The World and Its People

Features and Benefits

Dynamic Instructional Structure	**. . . presents a clear and comprehensive coverage of geography and world cultures.** • Each engaging section introduction includes a Main Idea, Terms to Know, a Reading Strategy, and a National Geographic Exploring Our World feature. • The Reading Review offers concise synopses of important chapter topics and can be used to preview, review, or summarize chapter content. • The Study and Writing, Technology, Critical Thinking, and Social Studies Skills features teach students the skills they need to be successful in their study of geography and world cultures.
A Strong Reading Strand	**. . . encourages active reading and learning for students of all reading levels.** • The Reading Skills Handbook provides students with vital strategies to improve their reading comprehension. • Foldables help students organize and process key concepts as they read the chapters. • Reading Checks help students check their reading comprehension. • Reading Strategies in the Teacher Wraparound Edition provide a wealth of activities designed to involve students at all reading levels.
Differentiated Instruction	**. . . makes *The World and Its People* accessible to students of all learning levels.** • Differentiated Instruction activities and strategies are designed for students of varying ability levels and learning styles. • A variety of question types and strategies provide students of differing ability levels and learning styles with assessment activities that cater to their strengths. • The comprehensive Teacher Wraparound Edition indicates which activities are suitable for various ability levels.
Standardized Test Preparation	**. . . gives students the opportunity to practice for state and national exams.** • Chapter Assessments and a Standardized Test Practice question at the end of each chapter provide a variety of forms of standardized test practice questions, including multiple choice, open-ended short response, and open-ended extended response. • Test-Taking Tips help students learn how to approach test questions successfully.
A Variety of History Activities and Features	**. . . are essential for student success and get students excited about geography and world cultures.** • The Regional Atlas provides a preview of the land, climates, economies, and people that will be presented in the unit. • Geography and History features show students how geography and history are intertwined. • Eye on the Environment features examine regional environmental challenges and how people are attempting to resolve them. • TIME Reports present information about current events and how they are relevant to students' lives.
Teacher Resources	**. . . provide convenient strategies to help new and experienced teachers.** • Unit and Chapter Resources provide background and extension material to help in lesson preparation. • Unit Resource books contain important unit, chapter, and section reproducible masters.
Technology	**. . . provides time-saving software products to help you creatively engage students and reduce prep time.** • *The World and Its People* Video Program offers interesting and diverse content extension. • TeacherWorks includes an Interactive Teacher Edition as well as an Interactive Lesson Planner that contains all resources available with the program on a CD-ROM. • StudentWorks includes an electronic version of the Student Edition, along with all of the program's workbooks. • Social Studies Online at twip.glencoe.com provides resources and activities designed for your book.

Improving Active Reading and Study Skills

Dinah Zike's FOLDABLES™

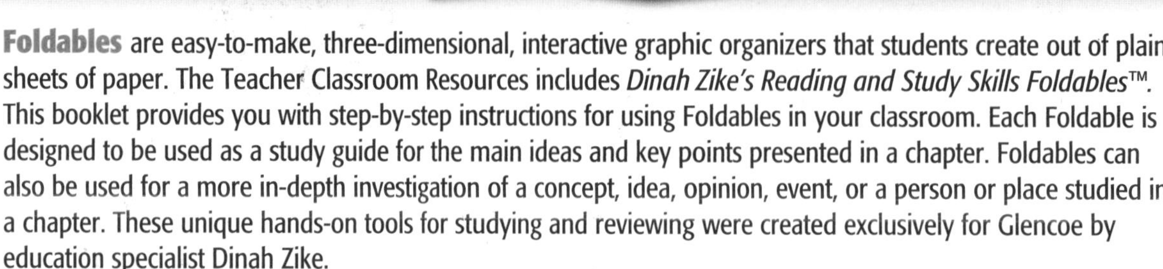

Foldables are easy-to-make, three-dimensional, interactive graphic organizers that students create out of plain sheets of paper. The Teacher Classroom Resources includes *Dinah Zike's Reading and Study Skills Foldables™*. This booklet provides you with step-by-step instructions for using Foldables in your classroom. Each Foldable is designed to be used as a study guide for the main ideas and key points presented in a chapter. Foldables can also be used for a more in-depth investigation of a concept, idea, opinion, event, or a person or place studied in a chapter. These unique hands-on tools for studying and reviewing were created exclusively for Glencoe by education specialist Dinah Zike.

Why Use Foldables in Social Studies?

Because they:

- organize, display, and arrange information, making it easier for students to grasp social studies concepts, theories, facts, opinions, questions, research, and ideas.
- are student-made study guides that are compiled as students listen for main ideas, read main ideas, or conduct research.
- integrate language arts, the sciences, and mathematics into the study of social studies.
- provide a multitude of creative formats in which students can present projects, research, interviews, and inquiry-based reports.
- replace teacher-generated writing or photocopied sheets with student-generated print.
- incorporate the use of such skills as comparing and contrasting, recognizing cause-and-effect, and finding similarities and differences.
- continue to immerse students in previously learned vocabulary, concepts, information, generalizations, ideas, and theories, providing them with a strong foundation that they can build upon with new observations, concepts, and knowledge.
- can be used by students or teachers to easily communicate data through graphs, tables, charts, models, and diagrams, including Venn diagrams.
- allow students to make their own journals for recording observations, research information, primary and secondary source data, surveys, and so on.
- can be used as alternative assessment tools by teachers to evaluate student progress or by students to evaluate their own progress.
- provide a sense of student ownership or investiture in the social studies curriculum.

▼ *Student Edition, p. 79*

FOLDABLES™ Study Organizer

Organizing Information Make this foldable to help you organize what you learn about culture, the world's population, resources, and the effect of technology on the world.

Step 1 Fold the sides of a piece of paper into the middle to make a shutter fold.

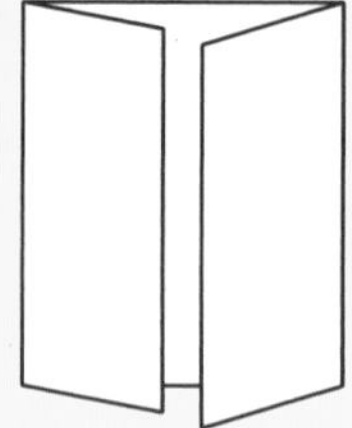

Step 2 Fold in half from side to side.

The World's People

Step 3 Open and cut along the inside fold lines to form four tabs.

Cut along the fold lines on both sides.

Step 4 Label the tabs as shown.

Understanding Culture | Population Patterns | Resources & World Trade | Technology "Shrinks" the World

Reading and Writing As you read each section in the chapter, write notes under the correct tab of your foldable.

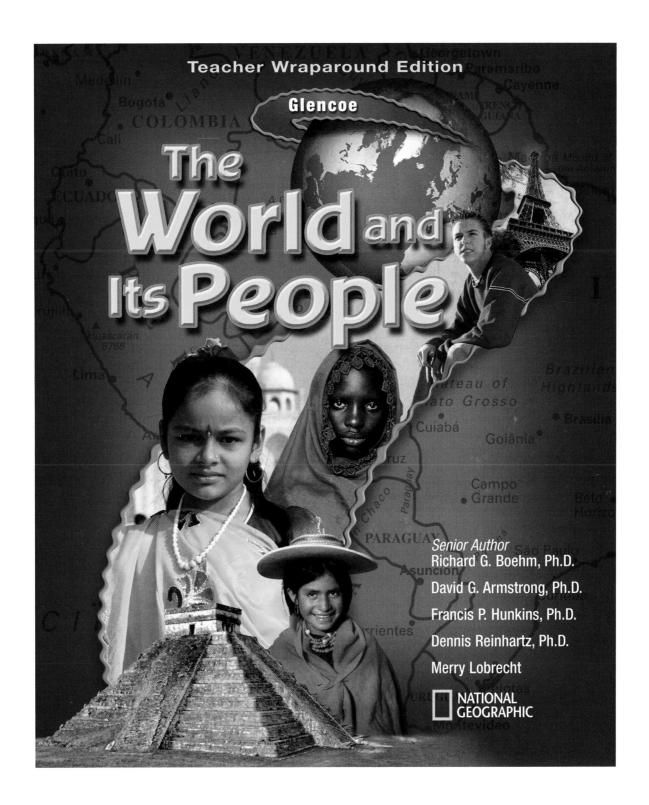

Teacher Wraparound Edition

Glencoe

The World and Its People

Senior Author
Richard G. Boehm, Ph.D.

David G. Armstrong, Ph.D.

Francis P. Hunkins, Ph.D.

Dennis Reinhartz, Ph.D.

Merry Lobrecht

NATIONAL GEOGRAPHIC

New York, New York   Columbus, Ohio   Chicago, Illinois   Peoria, Illinois   Woodland Hills, California

ABOUT THE AUTHORS

The National Geographic Society, founded in 1888 for the increase and diffusion of geographic knowledge, is the world's largest nonprofit scientific and educational organization. The Society uses sophisticated communication technologies to convey geographic knowledge to a worldwide membership. The School Publishing Division supports the Society's mission by developing innovative educational programs—ranging from traditional print materials to multimedia programs including CD-ROMS, videos, and software.

David G. Armstrong

David G. Armstrong, Ph.D., served as Dean of the School of Education at the University of North Carolina at Greensboro. A social studies education specialist with additional advanced training in geography, Dr. Armstrong was educated at Stanford University, University of Montana, and University of Washington.

Merry Lobrecht

Merry Lobrecht is the Social Studies Curriculum Coordinator for the Humble ISD. She was the recipient of both the 2001 National Council for Geographic Education Distinguished Teacher Achievement Award and the Texas Council of Social Studies Texas Alliance for Geographic Distinguished Teacher Award for 2001.

Senior Author

Richard G. Boehm

Richard G. Boehm, Ph.D., was one of seven authors of *Geography for Life,* national standards in geography, prepared under Goals 2000: Educate America Act. In 1991 he received the George J. Miller award from the National Council for Geographic Education (NCGE) for distinguished service to geographic education. He has twice won the *Journal of Geography* award for best article. He presently holds the Jesse H. Jones Distinguished Chair in Geographic Education at Southwest Texas State University in San Marcos, Texas.

Francis P. Hunkins

Francis P. Hunkins, Ph.D., is Professor of Education at the University of Washington. He began his career as a teacher in Massachusetts. He received his master's degree in education from Boston University and his doctorate from Kent State University with a major in general curriculum and a minor in geography. Dr. Hunkins has written numerous books and articles.

Dennis Reinhartz

Dennis Reinhartz, Ph.D., is Professor of History and Russian at the University of Texas at Arlington. A specialist in Russian and East European history, as well as in the history of cartography and historical geography, Dr. Reinhartz has written numerous books in these fields. He is a consultant to the U.S. State and Justice Departments and to the U.S. Holocaust Memorial Museum in Washington, D.C.

Glencoe

The McGraw-Hill Companies

Printed in the United States of America

Send all inquiries to:
Glencoe/McGraw-Hill
8787 Orion Place
Columbus, Ohio 43240-4027

ISBN 0-07-860976-3 (Student Edition) ISBN 0-07-860977-1 (Teacher Wraparound Edition)
3 4 5 6 7 8 027/055 09 08 07 06 05

ACADEMIC CONSULTANTS

Karl Barbir, Ph.D.
Professor of History
Sienna College
Loudonville, New York

Brock Brown, Ph.D.
Associate Professor of Geography and Planning
Southwest Texas State University
San Marcos, Texas

Thomas H. Buckley, Ph.D.
Professor of History
University of Tulsa
Tulsa, Oklahoma

Ramesh Dhussa, Ph.D.
Assistant Professor of Geography
Drake University
Des Moines, Iowa

Charles A. Endress, Ph.D.
Professor of History
Angelo State University
San Angelo, Texas

Dana A. Farnham, Ph.D.
Professor of Anthropology
Lincoln College at Normal
Normal, Illinois

Anne Hardgrove, Ph.D.
Assistant Professor of History
University of Texas at San Antonio
San Antonio, Texas

Ken Hendrickson, Ph.D.
Professor of History
Sam Houston State University
Huntsville, Texas

Terry G. Jordan, Ph.D.
Professor of Geography
University of Texas at Austin
Austin, Texas

Monica Najar, Ph.D.
Assistant Professor of History
Lehigh University
Bethlehem, Pennsylvania

Reverend Marvin O'Dell
Faith Baptist Church
Thousand Oaks, California

Rex Peebles
Dean of Social and Behavioral Sciences
Austin Community College
Austin, Texas

Bernard Reich, Ph.D.
Professor of Political Science and International Affairs
George Washington University
Washington, D.C.

FOLDABLES **Dinah Zike**
Educational Consultant
Dinah-Might Activities, Inc.
San Antonio, Texas

READING CONSULTANTS

Carol M. Santa, Ph.D.
CRISS: Project Developer
Director of Education
Montana Academy
Kalispell, Montana

Bonnie Valdes
Master CRISS Trainer
Project CRISS
Largo, Florida

Steve Qunell
Social Studies Instructor
Montana Academy
Kalispell, Montana

TEACHER REVIEWERS

Diana Bradford
Scobee Middle School
San Antonio, Texas

Kenneth E. Bridges
Huffines Middle School
Lewisville, Texas

Rosemary Conroy
St. Luke School
Shoreline, Washington

Nancy Eudy
Bammel Middle School
Houston, Texas

Carolyn Grogan
Mesa Elementary School
Somis, California

Pamela Kniffin
Navasota Intermediate School
Navasota, Texas

Sarah L. Matt
Irma Marsh Middle School
Fort Worth, Texas

Karen Muir
George Fox Middle School
Pasadena, Maryland

David Nienkamp
Sandy Creek Junior/Senior High School
Fairfield, Nebraska

Susan Pearson
The Academy For Science and Foreign Languages
Huntsville, Alabama

Megan Phelps
Moorpark Community College
Moorpark, California

Julie Scott
East Valley Middle School
Spokane, Washington

Michael Yell
Hudson Middle School
Hudson, Wisconsin

Marsha Yoder
Lawton Chiles Middle Academy
Lakeland, Florida

Contents

Scope and Sequence T18

NCSS Ten Thematic Strands T24

Geography Themes to Standards.....................................T30

Classroom Solutions: Teacher Professional Handbook............T38

Previewing Your Textbook T50

Scavenger Hunt..........................T55

Reading Skills Handbook........RH1

NATIONAL GEOGRAPHIC Reference Atlas

The World: Political..................................RA2

North America: Political..........................RA4

North America: Physical..........................RA5

United States: Political............................RA6

United States: Physical............................RA8

Canada: Physical/Political.....................RA10

Middle America: Physical/Political......RA12

South America: Political........................RA14

South America: Physical........................RA15

Europe: Political....................................RA16

Europe: Physical....................................RA18

Africa: Political.......................................RA20

Africa: Physical.......................................RA21

Asia: Political..RA22

Asia: Physical..RA24

Middle East: Physical/Political.............RA26

Pacific Rim: Physical/Political..............RA28

Arctic Ocean: Physical...........................RA30

Antarctica: Physical................................RA30

NATIONAL GEOGRAPHIC Geography Handbook

How Do I Study Geography?..............................2

How Do I Use Maps and Globes?........................4

Understanding Latitude and Longitude..............5

From Globes to Maps 6

Common Map Projections...................................7

Parts of Maps 8

Types of Maps...9

Using Graphs, Charts, and Diagrams.................11

Geographic Dictionary..14

Be an Active Reader 16

Unit 1 The World 18

Chapter 1 Looking at the Earth 20

1 Thinking Like a Geographer........................22

2 The Earth in Space 29

3 Forces Shaping the Earth 34

4 Landforms and Waterways 39

Chapter 2 Water, Climate, and Vegetation 46

1 The Water Planet...48

2 Climate 52

3 Climate Zones and Vegetation.....................61

4 An Environmental Balance 69

Chapter 3 The World's People..............78

1 Understanding Culture 80

2 Population Patterns 87

3 Resources and World Trade.........................92

4 Technology "Shrinks" the World.................97

Unit 2 The United States and Canada 112

Regional Atlas 114

Chapter 4 The United States 124

1 From Sea to Shining Sea 126
2 An Economic Leader 131
3 The Americans 145

Chapter 5 Canada 156

1 A Resource-Rich Country 158
2 The Canadians 165

Unit 3 Latin America..........174

Regional Atlas 176

Chapter 6 Mexico 188

1 Mexico's Land and Economy............190
2 Mexico's History............197
3 Mexico Today 202

Chapter 7 Central America and the Caribbean Islands............210

1 Central America............212
2 Cultures of the Caribbean 219

Chapter 8 Brazil and Its Neighbors............230

1 Brazil—Emerging Giant 232
2 Argentina to Venezuela 239

Chapter 9 The Andean Countries......252

1 Colombia's Culture and Challenges 254
2 Land and People of Peru and Ecuador......266
3 The Bolivians and Chileans 271

Unit 4 Europe............278

Regional Atlas..............280

Chapter 10 Europe—Early History....292

1 Classical Greece and Rome 294
2 Medieval Europe............299
3 From Renaissance to Revolution............303

Chapter 11 Europe—Modern History............312

1 The Modern Era Emerges 314
2 A Divided Continent............319
3 Moving Toward Unity............324

Chapter 12 Western Europe Today....338

1 The British Isles 340
2 France and the Benelux Countries............345
3 Germany and the Alpine Countries 350
4 The Nordic Nations 354
5 Southern Europe 358

Chapter 13 The New Eastern Europe............366

1 Poland and the Baltic Republics............368
2 Hungarians, Czechs, and Slovaks 372
3 Rebuilding the Balkan Countries............377
4 Ukraine, Belarus, and Moldova............383

Unit 5 Russia and the Eurasian Republics 390

NATIONAL GEOGRAPHIC Regional Atlas 392

Chapter 14 Russia's Landscape and History 402

1 A Vast Land 404

2 A Troubled History 410

Chapter 15 The New Russia and Independent Republics 422

1 From Communism to Free Enterprise.......424

2 Russia's People and Culture 429

3 The Republics Emerge 436

Unit 6 North Africa and Southwest Asia 452

NATIONAL GEOGRAPHIC Regional Atlas 454

Chapter 16 Birthplace of Civilization 464

1 Mesopotamia and Ancient Egypt 466

2 Three World Religions...............................473

Chapter 17 North Africa Today 482

1 Egypt...484

2 Libya and the Maghreb.............................490

Chapter 18 Southwest Asia 500

1 Turkey, Syria, Lebanon, Jordan 502

2 Israel and the Palestinian Territories.........508

3 The Arabian Peninsula...............................513

4 Iraq, Iran, and Afghanistan 517

Unit 7 Africa South of the Sahara 532

NATIONAL GEOGRAPHIC Regional Atlas 534

Chapter 19 West Africa 548

1 Nigeria—African Giant 550

2 The Sahel and Coastal West Africa 556

Chapter 20 Central and East Africa...568

1 Central Africa 570

2 People of Kenya and Tanzania...................577

3 Uganda, Rwanda, and Burundi...................582

4 The Horn of Africa 586

Chapter 21 Southern Africa— A Varied Region....................................602

1 The New South Africa 604

2 Zambia, Malawi, Zimbabwe, Botswana 609

3 Coastal and Island Countries.....................614

Unit 8 Asia 622

NATIONAL GEOGRAPHIC Regional Atlas 624

Chapter 22 South Asia 636

1 India—Past and Present 638

2 Pakistan and Bangladesh 644

3 Mountain Kingdoms, Island Republics 649

Chapter 23 China and Its Neighbors ..658

1 China's Land and New Economy 660

2 Dynasties to Communism 666

3 China's Neighbors 678

Chapter 24 Japan and the Koreas 688

1 Japan—Past and Present 690

2 The Two Koreas 698

Chapter 25 Southeast Asia 706

1 Life on the Mainland 708

2 Diverse Island Cultures 714

Unit 9 Australia, Oceania, and Antarctica 722

NATIONAL GEOGRAPHIC Regional Atlas 724

Chapter 26 Australia and New Zealand 734

1 Australia—Land Down Under 736

2 New Zealand 741

Chapter 27 Oceania and Antarctica 756

1 Pacific Island Cultures and Economies 758

2 The Frozen Continent 764

Appendix 774

What Is an Appendix? 775

Nations of the World Data Bank....................776

Standardized Test Skills Handbook...............786

Honoring America 798

Gazetteer 799

Glossary 807

Spanish Glossary....................814

Index 823

Acknowledgments....................841

One-Stop Internet Resources

This textbook contains one-stop Internet resources for teachers, students, and parents. Log on to twip.glencoe.com for more information. Online study tools include Chapter Overviews, Self-Check Quizzes, an Interactive Tutor, and E-Flashcards. Online research tools include Student Web Activities, Beyond the Textbook Features, Current Events, Web Resources, and State Resources. The interactive online student edition includes the complete Interactive Student Edition along with textbook updates. Especially for teachers, Glencoe offers an online Teacher Forum, Web Activity Lesson Plans, and Literature Connections.

Getty Images

Features

Endangered Spaces 76
Vanishing Rain Forests 250
A Water Crisis 498
Ozone: Earth's Natural Sunscreen 772

The Columbian Exchange 228
Russia's Strategy: Freeze Your Foes 420
Please Pass the Salt: Africa's Salt Trade 566
The Silk Road 686

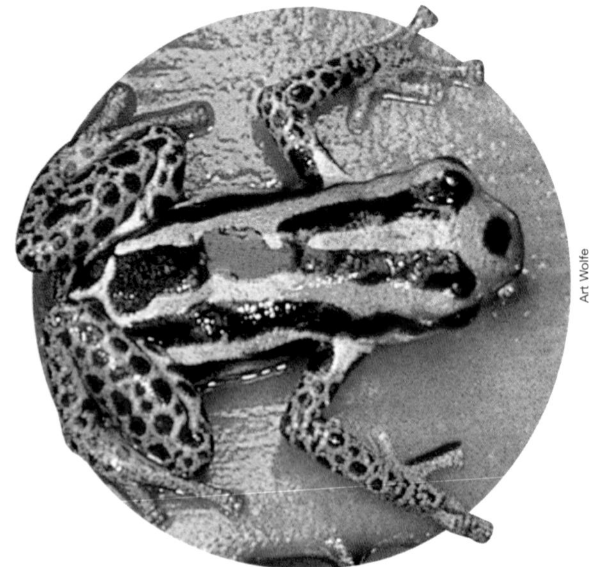
Art Wolfe

▲ Poison arrow frog

Skills

Social Studies Skills

Using a Map Key 33
Using Latitude and Longitude 60
Reading a Thematic Map 86
Mental Mapping 144
Reading a Physical Map 196
Interpreting an Elevation Profile 224
Using B.C. and A.D. 298
Reading a Population Map 334
Reading a Vegetation Map 349
Reading a Time Zones Map 613
Reading a Circle Graph 648
Reading a Contour Map 713

Critical Thinking Skills

Sequencing and Categorizing Information 238
Understanding Cause and Effect 416
Drawing Inferences and Conclusions 555
Making Predictions 598
Distinguishing Fact From Opinion 682
Making Comparisons 702

Technology Skills

Developing Multimedia Presentations 164
Using a Database 258
Using a Spreadsheet 494
Evaluating a Web Site 528

Study and Writing Skills

Taking Notes 376
Using Primary and Secondary Sources 448
Using Library Resources 478
Outlining 752
Writing a Report 763

Making Connections

Art

Leonardo da Vinci 308
Ukrainian Easter Eggs 382
Carpet Weaving 507
Shadow Puppets 718

Science

Exploring Earth's Water 51
The Aztec Calendar Stone 201
The Galápagos Islands 270
Battling Sleeping Sickness 576
Australia's Amazing Animals 740
Antarctica's Environmental Stations 768

Culture

Americans All 152
Matthews Coon Come: Man With a Mission 170
Poetry on the Pampas 246
The Holocaust 318
Count Leo Tolstoy 435
An Egyptian Folktale 489
Great Mosque of Djenné 562
The Taj Mahal 643
Haiku 697

Technology

Geographic Information Systems 28
Counting Heads 108
The Panama Canal Locks 218
Stonehenge 344
Cooperative Space Ventures 409
The Egyptian Pyramids 472
Mining and Cutting Diamonds 608
The Three Gorges Dam 665

▲ Inuit greet with a nose rub.

Architecture: Quake-Proof Structures 37
Clothing: The Inuit 166
Art: Diego Rivera and His Murals 203
Sports: Peru 268
Architecture: Leaning Tower of Pisa 361
Food: Slovakia and the Czech Republic 374
Art: Fabergé Eggs 433
Food: Egypt 487
Clothing: The Tuareg 557
Sculpture: Shona Artists 611
Clothing: Dyeing Cloth 640
Customs: Greetings 695
Architecture: Angkor Wat 711
Architecture: Sydney Opera House 738

Fighting Pollution 428
Stable Democracy....................................612

Surf's Up! 133
Time to Play..168
What a Catch! 216
Cozy Ballet? 356
Bazaar! 491
Festival Time..504
I Am a Samburu 581
What's for Dinner?.......................................610
School's Out! 646
The Race Is On!...681
Hard Hats to School? 694
Life as a Monk 710
Dreamtime...739

Teen from Senegal ▶

Owen Franken/CORBIS

Believe It or Not!

Solar Eclipse 30
Mt. Pinatubo 55
Saffron—A Valuable Resource 93
San Xavier del Bac 146
Bee Hummingbird 222
Roping a Capybara 242
Islamic Art 359
Transylvania 378
The Aral Sea...439
The Rosetta Stone 470
Petra...505
The Okapi...571
Ship Breakers...647
Clay Warriors...667
The *Endurance* 766

Primary Source

Globalization 99
A Declaration of First Nations 167
Zlata's Diary...380
Alexander Solzhenitsyn 432
Comparing Scripture....................................475
Nelson Mandela 606

Literature

Botoque 235
The Scarlet Pimpernel 306
Where Are Those Songs? 578
Sadako and the Thousand Paper Cranes ..692
Great Mother Snake.....................................737

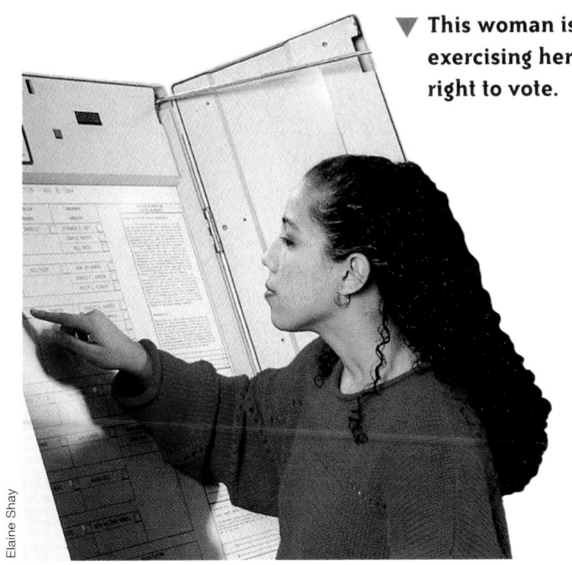

This woman is exercising her right to vote.

Elaine Shay

Public and Private Needs 187
Participation 291
Initiative 401
Religious Tolerance 463
Closing the Door on Racism 546
Women's Rights 634
Voting 733

Our Shrinking World 101
Protecting America's Freedoms from Terror 137
Waging War on Drugs 259
The European Union: Good for Everyone? ... 327
The New Russia 441
The Fight for Peace in Southwest Asia 521
Refugees on the Move 591
East Asia: Report Card on Democracy 671
Closing the Gap 745

Exploring Economics

The "Third World" 96
The Quipu 267
Manor Economy 300
Restructuring 321
Centers of Trade 468
Monoculture 558
Labor Costs 664
Exchange of Knowledge 715
East Timor's Challenges 715
The Fate of Nauru 761

An illustration of the new World Trade Center memorial site, New York City

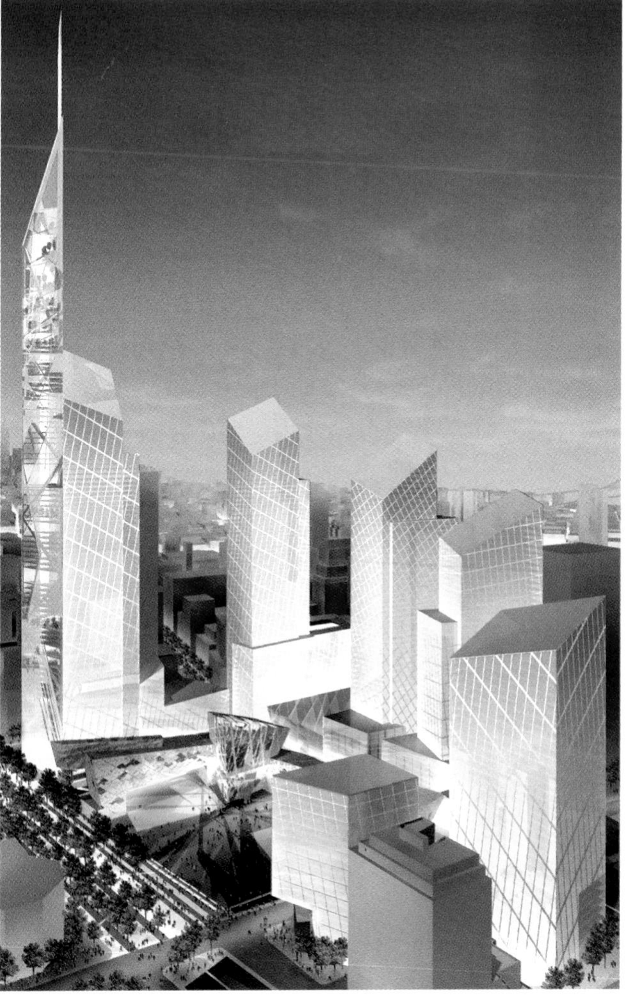

Torsten Sedel

Maps

NATIONAL GEOGRAPHIC Reference Atlas

The World: Political RA2
North America: Political RA4
North America: Physical RA5
United States: Political RA6
United States: Physical RA8
Canada: Physical/Political RA10
Middle America: Physical/Political RA12
South America: Political RA14
South America: Physical RA15
Europe: Political RA16
Europe: Physical RA18
Africa: Political RA20
Africa: Physical RA21
Asia: Political RA22
Asia: Physical RA24
Middle East: Physical/Political RA26
Pacific Rim: Physical/Political RA28
Arctic Ocean: Physical RA30
Antarctica: Physical RA30

NATIONAL GEOGRAPHIC Geography Handbook

Great Circle Route 6
Climate Regions of the United States 8
Spain: Political 9
Sri Lanka: Physical 9
Sri Lanka: Contour 10
Egypt: Population Density 10

Unit 1 The World

Washington, D.C. 33
World Continents and Oceans 41
Continental Drift 45
Prevailing Wind Patterns 54
World Ocean Currents 57
Map of the World 60
World Climate Regions 63
World Natural Vegetation Regions 64
World Religions 81
World Culture Regions 84
Early Civilizations 86
World Population Density 89
World Economic Activity 95
A Sweatshirt's Global Journey 102

Unit 2 The United States and Canada

The United States and Canada: Physical 118
The United States and Canada: Political 119
The United States and Canada: Food Production 120
Contiguous United States and Canada: Land Comparison 120
The United States: Physical 127
The United States: Economic Activity 132
Downtown Chicago, Illinois 144
The United States: Population Density 149
Canada: Economic Activity 161

Unit 3 Latin America

Latin America: Physical 180
Latin America: Political 181
South America: Urban Population Growth 182
Contiguous United States and Latin America: Land Comparison 182
Mexico: Political 191
Mexico: Physical 196
Mexico's Native American Civilizations 198
Mexico: Population Density 205
Central America and the Caribbean Islands: Political 213
Central America and the Caribbean Islands: Economic Activity 214
Contiguous U.S. and Latin America 227
The Spread of Plants and Animals 229
Brazil and Its Neighbors: Physical/Political 233
Brazil and Its Neighbors: Economic Activity 240
The Andean Countries: Political 255
The Drug War in the Andes 260
The Andean Countries: Climate 273

Unit 4 Europe

Europe: Physical 284
Europe: Political 285
Europe: Languages 286
Contiguous United States and Europe: Land Comparison 286
Greek and Roman Empires 295
Medieval Europe c. A.D. 1200 301
Western and Eastern Europe (c. 1950) 320
Europe in 2004 328
Spain and Portugal: Population Density 334
Occupation of Germany 1945 337
Western Europe: Political 341
France: Vegetation 349
Eastern Europe: Political 369
Eastern Europe: Population Density 384
European Union 2004 389

NATIONAL GEOGRAPHIC

Eastern Europe: Political

Unit 5 Russia and the Eurasian Republics

Russia and the Eurasian Republics: Physical......396
Russia and the Eurasian Republics: Political......397
The Russian Winter......398
Contiguous United States and Russia: Land Comparison......398
Russia: Climate......405
Expansion of Russia......412
Average Winter Temperatures......421
Russia: Economic Activity......425
Eurasian Republics: Economic Activity......437
Russia's 11 Time Zones......447
Chechnya......451

Unit 6 North Africa and Southwest Asia

North Africa and Southwest Asia: Physical......458
North Africa and Southwest Asia: Political......459
North Africa and Southwest Asia: Oil and Gas Production and Distribution......460
Contiguous United States and North Africa and Southwest Asia: Land Comparison......460
Mesopotamia and Ancient Egypt......467
Jerusalem......474
Mesopotamian Civilizations, c. 4000 B.C.......481
Ancient Egypt, c. 3100 B.C.......481
North Africa: Physical/Political......485
Southwest Asia: Physical/Political......503
Southwest Asia: Climate......509
Israel and Its Neighbors......511
Spread of Islam......518
Where Iraq's Muslims Live......522

Unit 7 Africa South of the Sahara

Africa South of the Sahara: Physical......538
Africa South of the Sahara: Political......539
Africa South of the Sahara: Gems and Minerals......540
Contiguous United States and Africa South of the Sahara: Land Comparison......540
West Africa: Political......551
West Africa: Physical......552
West Africa: Population Density......560
Salt Trade Routes......567
Central and East Africa: Physical......572
Central and East Africa: Political......580
East Africa: Economic Activity......583
East Africa: Population Density......587
Major African Ethnic Groups......589
Africans on the Move......592
Kenya......601
Southern Africa: Political......605
World Time Zones......613
African Independence Dates......615
Population Density of Southern African Countries......621

Unit 8 Asia

Asia: Physical......628
Asia: Political......629
Asia: Monsoons......630
Contiguous United States and Asia: Land Comparison......630
South Asia: Physical......645
South Asia: Economic Activity......650
South Asia: Population Density......653
China and Its Neighbors: Physical/Political......661
China and Its Neighbors: Population Density....668
Who's Free, Who's Not in East Asia......672
China's Defenses......685
Silk Road Routes......687
Japan and the Koreas: Physical/Political......691
Japan and the Koreas: Population Density......700
Asia's Pacific Rim......702
Southeast Asia: Political......709
Borneo: Contour Map......713

Unit 9 Australia, Oceania, and Antarctica

Australia, Oceania, and Antarctica: Physical......728
Australia, Oceania, and Antarctica: Political......729
Australia, Oceania, and Antarctica: Endangered Environments......730
Contiguous United States and Australia, Oceania, and Antarctica: Land Comparison......730
Australia and New Zealand: Physical/Political......742
Maori Iwi Lands......746
Oceania and Antarctica: Political......759

Charts and Graphs

NATIONAL GEOGRAPHIC Geography Handbook

Hemispheres 4
Comparing World Languages 11
U.S. Farms, 1940–2000 11
World Population 12
Major Automobile-Producing Countries, 2001 12
Climograph: Moscow, Russia 13
Africa: Elevation Profile 13
Landforms and Water Bodies 14

Unit 1 The World

The Solar System 30
Seasons 31
Earth's Layers 35
Tectonic Plate Boundaries 36
The Water Cycle 49
El Niño 56
Rain Shadow 58
Number of Hurricanes in a Year 75
Major World Religions 82
Types of Government 83
World Population: Population Growth 88
World Population: Most Populous Countries 88
Types of Economic Systems 94
Modern Inventions 98
The Digital Divide 107
Exports by World Region 111

Unit 2 The United States and Canada

Data Bits 117
Population: Urban vs. Rural 117
The United States Labor Force 117
Elevation Profile 118
Comparing Population: United States and Canada 121
Ethnic Groups: United States and Canada 121
Country Profiles 122
U.S. State Names: Meaning and Origin 122
Canadian Province and Territory Names: Meaning and Origin 123
Balancing Freedom and Safety 138
Ground Zero: A Proposal for Renewal 143
Branches of the United States Government 148
Top 6 Tourist Destinations, 2001 155
St. Lawrence Seaway 159
Native North American Populations by Canadian Province in 2001 173

Unit 3 Latin America

Data Bits 179
Population: Urban vs. Rural 179
Elevation Profile 180
Comparing Population: United States and Selected Countries of Latin America 183
Ethnic Groups: Selected Countries of Latin America 183
Country Profiles 184

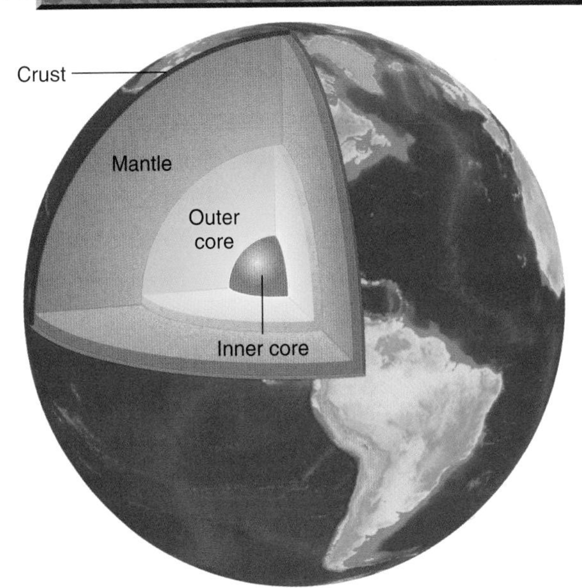

Mexico's Altitude Zones 193
The Panama Canal Locks 218
Jamaica: Elevation Profile 224
Leading Coffee-Producing Countries 234
What Drug and Alcohol Abuse Cost 265

Unit 4 Europe

Data Bits 283
Population: Urban vs. Rural 283
Elevation Profile 284
Comparing Population: United States and Selected Countries of Europe 287
Religions: Selected Countries of Europe 287
Country Profiles 288
Classical Europe 298
It's All About Jobs! 333
Number of Personal Computers per 1,000 People 365
Language Families of Europe 385

Unit 5 Russia and the Eurasian Republics

Data Bits 395
Ethnic Makeup 395
World Ranking 395
Population: Urban vs. Rural 395
Elevation Profile 396
Comparing Population: United States and Russia 399
Comparing Area and Population: Russia East and West of the Ural Mountains 399
Country Profiles 400
International Space Station 409
Where Russians Work 443

Unit 6 North Africa and Southwest Asia

Data Bits 457
Population: Urban vs. Rural 457

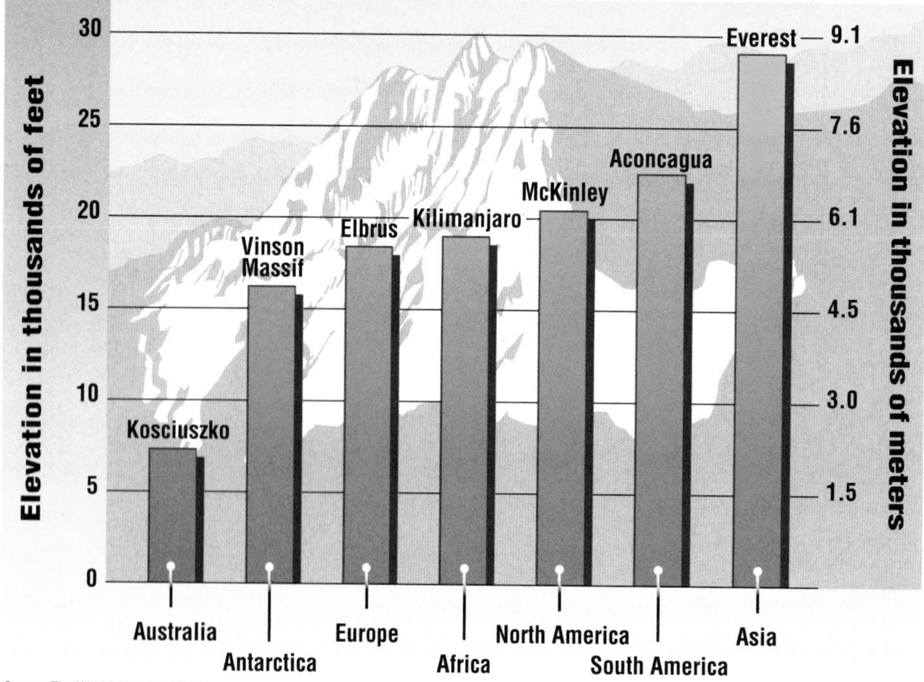

Source: *The World Almanac*, 2002.

Elevation Profile 458
Comparing Population: United States and Selected Countries of North Africa and Southwest Asia 461
Urban Populations: Selected Cities of North Africa and Southwest Asia 461
Country Profiles 462
Percentage of North Africa's People Living in Each Country 497
World Oil Reserves 514
Believers Who Share a Common Ground 527
Countries With the Largest Oil Reserves 531

Unit 7 Africa South of the Sahara

Data Bits 537
Religions 537
Elevation Profile 538
Comparing Population: United States and Selected Countries of Africa South of the Sahara 541
Selected Rural and Urban Populations: Africa South of the Sahara 541
Country Profiles 542
Leading Cacao-Producing Countries 565
Leading Diamond-Producing Countries 571
Where the World's Refugees Come From 597
Tourism in Kenya 598

Unit 8 Asia

Data Bits 627
Ethnic Makeup 627
World Ranking 627
Population: Urban vs. Rural 627
Elevation Profile 628
Comparing Population: United States and Selected Countries of Asia 631
World Population: Asia's Share of the World's People 631
Country Profiles 632
Religions of South Asia 648

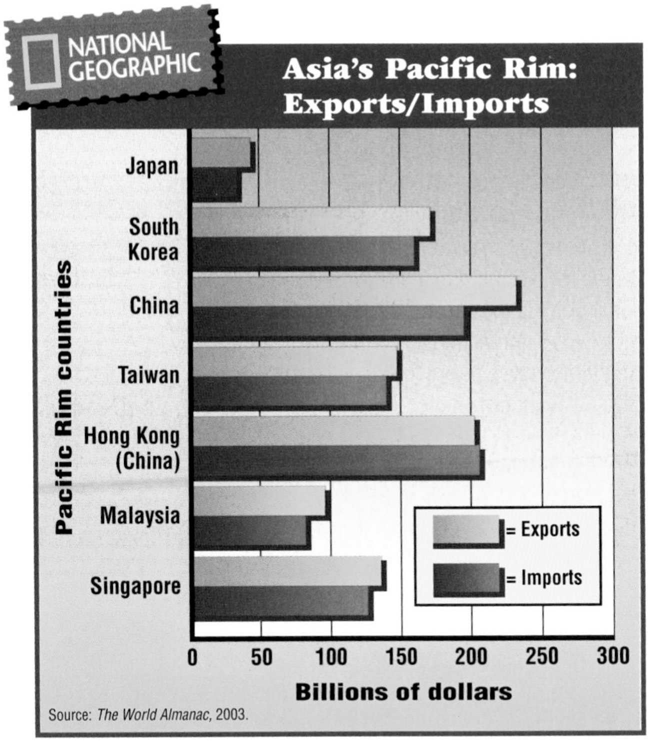

Highest Mountain on Each Continent 652
Comparing Population 657
Leading Rice-Producing Countries 662
Taiwan: From Dictatorship to Democracy 677
Asia's Pacific Rim: Exports/Imports 702
Top Tin Producers 721

Unit 9 Australia, Oceania, and Antarctica

Data Bits 727
Ethnic Makeup 727
World Ranking 727
Population: Urban vs. Rural 727
Elevation Profile 728
Comparing Population: United States and Selected Countries of Australia, Oceania, and Antarctica 731
Population Growth: Australia, 1958–2008 731
Country Profiles 732
The Making of a Multicultural Society 751
Leading Wool-Producing Countries 755

Scope and Sequence

Themes and Concepts

Each section of *The World and Its People* focuses on one of the National Council for the Social Studies (NCSS) 10 themes. These themes serve as organizing strands for social studies curriculum at every school level. The section numbers highlighted here in **red** indicate that the theme is the main focus of that section. Section numbers in black indicate that the theme can be found in the section, but it is not necessarily the main focus. For a complete description of the NCSS themes and a list of Student Edition pages where these themes can be found, refer to pages T24–T29.

Chapter	1	2
Culture		
Time, Continuity, and Change		
People, Places, and Environments	Section 1, 2, 3, 4	Section 1, 2, 3, 4
Individual Development and Identity		
Individuals, Groups, and Institutions		
Power, Authority, and Governance		
Production, Distribution, and Consumption		
Science, Technology, and Society	Section 1	
Global Connections		
Civic Ideals and Practices		

Skills

These are the skills taught in the Chapter Skills lesson. Each skill is reinforced in the ***Chapter Skills Review*** activities in the Unit Resource books in the TCR and **Glencoe's Skillbuilder Interactive Workbook CD-ROM.**

Chapter	1	2
Skill Category	*Social Studies*	*Social Studies*
Specific Skill	Using a Map Key	Using Latitude and Longitude

3	4	5	6	7
Section 1, 2	Section 3		Section 3	Section 2
Section 2		Section 1, 2	Section 1, 2	Section 1
Section 2	Section 1, 2	Section 1, 2	Section 1, 3	Section 1
			Section 2	Section 2
	Section 3	Section 2	Section 3	Section 2
Section 3	Section 2		Section 1	
Section 4				
Section 3, 4		Section 2		
Social Studies	*Social Studies*	*Technology*	*Social Studies*	*Social Studies*
Reading a Thematic Map	Mental Mapping	Developing Multimedia Presentations	Reading a Physical Map	Interpreting an Elevation Profile

Chapter	8	9	10	11
Themes and Concepts				
Culture	Section 1, 2	Section 1, 2, 3	Section 1	Section 1
Time, Continuity, and Change		Section 1, 2, 3	Section 2, 3	Section 1
People, Places, and Environments	Section 1, 2	Section 1, 2, 3,		
Individual Development and Identity			Section 3	
Individuals, Groups, and Institutions			Section 2	Section 2, 3
Power, Authority, and Governance		Section 1, 2, 3	Section 1	Section 2, 3
Production, Distribution, and Consumption	Section 1, 2	Section 1, 2, 3,	Section 2	
Science, Technology, and Society				Section 3
Global Connections	Section 1			
Civic Ideals and Practices				
Skills				
Skill Category	*Critical Thinking*	*Technology*	*Social Studies*	*Social Studies*
Specific Skill	Sequencing and Categorizing Information	Using a Database	Using B.C. and A.D.	Reading a Population Map

12	13	14	15	16
Section 1, 2, 3, 4, 5				Section 1
		Section 2	Section 1	
Section 1, 2, 3, 4, 5	Section 1, 2, 3, 4	Section 1		Section 1
			Section 2	
			Section 2	Section 2
			Section 3	
	Section 1, 2, 3, 4			Section 2
			Section 2	
Social Studies	*Study and Writing*	*Critical Thinking*	*Study and Writing*	*Study and Writing*
Reading a Vegetation Map	Taking Notes	Understanding Cause and Effect	Using Primary and Secondary Sources	Using Library Resources

Chapter	17	18	19	20	21
Themes and Concepts					
Culture		Section 1, 2, 3, 4	Section 1, 2	Section 1, 2, 3, 4	Section 1, 2, 3
Time, Continuity, and Change	Section 1, 2	Section 1, 2, 3, 4			
People, Places, and Environments		Section 1, 2, 3, 4	Section 1, 2	Section 1, 2, 3, 4	Section 1, 2, 3
Individual Development and Identity					
Individuals, Groups, and Institutions					
Power, Authority, and Governance	Section 1, 2	Section 2			
Production, Distribution, and Consumption	Section 1, 2		Section 1, 2	Section 1, 2, 3, 4	Section 1, 2, 3
Science, Technology, and Society					
Global Connections					
Civic Ideals and Practices					
Skills					
Skill Category	*Technology*	*Technology*	*Critical Thinking*	*Critical Thinking*	*Social Studies*
Specific Skill	Using a Spreadsheet	Evaluating a Web Site	Drawing Inferences and Conclusions	Making Predictions	Reading a Time Zones Map

	22	23	24	25	26	27
	Section 2, 3	Section 1	Section 1	Section 1, 2	Section 1, 2	Section 1
	Section 1, 2, 3	Section 1, 2	Section 1		Section 1, 2	
	Section 3	Section 1, 3	Section 1	Section 1, 2	Section 1, 2	Section 1, 2
	Section 1	Section 1, 3				
		Section 1	Section 1, 2			
	Section 1	Section 1, 2				Section 1
					Section 2	Section 2
			Section 2			Section 2
	Social Studies	*Critical Thinking*	*Critical Thinking*	*Social Studies*	*Study and Writing*	*Study and Writing*
	Reading a Circle Graph	Distinguishing Fact from Opinion	Making Comparisons	Reading a Contour Map	Outlining	Writing a Report

Correlation of

The World and Its People To the NCSS Thematic Strands

In *Curriculum for Social Studies: Expectations of Excellence,* the National Council for the Social Studies (NCSS) identified 10 themes that serve as organizing strands for the social studies curriculum at every school level. These themes are interrelated and draw from all of the social science disciplines. Each theme provides student performance expectations in the areas of knowledge, processes, and attitudes. The 10 NCSS themes were the basis for the themes used in *The World and Its People.*

Theme and Performance Expectation	Student Pages
I. *Culture* The study of culture helps students understand similarities and differences within groups of people. By studying a culture's beliefs, values, and traditions, students begin to gain a perspective that helps them relate to different groups. In the middle grades, students begin to examine aspects of culture and how culture influences human behavior.	
A. Compare similarities and differences in the ways groups, societies, and cultures meet human needs and concerns.	80, 82, 85, 169, 179, 198–199, 202–203, 216, 237, 241–242, 246, 298, 301, 304, 379, 393–394, 433–434, 440, 462–466, 473–478, 487–488, 556–61, 566, 570–575, 584–587, 609–612, 668–669, 679, 694–696, 708–712, 737–739, 743–744, 759–762
B. Explain how information and experiences may be interpreted by people from diverse cultural perspectives and frames of reference.	82, 201, 242, 246, 298, 307, 347, 382, 435, 473–478, 489, 552–554, 557, 560–561, 572–573, 577–581, 582–583, 605–607, 610–611, 617–618, 693–694, 708–712, 738–739, 759–762
C. Explain and give examples of how language, literature, the arts, architecture, other artifacts, traditions, beliefs, values, and behaviors contribute to the development and transmission of culture.	37, 80–82, 150–151, 166, 169, 198–199, 201–204, 216–217, 222, 228, 237, 241–242, 246, 257, 268–269, 274, 282, 295–296, 300–301, 303–304, 308, 340, 342, 344, 347–348, 352–353, 355, 357, 359–361, 371, 374, 375, 378–382, 386, 394, 433–435, 463–464, 473–478, 487, 489, 557, 611, 640, 643, 669–670, 681, 694–697, 711, 718, 737, 738
D. Explain why individuals and groups respond differently to their physical and social environments and/or changes to them on the basis of shared assumptions, values, and beliefs.	217, 223, 241, 301, 318, 343, 359, 380, 381, 412, 434, 473–478, 487, 515–516, 520, 552–554, 557, 559, 572–573, 578, 585, 605–607, 610–611, 617–618, 679, 694–696, 708–712, 737, 743–744, 759–762
E. Articulate the implications of cultural diversity, as well as cohesion, within and across groups.	81, 99, 100, 149, 166, 167, 168, 169, 170, 179, 217, 222, 236, 242, 267, 268, 282, 301, 305, 318, 340, 343, 347, 348, 351, 353, 359, 361, 379, 380, 381, 393, 394, 432–434, 436, 438–440, 473–478, 559, 566–567, 578, 605–607, 614–615, 666, 671–677, 698–701, 708–712, 714–717, 759–760, 766–767
II. *Time, Continuity, and Change* Understanding time, continuity, and change involves being knowledgeable about what things were like in the past and how things change and develop over time. Knowing how to read and reconstruct the past helps students gain a historical perspective. In the middle grades, students will continue to increase their knowledge of the past and of historical concepts. Students will also begin to learn how individual experiences, social values, and cultural traditions influence interpretations of the past.	
A. Demonstrate an understanding that different scholars may describe the same event or situation in different ways but must provide reasons or evidence for their views.	23–24, 190, 191, 344, 445, 472, 682
B. Identify and use key concepts such as chronology, causality, change, conflict, and complexity to explain, analyze, and show connections among patterns of historical change and continuity.	27, 84, 85, 89, 98, 108, 145, 146, 147, 148, 149, 150, 151, 159, 165, 166, 167, 179, 192, 197, 198, 199, 200, 215, 216, 222, 236, 240, 241, 242, 243, 244, 245, 256, 270, 283, 294–297, 300, 304, 307, 314, 321, 322, 323, 351, 370, 373, 374, 379, 380, 381, 384–386, 410–415, 424, 429–430, 436–437, 439, 445, 472–474, 487–488, 493, 557, 663–664, 668–669, 693–696, 712
C. Identify and describe selected historical periods and patterns of change within and across cultures, such as the rise of civilizations, the development of transportation systems, the growth and breakdown of colonial systems, and others.	27, 84, 85, 87, 147, 150, 165, 166, 167, 179, 197, 198, 199, 200, 216, 221, 222, 241, 242, 243, 244, 245, 256, 283, 295, 296, 297, 299, 303, 306, 307, 314, 321, 323, 356, 369, 370, 373, 374, 384–386, 410, 411, 412, 414, 424, 429–430, 436–437, 471–472, 473–478, 487–488, 493, 553–554, 557, 559, 598, 605–607, 640–641, 666–667, 743–744
D. Identify and use processes important to reconstructing and reinterpreting the past, such as using a variety of sources, providing, validating, and weighing evidence for claims, checking credibility of sources, and searching for causality.	27, 88, 238, 307, 413, 415, 448, 466, 471, 477, 555, 568, 598, 613, 654, 665, 682, 685, 739

Theme and Performance Expectation	Student Pages
E. Develop critical sensitivities such as empathy and skepticism regarding attitudes, values, and behaviors of people in different historical contexts.	22–23, 83–84, 90–91, 379, 471, 606, 612, 670, 692, 711, 737
F. Use knowledge of facts and concepts drawn from history, along with methods of historical inquiry, to inform decision-making about and action-taking on public issues.	76–77, 151, 250–251, 414, 448
III. *People, Places, & Environments* The study of people, places, and environments will help students as they create their spatial views and geographic perspective of the world. Students begin to make informed and critical decisions about the relationship between humans and their environment. In the middle school years, students can relate their personal experiences to happenings in other environments. These experiences will help students increase their abstract thought when analyzing human behavior in relation to physical and cultural environments.	
A. Elaborate mental maps of locales, regions, and the world that demonstrate understanding of relative location, direction, size, and shape.	24, 29, 30, 32, 63, 114, 116, 126, 127, 128, 129, 133, 134, 135, 144, 158, 160, 161, 162, 163, 176, 177, 187, 190, 191, 192, 193, 194, 212, 213, 214, 219, 220, 223, 232, 233, 239, 240, 242, 243, 254, 255, 266, 268, 269, 270, 272, 273, 280, 282, 340, 342, 345, 347, 350, 351, 354, 358, 360, 361, 368, 369, 371–374, 375, 377–380, 381, 383, 384, 392–394, 404–408, 426, 427, 436–439, 440, 477–478, 484, 490–493, 613, 685
B. Create, interpret, use, and distinguish various representations of the earth such as maps, globes, and photographs.	22, 23, 30, 33, 41, 42, 45, 49, 54, 56, 57, 58, 60, 63, 64, 66, 81, 84, 86, 89, 95, 102, 115, 116, 117, 118, 119, 120, 121, 122, 123, 126, 127, 128, 129, 132, 144, 147, 147, 149, 159, 161, 168, 180, 181, 182, 183, 191, 196, 198, 205, 213, 214, 227, 229, 233, 240, 255, 260, 271, 273, 284–286, 295, 301, 320, 334, 337, 341, 349, 369, 384, 389, 394–401, 405–407, 421, 427, 437, 438, 447, 451, 457, 460, 472, 477, 481, 484–485, 490, 503, 509, 511, 518, 522, 538–540, 551, 555, 560, 574, 580, 583, 587, 589, 601, 605, 613, 615, 621, 628, 630, 645, 650, 653, 654, 661, 668, 672, 685, 687, 691, 700, 702, 709, 713, 728–730, 742, 759, 765
C. Use appropriate resources, data sources, and geographic tools such as aerial photographs, satellite images, geographic information systems (GIS), map projections, and cartography to generate, manipulate, and interpret information such as atlases, databases, grid systems, charts, graphs, and maps.	24, 28, 83, 88, 100, 120, 121, 160, 168, 182, 183, 184, 185, 186, 187, 196, 205, 218, 224, 284, 286–291, 385, 395, 396–399 405, 427, 437, 443, 447, 457, 565, 566–567, 571, 575, 598, 648, 649–650, 662, 702, 712, 767
D. Estimate distance, calculate scale, and distinguish other geographic relationships such as population density and spatial distribution patterns.	31, 86, 89, 90, 215, 224, 229, 232, 233, 254, 270, 273, 334, 348, 385, 399, 405, 427, 431, 457, 520, 551-552, 560, 572, 642, 691, 708–712, 742
E. Locate and describe varying landforms and geographic features, such as mountains, plateaus, islands, rain forests, deserts, and oceans, and explain their relationship within the ecosystem.	22, 23, 24, 25, 34, 35, 36, 37, 38, 39, 40, 41, 42, 48, 49, 50, 52, 53, 54, 55, 56, 57, 58, 59, 61, 62, 63, 64, 65, 66, 67, 68, 69, 70, 71, 72, 130, 192, 193, 212, 213, 214, 219, 220, 239, 243, 250, 255, 266, 268, 271, 272, 273, 280, 340, 341, 347, 349, 350, 352, 353, 354, 357, 358, 360, 368, 372, 373, 374, 377, 378, 380, 381, 383, 392, 393, 407, 408, 438, 439, 440, 463, 492, 550, 558, 575, 577-578, 586-587, 610-612, 638, 660-662, 680, 690-691, 716, 736–737, 741-742, 758-759, 765-766, 768
F. Describe physical system changes such as seasons, climate and weather, and the water cycle and identify geographic patterns associated with them.	31, 48, 49, 130, 176, 177, 190, 192, 193, 194, 212, 250, 254, 268, 280, 353, 354, 355, 356, 398, 399, 404, 406-407, 426, 484, 490, 492, 556-557, 638-639, 665, 699-700, 714-715, 760, 765
G. Describe how people create places that reflect cultural values and ideals as they build neighborhoods, parks, shopping centers, and the like.	91, 202, 223, 302, 322, 344, 348, 356, 372, 408, 426, 431, 432, 437, 438, 440, 462, 467, 478, 550-551, 574, 579, 581, 616, 643-647, 669-670, 681, 694-696, 711, 718, 766-767
H. Examine, interpret, and analyze physical and cultural patterns and their interactions, such as land use, settlement patterns, cultural transmission of customs and ideas, and ecosystem changes.	58, 59, 70, 72, 76, 91, 92, 93, 133, 134, 135, 136, 145, 146, 204, 205, 212, 215, 218, 235, 243, 250, 266, 269, 271, 274, 282, 302, 322, 326, 342, 343, 345, 347, 352, 354, 355, 357, 385, 386, 392, 393, 404, 406-408, 426-428, 431-433, 437-438, 440, 462-463, 466, 477-479, 485, 491, 513-514, 553-554, 561, 584-585, 604-607, 617, 640, 654, 666-667, 680-681, 690-691, 715, 736-737, 739, 744, 760-761, 766-767

Theme and Performance Expectation	Student Pages
I. Describe ways that historical events have been influenced by, and have influenced, physical and human geographic factors in local, regional, national, and global settings.	24, 88, 95, 162, 163, 194, 214, 223, 235, 296, 343, 346, 355, 357, 399, 408, 427, 431, 432, 466, 640–642, 666–667, 670, 685, 693–694, 698–699, 701, 711–712
J. Observe and speculate about social and economic effects of environmental changes and crises resulting from phenomena such as floods, storms, and drought.	351, 428, 438, 463–466, 551, 556–557, 576, 582, 646–647, 662–663
K. Propose, compare, and evaluate alternative uses of land and resources in communities, nations, and the world.	77, 184, 185, 186, 187, 252, 357, 663, 693, 743, 766–770
IV. *Individual Development & Identity* People and culture influence a person's identity. Examining the different forms of human behavior improve one's understanding of social relationships and the development of personal identity. The study of human behavior helps students become aware of how social processes influence a person's identity. In the middle years, issues of personal identity become important as students begin to view themselves in relation to others.	
A. Relate personal changes to social, cultural, and historical contexts.	308, 425, 430, 444, 445, 578, 606, 679, 681, 692
B. Describe personal connections to place—as associated with community, nation, and world.	444, 459, 640–642, 646–647, 669–670, 679, 692, 697, 767
C. Describe the ways family, gender, ethnicity, nationality, and institutional affiliations contribute to personal identity.	148, 346, 430, 442, 444, 473–478, 510–512, 520, 552–553, 578, 585, 605–607, 640–642, 694–695, 737, 743–744
D. Relate such factors as physical endowment and capabilities, learning, motivation, personality, perception, and behavior to individual development.	308, 474, 477–478, 606, 640–641, 667, 692, 695–696, 737
E. Identify and describe ways regional, ethnic, and national cultures influence individuals' daily lives.	319, 425, 442, 444–445, 473–478, 516, 520, 552–553, 557, 559, 572–573, 578–579, 605–607, 610–611, 617–618, 679, 694–696, 699, 708–712, 737, 743–744, 759–762
F. Identify and describe the influence of perception, attitudes, values, and beliefs on personal identity.	80–81, 86–89, 93–94, 469, 477–478, 565, 606, 640–641, 643, 667, 692, 695–696, 737
G. Identify and interpret examples of stereotyping, conformity, and altruism.	82–83, 87, 95, 578, 606–607, 640–642, 663, 668, 692
H. Work independently and cooperatively to accomplish goals.	24, 92, 401, 446, 565, 686, 702, 737
V. *Individuals, Groups, & Institutions* Institutions, such as schools, governments, and churches, influence people and often reflect a society's values. Because of the vital role that institutions play in people's lives, it is important that students know how institutions develop, what controls and influences them, and how humans react to them. Middle school students will gain experience by studying how institutions change over time. They should also be able to use their understanding to suggest ways how institutions can work for the common good.	
A. Demonstrate an understanding of concepts such as role, status, and social class in describing the interactions of individuals and social groups.	81, 200, 301, 302, 412, 463–464, 514–516, 554, 559, 578, 605–607, 640–642, 693–694, 743–744
B. Analyze group and institutional influences on people, events, and elements of culture.	299, 300, 305, 307, 318, 360, 371, 413, 432, 473–478, 553–554, 651, 701, 717
C. Describe the various forms institutions take and the interactions of people with institutions.	204, 222, 301, 304, 305, 323, 341, 351, 361, 362, 370, 411, 432, 459, 473–478, 506, 559, 581, 663, 693–694, 766–767
D. Identify and analyze examples of tensions between expressions of individuality and group or institutional efforts to promote social conformity.	432, 438, 443 502, 606–607, 668–669, 681, 701
E. Identify and describe examples of tensions between belief systems and government policies and laws.	343, 359, 413, 430, 443, 469, 471, 502, 519–520, 606–607, 667, 681, 739

Theme and Performance Expectation	Student Pages
F. Describe the role of institutions in furthering both continuity and change.	200, 299, 300, 305, 317, 323, 459, 473–478, 508–510, 553–554, 581, 651, 663, 693–694, 701, 717, 766–767
G. Apply knowledge of how groups and institutions work to meet individual needs and promote the common good.	84, 91, 94–96, 257, 471, 576, 606, 767
VI. *Power, Authority, & Governance* Studying structures of power, authority, and governance and their functions in the United States and around the world is important for developing a notion of civic responsibility. Students will identify the purpose and characteristics of various types of government and how people try to resolve conflicts. Students will also examine the relationship between individual rights and responsibilities. During the middle school years, students apply what they have learned about rights and responsibilities in more complex contexts.	
A. Examine persistent issues involving the rights, roles, and status of the individual in relation to the general welfare.	83, 301, 318, 411, 413, 444, 473–478, 520, 559, 606, 640–642, 668–669, 767
B. Describe the purpose of government and how its powers are acquired, used, and justified.	83, 204, 241, 256, 429, 431, 463, 508–509, 520, 553–554, 581, 639–640, 646–647, 668–669
C. Analyze and explain ideas and governmental mechanisms to meet needs and wants of citizens, regulate territory, manage conflict, and establish order and security.	149, 216, 221, 223, 257, 267, 351, 352, 414, 428, 429, 431, 443, 506, 508, 520, 553–554, 566–567, 584, 606–607, 664, 679, 694, 712, 744, 767
D. Describe the ways nations and organizations respond to forces of unity and diversity affecting order and security.	243, 245, 257, 267, 300, 303, 317, 319, 360, 393, 431–432, 443, 473–478, 503–504, 518–520, 559, 588, 605–607, 640–642, 668–669, 679, 685, 694, 712
E. Identify and describe the basic features of the political system in the United States and identify representative leaders from various levels and branches of government.	148
F. Explain conditions, actions, and motivations that contribute to conflict and cooperation within and among nations.	96, 100, 163, 243, 317, 318, 319, 323, 370, 379, 384, 386, 411, 414, 430, 444, 503–504, 508, 518–520, 559, 588, 605–607, 640–642, 668–669, 679, 685, 694, 712, 766–767
G. Describe and analyze the role of technology in communications, transportation, information processing, weapons development, or other areas as it contributes to or helps resolve conflicts.	257, 315, 316, 317, 319, 414, 428, 513–516, 518, 566, 647, 664–665, 678–679, 692–694, 701, 767
H. Explain and apply concepts such as power, role, status, justice, and influence to the examination of persistent issues and social problems.	221, 257, 401, 412, 473–478, 512, 520, 559, 606, 640–642, 668–669, 767
I. Give examples and explain how governments attempt to achieve their stated ideals at home and abroad.	352, 512, 506, 517, 520, 554, 579, 588, 605–606, 647, 663, 679, 694, 712
VII. *Production, Distribution, & Consumption* Societies try to meet people's needs and wants by trying to answer the basic economic questions: What is to be produced? How should goods be produced? How should goods and services be distributed? How should land, labor, capital, and management be allocated? By studying how needs and wants are met, students learn how trade and government economic policies develop. In the middle grades, students increase their knowledge of economic concepts, principles, and reasoning.	
A. Give and explain examples of ways that economic systems structure choices about how goods and services are to be produced and distributed.	93, 94, 133, 134, 135, 195, 220, 234, 240, 256, 282, 301, 303, 306, 321, 341, 351, 361, 362, 377, 393, 414, 425, 438, 439, 486, 508–512, 513–516, 578–579, 582–583, 610–611, 616, 639, 663–664, 678–679, 682, 692–694, 701, 711–712, 743
B. Describe the role that supply and demand, prices, incentives, and profits play in determining what is produced and distributed in a competitive market system.	131, 136, 195, 237, 256, 291, 346, 357, 359, 360, 425, 438, 551, 554, 558, 571, 575, 663–664, 678–679, 693, 709, 715
C. Explain the difference between private and public goods and services.	162, 187, 220, 243, 306, 425–426

Theme and Performance Expectation	Student Pages
D. Describe a range of examples of the various institutions that make up economic systems such as households, business firms, banks, government agencies, labor unions, and corporations.	132, 213, 215, 240, 266, 267, 272, 301, 315, 321, 370, 374, 425–426, 468, 506, 512, 516, 639, 663, 664, 678–679
E. Describe the role of specialization and exchange in the economic process.	117, 132, 187, 193, 194, 213, 240, 243, 267, 272, 282, 300, 314, 315, 341, 342, 346, 356, 357, 359, 360, 362, 369, 370, 371, 373, 374, 375, 377, 378, 424, 512, 513–514, 519, 551–552, 557, 559, 571, 663–664, 693, 715, 761
F. Explain and illustrate how values and beliefs influence different economic decisions.	131, 193, 237, 300, 302, 305, 306, 315, 316, 355, 375, 378, 413, 414, 557, 639, 665, 694, 744, 766–767
G. Differentiate among various forms of exchange and money.	228, 301, 325, 464, 486, 554, 566, 572–573, 588, 613, 667, 715, 761
H. Compare basic economic systems according to who determines what is produced, distributed, and consumed.	93, 94, 96, 301–302, 321, 355, 369, 393, 413, 424–425, 486, 510–511, 513–515, 558, 578–579, 582–583, 610–611, 616, 639, 663–664, 678–679, 682, 692–694, 701, 711, 743
I. Use economic concepts to help explain historical and current developments and issues in local, national, or global contexts.	93, 94, 95, 96, 187, 194, 195, 206, 228, 233, 234, 236, 244, 253, 256, 267, 272, 274, 300, 316, 317, 320, 321, 342, 351, 356, 359, 362, 375, 383, 393, 414, 424–425, 427, 437, 438, 488, 513–515, 558, 566–567, 639, 666–670
J. Use economic reasoning to compare different proposals for dealing with a contemporary social issue such as unemployment, acid rain, or high quality education.	70–72, 131–132, 406–407, 428, 667, 693
VIII. *Science, Technology, & Society* The study of science, technology, and society is ever changing. It raises questions about who will benefit from it and how fundamental values and beliefs can be preserved in a technology-driven society. By the middle grades, students research the complex relationships among technology, human values, and behavior. Students will learn how technology and science have brought about change and how they have often challenged accepted societal beliefs.	
A. Examine and describe the influence of culture on scientific and technological choices and advancement, such as in transportation, medicine, and warfare.	98, 218, 304, 325, 374, 409, 512–515, 553–554, 566, 576, 642, 667, 694, 696, 710, 760
B. Show through specific examples how science and technology have changed people's perceptions of the social and natural world, such as in their relationship to the land, animal life, family life, and economic wants, needs, and security.	28, 51, 97, 98, 108, 218, 298, 315, 409, 428, 566–567, 578, 616, 665, 693–694, 739, 766–767
C. Describe examples in which values, beliefs, and attitudes have been influenced by new scientific and technological knowledge, such as the invention of the printing press, conceptions of the universe, applications of atomic energy, and genetic discoveries.	218, 304, 315, 325, 409, 553–554, 566, 665, 679, 692
D. Explain the need for laws and policies to govern scientific and technological applications, such as the safety and well-being of workers and consumers and the regulation of utilities, radio, and television.	89–90, 315, 428
E. Seek reasonable and ethical solutions to problems that arise when scientific advancements and social norms or values come into conflict.	72, 250–251, 498, 768, 772
IX. *Global Connections* As countries grow more interdependent, understanding global connections among world societies becomes important. Students will analyze emerging global issues in many different fields. They will also investigate relationships among the different cultures of the world. In the middle years, students analyze the interactions among states and countries and respond to global events and changes.	
A. Describe instances in which language, art, music, belief systems, and other cultural elements can facilitate global understanding or cause misunderstanding.	81, 199, 414, 466, 468, 551, 562, 578, 610, 641–642, 669–670, 681, 696, 718, 737

Theme and Performance Expectation	Student Pages
B. Analyze examples of conflict, cooperation, and interdependence among groups, societies, and nations.	195, 228, 244, 245, 296, 297, 316, 317, 320, 321, 324, 325, 326, 351, 370, 414, 439, 446, 473–478, 493, 517–520, 584–585, 605–607, 664, 668–669, 698–701, 744, 766, 768
C. Describe and analyze the effects of changing technologies on the global community.	97, 98, 317, 462–464, 467, 512–515, 554, 576, 578, 616, 642, 663–664, 667, 679, 693–694, 696, 710, 739, 760, 766–768
D. Explore the causes, consequences, and possible solutions to persistent, contemporary, and emerging global issues, such as health, security, resource allocation, economic development, and environmental quality.	205, 206, 231, 250, 256, 320, 402, 508–509, 517–520, 576, 607, 664, 668–670
E. Describe and explain the relationships and tensions between national sovereignty and global interests in such matters as territory, natural resources, trade, use of technology, and welfare of people.	96, 187, 231, 235, 270, 283, 316, 320, 321, 324, 326, 328–333, 379, 380, 411, 512–513, 517–520, 605–607, 668–669
F. Demonstrate understanding of concerns, standards, issues, and conflicts related to universal human rights.	99, 317, 402, 512–515, 584–585, 591–597, 605–607, 668–669
G. Identify and describe the roles of international and multinational organizations.	96, 205, 348, 513, 766
X. *Civic Ideals & Practices* Understanding civic ideals and practices is crucial to complete participation in society and is the main purpose of social studies. Students will learn about civic participation and the role of the citizen within his or her community, country, and world. By the middle grades, students will broaden their understanding to analyze and evaluate relationships between civic ideals and practices.	
A. Examine the origins and continuing influence of key ideals of the democratic republican form of government, such as individual human dignity, liberty, justice, equality, and the rule of law.	146, 147, 294, 296, 306, 307, 362, 445, 446, 639–640, 668–669
B. Identify and interpret sources and examples of the rights and responsibilities of citizens.	99, 167, 187, 291, 307, 401, 413, 414, 463, 546, 634, 668–669, 733
C. Locate, access, analyze, organize, and apply information about selected public issues—recognizing and explaining multiple points of view.	76, 170, 250, 401, 448, 459, 498, 520, 654, 670, 682, 705, 772
D. Practice forms of civic discussion and participation consistent with the ideals of citizens in a democratic republic.	318–319, 446, 459
E. Explain and analyze various forms of citizen action that influence public policy decisions.	170, 252, 606, 668, 733
F. Identify and explain the roles of formal and informal political actors in influencing and shaping public policy and decision-making.	170, 445, 606, 640, 646–647, 667–668
G. Analyze the influence of diverse forms of public opinion on the development of public policy and decision-making.	606, 668
H. Analyze the effectiveness of selected public policies and citizen behaviors in realizing the stated ideals of a democratic republican form of government.	579, 639–640, 668–669, 733
I. Explain the relationship between policy statements and action plans used to address issues of public concern.	605–607, 639, 653, 665, 766
J. Examine strategies designed to strengthen the "common good," which consider a range of options for citizen action.	250–251, 409, 498, 576

From Geography Themes

In the past decade, instruction in geography has been organized around the five themes of geography: location, place, human/environment interaction, movement, and regions. The popularity of these content organizers set the stage for the development of two additional, more comprehensive instructional frameworks: the "Six Essential Elements" and the "Eighteen Geography Standards" within the elements. These two interlocking frameworks provide the structure of the publication *Geography for Life: National Geography Standards 1994.*

6 Essential Elements and

1 The World in Spatial Terms

Geography studies the relationships between people, places, and environments by mapping information about them into a spatial context.

The geographically informed person knows and understands:

1. How to use maps and other geographic representations, tools, and technologies to acquire, process, and report information from a spatial perspective
2. How to use mental maps to organize information about people, places, and environments in a spatial context
3. How to analyze the spatial organization of people, places, and environments on Earth's surface

2 Places and Regions

The identities and lives of individuals and peoples are rooted in particular places and in those human constructs called regions.

The geographically informed person knows and understands:

4. The physical and human characteristics of places
5. That people create regions to interpret Earth's complexity
6. How culture and experience influence people's perception of places and regions

3 Physical Systems

Physical processes shape Earth's surface and interact with plant and animal life to create, sustain, and modify ecosystems.

The geographically informed person knows and understands:

7. The physical processes that shape the patterns of Earth's surface
8. The characteristics and spatial distribution of ecosystems on Earth's surface

to Geography Standards

How the Themes and Standards Compare It is important to keep in mind that the five themes and the standards look at the same geographic universe. The themes represent an instructional approach; they allow a particular focus to be given to the lesson of the moment. The standards comprise the geographic subject matter, skills, and perspectives of geography. The 5 themes flow through all the 18 geography standards and can be used in the instruction of all of them, at any grade level.

The chart below explains the 6 essential elements and lists the standards within each. The chart on pages T32–T37 provides:

- An explanation of the 18 standards
- Which of the five themes relate most closely to each standard
- Page numbers in the student edition of *The World and Its People* that utilize each standard

18 Geography Standards

4 Human Systems

People are central to geography in that human activities help shape Earth's surface, human settlements and structures are part of Earth's surface, and humans compete for control of Earth's surface.

The geographically informed person knows and understands:

9. The characteristics, distribution, and migration of human populations on Earth's surface
10. The characteristics, distribution, and complexity of Earth's cultural mosaics
11. The patterns and networks of economic interdependence on Earth's surface
12. The processes, patterns, and functions of human settlement
13. How the forces of cooperation and conflict among people influence the division and control of Earth's surface

5 Environment and Society

The physical environment is modified by human activities, largely as a consequence of the ways in which human societies value and use Earth's natural resources, and human activities are also influenced by Earth's physical features and processes.

The geographically informed person knows and understands:

14. How human actions modify the physical environment
15. How physical systems affect human systems
16. The changes that occur in the meaning, use, distribution, and importance of resources

6 The Uses of Geography

Knowledge of geography enables people to develop an understanding of the relationships between people, places, and environments over time—that is, of Earth as it was, is, and might be.

The geographically informed person knows and understands:

17. How to apply geography to interpret the past
18. How to apply geography to interpret the present and plan for the future

Correlation of *The World and Its People* to the National Geography Standards

National Geography Standards & Related Themes	Student Edition Pages
STANDARD 1 **How to use maps and other geographic representations, tools, and technologies to acquire, process, and report information from a spatial perspective** Maps are the most commonly used representations of detailed geographic information on features or places. Along with other tools such as globes, aerial photographs, satellite images, and statistical databases, they bring the whole world into focus. Maps range from simple sketch maps to complex Geographic Information Systems (GIS) analyses. **Related Themes: Location, Place**	22–23, 25, 28, 29–31, 33, 41, 56, 57, 58, 60, 63–64, 84, 86, 89, 98, 118, 119–123, 127, 130, 132, 160, 180–186, 196, 213, 224, 233, 240, 255, 273, 284–292, 298, 301, 334, 341, 342, 349, 364–365, 369, 383, 395–401, 405, 406, 427, 437, 458–463, 485, 503, 509, 510, 518, 538–546, 551, 552, 560, 573, 580, 583, 587, 589, 613, 615, 628–634, 648, 650, 652, 653, 661, 668, 684, 689, 691, 695, 702, 709, 713
STANDARD 2 **How to use mental maps to organize information about people, places, and environments in a spatial context** A mental map exists only in the mind's eye. It represents each individual's knowledge of the location of geographic features such as countries, cities, seas, mountain ranges, and rivers. A mental map is also made up of approximate size dimensions and cultural characteristics. In scale, it may include our route to a local store or theater, or it may serve as the framework for the location of the Khyber Pass, Brasília, or the Yangtze Gorges. This map grows in complexity as experience, study, and the media bring us new geographic information. **Related Themes: Location, Place, Regions**	23–24, 29–31, 88–90, 97, 114, 116, 126, 127, 128, 129, 144, 158, 159, 160, 161, 176, 212, 218, 232, 239, 242, 244, 266, 267, 268, 273, 280, 284–287, 340, 341, 342, 345, 350, 353–361, 368, 369, 370, 371, 375, 377–379, 381, 383, 404, 406, 407, 410, 427, 436, 437, 439, 466, 469, 470, 483, 484, 485, 486, 488, 490–492, 502, 504–506, 508, 509, 510, 513, 515, 516, 517, 519, 520, 550, 556, 570, 571, 573, 577, 580, 582, 583, 586, 587, 588, 590, 604, 609, 610, 612, 614, 616, 617, 618, 624, 638, 640, 644, 646, 649, 651, 652, 666, 678, 680, 685, 698, 699, 701, 710
STANDARD 3 **How to analyze the spatial organization of people, places, and environments on Earth's surface** Human structures organize space. Pattern, regularity, and reason are inherent in the locations of cities, factories, malls, cemeteries, and other human landscape creations. To understand the spatial patterns and processes that organize Earth's surface, it is essential to know concepts such as distance, direction, location, connections, and association. Understanding these concepts enables one to say what factors influence a locational decision for a hospital, a county seat, a sanitary landfill, or a regional shopping center. **Related Themes: Place, Human/Environment Interaction**	24–26, 28, 29–31, 86, 89–91, 97–98, 120, 162, 163, 170, 178, 179, 187, 212, 213, 215, 218, 222, 236, 241, 250, 268, 280, 282, 285–291, 301, 322, 323, 325–326, 341, 342, 349, 350, 354, 357–360, 370, 371, 372, 374, 395–401, 404, 405, 406, 407, 410, 427, 436, 437, 439, 454, 458, 460–463, 469, 470, 485, 486, 493, 517, 519, 520, 550, 570, 571, 580, 583, 609, 626, 666, 678, 691, 698, 708, 713, 716

National Geography Standards & Related Themes	Student Edition Pages
STANDARD 4 **The physical and human characteristics of places** Places may be distinguished by their physical and human characteristics. Physical characteristics include landforms, climate, soils, hydrology, vegetation, and animal life. Human characteristics include language, religion, political and economic systems, population, and quality of life. Places change over time as new technologies, resources, knowledge, and ideologies are introduced and become part of a place's geography. Such change leads to the rise and fall of empires, may derive from shifts in climate or other physical systems, or may be generated by population expansion. **Related Themes: Place, Human/Environment Interaction**	23, 24, 53–57, 61–72, 80–81, 88–91, 114, 116, 117, 126, 127–130, 133–135, 143, 147–149, 158–163, 165–170, 176, 178, 190–192, 198, 212, 213, 215, 217–222, 232, 236, 239–243, 256, 268, 271, 272, 273, 280, 282, 283, 296, 299, 301, 303–304, 306, 314, 319–321, 342, 343, 344, 345, 350–354, 357–360, 362, 369–374, 381, 383–385, 392–395, 399, 404, 406, 407, 410, 424–429, 431, 434, 436, 437, 439, 454, 455, 461–463, 466–471, 473, 474, 476, 484, 486–488, 490–492, 493, 502, 505, 506, 508, 509, 513, 517, 519, 534, 536, 541, 550, 551, 556–558, 570–572, 575, 582, 585, 586, 588, 589, 595–596, 607, 609, 610, 611, 612, 614, 615, 616, 617, 618, 631, 638, 639, 640, 645, 649, 652, 660–664, 666–670, 678–781, 690–695, 698–701, 708–712, 714–717
STANDARD 5 **That people create regions to interpret Earth's complexity** Regions are defined as having one or more common characteristics that give them a measure of unity and make them distinct from surrounding areas. As worlds within worlds, regions simplify geographic analysis by organizing a specific area into a unit of explicit physical and human elements. The criteria in the definition of a region can be as precise as coastline or political boundaries, or as arbitrary as the general location of people loyal to a specific athletic team. Regions are human constructs, created to facilitate the understanding of a large, varied, complex, and changing world. **Related Themes: Regions, Human/Environment Interaction**	26–27, 61, 62, 63, 65–68, 84–85, 127–129, 133, 134, 135, 148, 158, 159, 176, 178, 190, 191, 192, 199, 212, 213, 221, 240, 243, 268, 273, 282, 296, 301, 304, 319–322, 324–326, 345, 347, 351, 352, 371, 379, 383–385, 394, 395, 407, 426, 427, 436, 437, 454, 455, 467, 474, 486, 490, 491, 493, 519, 534, 536, 550, 556, 557, 572, 586, 607, 609, 624, 652, 661, 678, 699, 708, 710, 711, 714
STANDARD 6 **How culture and experience influence people's perceptions of places and regions** Perception of all places and regions depends upon personal experience, culture, age, gender, and other factors. It is sometimes said that there is no reality, only perception. In geography there is always a mixture of both. For example, a wilderness can be attractive to a camper, a source of anxiety for a child, and a nuisance to a pioneering farmer. **Related Themes: Regions, Place, Movement**	26–27, 80–83, 97, 98, 100, 146, 148, 168, 170, 215, 216, 219, 222, 233, 234, 240, 241, 283, 303, 306, 308, 315, 319, 320, 343, 351, 352, 353, 357, 360, 362, 379, 406, 415, 439, 466, 468, 470, 473, 474, 476, 477, 487, 493, 510, 514, 550, 572, 586, 588, 606, 607, 615, 616, 664, 665, 667, 669, 693, 694, 695, 707, 715

National Geography Standards & Related Themes	Student Edition Pages
STANDARD 7 **The physical processes that shape the patterns of Earth's surface** Physical processes create natural landscapes and environments arrayed across Earth's surface in spatial patterns. Understanding these forces is indispensable in daily decision-making, such as evaluating home-building sites in earthquake zones or floodplains, or building a highway along the ocean coastline. There is a systematic order in this continual remaking of Earth's surface. The geographically informed person understands the interplay of systems, forces, boundaries, thresholds, and equilibrium as they influence patterns on Earth's surface. **Related Themes: Place, Regions**	29–32, 34–42, 48–58, 62–67, 100, 114, 159, 192, 193, 219, 220, 232, 280, 357, 362, 363, 392, 484, 485, 502, 503, 509, 534, 536, 558, 571, 575, 588, 589, 608, 612, 618, 624, 639, 645, 646, 649, 654, 661–663, 694, 714, 741, 760, 764, 766
STANDARD 8 **The characteristics and spatial distribution of ecosystems on Earth's surface** Ecosystems are communities of living things—plants and animals—interacting with each other and with the physical environment. Ecosystems are dynamic and ever changing. They are self-regulating, open systems that maintain flows of energy and matter that naturally move toward maturity, stability, and balance. By understanding how these systems and processes work in shaping the physical environment, students will be better able to comprehend the basic principles that guide environmental management. Such knowledge will enable them to anticipate the consequences of ongoing human effort to transform Earth's landscapes. **Related Themes: Location, Place, Regions**	31, 32, 34, 35, 39–42, 49, 50, 53–58, 62–68, 69–71, 100, 145–146, 159–161, 192, 193, 213, 219, 220, 232, 243, 250, 255, 266, 267, 271, 273, 358, 362, 363, 392, 407, 408, 454, 455, 484, 485, 492, 503, 505–506, 509, 513, 534, 536, 556, 557, 571, 588, 614, 616, 624, 625, 638, 639, 640, 645, 646, 650, 654, 660, 685, 768
STANDARD 9 **The characteristics, distribution, and migration of human populations on Earth's surface** The characteristics and distribution of human populations are never static. Factors such as natural increase, war, famine, disease, and rate of urbanization play decisive roles in where people live. At any one time, some populations are bound to be migrating—leaving one place, striking out for a second, or possibly settling in a third. The factors that give definition to a nation's population profile, patterns of growth or decline, and inclinations toward migration combine to be significant geographic information. **Related Themes: Human/Environment Interaction, Movement, Regions**	58, 70–71, 87, 88, 89, 90, 91, 108, 145, 146, 150, 165, 166, 169, 179, 197, 199, 201, 202, 212, 215, 216, 217, 220, 222, 237, 240, 241, 242, 254, 267, 272, 273, 274, 282, 283, 294–297, 299–302, 304–306, 307, 315–318, 322, 323, 344, 346–348, 350, 352, 353, 355, 358–360, 361, 373, 374, 375, 377, 380, 381, 384–386, 414, 424, 426, 430–433, 434, 437, 438, 440, 467, 473, 474, 475, 476, 477, 484, 487, 488, 493, 503, 505–506, 508, 510, 511–516, 518, 519, 520, 523, 551, 552, 554, 557–561, 571, 572, 573–575, 577–579, 583, 604, 605, 606, 607, 609, 612, 614, 615, 640, 641, 642, 646, 647, 650, 651, 654, 661–662, 669, 678–680, 694, 695, 700, 709, 710, 712, 715–716, 738–739, 761, 767

National Geography Standards & Related Themes	Student Edition Pages
STANDARD 10 **The characteristics, distribution, and complexity of Earth's cultural mosaics** Culture defines each group's unique view of itself and others, and includes the material goods, skills, and social behavior transmitted to successive generations. It is expressed through art, language, beliefs and institutions, the built environment, and numerous other features. Cultural patterns are never static. They change in response to human migration, diffusion, and the steady introduction of new and competing cultural traits. **Related Themes: Location, Regions, Place**	80–85, 91, 117, 150, 151, 167, 168, 169, 170, 179, 198, 199, 203, 204, 216, 220, 222, 235, 236, 242, 244, 245, 246, 256, 257, 267, 268, 269, 270, 273, 274, 282, 295–297, 299–302, 303, 304, 305, 308, 317, 344, 346–348, 351, 352, 355, 356, 359, 361, 362, 370, 371, 373, 374, 375, 378–382, 385, 386, 394, 395, 411, 412, 414, 415, 425, 426, 430–433, 434, 437, 438, 440, 455, 456, 467, 468, 469, 470, 471, 473–477, 487–489, 491, 493, 503–505, 507, 510–512, 514–516, 518–520, 524–526, 536–537, 552–555, 557, 558, 560–562, 572, 573–575, 577–579, 581, 583, 584, 588, 590, 604, 605, 606, 607, 610, 611, 616, 617, 618, 625, 640, 641, 642, 643, 644, 646, 647, 651, 652, 653, 654, 667, 670, 680, 692, 694–697, 700–701, 711, 717, 718, 737–739, 743–744, 759–762, 767
STANDARD 11 **The patterns and networks of economic interdependence on Earth's surface** The goods that we need daily to make life work have sources all over the world. Economic networks at all scales, from local to global, have been developed to promote the efficient interchange of goods. Linkages of transportation, communication, language, currency, and custom have been fashioned out of the human desire to have more than what is available locally. For United States citizens, learning about the nature and significance of global interdependence is an essential aspect of being geographically well-informed. **Related Themes: Movement, Regions, Human/Environment Interaction, Location**	71–72, 83, 93, 94, 95, 96, 100, 131, 132–136, 146, 160, 161, 162, 163, 168, 179, 194, 195, 204, 205, 213, 220, 222, 223, 228, 233, 234, 240, 242, 243, 250, 253, 256, 257, 268, 274, 282, 295–297, 300–302, 315, 319–321, 324–325, 346–348, 351, 352, 355–357, 359, 360, 362, 369, 375, 377, 378, 380, 384, 412, 415, 424, 425, 427, 428, 438, 455, 467, 469, 470, 486, 488, 491, 492, 503, 505–506, 509, 510, 511, 514, 515, 536, 551, 557, 559–561, 571, 573, 578, 580, 582, 584, 589, 605, 610, 612, 614, 616, 618, 625, 639, 646, 647, 650, 652, 663, 678–679, 702, 710, 711, 716, 739, 743, 758–759, 761–762
STANDARD 12 **The processes, patterns, and functions of human settlement** Settlement is one of the most basic human responses to the environment. As social animals, humans achieve proximity, shared environments, and the opportunity to engage in effective economic and social interaction through settlement. Nearly half the human population has opted for city residence. However, there is a vast variety of cultural landscapes in urban settings, just as there is in village and town settings for most of the rest of the population. In all varieties of settlements, cultural landscapes reflect local resources and human preferences. **Related Themes: Place, Regions, Movement**	52, 72, 83–84, 90–91, 92, 98, 117, 132–135, 146–150, 159, 165, 166, 168, 169, 179, 197, 198, 199, 203, 204, 223, 228, 234, 242, 244, 256, 269, 274, 283, 294, 295–297, 300–301, 305, 307, 315–316, 319, 322, 346–348, 352, 355–357, 361, 369, 378, 379, 386, 406, 411, 412, 414, 430–433, 467, 468, 470, 474, 476, 486, 487, 488, 491, 492, 493, 503, 504, 505–506, 510–512, 514–516, 518, 519, 523, 537, 552–554, 557–560, 572, 573–575, 578, 579, 583, 584, 587, 590, 591–596, 604, 605, 606, 607, 610, 611, 612, 614, 615, 616, 617, 618, 625, 626, 640, 641, 646, 647, 651, 653, 663–665, 669, 681, 692, 700–701, 709–712, 717, 736, 738–739, 743–744, 760

National Geography Standards & Related Themes	Student Edition Pages
STANDARD 13 **How the forces of cooperation and conflict among people influence the division and control of Earth's surface** The tendency to divide space into segments that provide identity and a sense of security is universal. This human drive covers all scales, from individual homesteads through neighborhood and city limits to state and national boundaries. We have long declared borders, built walls, demarcated rivers and mountain ridges, and had arbitrary lines mapped across deserts. This trait relates to a wish to enclose that which we desire or perhaps exclude that which is feared. Multinational alliances as well as community interest groups are all motivated by the human capacity for expression of cooperation and conflict in the control of Earth's surface. **Related Themes: Regions, Movement, Human/Environment Interaction**	71, 72, 84–85, 88, 96, 99–100, 146–149, 163, 166, 170, 179, 199, 200, 205, 215, 216, 218, 221, 222, 223, 228, 233, 234, 237, 243, 244, 245, 253, 256, 257, 267, 271, 283, 295–297, 300–302, 305, 306, 307, 315–317, 319, 321–323, 324–326, 347–348, 355–357, 360, 361, 362, 369, 370, 373, 374, 375, 378, 380, 384–386, 408, 409, 411, 412, 413, 414, 430, 438, 439, 440, 455, 456, 468, 470, 471, 474, 475, 476, 487, 493, 503, 504, 509, 510, 511, 512, 514, 515, 518, 522–526, 557, 559, 561, 571, 573, 574, 579, 583, 587, 588, 589, 590, 592–596, 603, 605, 606, 610, 611, 615, 617, 641, 642, 644, 645, 647, 650, 652, 653, 654, 667–668, 679, 699, 761, 767
STANDARD 14 **How human actions modify the physical environment** When humans first occupied the environment, levels of technology were low enough that modifications of the physical setting were generally simple, although significant over time. However, as we have developed more powerful technology to assist us in such modifications, we have made hot areas cool, cold areas warm, dry areas garden-like, and wet areas habitable. Changing the landscape has become a signature of human use of Earth, and will be a significant theme as we see just what we have gained (and lost) in such transformations. **Related Themes: Human/Environment Interaction, Place, Regions**	58–59, 69–72, 76, 92–93, 136, 147–148, 160, 168, 193, 194, 206, 214, 231, 235, 250, 251, 267, 270, 271, 272, 300–302, 305, 315–318, 344, 370, 378, 394, 408, 411, 413, 428, 472, 486, 490, 504, 511, 512, 553, 558, 574, 584, 585, 604, 606, 639, 640, 651, 653, 664–665, 693, 708
STANDARD 15 **How physical systems affect human systems** Expanding settlement of floodplains, coastal margins, and seismic zones has brought us face-to-face with striking evidence of ways in which physical systems have profound effects on human systems. Less dramatic—but ultimately more significant—aspects of the effect of physical systems on human systems are such issues as freshwater use, ozone depletion, global warming, and soil loss. Knowledge of Earth's physical systems will be critical to the human use of Earth in the years to come and is central to *Geography for Life.* **Related Themes: Place, Regions, Human/Environment Interaction**	31–32, 34, 41, 58, 59, 69, 70, 71, 72, 95, 117, 162–163, 201, 212, 220, 231, 235, 242, 243, 244, 250, 251, 274, 300, 304, 305, 314–315, 351, 353, 356, 359, 370, 373, 378, 392, 405, 406, 413, 426, 427, 428, 437, 467, 469, 484, 490, 509, 516, 557, 566, 571, 576, 582, 584, 585, 587, 616, 639, 645, 647, 651, 654, 662, 690, 714, 760

National Geography Standards & Related Themes	Student Edition Pages
STANDARD 16 **The changes that occur in the meaning, use, distribution, and importance of resources** We extract, process, market, and consume those things we value in the environment. The activity related to putting values on resources, and the subsequent demands on the environment, establish patterns of economic, political, and cultural interaction. Some natural resources we require: air, water, vegetation—and space. Others commonly used, such as oil, tin, diamonds, bananas, and coffee, have gained their value by human decisions that generally relate to levels of technology and economic development. A geographer must understand what makes an item a resource, and what the subsequent geographic implications of such an appraisal might be. **Related Themes: Human/Environment Interaction, Place, Regions**	70, 71, 72, 88, 92–96, 99, 135–136, 147–149, 162–163, 195, 200, 213, 214, 220, 253, 269, 270, 274, 301, 302, 304, 305, 314–315, 356, 370, 380, 394, 408, 413, 414, 428, 438, 440, 455, 486, 487, 490, 491, 492, 558, 578, 580, 583, 585, 606, 610, 611, 617, 639, 642, 645, 662, 665, 679, 693, 700–701, 708–709, 715, 737–738, 740–743, 758–759, 761–762, 764, 766
STANDARD 17 **How to apply geography to interpret the past** An understanding of spatial and environmental perspectives leads to a fuller appreciation of the human use of Earth in the past. By determining how people have assessed their own settings, and gaining understanding of why they used their settings as they did—or changed them the way they did—we can see the role that geography has played in our histories. **Related Themes: Human/Environment Interaction, Movement, Regions**	27, 61, 145, 146, 147, 165–166, 199, 200, 216, 220, 223, 235, 240, 244, 245, 267, 270, 272, 283, 296, 305, 307, 314–315, 321, 322, 323, 326, 341, 351, 403, 410, 414, 415, 424, 441–447, 469, 473, 475, 476, 504, 507, 517, 518, 520, 549, 553, 562, 566, 594, 606, 663, 665–670, 679–681, 692–694, 698, 699, 701, 709, 711–712, 715–717, 738–739, 743–744, 761–762, 766, 768
STANDARD 18 **How to apply geography to interpret the present and plan for the future** Geography leads people to think about spatial patterns, connections between places, integration of local to global scales, diversity, and systems. With such a scope, it is easy to see how completely geography influences the present, and how it can be significant in achieving effective planning for the future. Issues that range from resources to population to paths of movement all relate to the essence of geography. Being able to put this breadth of impact to work in planning for the future is one of the benefits of being geographically well-informed. **Related Themes: Regions, Human/Environment Interaction, Place**	22, 23, 24, 25, 26, 51, 77, 88, 135, 136, 168–169, 250, 251, 269, 307, 314, 318, 323, 326, 327–333, 343, 403, 409, 441–447, 465, 501, 526, 546, 566, 581, 596, 603, 681, 712, 742, 768

Classroom Solutions

Project CRISS

How Can I Teach My Students How to Learn Social Studies?

by Carol M. Santa, Ph.D.

We all know that teaching social studies involves far more than teaching just course content. We understand that students need to become engaged, confident learners. Achieving that goal means helping them to understand, organize, and retain information.

Teaching Both Content and Skills

In other words, we want our students to have the skills and confidence to be life-long learners. With its rich content, social studies offer an ideal arena for teaching both content and skills.

✔ **A Dual Responsibility** Let's take a moment to consider why the dual responsibility of teaching both content and skills is so important. Think back to your own middle and high school years. What do you remember about the content you learned? If I recall my experiences, I find I remember remarkably little content. What did I learn in biology or history? What did my textbooks look like? As the years go by, I don't even remember the names of most of my teachers.

✔ **An Inspiring Teacher** Yet I have vivid memories of my eighth-grade social studies teacher, who came out of retirement to fill in for a history teacher who left on maternity leave. I remember how fascinated I became with ancient history; I recall giving oral reports and how she helped me become comfortable speaking before a group. In fact, I remember more from her class than any other I took during high school.

✔ **Teach How to Learn** More important, I now understand that she taught me how to learn to learn. She showed me how to underline, how to organize information using different note-taking formats, and how to write coherent answers on essay tests. She taught me the need to test myself on what I knew. And during that vulnerable, adolescent year, I went from being a mediocre student to being an excellent one.

This inspirational teacher did something else for me. At some point during that eighth-grade year, I decided to become a teacher. Later I realized that she had launched me on my professional mission—to spread her wisdom to others. Eventually this led to Project CRISS.

What is CRISS?

CRISS stands for **CR**eating **I**ndependence through **S**tudent-owned **S**trategies. It is a staff development program that I created in collaboration with middle and high school teachers in Kalispell, Montana.

✔ **Origin of CRISS** CRISS had its start 20 years ago in a lunchtime conversation in a teacher's lounge. One of the social studies teachers said, "My students aren't doing a good job of answering chapter questions. In fact, I don't think they even read my assignments. My reading assignments are becoming a waste of time!" His words struck a chord. "My students don't have a clue about how to study, and they don't write very well either," another teacher lamented.

✔ **Evolving Strategies** Supported by a state grant, we started working together to find practical ways to help students read, write, and learn content. We met in teams, read professional literature, and designed studies to test classroom strategies. From these efforts, we evolved a project to help students become better readers, writers, and

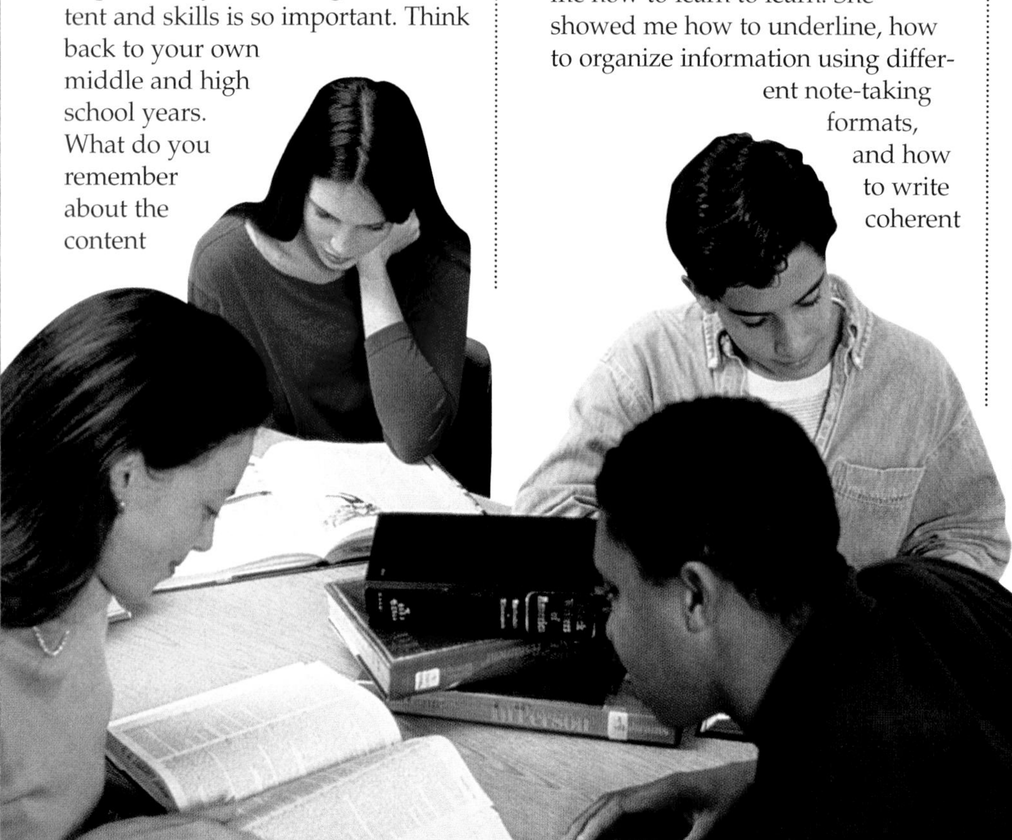

Tom & DeeAnn McCarthy/CORBIS STOCK MARKET

learners. Once the project took shape, we shared our discoveries with other teachers by offering a two- or three-day CRISS workshop to schools and districts in the state.

✔ ***Constant Growth*** Over the last two decades, Project CRISS has spread from teacher to teacher across this country, into Canada, and to several European countries. The project seems to sell itself. Teachers who use CRISS principles and strategies find that their students attain a deeper understanding of course content and become better readers, writers, and learners at the same time. In fact, data from numerous quantitative studies shows that using CRISS strategies improves student learning. (For the most recent data and for information on CRISS workshops, see www.projectcriss.com.)

CRISS Strategies in the Teacher Edition

When the editors of Glencoe/McGraw-Hill asked me and my colleagues to help them integrate CRISS strategies into their social studies texts, we welcomed the opportunity. In this teacher wraparound edition, we offer many references to CRISS strategies. We have packed the pages with strategies that help students gain a deeper understanding of specific content.

CRISS Training

We have one word of caution, however: the integration of CRISS strategies within this teacher wraparound edition does not take the place of a Project CRISS workshop, which provides an in-depth knowledge of CRISS. So, if you haven't yet participated in a CRISS workshop, we encourage you to do so. During a workshop, CRISS trainers take you step-by-step through the philosophy and instructional strategies. Participants are actively involved in all aspects of the program—practicing, adapting, and applying strategies to meet teaching needs.

Long-lasting change occurs when teachers and administrators work together to share, extend ideas, and problem solve. The most effective implementations occur when the initial workshop is supported by follow-up sessions, including a specific follow-up day. At this session, teachers bring examples of strategies they have used since the initial training. Part of this time may be spent in review and in learning new strategies. The rest of the time is for sharing applications. Additional on-going support can occur in teacher planning periods.

In any case, for those of you unfamiliar with Project CRISS, let's begin with a little background knowledge. In this way you will have some context for the various activities suggested throughout the teacher wraparound edition.

The CRISS Philosophy

The first thing to know is that Project CRISS is more than a collection of learning strategies. Its underlying power rests not on the individual strategies but on the teaching philosophy behind them. This philosophy integrates work from cognitive psychology, social learning theory, and neurological research about how the brain learns. It includes these overlapping principles:

- ✔ background knowledge and purposeful reading
- ✔ author's craft
- ✔ active involvement
- ✔ discussion
- ✔ organization
- ✔ writing
- ✔ teacher modeling

Let's look at each of these principles in more detail, along with examples of instructional strategies that illustrate them.

Background knowledge and purposeful reading are powerful determinants of reading comprehension.

Teachers involved in Project CRISS often talk about the importance of background knowledge. Readers are

(Continued on next page)

Using CRISS to Set a Purpose

Advice from Malla S. Kolhoff
Palm Harbor University High School
International Baccalaureate Program
Palm Harbor, Florida

As educators, it is our responsibility to set a purpose for historical reading. Students often must struggle to connect history with their own lives. To compare and contrast, establish cause and effect, and sequence events in chronological order presents a challenge for even the best reader. CRISS strategies allow students to move beyond words to the real significance for their society. With CRISS, my students are able to become engaged in the learning process through:

a. background knowledge
b. active reading, listening, and learning
c. discussion
d. metacognition
e. writing
f. organization
g. understanding

I have found that these strategies help my students attain a higher level of historical thinking and understanding.

Classroom Solutions

Project CRISS

far more likely to learn new information when they have some previous knowledge and have a purpose in mind before they read or listen.

- ✔ ***More Than Simply Reading*** We warn students not to simply begin reading. We ask them, *"What might you already know about the topic? What questions do you have about the topic?"* We also remind them to preview the assignment and think about their goals for reading. We often have to be very explicit about the goals. For example, we might tell students, *"After reading this selection, you should be able to . . . ,"* or, *"After viewing the video, you should be able to identify. . . ."*
- ✔ ***KWLH*** In the teaching strategies included for each chapter in this book, we offer ideas for helping students tap into their background knowledge. For example, we suggest that students preview their reading assignment and consider what they already know about a topic. Or, we might develop a whole class **KWLH** chart (**K**now, **W**ant to learn, **L**earned, **H**ow to learn more), where students work on this task together. They can generate questions about what they want to learn, and then, after completing the assignment, they can list the new information they have learned and how they can learn more.

K	W	L	H
What I **Know**	What I **Want** to Find Out	What I **Learned**	**How I** Can Learn More

✔ ***Reading Goals*** We also suggest ways to make sure your students have clear goals for their reading. Each section opener lists reading strategies and main ideas that outline reading goals. Most students will skip over this material and simply start reading. Teachers need to help students understand that the reading goals are important tools for understanding. We tell students, *"Don't ignore your purposes for reading. Take time to think about them before delving into your reading."* Project CRISS also provides hints about how to get students to use these purpose statements to evaluate whether they have understood their reading.

Good readers have an intuitive understanding of the author's craft.

When students know how authors craft their writing, they can more readily understand and remember what they read.

- ✔ ***Pay Attention*** Good readers and writers know that paying attention to how text is organized—its headings and paragraphs, for example—makes it easier to comprehend its content. Good readers will analyze the author's style of presentation as they read. They might ask themselves, *"What is this author doing to help me learn key concepts? How does the writer lead me from one idea to the next?"* When students become aware of what the author is doing to impart content, they have a clearer idea of what the author is saying.
- ✔ ***The Walk Through*** In the sample lesson on pages T42–T43, we offer advice about "walking through" the text to discover the author's style of presentation. Our suggestions go beyond examining the surface structure (headings, bold print, color coding of topical headings, italicized words) to analyzing how the author elaborates on key topics.

Effective learners are actively involved when they listen and read.

We learn best when we act on the information presented. We can do this by using a variety of organizing activities that require us to write, talk, and transform the information we are absorbing. None of us learns much from reading alone—it's far too passive.

CRISS strategies encourage active engagement in learning. We might ask students to read a section and describe what they are learning to a partner, or we might be more elaborate and have students develop concept maps or write summaries.

Students need many opportunities to talk with one another about what they are learning.

Discussion is critical to learning. The discussions we advocate are different from those in which the teacher remains the authority figure, with students simply reciting answers to

(Continued on next page)

Jose L. Pelaez/CORBIS STOCK MARKET

questions. If discussion becomes mere recitation and there is little interaction among students, little learning occurs. Thus we focus on how to get students to lead their own discussions about a topic. We want them to understand that it is their discussing, their oral grappling with meaning—not ours—that leads to deeper understanding.

Competent readers know several ways to organize information for learning.

Learning depends on organization. We show students different ways to organize information. They can take notes, underline selectively, develop concept maps, and summarize ideas in charts. Once we have taught students these techniques, we tell them, *"You have to do more than just read this assignment. How are you going to organize the information from this assignment? You have to change it, to transform it so that it becomes your own."*

For each chapter of this text, we offer ideas for assisting students in organizing information. Once students have learned a variety of organizing systems, we suggest ways to help them apply these structures independently.

Students deserve opportunities to write about what they are learning.

Writing is an integral part of the CRISS project. Writing lets us figure out what we know and what we still need to know. We cannot write about something we do not understand. While we teach students how to write expository papers and essay exams, we also encourage students to write more informally by questioning, speculating, and writing explanations in learning logs. We make sure that students are writing continually about what they are learning.

For each chapter of this text, we offer ideas for assisting students in organizing information. Once students have learned a variety of organizing systems, we suggest ways to help them apply these structures independently.

Teaching involves explanation and modeling.

Our final principle has to do with our own teaching. Students learn to think strategically when we use these processes as part of our instruction. Our demonstrations are especially critical for struggling readers. Most have never been taught how to learn. We have to show them how.

- ✔ ***Take Center Stage*** When you introduce a new strategy, you should take the center stage: showing, telling, modeling, demonstrating, and explaining not only the content but the process of active reading. As students learn, gradually release responsibility to them. Strategy instruction involves two overlapping steps. First we explain what the strategy is and why students should use it. If students do not know why they are performing an activity, they will rarely use the activity on their own. Next, we demonstrate and talk about procedures for carrying out the strategy. We discuss, demonstrate, and think aloud while modeling. Then, students practice under our guidance and feedback.
- ✔ ***A Systematic Approach*** Project CRISS is a valuable basis for instruction. It provides a systematic approach for using what we now know about teaching and learning. The following chart lists questions we need to continually ask ourselves while we are teaching. Use this chart to monitor your efforts to incorporate CRISS principles into your teaching.

CRISS Principles	The CRISS Philosophy	Yes	No	Somewhat
Background knowledge:	Did I assist students in thinking about what they already knew about the topic before beginning the unit? Did I develop necessary concepts before students read?			
Purpose setting:	Did my students have a clear purpose about what they were going to learn before beginning the lesson?			
Author's craft:	Can my students use the author's style of presentation to facilitate their understanding?			
Active involvement:	Were my students engaged in the topic? Did I help students become actively involved in their learning?			
Discussion:	Did my students have opportunities to talk about what they were learning?			
Organization:	Did my students organize information in a variety of ways?			
Writing:	Did my students write about what they were learning?			
Teacher modeling:	Did I do enough teacher modeling of learning strategies so that students could begin doing them on their own?			

Classroom Solutions

Project CRISS

How Do I Use Project CRISS to Teach The World and Its People?

When students know how authors structure their writing, they can more readily understand and remember what they read. For the first several chapters of this book, show students how to analyze the author's craft by "walking through" features of the text. Then demonstrate how to use the author's organization to develop two-column notes.

To demonstrate these strategies, make transparencies of the first several pages of Chapter 1 "Looking at the Earth."

Introducing the Chapter

Place a transparency of pages 20–21 on the overhead and begin modeling.

Tell students: *"Before reading a text, I take time to figure out how the author has presented the information. If I understand the author's craft, I can do a better job of reading and learning. The authors of this book have a consistent organizational plan for presenting information. Let's discover what they do."*

Have students open their books to pages 20–21. Together, preview these pages, noticing the video information, the Social Studies online reference (twip.glencoe.com), the *Why It Matters* information, and the foldable activity. *"How might you use Social Studies online to expand your understanding of the chapter content?"* (Ask one or more students to explore what is available online for this chapter and report to the class on ways that this information could be used.)

Eugene Fisher & Barbara Brundege

Introducing the Section

Ask students to turn to page 22. *"Notice how this page is organized."* (It begins with a Guide to Reading that includes: Main Idea, Terms to Know, and Reading Strategy.) *"Let's take a moment and talk about how these features might help you."*

Main Idea

"Why has the author included the main idea at the beginning of the section?" (The main idea helps the readers focus on what they are going to learn, helps them think about what they might already know about the section information, and helps them set goals for reading.)

Terms to Know

"Now look at the list of key terms (geography, landform, environment, and so on) *and skim the first several pages of each section. What do you notice about how the Terms to Know are sequenced and highlighted in this chapter?"* (The Terms to Know are highlighted in blue and presented in the same order as in the list at the beginning of each section.)

Reading Strategy

"Notice the reading strategy suggested for this section. Why is it important to organize information you read? How might the strategy suggested here help you?"

National Geographic

"Notice the references to National Geographic on pages 22, 23, 25, and 26. Why do you think the author has included these references? Why should you pay attention to them? It is a good idea to read through these references before reading the chapter." (These references make the topics more interesting, provide background knowledge, include important information for understanding the content, and so on.)

Walking Through the Chapter

As you talk aloud, note features on the transparencies for pages 22–27. *"Now let's see how the authors have helped us figure out the main topics covered in this chapter. Notice the bold print headings. The main topics are printed in larger red print and the subtopics are printed in smaller blue print. Vocabulary terms are noted in blue. This organization and color coding should help you figure out what is important."*

"At the end of each subsection, notice the Reading Check question. There are also assessment questions at the end of each section (page 27). *The Reading Check questions will help you know if you have comprehended each subsection. When you come to a Reading Check, you should stop and try to answer the question. If you can't answer the question, you should reread. You should also read through these questions before you begin to read. In this way, you will know what you are supposed to get out of this section. The end-of-section assessment questions will also help you know what you are to learn."*

Have students read the topical headings for the first section of the chapter (A Geographer's View of Place, The Tools of Geography, Uses of Geography, and Clues to Our Past). Have students make some predictions about what they will learn. Explain that good readers take time to preview and to make predictions before reading. Talk about how using the topic headings helps with this process.

Reading the Chapter

Assign students to read the introduction to the section, stopping on page 23 at the heading, A Geographer's View of Place. Have them turn to a partner and retell what they have just read.

"Good readers are active when they read. They stop and think about what they have just read. If they can't remember the information, they go back and reread."

Continue having students read the rest of Section 1. After each subsection, have them turn to a partner, and, without looking back at the text, retell what they have just read. Also, model how to turn topical headings into questions as a way to evaluate comprehension. *"Only you know if you understand. No one else can do that for you. Constantly check your comprehension by retelling, asking yourself questions, and explaining to yourself or to a partner what you are learning."*

Main Idea-Detail Notes

Ask students to divide their notebook paper into two columns. Explain that they will record main ideas in the left-hand column and details explaining the main ideas in the right-hand column. Main ideas may be questions or key words. They cover the information on the right. Students can use the questions or key words to quiz themselves.

- ✔ Demonstrate how to use the author's clues (headings, bold print vocabulary) to develop main idea-detail notes. The authors also might include rhetorical questions which assist readers in determining main ideas. Talk about how the examples help clarify content, and show students how to include these rhetorical questions and examples within their notes. On a blank transparency, develop two-column notes over the first section of the chapter while students take notes at their desks. Model how to include main ideas, rhetorical questions, and vocabulary essential to understanding the content in the left-column. On the right, record details that elaborate on the main ideas. Talk to students about the importance of being brief and using their own words. Explain that making the author's message their own ensures better comprehension and retention.
- ✔ Continue modeling note-taking for the rest of this section. Then ask students to work in pairs or small groups to develop two-column notes for the rest of the chapter. Ask them to share their notes in a class discussion.
- ✔ Demonstrate how to use the notes for self-testing. Show students how you cover the right-hand column with a sheet of paper and recite what you can remember. Talk about why self-testing is so important for learning. *"You are the only one who knows if you know. Self-testing is an excellent way to learn and to check your understanding."*
- ✔ Take time for reflection. Allow time for discussion about these reading strategies. Ask students to write and then talk about how analyzing the author's craft and developing two-column notes helped them read and learn content. How might they use these strategies in the future?

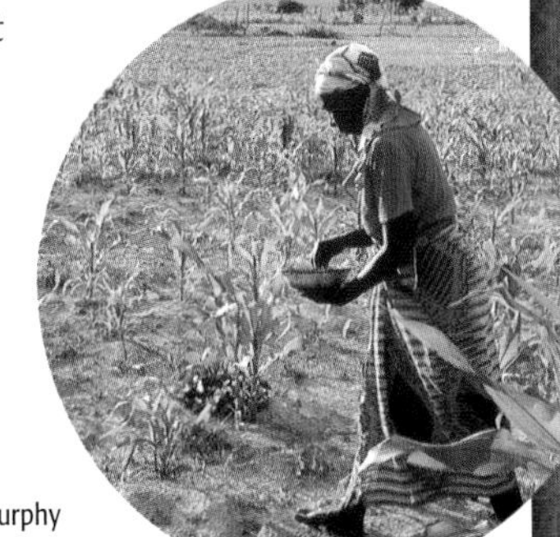

Stone/Ian Murphy

SAMPLE ORGANIZER

Main Ideas	Details
What is geography? **What are two types of geography?**	study of the earth 1. physical geography: land, water, plants, animals, how continents were formed, causes of erosion 2. human geography: people, how they live, effects of the environment, comparing different groups
Questions geographers study 1. Place: What physical features make a place similar or different?	1. landforms 2. water 3. climate 4. natural resources
2. What are the human characteristics that describe the people in a place?	1. population density 2. government 3. religions 4. occupations 5. languages 6. ancestry
3. How do people interact with their environments?	1. building dams 2. fishermen, shipbuilders, farmers
4. What is a region?	areas that have common characteristics; can be small (town) or big (western United States)

Classroom Solutions

Reading in the Content Areas

How Can I Use Jamestown Education Products to Help Struggling Readers?

For over 30 years, Jamestown Education has made its primary focus helping older readers become better readers. The Jamestown products shown on this page support the basic elements of reading cited by the National Reading Panel. Each of them can help your struggling readers become better readers.

Timed Readings Plus in Social Studies

✔ **Reading Levels:** 4-13+

✔ **Benefits:**

This ten-book series will help your students increase both reading rate and comprehension. The nonfiction passages cover current social studies topics and are similar to those found on both state and national tests. Each of the two-part lessons focuses on reading rate, factual recall, comprehension strategies, and higher-level critical thinking skills.

Reading in the Content Areas: Social Studies

✔ **Reading Levels:** 4-12+

✔ **Benefits:**

This book concentrates on six essential reading skills that will help your students better comprehend what they read. Seventy-five high-interest nonfiction passages written at increasing levels of difficulty, followed by consistent, targeted skills, teach the techniques needed to organize, understand, and apply information.

Reading Fluency

✔ **Reading Levels:** 1-10

✔ **Benefits:**

This seven-book series will help your students read smoothly, accurately and expressively. Students work in pairs to provide immediate feedback and self-assessment. Author Camille Blachowicz states that "the ability to read fluently is highly correlated with many other measures of reading competence."

Jamestown's Reading Improvement

✔ **Reading Levels** 4-10

✔ **Benefits:**

Authored by renowned reading expert Edward Fry, this eight-book series focuses on helping build your students' comprehension, vocabulary, and skimming and scanning skills. Repeated practice with targeted exercises ensures mastery of valuable reading skills.

Critical Reading Series

✔ **Reading Levels:** 2-8

✔ **Benefits:**
This twenty-four book high-interest series, written at three reading spans, encourages your reluctant readers to build a love for nonfiction while focusing on critical reading skills. Topics ranging from Fateful Journeys to Weird Science to Heroes draw students in, while giving students ample opportunities to master important skills found on both state and national tests.

In addition to the Project CRISS Reading Strategies, you may find it effective to implement some of the following instructional methods. They help *your* struggling students take increasing ownership of the reading process.

Reciprocal Teaching

Reciprocal teaching is characterized by a dialogue between you and your student, and ultimately among students in a group, in which students take the role of dialogue reader. Construction of meaning is built upon four reading strategies:

✔ **Summarizing** Readers identify the most important information in a segment of text and state that information in their own words. Summarizing involves students in recognizing and communicating the significant ideas in a text.

✔ **Questioning** Readers ask themselves questions about the text segment. Self-questioning aids comprehension by helping students identify where their understanding of the text has broken down and what they still need to know in order to understand what they have read.

✔ **Clarifying** Readers try to find answers to the questions they have raised and to make sense of parts of the text that have caused confusion. They seek clarification by rereading, reading ahead or by seeking outside help, such as through a peer or a reference source.

✔ **Predicting** Readers tell what they think will happen next, basing their predictions on evidence from the text they have already read.

Modeling

An important element of strategic instruction is teacher modeling. As a part of the modeling process, think aloud as you apply a strategy to solve a reading problem, putting words to the inner voice that successful readers have with text, and demonstrating the strategy used for understanding. To construct a "think-aloud," read aloud a passage, stopping at pertinent points to talk about what you are thinking. A think-aloud demonstrates the cognitive process and allows students to observe how a proficient reader approaches a problem with reading.

"Fix-Up" Strategies

Explain that readers perform certain tasks. Guide them through these following steps:

✔ **Stop** Tell students to stop and fix the problem when they do not understand.

✔ **Identify the Problem** Have students ask themselves when they stopped understanding and what they don't understand.

✔ **Apply a Fix-up Strategy** Encourage students to try these strategies:

✔ **Reread**

✔ **Read ahead**

✔ **Alter** the pace or voice

✔ **Ask** for help

CRISS and the Jamestown Reader

Advice from Dr. Sara Wartenberg
Palm Harbor University High School
International Baccalaureate Program
Palm Harbor, Florida

Help your students achieve testing success by combining CRISS strategies with the Jamestown Readers. The stories appeal to students of all reading levels. The stories are interesting and informative for students and teachers alike. Implementing CRISS strategies as students read the selections will help them respond with greater success to the questions that accompany each selection. Students will gain confidence and thus work for greater skill in reading comprehension and critical thinking.

Classroom Solutions

Test-Taking Strategies

How Can I Help My Students Succeed on Tests?

It's not enough for students to learn social studies facts and concepts—they must be able to show what they know in a variety of test-taking situations.

How Can I Help My Students Do Well On Objective Tests?

Objective tests may include multiple choice, true/false, and matching questions. Applying the following strategies can help students do their best on objective tests.

Multiple Choice Questions

- ✔ Students should read the directions carefully to learn what answer the test requires—the best answer or the right answer. This is especially important when answer choices include "all of the above" or "none of the above."
- ✔ Advise students to watch for negative words in the questions, such as *not, except, unless, never,* and so forth. If the question contains a negative, the correct answer choice is the one that does not fit.
- ✔ Students should try to mentally answer the question before reading the answer choices.
- ✔ Students should read all the answer choices and cross out those that are obviously wrong. Then they should choose an answer from those that remain.

True/False Questions

- ✔ It is important that students read the entire question before answering. For an answer to be true, the entire statement must be true. If one part of a statement is false, the answer should be marked *False*.
- ✔ Remind students to watch for words like *all, never, every,* and *always*. Statements containing these words are often false.

Matching Questions

- ✔ Students should read through both lists before they mark any answers.
- ✔ Unless an answer can be used more than once, students should cross out each choice as they use it.
- ✔ Using what they know about grammar can help students find the right answer. For instance, when matching a word with its definition, the definition is often the same part of speech (noun, verb, adjective, and so forth) as the word.

How Can I Help My Students Do Well On Essay Tests?

Essay tests require students to provide thorough and well-organized written responses, in addition to telling what they know. Help students use the following strategies on essay tests.

Analyze:	*To **analyze** means to systematically and critically examine all parts of an issue or event.*
Classify or Categorize:	*To **classify** or **categorize** means to put people, things, or ideas into groups, based on a common set of characteristics.*
Compare and Contrast:	*To **compare** is to show how things are similar, or alike. To **contrast** is to show how things are different.*
Describe:	*To **describe** means to present a sketch or impression. Rich details, especially details that appeal to the senses, flesh out a description.*
Discuss:	*To **discuss** means to systematically write about all sides of an issue or event.*
Evaluate:	*To **evaluate** means to make a judgment and support it with evidence.*
Explain:	*To **explain** means to clarify or make plain.*
Illustrate:	*To **illustrate** means to provide examples or to show with a picture or other graphic.*
Infer:	*To **infer** means to read between the lines or to use knowledge and experience to draw conclusions, make a generalization, or form a prediction.*
Justify:	*To **justify** means to prove or to support a position with specific facts and reasons.*
Predict:	*To **predict** means to tell what will happen in the future, based on an understanding of prior events and behaviors.*
State:	*To **state** means to briefly and concisely present information.*
Summarize:	*To **summarize** means to give a brief overview of the main points of an issue or event.*
Trace:	*To **trace** means to present the steps or stages in a process or event in sequential or chronological order.*

Read the Question

The key to writing successful essay responses lies in reading and interpreting questions correctly. Teach students to identify and underline key words in the questions, and to use these words to guide them in understanding what the question asks. Help students understand the meaning of some of the most common key words, listed in the chart on page T46.

Plan and Write the Essay

After students understand the question, they should follow the writing process to develop their answer. Encourage students to follow the steps below to plan and write their essays.

1. Map out an answer. Make lists, webs, or an outline to plan the response.

2. Decide on an order in which to present the main points.

3. Write an opening statement that directly responds to the essay question.

4. Write the essay. Expand on the opening statement. Support key points with specific facts, details, and reasons.

5. Write a closing statement that brings the main points together.

6. Proofread to check for spelling, grammar, and punctuation.

How Can I Help My Students Prepare for Standardized Tests?

Students can follow the steps below to prepare for a test.

Bill Aron/PhotoEdit

- ✔ ***Read About the Test*** Students can familiarize themselves with the format of the test, the types of questions that will be asked, and the amount of time they will have to complete the test.
- ✔ ***Review the Content*** Consistent study throughout the school year will help students build social studies knowledge and understanding. If there are specific objectives or standards that are tested on the exam, help students review these facts or skills to be sure they are proficient.
- ✔ ***Practice*** Provide practice, ideally with real released tests, to build students' familiarity with the content, format, and timing of the real exam. Students should practice all the types of questions they will encounter on the test—multiple choice, short answer, and extended response.
- ✔ ***Analyze Practice Results*** Help students improve test-taking performance by analyzing their test-taking strengths and weaknesses. Spend time discussing students' completed practice tests, explaining why particular answers are right or wrong. Help students identify what kinds of questions they had the most difficulty with. Look for patterns in errors and then tailor instruction to review the appropriate test-taking skills or social studies content.✦

Help Students Learn by Reviewing Graded Tests

Advice from Tara Musslewhite
Humble Independent School District
Humble, Texas

Frequently reviewing graded tests is a great way for students to assess their test-taking skills. It also gives teachers the opportunity to teach test-taking strategies and review content. As the class rereads each test question, guide students to think logically about their answer choices. Show students how to:

1. Read each question carefully to determine its meaning.
2. Look for key words in the question to support their answers.
3. Recognize synonyms in the answer choices that may match phrases in the question.
4. Narrow down answer choices by eliminating ones that don't make sense.
5. Anticipate the answer before looking at the answer choices.
6. Circle questions of which they are unsure and go back to them later. Sometimes a clue will be found in another question on the test.

Classroom Solutions

Alternative Assessment Strategies

How Can I Go Beyond Tests to Assess Students' Understanding of Social Studies Facts and Concepts?

In response to the growing demand for accountability in the classroom, educators must use multiple assessment measures to accurately gauge student performance. In addition to quizzes, tests, essay exams, and standardized tests, assessment today incorporates a variety of performance-based measures and portfolio opportunities.

What Are Some Typical Performance-Based Assessments?

There are many kinds of performance-based assessments. They all share one common characteristic—they challenge students to create products that demonstrate what they know. One good way to present a performance assessment is in the form of an open-ended question.

Writing

Performance-based writing assessments challenge students to apply their knowledge of social studies concepts and information in a variety of written ways. Writing activities are most often completed by one student, rather than by a group.

- ✔ ***Journals*** Students write from the perspective of a historical character or a citizen of a particular historical era.
- ✔ ***Letters*** Students write a letter from one historical figure to another or from a historical figure to a family member or other audience.
- ✔ ***Position Paper or Editorial*** Students explain a controversial issue and present their own opinion and recommendations, supported with strong evidence and convincing reasons.
- ✔ ***Newspaper*** Students write a variety of stories from the perspective of a reporter living in a particular historical time period.
- ✔ ***Biographies and Autobiographies*** Students write about historical figures either from the third person point of view (biography) or from the first person (autobiography).
- ✔ ***Creative Stories*** Students integrate historical events into a piece of fiction, incorporating the customs, language, and geography of the period.
- ✔ ***Poems and Songs*** Students follow the conventions of a particular type of song or poem as they tell about a historical event or person.
- ✔ ***Research Reports*** Students synthesize information from a variety of sources into a well-developed research report.

Oral Presentations

Oral presentations allow students to demonstrate their social studies literacy before an audience. Oral presentations are often group efforts, although this need not be the case.

- ✔ ***Simulations*** Students hold simulations, or reenactments, of actual events, such as trials, acts of civil disobedience, battles, speeches, and so forth.
- ✔ ***Debates*** Students debate two or more sides to a historical policy or issue. Students can debate from a contemporary perspective or in a role play in which they assume a viewpoint held by a historical character.
- ✔ ***Interview*** Students conduct a mock interview of an historical character or bystander.
- ✔ ***Oral Reports*** Students present the results of research efforts in a lively oral report.
- ✔ ***Skits and Plays*** Students use historical events as the basis for a play or skit. Details should accurately reflect customs, language, and the setting of the period.

Visual Presentations

Visual presentations allow students to demonstrate their social studies understandings in a variety of visual formats. Visual presentations can be either group or individual projects.

- ✔ ***Model*** Students make a model to demonstrate or represent a process, place, event, battle, artifact, or custom.
- ✔ ***Museum Exhibit*** Students create a rich display of materials around a topic. Typical displays might include models, illustrations, photographs, videos, writings, and audiotaped explanations.
- ✔ ***Graph or Chart*** Students analyze and represent historical data in a line graph, bar graph, table, or other chart format.
- ✔ ***Drawing*** Students represent or interpret a historical event or period through illustration, including political cartoons.
- ✔ ***Posters and Murals*** Posters and murals may include maps, time lines, diagrams, illustrations, photographs, and written explanations that reflect students' understandings of historical information.

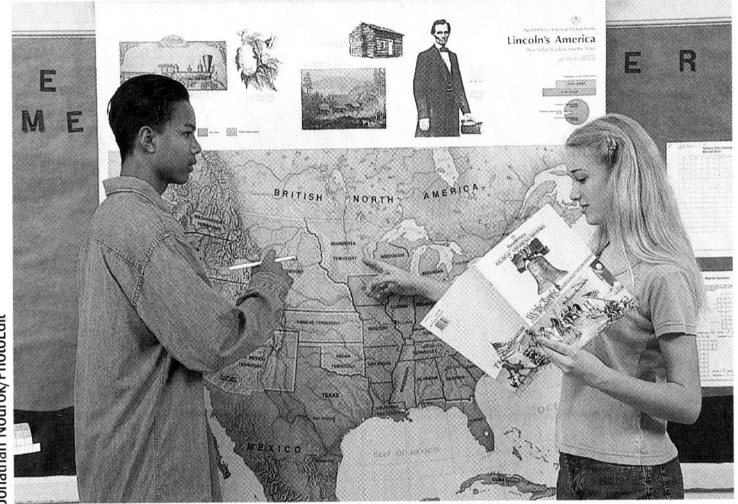

Jonathan Nourok/PhotoEdit

- ✔ ***Quilt*** Students sew or draw a design for a patchwork quilt that shows a variety of perspectives, events, or issues related to a key topic.
- ✔ ***Videotapes*** Students film a video to show historical fiction or to preserve a simulation of a historical event.
- ✔ ***Multimedia Presentation or Slide Show*** Students create a computer-generated multimedia presentation containing historical information and analysis.

How Are Performance Assessments Scored?

There are a variety of means used to evaluate performance tasks. Some or all of the following methods may be used.

- ✔ ***Scoring Rubrics*** A scoring rubric is a set of guidelines for assessing the quality of a process and/or product. It sets out criteria used to distinguish acceptable responses from unacceptable ones, generally along a scale from excellent to poor.
- ✔ ***Models of Excellent Work*** Teacher-selected models of excellent work concretely illustrate expectations and help students set goals for their own projects.
- ✔ ***Student Self-Assessment*** Common methods of self-assessment include ranking work in relation to the model, using a scoring rubric, and writing their own goals and then evaluating how well they have met the goals they set for themselves. Regardless of which method or methods students use, they should be encouraged to evaluate their behaviors and processes, as well as the finished product.
- ✔ ***Peer or Audience Assessment*** Many of the performance tasks target an audience other than the classroom teacher. If possible, the audience of peers should give the student feedback. Have the class create rubrics for specific projects together.
- ✔ ***Observation*** As students carry out their performance tasks, you may want to formally observe students at work. Start by developing a checklist, identifying all the specific behaviors and understandings you expect students to demonstrate. Then observe students as they carry out performance tasks and check off the behaviors as you observe them.
- ✔ ***Interviews*** As a form of ongoing assessment, you may want to conduct interviews with students, asking them to analyze, explain, and assess their participation in performance tasks. When projects take place over an extended period of time, you can hold periodic interviews as well as exit interviews. In this way the interview process allows you to gauge the status of the project and to guide students' efforts along the way.✦

Targeting Multiple Intelligences

Advice from John Cartaina
Consultant, New Jersey Council of Social Studies

Authentic performance assessment provides students with different learning styles opportunities to demonstrate their successful learning. The table below lists types of learning styles.

Learning Style	***Characteristics of Students***
Linguistic	*Read regularly, write clearly, and easily understand the written word*
Logical-Mathematical	*Use numbers, logic, and critical thinking skills*
Visual-Spatial	*Think in terms of pictures and images*
Auditory-Musical	*Remember spoken words and produce rhythms and melodies*
Kinesthetic	*Learn from touch, movement, and manipulating objects*
Interpersonal	*Understand and work well with other people*
Intrapersonal	*Have a realistic understanding of their strengths and weaknesses*
Naturalist	*Can distinguish among, classify, and use features of the environment*

You may want to assign activities to students that accommodate their strongest learning styles, but frequently ask them to use their weakest learning styles.

Previewing Your Textbook

Your textbook has been organized to help you learn about the many people and places that make up our world. Before you start reading, though, here is a road map to help you understand what you will encounter in the pages of this textbook. Follow this road map before you read so that you can understand how your textbook works.

Units

Your textbook is divided into units. Each unit begins with two pages of photographs and an introduction to the region. These pages will help you begin your study of the geography, culture, and history of that particular region. Next comes a Regional Atlas with a feature that focuses on the region and includes National Geographic maps. You will also find country profiles with facts about each country in the region.

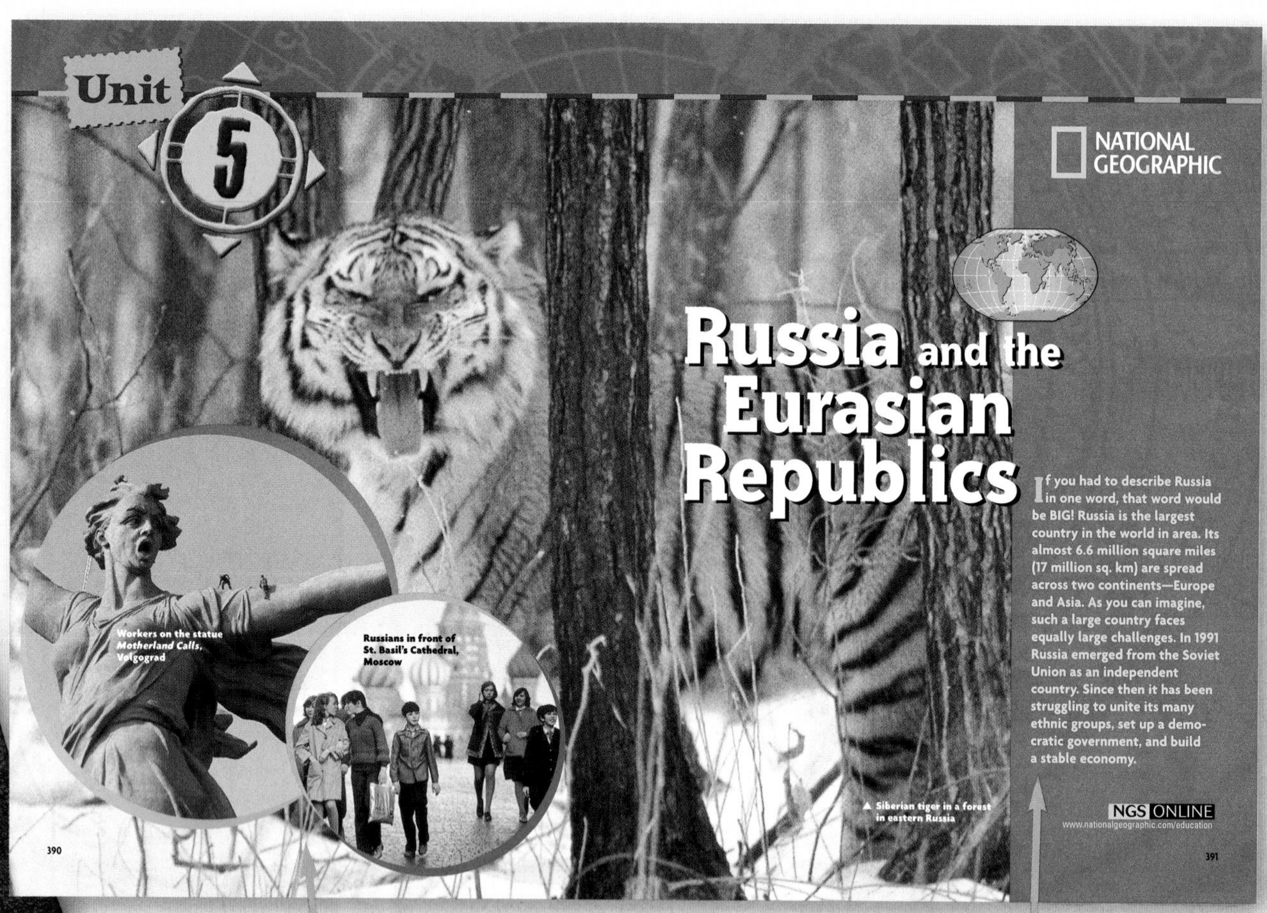

VISUALS

Photographs show you glimpses of landscapes, life, and culture from the region.

INTRODUCTION

An introductory paragraph gives you information and interesting facts about the region you are about to study.

Chapters

Each unit in *The World and Its People* is made up of chapters. Each chapter starts by providing you with background information to help you get the most out of the chapter.

Chapter Title

The chapter title tells you the main topic you will be reading about.

Visuals

A photograph shows people or places from the region.

Foldables

Use the Foldables Study Organizer to take notes as you read.

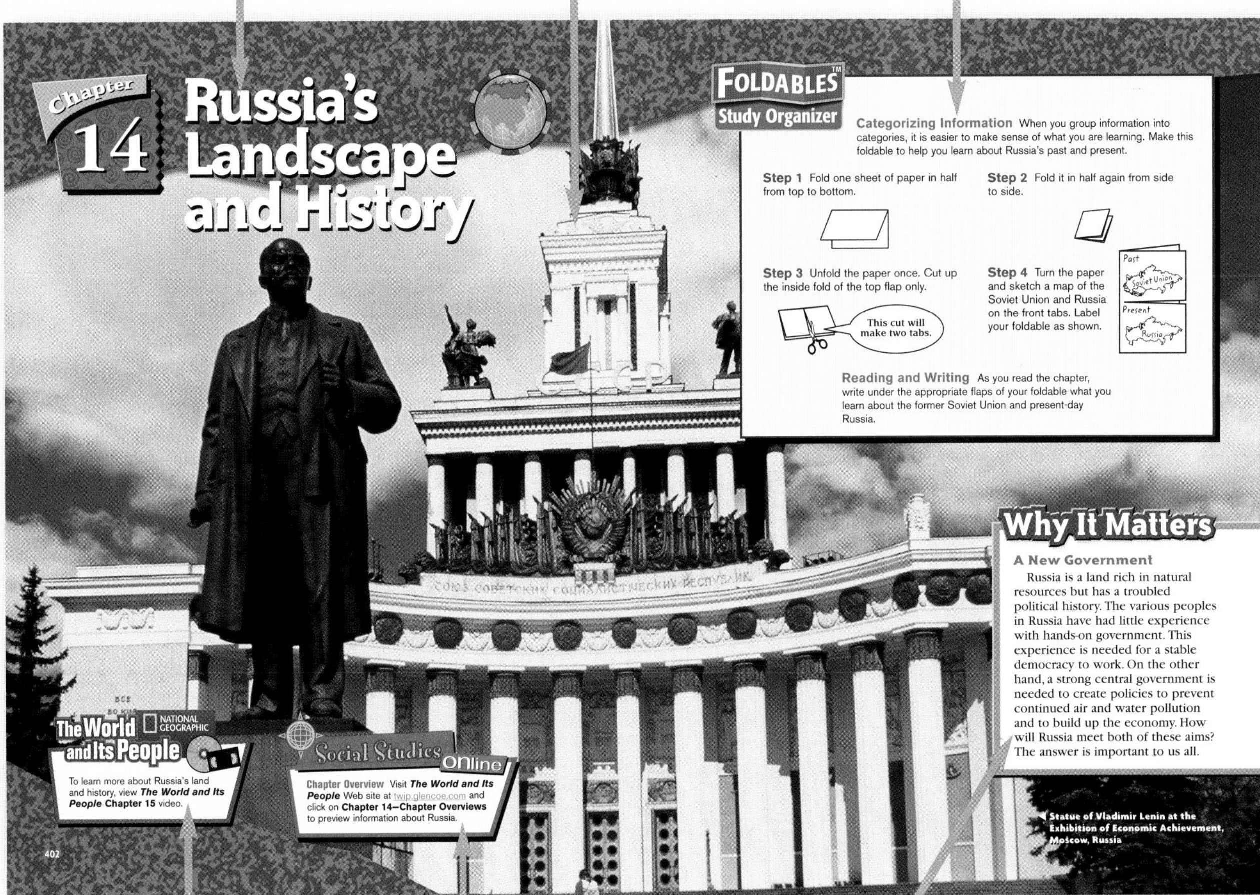

Chapter 14

Russia's Landscape and History

FOLDABLES™ Study Organizer

Categorizing Information When you group information into categories, it is easier to make sense of what you are learning. Make this foldable to help you learn about Russia's past and present.

Step 1 Fold one sheet of paper in half from top to bottom.

Step 2 Fold it in half again from side to side.

Step 3 Unfold the paper once. Cut up the inside fold of the top flap only.

Step 4 Turn the paper and sketch a map of the Soviet Union and Russia on the front tabs. Label your foldable as shown.

Reading and Writing As you read the chapter, write under the appropriate flaps of your foldable what you learn about the former Soviet Union and present-day Russia.

Why It Matters

A New Government

Russia is a land rich in natural resources but has a troubled political history. The various peoples in Russia have had little experience with hands-on government. This experience is needed for a stable democracy to work. On the other hand, a strong central government is needed to create policies to prevent continued air and water pollution and to build up the economy. How will Russia meet both of these aims? The answer is important to us all.

The World and Its People — National Geographic

To learn more about Russia's land and history, view ***The World and Its People* Chapter 15** video.

Social Studies Online

Chapter Overview Visit ***The World and Its People*** Web site at twip.glencoe.com and click on **Chapter 14—Chapter Overviews** to preview information about Russia.

Statue of Vladimir Lenin at the Exhibition of Economic Achievement, Moscow, Russia

402

Videos

You can view these National Geographic videos to learn more about the region in the chapter. You will see first-hand the amazing people and places of our world.

Web Site

Social Studies Online directs you to the Internet where you can find more information, activities, and quizzes. There are also links to additional resources.

Why It Matters

Why It Matters tells you how the region you will study is connected to the rest of the world. It also tells you why the region is unique.

Sections

A section is a division, or part, of the chapter. The first page of the section, the section opener, helps you set a purpose for reading.

Main Idea

The *Main Idea* of this section is introduced here. Below it are important terms you will come upon as you read the section.

Exploring Our World

This National Geographic feature gives you a unique perspective of the world with a story and photograph about an interesting aspect of the region.

Reading Strategy

Completing the *Reading Strategy* activity will help you organize the information as you read the section.

Section 1

A Vast Land

Guide to Reading

Main Idea

Russia is a huge country with a cold climate due to its far northern location.

Terms to Know

- steppe
- tundra
- permafrost
- taiga

Reading Strategy

Create a chart like this one. Give a specific name for each type of physical feature listed.

Russia	
Plains	
Mountains	
Rivers	

Siberian tigers hunt in the eastern forests of Russia—sometimes even climbing trees to find food. Only a few hundred now live in the wild, though. The animals they hunt—elk, deer, and wild boar—are dwindling, and the tigers are hunted by people. Poachers who kill the tigers illegally can sell a skin for $15,000. Russia is trying to enforce laws to save these animals.

Russia is the world's largest country. Nearly twice as big as the United States, Russia is called a Eurasian country because its lands lie on two continents—Europe and Asia. The **Ural Mountains** form the dividing line between the two continents. The European or western part of Russia borders countries such as Finland, Belarus, and Ukraine. The much larger eastern part of Russia stretches across Asia to the Pacific Ocean. The Chukchi Peninsula, on Russia's far eastern border, is separated from Alaska by only about 50 miles (80 km).

Russia is so wide that it shares borders with 14 other countries. It also includes 11 time zones from east to west. When it is 12:00 P.M. (noon) in eastern Russia and people are eating lunch, people in western Russia are still sound asleep at 1:00 A.M.

Russia's Climate

As you can see from the climate map on page 405, Russia's southern border is in the middle latitudes, but the north reaches past the Arctic Circle. Most of the western part of Russia has a humid continental climate. Summers are warm and rainy, while winters are cold

404 CHAPTER 14

Reading Roadmap

You will get more out of your textbook if you recognize the different elements that help you to understand what you read.

Maps

Easy-to-read maps show you where countries and regions are located in the world. Questions test your understanding of the map's information.

Reading Checks

Reading Checks help you check your understanding of the main ideas.

Outline

Think of the headings as forming an outline. The red titles are the main headings. The blue titles that follow are the subheadings.

Vocabulary

The words in blue are the key terms. The definition is also included here.

Photographs

Photographs show you important people, places, and events from the region. Questions help you interpret the photographs and relate them to what you are learning.

Section Assessment

The *Section Assessment* is the last item in every section. Here, you can check your understanding of what you have read.

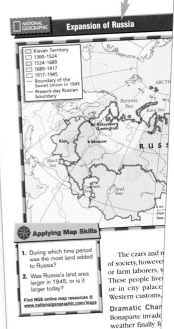

NATIONAL GEOGRAPHIC **Expansion of Russia**

Kievan Territory
1360–1524
1524–1689
1689–1917
1917–1945
Boundary of the Soviet Union in 1945
Present-day Russian boundary

Barents Sea, Kara Sea, ARCTIC, St. Petersburg (Leningrad), Kiev, Moscow, RUSS, Black Sea, Caspian Sea, Aral Sea

Applying Map Skills

1. During which time period was the most land added to Russia?
2. Was Russia's land area larger in 1945, or is it larger today?

Find NGS online map resources @ www.nationalgeographic.com/maps

The czars and n
of society, however
or farm laborers, v
These people live
or in city palace
Western customs,

Dramatic Chan
Bonaparte invade
weather finally f
1812 Overture,
and bursts of c
Tchaikovsky (ch
the Russian vic
about Napoleon
In the late 1
change. The Ru
Mountains and
Alexander II, k
tied to the lan
though. Russia

412

boundary. West of the Urals lies the North European Plain. This fertile plain has Russia's mildest climate, and about 75 percent of the population live here. This region holds Russia's capital, **Moscow,** and other important cities, such as **St. Petersburg** and **Volgograd.** Much of Russia's agriculture and industry is found on the North European Plain.

Good farmland also lies south of the North European Plain, along the Don and Volga Rivers. This area is part of the steppe, the nearly treeless grassy plain that stretches through Ukraine. To the far south of European Russia lie the high, rugged **Caucasus** (KAW•kuh•suhs) **Mountains.** Thickly covered with pines and other trees, the Caucasus are much taller than the Urals.

✓Reading Check What is the steppe?

East of the Urals

The huge Asian part of Russia lies east of the Ural Mountains and is known as **Siberia.** Northern Siberia has one of the coldest climates in the world. Not even hardy evergreens can grow here. Instead, you find tundra, a vast and rolling treeless plain in which only the top few inches of the ground thaw during the summer. The permanently frozen lower layers of soil are called permafrost and cover 40 percent of Russia.

The few people who live in the tundra make their living by fishing, hunting seals and walruses, or herding reindeer. With so few trees, many of the houses are made of walrus skins. Because the distances are so great and the land is usually covered in ice and snow, people may use helicopters for travel.

The Taiga South of the tundra is the world's largest forest, the taiga (TY•guh). Here, evergreen trees stretch about 4,000 miles (6,436 km) across the country in a belt 1,000 to 2,000 miles (1,609 to 3,218 km) wide. As with the tundra, few people live in this area. Those who do support themselves by lumbering or hunting. This area is so sparsely populated that forest fires sometimes burn for weeks before anyone notices.

NATIONAL GEOGRAPHIC **On Location**

Siberia

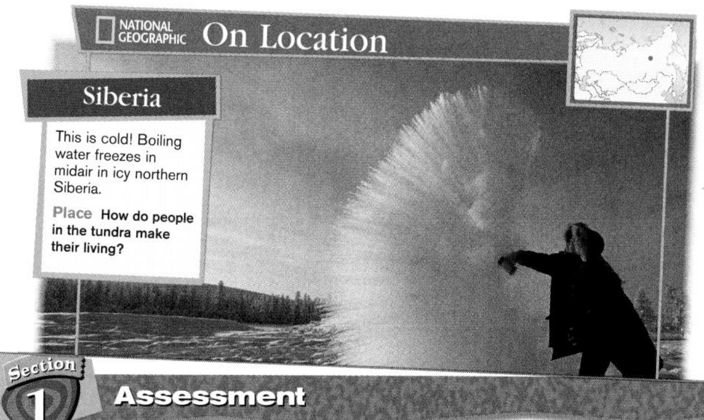

This is cold! Boiling water freezes in midair in icy northern Siberia.

Place **How do people in the tundra make their living?**

Section 1 **Assessment**

Defining Terms

1. Define steppe, tundra, permafrost, taiga.

Recalling Facts

2. Location What mountain range separates Europe and Asia?
3. Region How many countries does Russia border?
4. Place What is unique about Lake Baikal?

Critical Thinking

5. Analyzing Information Why do you think trains are more important than other kinds of vehicles for moving people and goods across Russia?
6. Making Comparisons How do the waters of the Caspian Sea and Lake Baikal differ?

Graphic Organizer

7. Categorizing Information Create a chart like this one. Then place each of the following items into the column in which it is located: Moscow, Lake Baikal, Kamchatka Peninsula, St. Petersburg, Volga River, Volgograd, taiga.

European Russia	Asian Russia

Applying Social Studies Skills

8. Analyzing Maps Turn to the climate map on page 405. Select a Russian city. Now look at the map of "The Russian Winter" on page 398. On average, how many days of snow cover does your selected city have per year?

408 CHAPTER 14

Special Features

A variety of special features will help you as you study *The World and Its People.*

MAKING CONNECTIONS

This feature connects you with various art, science, culture, and technology contributions in a particular region.

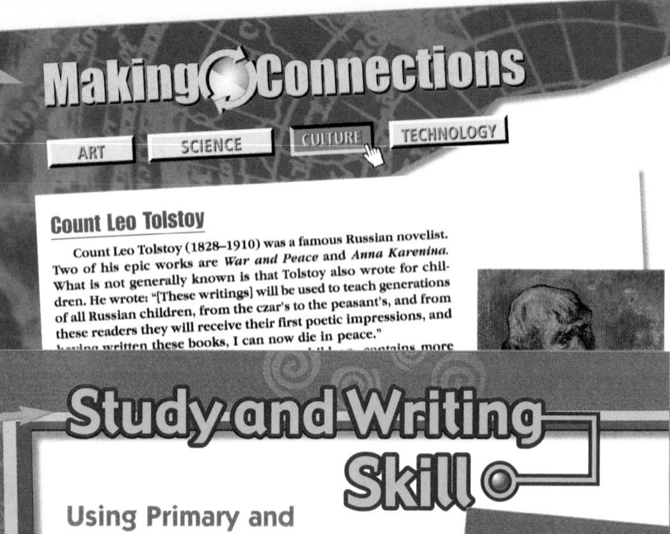

Making Connections
ART
SCIENCE
CULTURE
TECHNOLOGY
Count Leo Tolstoy
Count Leo Tolstoy (1828–1910) was a famous Russian novelist. Two of his epic works are *War and Peace* and *Anna Karenina.* What is not generally known is that Tolstoy also wrote for children. He wrote: "[These writings] will be used to teach generations of all Russian children, from the czar's to the peasant's, and from these readers they will receive their first poetic impressions, and
Study and Writing Skill
Using Primary and Secondary Sources
So much information comes our way in today's world. How can you analyze it to decide what is truly useful and accurate?
Practicing t

SKILLS ACTIVITIES

These activities help you learn and practice social studies, critical thinking, technology, and study and writing skills.

EXPLORING CULTURE

Exploring Culture examines art, architecture, clothing, and more in a particular region.

Art

Peter Carl Fabergé was no ordinary Russian jeweler. His successful workshop designed extravagant jeweled flowers, figures, and animals. He is most famous for crafting priceless gold Easter eggs for the czar of Russia and other royalty in Europe and Asia. Each egg was unique and took nearly a year to create. Lifting the lid of the egg revealed a tiny surprise. One egg Fabergé created (shown here) held an intricate ship inside.

Looking Closer **Why do you think Fabergé's workshop closed after the Russian Revolution of 1917?**

that at one time lived in Russia have emigrated to other areas. Few than 1 million Jews live in Russia today.

Celebrations, Foods, and Sports Russians enjoy small family g togethers as well as national holidays. New Year's Eve is the most f tive nonreligious holiday. Russian children decorate a fir tree a exchange presents with others in their families. Russians also celebr May 1 with parades and speeches. May Day honors Russian worke

If you were to have dinner with a Russian family, you might begin w a big bowl of *borscht,* a soup made from beets, or *shchi,* a soup m from cabbage. Next, you might have meat turnovers called *piroshki.* the main course, you are likely to eat meat, poultry, or fish with bo potatoes. On special occasions, Russians like to eat caviar. This delic is made from eggs of the sturgeon, a fish from the Caspian Sea.

Have you ever watched the Olympics? If so, you probably l seen Russian hockey players, figure skaters, and gymnasts. Du Russia's cold climate, winter and indoor sports are popular. Russ also enjoy soccer, tennis, hiking, camping, and mountain climbing

Reading Check **How have Russia's cities changed in recent years?**

Rich Cultural Traditions

Russia has a rich tradition of literature, art, and music. The Ru storytelling tradition is one of the oldest and richest in the w These stories, or *skazki,* were passed down orally from generation to generation, until finally they were recorded in print. Beasts and creatures with magical powers are common in these tales that grew out of a land with dark forests and long, cold winters.

The New Russia and Independent Republics 433

TIME PERSPECTIVES

Time Perspectives: Exploring World Issues takes an in-depth look at issues in the region and helps you understand and analyze those issues.

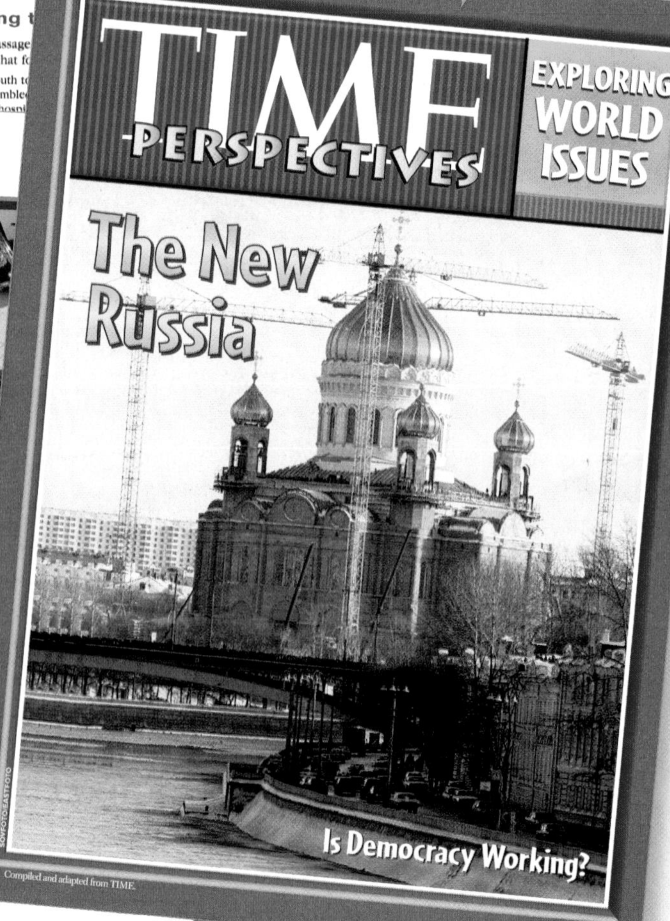

The World and Its People contains a wealth of information. The trick is to know where to look to access all the information in the book. If you complete this scavenger hunt exercise with your teachers or parents, you will see how the textbook is organized and how to get the most out of your reading and study time. Let's get started!

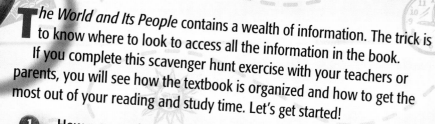

1. How many units and how many chapters are in the book?
   9 units and 27 chapters
2. What region does Unit 3 cover?
   Latin America
3. Where can you find facts about each country in a unit?
   country profile stamps in the Regional Atlas
4. In what four places can you find the key terms for Section 1 of Chapter 10? Section opener under "Terms to Know," Section Assessment, Reading Review at the end of the chapter, and the Chapter Assessment
5. What does the Foldables Study Organizer at the beginning of Chapter 4 ask you to do? make a foldable journal to identify main ideas in the chapter
6. How are the key terms throughout your book highlighted in the narrative?
   They are blue.
7. Where do you find graphic organizers in your textbook? Section opener: Reading Strategy, Section Assessment, and Chapter Assessment
8. You want to quickly find all the maps in the book about Europe. Where do you look?
   in the Table of Contents: Maps: Unit 4
9. Each Unit's Regional Atlas includes country profile stamps. Where else can you find information about countries in the textbook?
   Data Bank in the Index
10. Where can you learn the definition of a physical map, a political map, and a special purpose map?
    Geography Handbook at the front of the book

Why Should I Teach Reading to My Social Studies Students?

For many social studies teachers, helping students develop reading skills is a low priority–nice to do if there's time, but not necessary. After all, there is scarcely time to meet many of the state-mandated subject-area learning objectives. Why add reading instruction to the list? The answer is that reading skills are essential to the learning of subjects. In the social studies, students must read to learn. Struggling readers risk learning less than those who are proficient in reading.

Teachers who infuse literacy strategies with social studies content actively engage students in learning. Once students internalize reading strategies such as visualizing, predicting, and making connections, they inevitably become better social studies students.

Reading Skills Handbook

READING TO LEARN

This handbook focuses on skills and strategies that can help you understand the words you read. The strategies you use to understand whole texts depend on the kind of text you are reading. In other words, you do not read a textbook the way you read a novel. You read a textbook mainly for information; you read a novel mainly for fun. To get the most out of your reading, you need to choose the right strategy to fit the reason you're reading.

USE THIS HANDBOOK TO HELP YOU LEARN

- how to identify new words and build your vocabulary;
- how to adjust the way you read to fit your reason for reading;
- how to use specific reading strategies to better understand what you read;
- how to use critical thinking strategies to think more deeply about what you read.

You will also learn about

- text structures;
- reading for research.

TABLE OF CONTENTS

Identifying Words and Building Vocabulary RH1
Reading for a Reason RH3
Understanding What You Read RH4
Thinking About Your Reading RH5
Understanding Text Structure RH7

Professional Development: Teaching Reading

The following sources will help you teach reading skills:

- *Subjects Matter: Every Teacher's Guide to Content-Area Reading,* by Harvey Daniels and Steven Zemelman. Portsmouth, NH: Heineman, 2004.
- *When Kids Can't Read, What Teachers Can Do: A Guide for Teachers, 6–12,* by G. Kylene Beers. Portsmouth, NH: Heinemann, 2003.
- *I Read It But I Don't Get It: Comprehension Strategies for Adolescent Readers,* by Cris Tovani. Portland, ME: Stenhouse Publishers, 2000.
- *Teaching Reading in the Middle School,* by Laura Robb. New York, NY: Scholastic Professional Books, 2000.

Identifying Words and Building Vocabulary

What do you do when you come across a word you do not know as you read? Do you skip over the word and keep reading? If you are reading for fun or entertainment, you might. But if you are reading for information, an unfamiliar word may get in the way of your understanding. When that happens, try the following strategies to figure out how to say the word and what the word means.

Reading Unfamiliar Words

Sounding out the word One way to figure out how to say a new word is to sound it out, syllable by syllable. Look carefully at the word's beginning, middle, and ending. Inside the word, do you see a word you already know how to pronounce? What vowels are in the syllables? Use the following tips when sounding out new words.

- **Roots and base words** The main part of a word is called its root. When the root is a complete word, it may be called the base word. When you come across a new word, check whether you recognize its root or base word. It can help you pronounce the word and figure out the word's meaning.

ASK YOURSELF

- What letters make up the beginning sound or beginning syllable of the word?

  Example: In the word *coagulate, co* rhymes with *so.*
- What sounds do the letters in the middle part of the word make?

  Example: In the word *coagulate,* the syllable *ag* has the same sound as the *ag* in *bag,* and the syllable *u* is pronounced like the letter *u.*
- What letters make up the ending sound or syllable?

  Example: In the word *coagulate, late* is a familiar word you already know how to pronounce.
- Now try pronouncing the whole word: *co ag u late.*

- **Prefixes** A prefix is a word part that can be added to the beginning of a root or base word. For example, the prefix *pre-* means "before," so *prehistory* means "before history." Prefixes can change, or even reverse, the meaning of a word. For example, *un-* means "not," so *unconstitutional* means "not constitutional."
- **Suffixes** A suffix is a word part that can be added to the end of a root or base word to change the word's meaning. Adding a suffix to a word can also change that word from one part of speech to another. For example, the word *joy,* which is a noun, becomes an adjective when the suffix *-ful* (meaning "full of") is added. *Joyful* means "full of joy."

Determining a Word's Meaning

Using syntax Like all languages, English has rules and patterns for the way words are arranged in sentences. The way a sentence is organized is called the **syntax.**

In a simple sentence in English, someone or something (the *subject*) does something (the *predicate* or *verb*) to or with another person or thing (the *object*): The *soldiers attacked* the *enemy.*

RH1

Reading Skills Handbook

Identifying Words and Building Vocabulary

Why It's Important

Research documents the relationship between a strong vocabulary and the ability to read and write proficiently. Vocabulary may be the most important factor in comprehension, showing that ongoing, specific vocabulary instruction must be an integral part of every lesson.

Before Reading

Activating Prior Knowledge
Distribute index cards with a key word from the chapter written on each card. Organize students into groups of four, and give them time to discuss their words. After the group discussion, ask each group to write what they think the word means on the back of the card. Then have groups present the words to the class by writing their words and definitions on the board. Other students should help confirm or revise the definitions. Use pictures or graphs to enhance or correct the students' definitions.

Differentiated Instruction

Meeting Special Needs: Less-proficient Readers One way to help students increase their vocabularies is to have them play word games before they read the chapter. Give students a word from the chapter that they do not know, and allow them to ask questions about its definition. When a student correctly guesses its meaning, he or she can then be "it," choosing a new word for the class to question. This type of game demonstrates that there are often many definitions for a word, and it allows students to learn from each other.

During Reading

Learning Vocabulary Post a chart on the wall listing the steps for learning new vocabulary. Students may refer to the chart as they read. Steps include: sound out the word; look at prefixes, suffixes, and roots; look at how the word is used in the sentence; use context clues in surrounding sentences; use reference materials such as dictionaries and thesauruses; ask someone the meaning of the word. Encourage students to experiment with different steps to find the one that works best for them.

After Reading

Reinforcing Vocabulary Students should use graphic organizers and web diagrams to explain the definition of a word. Have students write the word in the center of a sheet of notebook paper. Then have them write *What it is* at the top left of the page, *What it is like* at the top right, *Examples of its meaning* at the bottom left of the page, and *What it is not* at the bottom right. Have students write the appropriate information under each head.

CHECK IT OUT

Knowing about syntax can help you figure out the meaning of an unfamiliar word. Just look at how syntax can help you figure out the following nonsense sentence.

The blizzy kwarkles sminched the flerky fleans.

Your experience with English syntax tells you that the action word, or verb, in this sentence is *sminched.* Who did the *sminching?* The *kwarkles.* What kind of kwarkles were they? *Blizzy.* Whom did they *sminch?* The fleans. What kind of fleans were they? *Flerky.* Even though you don't know the meaning of the words in the nonsense sentence, you can make some sense of the sentence by studying its syntax.

Using context clues You can often figure out the meaning of an unfamiliar word by looking at its context, or the words and sentences that surround it. To learn new words as you read, follow these steps for using context clues.

1. Look before and after the unfamiliar word for:
   - a definition or a synonym, another word that means the same as the unfamiliar word.
   - a general topic associated with the word.
   - a clue to what the word is similar to or different from.
   - an action or a description that has something to do with the word.
2. Connect what you already know with what the author has written.
3. Predict a possible meaning.
4. Use the meaning in the sentence.
5. Try again if your guess does not make sense.

Using reference materials Dictionaries and other reference sources can help you learn new words. Check out these reference sources:

- A **dictionary** gives the pronunciation and the meaning or meanings of words. Some dictionaries also give other forms of words, their parts of speech, and synonyms. You might also find the historical background of a word.
- A **glossary** is a word list that appears at the end—or appendix—of a book or other written work. It includes only words that are in that work. Like dictionaries, glossaries have the pronunciation and definitions of words.
- A **thesaurus** lists groups of words that have the same, or almost the same, meaning. Words with similar meanings are called *synonyms.* Seeing the synonyms of words can help you build your vocabulary.

Recognizing Word Meanings Across Subjects

Have you ever learned a new word in one class and then noticed it in your reading for other subjects? The word probably will not mean exactly the same thing in each class. But you can use what you know about the word's meaning to help you understand what it means in a different subject area.

More About the Reading Strategy

How can teachers help students understand word concepts instead of just learning simple definitions? One way is to use words often and in a variety of ways. Teams of teachers can choose common vocabulary words which they will present in various content area classes. Teachers should provide opportunities for integrating the words into meaningful contexts. The goal is for students to develop full knowledge of the words so that they become fixed parts of their vocabularies.

CHECK IT OUT

Look at the following example from three subjects:

Social studies: One major **product** manufactured in southern U.S. states is cotton cloth.

Math: After you multiply those two numbers, explain how you arrived at the **product.**

Science: One **product** of photosynthesis is oxygen.

Reading for a Reason

Why are you reading that paperback mystery? What do you hope to get from your geography textbook? And are you going to read either of these books in the same way that you read a restaurant menu? The point is, you read for different reasons. The reason you are reading something helps you decide on the reading strategies you use. In other words, how you read will depend on **why** you're reading.

Knowing Your Reason for Reading

In school and in life, you will have many reasons for reading, and those reasons will lead you to a wide range of materials. For example,

- **to learn and understand new information,** you might read news magazines, textbooks, news on the Internet, books about your favorite pastime, encyclopedia articles, primary and secondary sources for a school report, instructions on how to use a calling card, or directions for a standardized test.
- **to find specific information,** you might look at a weather report, a bank statement, television listings, the sports section for the score of last night's game, or a notice on where to register for a field trip.
- **to be entertained,** you might read your favorite magazine, e-mails or letters from friends, the Sunday comics, or even novels, short stories, plays, or poems.

Adjusting How Fast You Read

How quickly or how carefully you should read a text depends on your purpose for reading it. Because there are many reasons and ways to read, think about your purpose and choose a strategy that works best. Try out these strategies:

- **Scanning** means quickly running your eyes over the material, looking for *key words or phrases* that point to the information you're looking for. Scan when you need to find a particular piece or type of information. For example, you might scan a newspaper for movie show times.
- **Skimming** means quickly reading a piece of writing *to find its main idea* or to *get a general overview* of it. For example, you might skim the sports section of the daily newspaper to find out how your favorite teams are doing. Or you might skim a chapter in your textbook to prepare for a test.
- **Careful reading** involves *reading slowly and paying attention* with a purpose in mind. Read carefully when you're learning new concepts, following complicated directions, or preparing to explain information to someone else.

Reading Skills Handbook

Reading for a Reason

Why It's Important

When students have a reason or purpose for reading, the task becomes relevant and meaningful, both of which are necessary for comprehension. Good readers inherently set purposes for themselves, but less-proficient readers might need help finding a reason for reading.

Before Reading

Skimming Help students establish a reason for reading by skimming the text. Point out section headings, illustrations, and boldfaced words. Tell students that these text features can help establish a purpose for reading.

During Reading

Identifying a Reason for Reading Give students a specific task to perform while they read, such as looking for a specific piece of information, summarizing content, finding details to support a position, or writing a response to what they have read.

Differentiated Instruction

Meeting Special Needs: Less-proficient Readers Students need practice with establishing a reason for reading. Encourage students to read news magazines, newspapers, historical novels, nonfiction books, or Internet articles. Before reading, have students write a rationale for why they have chosen that type of reading. Students should describe what they will do after they read, such as present an oral report.

After Reading

Paraphrasing When students finish reading, have them work with a partner to paraphrase what they have read. Encourage them to reread sections of text or share notes and answers to questions in order to clarify the reading.

Understanding What You Read

Why It's Important

Students who read but don't "get it" or who simply will not read at all cannot adequately master the content of their courses. Helping students learn to use a variety of reading strategies as tools for comprehension will lead to long-term benefits in school and everyday life.

Before Reading

Making Predictions On index cards, write important words from the chapter–one word per card. Place the cards on various desks around the room. Allow students to move from desk to desk until they find a word that they think they may know something about. Have students use the word to make predictions about what they will learn in the chapter.

Understanding What You Read

Skilled readers adopt a number of strategies before, during, and after reading to make sure they understand what they read.

Previewing

When you preview a piece of writing, you are trying to get an idea about that piece of writing. If you know what to expect before reading, you will have an easier time understanding ideas and relationships.

DO IT!

1. Look at the title and any illustrations that are included.
2. Read the headings, subheadings, and anything in bold letters.
3. Skim over the passage to see how it is organized. Is it divided into many parts? Is it a long poem or short story? Do not forget to look at the graphics—pictures, maps, or diagrams.
4. Set a purpose for your reading. Are you reading to learn something new? Are you reading to find specific information?

Using What You Know

Believe it or not, you already know quite a bit about what you are going to read. You bring knowledge and personal experience to a selection. Drawing on your own background is called *activating prior knowledge,* and it can help you create meaning in what you read. Ask yourself, *What do I already know about this topic?*

Predicting

You do not need any special knowledge to make *predictions* when you read. The predictions do not even have to be accurate. Take educated guesses before and during your reading about what might happen in the story or article you are reading.

Visualizing

Creating pictures in your mind as you read—called *visualizing*—is a powerful aid to understanding. As you read, set up a movie theater in your imagination. Picture the setting—city streets, the desert, or the surface of the moon. If you can visualize what you read, selections will be more vivid, and you will recall them better later on.

Identifying Sequence

When you discover the logical order of events or ideas, you are identifying *sequence.* Look for clues and signal words that will help you find the way information is organized.

Determining the Main Idea

When you look for the *main idea* of a selection, you look for the most important idea. The examples, reasons, and details that further explain the main idea are called *supporting details.*

More About the Reading Strategy

What does it mean to read? What do we know about how the brain processes the written word? Consider forming a study group with other teachers interested in learning more about the process of reading. There are books available through several educational presses that focus on new research about the learning process and comprehension.

Questioning

Keep up a conversation with yourself as you read by *asking questions* about the text. Ask about the importance of the information you are reading. Ask how one event relates to another. Ask yourself if you understand what you just read. As you answer your questions, you are making sure that you understand what is going on.

Clarifying

Clear up, or *clarify,* confusing or difficult passages as you read. Reread the passage using these techniques.

- *Reread* the confusing parts slowly and carefully.
- *Look up* unfamiliar words.
- Simply *"talk out"* the part to yourself.

Reviewing

You probably *review* in school what you learned the day before so that the ideas are firm in your mind. Reviewing when you read does the same thing. Take time now and then to pause and review what you have read. Think about the main ideas and reorganize them for yourself so you can recall them later. Filling in study aids such as graphic organizers can help you review.

Monitoring Your Comprehension

As you read, check your understanding by using the following strategies.

- **Summarize** what you read by pausing from time to time and telling yourself the main ideas of what you have just read. Answer the questions *Who? What? Where? When? Why?* and *How?* Summarizing tests your comprehension by encouraging you to clarify key points in your own words.
- **Paraphrase** Use paraphrasing as a test to see whether you really got the point. *Paraphrasing* is retelling something in your own words. Try putting what you have just read into your own words. If you cannot explain it clearly, you should probably have another look at the text.

Thinking About Your Reading

Sometimes it is important to think more deeply about what you have read so you can get the most out of what the author says. These critical thinking skills will help you go beyond what the words say and understand the important messages of your reading.

Interpreting

To *interpret* a text, first ask yourself, *What is the writer really saying here?* Then use what you know about the world to help answer that question.

Inferring

Writers provide clues and interesting details that suggest certain information. *Inferring* involves thinking and using your own experience to come up with an idea based on what an author implies or suggests. In reading, you *infer* when you use context clues and your own knowledge to figure out the author's meaning.

Reading Skills Handbook

During Reading

Engaging With the Text Encourage students to write questions or mark confusing parts of the text with a sticky note as they read. Discuss as a class the sections of the reading that were difficult or confusing, and help clarify the material for the students.

After Reading

Reviewing Remind students to use the following strategies after each section or chapter to ensure greater comprehension:

- Readers should summarize the most important parts of the text in their own words.
- Readers should clarify confusing content by rereading, asking questions, or seeking outside help.
- Readers should predict what might happen next.

Thinking About Your Reading

Why It's Important

Understanding subtleties of meaning or thinking critically may be difficult for some students. Students become better readers, writers, and thinkers when they know how to use critical thinking skills.

Differentiated Instruction

Meeting Special Needs: Less-proficient Readers Prediction guides (often called anticipation guides) are an effective way of setting a purpose for reading, engaging students during reading, and monitoring comprehension after reading. Create statements related to the upcoming section or chapter. Write some statements that are true, some that are false, and some that are outrageous or funny. Have students write *True* or *False* beside each statement. Students should then check and make corrections to their predictions as they read.

Before Reading

Modeling When teaching critical thinking skills, it is best to focus on teaching only one or two skills prior to reading. Explain the skill, and model how you, as a reader, use it to comprehend the reading.

During Reading

Thinking Critically Students who interact with the text will have a better chance of thinking more critically about it. Organize students into small groups, and assign a section of text for each group to read. Have students discuss questions such as, "Why did the stock market fall at this particular time?" or "Is the reason why this event occurred based on fact or opinion?" Encourage students to examine the questions from different perspectives. Have students share their discussions with the class.

After Reading

Writing Questions Tell students that after they read, they will write one question that reflects each type of the thinking skills described in the *Reading Skills Handbook.* Knowing that they will have to write questions about the text will help students think more about it as they read.

Drawing Conclusions

Skillful readers are always *drawing conclusions,* or figuring out much more than an author says directly. The process is like a detective solving a mystery. You combine information and evidence that the author provides to come up with a statement about the topic. Drawing conclusions helps you find connections between ideas and events and gives you a better understanding of what you are reading.

Analyzing

Analyzing, or looking at separate parts of something to understand the entire piece, is a way to think critically about written work. In analyzing *informational text,* you might look at how the ideas are organized to see what is most important.

Distinguishing Fact From Opinion

Distinguishing between fact and opinion is one of the most important reading skills you can learn. A *fact* is a statement that can be proved with supporting information. An *opinion,* on the other hand, is what a writer believes, on the basis of his or her personal viewpoint.

FOR EXAMPLE

Look at the following examples of fact and opinion.

Fact: George III was the British king during the American Revolution.

Opinion: King George III was an evil tyrant.

You could prove that George III was king during that period. It is a fact. However, not everyone might see that King George III was a tyrant. That is someone's opinion.

As you examine information, always ask yourself, *Is this a fact or an opinion?* Do not think that opinions are always bad. Very often they are just what you want. You read editorials and essays for their authors' opinions. Reviews of books, movies, plays, and CDs can help you decide whether to spend your time and money on something. It's when opinions are based on faulty reasoning or prejudice or when they are stated as facts that they become troublesome.

Evaluating

When you form an opinion or make a judgment about something you are reading, you are *evaluating.* Ask yourself whether the author seems biased, whether the information is one-sided, and whether the argument that is presented is logical.

Synthesizing

When you *synthesize,* you combine ideas (maybe even from different sources) to come up with something new. For example, you might read a manual on coaching soccer, combine that information with your own experiences playing soccer, and come up with a winning plan for coaching your sister's team this spring.

More About the Reading Strategy

Have students evaluate their proficiency with using different types of critical thinking skills. Draw a continuum on the board for each skill, with 0 representing great difficulty using the skill and 10 indicating mastery of it. Have students rate their abilities by answering questions such as: Am I usually able to infer and understand what the author is suggesting, even if it is not stated? Can I usually draw conclusions when I read? Can I easily tell facts from opinions?

Understanding Text Structure

Good writers structure each piece of their writing in a specific way for a specific purpose. That pattern of organization is called *text structure.* When you know the text structure of a selection, you will find it easier to locate and recall an author's ideas. Here are four ways that writers organize text.

Comparison and Contrast

Comparison-and-contrast structure shows the similarities and differences among people, things, and ideas. When writers use comparison-and-contrast structure, often they want to show you *how things that seem alike are different,* or *how things that seem different are alike.*

- **Signal words and phrases:** *similarly, on the other hand, in contrast to*

Cause and Effect

Just about everything that happens in life is the cause or the effect of some other event or action. Writers use cause-and-effect structure to explore the reasons for something happening and to examine the results of previous events. This structure helps answer the question that everybody is always asking: *Why?* Cause-and-effect structure is all about explaining things.

- **Signal words and phrases:** *so, because, as a result, therefore*

Problem and Solution

How did scientists overcome the difficulty of getting a person to the moon? How will I brush my teeth when I have forgotten my toothpaste? These questions may be very different in importance, but they have one thing in common: Each identifies a problem and asks how to solve it. *Problems* and *solutions* are part of what makes life interesting. Problems and solutions also occur in fiction and nonfiction writing.

- **Signal words and phrases:** *how, help, problem, obstruction, difficulty, need, attempt, have to, must*

Sequence

Take a look at three common types of sequences, or the order in which thoughts are arranged.

1. **Chronological order** refers to the order in which events take place. First you wake up; next you have breakfast; then you go to school. Those events don't make much sense in any other order.
   - **Signal words:** *first, next, then, later, finally*
2. **Spatial order** tells you the order in which to look at objects. For example, take a look at this description of an ice cream sundae: *At the bottom of the dish are two scoops of vanilla. The scoops are covered with fudge and topped with whipped cream and a cherry.* Your eyes follow the sundae from the bottom to the top. Spatial order is important in descriptive writing because it helps you as a reader to see an image the way the author does.
   - **Signal words:** *above, below, behind, next to*
3. **Order of importance** is going from most important to least important or the other way around. For example, a typical news article has a most-to-least-important structure.
   - **Signal words:** *principal, central, important, fundamental*

Reading Skills Handbook

Understanding Text Structure

Why It's Important

Students can make sense of the text more easily when they learn how authors organize it.

Before Reading

Skimming Before students read the chapter, walk them through it. Ask students questions such as: How does this map relate to the topic described in the title? What do you think the author intends for you to learn in this section?

During Reading

Identifying Text Structure
Organize students into groups of four, and assign different sections of the text to each group. Have groups choose a facilitator, a reader, a recorder, and a reporter. As the reader reads a section aloud, have the recorder note all the signal words. The facilitator will help the group identify the section's text structure. The reporter will describe to the class the signal words and the text structure that the group identified.

After Reading

Organizing Information
Have a variety of blank graphic organizers available for students to choose from to help them organize text information, including flow charts, time lines, and Venn diagrams.

Differentiated Instruction

Meeting Special Needs: Less-proficient Readers When students find connections to their own lives in the text, their ability to comprehend it improves. Offer projects that build upon these connections. Projects may include: debating issues presented in the text; writing articles for the school or local paper; conducting interviews with others who have knowledge of the subject; role playing; finding relevant poetry, art, or music to share with the class; and reading and reporting on books or magazine articles related to the subject.

Reference Atlas

World: Political	RA2	Europe: Political	RA16
North America: Political	RA4	Europe: Physical	RA18
North America: Physical	RA5	Africa: Political	RA20
United States: Political	RA6	Africa: Physical	RA21
United States: Physical	RA8	Asia: Political	RA22
Canada: Physical/Political	RA10	Asia: Physical	RA24
Middle America: Physical/Political	RA12	Middle East: Physical/Political	RA26
South America: Political	RA14	Pacific Rim: Physical/Political	RA28
South America: Physical	RA15	Polar Regions	RA30

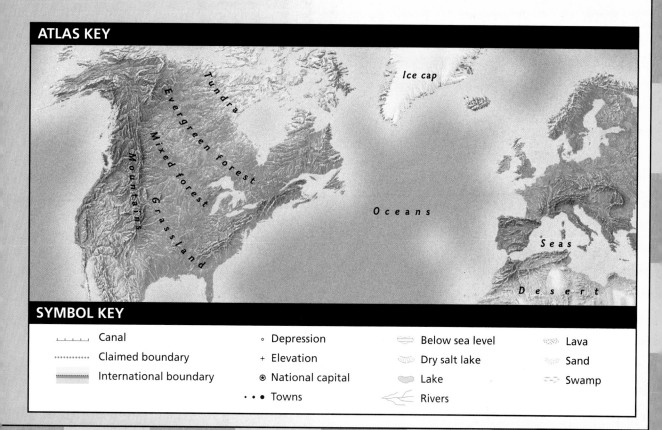

ATLAS KEY

SYMBOL KEY

- Canal
- Claimed boundary
- International boundary
- Depression
- Elevation
- National capital
- Towns
- Below sea level
- Dry salt lake
- Lake
- Rivers
- Lava
- Sand
- Swamp

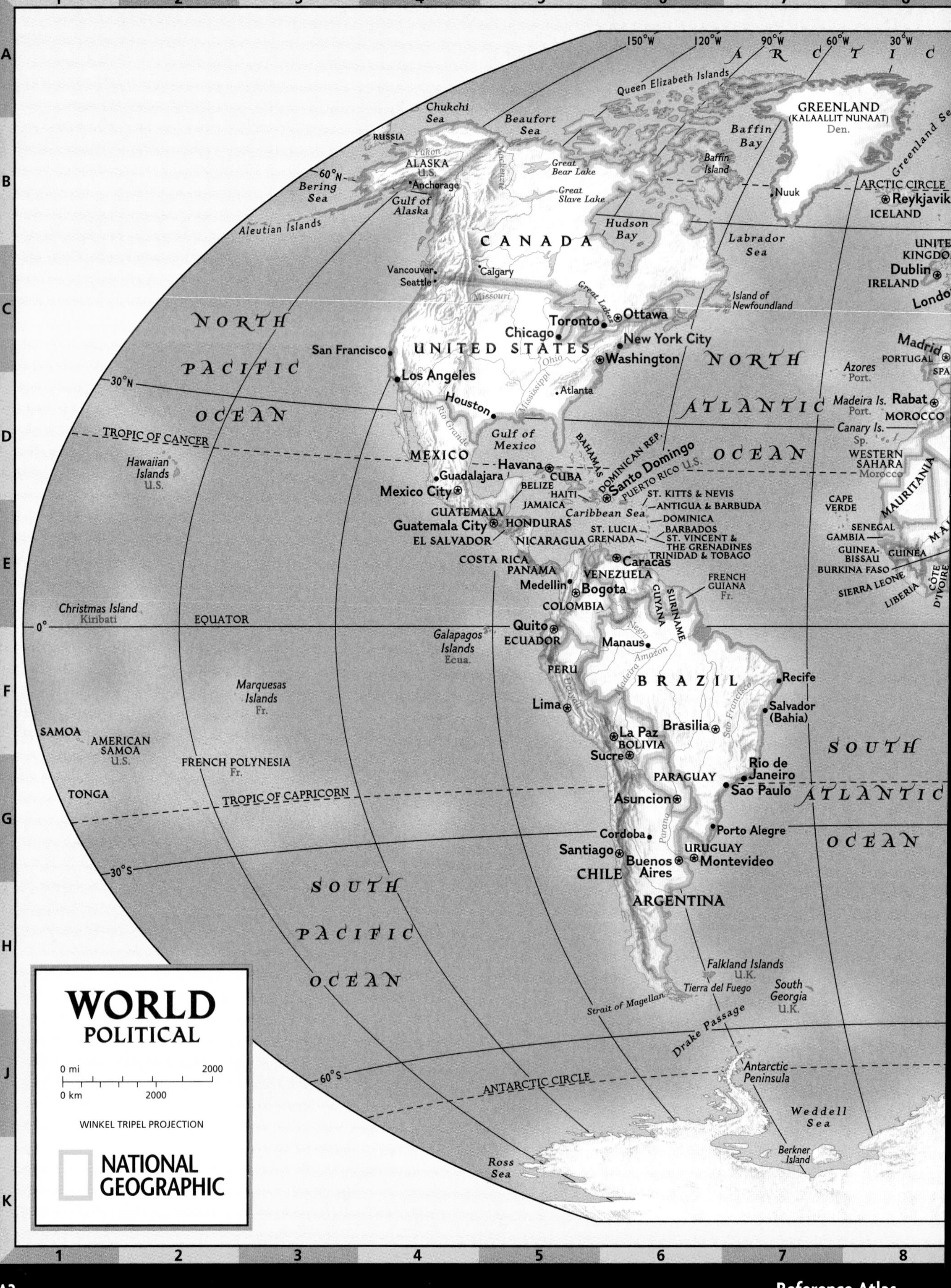
WORLD
POLITICAL
0 mi 2000
0 km 2000
WINKEL TRIPEL PROJECTION
NATIONAL GEOGRAPHIC
NORTH PACIFIC OCEAN
SOUTH PACIFIC OCEAN
NORTH ATLANTIC OCEAN
SOUTH ATLANTIC OCEAN
ARCTIC
CANADA
UNITED STATES
MEXICO
BRAZIL
ARGENTINA
CHILE
GREENLAND (KALAALLIT NUNAAT) Den.
ALASKA U.S.
RUSSIA
ICELAND
IRELAND
Ottawa
Washington
Mexico City
Havana
Bogota
Caracas
Quito
Lima
La Paz
Sucre
Brasilia
Asuncion
Santiago
Buenos Aires
Montevideo
EQUATOR
TROPIC OF CANCER
TROPIC OF CAPRICORN
ARCTIC CIRCLE
ANTARCTIC CIRCLE

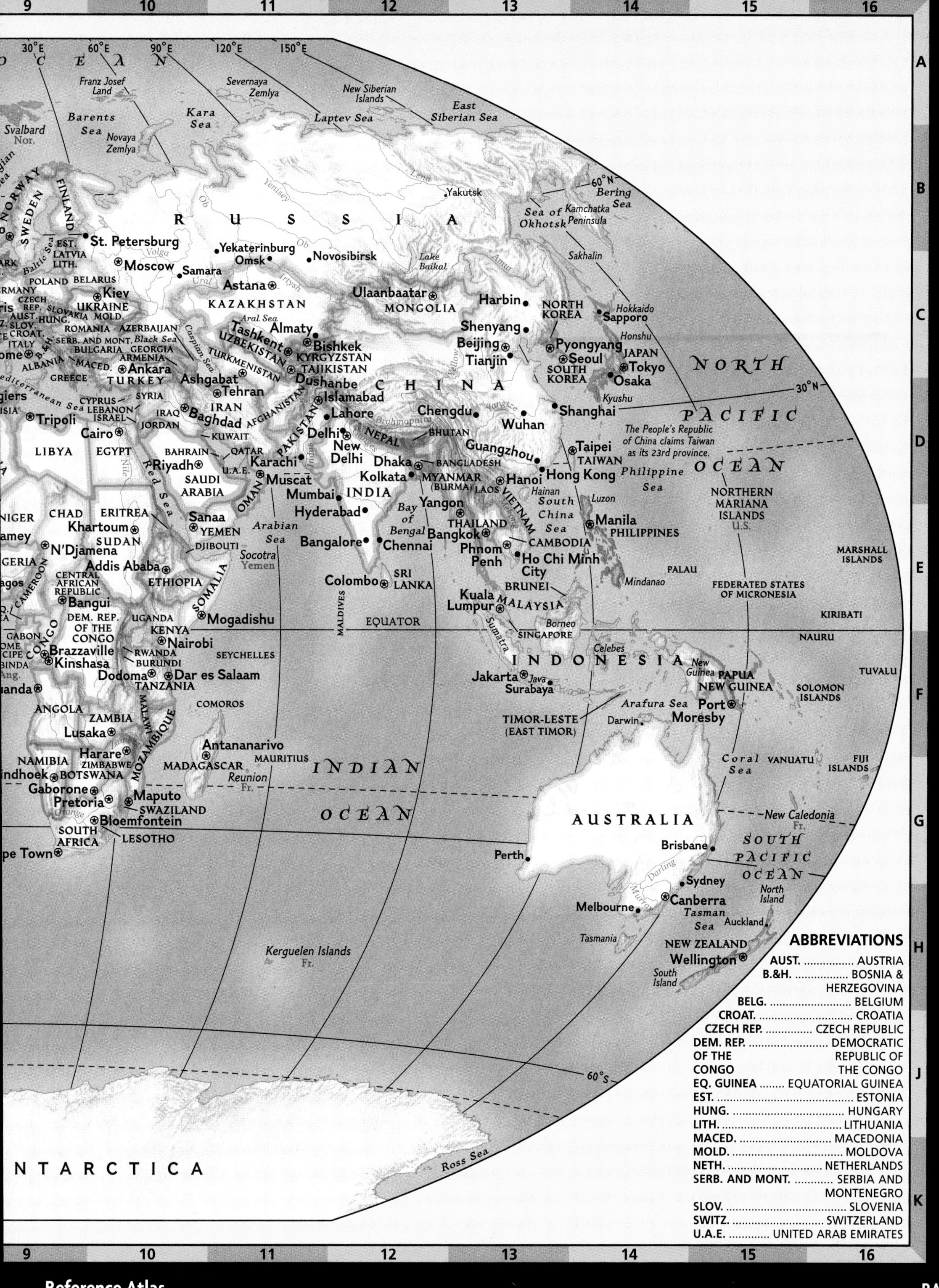
9
10
11
12
13
14
15
16
A
B
C
D
E
F
G
H
J
K
30°E
60°E
90°E
120°E
150°E
Franz Josef Land
Severnaya Zemlya
New Siberian Islands
East Siberian Sea
Laptev Sea
Kara Sea
Barents Sea
Svalbard Nor.
Novaya Zemlya
NORWAY
SWEDEN
FINLAND
Lena
Yenisey
Ob
Yakutsk
60°N
Bering Sea
Sea of Okhotsk
Kamchatka Peninsula
R U S S I A
St. Petersburg
Volga
Yekaterinburg
Omsk
Novosibirsk
Lake Baikal
Amur
Sakhalin
Moscow
Samara
Ural
Irtysh
EST.
LATVIA
LITH.
Baltic Sea
POLAND
BELARUS
Astana
Ulaanbaatar
MONGOLIA
Harbin
NORTH KOREA
Hokkaido
Sapporo
CZECH REP.
SLOVAKIA
AUST.
HUNG.
SLOV.
CROAT.
Kiev
UKRAINE
MOLD.
KAZAKHSTAN
Aral Sea
Tashkent
Almaty
Shenyang
Honshu
ITALY
B.&H.
SERB. AND MONT.
ROMANIA
BULGARIA
AZERBAIJAN
Black Sea
GEORGIA
ARMENIA
Caspian Sea
UZBEKISTAN
Bishkek
KYRGYZSTAN
Beijing
Tianjin
Yellow
Pyongyang
Seoul
SOUTH KOREA
JAPAN
Tokyo
Osaka
ALBANIA
MACED.
Ankara
TURKEY
GREECE
TURKMENISTAN
TAJIKISTAN
Ashgabat
Dushanbe
C H I N A
NORTH
Tehran
Mediterranean Sea
CYPRUS
LEBANON
ISRAEL
SYRIA
IRAQ
Baghdad
IRAN
AFGHANISTAN
Islamabad
PAKISTAN
Lahore
Chengdu
Yangtze
Wuhan
Shanghai
Kyushu
30°N
Tripoli
Cairo
JORDAN
KUWAIT
Brahmaputra
Delhi
New Delhi
NEPAL
BHUTAN
Ganges
Indus
PACIFIC
The People's Republic of China claims Taiwan as its 23rd province.
LIBYA
EGYPT
Nile
BAHRAIN
QATAR
U.A.E.
Riyadh
SAUDI ARABIA
Red Sea
Karachi
OMAN
Muscat
Dhaka
BANGLADESH
Kolkata
Guangzhou
Taipei
TAIWAN
Hong Kong
Philippine Sea
OCEAN
MYANMAR (BURMA)
LAOS
Hanoi
VIETNAM
Hainan
INDIA
Mumbai
South China Sea
Luzon
NORTHERN MARIANA ISLANDS U.S.
NIGER
CHAD
ERITREA
Khartoum
SUDAN
Sanaa
YEMEN
Arabian Sea
Hyderabad
Bay of Bengal
Yangon
THAILAND
Bangkok
Mekong
Manila
PHILIPPINES
N'Djamena
DJIBOUTI
Bangalore
Chennai
CAMBODIA
Phnom Penh
Ho Chi Minh City
CAMEROON
Addis Ababa
ETHIOPIA
Socotra Yemen
SOMALIA
CENTRAL AFRICAN REPUBLIC
Bangui
Colombo
SRI LANKA
MALDIVES
BRUNEI
MALAYSIA
Kuala Lumpur
Mindanao
PALAU
FEDERATED STATES OF MICRONESIA
MARSHALL ISLANDS
DEM. REP. OF THE CONGO
UGANDA
KENYA
Mogadishu
EQUATOR
Sumatra
Borneo
SINGAPORE
KIRIBATI
NAURU
GABON
CONGO
Brazzaville
Kinshasa
RWANDA
BURUNDI
Nairobi
SEYCHELLES
Celebes
I N D O N E S I A
New Guinea
PAPUA NEW GUINEA
TUVALU
Ang.
Dodoma
Dar es Salaam
TANZANIA
Jakarta
Java
Surabaya
SOLOMON ISLANDS
ANGOLA
COMOROS
MALAWI
ZAMBIA
Lusaka
Arafura Sea
Port Moresby
TIMOR-LESTE (EAST TIMOR)
Darwin
NAMIBIA
Harare
ZIMBABWE
MOZAMBIQUE
Antananarivo
MAURITIUS
MADAGASCAR
INDIAN
Reunion Fr.
Coral Sea
VANUATU
FIJI ISLANDS
BOTSWANA
Gaborone
Pretoria
Orange
Maputo
SWAZILAND
OCEAN
Bloemfontein
LESOTHO
SOUTH AFRICA
AUSTRALIA
New Caledonia Fr.
SOUTH PACIFIC OCEAN
Brisbane
Perth
Darling
Murray
Sydney
Canberra
Melbourne
North Island
Tasman Sea
Auckland
Tasmania
NEW ZEALAND
Wellington
South Island
Kerguelen Islands Fr.
60°S
Ross Sea
NTARCTICA
ABBREVIATIONS
AUST. .... AUSTRIA
B.&H. .... BOSNIA & HERZEGOVINA
BELG. .... BELGIUM
CROAT. .... CROATIA
CZECH REP. .... CZECH REPUBLIC
DEM. REP. OF THE CONGO .... DEMOCRATIC REPUBLIC OF THE CONGO
EQ. GUINEA .... EQUATORIAL GUINEA
EST. .... ESTONIA
HUNG. .... HUNGARY
LITH. .... LITHUANIA
MACED. .... MACEDONIA
MOLD. .... MOLDOVA
NETH. .... NETHERLANDS
SERB. AND MONT. .... SERBIA AND MONTENEGRO
SLOV. .... SLOVENIA
SWITZ. .... SWITZERLAND
U.A.E. .... UNITED ARAB EMIRATES

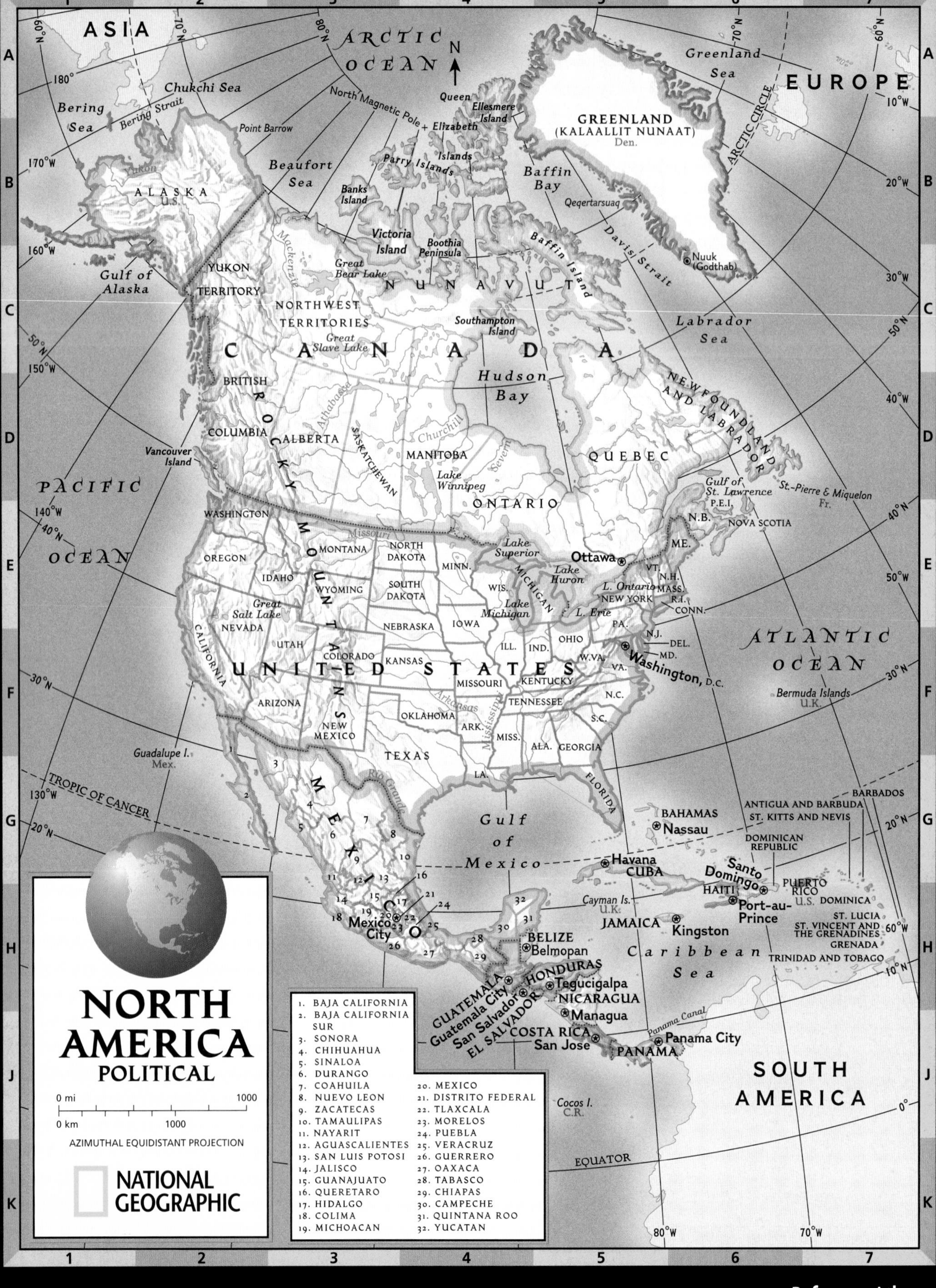
NORTH
AMERICA
POLITICAL
0 mi 1000
0 km 1000
AZIMUTHAL EQUIDISTANT PROJECTION
NATIONAL
GEOGRAPHIC
1. BAJA CALIFORNIA
2. BAJA CALIFORNIA SUR
3. SONORA
4. CHIHUAHUA
5. SINALOA
6. DURANGO
7. COAHUILA
8. NUEVO LEON
9. ZACATECAS
10. TAMAULIPAS
11. NAYARIT
12. AGUASCALIENTES
13. SAN LUIS POTOSI
14. JALISCO
15. GUANAJUATO
16. QUERETARO
17. HIDALGO
18. COLIMA
19. MICHOACAN
20. MEXICO
21. DISTRITO FEDERAL
22. TLAXCALA
23. MORELOS
24. PUEBLA
25. VERACRUZ
26. GUERRERO
27. OAXACA
28. TABASCO
29. CHIAPAS
30. CAMPECHE
31. QUINTANA ROO
32. YUCATAN
ASIA
ARCTIC OCEAN
N
EUROPE
Greenland Sea
GREENLAND
(KALAALLIT NUNAAT)
Den.
Chukchi Sea
Bering Sea
Bering Strait
Point Barrow
North Magnetic Pole
Queen Elizabeth Islands
Ellesmere Island
Parry Islands
Beaufort Sea
Banks Island
Victoria Island
Boothia Peninsula
Baffin Bay
Qeqertarsuaq
Baffin Island
Davis Strait
Nuuk (Godthab)
ARCTIC CIRCLE
ALASKA
U.S.
Yukon
Gulf of Alaska
YUKON TERRITORY
Mackenzie
Great Bear Lake
NUNAVUT
NORTHWEST TERRITORIES
Southampton Island
Labrador Sea
Great Slave Lake
CANADA
Hudson Bay
NEWFOUNDLAND AND LABRADOR
BRITISH COLUMBIA
ALBERTA
Athabasca
SASKATCHEWAN
Churchill
MANITOBA
Severn
Lake Winnipeg
QUEBEC
ROCKY MOUNTAINS
Vancouver Island
PACIFIC OCEAN
ONTARIO
Gulf of St. Lawrence
P.E.I.
St.-Pierre & Miquelon Fr.
N.B.
NOVA SCOTIA
WASHINGTON
Missouri
Lake Superior
Ottawa
ME.
MONTANA
NORTH DAKOTA
MINN.
OREGON
Lake Huron
VT.
N.H.
MASS.
R.I.
CONN.
IDAHO
WYOMING
SOUTH DAKOTA
WIS.
MICHIGAN
L. Ontario
NEW YORK
Great Salt Lake
Lake Michigan
L. Erie
NEVADA
NEBRASKA
IOWA
PA.
N.J.
DEL.
MD.
UTAH
COLORADO
ILL.
IND.
OHIO
W.VA.
VA.
Washington, D.C.
CALIFORNIA
KANSAS
UNITED STATES
MISSOURI
KENTUCKY
ATLANTIC OCEAN
ARIZONA
Arkansas
TENNESSEE
N.C.
Bermuda Islands U.K.
OKLAHOMA
Mississippi
NEW MEXICO
ARK.
S.C.
Guadalupe I. Mex.
TEXAS
MISS.
ALA.
GEORGIA
Rio Grande
LA.
FLORIDA
TROPIC OF CANCER
MEXICO
Gulf of Mexico
BAHAMAS
Nassau
BARBADOS
ANTIGUA AND BARBUDA
ST. KITTS AND NEVIS
DOMINICAN REPUBLIC
Havana
CUBA
Santo Domingo
HAITI
PUERTO RICO U.S.
DOMINICA
Port-au-Prince
Cayman Is. U.K.
JAMAICA
Kingston
ST. LUCIA
ST. VINCENT AND THE GRENADINES
GRENADA
Mexico City
BELIZE
Belmopan
Caribbean Sea
TRINIDAD AND TOBAGO
HONDURAS
Tegucigalpa
GUATEMALA
Guatemala City
San Salvador
EL SALVADOR
NICARAGUA
Managua
COSTA RICA
San Jose
Panama Canal
Panama City
PANAMA
SOUTH AMERICA
Cocos I. C.R.
EQUATOR
180°
170°W
160°W
150°W
140°W
130°W
80°W
70°W
60°W
10°W
20°W
30°W
40°W
50°W
60°N
70°N
80°N
50°N
40°N
30°N
20°N
10°N
0°

NORTH AMERICA
PHYSICAL
0 mi 1000
0 km 1000
AZIMUTHAL EQUIDISTANT PROJECTION
NATIONAL GEOGRAPHIC
ASIA
ARCTIC OCEAN
Lincoln Sea
Greenland Sea
EUROPE
GREENLAND
Chukchi Sea
Bering Sea
Beaufort Sea
Baffin Bay
ALASKA
Mt. McKinley (Denali) 20,320 ft 6,194 m
Gulf of Alaska
PACIFIC OCEAN
CANADA
Hudson Bay
Labrador Sea
ROCKY MOUNTAINS
GREAT PLAINS
CANADIAN SHIELD
UNITED STATES
CENTRAL LOWLAND
APPALACHIAN MOUNTAINS
COASTAL PLAIN
ATLANTIC OCEAN
Gulf of Mexico
MEXICO
Mexico City
Washington
Ottawa
Havana
CUBA
Caribbean Sea
WEST INDIES
CENTRAL AMERICA
SOUTH AMERICA
TROPIC OF CANCER
ARCTIC CIRCLE
EQUATOR

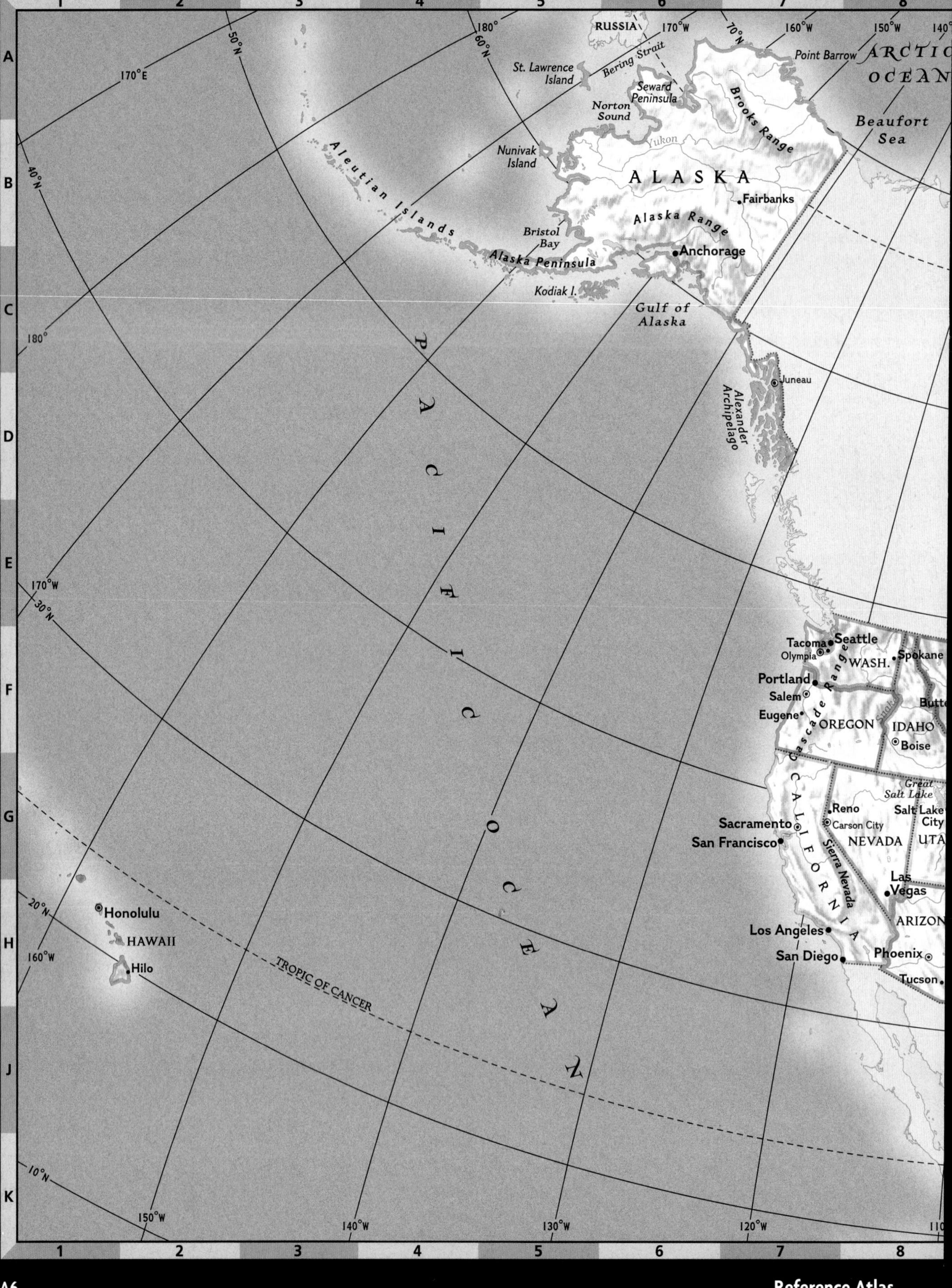
RUSSIA
Bering Strait
St. Lawrence Island
Seward Peninsula
Norton Sound
Point Barrow
ARCTIC OCEAN
Beaufort Sea
Brooks Range
Yukon
Nunivak Island
ALASKA
Fairbanks
Alaska Range
Aleutian Islands
Bristol Bay
Anchorage
Alaska Peninsula
Kodiak I.
Gulf of Alaska
Juneau
Alexander Archipelago
PACIFIC OCEAN
Tacoma
Seattle
Olympia
WASH.
Spokane
Portland
Salem
Cascade Range
Eugene
OREGON
IDAHO
Boise
Great Salt Lake
Salt Lake City
Reno
Carson City
Sacramento
San Francisco
NEVADA
Sierra Nevada
CALIFORNIA
Las Vegas
Los Angeles
San Diego
Phoenix
Tucson
Honolulu
HAWAII
Hilo
TROPIC OF CANCER
170°E
180°
170°W
160°W
150°W
140°W
130°W
120°W
70°N
60°N
50°N
40°N
30°N
20°N
10°N

UNITED STATES
POLITICAL
0 mi
600
0 km
600
OBLIQUE AZIMUTHAL EQUIDISTANT PROJECTION
NATIONAL GEOGRAPHIC
GREENLAND
(KALAALLIT NUNAAT)
Den.
ARCTIC CIRCLE
CANADA
ATLANTIC OCEAN
Gulf of Mexico
Caribbean Sea
MEXICO
BAHAMAS
CUBA
HAITI
DOMINICAN REPUBLIC
PUERTO RICO
U.S.
JAMAICA
DOMINICA
ANTIGUA & BARBUDA
ST. KITTS & NEVIS
San Juan
Bermuda Is.
U.K.
Straits of Florida
Lake Superior
Lake Huron
L. Michigan
L. Erie
Lake Ontario
MONTANA
NORTH DAKOTA
SOUTH DAKOTA
MINNESOTA
WISCONSIN
MICHIGAN
IOWA
NEBRASKA
WYOMING
COLORADO
KANSAS
MISSOURI
ILLINOIS
IND.
OHIO
KENTUCKY
TENNESSEE
NORTH CAROLINA
SOUTH CAROLINA
GEORGIA
ALABAMA
MISS.
LOUISIANA
ARKANSAS
OKLAHOMA
TEXAS
NEW MEXICO
FLORIDA
VIRGINIA
W. VA.
PA.
NEW YORK
VT.
MAINE
ROCKY MOUNTAINS
APPALACHIAN
Billings
Bismarck
Pierre
Minneapolis
St. Paul
Milwaukee
Madison
Lansing
Detroit
Cleveland
Toledo
Buffalo
Albany
Montpelier
Augusta
Portland
Concord, N.H.
Boston, MASS.
Providence, R.I.
Hartford, CONN.
New York City
Trenton, N.J.
Philadelphia
Harrisburg
Pittsburgh
Baltimore
Dover, DEL.
Annapolis, MD.
Washington, D.C.
Richmond
Virginia Beach
Casper
Cheyenne
Sioux City
Des Moines
Omaha
Lincoln
Chicago
Columbus
Indianapolis
Dayton
Cincinnati
Charleston
Denver
Kansas City
Topeka
Springfield
Jefferson City
St. Louis
Frankfort
Louisville
Nashville
Raleigh
Charlotte
Columbia
Charleston
Santa Fe
Albuquerque
Oklahoma City
Tulsa
Memphis
Little Rock
Atlanta
Birmingham
Montgomery
Jackson
Savannah
Jacksonville
Tallahassee
Fort Worth
Dallas
El Paso
Austin
San Antonio
Houston
Baton Rouge
New Orleans
Tampa
Miami
Missouri
Mississippi
Arkansas
Rio Grande

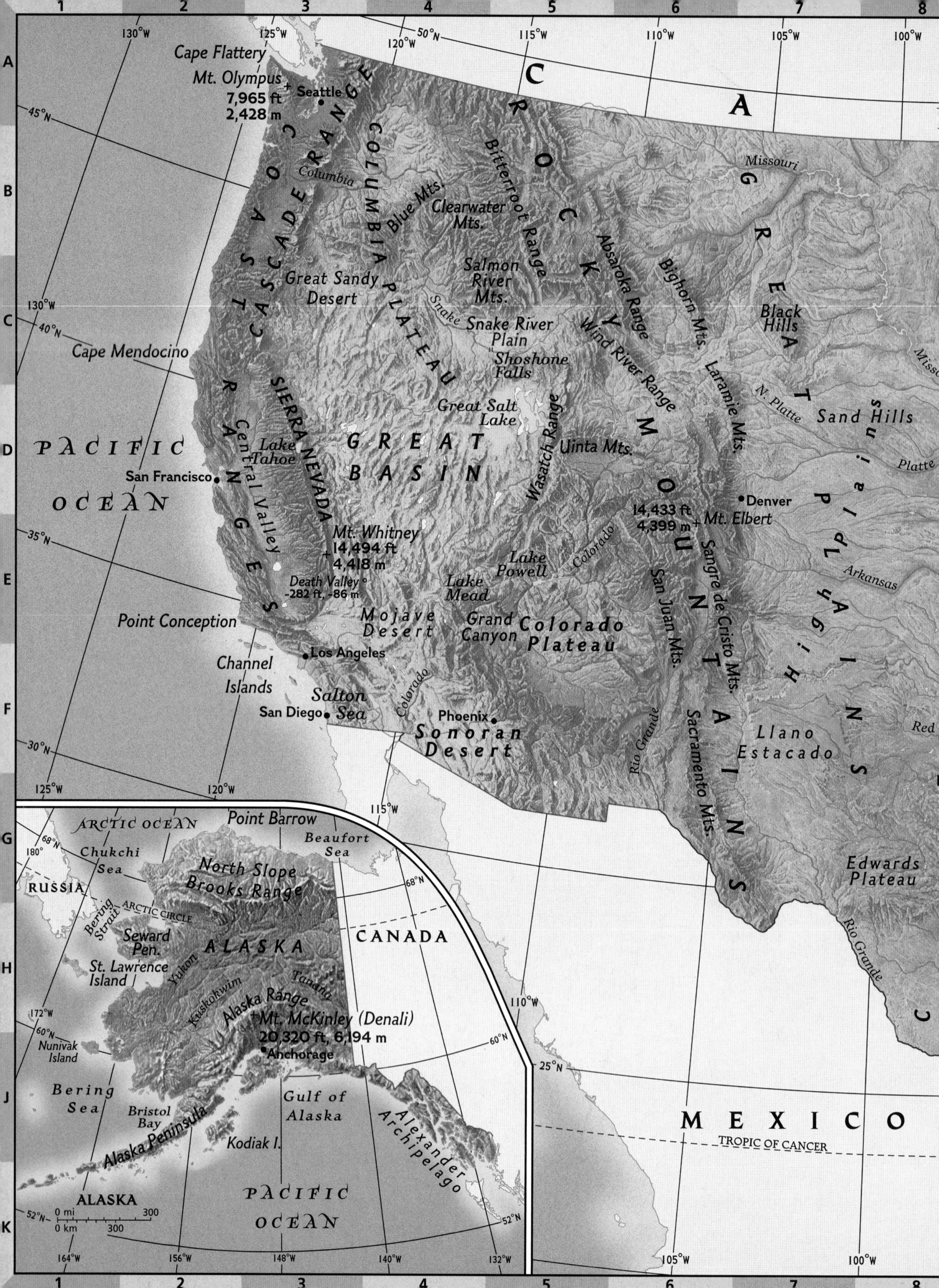

PACIFIC OCEAN
CASCADE RANGE
COAST RANGES
SIERRA NEVADA
COLUMBIA PLATEAU
GREAT BASIN
ROCKY MOUNTAINS
GREAT PLAINS
High Plains
Cape Flattery
Mt. Olympus
7,965 ft
2,428 m
Seattle
Columbia
Blue Mts.
Clearwater Mts.
Bitterroot Range
Salmon River Mts.
Great Sandy Desert
Snake
Snake River Plain
Shoshone Falls
Absaroka Range
Wind River Range
Bighorn Mts.
Black Hills
Missouri
Laramie Mts.
N. Platte
Platte
Sand Hills
Cape Mendocino
Great Salt Lake
Wasatch Range
Uinta Mts.
Lake Tahoe
Central Valley
San Francisco
Denver
14,433 ft
4,399 m
Mt. Elbert
Mt. Whitney
14,494 ft
4,418 m
Death Valley
-282 ft, -86 m
Lake Powell
Colorado
Lake Mead
Arkansas
San Juan Mts.
Sangre de Cristo Mts.
Point Conception
Mojave Desert
Grand Canyon
Colorado Plateau
Los Angeles
Channel Islands
Salton Sea
San Diego
Phoenix
Sonoran Desert
Rio Grande
Sacramento Mts.
Llano Estacado
Red
Edwards Plateau
MEXICO
TROPIC OF CANCER
ARCTIC OCEAN
Point Barrow
Beaufort Sea
Chukchi Sea
RUSSIA
North Slope
Brooks Range
Bering Strait
ARCTIC CIRCLE
Seward Pen.
ALASKA
CANADA
St. Lawrence Island
Yukon
Tanana
Kuskokwim
Alaska Range
Mt. McKinley (Denali)
20,320 ft, 6,194 m
Anchorage
Nunivak Island
Bering Sea
Bristol Bay
Gulf of Alaska
Alexander Archipelago
Kodiak I.
Alaska Peninsula
PACIFIC OCEAN
0 mi 300
0 km 300

UNITED STATES
PHYSICAL
0 mi 300
0 km 300
ALBERS CONIC EQUAL-AREA PROJECTION
NATIONAL GEOGRAPHIC
Lake of the Woods
Isle Royale
Lake Superior
Upper Peninsula
Lake Michigan
Lower Peninsula
Lake Huron
Lake Ontario
Lake Erie
Niagara Falls
Lake Champlain
Adirondack Mts.
Green Mts.
White Mts.
Gulf of Maine
APPALACHIAN MOUNTAINS
Appalachian Plateau
Allegheny Mts.
Blue Ridge
Cumberland Plateau
Piedmont
Mt. Mitchell 6,684 ft 2,037 m
CENTRAL LOWLAND
Ozark Plateau
Boston Mts.
Black Belt
ATLANTIC OCEAN
Gulf of Mexico
Mississippi River Delta
Cape Cod
Long Island
Delaware Bay
Chesapeake Bay
Cape Hatteras
Cape Canaveral
Lake Okeechobee
The Everglades
Florida Keys
Straits of Florida
TROPIC OF CANCER
CUBA
Boston
New York City
Philadelphia
Baltimore
Washington
Pittsburgh
Cleveland
Detroit
Chicago
Milwaukee
Indianapolis
St. Louis
Memphis
Atlanta
Jacksonville
New Orleans
Houston
Miami
Mississippi
Ohio
Wabash
Cumberland
Tennessee
Savannah
Red
Hudson
Connecticut
PRINCIPAL HAWAIIAN ISLANDS
Niihau
Kauai
Oahu
Honolulu
Molokai
Maui
Lanai
Kahoolawe
Hawaii
Mauna Kea 13,796 ft 4,205 m
PACIFIC OCEAN
0 mi 100
0 km 100

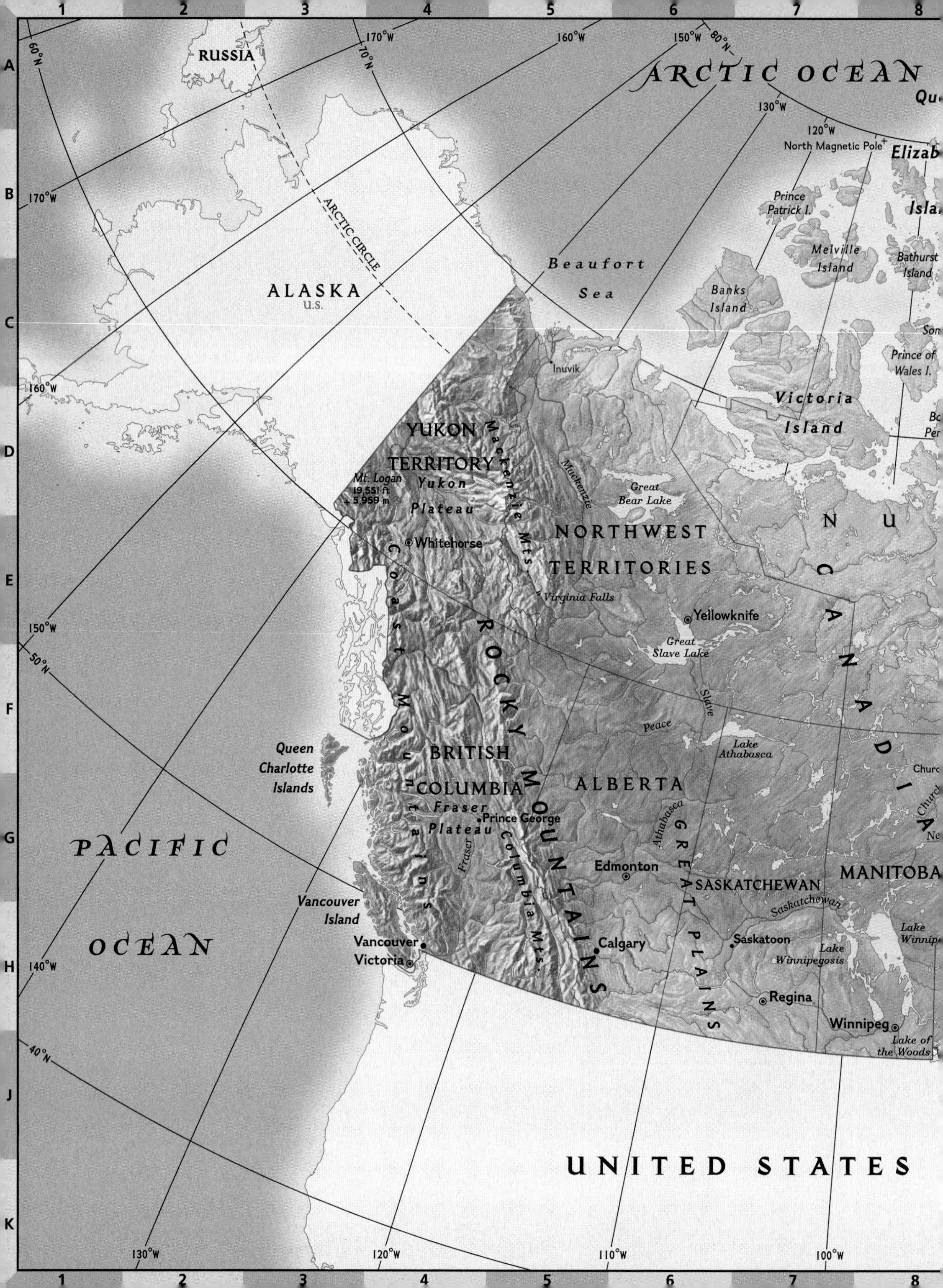

RUSSIA
ARCTIC OCEAN
ARCTIC CIRCLE
North Magnetic Pole
Prince Patrick I.
Melville Island
Bathurst Island
Beaufort Sea
Banks Island
ALASKA
U.S.
Inuvik
Prince of Wales I.
Victoria Island
YUKON TERRITORY
Mackenzie Mts.
Mt. Logan 19,551 ft 5,959 m
Yukon Plateau
Mackenzie
Great Bear Lake
Whitehorse
NORTHWEST TERRITORIES
Coast Mountains
Virginia Falls
Yellowknife
ROCKY MOUNTAINS
Great Slave Lake
Slave
Peace
Lake Athabasca
Queen Charlotte Islands
BRITISH COLUMBIA
ALBERTA
Fraser Plateau
Prince George
Athabasca
GREAT PLAINS
PACIFIC OCEAN
Fraser
Columbia Mts.
Edmonton
SASKATCHEWAN
MANITOBA
Saskatchewan
Vancouver Island
Vancouver
Victoria
Calgary
Saskatoon
Lake Winnipegosis
Regina
Winnipeg
Lake of the Woods
UNITED STATES

CANADA
PHYSICAL/POLITICAL
0 mi
400
0 km
400
AZIMUTHAL EQUIDISTANT PROJECTION
NATIONAL GEOGRAPHIC
GREENLAND
(KALAALLIT NUNAAT)
Den.
ICELAND
Baffin Bay
Baffin Island
Davis Strait
Labrador Sea
Melville Peninsula
Foxe Basin
Southampton Island
Iqaluit
Hudson Strait
Ungava Bay
Hudson Bay
Belcher Islands
James Bay
QUEBEC
SHIELD
ONTARIO
NEWFOUNDLAND AND LABRADOR
Cartwright
Schefferville
Happy Valley-Goose Bay
Smallwood Reservoir
Churchill Falls
Island of Newfoundland
St. John's
Avalon Peninsula
Manicouagan Reservoir
Sept-Iles
Anticosti I.
Gulf of St. Lawrence
St.-Pierre & Miquelon
Fr.
Gaspe Pen.
PRINCE EDWARD ISLAND
Charlottetown
Cape Breton I.
NEW BRUNSWICK
NOVA SCOTIA
Halifax
Fredericton
Saint John
Bay of Fundy
Chicoutimi
Quebec City
St. Lawrence
Rouyn-Noranda
Montreal
Ottawa
Sudbury
Lake Nipigon
Thunder Bay
Lake Superior
Lake Huron
Lake Michigan
Toronto
L. Ontario
Niagara Falls
London
L. Erie
ATLANTIC OCEAN
Ellesmere Island
Baffin Island

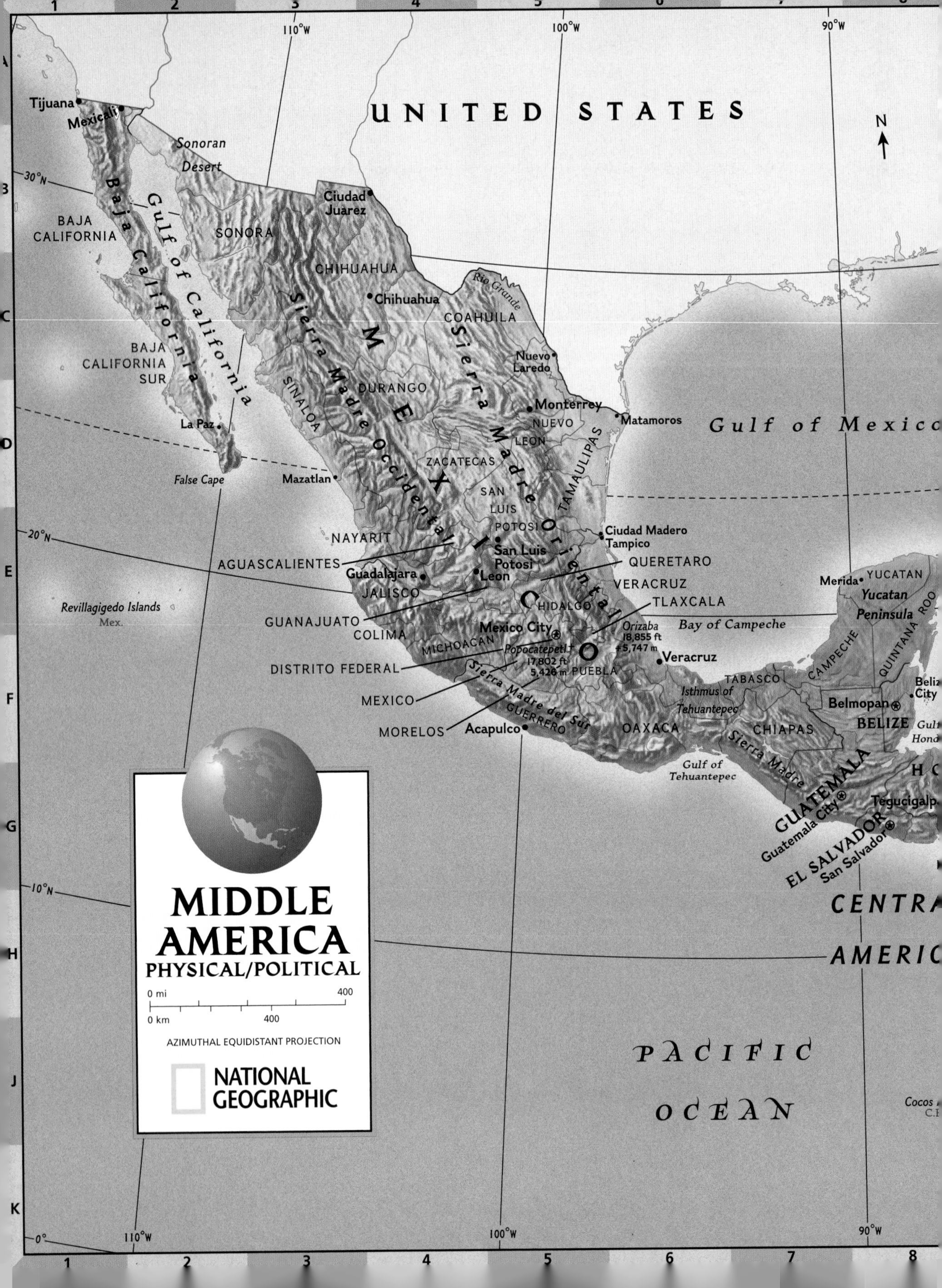

MIDDLE AMERICA
PHYSICAL/POLITICAL
0 mi
400
0 km
400
AZIMUTHAL EQUIDISTANT PROJECTION
NATIONAL GEOGRAPHIC
UNITED STATES
MEXICO
Gulf of Mexico
PACIFIC OCEAN
CENTRAL AMERICA
GUATEMALA
EL SALVADOR
BELIZE
Tijuana
Mexicali
Sonoran Desert
Baja California
Gulf of California
BAJA CALIFORNIA
BAJA CALIFORNIA SUR
SONORA
CHIHUAHUA
Ciudad Juarez
Chihuahua
COAHUILA
Rio Grande
Sierra Madre Occidental
Sierra Madre Oriental
Nuevo Laredo
Monterrey
NUEVO LEON
Matamoros
TAMAULIPAS
SINALOA
DURANGO
La Paz
False Cape
Mazatlan
ZACATECAS
SAN LUIS POTOSI
NAYARIT
Ciudad Madero
Tampico
San Luis Potosi
AGUASCALIENTES
QUERETARO
Guadalajara
Leon
JALISCO
VERACRUZ
HIDALGO
TLAXCALA
Revillagigedo Islands
Mex.
GUANAJUATO
COLIMA
Mexico City
Orizaba
18,855 ft
5,747 m
Bay of Campeche
MICHOACAN
Popocatepetl
17,802 ft
5,426 m
Veracruz
DISTRITO FEDERAL
PUEBLA
TABASCO
MEXICO
Sierra Madre del Sur
GUERRERO
Isthmus of Tehuantepec
MORELOS
Acapulco
OAXACA
CHIAPAS
Gulf of Tehuantepec
Sierra Madre
Merida
YUCATAN
Yucatan Peninsula
CAMPECHE
QUINTANA ROO
Belmopan
Guatemala City
San Salvador
Tegucigalp
Cocos
110°W
100°W
90°W
30°N
20°N
10°N
0°
N

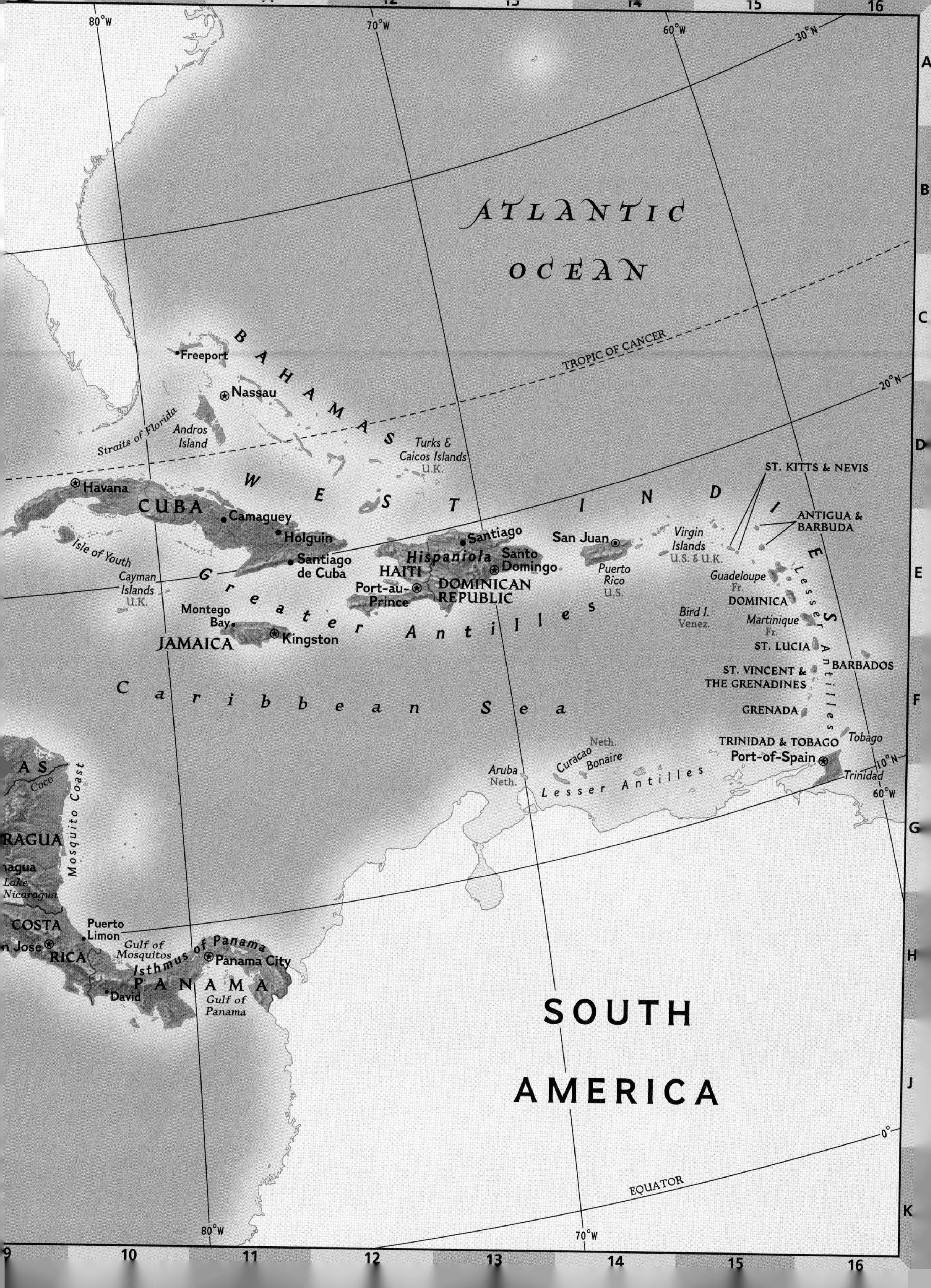

ATLANTIC OCEAN
BAHAMAS
Freeport
Nassau
Andros Island
Straits of Florida
TROPIC OF CANCER
Turks & Caicos Islands U.K.
W E S T I N D I E S
Havana
CUBA
Camaguey
Holguin
Santiago de Cuba
Isle of Youth
Cayman Islands U.K.
Santiago
Hispaniola
Santo Domingo
HAITI
Port-au-Prince
DOMINICAN REPUBLIC
San Juan
Puerto Rico U.S.
Virgin Islands U.S. & U.K.
ST. KITTS & NEVIS
ANTIGUA & BARBUDA
Guadeloupe Fr.
DOMINICA
Martinique Fr.
Bird I. Venez.
ST. LUCIA
BARBADOS
ST. VINCENT & THE GRENADINES
GRENADA
TRINIDAD & TOBAGO
Tobago
Port-of-Spain
Trinidad
Lesser Antilles
Greater Antilles
Montego Bay
Kingston
JAMAICA
Caribbean Sea
Aruba Neth.
Curacao
Bonaire
Neth.
Lesser Antilles
Mosquito Coast
Coco
Lake Nicaragua
COSTA RICA
Puerto Limon
Gulf of Mosquitos
Isthmus of Panama
Panama City
PANAMA
David
Gulf of Panama
SOUTH AMERICA
EQUATOR
80°W
70°W
60°W
30°N
20°N
10°N
0°

SOUTH AMERICA
POLITICAL
0 mi 800
0 km 800
AZIMUTHAL EQUIDISTANT PROJECTION
NATIONAL GEOGRAPHIC
Caribbean Sea
ATLANTIC OCEAN
PACIFIC OCEAN
VENEZUELA
GUYANA
SURINAME
FRENCH GUIANA
Fr.
COLOMBIA
ECUADOR
PERU
BRAZIL
BOLIVIA
PARAGUAY
URUGUAY
ARGENTINA
AMAZON BASIN
ANDES
Barranquilla
Cartagena
Santa Marta
Maracaibo
Lake Maracaibo
Barquisimeto
Caracas
Valencia
Ciudad Guayana
Orinoco
Georgetown
Paramaribo
Cayenne
Bucaramanga
San Cristobal
Medellin
Bogota
Cali
Malpelo I.
Col.
Boa Vista
Boundary claimed by Suriname
Esmeraldas
Quito
Guayaquil
Negro
Marajo Island
Belem
Amazon
Manaus
Santarem
Iquitos
Amazon (Solimoes)
Maranon
Madeira
Tapajos
Xingu
Purus
Fortaleza
Teresina
Natal
Campina Grande
Recife
Rio Branco
Porto Velho
Teles Pires
Tocantins
Sao Francisco
Ucayali
Callao
Lima
Machu Picchu
Cuzco
Ayacucho
Lake Titicaca
Trinidad
Salvador (Bahia)
Brasilia
Goiania
Arequipa
La Paz
Oruro
Santa Cruz
Sucre
Arica
Uberandia
Uberaba
Iquique
Campo Grande
Belo Horizonte
Paraguay
Tarija
Campinas
Nova Iguacu
Londrina
Rio de Janeiro
Sao Paulo
Santos
Antofagasta
Salta
TROPIC OF CAPRICORN
Asuncion
Curitiba
San Miguel de Tucuman
San Felix I.
San Ambrosio I.
Chil.
Parana
Uruguay
Uruguaiana
Porto Alegre
Santa Maria
La Serena
Coquimbo
Cordoba
Rosario
Valparaiso
Mendoza
Santiago
Buenos Aires
Montevideo
La Plata
Rio de la Plata
Juan Fernandez Is.
Chil.
Concepcion
Mar del Plata
Bahia Blanca
Negro
Puerto Montt
Comodoro Rivadavia
Falkland Islands (Islas Malvinas)
Stanley
Administered by United Kingdom
(Claimed by Arg.)
Rio Gallegos
Strait of Magellan
Punta Arenas
TIERRA DEL FUEGO
Ushuaia
Cape Horn
South Georgia I.
U.K.
EQUATOR
N
80°W
60°W
50°W
40°W
10°N
0°
10°S
20°S
30°S
40°S
50°S
100°W
90°W
70°W
30°W
20°W
1 2 3 4 5 6 7
A B C D E F G H J K

SOUTH AMERICA
PHYSICAL
0 mi
800
0 km
800
AZIMUTHAL EQUIDISTANT PROJECTION
NATIONAL GEOGRAPHIC
Caribbean Sea
ATLANTIC OCEAN
PACIFIC OCEAN
Lake Maracaibo
Caracas
Orinoco
VENEZUELA
LLANOS
GUYANA
Georgetown
SURINAME
Paramaribo
Cayenne
FRENCH GUIANA
Angel Falls
Total drop
3,212 ft 979 m
GUIANA HIGHLANDS
Boundary claimed by Suriname
Bogota
COLOMBIA
Malpelo I.
Quito
ECUADOR
Negro
Amazon
Marajo Island
EQUATOR
AMAZON
Selvas
BASIN
Madeira
Tapajos
Xingu
Purus
Ucayali
Teles Pires
Tocantins
BRAZIL
Sao Francisco
ANDES
Lima
Machu Picchu
Lake Titicaca
MATO GROSSO
PLATEAU
BRAZILIAN
HIGHLANDS
Brasilia
BOLIVIA
La Paz
Altiplano
Sucre
Salar de Uyuni
Paraguay
PARAGUAY
GRAN CHACO
Asuncion
Iguazu Falls
TROPIC OF CAPRICORN
San Felix I.
San Ambrosio I.
Parana
Uruguay
ARGENTINA
Aconcagua 22,834 ft 6,960 m
Santiago
CHILE
Juan Fernandez Is.
Buenos Aires
URUGUAY
Montevideo
Rio de la Plata
PAMPAS
Negro
-131 ft -40 m
Valdes Peninsula
Chiloe Island
PATAGONIA
Gulf of San Jorge
Taitao Peninsula
Wellington I.
Falkland Islands (Islas Malvinas)
Stanley
Strait of Magellan
Tierra del Fuego
Cape Horn
South Georgia I.
10°N
0°
10°S
20°S
30°S
40°S
50°S
100°W
90°W
80°W
70°W
60°W
50°W
40°W
30°W
20°W
N

EUROPE
POLITICAL
0 mi 400
0 km 400
AZIMUTHAL EQUIDISTANT PROJECTION
NATIONAL GEOGRAPHIC
ATLANTIC OCEAN
ICELAND
Reykjavik
Akureyri
ARCTIC CIRCLE
MERIDIAN OF GREENWICH (LONDON)
Norwegian Sea
Faroe Islands
Den.
Torshavn
Shetland Islands
Lerwick
Orkney Islands
Rockall
U.K.
Isle of Lewis
Inverness
UNITED KINGDOM
SCOTLAND
Aberdeen
Glasgow
Edinburgh
NORTHERN IRELAND
Belfast
IRELAND
Dublin
Cork
Irish Sea
Liverpool
Manchester
WALES
Cardiff
Birmingham
ENGLAND
London
Celtic Sea
Land's End
Southampton
English Channel
North Sea
NORWAY
Trondheim
Alesund
Bergen
Stavanger
Oslo
Skagerrak
SWEDEN
Are
Sundsvall
Uppsala
Stockholm
Goteborg
Gotland
DENMARK
Arhus
Copenhagen
Malmo
Kiel
Hamburg
NETH.
The Hague
Amsterdam
Brussels
BELGIUM
LUX.
GERMANY
Berlin
Bonn
Rhine
Frankfurt
Munich
POLAND
Gdansk
Bydgoszcz
Wroclaw
Prague
CZECH REP.
Bratislava
Vienna
AUSTRIA
LIECH.
SWITZERLAND
Zurich
Bern
Geneva
ALPS
FRANCE
Le Havre
Brest
Rennes
Paris
Nantes
Strasbourg
La Rochelle
Limoges
Bordeaux
Lyon
Toulouse
Bay of Biscay
Donostia-San Sebastian
Pyrenees
ANDORRA
MONACO
Nice
Marseille
Corsica
Fr.
ITALY
Milan
Turin
Genoa
Venice
SAN MARINO
VATICAN CITY
Rome
Naples
Sardinia
It.
Cagliari
Tyrrhenian Sea
Palermo
Messina
Sicily
Catania
Valletta
MALTA
SLOVENIA
Ljubljana
Zagreb
CROATIA
HUNGARY
Budapest
BOSNIA HERZEGOVINA
Sarajevo
Adriatic Sea
SPAIN
Madrid
A Coruna
Vigo
Bilbao
Valladolid
Zaragoza
Barcelona
Valencia
Palma
Balearic Islands
Sp.
Cordoba
Seville
Murcia
Cartagena
Cadiz
Malaga
GIBRALTAR
U.K.
Strait of Gibraltar
PORTUGAL
Porto
Coimbra
Lisbon
Cape St. Vincent
Mediterranean
AFRICA
60°N
50°N
40°N
30°N
40°W
30°W
20°W
10°W
0°
10°E
70°N

A commonly accepted division between Asia and Europe—here marked by a gray line—is formed by the Ural Mountains, Ural River, Caspian Sea, Caucasus Mountains, and the Black Sea with its outlets, the Bosporus and the Dardanelles.
Europe-Asia boundary
RUSSIA
ASIA
KAZAKHSTAN
URAL MOUNTAINS
Barents Sea
White Sea
Kola Peninsula
LAPLAND
FINLAND
ESTONIA
LATVIA
LITHUANIA
BELARUS
UKRAINE
MOLDOVA
ROMANIA
BULGARIA
TURKEY
GEORGIA
AZERBAIJAN
GREECE
CYPRUS
Caspian Sea
Black Sea
Sea of Azov
Sea of Marmara
Aegean Sea
Caucasus Mountains
Carpathian Mts.
Balkan Mts.
Crimea
Bosporus
Dardanelles
Lake Onega
Lake Ladoga
Volga
Ural
Dniester
Danube
Peloponnesus
Rhodes
Crete
Murmansk
Kirovsk
Umba
Ivalo
Kemi
Lulea
Oulu
Vaasa
Kuopio
Pori
Tampere
Turku
Helsinki
St. Petersburg
Tallinn
Riga
Daugavpils
Vitsyebsk
Vilnius
Kaunas
Minsk
Homyel
Archangel
Severodvinsk
Kem
Pechora
Tobseda
Syktyvkar
Perm
Kirov
Ufa
Kazan
Yaroslavl
Nizhniy Novgorod
Tver
Moscow
Velikiy Novgorod
Smolensk
Bryansk
Kursk
Ryazan
Penza
Samara
Orenburg
Oral
Saratov
Volgograd
Astrakhan
Chernihiv
Sumy
Kharkiv
Kiev
Poltava
Lviv
Vinnytsya
Donetsk
Dnipropetrovsk
Rostov
Chisinau
Odesa
Kerch
Simferopol
Yalta
Sevastopol
Stavropol
Groznyy
Baku
Bucharest
Constanta
Varna
Sofia
Skopje
Istanbul
Thessaloniki
Athens
Iraklio
Nicosia
Belgrade
Warsaw
Krakow
30°E
40°E
50°E
60°E
70°E
80°E
30°N
40°N
50°N
60°N
70°N

EUROPE
PHYSICAL
0 mi
400
0 km
400
AZIMUTHAL EQUIDISTANT PROJECTION
NATIONAL GEOGRAPHIC
ATLANTIC OCEAN
Reykjavik
ICELAND
ARCTIC CIRCLE
Norwegian Sea
MERIDIAN OF GREENWICH (LONDON)
Faroe Islands
Shetland Islands
Orkney Islands
Outer Hebrides
Highlands
British Isles
Edinburgh
Belfast
UNITED KINGDOM
IRELAND
Dublin
Irish Sea
Great Britain
Cardiff
London
North Sea
Jutland
DENMARK
Copenhagen
Zealand
Oslo
Stockholm
SCANDINAVIA
NORWAY
SWEDEN
Amsterdam
NETH.
Berlin
BELGIUM
Brussels
LUX.
GERMANY
POLAND
Oder
Elbe
Prague
CZECH REP.
Rhine
Danube
English Channel
Brittany
Seine
Paris
Loire
FRANCE
Bay of Biscay
Mont Blanc
15,771 ft
4,807 m
Bern
SWITZ.
LIECH.
AUSTRIA
Vienna
Bratislava
SLOVAKIA
Budapest
HUNGARY
ALPS
Massif Central
Rhone
SLOVENIA
Ljubljana
Drava
Zagreb
CROATIA
Sava
Po
MONACO
Riviera
SAN MARINO
BOSNIA & HERZEGOVINA
Sarajevo
Adriatic Sea
Apennines
Cantabrian Mountains
Pyrenees
ANDORRA
Douro
PORTUGAL
IBERIAN PENINSULA
SPAIN
Madrid
Lisbon
Tagus
Ebro
Corsica
ITALY
VATICAN CITY
Rome
Tirana
ALBANIA
Sardinia
Tyrrhenian Sea
Balearic Islands
Baetic Mountains
GIBRALTAR
Strait of Gibraltar
Mediterranean
Ionian Sea
Sicily
Etna
10,902 ft
3,323 m
Valletta
MALTA
AFRICA
60°N
50°N
40°N
30°N
70°N
40°W
30°W
20°W
10°W
0°
10°E
N

North Cape
Barents Sea
Kola Peninsula
White Sea
Pechora
URAL MOUNTAINS
FINLAND
Bothnia
Northern Dvina
EUROPEAN PLAIN
Europe-Asia boundary
Lake Region
Lake Onega
Lake Ladoga
ASIA
RUSSIA
Helsinki
Gulf of Finland
Tallinn
ESTONIA
Kama
Ural
Volga
Riga
LATVIA
Moscow
LITHUANIA
Oka
Vilnius
CENTRAL RUSSIAN UPLAND
Minsk
BELARUS
Dnieper
Don
Warsaw
KAZAKHSTAN
Caspian Depression
Vistula
Kiev
UKRAINE
Dniester
Carpathian Mountains
MOLDOVA
Chisinau
Sea of Azov
Crimea
Elbrus 18,510 ft 5,642 m
Caucasus Mountains
ROMANIA
Belgrade
Bucharest
Danube
GEORGIA
AZERBAIJAN
Baku
Caspian Sea
BALKAN PENINSULA
BULGARIA
Balkan Mountains
Sofia
Skopje
MACED.
Black Sea
Bosporus
TURKEY
Dardanelles
Sea of Marmara
GREECE
Aegean Sea
Athens
Peloponnesus
Rhodes
Nicosia
CYPRUS
Crete
Sea

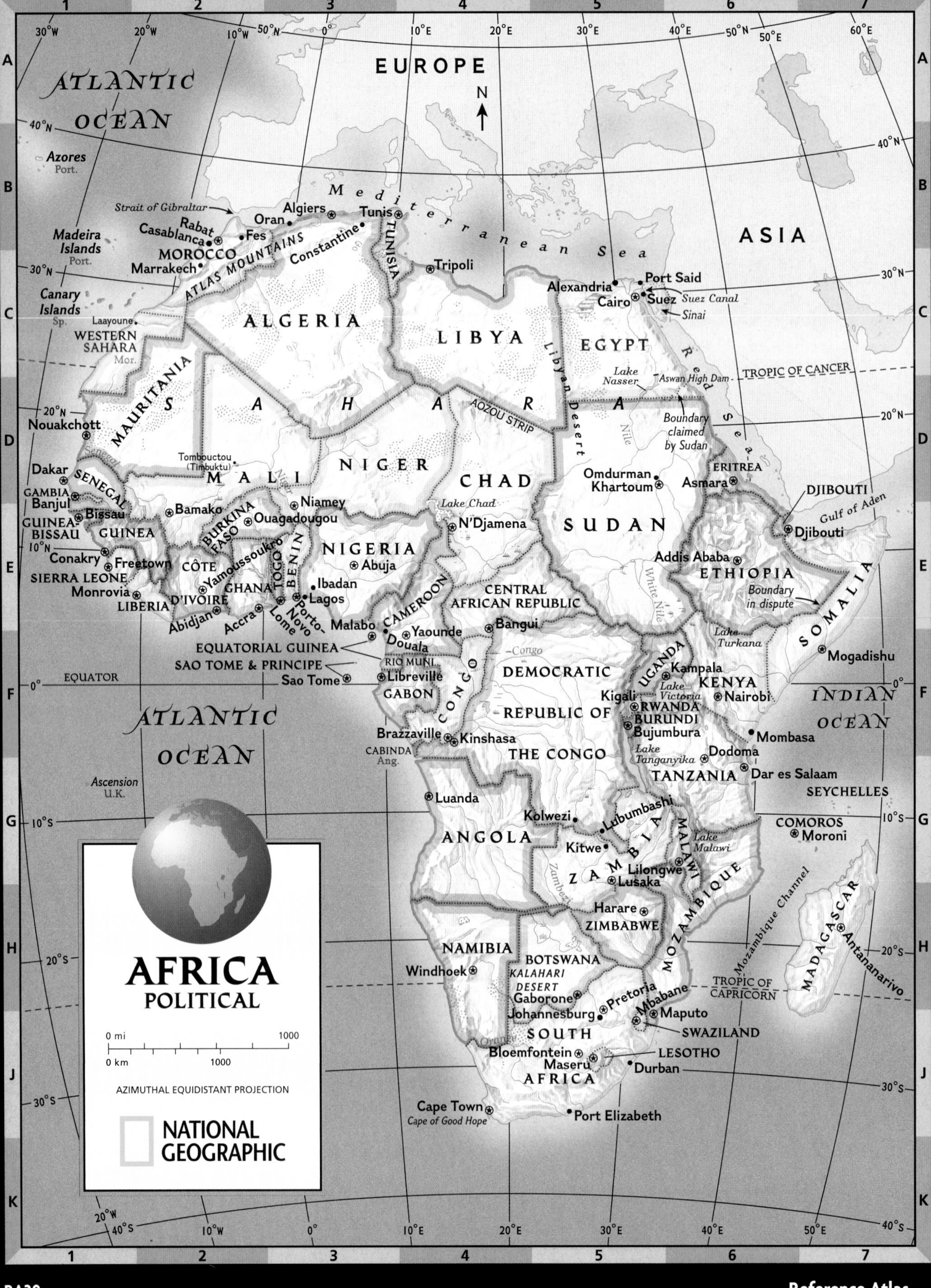
AFRICA
POLITICAL
AZIMUTHAL EQUIDISTANT PROJECTION
NATIONAL GEOGRAPHIC
EUROPE
ASIA
ATLANTIC OCEAN
INDIAN OCEAN
Mediterranean Sea
Red Sea
ALGERIA
LIBYA
EGYPT
MOROCCO
TUNISIA
WESTERN SAHARA
MAURITANIA
MALI
NIGER
CHAD
SUDAN
ERITREA
DJIBOUTI
ETHIOPIA
SOMALIA
SENEGAL
GAMBIA
GUINEA-BISSAU
GUINEA
SIERRA LEONE
LIBERIA
CÔTE D'IVOIRE
BURKINA FASO
GHANA
TOGO
BENIN
NIGERIA
CAMEROON
CENTRAL AFRICAN REPUBLIC
EQUATORIAL GUINEA
SAO TOME & PRINCIPE
GABON
CONGO
DEMOCRATIC REPUBLIC OF THE CONGO
UGANDA
KENYA
RWANDA
BURUNDI
TANZANIA
ANGOLA
ZAMBIA
MALAWI
MOZAMBIQUE
ZIMBABWE
NAMIBIA
BOTSWANA
SOUTH AFRICA
LESOTHO
SWAZILAND
MADAGASCAR
SEYCHELLES
COMOROS
Reference Atlas

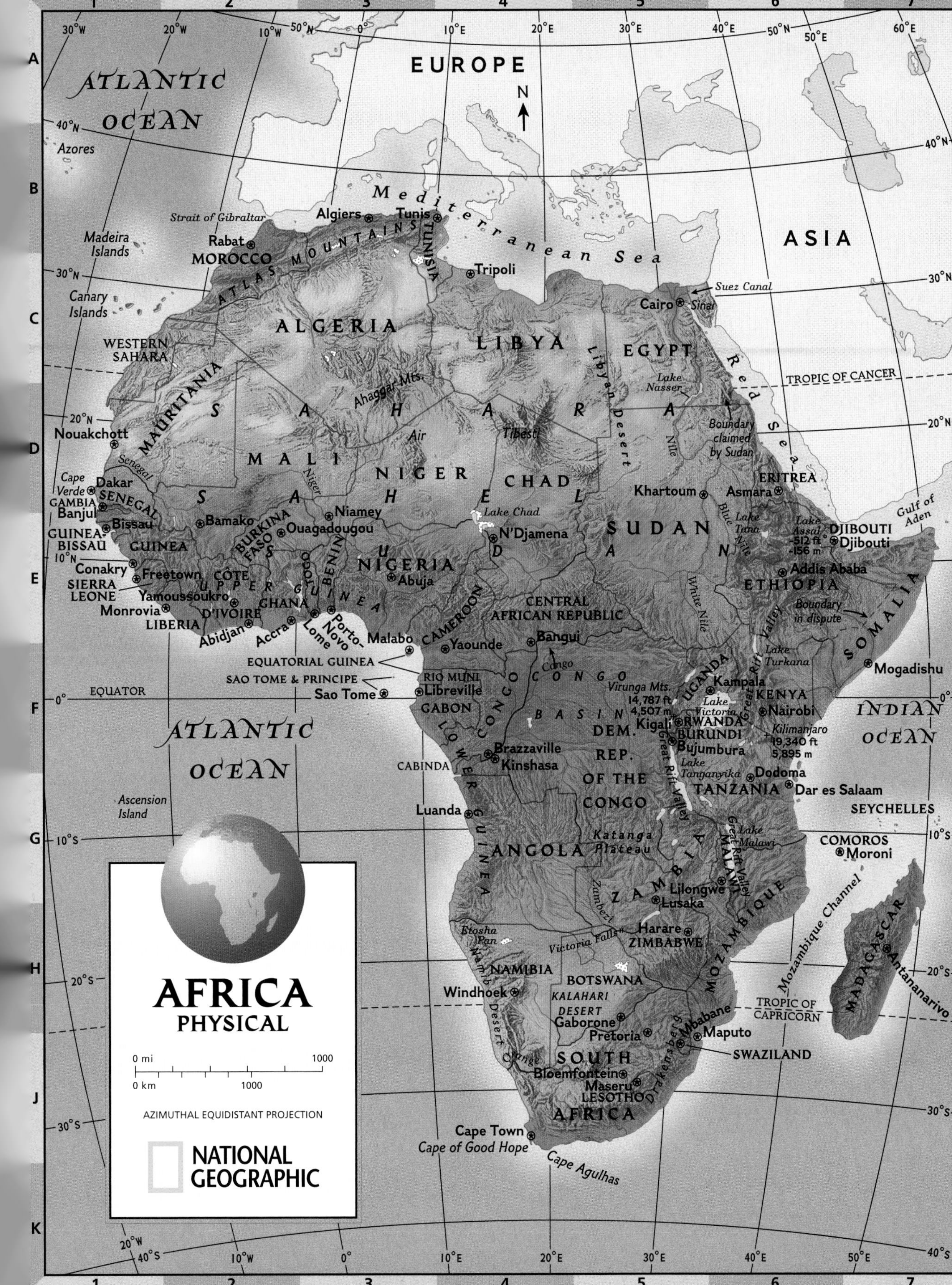

AFRICA
PHYSICAL
EUROPE
ASIA
ATLANTIC OCEAN
INDIAN OCEAN
Mediterranean Sea
Red Sea
Gulf of Aden
Mozambique Channel
TROPIC OF CANCER
EQUATOR
TROPIC OF CAPRICORN
SAHARA
SAHEL
ATLAS MOUNTAINS
Ahaggar Mts.
Tibesti
Air
Libyan Desert
CONGO BASIN
Katanga Plateau
KALAHARI DESERT
Namib Desert
Great Rift Valley
Virunga Mts. 14,787 ft 4,507 m
Kilimanjaro 19,340 ft 5,895 m
Lake Assal -512 ft -156 m
Lake Chad
Lake Victoria
Lake Tanganyika
Lake Malawi
Lake Turkana
Lake Nasser
Lake Tana
Nile
Blue Nile
White Nile
Niger
Congo
Zambezi
Orange
Senegal
Victoria Falls
Etosha Pan
Drakensberg
Cape Verde
Cape of Good Hope
Cape Agulhas
Strait of Gibraltar
Suez Canal
Sinai
Boundary claimed by Sudan
Boundary in dispute
UPPER GUINEA
LOWER GUINEA
Azores
Madeira Islands
Canary Islands
Ascension Island
MOROCCO
WESTERN SAHARA
ALGERIA
TUNISIA
LIBYA
EGYPT
MAURITANIA
MALI
NIGER
CHAD
SUDAN
ERITREA
DJIBOUTI
ETHIOPIA
SOMALIA
SENEGAL
GAMBIA
GUINEA-BISSAU
GUINEA
SIERRA LEONE
LIBERIA
CÔTE D'IVOIRE
BURKINA FASO
GHANA
TOGO
BENIN
NIGERIA
CAMEROON
CENTRAL AFRICAN REPUBLIC
EQUATORIAL GUINEA
SAO TOME & PRINCIPE
RIO MUNI
GABON
CONGO
DEM. REP. OF THE CONGO
CABINDA
UGANDA
KENYA
RWANDA
BURUNDI
TANZANIA
SEYCHELLES
COMOROS
ANGOLA
ZAMBIA
MALAWI
MOZAMBIQUE
ZIMBABWE
NAMIBIA
BOTSWANA
SOUTH AFRICA
LESOTHO
SWAZILAND
MADAGASCAR
Rabat
Algiers
Tunis
Tripoli
Cairo
Nouakchott
Dakar
Banjul
Bissau
Conakry
Freetown
Monrovia
Yamoussoukro
Abidjan
Accra
Lome
Porto-Novo
Bamako
Ouagadougou
Niamey
Abuja
N'Djamena
Khartoum
Asmara
Djibouti
Addis Ababa
Mogadishu
Malabo
Yaounde
Bangui
Sao Tome
Libreville
Brazzaville
Kinshasa
Luanda
Kampala
Nairobi
Kigali
Bujumbura
Dodoma
Dar es Salaam
Moroni
Lilongwe
Lusaka
Harare
Windhoek
Gaborone
Pretoria
Mbabane
Maputo
Bloemfontein
Maseru
Cape Town
Antananarivo
0 mi 1000
0 km 1000
AZIMUTHAL EQUIDISTANT PROJECTION
NATIONAL GEOGRAPHIC

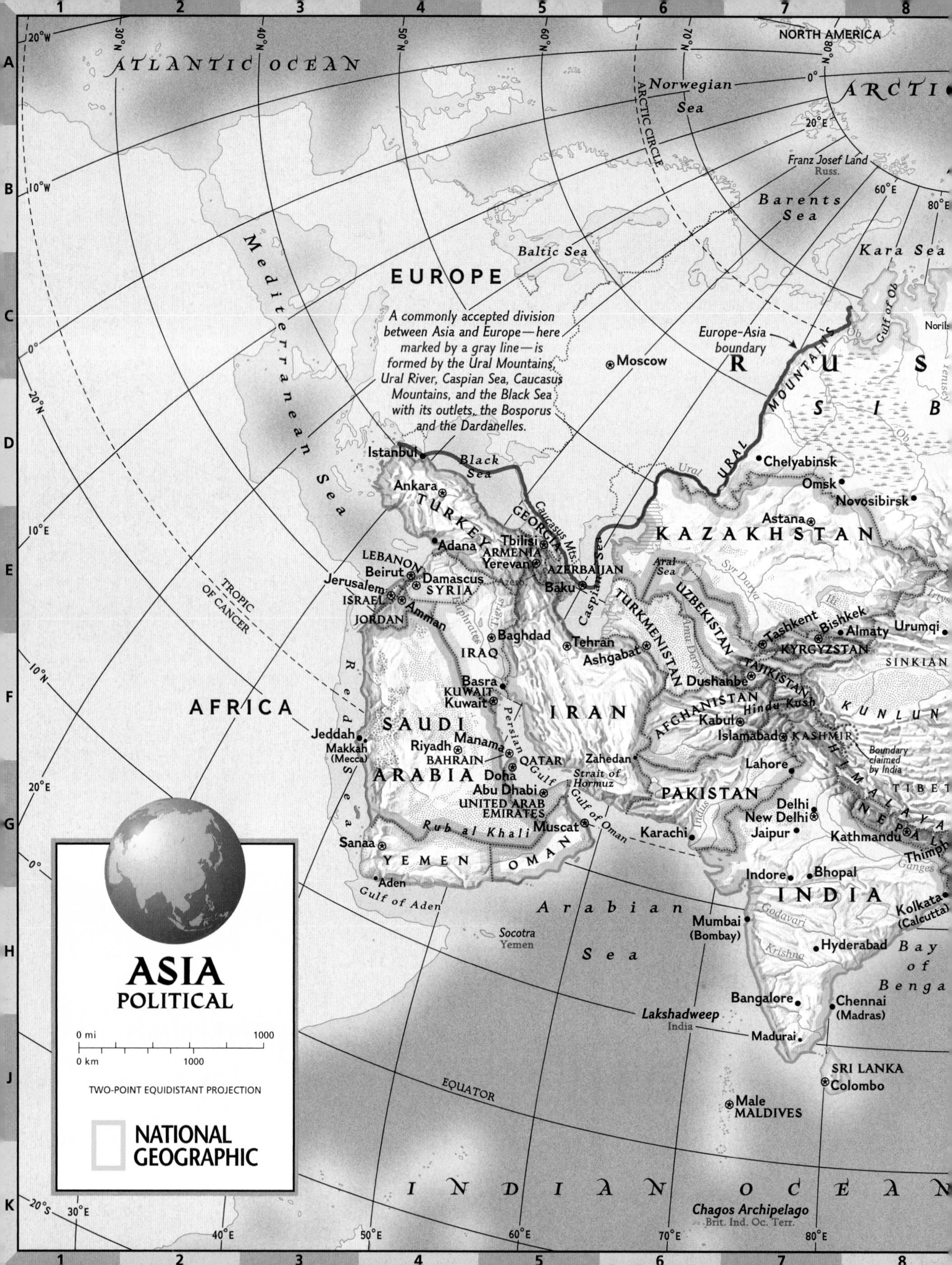

ASIA
POLITICAL
TWO-POINT EQUIDISTANT PROJECTION
NATIONAL GEOGRAPHIC
0 mi 1000
0 km 1000
A commonly accepted division between Asia and Europe—here marked by a gray line—is formed by the Ural Mountains, Ural River, Caspian Sea, Caucasus Mountains, and the Black Sea with its outlets, the Bosporus and the Dardanelles.
ATLANTIC OCEAN
EUROPE
AFRICA
NORTH AMERICA
Norwegian Sea
ARCTIC CIRCLE
Barents Sea
Kara Sea
Baltic Sea
Mediterranean Sea
Black Sea
Franz Josef Land Russ.
Europe-Asia boundary
URAL MOUNTAINS
Moscow
Chelyabinsk
Omsk
Novosibirsk
Astana
KAZAKHSTAN
Istanbul
Ankara
TURKEY
Adana
GEORGIA
Tbilisi
ARMENIA
Yerevan
AZERBAIJAN
Baku
Caucasus Mts.
Caspian Sea
Aral Sea
Syr Darya
Amu Darya
UZBEKISTAN
TURKMENISTAN
Tashkent
Bishkek
Almaty
KYRGYZSTAN
Urumqi
TAJIKISTAN
Dushanbe
Ashgabat
Tehran
LEBANON
Beirut
Damascus
SYRIA
Jerusalem
ISRAEL
Amman
JORDAN
Baghdad
IRAQ
Euphrates
Tigris
Basra
KUWAIT
Kuwait
IRAN
AFGHANISTAN
Kabul
Hindu Kush
Islamabad
KASHMIR
Boundary claimed by India
Lahore
PAKISTAN
Karachi
Indus
Zahedan
SAUDI ARABIA
Riyadh
Manama
BAHRAIN
QATAR
Doha
Abu Dhabi
UNITED ARAB EMIRATES
Persian Gulf
Strait of Hormuz
Gulf of Oman
Muscat
OMAN
Rub al Khali
Jeddah
Makkah (Mecca)
Red Sea
Sanaa
YEMEN
Aden
Gulf of Aden
Socotra Yemen
Arabian Sea
TROPIC OF CANCER
EQUATOR
INDIA
Delhi
New Delhi
Jaipur
Kathmandu
NEPAL
HIMALAYA
Thimphu
Ganges
Indore
Bhopal
Mumbai (Bombay)
Godavari
Krishna
Hyderabad
Kolkata (Calcutta)
Bay of Bengal
Bangalore
Chennai (Madras)
Madurai
Lakshadweep India
SRI LANKA
Colombo
Male
MALDIVES
INDIAN OCEAN
Chagos Archipelago Brit. Ind. Oc. Terr.
KUNLUN
SINKIANG
TIBET
ARCTIC
RUSSIA
SIBERIA
Ob
Gulf of Ob
Norilsk
Irtysh
Ili
Ural

NORTH AMERICA
Bering Strait
Chukchi Sea
Wrangel I.
Gulf of Anadyr
Anadyr
Bering Sea
East Siberian Sea
New Siberian Islands
North Land
Laptev Sea
Commander Is.
Kamchatka Peninsula
Cherskiy Range
Kolyma Range
Verkhoyansk Range
Magadan
Sea of Okhotsk
Yakutsk
Lena
Aldan
Sakhalin
Kuril Islands
Lake Baikal
Amur
Hokkaido
Sapporo
Irkutsk
Yenisey
MANCHURIA
Vladivostok
Sea of Japan (East Sea)
Ulaanbaatar
Herlen
Changchun
JAPAN
Tokyo
MONGOLIA
ALTAY MTS.
GOBI
Shenyang
NORTH KOREA
Honshu
Kyoto
Osaka
Pyongyang
Seoul
SOUTH KOREA
Hiroshima
Beijing
Qingdao
Kyushu
Shijiazhuang
Yellow Sea
Yellow
Xuzhou
Marcus I. Jap.
TROPIC OF CANCER
Bonin Is. Jap.
Volcano Is. Jap.
Lanzhou
Xian
East China Sea
Shanghai
Nanjing
Ryukyu Islands
Okinawa
CHINA
Yangtze
Nanchang
Chengdu
Fuzhou
Changsha
Taipei
TAIWAN
Parece Vela Jap.
Boundary claimed by China
Guiyang
The People's Republic of China claims Taiwan as its 23rd province.
BHUTAN
BANGLADESH
Dhaka
Kunming
Guangzhou
Hong Kong
Macau
Irrawaddy
Hanoi
Haiphong
Philippine Sea
MYANMAR (BURMA)
LAOS
South China Sea
Hainan
Luzon
Quezon City
Manila
Samar
PHILIPPINES
Leyte
Mindoro
Panay
Negros
Vientiane
Yangon (Rangoon)
Da Nang
THAILAND
Bangkok
CAMBODIA
VIETNAM
Palawan
Mindanao
Andaman Islands India
Phnom Penh
Ho Chi Minh City
PACIFIC OCEAN
EQUATOR
Gulf of Thailand
Andaman Sea
Bandar Seri Begawan
BRUNEI
SABAH
SARAWAK
MALAYSIA
Halmahera
Morotai
Biak
Jayapura
New Guinea
Nicobar Islands India
Kuala Lumpur
Medan
SINGAPORE
Borneo
Celebes
Buru
Moluccas
Ceram
Aru Is.
Kepi
Merauke
Dolak
INDONESIA
Sumatra
Jambi
Tanimbar Is.
GREATER SUNDA ISLANDS
Mentawai Islands
Java Sea
Dili
TIMOR-LESTE (EAST TIMOR)
Timor Sea
Kupang
AUSTRALIA
Jakarta
Java
North Pole
OCEAN
ASIA
SIBERIA
80°N
70°N
60°N
50°N
40°N
30°N
20°N
10°N
0°
10°S
20°S
180°
160°E
120°E
100°E
110°E
130°E
140°E
150°E
160°W
170°W
170°E
160°E
9
10
11
12
13
14
15
16
A
B
C
D
E
F
G
H
J
K

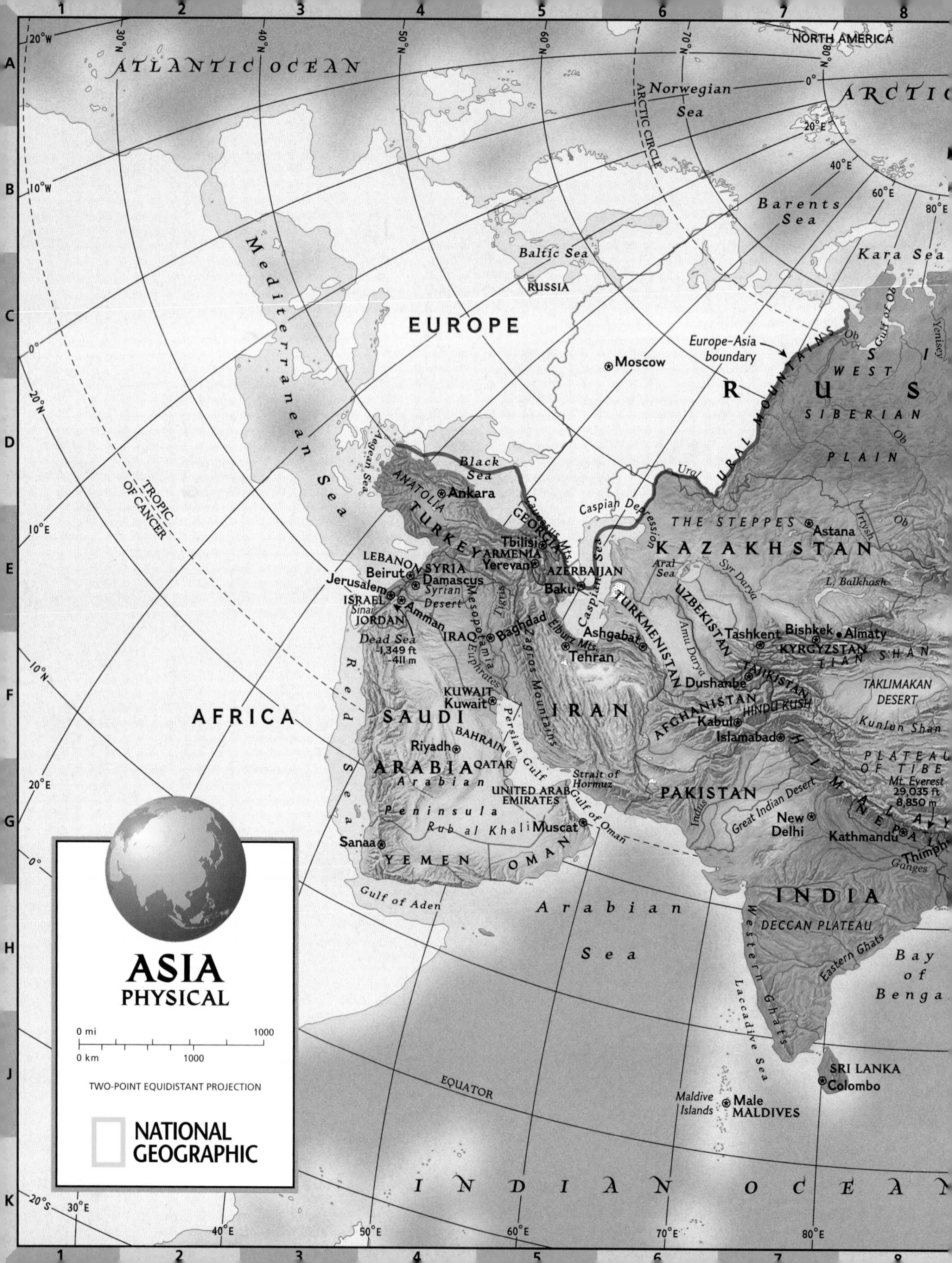

ASIA
PHYSICAL
TWO-POINT EQUIDISTANT PROJECTION
NATIONAL GEOGRAPHIC
ATLANTIC OCEAN
NORTH AMERICA
ARCTIC
Norwegian Sea
ARCTIC CIRCLE
Barents Sea
Kara Sea
Baltic Sea
RUSSIA
EUROPE
Mediterranean Sea
Moscow
Europe-Asia boundary
URAL MOUNTAINS
RUSSIA
WEST SIBERIAN PLAIN
Black Sea
Aegean Sea
ANATOLIA
Ankara
TURKEY
GEORGIA
Caucasus Mts.
Tbilisi
ARMENIA
Yerevan
AZERBAIJAN
Baku
Caspian Depression
Caspian Sea
THE STEPPES
Astana
KAZAKHSTAN
Aral Sea
Syr Darya
L. Balkhash
LEBANON
SYRIA
Beirut
Damascus
Syrian Desert
Jerusalem
ISRAEL
Sinai
JORDAN
Amman
Dead Sea -1,349 ft -411 m
IRAQ
Baghdad
Mesopotamia
Tigris
Euphrates
Elburz Mts.
Tehran
Zagros Mountains
TURKMENISTAN
Ashgabat
UZBEKISTAN
Amu Darya
Tashkent
Bishkek
Almaty
KYRGYZSTAN
TIAN SHAN
TAJIKISTAN
Dushanbe
TAKLIMAKAN DESERT
AFRICA
Red Sea
KUWAIT
Kuwait
SAUDI ARABIA
Riyadh
BAHRAIN
QATAR
Persian Gulf
IRAN
AFGHANISTAN
Kabul
HINDU KUSH
Islamabad
Kunlun Shan
PLATEAU OF TIBET
Mt. Everest 29,035 ft 8,850 m
HIMALAYA
Strait of Hormuz
Arabian Peninsula
UNITED ARAB EMIRATES
Gulf of Oman
Muscat
PAKISTAN
Indus
Great Indian Desert
New Delhi
Kathmandu
NEPAL
Thimphu
Ganges
Rub al Khali
Sanaa
YEMEN
OMAN
Gulf of Aden
Arabian Sea
INDIA
DECCAN PLATEAU
Western Ghats
Eastern Ghats
Bay of Bengal
Laccadive Sea
SRI LANKA
Colombo
Maldive Islands
Male
MALDIVES
EQUATOR
INDIAN OCEAN
TROPIC OF CANCER
Ob
Gulf of Ob
Yenisey
Irtysh
Ural

NORTH AMERICA
Bering Strait
Chukchi Sea
Chukchi Peninsula
Wrangel Island
Gulf of Anadyr
Bering Sea
East Siberian Sea
New Siberian Islands
North Land
Laptev Sea
Aleutian Islands
Commander Islands
Kamchatka Peninsula
Kolyma
Kolyma Range
Cherskiy Range
Verkhoyansk Range
Lena
Aldan
CENTRAL SIBERIAN PLATEAU
SIBERIA
ASIA
Sea of Okhotsk
Sakhalin
Kuril Islands
Amur
Angara
Lake Baikal
Yablonovyy Range
Sikhote Alin Range
Hokkaido
Yenisey
Greater Khingan Range
Manchurian Plain
Sea of Japan (East Sea)
JAPAN
Tokyo
Honshu
Ulaanbaatar
MONGOLIA
ALTAY MOUNTAINS
GOBI
NORTH KOREA
Pyongyang
Seoul
SOUTH KOREA
Beijing
North China Plain
Yellow
Yellow Sea
Shikoku
Kyushu
Nampo Shoto
PACIFIC OCEAN
TROPIC OF CANCER
Qaidam Basin
CHINA
East China Sea
Ryukyu Islands
Yangtze
Mekong
Salween
Sichuan Basin
Gongga Shan 24,790 ft 7,556 m
Taipei
TAIWAN
Philippine Sea
Mariana Islands
BHUTAN
Brahmaputra
BANGLADESH
Dhaka
MYANMAR (BURMA)
Hanoi
LAOS
Vientiane
Yangon (Rangoon)
Hainan
South China Sea
Luzon
Manila
PHILIPPINES
PHILIPPINE ISLANDS
Caroline Islands
EQUATOR
THAILAND
Bangkok
CAMBODIA
VIETNAM
Phnom Penh
Andaman Islands
Sulu Sea
Mindanao
Andaman Sea
Gulf of Thailand
Malay Peninsula
Nicobar Islands
Bandar Seri Begawan
BRUNEI
MALAYSIA
Celebes Sea
Moluccas
New Guinea
Kuala Lumpur
SINGAPORE
Borneo
Celebes
INDONESIA
Sumatra
Arafura Sea
GREATER SUNDA ISLANDS
Java Sea
Java
Jakarta
Mentawai Islands
TIMOR-LESTE (EAST TIMOR)
Dili
Timor Sea
AUSTRALIA
80°N
70°N
60°N
50°N
40°N
30°N
20°N
10°N
0°
10°S
20°S
180°
160°E
120°E
100°E
110°E
130°E
140°E
150°E
170°E
160°W
170°W
9 10 11 12 13 14 15 16
A B C D E F G H J K

EUROPE
Black Sea
Sea of Marmara
Istanbul
ANATOLIA
Ankara
TURKEY
Tunis
TUNISIA
Mediterranean Sea
Tripoli
LIBYA
Taurus Mountains
Aleppo
CYPRUS
SYRIA
LEBANON
Damascus
Beirut
ISRAEL
Syrian Desert
Jerusalem
Amman
Alexandria
Cairo
JORDAN
El Giza
Sinai Pen.
See inset below
EGYPT
Nile R.
Hejaz
Aswan High Dam
Red Sea
SAHARA
Boundary claimed by Sudan
SUDAN
AFRICA
Khartoum
Eastern Mediterranean Area
TURKEY
N
Aleppo
CYPRUS
SYRIA
LEBANON
Mediterranean Sea
Beirut
Damascus
Sea of Galilee
Golan Heights
Jordan River
Tel Aviv–Yafo
West Bank
Jerusalem
Amman
Suez Canal
Gaza Strip
Dead Sea
ISRAEL
JORDAN
El Giza
Cairo
EGYPT
SAUDI ARABIA
Gulf of Suez
Gulf of Aqaba
Nile River
Red Sea
0 mi 100
0 km 100

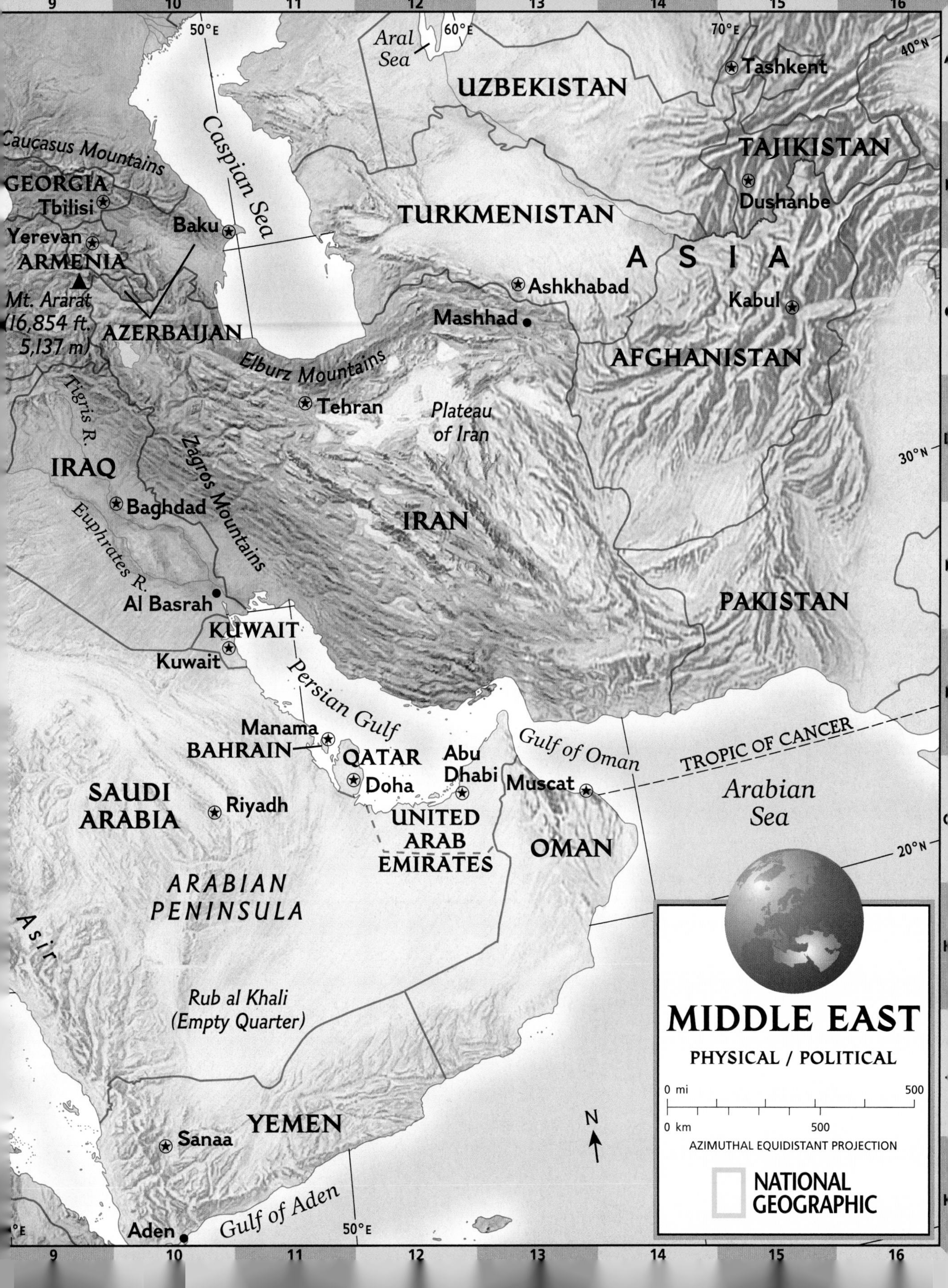

MIDDLE EAST
PHYSICAL / POLITICAL
0 mi
500
0 km
500
AZIMUTHAL EQUIDISTANT PROJECTION
NATIONAL GEOGRAPHIC
UZBEKISTAN
TAJIKISTAN
TURKMENISTAN
ASIA
AFGHANISTAN
PAKISTAN
IRAN
IRAQ
GEORGIA
ARMENIA
AZERBAIJAN
KUWAIT
BAHRAIN
QATAR
UNITED ARAB EMIRATES
OMAN
SAUDI ARABIA
YEMEN
ARABIAN PENINSULA
Tashkent
Dushanbe
Kabul
Ashkhabad
Mashhad
Tehran
Baku
Tbilisi
Yerevan
Baghdad
Al Basrah
Kuwait
Manama
Doha
Abu Dhabi
Muscat
Riyadh
Sanaa
Aden
Aral Sea
Caspian Sea
Caucasus Mountains
Mt. Ararat (16,854 ft. 5,137 m)
Elburz Mountains
Zagros Mountains
Plateau of Iran
Tigris R.
Euphrates R.
Persian Gulf
Gulf of Oman
Arabian Sea
Gulf of Aden
TROPIC OF CANCER
Asir
Rub al Khali (Empty Quarter)
50°E
60°E
70°E
40°N
30°N
20°N
N
9
10
11
12
13
14
15
16

RUSSIA
Lake Baikal
Yablonovyy Range
Ulaanbaatar
MONGOLIA
ALTAY MOUNTAINS
GOBI
Greater Khingan Range
Manchurian Plain
Amur
Sikhote Alin Range
Sakhalin
KAMCHATKA PENINSULA
Sea of Okhotsk
Bering Sea
ALEUTIAN ISLANDS
KURIL ISLANDS
Hokkaido
Beijing
Pyongyang
NORTH KOREA
Seoul
SOUTH KOREA
Sea of Japan (East Sea)
Honshu
JAPAN
Tokyo
Yellow
Yellow Sea
CHINA
Yangtze
Mekong
Kyushu
Shikoku
NAMPO SHOTO
NORTH PACI
East China Sea
RYUKYU ISLANDS
Taipei
TAIWAN
INDIA
MYANMAR (BURMA)
Hanoi
Hainan
LAOS
VIETNAM
Vientiane
Yangon (Rangoon)
THAILAND
Bangkok
CAMBODIA
Phnom Penh
Andaman Sea
South China Sea
Luzon
Manila
PHILIPPINE ISLANDS
PHILIPPINES
Philippine Sea
Hawaiia
NORTHERN MARIANA ISLANDS U.S.
MARIANA ISLANDS
GUAM U.S.
MICRONESIA
PALAU
Koror
CAROLINE ISLANDS
FEDERATED STATES OF MICRONESIA
Palikir
MARSHALL ISLANDS
Ratak Chain
Ralik Chain
Majuro
Tarawa
Gilbert Islands
KIRIBAT
Phoenix Is.
PO
Sulu Sea
Mindanao
Bandar Seri Begawan
BRUNEI
Kuala Lumpur
MALAYSIA
SINGAPORE
Celebes Sea
Borneo
Sumatra
INDONESIA
GREATER SUNDA ISLANDS
Celebes
MOLUCCAS
Java Sea
Jakarta
Java
LESSER SUNDA ISLANDS
Dili
TIMOR-LESTE (EAST TIMOR)
Arafura Sea
NEW GUINEA
PAPUA NEW GUINEA
Port Moresby
Yaren
NAURU
MELANESIA
Solomon Is.
SOLOMON ISLANDS
Honiara
Santa Cruz Islands
TUVALU
Funafuti
Tokelau N.Z.
WALLIS AND FUTUNA IS. Fr.
AMERICA SAMO
SAMOA
Apia
CORAL SEA ISLANDS TERRITORY Austral.
VANUATU
Port-Vila
NEW CALEDONIA Fr.
Suva
FIJI ISLANDS
TONGA
Nuku'alof
TROPIC OF CAPRICORN
Coral Sea
AUSTRALIA
Norfolk Island Austral.
Lord Howe Island Austral.
Kermadec Islands N.Z.
Darling
Great Australian Bight
Canberra
Tasman Sea
NEW ZEALAND
Wellington
Tasmania
Chatham Island N.Z.
INDIAN OCEAN
105°E
120°E
135°E
150°E
165°E
180°

PACIFIC RIM
PHYSICAL/POLITICAL
0 mi 1500
0 km 1500
MILLER CYLINDRICAL PROJECTION
NATIONAL GEOGRAPHIC
CANADA
UNITED STATES
MEXICO
Gulf of Alaska
Kodiak I.
Alexander Archipelago
Queen Charlotte Islands
Vancouver Island
Coast Mountains
ROCKY MOUNTAINS
Cascade Range
GREAT PLAINS
CANADIAN SHIELD
Hudson Bay
Ottawa
Great Lakes
Missouri
CENTRAL LOWLAND
Washington
APPALACHIAN MTS.
Mississippi
COASTAL PLAIN
ATLANTIC OCEAN
Baja California
Gulf of California
Sierra Madre Occidental
Sierra Madre Oriental
Gulf of Mexico
TROPIC OF CANCER
Nassau
BAHAMAS
Havana
CUBA
JAMAICA
HAITI
DOMINICAN REPUBLIC
Santo Domingo
Mexico City
BELIZE
HONDURAS
GUATEMALA
Guatemala City
Tegucigalpa
San Salvador
EL SALVADOR
NICARAGUA
Managua
San Jose
COSTA RICA
Panama City
PANAMA
Caribbean Sea
Caracas
LLANOS
VENEZ.
Bogota
COLOMBIA
Quito
ECUADOR
AMAZON BASIN
BRAZIL
PERU
Lima
ANDES
La Paz
BOLIVIA
Santiago
CHILE
ARGENTINA
PATAGONIA
Chiloe Island
Galapagos Islands Ecua.
EQUATOR
HAWAII U.S.
Kiritimati
Line Islands
Marquesas Is.
Tuamotu Archipelago
Society Is.
COOK ISLANDS N.Z.
FRENCH POLYNESIA Fr.
Austral Is.
Pitcairn Island U.K.
SOUTH PACIFIC OCEAN
45°N
30°N
15°N
0°
15°S
30°S
45°S
150°W
135°W
120°W
105°W
90°W
75°W

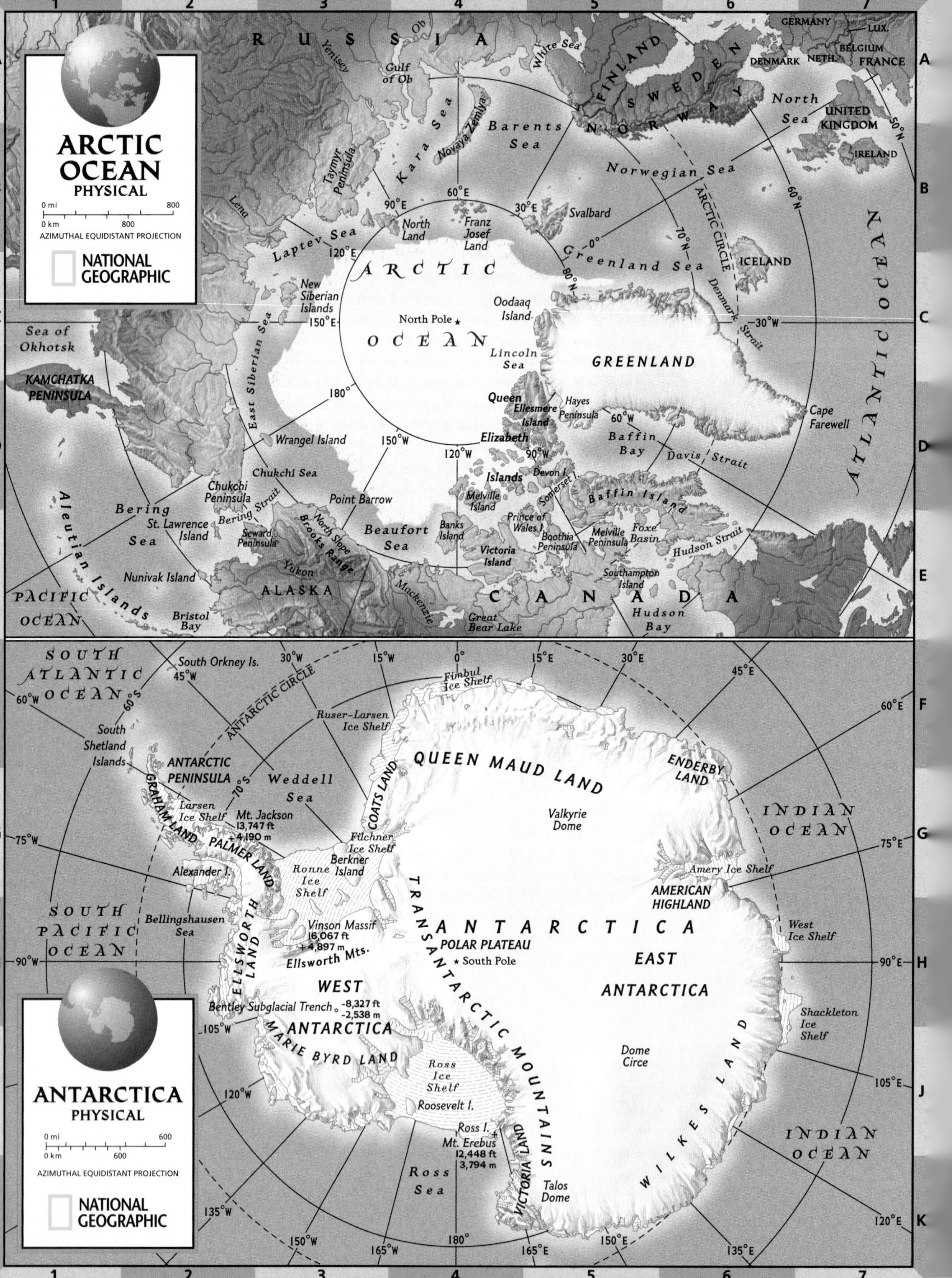

ARCTIC OCEAN
PHYSICAL
AZIMUTHAL EQUIDISTANT PROJECTION
NATIONAL GEOGRAPHIC
RUSSIA
FINLAND
SWEDEN
NORWAY
GERMANY
LUX.
BELGIUM
DENMARK
NETH.
FRANCE
UNITED KINGDOM
IRELAND
North Sea
Norwegian Sea
Barents Sea
Kara Sea
Novaya Zemlya
Taymyr Peninsula
Gulf of Ob
White Sea
Yenisey
Lena
Laptev Sea
North Land
Franz Josef Land
Svalbard
Greenland Sea
ICELAND
ARCTIC CIRCLE
Denmark Strait
ARCTIC OCEAN
North Pole
New Siberian Islands
East Siberian Sea
Sea of Okhotsk
KAMCHATKA PENINSULA
Oodaaq Island
Lincoln Sea
GREENLAND
Queen Elizabeth Islands
Ellesmere Island
Hayes Peninsula
Cape Farewell
Baffin Bay
Davis Strait
ATLANTIC OCEAN
Wrangel Island
Chukchi Sea
Chukchi Peninsula
Bering Strait
Bering Sea
St. Lawrence Island
Seward Peninsula
Point Barrow
North Slope
Brooks Range
Beaufort Sea
Banks Island
Melville Island
Prince of Wales I.
Devon I.
Somerset I.
Baffin Island
Boothia Peninsula
Melville Peninsula
Foxe Basin
Hudson Strait
Victoria Island
Southampton Island
Aleutian Islands
Nunivak Island
Yukon
ALASKA
Mackenzie
CANADA
PACIFIC OCEAN
Bristol Bay
Great Bear Lake
Hudson Bay
SOUTH ATLANTIC OCEAN
South Orkney Is.
ANTARCTIC CIRCLE
Fimbul Ice Shelf
Riiser-Larsen Ice Shelf
South Shetland Islands
ANTARCTIC PENINSULA
GRAHAM LAND
Weddell Sea
COATS LAND
QUEEN MAUD LAND
ENDERBY LAND
INDIAN OCEAN
Valkyrie Dome
Larsen Ice Shelf
Mt. Jackson 13,747 ft 4,190 m
PALMER LAND
Filchner Ice Shelf
Berkner Island
Alexander I.
Ronne Ice Shelf
Amery Ice Shelf
AMERICAN HIGHLAND
SOUTH PACIFIC OCEAN
Bellingshausen Sea
ELLSWORTH LAND
Vinson Massif 16,067 ft 4,897 m
Ellsworth Mts.
TRANSANTARCTIC MOUNTAINS
ANTARCTICA
POLAR PLATEAU
South Pole
EAST ANTARCTICA
West Ice Shelf
WEST ANTARCTICA
Bentley Subglacial Trench -8,327 ft -2,538 m
Shackleton Ice Shelf
MARIE BYRD LAND
Ross Ice Shelf
Dome Circe
Roosevelt I.
WILKES LAND
Ross I.
Mt. Erebus 12,448 ft 3,794 m
VICTORIA LAND
Ross Sea
Talos Dome
ANTARCTICA
PHYSICAL
AZIMUTHAL EQUIDISTANT PROJECTION
NATIONAL GEOGRAPHIC

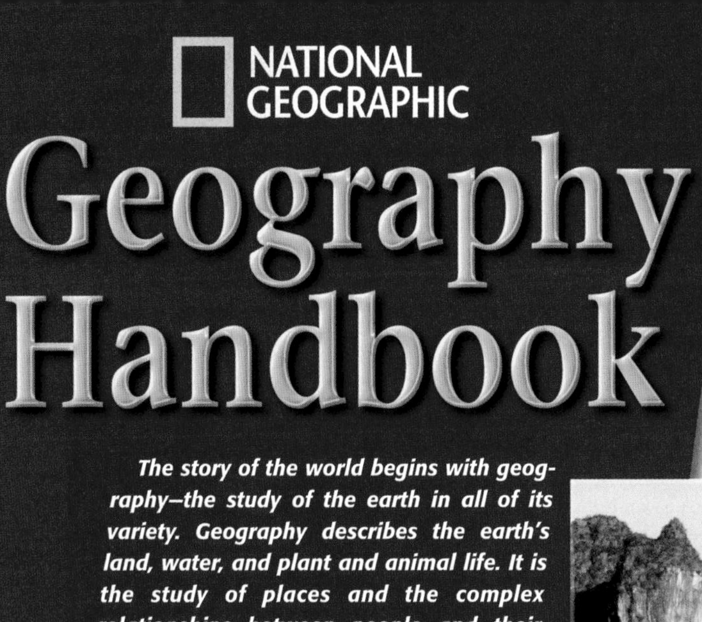

The story of the world begins with geography—the study of the earth in all of its variety. Geography describes the earth's land, water, and plant and animal life. It is the study of places and the complex relationships between people and their environment.

The resources in this handbook will help you get the most out of your textbook—and provide you with skills you will use for the rest of your life.

The Gui River, Guilin, China

Saharan sand dunes, Morocco

The Amazon, Brazil

TEACH

Handbook Objectives

After studying this handbook, students should be able to:

1. understand the themes and elements associated with the study of geography;
2. understand the purpose and uses of globes and map projections;
3. describe how to use maps, graphs, and charts;
4. identify the most commonly used geographic terms.

Preteaching Vocabulary

Survey the students' knowledge of geographic terms. Create three columns on the board with the headings *landforms, map elements,* and *bodies of water.* List one term that fits each column, such as "canyon," "meridian," and "bay." Ask students to identify as many other terms for each column as they can. Then have students turn to the Geographic Dictionary on pages 14–15 and identify additional terms for each column. Write the terms on the board in the appropriate columns of the chart. L1

Geography Handbook Resources

Reproducible Masters

- Glencoe Social Studies Outline Map Resource Book
- Building Geography Skills for Life Workbook

Transparencies

- Geography Handbook Transparencies
- NGS PicturePack Transparencies: Physical Geography of the World

Multimedia

- NGS Dynamic Earth CD-ROM
- Picture Atlas of the World, Revised Edition CD-ROM

NATIONAL GEOGRAPHIC
Geography Handbook

Understanding the Six Essential Elements Have students complete the following activities to learn more about the Six Essential Elements of Geography.

Element 1: The World in Spatial Terms Have students create a map that shows the route they traveled from their homes to school. Students should identify major roads and human-made landmarks on their maps. Display the maps on the class bulletin board. **L2**

Element 2: Places and Regions Explain that physical characteristics play a part in shaping human characteristics in a given place. For example, Native Americans in Alaska and Native Americans in Mexico had widely differing clothing, economic pursuits, architecture, and lifestyles because of the physical characteristics of their regions. Ask students to describe a favorite city, state, or country. Ask them how the physical characteristics of the place might influence characteristics or customs of the inhabitants. **L1**

Element 3: Physical Systems Ask students to think of ways that physical systems affect their lives and cultures. Have students explain how events such as hurricanes influence a region's population and economy. **L2**

How Do I Study Geography?

To understand how our world is connected, some geographers have broken down the study of geography into five themes. The ***Five Themes of Geography*** *are (1) location, (2) place, (3) human/environment interaction, (4) movement, and (5) regions. You will see these themes highlighted in the Section and Chapter Assessments in* The World and Its People.

Six Essential Elements

Recently, geographers have broken down the study of geography into **Six Essential Elements,** which are explained here. Being aware of these elements will help you sort out what you are learning about geography.

Element 1

The World in Spatial Terms

Geographers first take a look at where a place is located. **Location** serves as a starting point by asking "Where is it?" Knowing the location of places helps you develop an awareness of the world around you.

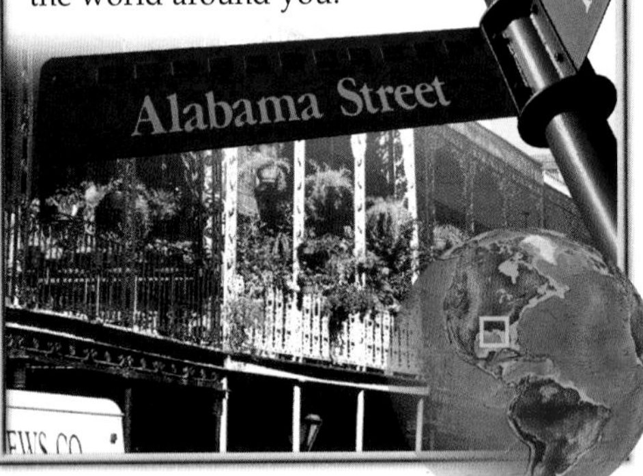

Element 2

Places and Regions

Place has a special meaning in geography. It is not just a geographic location. It also describes characteristics. It might describe physical characteristics such as landforms, climate, and plant or animal life. Or it might describe human characteristics, including language and way of life.

To help organize their study, geographers often group places into regions. **Regions** are united by one or more common characteristics.

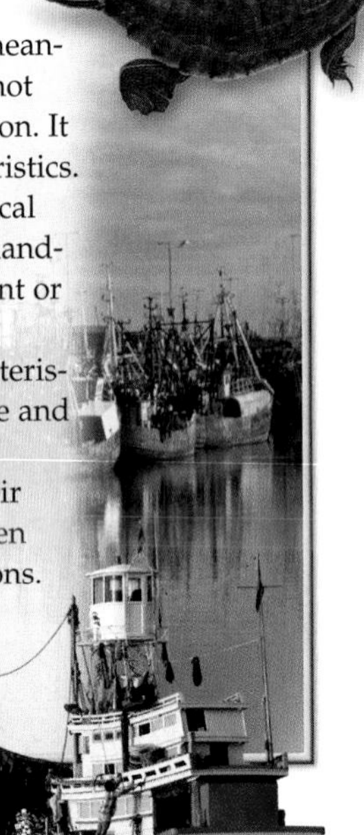

Element 3

Physical Systems

When studying places and regions, geographers analyze how **physical systems**—such as hurricanes, volcanoes, and glaciers—shape the earth's surface. They also look at communities of plants and animals that depend upon one another and their surroundings for survival.

Differentiated Instruction

Meeting Special Needs: Less-proficient Readers Students who have trouble understanding the Six Essential Elements of Geography should use graphic organizers to help them organize the information. Students should create two-column tables with the labels *Element* and *Description.* As they read each element, they should complete their tables. **L1**

Refer to *Inclusion for the Middle School Social Studies Classroom Strategies and Activities* in the TCR.

Element 4

Human Systems

Geographers also examine **human systems,** or how people have shaped our world. They look at how boundary lines are determined and analyze why people settle in certain places and not in others. A key theme in geography is the continual **movement** of people, ideas, and goods.

Element 5

Environment and Society

How does the relationship between people and their natural surroundings influence the way people live? Geographers study how people use the **environment** and how their actions affect the environment.

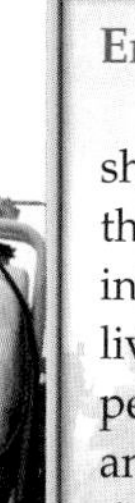

Element 6

The Uses of Geography

Knowledge of geography helps us understand the relationships among people, places, and environments over time. Applying geographic skills helps you understand the past and prepare for the future.

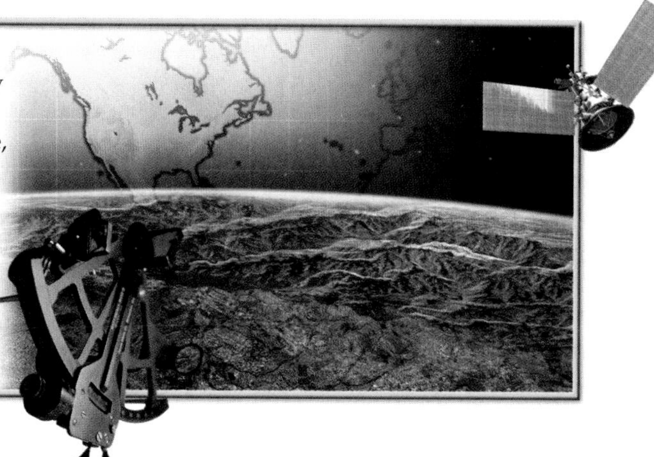

Element 4: Human Systems Call on volunteers to name places from which their family or ancestors moved. Students may describe a move within the United States or a migration from another country. Discuss the reasons that people move to different places. **ELL**

Element 5: Environment and Society Give examples of ways that humans use and modify the environment in places they live. For example, people convert fields and forests into towns and irrigate arid land to support farming. Call on students to give examples of the ways people have modified the environment where they live in both positive and negative ways. **L2**

Element 6: The Uses of Geography Have students give examples of ways businesses use geography. Have students explain how geography influences where businesses such as gas stations and shopping malls are built. **L2**

Content Background

Regions Geographers organize regions into three categories. Formal regions are characterized by the presence of a common human property (for example, language, religion, nationality, and political identity) or common physical property (for example, climate, landforms, and vegetation cover). Functional regions are organized around a node or focal point with surrounding areas linked to that node through transportation or communication systems or economic associations. Perceptual regions reflect human feelings or attitudes and are defined by subjective images of the area (for example, New England and the Corn Belt).

How Do I Use Maps and Globes?

TEACH

Synthesizing Information Emphasize the difficulty in portraying the curved surface of the earth on a flat map by giving each student an orange. Using permanent markers, have students draw the outlines of the continents on their oranges. Then ask students to peel the oranges and try to place the peel flat on their desks. Point out that they have to tear the peel to get it to lay flat. L1

There is a place with no latitude and no longitude. The absolute location where the Prime Meridian and the Equator intersect is 0°N–S, 0°E–W.

Each Geography Handbook Transparency is accompanied by a Student Activity.
Geography Handbook Transparency 1
HEMISPHERES OF THE WORLD

Hemispheres

To locate places on the earth, geographers use a system of imaginary lines that crisscross the globe. One of these lines, the **Equator,** circles the middle of the earth like a belt. It divides the earth into "half spheres," or **hemispheres.** Everything north of the Equator is in the Northern Hemisphere. Everything south of the Equator is in the Southern Hemisphere.

Another imaginary line runs from north to south. It helps divide the earth into half spheres in the other direction. Find this line—called the **Prime Meridian**—on a globe. Everything east of the Prime Meridian for 180 degrees is in the Eastern Hemisphere. Everything west of the Prime Meridian for 180 degrees is in the Western Hemisphere.

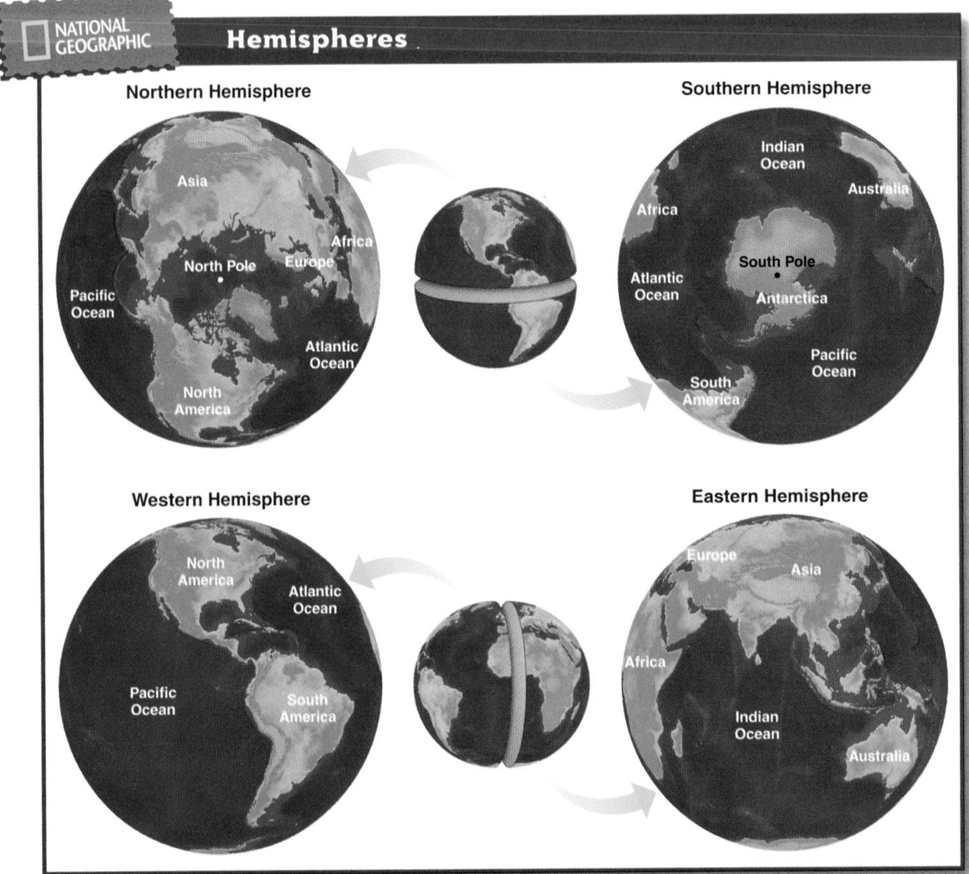

Cooperative Learning Activity

Creating a Presentation Organize the class into two groups. Assign one group to research the National Geographic Society and the other group to research the United States Geological Survey. Have each group prepare a presentation on what the organization does, what research and resources it provides, how it is funded, and career opportunities. Encourage students to contact their assigned organization and, if possible, arrange for a speaker to talk to the class about the organization's purpose and goals. L2

Understanding Latitude and Longitude

Lines on globes and maps provide information that can help you easily locate places on the earth. These lines—called ***latitude*** *and* ***longitude***—*cross one another, forming a pattern called a grid system.*

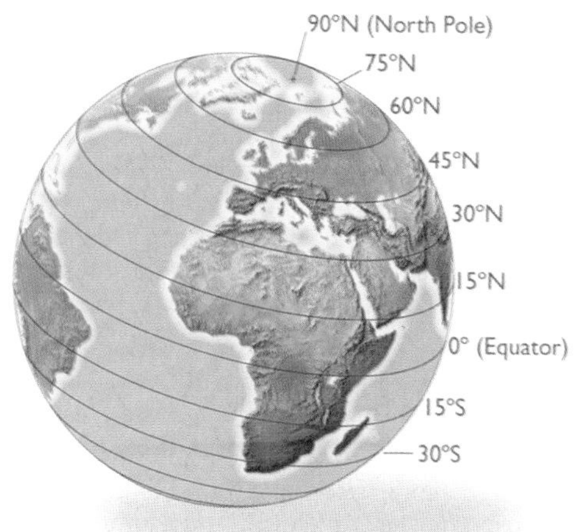

Latitude

Lines of latitude, or **parallels,** circle the earth parallel to the **Equator** and measure the distance north or south of the Equator in degrees. The Equator is at 0° latitude, while the North Pole lies at latitude 90°N (north).

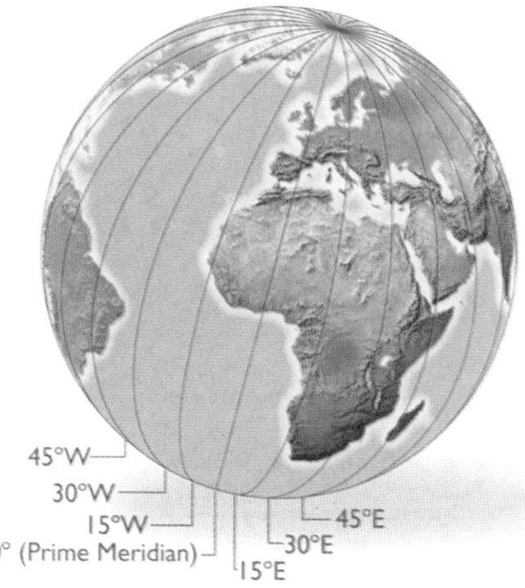

Longitude

Lines of longitude, or **meridians,** circle the earth from Pole to Pole. These lines measure distances east or west of the starting line, which is at 0° longitude and is called the **Prime Meridian.** The Prime Meridian runs through the Royal Observatory in Greenwich, England.

Absolute Location

The grid system formed by lines of latitude and longitude makes it possible to find the absolute location of a place. Only one place can be found at the point where a specific line of latitude crosses a specific line of longitude. By using degrees (°) and minutes (′) (points between degrees), people can pinpoint the precise spot where one line of latitude crosses one line of longitude—an **absolute location.**

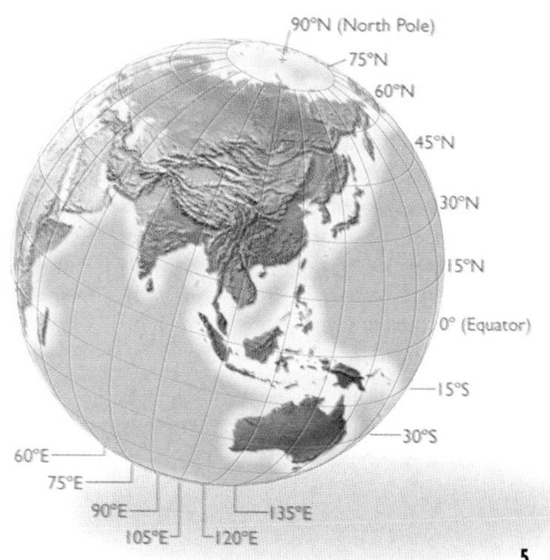

NATIONAL GEOGRAPHIC
Geography Handbook

TEACH

Monitoring Comprehension
After students read this page, check their comprehension by asking them the following questions: **What line is at 0° latitude?** *(Equator)* **What is the latitude of the North Pole?** *(90° N)* **Through which continents does the Prime Meridian pass?** *(Africa, Europe)* L1

Interdisciplinary Connections

Language Arts The word *longitude* comes from the Latin word for "length," and the word *latitude* comes from the Latin word for "breadth."

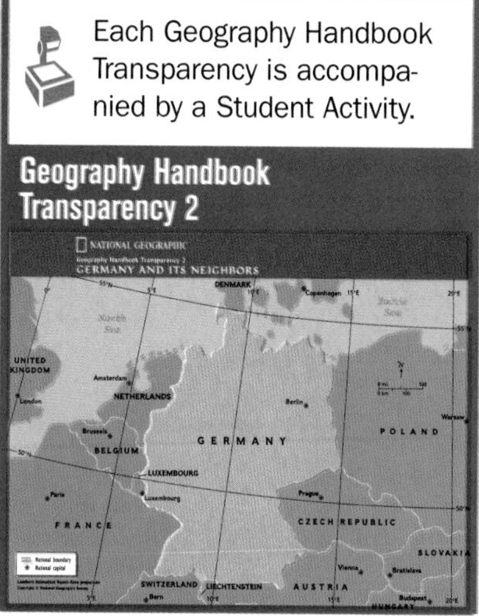

Differentiated Instruction

Meeting Special Needs: Less-proficient Readers Knowing how to use the grid system is a prerequisite for understanding other aspects of geography, so ensure that all students grasp it at this point. To help students who are having difficulty understanding the grid system, make a simplified grid of three horizontal lines labeled A, B, and C, and three vertical lines labeled 1, 2, and 3. Have students practice naming locations with this simple grid system. When they are comfortable with the basic concept, make a more complex grid of 10 horizontal and three vertical lines labeled with degrees. Finally, have students practice finding a city's absolute location on a globe or map. L1

From Globes to Maps

The most accurate way to depict the earth is as a ***globe,*** *a round scale model of the earth. A globe gives a true picture of the continents' relative sizes and the shapes of landmasses and bodies of water. Globes accurately represent distance and direction.*

A ***map*** *is a flat drawing of all or part of the earth's surface. Unlike globes, maps can show small areas in great detail. Maps can also display political boundaries, population densities, or even voting returns.*

From Globes to Maps

Maps, however, do have their limitations. As you can imagine, drawing a round object on a flat surface is very difficult. **Cartographers,** or mapmakers, use mathematical formulas to transfer information from the round globe to a flat map. However, when the curves of a globe become straight lines on a map, the size, shape, distance, or area can change or be distorted.

Great Circle Routes

Mapmakers have solved some problems of going from a globe to a map. A **great circle** is an imaginary line that follows the curve of the earth. A line drawn along the Equator is an example of a great circle. Traveling along a great circle is called following a **great circle route.** Airplane pilots use great circle routes because they represent the shortest distances from one city to another.

The idea of a great circle shows one important difference between a globe and a map. Because a globe is round, it accurately shows great circles. On a flat map, however, the great circle route between two points may not appear to be the shortest distance. See the maps to the right.

Mapmaking with Technology

Technology has changed the way maps are made. Most cartographers use software programs called **geographic information systems (GIS).** This software layers map data from satellite images, printed text, and statistics. A **Global Positioning System (GPS)** helps mapmakers and consumers locate places based on coordinates broadcast by satellites.

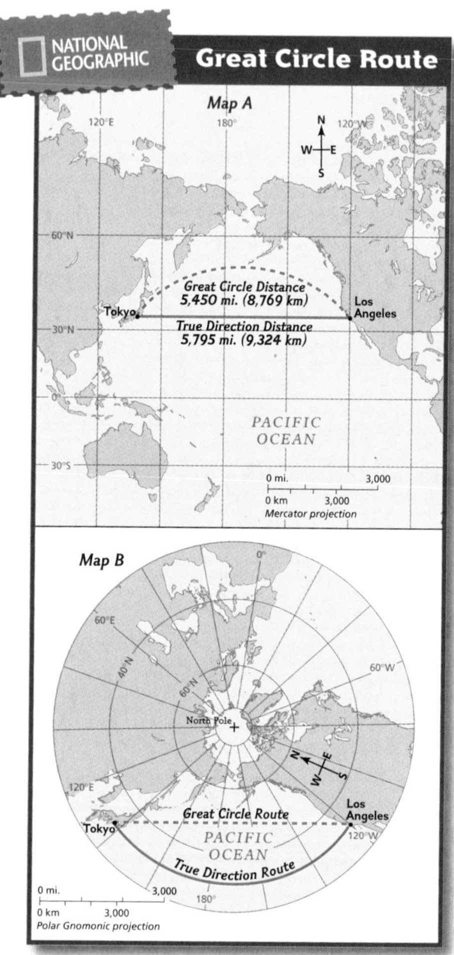

TEACH

Understanding Maps Give students a copy of a world map and ask them to draw a line connecting San Francisco, California, to Istanbul, Turkey, by the most direct route. Give two students a piece of string and, using a classroom globe, ask them to connect those same two cities by the most direct route. Ask all students to note the location of the string on the globe and trace its course on their maps. Discuss with students how both these exercises illustrate the difficulty of projecting the earth's curved surface on a flat map. L1

Each Geography Handbook Transparency is accompanied by a Student Activity.

Geography Handbook Transparency 3

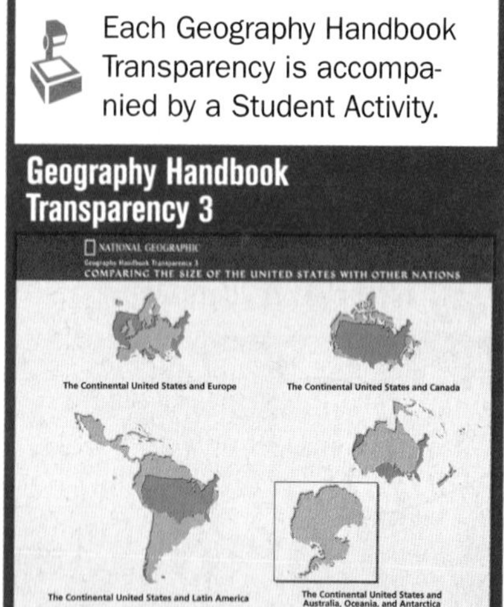

Cultural Kaleidoscope

"Grid Language" Citizens of all countries speak the same language of latitude and longitude.

Content Background

Geographers Geographers work for the federal government in the Defense Mapping Agency, United States Geological Survey, Central Intelligence Agency, Army Corps of Engineers, National Science Foundation, Smithsonian Institution, and the Office of the Geographer in the Department of State. State environmental and transportation agencies hire geographers as analysts, planners, and cartographers. In the private sector, geographers work as professors, researchers, and cartographers for high-tech computer mapmakers. Businesses as varied as fast-food chains and ski resorts consult geographers about finding optimal locations for new restaurants and understanding the effects of pollution on the ski slopes.

Common Map Projections

Imagine taking the whole peel from an orange and trying to flatten it on a table. You would either have to cut it or stretch parts of it. Mapmakers face a similar problem in showing the surface of the round earth on a flat map. When the earth's surface is flattened, big gaps open up. To fill in the gaps, mapmakers stretch parts of the earth. They choose to show either the correct shapes of places or their correct sizes. It is impossible to show both. As a result, mapmakers have developed different ***projections,*** *or ways of showing the earth on a flat piece of paper.*

Goode's Interrupted Equal-Area Projection

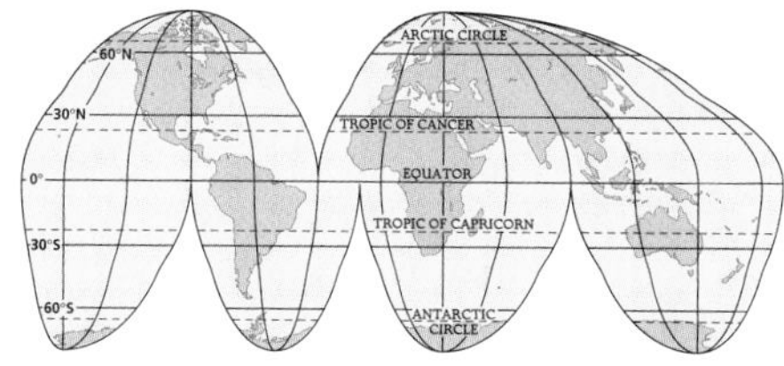

▲ Take a second look at your peeled, flattened orange. You might have something that looks like a map based on **Goode's Interrupted Equal-Area** projection. A map with this projection shows continents close to their true shapes and sizes. This projection is helpful to compare land areas among continents.

Robinson Projection

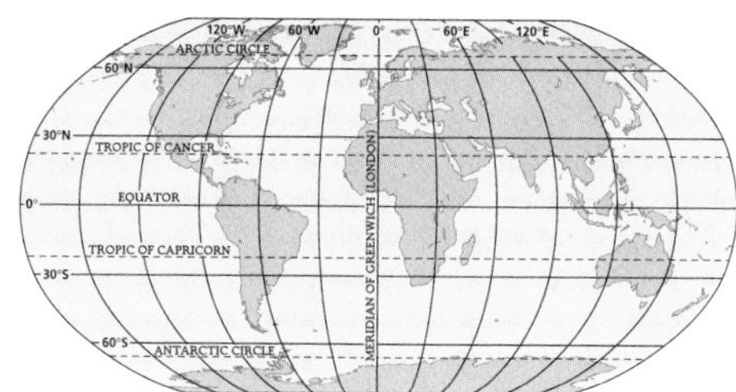

▲ A map using the **Robinson** projection has minor distortions. Land on the western and eastern sides of the Robinson map appears much as it does on a globe. The areas most distorted on this projection are near the North and South Poles.

Winkel Tripel Projection

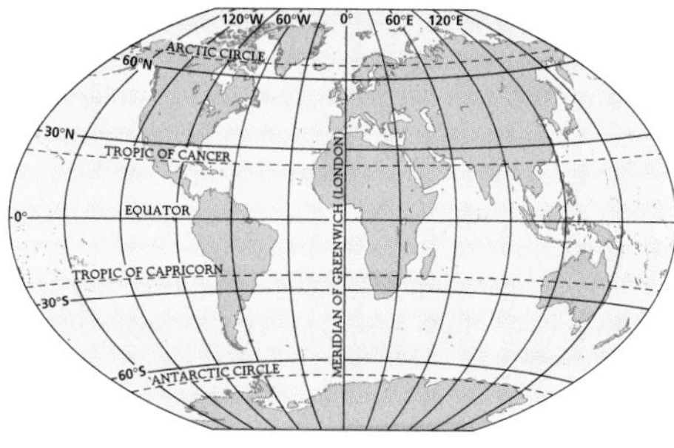

▲ The **Winkel Tripel** projection gives a good overall view of the continents' shapes and sizes. Land areas in a Winkel Tripel projection are not as distorted near the Poles as they are in the Robinson projection.

Mercator Projection

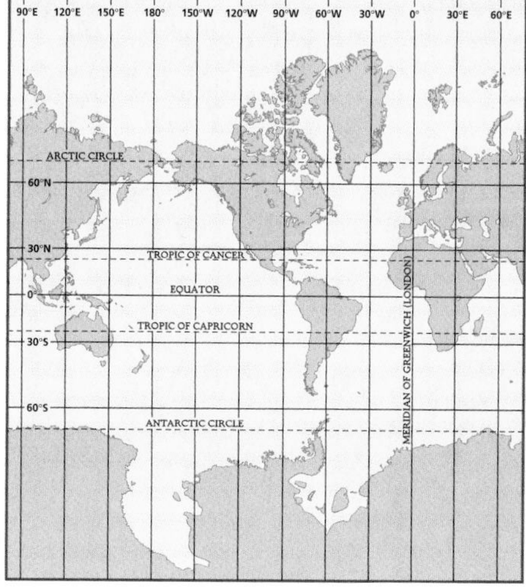

▲ The **Mercator** projection shows true direction and land shapes fairly accurately, but not size or distance. Areas that are located far from the Equator are quite distorted on this projection. Alaska, for example, appears much larger on a Mercator map than it does on a globe.

TEACH

Understanding Information

The National Geographic Society is renowned for the quality and accuracy of its maps. The Society changed from the Robinson projection to the Winkel Tripel projection in 1998. Ask students to research why the Society made the change. Students should write a brief paper describing the results of their research. L3

Did You Know

Flemish mathematician, geographer, and cartographer Gerardus Mercator created his well-known projection in 1568. The Mercator projection exaggerates areas as they increase in distance from the Equator, and has been favored by sailors for more than 400 years.

Content Background

Tactile Maps The Americans with Disabilities Act is opening the door to the production of tactile maps—maps that can be accessed with senses other than sight. Examples include a tactile subway map and a three-dimensional talking map. These maps are, by necessity, much simpler and handle less data since the sense of touch distinguishes less information than the eye. Cartographers are convinced, however, that with increased computer capabilities and innovations in technology, tactile maps will soon be as detailed and informative as any visual maps currently being produced.

TEACH

Using Scale Write the words *Distance* and *Direction* on the board. **Ask:** How do maps show distance and direction? *(scales and compass roses)* Give students practice in determining distance by showing them how to mark a map scale on the edge of a piece of paper. Have students practice measuring the distance between cities on the map. **L1**

Understanding Direction Have students practice cardinal directions by asking questions such as: What state is to the west of Indiana? *(Illinois)* Is Los Angeles located in northern or southern California? *(southern)* Where is Alabama located in relation to Georgia? *(to the west)* **L1**

Parts of Maps

Map Key An important first step in reading a map is to note the map key. The **map key** explains the lines, symbols, and colors used on a map. For example, the map on this page shows the various climate regions of the United States and the different colors representing them. Cities are usually symbolized by a solid circle (•) and capitals by a star (⊛). On this map, you can see the capital of Texas and the cities of Los Angeles, Seattle, New Orleans, and Chicago.

Scale Bar A measuring line, often called a **scale bar,** helps you figure distance on the map. The map scale tells you what distance on the earth is represented by the measurement on the scale bar.

Compass Rose A map has a symbol that tells you where the **cardinal directions**—north, south, east, and west—are positioned. This symbol is called a compass rose.

Cooperative Learning Activity

Making Maps Organize students into several groups to work as cartographers. Assign each group a particular map—a map of the classroom, the school grounds, or another small area, for example. Different group members should be responsible for the following tasks: measuring and making a scale, using a compass to determine direction and making a compass rose, creating a map key, and creating the map itself. Group members should cooperate to coordinate their work. Display students' maps around the classroom. **ELL**

Types of Maps

NATIONAL GEOGRAPHIC
Geography Handbook

General Purpose Maps

Maps are amazingly useful tools. You can use them to preserve information, to display data, and to make connections between seemingly unrelated things. Geographers use many different types of maps. Maps that show a wide range of general information about an area are called **general purpose maps.** Two of the most common general purpose maps are physical and political maps.

Physical Maps ▼

Physical maps call out landforms and water features. The physical map of Sri Lanka below shows rivers and mountains. The colors used on physical maps include brown or green for land, and blue for water. These colors and shadings may show **relief**—or how flat or rugged the land surface is. In addition, physical maps may use colors to show **elevation**—the height of an area above sea level. A key explains what each color and symbol stands for.

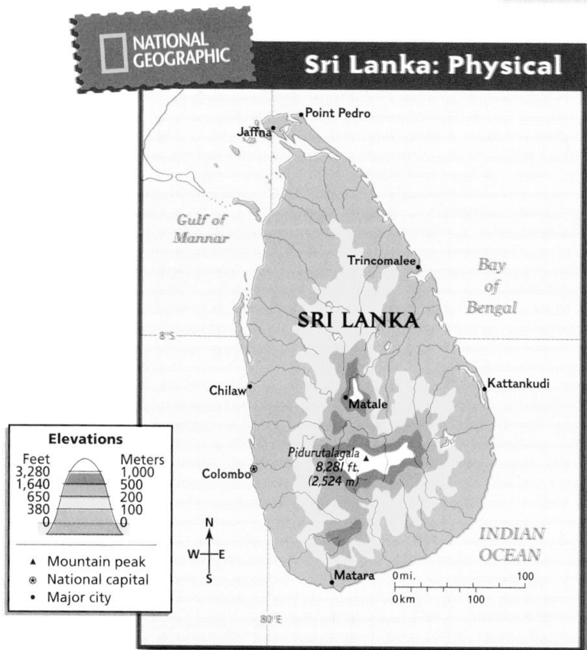

Political Maps ▲

Political maps show the names and boundaries of countries, the location of cities and other human-made features of a place, and often identify major physical features. The political map of Spain above, for example, shows the boundaries between Spain and other countries. It also shows cities and rivers within Spain and bodies of water surrounding Spain.

TEACH

Classifying Maps Have students work in groups to scan the textbook and classify ten maps according to type: physical, political, or special purpose. Give each group the task of listing page numbers for maps of each type. Have students describe the maps to the class. L1

Each Geography Handbook Transparency is accompanied by a Student Activity.

Geography Handbook Transparency 4

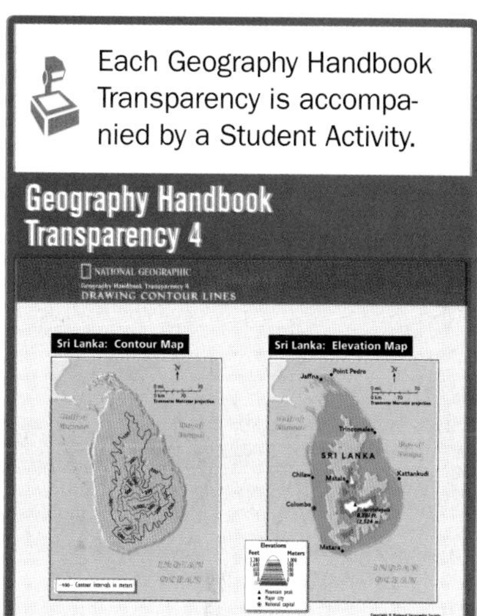

Differentiated Instruction

Meeting Special Needs: Less-proficient Readers To help students remember the different categories and examples of maps discussed in the National Geographic Geography Handbook, guide them in creating a graphic organizer entitled "Types of Maps." Branching from this main head should be three boxes labeled "Political," "Physical," and "Special Purpose." Have students complete the organizer by taking notes on each of the different types of maps. L1

Refer to *Inclusion for the Middle School Social Studies Classroom Strategies and Activities* in the TCR.

TEACH

Using Special Purpose Maps Ask volunteers to bring special purpose maps to class to show how they are used in everyday life. Students may bring in maps showing bus routes, weather forecasts, or bike routes. L1

Each Geography Handbook Transparency is accompanied by a Student Activity.

Geography Handbook Transparency 5

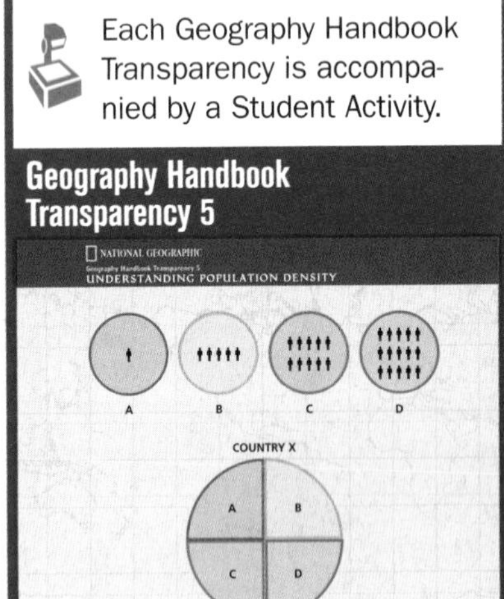

Contour Maps ▼

One kind of physical map, called a **contour** map, also shows elevation. A contour map has **contour lines**—one line for each major level of elevation. All the land at the same elevation is connected by a line. These lines usually form circles or ovals—one inside the other. If contour lines come very close together, the surface is steep. If the lines are spread apart, the land is flat or rises very gradually. Compare the contour map of Sri Lanka below to its physical map on page 9.

Special Purpose Maps ▶

Some maps are made to present specific kinds of information. These are called **thematic** or **special purpose maps.** They usually show specific topics in detail. Special purpose maps might present climate, natural resources, or population density. They might also display historical information, such as battle sites or territorial expansions. The map's title tells what kind of special information it shows. Colors and symbols in the map key are especially important on these types of maps.

One type of special purpose map uses colors to show population density, or the average number of people living in a square mile or square kilometer. As with other maps, it is important to first read the title and the key. The population density map of Egypt above shows that the Nile River valley and delta are very densely populated.

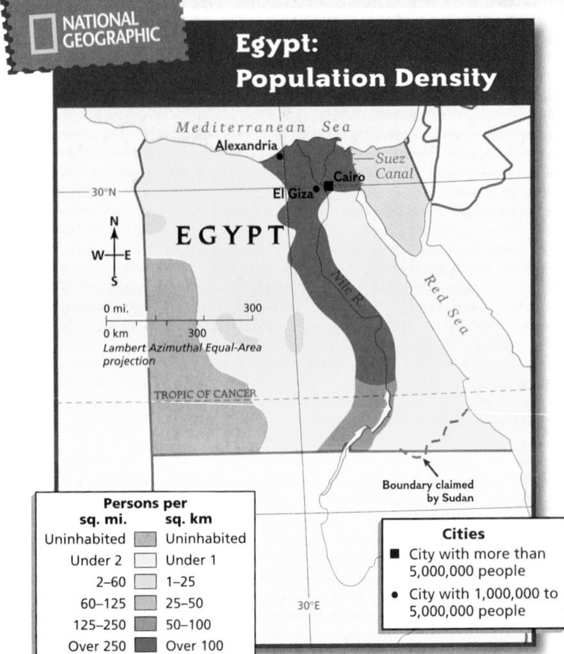

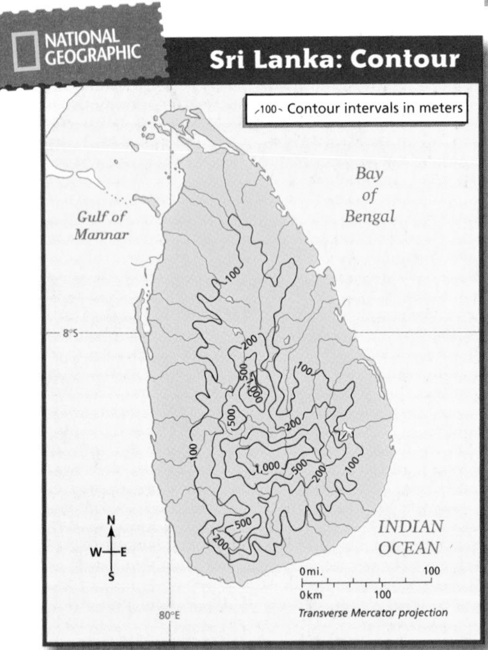

Content Background

Longitude Until the 1700s, sailors seldom knew exactly where they were because they had only lines of latitude to guide them. John Harrison, an English instrument maker, invented a clock that could keep accurate time at sea. A navigator can determine longitude by figuring the difference between Greenwich Mean Time and the time at the ship's location.

Using Graphs, Charts, and Diagrams

Graphs

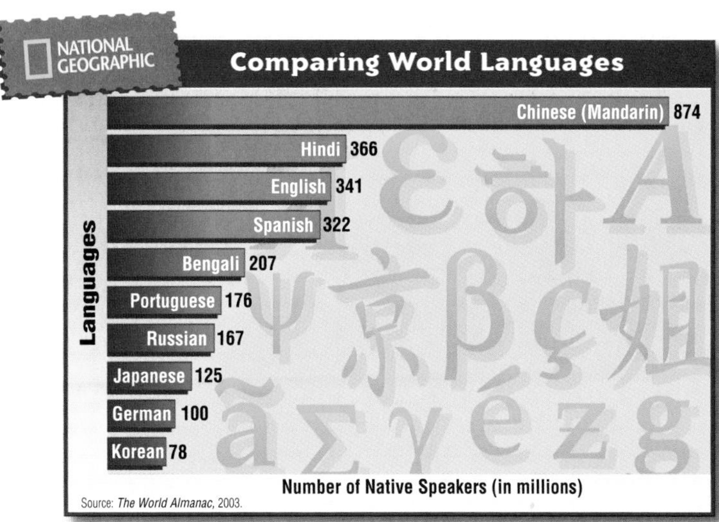

A graph is a way of summarizing and presenting information visually. Each part of a graph gives useful information. First read the graph's title to find out its subject. Then read the labels along the graph's **axes**—the vertical line along the left side of the graph and the horizontal line along the bottom. One axis will tell you what is being measured. The other axis tells what units of measurement are being used.

Bar and Line Graphs

Graphs that use bars or wide lines to compare data visually are called **bar graphs.** Look carefully at the bar graph above, which compares world languages. The vertical axis lists the languages. The horizontal axis measures the number of speakers of the language in millions. By comparing the lengths of the bars, you can quickly tell which language is spoken by the most people. Bar graphs are especially useful for comparing quantities.

A **line graph** is a useful tool for showing changes over a period of time. The amounts being measured are plotted on the grid above each year, and then are connected by a line. Line graphs sometimes have two or more lines plotted on them. The line graph to your left shows that the number of farms in the United States has decreased since 1940.

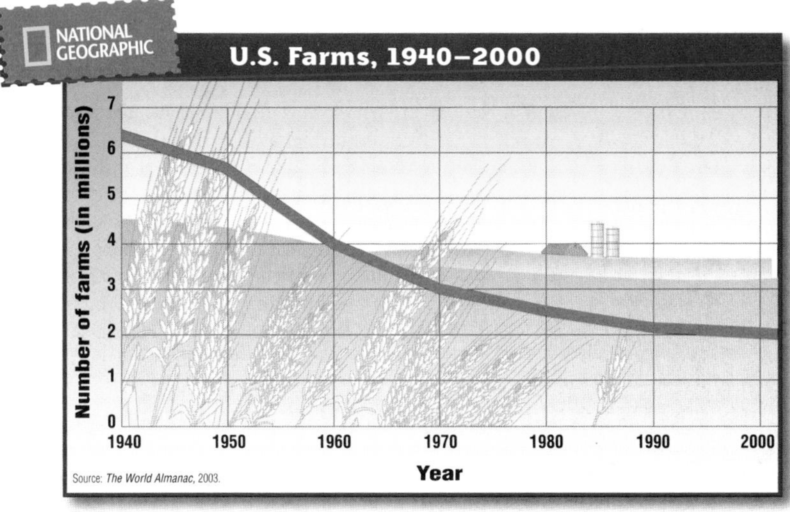

NATIONAL GEOGRAPHIC
Geography Handbook

Teach

Understanding Information
Bring several newspapers to class, and have students look through them for charts, graphs, and diagrams. Ask students to summarize the information that several of these visuals portray. L1

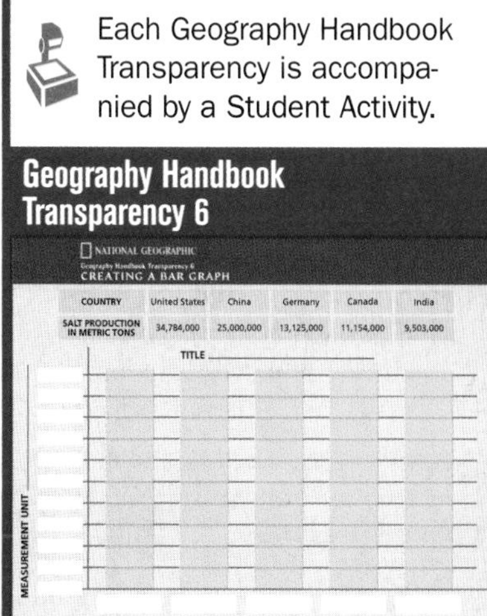

Each Geography Handbook Transparency is accompanied by a Student Activity.

Geography Handbook Transparency 6

Differentiated Instruction

Meeting Special Needs: Kinesthetic
Students who do well with the kinesthetic mode of learning can benefit by translating some two-dimensional models. For example, students can make a line graph using tacks and string, make a bar graph out of blocks, or create a circle graph using clay in a pie tin. L1 ELL

Each Geography Handbook Transparency is accompanied by a Student Activity.

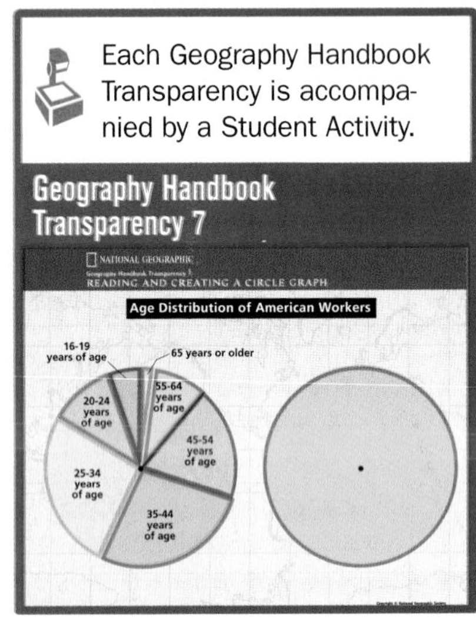

Each Geography Handbook Transparency is accompanied by a Student Activity.

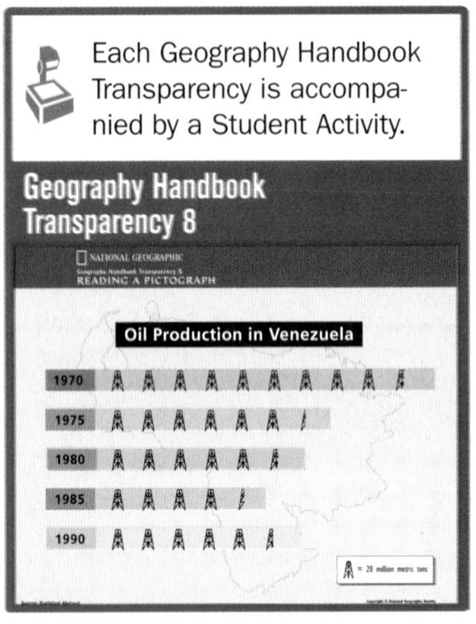

Analyzing Graphs Have students look at the pictograph on this page. **Ask:** About how many passenger cars did the United States produce in 2001? *(about 5 million)* Japan? *(8 million)* Have students study the climograph on the next page. **Ask:** What are the two coldest months in Moscow? *(January and February)* L1

Circle Graphs ▼

You can use **circle graphs** when you want to show how the *whole* of something is divided into its *parts.* Because of their shape, circle graphs are often called pie graphs. Each "slice" represents a part or percentage of the whole "pie." On the circle graph below, the whole circle (100 percent) represents the world's population in 2002. The slices show how this population is divided among the world's five largest continents.

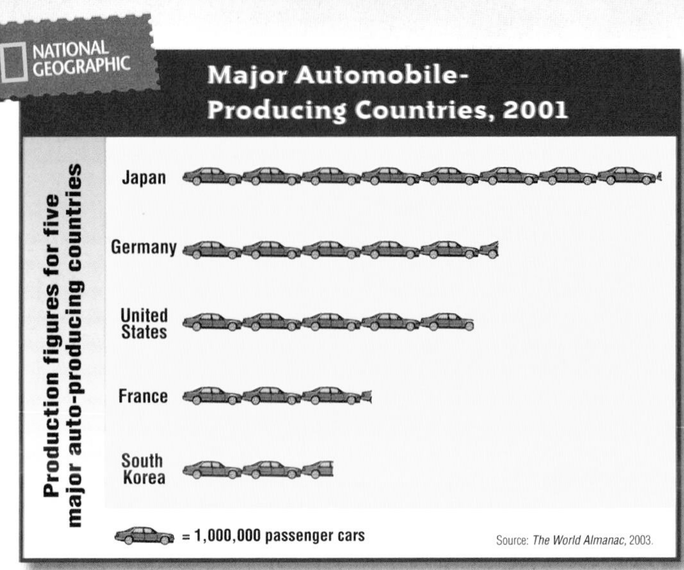

Charts

Charts present facts and numbers in an organized way. They arrange data, especially numbers, in rows and columns for easy reference. Look at the chart called "Population Growth" on page 88. To interpret the chart, first read the title. It tells you what information the chart contains. Next, read the labels at the top of each column and on the left side of the chart. They explain what the numbers or data on the chart are measuring.

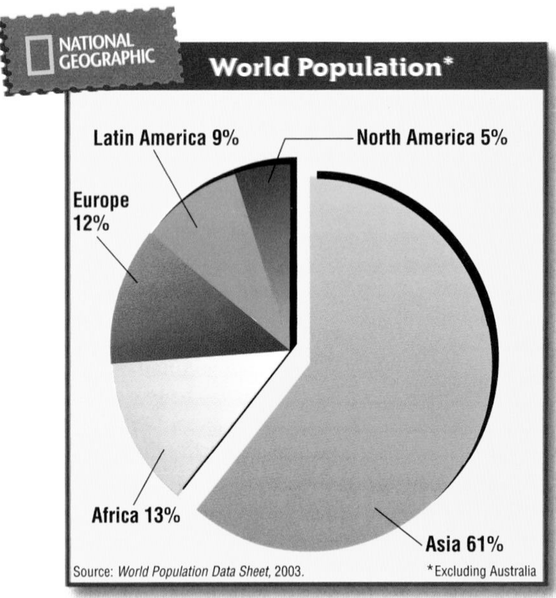

Pictographs ▲

Like bar and circle graphs, pictographs are good for making comparisons. **Pictographs** use rows of small pictures or symbols, with each picture or symbol representing an amount. Look at the pictograph showing the number of automobiles produced in the world's five major automobile-producing countries above. The key tells you that one car symbol stands for 1 million automobiles. The total number of car symbols in a row adds up to the auto production in each selected country.

Critical Thinking Activity

Recognizing Bias Point out the source lines at the bottom of the graphs and charts. Make sure students understand what source lines signify. Then ask students what qualities make an organization a good source of information. Ask them what qualities make a bad source of information. Tell them that some organizations bias their information or delete information in order to support their point of view. Ask them what biases the following sources might have: an industry trade group, a foreign government, and an environmental group. L3

NATIONAL GEOGRAPHIC Geography Handbook

Climographs ▸

A **climograph,** or climate graph, combines a line graph and a bar graph. It gives an overall picture of the long-term weather patterns in a specific place. Climographs include several kinds of information. The green vertical bars on the climograph of Moscow to your right show average monthly amounts of precipitation (rain, snow, or sleet). These bars are measured against the axis on the right side of the graph. The red line plotted above the bars represents changes in the average monthly temperature. You measure this line against the axis on the left side.

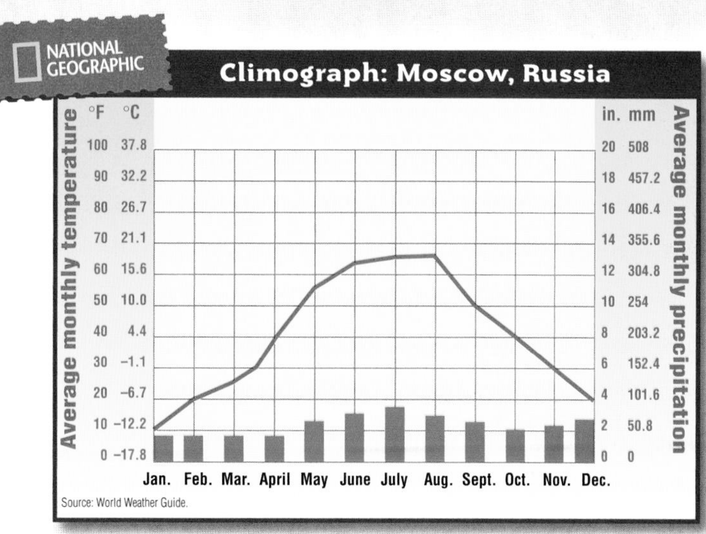

Diagrams ▾

Diagrams are drawings that show steps in a process, point out the parts of an object, or explain how something works. An **elevation profile** is a type of diagram that can be helpful when comparing the elevations—or heights—of an area. It shows an exaggerated side view of the land as if it were sliced and you were viewing it from the side. The elevation profile of Africa below clearly shows sea level, low areas, and mountains.

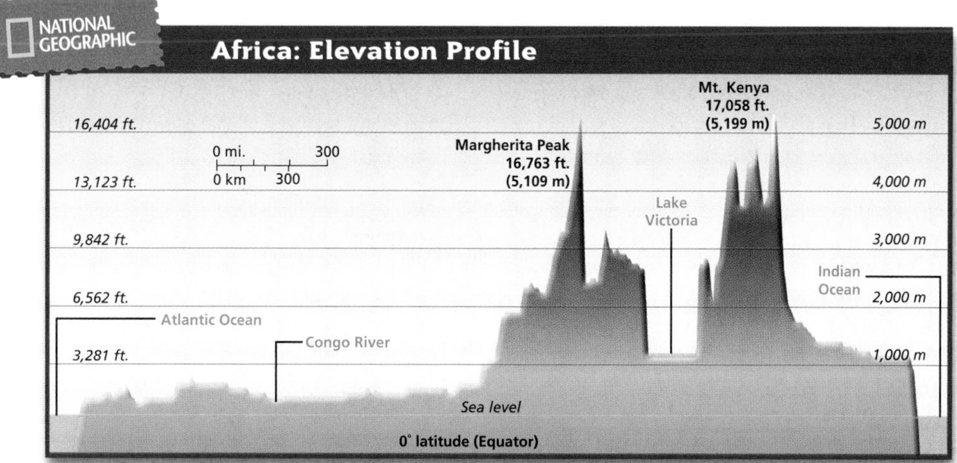

Each Geography Handbook Transparency is accompanied by a Student Activity.

Geography Handbook Transparency 9

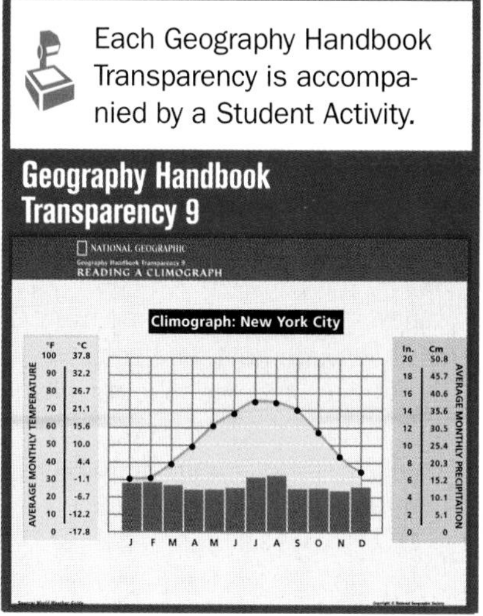

Displaying Information

Have students use a decision-making process to identify the best way to graphically display the following information: 1) the total number of students in the class, including the number of boys and girls *(circle graph);* 2) a record of the number of students who attend class each day for a month *(line graph);* 3) a comparison of the number of students who are of certain heights *(bar graph);* the number of books read by each student during the summer *(pictograph or bar graph).* **L2**

Content Background

James Cook British sea captain James Cook was one of the greatest explorers and cartographers of the eighteenth century. In the three voyages that he undertook between 1768 and 1779, Cook surveyed and charted large areas of the Pacific Ocean. He made the first recorded crossing of the Antarctic Circle and provided a wealth of information about the south Atlantic, south Indian, and Arctic Oceans. Using the latest scientific developments, Cook created incredibly accurate charts of his journeys. These charts revolutionized cartographic knowledge and practices.

TEACH

Writing a Brochure Assign students to create a travel brochure for the destination of their choice. The brochure should contain information about its absolute location, place and region, physical and human systems, environment, and society. Encourage students to review the beginning of the National Geographic Geography Handbook before they begin writing. L2

Cultural Kaleidoscope

The Geographer's Language The terms that geographers use to describe the earth originate from different languages. The term *tsunami* is a Japanese word meaning "overflowing wave." *Mesa* is a Spanish word meaning "table." *Fjord* is a Norwegian word meaning "long, narrow bay."

NATIONAL GEOGRAPHIC Geographic Dictionary

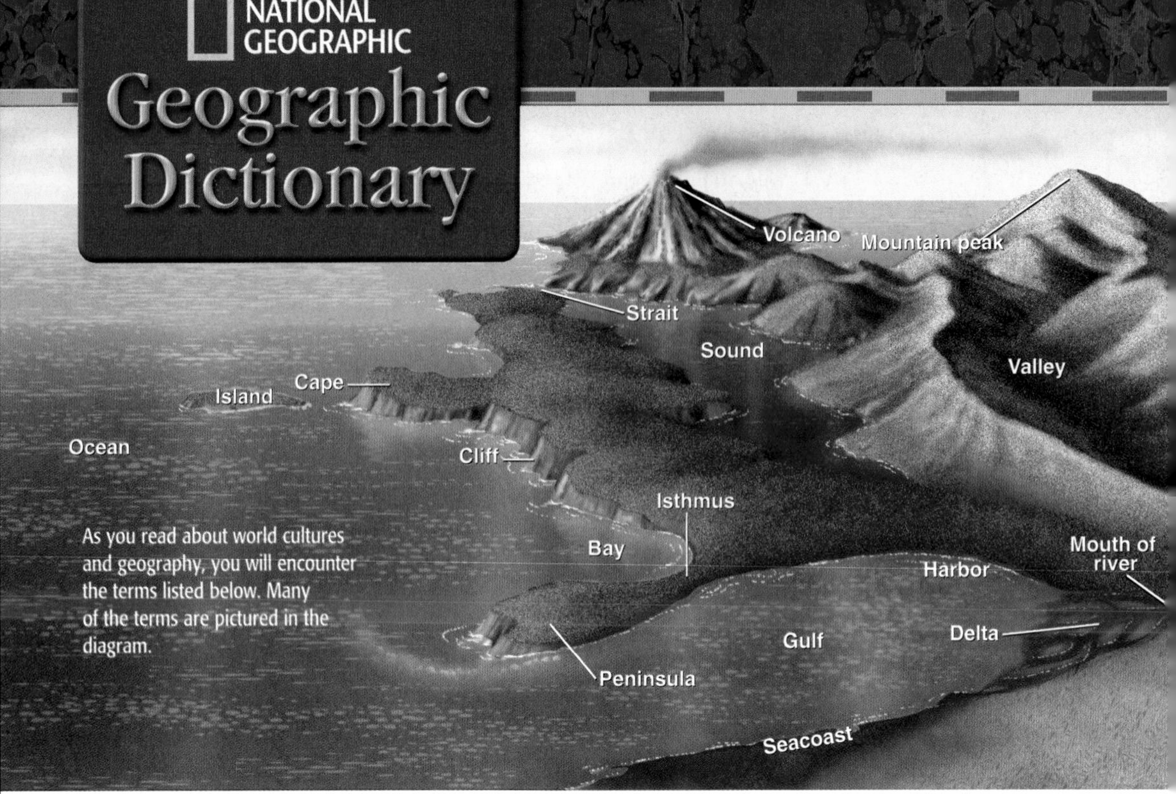

As you read about world cultures and geography, you will encounter the terms listed below. Many of the terms are pictured in the diagram.

absolute location exact location of a place on the earth described by global coordinates

basin area of land drained by a given river and its branches; area of land surrounded by lands of higher elevation

bay part of a large body of water that extends into a shoreline, generally smaller than a gulf

canyon deep and narrow valley with steep walls

cape point of land that extends into a river, lake, or ocean

channel wide strait or waterway between two landmasses that lie close to each other; deep part of a river or other waterway

cliff steep, high wall of rock, earth, or ice

continent one of the seven large landmasses on the earth

cultural feature characteristic that humans have created in a place, such as language, religion, housing, and settlement pattern

delta flat, low-lying land built up from soil carried downstream by a river and deposited at its mouth

divide stretch of high land that separates river systems

downstream direction in which a river or stream flows from its source to its mouth

elevation height of land above sea level

Equator imaginary line that runs around the earth halfway between the North and South Poles; used as the starting point to measure degrees of north and south latitude

glacier large, thick body of slowly moving ice

gulf part of a large body of water that extends into a shoreline, generally larger and more deeply indented than a bay

harbor a sheltered place along a shoreline where ships can anchor safely

highland elevated land area such as a hill, mountain, or plateau

hill elevated land with sloping sides and rounded summit; generally smaller than a mountain

island land area, smaller than a continent, completely surrounded by water

isthmus narrow stretch of land connecting two larger land areas

lake a sizable inland body of water

latitude distance north or south of the Equator, measured in degrees

longitude distance east or west of the Prime Meridian, measured in degrees

lowland land, usually level, at a low elevation

map drawing of the earth shown on a flat surface

meridian one of many lines on the global grid running from the North Pole to the South Pole; used to measure degrees of longitude

mesa broad, flat-topped landform with steep sides; smaller than a plateau

Cooperative Learning Activity

Map Quiz Organize the class into two teams. Provide one team with a map of their county and the other team with a map of their state. Assign each team the following task: Locate every major body of water in your assigned area. Record your findings, including 1) the name of each major body of water; 2) what type of body of water it is—lake, river, bay, and so on; and 3) its absolute location. When each team has completed its task, have them create a map quiz based on their work. The teams should then trade maps and challenge each other with their quizzes. L2

mountain land with steep sides that rises sharply (1,000 feet [305 m] or more) from surrounding land; generally larger and more rugged than a hill

mountain peak pointed top of a mountain

mountain range a series of connected mountains

mouth (of a river) place where a stream or river flows into a larger body of water

ocean one of the four major bodies of salt water that surround the continents

ocean current stream of either cold or warm water that moves in a definite direction through an ocean

parallel one of many lines on the global grid that circle the earth north or south of the Equator; used to measure degrees of latitude

peninsula body of land jutting into a lake or ocean, surrounded on three sides by water

physical feature characteristic of a place occurring naturally, such as a landform, body of water, climate pattern, or resource

plain area of level land, usually at a low elevation and often covered with grasses

plateau area of flat or rolling land at a high elevation, about 300–3,000 feet (91–914 m) high

Prime Meridian line of the global grid running from the North Pole to the South Pole through Greenwich, England; starting point for measuring degrees of east and west longitude

relief changes in elevation over a given area of land

river large natural stream of water that runs through the land

sea large body of water completely or partly surrounded by land

seacoast land lying next to a sea or ocean

sea level position on land level with the surface of a nearby ocean or sea

sound body of water between a coastline and one or more islands off the coast

source (of a river) place where a river or stream begins, often in highlands

strait narrow stretch of water joining two larger bodies of water

tributary small river or stream that flows into a larger river or stream; a branch of the river

upstream direction opposite the flow of a river; toward the source of a river or stream

valley area of low land between hills or mountains

volcano mountain created as liquid rock or ash erupts from inside the earth

Did You Know?

One of the most violent volcanic eruptions in history occurred in 1883 on the island of Krakatau in Indonesia. The volcano collapsed from a height of 2,640 feet (692 m) to 1,000 feet (300 m) below sea level. Its collapse triggered a tidal wave that killed 36,000 people in nearby Java and Sumatra.

CLOSE

Making a Shoe Map To help give students a sense of appreciation for the complexities of map making, conduct the following activity. Students will need drawing paper and no more than five different colored crayons or markers. Their assignment is to "draw" a map of their shoe, designing a projection or system that would indicate the shoe's three-dimensional, or curved characteristics.

Allow students to attempt to draw a cross-section, top view, or other perspective that they choose. Remind students that they will need a key and a scale bar on their completed maps. L3

Reading Strategy — Reading the Text

Understanding Cause and Effect As students read the textbook, remind them to think about how geography affects a region. Students should create graphic organizers for each chapter that shows how geography has shaped the environment, people, culture, and events in a region. As students study the chapters, ask questions that focus on geographical cause-and-effect relationships.

Reading Strategies

Helping students become active readers is only the first step in training students for success.The second step is helping students retain and use the knowledge they have gained through reading.

How Can You Help Students Retain What They Read?

The better students understand what they read, the more they will remember—so teaching students to use the reading strategies on these pages aids retention. In addition, you can help students use formal study systems such as working with graphic organizers.

Graphic Organizers That Help Students Read and Comprehend

Graphic organizers provide a visual format that requires students to restructure information as they analyze and interpret it. In addition, presenting information graphically helps students remember facts and concepts more easily, since they can "picture" it in their mind's eye. Students can productively use graphic organizers prior to reading to activate prior knowledge, during reading to process and analyze information, and after instruction to summarize and draw conclusions. Encourage students to use graphic organizers in the following ways *(see next page)*.

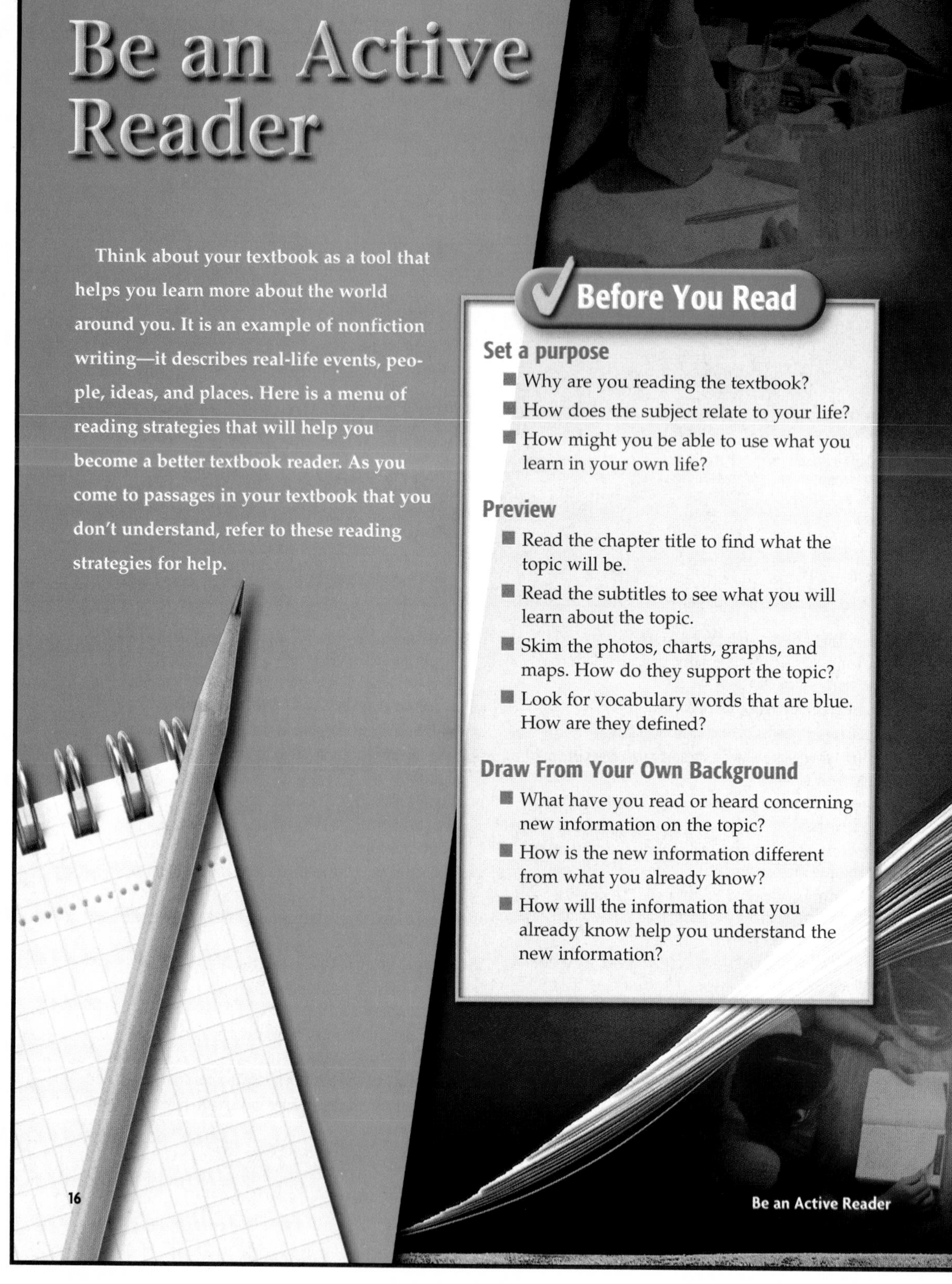

Be an Active Reader

Think about your textbook as a tool that helps you learn more about the world around you. It is an example of nonfiction writing—it describes real-life events, people, ideas, and places. Here is a menu of reading strategies that will help you become a better textbook reader. As you come to passages in your textbook that you don't understand, refer to these reading strategies for help.

Before You Read

Set a purpose

- Why are you reading the textbook?
- How does the subject relate to your life?
- How might you be able to use what you learn in your own life?

Preview

- Read the chapter title to find what the topic will be.
- Read the subtitles to see what you will learn about the topic.
- Skim the photos, charts, graphs, and maps. How do they support the topic?
- Look for vocabulary words that are blue. How are they defined?

Draw From Your Own Background

- What have you read or heard concerning new information on the topic?
- How is the new information different from what you already know?
- How will the information that you already know help you understand the new information?

16 Be an Active Reader

Good Study Habits for Successful Students

As you work with students on reading strategies, keep in mind and share the following tips for helping students retain what they read and prepare for all types of tests.

- **Keep Up:** Frequent review will help students build long-term memory and understanding.
- **Visualize and Recite Information:** Visual images are powerful ones. Students should try to associate a name, event, or idea with a picture. They can visualize the steps in a process or a sequence of events. Students should repeat important information aloud, whenever possible.

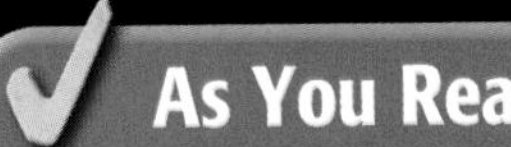

As You Read

Question

- What is the main idea?
- How do the photos, charts, graphs, and maps support the main idea?

Connect

- Think about people, places, and events in your own life. Are there any similarities with those discussed in your textbook?
- Can you relate the textbook information to other areas of your life?

Predict

- Predict events or outcomes by using clues and information that you already know.
- Change your predictions as you read and gather new information.

Visualize

- Pay careful attention to details and descriptions.
- Create graphic organizers to show relationships that you find in the information.

Look For Clues As You Read

Comparison and Contrast Sentences

- Look for clue words and phrases that signal comparison, such as *similarly, just as, both, in common, also,* and *too.*
- Look for clue words and phrases that signal contrast, such as *on the other hand, in contrast to, however, different, instead of, rather than, but,* and *unlike.*

Cause-and-Effect Sentences

- Look for clue words and phrases such as *because, as a result, therefore, that is why, since, so, for this reason,* and *consequently.*

Chronological Sentences

- Look for clue words and phrases such as *after, before, first, next, last, during, finally, earlier, later, since,* and *then.*

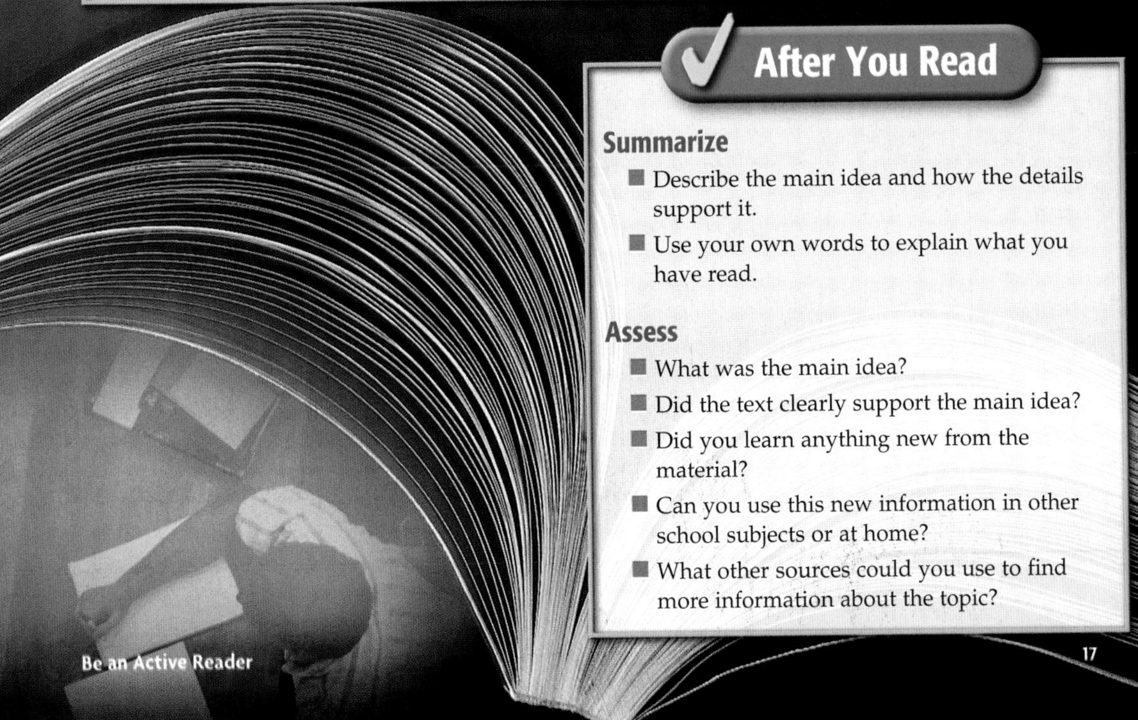

After You Read

Summarize

- Describe the main idea and how the details support it.
- Use your own words to explain what you have read.

Assess

- What was the main idea?
- Did the text clearly support the main idea?
- Did you learn anything new from the material?
- Can you use this new information in other school subjects or at home?
- What other sources could you use to find more information about the topic?

Reading Strategies

- Use a web to show connections between related ideas, to describe the characteristics of a place or group, or to list examples.
- Use a tree to show a hierarchy of ideas or the structure of an organization or group.
- Use a flowchart to explain steps in a process. Use a time line or chain-of-events diagram to show a chronology or the order of events.
- Analyze causal relationships with a cause-and-effect chart or a problem-and-solution diagram.
- Use a Venn diagram to compare and contrast attributes or characteristics.

Use Writing to Help Students Understand What They Read

Writing provides a way for students to demonstrate what they have learned. More significantly, writing can facilitate greater understanding and richer learning by encouraging writers to transform knowledge into something new. Appropriate writing assignments can help students build social studies concepts in the following ways.

- Writing challenges students to analyze, evaluate, and interpret events.
- Writing invites students to synthesize information from a variety of sources, including students' own prior knowledge and experiences.
- Writing requires students to make connections, draw conclusions, and support their judgments with facts and details.
- The writing process promotes a systematic approach to content analysis by teaching students to focus their thoughts, expand and refine their ideas, and express their viewpoints precisely.

Good Study Habits for Successful Students

- **Use the Body:** Incorporate movement into study routines, if possible. Students can march in place or pace while reciting a sequence of events or saying a list of items.
- **Study Groups:** Encourage students to work with others to review for a test. They can discuss important topics and take turns asking and answering questions.
- **The Big Picture:** Essay tests often ask "big picture" questions. To help students get the big picture, have them identify main ideas in reading selections; develop summaries of important topics; and create webs, maps, or other graphic organizers to draw conclusions and analyze relationships.

Unit 1 Planning Guide

- If you teach BOTH Eastern and Western world regions in one year, use the columns in red to help you pace your lessons.
- If you teach ONLY Eastern or Western world regions in one year, use the columns in blue to help you pace your lessons.

ALTERNATIVE PACING CHARTS

Geography Handbook		Unit 1		Chapter 1		Chapter 2		Chapter 3	
Both East and West	Either East or West	Both East and West	Either East or West	Both East and West	Either East or West	Both East and West	Either East or West	Both East and West	Either East or West
Day 1 Geography Handbook **Day 2** Geography Handbook	**Day 1** Geography Handbook **Day 2** Geography Handbook	**Day 1** Be an Active Reader! Unit Opener	**Day 1** Be an Active Reader! Unit Opener	**Day 1** Chapter Opener, Section 1 **Day 2** Making Connections, Section 2 **Day 3** Social Studies Skill, Section 3 **Day 4** Section 4, Review **Day 5** Chapter Assessment	**Day 1** Chapter Opener, Section 1 **Day 2** Section 1 **Day 3** Section 1, Making Connections **Day 4** Section 2 **Day 5** Social Studies Skill, Section 3 **Day 6** Section 3 **Day 7** Section 4 **Day 8** Section 4, Review **Day 9** Chapter Assessment	**Day 1** Chapter Opener, Section 1 **Day 2** Making Connections, Section 2 **Day 3** Section 2, Social Studies Skill **Day 4** Section 3 **Day 5** Section 3 **Day 6** Section 4, Review **Day 7** Chapter Assessment **Day 8** Eye on the Environment	**Day 1** Chapter Opener, Section 1 **Day 2** Section 1, Making Connections **Day 3** Section 2 **Day 4** Section 2 **Day 5** Social Studies Skill, Section 3 **Day 6** Section 3 **Day 7** Section 4 **Day 8** Section 4 **Day 9** Review **Day 10** Chapter Assessment **Day 11** Eye on the Environment	**Day 1** Chapter Opener, Section 1 **Day 2** Social Studies Skill, Section 2 **Day 3** Section 3 **Day 4** Section 4 **Day 5** TIME Reports **Day 6** Making Connections, Review **Day 7** Chapter Assessment	**Day 1** Chapter Opener, Section 1 **Day 2** Section 1 **Day 3** Social Studies Skill **Day 4** Section 2 **Day 5** Section 3 **Day 6** Section 4 **Day 7** TIME Reports **Day 8** Making Connections, Review **Day 9** Chapter Assessment

Note: The following materials may be used when teaching Unit 1.
Chapter level support materials can be found on the chapter resource pages.

TEACHING TRANSPARENCIES

Political Map Transparency L2

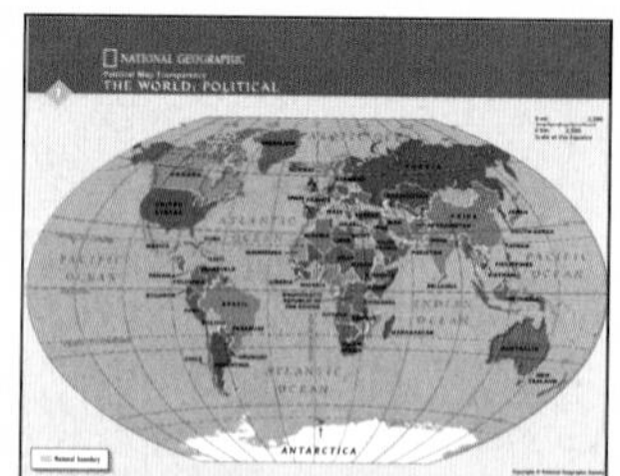

Map Overlay Transparencies L2

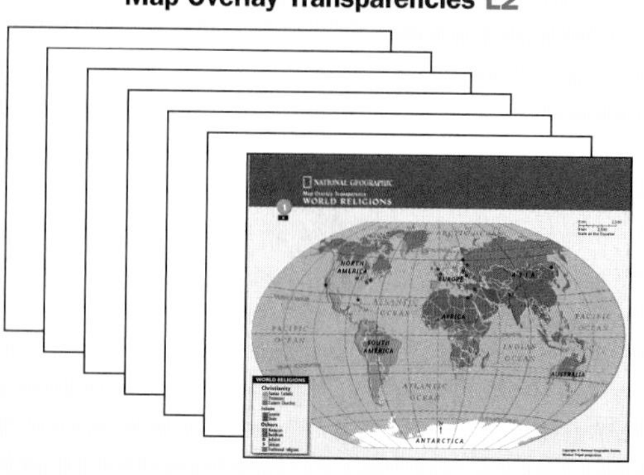

Unit 1 Resources

INTERDISCIPLINARY CONNECTIONS

World Literature Reading L2

Economics and Geography Activity L2

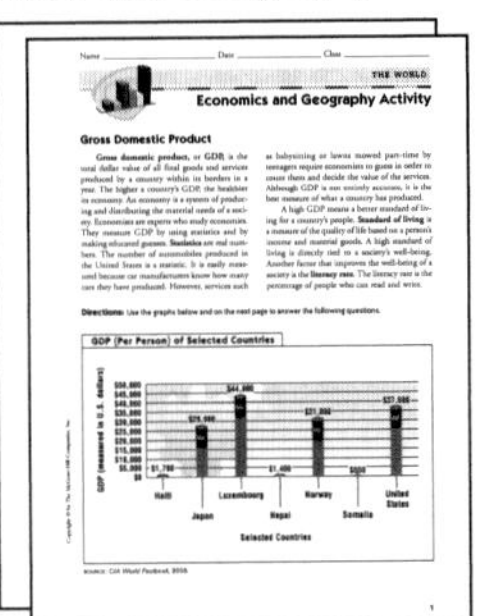

History and Geography Activity L2

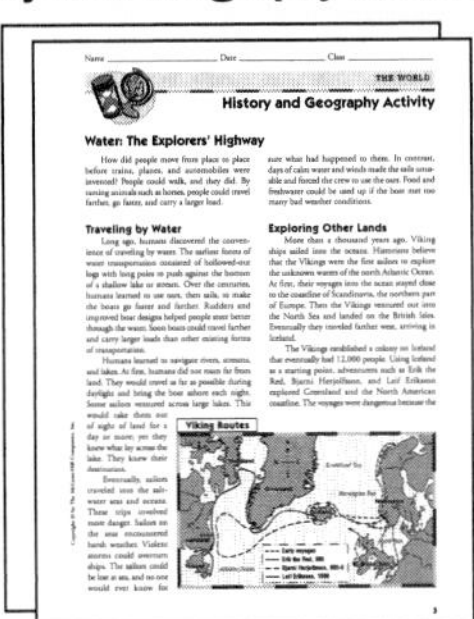

INTERDISCIPLINARY CONNECTIONS

Foods Around the World L1/ELL

World Music: A Cultural Legacy

CIVIC INVOLVEMENT

Citizenship Activity L1

Environmental Case Study L2

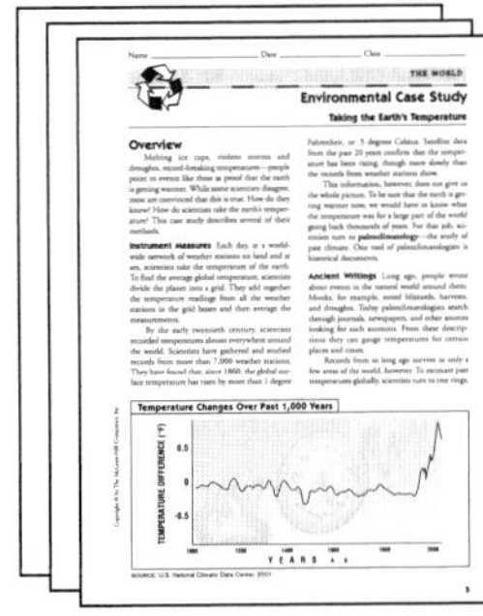

MAP AND GEOGRAPHY SKILLS

Building Geography Skills for Life

NGS Focus on Geography Literacy L2

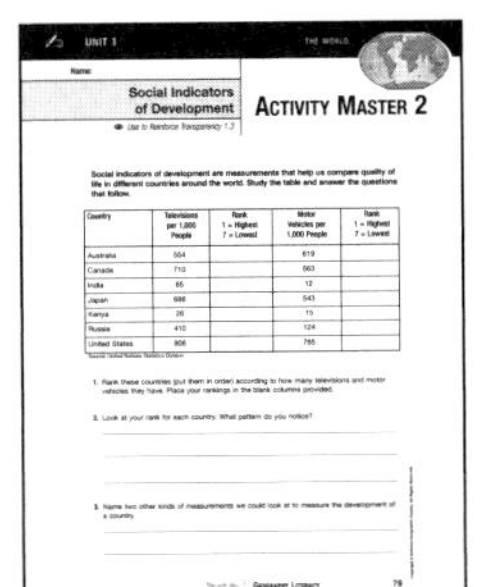

KEY TO ABILITY LEVELS

Teaching strategies have been coded for varying learning styles and abilities.

- L1 **BASIC** activities for all students
- L2 **AVERAGE** activities for average to above-average students
- L3 **CHALLENGING** activities for above-average students
- ELL **ENGLISH LANGUAGE LEARNER** activities

ASSESSMENT

Unit Pretests L2

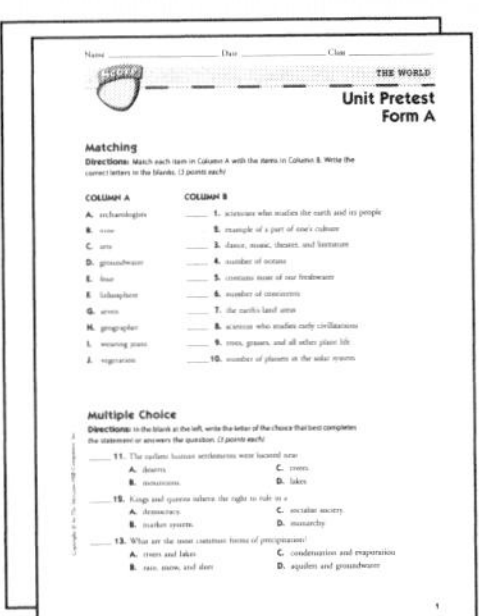

Unit Posttests L2

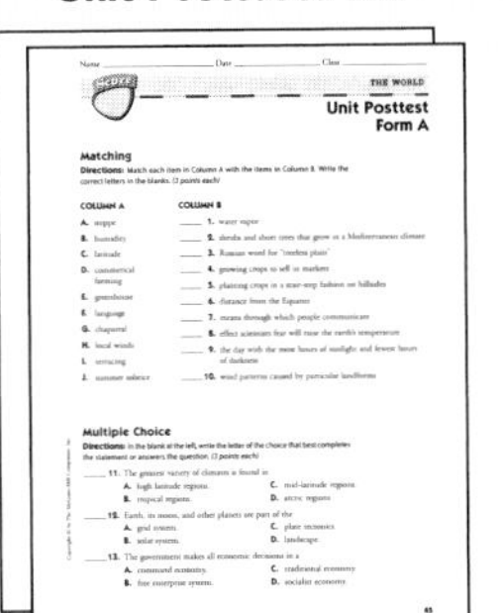

Glencoe Professional Development and Teacher Support Materials

- Reading in the Content Area for the Middle School Classroom
- Inclusion Strategies for the Middle School Social Studies Classroom
- Character Education for the Middle School Classroom
- Teaching Strategies for the Social Studies Classroom
- Reproducible Lesson Plans
- Outline Map Resource Book
- Writing Process Transparencies for Middle School
- Social Studies: Reading Strategies

- **Timed Readings Plus in Social Studies** help students increase their reading rate and fluency while maintaining comprehension. The 400-word passages are similar to those found on state and national assessments.
- **Reading in the Content Area: Social Studies** concentrates on six essential reading skills that help students better comprehend what they read. The book includes 75 high-interest nonfiction passages written at increasing levels of difficulty.
- **Reading Fluency** helps students read smoothly, accurately, and expressively.
- **Jamestown's Reading Improvement,** by renowned reading expert Edward Fry, focuses on helping build your students' comprehension, vocabulary, and skimming and scanning skills.
- **Critical Reading Series** provides high-interest books, each written at three reading levels.

For more information about these products, see the Jamestown Education materials in the Classroom Solutions in the front of this Teacher Wraparound Edition. To order these products, call Glencoe at 1-800-334-7344.

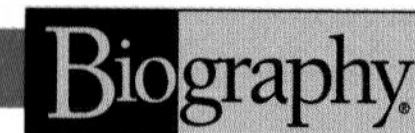

The following videotape programs are available from Glencoe:

- **Seven Wonders of the Ancient World** 0-7670-0401-9
- **The Television: Window to the World** 0-7670-0137-0
- **The Mighty Mississippi** 0-7670-1090-6

To order, call Glencoe at 1-800-334-7344. To find classroom resources to accompany many of these, check:

A&E Television: www.aetv.com

The History Channel: www.historychannel.com

Reading List Generator CD-ROM

Glencoe BookLink

The Glencoe BookLink CD-ROM is a database that allows you to search more than 15,000 titles to create a customized reading list for your students.

- Reading lists can be organized by students' reading level, author, genre, theme, or area of interest.
- The database provides Degrees of Reading Power™ (DRP) and Lexile™ readability scores for all selections.
- A brief summary of each selection is included.

Leveled reading suggestions for this unit:

For students at a Grade 5 reading level:

- ***Protecting Rivers and Seas,*** by Kamini Khanduri.

For students at a Grade 6 reading level:

- ***50 Simple Things Kids Can Do to Recycle,*** by Earth Works Group.

For students at a Grade 7 reading level:

- ***The Gentle Desert: Exploring an Ecosystem,*** by Laurence Pringle.

To order this CD-ROM, call Glencoe at 1-800-334-7344.

Extending the Content

Readings for the Teacher

- ***Encyclopedia of Biomes,*** 3 vols., by Marlene Weigel, ed. Farmington Hills, Mich.: U*X*L, 1999.
- ***The Encyclopedia of World Religions,*** by Robert S. Ellwood and Gregory D. Alles, eds. New York: Facts On File, 1998.

Multimedia Resources

- **Glencoe World History Primary Source Document Library CD-ROM**
- ***Mapmakers Toolkit.*** Watertown, Mass.: Tom Snyder Productions. Mac/Windows CD-ROM.

Service Learning Project

Keeping the Earth Clean

In many communities across the country, local governments participate in "adopt a highway" programs, in which organizations take responsibility for keeping one stretch of a local roadway clear of litter. Have the class investigate what such a program entails and how to arrange to participate in it. If possible, have the class adopt a part of a local roadway. If that is not possible, have the students work in the community to convince others to do so.

Content Background Notes

Use this additional information as lecture notes or discussion prompts throughout the study of Unit 1.

Chapter 1 Looking at the Earth (pp. 20–45)

Earth in the Solar System Some scientists hope to learn more about Mars by studying Earth. A huge crater north of Baffin Island shows where a meteorite slammed into the earth 23 million years ago. Today Haughton Crater, in Canada's Arctic region, shows evidence of surface structures similar to those found on Mars. Scientists are studying Haughton Crater hoping to unlock some secrets of Mars's natural history. One way is to use a spectrometer to identify the chemical makeup of the crater's rocks. Later, these records can be compared to measurements made of Mars's surface to see if the same minerals are found in both places. Scientists also study the remains of lake sediments in the crater to find patterns they can look for in Martian craters.

A group called the International Mars Society has constructed a permanent structure on the edge of the crater. It allows scientists to live and work there. The structure is the Society's suggested prototype for a similar structure on Mars itself—because the Mars Society wants the landing of humans on Mars to be the next important goal of the space program.

The Great Rift Valley Africa's Great Rift Valley is a 3,500-mile (5,633-km) long gash in the earth stretching from Mozambique to the Red Sea. The valley helps demonstrate the theory of plate tectonics. This gash is formed by the separation of the Somali and African Plates. As the plates move apart, hot magma rises to the surface, creating a thin new layer of the earth. The magma sometimes breaks to the surface in volcanoes such as the Virunga Mountains of Uganda. The upwelling of land also builds the highlands of Kenya and Ethiopia.

The Great Rift Valley shows evidence of climate change. Scientists have found the 5,000- to-10,000-year-old shells of freshwater snails in a dry region of Djibouti. Their presence establishes that the climate of East Africa was much wetter then than it is now.

Chapter 2 Water, Climate, and Vegetation (pp. 46–75)

Biodiversity Scientists argue over exactly how many species of plants and animals actually live on the earth. One suggested as many as 30 million different species. Others believe that this figure is far too high. Whatever the actual total, it is clear that to date we have identified only a fraction of them all—only about 1.75 million.

One reason for such concern over the destruction of the rain forest is that this biological region is rich in living things. Studies show that a hectare (about 2.5 acres) of Panama's rain forest yields as many as 60,000 insect species alone. Yet rain forests—and other environments—yield valuable resources for humans:

- A plant from Madagascar contains a chemical used to treat cancer.
- A microorganism in the hot springs of Yellowstone National Park furnishes a chemical used in easily creating DNA in the laboratory.
- African clawed frogs secrete a powerful chemical that kills bacteria, a chemical that may become an important medicine as antibiotics lose their effectiveness.
- A chemical in the liver of the dogfish shark contains a potential cancer-fighting compound.

Protecting the Environment One obstacle to efforts to save the rain forest is the need of indigenous populations to feed their growing numbers. A World Wildlife Fund effort in Madagascar is hoping to overcome this problem. The first step is to revive local peoples' traditions in viewing the land as sacred. Then the planners hope to develop the area for ecotourism so that local peoples can earn a living while still maintaining the land in its wild state.

Chapter 3 The World's People (pp. 78–111)

Global Culture The signs of the globalization of world culture are all around us. Many Chinese now earn extra money by selling products through home party retailing—and they sell the same American makeup, cleaning, and plastic storage products that made product demonstrations a staple of suburban American life. Meanwhile, an American has launched an Internet version of the ancient Chinese game of mah-jongg, which he plays online with fellow enthusiasts in Germany and Wales. In India, diners in one restaurant enjoy Lebanese food while listening to Filipino music and looking at posters of the Grand Ole Opry.

Some critics decry the role that American-based corporations play in this globalization. They say that countries around the world are losing their uniqueness. But multinationals cannot impose American culture everywhere. One makeup company changed the colors it sold in India to adapt to the skin of Indian women, and a major fast-food chain in that country dropped beef from its burgers and served mutton instead.

Languages Anthropologists estimate that about 10,000 languages have been spoken by humans throughout history. Of that number, 6,000 are still in use today. Many are about to die out because parents in some traditional cultures no longer teach their language to children. As many as 3,000 languages may disappear in the next hundred years.

00:00 Out of Time?

If time does not permit teaching each chapter in this unit, you may use the **Reading Essentials and Study Guide** for each chapter.

Unit Overview

The three chapters of this unit introduce students to the basic concepts of geography and the study of the earth. The topics include:

- the structure of the earth and how its motion creates the seasons
- the landforms of the earth and the forces that shape the land
- the role of wind and water in creating climate
- the different climate and vegetation zones found on the earth
- the factors that make up all the world's cultures
- the growth and movement of the world's population
- how people use resources and affect the environment

Glencoe Literature Library

As students study the unit, have them read *Mrs. Frisby and the Rats of NIMH* by Robert C. O'Brien from the **Glencoe Literature Library.** The Glencoe Literature Library consists of novels and other readings for middle school students, along with study guides that offer instructional support and student activities.

Unit 1

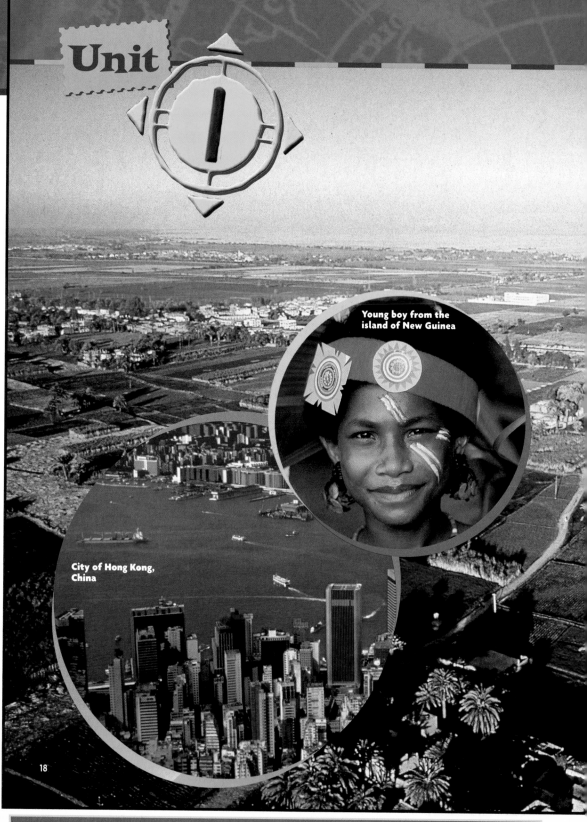

Young boy from the island of New Guinea

City of Hong Kong, China

18

Using the Illustration

Visual Instruction Although modern technology has caused many cultures to blend together, there is still diversity in the world. Hong Kong is one of the most crowded areas on Earth: about 6.8 million people live in an area of 413 square miles (1,070 sq. km). It is an important source center of commerce, trade, and shipping. Papua New Guinea, however, is located approximately 2,000 miles (3,218 km) from Hong Kong and has a population of 5.5 million people living in an area of 178,703 square miles (462,841 sq. km). There is very little industry, and the people produce only enough to meet their own needs, with few products for export. **Ask:** **Why might some cultures develop differently from others?** *(Cultures might develop in relative isolation as a result of geographic features such as mountains and bodies of water.)*

NATIONAL GEOGRAPHIC

The World

You are about to journey to dense rain forests, bleak deserts, bustling cities and marketplaces, and remote villages. In your study of the earth, you will learn about different places and different peoples. Imagine that you could visit any place in the world. Where would you want to go? What would you want to see?

▲ Hot air balloon floating over cultivated fields, Egypt

NGS ONLINE
www.nationalgeographic.com/education

19

Current Events Journal

Tell students to think about the variety of physical features on the earth. Have them list in their journals all the different landforms, climates, and types of vegetation they can name. Then have them write a paragraph explaining what meaning all this diversity has for them.

NGS ONLINE

www.nationalgeographic.com/education

This online resource provides lesson plans, atlas updates, cartographic activities with interactive maps, an online map store, and geography links.

Unit Launch Activity

Why Study Other Cultures? Point out that people around the world have many different ways of life—different foods, different kinds of clothing, different housing. Have students offer examples of some of these differences, such as the igloos that the Inuit use for shelter in the cold Arctic or the thatch-built houses on stilts that some Pacific Islanders use. **Ask:** Why do you think people follow different ways of life around the world? Have students write the question in their notebooks and refer to it as they study the unit. After completing the unit, ask for volunteers to suggest answers to the question and then discuss each suggestion.

EE4 Human Systems: Standard 9

Chapter 1 Resources

Note: The following materials may be used when teaching Chapter 1.
Section level support materials are shown at point of use in the margins of the Teacher Wraparound Edition.

Timesaving Tools

TeacherWorks™ All-In-One Planner and Resource Center

- **Interactive Teacher Edition** See the **Interactive Teacher Edition** CD-ROM to electronically integrate your Teacher Wraparound Edition and blackline masters.
- **Interactive Lesson Planner** Organize your week, month, semester, or year with all the lesson helps you need. The **Interactive Lesson Planner** CD-ROM contains all Chapter 1 resources.

Use Glencoe's **Presentation Plus!** multimedia teacher tool to easily present dynamic lessons that visually excite your students. Using Microsoft PowerPoint® you can customize the presentations to create your own personalized lessons.

TEACHING TRANSPARENCIES

Graphic Organizer Transparency 14 L2

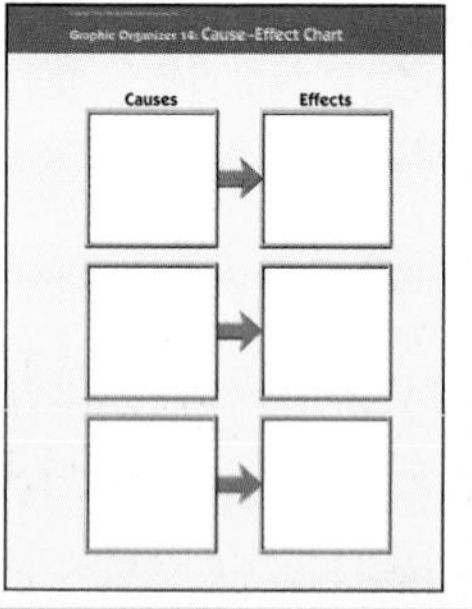

In-text Map Transparency L1

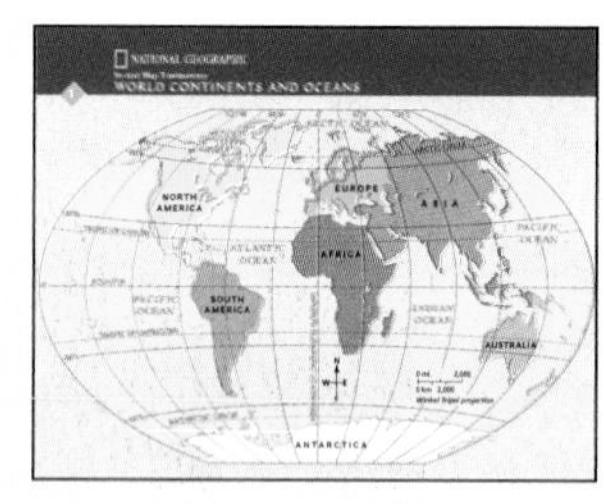

FOLDABLES™ Study Organizer **Dinah Zike's Foldables**

Foldables are three-dimensional, interactive graphic organizers that help students practice basic writing skills, review key vocabulary terms, and identify main ideas. Additional chapter activities can be found in the ***Reading and Study Skills Foldables*** booklet.

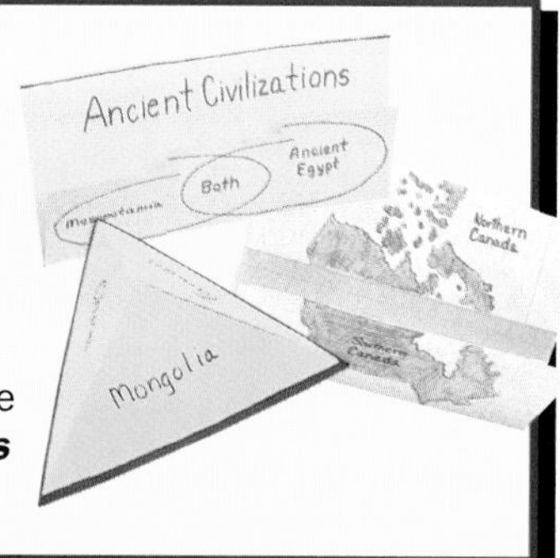

MAP AND GEOGRAPHY SKILLS

Chapter Map Activity L2

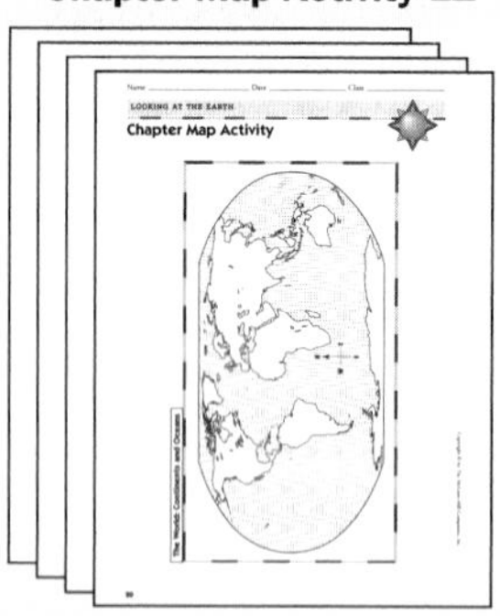

GeoLab Activity L2

READING SUPPORT

Vocabulary Activity L1

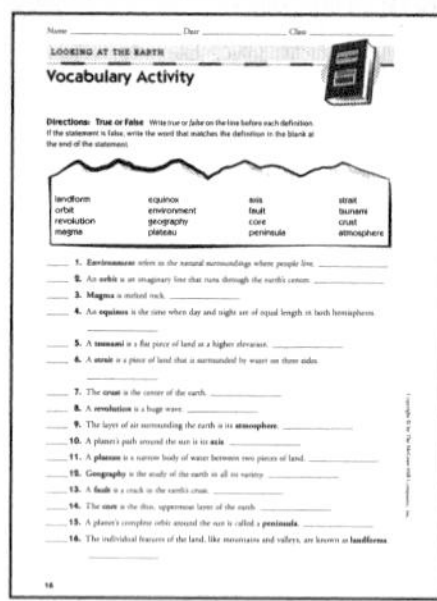

Workbook Activity L1

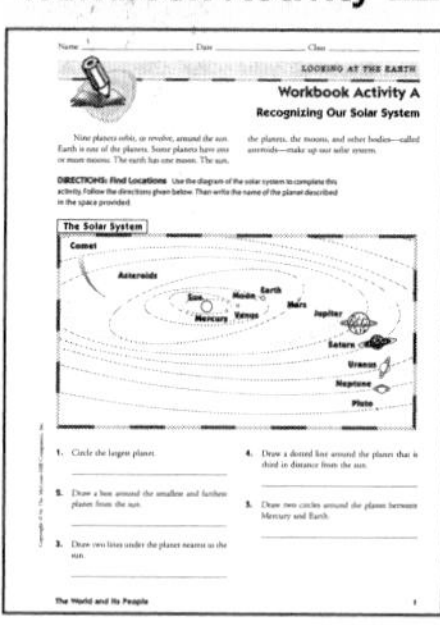

Reading and Writing Skills Activity L1/ELL

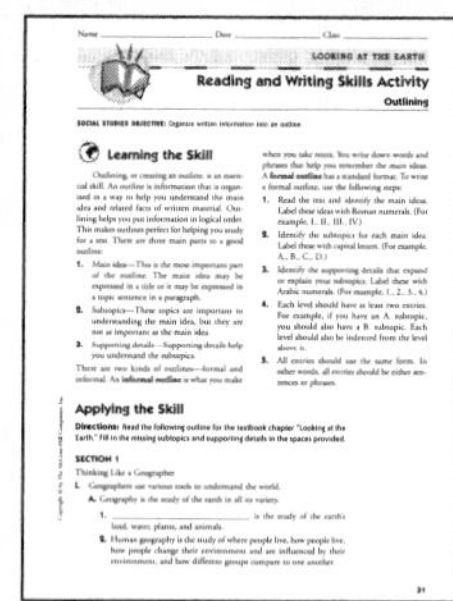

DIFFERENTIATED INSTRUCTION

Use these review and reinforcement materials to help less-proficient readers, English learners, and gifted and talented students.

Reteaching Activity L1

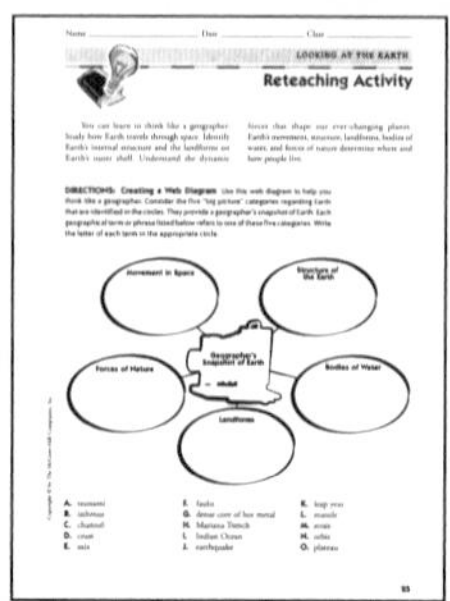

Chapter Skills Review L2

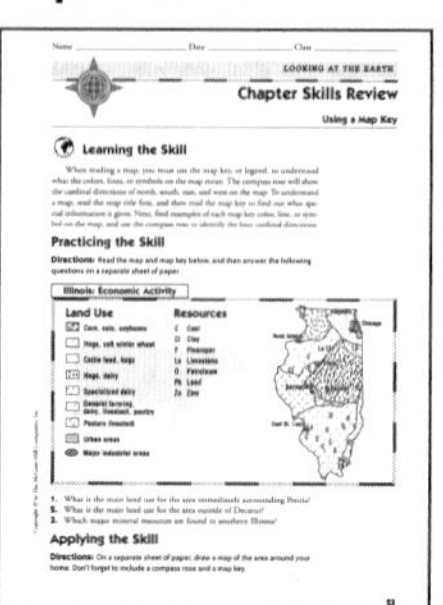

Cooperative Learning Activity L1/ELL

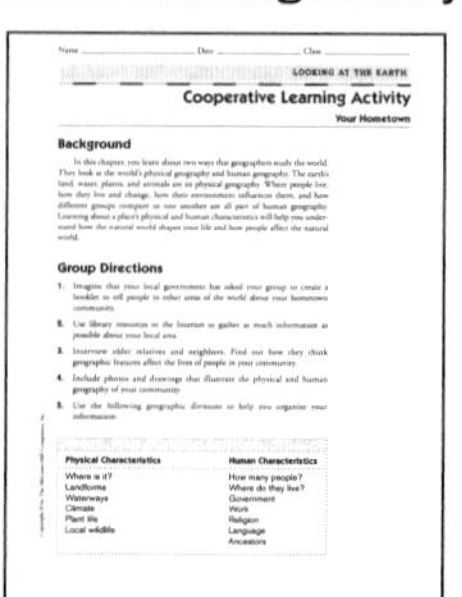

Enrichment Activity L3

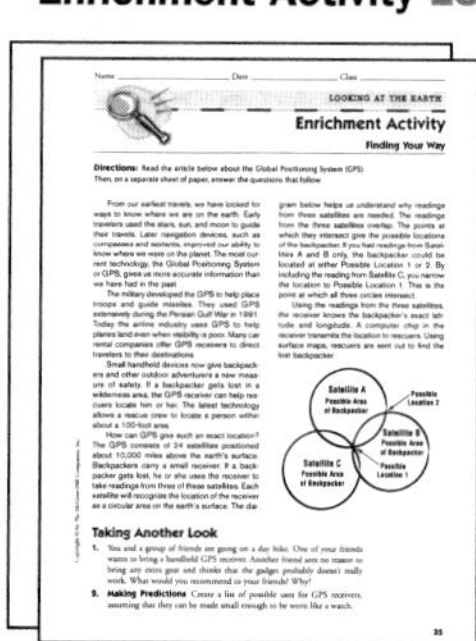

ASSESSMENT

Chapter Test, Form A L2

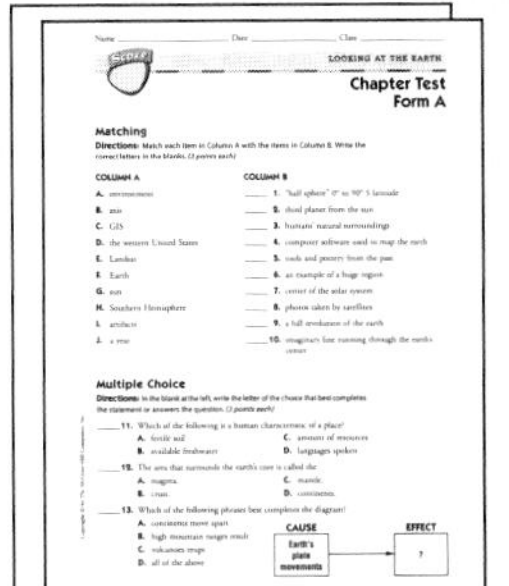

Chapter Test, Form B L2

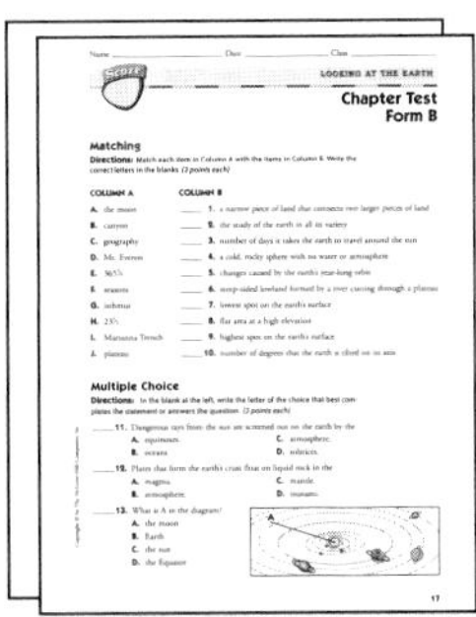

Performance Assessment Activity L1/ELL

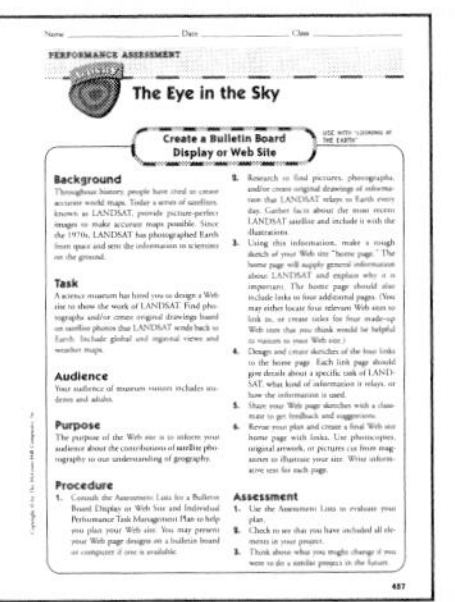

ExamView® Pro Testmaker CD-ROM

STANDARDIZED ASSESSMENT SKILLS

Critical Thinking Skills Activity L2

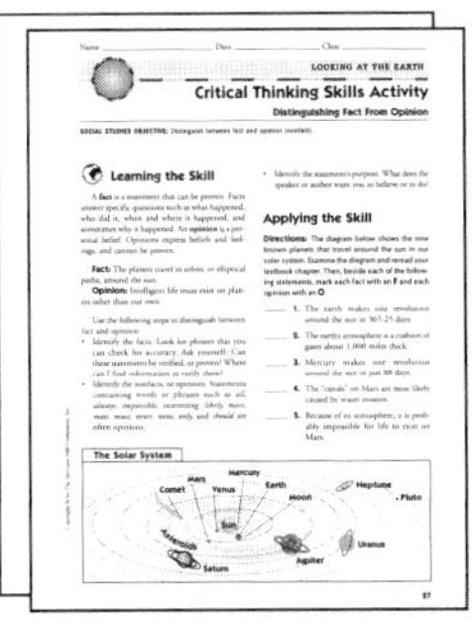

Map and Graph Skills Activity L2

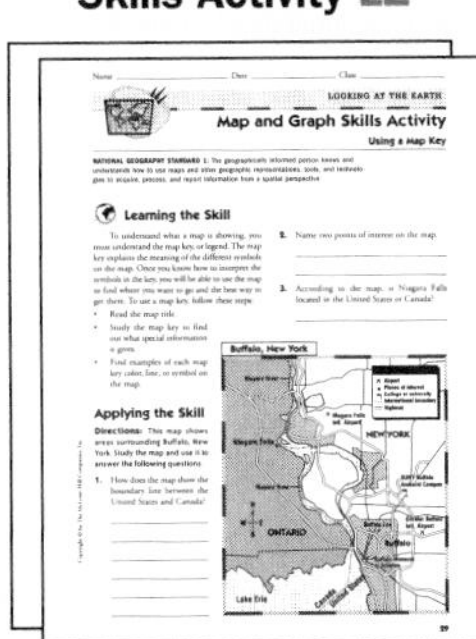

Standardized Test Skills Practice Workbook Activity L2

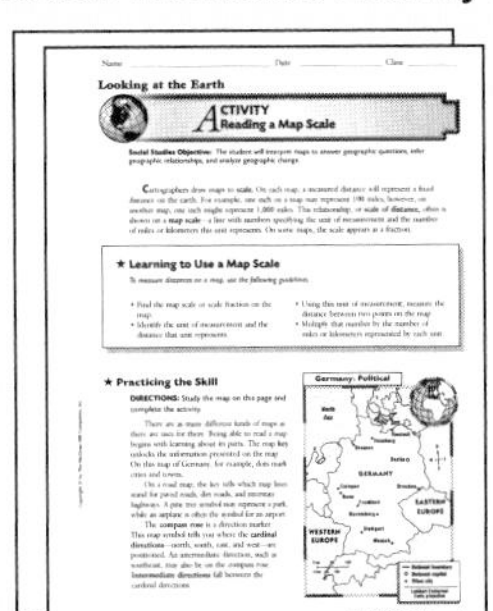

HOME INVOLVEMENT

Take-Home Review Activity L1

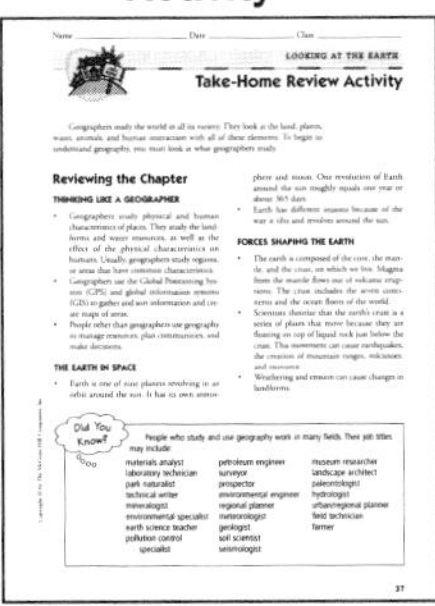

MULTIMEDIA

- **National Geographic's The World and Its People**
- **MindJogger Videoquiz**
- **Vocabulary PuzzleMaker CD-ROM**
- **Interactive Tutor Self-Assessment CD-ROM**
- **ExamView® Pro Testmaker CD-ROM**
- **TeacherWorks CD-ROM**
- **StudentWorks CD-ROM**
- **Skillbuilder Interactive Workbook CD-ROM, Level 1**
- **Presentation Plus! CD-ROM**
- **Audio Program**

SPANISH RESOURCES

The following Spanish language materials are available in the Spanish Resources binder:

- **Spanish Summaries**
- **Spanish Vocabulary Activities**
- **Spanish Guided Reading Activities**
- **Spanish Quizzes and Tests**
- **Spanish Take-Home Review Activities**
- **Spanish Reteaching Activities**

Meeting National Standards

Geography for Life

The following standards are covered in Chapter 1:

Section 1	**EE1 The World in Spatial Terms: Standards 1, 2, 3**
	EE2 Places and Regions: Standards 4, 5, 6
Section 2	**EE1 The World in Spatial Terms: Standards 1, 2, 3**
	EE5 Environment and Society: Standard 15
Section 3	**EE3 Physical Systems: Standards 7, 8**
	EE5 Environment and Society: Standard 15
Section 4	**EE3 Physical Systems: Standards 7, 8**
	EE5 Environment and Society: Standard 15

State and Local Objectives

Chapter 1 Planning Guide

SECTION RESOURCES

Daily Objectives	Reproducible Resources	Multimedia Resources
Section 1 **Thinking Like a Geographer** **1.** Describe how geographers look at the world. **2.** Discuss what tools geographers use. **3.** Explain how geographers use their knowledge of the earth.	Reproducible Lesson Plan Daily Lecture and Discussion Notes Note-taking Guide Guided Reading Activity* Reading Essentials and Study Guide* Section Quiz*	Daily Focus Skills Transparency GeoQuiz Transparency Vocabulary PuzzleMaker CD-ROM Interactive Tutor Self-Assessment CD-ROM ExamView® Pro Testmaker CD-ROM Presentation Plus! CD-ROM
Section 2 **The Earth in Space** **1.** Identify what makes up the solar system. **2.** Describe how Earth moves in space. **3.** Explain why Earth's seasons change.	Reproducible Lesson Plan Daily Lecture and Discussion Notes Note-taking Guide Guided Reading Activity* Reading Essentials and Study Guide* Section Quiz*	Daily Focus Skills Transparency Vocabulary PuzzleMaker CD-ROM Interactive Tutor Self-Assessment CD-ROM ExamView® Pro Testmaker CD-ROM Presentation Plus! CD-ROM
Section 3 **Forces Shaping the Earth** **1.** Describe the layers found within the earth. **2.** Discuss the forces that change the earth's surface.	Reproducible Lesson Plan Daily Lecture and Discussion Notes Note-taking Guide Guided Reading Activity* Reading Essentials and Study Guide* Section Quiz*	Daily Focus Skills Transparency Vocabulary PuzzleMaker CD-ROM Interactive Tutor Self-Assessment CD-ROM ExamView® Pro Testmaker CD-ROM Presentation Plus! CD-ROM
Section 4 **Landforms and Waterways** **1.** Describe the earth's major landforms. **2.** Explain how landforms affect where people live.	Reproducible Lesson Plan Daily Lecture and Discussion Notes Note-taking Guide Guided Reading Activity* Reading Essentials and Study Guide* Section Quiz*	Daily Focus Skills Transparency In-text Map Transparency Vocabulary PuzzleMaker CD-ROM Interactive Tutor Self-Assessment CD-ROM ExamView® Pro Testmaker CD-ROM Presentation Plus! CD-ROM MindJogger Videoquiz

00:00 **Out of Time?** Assign the **Reading Essentials and Study Guide*** for this chapter.

*Also available in Spanish

KEY TO ABILITY LEVELS

Teaching strategies have been coded for varying learning styles and abilities.

L1 **BASIC** activities for all students
L2 **AVERAGE** activities for average to above-average students
L3 **CHALLENGING** activities for above-average students
ELL **ENGLISH LANGUAGE LEARNER** activities

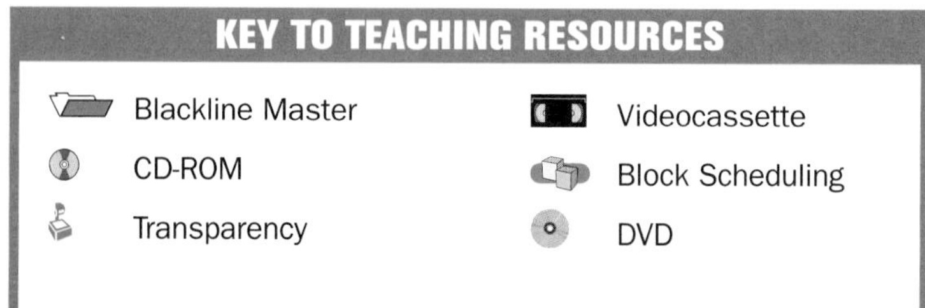

Teacher to Teacher

Learning Latitude and Longitude

Beverly A. Blamer
Fremont Middle School
Fremont, Michigan

This activity can be used to help students learn about latitude and longitude and how the grid system shows exact locations. Before class, make large signs for every tenth parallel north and south of the Equator and every fifteenth meridian east and west of the Prime Meridian. Also make signs for the Equator, Arctic and Antarctic Circles, Tropics of Cancer and Capricorn, Prime Meridian, and International Date Line. Take your students and signs to the gymnasium. Have students help you arrange and tape the signs around the room to set up a grid system. Then call out commands such as "Everybody stand on 40°N. Raise your hand if you are also standing at 50°E. You are standing on [name of city]." Repeat with new coordinates until students understand the grid system.

Meeting Special Needs

In addition to the Differentiated Instruction strategies found in each section, the following resources are also suitable for your special needs students:

- ***ExamView® Pro Testmaker CD-ROM*** allows teachers to tailor tests by reducing answer choices.
- The ***Audio Program*** includes the entire narrative of the student edition so that less-proficient readers can listen to the words as they read them.
- The ***Reading Essentials and Study Guide*** provides the same content as the student edition but is written two grade levels below the textbook.
- ***Guided Reading Activities*** give less-proficient readers point-by-point instructions to increase comprehension as they read each textbook section.
- ***Enrichment Activities*** include a stimulating collection of readings and activities for gifted and talented students.

NATIONAL GEOGRAPHIC TEACHER'S CORNER

Index to National Geographic Magazine:

The following articles may be used for research relating to this chapter:

- "John Glenn: Man With a Mission," by William R. Newcott, June 1999.
- *Physical World,* a National Geographic Special Edition, May 1998.
- "Landsat's Views of a Changing Earth," by Boris Weintraub, November 1997.

National Geographic Society Products:

To order the following products for use with this chapter, call National Geographic Society at 1-800-368-2728:

- *Water: A Precious Resource* (Video)
- *Physical Geography of North America Series* (6 Videos)
- *Geography: Five Themes for Planet Earth* (Video)
- *PicturePack: Physical Geography of the World* (Transparencies)

NGS ONLINE

Access National Geographic's Web site for current events, activities, links, interactive features, and archives.
www.nationalgeographic.com

NATIONAL GEOGRAPHIC MapMachine

Find the latest coverage of geography in the news, atlas updates, cartographic activities with interactive maps, an online map store, and links at www.nationalgeographic.com/maps

SOCIAL STUDIES Online

Use our Web site for additional resources. All essential content is covered in the Student Edition.

You and your students can visit twip.glencoe.com, the Web site companion to *The World and Its People.* This innovative integration of electronic and print media offers your students a wealth of opportunities. The student text directs students to the Web site for the following options:

- Chapter Overviews
- Student Web Activities
- Self-Check Quizzes
- Textbook Updates

Answers are provided for you in the Web Activity Lesson Plan. Additional Web resources and Interactive Tutor puzzles are also available.

Introducing
Chapter 1

Social Studies Online

Introduce students to chapter content and key terms by having them access Chapter Overview 1 at twip.glencoe.com

Chapter Objectives

1. Discuss how geographers look at the world and what tools they use.
2. Explain how the earth moves in space and why the seasons change.
3. Describe the structure of the earth's interior.
4. Identify different landforms.

GLENCOE TECHNOLOGY

NATIONAL GEOGRAPHIC

The World and Its People Video Program

Chapter 1 The World

The following segments enhance the study of this chapter:

- **Global Sunrise**
- **Kilauea Volcano**

MindJogger Videoquiz

Use MindJogger Videoquiz to preview the Chapter 1 content.

Both programs available in DVD and VHS

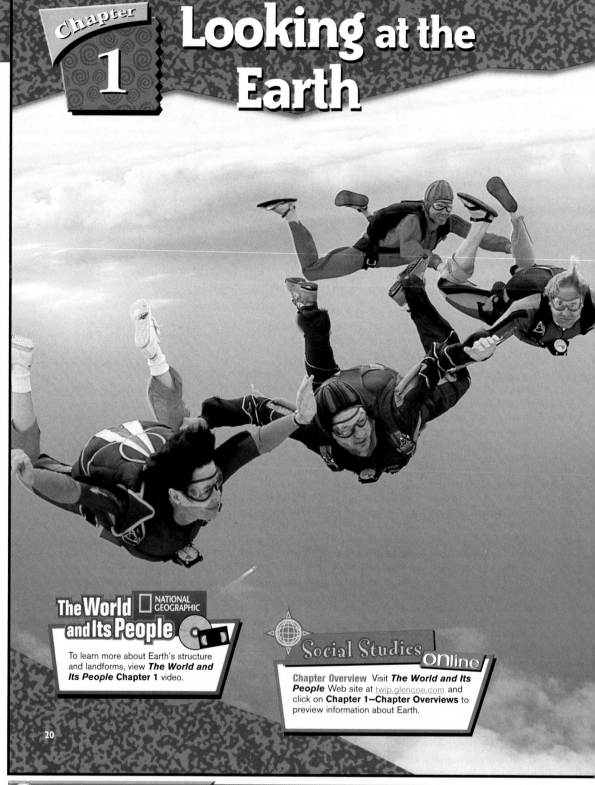

Chapter 1 Looking at the Earth

The World and Its People NATIONAL GEOGRAPHIC

To learn more about Earth's structure and landforms, view ***The World and Its People*** **Chapter 1** video.

Social Studies Online

Chapter Overview Visit ***The World and Its People*** Web site at twip.glencoe.com and click on **Chapter 1—Chapter Overviews** to preview information about Earth.

20

Reading Strategy — Purpose for Reading

The **Book Tour** is an important tool in showing students how their text is structured. Once they understand how the text is structured, they will be more successful readers. Beginning with Section 1, **ask:** **How has the author designed the text? What are the main features? What does the author do to tap in to what you already know? How does the author identify the main ideas and highlight important vocabulary?** Have pairs of students write the main features of the author's craft. Discuss as a class what students have noted and tell the students to pay attention to these features of the text as they read the book. **L1**

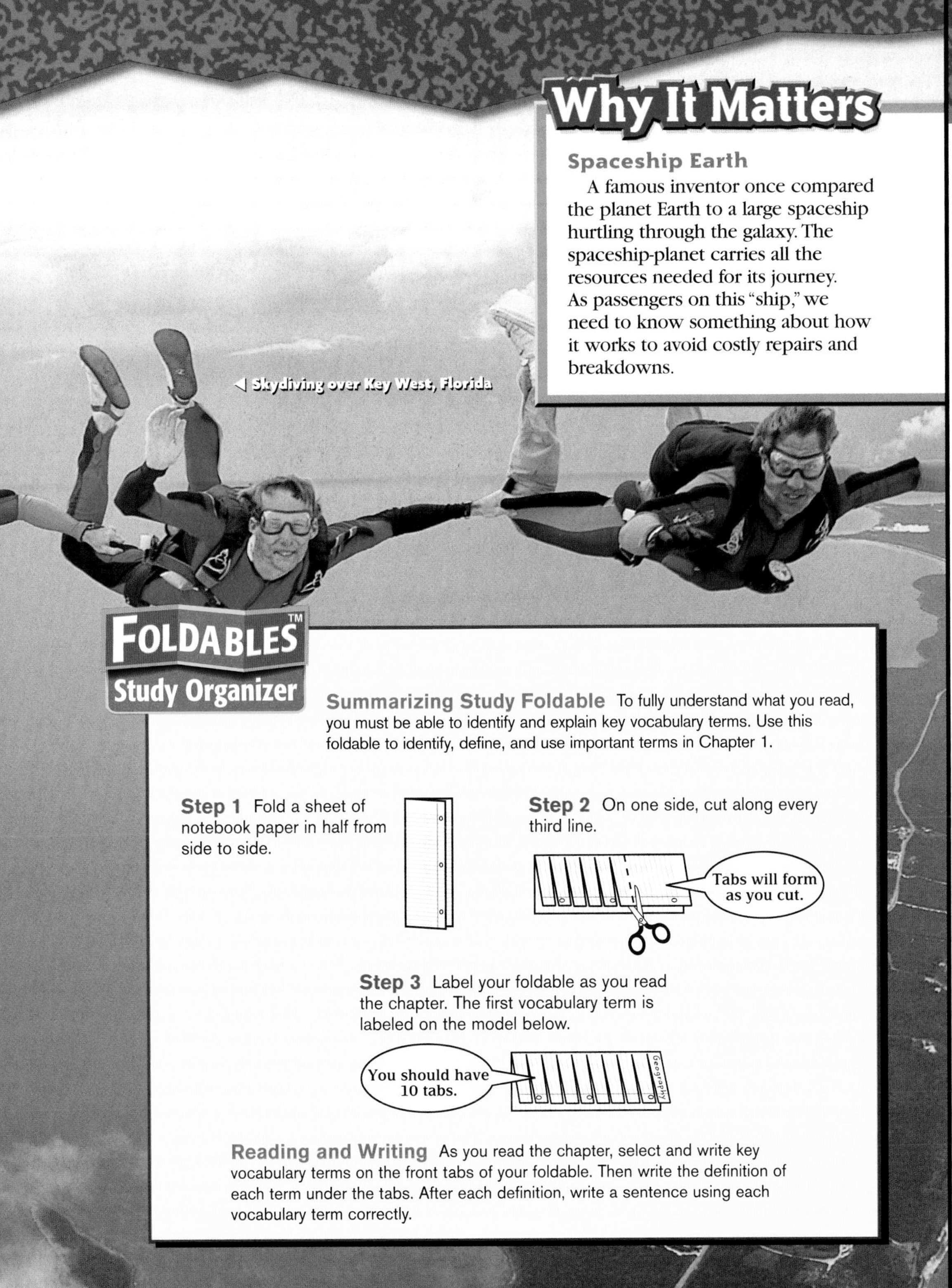

Why It Matters

Spaceship Earth

A famous inventor once compared the planet Earth to a large spaceship hurtling through the galaxy. The spaceship-planet carries all the resources needed for its journey. As passengers on this "ship," we need to know something about how it works to avoid costly repairs and breakdowns.

◀ Skydiving over Key West, Florida

FOLDABLES™ Study Organizer

Summarizing Study Foldable To fully understand what you read, you must be able to identify and explain key vocabulary terms. Use this foldable to identify, define, and use important terms in Chapter 1.

Step 1 Fold a sheet of notebook paper in half from side to side.

Step 2 On one side, cut along every third line.

Tabs will form as you cut.

Step 3 Label your foldable as you read the chapter. The first vocabulary term is labeled on the model below.

You should have 10 tabs.

Geography

Reading and Writing As you read the chapter, select and write key vocabulary terms on the front tabs of your foldable. Then write the definition of each term under the tabs. After each definition, write a sentence using each vocabulary term correctly.

FOLDABLES™ Study Organizer — Dinah Zike's Foldables

Purpose Students will make and use a foldable to define key vocabulary terms found in the chapter. Students may want to create a foldable for each section of the chapter. They should write the term on the front of each tab and its definition on the back of the tab. Students should write a complete sentence on the back of the tab using the vocabulary term to be sure that they understand its meaning.

Have students complete the ***Reading and Study Skills Foldables*** activity for this chapter.

Why It Matters

About 77 percent of all pollution in the oceans originates on land. Plastic and other trash in ocean waters kill fish, sea birds, turtles, seals, and whales. People can help the oceans by recycling. Have your students find out what local arrangements have been made for recycling at your school and in the community. Then have them create posters urging others to recycle and providing information about how to recycle.

About the Photo

These skydivers have a bird's-eye view of the Florida Keys' beautiful blue waters. What they can't see is the destruction that is taking place within these once-clear waters. The coral reefs—home to sea turtles, spiny lobsters, sea urchins, fish, and many other types of marine life—are disappearing rapidly. The living corals are being killed by disease and smothered by algae that thrives on pollutants from treated sewage and storm water run-off. The Environmental Protection Agency (EPA) is monitoring Florida's coastal waters to determine changes in the coral reef due to increased human population. They will implement a Water Quality Protection Program based on their findings.

Chapter 1

Section 1, pages 22–27

Focus

Section Objectives

1. Describe how geographers look at the world.
2. Discuss what tools geographers use.
3. Explain how geographers use their knowledge of the earth.

BELLRINGER
Skillbuilder Activity

Project transparency and have students answer the question.

Daily Focus Skills Transparency

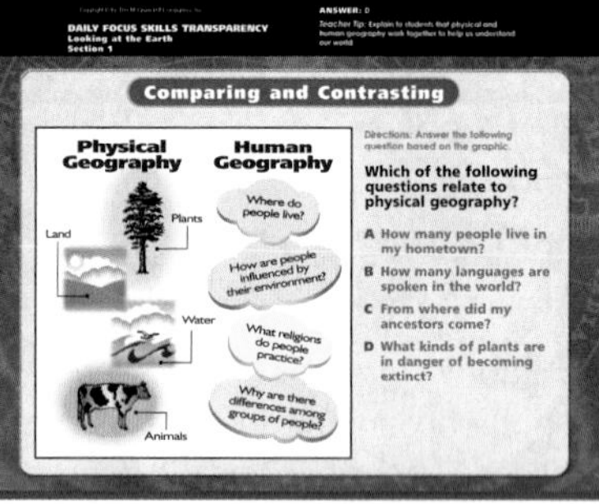

Reading Preview

■ **Activating Prior Knowledge**
Ask: Have you ever given directions to someone? Lead students to see that maps are ways of representing spatial reality.

■ **Preteaching Vocabulary**
Remind students that when they are faced with multipart terms like GPS and GIS, they should break down the terms by analyzing each of the words.

Guide to Reading

Main Idea

Geographers use various tools to understand the world.

Terms to Know

- geography
- landform
- environment
- Global Positioning System (GPS)
- geographic information systems (GIS)
- artifact
- fossil

Reading Strategy

Create a chart like this, and write three examples for each heading.

How Geographers View the World 1. 2. 3.
Tools of Geography 1. 2. 3.
Uses of Geography 1. 2. 3.

Section 1 Thinking Like a Geographer

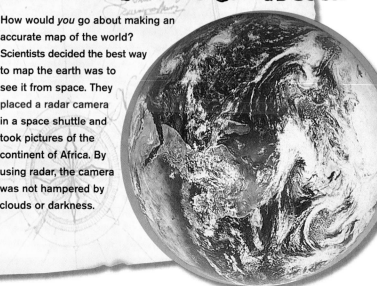

How would *you* go about making an accurate map of the world? Scientists decided the best way to map the earth was to see it from space. They placed a radar camera in a space shuttle and took pictures of the continent of Africa. By using radar, the camera was not hampered by clouds or darkness.

Why do geographers want to know exactly what the earth looks like? Think about the following: Mount Etna in **Italy** is one of the world's most active volcanoes. Two eruptions between 2001 and 2003 were the most explosive in the volcano's history. Scientists who study volcanoes constantly watch Mount Etna. By doing so, they hope to learn enough about the volcano to be able to predict eruptions and warn the people living nearby. Earthquakes, which usually happen before a volcanic eruption, can also give local residents advance warning. In addition, scientists study movements under the surface of the earth to predict volcanic activity.

This is just one example of how people around the world use geographic knowledge collected from various sources. **Geography** is the study of the earth in all its variety. When you study geography, you learn about the earth's land, water, plants, and animals. This is physical geography. You also learn about how the continents were

Section Resources

Reproducible Masters
- Reproducible Lesson Plan
- Daily Lecture and Discussion Notes
- Note-taking Guide
- Guided Reading Activity
- Reading Essentials and Study Guide
- Section Quiz

Transparencies
- Daily Focus Skills Transparency
- GeoQuiz Transparency

Multimedia
- Vocabulary PuzzleMaker CD-ROM
- Interactive Tutor Self-Assessment CD-ROM
- Presentation Plus! CD-ROM
- ExamView® Pro Testmaker CD-ROM

formed and what causes erosion. You also study people—where they live, how they live, how they change and are influenced by their environment, and how different groups compare to one another. This is human geography.

A Geographer's View of Place

Geographers look at major issues—like the eruptions of Mount Etna, which affect many people over a wide area. They also look at local issues—such as where the best place is for a company to build a new store in town. Whether an issue is global, national, or local, geographers try to understand both the physical and human characteristics, or features, of the issue.

Physical Characteristics Geographers study places. They look at *where* something is located on the earth. They also try to understand what the place is *like*. They ask: What features make a place similar to or different from other places?

To answer this question, geographers identify the landforms of a place. **Landforms** are individual features of the land, such as mountains and valleys. Geographers also look at water. Is the place near the ocean or on a river? Does it have plentiful or very little freshwater? They consider whether the soil will produce crops. They see how much rain the place usually receives and how hot or cold the area is. They find out whether the place has minerals, trees, or other resources.

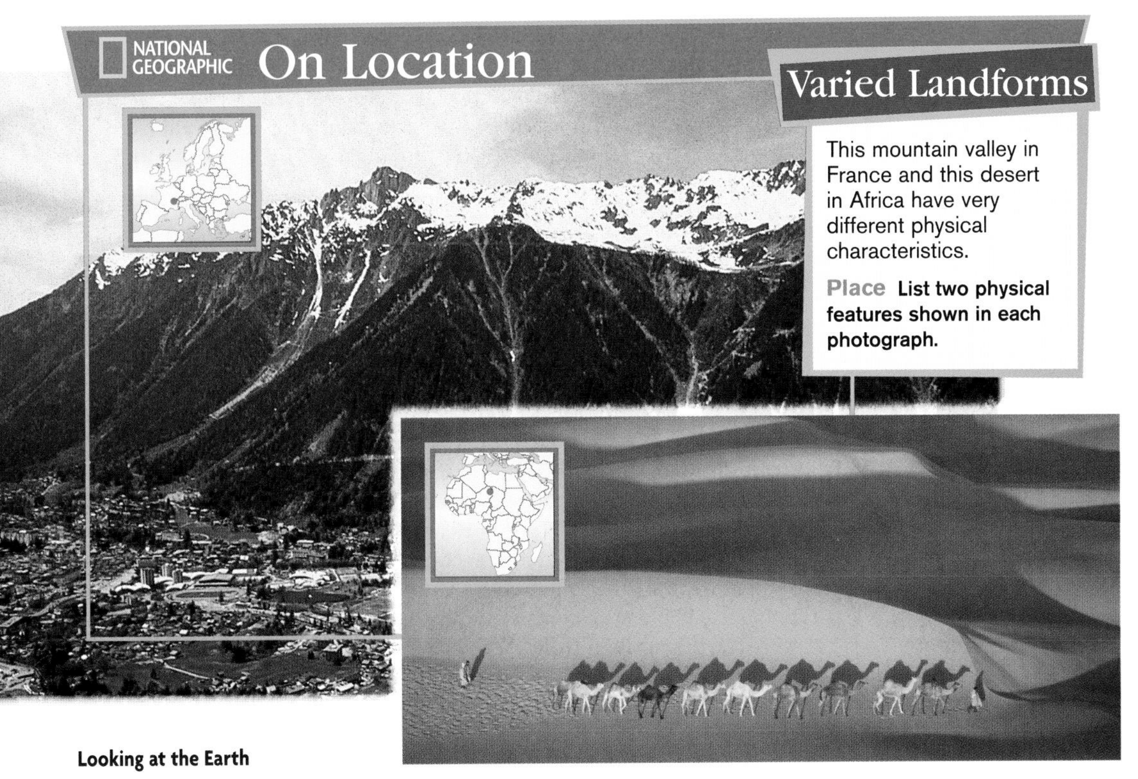

NATIONAL GEOGRAPHIC On Location

Varied Landforms

This mountain valley in France and this desert in Africa have very different physical characteristics.

Place **List two physical features shown in each photograph.**

2 TEACH

Making Inferences Ask students to describe the physical characteristics of your area. Then have them think again about your area in terms of human characteristics. How would they describe your area in terms of the human impact on the environment? L1

Daily Lecture and Discussion Notes

LOOKING AT THE EARTH

Daily Lecture and Discussion Notes

Thinking Like a Geographer

Did You Know?

Geography is the science of space and place on the earth's surface. We human beings are constantly interacting with the earth. The earth shapes our lives just as we shape the face of the earth. Studying geography enables us to better see and understand our own home and culture and our relationships to other cultures and environments. Clear vision and understanding form a basis for nearly any kind of communication and constructive action.

I. A Geographer's View of Place

A. **Geography** is the study of land as well as water, plants, animals, and people.

B. Geographers study the physical and human characteristics of places.

of the land, such as mountains and valleys

More About the Photos

Varied Landforms Mont Blanc rises on the border of France and Italy. Its name—which means "white mountain"—comes from the glacier that covers about 40 square miles (104 sq. km) of its surface. The Sahara, the world's largest hot desert, covers about 3.5 million square miles (9 million sq. km).

Caption Answer *Possible answers:* for Mont Blanc—mountain, valley, forests; for Sahara—desert, shifting dunes, rocky and sandy soil

Reading Strategy — Reading the Text

Previewing Have students preview the text's structure before they begin reading. Text structure is the way ideas are organized in a selection. Text structures in this textbook include time order, compare-contrast, description, cause and effect, and problem-solution. Noticing how ideas are organized will prepare students for the types of information they will receive. L1

*Use the **Reading Skills Handbook** for more reading strategies.*

Chapter 1

Section 1, pages 22–27

Current Events Journal

Have students create a chart with four column headings: "Physical Characteristics," "Human Characteristics," "People and Places," and "Regions." In the first row, have them write a definition of each approach to studying the earth. In the second row, have them write two examples of each approach.

✓ Reading Check Answer

Possible answers: settlement patterns, form of government, types of religion, kinds of work, languages spoken, ancestors' homes

L1/ELL

Guided Reading Activity

Name ______ Date ______ Class ______

LOOKING AT THE EARTH

Guided Reading Activity 1

Thinking Like a Geographer

DIRECTIONS: Reading for Accuracy Reading the section and completing the activity below will help you learn more about thinking like a geographer. Use your textbook to decide if a statement is true or false. Write **T** or **F**, and if a statement is false, rewrite it correctly.

____ 1. Geography is only the study of the earth's land, water, plants, and animals.

____ 2. Landforms are individual features of the land like mountains and valleys.

____ 3. People do not have much impact on the environment.

Social Studies Online

Objectives and answers to the Student Web Activity can be found in the Web Activity Lesson Plan at twip.glencoe.com

Human Characteristics Geographers also look at the social characteristics of the people living in the place. Do many or only a few people live there? Do they live close together or far apart? Why? What kind of government do they have? What religions do they follow? What kinds of work do they do? What languages do they speak? From where did the people's ancestors come?

People and Places Geographers are especially interested in how people interact with their **environment,** or natural surroundings. People can have a major impact on the environment. In many parts of the world, people have built dams along rivers. As a result, they have changed the ways that rivers behave in flood season.

Where people live often has a strong influence on *how* they live. The earliest settlements were near rivers, which provided water for crops and transportation. Today people near the sea might catch fish and build ships for trade. Those living inland might farm or take up ranching. More and more people are using computers and other technology in their work today. This means people depend less on their physical environment to make a living.

Regions Geographers carefully study individual cities, rivers, and other landforms. They also look at the big picture, or how individual places relate to other places. In other words, geographers look at a region, or an area that shares common characteristics. Regions can be relatively small—like your state, town, or school district. They can also be huge—like the western **United States.** Some regions may even include several countries if they have similar environments or their people follow similar ways of life and speak the same language. The countries of western South America are often discussed as a region. They are called the Andean countries because the **Andes,** a series of mountain ranges, run through all of them.

✓ **Reading Check** **What do geographers study to determine the human characteristics of a place?**

The Tools of Geography

Geographers need tools to study people and places. Maps and globes are the main tools they use. As you read in the **Geography Handbook** on page 9, geographers use many different types of maps. Each type gives geographers a particular kind of information about a place.

Social Studies Online

Web Activity Visit ***The World and Its People*** Web site at twip.glencoe.com and click on **Chapter 1—Student Web Activities** to learn more about geographic information systems.

Collecting Data for Mapping Earth How do geographers gather information so they can make accurate maps? One way is to take photographs from high above the earth. Landsat images are photographs taken by satellites that circle the earth. These images show details such as the shape of the land, what plants cover an area, and how land is being used. Radar cameras can even reveal hidden information. Photos of **Antarctica** taken from radar cameras show rivers of ice 500 miles (805 km) long—all hidden by snow.

Differentiated Instruction

Meeting Special Needs: Visual/Spatial To help students understand the idea that a place can belong to many different regions, display a map that shows all of one country. Focus on a single city and draw a circle around it. Then draw a slightly larger circle around the metropolitan area, which includes the city's suburbs. Draw another circle around a physical region that includes the city and surrounding areas—for example, the river valley or coastal region to which the city belongs. Draw another circle around the state or other administrative division in which the city sits, and yet one more around the country as a whole. Point out that many of the circles overlap, but all show how the place is linked to other regions in certain ways. **L1**

NATIONAL GEOGRAPHIC On Location

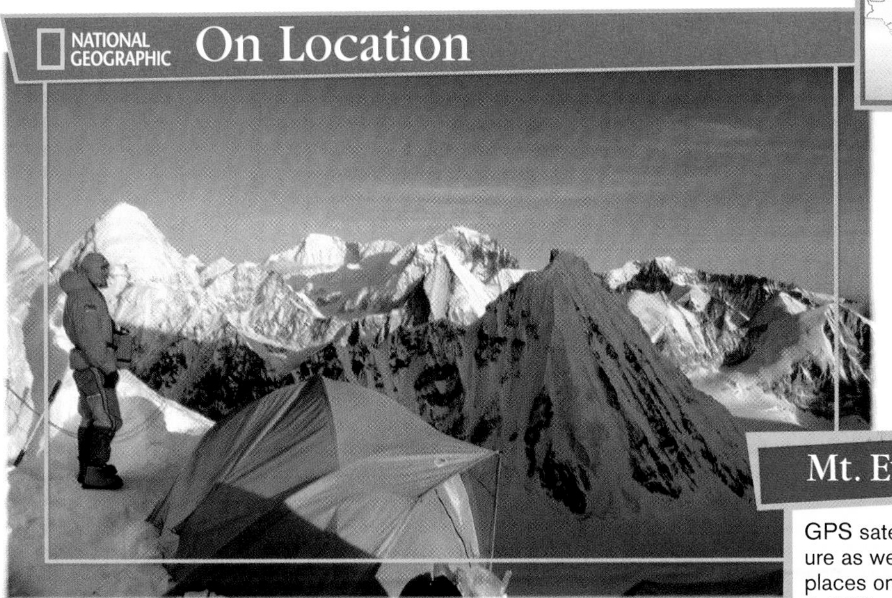

Mt. Everest

GPS satellites measure as well as locate places on the earth. A GPS receiver placed on top of Mt. Everest, the tallest mountain in the world, showed that it is 7 feet (2.1 m) higher than people previously thought.

Location **Why is it important for geographers to know exactly where places are located on the earth?**

How do geographers accurately label the exact locations of places on a map? Believe it or not, the best way to find a location is from outer space. Another group of satellites traveling around the earth makes up the **Global Positioning System (GPS).** A GPS receiver is a special device that receives signals from these satellites. When the receiver is placed at a location, the GPS satellite can tell the exact latitude and longitude of that location. As a result, a mapmaker can know where exactly on the earth the particular area is located. GPS devices are even installed in vehicles to help drivers find their way.

Geographic Information Systems Today geographers use another powerful tool in their work—computers. Special computer software called **geographic information systems (GIS)** helps geographers gather many different kinds of information about the same place. First geographers input all the data they collect. Then they use the software to combine and overlap the information on special maps.

In the early 2000s, scientists developed GIS technology to help conserve the plants and animals that live in the Amazon rain forest. More than 50 million acres of the rain forest are destroyed each year because of logging, mining, and other such activities. Using GIS technology, scientists can compare data gathered from the ground to data taken from satellite pictures. For example, they can see what species live where within the rain forest. Land use planners use this information to help local people make good decisions about how to use the land. These activities help prevent the rain forest from being destroyed.

Reading Check **What is the difference between GPS and GIS?**

More About the Photo

GPS Satellites At the heart of the GPS system are 24 satellites that orbit the earth and give off signals. These signals are picked up by receivers, revealing the latitude, longitude, and altitude of the receivers.

Caption Answer to make accurate maps

Reading Check Answer

GPS includes a group of satellites used to identify location; GIS is special computer software used to analyze data and create maps.

Measure student knowledge of physical features.

GeoQuiz Transparency

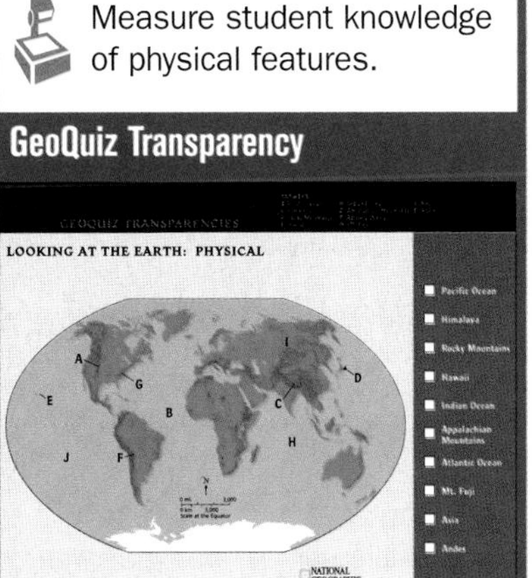

3 Assess

Assign Section 1 Assessment as homework or an in-class activity.

Have students use the Interactive Tutor Self-Assessment CD-ROM to review Section 1.

Critical Thinking Activity

Categorizing Information Have students skim the chapter about the United States to find political, physical, climate, economic activity, and population density maps. Have them find the state in which they live. Tell them to write five column headings on a sheet of paper: "Political," "Physical," "Climate," "Land Use," and "Population Density." Have them write under each column the information they can learn about their state from the appropriate map. When they have completed this work, point out that they have just made use of geographic information systems (GIS)—they have been able to interpret different information about the same place. L1

EE1 The World in Spatial Terms: Standard 1

Chapter 1

Section 1, pages 22–27

L2

Section Quiz

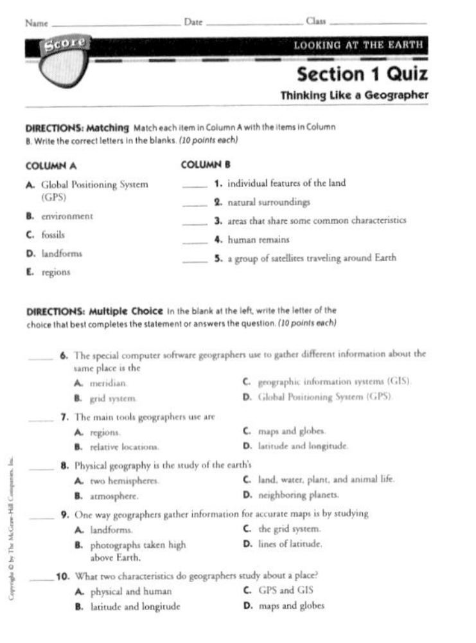

Name ________ Date ________ Class ________

Score

LOOKING AT THE EARTH

Section 1 Quiz

Thinking Like a Geographer

DIRECTIONS: Matching Match each item in Column A with the items in Column B. Write the correct letters in the blanks. *(10 points each)*

COLUMN A	COLUMN B
A. Global Positioning System (GPS)	____ 1. individual features of the land
B. environment	____ 2. natural surroundings
C. fossils	____ 3. areas that share some common characteristics
D. landforms	____ 4. human remains
E. regions	____ 5. a group of satellites traveling around Earth

DIRECTIONS: Multiple Choice In the blank at the left, write the letter of the choice that best completes the statement or answers the question. *(10 points each)*

____ 6. The special computer software geographers use to gather different information about the same place is the
A. meridian.
B. grid system.
C. geographic information systems (GIS).
D. Global Positioning System (GPS).

____ 7. The main tools geographers use are
A. regions.
B. relative locations.
C. maps and globes.
D. latitude and longitude.

____ 8. Physical geography is the study of the earth's
A. two hemispheres.
B. atmosphere.
C. land, water, plant, and animal life.
D. neighboring planets.

____ 9. One way geographers gather information for accurate maps is by studying
A. landforms.
B. photographs taken high above Earth.
C. the grid system.
D. lines of latitude.

____ 10. What two characteristics do geographers study about a place?
A. physical and human
B. latitude and longitude
C. GPS and GIS
D. maps and globes

9

Reading Strategy

Reteach

Have students prepare an outline of the section.

More About the Photos

Arrowheads Arrowheads are known as projectile points. Archaeologists group these projectile points into types that are assigned to a specific cultural group and time period.

Caption Answer Students may note that the arrowhead shows that the society may have hunted or had military strength.

Reading Check Answer

so they are not all used up

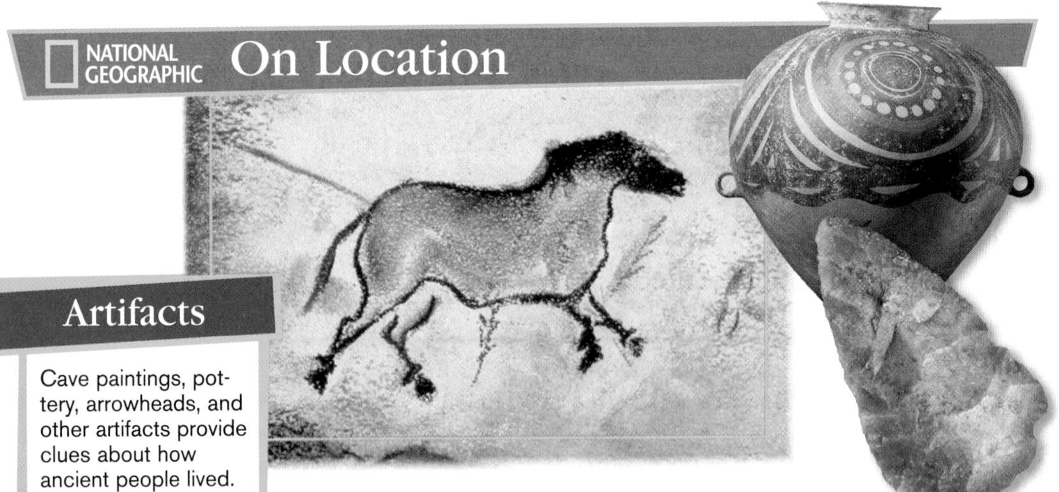

Artifacts

Cave paintings, pottery, arrowheads, and other artifacts provide clues about how ancient people lived.

History What clues can you gather about the society that made this arrowhead?

Uses of Geography

Have you ever gone on a long-distance trip in a car or taken a subway ride? If you used a road map or subway map to figure out where you were going, you were using geography. This is just one of the many uses of geographic information.

Geographic information is used in planning. Government leaders use geographic information to plan new services in their communities. They might plan how to handle disasters or how much new housing to allow in an area. Businesses study population trends to see where people are moving in a region. If people are moving out of an area, for example, a business may decide to close or relocate.

In addition, geographic information helps people make sound decisions. Perhaps a question arises over whether a new building should be constructed. City leaders look at street use to see if the area can handle additional traffic. They make sure the area has the power, water, and sewage systems the building will need.

Finally, geographic information helps people manage resources. Resources such as trees or water can be replaced or renewed. Other natural resources, such as oil or coal, are available only in limited supply. People can use geographic information both to locate more of these limited natural resources and to manage them wisely.

Reading Check **Why do people have to manage resources carefully?**

Clues to Our Past

So far, you have learned about the tools geographers use to study the world and how to think like a geographer. You will use these tools as you read about the people and places of today, as well as learn about the past—from ancient civilizations to modern history. Historians, archaeologists, and anthropologists are scientists who try to unravel

Differentiated Instruction

Meeting Special Needs: Less-proficient Readers To assess students' understanding of the information in the section, have them write one or two sentences that summarize the information for each main head. Sentences should be concise and contain the main idea. Have volunteers share their sentences with the class, and write them on the board. Students should identify the sentences that best explain the main ideas of the section and write them in their notebooks to help them as they study the chapter. L1

Refer to *Inclusion for the Middle School Social Studies Classroom Strategies and Activities* in the TCR.

the mysteries of early times. Like geographers, these scientists also have tools to help them in their work.

Written Records Historians rely mostly on written records to create their stories of the past. For example, they search through diaries, newspapers, and legal documents for information about how people used to live. However, no written records exist for the prehistory of humankind. In fact, *prehistory* means the time before writing was developed. How, then, do we know about ancient times and early humans?

Artifacts and Fossils Much of what is known about ancient people comes from studies by archaeologists and anthropologists. These scientists study past societies by analyzing what people have left behind. They dig up and examine **artifacts**—tools, pottery, paintings, weapons, and other items. They also study the remains of humans, or human **fossils**, to determine how ancient people lived. By examining artifacts such as tools and weapons, for example, scientists may learn that an early society was able to farm and had military strength. By analyzing bones, animal skins, and plant seeds, they are able to piece together what early people ate and what animals they hunted.

✓ **Reading Check** How is prehistory different from history?

Assessment

Defining Terms

1. **Define** geography, landform, environment, Global Positioning System (GPS), geographic information systems (GIS), artifact, fossil.

Recalling Facts

2. **Place** What two kinds of characteristics of a place do geographers study?
3. **Technology** What are the main tools of geography?
4. **Human/Environment Interaction** What are three uses for geography?

Critical Thinking

5. **Understanding Cause and Effect** How have the physical characteristics of your region affected the way people live there?
6. **Categorizing Information** Give five examples of regions. Begin with an area near you that shares common characteristics, then think of larger and larger regions.

Graphic Organizer

7. **Organizing Information** Draw a diagram like this one. In the center, write the name of a place you would like to visit. In the outer ovals, identify the types of geographic information you would like to learn about this place.

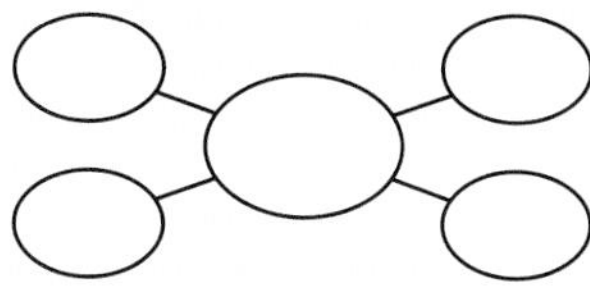

Applying Social Studies Skills

8. **Analyzing Maps** Find Egypt on the map on page RA21 of the **Reference Atlas**. Along what physical feature do you think most Egyptians live? Why? Turn to the population density map of Egypt on page 10 of the **Geography Handbook** to see if you are correct.

Section 1 Assessment

1. The terms are defined in the Glossary.
2. physical, human
3. maps, globes
4. to find a location, planning, making good decisions, using resources wisely
5. Answers will vary. Students may mention landforms, climate, resources, and location near water as affecting people.
6. Answers will vary depending on location. Students may mention their suburb, city, county, state, country, and continent.
7. Students may mention location, natural resources, landforms, climate, and population density.
8. Nile River; because desert covers the rest of the country and water is an important resource

Chapter 1

Section 1, pages 22–27

L1/ELL

Reading Essentials and Study Guide

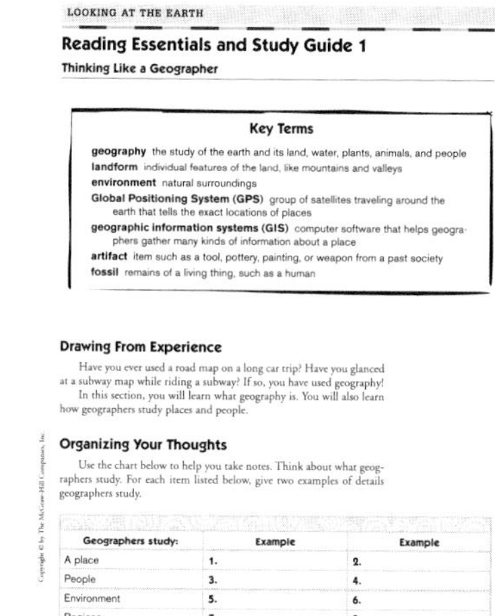

Name ______ Date ______ Class ______

LOOKING AT THE EARTH

Reading Essentials and Study Guide 1

Thinking Like a Geographer

Key Terms

geography the study of the earth and its land, water, plants, animals, and people
landform individual features of the land, like mountains and valleys
environment natural surroundings
Global Positioning System (GPS) group of satellites traveling around the earth that tells the exact locations of places
geographic information systems (GIS) computer software that helps geographers gather many kinds of information about a place
artifact item such as a tool, pottery, painting, or weapon from a past society
fossil remains of a living thing, such as a human

Drawing From Experience

Have you ever used a road map on a long car trip? Have you glanced at a subway map while riding a subway? If so, you have used geography!

In this section, you will learn what geography is. You will also learn how geographers study places and people.

Organizing Your Thoughts

Use the chart below to help you take notes. Think about what geographers study. For each item listed below, give two examples of details geographers study.

Geographers study:	Example	Example
A place	1.	2.
People	3.	4.
Environment	5.	6.
Regions	7.	8.

1

Enrich

Have students research to learn more about the global positioning system. Have them prepare a drawing, diagram, or model showing how the GPS works.

✓ Reading Check Answer

Prehistory is the time before writing was developed.

Close

Reading Strategy

Summarizing Have students create a concept web for the word *geography*. Tell them that their web should include such subcategories as ways of studying places, tools, and uses.

TEACH

Create a map of the area around the school, showing the school building and the main streets. Make five copies of the map. Form students into groups and give each group a copy. Have each group fill in the map with different information. This could include places to eat, parking areas, houses, traffic lights, gas stations, or other important features. Display the different maps on an overhead transparency. **Ask:** **How are these maps like GIS?** *(They display different information about the same area.)* **L1**

More About GIS

One key to GIS is that a computer can create exact copies of the same base map so that the different layers of information can all be stored on the same scale. When two or more sets of data are displayed together, the resulting map can be used reliably.

Interdisciplinary Connections

Technology Salt Lake City sits on a major fault in the earth's crust, creating the danger of an earthquake. Emergency planners used GIS to simulate damage to roads so they could plot the response time of fire and rescue crews.

Making Connections

ART | SCIENCE | CULTURE | TECHNOLOGY

Geographic Information Systems

What if a farmer could save money by applying fertilizer only to the crops that needed it? Today, thanks to computer technology called geographic information systems (GIS), farmers can do just that.

The Technology

Geographic information systems (GIS) use computer software to combine and display a wide range of information about an area. GIS programs start with a map showing a specific location on the earth. This map is then linked with other information about that same place, such as satellite photos, amounts of rainfall, or where houses are located.

Think of geographic information systems as a stack of overhead transparencies. Each transparency shows the same general background but highlights different information. The first transparency may show a base map of an area. Only the borders may appear. The second transparency may show only rivers and highways. The third may highlight mountains and other physical features, buildings, or cities.

In a similar way, GIS technology places layers of information onto a base map. It can then switch each layer of information on or off, allowing data to be viewed in many different ways. In the case of the farmer mentioned above, GIS software combines information about soil type, plant needs, and last year's crop to pinpoint exact areas that need fertilizer.

How It Is Used

GIS technology allows users to quickly pull together data from many different sources and construct maps tailored to specific needs. This helps people analyze past events, predict future possibilities, and make sound decisions.

A person who is deciding where to build a new store can use GIS technology to help select the best location. The process might begin with a list of possible sites. The store owner gathers information about the areas surrounding each place. This could include shoppers' ages, incomes, and educations; where shoppers live; traffic patterns; and other stores in the area. The GIS software then builds a computerized map composed of these layers of information. The store owner can use the information to decide on a new store location.

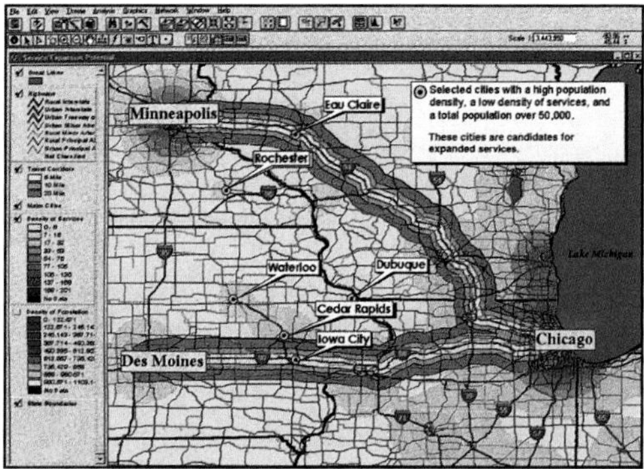

Graphic image created using ArcView® GIS software, and provided courtesy of Environmental Systems Research Institute, Inc.

Making the Connection

1. What is GIS technology?
2. In what ways do GIS programs analyze data?
3. **Asking Questions** What questions would you ask to locate the best place to add a new school to your district?

28 CHAPTER 1

Making the Connection

1. computer software that can combine and display a variety of information about the same area
2. *Possible answer:* GIS layers different types of information on a base map. The user can choose to display different sets of data at the same time, allowing comparisons.
3. Questions should address settlement patterns, population growth patterns, traffic patterns, and land use information for the community.

The Earth in Space

Guide to Reading

Main Idea

Earth has life because of the sun. Earth has different seasons because of the way it tilts and revolves around the sun.

Terms to Know

- solar system
- orbit
- atmosphere
- axis
- revolution
- leap year
- summer solstice
- winter solstice
- equinox

Reading Strategy

Draw a diagram like this one and list three facts about the sun in the first column. In the second column, write how these facts contribute to life on Earth.

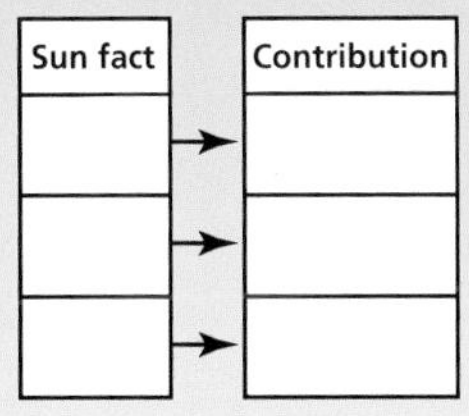

NATIONAL GEOGRAPHIC **Exploring Our World**

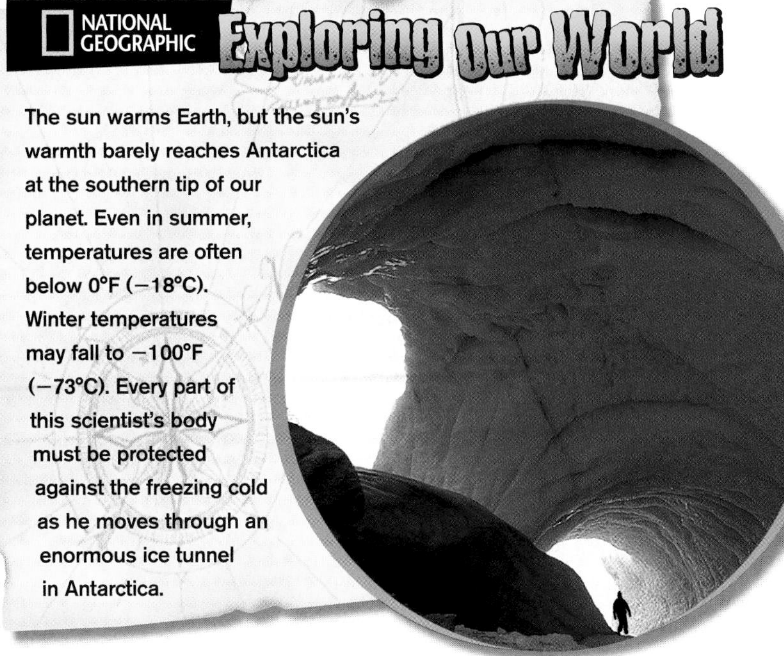

The sun warms Earth, but the sun's warmth barely reaches Antarctica at the southern tip of our planet. Even in summer, temperatures are often below 0°F (−18°C). Winter temperatures may fall to −100°F (−73°C). Every part of this scientist's body must be protected against the freezing cold as he moves through an enormous ice tunnel in Antarctica.

The sun's heat provides life on our planet. Earth, eight other planets, and thousands of smaller bodies all revolve around the sun. Together with the sun, these bodies form the solar system. Look at the diagram of the **solar system** on page 30. As you can see, Earth is the third planet from the sun.

The Solar System

Each planet travels along its own path, or **orbit,** around the sun. The paths they travel are ellipses, which are like stretched-out circles. Each planet takes a different amount of time to complete one full trip around the sun. Earth makes one trip in 365¼ days. Mercury orbits the sun in just 88 days. Far-off Pluto takes almost 250 years!

Planets can be classified into two types—those that are like Earth and those that are like Jupiter. Earthlike planets are Mercury, Venus, Mars, and Pluto. These planets are solid and small. They have few or no moons. They also rotate, or spin, fairly slowly.

The other four planets—Jupiter, Saturn, Neptune, and Uranus—are huge. Uranus, the smallest of the four, is 15 times larger than Earth.

1 Focus

Section Objectives

1. Identify what makes up the solar system.
2. Describe how Earth moves in space.
3. Explain why Earth's seasons change.

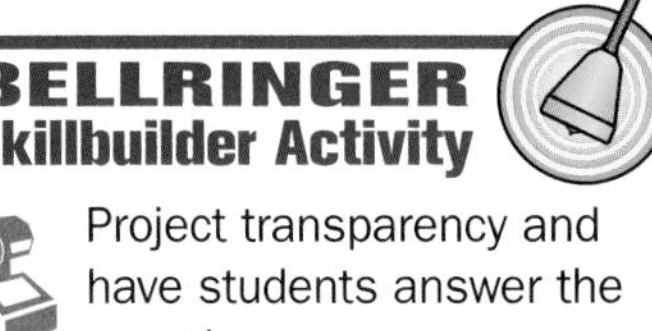

BELLRINGER Skillbuilder Activity

Project transparency and have students answer the question.

Daily Focus Skills Transparency

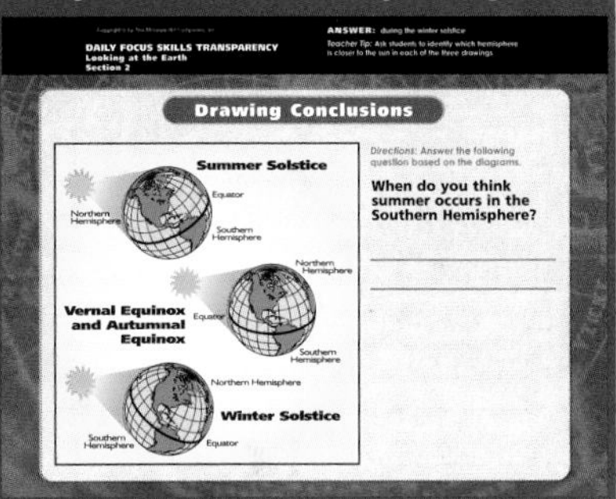

Reading Preview

■ **Activating Prior Knowledge** Have students describe how temperature, precipitation, length of the day, and vegetation differ in your area in the four seasons.

■ **Preteaching Vocabulary** Point out that the terms *solar* and *solstice* are derived from the Latin word for *sun.* Have students find the terms and note how they are related to the sun.

Section Resources

Reproducible Masters

- Reproducible Lesson Plan
- Daily Lecture and Discussion Notes
- Note-taking Guide
- Guided Reading Activity
- Reading Essentials and Study Guide
- Section Quiz

Transparencies

- Daily Focus Skills Transparency

Multimedia

- Vocabulary PuzzleMaker CD-ROM
- Interactive Tutor Self-Assessment CD-ROM
- Presentation Plus! CD-ROM
- ExamView® Pro Testmaker CD-ROM

TEACH

Constructing Models Have students work in small groups to create a model of the solar system. Encourage groups to write a brief description of the movement of the planets. L1

Daily Lecture and Discussion Notes

LOOKING AT THE EARTH

Daily Lecture and Discussion Notes

The Earth in Space

The fifth-largest planet, Earth, orbits the sun at 18.5 miles per second. Earth spins at about 1,000 miles per hour at the Equator. The centrifugal force of this rotation causes Earth to bulge at the Equator and to be flatter at the Poles.

I. The Solar System

A. The **solar system** is made up of the sun, Earth, eight other planets, and thousands of smaller bodies (moons, comets, and asteroids). The planets and smaller bodies revolve around the sun.

B. A planet follows an elliptical path around the sun. This is known as its **orbit.**

C. There are two types of planets—those solid and small like Earth, and those that resemble balls of gas like Jupiter.

D. Earth is surrounded by a layer of air called the **atmosphere.** Nitrogen and oxygen make up about 99 percent of this layer.

E. Earth makes two motions in space. It spins on an imaginary line **(axis)** that runs through the center of Earth between the North and South Poles. It takes 24 hours for Earth to complete one spin on this axis. The other motion is its complete orbit around the sun, or revolution. This **revolution** takes 365¼ days, which accounts for our need for a **leap year** once every four years.

DISCUSSION QUESTION

How does Earth's axis affect you? *(As Earth turns on its axis, different parts of the world are in sunlight or darkness, creating day and night. The tilt of the axis is responsible for the four seasons on Earth.)*

II. The Sun and the Seasons

A. Earth is tilted 23½ degrees on its axis. Because of this, we have seasons as Earth rotates around the sun.

3

Analyzing the Diagram

Answer
Venus and Mars

Skills Practice
What is unusual about Pluto's orbit? *(It crosses the orbit of another planet, Neptune.)*

Solar Eclipse

One of the most spectacular sights in the sky is a solar eclipse. This event takes place when the moon passes between Earth and the sun and covers some or all of the sun. The photograph here shows a total eclipse, when the moon completely blocks the sun. When the moon blocks the sun's light, a large shadow is cast on part of Earth.

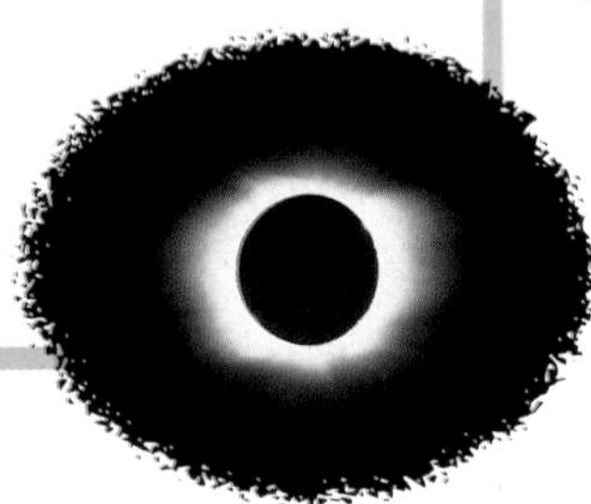

These planets are more like balls of gas than rockier Earthlike planets. They spin rapidly and have many moons. Surrounding each one is a series of rings made of bits of rock and dust.

Sun, Earth, and Moon The sun—about 93 million miles (150 million km) from Earth—is made mostly of intensely hot gases. Reactions that occur inside the sun make it as hot as 27 million degrees Fahrenheit (about 15 million degrees Celsius). As a result, the sun gives off light and warmth. Life on Earth could not exist without the sun.

The layer of air surrounding Earth—the atmosphere—also supports life. This cushion of gases measures about 1,000 miles (1,609 km) thick. Nitrogen and oxygen form about 99 percent of the atmosphere, with other gases making up the rest.

Humans and animals need oxygen to breathe. The atmosphere is important in other ways, too. This protective layer holds in enough of the sun's heat to make life possible, just as a greenhouse keeps in enough heat to protect plants. Without this protection, Earth would be too cold for most living things. At the same time, the atmosphere also reflects some heat back into space. As a result, Earth does not become too warm. Finally, the atmosphere shields living things. It screens out some rays from the sun that are dangerous. You will learn more about the atmosphere in Chapter 2.

Earth's nearest neighbor in the solar system is its moon. The moon orbits Earth, taking about 30 days to complete each trip. A cold, rocky sphere, the moon has no water and no atmosphere. The moon also gives off no light of its own. When you see the moon shining, it is actually reflecting light from the sun.

The Solar System

Analyzing the Diagram

Earth and eight other planets in our solar system travel around the sun.

Movement Between which two planets' orbits is Earth's orbit?

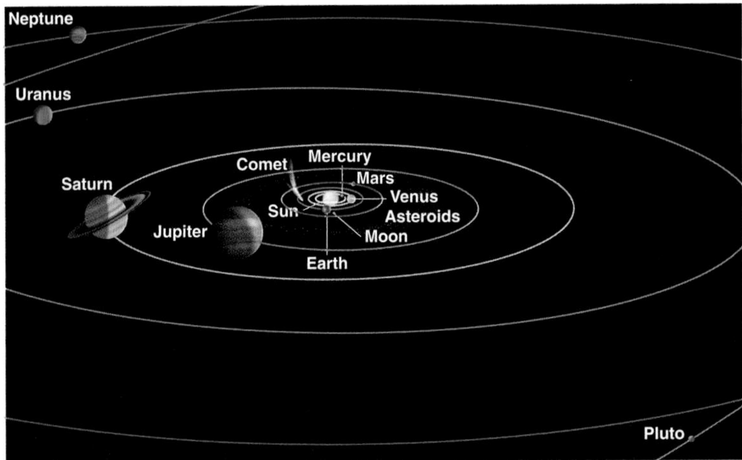

Reading Strategy Reading the Text

Previewing Students can quickly gain an understanding of what the text will be about by looking over features such as headings and subheadings, charted information, illustrations, captions, and graphics. Students should preview the section by looking at these elements before they begin reading so that they know what they will be reading about. L1

*Use the **Reading Skills Handbook** for more reading strategies.*

Seasons

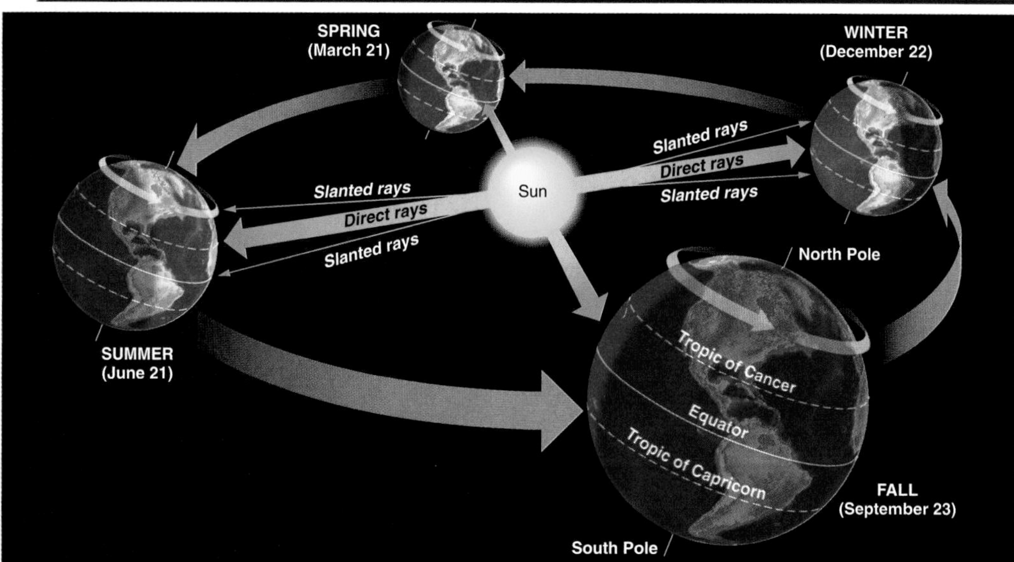

Analyzing the Diagram

Because Earth is tilted, different areas receive direct rays from the sun at different times of the year.

Movement How does this fact cause changes in seasons?

Earth's Movement Like all the planets, Earth rotates, or spins, on its axis. The **axis** is an imaginary line that runs through Earth's center between the North and South Poles. Earth takes 24 hours to finish one complete spin on its axis. As a result, one day is 24 hours. As Earth turns, different parts of the planet are in sunlight or in darkness. The part facing the sun has day, and the part facing away has night.

Earth has another motion, too. The planet makes one **revolution**, or complete orbit around the sun, in 365¼ days. This period is what we define as one year. Every four years, the extra one-fourths of a day are combined and added to the calendar as February 29. A year that contains one of these extra days is called a **leap year**.

✓Reading Check How does Earth's orbit affect you?

The Sun and the Seasons

Earth is tilted 23½ degrees on its axis. As a result, seasons change as Earth makes its year-long orbit around the sun. To see why this happens, look at the four globes in the diagram above. Notice how sunlight falls directly on the northern or southern halves of Earth at different times of the year. Direct rays from the sun bring more warmth than the slanted rays. When the people in a hemisphere receive those direct rays from the sun, they enjoy the warmth of summer. When they receive only indirect rays, they experience winter, which is colder.

Chapter 1

Section 2, pages 29–32

L1/ELL

Guided Reading Activity

Name ____ Date ____ Class ____

LOOKING AT THE EARTH

Guided Reading Activity 2

The Earth in Space

DIRECTIONS: Filling in the Blanks Reading the section and completing the sentences below will help you learn more about Earth. Refer to your textbook to fill in the blanks.

Earth, eight other planets, thousands of smaller bodies, and the (1) ____ form the (2) ____. The planets travel in paths called (3) ____ around the (4) ____. The Earthlike planets are Mercury, (5) ____, Mars, and Pluto. They are solid and ... few or no (7) ____.

Analyzing the Diagram

Answer
Sun's direct rays bring warmth and summer; indirect rays result in cold, or winter.

Skills Practice
What does September 23 mark in the Northern Hemisphere? *(fall)* In the Southern Hemisphere? *(spring)*

✓ Reading Check Answer

Earth's orbit lasts a year and causes the seasons.

Assign Section 2 Assessment as homework or an in-class activity.

Have students use the Interactive Tutor Self-Assessment CD-ROM to review Section 2.

Differentiated Instruction

Meeting Special Needs: Kinesthetic Have students act out the earth's revolution around the sun and the subsequent change of seasons. Choose a student to stand in the center of that space with a flashlight. Have another student—holding a large ball that represents the earth—stand at the outer edge of a circle. Remind the student to tilt the ball slightly. Have the student in the center shine the light on the ball and ask students to identify which half—upper or lower—gets the most light. Have the student holding the ball move to three other positions, representing the three other seasons. **L1**

Refer to *Inclusion for the Middle School Social Studies Classroom Strategies and Activities* in the TCR.

Chapter 1

Section 2, pages 29–32

L2

Section Quiz

Name ______ Date ______ Class ______

LOOKING AT THE EARTH

Score

Section 2 Quiz

The Earth in Space

DIRECTIONS: Matching Match each item in Column A with the items in Column B. Write the correct letters in the blanks. *(10 points each)*

COLUMN A	COLUMN B
A. orbit	____ 1. the first day of summer and of winter
B. solstice	____ 2. when day and night are of equal length in both the Northern and Southern Hemispheres
C. the solar system	____ 3. a planet's path around the sun
D. a revolution	____ 4. the earth's complete trip around the sun
E. equinox	____ 5. the sun, planets, and other smaller bodies

Reading Check Answer

spring, autumn

L1/ELL

Reading Essentials and Study Guide

Name ______ Date ______ Class ______

LOOKING AT THE EARTH

Reading Essentials and Study Guide 2

The Earth in Space

Key Terms

solar system group of planets and other bodies that revolve around the sun
orbit path a planet follows in revolving around the sun
atmosphere layer of air surrounding Earth
axis imaginary line that runs through Earth's center between the North and South Poles
revolution one complete orbit of a planet around the sun
leap year a year that has an extra day; occurs every fourth year
summer solstice the day in June when the sun appears directly over the ... the day in the Northern Hemisphere with the most hours

Enrich

Have students research attempts to explore the solar system.

Close

Have students draw a diagram of the earth's two types of movement, explaining how they cause day and night and the seasons.

Solstices and Equinoxes Four days in the year have special names because of the position of the sun in relation to Earth. These days mark the beginnings of the four seasons. On or about June 21, the North Pole is tilted toward the sun. On noon of this day, the sun appears directly overhead at the line of latitude called the Tropic of Cancer (23½°N latitude). In the Northern Hemisphere, this day is the **summer solstice,** the day with the most hours of sunlight and the fewest hours of darkness. It is the beginning of summer—but only in the Northern Hemisphere. Remember that the Northern Hemisphere includes everything north of the Equator. Everything south of the Equator is in the Southern Hemisphere. In the Southern Hemisphere, that same day is the day with the fewest hours of sunlight and marks the beginning of winter.

Six months later—on or about December 22—the North Pole is tilted away from the sun. At noon, the sun's direct rays strike the line of latitude known as the Tropic of Capricorn (23½°S latitude). In the Northern Hemisphere, this day is the **winter solstice**—the day with the fewest hours of sunlight. This same day, though, marks the beginning of summer in the Southern Hemisphere.

Spring and autumn begin midway between the two solstices. These are the **equinoxes,** when day and night are of equal length in both hemispheres. On or about March 21, the vernal equinox (spring) occurs. On or about September 23, the autumnal equinox occurs. On both of these days, the noon sun shines directly over the Equator.

Reading Check **Which seasons begin on the two equinoxes?**

Section 2 Assessment

Defining Terms

1. **Define** solar system, orbit, atmosphere, axis, revolution, leap year, summer solstice, winter solstice, equinox.

Recalling Facts

2. **Region** Which bodies make up the solar system?
3. **Science** List two gases in the atmosphere.
4. **Movement** Which two motions does Earth make in space?

Critical Thinking

5. **Analyzing Information** How does the position of Earth determine whether a day is one of the solstice or equinox days?
6. **Summarizing Information** In a paragraph, describe why the seasons change.

Graphic Organizer

7. **Organizing Information** Draw two diagrams like those below. First, list the effects of Earth's rotation on human, plant, and animal life. Then list the effects if Earth were to stop rotating.

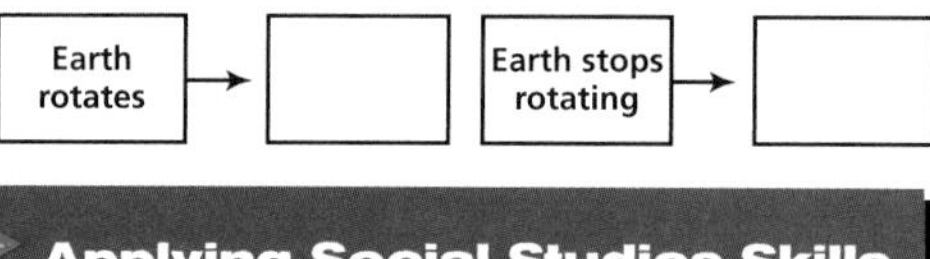

Applying Social Studies Skills

8. **Analyzing Diagrams** Look at the diagram on page 31. When the sun's direct rays hit the Tropic of Capricorn, what season is it in the Northern Hemisphere?

32

Section 2 Assessment

1. The terms are defined in the Glossary.
2. the sun, Earth, eight other planets, thousands of smaller bodies including Earth's moon
3. nitrogen, oxygen
4. rotates on its axis and revolves around the sun
5. If the sun is directly over one of the tropics at noon, the day is a solstice. If it is directly over the Equator at noon, the day is an equinox.
6. Winter occurs where a part of Earth is tilted away from the sun. Summer occurs where that part of Earth is tilted toward the sun. Autumn and spring occur midway between summer and winter.
7. *Possible answers:* Earth's rotation brings light to all areas of Earth. If Earth stopped rotating, only one side would receive light, and plants and animals would not be able to live on the other side.
8. winter

Social Studies Skill

Using a Map Key

To understand what a map is showing, you must read the **map key,** or legend. The map key explains the meaning of special colors, symbols, and lines on the map.

Learning the Skill

Colors in the map key may represent different elevations or heights of land, climate areas, or languages. Lines may stand for rivers, streets, or boundaries.

Maps also have a compass rose showing directions. The cardinal directions are north, south, east, and west. North and south are the directions of the North and South Poles. If you stand facing north, east is the direction to your right. West is the direction to your left. The compass rose might also show intermediate directions, or those that fall between the cardinal directions. For example, the intermediate direction *northeast* falls between north and east. To use a map key, follow these steps:

- Read the map title.
- Read the map key to find out what special information it gives.
- Find examples of each map key color, line, or symbol on the map.
- Use the compass rose to identify the four cardinal directions.

Practicing the Skill

Look at the map of Washington, D.C., below to answer the following questions.

1. What does the red square represent?
2. What does the blue square represent?
3. Does the Washington Monument lie east or west of the Lincoln Memorial?
4. From the White House, in what direction would you go to get to the Capitol?

Applying the Skill

Find a map in a newspaper or magazine. Use the map key to explain three things the map is showing.

GO TO Practice key skills with **Glencoe Skillbuilder Interactive Workbook, Level 1.**

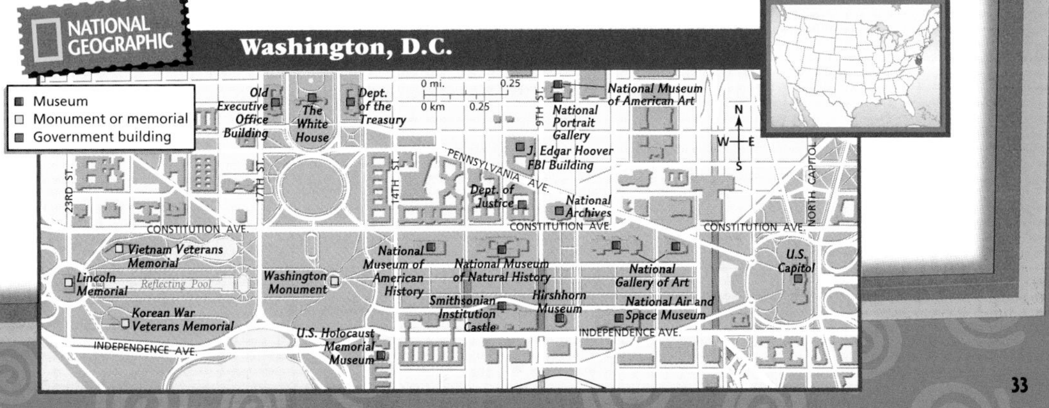

Social Studies Skill

Teach

Draw a map of the classroom on the board. Draw the perimeter of the room, and then add windows, doors, desks, bookcases, and other features. Before adding each feature, ask students to suggest how it might be represented on the map. *(with different colors or symbols)* Record the suggestions on a key next to the map. Be sure to include a compass rose. Working from the map, have students answer such questions as: **How many windows does the room have? How many desks?** Then direct students to read the feature and answer the questions. L1

Additional Skills Practice

1. **How are monuments and memorials shown on the map?** *(by yellow squares)*
2. **What direction is the top of the map?** *(north)*
3. **On what street is the Hirshhorn Museum located?** *(Independence Avenue)*

Additional Skills Resources

 Chapter Skills Review

 Building Geography Skills for Life

GLENCOE TECHNOLOGY

 **Skillbuilder Interactive Workbook CD-ROM, Level 1**

This interactive CD-ROM reinforces student mastery of essential social studies skills.

Practicing the Skill Answers

1. government building
2. museum
3. east
4. southeast

Applying the Skill

Students' responses should demonstrate correct interpretations of the map key in question.

Chapter 1

Section 3, pages 34–38

1 Focus

Section Objectives

1. Describe the layers found within the earth.
2. Discuss the forces that change the earth's surface.

BELLRINGER
Skillbuilder Activity

Project transparency and have students answer the question.

Daily Focus Skills Transparency

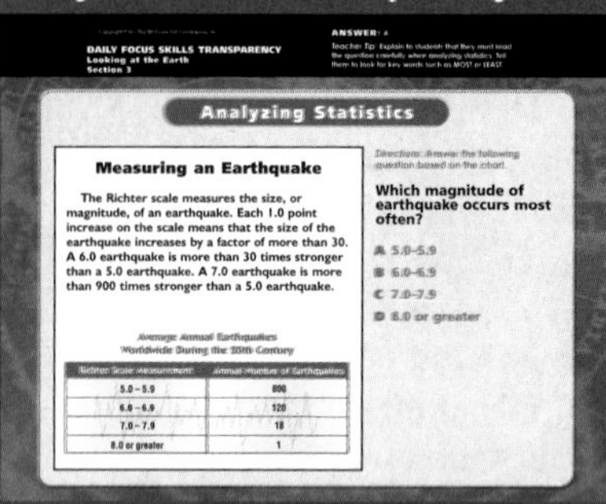

ANSWER: A

Teacher Tip: Explain to students that they must read the question carefully when analyzing statistics. Tell them to look for key words such as MOST or LEAST.

DAILY FOCUS SKILLS TRANSPARENCY
Looking at the Earth
Section 3

Analyzing Statistics

Measuring an Earthquake

The Richter scale measures the size, or magnitude, of an earthquake. Each 1.0 point increase on the scale means that the size of the earthquake increases by a factor of more than 30. A 6.0 earthquake is more than 30 times stronger than a 5.0 earthquake. A 7.0 earthquake is more than 900 times stronger than a 5.0 earthquake.

Average Annual Earthquakes Worldwide During the 20th Century

Richter Scale Measurement	Annual Number of Earthquakes
5.0–5.9	800
6.0–6.9	120
7.0–7.9	18
8.0 or greater	1

Directions: Answer the following question based on the chart.

Which magnitude of earthquake occurs most often?

A 5.0–5.9
B 6.0–6.9
C 7.0–7.9
D 8.0 or greater

Reading Preview

Activating Prior Knowledge Bring a baseball to class. Explain to students that the earth is like a baseball. It has an outer shell, like the ball's stitched covering, and two inner sections that support it.

Preteaching Vocabulary Explain that *crust* and *core* both refer to parts of the earth. **Ask:** What other objects have these features? *(pie, apple)* Have them guess at the meaning of these words regarding the earth.

Guide to Reading

Main Idea

Forces both inside the earth and on its surface affect the shape of the land.

Terms to Know

- core
- mantle
- magma
- crust
- continent
- plate tectonics
- earthquake
- tsunami
- fault
- weathering
- erosion
- glacier

Reading Strategy

Create a chart like this one. Write three forces that change the shape of the land. Then write three effects these forces can have on Earth.

Forces	Effects
→	
→	
→	

Section 3

Forces Shaping the Earth

NATIONAL GEOGRAPHIC **Exploring Our World**

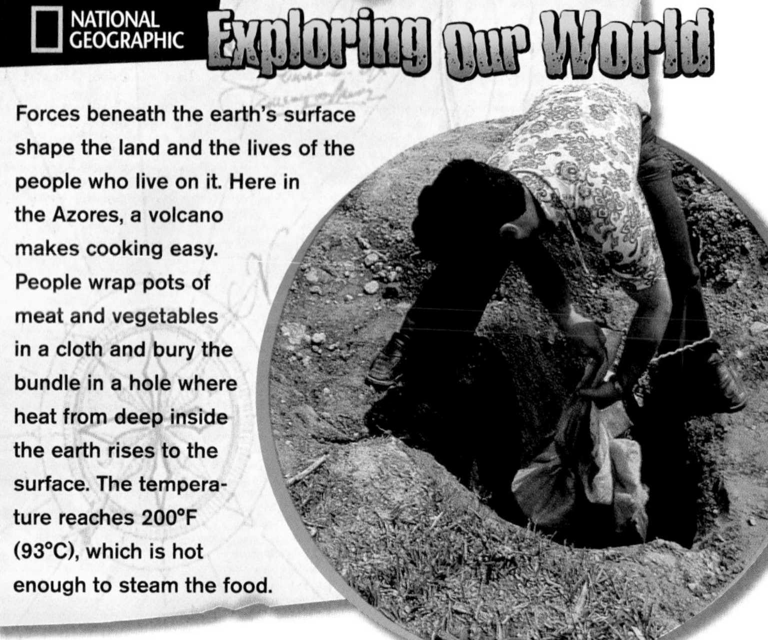

Forces beneath the earth's surface shape the land and the lives of the people who live on it. Here in the Azores, a volcano makes cooking easy. People wrap pots of meat and vegetables in a cloth and bury the bundle in a hole where heat from deep inside the earth rises to the surface. The temperature reaches 200°F (93°C), which is hot enough to steam the food.

Thousands of miles beneath your feet, the earth's heat has turned metal into liquid. You may not feel these forces, but what lies inside the earth affects what lies on top. Mountains, deserts, and other landscapes were formed over millions of years by forces acting below the earth's surface—and they are still changing today. Some forces work slowly and show no results for thousands of years. Others appear suddenly and have dramatic, and sometimes very destructive, effects.

Inside the Earth

Scientists have only been able to study the top layer of the earth, but have developed a picture of what lies inside. They have found that Earth has three layers—the core, the mantle, and the crust. Have you ever seen a cantaloupe cut in half? The earth's core is like the center of a cantaloupe, where you find the seeds. The mantle is like the part of the fruit that you eat, between the center and the rind, or outer

Section Resources

Reproducible Masters

- Reproducible Lesson Plan
- Daily Lecture and Discussion Notes
- Note-taking Guide
- Guided Reading Activity
- Reading Essentials and Study Guide
- Section Quiz

Transparencies

- Daily Focus Skills Transparency

Multimedia

- Vocabulary PuzzleMaker CD-ROM
- Interactive Tutor Self-Assessment CD-ROM
- Presentation Plus! CD-ROM
- ExamView® Pro Testmaker CD-ROM

layer. The crust is like the melon's rind. Let us look closer at Earth's three layers.

In the center of the earth is a dense **core** of hot iron mixed with other metals and rock. The inner core is solid, but the outer core is so hot that the metal has melted into liquid. Surrounding the core is the **mantle,** a layer of rock about 1,800 miles (2,897 km) thick. Like the core, the mantle also has two parts. The section nearest the core remains solid, but the rock in the outer mantle sometimes melts. If you have seen photographs of an active volcano, then you have seen this melted rock, called **magma.** It flows to the surface during a volcanic eruption.

The uppermost layer of the earth, the **crust,** is relatively thin. It reaches only 31 to 62 miles (50 to 100 km) deep. The crust includes the ocean floors. It also includes seven massive land areas known as **continents.** The crust is thinnest on the ocean floor. It is thicker below the continents. Turn to the map on page 41 to see where the earth's seven continents are located.

✓Reading Check Which layer of the earth is thinnest?

NATIONAL GEOGRAPHIC **Earth's Layers**

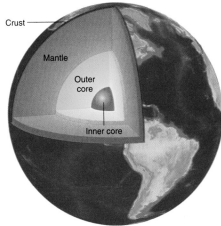

Crust
Mantle
Outer core
Inner core

Analyzing the Diagram

Hot rock and metal—some of it liquid—fill the center of the earth.

Region What is the innermost layer inside the earth called? In which layer do you find the continents?

Forces Beneath the Earth's Crust

You have probably watched science shows about earthquakes and volcanoes. You have probably also seen news on television discussing the destruction caused by earthquakes. These events result from forces at work inside the earth.

Plate Movements Scientists have developed a theory called **plate tectonics** to explain the earth's structure. This theory states that the crust is not an unbroken shell but consists of plates, or huge slabs of rock, that move. The plates float on top of liquid rock just below the earth's crust. They move—but often in different directions. Oceans and continents sit on these gigantic plates, as shown on page 36.

Have you ever noticed that the eastern part of **South America** seems to fit into the western side of **Africa?** That is because these two continents were once joined together in a landmass that scientists call **Pangaea.** Millions of years ago, however, the continents moved apart. Tectonic activity caused them to move. The plates are still moving today, but they move so slowly that you do not feel it. The plate under the Pacific Ocean moves to the west at the rate of about 4 inches (10 cm) per year. That is about the same rate that a man's beard grows. The plate along the western edge of South America moves east at the rate of about 1.8 inches (5 cm) per year. That is a little faster than your fingernails grow. Turn to page 45 to see what Pangaea looked like before and after it experienced this movement, known as continental drift.

Chapter 1

Section 3, pages 34–38

TEACH

Reading Strategy

Outlining Tell students that the hierarchical structure of the text can help them remember the content. Have them create outlines using the headings and subheadings, and then add important notes under each subheading. L1

Daily Lecture and Discussion Notes

LOOKING AT THE EARTH

Daily Lecture and Discussion Notes

Forces Shaping the Earth

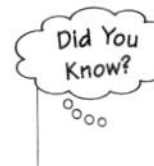

The ancient Greeks knew the size of the earth, but it was not until the turn of the twentieth century that scientists determined that our planet is made up of three main layers. This layered structure can be compared to that of a boiled egg. The crust, or the outermost layer, is rigid and very thin compared with the other two. Like the shell of an egg, the earth's crust is brittle and can break.

I. Inside the Earth

A. The inside of the earth is made up of three layers. The **core** consists of hot iron mixed with other metals and rock.

B. The **mantle** is a layer of rock surrounding the core.

rock called **magma** flows to the earth's surface.

✓Reading Check Answer

the crust

Analyzing the Diagram

Answers

core, crust

Skills Practice

What causes volcanoes? *(when two plates move against each other and the hot magma inside the earth's mantle erupts to the surface)*

Reading Strategy — Reading the Text

Visualizing As students read the information about plate tectonics, suggest that they visualize how plates move in different ways (pull away, collide, move against). Tell students to form an image in their minds about each type of movement after they read the text. Using imagery will help students recall the different types of plate movement more easily. L1

*Use the **Reading Skills Handbook** for more reading strategies.*

Building Skills

Drawing Conclusions Have students read "When Plates Meet" with these questions in mind: **What areas are more likely to experience earthquakes?** *(areas where plates meet)* **What areas are more likely to experience tsunamis?** *(coastal areas)*

Analyzing the Diagram

Answer
Most earthquakes and volcanoes occur along plate boundaries.

Skills Practice
What is the name of an area where two plates are pulling apart? *(fault)*

L1/ELL

Guided Reading Activity

Name ______ Date ______ Class ______

LOOKING AT THE EARTH

Guided Reading Activity 3

Forces Shaping the Earth

DIRECTIONS: Outlining Reading the section and completing the outline below will help you learn more about the earth's structure. Refer to your textbook to fill in the blanks.

I. The inside of the earth has ______ layers.
 A. The ______ is the center of the earth.
  1. The very center is ______.
  2. The ______ ______ is so hot that the metal is liquid.
 B. The ______ surrounds the core.
  1. The part nearest the core is ______.
  ...ter section ______.

Tectonic Plate Boundaries

NATIONAL GEOGRAPHIC

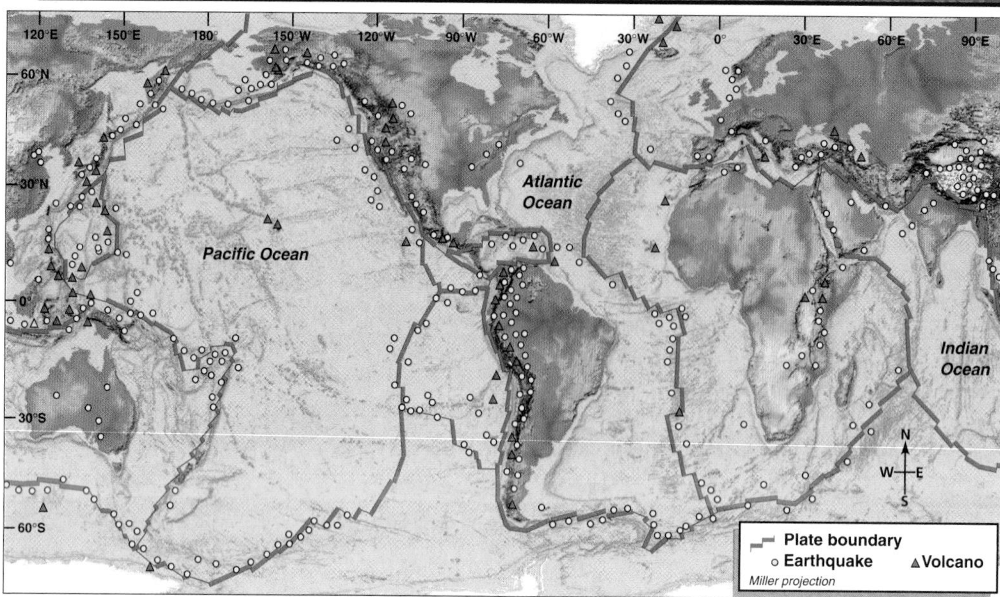

Analyzing the Diagram

Most of North America sits on one plate.

Region **What pattern do you see among plate boundaries, earthquakes, and volcanoes?**

When Plates Meet The movements of the earth's plates have actually shaped the surface of the earth. Sometimes the plates spread, or pull away from each other. That type of tectonic action separated South America and Africa millions of years ago. Sometimes, though, the plates push against each other. When this happens, one of three events occurs, depending on what kinds of plates are involved.

If two continental plates smash into each other, the collision produces high mountain ranges. This kind of collision produced the **Himalaya** in South Asia.

If a continental plate and an ocean plate move against each other, the thicker continental plate slides over the thinner ocean plate. The downward force of the lower plate causes molten rock to build up. Then, as magma, it erupts to form volcanic mountains. Another result may occur from the pressure that builds up between the two sliding plates. This pressure may cause one plate to move suddenly. The result is an **earthquake,** or a violent and sudden movement of the earth's crust.

Earthquakes can be very damaging to both physical structures and human lives. They can collapse buildings, destroy bridges, and break apart underground water or gas pipes. Undersea earthquakes can cause huge waves called **tsunamis** (tsu•NAH•mees). These waves may reach as high as 98 feet (30 m). Such waves can cause severe flooding of coastal towns.

Differentiated Instruction

Meeting Special Needs: English Learners Tell students that they can use word play to help them remember concepts. For instance, the initials *C-2M-2C* can help them remember the structure of the earth: the core (the first *C*) lies beneath the mantle that holds magma (the two *Ms*), which lies beneath the crust where the continents are found (the two *Cs*). Have the class see if they can think of a mnemonic device for remembering the three forces that cause erosion. **ELL**

Refer to *Inclusion for the Middle School Social Studies Classroom Strategies and Activities* in the TCR.

Sometimes two plates do not meet head-on but move alongside each other. To picture this, put your hands together and then move them in opposite directions. When this action occurs in the earth, the two plates slide against each other. This movement creates **faults,** or cracks in the earth's crust. Violent earthquakes can happen near these faults. In 1988, for example, an earthquake struck the country of Armenia. About 25,000 people were killed, and another 500,000 lost their homes. One of the most famous faults in the United States is the **San Andreas Fault** in California. The earth's movement along this fault caused a severe earthquake in San Francisco in 1906 and another less serious earthquake in 1989.

✓ Reading Check **What happens when two continental plates collide?**

Forces Shaping Landforms

The forces under the earth's crust that move tectonic plates cause volcanoes and earthquakes to change the earth's landforms. Once formed, however, these landforms will continue to change because of forces that work on the earth's surface.

Weathering **Weathering** is the process of breaking surface rock into boulders, gravel, sand, and soil. Water and frost, chemicals, and even plants cause weathering. Water seeps into cracks of rocks and then freezes. As it freezes, the ice expands and splits the rock. Sometimes entire sides of cliffs fall off because frost has wedged the rock apart. Chemicals, too, cause weathering when acids in air pollution mix with rain and fall back to the earth. The chemicals eat away the surfaces of stone structures and natural rocks. Even tiny seeds that fall into cracks can spread out roots, causing huge boulders to eventually break apart.

Architecture

In earthquake-prone parts of the world, engineers design new buildings to stand up to tremors, or shaking of the earth. Flexible structures allow buildings to sway rather than break apart. Placing a building on pads or rollers cushions the structure from the motion of the ground. Some so-called intelligent buildings automatically respond to tremors, shifting their weight or tightening and loosening joints.

Looking Closer **How can studying earthquake-damaged buildings help designers improve future construction?**

San Francisco, California, 1989 ▶

Chapter 1

Section 3, pages 34–38

Assess

Assign Section 3 Assessment as homework or an in-class activity.

Have students use the Interactive Tutor Self-Assessment CD-ROM to review Section 3.

L2

Section Quiz

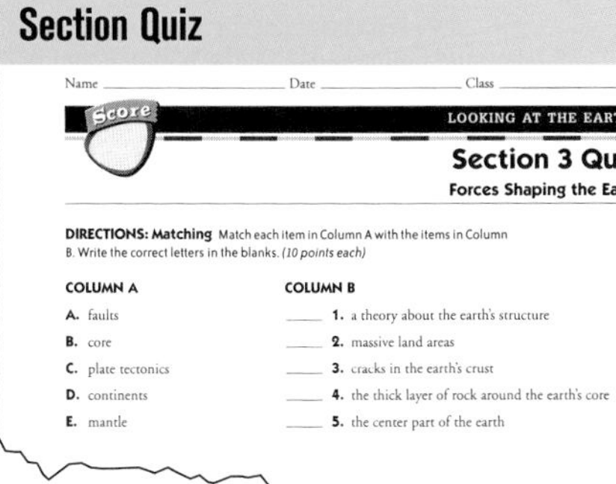

Name ______ Date ______ Class ______

Score

LOOKING AT THE EARTH

Section 3 Quiz

Forces Shaping the Earth

DIRECTIONS: Matching Match each item in Column A with the items in Column B. Write the correct letters in the blanks. *(10 points each)*

COLUMN A	COLUMN B
A. faults	____ 1. a theory about the earth's structure
B. core	____ 2. massive land areas
C. plate tectonics	____ 3. cracks in the earth's crust
D. continents	____ 4. the thick layer of rock around the earth's core
E. mantle	____ 5. the center part of the earth

✓ Reading Check Answer

The collision produces high mountain ranges.

Answer by helping them see how to make structures that stand up to tremors

Ask students: **What areas of the world would especially need to study these building techniques?** *(areas near where tectonic plates meet)*

Critical Thinking Activity

Identifying Central Issues Have students identify the characteristics of cities and towns. Have them think in terms of how many people live in the area, what kind of emergency facilities (such as hospitals and fire and rescue teams) the area has, what kinds of buildings there are, and how many underground materials such as pipes and wires the area would have. As they make suggestions, write the characteristics on the board. After the list is compiled, have students predict the damage that might be caused if a severe earthquake struck. Ask them to suggest steps government officials might take to prepare for such a disaster. L2

EE2 Places and Regions: Standard 5

Reading Check Answer

water and frost, chemicals, and plants

L1/ELL

Reading Essentials and Study Guide

Name ______ Date ______ Class ______

LOOKING AT THE EARTH

Reading Essentials and Study Guide 3

Forces Shaping the Earth

Key Terms

core center of the earth that is solid metal and rock surrounded by hot liquid metal
mantle layer of solid and melted rock surrounding the earth's core
magma melted rock from the earth's mantle that flows to the earth's surface during volcanic eruptions
crust outer layer of the earth
continent one of the seven major land areas of the earth
plate tectonics theory that the earth's crust is made up of huge, moving plates of rock
earthquake violent and sudden movement of the earth's crust
tsunami huge wave caused by undersea earthquakes
fault crack in the earth's crust
weathering the breaking down of surface rocks into smaller pieces by water, frost, chemicals, and plants
erosion the moving or wearing away of weathered material by water, wind, and ice
glacier giant sheet of ice

Drawing From Experience

Have you ever picked up rocks along a stream? Were many of them smooth? Did you wonder how they got that way?

In the last section, you learned about the sun, planets, and seasons. This section describes forces inside and on top of the earth. These forces shape the land.

Organizing Your Thoughts

Use the diagram on the next page to help you take notes. Name the layers of the earth. Some layers have two parts. Write what each layer is

9. Give an example of one of the earth's forces that can destroy things.

CLOSE

Have students prepare an annotated diagram that explains the structure of the earth, the movement of plates, or the forces shaping the surface of the earth.

Erosion Erosion is the process of wearing away or moving weathered material. Water, wind, and ice are the greatest factors that erode, or wear away, surface material. Rain and moving water in oceans, rivers, and streams can erode even the hardest stone over time. Rainwater that works its way to streams and rivers picks up and moves soil and sand. These particles make the river water similar to a giant scrub brush that grinds away at riverbanks and any other surface in the water's path.

Wind is also a major cause of erosion as it lifts weathered soil and sand. The areas that lose soil often become unable to grow crops and support life. The areas that receive the windblown soil often benefit from the additional nutrients to the land. When wind carries sand, however, it acts like sandpaper. Rock and other structures are carved into smooth shapes.

The third cause of erosion is ice. Giant, slow-moving sheets of ice are called glaciers. Forming high in mountains, glaciers change the land as they inch over it. Similar to windstorms, glaciers act like sandpaper as they pick up and carry rocks down the mountainside, grinding smooth everything beneath them. Some glaciers are thousands of feet thick. The weight and pressure of thousands of feet of ice also cut deep valleys at the mountain's base.

Reading Check List three things that can cause weathering.

Assessment

Defining Terms

1. **Define** core, mantle, magma, crust, continent, plate tectonics, earthquake, tsunami, fault, weathering, erosion, glacier.

Recalling Facts

2. **Region** What are the three layers of the earth?
3. **Movement** In what three ways can tectonic plates move?
4. **Science** What are the three greatest factors that cause erosion?

Critical Thinking

5. **Making Comparisons** How does water play a role in the processes of weathering and erosion?
6. **Understanding Cause and Effect** How does erosion hurt some areas yet benefit others?

Graphic Organizer

7. **Organizing Information** Draw a diagram like this one, then label the inner arrows with inside forces that shape landforms. Label the outer arrows with surface forces that change the earth's landforms.

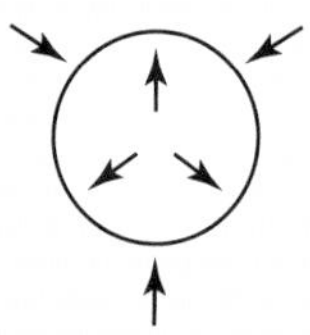

Applying Social Studies Skills

8. **Analyzing Diagrams** Look at the diagram of tectonic plate boundaries on page 36. Why might it be a problem that many of the world's people live along the western edge of the Pacific Ocean?

38 CHAPTER 1

Section 3 Assessment

1. The terms are defined in the Glossary.
2. core, mantle, crust
3. Two plates can collide, one can move over the other, or they can move against each other sideways.
4. wind, water, ice
5. Water seeps into rock, then freezes and expands and splits the rock. Water can also carry away the weathered rock in erosion.
6. Wind can blow nutrient-rich soils from one place to another. The place that receives the soils will benefit.
7. *Inside arrows:* plate movements, volcanoes, earthquakes; *Outside arrows:* water, wind, ice
8. because the area is likely to have many earthquakes

Section 4 Landforms and Waterways

Guide to Reading

Main Idea

Landforms in all their variety affect how people live.

Terms to Know

- elevation
- plain
- plateau
- isthmus
- peninsula
- island
- continental shelf
- trench
- strait
- channel
- delta

Reading Strategy

Draw a diagram like this one. In each of the surrounding circles, write the name of a landform and a fact about it.

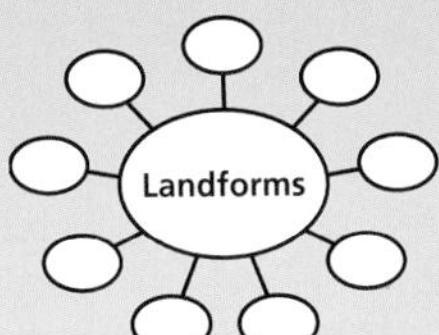

NATIONAL GEOGRAPHIC **Exploring Our World**

Mountains and other landforms are usually formed by forces under the earth's crust. Yet some landforms are not created by the earth's forces—they are made by animals. Here, off Australia's northeast coast, coral and algae have joined together underwater, creating the Great Barrier Reef. They worked hard—the reef stretches more than 1,250 miles (2,012 km).

The earth's land surface consists of seven continents—North America, South America, Europe, Africa, Asia, Australia, and Antarctica. All have a variety of landforms—even icy Antarctica.

Types of Landforms

Look at the illustration on pages 14–15 of the Geography Handbook. Notice the many different forms that the land may take. Which ones are familiar to you? Which ones are new to you?

On Land Mountains are huge towers of rock formed by the collision of the earth's tectonic plates or by volcanoes. Some mountains may be a few thousand feet high. Others can soar higher than 20,000 feet (6,096 m). The world's tallest mountain is **Mt. Everest,** located in South Asia's Himalaya mountain ranges. It towers at 29,035 feet (8,850 m)—nearly 5.5 miles (8.9 km) high.

Section Resources

Reproducible Masters

- Reproducible Lesson Plan
- Daily Lecture and Discussion Notes
- Note-taking Guide
- Guided Reading Activity
- Reading Essentials and Study Guide
- Section Quiz

Transparencies

- Daily Focus Skills Transparency
- In-text Map Transparency

Multimedia

- Vocabulary PuzzleMaker CD-ROM
- Interactive Tutor Self-Assessment CD-ROM
- Presentation Plus! CD-ROM
- ExamView® Pro Testmaker CD-ROM
- MindJogger Videoquiz

1 Focus

Section Objectives

1. Describe the earth's major landforms.
2. Explain how landforms affect where people live.

Project transparency and have students answer the question.

Daily Focus Skills Transparency

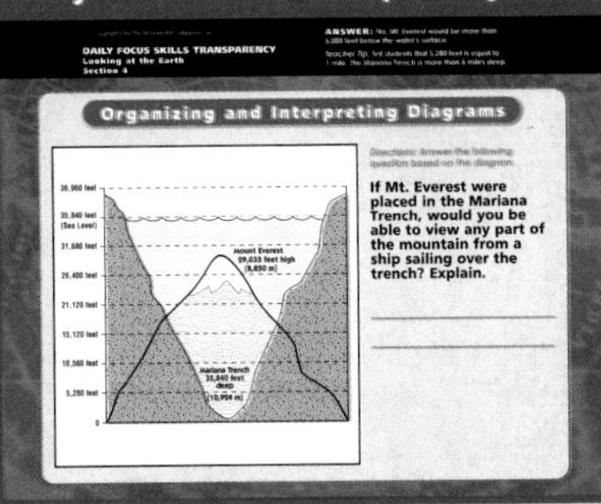

Reading Preview

- **Activating Prior Knowledge** Have students give examples of landforms that they know, such as Mt. Everest and the Great Plains.
- **Preteaching Vocabulary** Point out to students that some words can be learned in pairs. For instance, a *peninsula* is land that has water on three sides; an *island* is land completely surrounded by water. Suggest that they find other related words as they read.

2 TEACH

Reading Strategy

Classifying Information Have students scan the photographs in the text to find examples of the different landforms. L1

Daily Lecture and Discussion Notes

LOOKING AT THE EARTH

Daily Lecture and Discussion Notes

Landforms and Waterways

Did You Know?

The Mississippi River delta forms in the Gulf of Mexico. Deltas are usually shaped like a rough triangle. They are built up by mud and sand. Both the Nile and Mississippi River deltas produce valuable crops of high-grade cotton. The strength of the river current determines the size of the delta.

I. Types of Landforms

A. Mountains and hills differ in that mountains have high peaks and steep, rugged slopes. Hills are lower and more rounded.

B. Between mountains and hills lie valleys. A valley is a long stretch of land lower than the land on either side. Canyons are steep-sided lowlands that rivers have [cut] through a plateau.

More About the Photos

The Great Rift Valley and the Grand Canyon The Grand Canyon, about a mile deep, was formed fairly recently—about six million years ago. The Great Rift Valley of Africa is less steep—about 2,000 to 3,000 feet (610 to 914 m). It is much older—about 30 million years old.

Caption Answer Both valleys and canyons are lowlands, but canyons are more steep-sided.

NATIONAL GEOGRAPHIC **On Location**

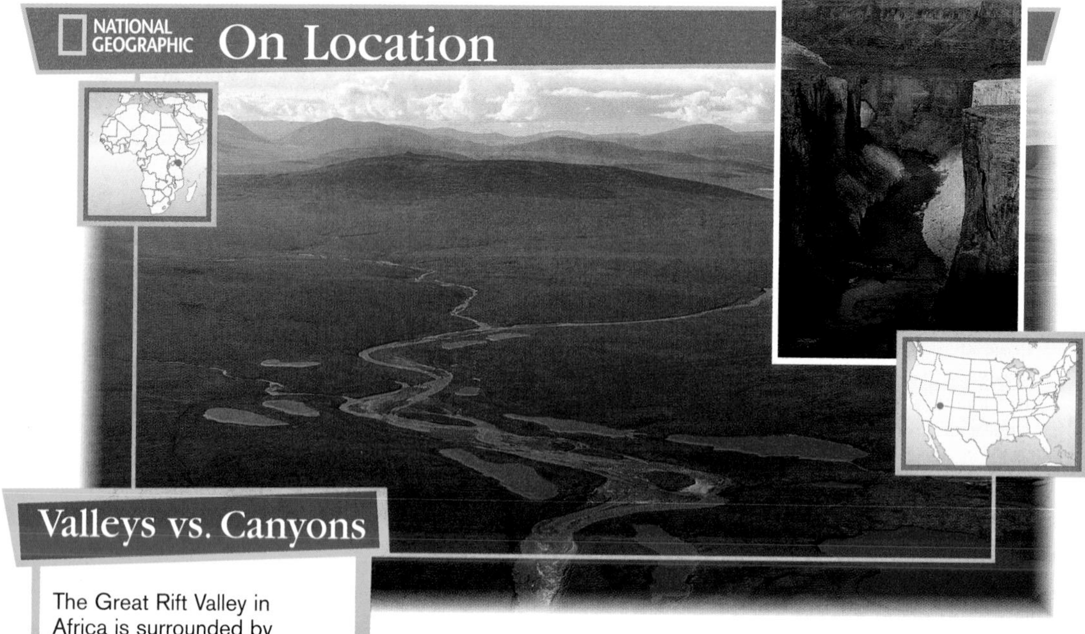

Valleys vs. Canyons

The Great Rift Valley in Africa is surrounded by mountains (above). Canyons, like the Grand Canyon in Arizona (right), are carved from plateaus.

Place How are valleys and canyons similar?

Mountains often have high peaks and steep, rugged slopes. Hills are lower and more rounded. Some hills form at the foot, or base, of mountains. As a result, these hills are called foothills.

In contrast, plains and plateaus are mostly flat. What makes them different from one another is their **elevation,** or height above sea level. **Plains** are low-lying stretches of flat or gently rolling land. Many plains reach from the middle of a continent to the coast, such as the **North European Plain. Plateaus** are also flat but have higher elevation. With some plateaus, a steep cliff forms on one side where the plateau rises above nearby lowlands. With others, such as the **Plateau of Tibet** in Asia, the plateau is surrounded by mountains.

Between mountains and hills lie valleys. A valley is a long stretch of land lower than the land on either side. Rivers are often found at the bottom of valleys. Canyons are steep-sided lowlands that rivers have cut through a plateau. One of the most famous canyons is the **Grand Canyon** in Arizona. For millions of years, the Colorado River flowed over a plateau and carved through rock, forming the Grand Canyon.

Geographers describe some landforms by their relationship to larger land areas or to bodies of water. An **isthmus** is a narrow piece of land that connects two larger pieces of land. A **peninsula** is a piece of land with water on three sides. A body of land smaller than a continent and completely surrounded by water is an **island.**

Under the Oceans If you were to explore the oceans, you would see landforms under the water that are similar to those on land. Off each coast of a continent lies a plateau called a **continental shelf** that

Reading Strategy — Reading the Text

Varying Reading Rate Students will learn that some text is more difficult to read than others, and they must make adjustments to their reading rate. Remind students to slow down when they encounter difficult concepts, connections to previous ideas, new vocabulary, or text that contains a great deal of information.

*Use the **Reading Skills Handbook** for more reading strategies.*

stretches for several miles underwater. At the edge of the shelf, steep cliffs drop down to the ocean floor.

Tall mountains and very deep valleys line the ocean floor. Valleys here are called trenches, and they are the lowest spots in the earth's crust. The deepest one, in the western Pacific Ocean, is called the **Mariana Trench.** This trench plunges 35,840 feet (10,924 m) below sea level. How deep is this? If Mt. Everest were placed into this trench, the mountain would have to grow 1.3 miles (2 km) higher just to reach the ocean's surface.

Landforms and People Humans have settled on all types of landforms. Some people live at high elevations in the Andes mountain ranges of South America. The people of Bangladesh live on a low coastal plain. Farmers in Ethiopia work the land on a plateau called the Ethiopian Highlands.

Why do people decide to live in a particular area? Climate—the average temperature and rainfall of a region—is one reason. You will read more about climate in the next chapter. The availability of resources is another reason. People settle where they can get freshwater and where they can grow food, catch fish, or raise animals. They might settle in an area because it has good supplies of useful items such as trees for building, iron for manufacturing, or petroleum for making energy. You will read more about resources in Chapter 3.

Reading Check How are plains and plateaus similar? How are they different?

Applying Map Skills

1. What are the names of the seven large landmasses on the earth?
2. What are the earth's four major oceans?

Find NGS online map resources @ www.nationalgeographic.com/maps

NATIONAL GEOGRAPHIC **World Continents and Oceans**

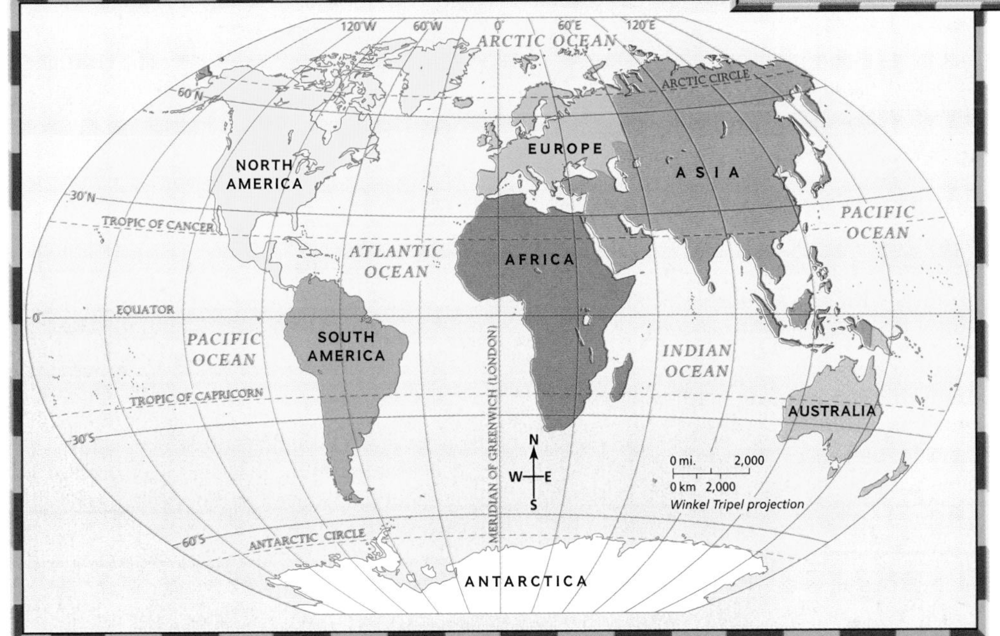

Chapter 1

Section 4, pages 39–42

L1/ELL

Guided Reading Activity

Name ______ Date ______ Class ______

LOOKING AT THE EARTH

Guided Reading Activity 4

Landforms and Waterways

DIRECTIONS: Answering Questions Reading the section and answering the questions below will help you learn about landforms and waterways. Refer to your textbook to answer the questions.

1. Name the earth's seven continents.
2. What are the differences among mountains, hills, plains, and plateaus?

Reading Check Answer

Both are generally flat, but plateaus have a higher elevation than plains.

Applying Map Skills

Answers

1. continents (North and South America, Africa, Europe, Asia, Australia, and Antarctica)
2. Pacific, Atlantic, Indian, and Arctic Oceans

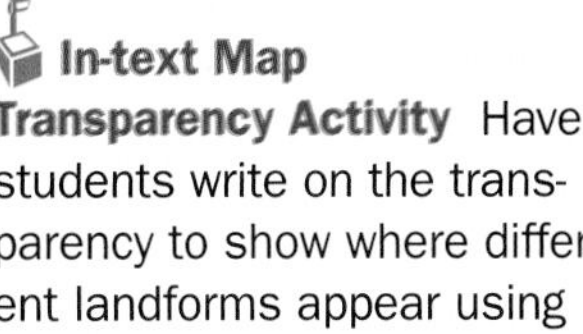

In-text Map Transparency Activity Have students write on the transparency to show where different landforms appear using information in the section.

3 ASSESS

Assign Section 4 Assessment as homework or an in-class activity.

Have students use the Interactive Tutor Self-Assessment CD-ROM to review Section 4.

Differentiated Instruction

Meeting Special Needs: Naturalist Organize the class into teams. Give each team an example of a landform or body of water, such as mountain, valley, ocean, or river. Have teams brainstorm to identify the influence that this geographical feature might have on the lives of people. Remind students that the influence can be both positive and negative (for example, a river can supply freshwater but also flood its banks, endangering the lives of people living near it). Have the groups present their lists to the rest of the class and discuss their findings. **L2**

Refer to *Inclusion for the Middle School Social Studies Classroom Strategies and Activities* in the TCR.

L2

Section Quiz

Name ____ Date ____ Class ____

LOOKING AT THE EARTH

Score

Section 4 Quiz

Landforms and Waterways

DIRECTIONS: Matching Match each item in Column A with the items in Column B. Write the correct letters in the blanks. *(10 points each)*

COLUMN A	COLUMN B
A. source	____ 1. an underwater plateau
B. continental shelf	____ 2. the earth's largest bodies of water
C. elevation	____ 3. height above sea level
D. peninsula	____ 4. point at which a river originates
E. oceans	____ 5. piece of land with water on three sides

Reading Check Answer

The source is where a river begins; the mouth is where it empties into another body of water.

L1/ELL

Reading Essentials and Study Guide

Name ____ Date ____ Class ____

LOOKING AT THE EARTH

Reading Essentials and Study Guide 4

Landforms and Waterways

Key Terms

elevation height above sea level
plain low-lying stretch of flat or gently rolling land
plateau flat land at higher elevations than plains
isthmus narrow piece of land that connects two larger pieces of land
peninsula piece of land with water on three sides
island piece of land smaller than a continent and completely surrounded by water
continental shelf underwater plateau that lies off each coast of a continent
oceans ... the ocean floor

CLOSE

Have students create an annotated drawing showing six to eight different landforms, with callouts identifying each and describing its characteristics.

Bodies of Water

About 70 percent of the earth's surface is water. Most of that water is salt water, which people and most animals cannot drink. Only a small percentage is freshwater, which is drinkable. Oceans, consisting of salt water, are the earth's largest bodies of water. Smaller bodies of salt water are connected to oceans but are at least partly enclosed by land. These bodies include seas, gulfs, and bays.

Two other kinds of water form passages that connect two larger bodies of water. A **strait** is a narrow body of water between two pieces of land. The **Strait of Magellan** flows between the southern tip of South America and an island called Tierra del Fuego (tee•EHR•uh DEHL fu•AY•GOH). This strait connects the Atlantic and the Pacific Oceans. A wider passage is called a **channel**. The Mozambique Channel separates southeastern Africa from the island of Madagascar.

Bodies of freshwater appear on the world's continents and islands. They include larger bodies like lakes and rivers as well as smaller ones such as ponds and streams. The point at which a river originates—usually high in the mountains—is called its source. The mouth of a river is where it empties into another body of water. As you learned in Section 3, rivers carry soil and sand. They eventually deposit this soil at the mouth, which builds up over time to form a **delta**.

Reading Check What is the difference between the source and the mouth of a river?

Section 4 Assessment

Defining Terms

1. **Define** elevation, plain, plateau, isthmus, peninsula, island, continental shelf, trench, strait, channel, delta.

Recalling Facts

2. **Place** What is the difference between mountains and hills?
3. **Place** How are straits and channels similar? How are they different?
4. **Culture** What are two reasons people decide to settle in a particular area?

Critical Thinking

5. **Analyzing Information** What two landforms are created by rivers?
6. **Making Inferences** Why do people often settle on the edges of rivers?

Graphic Organizer

7. **Organizing Information** Make a chart like this and give three examples for each item.

Landforms			
Landforms Under the Ocean			
Types of Bodies of Water			

Applying Social Studies Skills

8. **Analyzing Maps** Look at the map of Asia on pages RA24–RA25 of the **Reference Atlas**. Find an example of the following: plain, plateau, peninsula, island, strait. List the specific names of each landform.

Section 4 Assessment

1. The terms are defined in the Glossary.
2. Mountains are taller and have more rugged slopes. Hills are lower and more rounded.
3. *Similar:* Both are passages that connect two larger bodies of water. *Different:* Straits are more narrow, and channels are broader.
4. climate, availability of resources
5. valleys and canyons (also deltas)
6. *Possible answer:* settling there gives access to freshwater and transportation
7. *Landforms*—mountain, hill, plain, plateau, valley, canyon, peninsula, island; *Landforms under the ocean*—continental shelf (plateau), mountain, trench (valley); *Types of bodies of water*—ocean, sea, gulf, bay, strait, lake, river, pond, stream
8. Answers will vary. Students should specifically name the landforms.

Reading Review

Section 1 Thinking Like a Geographer

Terms to Know

- geography
- landform
- environment
- Global Positioning System (GPS)
- geographic information systems (GIS)
- artifact
- fossil

Main Idea

Geographers use various tools to understand the world.

✓ Place Geographers study the physical and social characteristics of places.

✓ Human/Environment Interaction Geographers are especially interested in how people interact with their environment.

✓ Technology To study the earth, geographers use maps, globes, photographs, the Global Positioning System, and geographic information systems.

✓ Economics People can use information from geography to plan, make decisions, and manage resources.

Section 2 The Earth in Space

Terms to Know

- solar system
- orbit
- atmosphere
- axis
- revolution
- leap year
- summer solstice
- winter solstice
- equinox

Main Idea

Earth has life because of the sun. Earth has different seasons because of the way it tilts and revolves around the sun.

✓ Science The sun's light and warmth allow life to exist on Earth.

✓ Science The atmosphere is a cushion of gases that protects Earth and provides air to breathe.

✓ Movement Earth spins on its axis causing day and night.

✓ Movement The tilt of Earth and its revolution around the sun cause the changes in seasons.

Section 3 Forces Shaping the Earth

Terms to Know

- core
- mantle
- magma
- crust
- continent
- earthquake
- plate tectonics
- tsunami
- fault
- weathering
- erosion
- glacier

Main Idea

Forces both inside the earth and on its surface affect the shape of the land.

✓ Region Earth has an inner and outer core, a mantle, and a crust.

✓ Movement The continents are on large plates of rock that move.

✓ Movement Earthquakes and volcanoes can reshape the land.

✓ Science Wind, water, and ice can change the look of the land.

Section 4 Landforms and Waterways

Terms to Know

- elevation
- plain
- plateau
- isthmus
- peninsula
- island
- continental shelf
- trench
- strait
- channel
- delta

Main Idea

Landforms in all their variety affect how people live.

✓ Location Mountains, plateaus, valleys, and other landforms are found on land and under the oceans.

✓ Science About 70 percent of the earth's surface is water.

✓ Culture People have adapted in order to live on various landforms.

Reading Review

Use the Chapter 1 Reading Review to preview, review, condense, or reteach the chapter.

Preview/Review

Use the Terms to Know lists to help students review and study.

Activity Play a game in which you challenge teams of students to be the first to identify the correct term from a definition.

Vocabulary PuzzleMaker CD-ROM reinforces the vocabulary terms used in Chapter 1.

The Interactive Tutor Self-Assessment CD-ROM allows students to review Chapter 1 content.

Condense

Have students read the Chapter 1 summary statements.

Guided Reading Activities

Audio Program

Reteach

Reteaching Activity

Reading Essentials and Study Guide

Reading Strategy Read to Write

Summarizing Ask students: Why does the earth look the way it looks? Have students review the chapter to help them answer the question. Students should answer the question by writing a one-page essay that describes the forces that shape the face of the earth. They may write about all the forces (both those inside the earth and on the surface), focus on only one set of forces (those inside or outside), or explore the various impacts of one particular force (weathering or the movement of plates). L1

EE3 Physical Systems: Standard 7

GLENCOE TECHNOLOGY

MindJogger Videoquiz
Use MindJogger Videoquiz to review the Chapter 1 content.

Available in DVD and VHS

Using Key Terms

1. a
2. j
3. i
4. c
5. e
6. d
7. b
8. f
9. h
10. g

Reviewing the Main Ideas

11. *Any three:* landforms such as mountains, valleys, hills; bodies of water; typical rainfall and temperature; soil; resources
12. *Possible answer:* A place is a specific location; a region is a group of places that have some characteristic in common.
13. *Possible answers:* government leaders planning new community services, civic leaders expanding city services, realtors identifying apartment locations
14. nine
15. rotating on its axis every 24 hours
16. As Earth revolves around the sun, the sun's rays hit parts of the earth more or less directly. Areas that are struck by the sun directly have summer; those with only indirect sunlight have winter.
17. They float on liquid rock in the mantle.
18. *Possible answer:* River water wears away the soil on riverbanks.
19. plateaus
20. climate, availability of resources

Chapter 1 Assessment and Activities

Using Key Terms

Match the terms in Part A with their definitions in Part B.

A.

1. elevation
2. landform
3. summer solstice
4. plate tectonics
5. geographic information systems
6. Global Positioning System
7. erosion
8. equinox
9. fault
10. weathering

B.

a. height above sea level
b. wearing away of the earth's surface
c. theory that the earth's crust consists of huge slabs of rock that move
d. a group of satellites around the earth
e. special software that helps geographers gather and use information
f. when day and night are of equal length
g. a process that breaks surface rocks into gravel, sand, or soil
h. a crack in the earth's crust
i. the day with the most hours of sunlight
j. particular features of the land

Reviewing the Main Ideas

Section 1 Thinking Like a Geographer

11. **Place** Give three examples of the physical characteristics of a place.
12. **Region** How is a region different from a place?
13. **Human/Environment Interaction** Give an example of how people use geographic knowledge.

Section 2 The Earth in Space

14. **Region** How many planets are in the solar system?
15. **Movement** What movement of Earth causes day and night?
16. **Movement** How does Earth's revolution around the sun relate to the seasons?

Section 3 Forces Shaping the Earth

17. **Movement** How do the plates in the earth's crust move?
18. **Movement** Give an example of erosion.

Section 4 Landforms and Waterways

19. **Place** Which has a higher elevation—plains or plateaus?
20. **Movement** What are two reasons people settle in a particular region?

The World

Place Location Activity

On a separate sheet of paper, match the letters on the map with the numbered places listed below.

1. North America
2. Pacific Ocean
3. Africa
4. South America
5. Antarctica
6. Australia
7. Atlantic Ocean
8. Asia

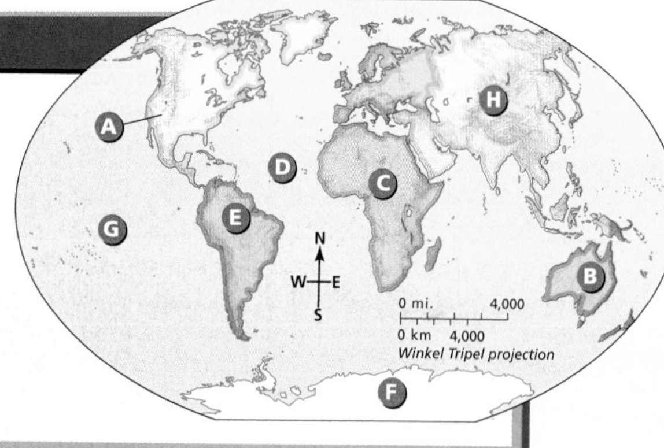

NATIONAL GEOGRAPHIC Place Location Activity

1. A
2. G
3. C
4. E
5. F
6. B
7. D
8. H

Critical Thinking

21. because it is winter in the Southern Hemisphere at that time
22. Plate movements caused continents to reach current positions, mountains to form, and volcanoes, earthquakes, tsunamis, and faults to occur. Earthquakes cause the land to change or damage to buildings and other structures. Volcanoes may cause mountains to form or damage to cities near them. Weathering breaks surface rock into gravel, sand, and

Self-Check Quiz Visit ***The World and Its People*** Web site at twip.glencoe.com and click on **Chapter 1—Self-Check Quizzes** to prepare for the Chapter Test.

Critical Thinking

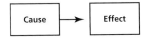

21. **Drawing Conclusions** Why do people in Australia snow-ski during the Northern Hemisphere's summer months?
22. **Understanding Cause and Effect** Create a diagram like this one. In the "Cause" box, write "plate movements." In the "Effect" box, describe the effect that this force has on the earth. Draw four more pairs of boxes and do the same for the other forces that shape the earth: earthquakes, volcanoes, weathering, and erosion.

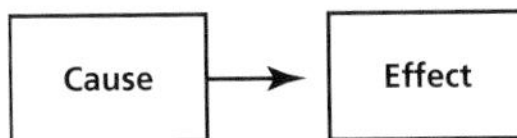

Comparing Regions Activity

23. **Geography** Think about your neighborhood. List the characteristics that make it a region. Organize into pairs and compare the characteristics of your region to your partner's region.

Mental Mapping Activity

24. **Focusing on the Region** Draw a simple outline map of the earth, then label the following:
    - core
    - mantle
    - crust
    - atmosphere

Technology Skills Activity

25. **Building a Database** Use a word processing program to make a database like the following. In the first column, list forces inside Earth that have shaped the land. Then write the result of the force in the second column. In the third column, research to find an example of each result. The first row has been filled in for you.

Force	Result	Example
collision of plates	mountains	Himalaya

Standardized Test Practice

Directions: Study the maps below, and then answer the question that follows.

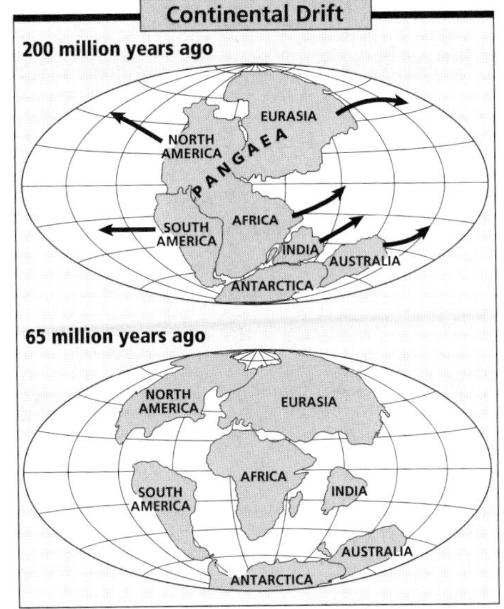

1. What "supercontinent" do many scientists believe existed 200 million years ago?

A Eurasia
B Pangaea
C Gondwana
D Antarctica

Test-Taking Tip: Use information on the maps to answer this question. Read the title above the maps and then the two subtitles. If you reread the question, you see it is asking about a certain time period. Make sure you use the correct map above to answer the question.

45

soil. Erosion wears away the surface. Ice in the form of glaciers can erode mountains and create valleys.

Comparing Regions Activity

23. Students should note their neighborhoods' physical and human characteristics.

Mental Mapping Activity

24. This exercise helps students visualize the structure of the earth and understand the relationship among various parts. All attempts at freehand mapping should be accepted.

Technology Skills Activity

25. Students' databases should contain the required information.

Assessment and Activities

Standardized Test Practice

1. B

Tested Objectives:
Analyzing information, reading a map

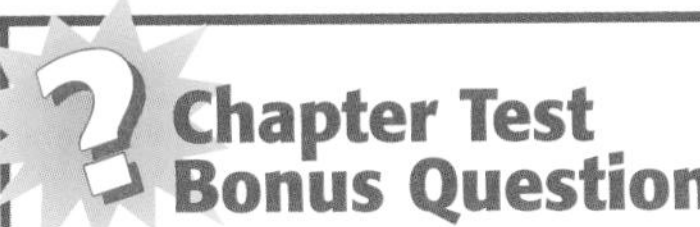

This question may be used for extra credit on the chapter test.

You are a rugged and steep natural landmark. Some people put on all types of clothing and special equipment to see your highest point. What are you? *(a mountain)*

Have students visit the Web site at twip.glencoe.com to review Chapter 1 and take the Self-Check Quiz.

Dinah Zike's Foldables

Culminating Activity Have students quiz each other using the vocabulary terms. Answers should be checked against the information found on their foldables.

Chapter 2 Resources

Note: The following materials may be used when teaching Chapter 2.
Section level support materials are shown at point of use in the margins of the Teacher Wraparound Edition.

Timesaving Tools

TeacherWorks™ All-In-One Planner and Resource Center

- **Interactive Teacher Edition** See the **Interactive Teacher Edition** CD-ROM to electronically integrate your Teacher Wraparound Edition and blackline masters.
- **Interactive Lesson Planner** Organize your week, month, semester, or year with all the lesson helps you need. The **Interactive Lesson Planner** CD-ROM contains all Chapter 2 resources.

Use Glencoe's **Presentation Plus!** multimedia teacher tool to easily present dynamic lessons that visually excite your students. Using Microsoft PowerPoint® you can customize the presentations to create your own personalized lessons.

TEACHING TRANSPARENCIES

Graphic Organizer Transparency 9 L2

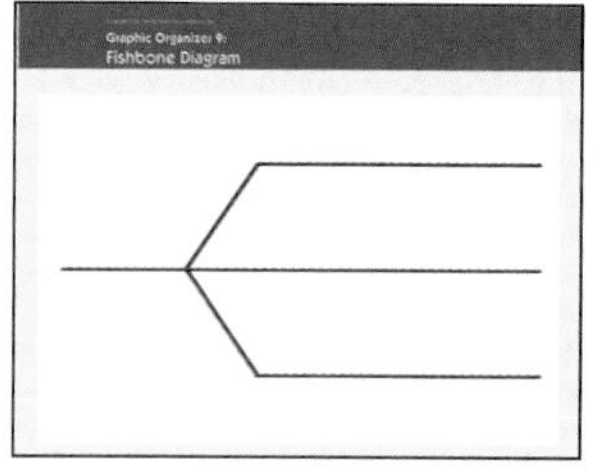

In-text Map Transparency L1

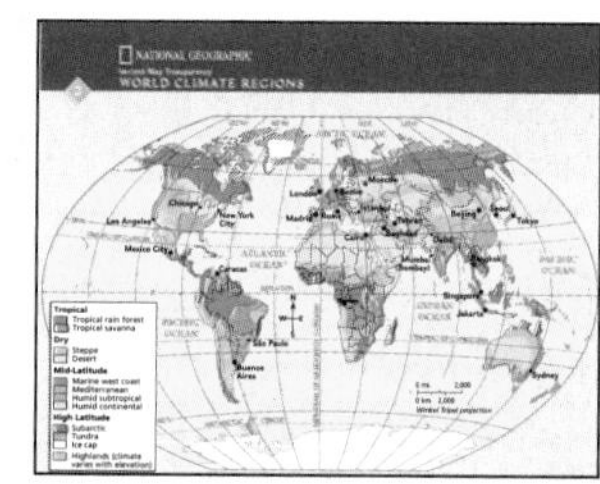

FOLDABLES™ Study Organizer

Dinah Zike's Foldables

Foldables are three-dimensional, interactive graphic organizers that help students practice basic writing skills, review key vocabulary terms, and identify main ideas. Additional chapter activities can be found in the ***Reading and Study Skills Foldables*** booklet.

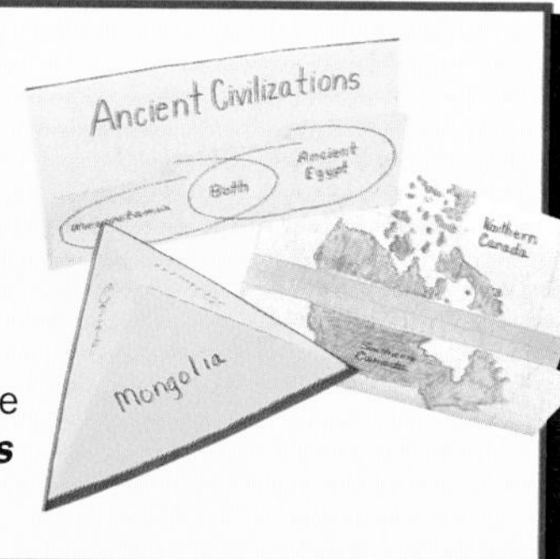

MAP AND GEOGRAPHY SKILLS

Chapter Map Activity L2

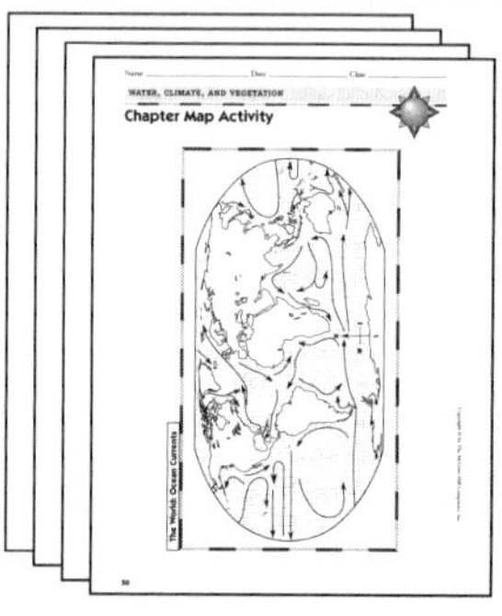

GeoLab Activity L2

READING SUPPORT

Vocabulary Activity L1

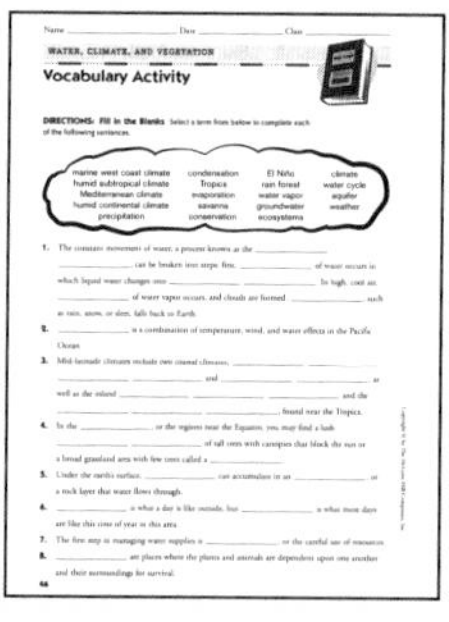

Workbook Activity L1

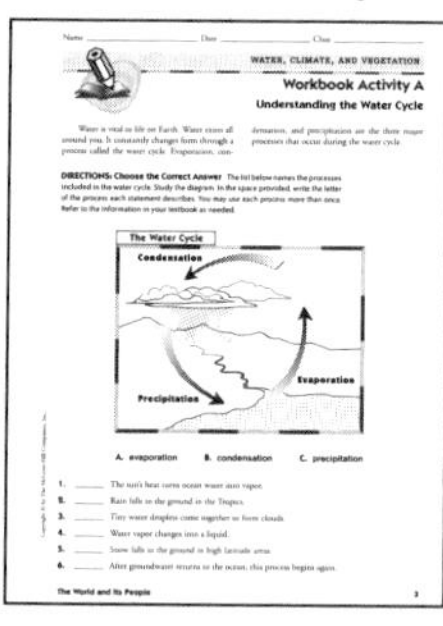

Reading and Writing Skills Activity L1/ELL

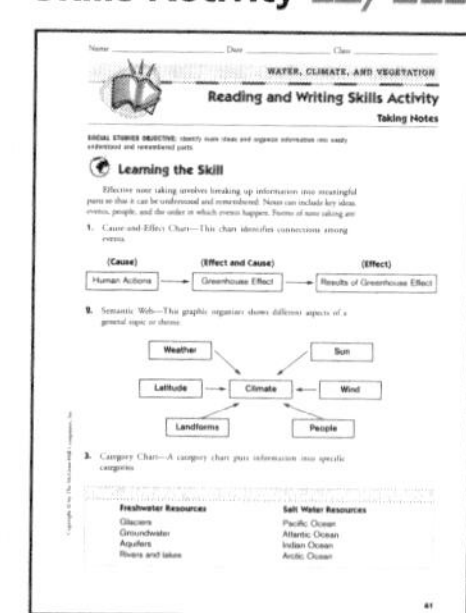

DIFFERENTIATED INSTRUCTION

Use these review and reinforcement materials to help less-proficient readers, English learners, and gifted and talented students.

Reteaching Activity L1

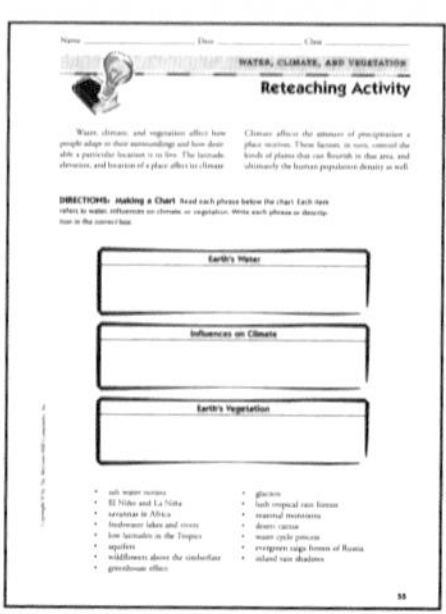

Chapter Skills Review L2

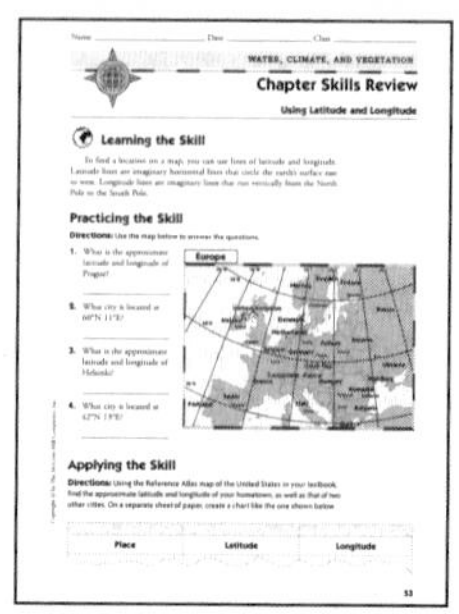

Cooperative Learning Activity L1/ELL

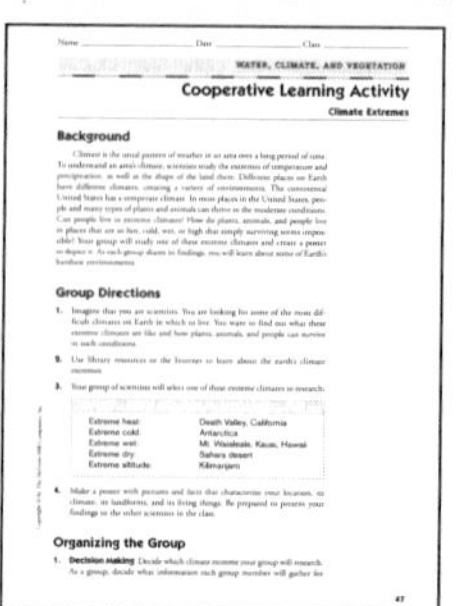

Enrichment Activity L3

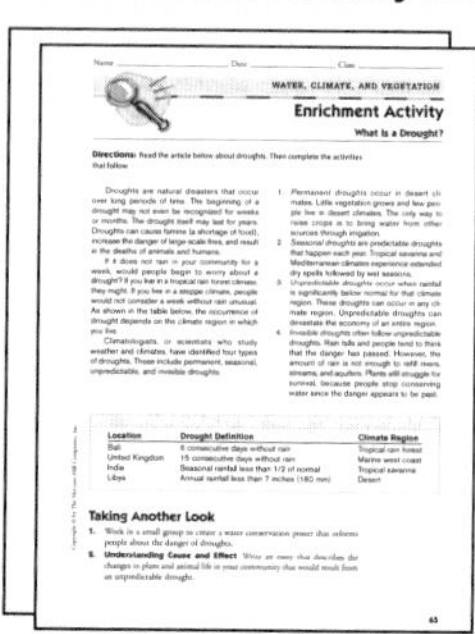

ASSESSMENT

Chapter Test, Form A L2

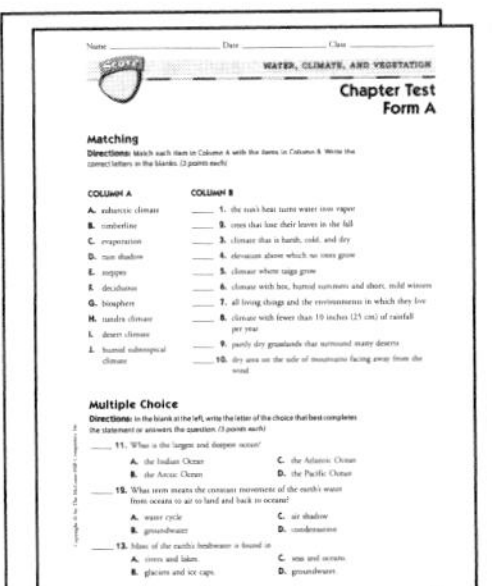

Chapter Test, Form B L2

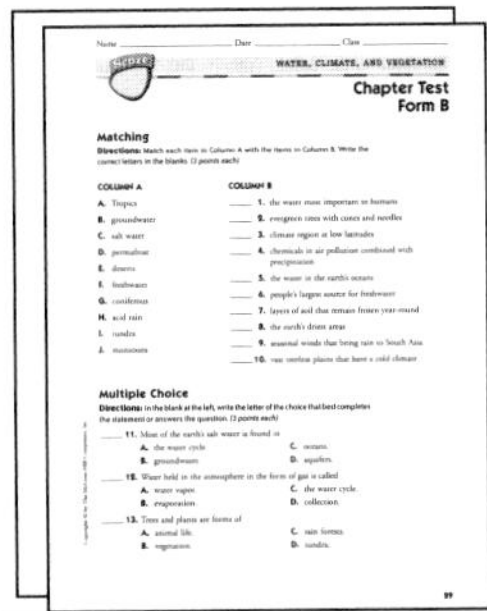

Performance Assessment Activity L1/ELL

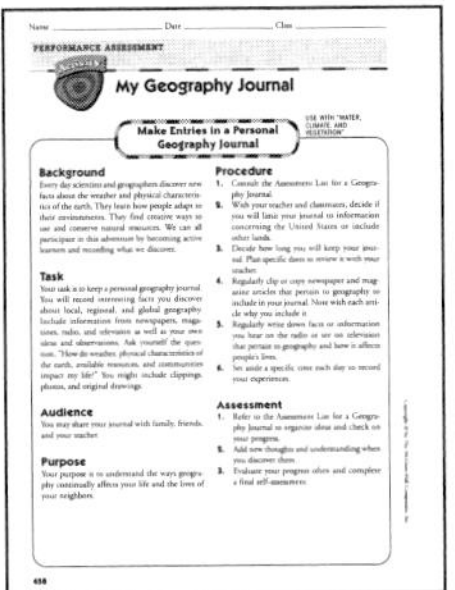

ExamView® Pro Testmaker CD-ROM

STANDARDIZED ASSESSMENT SKILLS

Critical Thinking Skills Activity L2

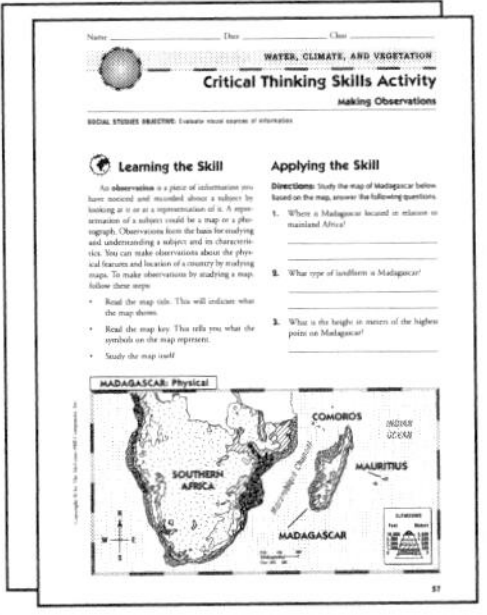

Map and Graph Skills Activity L2

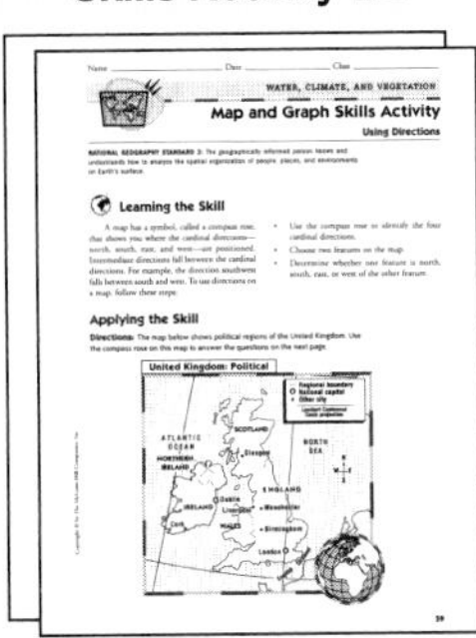

Standardized Test Skills Practice Workbook Activity L2

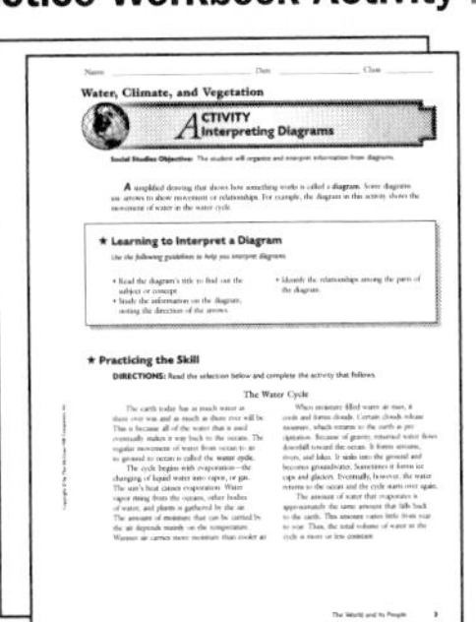

HOME INVOLVEMENT

Take-Home Review Activity L1

MULTIMEDIA

- National Geographic's The World and Its People
- MindJogger Videoquiz
- Vocabulary PuzzleMaker CD-ROM
- Interactive Tutor Self-Assessment CD-ROM
- ExamView® Pro Testmaker CD-ROM
- TeacherWorks CD-ROM
- StudentWorks CD-ROM
- Skillbuilder Interactive Workbook CD-ROM, Level 1
- Presentation Plus! CD-ROM
- Audio Program

SPANISH RESOURCES

The following Spanish language materials are available in the Spanish Resources binder:

- Spanish Summaries
- Spanish Vocabulary Activities
- Spanish Guided Reading Activities
- Spanish Quizzes and Tests
- Spanish Take-Home Review Activities
- Spanish Reteaching Activities

Meeting National Standards

Geography for Life

The following standards are covered in Chapter 2:

Section 1	EE3 Physical Systems: Standards 7, 8
Section 2	EE3 Physical Systems: Standards 7, 8
	EE4 Human Systems: Standards 9, 12
	EE5 Environment and Society: Standards 14, 15
Section 3	EE3 Physical Systems: Standards 7, 8
	EE6 The Uses of Geography: Standard 17
Section 4	EE3 Physical Systems: Standard 8
	EE4 Human Systems: Standards 9, 11, 12, 13
	EE5 Environment and Society: Standards 14, 15, 16

Chapter 2 Planning Guide

SECTION RESOURCES

Daily Objectives	Reproducible Resources	Multimedia Resources
Section 1 **The Water Planet** **1.** Describe how the earth's water moves in a cycle. **2.** Explain where people get freshwater. **3.** Discuss where the world's salt water is found.	Reproducible Lesson Plan Daily Lecture and Discussion Notes Note-taking Guide Guided Reading Activity* Reading Essentials and Study Guide* Section Quiz*	Daily Focus Skills Transparency GeoQuiz Transparency Vocabulary PuzzleMaker CD-ROM Interactive Tutor Self-Assessment CD-ROM ExamView® Pro Testmaker CD-ROM Presentation Plus! CD-ROM
Section 2 **Climate** **1.** Explain what climate is. **2.** Describe how wind and water move around the earth. **3.** Discuss what causes precipitation and storms. **4.** Describe what El Niño and La Niña are.	Reproducible Lesson Plan Daily Lecture and Discussion Notes Note-taking Guide Guided Reading Activity* Reading Essentials and Study Guide* Section Quiz*	Daily Focus Skills Transparency GeoQuiz Transparency Vocabulary PuzzleMaker CD-ROM Interactive Tutor Self-Assessment CD-ROM ExamView® Pro Testmaker CD-ROM Presentation Plus! CD-ROM
Section 3 **Climate Zones and Vegetation** **1.** Describe what major world climate zones are like. **2.** Identify where each major world climate zone is located. **3.** Explain what kinds of vegetation are grown in each climate zone.	Reproducible Lesson Plan Daily Lecture and Discussion Notes Note-taking Guide Guided Reading Activity* Reading Essentials and Study Guide* Section Quiz*	Daily Focus Skills Transparency In-text Map Transparency Vocabulary PuzzleMaker CD-ROM Interactive Tutor Self-Assessment CD-ROM ExamView® Pro Testmaker CD-ROM Presentation Plus! CD-ROM
Section 4 **An Environmental Balance** **1.** Describe the four basic parts of Earth's geography. **2.** Explain how the soil can be damaged by people. **3.** Identify the effects of air pollution.	Reproducible Lesson Plan Daily Lecture and Discussion Notes Note-taking Guide Guided Reading Activity* Reading Essentials and Study Guide* Section Quiz*	Daily Focus Skills Transparency Vocabulary PuzzleMaker CD-ROM Interactive Tutor Self-Assessment CD-ROM ExamView® Pro Testmaker CD-ROM Presentation Plus! CD-ROM MindJogger Videoquiz

00:00 **Out of Time?** Assign the **Reading Essentials and Study Guide*** for this chapter.

*Also available in Spanish

KEY TO ABILITY LEVELS

Teaching strategies have been coded for varying learning styles and abilities.

L1 **BASIC** activities for all students
L2 **AVERAGE** activities for average to above-average students
L3 **CHALLENGING** activities for above-average students
ELL **ENGLISH LANGUAGE LEARNER** activities

KEY TO TEACHING RESOURCES

Blackline Master
CD-ROM
Transparency
Videocassette
Block Scheduling
DVD

Teacher to Teacher

Hurricane Season

Kim Cavanaugh
Congress Middle School
Boynton Beach, Florida

Provide students with some basic background information about hurricanes. Explain that cyclones are intense storms. Cyclones that form over land are called tornadoes. Tropical cyclones with winds of 74 miles (119 km) per hour that form over the North Atlantic or eastern North Pacific are called hurricanes. They are called typhoons in the western Pacific. Then have students plot the year's current hurricanes. Students should create maps that illustrate the hurricanes' paths and note, in a chart, their average wind speeds.

Meeting Special Needs

In addition to the Differentiated Instruction strategies found in each section, the following resources are also suitable for your special needs students:

- ***ExamView® Pro Testmaker CD-ROM*** allows teachers to tailor tests by reducing answer choices.
- The ***Audio Program*** includes the entire narrative of the student edition so that less-proficient readers can listen to the words as they read them.
- The ***Reading Essentials and Study Guide*** provides the same content as the student edition but is written two grade levels below the textbook.
- ***Guided Reading Activities*** give less-proficient readers point-by-point instructions to increase comprehension as they read each textbook section.
- ***Enrichment Activities*** include a stimulating collection of readings and activities for gifted and talented students.

NATIONAL GEOGRAPHIC TEACHER'S CORNER

Index to National Geographic Magazine:

The following articles may be used for research relating to this chapter:

- "Arctic Submarine," by Glenn Hodges, March 2000.
- "El Niño/La Niña," by Curt Suplee, March 1999.
- *Physical World,* a National Geographic Special Edition, May 1998.
- "Unlocking the Climate Puzzle," by Curt Suplee, May 1998.

National Geographic Society Products:

To order the following products for use with this chapter, call National Geographic Society at 1-800-368-2728:

- *PictureShow: U.S. Regional Geography* (CD-ROM)
- *Physical Geography of the Continents Series* (6 Videos)
- *National Geographic Desk Reference* (Book)
- *National Geographic Atlas of the World, Seventh Edition* (Book)
- *Living Earth* (Video)
- *Water: A Precious Resource* (Video)
- *Living Ocean* (Video)

NGS ONLINE

Access National Geographic's Web site for current events, activities, links, interactive features, and archives. www.nationalgeographic.com

Find the latest coverage of geography in the news, atlas updates, cartographic activities with interactive maps, an online map store, and links at www.nationalgeographic.com/maps

SOCIAL STUDIES Online

Use our Web site for additional resources. All essential content is covered in the Student Edition.

You and your students can visit twip.glencoe.com, the Web site companion to *The World and Its People*. This innovative integration of electronic and print media offers your students a wealth of opportunities. The student text directs students to the Web site for the following options:

- Chapter Overviews
- Student Web Activities
- Self-Check Quizzes
- Textbook Updates

Answers are provided for you in the Web Activity Lesson Plan. Additional Web resources and Interactive Tutor puzzles are also available.

Introducing Chapter 2

Social Studies Online

Introduce students to chapter content and key terms by having them access Chapter Overview 2 at twip.glencoe.com

Chapter Objectives

1. Describe how the water of the earth moves in a cycle.
2. Outline the factors that influence climate.
3. Identify each major climate zone.

GLENCOE TECHNOLOGY

NATIONAL GEOGRAPHIC

The World and Its People Video Program

Chapter 2 Water, Climate, and Vegetation

The following segments enhance the study of this chapter:

- **Exploring the Ocean**
- **Monsoon**
- **The Sahara**

MindJogger Videoquiz

Use MindJogger Videoquiz to preview the Chapter 2 content.

Both programs available in DVD and VHS

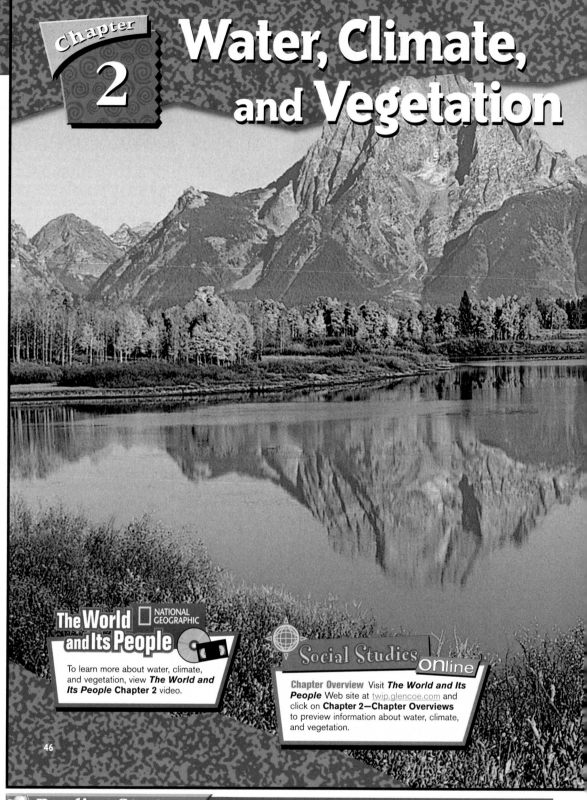

Chapter 2 Water, Climate, and Vegetation

The World and Its People — NATIONAL GEOGRAPHIC

To learn more about water, climate, and vegetation, view ***The World and Its People*** **Chapter 2** video.

Social Studies Online

Chapter Overview Visit ***The World and Its People*** Web site at twip.glencoe.com and click on **Chapter 2—Chapter Overviews** to preview information about water, climate, and vegetation.

46

Reading Strategy — Purpose for Reading

Think-Pair-Share is one strategy for engaging students in subject material through student discussion. **Think**—Tell your students that after the first astronauts sent back pictures of the earth from space, the planet was called "big blue marble." Using a globe for reference, ask them to write why this nickname is appropriate. **Pair**—Have the students pair up and discuss what they wrote by being specific in their descriptions. **Share**—Have students share their responses with the entire class. Point out similarities and differences in their responses. Wrap up by discussing how water affects the earth's climate and vegetation. L1

Introducing

Chapter 2

Why It Matters

A Balancing Act

Many of the daily decisions you make pertain to the weather and climate. Climate affects where you live, what you wear, what you eat, and what activities you participate in. Climate also affects what types of vegetation will grow in certain areas. Understanding climate—and the human activities that can change it—is the first step in understanding the need to have a balance in the global environment.

Grand Teton National Park, Wyoming, United States

FOLDABLES™ Study Organizer

Summarizing Make this foldable and use it to organize note cards with information about water, climate, and vegetation.

Step 1 Fold a two-inch tab along the long edge of a sheet of paper.

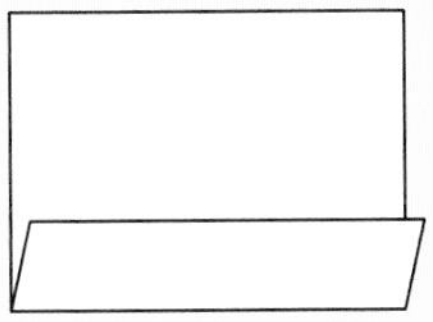

Step 2 Fold the paper in thirds so the tab is on the inside.

Step 3 Open the paper pocket foldable, turn it, and glue the edges of the pockets together.

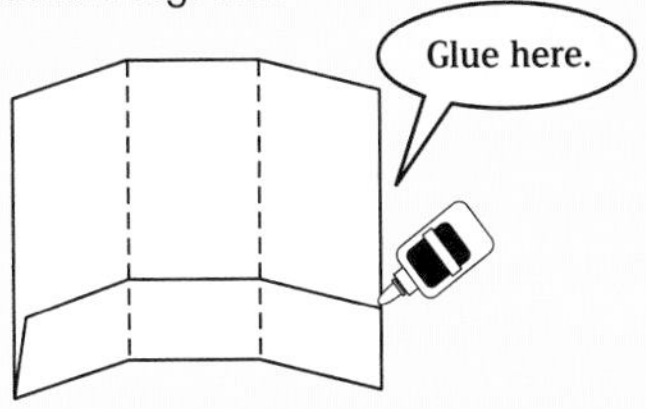

Step 4 Label the pockets as shown.

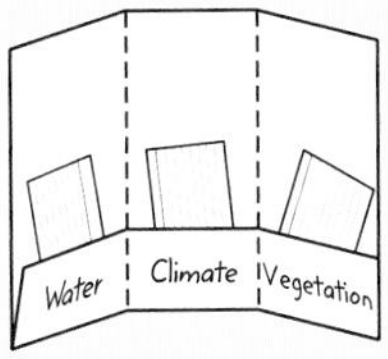

Reading and Writing As you read each section in the chapter, summarize key facts about water, climate, and vegetation on note cards or on quarter sheets of notebook paper. Organize your notes by placing them in your foldable inside the appropriate pocket.

FOLDABLES™ Study Organizer — Dinah Zike's Foldables

Purpose Students will make and use this foldable to organize information about the earth's water, climate, and vegetation. As students read, they should take notes on index cards and place them in the appropriate category pocket. Students' notes should include the main ideas about water, climate, and vegetation. Index cards can be used to review for chapter and unit tests.

 Have students complete the ***Reading and Study Skills Foldables*** activity for this chapter.

Why It Matters

Climate can change, as has been seen in recent years all over the world. Much of Africa north of the Equator receives very little rainfall. The world's largest tropical desert is found in this region—the Sahara. However, at one time the Sahara was a fertile region that supported a thriving civilization. Because of a gradual lack of rainfall, most of this area is now uninhabitable. On the southern border of this desert is the Sahel, which in Arabic means "coastal land." Between 1968 and 1980, a drought in the Sahel destroyed livestock and caused the starvation of many West Africans. Have students research how their state has changed as a result of climate and explain their findings in a brief oral report.

About the Photo

Grand Teton National Park is located in northwestern Wyoming. Located in the park is the Teton Range, a 40-mile-long mountain front. There are eight peaks over 12,000 feet (3,658 m), including the Grand Teton at 13,770 feet (4,198 m). Elk, moose, and bison roam throughout the park, along with black bears and grizzlies.

FOCUS

Section Objectives

1. Describe how the earth's water moves in a cycle.
2. Explain where people get freshwater.
3. Discuss where the world's salt water is found.

BELLRINGER
Skillbuilder Activity

Project transparency and have students answer the question.

Daily Focus Skills Transparency

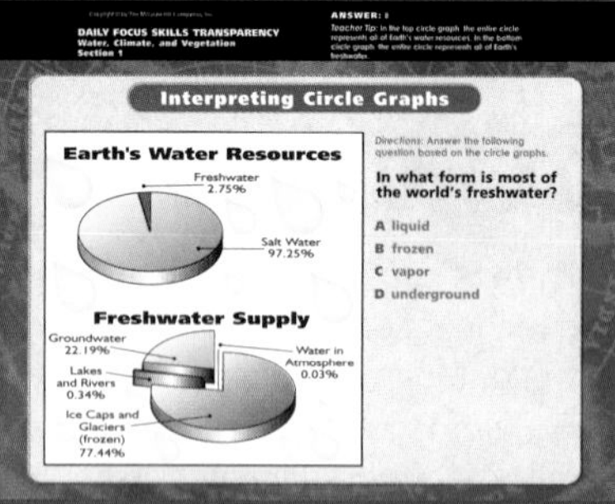

Reading Preview

- **Activating Prior Knowledge** **Ask:** How do you use water? As students respond, write their answers on the board.
- **Preteaching Vocabulary** Ask students what bicycles and motorcycles have in common. *(wheels that go around)* Ask them to use this information to suggest the meaning of the term *water cycle*.

Guide to Reading

Main Idea

Water is one of the earth's most precious resources.

Terms to Know

- water vapor
- water cycle
- evaporation
- condensation
- precipitation
- collection
- glacier
- groundwater
- aquifer

Reading Strategy

Draw a diagram like this one. Starting at the top, write the steps of the water cycle—each in a separate square—in the correct sequence.

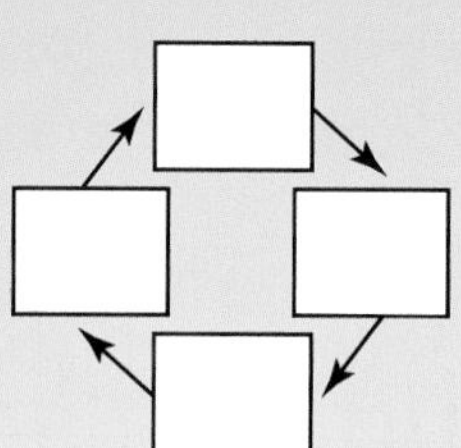

Section 1

The Water Planet

NATIONAL GEOGRAPHIC **Exploring Our World**

Humans, trees, other plants, and animals all need water. We cannot survive without it. Here, a swimmer enjoys a remarkable sight—a permanent pool of water in the middle of Mexico's Chihuahuan Desert. The water bubbles to the surface from an underground spring. The clear water does more than attract swimmers, though. It supports a variety of animal and plant life.

Some people call Earth "the water planet." Why? Water covers about 70 percent of the earth's surface. Water exists all around you in many different forms. Streams, rivers, lakes, seas, and oceans contain water in liquid form. The atmosphere holds **water vapor,** or water in the form of gas. Glaciers and ice sheets are masses of water that have been frozen solid. As a matter of fact, the human body itself is about 60 percent water.

The Water Cycle

The total amount of water on the earth does not change. It does not stay in one place, either. Instead, the water moves constantly. In a process called the **water cycle,** the water goes from the oceans to the air to the ground and finally back to the oceans.

Look at the diagram on page 49 to see how the water cycle works. The sun drives the cycle by evaporating water mostly from the surface of oceans, but also from lakes and streams. In **evaporation,** the sun's heat turns liquid water into water vapor—also called humidity. The amount of water vapor that the air holds depends on the air

Section Resources

Reproducible Masters
- Reproducible Lesson Plan
- Daily Lecture and Discussion Notes
- Note-taking Guide
- Guided Reading Activity
- Reading Essentials and Study Guide
- Section Quiz

Transparencies
- Daily Focus Skills Transparency
- GeoQuiz Transparency

Multimedia
- Vocabulary PuzzleMaker CD-ROM
- Interactive Tutor Self-Assessment CD-ROM
- Presentation Plus! CD-ROM
- ExamView® Pro Testmaker CD-ROM

temperature. Warm air can hold more humidity than cool air. This explains those warm, muggy summer days.

In addition, warm air tends to rise. As warm air rises higher in the atmosphere, it cools. The cooler air loses its ability to hold as much humidity. As a result, the water vapor changes back into a liquid in a process called condensation. Tiny droplets of water come together to form clouds. Eventually, the water falls back to the earth as some form of precipitation—rain, snow, sleet, or hail—depending on the temperature of the surrounding air.

When this precipitation reaches the earth's surface, it soaks into the ground and collects in streams and lakes. During collection, streams and rivers both above and below the ground carry the water back to the oceans. Then the cycle begins again.

Reading Check Which kind of air—warm or cold—holds the most water vapor?

Water Resources

It is a hot day, and you rush home for a glass of water. Like all other people, and all plants and animals, you need water to survive. Think about the many ways you use water in a single day. You use it to bathe, to brush your teeth, to cook your food, and to quench your thirst. People and most animals need freshwater to live. Other creatures make their homes in the earth's more plentiful kind of water: salt water.

Freshwater Only about 2 percent of the water on the earth is freshwater. Eighty percent of that freshwater is frozen in polar ice caps or glaciers, which are giant sheets of ice. Only a tiny fraction of all freshwater—not even four-hundredths of a percent—is found in lakes and rivers.

NATIONAL GEOGRAPHIC

The Water Cycle

Analyzing the Diagram

The water cycle involves evaporation, condensation, precipitation, and the collection of water above and below the ground.

Movement How does water get from the ground to the oceans?

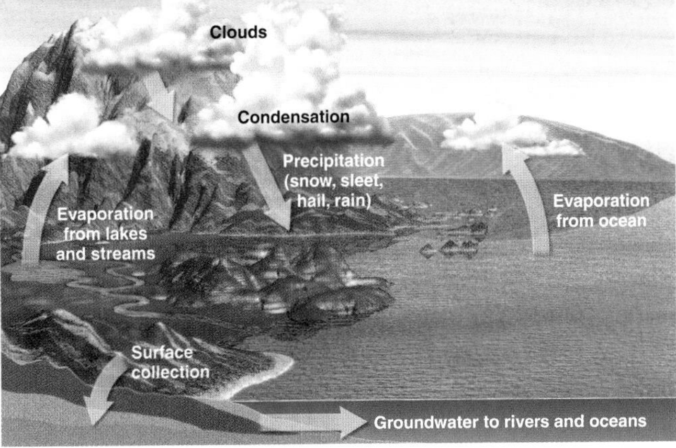

Chapter 2

Section 1, pages 48–50

2 TEACH

Seeing the Big Picture

Point out that there are about a trillion gallons in a cubic mile of water. Then mention that there are about 326 million cubic miles of water on Earth. Use these figures as a springboard for a discussion of water's importance to geographical processes. L1

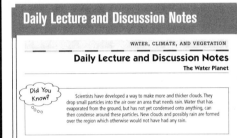

Daily Lecture and Discussion Notes

WATER, CLIMATE, AND VEGETATION

Daily Lecture and Discussion Notes

The Water Planet

Did You Know? Scientists have developed a way to make more and thicker clouds. They drop small particles into the air over an area that needs rain. Water that has evaporated from the ground, but has not yet condensed onto anything, can then condense around these particles. New clouds and possibly rain are formed over the region which otherwise would not have had any rain.

I. The Water Cycle

A. Seventy percent of the earth's surface is covered with water. There is water literally all around us in the form of **water vapor,** or water in the atmosphere in

Reading Check Answer

warm air

Analyzing the Diagram

Answer

Streams and rivers on and below the ground carry it to oceans during collection.

3 ASSESS

Assign Section 1 Assessment as homework or an in-class activity.

Reading Strategy **Reading the Text**

Monitoring Comprehension One of the most important reading strategies a student can learn is that he or she must monitor his or her reading comprehension. As students read, they should be aware of when they have missed an important idea. They can monitor comprehension by questioning themselves as they read. If they do not understand an important idea, they need to reread, review, or read on to clarify what is unclear. L1

*Use the **Reading Skills Handbook** for more reading strategies.*

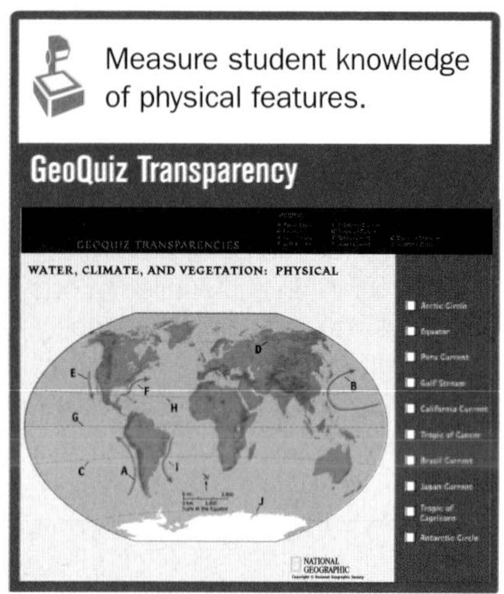

Measure student knowledge of physical features.
GeoQuiz Transparency
WATER, CLIMATE, AND VEGETATION: PHYSICAL

Reading Check Answer

Groundwater is water in rocks beneath the earth's surface. Aquifers are underground rock layers that water flows through.

L1/ELL

Reading Essentials and Study Guide

Name ______ Date ______ Class ______

WATER, CLIMATE, AND VEGETATION

Reading Essentials and Study Guide 1

The Water Planet

Key Terms

water vapor water in the form of gas
water cycle movement of water from oceans to air to ground and back to oceans
evaporation process in which the sun's heat turns liquid water into water vapor
condensation process in which water vapor turns into liquid water
precipitation water that falls to earth as rain, snow, sleet, or hail
collection process in which streams and rivers carry water back to the oceans
glacier giant sheet of ice
groundwater water that fills tiny cracks and holes in the rock layers below the

4 Close

Reading Strategy

Summarizing Have students describe the water cycle in their own words.

When you think of freshwater, you probably think of mighty rivers and huge lakes. People can get freshwater from another source, though. **Groundwater** is water that fills tiny cracks and holes in the rock layers below the surface of the earth. This is a vital source of water because there is 10 times more groundwater than there is water in rivers and lakes. Groundwater can be tapped by wells. Some areas have **aquifers,** or underground rock layers that water flows through. In regions with little rainfall, both farmers and city dwellers sometimes have to depend on aquifers and other groundwater for most of their water supply.

Salt Water All the oceans on the earth are part of a huge, continuous body of salt water—almost 98 percent of the planet's water. Look at the map on page 57. You will see that the four major oceans are the **Pacific Ocean,** the **Atlantic Ocean,** the **Indian Ocean,** and the **Arctic Ocean.**

The Pacific Ocean is the largest and deepest of these four oceans. It covers almost 64 million square miles (166 million sq. km)—more than all the land areas of the earth combined. As you learned in Chapter 1, bodies of salt water smaller than the oceans are called seas, gulfs, bays, or straits. Look back at the diagram on pages 14–15 of the Geography Handbook to see these features again.

Reading Check What is the difference between groundwater and aquifers?

Section 1 Assessment

Defining Terms

1. **Define** water vapor, water cycle, evaporation, condensation, precipitation, collection, glacier, groundwater, aquifer.

Recalling Facts

2. **Region** What percentage of the earth is covered by water?
3. **Movement** In which part of the water cycle does water return to the earth?
4. **Region** What are the world's four oceans?

Critical Thinking

5. **Understanding Cause and Effect** How does the temperature of the air affect the amount of humidity that you feel? How does the air's temperature also influence the form of precipitation that falls?
6. **Drawing Conclusions** Why do you think it is important to keep groundwater free of dangerous chemicals?

Graphic Organizer

7. **Organizing Information** Draw a diagram like this one. List at least four sources of freshwater and salt water on the lines under each heading.

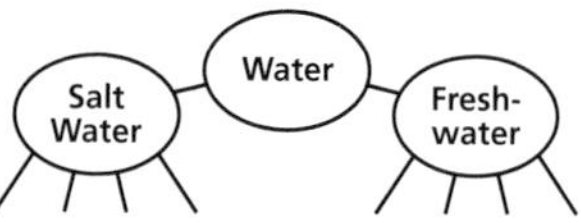

Applying Social Studies Skills

8. **Analyzing Diagrams** Look at the diagram of the water cycle on page 49. From where does water evaporate?

Section 1 Assessment

1. The terms are defined in the Glossary.
2. 70 percent
3. precipitation
4. Arctic, Atlantic, Indian, Pacific
5. The warmer the air, the more water vapor it can hold. When precipitation occurs, it takes one of four forms—rain, snow, sleet, or hail—depending on the temperature of the surrounding air.
6. *Possible answers:* because there is more freshwater in the ground than on the surface; because people in some areas depend on groundwater for survival
7. *Freshwater:* glaciers, lakes, rivers, groundwater; *Salt water (any four):* oceans, seas, gulfs, bays, straits
8. from lakes, streams, and oceans (*or* from any body of water on the earth's surface)

Making Connections

ART | SCIENCE | CULTURE | TECHNOLOGY

Exploring Earth's Water

More than two-thirds of the earth's surface is covered with water, yet scientists know more about the surface of the moon than they do about the ocean floor. Using an AUV, or autonomous underwater vehicle, called *Autosub,* researchers hope to gain a new understanding about the earth's watery surface.

What It Does

It looks like a giant torpedo, but *Autosub* is really a battery-powered robotic submarine that is 23 feet (7 m) long. Its mission is to explore parts of the ocean that are beyond the reach of other research vessels or are too dangerous for humans. Although it is still being tested, *Autosub* has already conducted hundreds of underwater missions.

Exploring Ice Shelves

One of the most promising areas of research for *Autosub* lies in seawater under the ice shelves near Greenland in the Arctic and near Antarctica at the southern extreme of the globe. Traditional submarines are unable to explore these places safely. Satellite photographs show that the area of the ice shelves is changing. Scientists want to use *Autosub*'s technology to measure changes in the thickness of sea ice. They believe that this information may give important clues about the possible rise in the earth's temperature.

Sea ice plays an important role in keeping the earth's climate stable. It acts as insulation—a kind of protection—between the ocean and the atmosphere. Sea ice reflects light, so it limits the amount of heat absorbed into the water. This keeps the ocean from getting too warm. In winter, sea ice helps prevent heat from escaping the warmer oceans into the atmosphere.

What the Future Holds

So far, *Autosub*'s missions have been fairly short. Scientists hope to someday program *Autosub* to make long voyages, sampling seawater and collecting data from ocean floors. The information that *Autosub* provides will help scientists make better predictions about the earth's climate.

▲ ***Autosub*** **can be launched from shore, towed out to sea by a small boat, or lowered by a crane into the water.**

Making the Connection

1. What is *Autosub*?
2. Why do scientists want to use *Autosub* to explore under the ice shelves?
3. **Understanding Cause and Effect** How could a loss of sea ice affect the earth's climate?

TEACH

Tell students that in May 1961, President John F. Kennedy announced the goal of landing an American on the moon before the end of the 1960s. This goal was met in July 1969. Point out that no similar goal has ever been stated relating to oceanographic research. **Ask:** **Which do you think is more important—exploration of space or under the sea? Why? L1**

More About *Autosub*

In addition to exploring sea ice, *Autosub* should be useful in several other areas of oceanographic research, including tracking waste, spotting hazards in the ocean floor, monitoring changes in the environment, and identifying underwater sources of valuable resources and minerals. The team that developed the first *Autosub* is at work on a second, improved model.

Interdisciplinary Connections

Science One kind of instrument used by *Autosub* is sonar, which is used to detect the contours and depths of the ocean's floor. Have students investigate sonar and prepare a diagram or display showing how it works. **L3**

Making the Connection

1. a battery-powered robotic submarine 23 feet (7 m) long that explores the ocean floors
2. Traditional submarines cannot explore these areas safely. Scientists want to use the *Autosub* to measure changes in the thickness of the sea ice. They believe this information will provide clues about global warming.
3. Sea ice reflects the sun's heat, limiting the amount of heat absorbed by water and preventing the ocean from getting too warm. In winter, sea ice prevents heat from escaping from the warmer oceans, and so prevents the water from becoming too cold.

Chapter 2

Section 2, pages 52–59

1 Focus

Section Objectives

1. Explain what climate is.
2. Describe how wind and water move around the earth.
3. Discuss what causes precipitation and storms.
4. Describe what El Niño and La Niña are.

BELLRINGER Skillbuilder Activity

Project transparency and have students answer the question.

Daily Focus Skills Transparency

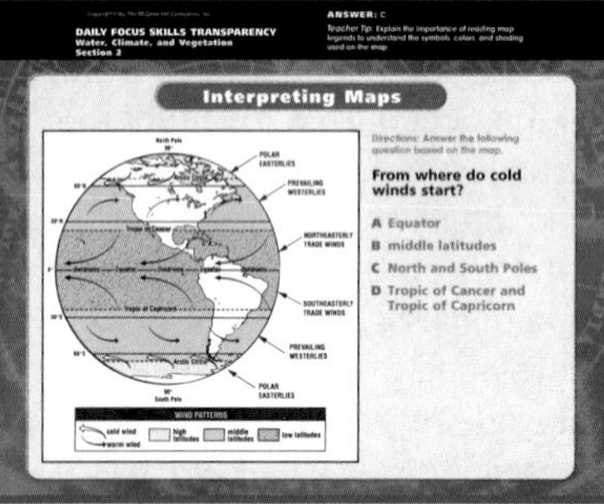

Reading Preview

■ **Activating Prior Knowledge** Write the words *climate* and *weather* on the board. Ask if students can suggest how the two terms differ in meaning.

■ **Preteaching Vocabulary** Point out to students that the *ñ* in *El Niño* and *La Niña* is pronounced "nyuh" (NEE • nyoh; NEE • nyah). Have them practice saying the words.

Guide to Reading

Main Idea

Wind and water carry rainfall and the sun's warmth around the world to create different climates.

Terms to Know

- weather
- climate
- Tropics
- drought
- El Niño
- La Niña
- current
- local wind
- rain shadow
- greenhouse effect
- rain forest

Reading Strategy

Create a chart like this one. Write at least two details that explain how each force contributes to climate.

Sun	Wind	Water

Section 2 Climate

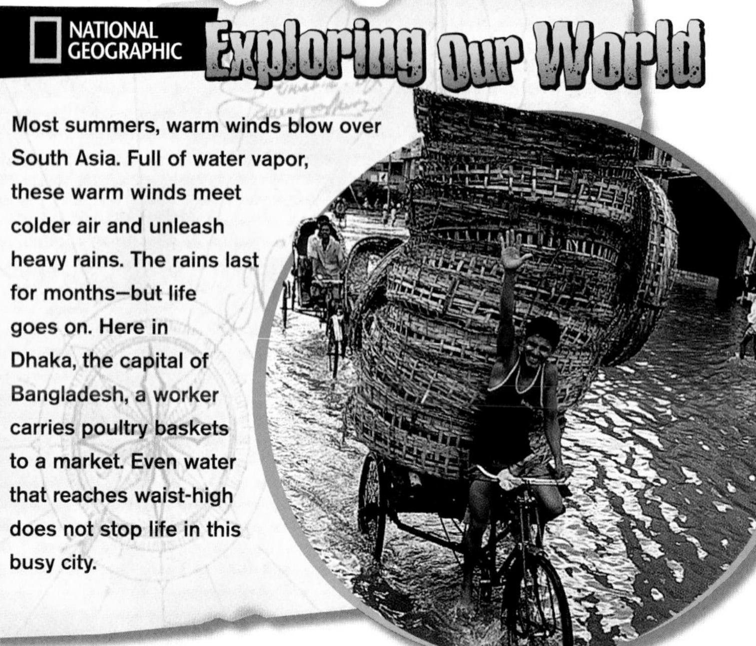

NATIONAL GEOGRAPHIC Exploring Our World

Most summers, warm winds blow over South Asia. Full of water vapor, these warm winds meet colder air and unleash heavy rains. The rains last for months—but life goes on. Here in Dhaka, the capital of Bangladesh, a worker carries poultry baskets to a market. Even water that reaches waist-high does not stop life in this busy city.

Why are some areas of the world full of lush forests, while others are covered with bone-dry deserts? Why do some people struggle through chilling winters, while others enjoy a day at the beach? To understand these mysteries, you need to unlock the secrets of climate.

Weather and Climate

As you learned in Chapter 1, the earth is surrounded by the atmosphere, which holds a combination of gases we call air. The many layers of the atmosphere protect life on the earth from harmful rays of the sun. The layer of atmosphere closest to the earth is also where you will find weather patterns. Suppose a friend calls you and asks what it is like outside. You might say, "It's a beautiful day—warm and sunny!" You are describing the weather. **Weather** refers to the unpredictable changes in air that take place over a short period of time.

Suppose that someone from another country asks what summers and winters are like in your area. You might say, "Summers are usually hot and rainy, and winters are cool but dry." This answer describes not the weather but your area's climate. **Climate** is the usual, predictable

Section Resources

Reproducible Masters
- Reproducible Lesson Plan
- Daily Lecture and Discussion Notes
- Note-taking Guide
- Guided Reading Activity
- Reading Essentials and Study Guide
- Section Quiz

Transparencies
- Daily Focus Skills Transparency
- GeoQuiz Transparency

Multimedia
- Vocabulary PuzzleMaker CD-ROM
- Interactive Tutor Self-Assessment CD-ROM
- Presentation Plus! CD-ROM
- ExamView® Pro Testmaker CD-ROM

pattern of weather in an area over a long period of time. Studies of climate show the highs and lows of temperature and precipitation over the course of 30 years or more.

✓ Reading Check **What is the difference between weather and climate?**

The Sun and Climate

What causes climate? The original source of climate is the sun. It gives off energy and light that all plants and animals need to survive. The sun's rays warm the air, water, and land on our planet. Warm gases and liquids are lighter than cool gases and liquids. Because they are lighter, the warmer gases and liquids rise. Then wind and water carry this warmth around the globe, spreading the sun's heat.

Latitude and Climate Climate is also affected by the angle at which the sun's rays hit the earth. As you learned in Chapter 1, the sun's rays hit various places at different angles at different times of the year. These changes are caused by the earth's tilt and revolution around the sun. The sun's rays hit places in low latitudes—regions near the **Equator**—more directly than places at higher latitudes. The low latitudes near the Equator, known as the **Tropics,** lie between the **Tropic of Cancer** (23½°N latitude) and the **Tropic of Capricorn** (23½°S latitude). If you lived in the Tropics, you would almost always experience a hot climate, unless you lived high in the mountains where temperatures are cooler. Find the Tropics on the map on page 54. (To learn how to use latitude and longitude, turn to page 60.)

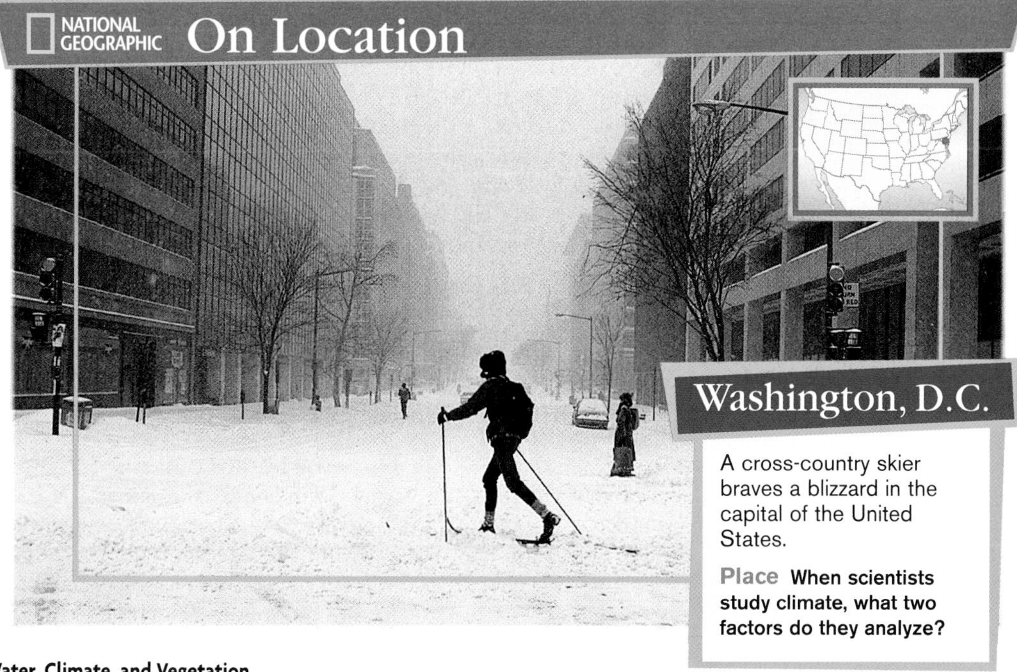

Washington, D.C.

A cross-country skier braves a blizzard in the capital of the United States.

Place **When scientists study climate, what two factors do they analyze?**

Formulating Questions

Have students suggest what kinds of questions geographers might ask to determine the climate of a region. *(How much precipitation falls on average each month? What are the extremes of precipitation? What is the average temperature each month? What are the extremes of temperature?)* L1

WATER, CLIMATE, AND VEGETATION

Daily Lecture and Discussion Notes

Climate

Did You Know? Climate changes over time. For example, a thousand years ago northern latitudes were milder than they are today. The warmer climate enabled Vikings from Iceland to settle on the southern coast of Greenland, but the colder climate that developed over the following centuries wiped out the settlements.

I. Weather and Climate

A. **Weather** refers to the unpredictable changes in air that take place over a short period of time. **Climate** is the usual, predictable pattern of weather in an area over a long period of time.

B. Climate is affected by the sun, the wind, the oceans and other bodies of water,

✓ Reading Check Answer

Weather includes unpredictable changes in the air over a short period of time; climate is the usual, predictable weather over a long period of time.

More About the Photo

Climate In 1870 the United States set up the world's first system for warning people of severe weather. It focused on the Great Lakes and aimed at preventing deaths to sailors.

Caption Answer extremes of temperature and precipitation

Reading Strategy — Reading the Text

Visualizing Share with students some of the photographs and verbal descriptions of severe storms in the *National Geographic* article "Living with Natural Hazards" (July 1998). Have students research tornadoes, hurricanes, floods, and drought-induced fires. Then, using information from their research, have them work in pairs to write their own first-person accounts of what it would be like to live through such an experience. Ask for pairs to read their accounts. L1

EE5 Environment and Society: Standard 15

Chapter 2

Section 2, pages 52–59

Reading Strategy

Making Inferences Have students read the paragraph describing monsoons. **Ask:** **Why do the summer monsoons in Africa and Asia bring rain?** *(Because they blow inland from the sea, they hold much moisture.)* L2

Applying Map Skills

Answers

1. generally west to east
2. northeasterly trade winds

Skills Practice

Where are the polar fronts located? *(along the Arctic and Antarctic Circles)*

Cultural Kaleidoscope

Pacific Winds The winds that blow near the Tropics in the Pacific generally move in a westward direction, which means that they were favorable for the sailing ships of earlier centuries to cross the ocean. Sailors from these periods called them trade winds because they aided in oceangoing commercial voyages.

Reading Check Answer

Because the earth is tilted, the sun's rays hit the surface in different amounts in different places. Areas in which the sun's rays hit more directly have warmer climates.

NATIONAL GEOGRAPHIC **Prevailing Wind Patterns**

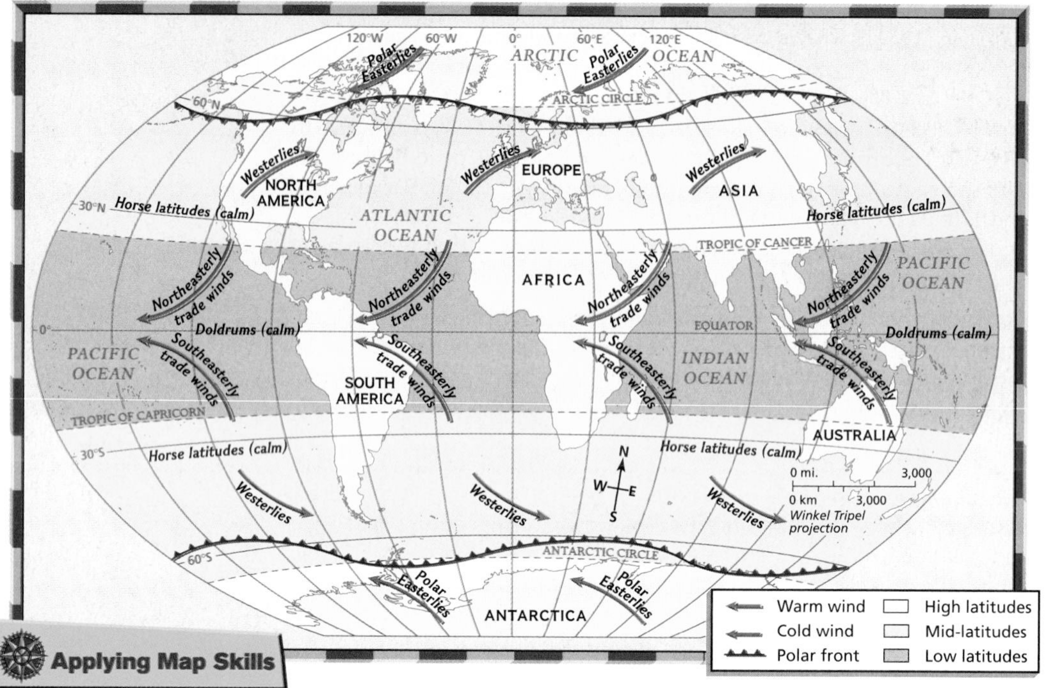

Applying Map Skills

1. In which general direction does the wind blow over North America?
2. What winds did European sailors use to get to South America and the islands north of it?

Find NGS online map resources @ www.nationalgeographic.com/maps

Outside the Tropics, the sun is never directly overhead. The mid-latitudes extend from the Tropics to about 60° both north and south of the Equator. When the North Pole is tilted toward the sun, the sun's rays fall more directly on the Northern Hemisphere. This affects our climate by giving us warm summer days. Six months later, the South Pole is tilted toward the sun, and the seasons are reversed. At the high latitudes near the North and South Poles, the sun's rays hit very indirectly. Climates in these regions are always cool or cold.

Reading Check **How does the tilt of the earth affect climate?**

The Wind's Effect on Climate

Movements of air are called winds. From year to year, winds follow prevailing, or typical, patterns. These patterns are very complex. One reason is that winds do more than move east and west or north and south. They also go up and down. As you learned earlier, warm air rises and cold air falls. Thus, the warmer winds near the Equator rise and move north and south toward the Poles of the earth. The colder winds from the Poles sink and move toward the Equator. This exchange is complicated by the fact that the earth rotates, which causes the winds to curve. Winds, then, are in constant motion in many directions.

54 CHAPTER 2

Differentiated Instruction

Meeting Special Needs: Visual/Spatial To better understand the idea that climate addresses the overall average of temperature and precipitation—as well as the extremes—have students review the climograph of Moscow, Russia, in the Geography Handbook. Point out that the bars represent precipitation and the line shows temperature. Have students compare the range of both measures for Moscow. **Ask:** **Are temperatures relatively even throughout the year? What about precipitation?** *(Moscow's temperature changes with the seasons; precipitation is fairly even, although summer months receive more precipitation.)* L1

Refer to *Inclusion for the Middle School Social Studies Classroom Strategies and Activities* in the TCR.

Another important wind pattern is the monsoon. Monsoons are tremendous seasonal winds that blow over continents for months at a time. They are found mainly in Asia and some areas in Africa. Although they often are destructive, the summer monsoons in South Asia bring much-needed heavy rains.

Storms As you read in Section 1, part of the water cycle is rain and other types of precipitation that fall to the earth. A little rain may ruin a picnic or spoil a ball game, but it is not a serious problem. Sometimes, though, people suffer through fierce storms. What causes these destructive events?

When warm, moist air systems meet cold air systems, thunderstorms may develop. These storms include thunder, lightning, and heavy rain. They tend to be short, lasting only about 30 minutes. Some areas are more likely to see thunderstorms than others. In central Florida, as many as 90 days per year may experience thunderstorms.

A thunderstorm can produce another danger—a tornado. Tornadoes are funnel-shaped windstorms that sometimes form during severe thunderstorms. They occur all over the world, but the United States has more tornadoes than any other area. Winds in tornadoes often reach 250 miles (402 km) per hour.

Hurricanes, or violent tropical storm systems, form over the warm Atlantic Ocean in late summer and fall. Hurricanes bring high winds that can reach more than 150 miles (241 km) per hour. They also produce rough seas and carry drenching rain. Hurricanes strike North America and the islands in the Caribbean Sea. They also rip through Asia, although in that region they are called typhoons. These storms can do tremendous damage. Their strong winds destroy buildings and snap power lines. Heavy rains can flood low-lying areas.

El Niño and La Niña In 1998 the world experienced unusual weather. Heavy rains brought floods to Peru, washing away whole villages. Europe, eastern Africa, and most of the southern United States also had severe flooding. In the western Pacific, normally heavy rains never came. Indonesia suffered a **drought,** a long period of extreme dryness. The land there became so dry that forest fires burned thousands of acres of trees. Thick smoke from the fires forced drivers to put their headlights on at noon!

Why did these disasters take place? They resulted from a combination of temperature, wind, and water effects in the Pacific Ocean called **El Niño** (ehl NEE•nyoh). The name "El Niño" was coined by early Spanish explorers in the Pacific. They used the phrase—which refers to the Christ child and means "the boy"—because the effect hits South America around Christmas.

El Niños form when cold winds from the east are weak. Without these cold winds, the central Pacific Ocean grows warmer than usual. More water evaporates, and more clouds form. The thick band of clouds changes wind and rain patterns. Some areas receive heavier than normal rains and others have less than normal rainfall.

Believe It or Not!

Mt. Pinatubo

Mt. Pinatubo (PEE•nah•TOO•boh) is a volcanic mountain in the Philippine Islands. Its eruption in the early 1990s impacted the world's climate. The powerful explosion shot ash and sulfur dioxide into the earth's atmosphere. This blocked some of the sun's rays from reaching the earth. The world's climate was cooler for two years after the volcano's blast.

Critical Thinking Activity

Determining Cause and Effect Organize students into several small groups. Have groups create a poster or some other form of visual that can be used to teach a lesson on the factors that affect climate in your region. Make certain that all group members have an assigned task. Some might do research, others might work on the design of the visual, and still others might create illustrations or write captions. Call on groups to display their finished visuals and use them to teach the rest of the class about these factors. L2

EE3 Physical Systems: Standard 7

Chapter 2

Section 2, pages 52–59

L1/ELL

Guided Reading Activity

Name ______ Date ______ Class ______

WATER, CLIMATE, AND VEGETATION

Guided Reading Activity 2

Climate

DIRECTIONS: Filling in the Blanks Reading the section and completing the sentences below will help you learn more about climate. Refer to your textbook to fill in the blanks.

(1) ______ describes the unpredictable changes in air that occur over a short period of time. (2) ______ is the usual, predictable pattern of weather in a certain area over a long period of time. It is affected by the sun, wind, ocean currents, (3) ______, and people. Scientists look at the extremes of (4) ______ and precipitation in order to understand the

Cultural Kaleidoscope

Australia In Australia, the tropical storms called hurricanes and typhoons elsewhere are given the colorful name *willy-willies.*

Did You Know?

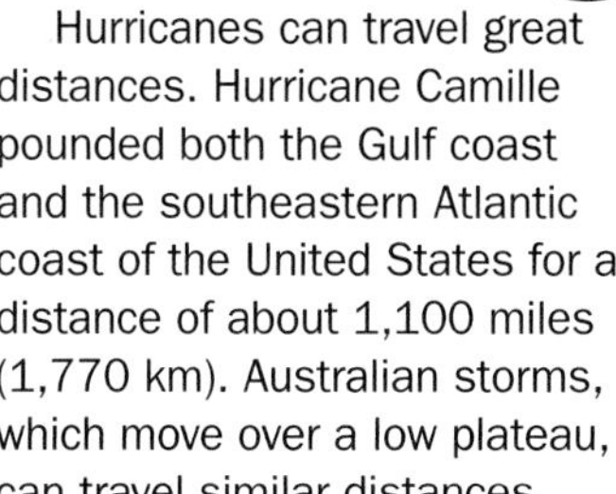

Hurricanes can travel great distances. Hurricane Camille pounded both the Gulf coast and the southeastern Atlantic coast of the United States for a distance of about 1,100 miles (1,770 km). Australian storms, which move over a low plateau, can travel similar distances.

Travel Guide

Hurricanes typically come at particular times of the year. The official hurricane season for the entire Gulf of Mexico region lasts from June 1 to November 1, but the likelihood of a hurricane is strongest in September.

Chapter 2

Section 2, pages 52–59

Note-taking tip

Suggest that students keep track of the differing effects of El Niño and La Niña by recording their notes on the two phenomena. They should create three columns in their notebooks with the headings "Region," "El Niño," and "La Niña." In the first column, they should list an area of the world. In the next two, they should record the effect that the phenomenon at the top of the column has on that area.

Reading Check Answer

When cold winds from the Pacific become weak, waters in the central Pacific Ocean grow warmer than usual, leading to more evaporation and rain in certain areas.

Analyzing the Diagram

Answer
The jet stream drops from northern North America to central North America (or closer to the Equator).

Skills Practice
How does El Niño affect Tahiti? *(The air pressure over Tahiti becomes lower than normal.)*

Reading Check Answer

east coast of North America and Western Europe

NORMAL CONDITIONS

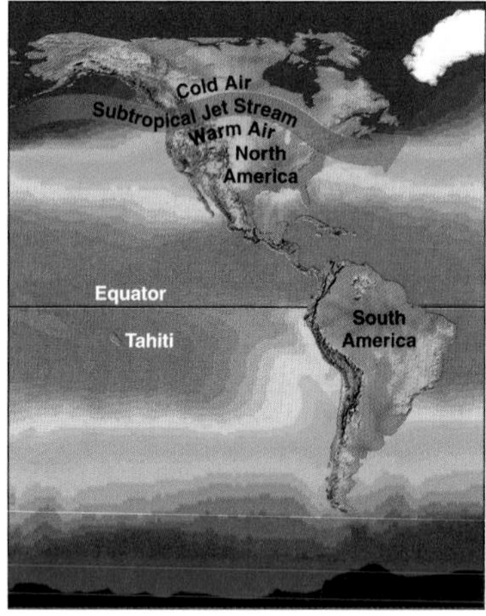

EL NIÑO CONDITIONS

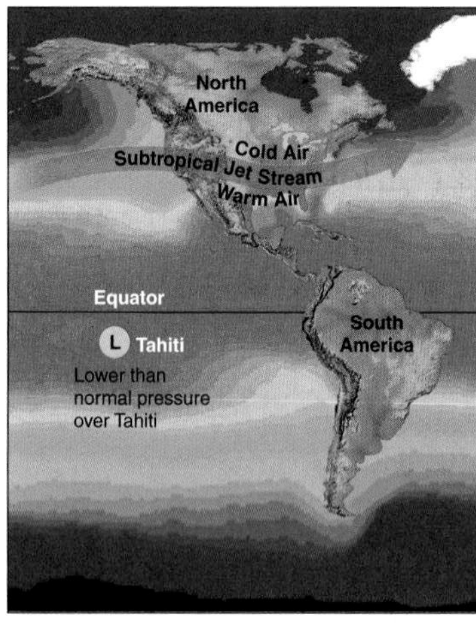

Analyzing the Diagram

The temperature of the oceans varies from warm (dark red) to very cold (dark purple).

Movement **What happens to the jet stream during El Niño conditions?**

Does El Niño happen every year? Scientists have found that El Niño occurs about every three years. They also found that in some years, the opposite kind of unusual weather takes place. This event is called **La Niña** (lah NEE•nyah), Spanish for "the girl," because the effects are the opposite of those in El Niño. Winds from the east become very strong, cooling more of the Pacific. When this happens, heavy clouds form in the western Pacific.

Reading Check **Why do El Niños occur?**

Ocean Currents

Winds carry large masses of warm and cool air around the earth. At the same time, moving streams of water called **currents** carry warm or cool water through the world's oceans. Look at the map on page 57. As you can see, these currents follow certain patterns. Notice how the warm currents tend to move along the Equator or from the Equator to the Poles. The cold currents carry cold polar water toward the Equator.

These currents affect the climate of land areas. Look at the warm current called the Gulf Stream. It flows from the Gulf of Mexico along the east coast of North America. Then it crosses the Atlantic Ocean toward Europe, where it is called the North Atlantic Current. Winds that blow over these warm waters bring warm air to western Europe. Because these winds blow from west to east, areas in Europe enjoy warmer weather than areas lying west of the Gulf Stream in Canada.

Reading Check **What areas of the world would be affected by a change in the Gulf Stream?**

Landforms and Climate

Wind and water affect climate, but the shape of the land has an effect on climate as well. Where the landforms are in relation to one another and to water influences climate too.

Landforms and Local Winds Although geographers study major wind patterns that blow over the earth, they also look at local winds. **Local winds** are patterns of wind caused by landforms in a particular area. Some local winds occur because land warms and cools more quickly than water does. As a result, cool sea breezes keep coastal areas cool during the

Team-Teaching Activity

Government Point out that Florida faces high probabilities for both hurricanes and tornadoes. Nevertheless, the population there more than doubled from 1970 to 2000. **Ask:** **What problems would this population growth cause in the event of a severe storm?** *(need to evacuate, rescue, or provide aid to larger numbers of people if a disaster occurs)* **What can governments do to try to address these problems?** *(plan evacuation routes, have emergency teams ready)* **L1** 

EE4 Human Systems: Standard 9

World Ocean Currents

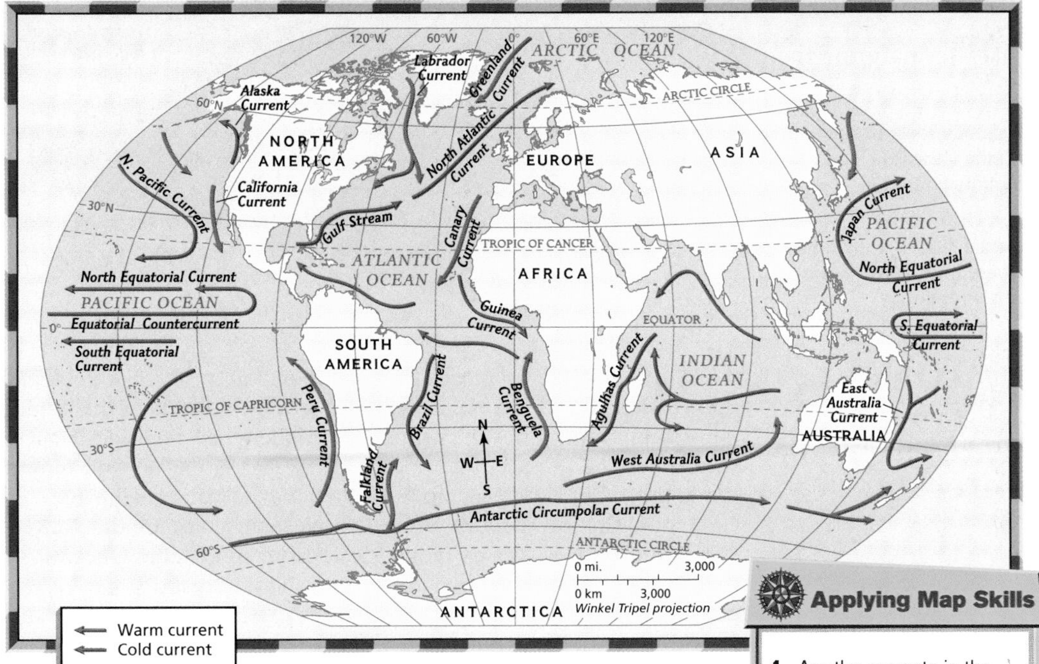

Applying Map Skills

1. Are the currents in the Indian Ocean warm or cold?
2. Where does the Peru Current flow?

Find NGS online map resources @ www.nationalgeographic.com/maps

day. After the sun sets, the opposite occurs. The air over the land cools more quickly than the air over water does. At night, then, a cool breeze blows from the land out to the sea.

A similar effect occurs near mountains. Air warmed by the sun rises up mountain slopes during the day. At night, cooler air moves down the mountain into the valley below. Have you ever seen fog lying on a valley floor on a cool morning? That fog was caused by the cool air that came down the mountain during the night.

Mountains, Temperature, and Rainfall The higher the elevation of a particular place, the lower the temperature that place will have. In high mountains, the air becomes thinner and cannot hold as much heat from the sun. The temperature drops. Even in the Tropics, snow covers the peaks of high mountains.

Mountains also have an effect on rainfall. When warm, moist winds blow inland from the ocean toward a coastal mountain range, the winds are forced upward over the mountains. As these warm winds rise, the air cools and loses its moisture. Rain or snow falls on the mountains. The climate on this windward—or wind-facing—side of mountain ranges is moist and often foggy. Trees are thick and green.

Applying Map Skills

Answers

1. warm
2. from south to north along the western coast of South America

Skills Practice

Which currents in the Pacific Ocean are warmer, those in the central part of the ocean or those along the eastern side? *(those in the central part)*

Building Skills

Outlining Have students prepare an outline of the section's contents. Remind them that their outlines should include notes explaining how each factor discussed in the section affects climate.

Measure student knowledge of political entities.

GeoQuiz Transparency

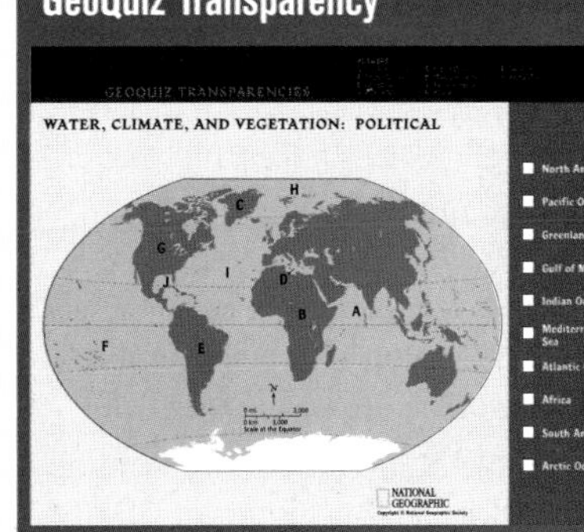

Content Background

Greenhouse Gases The main gases that contribute to the greenhouse effect are carbon dioxide and methane. Although carbon dioxide, released by the burning of fossil fuels, has risen less than 0.3 percent a year, the current levels are almost one-third higher than they were before the Industrial Revolution. Methane comes from bacteria found in rice fields, from the decomposition of garbage, from the release of gases by cattle, and from the production of fossil fuels. Although carbon dioxide is a serious threat as a greenhouse gas, the amount of methane in the atmosphere is actually increasing at a more rapid rate than the amount of carbon dioxide. Nitrous oxide and chlorofluorocarbons (CFCs) are other greenhouse gases. An international treaty forbids further use of CFCs due to their harmful effects on the ozone layer.

Analyzing the Diagram

Answer
windward side

Reading Check Answer

because the air becomes thinner and cannot hold as much heat from the sun

L2

Section Quiz

Name ____________ Date ____________ Class ____________

WATER, CLIMATE, AND VEGETATION

Score

Section 2 Quiz

Climate

DIRECTIONS: Matching Match each item in Column A with the items in Column B. Write the correct letters in the blanks. *(10 points each)*

COLUMN A	COLUMN B
A. currents	____ **1.** tropical storm systems that form over the Atlantic Ocean
B. typhoons	____ **2.** tropical storm systems in Asia
C. weather	____ **3.** unpredictable changes in the air during short periods of time
D. hurricanes	____ **4.** moving streams of ocean water
E. climate	____ **5.** an area's usual weather pattern over long periods of time

DIRECTIONS: Multiple Choice In the blank at the left, write the letter of the choice that best completes the statement or answers the question. *(10 points each)*

____ **6.** The climate on the windward side of coastal mountain ranges is
A. the same as the climate on the leeward side.
B. cool and dry.
C. humid and foggy.
D. hot and dry.

____ **7.** Dense forests called rain forests are located
A. at both Poles.
B. everywhere.
C. at all latitudes.
D. along the Equator.

____ **8.** The often destructive seasonal winds that bring much-needed rain to South Asia are called
A. typhoons.
B. monsoons.
C. hurricanes.
D. thunderstorms.

____ **9.** Land areas in latitudes near the Equator are called the
A. high latitudes.
B. currents.
C. Poles.
D. Tropics.

____ **10.** The dry area on the leeward side of coastal mountains is called a
A. monsoon.
B. rain shadow.
C. tropical climate.
D. natural landform.

22

Assess

Assign Section 2 Assessment as homework or an in-class activity.

Have students use the Interactive Tutor Self-Assessment CD-ROM to review Section 2.

Rain Shadow

Analyzing the Diagram

Rain shadows usually occur on the leeward sides of mountain ranges.

Location **What is the term for the side of a mountain where the climate is moist and often foggy?**

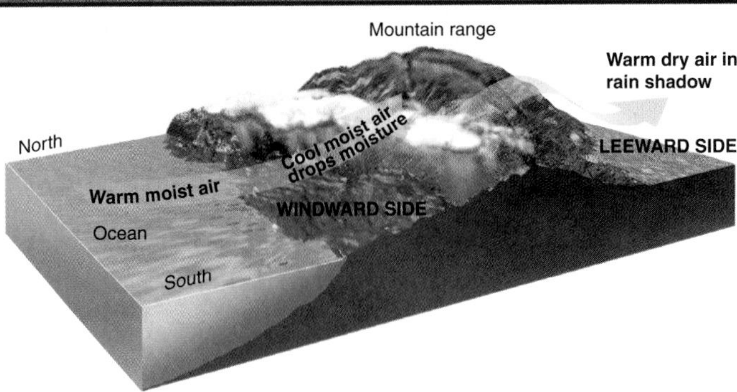

By the time the air moves over the mountain peaks, it is cool and dry. This creates a **rain shadow**, a dry area on the side of the mountains facing away from the wind. Geographers call this side the leeward side. The dry air of a rain shadow warms up again as it moves down the leeward side, giving the region a dry or desert climate.

A rain shadow occurs along the western coast of the United States and Canada. Winds moving east from the Pacific Ocean lose their moisture as they move upward on the windward slopes of the coastal mountains. Great deserts and dry basins are located on the leeward side of these ranges.

Reading Check **Why are areas of higher elevation often cooler?**

The Impact of People on Climate

People's actions can affect climate. You may have noticed that temperatures in large cities are generally higher than those in nearby rural areas. Why is that? The city's streets and buildings absorb more of the sun's rays than do the plants and trees of rural areas.

Cities are warmer even in winter. People burn fuels to warm houses, power industry, and move cars and buses along the streets. This burning raises the temperature in the city. The burning also releases a cloud of chemicals into the air. These chemicals blanket the city and hold in more of the sun's heat, creating a so-called heat island.

The Greenhouse Effect In the past two hundred years, people have burned coal, oil, and natural gas as sources of energy. Burning these fuels releases certain gases into the air. Some scientists warn that the buildup of these gases presents dangers. It creates a **greenhouse effect**—like a greenhouse, the gases prevent the warm air from rising and escaping into the atmosphere. As a result, the overall temperature of the earth will increase. Some scientists predict disastrous results from this global warming. They say the ice at the North and South Poles will melt. Then ocean levels will rise and flood coastal cities. Some areas that are now fertile will become unable to grow crops.

Content Background

Global Warming Scientists have found that the average global temperature has increased about 1°F (0.6°C) in the past 100 years. The amount seems very small, but researchers point out that a *drop* in temperature of the same magnitude occurred in the 1500s to the 1700s and brought about a period called the "Little Ice Age" in Europe—named because of the generally cold temperatures that significantly reduced crop yields. A study by the Intergovernmental Panel on Climate Change (IPCC), an independent group of scientists whose work is backed by the United Nations, suggests that an even sharper increase—perhaps as much as from 2°F to 7°F (1°C to 4°C)—may occur over the next century.

Not all scientists agree about the greenhouse effect. Some argue that the world is not warming. Others say that even if it is, the predictions of disaster are extreme. Many scientists are studying world temperature trends closely. They hope to be able to discover whether the greenhouse effect is a real threat.

Clearing the Rain Forests Along the Equator, dense forests called **rain forests** receive high amounts of rain each year. In some countries, people are clearing large areas of these forests. They want to sell the lumber from the trees. They also want to use the land to grow crops or as pasture for cattle. Clearing the rain forests, though, can hurt the world's climate.

One danger is related to the greenhouse effect. People often clear the forests by burning down the trees. This burning releases more gases into the air, just like burning oil or natural gas does. Another danger of clearing the rain forests is related to rainfall. Remember the water cycle discussed in Section 1? Water on the earth's surface evaporates into the air and then falls as rain. In the rain forests, much of this water evaporates from the leaves of trees. If the trees are cut, less water will evaporate. As a result, less rain will fall. Scientists worry that over time the area that now holds rain forests will actually become dry and unable to grow anything.

✓Reading Check **What are two dangers of clearing the rain forests?**

Social Studies Online

Web Activity Visit ***The World and Its People*** Web site at twip.glencoe.com and click on **Chapter 2—Student Web Activities** to learn more about the destruction of the rain forests.

Section 2 Assessment

Defining Terms

1. **Define** weather, climate, Tropics, drought, El Niño, La Niña, current, local wind, rain shadow, greenhouse effect, rain forest.

Recalling Facts

2. **Movement** What five elements affect climate?
3. **Location** Between what two lines of latitude are the Tropics?
4. **Place** Provide an example of how landforms influence climate.

Critical Thinking

5. **Making Comparisons** How does the amount of rainfall on the windward side of a mountain differ from that on the leeward side?
6. **Summarizing Information** What general patterns do wind and currents follow?

Graphic Organizer

7. **Organizing Information** Draw a diagram as shown. First, list three human actions that lead to the greenhouse effect. In the third box, list four results of the greenhouse effect.

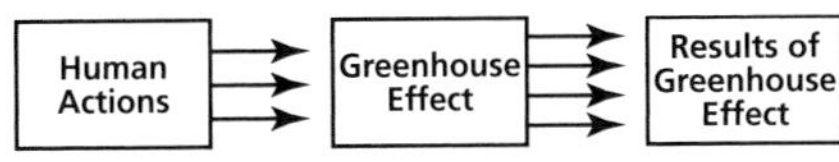

Applying Social Studies Skills

8. **Analyzing Maps** Look at the world ocean currents map on page 57. Which continent lies completely outside the Tropics?

Section 2 Assessment

1. The terms are defined in the Glossary.
2. the sun, wind, water, landforms, people
3. between 23 1/2°N (Tropic of Cancer) and 23 1/2°S (Tropic of Capricorn)
4. *Possible response:* Mountains are cooler because the thin air around them cannot hold as much of the sun's warmth.
5. The windward side receives more rain. As winds are forced up and over mountains, the air has less moisture on the leeward side.
6. Warmer Equator winds rise and move north and south toward the Poles, and colder polar winds sink and flow toward the Equator.
7. *Possible response:* First box—building cities, burning fuels, powering industries; third box—melting ice at Poles, rising ocean levels, flooding of cities, unable to grow crops
8. Antarctica

Chapter 2

Section 2, pages 52–59

Social Studies Online

Objectives and answers to the Student Web Activity can be found in the Web Activity Lesson Plan at twip.glencoe.com

✓ Reading Check Answer

Tree burning results in gases being released in the air, creating the greenhouse effect; fewer trees means less water evaporation, which might make rain forests dry and incapable of growing anything.

L1/ELL

Reading Essentials and Study Guide

Name ____ Date ____ Class ____

WATER, CLIMATE, AND VEGETATION

Reading Essentials and Study Guide 2

Climate

Key Terms

weather unpredictable changes in air that take place over a short time
climate usual, predictable pattern of weather in an area over a long time
Tropics areas near the Equator
drought long period of extreme dryness
El Niño period when cold winds over the Pacific Ocean are weak, making the water warmer than usual
La Niña period when cold winds over the Pacific Ocean are strong, making the water colder than usual

Close

Reading Strategy

Writing a Paragraph Have students write a brief paragraph summarizing what climate is and what factors influence it.

TEACH

Draw a map of the neighborhood around the school. Mark street names and include a number of local landmarks, such as the school, a park, and the library. Ask students to describe the locations of the various landmarks by using street names. Suggest that students use the street intersection nearest each landmark. Ask students to share their answers with the class. Point out that identifying locations by using lines of latitude and longitude follows the same principle. Have students read the skill and complete the questions. L1

Additional Skills Practice

1. What is another name used for lines of longitude? *(meridians)* For lines of latitude? *(parallels)*
2. What city on the map lies almost on the Equator? *(Singapore)* On the Prime Meridian (Meridian of Greenwich)? *(London)*

Additional Skills Resources

 Chapter Skills Review

 Building Geography Skills for Life

GLENCOE TECHNOLOGY

 **Skillbuilder Interactive Workbook CD-ROM, Level 1**

This interactive CD-ROM reinforces student mastery of essential social studies skills.

Social Studies Skill

Using Latitude and Longitude

Learning the Skill

To find an exact location, geographers use a set of imaginary lines. One set of lines—**latitude** lines—circles the earth's surface like a stack of rings. The starting point for numbering latitude lines is the Equator, which is 0° latitude. Lines of latitude are numbered from 1° to 90° and are followed by an N or S to show whether they are north or south of the Equator. Latitude lines are also called parallels.

A second set of lines—**longitude** lines—runs vertically from the North Pole to the South Pole. These lines are also called meridians. The starting point—0° longitude—is called the Prime Meridian (or Meridian of Greenwich). Longitude lines are numbered from 1° to 180° followed by an E or W—to show whether they are east or west of the Prime Meridian.

To find latitude and longitude, choose a place on a map. Identify the nearest parallel, or line of latitude. Is it located north or south of the Equator? Now identify the nearest meridian, or line of longitude. Is it located east or west of the Prime Meridian?

Practicing the Skill

1. On the map below, what is the exact location of Washington, D.C.?
2. Which cities on the map lie south of 0° latitude?
3. Which city is located near 30°N, 30°E?

Applying the Skill

Turn to pages RA2–RA3 of the **Reference Atlas.** Determine the latitude and longitude for one city. Ask a classmate to use the information to find and name the city.

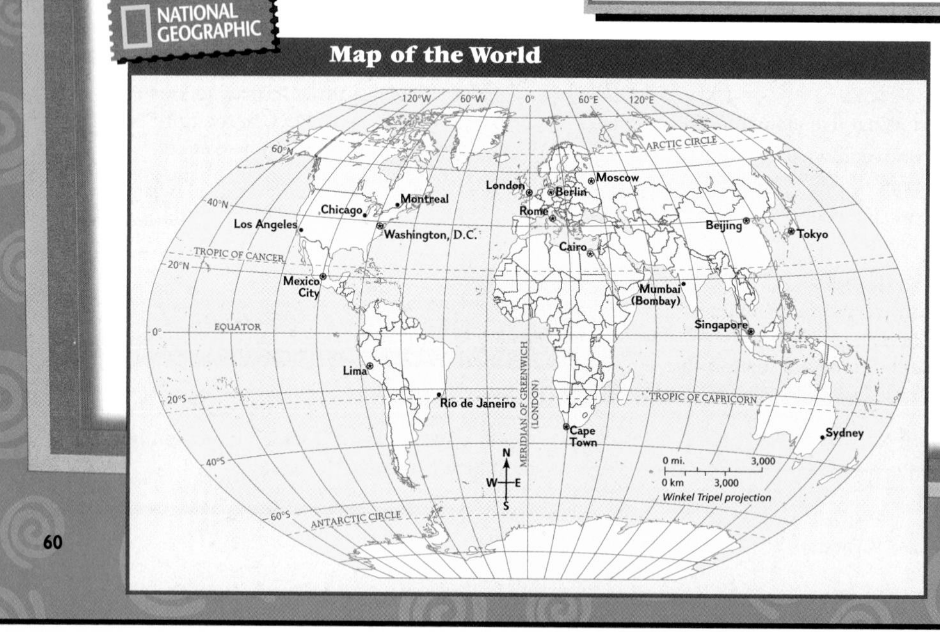

Practicing the Skill Answers

1. about 40°N, 80°W
2. Lima, Rio de Janeiro, Cape Town, Sydney
3. Cairo

Applying the Skill
Monitor students as they complete the activity.

Climate Zones and Vegetation

Guide to Reading

Main Idea

Geographers divide the world into different climate zones.

Terms to Know

- savanna
- marine west coast climate
- Mediterranean climate
- humid continental climate
- humid subtropical climate
- subarctic
- tundra
- steppe

Reading Strategy

Create a chart like this one by listing the categories of each type of climate next to the correct headings.

Climate Type	Categories
Tropical	
Mid-Latitude	
High Latitude	
Dry	
Highland	

NATIONAL GEOGRAPHIC Exploring Our World

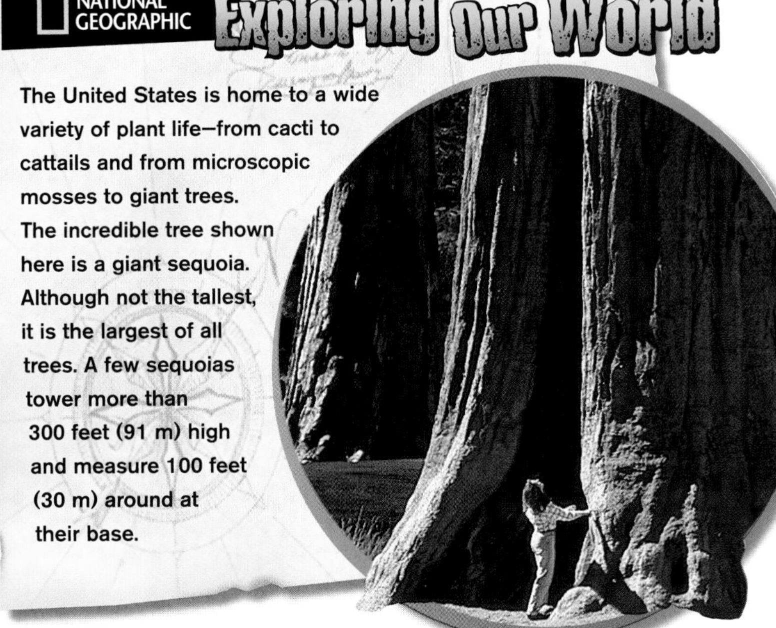

The United States is home to a wide variety of plant life—from cacti to cattails and from microscopic mosses to giant trees. The incredible tree shown here is a giant sequoia. Although not the tallest, it is the largest of all trees. A few sequoias tower more than 300 feet (91 m) high and measure 100 feet (30 m) around at their base.

Why do you think a photograph of a giant tree is in a chapter on climate? The reason is that climate and vegetation go together. Consider this: The state of Washington sits next to the state of Idaho. The plant life in western Washington, however, is much more similar to that of the United Kingdom, which is thousands of miles away, than it is to the plant life in eastern Washington and Idaho, which touch each other. Why? The patterns of temperature, wind, and precipitation in western Washington and the United Kingdom are similar.

Scientists use these patterns to group climates into many different types. They have put the world's climates into five major groups: tropical, mid-latitude, high latitude, dry, and highland. Three of these groups—tropical, mid-latitude, and high latitude—are based on an area's latitude, or distance from the Equator. Some of these major groups have subcategories of climate zones within them. In addition, each climate zone has particular kinds of plants that grow in it.

61

Focus

Section Objectives

1. Describe what major world climate zones are like.
2. Identify where each major world climate zone is located.
3. Explain what kinds of vegetation are grown in each climate zone.

BELLRINGER Skillbuilder Activity

Project transparency and have students answer the question.

Daily Focus Skills Transparency

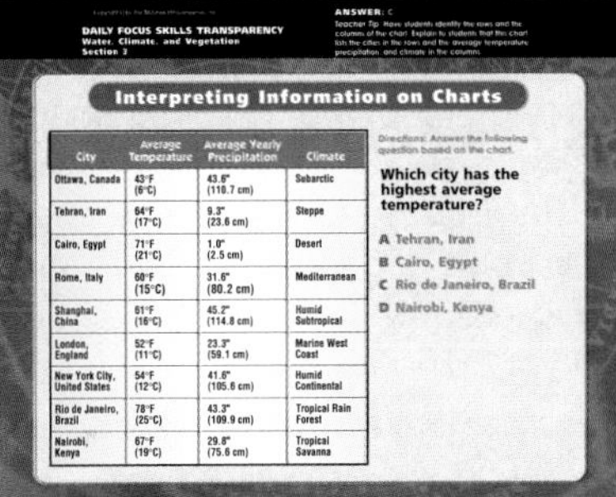

DAILY FOCUS SKILLS TRANSPARENCY
Water, Climate, and Vegetation
Section 3

ANSWER: C

Teacher Tip: Have students identify the rows and the columns of the chart. Explain to students that this chart lists the cities in the rows and the average temperature, precipitation, and climate in the columns.

Interpreting Information on Charts

City	Average Temperature	Average Yearly Precipitation	Climate
Ottawa, Canada	43°F (6°C)	43.6" (110.7 cm)	Subarctic
Tehran, Iran	64°F (17°C)	9.3" (23.6 cm)	Steppe
Cairo, Egypt	71°F (21°C)	1.0" (2.5 cm)	Desert
Rome, Italy	60°F (15°C)	31.6" (80.2 cm)	Mediterranean
Shanghai, China	61°F (16°C)	45.2" (114.8 cm)	Humid Subtropical
London, England	52°F (11°C)	23.3" (59.1 cm)	Marine West Coast
New York City, United States	54°F (12°C)	41.6" (105.6 cm)	Humid Continental
Rio de Janeiro, Brazil	78°F (25°C)	43.3" (109.9 cm)	Tropical Rain Forest
Nairobi, Kenya	67°F (19°C)	29.8" (75.6 cm)	Tropical Savanna

Directions: Answer the following question based on the chart.

Which city has the highest average temperature?

A Tehran, Iran
B Cairo, Egypt
C Rio de Janeiro, Brazil
D Nairobi, Kenya

Reading Preview

■ **Activating Prior Knowledge** Mention to students that the United States has the most varied climate on Earth—that is, it has more climate zones than any other country.

■ **Preteaching Vocabulary** Have students attempt to infer the meanings of the terms *permafrost* and *timberline* from their word parts.

Section Resources

Reproducible Masters

- Reproducible Lesson Plan
- Daily Lecture and Discussion Notes
- Note-taking Guide
- Guided Reading Activity
- Reading Essentials and Study Guide
- Section Quiz

Transparencies

- Daily Focus Skills Transparency
- In-text Map Transparency

Multimedia

- Vocabulary PuzzleMaker CD-ROM
- Interactive Tutor Self-Assessment CD-ROM
- Presentation Plus! CD-ROM
- ExamView® Pro Testmaker CD-ROM

Chapter 2

Section 3, pages 61–68

2 TEACH

Charting Climate Write the names of the months on the board. Ask students to describe the weather in your region over the course of a year. Have them recall any extremes of temperature or precipitation that they can remember from their lifetimes. Write their responses under the appropriate month. When the months are completely filled out, have them discuss the area's climate and reach a consensus on how to describe that climate. Tell students to write down their generalization and check it for accuracy as they read this section. L1

Reading Check Answer

in the Tropics—the region between the Tropic of Cancer and the Tropic of Capricorn

More About the Photos

Savannas Savannas tend to have sandy soil near the surface, allowing grasses to capture water quickly in the rainy season. Where rockier soils extend deeper into the earth, trees can grow.

Caption Answer broad grassland with few trees

Tropical Climates

The tropical climate gets its name from the Tropics—the areas along the Equator reaching from 23½°N to 23½°S. If you like warm weather, you would love a tropical climate. The tropical climate region can be separated into two types—tropical rain forest and tropical savanna. The tropical rain forest climate receives up to 100 inches (254 cm) of rain a year. As a result, the rain forest climate is wet in most months. The tropical savanna climate has two distinct seasons—one wet and one dry.

Tropical Rain Forest Climate Year-round rains in some parts of the Tropics produce lush vegetation and thick rain forests. These forests are home to millions of kinds of plant and animal life. Tall hardwood trees such as mahogany, teak, and ebony form the canopy, or top layer of the forest. The vegetation at the canopy layer is so thick that little sunlight reaches the forest floor. The Amazon Basin in South America is the world's largest rain forest area.

Tropical Savanna Climate In other parts of the Tropics, such as southern India and eastern Africa, rain falls in just a few months of the year. This is called the wet season. The rest of the year is hot and dry. **Savannas**, or broad grasslands with few trees, are the main type of vegetation in this climate region. Find the tropical savanna climate areas on the map on page 63.

Reading Check Where are the tropical climate zones found?

NATIONAL GEOGRAPHIC On Location

Tropical Vegetation

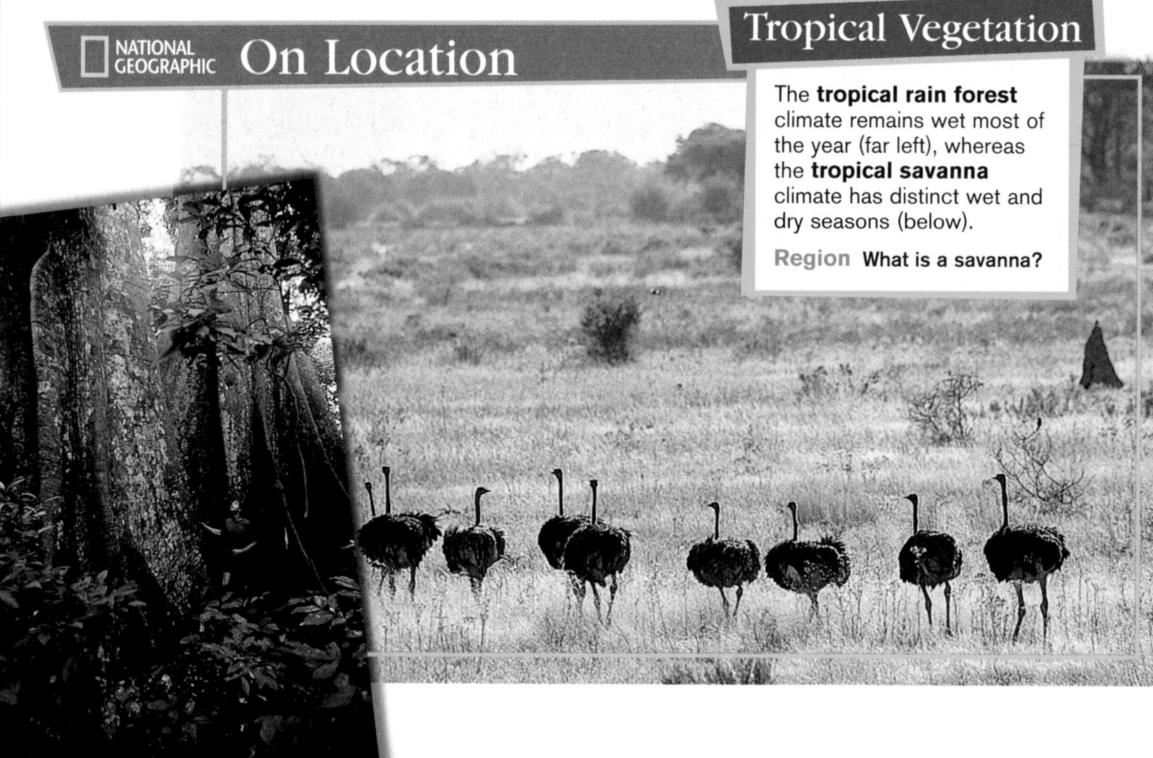

The **tropical rain forest** climate remains wet most of the year (far left), whereas the **tropical savanna** climate has distinct wet and dry seasons (below).

Region What is a savanna?

Reading Strategy — Reading the Text

Understanding Cause and Effect Have students create a chart with three headings: "Climate Zone," "Characteristics," and "Cause." Have them write the names of the different climate zones in the first column. In the second column, they should write the main characteristics of each zone. In the right column, they should describe the conditions that cause this climate. As an example, write on the board: *Marine west coast; Rainy and mild winters, cool summers, and heavy rain; Coastal area that receives moist ocean winds.* Have them complete the chart for each climate zone. L1

EE3 Physical Systems: Standard 8

NATIONAL GEOGRAPHIC

World Climate Regions

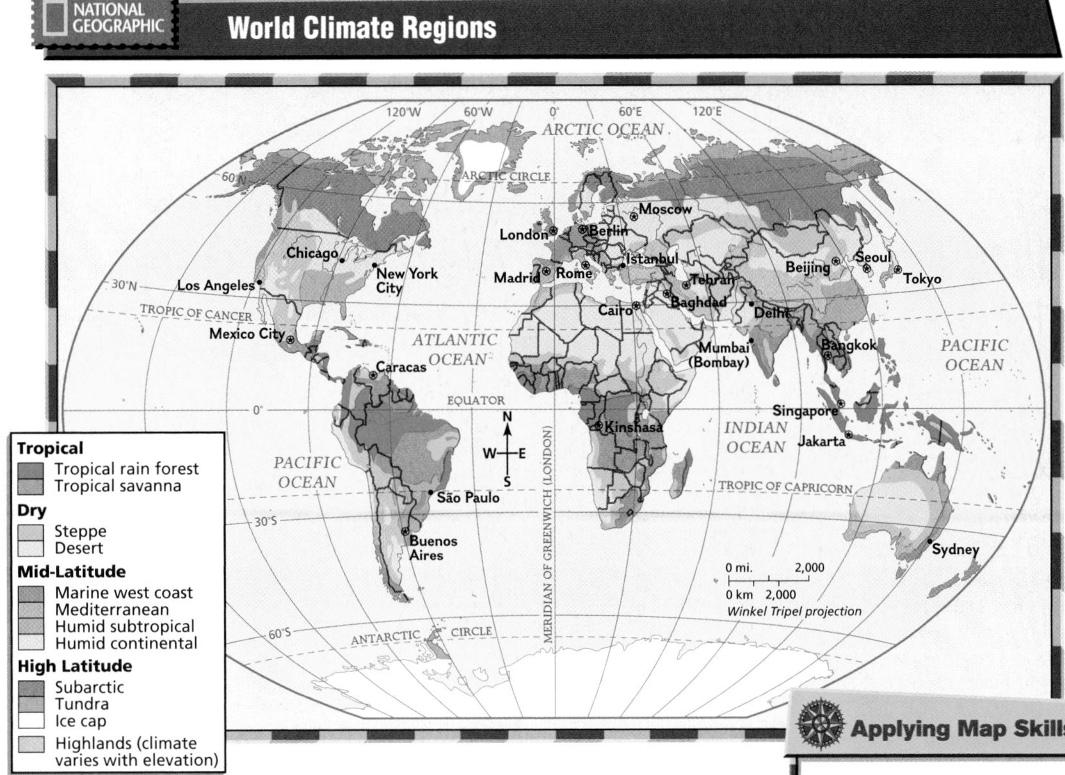

Applying Map Skills

1. Which climate covers most of the southeastern United States?
2. Which climate is most common in countries directly on the Equator?

Find NGS online map resources @ www.nationalgeographic.com/maps

Mid-Latitude Climates

Mid-latitude, or moderate, climates are found in the middle latitudes of the Northern and Southern Hemispheres. They extend from about 23½° to 60° both north and south of the Equator. Most of the world's people—probably including you—live within these two bands around the earth. The climate zones found here are called mid-latitude because they are in the middle of both the Northern Hemisphere and the Southern Hemisphere. The mid-latitude climates are neither as close to the Equator as the tropical climates nor as close to the Poles as the high latitude climates.

The mid-latitude region includes more and different climate zones than other regions. This variety results from a mix of air masses. As you remember from Section 2, warm air comes from the Tropics. Cool air comes from the polar regions. In most mid-latitude climates, the temperature changes with the seasons. Sometimes the climate zones in this region are called temperate climates.

Marine West Coast Climate Coastal areas that receive winds from the ocean usually have a mild **marine west coast climate.** If you lived in one of these areas, your winters would be rainy and mild, and your summers would be cool. Most areas with this climate—such as

Daily Lecture and Discussion Notes

WATER, CLIMATE, AND VEGETATION

Daily Lecture and Discussion Notes

Climate Zones and Vegetation

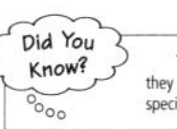

The world's rain forests cover only 7 percent of the earth's surface, but they provide a habitat for 50 to 90 percent of the world's plant and animal species.

I. Tropical Climates

A. There are two types of tropical climates—tropical rain forest and tropical savanna.

B. Areas with a tropical rain forest climate have year-round rains that produce lush vegetation and thick rain forests. Tall hardwood trees such as mahogany, teak, and ebony form a canopy, or top layer of the forest.

C. Tropical savanna areas have a definite wet season, while the remainder of the year is hot and dry. **Savannas,** or broad grasslands with few trees, are found in these areas.

DISCUSSION QUESTION

From where do the tropical climates get their name? *(The tropical climates get their name from the Tropics—the areas along the Equator reaching from 23½°N latitude to 23½°S latitude.)*

II. Mid-Latitude Climates

A. Mid-latitude climates include more and different climate zones. This is due to a mix of air masses: warm air from the Tropics and cool air from the polar regions.

B. The **marine west coast climate** occurs along coastal areas that receive winds from the ocean. Winters are rainy and summers are cool in these areas. Deciduous and coniferous trees grow in this climate.

C. The coastal **Mediterranean climate** also has rainy, mild winters. It differs from the marine west coast climate in that the Mediterranean climate experiences hot, dry summers. Shrubs and short trees grow in this climate.

15

Applying Map Skills

Answers

1. humid subtropical
2. tropical rain forest

In-text Map Transparency Activity Have students look at the map and write generalizations about different countries. For example, students may note that most of Russia has a subarctic climate. Then point to countries that students do not mention and ask them to provide verbal generalizations about them.

Differentiated Instruction

Meeting Special Needs: Less-proficient Readers Have students combine words and graphics to visualize the information in the section. Direct them to scan the section and note the five major climate groups. Then have them find the locations of the five climate regions on the World Climate Regions map. This activity provides students with a graphic reinforcement of the text. L1

Refer to *Inclusion for the Middle School Social Studies Classroom Strategies and Activities* in the TCR.

Chapter 2

Section 3, pages 61–68

Did You Know

The coastal redwood tree (*Sequoia sempervirens*) flourishes in the marine west coast climate of the Pacific coast of the United States. These trees, which typically grow taller than 300 feet (91 m), are the tallest trees alive today. The trees need several hundred years to mature. Some have been known to live as long as 1,500 years.

Applying Map Skills

Answers

1. deciduous and mixed deciduous-coniferous forest
2. tropical forest

Skills Practice

What kind of vegetation is found around Johannesburg? *(temperate grassland)*

Note-taking tip

Draw a four-column chart on the board with the following headings: "Climate Zone," "Location," "Characteristics," and "Typical Vegetation." Direct students to copy the chart into their notebooks. As students work through the section, have them add information to the chart.

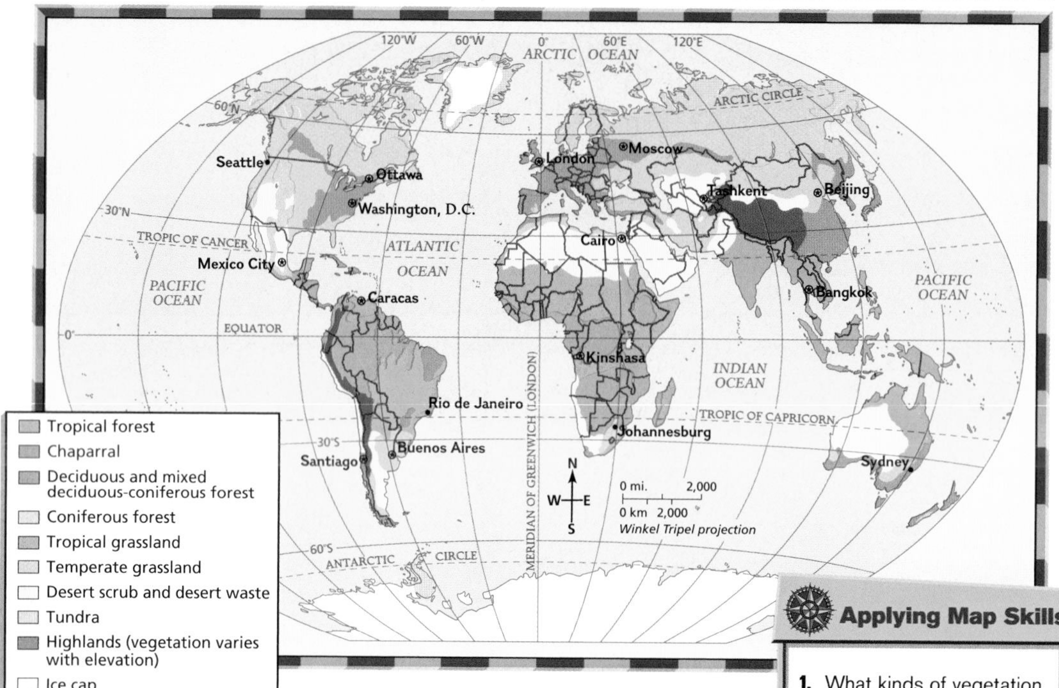

Applying Map Skills

1. What kinds of vegetation surround Washington, D.C., and Moscow?
2. What type of vegetation grows around Bangkok?

Find NGS online map resources @ www.nationalgeographic.com/maps

the northwestern United States—receive heavy rainfall. This supports the growth of deciduous trees, or those that lose their leaves in the fall. Coniferous forests, evergreens with cones and needles, also thrive.

Mediterranean Climate Another mid-latitude coastal climate is called a **Mediterranean climate** because it is similar to the climate found around the Mediterranean Sea. This climate has mild, rainy winters like the marine west coast climate. Instead of cool summers, however, people living in a Mediterranean climate experience hot, dry summers. The vegetation that grows in this climate includes chaparral, or shrubs and short trees. Some are evergreens, but others lose their leaves in the dry season.

Humid Continental Climate If you live in inland areas of North America, Europe, or Asia, you usually face a harsher **humid continental climate.** In these areas, winters can be long, cold, and snowy. Summers are short but may be very hot. Deciduous trees grow in forests, and vast grasslands flourish in some areas of this zone.

Team-Teaching Activity

Science Organize students into four or more groups. Assign each group a climate zone. Encourage group members to imagine that they will be stranded for one year in a remote area that has their assigned climate type. Have groups plan a survival strategy to live in that climate. Each group should identify the following: (1) the type of shelter they will need and be able to make; (2) the type of clothing they will need and be able to make; and (3) the way they will be able to obtain food and water. Have each group present their survival plan to the class, with other students challenging each plan with situations or conditions likely to arise in the climate zone. **L2**

EE5 Environment and Society: Standard 15

Humid Subtropical Climate Mid-latitude regions close to the Tropics have a **humid subtropical climate.** Rain falls throughout the year but is heaviest during the hot and humid summer months. Humid subtropical winters are generally short and mild. Trees like oaks, magnolias, and palms grow in this zone.

✓Reading Check What causes the mid-latitude region to have more and different climate zones than other regions?

High Latitude Climates

High latitude climate regions lie mostly in the high latitudes of each hemisphere, from 60°N to the North Pole and 60°S to the South Pole. These climates are generally cold, but some are more severely cold than others.

Subarctic Climate In the high latitudes nearest the mid-latitude zones, you will find the **subarctic** climate. The few people living here face very cold and bitter winters, but temperatures do rise above freezing during summer

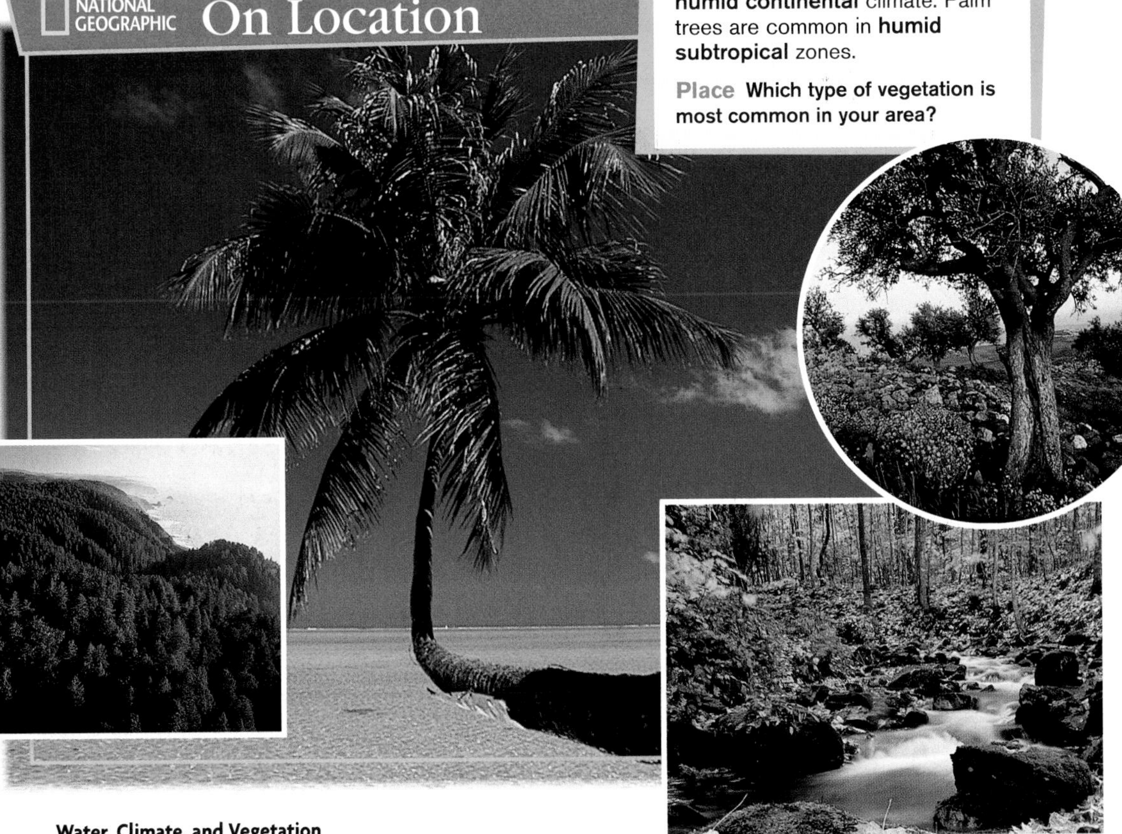

Mid-Latitude Vegetation

Fir trees (bottom left) thrive in a **marine west coast** climate. Shrubs and olive trees (top right) grow in a **Mediterranean** climate. Deciduous trees (bottom right) flourish in a **humid continental** climate. Palm trees are common in **humid subtropical** zones.

Place Which type of vegetation is most common in your area?

Chapter 2

Section 3, pages 61–68

Reading Strategy

Making Comparisons Have students look at the four groups of climates that have multiple zones—the tropical, mid-latitude, high latitude, and dry. Have them make a generalization about each group that explains what the different zones have in common with one another. L2

✓ Reading Check Answer

because of a mix of warm air masses from the Equator and cold ones from the Poles

More About the Photos

Humid Continental Vegetation In the colder climates of the humid continental zone, trees have developed leaves that are thin and live only a year. When cold winter temperatures come, the leaves are shed.

Caption Answer Check responses for accuracy.

L1/ELL

Guided Reading Activity

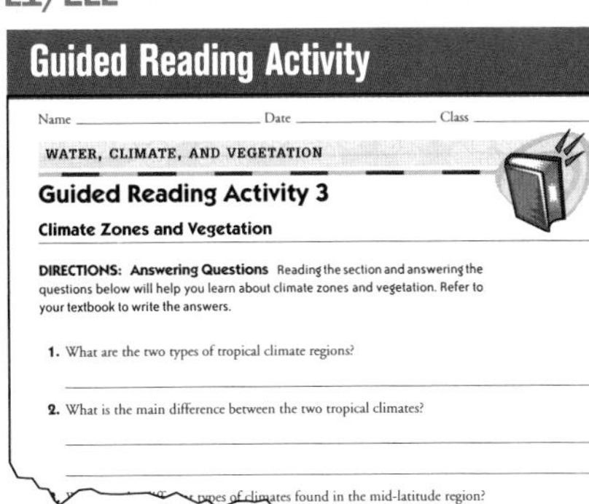
Name ______ Date ______ Class ______

WATER, CLIMATE, AND VEGETATION

Guided Reading Activity 3

Climate Zones and Vegetation

DIRECTIONS: Answering Questions Reading the section and answering the questions below will help you learn about climate zones and vegetation. Refer to your textbook to write the answers.

1. What are the two types of tropical climate regions?

2. What is the main difference between the two tropical climates?

types of climates found in the mid-latitude region?

Cooperative Learning Activity

The Steppes Discuss the role that nomads who lived on the Eurasian steppe played in history. Several times throughout history, peoples such as the Huns, Mongols, and Seljuk Turks broke out of the nomadic herding existence they followed on the steppes to confront the kingdoms and empires—such as Rome and China—on the fringes. The discussion should include information on the important role that the horse played in the lives of these nomads. Then form the class into groups, assign a different nomadic people to each group, and have them prepare an annotated map that explains the role of that group in history. L1

EE5 The Uses of Geography: Standard 17

3 ASSESS

Assign Section 3 Assessment as homework or an in-class activity.

Have students use the Interactive Tutor Self-Assessment CD-ROM to review Section 3.

Reading Check Answer

subarctic, tundra, ice cap

More About the Photos

Subarctic Vegetation The Russian *taiga* (evergreen forests of Siberia) is the largest single expanse of timber in the world.

Caption Answer Because the land is flat and the lower levels are frozen year-round, permafrost allows water to collect on top of the soil in the warmer months, giving plants the moisture they need to grow.

THE HUMANITIES CONNECTION

World Music: A Cultural Legacy

World Art and Architecture Transparencies

Focus on World Art Prints

months. Huge evergreen forests called taiga (TY•guh) grow in the subarctic region, especially in northern Russia.

Tundra Climate Closer to the Poles than the subarctic zone lie the tundra areas, or vast treeless plains. The climate in this zone is harsh and dry. In the tundra and parts of subarctic regions, the lower layers of soil are called permafrost because they stay permanently frozen. Only the top few inches of the ground thaw during summer months. Because of permafrost, melting snow does not seep into the ground. Instead, the tundra turns marshy during the summer. This provides the moisture that plants need to grow. Trees cannot set up roots, however, so only sturdy grasses and low bushes grow in the tundra.

Ice Cap Climate On the polar ice caps and the great ice sheets of Antarctica and Greenland, the climate is bitterly cold. Monthly temperatures average below freezing. Temperatures in Antarctica have been measured at −128°F (−89°C)! Although no other vegetation grows here, lichens—or funguslike plants and mosses—can live on rocks.

Reading Check What are the three types of high latitude climates?

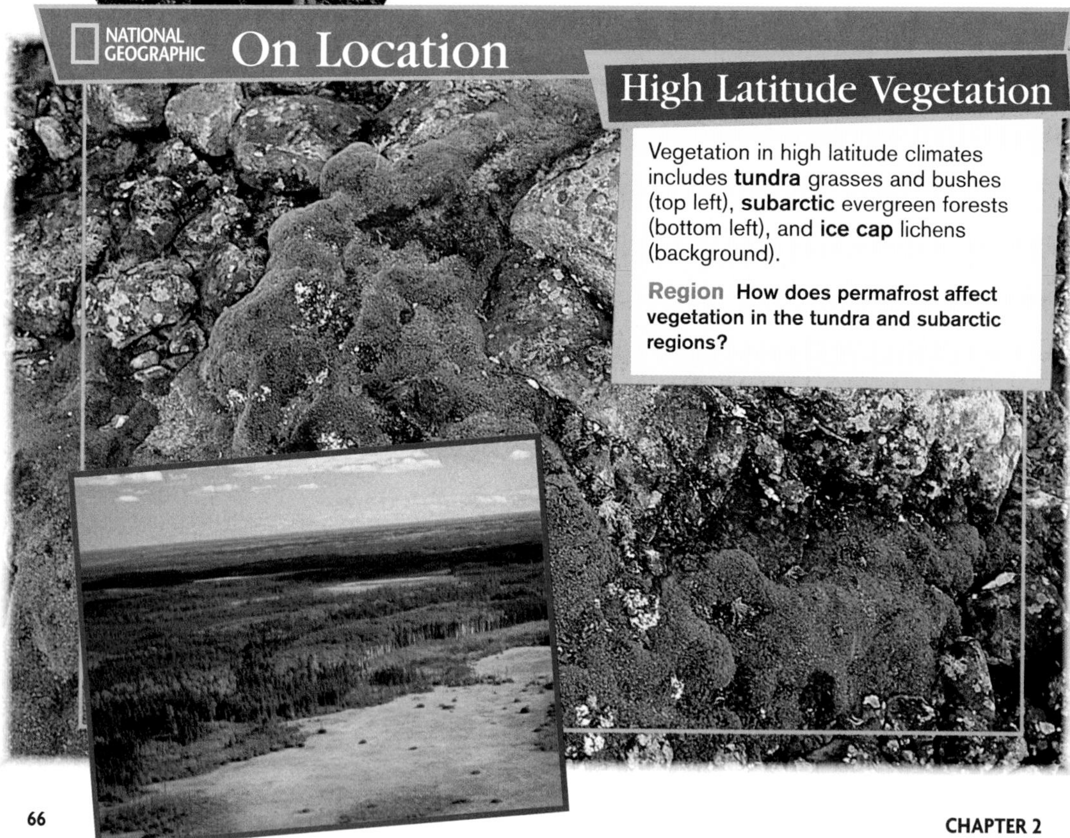

NATIONAL GEOGRAPHIC **On Location**

High Latitude Vegetation

Vegetation in high latitude climates includes **tundra** grasses and bushes (top left), **subarctic** evergreen forests (bottom left), and **ice cap** lichens (background).

Region How does permafrost affect vegetation in the tundra and subarctic regions?

66 CHAPTER 2

Content Background

Deserts When people think of deserts, they think of dryness and high heat. The lack of moisture is the defining characteristic of deserts, and rainfall ranges from an average of 0 inches a year to just over 20 inches (51 cm). A spot in the Chilean desert once went 45 years without any rain. Some coastal deserts, such as Africa's Namib, receive moisture from morning fog. Deserts may be hot—such as the Sahara—temperate, or cold. The temperate desert of Central Asia is dry because it is far from the coast and unable to receive moisture-bearing winds. The dry basin region of North America is the result of the rain shadow of the Pacific Coast Ranges and Sierra Nevada. Antarctica is considered the largest, coldest desert in the world.

NATIONAL GEOGRAPHIC On Location

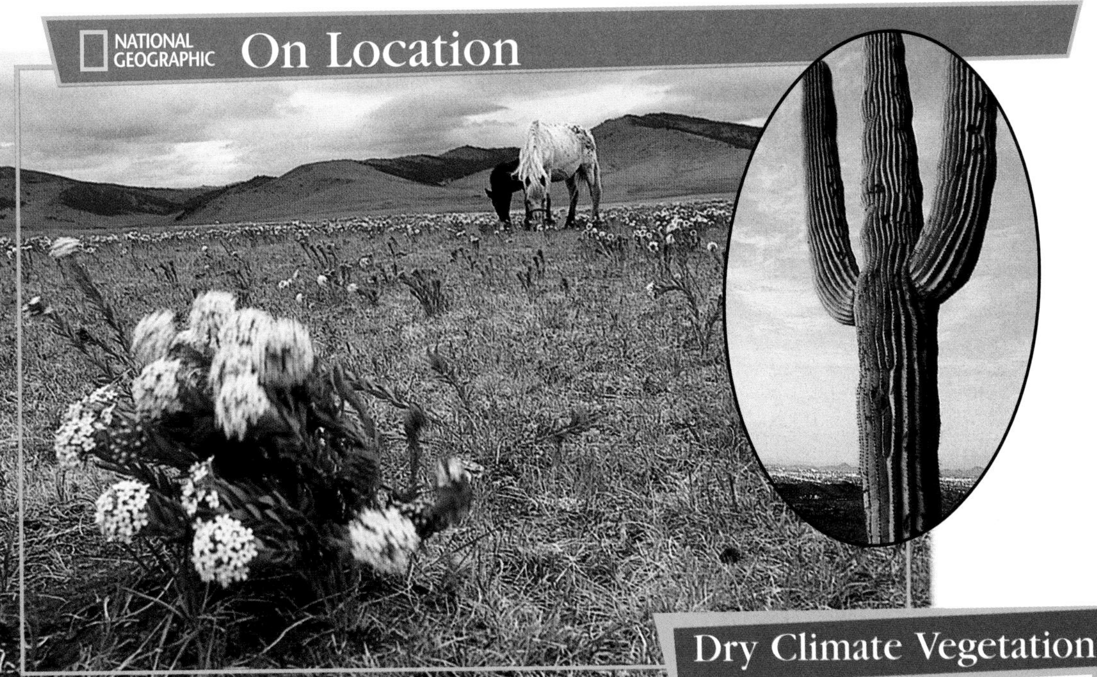

Dry Climate Vegetation

The vegetation that survives **desert** and **steppe** climates includes cacti (above) and short grasses (left).

Region **Are very dry climates always hot? Explain.**

Dry Climates

Dry climates refer to dry or partially dry areas that receive little or no rainfall. Temperatures can be extremely hot during the day and very cold at night. Dry climates can also have severely cold winters. You can find dry climate regions at any latitude.

Desert Climate The driest climates receive less than 10 inches (25 cm) of rainfall per year. Regions with such climates are called deserts. Only scattered plants such as scrub and cacti can survive a desert climate. With roots close to the surface, cacti can collect any rain that falls. Most cacti are found only in North America. In other countries, however, small areas of thick plant life dot the deserts. These arise along rivers or where underground springs reach the surface.

Steppe Climate Many deserts are surrounded by partly dry grasslands and prairies known as **steppes.** The word steppe comes from a Russian word meaning "treeless plain." The steppes receive more rain than deserts, averaging 10 to 20 inches (25 to 51 cm) per year. Bushes and short grasses cover the steppe landscape. The Great Plains of the United States has a steppe climate.

Reading Check **Where are steppe climate zones often located?**

Chapter 2

Section 3, pages 61–68

More About the Photos

Desert Vegetation There are many varieties of cacti found in the Americas. Only one genus is found in Europe, and many experts believe it is not native to the area.

Caption Answer No; dryness has to do with lack of precipitation, not temperature.

L2

Section Quiz

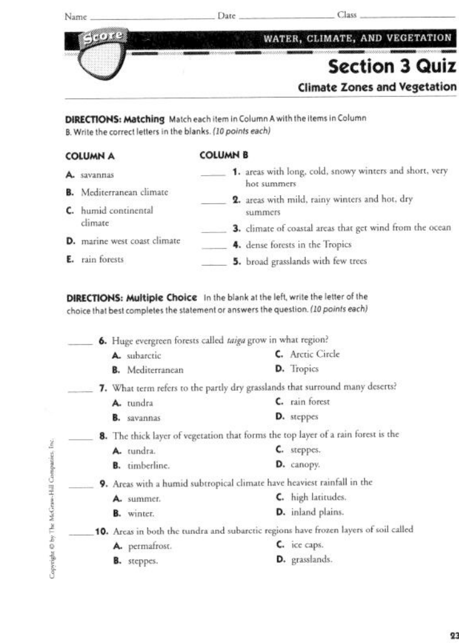

Name ______ Date ______ Class ______

Score WATER, CLIMATE, AND VEGETATION

Section 3 Quiz

Climate Zones and Vegetation

DIRECTIONS: Matching Match each item in Column A with the items in Column B. Write the correct letters in the blanks. *(10 points each)*

COLUMN A	COLUMN B
A. savannas	____ **1.** areas with long, cold, snowy winters and short, very hot summers
B. Mediterranean climate	____ **2.** areas with mild, rainy winters and hot, dry summers
C. humid continental climate	____ **3.** climate of coastal areas that get wind from the ocean
D. marine west coast climate	____ **4.** dense forests in the Tropics
E. rain forests	____ **5.** broad grasslands with few trees

DIRECTIONS: Multiple Choice In the blank at the left, write the letter of the choice that best completes the statement or answers the question. *(10 points each)*

____ **6.** Huge evergreen forests called *taiga* grow in what region?
A. subarctic **C.** Arctic Circle
B. Mediterranean **D.** Tropics

____ **7.** What term refers to the partly dry grasslands that surround many deserts?
A. tundra **C.** rain forest
B. savannas **D.** steppes

____ **8.** The thick layer of vegetation that forms the top layer of a rain forest is the
A. tundra. **C.** steppes.
B. timberline. **D.** canopy.

____ **9.** Areas with a humid subtropical climate have heaviest rainfall in the
A. summer. **C.** high latitudes.
B. winter. **D.** inland plains.

____ **10.** Areas in both the tundra and subarctic regions have frozen layers of soil called
A. permafrost. **C.** ice caps.
B. steppes. **D.** grasslands.

23

Reteach

Give students a quiz in which you read the characteristics of a climate zone and they have to identify the name of the zone.

Reading Check Answer

on the outskirts of deserts

Cooperative Learning Activity

Climatizing the Classroom Have students choose a climate region to re-create in the classroom. Suggest that they draw murals showing the vegetation found in that climate. Have students bring appropriate plants from home, such as a cactus for a desert climate or a rubber tree for a tropical one. They might also add a humidifier to simulate a wet climate or a dehumidifier for a dry climate. After the class is "climatized," declare a climate day and ask students to dress appropriately for the climate in the classroom. L2 ELL

EE3 Physical Systems: Standard 8

Chapter 2

Section 3, pages 61–68

More About the Photo

Highlands In the United States, you can find the highland climate in the higher elevations of the Rocky Mountains and Pacific Ranges. There are even some spots in Hawaii with cold, snowy peaks.

Caption Answer The higher the elevation of a place, the lower the temperature. Air becomes thinner as elevation increases, and it cannot hold as much heat from the sun.

✓ Reading Check Answer

the elevation above which no trees grow

L1/ELL

Reading Essentials and Study Guide

Name ______ Date ______ Class ______

WATER, CLIMATE, AND VEGETATION

Reading Essentials and Study Guide 3

Climate Zones and Vegetation

Key Terms

savanna broad grassland with few trees
marine west coast climate mid-latitude coastal climate with mild, rainy winters and cool summers
Mediterranean climate mid-latitude coastal climate with mild, rainy winters and hot, dry summers
humid continental climate inland mid-latitude climate with cold, snowy winters and short, hot summers
humid subtropical climate rainy mid-latitude climate with hot, humid summers

CLOSE

Provide each student with a copy of a world physical outline map and colored pencils. Have students draw and label the location of the climate zones.

NATIONAL GEOGRAPHIC **On Location**

Highland Vegetation

The wildflowers and shrubs that grow in meadows above the timberline are often called *alpine* vegetation.

Location **How does elevation affect climate?**

Highland Climate

As you read in Section 2, the elevation of a place changes its climate dramatically. Mountains tend to have cool climates—and the highest mountains have very cold climates. This is true even for mountains that are on the Equator. A highland, or mountain, climate has cool or cold temperatures year-round.

If you climb a mountain, you will reach an area called the timberline. The timberline is the elevation above which no trees grow. Once you reach the timberline, you will find only small shrubs and wildflowers growing in meadows.

✓ Reading Check **What is the timberline?**

Section 3 Assessment

Defining Terms

1. **Define** savanna, marine west coast climate, Mediterranean climate, humid continental climate, humid subtropical climate, subarctic, tundra, steppe.

Recalling Facts

2. **Region** What are the five types of climate regions?
3. **Region** How do the climate zones in the mid-latitude region differ?
4. **Region** What kind of vegetation grows in the tundra climate zone?

Critical Thinking

5. **Making Comparisons** What do the tropical savanna and humid continental climates have in common?
6. **Drawing Conclusions** How can snow exist in the Tropics along the Equator?

Graphic Organizer

7. **Organizing Information** Draw a globe like this one. Label the three climate regions that are based on latitude, then identify the lines of latitude that separate the climate regions.

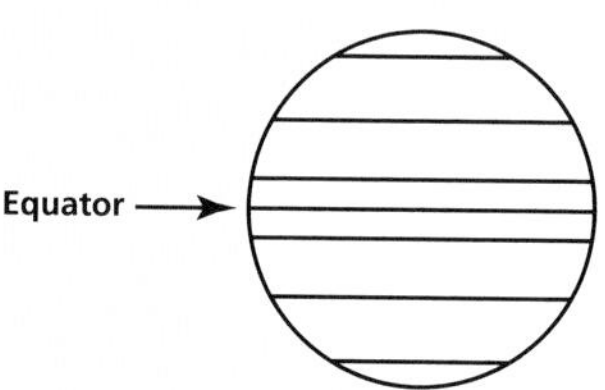

Applying Social Studies Skills

8. **Analyzing Maps** Look at the world natural vegetation regions map on page 64. What type of natural vegetation thrives around Cairo?

Section 3 Assessment

1. The terms are defined in the Glossary.
2. tropical, mid-latitude, high latitude, dry, and highland
3. *marine west coast:* cool summers and rainy, mild winters; *Mediterranean:* hot, dry summers and mild, rainy winters; *humid continental:* short, hot summers and long, cold, snowy winters; *humid subtropical:* hot, humid summers and short, mild winters
4. sturdy grasses and low-growing berry bushes
5. Both support vast grasslands.
6. Areas of high elevation have cool climates.
7. Tropical, from 23 1/2°N to 23 1/2°S; Mid-latitude, from 23 1/2° to 60° both North and South; High latitude, from 60°N to North Pole and 60°S to South Pole
8. desert scrub and desert waste

Section 4: An Environmental Balance

Guide to Reading

Main Idea

People's actions affect the environment.

Terms to Know

- acid rain
- deforestation
- crop rotation
- conservation
- irrigation
- pesticide
- ecosystem

Reading Strategy

Draw a diagram like this one. Then write at least two problems that arise with human use of water, land, and air.

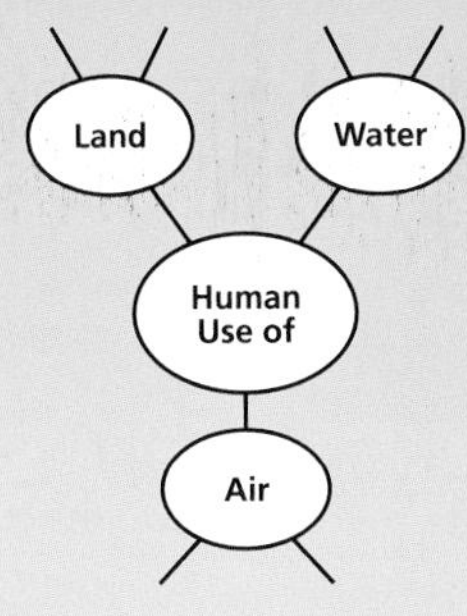

NATIONAL GEOGRAPHIC Exploring Our World

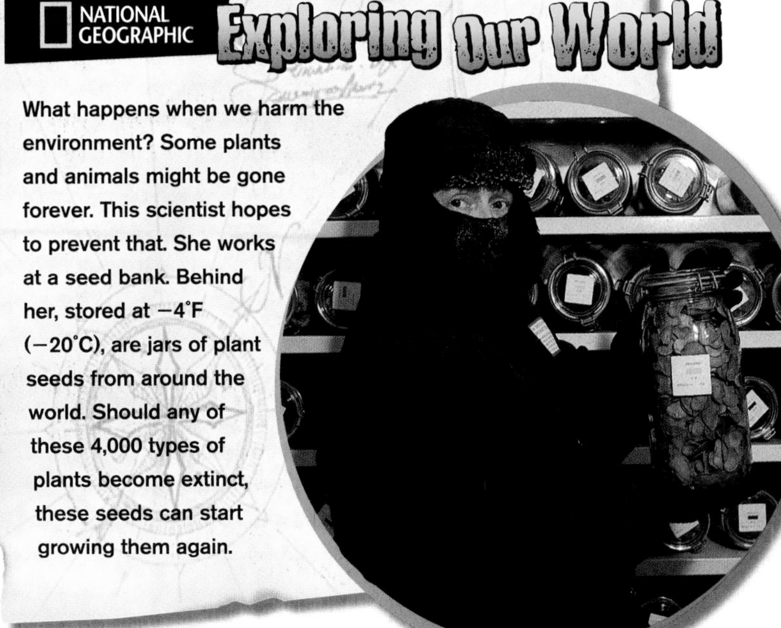

What happens when we harm the environment? Some plants and animals might be gone forever. This scientist hopes to prevent that. She works at a seed bank. Behind her, stored at −4°F (−20°C), are jars of plant seeds from around the world. Should any of these 4,000 types of plants become extinct, these seeds can start growing them again.

Earth's physical geography is made up of four basic parts. The atmosphere, as you read in Chapter 1, is the blanket of gases, or air, surrounding the earth. The lithosphere is the earth's hard outer shell, or what we view as land areas. The hydrosphere includes all the water in the oceans, lakes, rivers, and glaciers, plus all precipitation. Humans are part of the biosphere, which includes all living things and the environments in which they live. A delicate balance exists among these four "spheres." The world's people must act to preserve this balance.

The Atmosphere

Throughout the world, fumes and chemicals from vehicles and industries pollute the air. Air pollution also includes solid particles such as ash and dust. When air pollution is concentrated in urban areas, the air becomes harmful to breathe. Yet air pollution has an even greater effect on the earth as a whole.

69

1 Focus

Section Objectives

1. Describe the four basic parts of Earth's geography.
2. Explain how the soil can be damaged by people.
3. Identify the effects of air pollution.

BELLRINGER Skillbuilder Activity

Project transparency and have students answer the question.

Daily Focus Skills Transparency

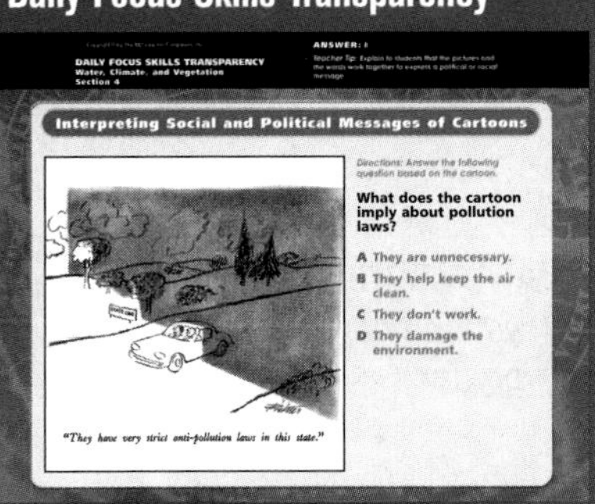

Reading Preview

■ **Activating Prior Knowledge** Have students volunteer ideas about how humans impact the environment. Suggest that they write their comments in their notebooks and check them as they read to see if they are true.

■ **Preteaching Vocabulary** Explain to students that the suffix *-tion* means "process" or "action." Have them use this information as they encounter new vocabulary.

Section Resources

Reproducible Masters

- Reproducible Lesson Plan
- Daily Lecture and Discussion Notes
- Note-taking Guide
- Guided Reading Activity
- Reading Essentials and Study Guide
- Section Quiz

Transparencies

- Daily Focus Skills Transparency

Multimedia

- Vocabulary PuzzleMaker CD-ROM
- Interactive Tutor Self-Assessment CD-ROM
- Presentation Plus! CD-ROM
- ExamView® Pro Testmaker CD-ROM
- MindJogger Videoquiz

Chapter 2

Section 4, pages 69–72

2 TEACH

Reading Strategy

Identifying Main Ideas

Ask: What are the most basic things that people need to live? *(food, water, and air)* What happens if those things are not available, or if they are not clean? *(People will become ill and perhaps die.)* Explain that in this section, students will learn about dangers that human actions pose to these fundamental resources. L1

Reading Check Answer

fumes, chemicals, ash, dust

More About the Photo

Air Pollution The earth's wind systems can carry pollutants very far. Scientists have found evidence of pesticides in Antarctica, where no such substances have ever been used.

Caption Answer damage to people's health, acid rain, and greenhouse effect

Reading Check Answer

Tree roots no longer hold the soil, and water can wash it away.

NATIONAL GEOGRAPHIC On Location

Taiwan

Vehicles and factories add harmful chemicals to the air.

Human/Environment Interaction What are some effects of air pollution?

The global effects of air pollution include global warming, ozone depletion, and acid rain. Some scientists believe that increasing amounts of pollutants in the atmosphere have caused the earth to warm. You learned earlier about this greenhouse effect.

Air pollution also affects the ozone layer in the atmosphere. The ozone layer serves as a protective shield as it filters out harmful rays of the sun. Certain chemicals, when they move into the upper atmosphere, destroy ozone molecules. Turn to page 772 to read more about the depletion—and repair—of the earth's "sunscreen."

Chemicals in air pollution can also combine with precipitation, which then falls as **acid rain.** Acid rain kills fish and eats away at the surfaces of buildings. It can even destroy entire forests.

Reading Check What are two forms of pollutants found in air?

The Lithosphere

The telephone you use, the microwave that heats your snacks, and the food you eat all come from land resources. Copper, iron, aluminum, and other minerals and ores are mined from the earth. To get to these resources, huge amounts of soil and rock must be removed. This harms the environment. In the United States, mining companies are required to restore the land and replant vegetation when their mining operations are finished.

Topsoil Rich topsoil is a vital part of the lithosphere. If people do not carefully manage the soil, it can be carried away by wind or water. In the Tropics, erosion by water presents a problem—especially if farmers plant their crops on sloping land. When heavy rains come, the soil may simply wash down the hillside. Some farmers have solved this problem by terracing their fields, or planting their crops in a stair-step fashion on slopes.

Deforestation, or cutting down forests without replanting, is another way in which topsoil is lost. When the tree roots are no longer there to hold the soil, wind and water can carry it away.

To enrich their topsoil, many farmers use fertilizers. Some also practice **crop rotation,** or changing what they plant in a field. This avoids using up all the minerals in the soil. Some crops, such as beans, actually restore valuable minerals to the soil. Many farmers now plant bean crops every three years to build up the soil.

Reading Check How does deforestation lead to erosion?

70 CHAPTER 2

Reading Strategy — Reading the Text

Using Context Clues Students can often determine the meaning of a word they do not know by using context—the words and sentences that surround an unfamiliar word. Synonyms often appear in context when two things are compared. Antonyms appear in context most often when two things are contrasted. Definitions often are surrounded by commas, dashes, or parentheses. The use of examples reveals the meaning of an unfamiliar word. As students read the section and encounter words they do not know, remind them to use these clues to identify the word's meaning. L1

*Use the **Reading Skills Handbook** for more reading strategies.*

The Hydrosphere

People, plants, and most animals need freshwater to live. Remember that only a small fraction of the world's freshwater is unfrozen, however. Since the earth's supply of water is limited, people must learn to manage freshwater carefully.

Water Management Managing water supplies involves two main steps. The first step is **conservation,** or the careful use of resources so they are not wasted. Did you know that 6 or 7 gallons (23 to 27 liters) of water go down the drain every minute that you shower? Taking shorter showers is an easy way to prevent wasting water.

Throughout most areas of the world, farmers use **irrigation,** or the practice of collecting water and distributing it to their crops. In fact, as much as 70 percent of all water used is for farming. Most irrigation methods are wasteful because water often evaporates or seeps into the ground before it reaches crops. Many farmers today, however, are trying to use more efficient practices, such as drip irrigation.

The second step in managing the water supply is to avoid polluting water. Most industrial processes use water. Sometimes those processes result in dangerous chemicals entering the water supply. Farmers who apply fertilizers to their soil may also use **pesticides,** or powerful chemicals that kill crop-destroying insects. These substances help increase food production, but they also seep into rivers and groundwater supplies, polluting the waterways.

✓Reading Check How can industry and farming harm the water supply?

NATIONAL GEOGRAPHIC **On Location**

Madeira Islands

This hillside has been terraced to allow the owner to build a house and plant crops.

Human/Environment Interaction How would terraced fields help prevent erosion?

Chapter 2

Section 4, pages 69–72

Daily Lecture and Discussion Notes

WATER, CLIMATE, AND VEGETATION

Daily Lecture and Discussion Notes

An Environmental Balance

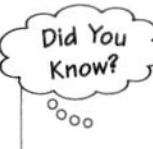

Did You Know? Forest areas in developed countries continue to increase slightly each year. Developing countries, however, reduce their forest areas each year when they clear land for agriculture, development, and logging. They lose forest area at a rate of at least 140,000 square kilometers every year.

I. The Atmosphere

A. The atmosphere is the blanket of gases, or air, surrounding the earth.

B. Air pollution consists of fumes and chemicals from vehicles and industries. It also includes solid particles such as ash and dust.

C. Global effects of air pollution include global warming, ozone depletion, and

✓ Reading Check Answer

Dangerous chemicals and pesticides can seep into the water supply.

More About the Photo

Landscape Art Terracing can be used in residential landscaping. Terracing allows for easier maintenance of sloped land plots and provides creative design alternatives for gardeners.

Caption Answer Terraces prevent water from rushing down slopes and washing soil away.

3 ASSESS

Assign Section 4 Assessment as homework or an in-class activity.

Have students use the Interactive Tutor Self-Assessment CD-ROM to review Section 4.

Differentiated Instruction

Meeting Special Needs: Naturalist Students may want to organize a school conservation club. Have interested students meet to discuss what they would like to achieve as a group. For example, students might want to promote water conservation or recycling at home or at the school. Then have students create a plan to promote their goal. Students should identify activities that they can perform to get their message out to other students. Students may want to create posters, write announcements to be read over the public address system, or hold a conservation fair to provide tips about conservation. **L1 ELL**

Refer to *Inclusion for the Middle School Social Studies Classroom Strategies and Activities* in the TCR.

Chapter 2

Section 4, pages 69–72

L2

Section Quiz

Name ______ Date ______ Class ______

WATER, CLIMATE, AND VEGETATION — Score

Section 4 Quiz

An Environmental Balance

DIRECTIONS: Matching Match each item in Column A with the items in Column B. Write the correct letters in the blanks. *(10 points each)*

COLUMN A	COLUMN B
A. erosion	____ 1. all of the earth's water and precipitation
B. ecosystem	____ 2. chemicals that kill crop-destroying insects
C. conservation	____ 3. place where plants and animals are dependent on one another and their surroundings for survival
D. pesticides	____ 4. wind or water carrying soil away
E. hydrosphere	____ 5. careful use of resources so they are not wasted

✓ Reading Check Answer

If farmers cannot clear the land, they will not have food.

L1/ELL

Reading Essentials and Study Guide

Name ______ Date ______ Class ______

WATER, CLIMATE, AND VEGETATION

Reading Essentials and Study Guide 4

An Environmental Balance

Key Terms

acid rain precipitation that combines with chemicals in air pollution
deforestation cutting down forests without replanting
crop rotation changing what is planted in a field
conservation careful use of resources so they are not wasted
irrigation process of collecting and distributing water to crops
pesticide powerful chemicals that kill crop-destroying insects
ecosystem places where plants and animals depend on each other and their surroundings to survive

Close

Reading Strategy

Writing a Paragraph Have students write a paragraph that highlights the potential damage that humans can do to the environment and steps that can be taken to prevent that impact.

The Biosphere

As the human population increases and people expand their communities, they invade **ecosystems.** These are places where the plants and animals are dependent upon one another and their surroundings for survival. Ecosystems can be found in every climate and vegetation region of the world. For example, some people may want to drain a wetland, or marshy area, to get rid of disease-carrying mosquitoes and to make the soil useful for farming or for building homes. When the area is drained, however, the ecosystem is destroyed. The delicate balance among the wetland's biodiversity—the various insects, reptiles, birds, and water plants—is upset.

People are becoming aware of the need to protect ecosystems, and communities are making increased efforts to do so. Wetlands are now recognized as valuable ecosystems. They are protected from development in the United States. Worldwide concern for rain forest ecosystems also has emerged.

Sometimes, though, protecting the environment for the future seems to clash with feeding people in the present. Remember that people, as well as plants and other animals, are also part of the biosphere. Thus, farmers in the rain forests burn or cut down trees not because they want to, but because they need to feed their families. Before they stop cutting down forests, these farmers will need to find new ways to meet their needs.

✓ Reading Check **How does saving the rain forests clash with current human needs?**

Section 4 Assessment

Defining Terms

1. **Define** acid rain, deforestation, crop rotation, conservation, irrigation, pesticide, ecosystem.

Recalling Facts

2. **Region** What are the four "spheres" of the earth?
3. **Human/Environment Interaction** What are two ways of managing water?
4. **Economics** Why do farmers practice crop rotation?

Critical Thinking

5. **Understanding Cause and Effect** Why are most irrigation methods inefficient?
6. **Analyzing Information** Which ecosystems were affected by the growth of your community?

Graphic Organizer

7. **Organizing Information** Draw a diagram like this and list three results of air pollution.

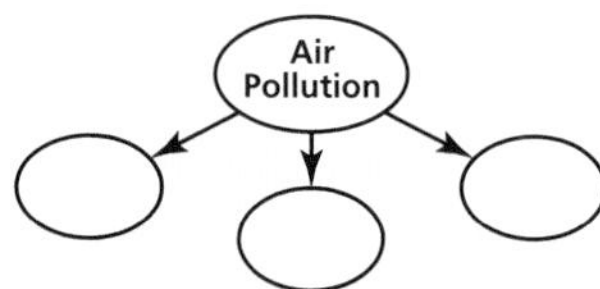

Applying Social Studies Skills

8. **Analyzing Maps** Look at the vegetation map on page 64. In what parts of the world are tropical rain forests located?

Section 4 Assessment

1. The terms are defined in the Glossary.
2. atmosphere, lithosphere, hydrosphere, biosphere
3. conservation and avoiding pollution
4. to restore minerals and keep the soil productive
5. Water evaporates or seeps into the ground before it reaches crops.
6. Answers will vary. Students should demonstrate knowledge of *ecosystem.*
7. global warming, ozone depletion, and acid rain
8. Central America, northern South America, west, central, and southern Africa, Madagascar, India, Southeast Asia

Reading Review

Section 1 The Water Planet

Terms to Know
- water vapor
- water cycle
- evaporation
- condensation
- precipitation
- collection
- glacier
- groundwater
- aquifer

Main Idea

Water is one of the earth's most precious resources.

✓Region Water covers about 70 percent of the earth's surface.

✓Movement Water follows a cycle of evaporation, condensation, precipitation, and collection on and beneath the ground.

✓Science Humans and most animals need freshwater to live. Only a small fraction of the world's water is found in rivers and lakes.

Section 2 Climate

Terms to Know
- weather
- climate
- Tropics
- drought
- El Niño
- La Niña
- current
- local wind
- rain shadow
- greenhouse effect
- rain forest

Main Idea

Wind and water carry rainfall and the sun's warmth around the world to create different climates.

✓Region Climate is the usual pattern of weather over a long period of time.

✓Region The Tropics, near the Equator, receive more of the sun's warmth than other regions.

✓Location Landforms and position near water affect climate in a local area.

✓Culture Human actions like building cities, burning fuels, and clearing the rain forests can affect climate.

Section 3 Climate Zones and Vegetation

Terms to Know
- savanna
- marine west coast climate
- Mediterranean climate
- humid continental climate
- humid subtropical climate
- subarctic
- tundra
- steppe

Main Idea

Geographers divide the world into different climate zones.

✓Region The world has five main climate regions that are based on latitude, amount of moisture, and/or elevation. These regions are tropical, mid-latitude, high latitude, dry, and highland.

✓Region Each climate zone has particular kinds of vegetation.

Section 4 An Environmental Balance

Terms to Know
- acid rain
- deforestation
- crop rotation
- conservation
- irrigation
- pesticide
- ecosystem

Main Idea

People's actions affect the environment.

✓Human/Environment Interaction A delicate balance exists among the earth's hydrosphere, lithosphere, atmosphere, and biosphere.

✓Human/Environment Interaction People need to carefully manage and conserve water and land resources.

Reading Strategy Read to Write

Writing a Paragraph **Ask students:** How does climate affect people? Have students review the chapter to help them answer the question. Students should answer the question by writing a paragraph describing the effects of climate on people. Remind them to include as many examples of the impact of climate on people as possible. Students' paragraphs should include a topic sentence stating how climate affects people. Supporting details should be described using factual evidence. L1

Reading Review

Use the Chapter 2 Reading Review to preview, review, condense, or reteach the chapter.

Preview/Review

Use the Terms to Know lists to help students review and study.

Activity Have students write the terms and definitions on index cards and group themselves into pairs. Have the pairs quiz each other on the terms.

Vocabulary PuzzleMaker CD-ROM reinforces the vocabulary terms used in Chapter 2.

The Interactive Tutor Self-Assessment CD-ROM allows students to review Chapter 2 content.

Condense

Have students read the Chapter 2 summary statements.

Guided Reading Activities

Audio Program

Reteach

Reteaching Activity

Reading Essentials and Study Guide

Assessment and Activities

GLENCOE TECHNOLOGY

MindJogger Videoquiz
Use MindJogger Videoquiz to review the Chapter 2 content.

Available in DVD and VHS

Using Key Terms

1.	i	6.	e
2.	j	7.	g
3.	d	8.	c
4.	b	9.	f
5.	h	10.	a

Reviewing the Main Ideas

11. evaporation, condensation, precipitation, collection
12. about 2 percent
13. groundwater
14. Wind and currents carry the sun's warmth around the earth.
15. Warm, moist winds blow in from oceans, then are forced up over mountains where they lose moisture and warmth, leaving the area on the other side of the mountain (the interior region) dry.
16. The streets and buildings in the city hold more of the sun's heat. Also, there are more people and industries burning fuels, raising the temperature and creating a heat island.
17. mid-latitudes, because they receive air from both the warm tropics and cold polar regions
18. shrubs and short trees
19. by rotating crops (crop rotation)
20. insects, reptiles, birds, and water plants

Chapter 2 Assessment and Activities

Using Key Terms

Match the terms in Part A with their definitions in Part B.

A.

1. evaporation	6. greenhouse effect
2. savanna	7. rain forest
3. crop rotation	8. El Niño
4. tundra	9. precipitation
5. condensation	10. current

B.

a. moving streams of water in the oceans
b. treeless plain in which only the top few inches of ground thaw in summer
c. weather pattern in the Pacific Ocean
d. alternating what is planted in a field
e. buildup of certain gases in the atmosphere that holds the sun's warmth
f. water that falls back to the earth
g. dense forest that receives much rain
h. water vapor changes back into a liquid
i. sun's heat turns water into water vapor
j. broad grassland in the Tropics

Reviewing the Main Ideas

Section 1 The Water Planet

11. **Movement** What are the four steps in the water cycle?
12. **Region** What percentage of the world's water is freshwater?
13. **Region** Which has more freshwater—lakes and rivers or groundwater?

Section 2 Climate

14. **Movement** How do wind and water affect climate?
15. **Location** How do mountains affect rainfall?
16. **Human/Environment Interaction** Why are cities warmer than nearby rural areas?

Section 3 Climate Zones and Vegetation

17. **Region** Which climate region has the most climate zones? Why?
18. **Place** What kind of vegetation grows in Mediterranean climates?

Section 4 An Environmental Balance

19. **Human/Environment Interaction** How can farmers restore the minerals in the soil?
20. **Region** What makes up a wetlands biodiversity?

World Oceans and Currents

Place Location Activity

On a separate sheet of paper, match the letters on the map with the numbered places listed below.

1. Arctic Ocean	4. Japan Current
2. Atlantic Ocean	5. Indian Ocean
3. California Current	6. Gulf Stream

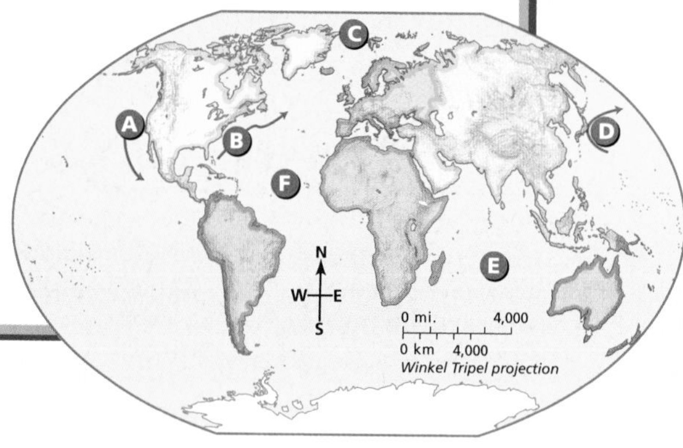

Place Location Activity

1. C	4. D
2. F	5. E
3. A	6. B

Critical Thinking

21. Encourage students to contact local officials to find the answers to these questions. Students may work in groups or individually on the task, and then present their findings to the class.
22. Check students' webs against the information presented in Section 3.

Self-Check Quiz Visit ***The World and Its People*** Web site at twip.glencoe.com and click on **Chapter 2—Self-Check Quizzes** to prepare for the Chapter Test.

Critical Thinking

21. **Analyzing Information** From where does the freshwater in your community come? How can you find out?
22. **Categorizing Information** Create five webs like the one shown here. In each large oval, write the name of a climate region. In the medium-sized ovals, write the name of each climate zone in that region. For each zone, fill in the three small ovals with the usual weather in summer, the usual weather in winter, and the kind of vegetation.

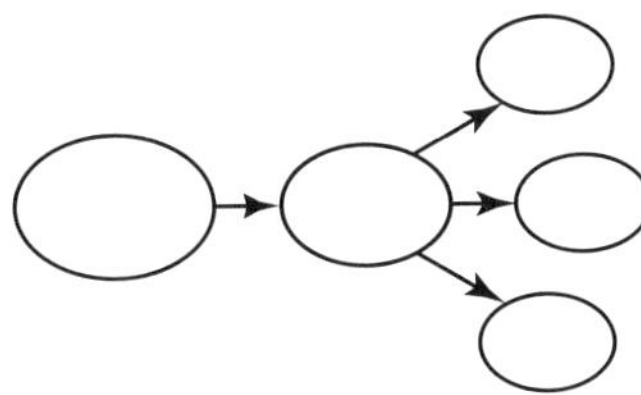

Comparing Regions Activity

23. **Culture** As you have learned, a region's climate helps determine how people live. Flip through your textbook or a geographic magazine to find pictures of people in their environments. What can you infer about their climates?

Mental Mapping Activity

24. **Focusing on the Region** Draw a freehand map of the world's oceans and continents. Label the following items:
    - Equator
    - North America
    - Pacific Ocean
    - Africa
    - high latitude climate regions
    - tropical climate regions

25. **Using the Internet** Research a recent hurricane or tornado. Find out when and where it occurred, how much force the storm had, and what damage it caused.

Standardized Test Practice

Directions: Study the graph below, and then answer the question that follows.

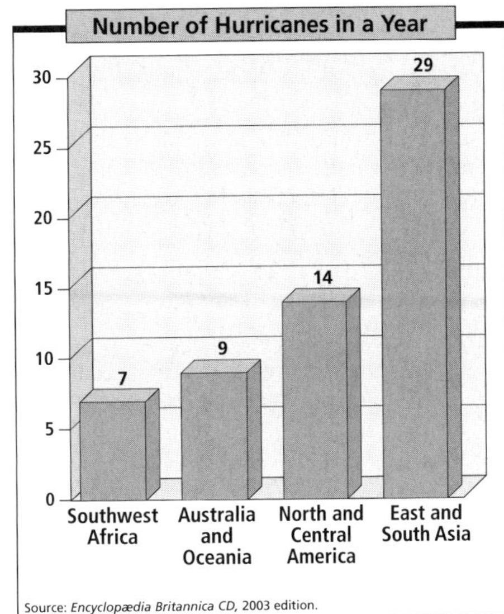

Source: *Encyclopædia Britannica CD,* 2003 edition.

1. How many more hurricanes do East and South Asia experience in a year than North and Central America?

F 29
G 14
H 9
J 15

Test-Taking Tip: Make sure you read the question carefully. It is not asking for the total number of hurricanes in East and South Asia. Instead, the question asks how many *more* hurricanes one region has than another.

75

Assessment and Activities

Standardized Test Practice

1. J

Tested Objectives:
Analyzing information, reading a graph

Chapter Test Bonus Question

This question may be used for extra credit on the chapter test.

The wettest climate zone, called the tropical rain forest, is found between what latitudes? *(23 1/2°N to 23 1/2°S)*

Social Studies Online

Have students visit the Web site at twip.glencoe.com to review Chapter 2 and take the Self-Check Quiz.

Dinah Zike's Foldables

Culminating Activity Have students write a paragraph that describes the relationship among water, climate, and vegetation.

Comparing Regions Activity

23. Students should make inferences from the pictures about people and their environments.

Mental Mapping Activity

24. This exercise helps students visualize the location of the world's ocean currents and continents. All attempts at freehand mapping should be accepted.

Technology Activity

25. Student presentations or reports should include the required information: when and where the hurricane or tornado took place, how much force the storm had, what damage it caused, and how the cleanup was carried out.

Write the word *extinction* and ask students what it means. If they have difficulty defining it, break the word into its root (*extinct,* "having ceased to exist"). Point out that plants and animals become extinct as their environments change. The pace of extinction today is much faster than in previous times.

Researching Wildlife Have students research an African animal. Aim for a variety of animals, including not only primates and well-known grazers and hunters, but also birds, fish, reptiles, and insects. Ask students to determine if their animal is threatened with extinction, why that is the case, and what steps are being taken to save the species. One source of information is the African Wildlife Foundation, which carries out programs to protect African species. L1

Meeting National Standards

Geography for Life

The following standards are met in the Student Edition feature:

EE1 The World in Spatial Terms: Standard 3

EE5 Environment and Society: Standard 14

EE6 The Uses of Geography: Standard 18

EYE on the Environment

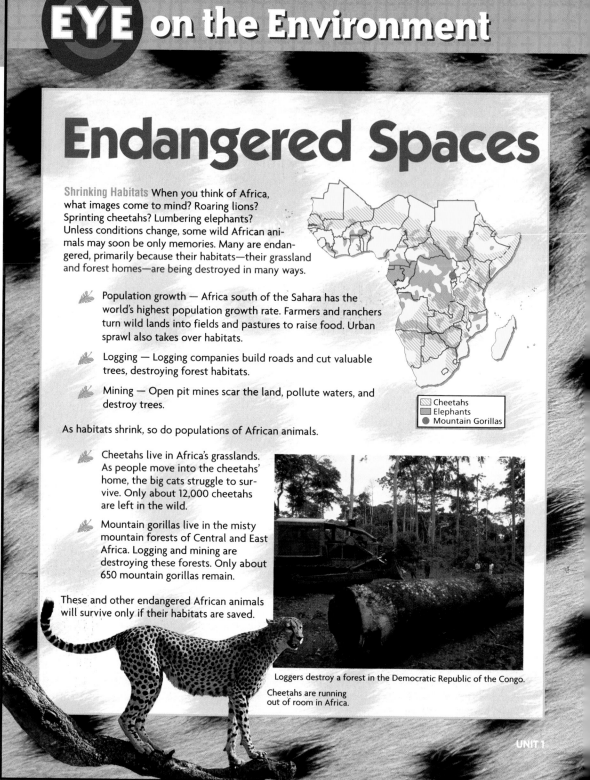

Endangered Spaces

Shrinking Habitats When you think of Africa, what images come to mind? Roaring lions? Sprinting cheetahs? Lumbering elephants? Unless conditions change, some wild African animals may soon be only memories. Many are endangered, primarily because their habitats—their grassland and forest homes—are being destroyed in many ways.

- Population growth — Africa south of the Sahara has the world's highest population growth rate. Farmers and ranchers turn wild lands into fields and pastures to raise food. Urban sprawl also takes over habitats.
- Logging — Logging companies build roads and cut valuable trees, destroying forest habitats.
- Mining — Open pit mines scar the land, pollute waters, and destroy trees.

Cheetahs
Elephants
Mountain Gorillas

As habitats shrink, so do populations of African animals.

- Cheetahs live in Africa's grasslands. As people move into the cheetahs' home, the big cats struggle to survive. Only about 12,000 cheetahs are left in the wild.
- Mountain gorillas live in the misty mountain forests of Central and East Africa. Logging and mining are destroying these forests. Only about 650 mountain gorillas remain.

These and other endangered African animals will survive only if their habitats are saved.

Loggers destroy a forest in the Democratic Republic of the Congo.

Cheetahs are running out of room in Africa.

UNIT 1

More About the Issues

Extinction Some biologists suggest that as many as 50 percent of plants and animals around the world are on the path to extinction. There have been five mass extinctions in the history of life on the earth, the most famous one being the extinction of the dinosaurs 65 million years ago. Even in a protected place like Everglades National Park—1.5 million acres in size—one species of sparrow has dropped in numbers from 6,400 in 1992 to 2,600 just three years later.

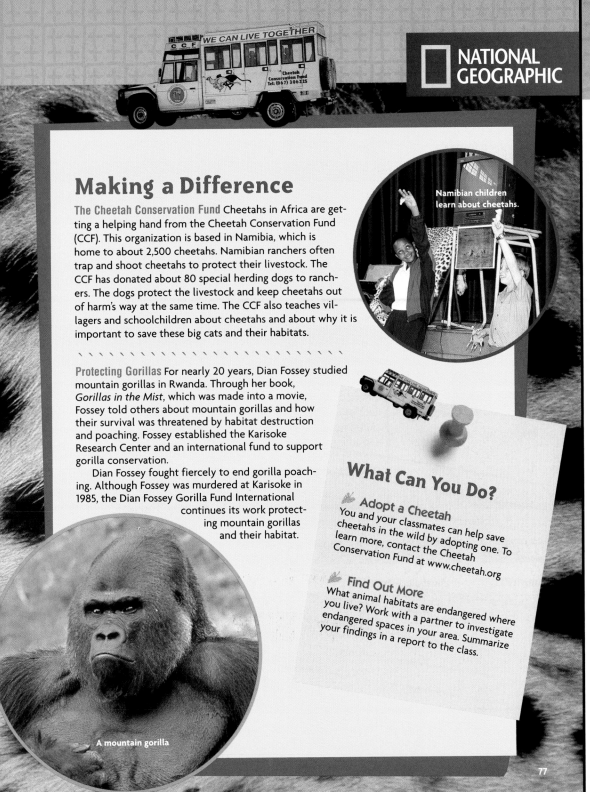

NATIONAL GEOGRAPHIC

Making a Difference

The Cheetah Conservation Fund Cheetahs in Africa are getting a helping hand from the Cheetah Conservation Fund (CCF). This organization is based in Namibia, which is home to about 2,500 cheetahs. Namibian ranchers often trap and shoot cheetahs to protect their livestock. The CCF has donated about 80 special herding dogs to ranchers. The dogs protect the livestock and keep cheetahs out of harm's way at the same time. The CCF also teaches villagers and schoolchildren about cheetahs and about why it is important to save these big cats and their habitats.

Namibian children learn about cheetahs.

Protecting Gorillas For nearly 20 years, Dian Fossey studied mountain gorillas in Rwanda. Through her book, *Gorillas in the Mist*, which was made into a movie, Fossey told others about mountain gorillas and how their survival was threatened by habitat destruction and poaching. Fossey established the Karisoke Research Center and an international fund to support gorilla conservation.

Dian Fossey fought fiercely to end gorilla poaching. Although Fossey was murdered at Karisoke in 1985, the Dian Fossey Gorilla Fund International continues its work protecting mountain gorillas and their habitat.

A mountain gorilla

What Can You Do?

Adopt a Cheetah
You and your classmates can help save cheetahs in the wild by adopting one. To learn more, contact the Cheetah Conservation Fund at www.cheetah.org

Find Out More
What animal habitats are endangered where you live? Work with a partner to investigate endangered spaces in your area. Summarize your findings in a report to the class.

77

GLOBAL ISSUES

Habitat Loss The problem of habitat loss affects places the world over. Tropical rain forests are being destroyed at the rate of about 11 square miles (28.5 sq. km) a day, with an estimated three species an hour becoming extinct. Deserts are expanding not only in Africa, but also in Asia, where both the Gobi and the Thar Desert are expanding. In the United States, about 3 million acres (1.2 million ha) of open space are lost each year.

Have students work individually or in groups to complete the What Can You Do? activities.

Discuss with students the What Can You Do? activities. You might want to have them write a paragraph explaining why they think endangered animal species should be protected.

For an additional regional case study, use the following:

Environmental Case Study

What Can You Do? Teacher Tips

Adopt a Cheetah: The Cheetah Conservation Fund's "Dog Page" on its Web site explains how using dogs to guard flocks actually helps cheetahs. The Web site has many other useful and informative pages.

Find Out More: The World Conservation Management Centre maintains the Red Book, which lists threatened species around the world. The U.S. Fish and Wildlife Service runs the Endangered Species Program, which includes a list, by state, of all endangered plants and animals in the United States.

Chapter 3 Resources

Note: The following materials may be used when teaching Chapter 3.
Section level support materials are shown at point of use in the margins of the Teacher Wraparound Edition.

Timesaving Tools

TeacherWorks™ All-In-One Planner and Resource Center

- **Interactive Teacher Edition** See the **Interactive Teacher Edition** CD-ROM to electronically integrate your Teacher Wraparound Edition and blackline masters.
- **Interactive Lesson Planner** Organize your week, month, semester, or year with all the lesson helps you need. The **Interactive Lesson Planner** CD-ROM contains all Chapter 3 resources.

Use Glencoe's **Presentation Plus!** multimedia teacher tool to easily present dynamic lessons that visually excite your students. Using Microsoft PowerPoint® you can customize the presentations to create your own personalized lessons.

TEACHING TRANSPARENCIES

Graphic Organizer Transparency 9 L2

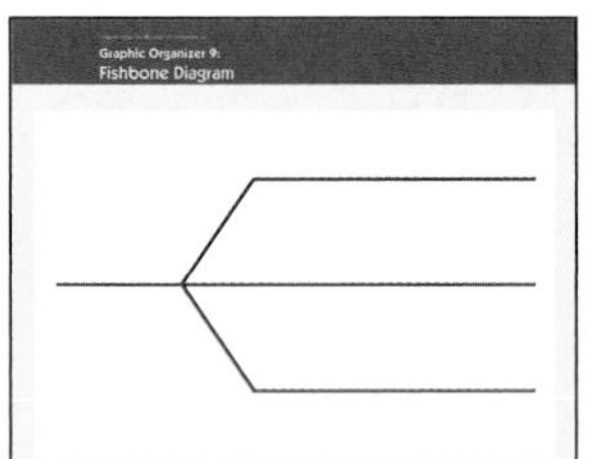

In-text Map Transparency L1

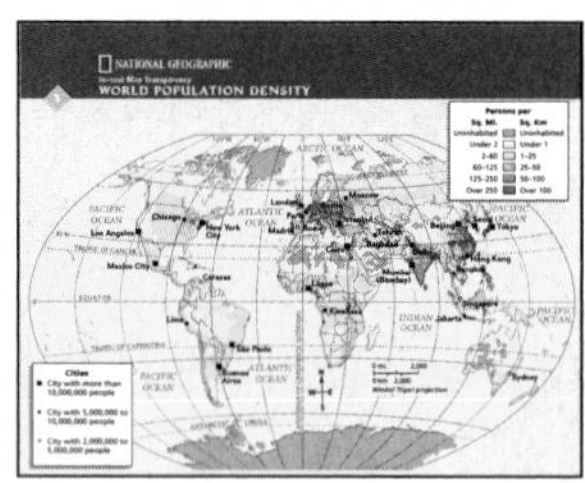

FOLDABLES™ Study Organizer

Dinah Zike's Foldables

Foldables are three-dimensional, interactive graphic organizers that help students practice basic writing skills, review key vocabulary terms, and identify main ideas. Additional chapter activities can be found in the ***Reading and Study Skills Foldables*** booklet.

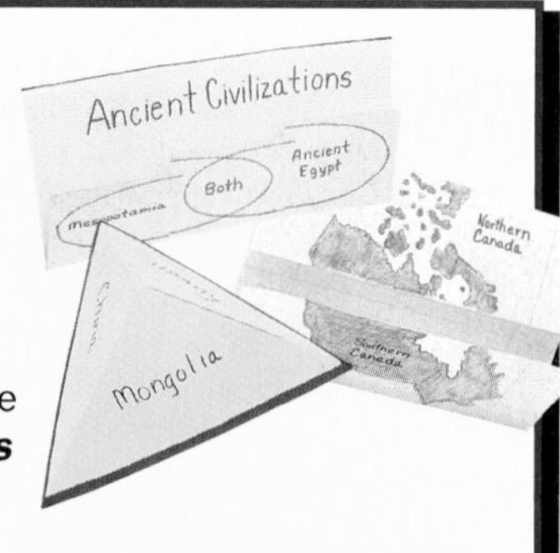

MAP AND GEOGRAPHY SKILLS

Chapter Map Activity L2

GeoLab Activity L2

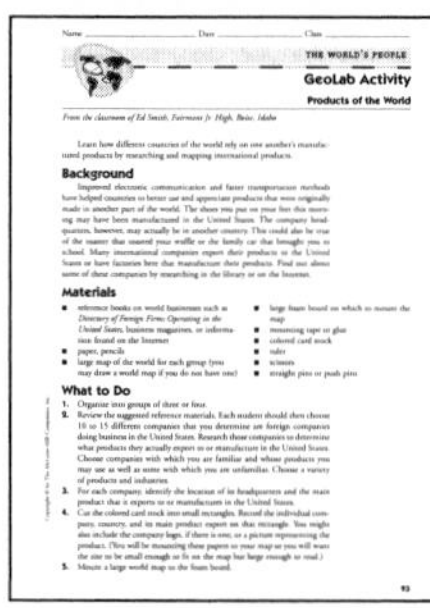

READING SUPPORT

Vocabulary Activity L1

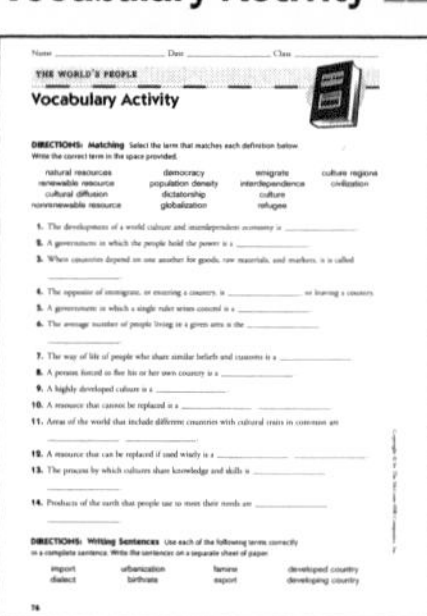

Workbook Activity L1

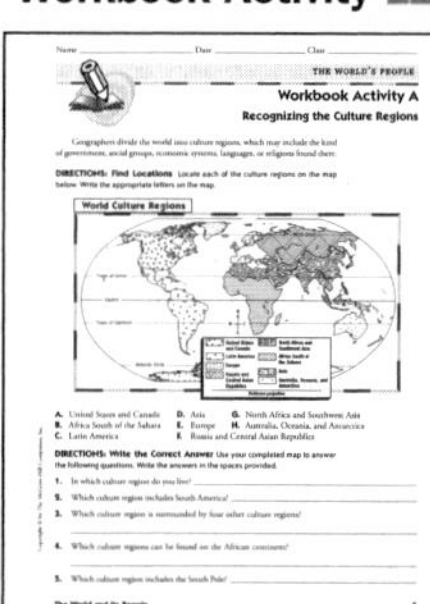

Reading and Writing Skills Activity L1

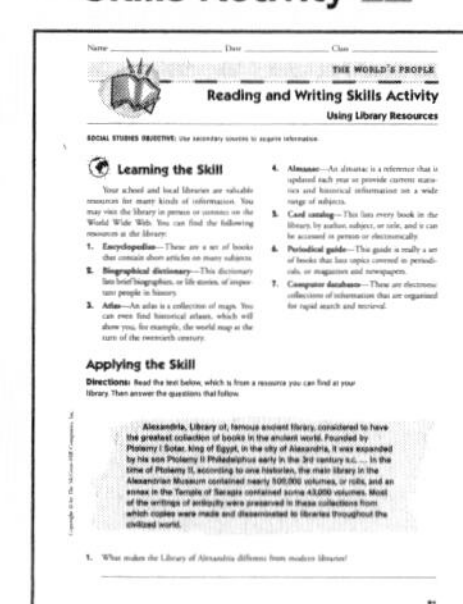

DIFFERENTIATED INSTRUCTION

Use these review and reinforcement materials to help less-proficient readers, English learners, and gifted and talented students.

Reteaching Activity L1

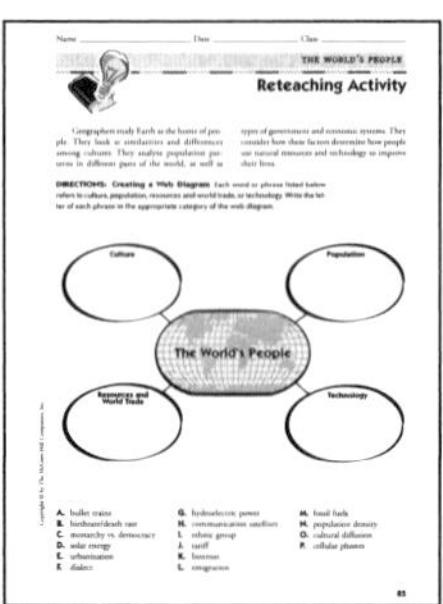

Chapter Skills Review L2

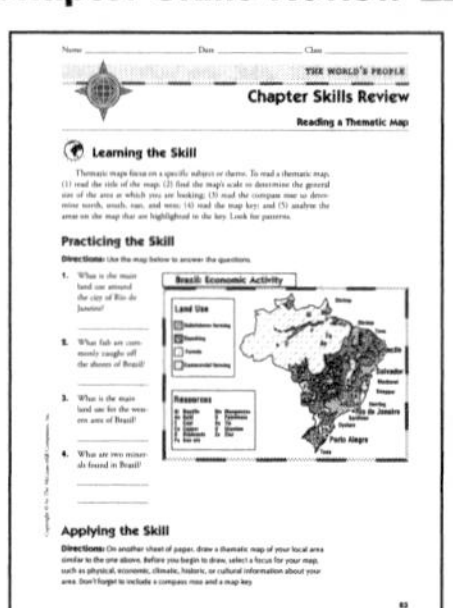

Cooperative Learning Activity L1/ELL

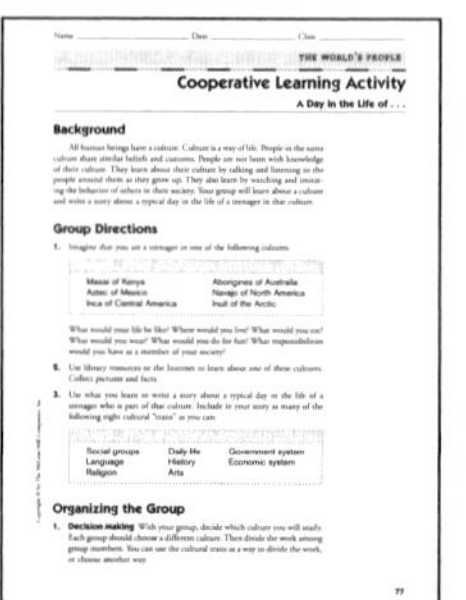

Enrichment Activity L3

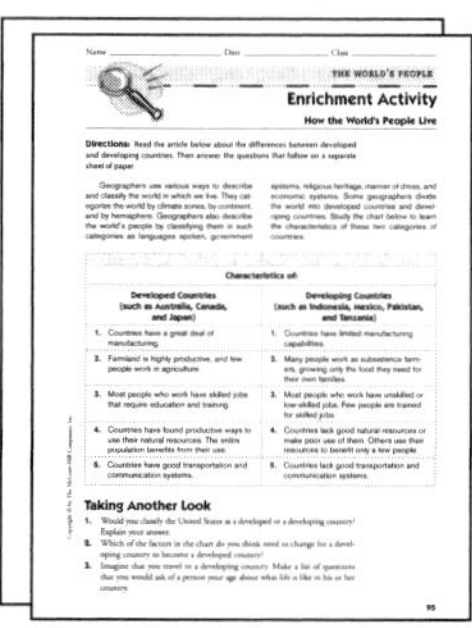

ASSESSMENT

Chapter Test, Form A L2

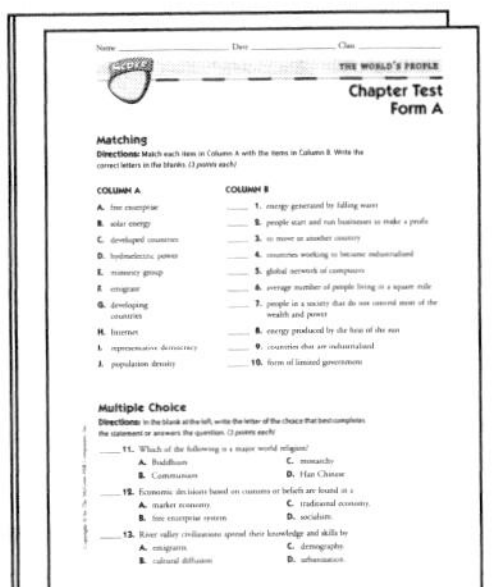

Chapter Test, Form B L2

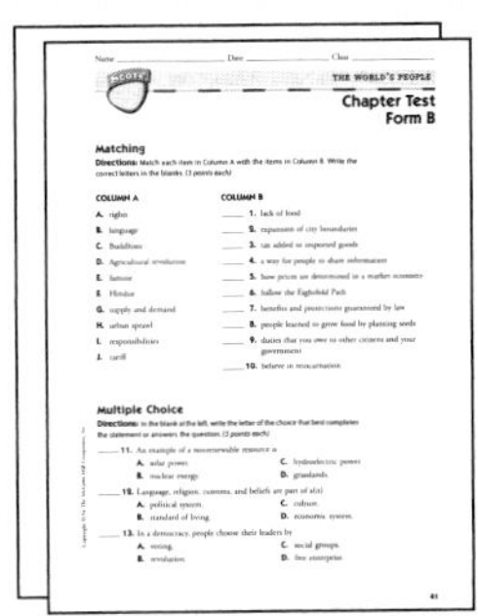

Performance Assessment Activity L1/ELL

ExamView® Pro Testmaker CD-ROM

STANDARDIZED ASSESSMENT SKILLS

Critical Thinking Skills Activity L2

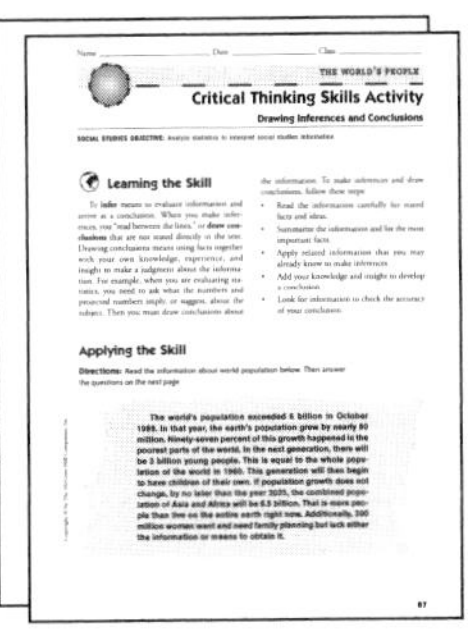

Map and Graph Skills Activity L2

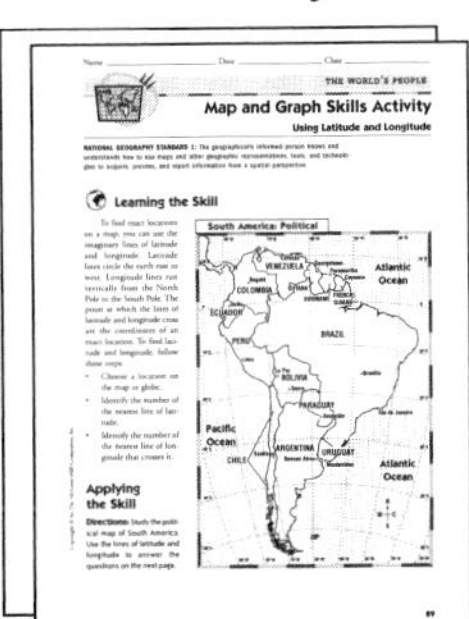

Standardized Test Skills Practice Workbook Activity L2

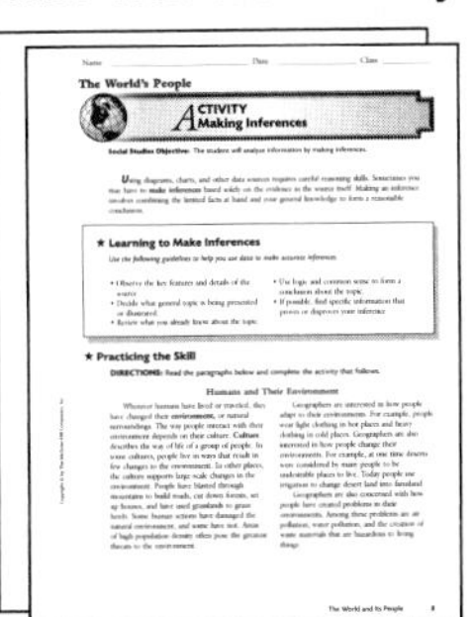

HOME INVOLVEMENT

Take-Home Review Activity L1

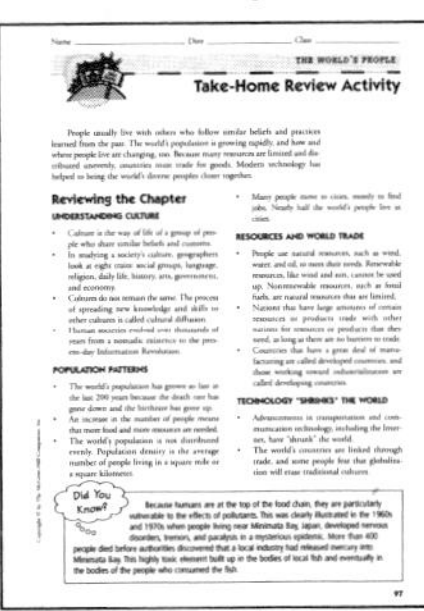

MULTIMEDIA

- **National Geographic's The World and Its People**
- **MindJogger Videoquiz**
- **Vocabulary PuzzleMaker CD-ROM**
- **Interactive Tutor Self-Assessment CD-ROM**
- **ExamView® Pro Testmaker CD-ROM**
- **TeacherWorks CD-ROM**
- **StudentWorks CD-ROM**
- **Skillbuilder Interactive Workbook CD-ROM, Level 1**
- **Presentation Plus! CD-ROM**
- **Audio Program**

SPANISH RESOURCES

The following Spanish language materials are available in the Spanish Resources binder:

- **Spanish Summaries**
- **Spanish Vocabulary Activities**
- **Spanish Guided Reading Activities**
- **Spanish Quizzes and Tests**
- **Spanish Take-Home Review Activities**
- **Spanish Reteaching Activities**

Meeting National Standards

Geography for Life

The following standards are covered in Chapter 3:

Section 1
- **EE2 Places and Regions: Standards 4, 5, 6**
- **EE4 Human Systems: Standards 10, 12, 13**

Section 2
- **EE1 The World in Spatial Terms: Standards 2, 3**
- **EE4 Human Systems: Standards 9, 10, 12, 13**

Section 3
- **EE4 Human Systems: Standards 11, 12, 13**
- **EE5 Environment and Society: Standards 14, 15, 16**

Section 4
- **EE1 The World in Spatial Terms: Standards 1, 2, 3**
- **EE3 Physical Systems: Standards 7, 8**
- **EE4 Human Systems: Standard 13**

Chapter 3 Planning Guide

SECTION RESOURCES

Daily Objectives	Reproducible Resources	Multimedia Resources
Section 1 **Understanding Culture** **1.** Define what *culture* means. **2.** Explain what elements make each culture unique. **3.** Describe how and why cultures change.	Reproducible Lesson Plan Daily Lecture and Discussion Notes Note-taking Guide Guided Reading Activity* Reading Essentials and Study Guide* Section Quiz*	Daily Focus Skills Transparency GeoQuiz Transparency Vocabulary PuzzleMaker CD-ROM Interactive Tutor Self-Assessment CD-ROM ExamView® Pro Testmaker CD-ROM Presentation Plus! CD-ROM
Section 2 **Population Patterns** **1.** Explain why the world's population is growing rapidly. **2.** Identify where most people in the world live. **3.** Discuss why more people are moving to cities.	Reproducible Lesson Plan Daily Lecture and Discussion Notes Note-taking Guide Guided Reading Activity* Reading Essentials and Study Guide* Section Quiz*	Daily Focus Skills Transparency GeoQuiz Transparency In-text Map Transparency Vocabulary PuzzleMaker CD-ROM Interactive Tutor Self-Assessment CD-ROM ExamView® Pro Testmaker CD-ROM Presentation Plus! CD-ROM
Section 3 **Resources and World Trade** **1.** Distinguish between renewable and nonrenewable resources. **2.** Explain why people trade. **3.** Describe how the world's economies are changing.	Reproducible Lesson Plan Daily Lecture and Discussion Notes Note-taking Guide Guided Reading Activity* Reading Essentials and Study Guide* Section Quiz*	Daily Focus Skills Transparency Vocabulary PuzzleMaker CD-ROM Interactive Tutor Self-Assessment CD-ROM ExamView® Pro Testmaker CD-ROM Presentation Plus! CD-ROM
Section 4 **Technology "Shrinks" the World** **1.** Describe how technology has changed the world. **2.** Define *interdependence* and how it has led to globalization.	Reproducible Lesson Plan Daily Lecture and Discussion Notes Note-taking Guide Guided Reading Activity* Reading Essentials and Study Guide* Section Quiz*	Daily Focus Skills Transparency Vocabulary PuzzleMaker CD-ROM Interactive Tutor Self-Assessment CD-ROM ExamView® Pro Testmaker CD-ROM Presentation Plus! CD-ROM MindJogger Videoquiz

00:00 **Out of Time?** Assign the **Reading Essentials and Study Guide*** for this chapter.

*Also available in Spanish

KEY TO ABILITY LEVELS

Teaching strategies have been coded for varying learning styles and abilities.

- L1 **BASIC** activities for all students
- L2 **AVERAGE** activities for average to above-average students
- L3 **CHALLENGING** activities for above-average students
- ELL **ENGLISH LANGUAGE LEARNER** activities

KEY TO TEACHING RESOURCES

- Blackline Master
- CD-ROM
- Transparency
- Videocassette
- Block Scheduling
- DVD

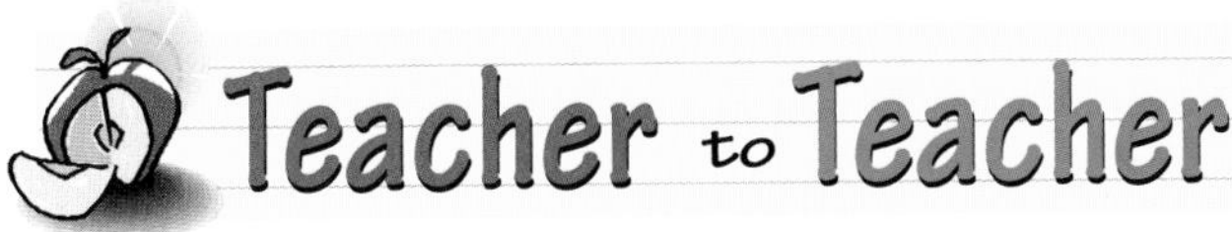

World Population and Food Supply

William Ball
West Central Jr./Sr. High
Francesville, Indiana

Organize the class into three groups, with 80 percent in group A, 15 percent in group B, and 5 percent in group C. Group A represents the world's poorest, developing nations. Group B represents mostly developed nations. Group C represents fully industrialized nations. Hold out a large candy bar and divide it among the three groups as follows: 80 percent goes to group C, 15 percent to group B, and 5 percent to group A. Explain to students that this is how the world's food supply is divided. Ask students to explain why this is so, then have groups work together for solutions that would provide a more equitable distribution of food.

Meeting Special Needs

In addition to the Differentiated Instruction strategies found in each section, the following resources are also suitable for your special needs students:

- ***ExamView® Pro Testmaker CD-ROM*** allows teachers to tailor tests by reducing answer choices.
- The ***Audio Program*** includes the entire narrative of the student edition so that less-proficient readers can listen to the words as they read them.
- The ***Reading Essentials and Study Guide*** provides the same content as the student edition but is written two grade levels below the textbook.
- ***Guided Reading Activities*** give less-proficient readers point-by-point instructions to increase comprehension as they read each textbook section.
- ***Enrichment Activities*** include a stimulating collection of readings and activities for gifted and talented students.

NATIONAL GEOGRAPHIC TEACHER'S CORNER

Index to National Geographic Magazine:

The following articles may be used for research relating to this chapter:

- "People Like Us," by Rick Gore, July 2000.
- *Global Culture,* a National Geographic Special Edition, August 1999.
- *Population,* a National Geographic Special Edition, October 1998

National Geographic Society Products:

To order the following products for use with this chapter, call National Geographic Society at 1-800-368-2728:

- *Nations of the World Series* (6 Videos)
- *Physical Geography of the Continents Series* (6 Videos)
- *National Geographic Desk Reference* (Book)
- *National Geographic Atlas of the World, Seventh Edition* (Book)
- *Healing the Earth* (Video)
- *Ozone: Protecting the Invisible Shield* (Video)

NGS ONLINE

Access National Geographic's Web site for current events, activities, links, interactive features, and archives. www.nationalgeographic.com

NATIONAL GEOGRAPHIC MapMachine

Find the latest coverage of geography in the news, atlas updates, cartographic activities with interactive maps, an online map store, and links at www.nationalgeographic.com/maps

Use our Web site for additional resources. All essential content is covered in the Student Edition.

You and your students can visit twip.glencoe.com, the Web site companion to *The World and Its People*. This innovative integration of electronic and print media offers your students a wealth of opportunities. The student text directs students to the Web site for the following options:

- Chapter Overviews
- Student Web Activities
- Self-Check Quizzes
- Textbook Updates

Answers are provided for you in the Web Activity Lesson Plan. Additional Web resources and Interactive Tutor puzzles are also available.

Introducing Chapter 3

Social Studies Online

Introduce students to chapter content and key terms by having them access Chapter Overview 3 at twip.glencoe.com

Chapter Objectives

1. Explain what makes up a people's culture.
2. Discuss issues related to human population and its growth.
3. Identify what resources are and explain why countries trade with one another.
4. Describe how technology has changed the world.

GLENCOE TECHNOLOGY

NATIONAL GEOGRAPHIC

The World and Its People Video Program

Chapter 3 The World's People

The following segments enhance the study of this chapter:

- **The Human Race**
- **Turkana Basin**

MindJogger Videoquiz

Use MindJogger Videoquiz to preview the Chapter 3 content.

Both programs available in DVD and VHS

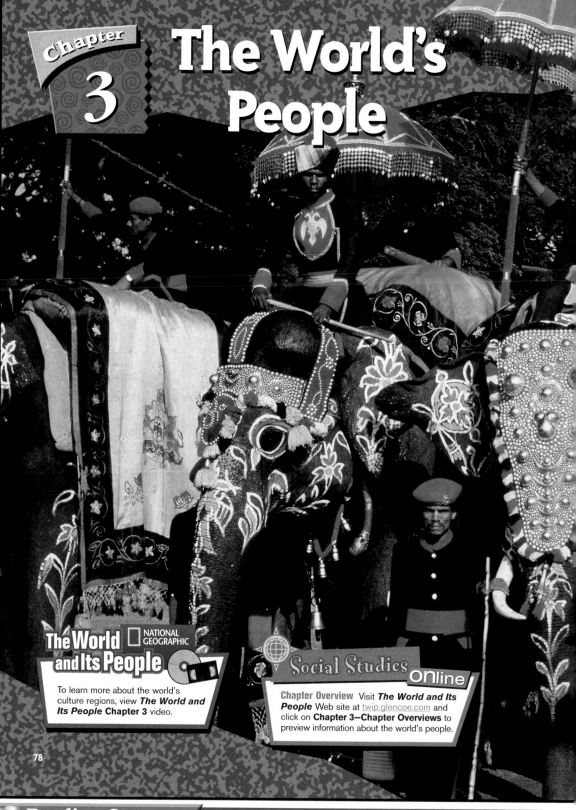

Chapter 3 The World's People

The World and Its People NATIONAL GEOGRAPHIC

To learn more about the world's culture regions, view ***The World and Its People* Chapter 3** video.

Social Studies Online

Chapter Overview Visit ***The World and Its People*** Web site at twip.glencoe.com and click on **Chapter 3—Chapter Overviews** to preview information about the world's people.

78

Reading Strategy — Purpose for Reading

Mindstreaming is a useful strategy to bring out students' background knowledge before starting a new unit or lesson. First organize the students into pairs. Next have student A talk for one minute about a visit he or she made to another country or another part of this country, telling everything he or she knows about food, clothing, languages, housing, and so on. Student B listens without saying anything. Reverse the roles for one more minute. Finally, solicit information discussed by random pairs. Conclude by discussing how culture includes many aspects of everyday life and that it defines the differences between one community and another. L1

Organizing Information Make this foldable to help you organize what you learn about culture, the world's population, resources, and the effect of technology on the world.

Step 1 Fold the sides of a piece of paper into the middle to make a shutter fold.

Step 2 Fold in half from side to side.

Step 3 Open and cut along the inside fold lines to form four tabs.

Cut along the fold lines on both sides.

Step 4 Label the tabs as shown.

Under-standing Culture | Population Patterns | Resources & World Trade | Technology "Shrinks" the World

Reading and Writing As you read each section in the chapter, write notes under the correct tab of your foldable.

Why It Matters

Discovering Other Cultures

A while ago it was common for people to spend most of their lives in the same town or place in which they were born. Today your neighbor may be someone from another state, another country, or another continent. How do people in the rest of the world live? How do we get along with them? This book will help you learn about other people and places and what issues are important to them.

◀ Painted elephants are part of the Dussehra festival in India.

Introducing Chapter 3

FOLDABLES Study Organizer — Dinah Zike's Foldables

Purpose Students will make and use the foldable to identify what they want to find out about the topics. After students have written the questions they have about the topics, they should read the sections to find the answers. These answers can be written on the inside of the tabs. Students should use other sources to research the questions that were not addressed in the section.

Have students complete the ***Reading and Study Skills Foldables*** activity for this chapter.

Why It Matters

Discuss with students how one's culture influences his or her beliefs. **Ask:** **What are some of the general beliefs in our culture about work, family, and religion?** Then have students choose a country and research it using the Internet, newspapers, or magazines. Students should find information about how that country's culture influences people's beliefs about work, family, and religion. Students should present their findings in a two-page essay. Discuss students' findings as a class.

About the Photo

Dussehra is one of the most important Hindu festivals celebrated in India. It commemorates the victory of Rama, a Hindu deity and hero, over the demon king Ravana, and the triumph of good over evil. It also marks the end of the hot summer and the beginning of the winter season. In Mysore, India, the day is celebrated with a magnificent procession. Richly decorated elephants carry actors dressed as deities. Different regions celebrate in their own particular ways, but it is always a joyous occasion, offering lively performances, food, firecrackers, and colorful effigies. Ask students to use this photo to explain the relationship among religious ideas, philosophical ideas, and cultures.

Chapter 3

Section 1, pages 80–85

Focus

Section Objectives

1. Define what *culture* means.
2. Explain what elements make each culture unique.
3. Describe how and why cultures change.

BELLRINGER Skillbuilder Activity

Project transparency and have students answer the question.

Daily Focus Skills Transparency

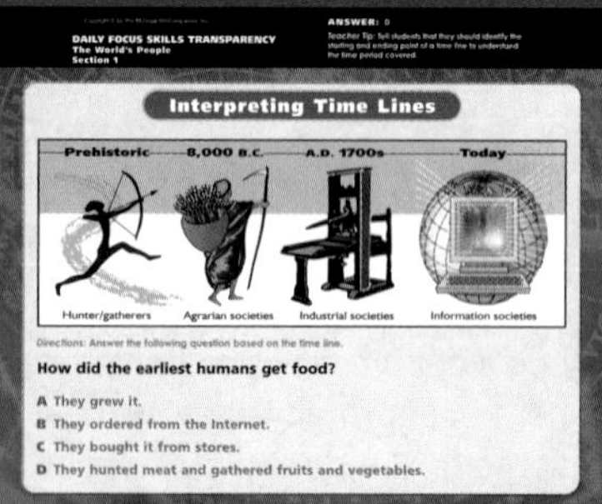

Reading Preview

■ **Activating Prior Knowledge** Have volunteers describe the ethnic foods they have eaten. Point out that food is one way cultures differ from one another.

■ **Preteaching Vocabulary** The word *economy* comes from a Greek word that means "household manager." Ask students what this tells them about the meaning of the word. *(It is concerned with managing resources.)*

Guide to Reading

Main Idea

People usually live with others who follow similar beliefs learned from the past.

Terms to Know

- culture
- ethnic group
- dialect
- democracy
- dictatorship
- monarchy
- cultural diffusion
- civilization
- culture region

Reading Strategy

Draw a diagram like this one. In each section, write one of the eight elements of culture and give an example of each from the United States today.

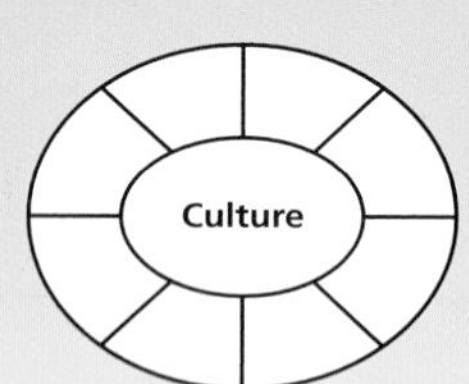

Section 1 Understanding Culture

NATIONAL GEOGRAPHIC Exploring Our World

Three thousand years ago, the Olmec people lived in Mexico. They sometimes wore skins of jaguars, cats that were sacred to them. This young boy lives in an area where the jaguar is still honored. He is preparing for a jaguar dance. An object from modern culture—a soft drink bottle—is used to make the "jaguar" spots of ash on the boy's clay-covered skin.

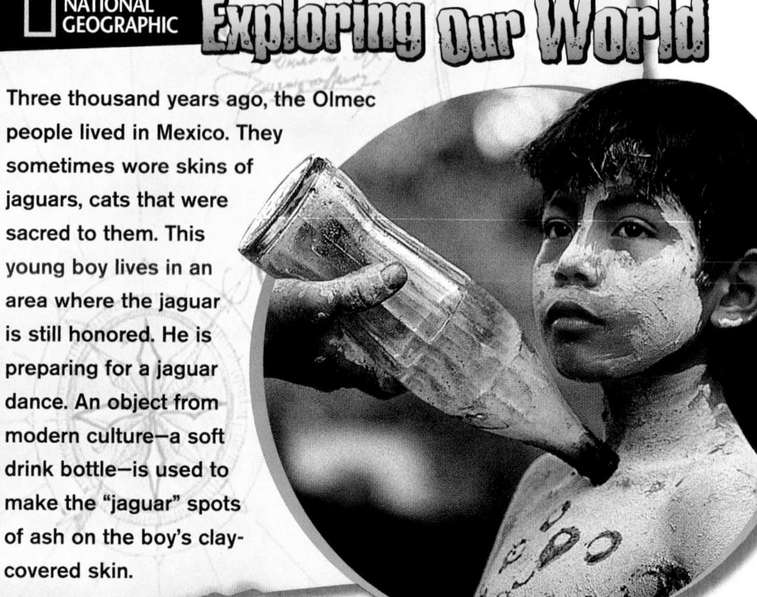

If you wake up to rock music, wear denim jeans, and celebrate the Fourth of July, these things are part of your culture. If you eat tortillas, speak Spanish, and honor the jaguar, these things are part of your culture.

What Is Culture?

Culture is the way of life of people who share similar beliefs and customs. Social scientists look at eight elements called traits. They study what groups a society is divided into, what language the people speak, and what religions they follow. They examine people's daily lives and look at their history and artwork. They also look at how a society is governed and how the people make a living.

Social Groups One way of studying cultures is by looking at the different groups of people in a society. For instance, scientists compare the number of rich, poor, and middle class people. They look at how the young and the old are treated. In addition, they study the differing

Section Resources

Reproducible Masters

- Reproducible Lesson Plan
- Daily Lecture and Discussion Notes
- Note-taking Guide
- Guided Reading Activity
- Reading Essentials and Study Guide
- Section Quiz

Transparencies

- Daily Focus Skills Transparency
- GeoQuiz Transparency

Multimedia

- Vocabulary PuzzleMaker CD-ROM
- Interactive Tutor Self-Assessment CD-ROM
- Presentation Plus! CD-ROM
- ExamView® Pro Testmaker CD-ROM

roles of men and women. Social scientists also examine a country's different ethnic groups. An **ethnic group** is a group of people who share a common history, language, religion, and some physical characteristics. One particular ethnic group in a country may be the majority group. This group in society controls most of the wealth and power. The other ethnic groups in that country are minority groups—people whose race or ethnic origin is different from that of the majority group in the region. The largest ethnic minority groups in the United States are African Americans and Hispanic Americans.

Language Sharing a language is one of the strongest unifying forces for a culture. Even within a culture, though, there are language differences. Some people may speak a **dialect,** or a local form of a language that differs from the same language in other areas. The differences may include pronunciation and the meaning of words. For example, people in the northeastern United States say "soda," whereas people in the Midwest say "pop." Both groups are referring to soft drinks, however.

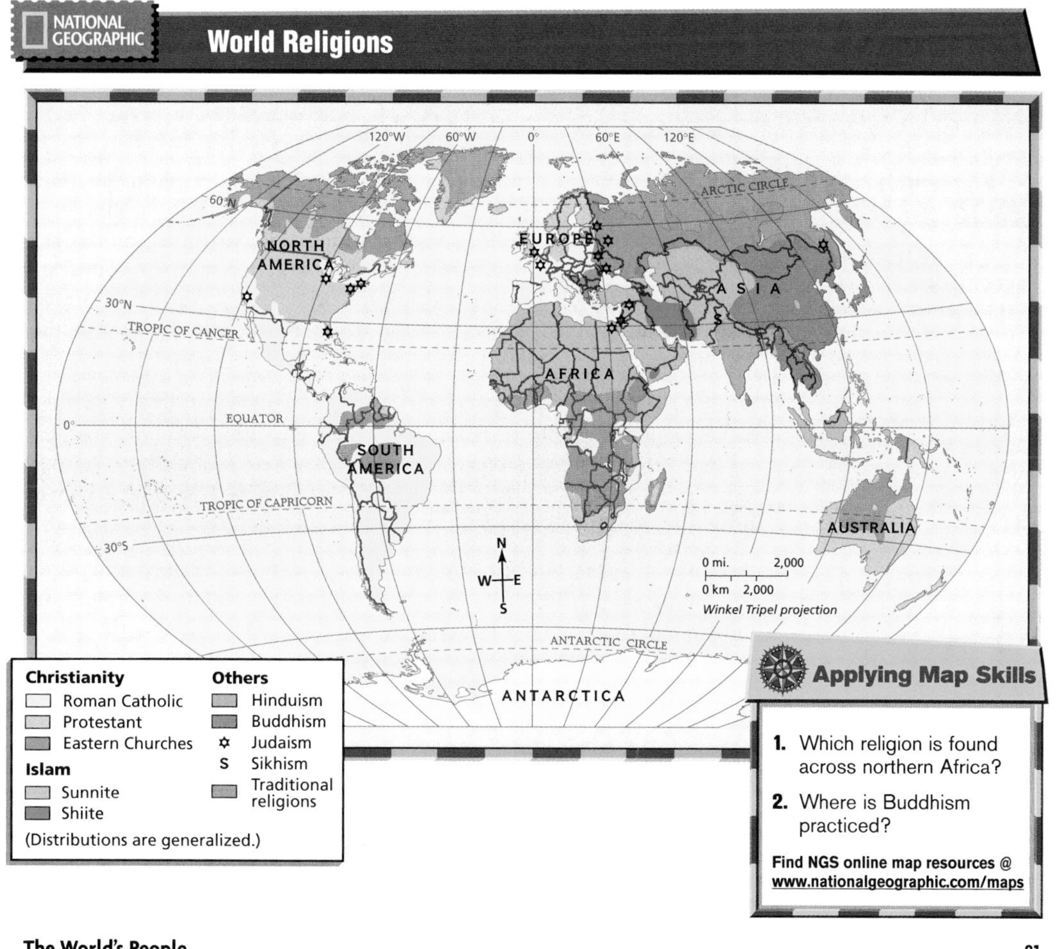

Applying Map Skills

1. Which religion is found across northern Africa?
2. Where is Buddhism practiced?

Find NGS online map resources @ www.nationalgeographic.com/maps

Chapter 3

Section 1, pages 80–85

Teach

Making Comparisons Make the concept of "culture" concrete for students by discussing it in the context of their own culture. For each cultural characteristic (social groups, language, and so on), have them identify examples from their culture. Write the examples on the board. Then work with students to provide comparative examples from other cultures. L1 

Daily Lecture and Discussion Notes

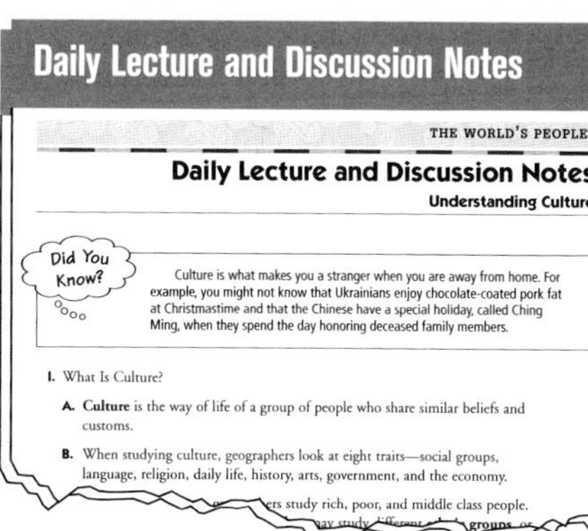
THE WORLD'S PEOPLE

Daily Lecture and Discussion Notes
Understanding Culture

Did You Know? Culture is what makes you a stranger when you are away from home. For example, you might not know that Ukrainians enjoy chocolate-coated pork fat at Christmastime and that the Chinese have a special holiday, called Ching Ming, when they spend the day honoring deceased family members.

I. What Is Culture?
A. **Culture** is the way of life of a group of people who share similar beliefs and customs.
B. When studying culture, geographers look at eight traits—social groups, language, religion, daily life, history, arts, government, and the economy.

Applying Map Skills

Answers
1. Islam (Sunnite)
2. East Asia

Skills Practice
What religions are predominant in Australia? *(Protestant and traditional religions)*

Reading Strategy: Reading the Text

Activating Prior Knowledge Before students begin to take in any new knowledge, prepare them by bringing to mind what they already know. Use the key concepts and boldfaced terms in the text to frame general questions that encourage students to think about the topic and to share ideas. Then provide specific information that will enhance their understanding of the subject. L1

*Use the **Reading Skills Handbook** for more reading strategies.*

Interdisciplinary Connections

Math Give students the following numbers from the *World Almanac, 2003:* Mandarin—874 million; Hindi—366 million; English—341 million; Spanish—322 million; and Bengali—207 million. Tell them that these represent the number of *native* speakers of the five most widely used languages in the world. Give them a world population figure of 6 billion and ask them to calculate the percentage of the world's people that speaks each of these languages. *(Mandarin—14.5%; Hindi—6.1%; English—5.7%; Spanish—5.4%; Bengali—3.5%)* L2

Analyzing the Chart

Answer
Siddhartha Gautama

Skills Practice
What is the Torah? *(the first five books of the Hebrew Bible)*

Major World Religions

Religion	Major Leader	Beliefs
Buddhism	Siddhartha Gautama, the Buddha	Buddhists believe that to escape the suffering caused by worldly desires, people must follow the Eightfold Path, or rules that lead to a life of morality, wisdom, and good thought. By following the Eightfold Path, one can achieve nirvana—a state of bliss.
Christianity	Jesus Christ	Christians believe that Jesus, the Son of God, was sent to Earth and died on the cross to save humanity. By having faith in Jesus and through God's grace, believers are saved from God's penalty for sin and receive eternal life with God.
Hinduism	Unknown	Hindus believe in reincarnation—after death, the soul is reborn in another person, animal, or vegetable. Where a soul is reborn depends upon a person's karma, or the spiritual force resulting from actions in past lives. The three main Hindu gods are Brahma, Vishnu, and Siva.
Islam	Muhammad	The followers of Islam, known as Muslims, believe in one God, Allah. Muslims follow the teachings of the Quran, which the prophet Muhammad said were revealed to him by Allah. By following the five pillars of faith—belief, prayer, charity, fasting, and pilgrimage—believers go to an eternal paradise.
Judaism	Abraham	Jews believe in one God, Yahweh. By following God's laws, Jews believe they will have peace with God and with each other. The main laws and practices of Judaism are contained in the Torah, the first five books of the Hebrew Bible.

Analyzing the Chart

How do we become good people? What happens when we die? These are some of the questions that religions attempt to answer.

Culture Who was the founder of Buddhism?

Religion Another important part of culture is religion. In many cultures, religion helps people answer basic questions about life's meaning. Religious beliefs vary significantly around the world. Struggles over religious differences are a challenge in many countries. Some of the major world religions are described in the chart above. The map on page 81 shows you the main areas where these religions are practiced.

Daily Life Do you eat pizza, tacos, yogurt, and egg rolls? All of these foods came from different cultures. What people eat and how they eat it—with their fingers, silverware, or chopsticks—reflect their culture. What people wear also reflects cultural differences. The same is true of how people build traditional homes in their societies.

History History shapes how we view the world. People remember the successes of the past. We often celebrate holidays to honor the heroes and heroines who brought about those successes. Stories about these heroes reveal the personal characteristics that the people think are important. A group also remembers the dark periods of history, when they met with disaster or defeat. These experiences, too, influence how a group of people sees itself.

Arts People express their culture through the arts. Art is not just paintings and sculptures, but also architecture, dance, music, theater, and literature. By viewing the arts of a culture, you can gain insight into what the people of that culture think is beautiful and important.

Differentiated Instruction

Meeting Special Needs: Visual/Spatial Students who do well with this mode of learning can benefit by studying a variety of photographs of people, activities, and artifacts of different cultures. Bring to class books showing photographs of various nations. Have students find photographs reflecting similar aspects of different cultures (for example, clothing, architecture, festivals). This will help students understand specific aspects of culture and the ways in which these aspects may vary. L1 ELL

Refer to *Inclusion for the Middle School Social Studies Classroom Strategies and Activities* in the TCR.

Government People need rules in order to live together without conflict. Rules or laws are created by governments. Countries may have limited governments or unlimited governments. In a limited government, all citizens—including the country's leaders—must obey the laws of the land as written in a constitution or statement of rights. A **democracy** is a form of limited government where power rests with the people of the nation. The United States has a representative democracy in which citizens vote to elect representatives who then make and enforce laws.

In unlimited governments, rulers have powers that are *not* limited by laws. One type of unlimited government is a **dictatorship,** where a dictator usually takes power by force. To stay in power, most dictators rely on the police and the military. Dictators are not responsible to the people, and they limit freedom of speech, assembly, and the press. In a **monarchy,** kings or queens are born into a ruling family and inherit their power to rule. Until about the 1600s, such rulers were absolute monarchs with unlimited power. Now, in most countries, absolute monarchy has given way to constitutional monarchy. The United Kingdom, for example, is both a constitutional monarchy and a democracy. The queen is the symbolic head of the country, but elected leaders hold the power to rule. The chart below summarizes forms of government.

The Economy Culture includes economic activities, or how the people in a society earn a living. Some people farm or manufacture products. Others provide services, such as designing a Web page or preparing food. You will learn more about economic systems in Section 3.

✓Reading Check What is culture?

Types of Government

Type of Government	Who Holds Power?	Examples
Direct Democracy	All citizens vote directly on issues.	• Parts of Switzerland • Some New England towns
Representative Democracy	People vote for representatives who lead the country and make laws.	• United States • Russia • France
Constitutional Monarchy	A monarch inherits the right to rule but is limited by laws and a lawmaking body elected by the people.	• United Kingdom • Japan • Sweden • Jordan
Absolute Monarchy	A monarch inherits the right to rule and has unlimited power.	• Saudi Arabia
Dictatorship	A dictator makes all laws and suppresses any opposition.	• Cuba • Iraq under Saddam Hussein • Germany under Adolf Hitler

Analyzing the Chart

The United States is one of many countries with a democratic type of government.

Government What is the difference between a direct democracy and a representative democracy?

Note-taking tip

Point out to students that the types of government and economic systems are important concepts they will refer to frequently in the course. Suggest that they put the definitions on a note card or some other material that they can keep handy and refer to often.

✓ Reading Check Answer

the way of life of a group of people who share similar beliefs and customs

Analyzing the Chart

Answer
direct democracy: people govern themselves by voting individually on issues; representative democracy: people elect representatives who make and enforce laws

L1/ELL

Guided Reading Activity

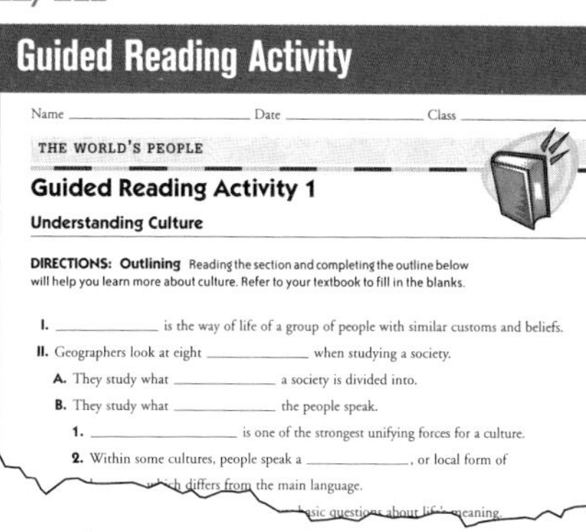
Name ____ Date ____ Class ____

THE WORLD'S PEOPLE

Guided Reading Activity 1
Understanding Culture

DIRECTIONS: Outlining Reading the section and completing the outline below will help you learn more about culture. Refer to your textbook to fill in the blanks.

I. ____ is the way of life of a group of people with similar customs and beliefs.
II. Geographers look at eight ____ when studying a society.
A. They study what ____ a society is divided into.
B. They study what ____ the people speak.
1. ____ is one of the strongest unifying forces for a culture.
2. Within some cultures, people speak a ____, or local form of

Critical Thinking Activity

Making Inferences Have students examine why cultural factors diffuse from one area to another. Create a three-column chart on the board with the headings "Trade," "Movement of People," and "War." Ask students to identify examples of each factor of cultural diffusion. One example for each factor would be the popularity of blue jeans around the world today; the presence of Christianity in the Americas; and the spread of Latin-based languages in Europe. Write students' suggestions under the appropriate column and discuss them. **Ask: Which factor of cultural diffusion is most prominent today? L2**

 **EE4 Human Systems: Standard 10**

Chapter 3

Section 1, pages 80–85

Applying Map Skills

Answers

1. Africa south of the Sahara
2. North Africa and Southwest Asia

Skills Practice

Do most continents have only one or more than one culture region? *(All but South America, Antarctica, and Australia have more than one.)*

3 ASSESS

Assign Section 1 Assessment as homework or an in-class activity.

Have students use the Interactive Tutor Self-Assessment CD-ROM to review Section 1.

Measure student knowledge of physical features.

GeoQuiz Transparency

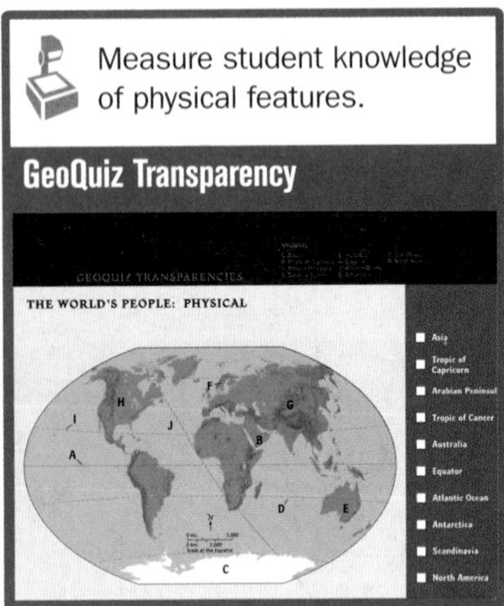

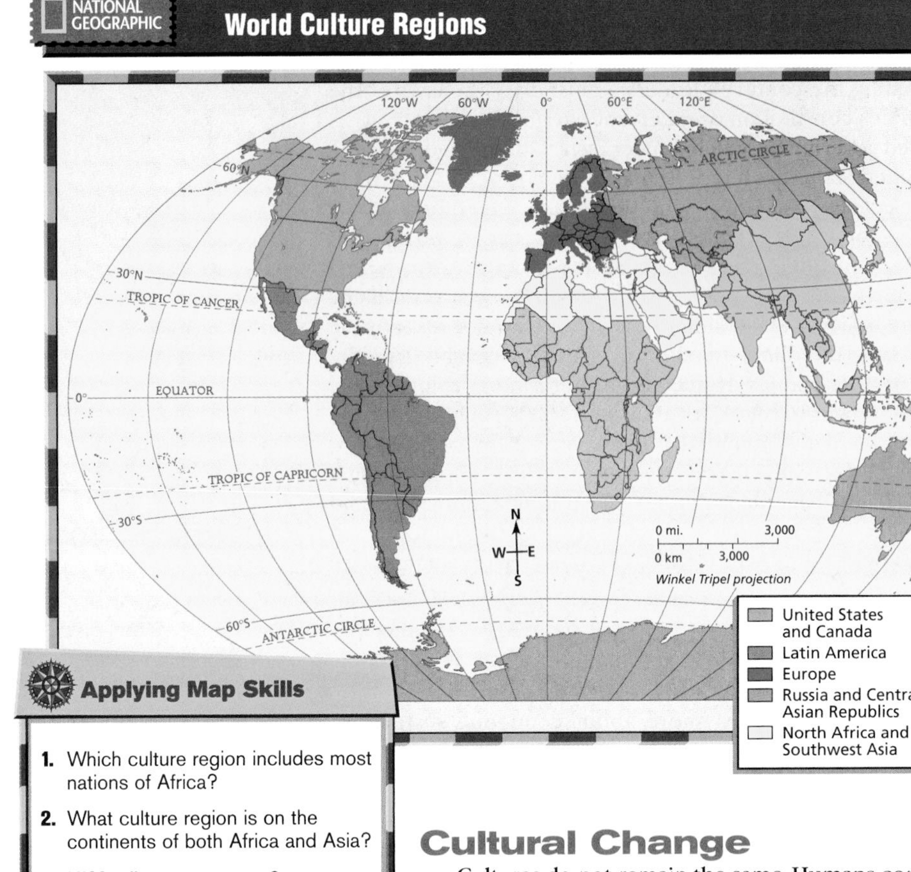

Applying Map Skills

1. Which culture region includes most nations of Africa?
2. What culture region is on the continents of both Africa and Asia?

Find NGS online map resources @ www.nationalgeographic.com/maps

Cultural Change

Cultures do not remain the same. Humans constantly invent new ideas and technologies and create new solutions to problems. Trade, the movement of people, and war can spread these changes to other cultures. The process of spreading new knowledge and skills to other cultures is called **cultural diffusion.** Today television and the Internet are making cultural diffusion take place more rapidly than ever before.

Culture Over Time Historians have traced the tremendous changes that humans have made in their cultures. In the first human societies, people lived by hunting animals and gathering fruits and vegetables. They were nomadic, moving from place to place, to follow sources of food.

Starting about 10,000 years ago, people learned to grow food by planting seeds. This change brought about the Agricultural Revolution. Groups stayed in one place and built settlements. Their societies became more complex. As a result, four **civilizations,** or highly developed cultures, arose in river valleys in present-day **Iraq, Egypt, India,** and **China.** These civilizations included cities,

Cooperative Learning Activity

Cultural Mural Organize students into eight groups. Inform groups that their task is to create an eight-section wall poster on aspects of cultures—both historical and modern. Assign each group one of the factors used to define culture regions—social groups, language, religion, daily life, history, arts, government, and the economy. Groups should develop or locate a number of images that illustrate their factor. Each group should then create its section of the poster. Some group members might do artwork or design, while others might write captions. Have groups combine their finished sections to create the wall poster. **L2 ELL** 

EE4 Human Systems: Standard 10

complex governments and religions, and systems of writing. The map on page 86 shows you where these civilizations were located.

Thousands of years later—in the 1700s and 1800s—came a new set of changes in the world. Some countries began to industrialize, or use machines and factories to make goods. These machines could work harder, faster, and longer than people or animals. As a result of the Industrial Revolution, people began to live longer, healthier, more comfortable lives.

Recently, the world began a new revolution—the Information Revolution. Computers make it possible to store and process huge amounts of information. They also allow people to instantly send this information all over the world. You will learn more about this revolution and how it connects the cultures of the world in Section 4.

Culture Regions As you recall, geographers use the term "regions" for areas that share common characteristics. Today geographers often divide the world into areas called culture regions. Each **culture region** includes different countries that have traits in common. They share similar economic systems, forms of government, and social groups. Their languages are related, and the people may follow the same religion. Their history and art are similar. The food, dress, and housing of the people may have common characteristics as well. In this textbook, you will study the different culture regions of the world.

Reading Check What three revolutions have changed the world?

Assessment

Defining Terms

1. **Define** culture, ethnic group, dialect, democracy, dictatorship, monarchy, cultural diffusion, civilization, culture region.

Recalling Facts

2. **Culture** What kinds of social groups do social scientists study?
3. **Government** What are the different forms of government a society may have?
4. **Culture** In what ways does cultural diffusion occur?

Critical Thinking

5. **Understanding Cause and Effect** How does history shape cultures?
6. **Making Comparisons** Describe the beliefs of two major religions.

Graphic Organizer

7. **Organizing Information** Create a diagram like this one that describes features of your culture. On the lines, write types of food, clothing, language, music, and so on.

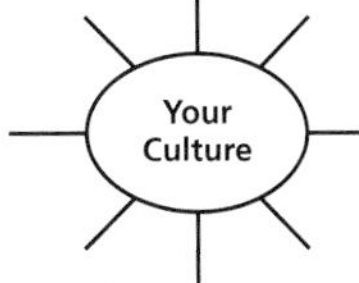

Applying Social Studies Skills

8. **Analyzing Maps** Look at the map on page 84. In which culture region do you live? In which culture region(s) did your ancestors live?

Chapter 3
Section 1, pages 80–85

L2

Section Quiz

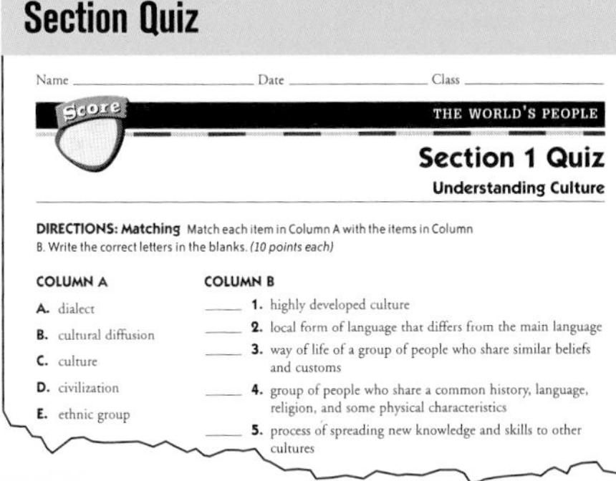
Name Date Class

THE WORLD'S PEOPLE

Section 1 Quiz
Understanding Culture

DIRECTIONS: Matching Match each item in Column A with the items in Column B. Write the correct letters in the blanks. (10 points each)

COLUMN A	COLUMN B
A. dialect	____ 1. highly developed culture
B. cultural diffusion	____ 2. local form of language that differs from the main language
C. culture	____ 3. way of life of a group of people who share similar beliefs and customs
D. civilization	____ 4. group of people who share a common history, language, religion, and some physical characteristics
E. ethnic group	____ 5. process of spreading new knowledge and skills to other cultures

Reading Check Answer

Agricultural Revolution, Industrial Revolution, Information Revolution

L1/ELL

Reading Essentials and Study Guide

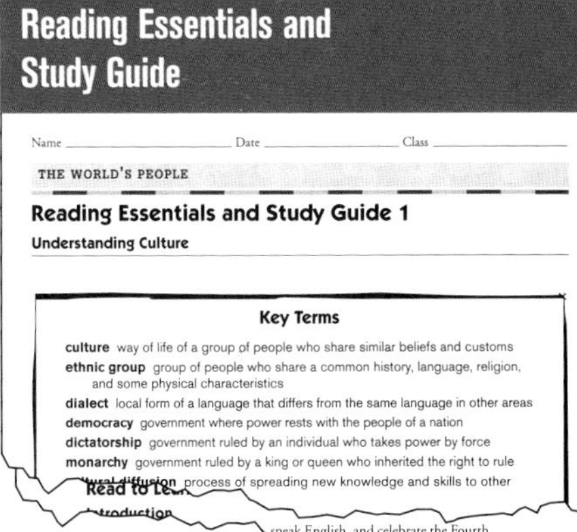
Name Date Class

THE WORLD'S PEOPLE

Reading Essentials and Study Guide 1
Understanding Culture

Key Terms

culture way of life of a group of people who share similar beliefs and customs
ethnic group group of people who share a common history, language, religion, and some physical characteristics
dialect local form of a language that differs from the same language in other areas
democracy government where power rests with the people of a nation
dictatorship government ruled by an individual who takes power by force
monarchy government ruled by a king or queen who inherited the right to rule
cultural diffusion process of spreading new knowledge and skills to other

Close

Reading Strategy

Writing an Essay Have students write a brief essay explaining each of the eight elements of culture.

Section 1 Assessment

1. The terms are defined in the Glossary.
2. rich, poor, middle class; age group; males and females; ethnic and religious groups
3. monarchy, dictatorship, and democracy
4. trade, movement of peoples, and war
5. Stories of heroes and of past misfortunes influence how a group of people sees itself.
6. Students should describe the beliefs of any two: Buddhism, Christianity, Hinduism, Islam, or Judaism.
7. Students should complete their diagrams with concrete examples of their cultures.
8. Students will likely answer *United States* and *Canada* to the first question. Answers to the second question will vary.

TEACH

Ask students if they have ever seen or used a road map to get from one place to another. Point out that road maps are special purpose maps. **Ask:** What special information do these maps contain? *(road locations; road types; government authority that has responsibility for the roads; relative size of cities and towns; in some cases, location of service stations, tolls, points of interest)* L1

Additional Skills Practice

1. What areas are shown on the map? *(parts of Africa, Asia, and Europe)*
2. What time period does the map cover? How long ago was that? *(from 3500 B.C. to 1700 B.C.; from 5,500 to 3,700 years ago)*
3. Which of these ancient civilizations covered the smallest area? *(Ancient Egypt)*

Additional Skills Resources

 Chapter Skills Review

 Building Geography Skills for Life

GLENCOE TECHNOLOGY

 **Skillbuilder Interactive Workbook CD-ROM, Level 1**

This interactive CD-ROM reinforces student mastery of essential social studies skills.

Social Studies Skill

Reading a Thematic Map

Thematic maps concentrate on a single theme. This theme may be to show the battles of a particular war or habitats of endangered species, for example.

Learning the Skill

To read a thematic map, follow these steps:

- Read the map title. It tells what kind of special information the map shows.
- Find the map's scale to determine the general size of the area.
- Read the key. Colors and symbols in the map key are especially important on this type of map.
- Analyze the areas on the map that are highlighted in the key. Look for patterns.

Practicing the Skill

Look at the map below to answer the following questions.

1. What is the title of the map?
2. Read the key. What four civilizations are shown on this map?
3. Which civilization was farthest west? East?
4. What do the locations of each of these civilizations have in common?

Applying the Skill

Find a thematic map in a newspaper or magazine. Write three questions about the map's purpose, then have a classmate answer the questions.

GO TO Practice key skills with **Glencoe Skillbuilder Interactive Workbook, Level 1.**

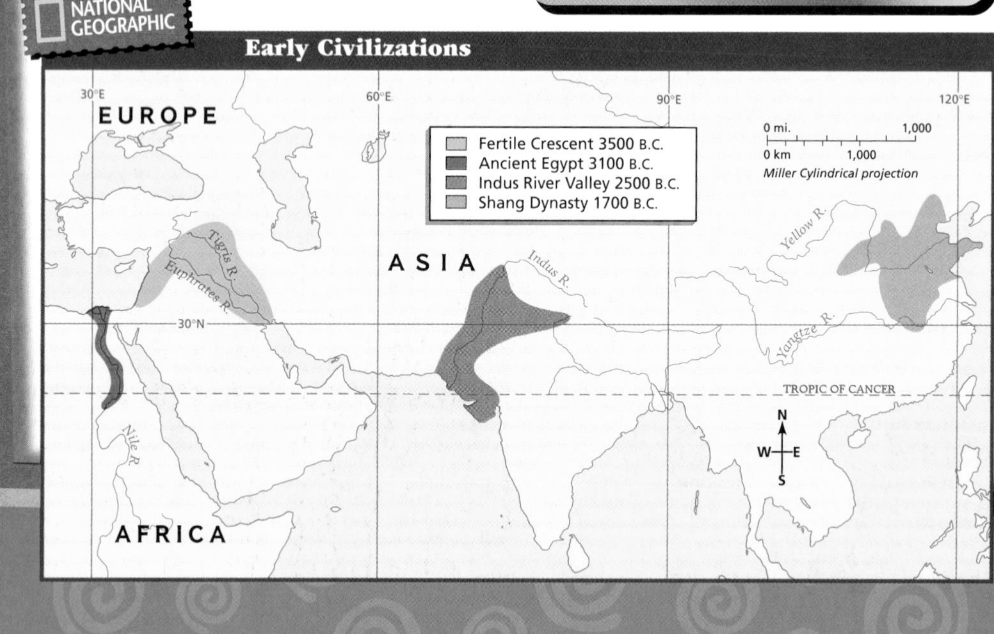

86

Practicing the Skill Answers

1. Early Civilizations
2. Fertile Crescent, Ancient Egypt, Indus River Valley, and Shang Dynasty
3. Ancient Egypt; Shang Dynasty
4. They all developed around rivers.

Applying the Skill
Students should include the map with the three questions.

Guide to Reading

Main Idea

The world's population is growing rapidly, and how and where people live are changing too.

Terms to Know

- death rate
- birthrate
- famine
- population density
- urbanization
- emigrate
- refugee

Reading Strategy

Draw a chart like this one. In the "Result" column, write a result of the fact listed in the left column.

Fact	Result
World population is increasing.	
Population is unevenly distributed.	
People move from place to place.	

Section 2 Population Patterns

NATIONAL GEOGRAPHIC Exploring Our World

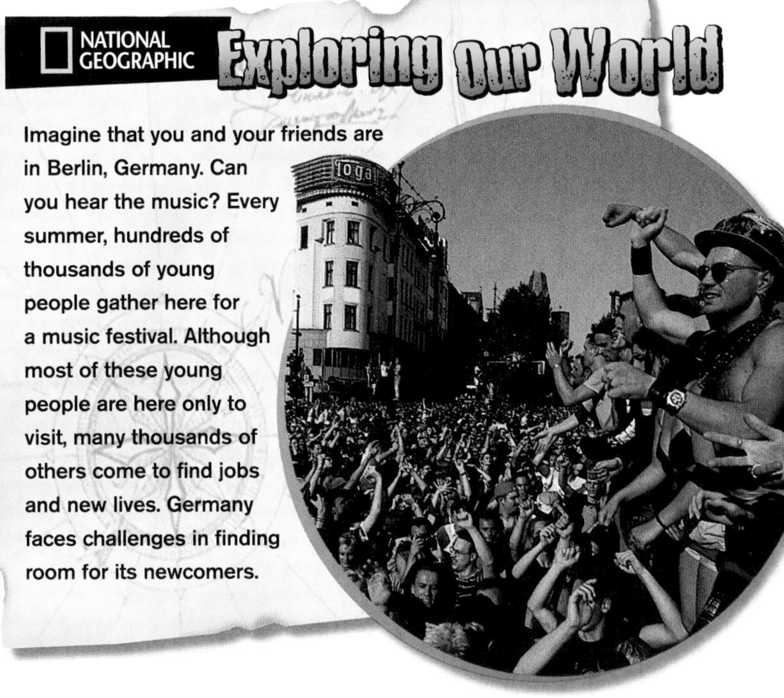

Imagine that you and your friends are in Berlin, Germany. Can you hear the music? Every summer, hundreds of thousands of young people gather here for a music festival. Although most of these young people are here only to visit, many thousands of others come to find jobs and new lives. Germany faces challenges in finding room for its newcomers.

On October 12, 1999, the world reached a significant point in its history. About 370,000 babies were born around the world that day. One of those babies—no one knows exactly which one—was the world's six billionth human being.

Population Growth

How fast has the earth's population grown? The graph on page 88 shows world population over the years. You will see that for more than fifteen hundred years, the world's population remained about the same. The world did not have 1 billion people until about 1800. It was not until 1930 that the population reached 2 billion. By 1974 the population had doubled to 4 billion. In 1999 it reached 6 billion.

Reasons for Population Growth Why has the world's population grown so fast in the past 200 years? One reason is that the death rate has gone down. The **death rate** is the number of people out of every 1,000 who die in a year. Better health care and living conditions have decreased the death rate.

1 Focus

Section Objectives

1. Explain why the world's population is growing rapidly.
2. Identify where most people in the world live.
3. Discuss why more people are moving to cities.

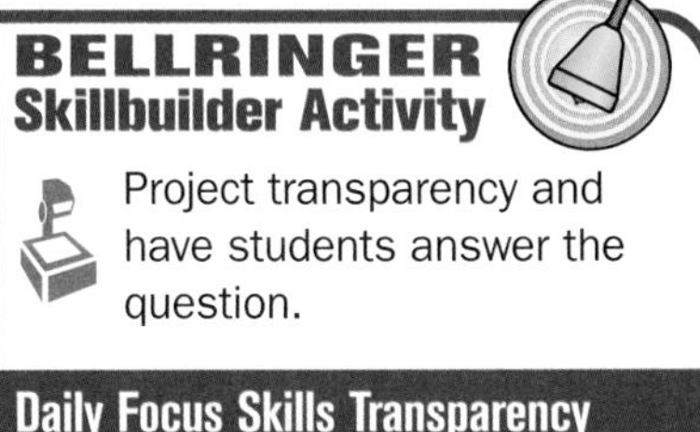

Project transparency and have students answer the question.

Daily Focus Skills Transparency

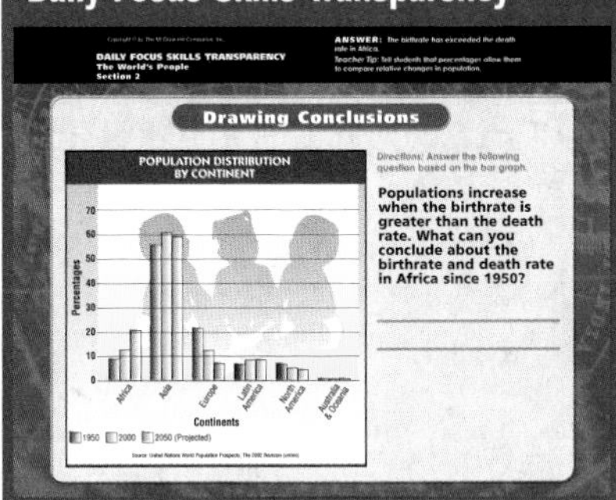

Reading Preview

■ **Activating Prior Knowledge** Ask students whether they believe their community is crowded. Have them explain their answer.

■ **Previewing Vocabulary** Have students identify and define the root words in the last four terms *(dense, urban, migrate, refuge)* and infer the meanings of the terms.

Section Resources

Reproducible Masters

- Reproducible Lesson Plan
- Daily Lecture and Discussion Notes
- Note-taking Guide
- Guided Reading Activity
- Reading Essentials and Study Guide
- Section Quiz

Transparencies

- Daily Focus Skills Transparency
- GeoQuiz Transparency
- In-text Map Transparency

Multimedia

- Vocabulary PuzzleMaker CD-ROM
- Interactive Tutor Self-Assessment CD-ROM
- Presentation Plus! CD-ROM
- ExamView® Pro Testmaker CD-ROM

Teach

Reading Strategy

Determining Cause and Effect Draw on the board a two-column chart titled "The Population Explosion." Write the words *Causes* and *Effects* as the column headings. Guide students in identifying the causes of the world's population explosion. *(causes: reduced death rates, high birthrates; effects: need for more food and resources, economic strains)* L1

Daily Lecture and Discussion Notes

THE WORLD'S PEOPLE

Daily Lecture and Discussion Notes

Population Patterns

During October 1999, world population reached 6 billion people, doubling in size in under 40 years. World population is still growing at a rate of 1.3 percent per year, with an average annual addition of 78 million people from 1995 to 2000.

I. Population Growth

A. The world's population continues to grow. The **death rate,** or the number of people out of every 1,000 who die in a year, has gone down because of better health care and living conditions. Meanwhile, the **birthrate,** or the number of children born each year for every 1,000 people, is very high in some regions.

...pulation growth include the rapid use of resources, a strain ... the lack of food ... ine.

Reading Check Answer

death rate: number out of every 1,000 who die in a year; birthrate: number born each year for every 1,000 people

Analyzing the Graph and Chart

Answer

India

Another reason for the rapid increase in the world's population is that in some regions of the world the birthrate is high. The **birthrate** is the number of children born each year for every 1,000 people. In Asia, Africa, and Latin America, families traditionally are large because children help with farming. High numbers of births have combined with low death rates to increase population growth in these areas. As a result, population in these areas has doubled every 25 years or so.

Challenges From Population Growth Rapid population growth presents many challenges. An increase in the number of people means that more food is needed. Fortunately, since 1950 world food production has increased faster than population on all continents except Africa. Because so many people there need food, disaster can result if bad weather or war ruin crops. Millions may suffer from **famine,** or lack of food.

Also, populations that grow rapidly may use resources more quickly than populations that do not grow as fast. Some countries face shortages of water and housing. Population growth also puts a strain on economies. More people means a country must create more jobs. Some experts claim that rapid population growth could harm the planet. Others are optimistic. They predict that as the number of humans rises, the levels of technology and creativity will also rise.

Reading Check How do the definitions of death rate and birthrate differ?

Where People Live

Where do all the people live? The world's people actually live on a surprisingly small part of the earth. As you learned in Chapter 2, land covers only about 30 percent of the earth's surface. Half of this land is

World Population

Analyzing the Graph and Chart

The world's population is expected to reach about 9 billion by 2050.

Place Which country has the second-largest number of people?

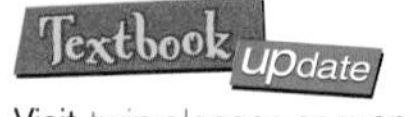

Visit twip.glencoe.com and click on **Chapter 3—Textbook Updates.**

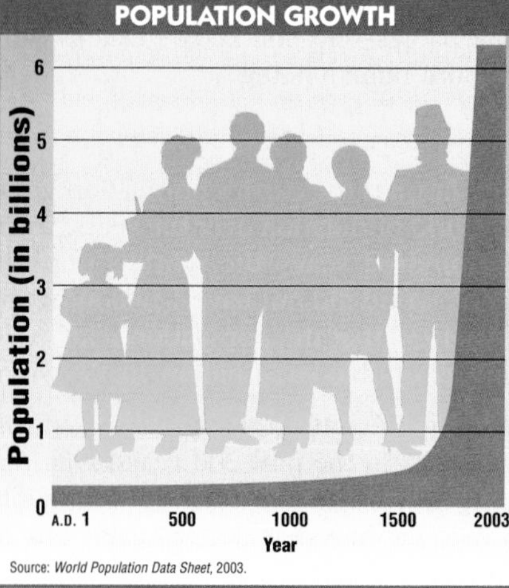

Source: *World Population Data Sheet*, 2003.

MOST POPULOUS COUNTRIES

Country	Millions of People
China	1,288.7
India	1,068.6
United States	291.5
Indonesia	220.5
Brazil	176.5
Pakistan	149.1
Russia	145.5

Source: *World Population Data Sheet*, 2003.

Reading Strategy — Reading the Text

Making Predictions Review the idea of population density as a function of usable land. Have students look at the map showing the population density of China. **Ask: What density patterns does China show?** *(very dense in the east and along rivers, not very dense in the west)* **Why do you think population follows these patterns?** *(because the western areas are less hospitable to people)* **What can government do to change these patterns?** *(possibly find ways of developing economic opportunities in those areas, but the climate or physical geography there may simply be too harsh to allow any significant population growth)* L1

 **EE4 Human Systems: Standard 12**

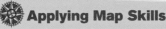

NATIONAL GEOGRAPHIC

World Population Density

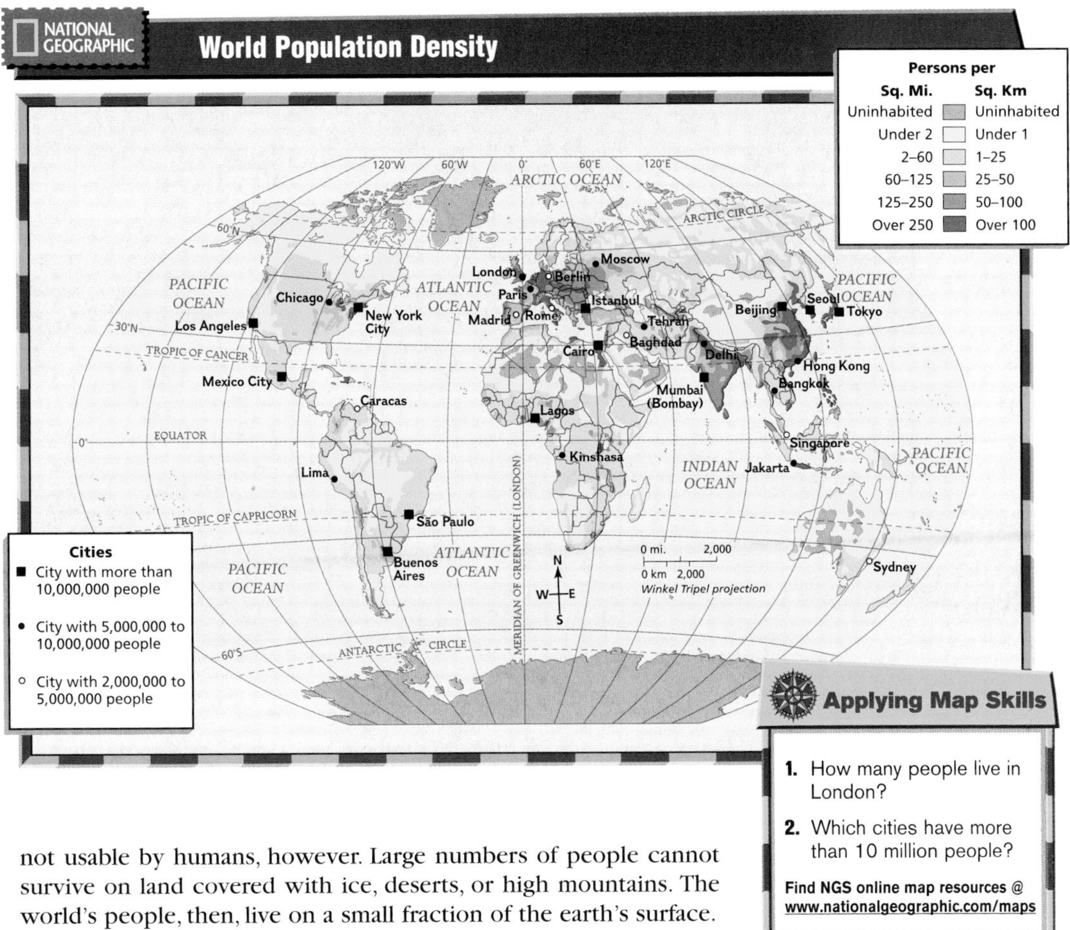

Applying Map Skills

1. How many people live in London?
2. Which cities have more than 10 million people?

Find NGS online map resources @ www.nationalgeographic.com/maps

not usable by humans, however. Large numbers of people cannot survive on land covered with ice, deserts, or high mountains. The world's people, then, live on a small fraction of the earth's surface.

Population Distribution Even on the usable land, population is not distributed, or spread, evenly. People naturally prefer to live in places that have plentiful water, good land, and a favorable climate. During the industrial age, people moved to places that had important resources such as coal or iron ore to run or make machines. People gather in other areas because these places hold religious significance or because they are government and transportation centers. The chart on page 88 shows you the most populous countries in the world. Four of these countries are located on the Asian continent.

Population Density Geographers have a way of determining how crowded a country or region is. They measure **population density**—the average number of people living in a square mile or square kilometer. To arrive at this figure, the total population is divided by the total land area. For example, the countries of **Afghanistan** and **Nepal** have about the same number of people. They are very different in terms of population density, though. With a smaller land area, Nepal has

Applying Map Skills

Answers

1. 5 to 10 million people
2. New York City, Los Angeles, Mexico City, São Paulo, Buenos Aires, Lagos, Mumbai (Bombay), Beijing, Seoul, and Tokyo

In-text Map Transparency Activity Ask students: What two continents have the lowest overall population densities? *(Australia and Antarctica)* Are there more uninhabited areas in Australia or Europe? *(Australia)*

L1/ELL

Guided Reading Activity

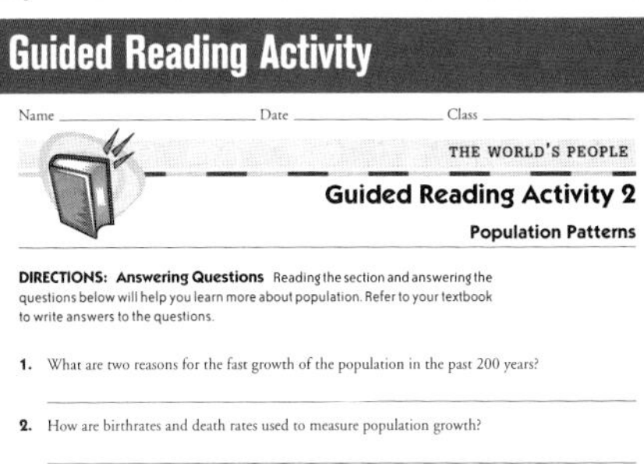
Name ____ Date ____ Class ____

THE WORLD'S PEOPLE

Guided Reading Activity 2

Population Patterns

DIRECTIONS: Answering Questions Reading the section and answering the questions below will help you learn more about population. Refer to your textbook to write answers to the questions.

1. What are two reasons for the fast growth of the population in the past 200 years?

2. How are birthrates and death rates used to measure population growth?

3 ASSESS

Assign Section 2 Assessment as homework or an in-class activity.

Have students use the Interactive Tutor Self-Assessment CD-ROM to review Section 2.

Differentiated Instruction

Meeting Special Needs: Interpersonal Have students consider the effects of different levels of population density. They should think about how life would be changed if there were more or fewer people in their community. Then have them create a chart that contains the characteristics of life in low-density and high-density areas. **L2**

Refer to *Inclusion for the Middle School Social Studies Classroom Strategies and Activities* in the TCR.

More About the Photo

Kosovo About 1.5 million Kosovars were driven from their homes during the civil war. Slightly more than half were forced to leave the country until NATO bombing forced Serbia to accept their return.

Caption Answer persecution or disaster

Reading Check Answer

the average number of people living in a square mile or square kilometer

Objectives and answers to the Student Web Activity can be found in the Web Activity Lesson Plan at twip.glencoe.com

Measure student knowledge of political entities.

GeoQuiz Transparency

Kosovo, Yugoslavia

In 1999 a civil war exploded in Kosovo, a province of Yugoslavia. Thousands of people were forced from their homes.

Movement What causes people to become refugees?

Social Studies Online

Web Activity Visit ***The World and Its People*** Web site at twip.glencoe.com and click on **Chapter 3—Student Web Activities** to learn more about the world population "clock."

443 people per square mile (171 people per sq. km). Afghanistan has an average of only 114 people per square mile (44 people per sq. km). Nepal, then, is more crowded than Afghanistan.

Remember that population density is an *average.* It assumes that people are distributed evenly throughout a country. Of course, this seldom happens. A country may have several large cities where most of the people actually live. In Egypt, for example, overall population density is 186 people per square mile (72 people per sq. km). In reality, about 99 percent of Egypt's people live within 20 miles (32 km) of the Nile River. The rest of Egypt is desert. Thus, some geographers prefer to figure a country's population density in terms of farmable or usable land rather than total land area. When Egypt's population density is measured this way, it equals about 6,550 people per square mile. The map on page 10 of the **Geography Handbook** shows how population density can vary within a country. The areas with high density in Egypt follow the path of the Nile River.

Reading Check **What is population density?**

Population Movement

Throughout the world, people are moving in great numbers from place to place. Some people move from city to city, or suburb to suburb. More and more people are leaving villages and farms and moving to cities. This movement to cities is called **urbanization.**

Team-Teaching Activity

Mathematics Organize students into six groups and assign each group one of the following continents: Africa, Asia, Australia, Europe, North America, and South America. Direct groups to locate the following information on their assigned continent: total population, population density, 10 largest cities, projected population for the year 2010 or 2025. Have each group list its findings on an outline map of the continent. Groups should mark their maps to show population distribution and the locations of the 10 cities. Arrange the maps to form a world map of population on the bulletin board. L1 

EE1 The World in Spatial Terms: Standard 3

People move to cities for many reasons. The most common reason is to find jobs. Rural populations have grown. The amount of land that can be farmed, however, has not increased to meet the growing number of people who need to work and eat. As a result, many people find city jobs in manufacturing or in services like tourism.

Nearly half the world's people live in cities—a far higher percentage than ever before. Between 1960 and 2000, the population of **Mexico City** more than tripled. Other cities in Latin America, as well as cities in Asia and Africa, have seen similar growth. Some of these cities hold a large part of a country's entire population. About one-third of Argentina's people, for instance, live in the city of **Buenos Aires.** As more and more people come to cities looking for work, the boundaries of cities and their suburbs keep expanding outward. This situation is called urban sprawl.

Some population movement occurs between countries. Some people emigrate, or leave the country where they were born and move to another. They are called emigrants in their homeland and immigrants in their new country. In the past 40 years, millions have left Africa, Asia, and Latin America to find jobs in the richer nations of Europe and North America. Many of these people were forced to flee their countries because of wars, political unrest, food shortages, or other problems. They are refugees, or people who flee to another country to escape persecution or disaster.

Reading Check What is urban sprawl?

Section 2 Assessment

Defining Terms

1. **Define** death rate, birthrate, famine, population density, urbanization, emigrate, refugee.

Recalling Facts

2. **Culture** What are three problems caused by overpopulation?
3. **Human/Environment Interaction** Why do people live on only a small fraction of the earth?
4. **Economics** What is the main reason for growing urbanization?

Critical Thinking

5. **Making Comparisons** What is the difference between an emigrant and an immigrant?
6. **Understanding Cause and Effect** Why have populations in areas of Asia, Africa, and Latin America doubled about every 25 years?

Graphic Organizer

7. **Organizing Information** Draw a diagram like this one, and list three causes of population growth.

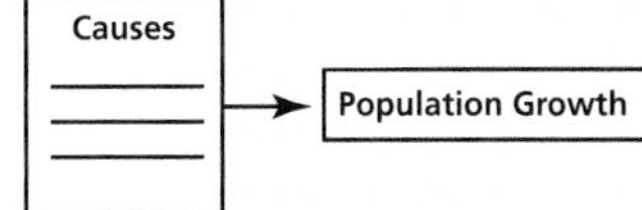

Applying Social Studies Skills

8. **Analyzing Maps** Look at the population density map on page 89. How would you describe the population density around Tokyo?

Chapter 3

Section 2, pages 87–91

L2

Section Quiz

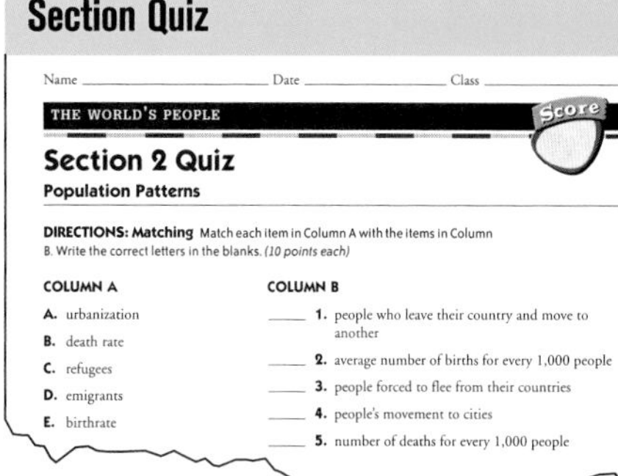

Name ____ Date ____ Class ____

THE WORLD'S PEOPLE

Section 2 Quiz
Population Patterns

DIRECTIONS: Matching Match each item in Column A with the items in Column B. Write the correct letters in the blanks. (10 points each)

COLUMN A	COLUMN B
A. urbanization	____ 1. people who leave their country and move to another
B. death rate	____ 2. average number of births for every 1,000 people
C. refugees	____ 3. people forced to flee from their countries
D. emigrants	____ 4. people's movement to cities
E. birthrate	____ 5. number of deaths for every 1,000 people

Reading Check Answer

the boundaries of cities and suburbs expanding outward as more people arrive looking for work

L1/ELL

Reading Essentials and Study Guide

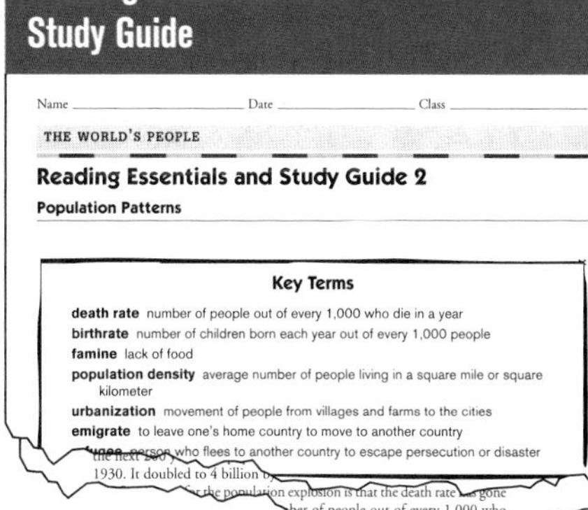

Name ____ Date ____ Class ____

THE WORLD'S PEOPLE

Reading Essentials and Study Guide 2
Population Patterns

Key Terms

death rate number of people out of every 1,000 who die in a year
birthrate number of children born each year out of every 1,000 people
famine lack of food
population density average number of people living in a square mile or square kilometer
urbanization movement of people from villages and farms to the cities
emigrate to leave one's home country to move to another country
refugee person who flees to another country to escape persecution or disaster

4 Close

Reading Strategy

Summarizing Have students write a summary that highlights the main ideas of the section.

Section 2 Assessment

1. The terms are defined in the Glossary.
2. more food is needed; more resources are needed; a country's economy is strained
3. Much of the earth is covered by water, ice, deserts, and mountains, which are not suitable conditions for human habitation.
4. People are moving to cities to find jobs.
5. An emigrant is someone who leaves a country. In the new country where the person arrives, he or she is an immigrant.
6. because the death rate has gone down, and the birthrate has gone up
7. Better health care has lowered the death rate; better living conditions have lowered the death rate; the birthrate has gone up.
8. very high—over 250 persons per square mile (over 100 persons per square kilometer)

Focus

Section Objectives

1. Distinguish between renewable and nonrenewable resources.
2. Explain why people trade.
3. Describe how the world's economies are changing.

BELLRINGER Skillbuilder Activity

Project transparency and have students answer the question.

Daily Focus Skills Transparency

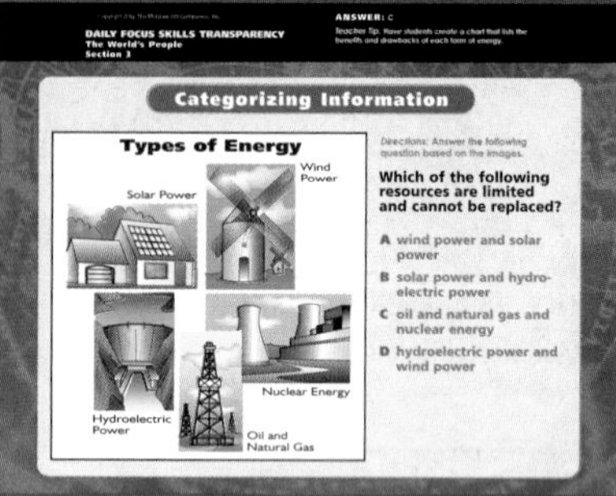

Reading Preview

■ **Activating Prior Knowledge** Have students name products they use that are produced in other countries. Then ask them to identify American goods that are sold in other countries.

■ **Preteaching Vocabulary** Call on a volunteer to look up the term *resource* in a dictionary and read its definitions. Ask students to select the definition that is appropriate for this section.

Guide to Reading

Main Idea

Many resources are limited and distributed unevenly, so countries must trade for goods.

Terms to Know

- natural resource
- renewable resource
- nonrenewable resource
- economic system
- export
- import
- tariff
- quota
- free trade
- developed country
- developing country

Reading Strategy

Draw a chart like this one. Write the names of different resources and how they are used.

Resource	Use

Section 3

Resources and World Trade

NATIONAL GEOGRAPHIC Exploring Our World

About 7,000 windmills stand on an 80-square-mile patch of hilly land near San Francisco. They turn in the strong winds that blow through a nearby pass in California's mountains. Why were they put there? These windmills generate electricity. In fact, they churn out enough electricity every year to meet the needs of all the homes in San Francisco.

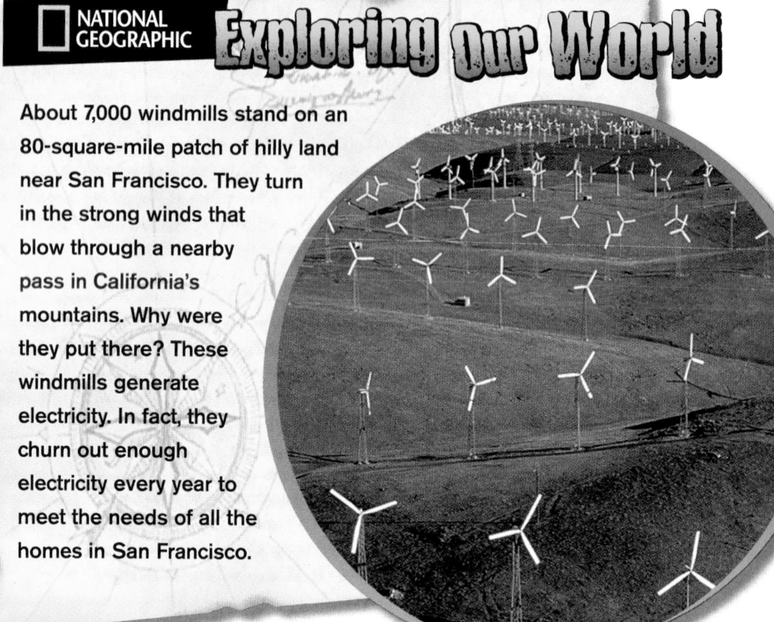

Natural Resources

As you learned in Section 2, people settle in some areas to gain access to resources. **Natural resources** are products of the earth that people use to meet their needs. Wind, water, and oil are resources that provide energy to power machines. Good soil and fish are resources that people use to produce food. Stones like granite and ores like iron ore are resources people can use for making products.

Renewable Resources People can use some natural resources as much as they want. These **renewable resources** cannot be used up or can be replaced naturally or grown again. Wind and sun cannot be used up. Forests, grasslands, plants and animals, and soil can be replaced—if people manage them carefully.

Today many countries are trying to find efficient ways of using renewable energy sources. Some produce hydroelectric power, the

Section Resources

Reproducible Masters
- Reproducible Lesson Plan
- Daily Lecture and Discussion Notes
- Note-taking Guide
- Guided Reading Activity
- Reading Essentials and Study Guide
- Section Quiz

Transparencies
- Daily Focus Skills Transparency

Multimedia
- Vocabulary PuzzleMaker CD-ROM
- Interactive Tutor Self-Assessment CD-ROM
- Presentation Plus! CD-ROM
- ExamView® Pro Testmaker CD-ROM

energy generated by falling water. Do you have a solar-powered calculator? If so, you know that the sun can provide energy to run people's machines. Solar energy is power produced by the heat of the sun. Making use of this energy on a large scale requires huge pieces of equipment. As a result, this energy source is not yet economical to use.

Nonrenewable Resources Minerals found in the earth's crust are also resources. They are **nonrenewable resources** because the earth provides limited supplies of them and they cannot be replaced. These resources were formed over millions of years by forces within the earth. Thus, it simply takes too long to generate new supplies.

One major nonrenewable source of energy is fossil fuels—coal, oil, and natural gas. People burn oil and gas to heat homes or run cars. They burn fossil fuels to generate electricity. Oil and coal are also used as raw materials to make plastics and medicines.

Another nonrenewable energy source is nuclear energy. Nuclear energy is power made by creating a controlled atomic reaction. Nuclear energy can be used to produce electricity, but some people fear its use. Nuclear reactions produce dangerous waste products that are difficult to dispose of. Still, some countries rely on nuclear energy to generate electricity. France and Japan are examples.

✓ Reading Check **List three fossil fuels.**

Economic Systems

People and nations use natural resources to produce and exchange goods and services. A country's **economic system** sets rules for deciding what goods and services to produce, how to produce them, and who will receive them. There are four main types of economic systems: traditional, command, market, and mixed.

Traditional Economies In a traditional economy, economic decisions are based on customs handed down from generation to generation. For example, if your grandparents and parents fished for a living, you will fish for a living. You will probably use the same fishing tools. To get other products you need, you may barter, or exchange part of your catch, instead of using money.

Command Economies Under a command economy, the government makes all economic decisions. Individuals have little or no say about what goods and services to produce and how to produce them. The government decides how much something will cost and which people receive training for particular jobs. The term "communism" applies to command economies.

Market Economies In a market economy, individuals make their own decisions about what to produce, how to produce it, and for whom to produce it. People and businesses make what they think customers want (supply). Consumers have choices about which goods or services to buy (demand). Prices are determined by supply and demand.

Believe It or Not!

Saffron— A Valuable Resource

A resource does not have to produce energy to be valued. The people in the Indian region of Kashmir are picking a resource that is precious to cooks—crocus flowers. Inside each crocus are three tiny orange stalks. When dried, the stalks become a spice called saffron. Cooks use it to add a delicate orange color and flavor to food. Saffron—the world's most expensive spice—is in short supply, though. Producers need nearly 4,700 flowers to produce just 1 ounce (28 g) of saffron!

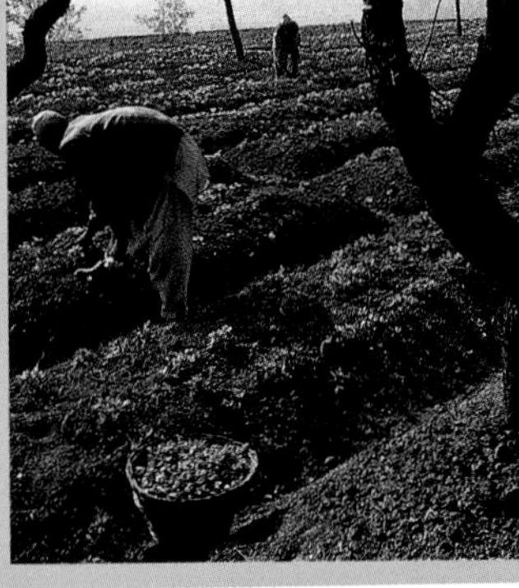

TEACH

Making Connections Lead a discussion about the manufacturing of objects in the classroom, such as desks, chairs, and so on. Guide students to identify (1) the resources from which they are made; (2) whether each resource is renewable or nonrenewable; (3) how agriculture, manufacturing, and service industries contributed to this product; and (4) what environmental effects might result from making this product. L2

Daily Lecture and Discussion Notes

THE WORLD'S PEOPLE

Daily Lecture and Discussion Notes

Resources and World Trade

In 1935 the United States made a historic commitment to the support of private land in the Soil Preservation Act. That act, passed during the Dust Bowl, recognized that the long-term welfare of all Americans rested in the hands of farmers and ranchers struggling to keep their land from eroding away.

I. Natural Resources

A. **Natural resources** are products of the earth that people use to meet their needs.

B. **Renewable resources** cannot be used up. They can be replaced naturally or grown again. People are trying to develop new ways of using renewable

✓ Reading Check Answer

coal, oil, and natural gas

Current Events Journal

Suggest that students create a two-column chart in their journals with the headings "Nonrenewable Resources" and "Renewable Resources." Have them fill out the chart with examples of each type.

Reading Strategy — Reading the Text

Summarizing Have students create a concept web of the section to identify the main ideas of this section. Webs should have three main parts: one about resources, one about trade, and one about development issues. After students complete their webs, have them summarize each of the three main ideas of the section in a sentence. L1

*Use the **Reading Skills Handbook** for more reading strategies.*

Analyzing the Chart

Answer
traditional: shared by group; command: government; market: individuals; mixed: individuals with some government regulation

✓ Reading Check Answer

the right to own property or businesses and to make a profit without government interference

L1/ELL

Guided Reading Activity

Name ________ Date ________ Class ________

THE WORLD'S PEOPLE

Guided Reading Activity 3

Resources and World Trade

DIRECTIONS: Outlining Reading the section and completing the outline below will help you learn more about resources and world trade. Refer to your textbook to fill in the blanks.

I. How can natural resources, or products people use from nature, be grouped?
  A. Renewable resources can be ________ naturally or ________ again.
    1. Forests, grasslands, plants, animals, and ________ can be replaced.
    2. ________ ________ is power produced by the sun.
  B. ________ ________ take too long to replace.
    1. ________ ________, such as coal, ________, and natural ________ are sources of energy.
    2. ________ ________ is power from an atomic reaction.

II. What are the different types of economic systems?
  A. A ________ economy is based on customs.
  B. The government makes all economic decisions in a ________ economy.
  C. In a ________ economy, individuals make their own decisions.

III. How do people get the resources they need?
  A. Countries ________, or focus on activities best suited to their resources.
  B. Countries ________ what they do not need, trading it to other countries.
  C. When they cannot produce enough of something, countries ________ it.

IV. How is world trade managed?
  A. ________ are taxes charged by some countries on imported goods.
  B. Other governments put a ________, or limit on the number of items allowed into a country.
  C. ________ ________ removes trade barriers.

V. What are differences in the development of countries?
  A. ________ ________ have a great deal of manufacturing.
  B. ________ ________ are working toward industrialization.

102

Types of Economic Systems

Analyzing the Chart

This chart shows economic systems in theory. In reality, most nations have a mixed economy.

Economics Who owns or controls resources in each type of system?

Economic System	WHAT, HOW, and FOR WHOM to produce	Examples (in theory)
Traditional	Customs and traditions determine what and how to produce. Resources are usually shared. Many traditional systems use bartering to exchange goods and services.	• Inuit • Some parts of Africa and South America
Command	Government owns resources and controls production, prices, and wages. Shortages of consumer goods occur because government sets prices low and resources are often used for military goods.	• China • North Korea • Former USSR
Market	Individuals own resources and determine what and how to produce. Prices and wages are determined by producer supply and consumer demand.	• United States
Mixed	Individuals own most resources and determine what and how to produce. Government regulates certain industries.	• Most nations

A market economy is based on "free enterprise." This is the idea that you have the right to own property or businesses and to make a profit without the government interfering. Capitalism is another name for a market or free enterprise economy.

Mixed Economies Most nations have a mixed economy. China, for example, has mostly a command economy, but the government has allowed some free enterprise. In the United States, most decisions are made by individuals, but the government regulates certain areas. Government agencies, for example, inspect meat and other products.

✓ **Reading Check** What is free enterprise?

World Trade

Resources, like people, are not distributed evenly around the world. Some areas have large amounts of one resource. Others have none of that resource but are rich in another one. These differences affect the economies of the world's countries. The competition for scarce resources may also lead to conflict.

Look at the map on page 95. Do you see the centers of manufacturing in the northern and eastern United States? There are large supplies of coal in the region and deposits of iron ore nearby. These areas became industrial centers because the people here took advantage of the resources they had.

In the western United States, you see another picture. People use much of the land for ranching. The soil and climate are well suited to raising livestock. Commercial farming—or growing food for sale in markets—occurs throughout much of the United States.

Differentiated Instruction

Meeting Special Needs: Logical/Mathematical Give an example of how tariffs work. Write the words *Brazilian car* and *American car* on the board. Under *Brazilian car,* write $15,000. Under *American car,* write $14,000. Explain that this is the situation before the tariff is imposed. **Ask:** **Which car would you buy if you lived in Brazil?** *(Most will probably answer the American car, because it costs less.)* **What would happen if Brazil's government put a 10 percent tariff on the American car?** *(The price would increase to $15,400.)* Cross out the old price of the American car and write down the new one. **Which car would you buy now?** *(Students will probably say the less-expensive Brazilian car.)* **L1**

Countries respond to the unequal distribution of resources by specializing, or focusing on the economic activities best suited to their resources. Parts of **Brazil** have the perfect soil and climate for growing coffee. As a result, Brazil produces more coffee beans than any other country.

Countries often cannot use all that they produce. Therefore, they export what they do not need, trading it to other countries. When they cannot produce as much as they need of a good, they import it, or buy it from another country. The world's countries, then, are connected to one another in a complex web of trade.

Barriers to Trade Governments try to manage trade to benefit their country's economy. Some charge a tariff, or a tax added to the price of goods that are imported. If there is a tariff on cars, for instance, people who buy an imported car pay extra. Governments often create tariffs to persuade their people to buy products made in their own country.

Governments sometimes create other barriers to trade. They might put a strict quota, or number limit, on how many items of a particular product can be imported from a particular country. A government may even stop trading with another country altogether as a way to punish it.

NATIONAL GEOGRAPHIC **World Economic Activity**

ARCTIC OCEAN
ARCTIC CIRCLE
PACIFIC OCEAN
ATLANTIC OCEAN
INDIAN OCEAN
PACIFIC OCEAN
TROPIC OF CANCER
EQUATOR
TROPIC OF CAPRICORN
ANTARCTIC CIRCLE
PRIME MERIDIAN OF GREENWICH (LONDON)
120°W 60°W 0° 60°E 120°E
60°N 30°N 0° 60°S
0 mi. 2,000
0 km 2,000
Winkel Tripel projection

Resources
Coal
Iron ore
Fishing
Petroleum

Land Use
Commercial farming
Subsistence farming
Ranching
Nomadic herding
Hunting and gathering
Forests
Manufacturing area
Little or no activity

Applying Map Skills

1. What symbol and color signify areas of manufacturing?
2. What kind of farming exists along the Equator?

Find NGS online map resources @ www.nationalgeographic.com/maps

Chapter 3

Section 3, pages 92–96

Applying Map Skills

Answers

1. an orange box or extended area
2. subsistence farming

Skills Practice
Which parts of the world might be leading exporters of lumber or wood products? Why? *(Canada, northern Europe, Russia; because forestry is shown as an economic activity in these places)*

3 ASSESS

Assign Section 3 Assessment as homework or an in-class activity.

Have students use the Interactive Tutor Self-Assessment CD-ROM to review Section 3.

THE HUMANITIES CONNECTION

World Music: A Cultural Legacy

World Art and Architecture Transparencies

World Art Prints

Team-Teaching Activity

Government Ask the government teacher to explain the rules of debating. Then organize the class into three groups and tell them that each group will debate an issue related to energy policy. Split each of the three groups into two parts—one to take the "pro" position and the other to take the "con" position on its issue. One group will debate whether the government should allow oil exploration on wilderness lands. The second group will debate whether money should be invested into finding more oil and gas or into identifying renewable energy resources. The third group will debate whether to allow nuclear power plants to be built and used. Allow groups time to conduct their research and prepare their arguments. Then stage the debates. **L3**

EE4 Human Systems: Standard 13

Chapter 3

Section 3, pages 92–96

L2

Section Quiz

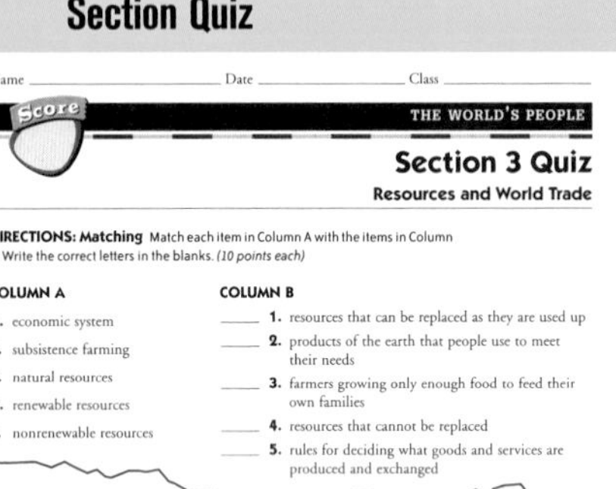

Name ______ Date ______ Class ______

THE WORLD'S PEOPLE

Score

Section 3 Quiz

Resources and World Trade

DIRECTIONS: Matching Match each item in Column A with the items in Column B. Write the correct letters in the blanks. *(10 points each)*

COLUMN A	COLUMN B
A. economic system	____ 1. resources that can be replaced as they are used up
B. subsistence farming	____ 2. products of the earth that people use to meet their needs
C. natural resources	____ 3. farmers growing only enough food to feed their own families
D. renewable resources	____ 4. resources that cannot be replaced
E. nonrenewable resources	____ 5. rules for deciding what goods and services are produced and exchanged

Reading Check Answer

tariffs, quotas, and complete bans on trade

L1/ELL

Reading Essentials and Study Guide

Name ______ Date ______ Class ______

THE WORLD'S PEOPLE

Reading Essentials and Study Guide 3

Resources and World Trade

Key Terms

natural resource product of the earth that people use to meet their needs
renewable resource resource that cannot be used up or can be replaced naturally
nonrenewable resource resource that cannot be replaced once it is used up
economic system rules for deciding what goods and services to produce, how to produce them, and who will receive them
export to sell goods to another country
import to buy goods from another country

Reading Check Answer

Industry generally brings greater wealth.

Close

Have students create a poster that shows many different ways that one basic resource—such as iron, oil, wood, or water—is used.

The "Third World"

Until the Soviet Union collapsed in 1991, developed and developing countries were divided into three groups. Developed countries with market economies were known as the "first world." Countries with communist command economies were known as the "second world." Developing countries outside of these two groups were together known as the "third world."

Free Trade Governments around the world are moving toward free trade. **Free trade** means removing trade barriers so that goods flow freely among countries. Several countries have joined together to create free trade agreements in certain parts of the world. The United States, Mexico, and Canada have agreed to eliminate all trade barriers to one another's goods. These three countries set up the North American Free Trade Agreement (NAFTA). The largest free trade organization—the European Union (EU)—includes many countries of Europe.

Reading Check What are three barriers to trade?

Differences in Development

Countries that have a great deal of manufacturing are called **developed countries.** Countries in Europe and North America are developed countries. So are Australia and Japan. Other countries have few, or no, manufacturing centers. Many people in these lands practice subsistence farming, which means they grow only enough food for their own families. These countries—mostly in Africa, Asia, and Latin America—are called **developing countries.** They may be rich in natural resources, however, and are working toward industrialization.

Countries want manufacturing centers because industry generally makes more money than agriculture. As a result, industrial countries are richer than agricultural ones. The spread of industry has created booming economies in Singapore, South Korea, China, and Taiwan.

Reading Check Why do developing countries want more industry?

Section 3 Assessment

Defining Terms

1. **Define** natural resource, renewable resource, nonrenewable resource, economic system, export, import, tariff, quota, free trade, developed country, developing country.

Recalling Facts

2. **Economics** What is the difference between commercial farming and subsistence farming?
3. **Economics** Why do countries specialize?
4. **Economics** How do developed and developing countries differ?

Critical Thinking

5. **Drawing Conclusions** Why are tariffs and quotas called "barriers" to trade?
6. **Making Comparisons** Describe two kinds of economic systems.

Graphic Organizer

7. **Organizing Information** Draw a chart like this one, listing three examples for each type of resource.

Renewable resources	Nonrenewable resources

Applying Social Studies Skills

8. **Analyzing Maps** Look at the economic activity map on page 95. What two types of farming are shown on the map?

Section 3 Assessment

1. The terms are defined in the Glossary.
2. Commercial farming is growing food for sale in markets; subsistence farming is growing only enough food to feed one's own family.
3. Countries produce what is most suited for the resources they have.
4. A developing country does not have an industrialized economy; a developed country does.
5. because they lower consumers' ability to buy imported goods, which reduces trade
6. Students should describe two of the four economies: traditional, command, market, or mixed.
7. *Renewable*—sun, wind, forests, grasslands, plants, animals, soil; *Nonrenewable*—minerals, coal, oil, natural gas, nuclear fuel
8. commercial and subsistence farming

Section 4

Technology "Shrinks" the World

Guide to Reading

Main Idea

Modern technology has helped to bring the world's diverse peoples closer together.

Terms to Know

- rights
- responsibilities
- interdependence
- globalization

Reading Strategy

Create a diagram like this one. On the spokes, list reasons why the world may seem to be getting smaller.

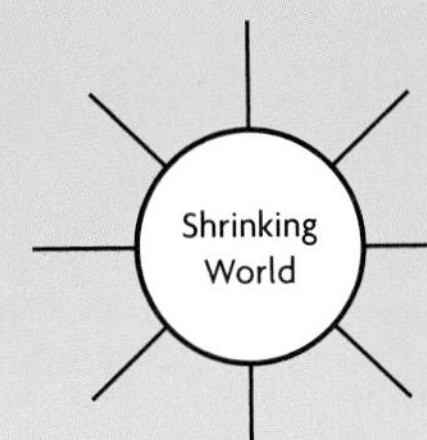

NATIONAL GEOGRAPHIC **Exploring Our World**

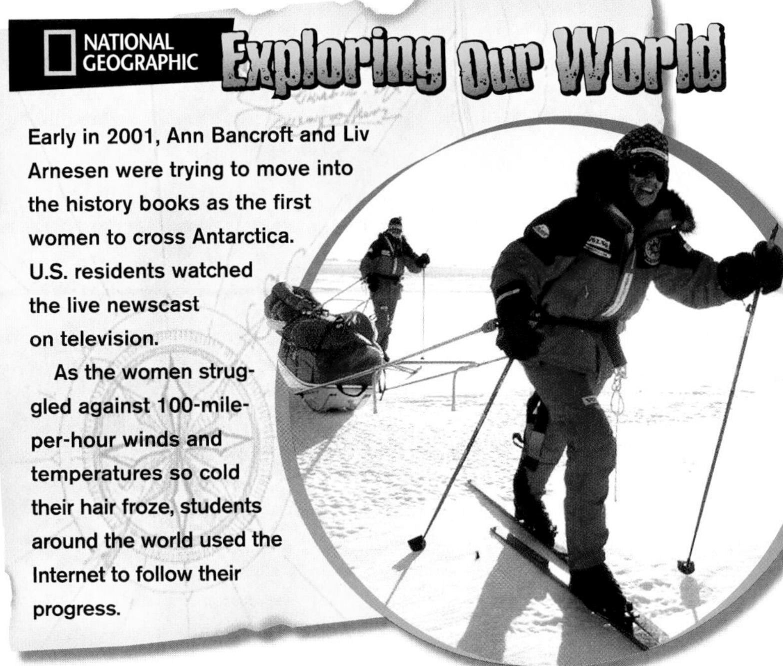

Early in 2001, Ann Bancroft and Liv Arnesen were trying to move into the history books as the first women to cross Antarctica. U.S. residents watched the live newscast on television.

As the women struggled against 100-mile-per-hour winds and temperatures so cold their hair froze, students around the world used the Internet to follow their progress.

People today can talk across an ocean as easily as across a backyard fence. This is what is meant when you hear people say that the world is "shrinking." The technology that has brought about the Information Revolution has enabled people to talk instantly with others practically everywhere on the earth.

Effects of Technology

The word "technology" refers to the ability of human beings to make things that will help them and give them some control over their environment. As you learned in Section 1, the first civilizations arose in about 8000 B.C. when humans learned farming technology—or how to grow crops on a regular basis. In just the past 100 years, new technology has emerged in transportation and communication. This new technology has possibly had an equal—if not greater—effect on human society than the Agricultural Revolution did 10,000 years ago.

97

FOCUS

Section Objectives

1. Describe how technology has changed the world.
2. Define *interdependence* and how it has led to globalization.

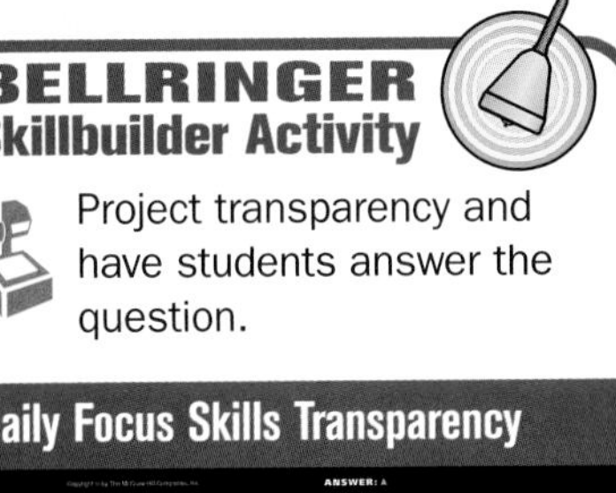

BELLRINGER
Skillbuilder Activity

Project transparency and have students answer the question.

Daily Focus Skills Transparency

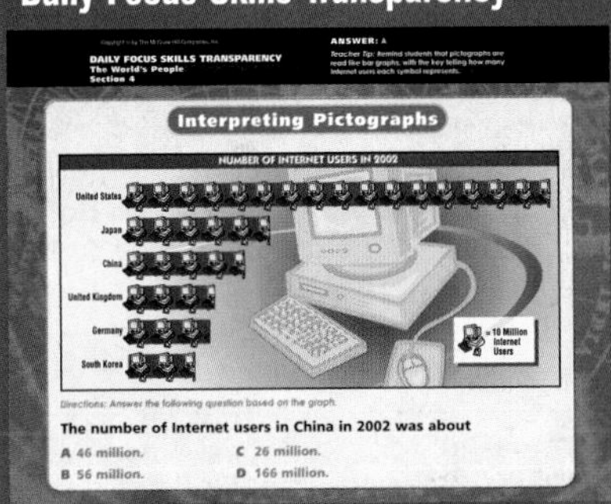

Reading Preview

- **Activating Prior Knowledge** Poll students to find out how many of them have purchased items using the Internet. Have them identify the benefits and drawbacks of Internet shopping.
- **Preteaching Vocabulary** Have students read the definitions of new vocabulary terms and explain them in their own words. This strategy helps students monitor their comprehension of the terms.

Section Resources

Reproducible Masters

- Reproducible Lesson Plan
- Daily Lecture and Discussion Notes
- Note-taking Guide
- Guided Reading Activity
- Reading Essentials and Study Guide
- Section Quiz

Transparencies

- Daily Focus Skills Transparency

Multimedia

- Vocabulary PuzzleMaker CD-ROM
- Interactive Tutor Self-Assessment CD-ROM
- Presentation Plus! CD-ROM
- ExamView® Pro Testmaker CD-ROM
- MindJogger Videoquiz

TEACH

Reading Strategy

Making Predictions Ask students for examples of technology that have transcended the boundaries of societies and helped shape the world. Then ask students to envision a future scientific discovery or technological innovation. Have them make predictions about the social, economic, and environmental consequences that might result from such progress. L2

Daily Lecture and Discussion Notes

THE WORLD'S PEOPLE

Daily Lecture and Discussion Notes

Technology "Shrinks" the World

Did You Know? In 1993, 22.8 percent of all United States households had computers. The U.S. Department of Commerce reported that this number had grown to 51 percent by 2000. In 2003, approximately 50 percent of U.S. households had Internet access.

I. Effects of Technology

A. Technology refers to the ability of humans to make things that help them and give them some control over their environment.

B. The Agricultural Revolution began 10,000 years ago. In just the past 100 years, important transportation and communication technologies have emerged.

Analyzing the Time Line

Answer
photography process, automobile, telephone, motion-picture camera, bicycle

Reading Check Answer

Communication technology links people around the world. Faster transportation makes it easy to travel long distances.

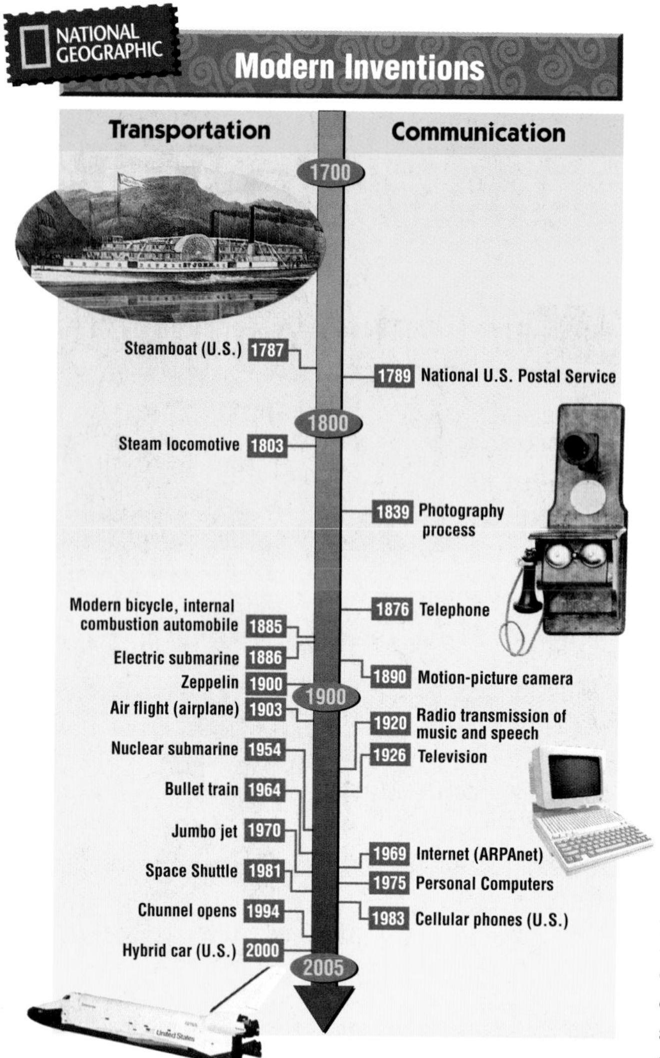

Analyzing the Time Line

In the last century, communication and transportation technologies have evolved at an amazing rate.

Technology Which nineteenth-century inventions are still used today?

Transportation Technology When steamboats first traveled upstream, people marveled at the technological feat. Settlers in western regions of the United States celebrated when railroad tracks were laid near their towns. Trains could carry passengers from New York City to San Francisco in about 10 days. Imagine their astonishment if early Americans could see how people travel today. Bullet trains speed workers from city to city, often moving well over 300 miles (483 km) per hour. Jet planes cross oceans in several hours, carrying people from one continent to another. The result is a shrinking world.

Communication Technology New inventions also have enabled people to communicate faster. For example, when the first telephone cable was laid along the bottom of the Atlantic Ocean in 1956, it could carry only 36 calls between Europe and North America at a time. Nearly forty years later, glass cables as fine as hairs were carrying 300,000 long-distance calls at once. Communication satellites surrounding the earth in space receive radio, television, and other signals. News can be broadcast live to the entire world so that more people than ever can see what is happening at the same time. Even cellular phones and fax machines have brought the world's cultures closer together.

Because of improved telephone cables and satellites, millions of people today use the **Internet,** a global network of computers. Other inventions made the Internet possible in the first place, however. The most important of these were the computer and the microchip. Today's personal computers have more processing power than the large computers of the 1960s that helped put an American on the moon! Millions of people use the Internet to exchange mail, shop, do research, take classes, play games with friends in other countries, and much more. The Internet helps make the world seem smaller yet.

Reading Check Name two ways in which technology makes the world seem smaller.

Reading Strategy — Reading the Text

Understanding Vocabulary Remind students about the difference between *synonyms,* which are words that have similar meanings, and *antonyms,* which are words that have opposite meanings. Help students remember this difference by telling them to remember the *s: s*ynonyms are the *s*ame. As students read the text and encounter words that they are unfamiliar with, have them use a thesaurus to identify appropriate synonyms and antonyms based on the words' contexts. L1

Use the ***Reading Skills Handbook*** *for more reading strategies.*

Globalization

Because the world seems to be getting smaller, it is likely that you know or will meet people from many other cultures. What is your role in this new, shrinking world?

Civic Participation First, you must learn civic participation. This means being an involved citizen and being concerned with the public affairs of your community, state, nation, and the world. You need to be aware of your rights and responsibilities. **Rights** are benefits and protections guaranteed to you by law. In a democracy like the United States, for example, you have the right to speak freely and to practice the religion of your choice. **Responsibilities** are duties that you owe to other citizens and your government. You have a responsibility to respect the property and privacy of others. When you turn 18 years old, you will be responsible for electing government leaders by voting.

Second, you can learn about the beliefs and values of other people in the world. By studying other cultures, you will become able to see connections between the United States and the world around us. Learning to understand and respect what makes each culture unique—and recognizing common experiences that link all people—will help you become an informed member of the global village.

Primary Source

GLOBALIZATION

Kofi Annan, secretary-general of the United Nations, spoke to the General Assembly about globalization.

"If one word [describes] the changes we are living through, it is 'globalization.' . . . What are [the] global issues? I have grouped them under three headings, each of which I relate to a fundamental human freedom . . . . First, freedom from want. How can we call human beings free and equal in dignity when over a billion of them are struggling to survive on less than one dollar a day? . . . The second . . . is freedom from fear. . . . We must do more to prevent conflicts from happening at all. . . . The third [is] the freedom of future generations to sustain their lives on this planet. . . . We need to remember the old African wisdom which I learned as a child—that the earth is not ours. It is a treasure we hold in trust for our descendents."

Millennium Report, April 3, 2000.

Analyzing Primary Sources

Do you think these are the only global issues? Do these issues affect you in your daily life? If they do, how? If they don't, do you think you should have to worry about them?

Chapter 3

Section 4, pages 97–100

Primary Source

Answer Answers will vary.

Activity Have your students use the Internet to find examples that illustrate Kofi Annan's three global issues. Have students present their findings to the class, using both pictures and facts. They should also describe the Web sites that they use as a source: what organization is behind it, how reliable is it, how up-to-date is the information?

L1/ELL

Guided Reading Activity

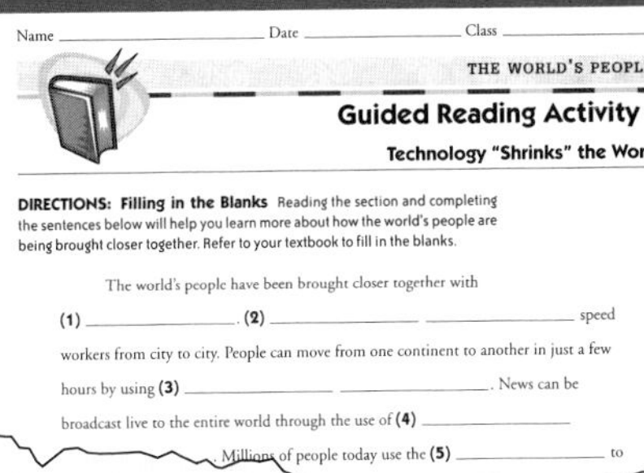
Name ______ Date ______ Class ______

THE WORLD'S PEOPLE

Guided Reading Activity 4

Technology "Shrinks" the World

DIRECTIONS: Filling in the Blanks Reading the section and completing the sentences below will help you learn more about how the world's people are being brought closer together. Refer to your textbook to fill in the blanks.

The world's people have been brought closer together with (1) ______ (2) ______ speed workers from city to city. People can move from one continent to another in just a few hours by using (3) ______. News can be broadcast live to the entire world through the use of (4) ______. Millions of people today use the (5) ______ to

Assign Section 4 Assessment as homework or an in-class activity.

Have students use the Interactive Tutor Self-Assessment CD-ROM to review Section 4.

Differentiated Instruction

Meeting Special Needs: Verbal/Linguistic Arrange your class into four groups. Groups 1 and 2 will represent eighteenth-century American and French governments, respectively. Groups 3 and 4 will be modern American and Russian governments. Present your class with the following problems: eighteenth-century America will have to go to war with France if France does not remove its warships from American territory. Modern America will have to go to war with Russia if Russia does not stop flying military planes over neutral territory. Have the groups research how they would communicate in their particular time period in order to stop the war. They should think about the time it would take, how messages would be carried, and who would be in communication. L2

EE6 The Uses of Geography: Standard 18

Chapter 3

Section 4, pages 97–100

L2

Section Quiz

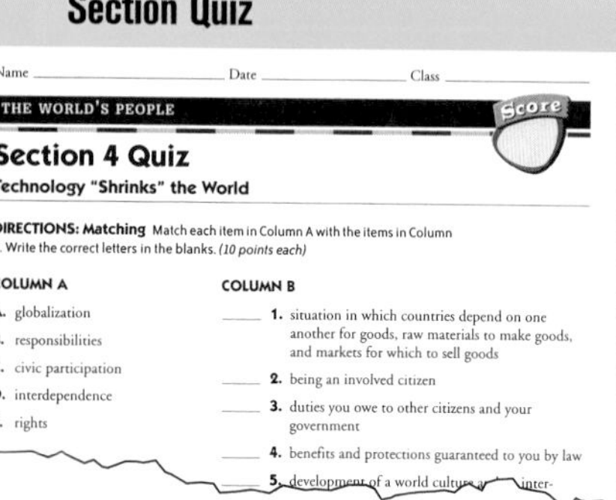
Name ______ Date ______ Class ______

THE WORLD'S PEOPLE

Score

Section 4 Quiz

Technology "Shrinks" the World

DIRECTIONS: Matching Match each item in Column A with the items in Column B. Write the correct letters in the blanks. *(10 points each)*

COLUMN A	COLUMN B
A. globalization	____ 1. situation in which countries depend on one another for goods, raw materials to make goods, and markets for which to sell goods
B. responsibilities	____ 2. being an involved citizen
C. civic participation	____ 3. duties you owe to other citizens and your government
D. interdependence	____ 4. benefits and protections guaranteed to you by law
E. rights	____ 5. development of a world culture and an inter-

Reading Check Answer

to see connections between the United States and the world; to become an informed member of the global community

L1/ELL

Reading Essentials and Study Guide

Date ______ Class ______

THE WORLD'S PEOPLE

Reading Essentials and Study Guide 4

Technology "Shrinks" the World

Key Terms

rights benefits and protections that are promised to you by law
responsibilities duties that you owe to other citizens and your government
interdependence when countries depend on each other for goods, raw materials, and places to sell goods
globalization development of a world culture and an interdependent economy

CLOSE

Reading Strategy

Summarizing Have students summarize the main ideas of the section in their own words.

Interdependence Why should we be concerned about what happens on the other side of the globe? The world's countries are interdependent. **Interdependence** exists when countries depend on one another for goods, raw materials to make goods, and markets in which to sell goods. Think of the many ways you use products from other countries. The fruit you put on your breakfast cereal might be from Mexico or South America. Your running shoes may be from China or Taiwan. Your book bag might have been made in India.

Events around the world have a rippling effect because of interdependence. A war or drought in another country, for example, causes instability in that country but also affects the people and economies that are linked to it through trade.

Many people perceive cultures in developing countries as backward because they do not have the same level of technology as developed countries. Others, however, appreciate the diverse cultures that exist in many developing countries. They fear that **globalization,** or the development of a world culture and an interdependent economy, might erase traditions and customs of smaller groups. Thus, an important issue in the world today is to make products, services, and technology available to developing countries yet still preserve local cultures and values. Read more about this challenge in **TIME Perspectives: Exploring World Issues** on pages 101–107.

Reading Check **Why is it important to learn about other cultures?**

Section 4 Assessment

Defining Terms

1. **Define** rights, responsibilities, interdependence, globalization.

Recalling Facts

2. **Technology** What are two examples of new transportation technology?
3. **Technology** What are two examples of new communication technology?
4. **Government** What responsibilities do people in democracies have?

Critical Thinking

5. **Synthesizing Information** What products found in your classroom were made in other countries?
6. **Making Comparisons** Which do you think had the greater impact on human society—the Agricultural Revolution or the Information Revolution? Explain.

Graphic Organizer

7. **Organizing Information** Draw a diagram like this one. On the outer spokes, write ways that people use the Internet.

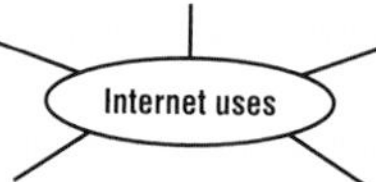

Applying Social Studies Skills

8. **Interpreting Time Lines** Look at the time line on page 98. About how many years after the internal combustion engine was invented was air flight invented?

Section 4 Assessment

1. The terms are defined in the Glossary.
2. bullet trains, jet planes
3. Answers may include the Internet, computers, cellular phones, and fax machines.
4. voting, respecting the property and privacy of others
5. Answers will vary.
6. Students' arguments should address how people learned to grow crops on a regular basis during the Agricultural Revolution but that people can travel around the world more easily and communicate faster in the Information Revolution, bringing the cultures closer together.
7. to exchange mail, shop, do research, take classes, play games with people in other countries
8. 18 years

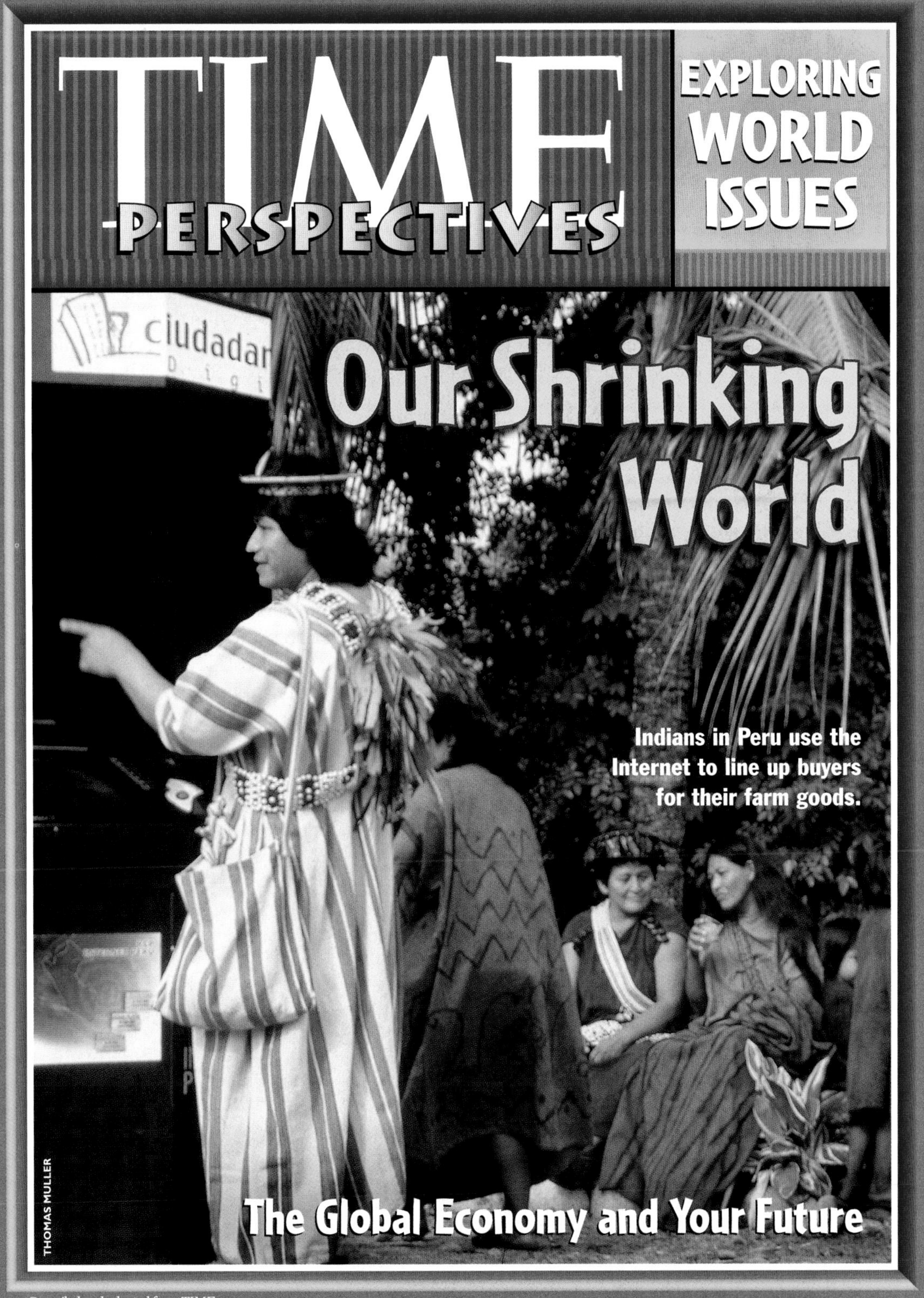

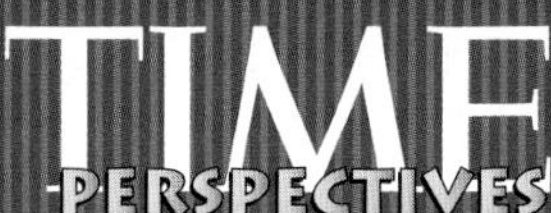

TIME
PERSPECTIVES
EXPLORING WORLD ISSUES
ciudadan
Our Shrinking World
Indians in Peru use the Internet to line up buyers for their farm goods.
The Global Economy and Your Future
THOMAS MULLER

Compiled and adapted from TIME.

Exploring World Issues

Teacher Background

Few topics are more controversial than globalization, which is changing the way virtually everyone works. Advocates state that globalization opens up new markets, provides consumers with the goods they want, and creates jobs. Opponents state that globalization discourages democracy, undermines the rights of workers and consumers, destroys the environment, subverts local development, and penalizes poor countries.

TIME
REPORTS
THE WORLD
Our Shrinking World
THEME: CULTURE AND SOCIETY
Guide To Teaching With This Unit

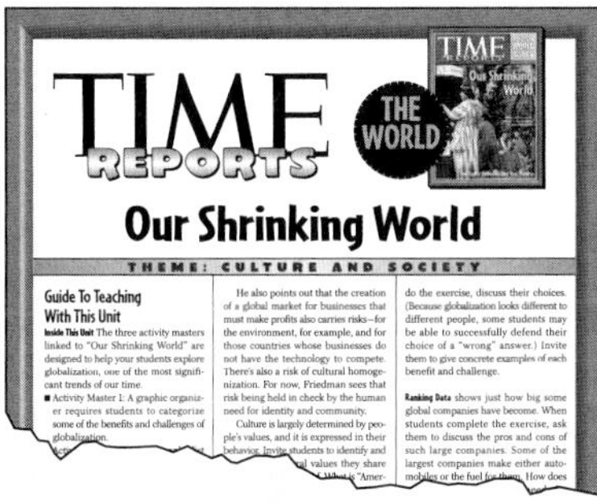

Preparing the Student

The term *globalization* came into common usage in the 1980s when countries became increasingly dependent on one another because of growing international trade and the freer flow of money around the world. However, globalization is nothing new—what is new is how the interests of corporations supersede laws passed by governments to protect their people.

Making Connections

Globalization Ask students: **What did you have for dinner last night?** List the foods on the board. The foods probably will have a variety of ethnic origins. Just a few generations ago, food such as chow mein and lasagna were considered exotic. Today, enchiladas and sushi are available practically everywhere in the United States. Ask students what they think this trend indicates. Encourage them to think of other ways in which their lives are influenced by the widespread interaction among world cultures. For example, how are our clothes, music, and sports influenced by other countries? Then ask students to come up with a definition of the term *globalization.* Emphasize the role that free trade plays in globalization. **L1**

1 Focus

Bring in pictures from magazines, newspapers, and so on that show how average people around the world (in particular, teenagers) have been affected by globalization and the mass media. For example, you might choose pictures of students in Africa accessing the Internet and Mexican children collecting reusable items in a dump to supplement the low wages earned by their parents in maquiladoras. Have students discuss the pictures in relationship to globalization. L2

A Sweatshirt's Global Journey

ANSWER
The cost would probably be higher because workers in the United States are paid more than those in the countries shown here.

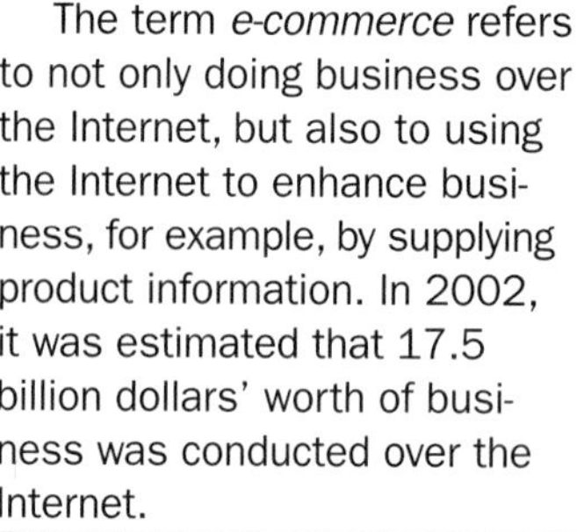
Did You Know

The term *e-commerce* refers to not only doing business over the Internet, but also to using the Internet to enhance business, for example, by supplying product information. In 2002, it was estimated that 17.5 billion dollars' worth of business was conducted over the Internet.

TIME PERSPECTIVES

EXPLORING WORLD ISSUES

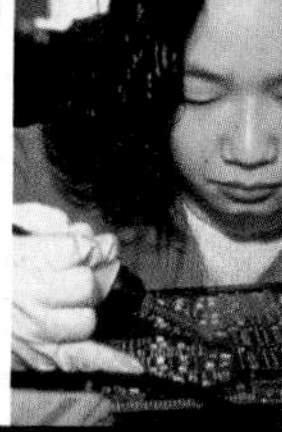

Two forms of globalization: In Cuba, a student and her professor develop medicines to sell abroad. A woman in China makes goods for export.

DAVID ALAN HARVEY/MAGNUM

How Trade Changes Lives

For Nora Lydia Urias Perez, life has never been easy. A single mother, she lived with her five-year-old daughter in the Mexican state of Veracruz. The only work she could find there was on a farm, earning $5 a day. That just wasn't enough.

In 2000 she moved to Nogales, a city just south of the New Mexico border. She got a job in a stapler factory that had moved to Nogales from New York City. Ms. Urias's job paid her $10 a day. To her, it was a fortune.

Thanks to the North American Free Trade Agreement (NAFTA), hundreds of thousands of Mexicans work in factories like Ms. Urias's. Companies in Mexico, Japan, and Europe hire their workers to assemble products with parts that come from the United States. They send the finished goods—everything from dresses to TVs—back to the United States and Canada.

Global Relationships

This relationship is an example of **globalization**, the linking together of the world's nations through trade. What's driving globalization today is the search for cheap labor. Cheap labor helps manufacturers keep costs low. Low costs can mean lower prices for many things you buy.

A Sweatshirt's Global Journey

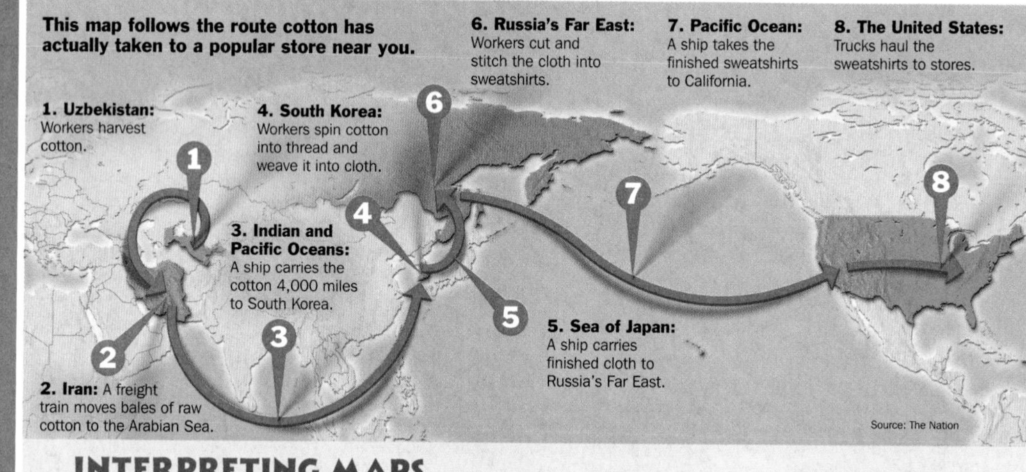
This map follows the route cotton has actually taken to a popular store near you.
1. Uzbekistan: Workers harvest cotton.
2. Iran: A freight train moves bales of raw cotton to the Arabian Sea.
3. Indian and Pacific Oceans: A ship carries the cotton 4,000 miles to South Korea.
4. South Korea: Workers spin cotton into thread and weave it into cloth.
5. Sea of Japan: A ship carries finished cloth to Russia's Far East.
6. Russia's Far East: Workers cut and stitch the cloth into sweatshirts.
7. Pacific Ocean: A ship takes the finished sweatshirts to California.
8. The United States: Trucks haul the sweatshirts to stores.
Source: The Nation

INTERPRETING MAPS

Making Inferences How do you think the price of the sweatshirt might be affected if the sweatshirt were made entirely in the United States?

102

Critical Thinking Activity

Formulating an Opinion Consumer advocate Ralph Nader has stated, "Globalization means control of world economies by giant corporations that don't have an allegiance to a community or don't have any allegiance to a particular country—even the one they're domiciled in—as long as they can make more profit elsewhere." Read this quote to the students. Then organize students into small groups to discuss whether they agree or disagree with this statement. When they are done, ask each group to share their discussion with the class. L2

 **EE4 Human Systems: Standard 11**

SERGE ATTAL/GAMMA LIASON NETWORK
ROBIN MOYER
Some fear global companies may neglect the environment.

ITSU INOUYE/AP
Police block a march by globalization's foes.

REUTERS/TIMEPIX
A U.S. resident made this Taiwanese movie in China.

Globalization is changing far more than prices. More people, money, and goods than ever before are crossing national borders.

Pop Goes Global

Popular entertainment is no exception. A movie popular in the United States is likely to be a favorite elsewhere. Asians love basketball as much as Americans do. Kids everywhere listen to Latin pop music and wear jeans and sneakers to school.

This doesn't mean all kids think and act the same way. "It is important to see individual differences from one country to the next," advises a woman who has studied teens in 44 nations.

Culture Clash

Companies that forget that advice can get into trouble. A U.S. company opened a theme park outside Paris, France. But the French stayed away. They hated the fast food the park sold. They didn't even like the park's name. It contained the word "Euro," short for "European." The French see themselves as French first, Europeans second.

When the park's owners figured all this out, they made the park more French. They offered food and drinks that suited French tastes, for example. They even put the word "Paris" in the park's name. Today that theme park is one of the most popular in the world.

Good for Everyone?

As the park's owners learned, globalization isn't **"Americanizing"** the world. Local **cultures,** or ways of life, are too strong for that.

But globalization hasn't been good for everyone. The poorest countries have seen little or no increase in trade. Many Americans' jobs have moved to countries where wages are low. And so far the lives of people like Ms. Urias haven't improved much. It costs more to live in Nogales than in Veracruz. So Ms. Urias is still poor.

Gaining Skills

Experts say these problems are only temporary. In recent years, trade has created millions of jobs. It has enabled people in poorer countries like Mexico to pick up new skills. The more skilled workers are, the more they get paid.

Ms. Urias looks forward to better times. "I am not saying it will be easy to start life [in Nogales]," she said. "But at last there is a chance that things for me will get better. There was no chance of that in Veracruz. I had no hope."

EXPLORING THE ISSUE

1. **Cause and Effect** How might the health of the U.S. economy shape Ms. Urias's life?
2. **Making Inferences** Why do you think that the poorest countries have seen few gains from globalization?

2 TEACH

Reading Strategy

Identifying Main Ideas

Have students read the subsection titled "Global Relationships." Ask them to write a one-sentence summary of this subsection. Ask volunteers to read their summaries to the class. L1

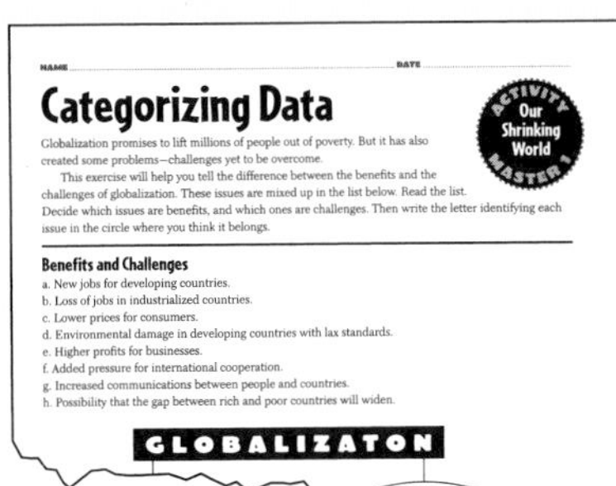
NAME ____ DATE ____

Categorizing Data

Activity Master 1: Our Shrinking World

Globalization promises to lift millions of people out of poverty. But it has also created some problems—challenges yet to be overcome.

This exercise will help you tell the difference between the benefits and the challenges of globalization. These issues are mixed up in the list below. Read the list. Decide which issues are benefits, and which ones are challenges. Then write the letter identifying each issue in the circle where you think it belongs.

Benefits and Challenges

a. New jobs for developing countries.
b. Loss of jobs in industrialized countries.
c. Lower prices for consumers.
d. Environmental damage in developing countries with lax standards.
e. Higher profits for businesses.
f. Added pressure for international cooperation.
g. Increased communications between people and countries.
h. Possibility that the gap between rich and poor countries will widen.

GLOBALIZATON

EXPLORING THE ISSUE

ANSWERS

1. *Possible answer:* Americans must make enough money to purchase the consumer goods she makes or she will not have work.
2. *Possible answer:* The jobs have gone to these countries because the people will work for very low wages. The workers generally have few skills, are not organized, and do not have the ability to fight for higher pay.

Differentiated Instruction

Meeting Special Needs: Kinesthetic

Dramatizing business activities can increase students' sensitivity to the difficulties in interacting with those from another culture. Organize students into pairs. Each pair should pick a foreign country and then research the business customs and conventions of that country. They should then use their knowledge of these customs to develop a short skit in which one person is an American visiting the country on business. The second person should be a native of the host country. The pair should then present their skit to the class. L2

Refer to *Inclusion for the Middle School Social Studies Classroom Strategies and Activities* in the TCR.

Recommended Internet Sites

www.wto.org
This is the official site of the World Trade Organization (WTO). The WTO deals with rules of trade among nations and attempts to aid in resolving trade disputes.

www.globaled.org/curriculum3.html
This site contains a number of lessons on global issues, human rights, and developing nations.

www.maryknoll.org/EDUCA/CORNER/studyguides/edup_la.htm
This site contains a set of four lessons on the effect of globalization on Latin America. One of the lessons ("Story Telling—the Human Face of Globalization") contains 16 case studies showing how globalization affects poor people.

EXPLORING THE ISSUE

ANSWERS

1. Trade increases communication among cultures and creates greater understanding of one another's customs and philosophies. People learn how other cultures are similar as well as different.
2. *Possible answers:* Vast amounts of information are available immediately; communication around the world is instantaneous; consumers can order items online in just a few minutes rather than going to a store.

TIME PERSPECTIVES

Globalization's New Face

The Phoenicians were great sailors. They lived in Southwest Asia, on the coast of Lebanon. They set up **trade routes** all around the Mediterranean Sea. Some experts think they may have sailed to England to bring back tin. They did all this as far back as 1200 B.C.

GARWOOD & AINSLIE, PLANET PROJECT

▲ **A Yagua (right) takes part in an Internet poll in the rain forests of Peru.**

As the Phoenicians showed, globalization is not new. People have traded in faraway lands, moved around, and mixed cultures for thousands of years.

What is new is the speed at which these exchanges take place. Technology is shrinking the world. Telephones zip our voices around the world. Jet planes carry us great distances in a few hours. High-speed cargo ships crisscross the oceans, carrying goods from nation to nation.

The Internet

The Internet has changed the way we swap goods, too. Twenty-five years ago, an American importer might have used "snail mail" to order a shipment of French bikes. Today she can check out the manufacturer's stock on his Web page. Then, in seconds, she can e-mail her order halfway around the world.

The deals she makes aren't much different from those the Phoenicians made. They traded timber for horses. She trades money for bicycles.

What's different is that she makes her trades in a flash, and without leaving her seat. She can do more business in less time, and she can do business anywhere. The Phoenicians could do business only where they could sail.

EXPLORING THE ISSUE

1. **Making Inferences** How might trade help people from different cultures understand one another?
2. **Analyzing Information** How does the Internet make growing up different for you than it was for your parents?

104

Team-Teaching Activity

Economics Have a teacher with a background in economics discuss the growth of e-commerce (electronic commerce) as it relates to globalization. He or she should talk about how e-commerce is used not only by consumers, but also by companies, particularly within manufacturing industries. Ask the teacher to discuss how treaties such as GATT and NAFTA and regional organizations such as the European Union have affected globalization. L2

 **EE4 Human Systems: Standard 11**

Sharing Globalization's Gains

A little more than 6 billion people live on Earth. About half of them get by on less than $2 a day. What does globalization mean to them? So far, not much.

Overall, the impact of increased trade has been amazing. The ability of people to make and spend money has grown almost everywhere.

Yet the fruits of globalization haven't been spread evenly. **Industrialized countries** have more to trade than **developing countries**. Foreign companies prefer to build more factories in rich countries than in poor ones.

The result is that countries like Kenya tend to create new jobs slowly. Places like Canada tend to create them more quickly. Some countries in Asia and Africa are barely able to create any new jobs at all.

A Wider Gap

These differences worry many people. If the trend continues, experts say that the gap between rich and poor countries can only get wider.

What can be done to narrow that gap? There are no easy answers. International businesses are certainly part of it. During the 1990s, private companies spent more than $1 trillion to build factories in developing countries.

Rich nations are also part of the answer. They are already helping poorer countries pay for new roads, phone lines, seaports, and airports. And they are encouraging poor nations to produce things that people elsewhere want to buy.

China figured out how to do that years ago. Thanks to trade, the ability of the Chinese to earn and spend money now doubles every 10 years. Finding ways to help about 200 other nations equal that success is one of today's biggest challenges.

MARIE DORIGNY/TIMEPIX

▲ Nowhere is the gap between rich and poor clearer than in Pakistan. Here a child laborer makes soccer balls for sale around the world.

EXPLORING THE ISSUE

1. **Making Inferences** Why do you think experts worry about the widening gap between rich and poor countries?
2. **Problem Solving** What would you do to help spread the fruits of globalization more evenly around the globe?

Reading Strategy

Synthesizing Information
Have students research the topic of child labor in developing countries. UNICEF is a good source for information. Have students then research child labor in the United States during the Industrial Revolution. **Ask:** **Compare the reasons for child labor during the Industrial Revolution to those for child labor in developing countries today. How was child labor stopped in the United States? Do you think these same methods would work in developing countries?** L1

NAME ______ DATE ______

Ranking Data

Activity Master 1 — Our Shrinking World

In baseball, teams keep score by adding up runs. In business, companies keep score by adding up the year's revenues. Revenues are the money companies collect for what they sell.

This activity isn't about baseball. (Sorry.) It's about 10 companies that sell their products all over the world. In the year 2003, these 10 companies led the pack in revenues. Every other company in the world took in less money than they did.

That's a very big deal. To see how big, rank the companies according to the size of their revenues. Then group the companies by the products they make or sell.

Top 10 Global Companies (in alphabetical order)

(a) BP – British oil and gas company, $179 billion
(b) DaimlerChrysler – German automaker, $141 billion
(c) Exxon Mobil – U.S. oil and gas company, $182 billion
(d) Ford Motor – U.S. automaker, $164 billion
(e) General Electric – U.S. manufacturer and finance company, $132 billion
(f) General Motors – U.S. automaker, $187 billion
(g) Mitsubishi – Japanese trading company, $109 billion
(h) Royal Dutch/Shell Group – Netherlands oil and gas company, $179 billion
(i) Toyota – Japanese automaker, $132 billion
(j) WalMart Stores – U.S. retailer, $247 billion

Source: *Fortune Magazine*

Top 10 Global Companies: Who Makes More?

GROUPED BY PRODUCT

EXPLORING THE ISSUE

ANSWERS

1. Poor people are less able to learn skills to improve their lives. They may be unable to afford food, medical care, or education for their children. They generally do not have the ability to fight for or participate in democratic governments. They may be more willing to engage in warfare because they have little to lose.
2. Answers will vary.

Interdisciplinary Activity

Literature Tell students to read selected essays in *War Talk* (South End Press, 2003) by Booker Prize winner Arundhati Roy. Have the readers briefly summarize their assigned essay for the class. Make certain each summary includes the situation described in the essay and the names of the groups involved. For example, in "The Greater Common Good," Roy discusses the nonviolent struggle of Indian activists against corporations building dams that would place thousands of Indian homes under water. After all the students have presented their summaries, ask: **What groups does Roy support in her writing?** *(Possible answers are the poor, the displaced, and the persecuted)* **Whom does Roy criticize?** *(Possible answers are politicians who favor corporations over people, the World Bank, the International Money Fund, and the WTO)* L3

TIME PERSPECTIVES

Current Events Journal

Have students read a summary of a recent meeting of an organization such as the World Trade Organization (www.wto.org). Ask students to make a list of the major topics of discussion at the meeting.

Drawing Conclusions Tell students that within recent years, many media companies have merged, resulting in a relatively few remaining organizations. A prime example occurred when America Online (AOL) and Time Warner merged, forming the world's largest media company. **Ask:** **What, if any, dangers can you see in an increasingly small number of companies controlling telecommunications and media businesses? L2**

EXPLORING THE ISSUE

ANSWERS

1. We can interact with people around the world quickly and cheaply.
2. Learning enhances people's skills and helps them think creatively.

TIME PERSPECTIVES

Preparing for a Smaller World: What Can One Person Do?

Every day in 2000, half a million airline passengers, 1.4 billion e-mail messages, and $1.5 trillion crossed national borders. All that shifting about of people, ideas, and money would have been unthinkable 10 years earlier. The Internet was a toddler. The World Wide Web had just been born.

DAVID STRICK/CORBIS OUTLINE

▲ Which of Pepperdine University's nine teammates was born in the U.S.? It's Anh Nguyen, fourth from left.

What will the world look like 10 years from now? No one can say. But two things are sure. Inventions that create faster ways to communicate will make the world seem a lot smaller than it is today. And more and more Americans will have jobs that require them to deal with people from other nations.

Learning About Other Cultures

You will be able to do that well if you have taken the time to learn about other countries. To really get to know people from other cultures, you need to understand what makes them tick. You can do that best by speaking to them in their own language.

You won't have to leave the United States to need that knowledge. Globalization has enabled more and more people to cross borders to find work. Employers will want to hire people who can work well with people born in other countries.

They will also want to know if you are committed to a lifetime of learning. As technology changes, your job will, too. Your need to learn new things won't stop when you leave high school or college.

Globalization is shaping tomorrow's job market. Only you can prepare yourself to thrive in it. And there's no time like today to start.

EXPLORING THE ISSUE

1. **Determining Cause and Effect** How does the Internet make the world seem smaller?
2. **Analyzing Information** Modern companies require employees at every level to solve problems they face on the job. Why are lifetime learners better equipped than others to solve problems?

Your Government and You

The Office of the United States Trade Representative is responsible for supporting U.S. trade throughout the world. It enforces U.S. trade regulations and aids in resolving international trade disputes. One important international dispute involves "intellectual property." Some countries, such as China, violate international copyright law by allowing companies to freely copy intellectual property such as books, videotapes, and software without paying royalties to authors. The USTR is active in trying to pressure worldwide enforcement of copyright law. Have students research more about what the USTR is doing on this issue and others by visiting its Web site (www.ustr.gov). Ask them to summarize their findings in a paragraph. L1

TIME REPORTS

REVIEW AND ASSESS

UNDERSTANDING THE ISSUE

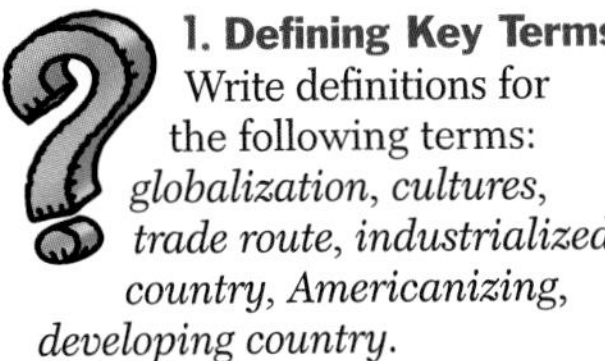

1. Defining Key Terms Write definitions for the following terms: *globalization, cultures, trade route, industrialized country, Americanizing, developing country.*

2. Writing to Inform Write a short article about how globalization shapes the way people live and what they do. Use as many words as you can from the above list.

3. Writing to Persuade Overall, is globalization good or bad for the world? Defend your answer in a letter to an imaginary friend who lives in a developing country in Africa.

INTERNET RESEARCH ACTIVITY

4. With your teacher's help, use Internet resources to contact two classrooms—one in an industrialized country and one in a developing country. Exchange lists on what imported goods kids in your country and theirs own or use. Compare the lists, and discuss what they say about the importance of trade.

5. Use the Internet to find information on the history of the Internet. Write an essay telling how the Internet sped up communication. Create a time line that notes important developments.

BEYOND THE CLASSROOM

6. Look through your local newspaper for a week. Find articles on topics related to globalization. For example, look for stories about the Internet, imports and exports, immigration, and even crimes like drug-smuggling. In an oral report, tell how the articles suggest that globalization is making the world smaller.

PHOTODISC

▲ **More and more Americans are crossing the borders for fun.**

7. Take an inventory of your room at home. Write down the name of each item made in another country. Count the items imported from the same country. Then make a bar graph to show how many imported items you own. Have each bar stand for one category—clothing, CDs, or sports equipment, for example. Write a caption explaining what the graph says about how important trade is to you.

The Digital Divide

(Individuals with home access to the Internet in 2001)

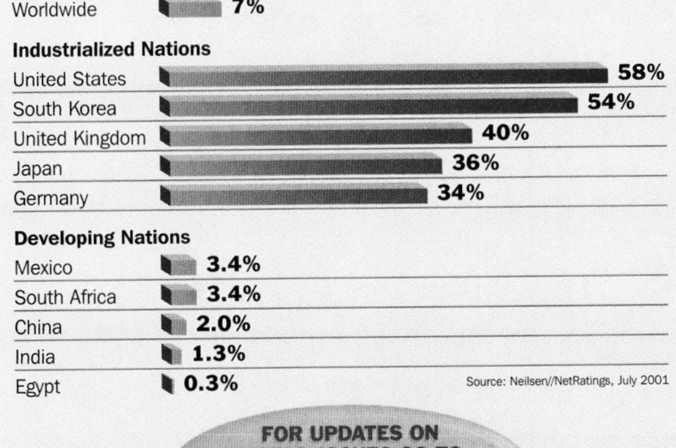

Worldwide	7%
Industrialized Nations	
United States	58%
South Korea	54%
United Kingdom	40%
Japan	36%
Germany	34%
Developing Nations	
Mexico	3.4%
South Africa	3.4%
China	2.0%
India	1.3%
Egypt	0.3%

Source: Neilsen//NetRatings, July 2001

Where in the world are people wired to the Internet at home? Almost everywhere. But industrialized nations have a big lead. People with home access make up a big chunk of the populations of these richer nations. It's just the opposite with developing nations. People with home access make up a tiny part of the populations of these poorer nations. Experts call this gap the "digital divide," and it worries them. The Internet is a tool. Nations must use it to participate fully in world trade.

BUILDING GRAPH READING SKILLS

1. **Comparing** Compare the amount of Internet use in industrialized and developing nations.
2. **Determining Cause and Effect** What does a nation need besides Internet access to succeed in world trade?

FOR UPDATES ON WORLD ISSUES GO TO www.timeclassroom.com/glencoe

107

3 ASSESS

Have students take the TIME Reports Quiz provided in the Teacher's Classroom Resources.

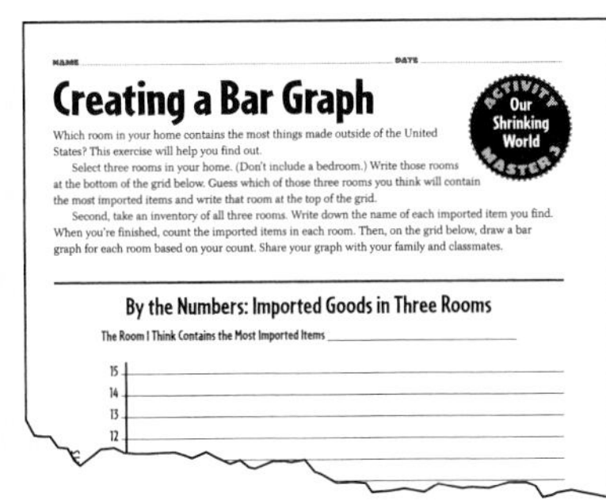

Creating a Bar Graph

Our Shrinking World Activity Master

By the Numbers: Imported Goods in Three Rooms

BUILDING GRAPH READING SKILLS

ANSWERS

1. It is higher in industrialized countries.
2. *Possible answers:* a hard-working, skilled workforce; a good transportation system; a stable government

4 CLOSE

Reading Strategy

Writing a Paragraph Ask students to write a paragraph starting with this topic sentence: *Some of the ways that globalization has changed the way companies conduct business are . . . .*

Culminating Activity

To close this lesson, have students complete the Review and Assess section questions and activities. Students should use classroom discussion, contextual clues, and their student dictionaries to write definitions for terms. Before assigning the Internet activities, it is recommended that you review your school district policy on student Internet use.

Focus on Debate
For further student understanding of the issue, have students debate the pro and con position of the following topic: **Industrialized countries have a responsibility to make certain that workers in developing countries are earning wages that allow them to meet their basic needs, including adequate food, clothing, and medical care. L2**

Teach

Before students read the feature, tell them to take the role of government officials. Inform them that their task is to make a count of every person in the country. Have them discuss how they would go about getting the information. **L2**

More About the Census

Two sets of national census records are not available to historians to study. During the War of 1812, when the British burned Washington, D.C., the fires destroyed some parts of the 1790 census, the nation's first count. Decades later, the census from 1890 was completely destroyed in another fire.

Interdisciplinary Connections

Technology The 2000 census became completely automated, using optical scanners to scan the questionnaires filled out by respondents—even scanning written words. The information was then stored immediately on computers. The process was 20 times faster than manually inputting the information.

Making Connections

ART | SCIENCE | CULTURE | TECHNOLOGY

Counting Heads

How did we know there were nearly 292 million people in the United States in 2000? Who counts the people? Every 10 years since 1790, the United States Census Bureau has counted heads in this country. Why and how do they do this?

The First Census

After the American colonies fought the Revolutionary War and won their independence, the new government ordered a census. By knowing how many people were in each state, the government could divide the war expenses fairly. The census would also determine the number of people that each state could send to Congress.

This census began in August 1790, about a year after George Washington became president. The law defined who would be counted and required that every household be visited by census takers. These workers walked or rode on horseback to gather their data. By the time it was completed, the census counted 3.9 million people.

The first census asked for little more than one's name and address. Over time, the census added questions to gather more than just population data. By 1820 there were questions about a person's job. Soon after, questions about crime, education, and wages appeared.

Changing Technology

As the country's population grew and the quantity of data increased, new technology helped census workers. In 1890 clerks began to use a keypunch device, invented by a Census Bureau worker, to add the numbers. The Tabulating Machine, as it was called, used an electric current to sense holes in punched cards and to keep a running total of the data. In 1950 the census used its first computer to process data. Now census data are released over the Internet.

Remarkably, one technology slow to change has been the way the government takes the census. Not until 1960 did the U.S. Postal Service become the major means of conducting the census. Even today, census takers go door-to-door to gather information from those who do not return their census forms in the mail.

▲ **The Electric Tabulating Machine processed the 1890 census in $2\frac{1}{2}$ years, a job that would have taken nearly 10 years to complete by hand.**

Making the Connection

1. In what two ways were population data from the first census used?
2. How has technology changed the way census data are collected and processed?
3. **Drawing Conclusions** Why do you think the national and state governments want information about people's education and jobs?

Making the Connection

1. to divide war expenses and to determine representation in Congress
2. Data is collected mostly through the mail rather than relying exclusively on door-to-door surveys. Instead of processing data by hand, it is now done by computers and results are posted on the Internet.
3. *Possible answer:* to help them make better plans about economic growth

Chapter 3 Reading Review

Section 1 Understanding Culture

Terms to Know
- culture
- ethnic group
- dialect
- democracy
- dictatorship
- monarchy
- cultural diffusion
- civilization
- culture region

Main Idea

People usually live with others who follow similar beliefs learned from the past.

✓ Culture Culture is the way of life of a group of people who share similar beliefs and customs.

✓ Culture Culture includes eight elements or traits: social groups, language, religion, daily life, history, arts, a government system, and an economic system.

✓ Culture Cultures change over time and influence other regions.

Section 2 Population Patterns

Terms to Know
- death rate
- birthrate
- famine
- population density
- urbanization
- emigrate
- refugee

Main Idea

The world's population is growing rapidly, and how and where people live are changing too.

✓ History In the past 200 years, the world's population has grown at a very rapid rate.

✓ Movement Some areas are more densely populated than others.

✓ Culture About 50 percent of the world's people live in cities.

Section 3 Resources and World Trade

Terms to Know
- natural resource
- renewable resource
- nonrenewable resource
- economic system
- export
- import
- tariff
- quota
- free trade
- developed country
- developing country

Main Idea

Many resources are limited and distributed unevenly, so countries must trade for goods.

✓ Human/Environment Interaction Renewable resources cannot be used up or can be replaced fairly quickly.

✓ Human/Environment Interaction Some resources—such as fossil fuels and minerals—are nonrenewable.

✓ Economics Countries specialize by producing what they can produce best with the resources they have.

✓ Economics Countries export their specialized products and import what they need.

Section 4 Technology "Shrinks" the World

Terms to Know
- rights
- responsibilities
- interdependence
- globalization

Main Idea

Modern technology has helped to bring the world's diverse peoples closer together.

✓ Technology Advancements in transportation and communication technology, including the Internet, have "shrunk" the world.

✓ Interdependence The world's countries are linked through trade, and some people fear that globalization will erase traditional cultures.

Reading Review

Use the Chapter 3 Reading Review to preview, review, condense, or reteach the chapter.

Preview/Review

Use the Terms to Know lists to help students review and study.

Activity Organize the class into teams and quiz them on the Terms to Know. Offer a definition and ask each team to identify the correct term. If they do so correctly, they win a point; if they do not, the other team has an opportunity to do so.

Vocabulary PuzzleMaker CD-ROM reinforces the vocabulary terms used in Chapter 3.

The Interactive Tutor Self-Assessment CD-ROM allows students to review Chapter 3 content.

Condense

Have students read the Chapter 3 summary statements.

Guided Reading Activities

Audio Program

Reteach

Reteaching Activity

Reading Essentials and Study Guide

Reading Strategy Read to Write

Summarizing **Ask students:** What do you think makes North American culture unique? Then have students work in groups to survey other students, faculty members, and family members. Have them ask the same question. Groups should collate the responses they receive and present their results to the class in a brief written report. Compile all the results and have the class discuss them. L1

Assessment and Activities

GLENCOE TECHNOLOGY

MindJogger Videoquiz
Use MindJogger Videoquiz to review the Chapter 3 content.

Available in DVD and VHS

Using Key Terms

1. h
2. g
3. a
4. j
5. f
6. d
7. i
8. e
9. c
10. b

Reviewing the Main Ideas

11. Buddhism, Christianity, Hinduism, Islam, and Judaism
12. Examples will vary but should reflect the principle of one culture influencing another.
13. falling death rates and high birthrates in some countries
14. divide the number of people in an area (total population) by the number of square miles or square kilometers in that area (total land area)
15. mainly to find jobs
16. wind power, solar power, and hydroelectric power
17. In a traditional economy, economic decisions are based on customs. In a market economy, individuals make their own economic decisions.
18. They produce what they can make best with the resources they have, or they specialize.
19. Technology is making it faster and easier to communicate with or travel to any place in the world.
20. Cultures might lose their traditions and customs.

Chapter 3 Assessment and Activities

Using Key Terms

Match the terms in Part A with their definitions in Part B.

A.

1. culture
2. developed country
3. democracy
4. globalization
5. population density
6. emigrate
7. urbanization
8. quota
9. developing country
10. cultural diffusion

B.

a. power rests with the people of a nation
b. spreading knowledge to other cultures
c. countries working toward industrialization
d. to move to another country
e. a number limit on imports from a country
f. the average number of people living in a square mile
g. country where much manufacturing is carried out
h. the way of life of a group of people who share similar beliefs and customs
i. movement to cities
j. development of a world culture and an interdependent world economy

Reviewing the Main Ideas

Section 1 Understanding Culture

11. **Culture** What are the major religions?
12. **Movement** Give an example of cultural diffusion.

Section 2 Population Patterns

13. **Culture** What has created rapid population growth?
14. **Culture** How do you calculate population density?
15. **Movement** Why have many people moved to cities?

Section 3 Resources and World Trade

16. **Human/Environment Interaction** What are three renewable energy sources?
17. **Economics** What is the difference between a traditional and market economy?
18. **Economics** How do countries respond to the unequal distribution of resources?

Section 4 Technology "Shrinks" the World

19. **Technology** In what ways is the world shrinking?
20. **Culture** How can globalization affect cultures in a negative way?

NATIONAL GEOGRAPHIC World Culture Regions

Place Location Activity

On a separate sheet of paper, match the letters on the map with the numbered places listed below.

1. Latin America
2. North Africa and Southwest Asia
3. Europe
4. Russia and Central Asian Republics
5. East Asia
6. United States and Canada
7. Australia, Oceania, and Antarctica
8. Africa South of the Sahara

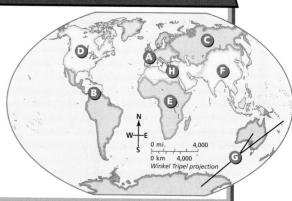

NATIONAL GEOGRAPHIC Place Location Activity

1. B
2. H
3. A
4. C
5. F
6. D
7. G
8. E

Critical Thinking

21. *Possible answers: Help*—provide jobs; raise standard of living; *Harm*—disrupt traditional relationships or ways of living
22. Answers will vary. In the first column, students should list their daily activities, such as waking to an alarm clock, listening to the radio, and cooking food. In the second column, they should list alternative ways to do these activities.

Self-Check Quiz Visit ***The World and Its People*** Web site at twip.glencoe.com and click on **Chapter 3—Self-Check Quizzes** to prepare for the Chapter Test.

Critical Thinking

21. **Making Predictions** In what ways do you think a company investing in a developing country could help the people there? How could that same company harm the culture?
22. **Sequencing Information** Make a chart like the one below, and list the ways you use electricity from the moment you wake up until you go to sleep. In the second column, write how you would perform the same activity if you had no electricity to rely on.

Activities With Electricity	Without Electricity

Comparing Regions Activity

23. **Culture** With your teacher's help, find a service that matches pen pals from different regions. In your first letter, describe your clothing, the sports you play, and what you do for fun. Ask your pal to describe the same.

Mental Mapping Activity

24. **Focusing on the Region** Draw a simple outline map of the United States. On your map, label the areas where the following activities take place:
    - Commercial farming
    - Manufacturing
    - Raising livestock
    - Fishing
    - Obtaining oil

Technology Skills Activity

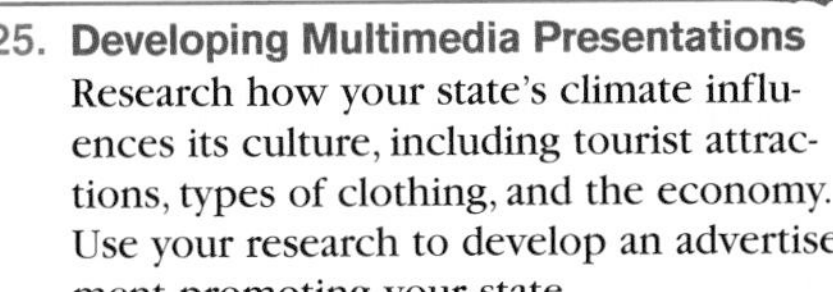

25. **Developing Multimedia Presentations** Research how your state's climate influences its culture, including tourist attractions, types of clothing, and the economy. Use your research to develop an advertisement promoting your state.

Standardized Test Practice

Directions: Study the graph below, and then answer the question that follows.

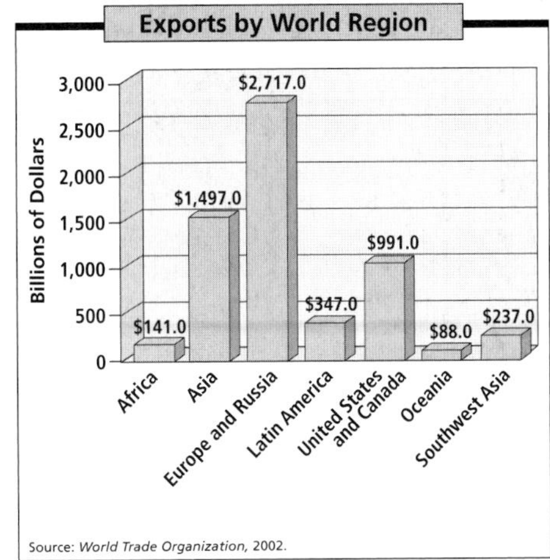

1. **According to the graph, how much do the United States and Canada export?**
   A $991,000,000,000
   B $991,000,000
   C $991,000
   D $991

Test-Taking Tip: In order to understand any type of graph, look carefully around the graph for keys that show how it is organized. On this bar graph, the numbers along the left side represent billions of dollars. Therefore, you need to multiply the number on the graph by 1,000,000,000 to get the correct answer.

Assessment and Activities

Standardized Test Practice

1. A

Tested Objectives:
Analyzing information, reading graphs

Social Studies Online

Have students visit the Web site at twip.glencoe.com to review Chapter 3 and take the Self-Check Quiz.

Chapter Test Bonus Question

This question may be used for extra credit on the chapter test.

In the past few decades, the number of people in the world has grown rapidly. Now more and more people live in cities. What are densely populated areas called? *(urban areas)*

FOLDABLES™ Study Organizer — Dinah Zike's Foldables

Culminating Activity Have students use their foldables to write a one-page essay that predicts what cultures, population patterns, and technology might be like in 2050.

Comparing Regions Activity

23. Letters should contain information that accurately describes aspects of students' lives.

Mental Mapping Activity

24. This exercise helps students visualize where specific economic activities are found in the United States. All attempts at freehand mapping should be accepted.

Technology Skills Activity

25. Students should research and summarize their state's climate before writing the advertisement. Students should advertise the unique benefits of their state, including examples of their state's climate, culture, tourist attractions, clothing worn/needed, and economic activities.

Unit 2 Planning Guide

• If you teach BOTH Eastern and Western world regions in one year, use the columns in red to help you pace your lessons.
• If you teach ONLY Eastern or Western world regions in one year, use the columns in blue to help you pace your lessons.

ALTERNATIVE PACING CHARTS

Unit 2		Chapter 4		Chapter 5	
Both East and West	Either East or West	Both East and West	Either East or West	Both East and West	Either East or West
Day 1 Unit Opener, Regional Atlas	**Day 1** Unit Opener, Regional Atlas	**Day 1** Chapter Opener, Section 1	**Day 1** Chapter Opener, Section 1	**Day 1** Chapter Opener, Section 1	**Day 1** Chapter Opener, Section 1
Day 2 Regional Atlas	**Day 2** Regional Atlas	**Day 2** Section 1	**Day 2** Section 1	**Day 2** Section 1, Technology Skill	**Day 2** Section 1
	Day 3 Regional Atlas	**Day 3** Section 2	**Day 3** Section 2	**Day 3** Section 2	**Day 3** Section 1, Technology Skill
		Day 4 TIME Reports	**Day 4** TIME Reports	**Day 4** Making Connections, Review	**Day 4** Section 2
		Day 5 TIME Reports, Social Studies Skill	**Day 5** Social Studies Skill Section 3,	**Day 5** Chapter Assessment	**Day 5** Section 2, Making Connections
		Day 6 Section 3	**Day 6** Section 3, Making Connections		**Day 6** Review
		Day 7 Section 3, Making Connections, Review	**Day 7** Review		**Day 7** Chapter Assessment
		Day 8 Chapter Assessment	**Day 8** Chapter Assessment		

Note: The following materials may be used when teaching Unit 2.
Chapter level support materials can be found on the chapter resource pages.

TEACHING TRANSPARENCIES

Political Map Transparency L2

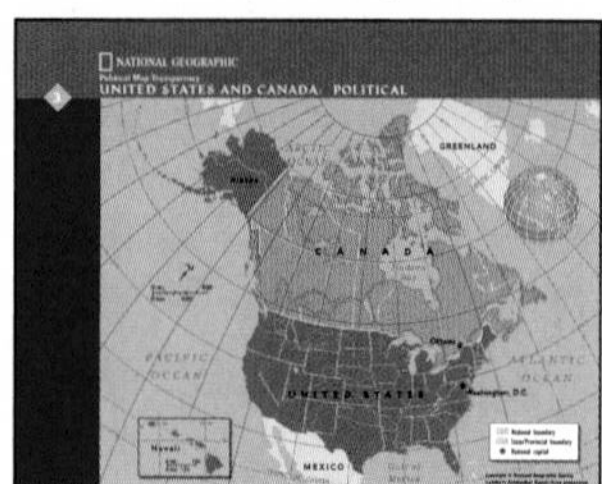

Map Overlay Transparencies L2

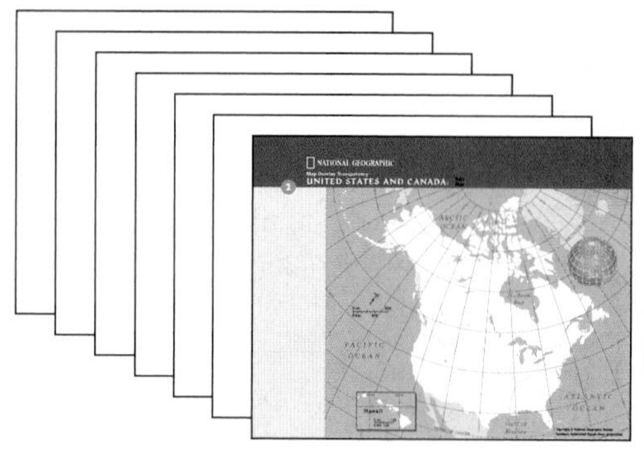

World Cultures Transparencies L2

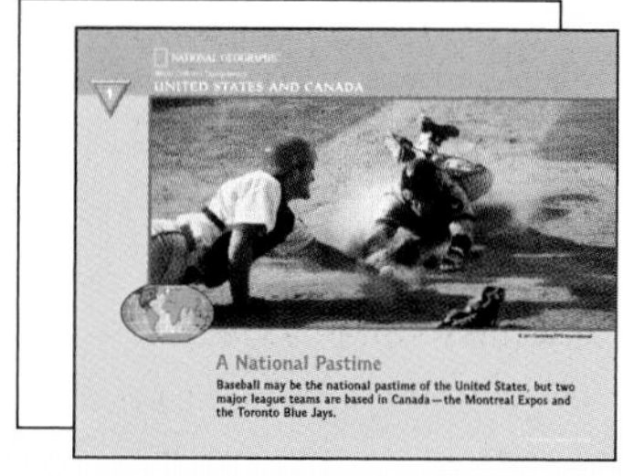

UNITED STATES AND CANADA
A National Pastime
Baseball may be the national pastime of the United States, but two major league teams are based in Canada—the Montreal Expos and the Toronto Blue Jays.

Unit 2 Resources

INTERDISCIPLINARY CONNECTIONS

World Literature Reading L2

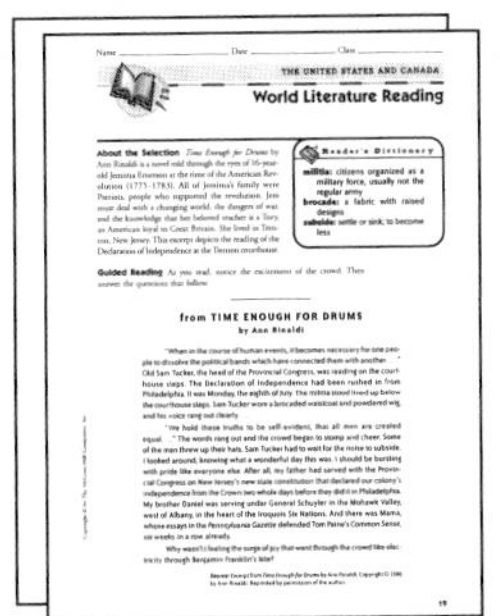

Economics and Geography Activity L2

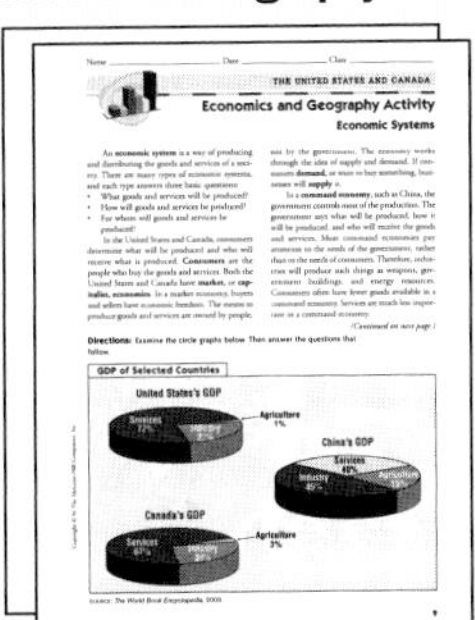

History and Geography Activity L2

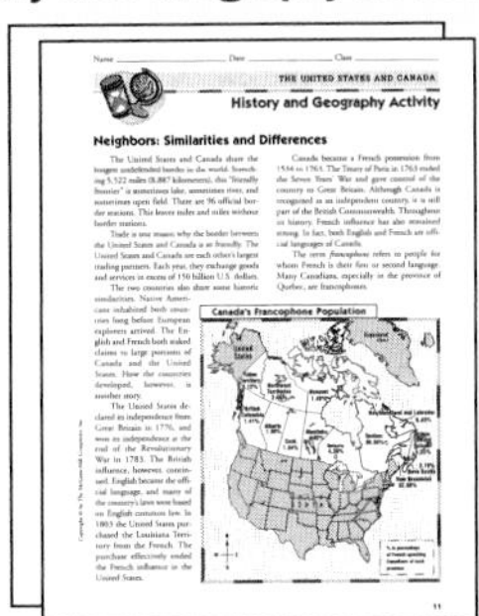

INTERDISCIPLINARY CONNECTIONS

Foods Around the World L1/ELL

World Music: A Cultural Legacy

CIVIC INVOLVEMENT

Citizenship Activity L1

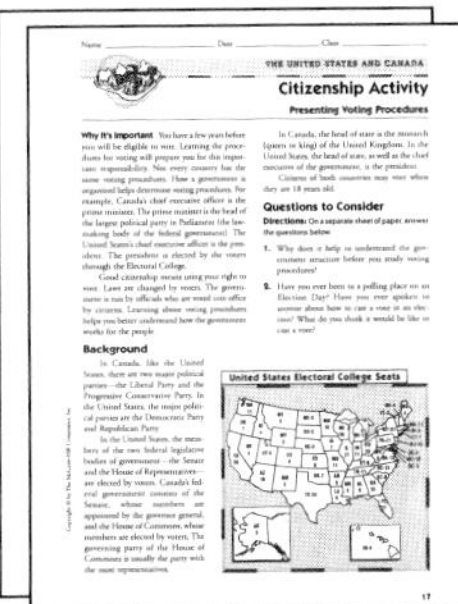

Environmental Case Study L2

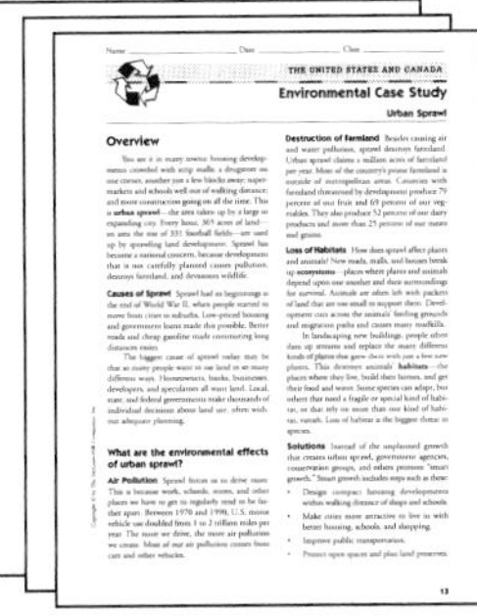

MAP AND GEOGRAPHY SKILLS

Building Geography Skills for Life

NGS Focus on Geography Literacy L2

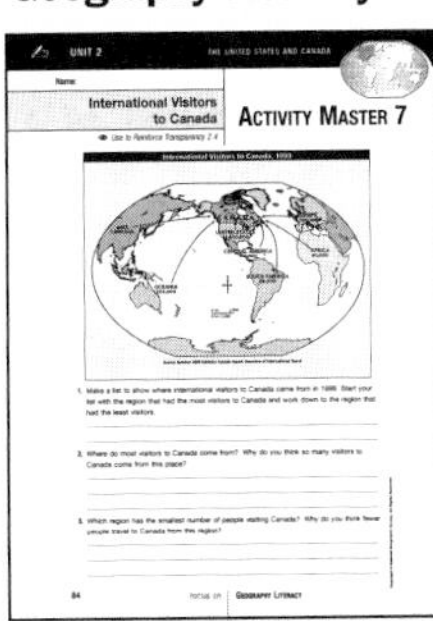

Regional Atlas Activity L2

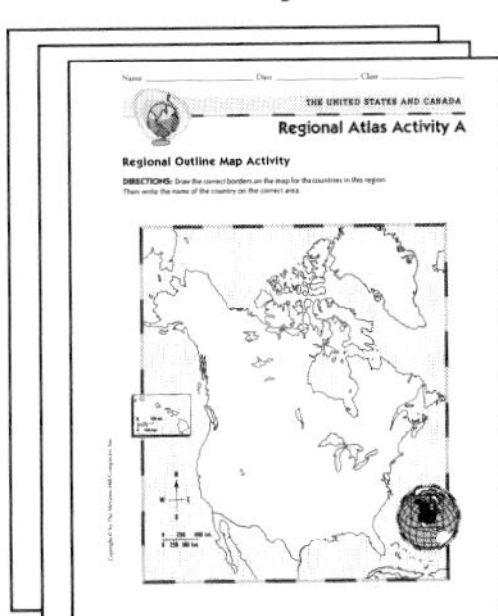

KEY TO ABILITY LEVELS

Teaching strategies have been coded for varying learning styles and abilities.

L1 **BASIC** activities for all students

L2 **AVERAGE** activities for average to above-average students

L3 **CHALLENGING** activities for above-average students

ELL **ENGLISH LANGUAGE LEARNER** activities

ASSESSMENT

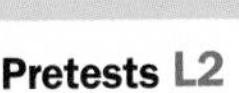

Unit Pretests L2

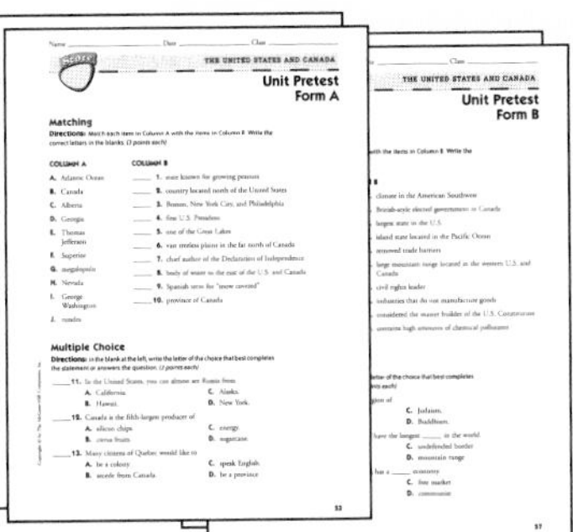

Unit Posttests L2

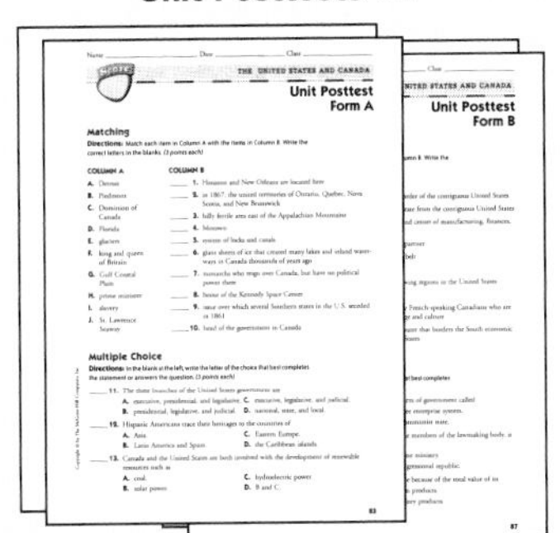

Glencoe Professional Development and Teacher Support Materials

- Reading in the Content Area for the Middle School Classroom
- Inclusion Strategies for the Middle School Social Studies Classroom
- Character Education for the Middle School Classroom
- Teaching Strategies for the Social Studies Classroom
- Reproducible Lesson Plans
- Outline Map Resource Book
- Writing Process Transparencies for Middle School
- Social Studies: Reading Strategies

Additional Unit 2 Resources

- **Timed Readings Plus in Social Studies** help students increase their reading rate and fluency while maintaining comprehension. The 400-word passages are similar to those found on state and national assessments.
- **Reading in the Content Area: Social Studies** concentrates on six essential reading skills that help students better comprehend what they read. The book includes 75 high-interest nonfiction passages written at increasing levels of difficulty.
- **Reading Fluency** helps students read smoothly, accurately, and expressively.
- **Jamestown's Reading Improvement,** by renowned reading expert Edward Fry, focuses on helping build your students' comprehension, vocabulary, and skimming and scanning skills.
- **Critical Reading Series** provides high-interest books, each written at three reading levels.

For more information about these products, see the Jamestown Education materials in the Classroom Solutions in the front of this Teacher Wraparound Edition. To order these products, call Glencoe at 1-800-334-7344.

The following videotape programs are available from Glencoe:

- **The Secret Mounds of Prehistoric America** 1-56501-681-5
- **The Vikings in North America** 1-56501-663-7
- **The Pueblo Cliffdwellers** 0-7670-0613-5
- **The Mighty Mississippi** 0-7670-1090-6
- **Lewis and Clark** 1-56501-592-4
- **Presidential Memorials—The Great American Monuments** 1-56501-641-6

To order, call Glencoe at 1-800-334-7344. To find classroom resources to accompany many of these, check:

A&E Television: www.aetv.com

The History Channel: www.historychannel.com

Reading List Generator CD-ROM — Glencoe BookLink

The Glencoe BookLink CD-ROM is a database that allows you to search more than 15,000 titles to create a customized reading list for your students.

- Reading lists can be organized by students' reading level, author, genre, theme, or area of interest.
- The database provides Degrees of Reading Power™ (DRP) and Lexile™ readability scores for all selections.
- A brief summary of each selection is included.

Leveled reading suggestions for this unit:

For students at a Grade 5 reading level:
- ***A Journey to the New World: The Diary of Remember Patience Whipple,*** by Kathryn Lasky.

For students at a Grade 6 reading level:
- ***The Native American Book of Life,*** by White Deer of Autumn.

For students at a Grade 7 reading level:
- ***Immigrant Kids,*** by Russell Freedman.

To order this CD-ROM, call Glencoe at 1-800-334-7344.

Extending the Content

Readings for the Teacher
- ***Gale Encyclopedia of Multicultural America: Primary Documents.*** Farmington Hills, Mich.: Gale Research, 2000.
- ***From Ellis Island to JFK,*** New Haven, CT: Yale University Press, 2000.

Multimedia Resources
- **Glencoe World History Primary Source Document Library CD-ROM**
- ***Canadian Treasures***, Burnaby, B.C.: Ingenuity Works. Mac/Windows CD-ROM.

Service Learning Project

Developing an Emergency Plan

Different areas of the United States are susceptible to different kinds of extreme weather or other natural hazards. The Southeast, for example, can be hit by hurricanes; the Plains states by tornadoes; the Northeast by heavy blizzards; and the West by wildfires. Have students find out what natural disasters are most likely to hit their area—and what recommendations public safety officials have for people to act responsibly and safely in such emergencies.

Content Background Notes

Use this additional information as lecture notes or discussion prompts throughout the study of Unit 2.

Chapter 4 The United States (pp. 124–155)

Unwelcome Insect Immigrants In the past, people coming to the United States have transformed the American landscape with many new plants and animals. A recent arrival, though, is turning out to be an unwelcome pest. In the 1940s, Formosan termites arrived in the South, probably on ships from Asia. Today they are eating their way through several southern cities.

They have made a particular home for themselves in New Orleans. A city official named the city "termite heaven" because of its warm temperatures and high humidity. The termites do about $300 million of damage each year. One library had about 70 million of the insects. In a New Orleans high school, the termites ate through the basketball court. They even traveled eight miles into nearby Lake Ponchartrain to eat the wooden bases of a bridge.

Damage to the Gulf Agricultural runoff from the Mississippi River basin is causing damage in the Gulf of Mexico. About 7 million tons of fertilizer is used on farms located in the vast, productive river basin each year. Some of that nitrogen-rich material washes into the river and, over time, flows out into the Gulf of Mexico. That is when the trouble starts. Algae thrive on the nitrogen, creating vast algae blooms that can spread as much as 7,000 square miles (18,130 sq. km). The algae suck up oxygen, which makes it impossible for other creatures to live. Scientists say that swimmers such as fish and shrimp can simply move elsewhere, but bottom-dwelling creatures such as starfish and clams die off in large numbers.

The New Madrid Earthquake The most powerful earthquake that ever shook the United States occurred not in California but along the Mississippi River. The New Madrid quake was actually not one but three quakes, which took place between mid-December 1811 and early February 1812. All three shocks were stronger than 8.0 on the Richter scale. Nearly 2,000 aftershocks followed. The movement was so intense that it could be felt as far away as Canada, New Orleans, and Boston.

The Missouri town of New Madrid—after which the quake is named—was the unfortunate site of the quake's epicenter. The movement dropped the town 12 feet (3.7 m), leaving it buried under the Mississippi River. The powerful forces destroyed lakes, swamps, and forests as well. But the shaking of the earth left a reminder—Reelfoot Lake, just east of the Mississippi in Tennessee. The lake, about 14 miles (23 km) long, was created by the earthquake.

The fault that caused the quake runs under the river for about 200 miles (322 km). Geologists say that the region is almost certain to experience another earthquake someday.

Chapter 5 Canada (pp. 156–173)

Canadian Pacific Rail System In the late 1800s, Canada, like the United States some decades earlier, dedicated itself to building a railroad across North America to link Atlantic coast and Pacific coast settlements. The Canadian Pacific Rail System (CPR) is the western heir to that original endeavor, and it is still running strong. Today the CPR includes about 19,000 miles (30,578 km) of track—some of which leads into the United States.

The CPR stretches from the Great Lakes across the Prairie Provinces through the Rocky Mountains to British Columbia. Work on the original line was completed in November 1885. William C. Van Horne was the manager of the CPR. Just before the line neared completion, he gave a short speech describing the work. "We were under the inspiration of a national idea," he said, "and went forward."

Quebec Perhaps the single most pressing political issue in Canada is the ongoing debate over the separation of Quebec. The separatist movement first gained prominence in the 1970s, and the separatist Parti Québécois (PQ) won a substantial majority of seats in the provincial legislature in 1976. In 1979 PQ leader René Lévesque, later prime minister of the province, made French the official language of Quebec. The next year he held a provincial referendum on the question of separation. By a nearly 60-40 margin, voters turned it down. Even a majority of French-speaking Quebecers voted no.

In the 1980s, the fortunes of the Parti Québécois declined, but the issue remained a hot topic. When Prime Minister Pierre Trudeau secured passage of the Constitution Act in 1982, giving Canada self-government, Quebec never agreed to certain aspects of the constitution. Brian Mulroney, prime minister in the late 1980s, tried to resolve this problem with the Meech Lake accord, but that agreement failed to win the required unanimous approval of all provinces because some charged it favored Quebec.

As a result, separatism in Quebec regained strength. In 1995 the province voted on a new separation referendum. This time, the vote was extremely close, with only 50.6 percent saying yes and 49.4 percent voting no. Interestingly, French speakers now approved separation by a 60-40 margin. Other groups, including English speakers and Native Americans, voted against separation by a 95-5 vote, however.

The current provincial prime minister has vowed to hold another referendum on the issue, but no date has been scheduled. For now, Quebecers are concentrating on rebuilding their economy. One strategy is to increase ties with the United States and Europe. More than 80 percent of the province's exports go to the United States, and these ties have generated nearly 300,000 new jobs.

00:00 Out of Time?

If time does not permit teaching each chapter in this unit, you may use the **Reading Essentials and Study Guide** for each chapter.

Unit Overview

The two chapters of this unit introduce students to the geography and peoples of the United States and Canada. The chapters detail the landforms, climate, economy, history, government, and lifestyles found in these countries. Before beginning to study the unit, point out to students that although these two countries have differences, they share the following features:

- large size and a wealth of resources
- varied economies and generally well-to-do people
- democratic governments and a high degree of freedom
- a diverse population

Glencoe Literature Library

As students study the unit, have them read *Bearstone* by Will Hobbs from the **Glencoe Literature Library.** The Glencoe Literature Library consists of novels and other readings for middle school students, along with study guides that offer instructional support and student activities.

Unit 2

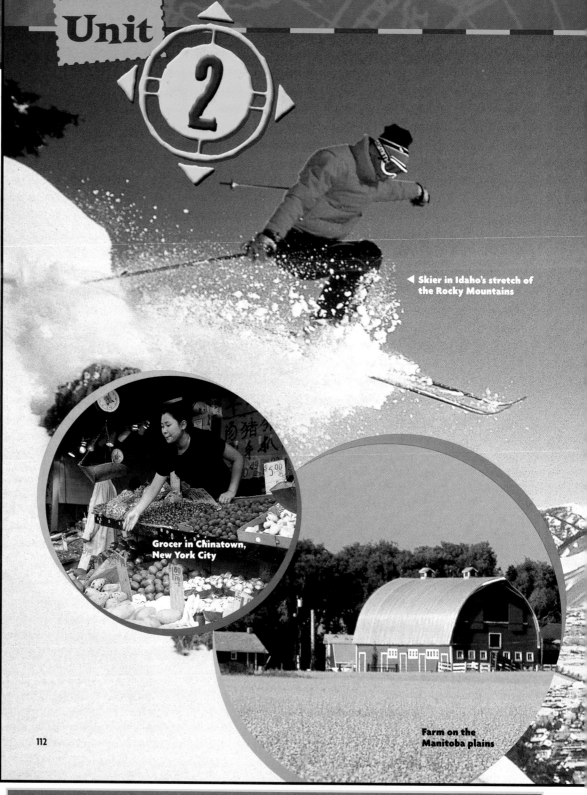

◀ Skier in Idaho's stretch of the Rocky Mountains

Grocer in Chinatown, New York City

Farm on the Manitoba plains

112

Using the Illustration

Visual Instruction The Rocky Mountains dominate the western landscapes of both the United States and Canada. The mountain system is actually a collection of about 100 distinct mountain ranges that are separated by plateaus and valleys. Though the ranges differ in their age and composition, they generally are very high, rugged, and rich in minerals. They also offer magnificent scenery and exciting opportunities for recreation. **Ask:** **How do you think having similar landforms affected the United States and Canada?** *(The similar landforms had a similar impact on development. High mountains like the Rockies, for instance, slowed communications between the western and eastern parts of both countries.)*

The United States and Canada

Which of the world's culture regions do you call home? It is probably the United States and Canada. If you look at a globe, you will see that the United States and Canada cover most of North America. These two nations share many of the same landforms, including rugged mountains in the west, rounded mountains in the east, and rolling plains in the center.

NGS ONLINE
www.nationalgeographic.com/education

113

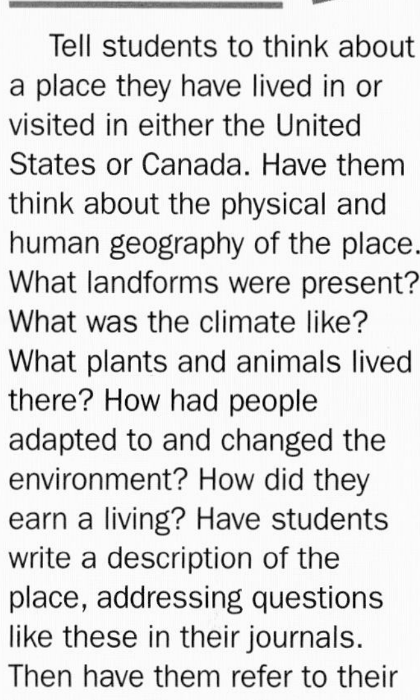

Current Events Journal

Tell students to think about a place they have lived in or visited in either the United States or Canada. Have them think about the physical and human geography of the place. What landforms were present? What was the climate like? What plants and animals lived there? How had people adapted to and changed the environment? How did they earn a living? Have students write a description of the place, addressing questions like these in their journals. Then have them refer to their journal entries as they study this unit.

NGS ONLINE
www.nationalgeographic.com/education

This online resource provides lesson plans, atlas updates, cartographic activities with interactive maps, an online map store, and geography links.

Unit Launch Activity

How Do Canada and the United States Compare? These two close neighbors enjoy many similarities—but they are different as well. **Ask:** How do the countries differ in land and climate? How are their economies both similar and different? In what ways are the people of the two countries like and unlike each other? Encourage students to keep a record of stories that they hear about the United States and Canada on television and radio or read in newspapers or magazines. Have them take notes on the content of the unit as well. When they are finished, ask for volunteers to recount their examples. Then have the class discuss the question: How are Canada and the United States similar and different?

 **EE2 Places and Regions: Standard 6**

Lesson Plan

Using the Regional Atlas
These features and activities may be used as an introduction to the unit or as teaching tools throughout the course of the unit.

Objectives

1. Outline the relative size and major physical features of the United States and Canada.
2. Identify the different climates found in the United States and Canada.
3. Summarize the main features of the economy of the United States and Canada.
4. Describe the people of the United States and Canada.

5-Minute Precheck

Ask students to name physical and cultural features that they know the United States and Canada share. If they have difficulty coming up with examples, have them look at the physical map of the region. They should be able to identify such features as the Rocky Mountains, the Great Plains, and the Great Lakes. Cultural examples include shared sports—such as baseball, football, basketball, hockey, skating, and skiing—and performers. Canadian singers Celine Dion and Alanis Morisette have gained popularity in both countries, for example.

Focus on:

The United States and Canada

SPANNING MORE THAN 7 MILLION square miles (18 million sq. km), the United States and Canada cover much of North America. These huge countries share many of the same landscapes, climates, and natural resources.

The Land

The United States and Canada make up a region bordered by the very cold Arctic Ocean in the north and bathed by the Gulf of Mexico's warm currents in the south. The western coast faces the Pacific Ocean. Eastern shores are edged by the Atlantic.

Landforms Rugged mountains are found in the western part of each country. The Pacific ranges follow the coastline. Farther inland are the massive, jagged peaks of the Rocky Mountains. Relatively young as mountains go, the Rockies stretch more than 3,000 miles (4,828 km) from Alaska to the southwestern United States.

East of the Rockies are the wide and windswept Great Plains. This gently rolling landscape covers the central part of both the United States and Canada.

The Appalachian range, much older than the Rockies, is the dominant landform in the eastern part of the region. East and south of the Appalachians' low, rounded peaks are coastal plains that end at the Atlantic shores.

Waterways The Mississippi River is the largest river system in North America. It flows through the heart of the Great Plains from near the United States–Canadian border in the north to the Gulf of Mexico in the south.

The largest lake system is the Great Lakes—Superior, Huron, Michigan, Erie, and Ontario. The waters of these connected lakes flow into the St. Lawrence River, which empties into the Atlantic Ocean. The St. Lawrence Seaway—built by the United States and Canada—provides large ships with a water route between the Great Lakes and the Atlantic Ocean. The diagram on page 159 shows you that the St. Lawrence Seaway includes a series of canals, rivers, and other inland waterways.

The Climate

This region's vast size and varied landforms help give it great diversity in climate and

Content Background

Shared Cities The United States and Canada share a 5,522-mile (8,887-km) border, the largest continuous border in the world. It is also an undefended border. In several spots, cities on both sides of the border share commerce, trade, and tourism. The two cities named Niagara Falls are one example, and the pair of Great Lakes cities named Sault Ste. Marie are another. The largest pairing, though, is Windsor, in Canada's province of Ontario, and Detroit, in the state of Michigan. The two cities sit on the opposite banks of the Detroit River and enjoy a thriving international trade. Each day thousands of people cross the two bridges and tunnels connecting these cities. Some cross to work in their jobs; others visit the sites of the neighboring city or use it as the launching point for travel in the other country.

UNIT 2

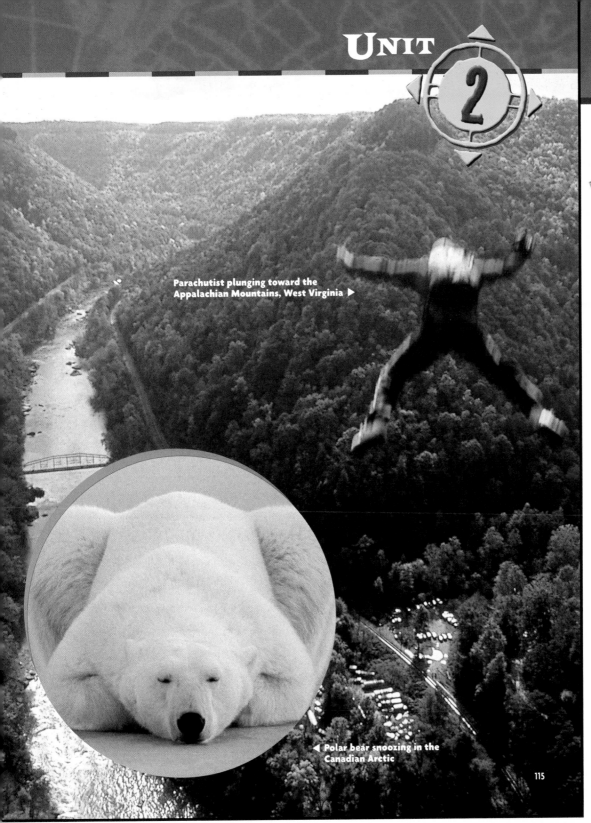

Parachutist plunging toward the Appalachian Mountains, West Virginia ▶

◀ Polar bear snoozing in the Canadian Arctic

115

Eyewitness to Geography

Quebec Samuel de Champlain was a leading figure in the French exploration and colonization of parts of North America. In this passage, he describes his first impressions of a site that would become one of the chief cities of the continent: "We came to anchor at Quebec, which is a narrow part of the said river of Canada, some three hundred paces broad. At these narrows on the north side is a very high mountain, which slopes down on both sides: all the rest is level and beautiful country, where there is good land covered with trees such as oaks, cypresses, birches, fir-trees and aspens, and also wild fruit-bearing trees, and vines; so that in my opinion, if this soil were tilled, it would be as good as ours."

Unit 2

2 TEACH

Reading Strategy

Comparing and Contrasting Have students draw two large, overlapping circles on a sheet of paper. Then have them take notes about the United States and Canada as they read the Regional Atlas. They should place information about only the United States in the left circle, information about only Canada in the right circle, and facts that apply to both countries in the center, overlapping area. L1

More About the Photos

West Virginia The Appalachian Mountains were formed from layers of rock deposits laid down by ancient rivers and seas. Erosion has worn down the softer rock layers, leaving long parallel ridges of harder rock and valleys in between. West Virginia's borders follow its mountains and river courses, so the state's boundary lines are crooked.

Polar Bears Polar bears live near Arctic Sea ice, water, islands, and continental coastlines. They travel throughout the year and feed mainly on seals.

Interviewing Have students interview an immigrant in the United States or Canada or someone whose recent ancestors came from another country. Have students prepare a list of questions in advance. Some suggested questions are: When did the person come? What country did he or she leave? Why? What was the trip to the new country like? How did the person find life different in the new country? Have students prepare an oral presentation for the rest of the class summarizing their findings. Assemble the presentations in a class booklet called "Coming to the Americas." **L2 ELL**

Cultural Kaleidoscope

North America The United States and Canada are sometimes called *Anglo America.* This is because many of the earliest European settlers in the two countries came from England. Also, in both countries English-speakers make up a majority of the population.

More About the Photo

Texas Service Industries The service sector in Texas, including film production and computer software, is the state's largest business sector and has been the engine for much of Texas's growth.

vegetation. In the far northern parts of Alaska and Canada, amid the treeless tundra and dense evergreen forests, brief summers and bitterly cold winters prevail. The Pacific coast, from southern Alaska to northern California, has a mild, wet climate. Rain clouds blowing in from the ocean are blocked by the Pacific ranges. Robbed of moisture, the land immediately east of these mountains is dry.

Hot, humid summers and cold, snowy winters are the norm in the Great Plains. This humid continental climate extends from the plains across southeastern Canada and the northeastern United States. The southeastern states, however, have much milder winters. The mildest of all are found on Florida's southern tip, the only part of the U.S. mainland that has a tropical climate.

The Economy

The United States and Canada are prosperous countries. Abundant natural resources and plenty of skilled workers have been key ingredients in creating two of the most successful economies in the world. Both countries operate under the free enterprise system, in which individuals and groups—not the government—control businesses and industries.

The region's strong economy was built on agriculture, which remains important today. Fertile soil, numerous waterways, a favorable climate, and high-tech equipment have made the United States and Canada two of the world's top food producers. Livestock, grains, vegetables, and fruits are all raised by the region's farmers.

Rich oil, coal, and natural gas deposits occur in this region. So do deposits of valuable minerals, including copper, iron ore, nickel, silver, and gold. These energy sources and raw materials have made it possible for the United States and Canada to develop large industrial economies. Today, however, people are more likely to work in offices than in factories. Service industries such as banking, communications, entertainment, insurance, and health care employ most people in the region.

The People

The United States and Canada have a rich mix of cultures. Native Americans were the nations' first inhabitants. Centuries later, settlers from Europe arrived. Immigrants from Africa, Asia, Latin America, and almost every other part of the world eventually followed. Some came looking for religious or political freedom. Some came as enslaved laborers. Some came for a fresh start in these immense lands of boundless

◀ Worker in sterile gown manufacturing computer chips in Texas

- **United States** Death Valley, in southeastern California, is the hottest and driest spot in North America. Temperatures have reached 190°F (88°C), and the average rainfall is a mere 1.66 inches (4.21 cm).
- **Canada** By contrast, parts of Canada are much colder. Areas of Baffin and Ellesmere Islands have permanent ice caps.

opportunity. Even today large numbers of immigrants continue to make the United States and Canada their new home. Every ethnic group and religion are represented in both countries. In many large cities, several different languages can be heard on the streets.

Today more than 324 million people call this region home. Thirty-two million of them live in Canada, while the remaining 292 million live in the United States. Most people live in urban areas on both sides of the border. Toronto, Vancouver, and Montreal are among Canada's largest cities. In the United States, New York City, Los Angeles, and Chicago are the most populous cities.

Inuit boys examining a Native American sculpture ▼

Data Bits

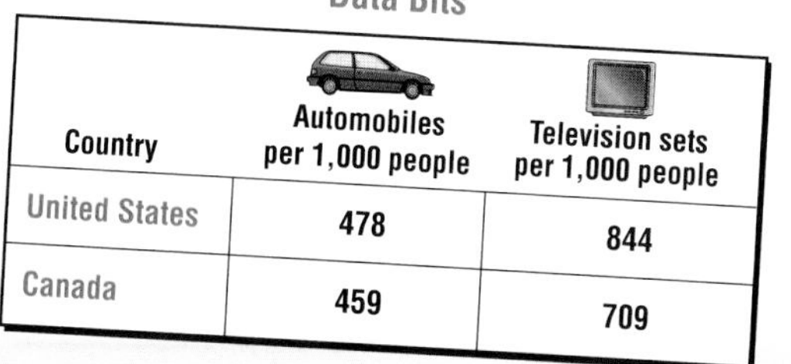

Country	Automobiles per 1,000 people	Television sets per 1,000 people
United States	478	844
Canada	459	709

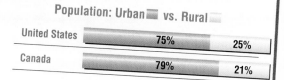

Population: Urban vs. Rural

	Urban	Rural
United States	75%	25%
Canada	79%	21%

The United States Labor Force

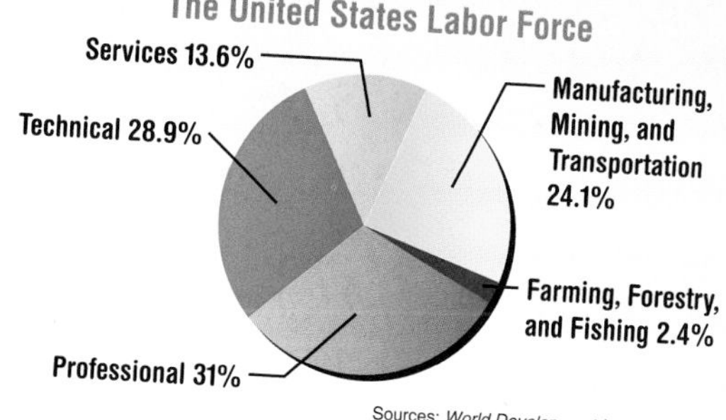

Sources: *World Development Indicators*, 2002; *The World Factbook*, 2003; *The World Almanac*, 2004.

Exploring the Region

1. **Which oceans border the region?**
2. **Why is the climate dry just east of the Pacific ranges?**
3. **What factors have helped make the region prosperous?**
4. **In which country do most of the region's people live?**

More About the Photo

Inuit Sculptures Inuit artists from the Canadian Arctic work with two main types of stone to create their sculptures—serpentine and steatite. These stones come in a variety of colors.

3 ASSESS

Assign the Exploring the Region questions as homework or as an in-class activity.

Reteach
Have students create a chart with four column headings—"Land," "Climate," "Economy," and "People." Have them write two key facts about the United States and Canada under each column heading.

Enrich
Have students research one of the cities mentioned under the subheading The People. Have them prepare an annotated map of the city, describing its main sites and key features.

4 CLOSE

Give students an outline map of the United States and Canada. Have them show the boundaries dividing the two countries. Then have them fill in the major geographic features and cities mentioned in the Regional Atlas.

Answers to Exploring the Region

1. the Arctic Ocean in the north, Atlantic Ocean on the east, and Pacific Ocean on the west
2. because the mountains block rain clouds moving in from the Pacific Ocean
3. abundant natural resources and plenty of skilled workers
4. the United States

LESSON PLAN

Using the Regional Atlas

These features and activities may be used as an introduction to the unit or as teaching tools throughout the course of the unit.

Focus

Objectives

1. Describe the relative size and location of the United States and Canada.
2. Name the major physical features of the United States and Canada.
3. Identify the smaller units into which the United States and Canada are divided.
4. Compare the populations of the United States and Canada.

5-Minute Precheck

Have students look at the political map and describe the locations of Washington, D.C., and Ottawa. *(between Maryland and Virginia; in eastern Ontario)*

More About the Profile

In order to show a variety of physical features, this cross section begins at Vancouver Island and ends at Nova Scotia.

NATIONAL GEOGRAPHIC **REGIONAL ATLAS**

The United States and Canada

Physical

118

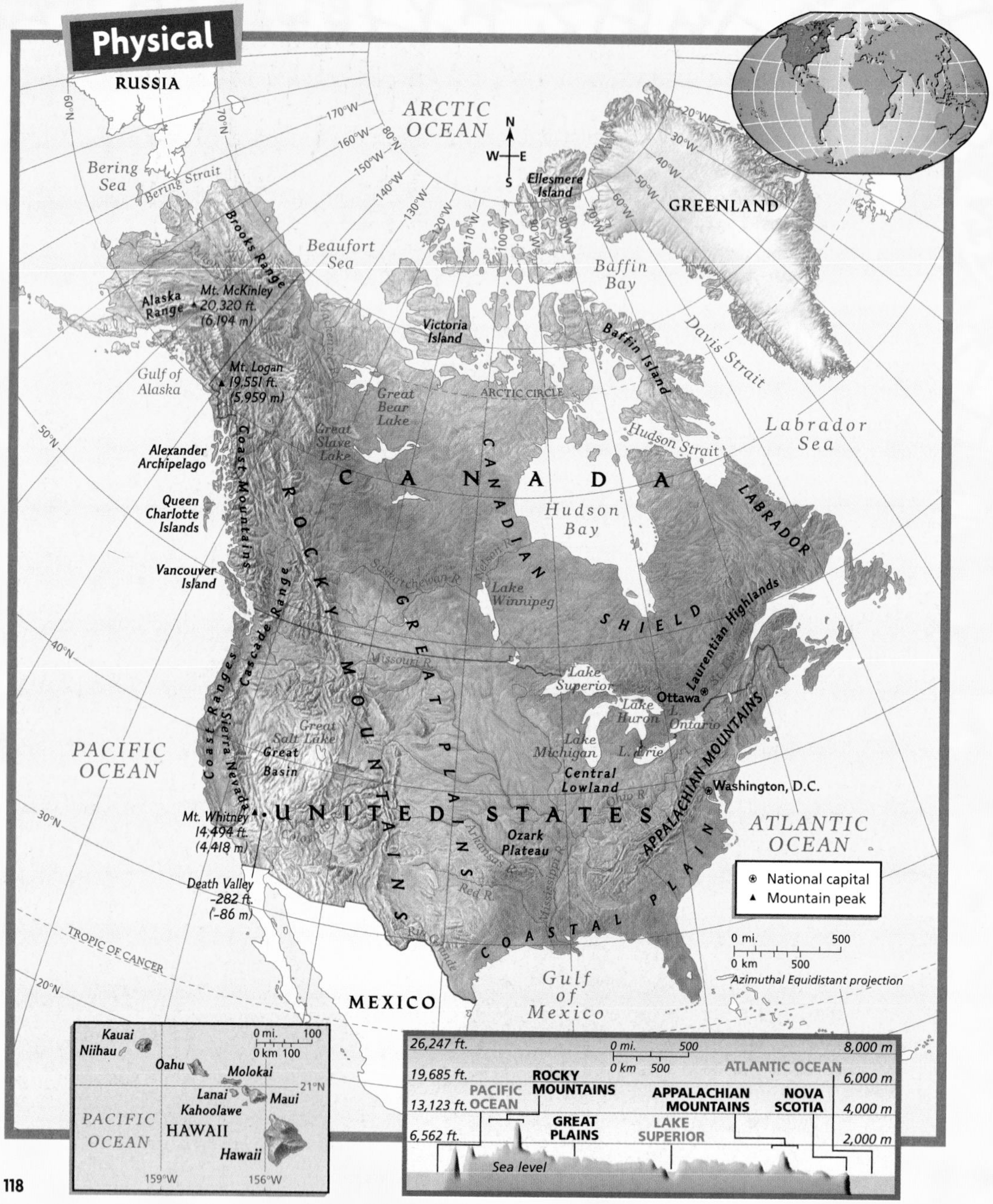

Regional Atlas Activity

Class Challenge Have students use atlases and other resources to plan a cross-country trip through the United States or Canada. Direct them to choose a definite starting point and destination and to plot the route between the two points. (Alternatively, you could assign starting and ending points to students.) Have them calculate the approximate distance of the journey and list specific points of interest along the way. Allow time for students to share their itineraries. **L1 ELL**

EE1 The World in Spatial Terms: Standard 1

UNIT 2

Political

RUSSIA
ARCTIC OCEAN
Bering Sea
Chukchi Sea
Ellesmere Island
GREENLAND (KALAALLIT NUNAAT) Den.
Beaufort Sea
Banks Island
Baffin Bay
ALASKA
Victoria Island
Baffin Island
Davis Strait
Gulf of Alaska
YUKON TERRITORY
NORTHWEST TERRITORIES
NUNAVUT
ARCTIC CIRCLE
Southampton Island
Hudson Strait
Labrador Sea
BRITISH COLUMBIA
ALBERTA
SASKATCHEWAN
MANITOBA
Hudson Bay
NEWFOUNDLAND and LABRADOR
QUEBEC
ONTARIO
Vancouver Island
P.E.I.
N.B.
NOVA SCOTIA
ME.
Ottawa
WASH.
OREGON
IDAHO
MONT.
N. DAK.
MINN.
WIS.
MICHIGAN
VT.
N.H.
MASS.
R.I.
CONN.
N.Y.
WYO.
S. DAK.
NEBR.
IOWA
PA.
N.J.
DEL.
MD.
Washington, D.C.
PACIFIC OCEAN
CALIFORNIA
NEVADA
UTAH
COLO.
KANSAS
ILL.
IND.
OHIO
W. VA.
VA.
UNITED STATES
MO.
KY.
ATLANTIC OCEAN
ARIZ.
NEW MEXICO
OKLA.
ARK.
TENN.
N.C.
S.C.
MISS.
ALA.
GA.
TEXAS
LA.
FLORIDA
ROCKY MOUNTAINS
MEXICO
Gulf of Mexico
TROPIC OF CANCER
HAWAII
PACIFIC OCEAN
⊛ National capital
Azimuthal Equidistant projection

MAP STUDY

1. What physical region covers much of the central part of the United States and Canada?
2. What is the capital of Canada?

Unit 2
Regional Atlas

TEACH

Making Comparisons Have the students look at the elevation profile of North America. **Ask: Which is higher, the Rocky or Appalachian Mountains?** *(the Rocky Mountains)* **Between what two landforms is Lake Superior located?** *(the Great Plains and Appalachian Mountains)* **L1**

Cultural Kaleidoscope

Canada Canadians call Alberta, Saskatchewan, and Manitoba, which are located on the Great Plains, the *Prairie Provinces. Prairie* is a French word that means "grassy field" or "meadow."

MAP STUDY

Answers

1. the Great Plains
2. Ottawa

Skills Practice

Which state in the United States does not touch either Canada or another state? *(Hawaii)* **What country borders the United States on the south?** *(Mexico)*

Regional Atlas Activity

Interpreting Maps Give students some time to study the physical features of the United States and Canada shown on the map. Then have them work in small groups to write five location questions based on the physical features. Offer the following question as an example: What mountain range extends through the western region of both the United States and Canada? *(Rocky Mountains)* Encourage groups to challenge one another with their questions. **L2**

EE1 The World in Spatial Terms: Standard 3

NATIONAL GEOGRAPHIC

REGIONAL ATLAS

The United States and Canada

Food Production

Arctic Ocean
Bering Sea
Beaufort Sea
Baffin Bay
Gulf of Alaska
Hudson Bay
Labrador Sea
Pacific Ocean
Gulf of Mexico
Atlantic Ocean
Arctic Circle
Tropic of Cancer
180°
160°W
140°W
120°W
100°W
80°W
60°W
80°N
70°N
60°N
50°N
40°N
30°N

Cattle
Citrus
Fruits
Hogs
Peanuts
Potatoes
Sugar
Corn
Rice
Wheat

0 mi. 600
0 km 600
Azimuthal Equidistant projection

Hawaii
Pacific Ocean
0 mi. 100
0 km 100
21°N
159°W
156°W

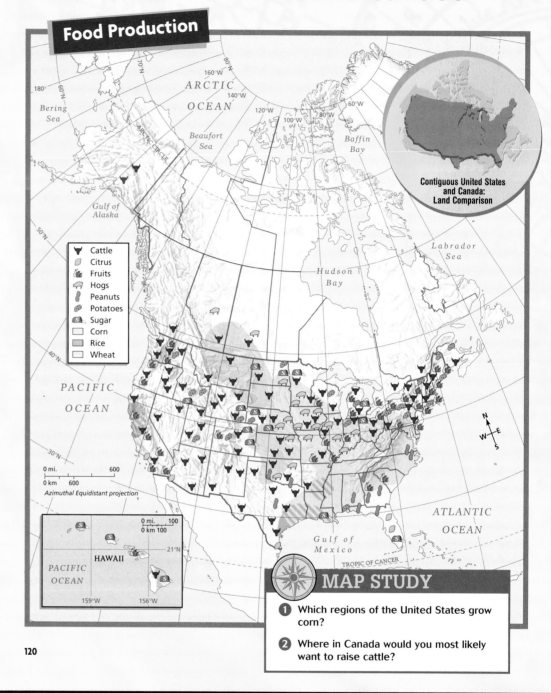

Contiguous United States and Canada: Land Comparison

N
W
E
S

MAP STUDY

1. Which regions of the United States grow corn?
2. Where in Canada would you most likely want to raise cattle?

120

Did You Know

The Reversing Falls of St. John is a waterfall near the mouth of the St. John River in New Brunswick, Canada. Twice each day, the high tides from the Bay of Fundy force water to flow upstream—up the falls.

MAP STUDY

Answers

1. mainly the central-eastern part of the country
2. eastern Ontario or southern British Columbia

Skills Practice

Citrus fruits are mainly grown in Florida, the southern tip of Texas, and in southern California. **What kind of climate do those locations suggest these crops need?** *(warm)*

THE HUMANITIES CONNECTION

World Music: A Cultural Legacy

World Art and Architecture Transparencies

Focus on World Art Prints

Regional Atlas Activity

Research Activity Point out that in earlier times, people in different regions of Canada and the United States developed particular styles of cooking that combined the traditions of the people who settled there with the foods available in that region due to its physical geography and climate. Have students choose a region of either country and generate a list of dishes typical of that region. You might ask them to devise a menu. Have them annotate their list or menu to explain whether the different dishes are based on the culture of those who settled there or the local availability of ingredients. L2

EE6 The Uses of Geography: Standard 17

UNIT 2

Geo Extremes

① HIGHEST POINT
Mount McKinley (Alaska)
20,320 ft. (6,194 m) high

② LOWEST POINT
Death Valley (California)
282 ft. (86 m)
below sea level

③ LONGEST RIVER
Mississippi-Missouri
(United States)
3,710 mi. (5,971 km) long

④ LARGEST LAKE
Lake Superior
31,700 sq. mi.
(82,103 sq. km)

⑤ LARGEST CANYON
Grand Canyon (Arizona)
277 mi. (446 km) long
1 mi. (1.6 km) deep

⑥ GREATEST TIDES
Bay of Fundy (Nova Scotia)
52 ft. (16 m)

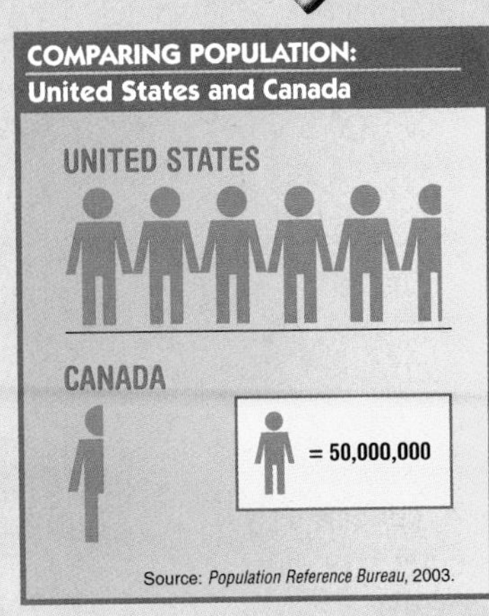

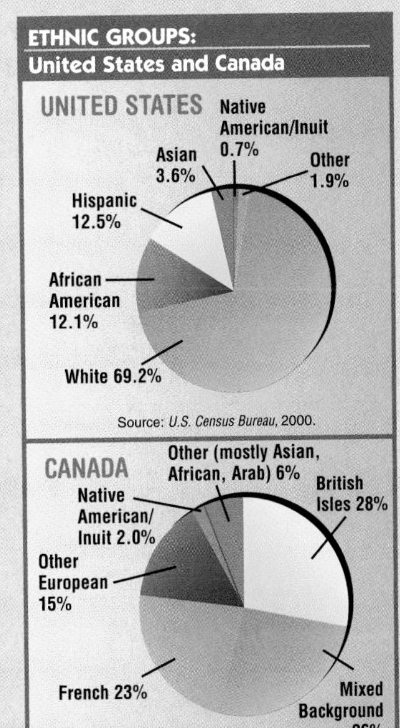

GRAPHIC STUDY

1. In what area of the United States do you find both the lowest point and largest canyon?
2. How does the percentage of Native American/Inuit population in the United States compare with their percentage of the population in Canada?

Interdisciplinary Connections

Economics Some of the world's largest deposits of silver and zinc lie in the Canadian Shield. Intense mining and smelting in the area resulted in such a bleak terrain that U.S. astronauts once trained there before the landscape was restored.

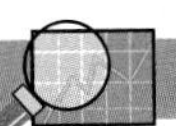

GRAPHIC STUDY

Answers

1. the Southwest
2. The percentage of Native Americans and Inuit in Canada is more than double the percentage of Native Americans and Inuit in the United States.

Skills Practice
About how many people live in the United States? *(290 million)*

Regional Atlas Activity

Analyzing Maps Have students examine the food production map. Then have them re-read the information on climate. **Ask:** Why do you think large areas of northern Canada do not show food production taking place? *(because the climate there is too harsh for raising food)* Why do you think there are more symbols for food production in the eastern and central regions of the United States than in the west? *(Much of the western region is too mountainous or too dry for food production.)* **L2**

EE5 Environment and Society: Standard 16

Making Inferences Point out to students that both Canada and the United States are divided into many smaller political units called states, provinces, or territories. **Ask:** **What is the significance of the fact that each of these smaller units has a capital?** *(They each have a government.)* **L2**

TRAVEL GUIDE 

The Cajun people of Louisiana are the descendants of French Canadians who were driven from their homes in an area called Acadia—now the province of Nova Scotia—by the British after the French and Indian War. *Cajun* is a slurred version of the word *Acadian.* The Cajuns enjoy many spicy dishes. Favorites include jambalaya, a dish that includes rice, ham, sausage, chicken, and seafood; and gumbo, a thick soup of vegetables and meat or seafood.

Did You Know 

On the shores of Canada's Georgian Bay are strange-looking landforms called flowerpots. Wind and water have worn away the bases of these tall rock formations. What remains are wide tops covered with flowers, plants, and shrubs.

NATIONAL GEOGRAPHIC **REGIONAL ATLAS**

Country Profiles

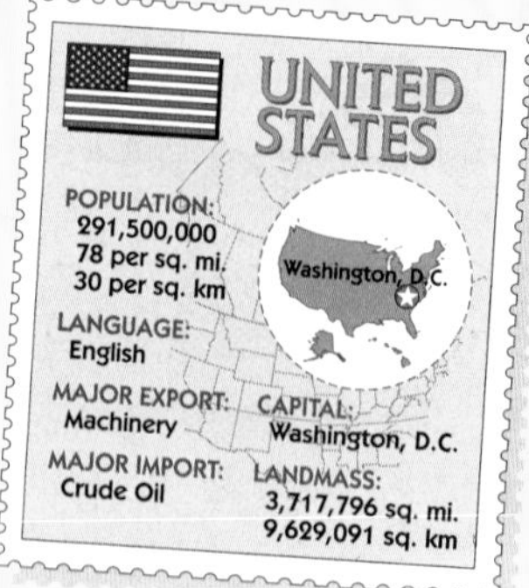

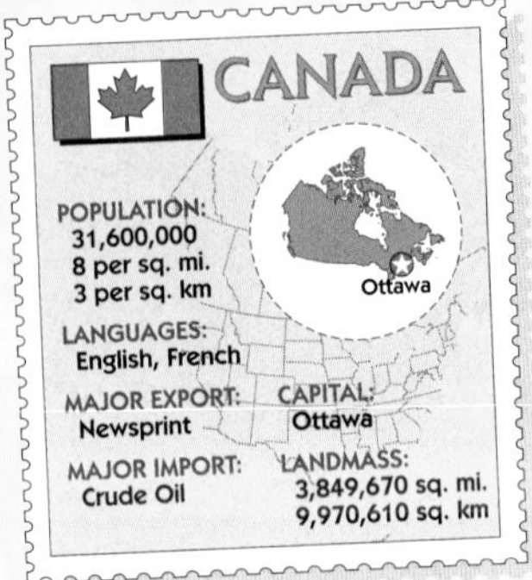

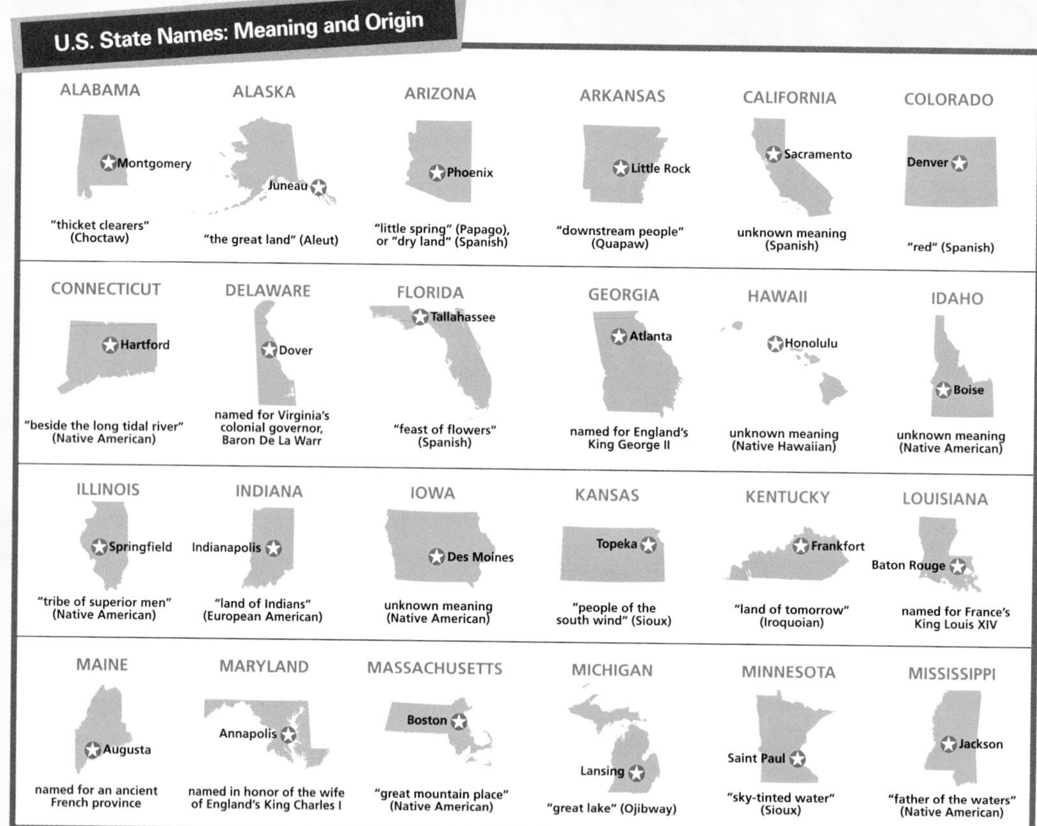

Countries, states, provinces, and flags not drawn to scale

Regional Atlas Activity

Analyzing Maps Have students study the state and provincial borders shown on the political map. **Ask:** **What patterns do you see?** *(Some are straight lines, and some are very ragged.)* **What geographical tool does it seem the straight lines are based on?** *(lines of latitude and longitude)* **On what do the ragged lines seem to be based?** *(Some are based on bodies of water forming coasts, while others seem to follow the courses of rivers.)* **L2**

EE1 The World in Spatial Terms: Standard 1

For more information on the U.S. and Canada, refer to the Nations of the World Data Bank in the Appendix.

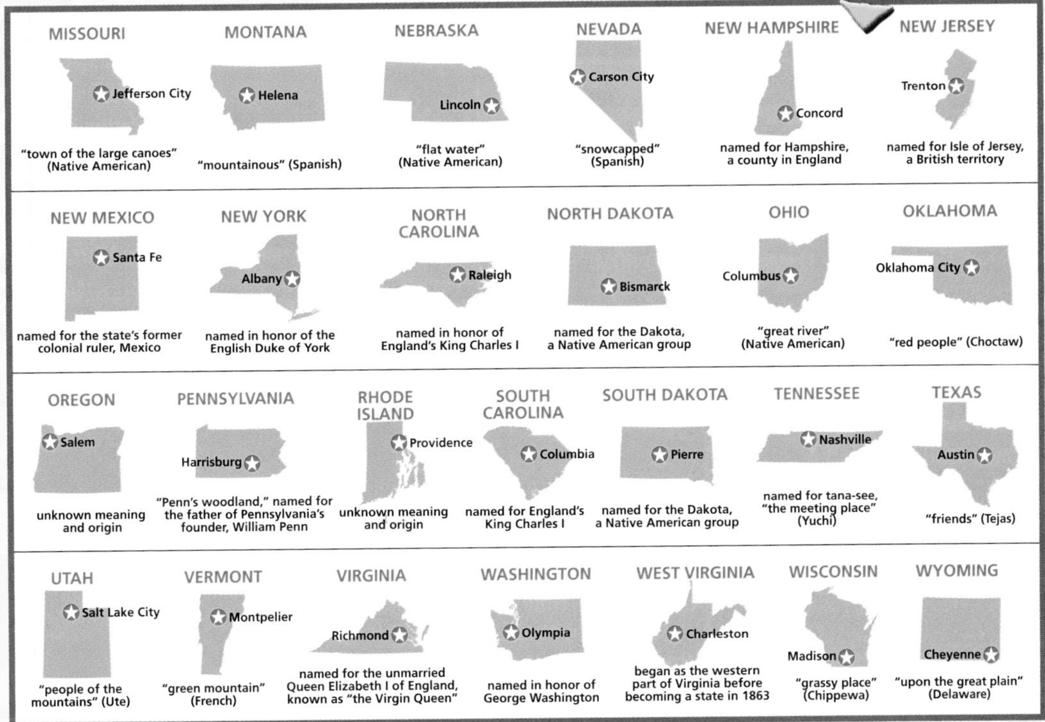

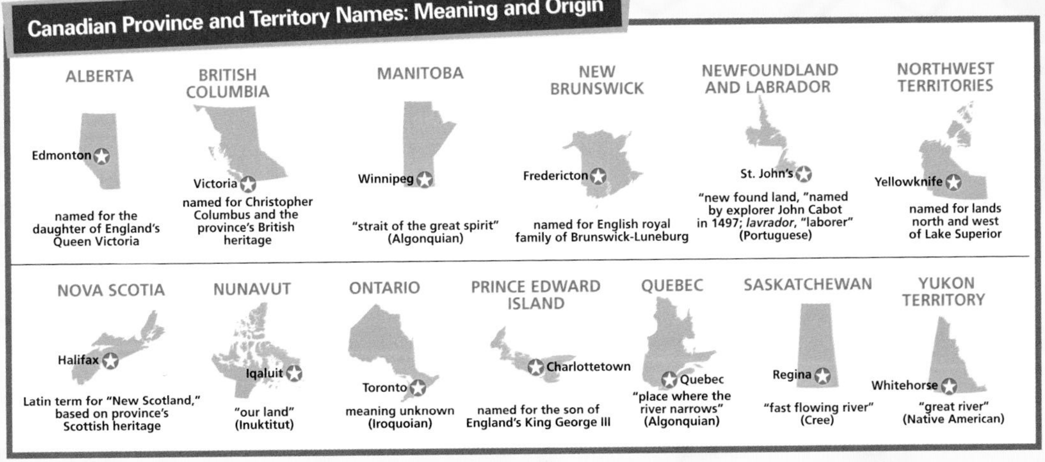

Canadian Province and Territory Names: Meaning and Origin
ALBERTA
Edmonton
named for the daughter of England's Queen Victoria
BRITISH COLUMBIA
Victoria
named for Christopher Columbus and the province's British heritage
MANITOBA
Winnipeg
"strait of the great spirit" (Algonquian)
NEW BRUNSWICK
Fredericton
named for English royal family of Brunswick-Luneburg
NEWFOUNDLAND AND LABRADOR
St. John's
"new found land, "named by explorer John Cabot in 1497; lavrador, "laborer" (Portuguese)
NORTHWEST TERRITORIES
Yellowknife
named for lands north and west of Lake Superior
NOVA SCOTIA
Halifax
Latin term for "New Scotland," based on province's Scottish heritage
NUNAVUT
Iqaluit
"our land" (Inuktitut)
ONTARIO
Toronto
meaning unknown (Iroquoian)
PRINCE EDWARD ISLAND
Charlottetown
named for the son of England's King George III
QUEBEC
Quebec
"place where the river narrows" (Algonquian)
SASKATCHEWAN
Regina
"fast flowing river" (Cree)
YUKON TERRITORY
Whitehorse
"great river" (Native American)

Regional Atlas Activity

Name Origins Have students review the explanations of the names of the states and provinces. **Ask:** **What do these names tell you about the people who lived in these areas? What varieties of influences are evident from the state and province names?** *(Native Americans, Pacific Islanders, and people from such different European places as the British Isles, France, and Spain all settled in these areas. Their influence is shown in the different names.)* If students are having difficulty finding the answers, suggest that they create a chart with several columns. In each column, they should list names that come from the same general group (such as Native Americans or British Isles). L3

EE6 The Uses of Geography: Standard 17

3 ASSESS

Organize students into groups. Have groups use the maps and graphs from the Regional Atlas to quiz one another on the geography of the United States and Canada.

Reteach

Give students an outline map of the United States and Canada. Have them complete the map by writing in the names of major physical features, including

- Mountains (Alaska Range, Brooks Range, Coast Ranges, Rocky Mountains, Cascade Range, Sierra Nevada, Appalachian Mountains)
- Highlands (Ozark Plateau)
- Other (Great Plains, Great Basin, Central Lowland, Canadian Shield)
- Bodies of water (Arctic, Atlantic, and Pacific Oceans; Gulf of Mexico; Lakes Superior, Michigan, Huron, Erie, Ontario; Mississippi, Missouri, and St. Lawrence Rivers)

Enrich

Have students research one of the states or provinces in these two countries. Then have them prepare a poster advertising the state's or province's attractions.

4 CLOSE

Summarizing Have students write a brief paragraph in which they summarize the physical and human characteristics of either country.

Chapter 4 Resources

Note: The following materials may be used when teaching Chapter 4.
Section level support materials are shown at point of use in the margins of the Teacher Wraparound Edition.

Timesaving Tools

TeacherWorks™ All-In-One Planner and Resource Center

- **Interactive Teacher Edition** See the **Interactive Teacher Edition** CD-ROM to electronically integrate your Teacher Wraparound Edition and blackline masters.
- **Interactive Lesson Planner** Organize your week, month, semester, or year with all the lesson helps you need. The **Interactive Lesson Planner** CD-ROM contains all Chapter 4 resources.

Use Glencoe's **Presentation Plus!** multimedia teacher tool to easily present dynamic lessons that visually excite your students. Using Microsoft PowerPoint® you can customize the presentations to create your own personalized lessons.

TEACHING TRANSPARENCIES

Graphic Organizer Transparency 3 L2

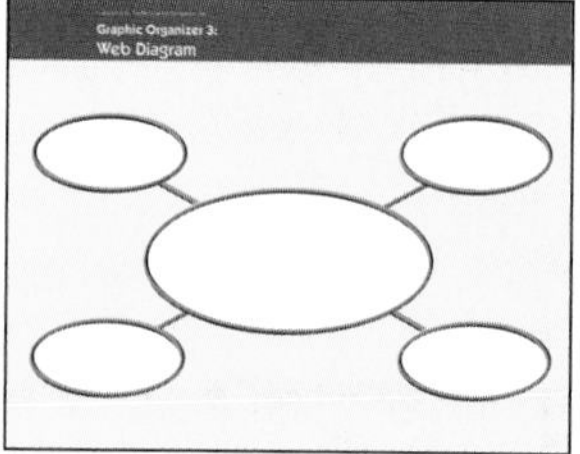

In-text Map Transparency L1

FOLDABLES™ Study Organizer

Dinah Zike's Foldables

Foldables are three-dimensional, interactive graphic organizers that help students practice basic writing skills, review key vocabulary terms, and identify main ideas. Additional chapter activities can be found in the ***Reading and Study Skills Foldables*** booklet.

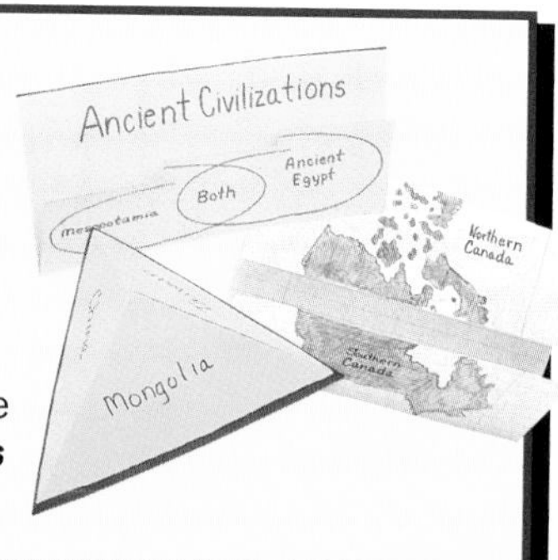

MAP AND GEOGRAPHY SKILLS

Chapter Map Activity L2

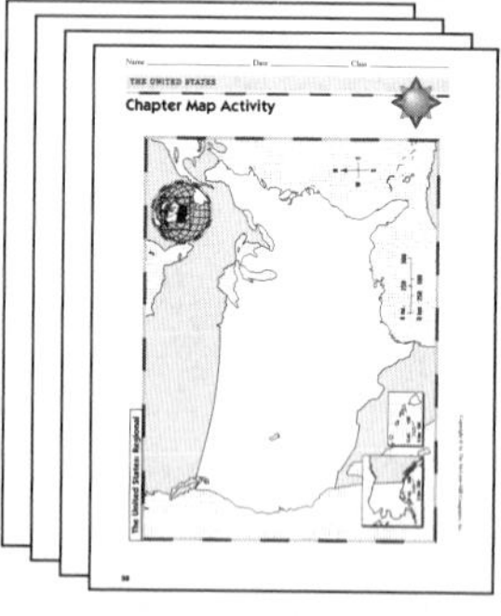

GeoLab Activity L2

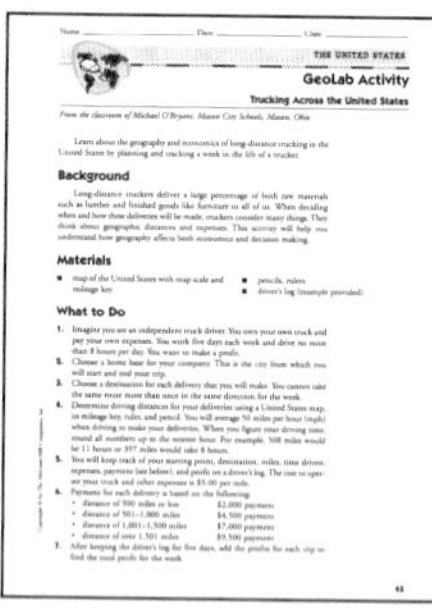

READING SUPPORT

Vocabulary Activity L1

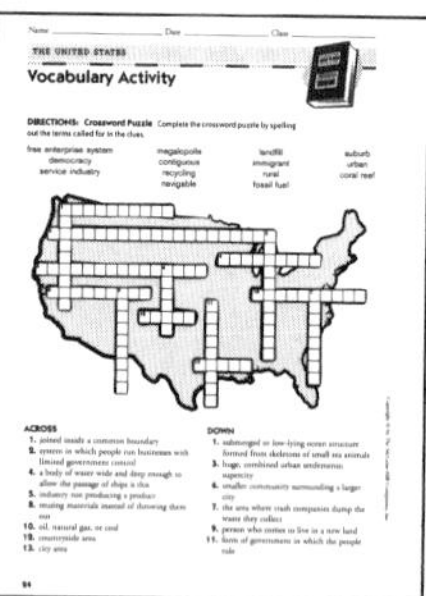

Workbook Activity L1

Reading and Writing Skills Activity L1/ELL

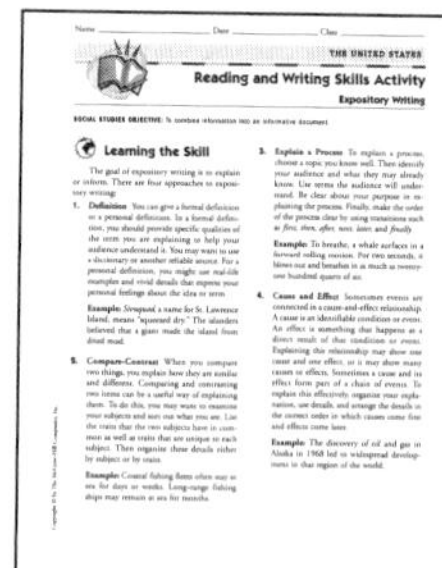

DIFFERENTIATED INSTRUCTION

Use these review and reinforcement materials to help less-proficient readers, English learners, and gifted and talented students.

Reteaching Activity L1

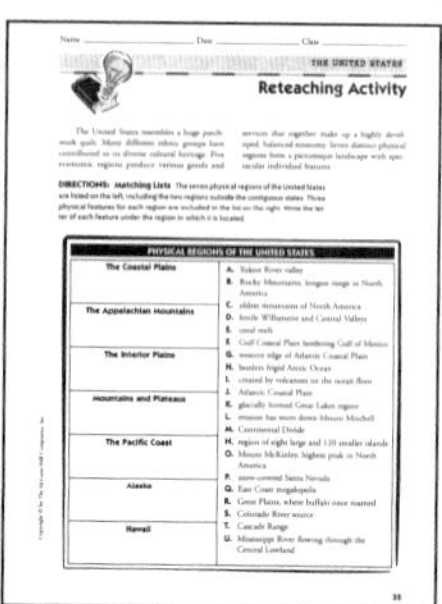

Chapter Skills Review L2

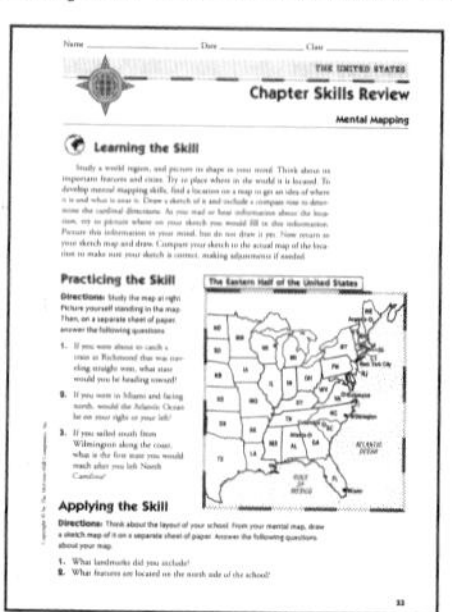

Cooperative Learning Activity L1/ELL

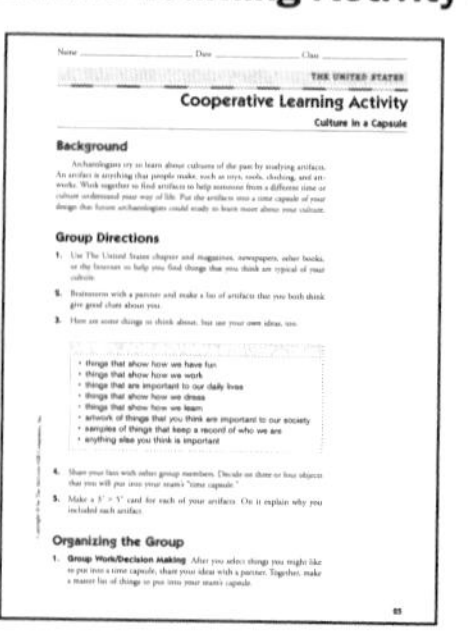

Enrichment Activity L3

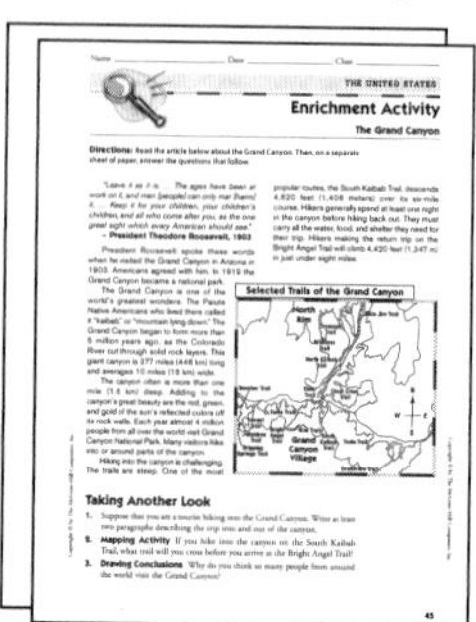

ASSESSMENT

Chapter Test, Form A L2

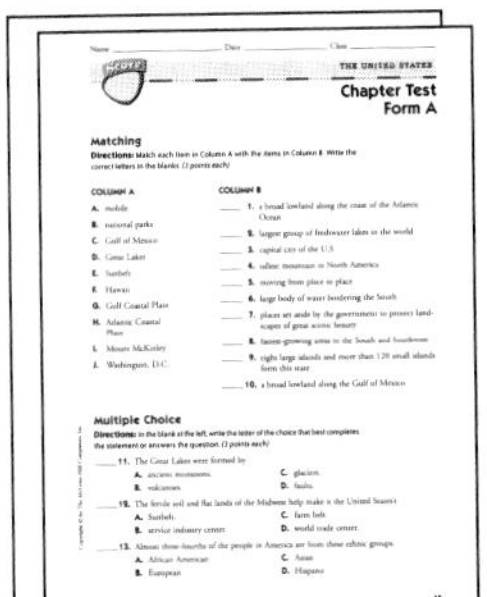

Chapter Test, Form B L2

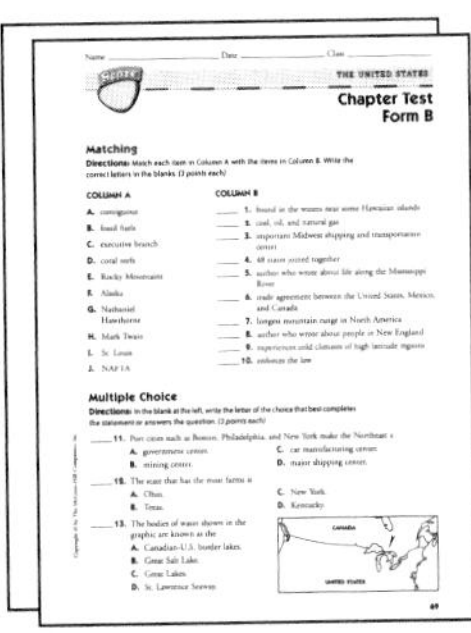

Performance Assessment Activity L1/ELL

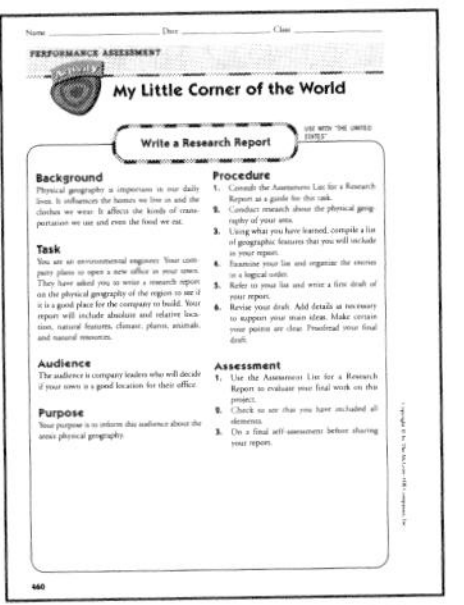

ExamView® Pro Testmaker CD-ROM

STANDARDIZED ASSESSMENT SKILLS

GLENCOE'S ASSESSMENT ADVANTAGE

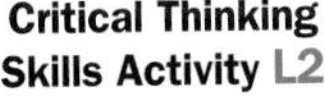

Critical Thinking Skills Activity L2

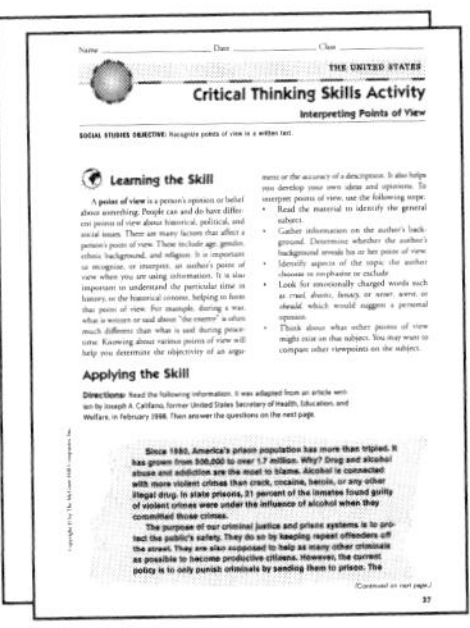

Map and Graph Skills Activity L2

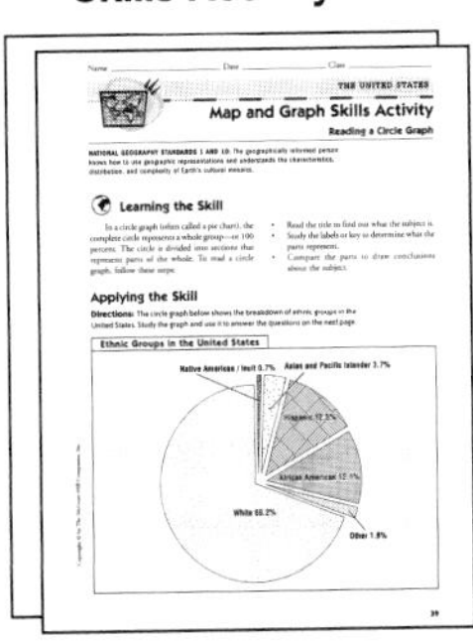

Standardized Test Skills Practice Workbook Activity L2

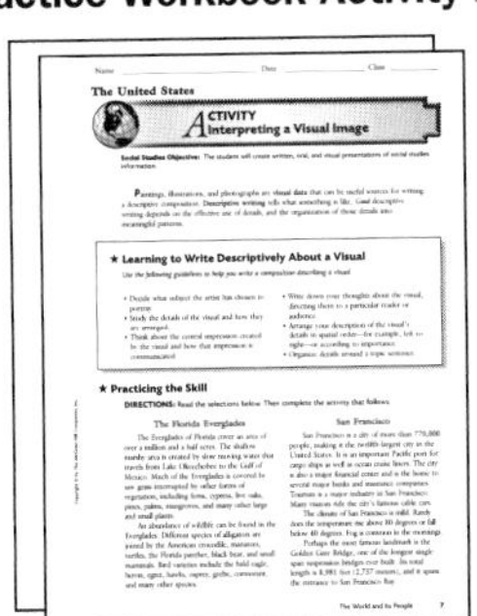

HOME INVOLVEMENT

Take-Home Review Activity L1

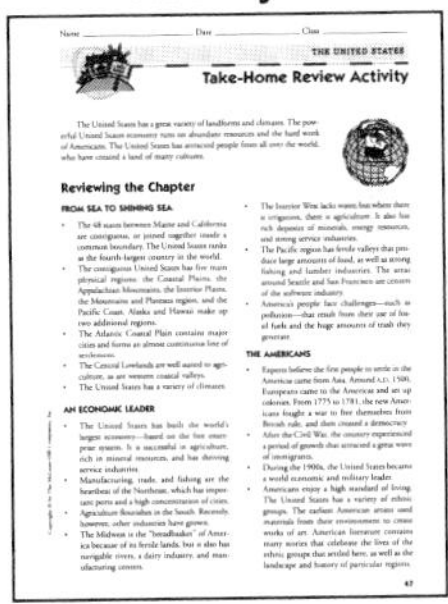

MULTIMEDIA

- **National Geographic's The World and Its People**
- **MindJogger Videoquiz**
- **Vocabulary PuzzleMaker CD-ROM**
- **Interactive Tutor Self-Assessment CD-ROM**
- **ExamView® Pro Testmaker CD-ROM**
- **TeacherWorks CD-ROM**
- **StudentWorks CD-ROM**
- **Skillbuilder Interactive Workbook CD-ROM, Level 1**
- **Presentation Plus! CD-ROM**
- **Audio Program**

SPANISH RESOURCES

The following Spanish language materials are available in the Spanish Resources binder:

- **Spanish Summaries**
- **Spanish Vocabulary Activities**
- **Spanish Guided Reading Activities**
- **Spanish Quizzes and Tests**
- **Spanish Take-Home Review Activities**
- **Spanish Reteaching Activities**

Meeting National Standards

Geography for Life

The following standards are covered in Chapter 4:

Section 1	**EE1 The World in Spatial Terms: Standards 1, 3**
	EE2 Places and Regions: Standards 4, 5
Section 2	**EE4 Human Systems: Standards 11, 12, 13**
	EE5 Environment and Society: Standards 14, 16
Section 3	**EE4 Human Systems: Standards 11, 12, 13**
	EE5 Environment and Society: Standards 14, 16

State and Local Objectives

Chapter 4 Planning Guide

SECTION RESOURCES

Daily Objectives	Reproducible Resources	Multimedia Resources
Section 1 **From Sea to Shining Sea** 1. Identify the landforms that are found in the United States. 2. Contrast the climates of different areas of the United States.	Reproducible Lesson Plan Daily Lecture and Discussion Notes Note-taking Guide Guided Reading Activity* Reading Essentials and Study Guide* Section Quiz*	Daily Focus Skills Transparency GeoQuiz Transparency Vocabulary PuzzleMaker CD-ROM Interactive Tutor Self-Assessment CD-ROM ExamView® Pro Testmaker CD-ROM Presentation Plus! CD-ROM
Section 2 **An Economic Leader** 1. Explain why the U.S. has the world's leading economy. 2. Identify how people in the United States earn their livings. 3. Describe the challenges facing the United States.	Reproducible Lesson Plan Daily Lecture and Discussion Notes Note-taking Guide Guided Reading Activity* Reading Essentials and Study Guide* Section Quiz*	Daily Focus Skills Transparency GeoQuiz Transparency Vocabulary PuzzleMaker CD-ROM Interactive Tutor Self-Assessment CD-ROM ExamView® Pro Testmaker CD-ROM Presentation Plus! CD-ROM
Section 3 **The Americans** 1. Describe how the United States changed throughout its history. 2. Explain what form of government the United States has. 3. Identify what groups make up the American people. 4. Discuss what has influenced American culture.	Reproducible Lesson Plan Daily Lecture and Discussion Notes Note-taking Guide Guided Reading Activity* Reading Essentials and Study Guide* Section Quiz*	Daily Focus Skills Transparency In-text Map Transparency Vocabulary PuzzleMaker CD-ROM Interactive Tutor Self-Assessment CD-ROM ExamView® Pro Testmaker CD-ROM Presentation Plus! CD-ROM MindJogger Videoquiz

00:00 **Out of Time?** Assign the **Reading Essentials and Study Guide*** for this chapter.

*Also available in Spanish

KEY TO ABILITY LEVELS

Teaching strategies have been coded for varying learning styles and abilities.

- L1 **BASIC** activities for all students
- L2 **AVERAGE** activities for average to above-average students
- L3 **CHALLENGING** activities for above-average students
- ELL **ENGLISH LANGUAGE LEARNER** activities

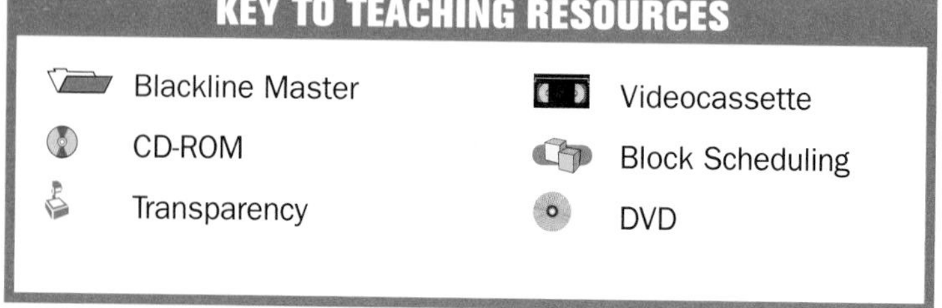

Sister Cities

Connie Dunn
Mulberry High School
Mulberry, Arkansas

Have your students learn and compare information about their hometown to other towns in the United States with the same name. By using an atlas or the Internet, find "your" city in other states. Have students contact the chamber of commerce or, if possible, a geography class in each of these other cities. Ask students to find out information such as population data, date of settlement, and main economic activities. They may also want to compare fun information such as school colors and team names. The information can be compiled to create a "HOMETOWN, U.S.A." booklet.

Meeting Special Needs

In addition to the Differentiated Instruction strategies found in each section, the following resources are also suitable for your special needs students:

- ***ExamView® Pro Testmaker CD-ROM*** allows teachers to tailor tests by reducing answer choices.
- The ***Audio Program*** includes the entire narrative of the student edition so that less-proficient readers can listen to the words as they read them.
- The ***Reading Essentials and Study Guide*** provides the same content as the student edition but is written two grade levels below the textbook.
- ***Guided Reading Activities*** give less-proficient readers point-by-point instructions to increase comprehension as they read each textbook section.
- ***Enrichment Activities*** include a stimulating collection of readings and activities for gifted and talented students.

NATIONAL GEOGRAPHIC TEACHER'S CORNER

Index to National Geographic Magazine:

The following articles may be used for research relating to this chapter:

- "The Way West," by John G. Mitchell, September 2000.
- "Cape Hatteras Lighthouse," by Angus Phillips, May 2000.
- "San Pedro River," by Barbara Kingsolver, April 2000.

National Geographic Society Products:

To order the following products for use with this chapter, call National Geographic Society at 1-800-368-2728:

- *PictureShow: U.S. Regional Geography Library* (CD-ROM)
- *PicturePack: U.S. Regional Geography Library* (Transparencies)
- *United States Geography Series* (Videos)
- *PictureShow: Native Americans, Part I* (CD-ROM)
- *PictureShow: Native Americans, Part II* (CD-ROM)

NGS ONLINE

Access National Geographic's Web site for current events, activities, links, interactive features, and archives. www.nationalgeographic.com

Find the latest coverage of geography in the news, atlas updates, cartographic activities with interactive maps, an online map store, and links at www.nationalgeographic.com/maps

SOCIAL STUDIES Online

Use our Web site for additional resources. All essential content is covered in the Student Edition.

You and your students can visit twip.glencoe.com, the Web site companion to *The World and Its People*. This innovative integration of electronic and print media offers your students a wealth of opportunities. The student text directs students to the Web site for the following options:

- Chapter Overviews
- Student Web Activities
- Self-Check Quizzes
- Textbook Updates

Answers are provided for you in the Web Activity Lesson Plan. Additional Web resources and Interactive Tutor puzzles are also available.

Introduce students to chapter content and key terms by having them access Chapter Overview 4 at twip.glencoe.com

Chapter Objectives

1. Compare the physical features and climates of the United States.
2. Describe the economy of the United States.
3. Discuss the challenges the United States faces in the twenty-first century.
4. Examine cultural influences on the people of the United States.

GLENCOE TECHNOLOGY

NATIONAL GEOGRAPHIC

The World and Its People Video Program

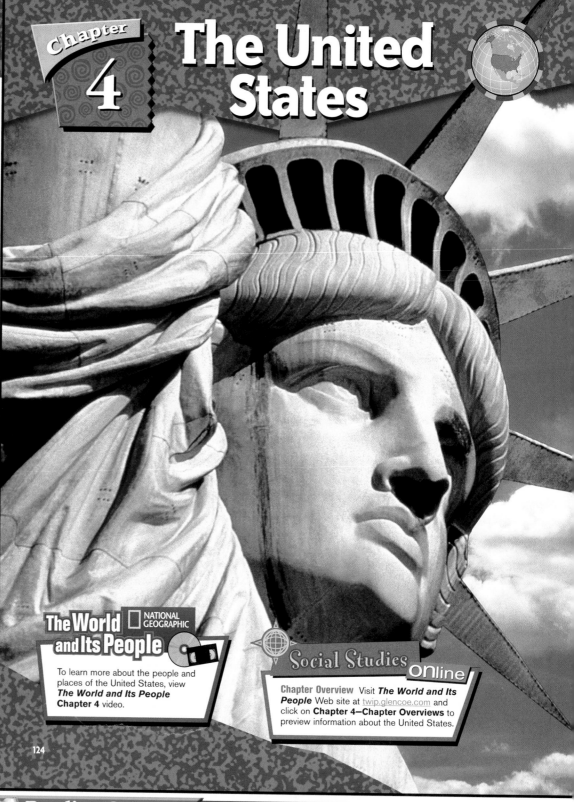

Chapter 4 The United States
The following segments enhance the study of this chapter:

- **America the Beautiful**
- **The American Bison**
- **Land of Opportunity**

MindJogger Videoquiz
Use MindJogger Videoquiz to preview the Chapter 4 content.

Both programs available in DVD and VHS

Chapter 4 The United States

The World and Its People NATIONAL GEOGRAPHIC

To learn more about the people and places of the United States, view ***The World and Its People*** **Chapter 4** video.

Social Studies Online

Chapter Overview Visit ***The World and Its People*** Web site at twip.glencoe.com and click on **Chapter 4—Chapter Overviews** to preview information about the United States.

124

Reading Strategy — Purpose for Reading

K-W-L Charts—what do you **K**now, what do you **W**ant to know, what have you **L**earned?–can be used before, during, and after a unit or lesson to activate student knowledge, establish a purpose for reading, and generate student interest. Have students divide a sheet of notebook paper into three columns. In the left column, have them write "What Do I Know About the United States?" In the middle column, have them write "What Do I Want to Know?" In the right column, have them write "What Have I Learned?" Ask them to complete the first two columns. Have students discuss what they wrote with a partner and share their responses with the class. Finally, ask them to add information to the right column as they study the chapter. L1

FOLDABLES™ Study Organizer

Identifying Main Ideas Asking yourself questions as you read helps you to focus on main ideas of the material and better understand it. Make this foldable and use it as a journal to record and answer your own questions about the United States.

Step 1 Fold a sheet of paper in half from top to bottom.

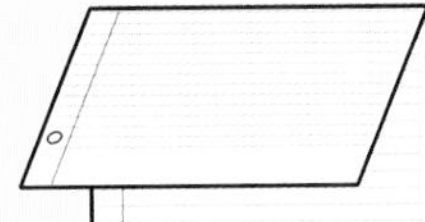

Step 2 Then fold the paper in half from side to side.

Step 3 Label the foldable as shown.

My United States Journal of Questions and Answers

Reading and Writing Before you read the chapter, list questions you have about the land, people, and economy of the United States. Then, as you read the chapter, write down more questions that occur to you on the pages of your journal. Be sure to review your questions and fill in all the correct answers.

◀ Statue of Liberty in New York Harbor, New York

Why It Matters

Leading the Free World

The United States is the most powerful nation in the world. It has the world's largest economy and is a leading representative democracy. Immigrants from nearly every other nation of the world have moved here in order to enjoy the freedom the United States Constitution provides.

Dinah Zike's Foldables

Purpose When making this foldable, students are required to ask themselves questions about the land, people, and economy of the United States. This reading strategy requires students to ask questions of the chapter material as they read it, thereby helping them focus on main ideas and better understand the material.

Have students complete the ***Reading and Study Skills Foldables*** activity for this chapter.

Why It Matters

Ask students to imagine they are from another country and have them write a letter to a relative explaining why they would like to move to the United States. Have them use outside sources to research geographic, economic, political, and social aspects of their "home" country and the United States. Tell them to include facts from their research in their letter when comparing the benefits of the United States to the negatives of their "home" country.

About the Photo

Located in New York Harbor, the Statue of Liberty was a gift of international friendship from the people of France to the people of the United States in recognition of the bond established between the two countries during the American Revolution. The monument was dedicated on October 28, 1886, and is one of the world's most universal symbols of political freedom and democracy. Visitors climb 354 steps to reach the crown. There are 25 windows in the crown that symbolize gemstones found on the earth and the heaven's rays shining over the world. The seven rays of the statue's crown represent the seven seas and continents of the world.

Chapter 4

Section 1, pages 126–130

FOCUS

Section Objectives

1. Identify the landforms that are found in the United States.
2. Contrast the climates of different areas of the United States.

BELLRINGER
Skillbuilder Activity

Project transparency and have students answer the question.

Daily Focus Skills Transparency

Interpreting Graphs

Highest Mountains in the United States

What is the highest point in the Appalachian Mountains?

A Mt. Elbert
B Mt. Ranier
C Mt. Michelson
D Mt. Mitchell

Reading Preview

■ **Activating Prior Knowledge** Have students recite the words to "America, the Beautiful." Write key phrases on the board. **Ask: What do these phrases tell you about the United States?** *(It has a variety of landforms.)*

■ **Preteaching Vocabulary** Tell students that roots derived from Greek words provide vocabulary clue meanings. For example, *mega* (great) and *polis* (city) mean "great city."

Guide to Reading

Main Idea

The United States has a great variety of landforms and climates.

Terms to Know

- contiguous
- megalopolis
- coral reef

Reading Strategy

Create a chart like the one below. Fill in details about each of the seven physical regions of the United States.

Region	Details

From Sea to Shining Sea

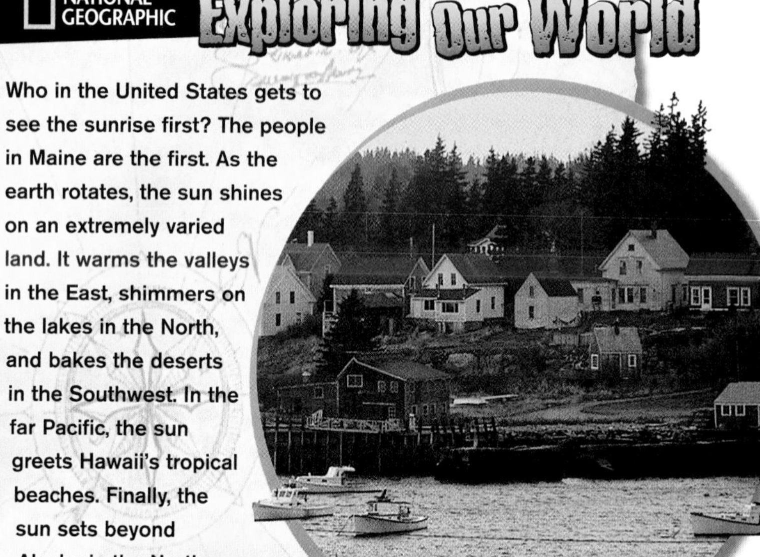

NATIONAL GEOGRAPHIC **Exploring Our World**

Who in the United States gets to see the sunrise first? The people in Maine are the first. As the earth rotates, the sun shines on an extremely varied land. It warms the valleys in the East, shimmers on the lakes in the North, and bakes the deserts in the Southwest. In the far Pacific, the sun greets Hawaii's tropical beaches. Finally, the sun sets beyond Alaska in the North.

The United States stretches 2,807 miles (4,517 km) across the middle part of North America. The 48 states in this part of the country are **contiguous,** or joined together inside a common boundary. These states touch the Atlantic Ocean, the Gulf of Mexico, and the Pacific Ocean. Two states lie apart from the other 48. Alaska lies in the northwestern portion of North America. Hawaii is in the Pacific Ocean about 2,400 miles (3,862 km) southwest of California. Find Alaska and Hawaii on page RA6 of the **Reference Atlas.**

A Vast, Scenic Land

The United States is the third-largest country in the world. Only Russia and Canada are larger. The contiguous states have five main physical regions: the Coastal Plains, the Appalachian Mountains, the Interior Plains, the Mountains and Plateaus, and the Pacific Coast. Alaska and Hawaii each has its own set of physical landforms.

Section Resources

Reproducible Masters
- Reproducible Lesson Plan
- Daily Lecture and Discussion Notes
- Note-taking Guide
- Guided Reading Activity
- Reading Essentials and Study Guide
- Section Quiz

Transparencies
- Daily Focus Skills Transparency
- GeoQuiz Transparency

Multimedia
- Vocabulary PuzzleMaker CD-ROM
- Interactive Tutor Self-Assessment CD-ROM
- Presentation Plus! CD-ROM
- ExamView® Pro Testmaker CD-ROM

The Coastal Plains A broad lowland runs along the eastern and southeastern coasts of the United States. The eastern lowlands are called the **Atlantic Coastal Plain.** The lowlands in the southeast border the Gulf of Mexico and are called the **Gulf Coastal Plain.** Find these coastal plains on the map below. Excellent harbors along the Atlantic Coastal Plain led to the growth of shipping ports. The soil in the northern part of the region tends to be thin and rocky, though.

Boston, New York City, Philadelphia, Baltimore, and Washington, D.C., all lie in the Atlantic Coastal Plain. These cities and their suburbs form an almost continuous line of settlement. Geographers call this kind of huge urban area a **megalopolis.**

The Gulf Coastal Plain is wider than the Atlantic plain. Soils in this region are better than those along the Atlantic coast. Large cities here include Houston and New Orleans, shown on the map on page 149.

Applying Map Skills

1. What river forms part of the boundary between the United States and Mexico?
2. What is the tallest mountain in the 50 states?

Find NGS online map resources @ www.nationalgeographic.com/maps

Chapter 4

Section 1, pages 126–130

Identifying Regions Have students identify the approximate location of their community on the map on this page. **Ask:** **In what physical region is your community located? What other physical regions are nearby? L1**

Daily Lecture and Discussion Notes

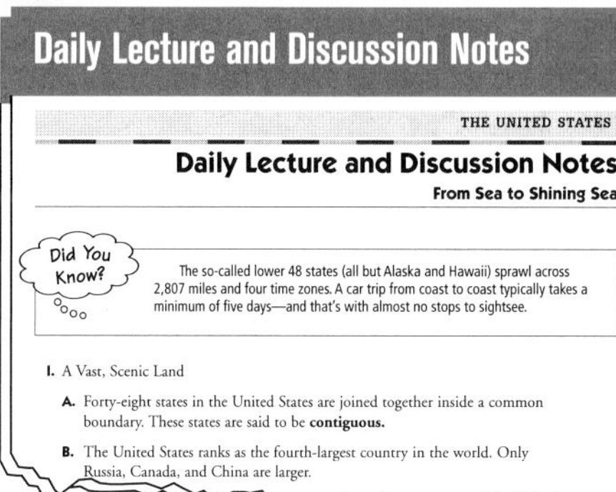
THE UNITED STATES

Daily Lecture and Discussion Notes

From Sea to Shining Sea

Did You Know? The so-called lower 48 states (all but Alaska and Hawaii) sprawl across 2,807 miles and four time zones. A car trip from coast to coast typically takes a minimum of five days—and that's with almost no stops to sightsee.

I. A Vast, Scenic Land

A. Forty-eight states in the United States are joined together inside a common boundary. These states are said to be **contiguous.**

B. The United States ranks as the fourth-largest country in the world. Only Russia, Canada, and China are larger.

...eastern and southeastern coasts of the United...

Applying Map Skills

Answers

1. the Rio Grande
2. Mt. McKinley, in Alaska

Skills Practice

Ask: **How does the landscape of the United States change when moving from west to east?** *(lowland on Pacific coast, then high mountains and plateaus, followed by high plains and lowlands in center, with mountains and lowlands in east)*

Reading Strategy Reading the Text

Predicting Create a chart using the seven physical regions of the United States as horizontal column headings and "Population" and "Economic Activities" as vertical row headings. Call on volunteers to identify physical characteristics of each region. **Ask:** **How might these physical characteristics affect population in each region?** Note responses in the appropriate column and row. **How might physical features influence economic activities in the region?** Note these responses on the chart as well. Have students copy the chart into their notebooks. Encourage them to review and adjust chart entries as they study the chapter. **L1**

Use the Reading Skills Handbook for more reading strategies.

Measure student knowledge of physical features.

GeoQuiz Transparency

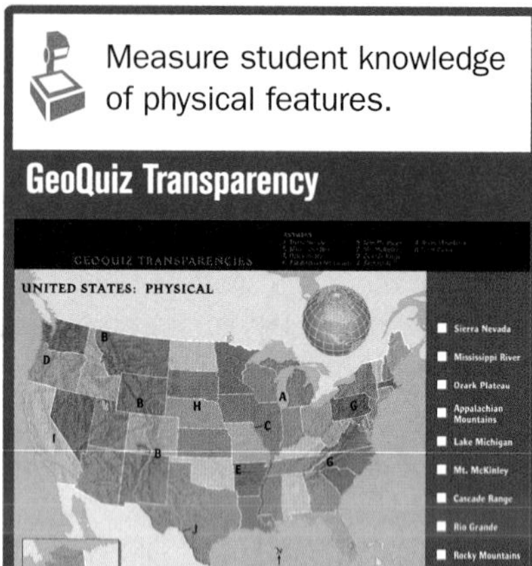

More About the Photos

Interior Plains Mineral resources in the Interior Plains helped build its industrial strength. Coal brought from nearby Appalachian foothills was used to power furnaces that make steel. To make that steel, workers used iron brought from the highlands near Lake Superior. The Mesabi Range in Minnesota was one of the richest sources of iron in the world. Cities such as Chicago, Detroit, Cleveland, and Pittsburgh became major industrial centers as a result of the availability of these resources.

Caption Answer the Mississippi River

NATIONAL GEOGRAPHIC On Location

City and Country

The Interior Plains of the United States include industrial cities of the North, such as Chicago (above), and the agricultural lands of the Great Plains, like this area in Texas (above right).

Region Which river divides much of the Interior Plains?

The Appalachian Mountains As you move west from the Atlantic Coastal Plain, you run into the hilly—yet very fertile—Piedmont area. These hills eventually turn into the **Appalachian** (A•puh•LAY•chuhn) **Mountains,** which run from eastern Canada to Alabama. The Appalachians are the oldest mountains on the continent. How can you tell? Their rounded peaks show their age. Erosion has worn them down over time. The highest peak, Mount Mitchell in North Carolina, reaches 6,684 feet (2,037 m).

The Interior Plains When you cross the Appalachians heading west, you enter the vast Interior Plains. This region has two parts. East of the **Mississippi River** is the **Central Lowland** area. Here you will find grassy hills, rolling flatlands, and thick forests. The land is fertile, and farms are productive. This area also contains important waterways.

The Great Lakes—the largest group of freshwater lakes in the world—lie in the Central Lowlands. Glaciers formed Lake Superior, Lake Michigan, Lake Huron, Lake Erie, and Lake Ontario in the distant past. The waters of these connected lakes flow into the St. Lawrence River, which empties into the Atlantic Ocean.

West of the Mississippi River stretch the **Great Plains.** The landscape in many places is blanketed with neat fields of grain and grassy pastures and takes on a checkerboard pattern. The Great Plains are about 500 miles (805 km) wide and stretch west to the Rocky Mountains, north into Canada, and south to the Mexican border. The rich grasslands of the Great Plains once provided food for millions of buffalo and the Native Americans who lived there. Today farmers grow grains and ranchers raise cattle on the Great Plains.

Differentiated Instruction

Meeting Special Needs: Naturalist Organize students into seven groups and assign each group one of the physical regions of the United States. Instruct group members to locate photographs or make sketches of landscapes found in their assigned regions. Encourage groups to use their images to create a bulletin board display titled "America the Beautiful." Have groups arrange their illustrations around a large wall map of the United States. Remind students to be sure that each illustration has a caption and a leader line connecting it to its approximate location on the map. **L1**

Mountains and Plateaus The **Rocky Mountains** begin in Alaska and run south to Mexico. Along the tops of these mountains is a ridge called the Continental Divide. This ridge separates rivers that flow west—toward the Pacific Ocean—from those that flow east—toward the Mississippi River. Many rivers begin in the high, snowy peaks of the Rockies. The Rio Grande as well as the Missouri, Platte, Arkansas, and Red Rivers flow east. The Colorado, Snake, and Columbia Rivers flow west.

Between the Rockies and the Pacific Coast are plateaus, canyons, and deserts. Plateaus are areas of flat land that rise above the land around them. A canyon is a deep valley with steep sides. The most famous of these is the Grand Canyon in Arizona.

The Pacific Coast Near the Pacific Coast rise two other mountain ranges. The Cascade Range reaches from Washington State south to California. Volcanoes formed these high peaks—and some of them still erupt. Along California's eastern side runs the Sierra Nevada. The name *Nevada* means "snow covered" in Spanish. Even in a place as far south as California, these high mountains remain covered with snow.

To the west of these Pacific ranges lie fertile valleys. The Willamette Valley in Oregon and the Central Valley in California both produce abundant crops. Many of the fruits and vegetables you eat may come from these valleys.

Alaska Mountain ranges form a semicircle over the northern, eastern, and southern parts of Alaska. **Mount McKinley**—the tallest mountain in North America—stands 20,320 feet (6,194 m) high in the Alaska Range. The northern part of the state borders on the frigid Arctic Ocean, and you can almost see Russia from Alaska's western shores. Most people in Alaska live along the southern coastal plain or in the central Yukon River valley.

Hawaii Eight large islands and more than 120 smaller islands make up Hawaii, the island state in the Pacific Ocean. Volcanoes on the ocean floor erupted and formed these islands. Some of the islands have coral reefs, formed by the skeletons of small sea animals. These structures lie just above or submerged just below the surface of the water.

Reading Check What is the Continental Divide?

NATIONAL GEOGRAPHIC **On Location**

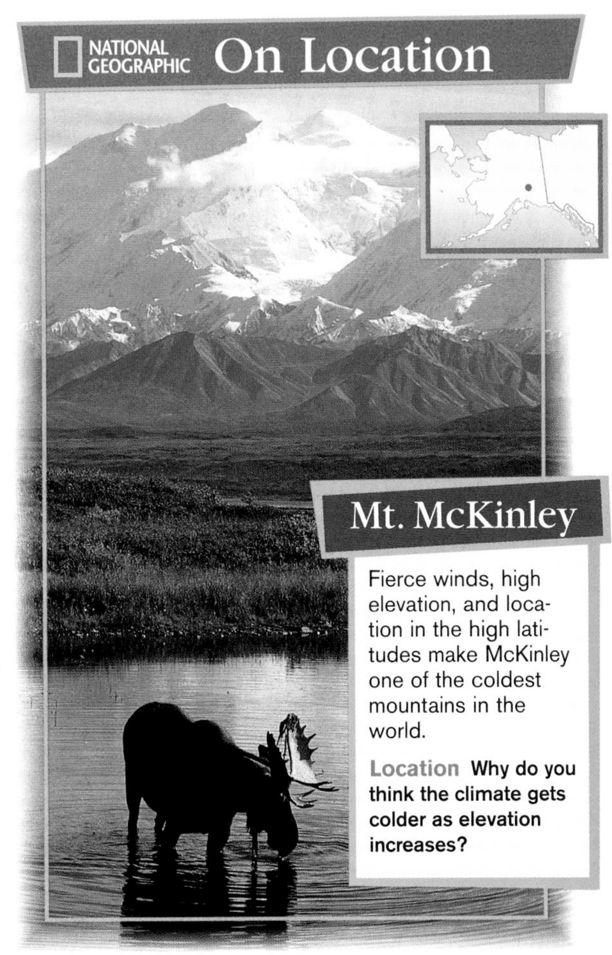

Mt. McKinley

Fierce winds, high elevation, and location in the high latitudes make McKinley one of the coldest mountains in the world.

Location **Why do you think the climate gets colder as elevation increases?**

Chapter 4

Section 1, pages 126–130

More About the Photo

Mt. McKinley In 1917, Mount McKinley National Park was established as a wildlife refuge. In 1980, the park area was enlarged by 4 million acres and renamed Denali National Park. Denali, or "high one," is the name native people gave the massive peak.

Caption Answer At higher elevations, the air is no longer warmed by the heat of the earth's surface.

L1/ELL

Guided Reading Activity

Name ________ Date ________ Class ________

THE UNITED STATES

Guided Reading Activity 1

From Sea to Shining Sea

DIRECTIONS: Outlining Reading the section and completing the outline below will help you learn more about the land in the United States. Use your textbook to fill in the blanks.

I. The 48 states are ________; two states lie apart, Alaska and ________.

II. The United States has ________ main physical regions.

A. The ________ Plains is a lowland that runs along the eastern and southeastern coasts of the United States.

B. The ________ Mountains are the oldest mountain range on the

Reading Check Answer

a ridge that runs along the Rocky Mountains separating rivers that flow west from those that flow east

3 Assess

Assign Section 1 Assessment as homework or an in-class activity.

Have students use the Interactive Tutor Self-Assessment CD-ROM to review Section 1.

Critical Thinking Activity

Understanding Cause and Effect A plateau called the Piedmont lies at the eastern edge of the Appalachians. The eastern edge of the Piedmont rises sharply from the low-lying Atlantic Coastal Plain. Here fast-moving rivers drop from the plateau to the plains, forming many rapids and waterfalls. The line formed where this drop takes place is called the fall line. Early European settlers were unable to travel beyond the fall line by boat. The waterfalls and rapids, however, later provided waterpower for industries. Thus, many cities—including Macon, Georgia; Columbia, South Carolina; Raleigh, North Carolina; and Richmond, Virginia—developed along the fall line. Have students trace how rivers helped power early American industry. L3

EE6 The Uses of Geography: Standard 17

Chapter 4

Section 1, pages 126–130

L2

Section Quiz

Name ______ Date ______ Class ______

THE UNITED STATES

Section 1 Quiz

From Sea to Shining Sea

DIRECTIONS: Matching Match each item in Column A with the items in Column B. Write the correct letters in the blanks. *(10 points each)*

COLUMN A	COLUMN B
A. Appalachian Mountains	___ 1. oldest mountains on the continent
B. contiguous	___ 2. mountain range running from Alaska south to Mexico
C. megalopolis	___ 3. an almost continuous line of huge, combined urban settlements
D. Rocky Mountains	___ 4. joined together inside a common boundary
E. coral reefs	___ 5. formed from skeletons of small sea animals

Reading Check Answer

The Pacific mountain ranges block humid winds, and hot, dry air gets trapped in between the Pacific ranges and the Rockies.

L1/ELL

Reading Essentials and Study Guide

Name ______ Date ______ Class ______

THE UNITED STATES

Reading Essentials and Study Guide 1

From Sea to Shining Sea

Key Terms

contiguous joined together inside a common boundary
megalopolis neighboring cities and suburbs that blend into one huge urban area
coral reef structure formed by the skeletons of small sea animals

Drawing From Experience

CLOSE

Have students make a list of state nicknames and determine which are related to physical geography.

A Variety of Climates

Because the United States is such a large country, you probably expect it to have many different climates. You are right! Most of the country lies squarely in the mid-latitude region—about 23½°N to 60°N latitude. As you recall from Chapter 2, this part of the earth has the greatest variety of climates.

Look at the climate map of the world on page 63. You can see that the northeastern United States has a humid continental climate. Winters here are cold, and summers are hot and long. Winter snows often blanket the region—especially around the Great Lakes. The southeastern states have a humid subtropical climate. Winters are mild, and summers are hot and humid. Nearness to the Gulf of Mexico and the Caribbean Sea often causes violent hurricanes and tornadoes in summer.

The Pacific coast from northern California up to Washington has a marine west coast climate. Temperatures are mild year-round, and Pacific winds bring much rain. Southern California, however, has a Mediterranean climate. People enjoy dry, warm summers and mild, rainy winters.

Much of the western Great Plains has a dry, steppe climate. Why? The Pacific mountain ranges block the humid ocean winds. Therefore, hot, dry air gets trapped in between the Pacific ranges and the Rockies. In the southwest, even less rain falls. This arid region has a hot, desert climate.

Alaska, in the high latitudes, has subarctic and tundra climates. Hawaii and southern Florida have warm, tropical climates with heavy rainfall much of the year.

Reading Check **Why are dry climates found in the western Great Plains?**

Section 1 Assessment

Defining Terms

1. Define contiguous, megalopolis, coral reef.

Recalling Facts

2. Place How does the United States rank in size among all the countries of the world?

3. History Which region once supported Native Americans and millions of buffalo?

4. Place What is the largest group of freshwater lakes in the world?

Critical Thinking

5. Understanding Cause and Effect How were the Hawaiian Islands formed?

6. Drawing Conclusions What challenges do you think result from the distance between Alaska, Hawaii, and the other states?

Graphic Organizer

7. Organizing Information Create a diagram like this one to compare the Atlantic and Gulf Coastal Plains. In the separate outer parts of the ovals, write the qualities that make each region different. In the overlapping area, write the characteristics that the two areas share.

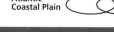

Atlantic Coastal Plain ◯◯ Gulf Coastal Plain

Applying Social Studies Skills

8. Analyzing Maps Look at the physical map on page 127 and the population density map on page 149. At what elevations do the cities with more than 5 million people lie?

Section 1 Assessment

1. The terms are defined in the Glossary.
2. fourth-largest country in the world
3. Great Plains
4. the Great Lakes
5. volcanic eruptions on the ocean floor
6. *Possible answers:* problems communicating; extra time needed to ship goods
7. *Atlantic Coastal Plain:* continuous line of settlement; *Gulf Coastal Plain:* wider, good soil, has oil and natural gas; *Both:* have major cities, low-lying areas
8. 0–1,000 feet (0–300 m)

Section 2

An Economic Leader

Guide to Reading

Main Idea

The United States economy runs on abundant resources and the hard work of Americans.

Terms to Know

- free enterprise system
- service industry
- navigable
- fossil fuel
- acid rain
- landfill
- recycling
- free trade

Reading Strategy

Complete a chart like this one. First, list the five economic regions of the United States. Then list the economic activities carried out in each region.

Region	Economic Activities

NATIONAL GEOGRAPHIC Exploring Our World

In the mid-1900s, many Southerners went north to find jobs. By the late 1900s, however, Northerners were flocking to cities in the South. Atlanta, Georgia, is one such growing city. In 1980 Atlanta had a population of 2.2 million. By 2000 it had more than 4 million people. Shown here, Atlanta's mayor Shirley Franklin (center) helps break ground for the city's new aquarium.

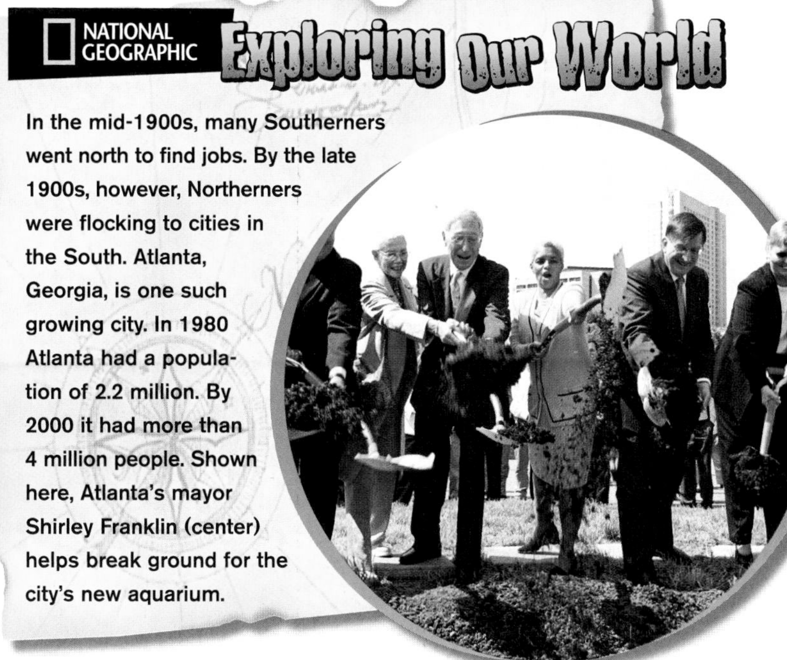

The United States has a large, energetic, and growing economy. Fueling all of this economic activity is freedom. As you recall from Chapter 3, the **free enterprise system** is built on the idea that individual people have the right to run businesses to make a profit. They do so with limited interference from the government. Americans are free to start their own businesses and to keep the profits they earn after paying taxes. They are free to work in whatever jobs they want. Freedom has helped create great economic success.

The World's Economic Leader

The United States is rich in resources and has hardworking, inventive people. As a result, the country has built the world's largest economy—in terms of how much money is made from the sale of its goods and services. In fact, the American economy is larger than the next two largest economies—China's and Japan's—combined.

Farms in the United States produce about one-half of the world's corn and about one-tenth of its wheat. American farmers raise about 20 percent of the world's beef, pork, and lamb. The country exports

1 Focus

Section Objectives

1. Explain why the U.S. has the world's leading economy.
2. Identify how people in the United States earn their livings.
3. Describe the challenges facing the United States.

BELLRINGER Skillbuilder Activity

Project transparency and have students answer the question.

Daily Focus Skills Transparency

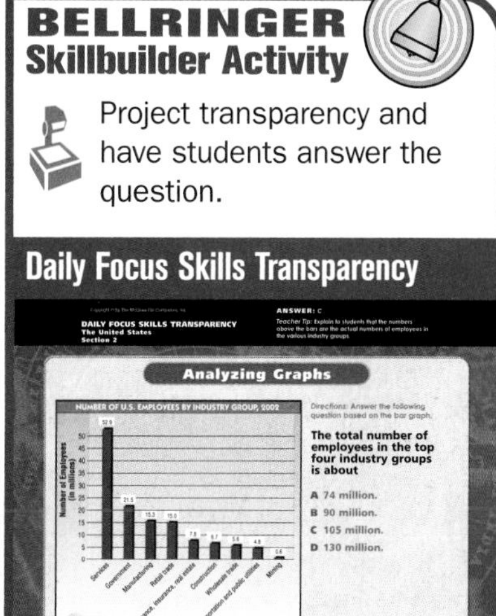

Reading Preview

■ **Activating Prior Knowledge** Have students give examples of American industries. Choose one and have students suggest what jobs the industry might include.

■ **Preteaching Vocabulary** Demonstrate how the meaning of a word changes when another word is added, such as *acid* in *acid rain.* Ask students to find other examples in the section.

Section Resources

Reproducible Masters
- Reproducible Lesson Plan
- Daily Lecture and Discussion Notes
- Note-taking Guide
- Guided Reading Activity
- Reading Essentials and Study Guide
- Section Quiz

Transparencies
- Daily Focus Skills Transparency
- GeoQuiz Transparency

Multimedia
- Vocabulary PuzzleMaker CD-ROM
- Interactive Tutor Self-Assessment CD-ROM
- Presentation Plus! CD-ROM
- ExamView® Pro Testmaker CD-ROM

Teach

Researching Jobs To reinforce the point that Americans are free to enter any career, bring in the want ads. Have each student find one job that interests him or her. Ask students to do research and create a fact sheet outlining what the job involves, what education or experience is needed, and how much it pays. L1

Daily Lecture and Discussion Notes

THE UNITED STATES

Daily Lecture and Discussion Notes

An Economic Leader

Did You Know?

The United States is the world's leading producer of electrical power from all sources. It also leads the world in production of natural gas, lead, aluminum, and several other minerals. It is among the leaders in the production of crude oil, coal, copper, iron ore, silver, and zinc. In total value of manufactured goods, the United States leads all other nations by a substantial margin.

I. The World's Economic Leader

A. In the United States, the **free enterprise system** allows individuals the right to run businesses and to make a profit with limited interference from the government. People are free to work in whatever job they wish.

Reading Check Answer

services

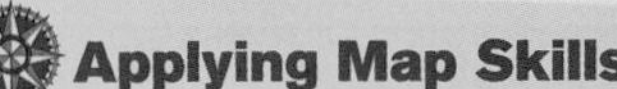

Applying Map Skills

Answers

1. iron, zinc, and copper
2. commercial farming

Skills Practice

What resources does Texas have? *(petroleum, natural gas, coal, and fishing)*

more food than any other nation. Yet agriculture is only a small part of the American economy. Food makes up about 2 percent of the value of all goods produced in the country.

The United States has rich mineral resources. About one-fifth of the world's coal and copper and one-tenth of the world's petroleum come from the United States. The country also has large amounts of iron ore, zinc, lead, silver, gold, and many other minerals. Mining, though, makes up less than 1 percent of the nation's economy.

American factory workers build cars and airplanes. They make computers and appliances. They process foods and make medicines. Manufacturing accounts for nearly one-fifth of the American economy.

By far, the largest part of the economy is services. A **service industry** is a business that provides services to people instead of producing goods. Banking and finance are services. So is entertainment—and people all over the world buy American movies and CDs. The United States is a leader in tourism, another service industry. Computer-based, online services have also emerged as an important American service industry.

Reading Check What is the largest part of the U.S. economy?

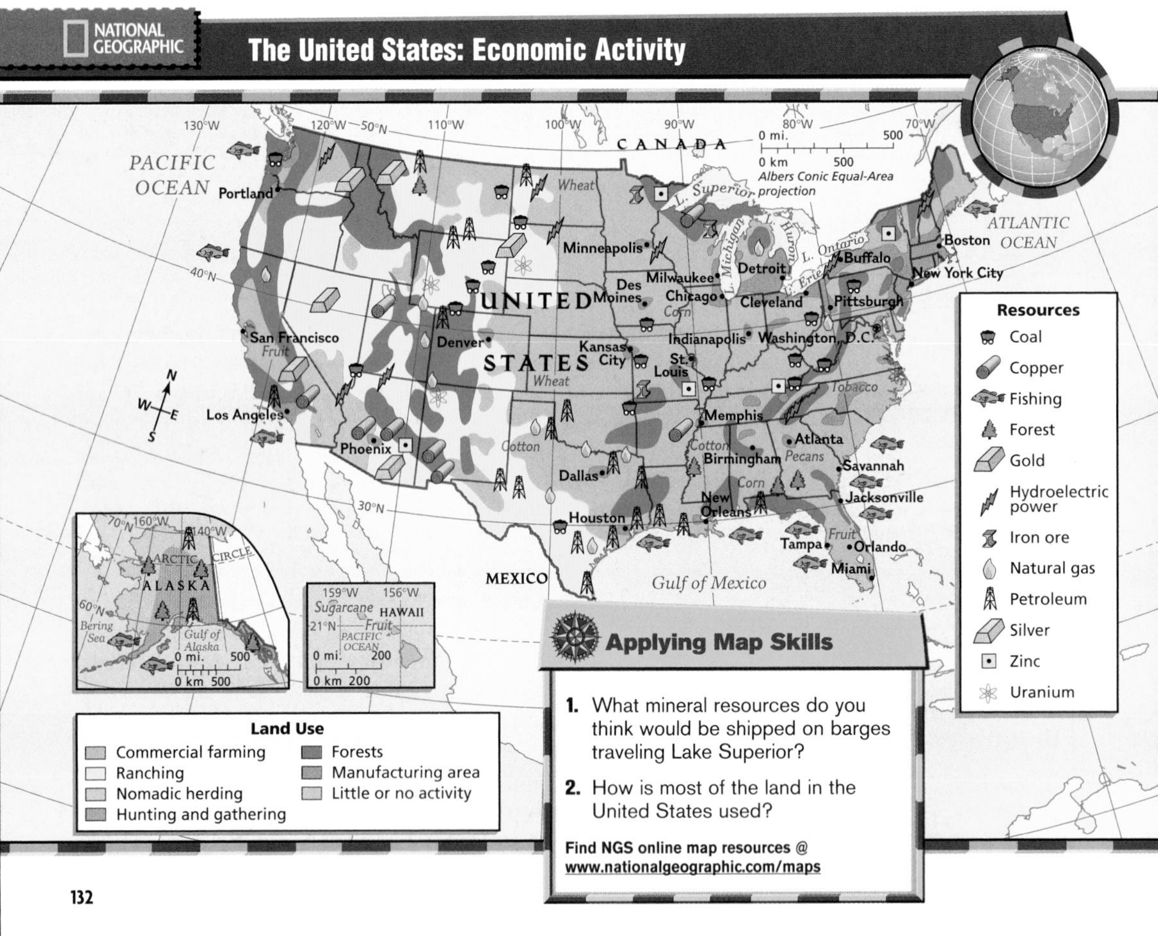

Applying Map Skills

1. What mineral resources do you think would be shipped on barges traveling Lake Superior?
2. How is most of the land in the United States used?

Find NGS online map resources @ www.nationalgeographic.com/maps

132

Reading Strategy — Reading the Text

Identifying the Main Idea Students should identify main ideas as they read. Text features, such as headings, subheadings, boldfaced terms, and graphics, are good indicators of main or key ideas. As students read, they should use the text features to help them create an outline or draw a graphic organizer of the main ideas. L1

*Use the **Reading Skills Handbook** for more reading strategies.*

America's Economic Regions

Geographers group states together into five economic regions—the Northeast, the South, the Midwest, the Interior West, and the Pacific.

The Northeast Some farmers in central Pennsylvania and western New York grow grains and fruits. Yet as you read in Section 1, the rocky soil and steep hills in this region are a challenge to the farmers. The area has plenty of deep water ports and swiftly moving rivers, though. As a result, manufacturing, trade, and fishing are the heartbeat of this region. In fact, the Northeast was home to the first mills powered by running water and coal. Look at the economic activity map on page 132. As you can see, coal mining takes place in Pennsylvania and West Virginia.

With their deep, natural harbors, Boston, New York City, Philadelphia, and Baltimore are all important ports. Goods are shipped all over the world to and from these ports. These cities are also important centers of banking, insurance, and finance. **New York City** is one of the financial capitals of the world. It is also a world center in the fashion, entertainment, and communications industries. Farther south, the nation's capital—**Washington, D.C.**—employs hundreds of thousands in government and tourism services.

The South With rich soil on most of the Coastal Plains, agriculture flourishes in the Southern states. Because of the region's warm, wet climate, farmers in Louisiana and Arkansas grow rice and sugarcane. Tobacco flourishes in Virginia and the Carolinas. In Florida you can sample the citrus fruits that farmers grow. Peanuts and pecans are found in Georgia. Alabama farmers grow corn and soybeans. You also see cotton growing in several Southern states, including Texas. Texas, in fact, has more farms than any other state. The people of Texas grow cotton, sorghum, and wheat and raise livestock as well.

The traditional image of the South as an agricultural region is changing, however. As you tour the South, you see expanding cities, growing industries, and diverse populations. New manufacturing centers have drawn new businesses and people to the South from the Northeast and elsewhere. Workers make textiles, electrical equipment, and airplane parts. Oil is found in Texas, Louisiana, and Alabama. As a result, these states produce petroleum-based products.

Service industries are important in the South as well. Florida is a major tourist center. People come to enjoy amusement parks in Orlando, the Kennedy Space Center at Cape Canaveral, and the beautiful beaches on both coasts. Millions of people flock to New Orleans each year to taste spicy food and hear lively music. Houston, Dallas, Atlanta, and Miami are just a few of this region's major centers of business and finance.

The Midwest This part of the United States has been called "America's breadbasket." Miles and miles of grain and soybean fields greet you as you travel over flat land and fertile soil. In this farm belt, farmers grow corn, soybeans, oats, and wheat to feed animals and people all over the world. Dairy farms in the upper Midwest produce

Surf's Up!

Fourteen-year-old Shawn Kilgore lives on Florida's Captiva Island, along the Gulf of Mexico. "I really like warm weather," he says. "Who needs snow? My dog Sunny and I couldn't go surfing if we lived in Ohio where my cousins are." Shawn's parents manage a resort for tourists. "My mom and dad are always reminding me that we live in one of the world's richest countries. So my older sister and I volunteer to grocery-shop for people around here who can't do it themselves."

Chapter 4

Section 2, pages 131–136

Reading Strategy

Synthesizing Information Have students use a map of the United States to identify the economic region in which they live. Direct them to make a list of the economic activities in and around their community. Then have them determine how these activities compare with those described in the text. L2

Making Comparisons Ask students if they have friends or family members living in another section of the country. Ask for volunteers to share descriptions of life in these areas. Then have the class compare these details to life in their own region. L1

L1/ELL

Guided Reading Activity

Name ______ Date ______ Class ______

THE UNITED STATES

Guided Reading Activity 2

An Economic Leader

DIRECTIONS: Answering Questions Reading the section and answering the questions below will help you learn more about the economy of the United States. Use your textbook to write answers to the questions.

1. Why are service industries important to the economy of the United States?
2. What are the main sources of income for the Northeast economic region?
3. What are some crops that are grown in the South?
4. What crops help make the Midwest economic region America's "breadbasket"?
5. What are two other attributes of the Midwest that are important to the economy?
6. What activities and resources are important to the economy of the Interior West?
7. What crops are grown in the Pacific region states?
8. What are some of the challenges the American economy faces in the twenty-first century?

51

Differentiated Instruction

Meeting Special Needs: Auditory/Musical Help students find the main ideas in the section describing the Northeast economic region. Then have them summarize the main ideas for the other sections describing economic regions. Suggest that while students write down the main ideas, they read the information aloud. Taking this step will help them better retain the information. L1

Refer to *Inclusion for the Middle School Social Studies Classroom Strategies and Activities* in the TCR.

More About the Photos

Florida Tourism More than 840,000 Floridians work in tourist-related activities, including the hotel and restaurant industries. Approximately 58 million people vacation in Florida each year, providing about $50 billion in revenue for the state.

Caption Answer Natural: Yellowstone National Park, Grand Canyon; human-made: amusement parks in Orlando, Kennedy Space Center, ruins of Mesa Verde

Assign Section 2 Assessment as homework or an in-class activity.

Have students use the Interactive Tutor Self-Assessment CD-ROM to review Section 2.

Measure student knowledge of political entities.

GeoQuiz Transparency

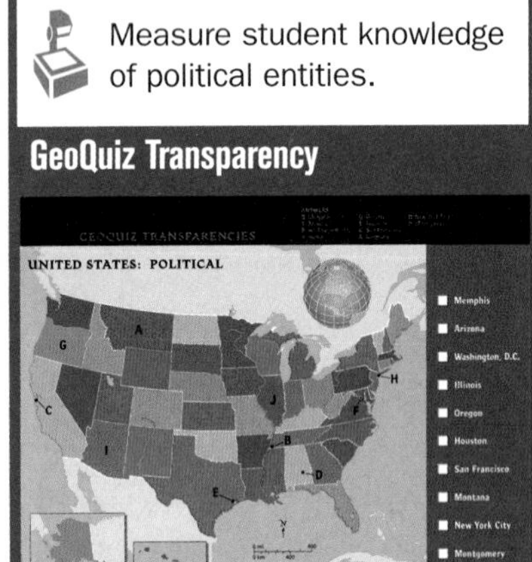

NATIONAL GEOGRAPHIC **On Location**

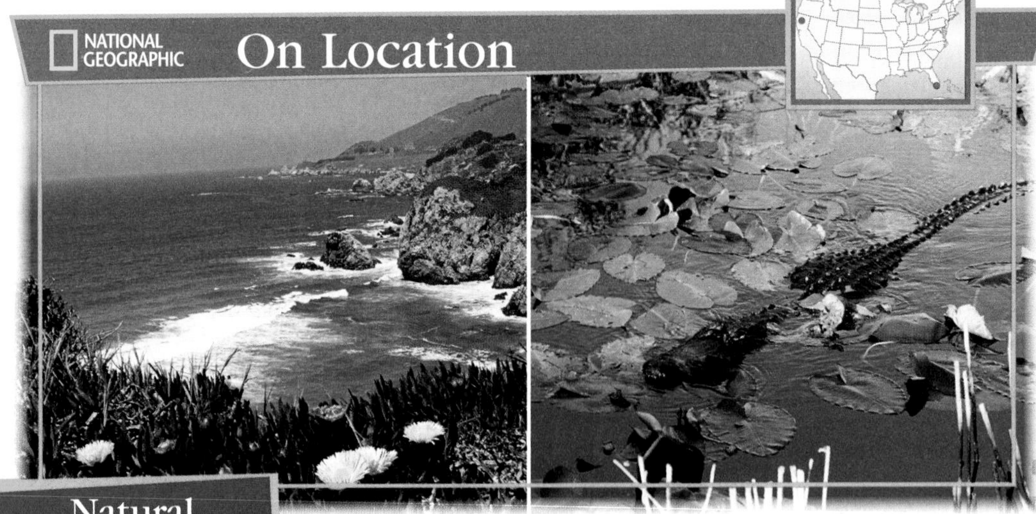

Natural Attractions

Tourists from all over the world visit the United States to see everything from Florida's Everglades (right) to California's surf (above).

Place **What other natural and human-made attractions draw tourists to our country?**

milk and cheese. However, technology has changed many farms from small, family-owned operations to big businesses. The graph on page 11 of the **Geography Handbook** shows you the decrease in the number of farms over the past few decades.

Many of the region's rivers are **navigable,** or wide and deep enough to allow the passage of ships. As a result, many cities here are major ports—even though they are far from an ocean. Businesses in Cincinnati and Louisville send goods down the Ohio River. St. Louis and Memphis serve as centers of trade along the Mississippi River. Chicago's and Cleveland's industries ship goods through the Great Lakes and St. Lawrence Seaway to ports around the world.

Because of their abundant coal and iron resources, many cities in the Midwest are manufacturing centers. A complex network of railroads also helps the region's many industries. Detroit is called Motown (short for Motor Town) because the country's auto industry started and grew there. Other major industries include steel, heavy machinery, and auto parts.

The Interior West Magnificent landscapes greet visitors to this region. However, this area is short on an important resource—water. With its dry climate, the region discourages farming. Yet grasses thrive in much of the land, and where the land is irrigated, you find agriculture. Large areas are used for raising cattle and sheep. Ranches here may be huge—as large as 4,000 acres (1,619 ha). In the past, cowhands worked the range on horseback. Although they still use horses today, you are just as likely to see them driving a sturdy truck.

Look at the map on page 132. You see rich deposits of minerals and energy resources in the Interior West. The discovery of gold and silver in the mountains and riverbeds drew settlers here more than 150 years ago. Mining still plays an important role in the economy.

Cooperative Learning Activity

Making Maps Organize students into five groups and assign each group one of the economic regions of the United States. Have groups prepare an annotated product map or economic activity map for their assigned region. Make certain that all group members have a task—some might conduct research, others might construct the map, and still others might write annotations. Have groups display and discuss their completed maps. L2 

EE5 Environment and Society: Standard 16

Many people work in service industries too. Every year tourists travel to Denver, Salt Lake City, Albuquerque, and Phoenix. They use these cities as starting points for trips to sites such as Yellowstone National Park or the Grand Canyon. Some visit the ruins of ancient Native American settlements, such as those found at Mesa Verde in southwestern Colorado.

The Pacific The Pacific region includes the states on the western coast plus Alaska and Hawaii. The fertile valleys of California, Oregon, and Washington produce large amounts of food. As you learned in Section 1, many of the fruits and vegetables you enjoy every day come from these states. Do you like pineapple? If so, it may have come from Hawaii. This state also grows sugarcane, coffee, and rice because of its tropical climate and rich volcanic soil.

In this region, just like the Atlantic coast, fishing is a major industry. The states of Washington and Oregon draw many people to work in the lumber industry. Mineral resources are important in the Pacific region too. California has gold, lead, and copper. Alaska has vast reserves of oil.

Factory workers in California and Washington make airplanes. The areas around San Francisco and Seattle are world-famous centers of research in computers and software. **Los Angeles** is the world capital of the movie industry. These states in the Pacific region also attract millions of tourists who visit California's redwood forests, Hawaii's tropical beaches, or the stunning glaciers of Alaska.

✓Reading Check **What goods are manufactured in the Pacific states?**

In the Twenty-First Century

The American economy, although strong, faces challenges in the twenty-first century. One of these challenges is how to clean up pollution and trash. Americans burn **fossil fuels**—coal, oil, and natural gas—to power their factories and run their cars. Burning these fuels pollutes the air, endangering all who breathe it. The pollution also mixes with water vapor in the air to make **acid rain,** or rain containing high amounts of chemical pollutants. Acid rain damages trees and harms rivers and lakes.

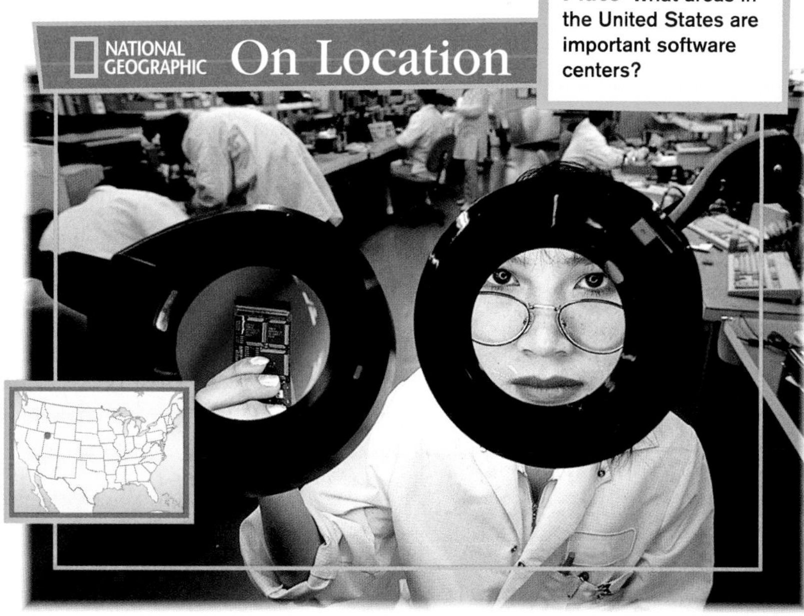

Technology

A worker inspects computer components. Along with agriculture, America's economy is strong in technology, science, education, and medicine.

Place **What areas in the United States are important software centers?**

Chapter 4

Section 2, pages 131–136

Cultural Kaleidoscope

Los Angeles Los Angeles is one of the most racially and ethnically diverse cities in the United States. About 40 percent of the people in Los Angeles are from Spanish-speaking countries, 37 percent are white, 13 percent are African American, and 10 percent are Asian. There are more people of Mexican, Chinese, Taiwanese, Korean, and Philippine backgrounds in Los Angeles than in any other city in the United States.

✓ Reading Check Answer

airplanes, computers, and software

More About the Photo

Computer Technology An area near San Francisco called Silicon Valley is important for producing electronic equipment.

Caption Answer areas around San Francisco and Seattle

L2

Section Quiz

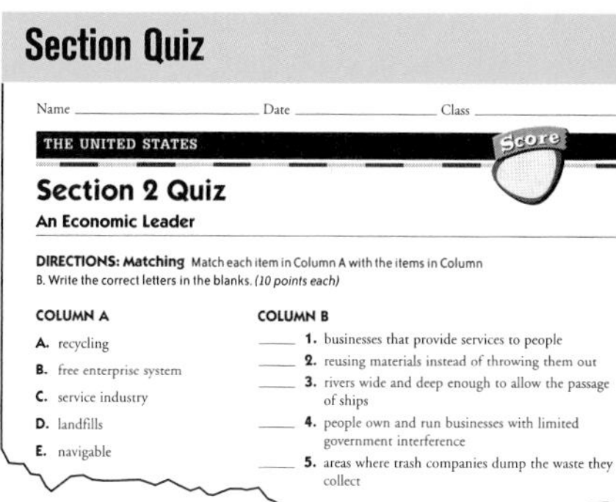
Name ______ Date ______ Class ______

THE UNITED STATES

Score

Section 2 Quiz

An Economic Leader

DIRECTIONS: Matching Match each item in Column A with the items in Column B. Write the correct letters in the blanks. *(10 points each)*

COLUMN A	COLUMN B
A. recycling	____ **1.** businesses that provide services to people
B. free enterprise system	____ **2.** reusing materials instead of throwing them out
C. service industry	____ **3.** rivers wide and deep enough to allow the passage of ships
D. landfills	____ **4.** people own and run businesses with limited government interference
E. navigable	____ **5.** areas where trash companies dump the waste they collect

Team-Teaching Activity

Science Recycling is an important way of contributing to a healthy environment. Many communities ask residents to recycle aluminum, glass, plastic, and paper. Work with the science teacher to outline for students the benefits of recycling, which include conserving resources and energy, reducing pollution, and saving landfill space. Ask the science teacher to discuss the different grades of plastic and explain why some can be recycled and others cannot. Finally, have students make a list of the things that they recycle—or could recycle—at home. Encourage them to carry out the practice. L2

EE5 Environment and Society: Standard 14

L1/ELL

Reading Essentials and Study Guide

Name ______ Date ______ Class ______

THE UNITED STATES

Reading Essentials and Study Guide 2

An Economic Leader

Key Terms

free enterprise system economic system in which individuals have the right to run businesses and make a profit with limited government interference
service industry businesses that provide services to people instead of producing goods
navigable body of water that is wide and deep enough to allow ships to pass
fossil fuel coal, oil, or natural gas
acid rain rain containing high amounts of chemical pollutants
landfill areas where trash companies dump the waste they collect

Reading Check Answer

The fuels burned for factories and in cars pollute the air. The pollution may then mix with water vapor and create acid rain.

Enrich

Have students investigate trade partnerships between the United States and other countries and present their findings in an annotated map.

Have students work in pairs or small groups to identify recent changes in technology and how they have affected jobs. Encourage students to use photos and other media to present their findings.

The fast-paced American way of life creates another problem. People generate huge amounts of trash. **Landfills,** the areas where trash companies dump the waste they collect, grow higher and higher each year. Many communities now promote **recycling,** or reusing materials instead of throwing them out. Recycling cuts down on the amount of trash.

New Technology The ability to develop new technology has been a major source of strength for the American economy. Researchers work constantly to find new products to make people's lives easier and healthier. Quality schools that produce educated and creative people have helped the country become a world leader in satellites, computers, medicine, and many other fields. You will need to learn and use new technologies to be productive and successful in your future jobs.

World Trade The United States leads the world in the value of all its imports and exports. Millions of Americans depend on trade for their jobs. American leaders have worked hard to promote free trade. **Free trade** means taking down trade barriers such as tariffs and quotas so that goods flow freely among countries. In 1993 the United States joined Mexico and Canada in the North American Free Trade Agreement (NAFTA). This agreement promised to remove all barriers to trade among these countries.

Reading Check How do factories and cars harm the environment in the United States?

Section 2 Assessment

Defining Terms

1. **Define** free enterprise system, service industry, navigable, fossil fuel, acid rain, landfill, recycling, free trade.

Recalling Facts

2. **Economics** Why is the Midwest called "America's breadbasket"?
3. **History** The discovery of which resources first brought settlers to the Interior West?
4. **Economics** What was the goal of NAFTA?

Critical Thinking

5. **Analyzing Information** Describe two characteristics of the United States that have made it a world economic leader.
6. **Understanding Cause and Effect** What reasons can you give for the economic changes taking place in the South?

Graphic Organizer

7. **Organizing Information** Draw a diagram like this one. Name one economic region of the United States in the center oval. In the outer ovals write examples for each subtopic.

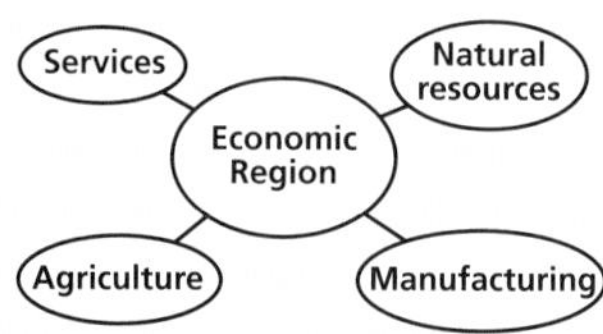

Applying Social Studies Skills

8. **Analyzing Maps** Study the economic activity map on page 132 and the physical map on page 127. What type of resources are found in or near the Rocky Mountains?

136

Section 2 Assessment

1. The terms are defined in the Glossary.
2. because so much food is grown there
3. gold and silver
4. to remove all barriers to trade among the United States, Canada, and Mexico (free trade)
5. The United States is rich in resources and has inventive people with the freedom to make profits.
6. Cities are expanding, and new manufacturing centers are drawing businesses there.
7. Webs will vary based on the region the student chooses.
8. coal, copper, natural gas, petroleum, uranium

TIME PERSPECTIVES

EXPLORING WORLD ISSUES

Protecting America's Freedoms from Terror

Keeping Liberty Safe

STAN HONDA/AFP/GETTY IMAGES

Compiled and adapted from TIME.

Exploring World Issues

Teacher Background

A long history of wars, displaced refugees, extreme poverty, and growing religious fundamentalism created the stew that boiled over into the horrific events of September 11, 2001. Many areas of Southwest Asia have long been ripe for extremist groups demanding retribution for perceived wrongs.

TIME REPORTS

THE UNITED STATES AND CANADA

Protecting America's Freedoms from Terror

THEME: CONFLICT AND CULTURES

Guide To Teaching With This Unit

Preparing the Student

Emphasize to students that most Muslims are peace-loving. Many different people—Basque separatists in Spain, Catholic and Protestant factions in Ireland, American Timothy McVeigh—have committed terrorist acts.

More About the Photo

Symbols Explain that the photo shows two light beams that serve as remembrances of the two fallen World Trade Center towers. **Ask:** What do you think the average American citizen feels when he or she sees this photo?

Making Connections

Terrorism Tell students that Secretary General Kofi Annan of the United Nations stated, "To defeat terrorism, we need a sustained effort and broad strategy that unites all nations." **Ask:** What do you think he meant by this statement? Do you think that working through the United Nations is the best way to fight terrorism? Or do you think it would be better for individual countries that are actually attacked by terrorists to fight them on their own? Have students support their opinions with examples. L1

1 Focus

Ask students to create a definition for *terrorism.* Write several definitions on the board. **Ask: How do you think terrorism differs from traditional warfare?**

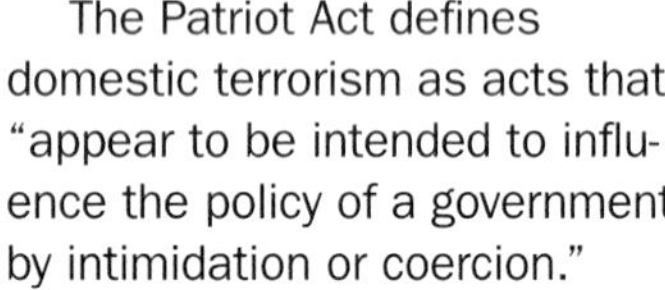

The Patriot Act defines domestic terrorism as acts that "appear to be intended to influence the policy of a government by intimidation or coercion."

More About the Photos

First Responders More than 300 rescue workers lost their lives trying to save others on September 11. **Ask: Do you think federal tax dollars should help support local fire and police departments—the "first responders" to a terrorist attack? Why or why not?**

TIME PERSPECTIVES

EXPLORING WORLD ISSUES

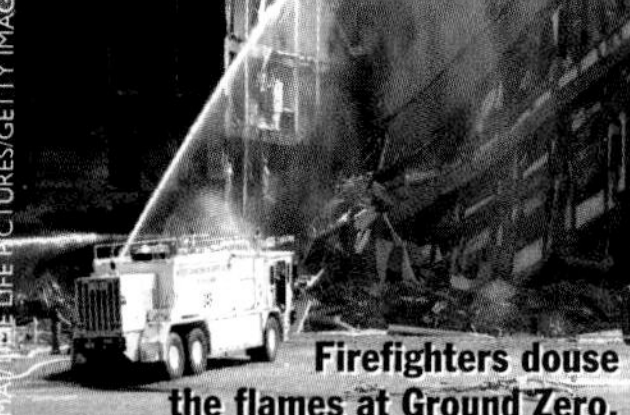

Firefighters douse the flames at Ground Zero.

The Day the Towers Fell

September 11, 2001, is a day no one will forget. At 8:46 A.M., a hijacked jumbo jet slammed into the north tower of the World Trade Center in New York City. A second hijacked plane plowed into the south tower at 9:03 A.M. About a half hour later, the south tower collapsed. Outside Washington, D.C., at 9:43 A.M., a third hijacked plane crashed into the Pentagon, the headquarters of the U.S. military. About 30 minutes later, a fourth jumbo jet crashed onto a field in Shanksville, Pennsylvania. Its target, which it never reached, may have been the White House, 124 miles away. Back in New York, the World Trade Center's north tower collapsed. It was 10:28 A.M. In less than two hours, 19 terrorists had murdered 2,976 innocent people.

America Reacts

The attacks stunned the world. They especially jarred the 4,000 students at the U.S. Military Academy at West Point, New York. These students realized they would soon be defending the nation against an entirely new kind of enemy.

"How do you fight this war and still stay true to the values of the United States?" a West Point professor asked her students shortly after the attack. She brought out a poster. It showed two curved lines facing each other. Outside one of the lines was the word *Liberty.* Outside the other line was the word *Security.* "What is the proper balance?" she asked. Americans have been wrestling with that question ever since that day—September 11, 2001.

Balancing Freedom and Safety

Freedom First

In the United States, the government can't take away people's right to...

- be free from unreasonable searches
- worship as they wish
- speak freely
- print and read what they want
- be free from cruel punishments
- protest government actions
- have fair, speedy, and public trials
- keep their personal affairs private

Compromises

To increase their safety, most Americans have seemed willing to accept...

- airport baggage searches
- metal detectors in schools
- court-okayed wiretaps
- concrete barriers in front of government buildings
- state bans on driving without a license
- police searches of people suspected of carrying weapons

Security First

In a country that puts security before freedom, the government might...

- search anyone without warning
- keep lists of members of a particular religion
- ban criticism of the government
- torture suspects
- hold trials in secret
- be free to access anyone's medical and financial records
- keep track of what people download to their computers
- close down newspapers it does not like

138

Differentiated Instruction

Meeting Special Needs: Interpersonal After the September 11, 2001, attacks on New York and Washington, D.C., many Americans said that they would not be defeated or frightened by the terrorists. Have students give an oral presentation, based on their personal experiences and what they have read and seen, that describes what they think is the essential American spirit. The presentation should discuss how and why Americans work as a group in times of crisis. Students should describe several instances they have personally witnessed and what it is about our culture, society, and government that encourages this type of behavior. L1

Refer to *Inclusion for the Middle School Social Studies Classroom Strategies and Activities* in the TCR.

Adults without proper I.D.s can't fly.

Blocked: the road to the Idaho Statehouse

National Guardsmen patrol the streets.

Airlines and Patriots

"September 11," or "**9/11,**" as the terrible event is called, made people everywhere more aware of the need for security. Governments reacted to those concerns in different ways. Some countries, like Japan, planned to require their citizens to carry electronic identification cards.

The United States tackled the problem in a different way. Shortly after 9/11, the United States Congress created new tools with which to combat terrorism. One of those tools was a new government agency, the Transportation Security Administration (TSA). The TSA's job is to find ways to make the nation's airlines and other transportation systems, such as railroads and trucking, safer.

The USA **Patriot Act** is another new weapon against terrorism. The law contains strong measures to prevent terrorism, detect it, and take legal action against it.

Most Americans welcomed the TSA and the Patriot Act. But many criticized them too. They worried that some freedoms might be taken away.

No-Fly Lists

The TSA created "no-fly" lists, which contained the names of people suspected of having links to terrorists. This means that airlines are not allowed to let anyone on the lists board an airplane. But many law-abiding Americans have been caught in TSA's web. One man complained that he was stopped every time he tried to fly. He had to prove each time that he was who he was—a 71-year-old, gray-haired, American-born English teacher.

The Patriot Act contained other measures that critics didn't like. One provision made it fairly easy for federal agents to search a citizen's library, business, and medical records.

This provision bothered Lynn Bradley, who works for an organization that represents librarians. She did not like the fact that the government could access private records. "People ask [me], 'Why are you interested in privacy when thousands of people were killed and there are soldiers at risk?'" she said. "We have in the United States a Constitution, a Bill of Rights, and all sorts of laws protecting privacy. One of the reasons we're fighting is to protect **rights** that [the terrorists] attacked us for in the first place." ■

EXPLORING THE ISSUE

1. **Analyzing Information** Why did the TSA create no-fly lists?
2. **Interpreting Points of View** Do you agree with Lynn Bradley that the Patriot Act might threaten individual rights? Why or why not?

139

2 TEACH

Reading Strategy

Identifying Main Ideas As students read each subsection in the "The Day the World Fell" section, have them write one sentence that expresses the main idea of that subsection. Have the class share and discuss their sentences. Repeat this process for the sections titled "Airlines and Patriots," "Protecting the Homeland," and "A Memorial for Heroes." L1

EXPLORING THE ISSUE

ANSWERS

1. The no-fly lists were an effort to make the airlines safer.
2. Answers will vary. A possible answer is *yes* because government officials might use the Patriot Act to persecute anyone who disagrees with them, not just terrorists.

Identifying Solutions Have small groups of students research terrorist actions or events that have involved or affected the United States. Instruct students to focus on results, effects, and solutions or countermeasures enacted by the United States. Ask students to discuss their findings and create charts identifying terrorist-related problems and possible solutions. L3

Critical Thinking Activity

Identifying Central Issues Adele Welty lost her son at the World Trade Center on September 11, 2001. Afterward she joined other family members of 9/11 victims in a group called September 11th Families for Peaceful Tomorrows. In September 2003 Welty spoke out in support of a bill that would cancel sections of the USA Patriot Act. Welty believed the sections posed a threat to Americans' "right to petition the government in cases where we believe the government's actions are contrary to the best interests of the American people." **Ask:** **Why might family members of 9/11 victims be especially concerned about the Patriot Act?** *(9/11 deaths are used to justify strong measures in the Patriot Act.)* L2

Recommended Internet Sites

www.un.org/terrorism
This United Nations Web site is titled "UN Action Against Terrorism." It contains UN statements and descriptions of current antiterrorist actions.

usinfo.state.gov
This Web site is maintained by the U.S. Department of State and contains information on a broad range of issues, including the U.S. government's response to terrorism.

www.pbs.org/americaresponds/educators.html
This site offers classroom resources and lesson plans in response to terrorist attacks.

EXPLORING THE ISSUE

ANSWERS

1. because the department is responsible for creating new medicines to protect Americans against smallpox and other biological agents
2. Possible answers are that in the course of protecting airports, borders, and seaports, the department may end up invading people's privacy and harassing travelers.

TIME PERSPECTIVES

Protecting the Homeland

On November 25, 2002, President George W. Bush signed a bill that gave birth to the U.S. government's third-largest department—the **Department of Homeland Security.** At its birth, the new department employed 170,000 people who worked for 22 different agencies. Among those agencies are the Coast Guard, the Border Patrol, the Secret Service, and the Customs Service. The president chose Tom Ridge, a former U.S. Congressman and governor of Pennsylvania, to head the department.

Department Responsibilities

The new department has four basic functions:

1. It analyzes information about terrorism provided by the Federal Bureau of Investigation (FBI) and the Central Intelligence Agency (CIA). It also helps state and local governments keep power plants and other possible homeland targets safe from terrorists.

2. It works to keep travelers safe and to protect airports, borders, and seaports.

3. It deals with natural and human-made disasters, ranging from hurricanes to terrorist attacks.

4. It oversees the development of new ways to detect weapons. It is also responsible for creating new medicines to protect Americans against smallpox and other biological agents.

The FBI and the CIA are not part of the new department. Secretary Ridge prefers it this way. "The CIA and the FBI provide reports and analysis to this department," he said. "We're a customer."

▲ At the U.S.–Canadian border, the U.S. Border Patrol has been working overtime since 9/11.

Americans cherish their right to be left alone. Can a government department dedicated to keeping citizens safe respect that right?

Secretary Ridge certainly thinks so. "Everyone from the president on down understands that protecting certain liberties and freedoms is at the very heart of who we are," he said. "[We intend] to make sure that we do everything we can within the law, within the Constitution, to improve our own security. It's a line that we have to walk carefully. There's a balance there, and I'm convinced it can be done."

EXPLORING THE ISSUE

1. **Making Inferences** Why should the Department of Homeland Security be involved with scientific research?
2. **Drawing Conclusions** What are some of the reasons people might be concerned about the new department's powers?

Critical Thinking Activity

Identifying Cause and Effect Some global issues, such as terrorism, unite people by creating common concerns, goals, and needs. Ask students to research various examples of how recent acts of terrorism have united people. Tell students to list possible advantages of such unification and ways in which it might lead to resolutions for problems of terrorism. Have students share their lists in a class discussion about what group measures might be taken in the future to combat or help prevent terrorism. **L3**

A Memorial for Heroes

Ancient people used to tell the story of the phoenix (FEE-nix). The phoenix was a sacred bird. When it reached the end of its life, it would burn itself up. Then it would rise from the ashes to begin its life again.

It took hundreds of workers eight months to haul away the smoldering remains of the World Trade Center. Then architects went to work. They drew up plans for a 16-acre city that would rise from the ashes like the phoenix.

A woman who lost her husband on 9/11 was happy to see the plans. "The greatest tribute to the people who died there," she said, "is to see life and rebirth."

A Long Process

It will take at least ten years to see exactly what will rise on the site. City planners, architects, political leaders, and builders will first have to agree on the size and shape of the buildings.

The memorial on the World Trade Center site has been chosen. It consists of two reflecting pools and a large grove of trees. This memorial, named "Reflecting Absence," occupies the towers' two "footprints." The names of all the 9/11 victims will be arranged around the pools to look like a ribbon of names.

The highest structure on the site will be the Freedom Tower. This twisting structure, exactly 1,776 feet (541 m) high, will be the first building to go up. Its height is a reminder of 1776, the year Americans declared their independence from Great Britain.

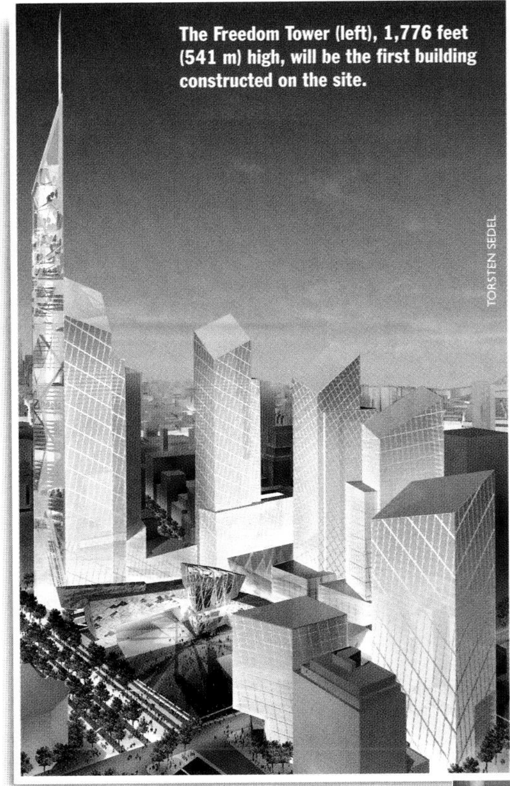

The Freedom Tower (left), 1,776 feet (541 m) high, will be the first building constructed on the site.

TORSTEN SEDEL

EXPLORING THE ISSUE

1. **Summarizing the Main Idea** Write a new title for this article. Tell your classmates why you think your title is a good one.
2. **Problem Solving** What sort of memorial would you like to see on the site?

Understanding Cause and Effect
Show several pictures of families, especially children, living in refugee camps. **Ask:** Do you think these young people are more or less likely to grow up to become followers of terrorist leaders than young people in America? Why or why not? If most students respond "yes," **Ask:** Do you think the United States can do anything to prevent this from happening? Encourage them to offer specific suggestions. L1

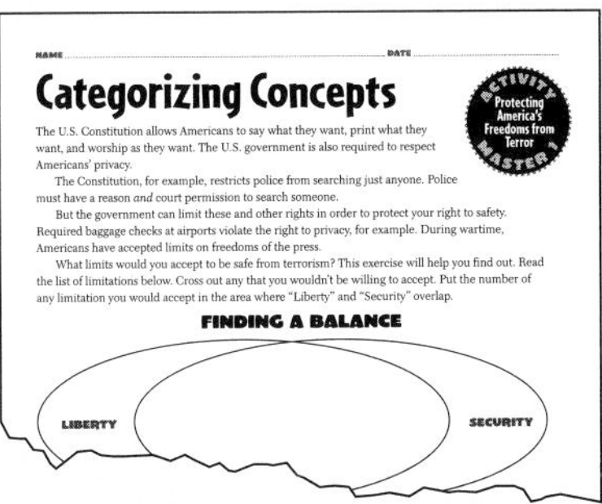

NAME ________ DATE ________

Categorizing Concepts

ACTIVITY Protecting America's Freedoms from Terror MASTER 1

The U.S. Constitution allows Americans to say what they want, print what they want, and worship as they want. The U.S. government is also required to respect Americans' privacy.

The Constitution, for example, restricts police from searching just anyone. Police must have a reason *and* court permission to search someone.

But the government can limit these and other rights in order to protect your right to safety. Required baggage checks at airports violate the right to privacy, for example. During wartime, Americans have accepted limits on freedoms of the press.

What limits would you accept to be safe from terrorism? This exercise will help you find out. Read the list of limitations below. Cross out any that you wouldn't be willing to accept. Put the number of any limitation you would accept in the area where "Liberty" and "Security" overlap.

FINDING A BALANCE

LIBERTY

SECURITY

EXPLORING THE ISSUE

ANSWERS

1. Titles will vary. Students' titles should focus on the main ideas of the article.
2. Answers will vary. Students should include descriptive details about the type of memorial that they would like to see on the site.

Interdisciplinary Activity

Art Have students design a monument that embodies the qualities shown by American citizens after the September 11, 2001, terrorist attacks. Students may want to look at newspaper and magazine articles, television reports, or Web sites about that time to inspire ideas. Students can use any medium, such as watercolors, acrylic or oil paints, collage, or clay. Ask for volunteers to show their designs to the class and explain the use of materials and symbolism. The rest of the class should then be encouraged to describe their emotional responses to the monument. L1

EE4 Human Systems: Standard 10

Current Events Journal

Have students find first-person accounts of three or four heroic acts that occurred in response to a terrorist attack. The attacks do not have to be in the United States. The students should write a brief description of each act. They should also write a discussion of what they believe motivated the person and how they might have acted under the same circumstances.

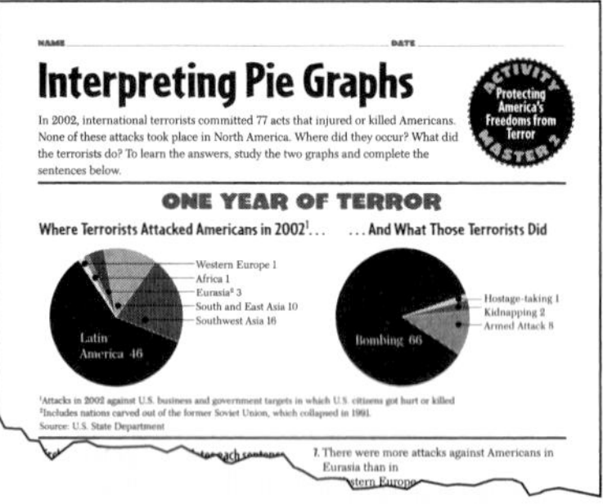

NAME ______ DATE ______

Interpreting Pie Graphs

ACTIVITY MASTER 2 — Protecting America's Freedoms from Terror

In 2002, international terrorists committed 77 acts that injured or killed Americans. None of these attacks took place in North America. Where did they occur? What did the terrorists do? To learn the answers, study the two graphs and complete the sentences below.

ONE YEAR OF TERROR

Where Terrorists Attacked Americans in 2002[1] . . .

Region	Attacks
Western Europe	1
Africa	1
Eurasia[2]	3
South and East Asia	10
Southwest Asia	16
Latin America	46

. . . And What Those Terrorists Did

Act	Number
Hostage-taking	1
Kidnapping	2
Armed Attack	8
Bombing	66

[1]Attacks in 2002 against U.S. business and government targets in which U.S. citizens got hurt or killed
[2]Includes nations carved out of the former Soviet Union, which collapsed in 1991
Source: U.S. State Department

7. There were more attacks against Americans in Eurasia than in

EXPLORING THE ISSUE

ANSWERS

1. Answers will vary. Students should support their suggestions with sound reasoning.
2. We should rally together and go on with our lives.

Defense Against Terror: What Can One Person Do?

"Terrorism forces us to make a choice," says Tom Ridge, secretary of the Department of Homeland Security. "We can be afraid. Or we can be ready."

It is very, very unlikely that terrorists will attack your neighborhood. But it can never hurt to prepare for the unexpected.

JOEL MEYEROWITZ

▲ **This New York firefighter survived 9/11. More than 300 did not.**

How can you do that? Prepare the same way you would if you were getting ready for a natural disaster like a hurricane or flood. Put together a kit of needed supplies: medicines, flashlights, batteries, a portable radio, and enough canned food and water to last three days. Add dense cotton cloth to your kit. Held over your mouth and nose, the cloth would filter out tiny airborne materials that could get into your lungs. Decide how family members will keep in touch with each other during a disaster. Get together with neighbors to figure out how you can help one another during an emergency.

Special Preparations

Terrorists use fear and misunderstanding to reach their goals. Make *understanding* one of your goals! Learn why some groups turn to terrorism. You'll find out that, in most cases, the terrorists cause as much fear and frustration in their own countries as they try to cause in the rest of the world. Promote communication and understanding by becoming pen pals with students in other regions.

As Secretary Ridge suggests, the mere fear of terrorism can leave scars. After 9/11, a West Point cadet knew what she would do to prevent that kind of fear. She recalled the Battle of Britain in 1940, when the Germans bombed English cities. The British "refused to let [the bombing] shut them down," she said. In the end, the British rallied together and won the battle. In the same way, we can prevent terrorists from shutting us down. ■

EXPLORING THE ISSUE

1. **Problem Solving** What suggestions would you give Secretary Ridge to help in the fight against terrorism?
2. **Making Inferences** What does the West Point cadet believe we should do to protect ourselves against the fear of terrorism?

Reading Strategy — Reading the Text

Responding and Reflecting After students have read "Defense Against Terror: What Can One Person Do?" have them think about how people can prepare for a terrorist attack. Discuss whether they believe the ideas presented in the reading are practical. **Ask:** **Can a country ever really be prepared for a terrorist attack?** Have students support their opinions with facts from the reading. L1

REVIEW AND ASSESS

UNDERSTANDING THE ISSUE

1. **Defining Key Terms** Write definitions for the following terms: *9/11, Patriot Act, rights, Department of Homeland Security.*

2. **Writing to Inform** In a brief essay, explain how 9/11 changed the nation. Use the words *airport, search, freedom,* and *security* in your essay.

3. **Writing to Persuade** A judge once said, "Your right to swing your arm stops at my nose." How might that statement apply to luggage searches at airports? Do you agree with the statement? Explain your answers in a short essay.

INTERNET RESEARCH ACTIVITIES

4. With your teacher's help, navigate to **www.ready.gov**. Explore one of the three main items on the page. Write a short essay that explains what you learned about preparing for a terrorist attack.

5. Navigate to **www.lifeandliberty.gov**, where the United States Department of Justice defends the Patriot Act. Jot down two arguments for the law. Then navigate to **www.epic.org/privacy/terrorism/usapatriot**. EPIC is a group that has some concerns about the law. Jot down two of EPIC's concerns. Explain to your classmates how these arguments shaped your view of the law.

BEYOND THE CLASSROOM

6. **In your local library,** research the impact of terrorism on nations such as Sri Lanka and Israel. Why is terrorism more common in those nations than in the United States? Summarize your conclusions and share them with your classmates.

7. **Working in groups,** create posters that explain how to prepare for any disaster, including a terrorist attack. Display your posters where other students in your school can see them.

PHOTODISC

▲ **The American flag is a symbol of freedom.**

Ground Zero: A Proposal for Renewal

This plan for rebuilding Ground Zero is sure to change as time goes by.

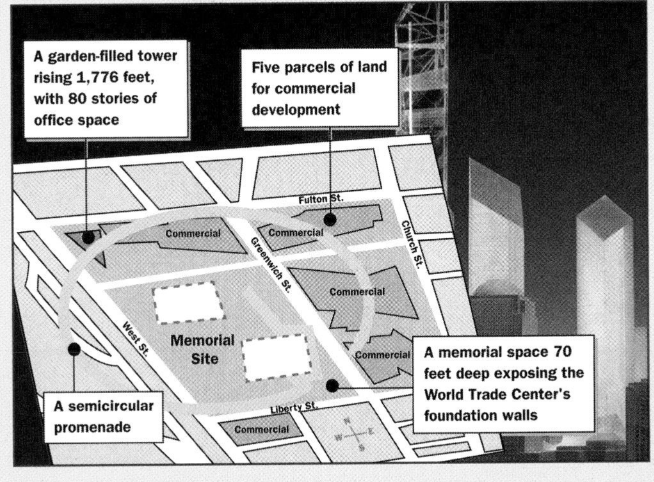

BACKGROUND PHOTO ©JOCK POTTLE

BUILDING MAP READING SKILLS

1. **Explaining** Two pools with cascading waterfalls will be placed in the two towers' "footprints." The architect named this memorial "Reflecting Absence." What does this mean to you?
2. **Making Generalizations** How do you think you would feel if you visited the site and saw the exposed foundation wall?

FOR UPDATES ON WORLD ISSUES GO TO www.timeclassroom.com/glencoe

143

3 ASSESS

Have students take the Time Reports Quiz or do the Alternative Assessment project for this unit provided in the Teacher's Classroom Resources.

BUILDING MAP READING SKILLS

ANSWERS

1. Answers will vary.
2. Answers will vary. Students should describe how the exposed wall would affect them.

CLOSE

Reading Strategy

Writing a Paragraph Ask students to write a paragraph starting with this topic sentence: *The best way that a democratic government can protect itself from terrorism is . . . .*

Culminating Activity

To close this lesson, have students complete the Review and Assess section questions and activities above. Students should use classroom discussion, contextual clues, and their student dictionaries to write definitions for terms. Before assigning the Internet activities, it is recommended that you review your school district policy on student Internet use.

Focus on Debate
Mohandas Gandhi, who led the nonviolent fight for India's freedom, stated, "There is no way to peace. Peace is the way." Ask students what this statement means to them and how it relates to terrorism. Then have them debate the pros and cons of Gandhi's philosophy. L2

 **EE4 Human Systems: Standard 10**

TEACH

Ask students to imagine that they have invited a new friend to visit them. Have them create a map of the route from the school to their home. Allow students a short time to make sketch maps. Then ask how many students made a mental picture of the route in order to create the map. Explain that the process of visualizing places and routes is called mental mapping. Direct students to read the skill and complete the practice questions. L1

Additional Skills Practice

1. **How would you create a map of the school?** *(Ask for volunteers to sketch their maps on the board.)*
2. **Why compare a map that you sketch to an actual map of the place?** *(to make any needed changes so it is accurate)*

Additional Skills Resources

 Chapter Skills Review

 Building Geography Skills for Life

GLENCOE TECHNOLOGY

 **Skillbuilder Interactive Workbook CD-ROM, Level 1**

This interactive CD-ROM reinforces student mastery of essential social studies skills.

Social Studies Skill

Mental Mapping

Think about how you get from place to place each day. In your mind you have a picture—or **mental map**—of your route. If necessary, you could probably create sketch maps like the one below of many familiar places.

Learning the Skill

To develop your mental mapping skills, follow these steps.

- When a country or city name is mentioned, find it on a map to get an idea of where it is and what is near it.
- Create a sketch map of it and include a compass rose to determine the cardinal directions.
- As you read or hear information about the place, try to picture where on your sketch you would fill in this information.
- Compare your sketch to an actual map of the place. Change your sketch if you need to, thus changing your mental map.

Practicing the Skill

Study the sketch map at the right. Picture yourself standing *in* the map, then answer the following questions.

1. If you were facing north, looking at the Chicago Cultural Center, what route would you take to reach the Chicago Harbor?
2. You are at the Sears Tower, one of the tallest buildings in the world. About how many miles would you have to walk to get to Medinah Temple?
3. If you met your friend at the cultural center, would it be too far to walk to the Art Institute? Should you take a taxi? Explain.

Applying the Skill

Think about your own neighborhood. Create a sketch map of it from your mental map. Which neighborhood streets or roads did you include? What are the three most important features on your map?

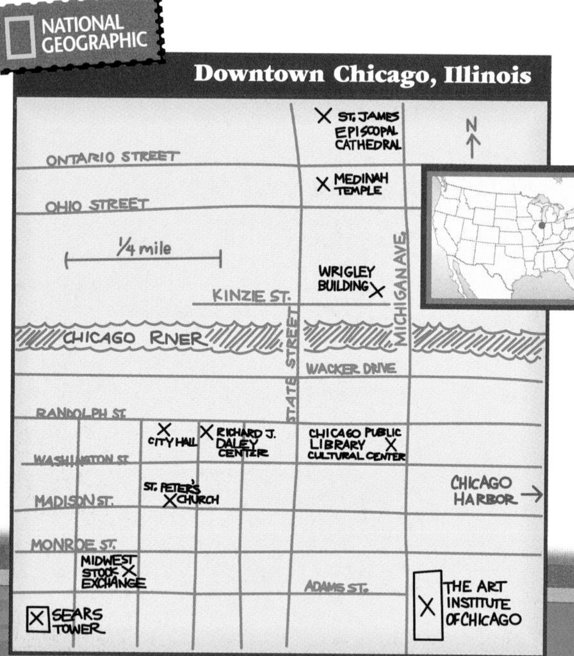

Practicing the Skill Answers

1. turn right and walk along Washington Street
2. about $1\frac{1}{4}$ miles
3. It would be easy to walk—the distance is only 3 blocks. There is no need to take a taxi.

Applying the Skill

Check students' mental maps for accuracy and to be sure they included at least three important features. Have students explain why they identified certain features as important.

Section 3 The Americans

Guide to Reading

Main Idea

The United States is a land of many cultures.

Terms to Know

- colony
- representative democracy
- federal republic
- secede
- immigrant
- rural
- urban
- suburb

Reading Strategy

Create a diagram like this one. In each outer oval, write one fact about American society as it relates to the topic given.

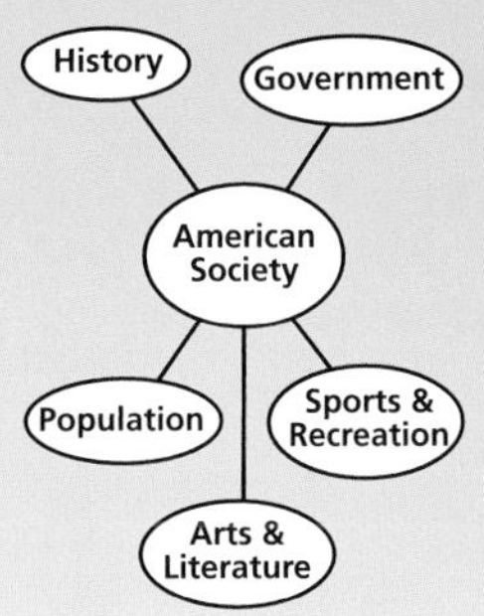

NATIONAL GEOGRAPHIC Exploring Our World

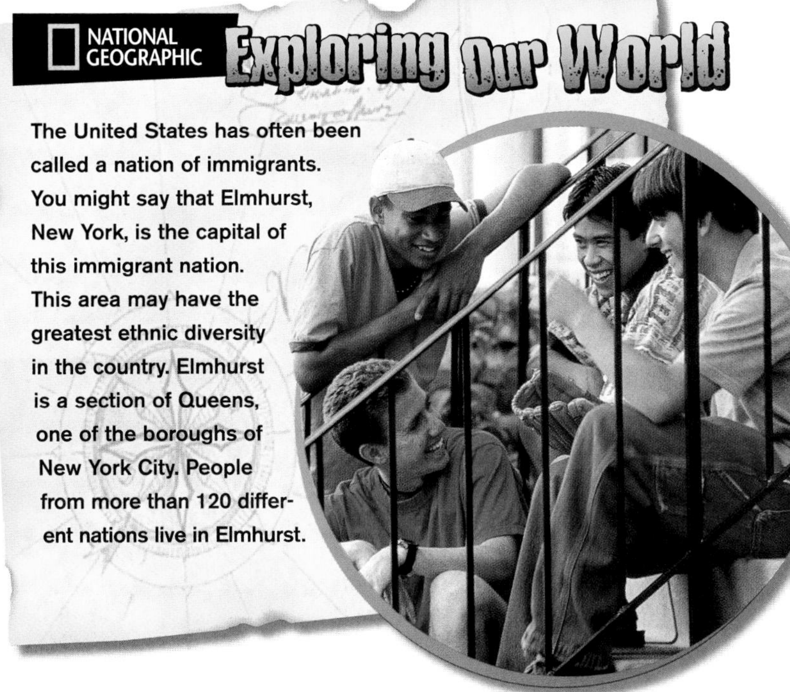

The United States has often been called a nation of immigrants. You might say that Elmhurst, New York, is the capital of this immigrant nation. This area may have the greatest ethnic diversity in the country. Elmhurst is a section of Queens, one of the boroughs of New York City. People from more than 120 different nations live in Elmhurst.

The United States is a young country compared to many others. It became an independent nation a little more than 225 years ago. American history starts much earlier than this, however.

A Rich History

Experts have long believed that the first people to settle in the Americas came from Asia about 15,000 years ago. At that time, the earth's climate was much colder than it is now. Huge sheets of ice covered much of the Northern Hemisphere. As a result, sea levels were lower, and a land bridge connected Asia and Alaska. Herd animals crossed this bridge—and the people who hunted them followed.

Native Americans The people who crossed the land bridge from Asia slowly fanned out over the Americas. Their descendants today are called Native Americans. Over time, they developed different ways of life using local resources. In the Northeast, the people hunted deer and fished. In the fertile lands of the Southeast and Mississippi Valley, they grew corn and other crops. On the dry, treeless Great Plains, the Native

Section Resources

Reproducible Masters

- Reproducible Lesson Plan
- Daily Lecture and Discussion Notes
- Note-taking Guide
- Guided Reading Activity
- Reading Essentials and Study Guide
- Section Quiz

Transparencies

- Daily Focus Skills Transparency
- In-text Map Transparency

Multimedia

- Vocabulary PuzzleMaker CD-ROM
- Interactive Tutor Self-Assessment CD-ROM
- Presentation Plus! CD-ROM
- ExamView® Pro Testmaker CD-ROM
- MindJogger Videoquiz

1 Focus

Section Objectives

1. Describe how the United States changed throughout its history.
2. Explain what form of government the United States has.
3. Identify what groups make up the American people.
4. Discuss what has influenced American culture.

BELLRINGER Skillbuilder Activity

Project transparency and have students answer the question.

Daily Focus Skills Transparency

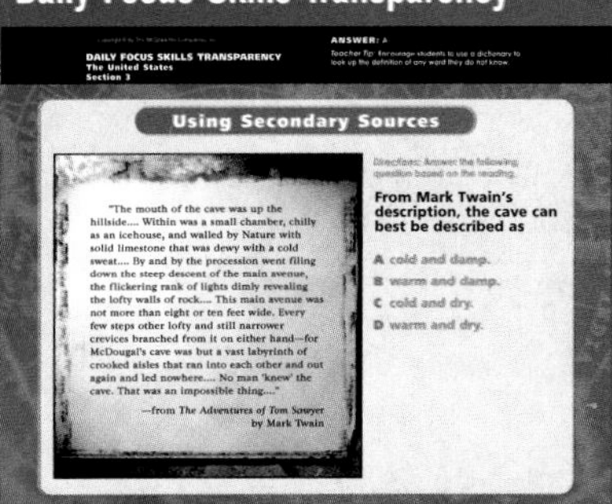

ANSWER: A

Teacher Tip: Encourage students to use a dictionary to look up the definition of any word they do not know.

DAILY FOCUS SKILLS TRANSPARENCY
The United States
Section 3

Using Secondary Sources

"The mouth of the cave was up the hillside.... Within was a small chamber, chilly as an icehouse, and walled by Nature with solid limestone that was dewy with a cold sweat.... By and by the procession went filing down the steep descent of the main avenue, the flickering rank of lights dimly revealing the lofty walls of rock.... This main avenue was not more than eight or ten feet wide. Every few steps other lofty and still narrower crevices branched from it on either hand—for McDougal's cave was but a vast labyrinth of crooked aisles that ran into each other and out again and led nowhere.... No man 'knew' the cave. That was an impossible thing...."

—from *The Adventures of Tom Sawyer* by Mark Twain

Directions: Answer the following question based on the reading.

From Mark Twain's description, the cave can best be described as

A cold and damp.
B warm and damp.
C cold and dry.
D warm and dry.

Reading Preview

■ **Activating Prior Knowledge** Have students suggest the names of different ethnic restaurants. Then ask them why they think the United States has such a variety of foods.

■ **Preteaching Vocabulary** Have students describe what they know about the terms *urban, rural,* and *suburbs.*

TEACH

Creating a Map Give students political maps of the United States. Have them write in the dates that each state entered the Union. Then have them color the states, grouping them by 1700s, 1800 to 1850, 1851 to 1900, and 1901 to today. Have them identify which period saw the most states enter the United States. *(1700s: 16; 1800–1850: 15; 1851–1900: 14: 1901–today: 5)* **L1**

Daily Lecture and Discussion Notes

THE UNITED STATES

Daily Lecture and Discussion Notes

The Americans

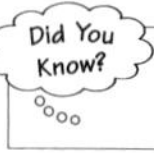

Within the span of 100 years—in the 1600s and early 1700s—a tide of immigrants from Europe to America built a nation out of a wilderness, and largely shaped the character and destiny of a previously uncharted continent.

I. A Rich History

A. Experts believe that the first Americans came from Asia on a land bridge that connected Asia with present-day Alaska. Their descendants today are known as Native Americans.

B. Around A.D. 1500, Europeans arrived in the Americas. Because of the ...dance of raw materials, European countries set up **colonies** in the ... colonists soon began to see themselves as Ameri...

Cultural Kaleidoscope

Spanish Settlements In 1565 the Spanish planted their first colony in what is today the United States, when Pedro Menéndez de Avilés founded a settlement at St. Augustine, Florida. In 1598, five years before the English settled in Jamestown, Virginia, the Spanish sent colonists to New Mexico. In 1610 they founded Santa Fe as the capital of this colony.

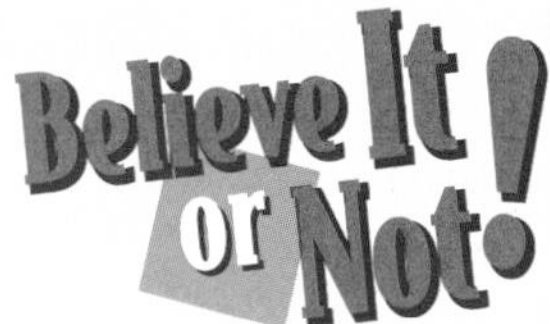

San Xavier del Bac

Is this Catholic church in Spain? In Mexico? No, this Spanish-style church, called San Xavier del Bac, stands near Tucson, Arizona. Settlers built the church in 1797, when the area was part of Spain's colonial empire. In fact, many Spanish settlements in the American Southwest were founded in the 1500s, long before the English Pilgrims sailed to the Americas on the *Mayflower*.

Americans hunted buffalo, which provided them with food, clothing, and shelter. In the dry Southwest, the people irrigated the land to grow corn and beans. In the Northwest, they fished.

Explorers and Colonists Around A.D. 1500, Europeans began to explore the Americas. The raw materials they saw—forests, animal furs, and rich soils—soon led them to set up **colonies.** These are overseas settlements tied to a parent country. The French built trading posts around the Great Lakes and interior river valleys. The Spanish built towns and missions in Florida and Georgia and from Texas to California. British and northern European colonists settled along the Atlantic coast from Massachusetts to Georgia.

By the mid-1700s, the people living in the British colonies had started to see themselves as Americans rather than as British citizens. They were frustrated with British policies that disregarded their rights. In 1775, thirteen of the British colonies rebelled. On July 4, 1776, they declared independence and created the United States of America. For the next five long years, colonial troops battled British soldiers in the American Revolution. With the help of France and Spain, the Americans won the war.

The U.S. Constitution The 13 former British colonies became the first 13 states. Each quickly wrote a state constitution, or plan of government. Developing a *national* plan of government proved harder, however. In 1787 a group of American leaders met in Philadelphia to create a new national government. They wrote the document called the United States Constitution.

The U.S. Constitution is still in place after more than 200 years. It is the basis for all our laws. It also explains how our national or central government is set up and works. Early American leaders' goal was to create a government strong enough to provide for the common good. They also wanted a government with limited powers so that people's rights would be protected from government interference. Because the U.S. Constitution has worked so well in achieving both goals, it has been used as a model by many other countries.

The U.S. Constitution went into effect in 1789, but it has grown and changed over the years. Through a process called amending, Americans have a peaceful way to change the basic laws of their government. A constitutional amendment is a change or addition to the Constitution. The first ten amendments, passed in 1791, are called the Bill of Rights. They list specific freedoms guaranteed to individual Americans, such as freedoms of speech and religion.

A Federal Republic Our government is based on the principle of democracy, or rule by the people. There are many different types of democracies. We have a **representative democracy,** in which voters choose leaders who make and enforce the laws.

When the Constitution was approved in 1788, each state kept its own government. Voters of each state also chose people to serve in the national government. This system makes the United States a

Reading Strategy — Reading the Text

Sequencing Information Organize students into groups and assign each group a time period in American history: pre-Columbian, colonial, Revolution to early 1800s, nineteenth century, and twentieth century. Have students use several sheets of butcher paper to construct a time line running along one or more walls of the classroom. Direct groups to research their time period and select 10 important events from that period to enter on the time line. Have group representatives write their selections in the correct places on the line. Ask them to add annotations explaining their entries. **L1**

Use the ***Reading Skills Handbook*** *for more reading strategies.*

federal republic. This is a form of government in which power is divided between the federal, or national, government and the state governments. A president serves as the leader of the nation. The Constitution also divided the national government into three branches so that no person or group could gain too much power. The chart on page 148 shows the three branches of the national government.

A Period of Growth From 1800 to 1900, the United States experienced tremendous growth. It expanded from the 13 states along the Atlantic coast to include 45 states that reached to the Pacific Ocean. The population boomed as millions of people settled here from other lands. Surveyors were hired to establish plot boundaries for land sales. In what is today the Midwest, settlers purchased rectangular plots, cleared forests, and grew corn. In the South, huge cotton plantations arose. When gold was discovered in California, miners surged past the Rocky Mountains. In their rush to grab land, settlers often fought with Native Americans who were being pushed out of the way.

The Industrial Revolution, which began in Great Britain, spread to the United States. Water-powered factories sprang up along fast-moving rivers. Roads and canals were built to help farmers move their products to ports. The emergence of steamboats allowed upstream travel.

In the mid-1800s, the nation experienced a crisis. The South had built its economy on slavery. Hundreds of thousands of enslaved Africans had been forced to work on Southern plantations. Over time, the issues of slavery and states' rights divided the country. In 1861 several Southern states seceded, or withdrew from the national government. For four years, the North and the South fought the bitter Civil War. In the end, the Southern states were brought back into the Union, and slavery was abolished.

The Civil War did more than end slavery. It also launched the country into a period of great economic and technological growth.

NATIONAL GEOGRAPHIC **On Location**

The Founders

With very few exceptions, the world knew only monarchies and absolute rulers when courageous leaders such as Thomas Jefferson (left), George Washington (center), and James Madison (right) risked their lives and fortunes to spearhead the drive for an independent United States. Jefferson was the chief author of the Declaration of Independence, which the Continental Congress formally issued on July 4, 1776. Washington led the new nation's army in the Revolution, chaired the Constitutional Convention, and became the first president under the U.S. Constitution. Madison is considered the master builder of the Constitution. He later served as president.

Beliefs Why do you think that the Founders were willing to risk their lives and fortunes to establish the United States?

Chapter 4

Section 3, pages 145–151

Analyzing Information

Have students define *culture region.* Write the following headings: "Cultures," "Homes," "Standard of Living," and "Recreation." Call on volunteers to identify characteristics of American people living in cities, suburbs, and rural areas under each heading. List the responses under the appropriate heading. Use this information to lead a discussion of why it is so difficult to describe a "typical American." L1

More About the Photos

The Founders The delegates to the Second Continental Congress were aware that by signing the Declaration of Independence they were signing their death warrants because they were declaring their open rebellion against Britain. In British eyes, they were committing treason.

Caption Answer Students might suggest that they were willing to sacrifice everything to safeguard individual liberty.

Differentiated Instruction

Meeting Special Needs: Less-proficient Readers Students who have difficulty understanding text structure may benefit from the following exercise. Have students tie the illustrations to the text by finding sentences or paragraphs that relate to each picture, map, or diagram in the section. Then have them compare what they learn from the illustrations with what they learn from the text. L1

Refer to *Inclusion for the Middle School Social Studies Classroom Strategies and Activities* in the TCR.

Analyzing the Diagram

Answer
the legislative branch

Skills Practice
What are the two lawmaking bodies of the federal government? *(Senate and House of Representatives)*

Interdisciplinary Connections

History The building of the transcontinental railroad in the 1860s opened up much of the West for settlement. The Union Pacific Railroad, which began in California, hired immigrant laborers, mostly from China, to lay track. Thousands of Chinese came to the United States to join this work.

Branches of the United States Government

Analyzing the Diagram

The United States government has three main branches.

Government Which branch makes the laws?

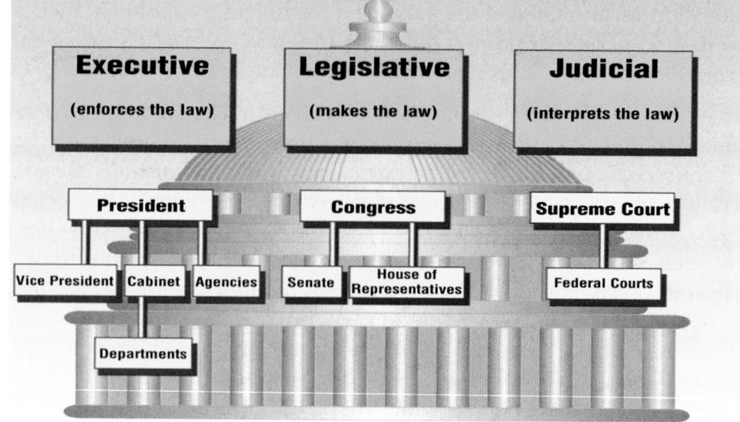

Railroads crisscrossed the land, and large factories were built, especially in the Northeast and Midwest. This economic expansion attracted another great wave of **immigrants**, or people who move to a new country to make a permanent home.

A World Leader During the early 1900s, the United States became one of the leading economies in the world. Automobiles rolled off assembly lines and electricity became common. Other technologies, such as the telephone and the radio, entered daily life.

The world plunged into two World Wars in the first half of the twentieth century. The United States took part in these wars. Our country's leaders urged the world's people to fight for freedom against dangerous dictators. American factories produced tanks and airplanes, while American soldiers helped win the wars.

After World War II, the United States enjoyed great influence around the world. American companies shipped their products to all continents. American leaders pushed for democracy and free enterprise in other countries. American culture spread around the globe.

At home, however, tensions existed among groups within American society. Many of the Americans who had fought in the two World Wars or had taken care of the home front were women, African Americans, Hispanic Americans, and Native Americans. After World War II, these groups became more active in seeking equal rights. Many people, including such leaders as Martin Luther King, Jr., developed methods that led to civil change. The poems on page 152 describe two views of Americans struggling to be accepted.

Security Americans have normally felt safe in their own country. After terrorists attacked New York City and Washington, D.C., on September 11, 2001, this feeling of security was tested, however.

Content Background

Steerage Many immigrants endured hardships as they traveled to the United States. By packing passengers aboard ships and giving them almost nothing in the way of privacy or comforts, ship operators were able to offer low fares. Third class, the most inexpensive ticket, offered noisy, cramped conditions. Third class was also referred to as steerage because accommodations were near the ship's steering mechanism. Unlike wealthier first- and second-class passengers who encountered brief inspections on board, steerage passengers were required to undergo a far more lengthy inspection when they arrived on Ellis Island.

President Bush responded by signing the Homeland Security Act into law. This act established a new cabinet department—the Department of Homeland Security—to coordinate government agencies charged with protecting the nation from terrorist attacks.

✓ Reading Check **How did a strong economy help spread American culture?**

One Out of Many

About 292 million people live in the United States, making it the third most populous country after China and India. Compared with people in most other countries, Americans enjoy a high standard of living. Americans, on the average, can expect to live about 77 years. Medical advances have helped people to live longer than earlier generations.

Almost three-fourths of the people in our country descended from European ethnic groups. African Americans form about 12 percent of the population. Hispanics, who trace their heritages to the countries of Latin America and Spain, are the fastest-growing ethnic group. Today many immigrants to the United States come from China, India, other

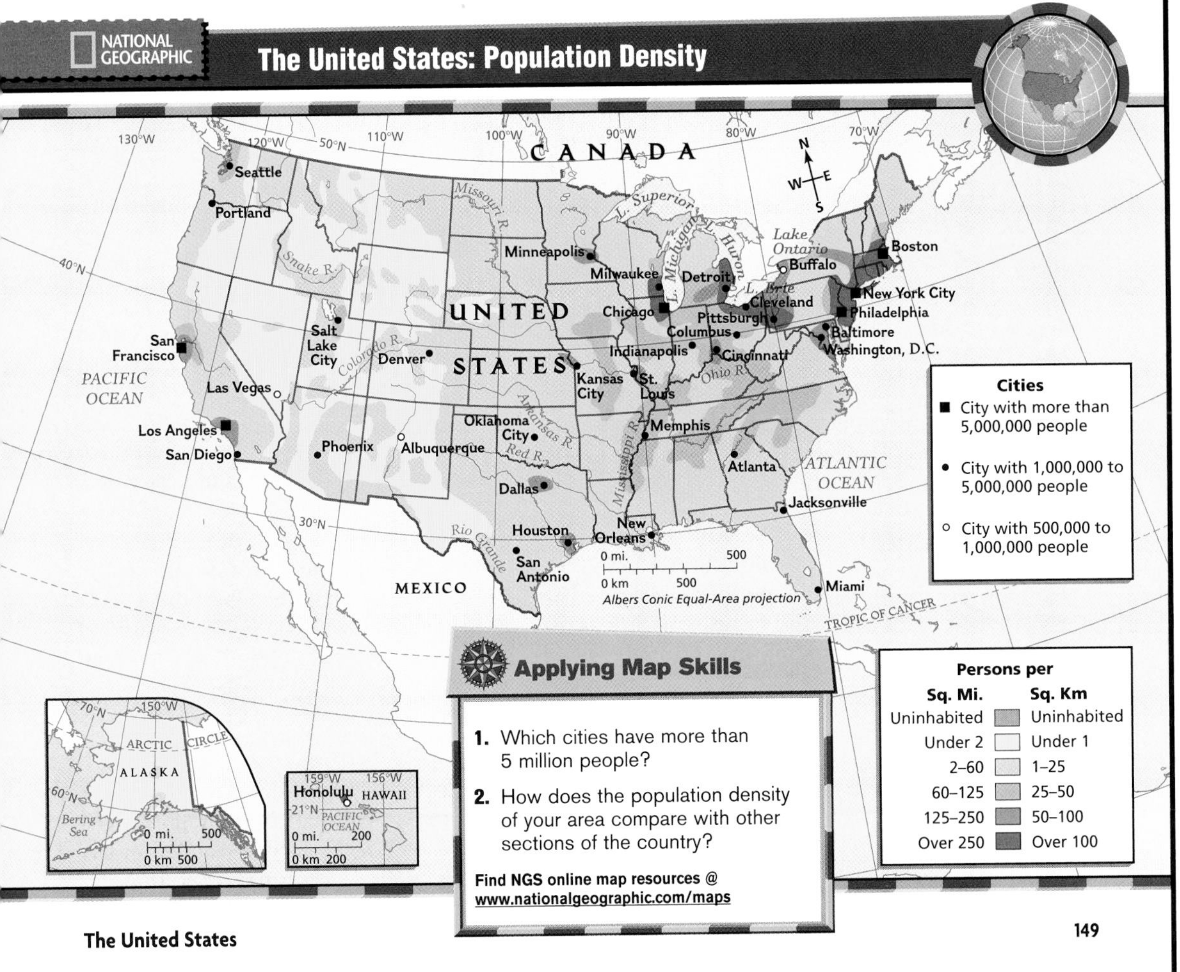

Chapter 4

Section 3, pages 145–151

✓ Reading Check Answer

After World War II, American companies shipped their products to all continents. American leaders worked to establish democracy and free enterprise in other countries.

Applying Map Skills

Answers

1. New York City, Chicago, Los Angeles, San Francisco, Boston, Philadelphia
2. Check answers for accuracy.

In-text Map Transparency Activity Point to the regions of the map that have the highest population densities. Ask students what these regions have in common. *(They are located near bodies of water or waterways.)* Then have students explain why these areas might be densely populated. *(These regions are easily accessed by water and are important areas for business and trade; the economies draw people to these regions.)*

L1/ELL

Guided Reading Activity

Name ______ Date ______ Class ______

THE UNITED STATES

Guided Reading Activity 3

The Americans

DIRECTIONS: Summarizing Reading the section and completing the summary below will help you learn more about the people of the United States. Use your textbook to fill in the blanks.

Experts believe the first Americans were from **(1)** ______ and followed their herds over a **(2)** ______. They developed **(3)** ______ ways of life using their **(4)** ______ ______. Around 1500 **(5)** ______ began to explore the Americas. The raw materials caused them to set up **(6)** ______. By the ... frustrated with **(7)** ______

Cooperative Learning Activity

Role Playing Assign student groups an ethnic group or minority that has had to fight for equal rights or been the victim of discrimination. Some possibilities are African Americans, Native Americans, Hispanics, Asians, Middle Eastern people, various religious groups, handicapped people, and women. Groups should research the history of their subject: examples of prejudice, significant events in the fight for equality or justice, important leaders. Each member of the group should write a short speech as if they were a member of the minority or one of its leaders, covering different aspects of their group's history. Have students make their speeches to the rest of the class. L1

EE4 Human Systems: Standard 13

More About the Photo

Cultural Influences The term *melting pot* implies that cultures blend together to form one. The term *mosaic* implies that each culture retains its identity within the whole.

Caption Answer Students should identify ethnic influences in their community.

Reading Check Answer

the Hispanic ethnic group

Assess

Assign Section 3 Assessment as homework or an in-class activity.

Have students use the Interactive Tutor Self-Assessment CD-ROM to review Section 3.

L2

Section Quiz

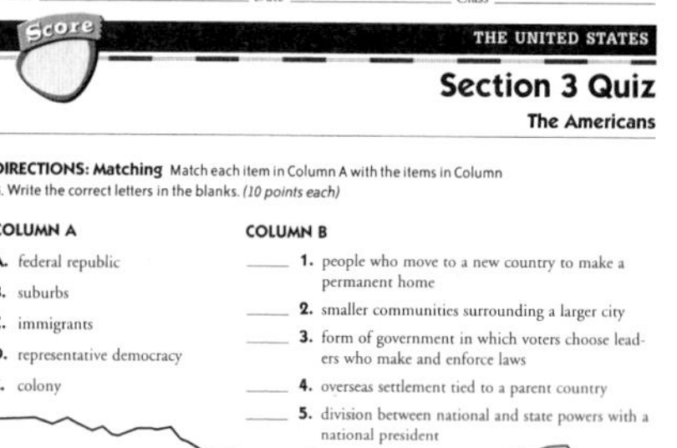

Name ________ Date ________ Class ________

Score

THE UNITED STATES

Section 3 Quiz

The Americans

DIRECTIONS: Matching Match each item in Column A with the items in Column B. Write the correct letters in the blanks. *(10 points each)*

COLUMN A	COLUMN B
A. federal republic	____ 1. people who move to a new country to make a permanent home
B. suburbs	____ 2. smaller communities surrounding a larger city
C. immigrants	____ 3. form of government in which voters choose leaders who make and enforce laws
D. representative democracy	____ 4. overseas settlement tied to a parent country
E. colony	____ 5. division between national and state powers with a national president

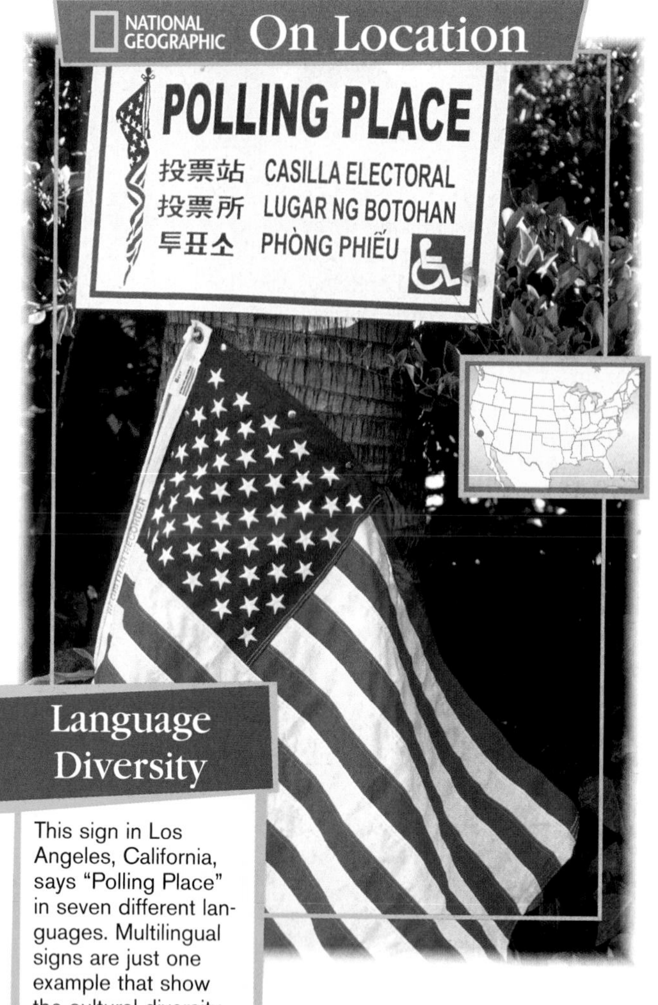

NATIONAL GEOGRAPHIC On Location
POLLING PLACE
投票站 CASILLA ELECTORAL
投票所 LUGAR NG BOTOHAN
투표소 PHÒNG PHIẾU

Language Diversity

This sign in Los Angeles, California, says "Polling Place" in seven different languages. Multilingual signs are just one example that show the cultural diversity in the United States.

Culture **What buildings or restaurants in your town reflect an ethnic group?**

Asian countries, and the Pacific Islands. The smallest ethnic group—Native American—has lived in the country the longest. A graph on page 121 shows the country's different ethnic groups.

Language and Religion The main language of the United States is English, but you can hear many languages spoken here. Spanish is commonly heard throughout Florida, Texas, and California. In California you can also read signs in Chinese and Korean.

Religion has always been an important influence on American life. About 80 percent of Americans consider themselves religious, and almost 50 percent attend a religious service on a regular basis. Most Americans follow some form of Christianity. Judaism, Islam, Buddhism, and Hinduism are also practiced in our country.

Mobility Americans have always been a mobile people, moving from place to place. At one time, our nation was made up entirely of **rural,** or countryside, areas. Now we are primarily a nation of **urban,** or city, dwellers. To find more room to live, Americans move from cities to the **suburbs,** or smaller communities surrounding a larger city. They also move from one region to another to seek a better climate or better jobs. Since the 1970s, the fastest-growing areas in the country have been in the South and Southwest—often called the Sunbelt.

Reading Check **Which ethnic group is the fastest growing?**

American Culture

American artists and writers have developed distinctly American styles. The earliest American artists used materials from their environments to create works of art. Native Americans carved wooden masks and totems or made beautiful designs on pottery from clay found in

Team-Teaching Activity

Language Arts Work with a foreign language teacher to help students learn a few common words in several different languages used in the United States. Words might include those for "hello," "goodbye," "dinner," and "friend." Languages could include Spanish, German, Italian, Chinese, Korean, Hindi, and Vietnamese, among others. If any students speak a language other than English at home, you might ask them to teach words from their language. **Ask:** **Why is it important to learn another language? L1 ELL**

EE4 Human Systems: Standard 10

their areas. Later artists were attracted to the beauty of the landscape. Winslow Homer painted the stormy waters of the North Atlantic. Georgia O'Keeffe painted the colorful deserts of the Southwest. Thomas Eakins and John Sloan often painted the gritty side of city life.

Two themes are common to American literature. One theme focuses on the rich diversity of the people in the United States. The poetry of Langston Hughes and the novels of Toni Morrison portray the triumphs and sorrows of African Americans. The novels of Amy Tan examine the lives of Chinese Americans. Oscar Hijuelos and Sandra Cisneros write about the country's Hispanics.

A second theme focuses on the landscape and history of particular regions. Mark Twain's books tell about life along the Mississippi River in the mid-1800s. Nathaniel Hawthorne wrote about the people of New England. Willa Cather and Laura Ingalls Wilder portrayed the struggles people faced in settling the Great Plains. William Faulkner wrote stories about life in the South.

Web Activity Visit ***The World and Its People*** Web site at twip.glencoe.com and click on **Chapter 4—Student Web Activities** to learn more about the national park system in the United States.

Sports and Recreation Many Americans spend their leisure time at home, reading books or using a computer. Many also pursue active lives outdoors. They may bike, ski, shoot baskets, or kick soccer balls. Spectator sports such as baseball and football draw large crowds. Millions each year travel to national parks, or areas set aside to protect wilderness and wildlife.

✓ Reading Check What are two common themes in American literature?

Section 3 Assessment

Defining Terms

1. **Define** colony, representative democracy, federal republic, secede, immigrant, rural, urban, suburb.

Recalling Facts

2. **History** What route do experts think the first Americans took to reach North America?
3. **Government** What document explains the form of government used in the United States?
4. **Culture** What theme do the works of Langston Hughes and Toni Morrison share?

Critical Thinking

5. **Analyzing Information** After World War II, what tensions existed at home?
6. **Drawing Conclusions** How do climate and culture influence the popularity of sports in your area?

Graphic Organizer

7. **Organizing Information** Draw a diagram like the one below. At the tops of the three arrows, list three reasons that Americans today are moving more frequently than ever.

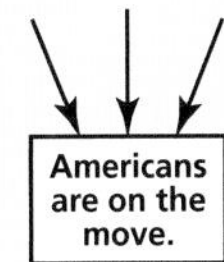

Applying Social Studies Skills

8. **Analyzing Maps** According to the population density map on page 149, what are the two largest cities in the Pacific Northwest?

Section 3 Assessment

1. The terms are defined in the Glossary.
2. They came from Asia across a land bridge to Alaska.
3. the Constitution of the United States
4. the triumphs and sorrows of African Americans
5. Tensions developed when women, African Americans, and Hispanic Americans wanted equal rights.
6. Students' answers will vary but should be supported by good reasoning.
7. to find more room to live, to seek a better climate, to find better jobs
8. Seattle and Portland

Objectives and answers to the Student Web Activity can be found in the Web Activity Lesson Plan at twip.glencoe.com

✓ Reading Check Answer

the rich diversity of the people; the landscape and history of regions

L1/ELL

Reading Essentials and Study Guide

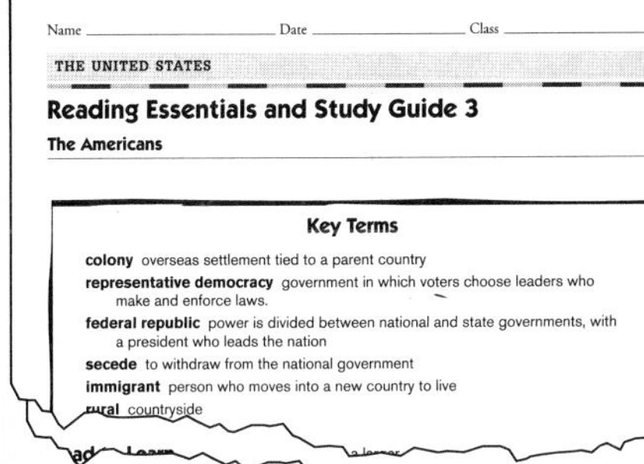
Name Date Class

THE UNITED STATES

Reading Essentials and Study Guide 3

The Americans

Key Terms

colony overseas settlement tied to a parent country
representative democracy government in which voters choose leaders who make and enforce laws.
federal republic power is divided between national and state governments, with a president who leads the nation
secede to withdraw from the national government
immigrant person who moves into a new country to live
rural countryside

4 Close

Reading Strategy

Writing a Paragraph Have students write a paragraph titled "What It Means to Be an American."

TEACH

Native American music and jazz, which influenced the work of Langston Hughes, both have strong rhythms. Play a selection of Native American music and a short jazz instrumental. **Ask:** How do the two musical styles compare? *(Possible answer: Native American music has simpler instrumentation.)* L2

More About the Poets

Simon Ortiz is an Acoma, one of the Pueblo peoples of the Southwest. His books include *A Good Journey* and *From Sand Creek*.

Langston Hughes first began writing poetry in high school. He became one of the leading figures of the Harlem Renaissance of the 1920s. He published many books, including collections of poems and short stories, plays, novels, essays, and two autobiographical works.

Interdisciplinary Connections

Literature Have students write their own poems about the experience of living in the United States. Encourage them to share their poems with the class.

Making Connections

ART | SCIENCE | CULTURE | TECHNOLOGY

Americans All

Native Americans and African Americans endured many years of injustice. Even so, the pride and determination of these Americans remained strong. Read the poems by Native American poet Simon J. Ortiz and African American poet Langston Hughes to see how they express these feelings.

▲ Picking cotton near Dallas, Texas, 1907

Survival This Way

by Simon J. Ortiz (1941–)

Survival, I know how this way.
This way, I know.
It rains.
Mountains and canyons and plants
grow.
We travelled this way,
gauged our distance by stories
and loved our children.
We taught them
to love their births.
We told ourselves over and over
again, "We shall survive
this way."

▲ Native Americans on the Great Plains, 1891

I, Too

by Langston Hughes (1902–1967)

I, too, sing America.

I am the darker brother.
They send me to eat in the kitchen
When company comes,
But I laugh,
And eat well,
And grow strong.

Tomorrow,
I'll be at the table
When company comes.
Nobody'll dare
Say to me,
"Eat in the kitchen,"
Then.

Besides,
They'll see how beautiful I am
And be ashamed—

I, too, am America.

Making the Connection

1. How does the poem "Survival This Way" tell how Native Americans feel about their children?
2. What does Langston Hughes mean by the phrase "I, too, sing America"?
3. **Making Comparisons** In what way do both poems convey a message of hope?

152

Making the Connection

1. *Possible answer:* With the lines "We taught them to love their births," Ortiz explains that they try to instill in their children a pride of their heritage to help them survive.
2. *Possible answer:* He is saying that even though the white majority often ignores African Americans, they also are beautiful Americans who have something to say about living in the United States.
3. *Possible answer:* The Ortiz poem affirms that Native Americans will survive and be proud of their heritage. The Hughes poem speaks of African Americans growing stronger, having a seat at the table, and being recognized.

Reading Review

Section 1 From Sea to Shining Sea

Terms to Know
contiguous
megalopolis
coral reef

Main Idea
The United States has a great variety of landforms and climates.

✓Region The United States has five main physical regions: the Coastal Plains, the Appalachian Mountains, the Interior Plains, the Mountains and Plateaus region, and the Pacific Coast. Alaska and Hawaii make up two additional regions.

✓History Forty-eight of the United States are contiguous, joined together inside a common boundary between the Atlantic and Pacific Oceans.

✓Economics The Central Lowlands area is well suited to agriculture, as are western coastal valleys.

✓Place The high Rocky Mountains have a ridge called the Continental Divide, which separates rivers that flow east from rivers that flow west.

Section 2 An Economic Leader

Terms to Know
free enterprise system
service industry
navigable
fossil fuel
acid rain
landfill
recycling
free trade

Main Idea
The United States economy runs on abundant resources and the hard work of Americans.

✓Economics Because of many natural resources and an inventive people, the United States has the world's most productive economy.

✓Economics Service industries contribute the most to the American economy, followed by manufacturing, agriculture, and mining.

✓Economics The United States has five economic regions—the Northeast, the South, the Midwest, the Interior West, and the Pacific.

✓Economics Creativity and hard work are needed to continue to develop new technologies and help the American economy grow.

Section 3 The Americans

Terms to Know
colony
representative democracy
federal republic
secede
immigrant
rural
urban
suburb

Main Idea
The United States is a land of many cultures.

✓Culture The American people are immigrants or the descendants of immigrants who have come from all over the world.

✓Government The United States is a republic. A republic is a type of representative democracy.

✓Culture Ethnic groups in America are descendants of five main peoples: Europeans, Africans, Hispanics, Asians and Pacific Islanders, and Native Americans.

✓Culture American arts celebrate the country's ethnic and regional diversity.

Reading Review

Use the Chapter 4 Reading Review to preview, review, condense, or reteach the chapter.

Preview/Review

Use the Terms to Know lists to help students review and study.

Activity Have students create a quiz in which 10 terms from the chapter are to be matched to their definitions. Then have them exchange quizzes with another student and take the quiz their partners prepared.

Vocabulary PuzzleMaker CD-ROM reinforces the vocabulary terms used in Chapter 4.

The Interactive Tutor Self-Assessment CD-ROM allows students to review Chapter 4 content.

Condense

Have students read the Chapter 4 summary statements.

Guided Reading Activities

Audio Program

Reteach

Reteaching Activity

Reading Essentials and Study Guide

Reading Strategy Read to Write

Making Comparisons Ask students if they have friends or relatives living in another section of the country. Ask for volunteers to share descriptions of life in these areas. List their answers under the name of the location. Group the descriptions under specific characteristics: physical, people, cultural, and so on. Then have the class compare these details to life in their own region. Afterwards, ask your students to find information about a part of the United States that they've never been to but would like to visit. Have them write a paragraph describing what that area offers that is not available in their own location. L1

EE2 Places and Regions: Standard 6

Assessment and Activities

GLENCOE TECHNOLOGY

MindJogger Videoquiz
Use MindJogger Videoquiz to review the Chapter 4 content.

Available in DVD and VHS

Using Key Terms

1.	c	6.	f
2.	g	7.	d
3.	e	8.	i
4.	a	9.	h
5.	b	10.	j

Reviewing the Main Ideas

11. the Coastal Plains, the Appalachian Mountains, the Interior Plains, the Mountains and Basins, and the Pacific Coast
12. Boston, New York City, Philadelphia, Baltimore, and Washington, D.C.
13. humid continental, humid subtropical, marine west coast, Mediterranean, steppe, desert, subarctic, tundra, tropical
14. Any four: coal, copper, petroleum, iron, zinc, lead, silver, gold
15. Any four: rice, sugarcane, citrus fruits, peanuts, pecans, cotton, sorghum, wheat, livestock
16. They are getting higher and higher because Americans are generating huge amounts of trash.
17. The amending process allows for laws to be changed to meet the changing needs of the people.
18. medical advances
19. the South and the Southwest

Chapter 4 Assessment and Activities

Using Key Terms

Match the terms in Part A with their definitions in Part B.

A.

1. contiguous
2. megalopolis
3. free enterprise system
4. fossil fuel
5. suburb
6. colony
7. recycling
8. free trade
9. secede
10. representative democracy

B.

a. oil, natural gas, and coal
b. smaller community surrounding a city
c. areas joined inside a common boundary
d. reusing materials
e. limited government control over the economy
f. overseas settlement tied to a parent country
g. huge urban area
h. withdraw from national government
i. goods flow freely between countries
j. voters choose government leaders

Reviewing the Main Ideas

Section 1 From Sea to Shining Sea

11. **Region** What are the five main physical regions of the United States?
12. **Place** What cities make up the huge urban area along the East Coast of the United States?
13. **Region** List nine kinds of climates found in the United States.

Section 2 An Economic Leader

14. **Economics** Name four of the mineral resources found in the United States.
15. **Economics** Name four of the South's agricultural products.
16. **Human/Environment Interaction** What is happening to America's landfills?

Section 3 The Americans

17. **Government** How has the United States Constitution been able to change over the years?
18. **Science** What has helped lengthen people's lives in the United States?
19. **Place** Which parts of the United States have the fastest-growing populations?

The United States

Place Location Activity

On a separate sheet of paper, match the letters on the map with the numbered places listed below.

1. Rocky Mountains
2. Mississippi River
3. Appalachian Mountains
4. Washington, D.C.
5. Chicago
6. Lake Superior
7. Ohio River
8. Gulf of Mexico
9. Texas
10. Los Angeles

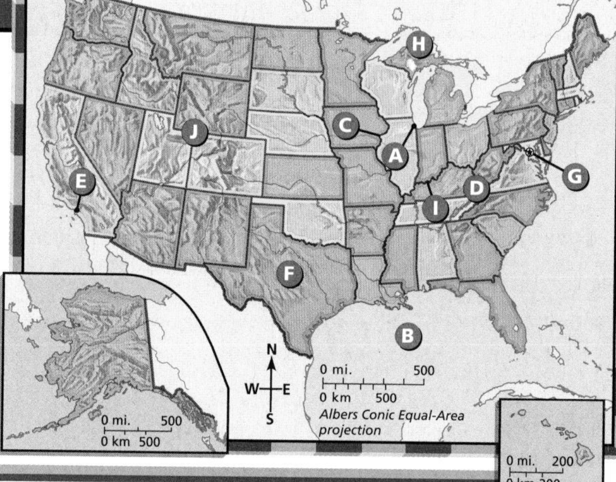

NATIONAL GEOGRAPHIC Place Location Activity

1.	J	6.	H
2.	C	7.	I
3.	D	8.	B
4.	G	9.	F
5.	A	10.	E

Critical Thinking

20. Flat land and fertile soil have made farming profitable. Its rivers are navigable, allowing Midwestern cities to become centers of trade. The Great Lakes also allow easy passage of shipping trade. Abundant mining resources have made many cities important manufacturing centers.
21. Answers will vary. Students should place facts from the textbook in the appropriate spaces.

Self-Check Quiz Visit ***The World and Its People*** Web site at twip.glencoe.com and click on **Chapter 4—Self-Check Quizzes** to prepare for the Chapter Test.

Critical Thinking

20. **Understanding Cause and Effect** What physical features of the Interior Plains have affected the economy of that region?
21. **Categorizing Information** Create a diagram like the one below. In the outer ovals, write two facts about the United States under each heading.

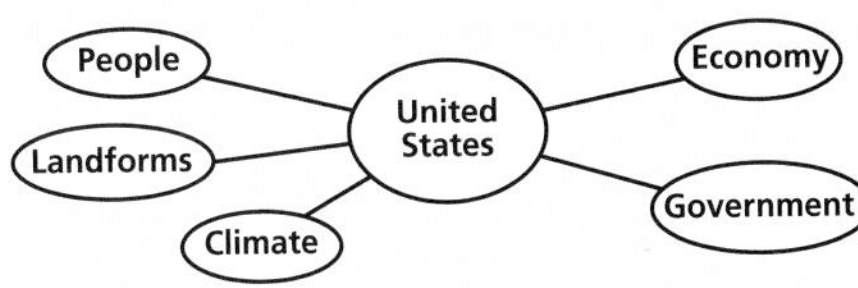

Comparing Regions Activity

22. **Geography** Research to find information on Death Valley in California and the Sahara in Africa. Write a paragraph comparing them.

Mental Mapping Activity

23. **Focusing on the Region** Create a simple outline map of the United States and then label the following:
    - Appalachian Mountains
    - Great Lakes
    - Alaska
    - Rocky Mountains
    - Hawaii
    - Mississippi River
    - Pacific Ocean
    - Atlantic Ocean
    - Gulf of Mexico
    - Great Plains

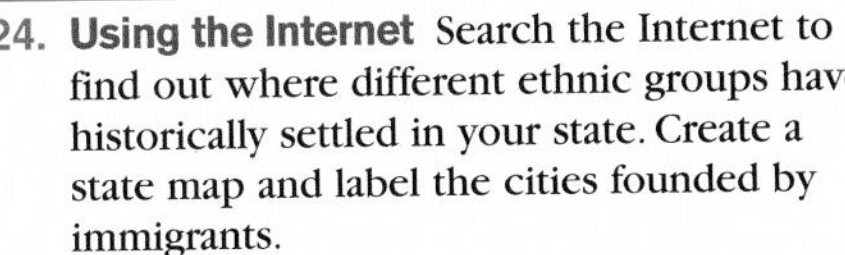

Technology Skills Activity

24. **Using the Internet** Search the Internet to find out where different ethnic groups have historically settled in your state. Create a state map and label the cities founded by immigrants.

Standardized Test Practice

Directions: Study the graph below, and then answer the questions that follow.

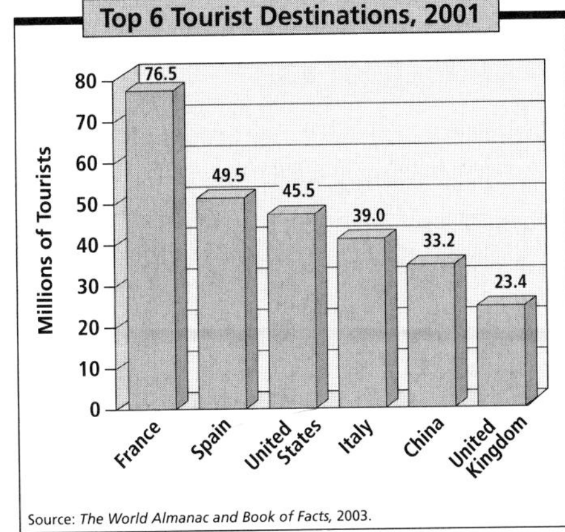

Source: *The World Almanac and Book of Facts, 2003.*

1. **According to the graph, about how many tourists visited the United States in 2001?**
   A 45.5
   B 76.5
   C 45,500
   D 45,500,000
2. **Which country on the graph had the least number of tourists?**
   F France
   G United Kingdom
   H Spain
   J Italy

Test-Taking Tip: A common error that occurs when you are reading graphs is to overlook the information on the bottom and the side of the graph. Check these areas to see what the numbers mean.

155

Assessment and Activities

Standardized Test Practice

1. D
2. G

Tested Objectives:
Analyzing information, reading bar graphs

Social Studies Online

Have students visit the Web site at twip.glencoe.com to review Chapter 4 and take the Self-Check Quiz.

Chapter Test Bonus Question

This question may be used for extra credit on the chapter test.

What branch of the United States government enforces the laws? *(executive)*

FOLDABLES™ Study Organizer — Dinah Zike's Foldables

Culminating Activity Have students summarize in their own words the main ideas that they listed on their foldables.

Comparing Regions Activity

22. Students' paragraphs should describe the similarities and differences between Death Valley and the Sahara.

Mental Mapping Activity

23. This exercise helps students visualize the geographic features of the United States. All attempts at freehand mapping should be accepted.

Technology Skills Activity

24. Students' maps should accurately present the data.

Chapter 5 Resources

Note: The following materials may be used when teaching Chapter 5.
Section level support materials are shown at point of use in the margins of the Teacher Wraparound Edition.

Timesaving Tools

TeacherWorks™ All-In-One Planner and Resource Center

- **Interactive Teacher Edition** See the **Interactive Teacher Edition** CD-ROM to electronically integrate your Teacher Wraparound Edition and blackline masters.
- **Interactive Lesson Planner** Organize your week, month, semester, or year with all the lesson helps you need. The **Interactive Lesson Planner** CD-ROM contains all Chapter 5 resources.

Use Glencoe's **Presentation Plus!** multimedia teacher tool to easily present dynamic lessons that visually excite your students. Using Microsoft PowerPoint® you can customize the presentations to create your own personalized lessons.

TEACHING TRANSPARENCIES

Graphic Organizer Transparency 4 L2

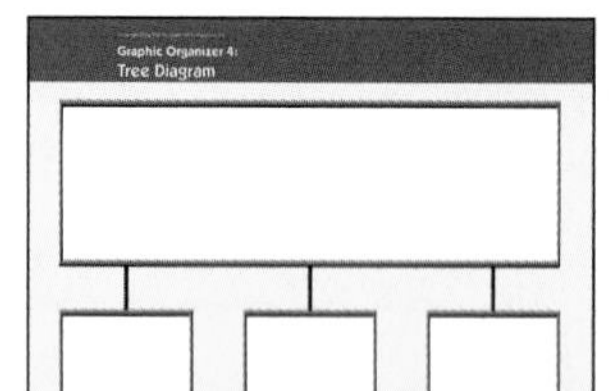

In-text Map Transparency L1

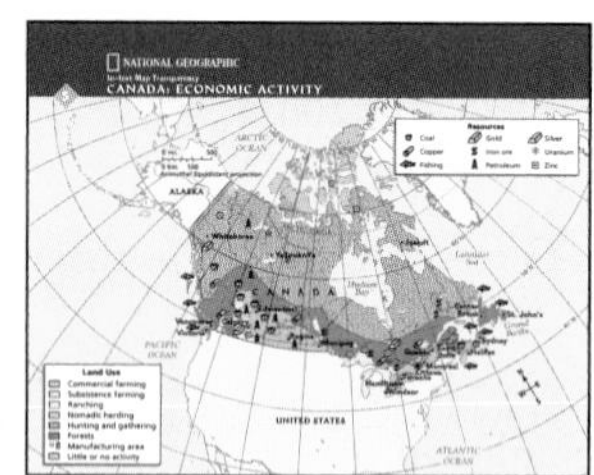

FOLDABLES™ Study Organizer

Dinah Zike's Foldables

Foldables are three-dimensional, interactive graphic organizers that help students practice basic writing skills, review key vocabulary terms, and identify main ideas. Additional chapter activities can be found in the ***Reading and Study Skills Foldables*** booklet.

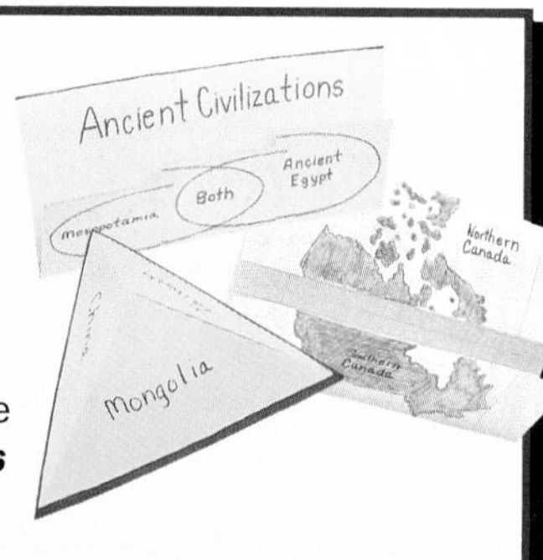

MAP AND GEOGRAPHY SKILLS

Chapter Map Activity L2

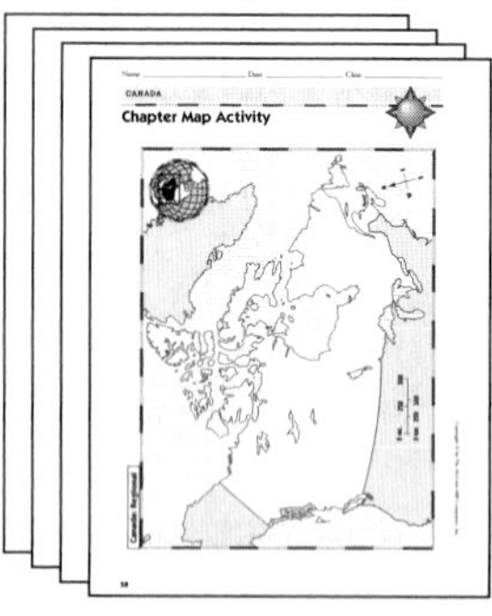

GeoLab Activity L2

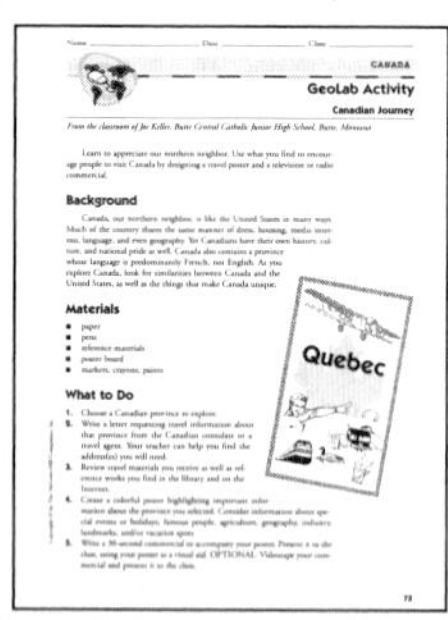

READING SUPPORT

Vocabulary Activity L1

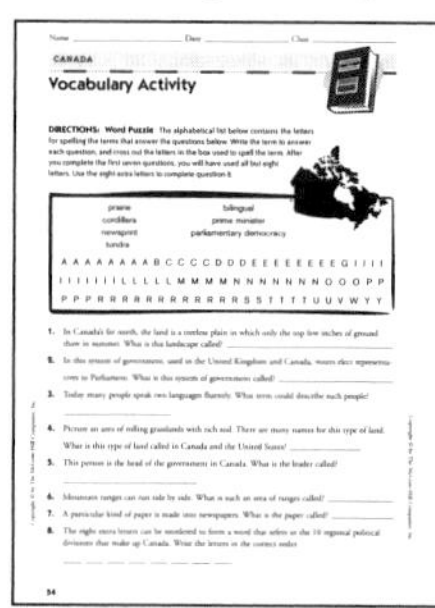

Workbook Activity L1

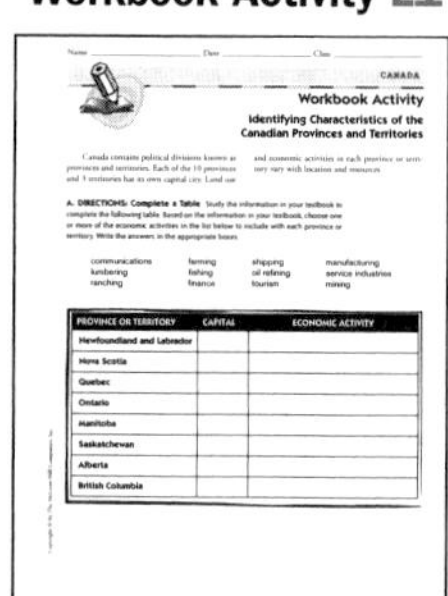

Reading and Writing Skills Activity L1/ELL

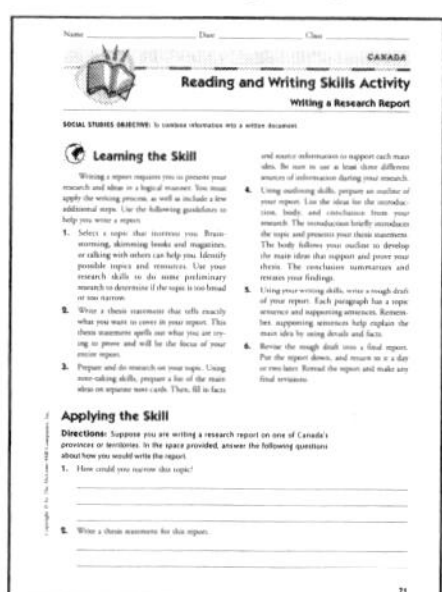

DIFFERENTIATED INSTRUCTION

Use these review and reinforcement materials to help less-proficient readers, English learners, and gifted and talented students.

Reteaching Activity L1

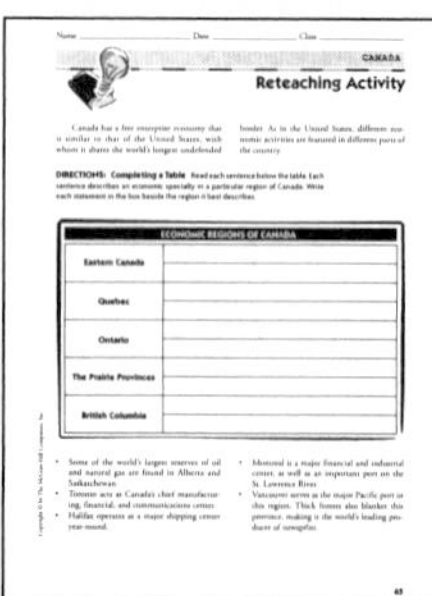

Chapter Skills Review L2

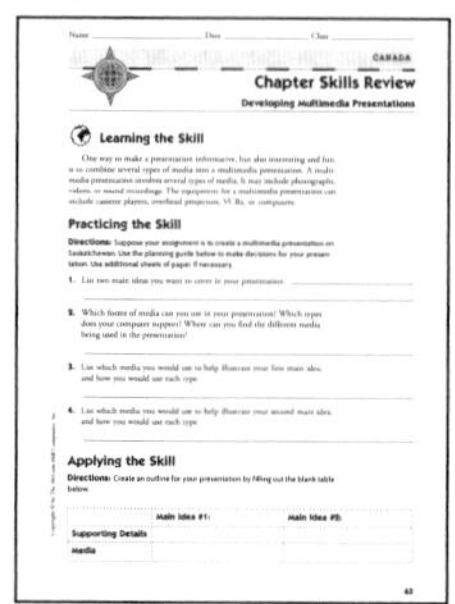

Cooperative Learning Activity L1/ELL

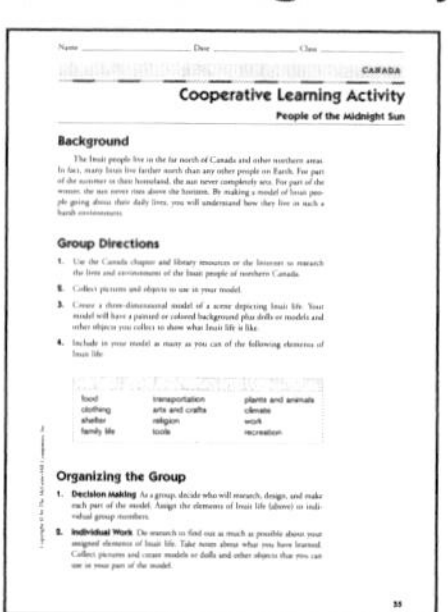

Enrichment Activity L3

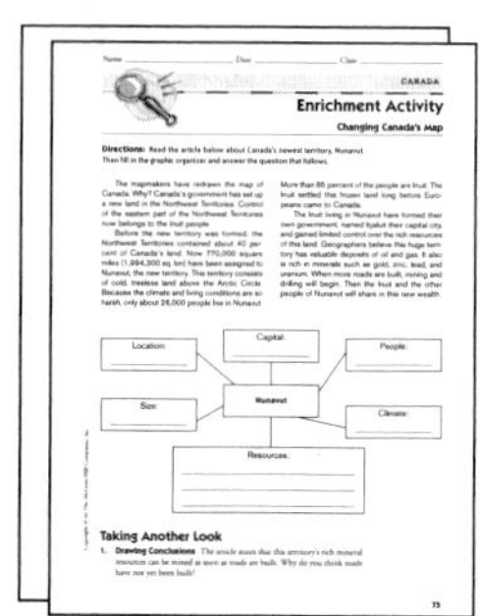

ASSESSMENT

Chapter Test, Form A L2

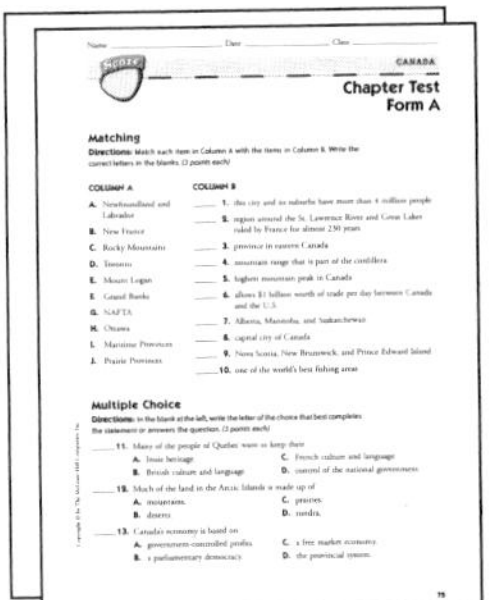

Chapter Test, Form B L2

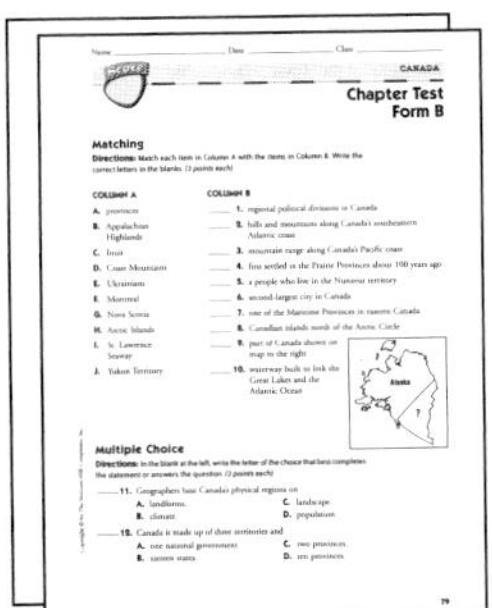

Performance Assessment Activity L1/ELL

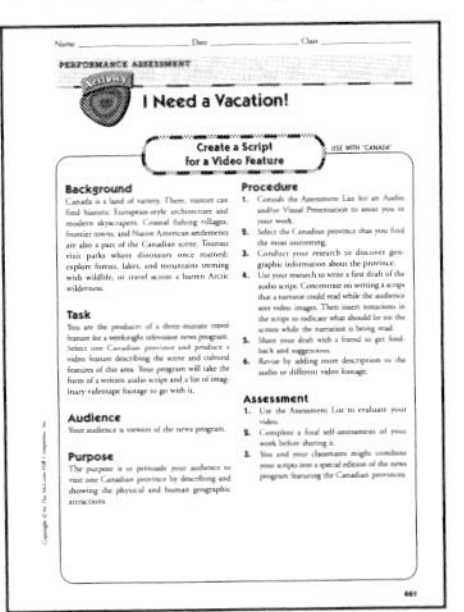

ExamView® Pro Testmaker CD-ROM

STANDARDIZED ASSESSMENT SKILLS

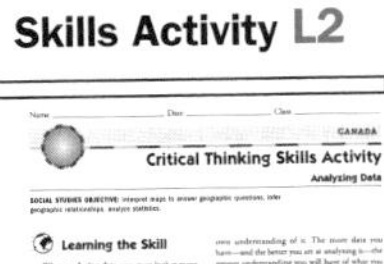

Critical Thinking Skills Activity L2

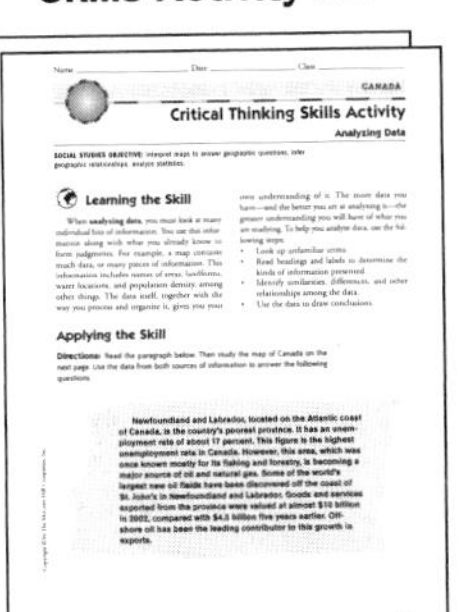

Map and Graph Skills Activity L2

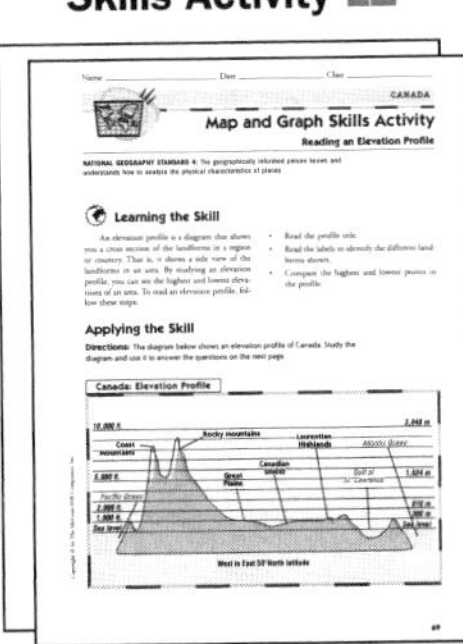

Standardized Test Skills Practice Workbook Activity L2

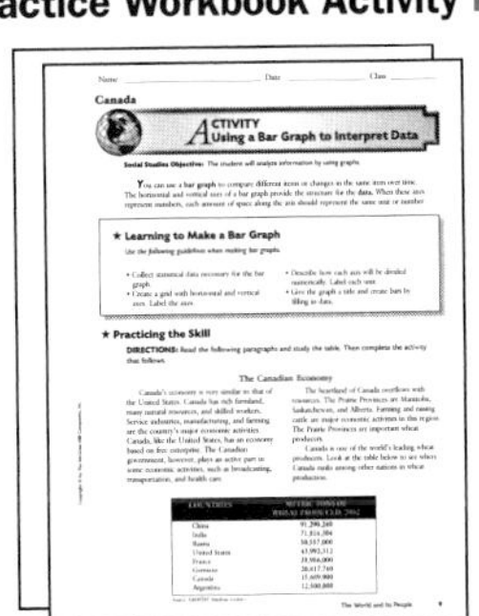

HOME INVOLVEMENT

Take-Home Review Activity L1

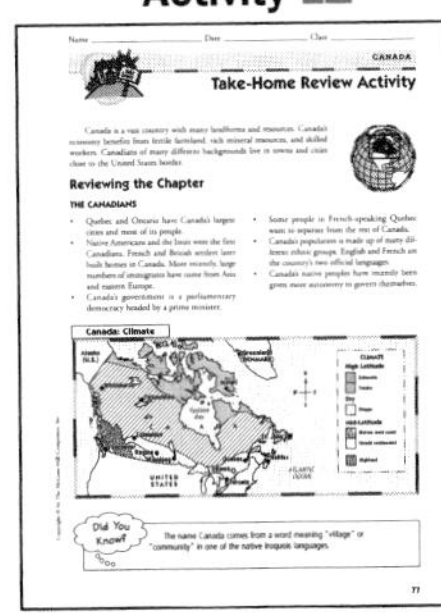

MULTIMEDIA

- **National Geographic's The World and Its People**
- **MindJogger Videoquiz**
- **Vocabulary PuzzleMaker CD-ROM**
- **Interactive Tutor Self-Assessment CD-ROM**
- **ExamView® Pro Testmaker CD-ROM**
- **TeacherWorks CD-ROM**
- **StudentWorks CD-ROM**
- **Skillbuilder Interactive Workbook CD-ROM, Level 1**
- **Presentation Plus! CD-ROM**
- **Audio Program**

SPANISH RESOURCES

The following Spanish language materials are available in the Spanish Resources binder:

- **Spanish Summaries**
- **Spanish Vocabulary Activities**
- **Spanish Guided Reading Activities**
- **Spanish Quizzes and Tests**
- **Spanish Take-Home Review Activities**
- **Spanish Reteaching Activities**

Meeting National Standards

Geography for Life

The following standards are covered in Chapter 5:

Section 1
EE3 Physical Systems: Standards 7, 8
EE5 Environment and Society: Standards 14, 15, 16

Section 2
EE4 Human Systems: Standards 9, 10, 11, 12, 13
EE5 Environment and Society: Standard 14
EE6 The Uses of Geography: Standards 17, 18

State and Local Objectives

____

____

____

____

Chapter 5 Planning Guide

SECTION RESOURCES

Daily Objectives	Reproducible Resources	Multimedia Resources
Section 1 **A Resource-Rich Country** 1. Explain how Canada's landforms and climate have affected where Canadians live. 2. Compare Canada's economy to that of the United States. 3. Compare the different economies of Canada's provinces.	Reproducible Lesson Plan Daily Lecture and Discussion Notes Note-taking Guide Guided Reading Activity* Reading Essentials and Study Guide* Section Quiz*	Daily Focus Skills Transparency GeoQuiz Transparency In-text Map Transparency Vocabulary PuzzleMaker CD-ROM Interactive Tutor Self-Assessment CD-ROM ExamView® Pro Testmaker CD-ROM Presentation Plus! CD-ROM
Section 2 **The Canadians** 1. Identify who first settled Canada. 2. Describe Canada's form of government. 3. Explain what groups make up the Canadian people.	Reproducible Lesson Plan Daily Lecture and Discussion Notes Note-taking Guide Guided Reading Activity* Reading Essentials and Study Guide* Section Quiz*	Daily Focus Skills Transparency Vocabulary PuzzleMaker CD-ROM Interactive Tutor Self-Assessment CD-ROM ExamView® Pro Testmaker CD-ROM Presentation Plus! CD-ROM MindJogger Videoquiz

00:00 **Out of Time?** Assign the **Reading Essentials and Study Guide*** for this chapter.

*Also available in Spanish

KEY TO ABILITY LEVELS

Teaching strategies have been coded for varying learning styles and abilities.

L1 **BASIC** activities for all students
L2 **AVERAGE** activities for average to above-average students
L3 **CHALLENGING** activities for above-average students
ELL **ENGLISH LANGUAGE LEARNER** activities

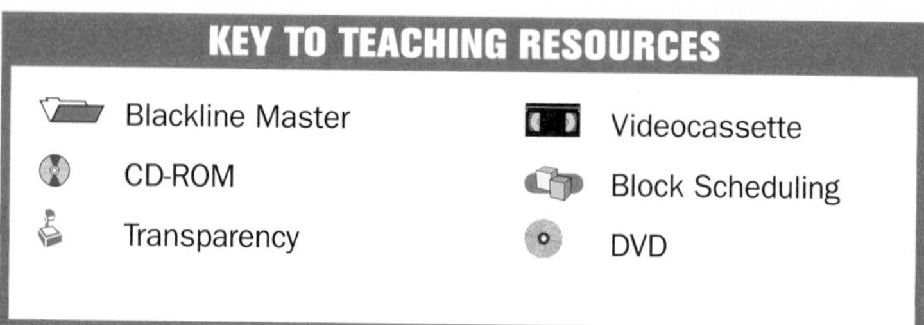

KEY TO TEACHING RESOURCES

Blackline Master
CD-ROM
Transparency
Videocassette
Block Scheduling
DVD

Teacher to Teacher

World Tour

William Sim
L.L. Wright Middle School
Ironwood, Michigan

Students travel the world. They select a city with a minimum population of 1 million people in 10 different countries. Then they construct a world map on a large piece of Styrofoam. Placing a pushpin into their hometown, they travel to their first city and add a pushpin there. They must research 5 items about the city: famous landmark, famous person from there and his or her significance, general physical landscape, year of founding, and flag of the country in which the city is located. For each city, students must draw or list the 5 items on small pieces of paper, and insert the papers with toothpicks near the city's pushpin. After the 10 cities are visited, the student connects all pushpins with a string in the order in which the cities were visited.

Meeting Special Needs

In addition to the Differentiated Instruction strategies found in each section, the following resources are also suitable for your special needs students:

- ***ExamView® Pro Testmaker CD-ROM*** allows teachers to tailor tests by reducing answer choices.
- The ***Audio Program*** includes the entire narrative of the student edition so that less-proficient readers can listen to the words as they read them.
- The ***Reading Essentials and Study Guide*** provides the same content as the student edition but is written two grade levels below the textbook.
- ***Guided Reading Activities*** give less-proficient readers point-by-point instructions to increase comprehension as they read each textbook section.
- ***Enrichment Activities*** include a stimulating collection of readings and activities for gifted and talented students.

NATIONAL GEOGRAPHIC TEACHER'S CORNER

Index to National Geographic Magazine:

The following articles may be used for research relating to this chapter:

- "The Untamed Yukon River," by Michael Parfit, July 1998.
- "Prince Edward Island: A World Apart No More," by Ian Darragh, May 1998.
- "A Dream Called Nunavut," by Michael Parfit, September 1997.

National Geographic Society Products:

To order the following products for use with this chapter, call National Geographic Society at 1-800-368-2728:

- *Physical Geography of North America Series* (6 Videos)
- *Technology's Price* (Video)
- *National Geographic Desk Reference* (Book)

NGS ONLINE

Access National Geographic's Web site for current events, activities, links, interactive features, and archives.
www.nationalgeographic.com

NATIONAL GEOGRAPHIC MapMachine

Find the latest coverage of geography in the news, atlas updates, cartographic activities with interactive maps, an online map store, and links at www.nationalgeographic.com/maps

SOCIAL STUDIES Online

Use our Web site for additional resources. All essential content is covered in the Student Edition.

You and your students can visit twip.glencoe.com, the Web site companion to *The World and Its People*. This innovative integration of electronic and print media offers your students a wealth of opportunities. The student text directs students to the Web site for the following options:

- Chapter Overviews
- Student Web Activities
- Self-Check Quizzes
- Textbook Updates

Answers are provided for you in the Web Activity Lesson Plan. Additional Web resources and Interactive Tutor puzzles are also available.

Introducing Chapter 5

Social Studies Online

Introduce students to chapter content and key terms by having them access Chapter Overview 5 at twip.glencoe.com

Chapter Objectives

1. Describe the landscapes and climates of Canada.
2. Explain Canada's economic resources, activities, and challenges.
3. Discuss the history and government of Canada.
4. Compare the Canadian peoples and their cultures.

GLENCOE TECHNOLOGY

NATIONAL GEOGRAPHIC

The World and Its People Video Program

Chapter 5 Canada
The following segments enhance the study of this chapter:

- **Newfoundland**
- **Seals in Winter**

MindJogger Videoquiz
Use MindJogger Videoquiz to preview the Chapter 5 content.

Both programs available in DVD and VHS

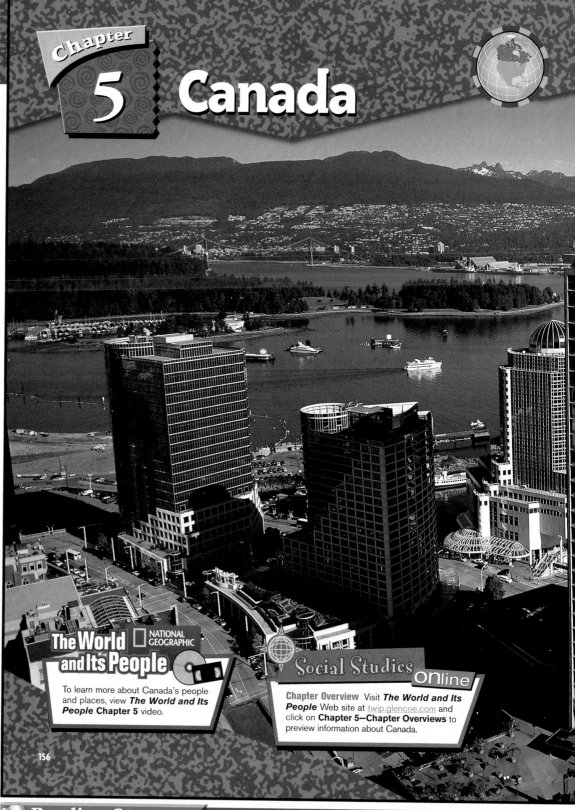

Chapter 5 Canada

The World and Its People NATIONAL GEOGRAPHIC

To learn more about Canada's people and places, view ***The World and Its People*** **Chapter 5** video.

Social Studies Online

Chapter Overview Visit ***The World and Its People*** Web site at twip.glencoe.com and click on **Chapter 5—Chapter Overviews** to preview information about Canada.

156

Reading Strategy — Purpose for Reading

Read and Say Something is a strategy to help students with reading comprehension and is especially useful when reading difficult material. It can also be used to introduce a unit using an original document or an item of special interest. Have students read the "Exploring our World" feature in Section 1. When they have finished reading, they should turn to a partner and say something about the reading. Students may comment about anything they want related to the selection, such as reactions to ideas, descriptions, images, or information that may be confusing. Elicit information from the entire class about what partners discussed. Tell the students they will be studying Canada in this chapter. L1

FOLDABLES™ Study Organizer

Compare-Contrast Make this foldable to help you analyze the similarities and differences between the landforms, climate, and cultures of northern and southern Canada.

Step 1 Mark the midpoint of the side edge of a sheet of paper.

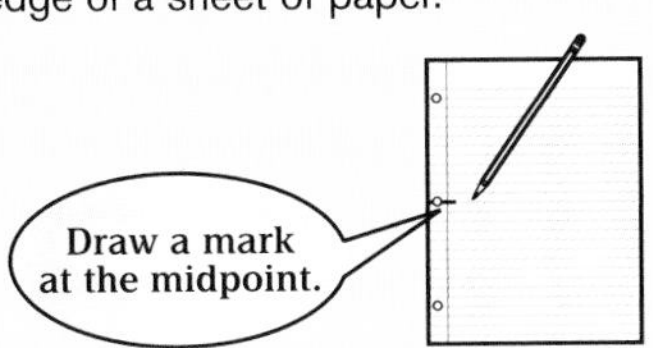

Step 2 Turn the paper and fold the outside edges in to touch at the midpoint.

Step 3 Turn and label your foldable as shown.

Reading and Writing As you read the chapter, collect and write information under the appropriate tab that will help you compare and contrast northern and southern Canada.

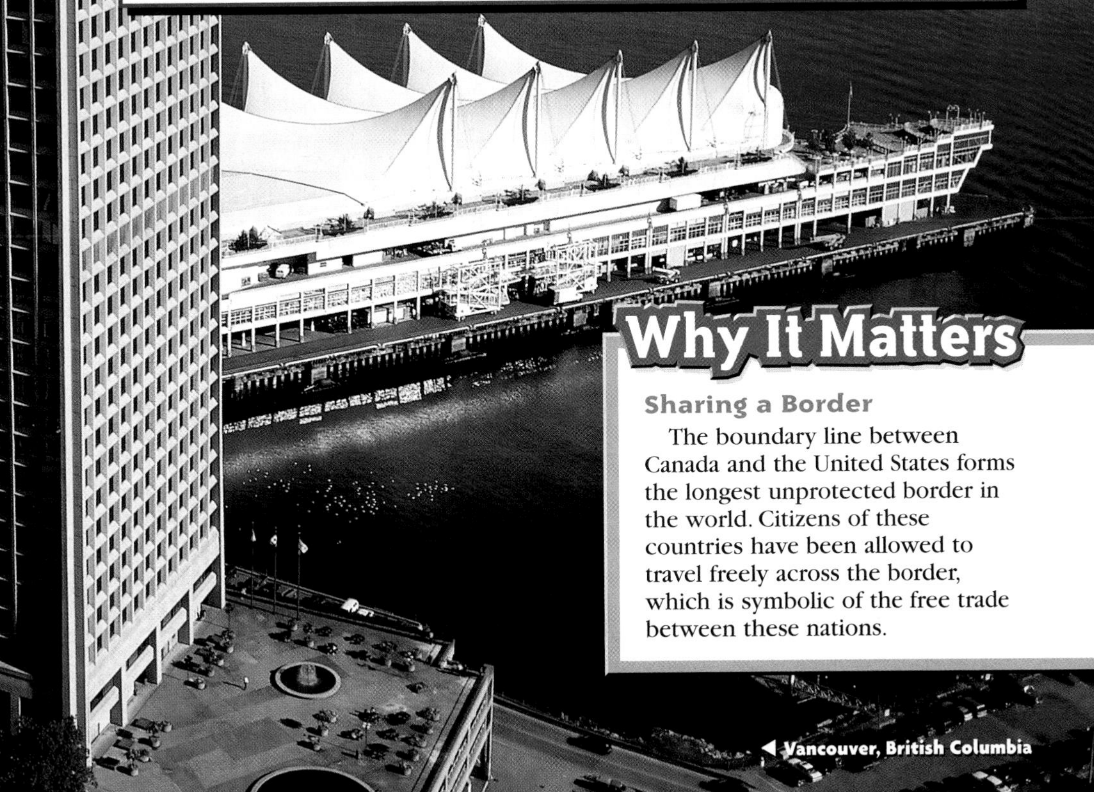

Why It Matters

Sharing a Border

The boundary line between Canada and the United States forms the longest unprotected border in the world. Citizens of these countries have been allowed to travel freely across the border, which is symbolic of the free trade between these nations.

◀ Vancouver, British Columbia

About the Photo

Vancouver is located on the Pacific Coast of Canada and is the country's main seaport and third largest city (after Toronto and Montreal). Although it has the most temperate climate in Canada, it often rains there. Vancouver's dramatic setting makes it a popular tourist destination, and it is known for its parks and many recreational and cultural activities. It's also the location of many Hollywood movies, which are filmed there because production is often less expensive than in the United States.

Dinah Zike's Foldables

Purpose Students will make and use a foldable to help them organize the similarities and differences between northern and southern Canada. As students read the chapter and fill in information on their foldables, they compare and contrast facts that show how the landforms, climate, and cultures are the same and different in northern and southern Canada.

Have students complete the ***Reading and Study Skills Foldables*** activity for this chapter.

Why It Matters

Ask students to name physical and cultural features that they know the United States and Canada share. If they have difficulty identifying examples, have them look at a physical map of the region. They should be able to identify such features as the Rocky Mountains, the Great Lakes, and the Great Plains. Cultural examples include a common language *(English)*, common sports, and popular performers. See if students can identify professional teams or sports figures from Canada. *(For example, the Toronto Blue Jays are in baseball's American League.)*

Chapter 5

Section 1, pages 158–163

Focus

Section Objectives

1. Explain how Canada's landforms and climate have affected where Canadians live.
2. Compare Canada's economy to that of the United States.
3. Compare the different economies of Canada's provinces.

BELLRINGER
Skillbuilder Activity

Project transparency and have students answer the question.

Daily Focus Skills Transparency

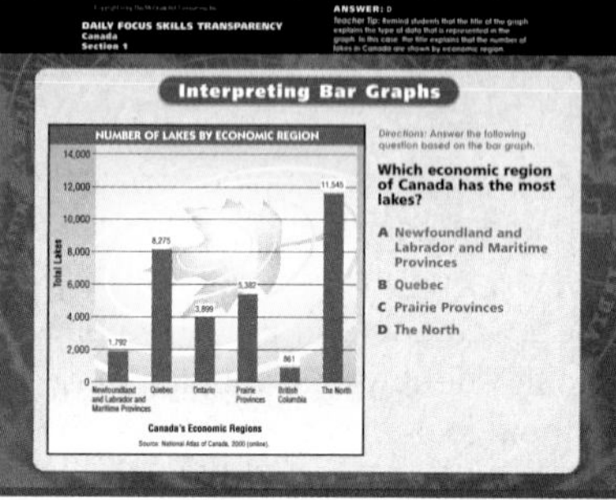

Reading Preview

■ **Activating Prior Knowledge**
Ask: How large do you think Canada is? Have students check their answers for accuracy as they read.

■ **Preteaching Vocabulary**
Have students skim the section for new vocabulary terms. Ask them to predict what they think the main ideas of the section might be.

Guide to Reading

Main Idea

Canada is a vast country with many landforms and resources.

Terms to Know

- province
- glacier
- tundra
- prairie
- cordillera
- newsprint

Reading Strategy

Create a chart like this one and list Canada's provinces in the left column. In the right column, list the main economic activities in each province.

Province	Economic Activities

Section 1

A Resource-Rich Country

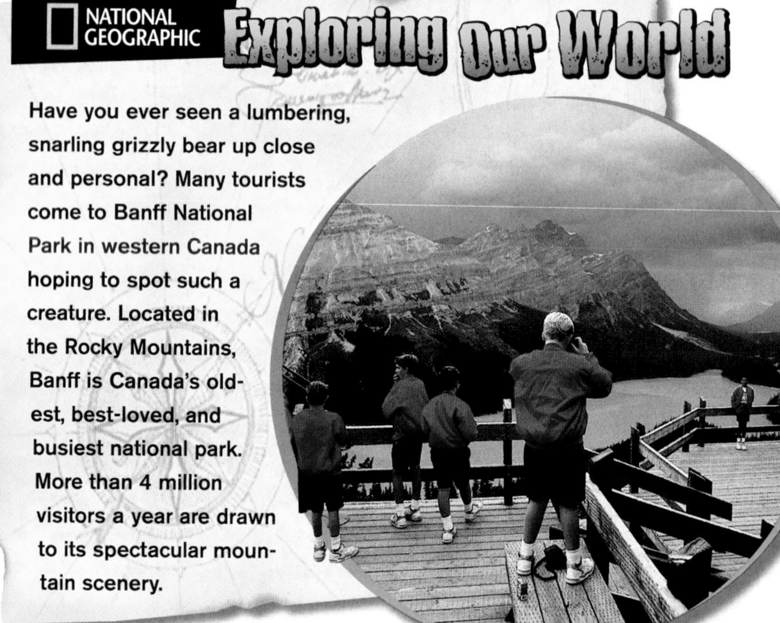

Have you ever seen a lumbering, snarling grizzly bear up close and personal? Many tourists come to Banff National Park in western Canada hoping to spot such a creature. Located in the Rocky Mountains, Banff is Canada's oldest, best-loved, and busiest national park. More than 4 million visitors a year are drawn to its spectacular mountain scenery.

Vikings landed their boats on its eastern coast around A.D. 1000. Niagara Falls thunders in the southeast. Grizzly bears roam its western regions. What country are we describing? It is **Canada.**

Canada's Landscape

Canada, located north of the contiguous United States, is the world's second-largest country in land area. Only Russia is larger. Between Canada and the United States lies the world's longest undefended border. The friendship between the two countries has allowed thousands of people to cross this 5,522-mile (8,887-km) border every day. Like the United States, Canada has the Atlantic Ocean on its eastern coast and the Pacific Ocean on its western coast. The Arctic Ocean lies to the far north.

Unlike the United States, Canada does not have states. Instead, it has 10 **provinces,** or regional political divisions. It also includes three

Section Resources

Reproducible Masters
- Reproducible Lesson Plan
- Daily Lecture and Discussion Notes
- Note-taking Guide
- Guided Reading Activity
- Reading Essentials and Study Guide
- Section Quiz

Transparencies
- Daily Focus Skills Transparency
- GeoQuiz Transparency
- In-text Map Transparency

Multimedia
- Vocabulary PuzzleMaker CD-ROM
- Interactive Tutor Self-Assessment CD-ROM
- Presentation Plus! CD-ROM
- ExamView® Pro Testmaker CD-ROM

territories. Look at the map on page 119 to find the eastern province of Newfoundland and Labrador. Now locate the Maritime Provinces of Nova Scotia, New Brunswick, and Prince Edward Island. Heading west, you see Quebec and Ontario, followed by the Prairie Provinces of Manitoba, Saskatchewan (suh•SKA•chuh•wuhn), and Alberta. On the far western coast lies British Columbia. Now find the Yukon Territory and the Northwest Territories. In 1999 a third territory—Nunavut (NOO•nuh•vuht)—was carved out of part of the Northwest Territories. This area is the homeland of the Inuit.

The Effect of Glaciers Thousands of years ago, huge glaciers, or giant sheets of ice, covered most of Canada. The weight of these glaciers pushed much of the land down and created a large, low basin. Highlands rose on the western, eastern, and northern edges of this basin. Water filled the land that was pushed very low. As a result, Canada today has many lakes and inland waterways—more than any other country in the world.

Look at the map on page 118 to see the horseshoe-shaped region known as the **Canadian Shield** that is wrapped around **Hudson Bay.** Rocky hills worn down by erosion along with thousands of lakes dot much of this wilderness region. Deep within the Canadian Shield are iron ore, copper, nickel, gold, and uranium deposits. Because of the region's location and cold climate, few people live here.

To the north lie the Arctic Islands. Much of the landscape here consists of tundra—vast rolling, treeless plains in which only the top few inches of ground thaw in summer. Glaciers blanket the islands that are farthest north.

Southern Canada From Atlantic to Pacific Many of southern Canada's physical features extend into the United States. Along Canada's southeastern Atlantic coast stretch the Appalachian Highlands

Analyzing the Diagram

The St. Lawrence Seaway provides a water link between the Great Lakes and the Atlantic Ocean.

Geography Which lake is completely above sea level?

St. Lawrence Seaway

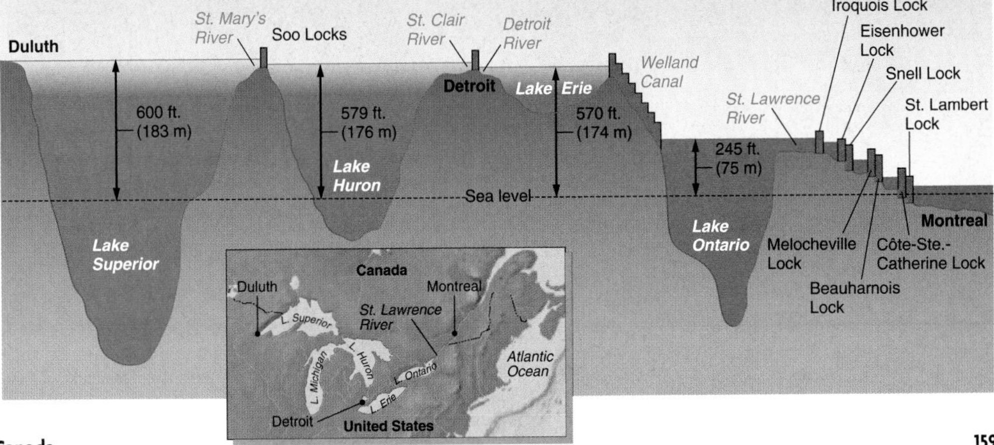

Chapter 5

Section 1, pages 158–163

TEACH

Making Comparisons
Canada and the United States both have free market economies, although there are differences between the two. Have students read "Canada's Economic Regions" and compare the economic practices of the two countries. **Ask:** **What are the various ways these countries organize their economic systems? L2**

Daily Lecture and Discussion Notes

CANADA

Daily Lecture and Discussion Notes
A Resource-Rich Country

The rocks of the Canadian Shield were formed in Precambrian times 500 million years ago. Two tectonic plates converged, causing the surface rock to be forced down into the interior of the earth, where it melted. Over millions of years, that rock slowly rose back to the surface and cooled.

I. Canada's Landscape
A. Canada lies north of the contiguous United States and is the world's second-largest country in land area.
B. Between Canada and the United States lies the world's longest undefended border. No military troops prevent thousands of people from crossing this

Analyzing the Diagram

Answer
Lake Erie

Skills Practice
Between which two lakes does the St. Lawrence Seaway show the biggest drop? *(between Lakes Erie and Ontario)*

Reading Strategy **Reading the Text**

Using Context Clues Provide students with these tips to use context to determine meaning: look before, at, and after the unfamiliar word for a context clue; connect what you already know with what the author has written; predict a possible meaning; apply the meaning in the sentence; decide if the meaning makes sense; if the meaning does not make sense, try again. **L1**

*Use the **Reading Skills Handbook** for more reading strategies.*

Chapter 5

Section 1, pages 158–163

Reading Strategy

Making Inferences Have students recall what they read about the physical features of Canada. Based on their recollections, have them make inferences to answer these questions: **Where might farming take place in Canada? Where would forestry be a major economic activity? Where would ranching be important?** Have them write their answers in their notebooks and check them as they read the section. L1

More About the Photo

Canada's Largest City Toronto has approximately 4.7 million inhabitants in its metropolitan area.

Caption Answer Ontario

Measure student knowledge of physical features.

GeoQuiz Transparency

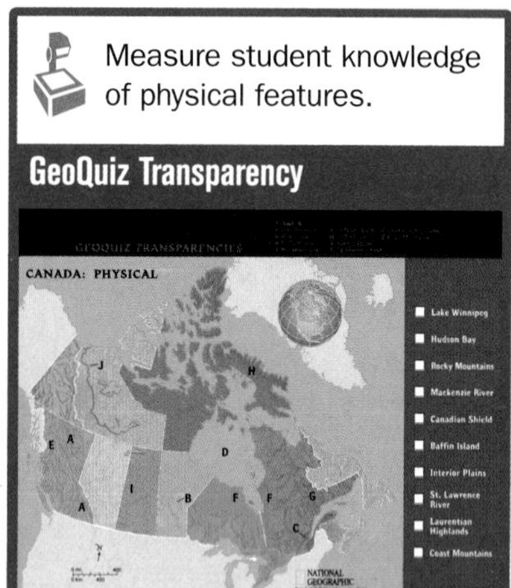

and the Laurentian Highlands. Traveling through this area of Canada, you see rolling hills. The valleys between them are dotted with farms. Forests also blanket much of the landscape. Many deepwater harbors nestle along the jagged, rocky coasts.

Cutting through these highland areas are the fertile lowlands of the **St. Lawrence River** and Great Lakes region. This area experiences a humid continental climate—long, cold winters and short, warm summers. Because of its rich soil and warm summers, this region holds most of Canada's urban centers, industries, and farms. Canada's largest city, **Toronto,** is located in this region. The St. Lawrence River and the Great Lakes form the major waterway linking central Canada with the Atlantic coast. A diagram on page 159 shows the St. Lawrence Seaway's system of locks and canals. Huge, slow-moving barges carry grain, ore, coal, and more through this waterway, which Canada shares with the United States.

Canada also shares the **Great Plains** with its southern neighbor. Look at the physical map on page 118 to locate this region. It is a huge prairie—a rolling, inland grassy area with fertile soil. Herds of buffalo once roamed here. Today large cattle ranches and farms occupy most of the land.

Another landform shared by Canada and the United States is the **Rocky Mountains,** part of an area called the cordillera (KAWR•duhl•YEHR•uh). A cordillera is a group of mountain ranges that run side by side. The Canadian Rockies are known for their scenic beauty and rich mineral resources. Tourists are drawn to this area, particularly to Banff and Jasper National Parks.

West of the Rockies you cross high plateaus until you reach the **Coast Mountains.** These mountains skirt Canada's Pacific shore and

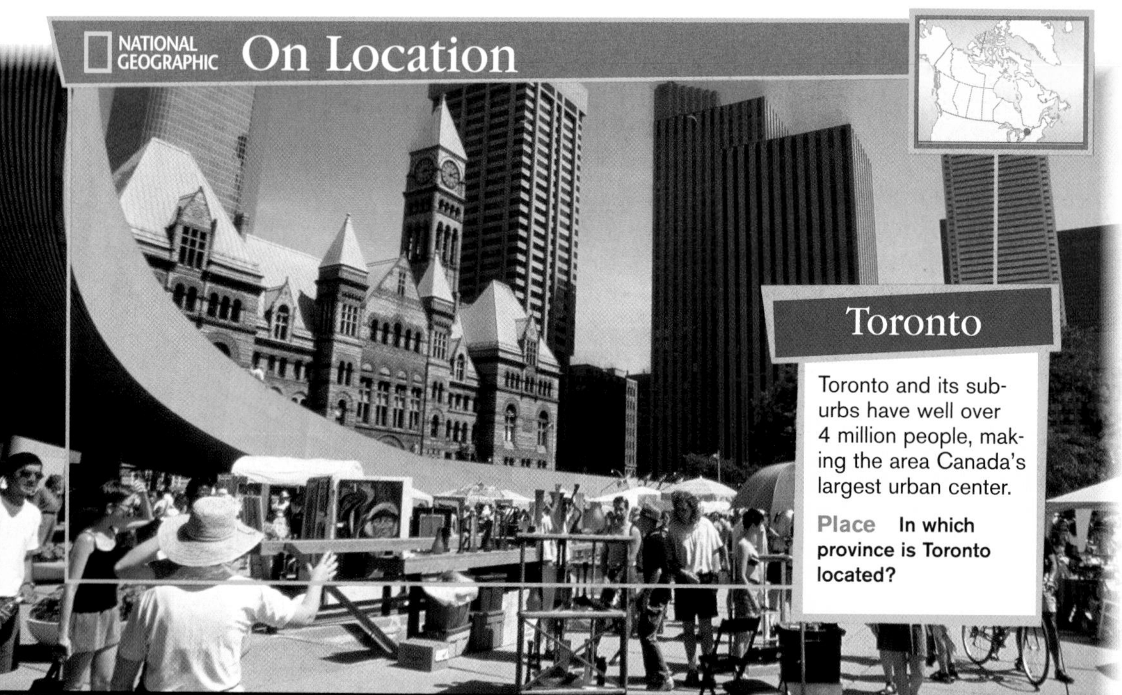

Toronto

Toronto and its suburbs have well over 4 million people, making the area Canada's largest urban center.

Place In which province is Toronto located?

Differentiated Instruction

Meeting Special Needs: Kinesthetic Help kinesthetic learners understand the effect of glaciers by demonstrating a glacier in the class. Place a layer of modeling clay in the bottom of a plastic container, like a dishpan. Make the surface uneven with some raised areas. Show the class the model and explain that this was similar to the landscape of northern Canada before the glaciers came. Then place a small towel over the plastic container and push down on the surface evenly with your hands. Explain that this simulates the action of the glaciers. Remove the towel, and discuss how the pressure from the glaciers changed the land, making it more level. L2

Refer to *Inclusion for the Middle School Social Studies Classroom Strategies and Activities* in the TCR.

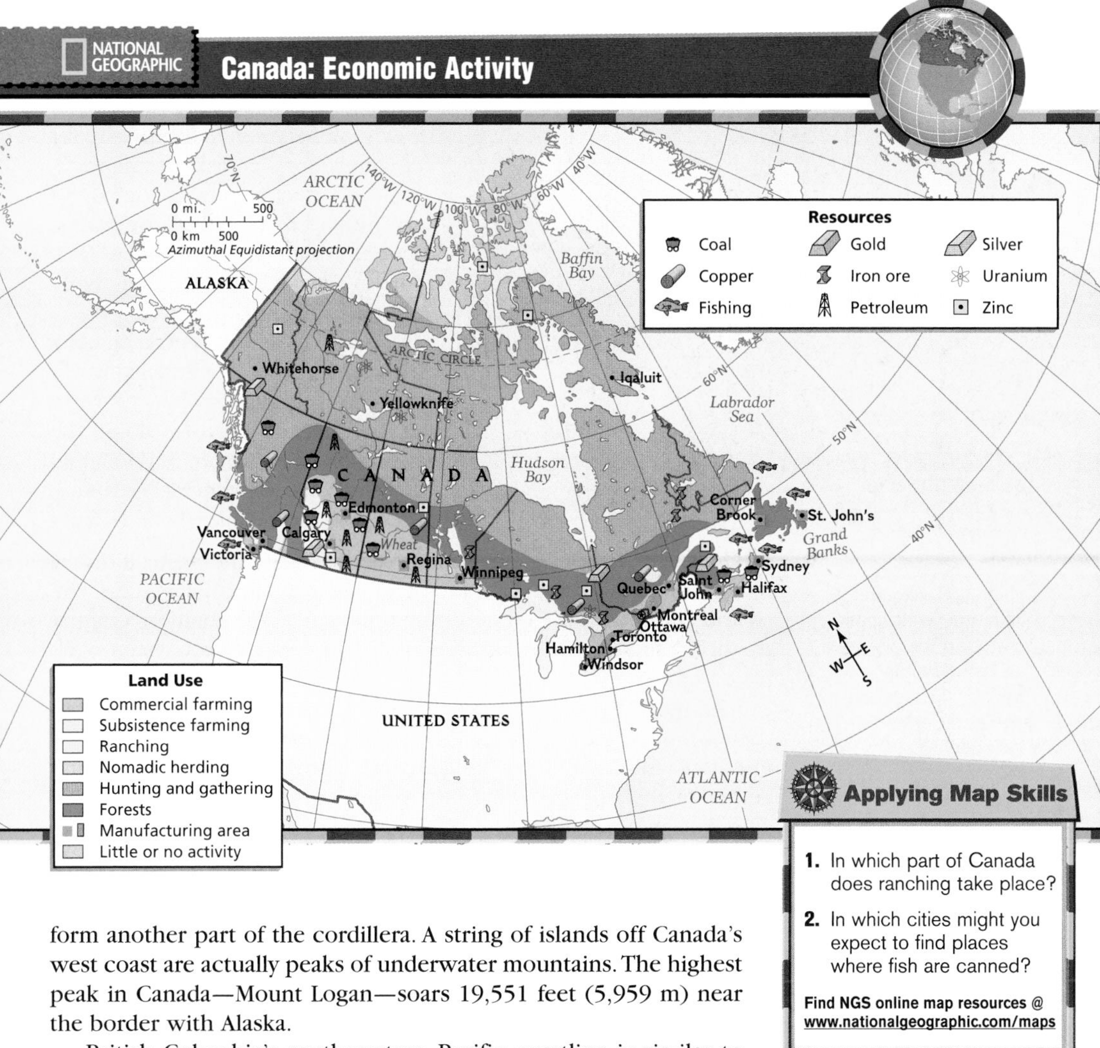

Applying Map Skills

1. In which part of Canada does ranching take place?
2. In which cities might you expect to find places where fish are canned?

Find NGS online map resources @ www.nationalgeographic.com/maps

form another part of the cordillera. A string of islands off Canada's west coast are actually peaks of underwater mountains. The highest peak in Canada—Mount Logan—soars 19,551 feet (5,959 m) near the border with Alaska.

British Columbia's southwestern Pacific coastline is similar to the coastlines of Washington and Oregon. With its marine west coast climate, this is the only area in Canada that has wet, mild winters. In fact, British Columbia's capital—Victoria—is known for its well-kept gardens that bloom year-round.

✓Reading Check **What are three landforms that Canada shares with the United States?**

Canada's Economic Regions

Canada is known for fertile farmland, rich natural resources, and skilled workers. Manufacturing, farming, and service industries are the country's major economic activities. Like the United States, Canada has a free market economy in which people start and run businesses with limited government involvement. Canada's government, however,

Chapter 5

Section 1, pages 158–163

Applying Map Skills

Answers

1. British Columbia, Alberta
2. St. John's, Corner Brook, Sydney, Halifax, Saint John, Victoria, and Vancouver

In-text Map Transparency Activity Use the transparency to help students identify why certain economic activities developed in specific regions. For example, ask students: **Where is most manufacturing in Canada concentrated?** *(in southern Ontario and Quebec, along the St. Lawrence River)* **Why do you think manufacturing developed here?** *(Students should note that there were available resources, and access to waterways allowed for the transportation of goods.)*

✓ Reading Check Answer

Appalachian and Laurentian Highlands, St. Lawrence River and Great Lakes region, Great Plains, Rocky Mountains

L1/ELL

Guided Reading Activity

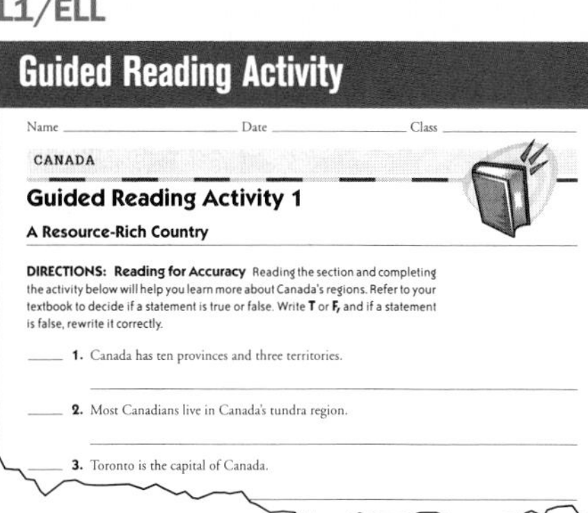
Name ______ Date ______ Class ______

CANADA

Guided Reading Activity 1

A Resource-Rich Country

DIRECTIONS: Reading for Accuracy Reading the section and completing the activity below will help you learn more about Canada's regions. Refer to your textbook to decide if a statement is true or false. Write **T** or **F**, and if a statement is false, rewrite it correctly.

____ 1. Canada has ten provinces and three territories.

____ 2. Most Canadians live in Canada's tundra region.

____ 3. Toronto is the capital of Canada.

Team-Teaching Activity

Government Have students work in pairs to draw up a list of social and economic challenges that face Canada's government leaders today. Then ask the pairs to rank the challenges they listed from the most pressing to the least important. Call on pairs to present and justify their rankings. **L2**

EE4 Human Systems: Standard 13

Chapter 5

Section 1, pages 158–163

More About the Photo

Saskatchewan More than half of Canada's wheat is grown in Saskatchewan. The building of the Canadian Pacific Railway in the late 1800s helped farmers migrate to Saskatchewan and provided a way for them to get their grain to market.

Caption Answer ranching, oil, and natural gas

ASSESS

Assign Section 1 Assessment as homework or an in-class activity.

Have students use the Interactive Tutor Self-Assessment CD-ROM to review Section 1.

L2

Section Quiz

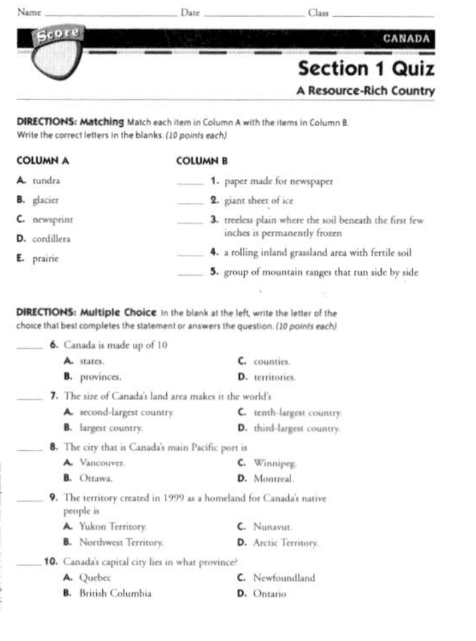

Name ______ Date ______ Class ______

Score

CANADA

Section 1 Quiz

A Resource-Rich Country

DIRECTIONS: Matching Match each item in Column A with the items in Column B. Write the correct letters in the blanks. *(10 points each)*

COLUMN A	COLUMN B
A. tundra	____ **1.** paper made for newspaper
B. glacier	____ **2.** giant sheet of ice
C. newsprint	____ **3.** treeless plain where the soil beneath the first few inches is permanently frozen
D. cordillera	____ **4.** a rolling inland grassland area with fertile soil
E. prairie	____ **5.** group of mountain ranges that run side by side

DIRECTIONS: Multiple Choice In the blank at the left, write the letter of the choice that best completes the statement or answers the question. *(10 points each)*

____ **6.** Canada is made up of 10
A. states. **C.** counties.
B. provinces. **D.** territories.

____ **7.** The size of Canada's land area makes it the world's
A. second-largest country. **C.** tenth-largest country.
B. largest country. **D.** third-largest country.

____ **8.** The city that is Canada's main Pacific port is
A. Vancouver. **C.** Winnipeg.
B. Ottawa. **D.** Montreal.

____ **9.** The territory created in 1999 as a homeland for Canada's native people is
A. Yukon Territory. **C.** Nunavut.
B. Northwest Territory. **D.** Arctic Territory.

____ **10.** Canada's capital city lies in what province?
A. Quebec **C.** Newfoundland
B. British Columbia **D.** Ontario

73

Nighttime Harvest

At harvest time in southern Saskatchewan, the work goes on around the clock. The farms in the Prairie Provinces are large and depend on machinery.

Economics **What other economic activities take place in the Prairie Provinces?**

plays a more direct role in the Canadian economy. For example, Canada's national and provincial governments provide health care for citizens. Broadcasting, transportation, and electric power companies are heavily regulated. These public services might not have been available in Canada's remote areas without government support.

As you would expect, geography plays a major role in where industries are located. Factors such as nearness to the ocean, location along the U.S.–Canadian border, and oil and coal deposits determine where industries, jobs, and people can be found.

Eastern Canada Fishing traditionally has been the major industry in Newfoundland and Labrador and the Maritime Provinces. The **Grand Banks,** off the coast of Newfoundland and Labrador, is one of the best fishing grounds in the world. These waters have been overfished, however. The government now regulates how many fish may be caught in these waters. As a result, fewer Canadians make a living from the sea. Instead, most people in the Maritime Provinces today hold jobs in manufacturing, mining, and tourism. **Halifax** is a major shipping center in this region. Its harbor remains open in winter when ice closes many other eastern Canadian ports.

Quebec and Ontario Manufacturing and service industries are dominant in Canada's largest province, Quebec. Almost one-fourth of Canadians live in Quebec, where agriculture and fishing are also important. **Montreal,** an important port on the St. Lawrence River, is Canada's second-largest city. It is also a major financial and industrial center. The city of **Quebec,** founded by the French in 1608, is the capital of the province of Quebec. Many historic sites and a European charm make it popular with tourists.

Canada's second-largest province is Ontario. It has the most people and greatest wealth, however. It produces more than half of Canada's manufactured goods. Southern Ontario also has fertile land and a growing season long enough for farming. Farmers here grow grains, fruits, and vegetables and raise beef and dairy cattle.

As you know, Toronto is Canada's largest city. It is also the capital of Ontario and the country's chief manufacturing, financial, and communications center. **Ottawa,** the national capital, lies in Ontario near the border with Quebec. Many Canadians work in government offices in Ottawa.

The Prairie Provinces and British Columbia Farming and ranching are major economic activities in the Prairie Provinces of Manitoba,

Content Background

The National Flag of Canada The National Flag of Canada, the official name for Canada's flag, is red and white and shows the maple leaf emblem. Red and white were designated as Canada's official colors by King George V in 1921. The maple leaf has been historically used to symbolize the land and the Canadian people. The maple leaf was first proposed as an emblem in 1834, but it did not become the official symbol of Canada until 1965.

Saskatchewan, and Alberta. Canada produces large amounts of wheat, most of which is exported to Europe and Asia. Some of the world's largest reserves of oil and natural gas are found in Alberta and Saskatchewan. Huge pipelines carry the oil and gas to other parts of Canada and the United States. Canada is the fifth-largest energy producer in the world.

Thick forests blanket much of British Columbia. The province helps make Canada the world's leading producer of newsprint, the type of paper used for printing newspapers. Timber and mining industries add to British Columbia's wealth. Fishing and tourism are also strong economic activities. Fishing fleets sail out into the Pacific Ocean to catch salmon and other kinds of fish. **Vancouver** is a bustling trade center and Canada's main Pacific port.

NAFTA About $1 billion worth of trade passes between Canada and the United States each day. In 1994 Canada, the United States, and Mexico entered into the North American Free Trade Agreement (NAFTA) to remove trade barriers among the three countries. Some Canadians fear that their economy is too dependent on the United States. They worry that the American economy is so large that it will dominate the partnership.

Reading Check Which city is Canada's chief manufacturing and communications center?

Section 1 Assessment

Defining Terms

1. **Define** province, glacier, tundra, prairie, cordillera, newsprint.

Recalling Facts

2. **History** What is unusual about the border between Canada and the United States?
3. **Place** Name four of the mineral resources found in the Canadian Shield.
4. **Economics** Which province is the world's leading producer of newsprint?

Critical Thinking

5. **Making Inferences** Why is Vancouver a useful port for Canadian trade with Asian countries?
6. **Drawing Conclusions** Explain why some Canadians worry about NAFTA.

Graphic Organizer

7. **Organizing Information** Create a chart like this one. Then list each province, the resources found in it, and major cities located there, if any.

Province	Resources	Cities

Canada largest city - Toronto

Applying Social Studies Skills

8. **Analyzing Maps** Look at the economic activity map on page 161. Name the resources and types of economic activity that can be found near the city of Edmonton.

Chapter 5

Section 1, pages 158–163

Reading Check Answer

Toronto

L1/ELL

Reading Essentials and Study Guide

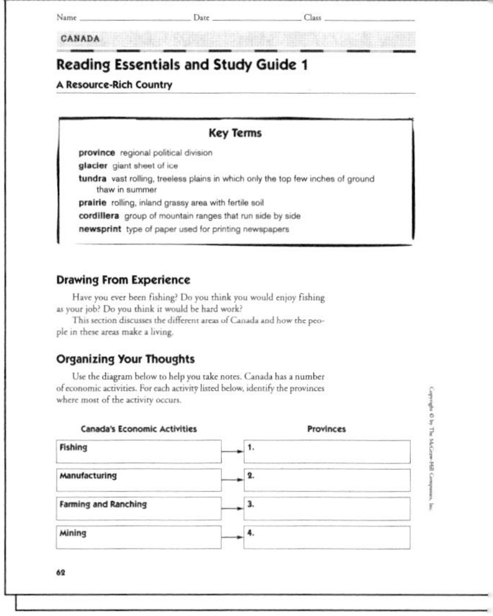

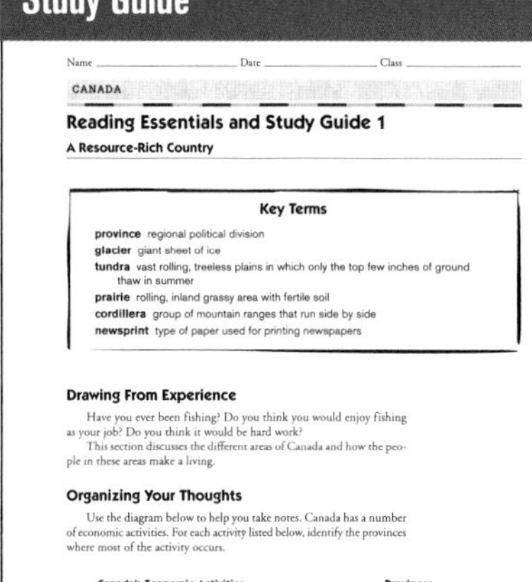

Name ________ Date ________ Class ________

CANADA

Reading Essentials and Study Guide 1

A Resource-Rich Country

Key Terms

province regional political division
glacier giant sheet of ice
tundra vast rolling, treeless plains in which only the top few inches of ground thaw in summer
prairie rolling, inland grassy area with fertile soil
cordillera group of mountain ranges that run side by side
newsprint type of paper used for printing newspapers

Drawing From Experience

Have you ever been fishing? Do you think you would enjoy fishing as your job? Do you think it would be hard work?

This section discusses the different areas of Canada and how the people in these areas make a living.

Organizing Your Thoughts

Use the diagram below to help you take notes. Canada has a number of economic activities. For each activity listed below, identify the provinces where most of the activity occurs.

Canada's Economic Activities	Provinces
Fishing	1.
Manufacturing	2.
Farming and Ranching	3.
Mining	4.

62

4 Close

Have students write want ads for jobs in Canada. Call on volunteers to read their ads and have the rest of the class identify in which regions the various jobs might exist.

Section 1 Assessment

1. The terms are defined in the Glossary.
2. The U.S.-Canadian border is the world's longest undefended border.
3. *Any four:* iron ore, copper, nickel, gold, uranium
4. British Columbia
5. The Pacific Ocean is easily accessed from it.
6. They fear that their economy is too dependent on the United States. They worry that the American economy is so large that it will dominate the partnership.
7. Students' completed charts may vary. Check facts for accuracy.
8. coal, petroleum, copper, zinc; commercial farming, manufacturing

Technology Skill

TEACH

Ask: **What is easier to remember—something you see and hear or something you read?** The question is likely to generate several different responses. Point out that this is why multimedia presentations are so effective—they appeal to the many different ways that people acquire information. Inform students that the skills they develop in this area might well be useful in their work lives.

Discuss the technologies mentioned and demonstrate some if needed. You might, for example, play Native American music on a cassette or CD player or show a clip from a documentary on a videocassette player. You could demonstrate several media at once using a CD-ROM encyclopedia on a computer. **L1**

Additional Skills Practice

1. **What type of media is used in the textbook to convey information?** *(print media, including photographs, maps, graphics)*
2. **Why are computers useful multimedia tools?** *(because you can use them to present information in many different formats)*

Additional Skills Resources

 Chapter Skills Review

 Building Geography Skills for Life

Technology Skill

Developing Multimedia Presentations

Your homework is to make a presentation about a Canadian province. You want to make your presentation informative but also interesting and fun. One way to do this is to combine several types of media into a **multimedia presentation.**

Learning the Skill

A multimedia presentation involves using several types of media, including photographs, videos, or sound recordings. The equipment can range from cassette players to overhead projectors to VCRs to computers. In your presentation on the Canadian province of Ontario, for example, you might show photographs of Niagara Falls. You could also find a video of people working in a large corporation in Toronto. You can then combine these items on a computer.

Computer multimedia programs allow you to combine text, video, audio, graphics, and animation. The tools you need include computer graphic and drawing programs, animation programs that make certain images move, and systems that tie everything together.

Practicing the Skill

Use the following questions as a guide when planning your presentation:

1. Which forms of media do I want to include? Video? Sound? Animation? Photographs? Graphics?
2. Which of the media forms does my computer support?
3. Which kinds of media equipment are available at my school or local library?
4. What types of media can I create to enhance my presentation?

Applying the Skill

Plan and create a multimedia presentation on a province in Canada. List three ideas you would like to cover. Use as many multimedia materials as possible and share your presentation with the class.

▼ Various equipment is needed to make multimedia presentations. For example, a photograph of the Ice Palace (left) will make your report on the province of Quebec more interesting.

Practicing the Skill Answers

1. Discuss with the class the benefits of each type of media.
2. You might wish to invite a computer teacher to class to discuss the different hardware and software in using media on computers.
3. Have students check with the school media center to find the answer to this question.
4. Have students debate the value of each of the different types of media.

Applying the Skill

If equipment is not available, suggest to students that they outline their presentation showing the kinds of content that they would include and the types of media they would use.

Guide to Reading

Main Idea

Canadians of many different backgrounds live in towns and cities close to the United States border.

Terms to Know

- dominion
- parliamentary democracy
- prime minister
- bilingual
- autonomy

Reading Strategy

Create a chart like this one and give at least two facts about Canada for each topic.

History		
Population		
Culture		

Section 2 The Canadians

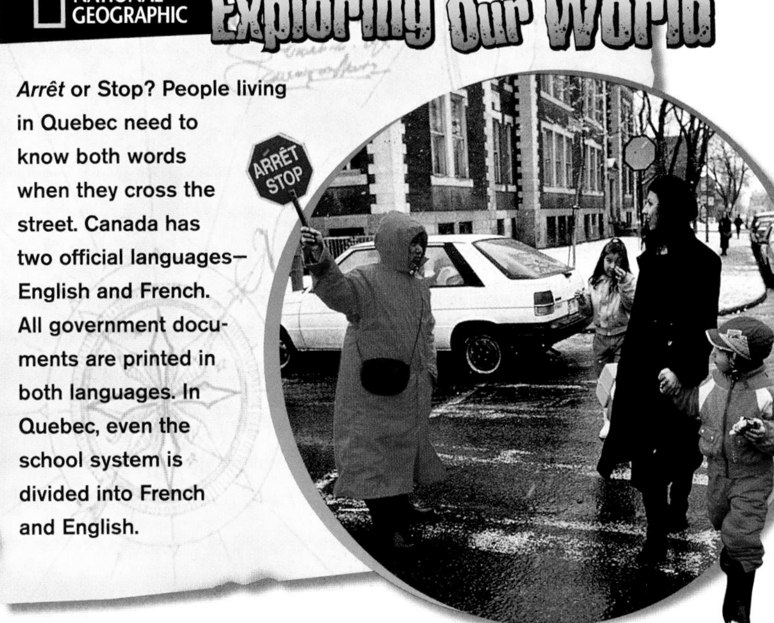

Arrêt or Stop? People living in Quebec need to know both words when they cross the street. Canada has two official languages—English and French. All government documents are printed in both languages. In Quebec, even the school system is divided into French and English.

About 32 million people live in Canada. Like the United States, Canada's population is made up of many different cultures. The largest group of Canadians has a European heritage, but the country is home to people from all countries. Unlike the United States, Canada has had difficulty achieving a strong sense of being one nation. The country's vast distances and separate cultures cause some Canadians to feel more closely attached to their own region than to Canada as a whole.

Canada's History

Inuit and other Native North Americans lived for thousands of years in Canada before European settlers arrived. Some lived in coastal fishing villages. Others were hunters and gatherers constantly on the move. Still others founded permanent settlements. The first Europeans in Canada were Viking explorers who landed in about A.D. 1000. They lived for a while on the Newfoundland coast but eventually left.

In the 1500s and 1600s, both Britain and France claimed areas of Canada. French explorers, settlers, and missionaries founded several cities. The most important were Quebec and Montreal. For almost 230

1 Focus

Section Objectives

1. Identify who first settled Canada.
2. Describe Canada's form of government.
3. Explain what groups make up the Canadian people.

BELLRINGER Skillbuilder Activity

Project transparency and have students answer the question.

Daily Focus Skills Transparency

Reading Preview

Activating Prior Knowledge The British, French, Dutch, and Spanish were early colonizers in the United States. Ask which of these groups might also have made colonies in Canada.

Preteaching Vocabulary Point out that the prefix *bi* means "two" and that *lingua* means "language." Have students use these clues to define the term *bilingual.*

Section Resources

Reproducible Masters

- Reproducible Lesson Plan
- Daily Lecture and Discussion Notes
- Note-taking Guide
- Guided Reading Activity
- Reading Essentials and Study Guide
- Section Quiz

Transparencies

- Daily Focus Skills Transparency

Multimedia

- Vocabulary PuzzleMaker CD-ROM
- Interactive Tutor Self-Assessment CD-ROM
- Presentation Plus! CD-ROM
- ExamView® Pro Testmaker CD-ROM
- MindJogger Videoquiz

TEACH

Making Comparisons After students have read the section, have them write a short paragraph in which they describe how the people of Canada are similar to and different from the people of the United States. L1/ELL

Daily Lecture and Discussion Notes

CANADA

Daily Lecture and Discussion Notes

The Canadians

Moose Jaw, Saskatchewan, was once home to Al "Scarface" Capone. Moose Jaw earned its nickname "Little Chicago" in the 1920s when American gangsters would ride the Soo Line north, direct from Chicago and Minneapolis, to avoid arrest during the Prohibition Era in the United States.

I. Canada's History

A. Canada's first inhabitants were the Inuit and other Native Americans.

B. The first Europeans in Canada were Viking explorers who arrived around A.D. 1000. English and French explorers followed. England and France fought for control of the territory, which Britain won in 1763. For about 100 years, ... Canada as a colony.

Answer The Inuit wore one layer of clothing with the fur against their skin, trapping warm air close to the body. They wore another layer with the fur outside, and the clothing moved to create a breeze which prevented overheating.

Clothing

The Inuit of the Canadian Arctic designed their clothes for protection from the harsh climate. Traditional clothing was made up of a caribou or sealskin parka, pants, mittens, and boots. In winter the Inuit wore their furs facing toward the skin. This created air pockets that trapped warm air close to the body. On top they wore another layer with the fur facing outward. The clothing flapped as the wearer moved, creating a breeze that kept the person from overheating while running or working.

Looking Closer **How does traditional clothing protect the Inuit from the harsh climate?**

years, France ruled the area around the St. Lawrence River and the Great Lakes. This region was called New France.

During the 1600s and 1700s, England and France fought each other for territory around the globe. Eventually, by 1763, the British gained control of all of Canada. Tragically, European warfare and diseases were destroying the Native American cultures during this time.

From Colony to Nation For about 100 years, Great Britain held Canada as a colony. As you recall from Chapter 4, a colony is an overseas territory with ties to the parent country. While Canada was ruled by Great Britain, English and French areas were kept separate. Each region had its own colonial government. In 1867 the different colonies of Canada became one nation known as the Dominion of Canada. As a **dominion,** Canada had its own government to run local affairs. Great Britain, however, still controlled Canada's relations with other countries.

The new Canadian government promised continued protection for the French language and culture in Quebec. Yet many English-speaking Canadians did not always keep this promise. French speakers often claimed that they were treated unfairly because of their heritage. Canada was often torn apart by disputes between the two ethnic groups.

During the 1900s, Canadians fought side by side with the British and Americans in the two World Wars. Canada's loyal support in these conflicts gradually led to the nation's full independence. In 1982 Canadians peacefully won the right to change their constitution without British approval. Today only one major link between Canada and Great Britain remains. The British king or queen still reigns as king or queen of Canada, but this is a ceremonial position with no real power.

Canada's Government The Canadians have a British-style parliamentary democracy. In a **parliamentary democracy,** voters elect

Reading Strategy Reading the Text

Sequencing Information Organize students into several groups and assign each group a time period in Canadian history. Determine reasonable time periods—perhaps 50- or 100-year increments starting in 1600. Using several sheets of butcher paper, have groups construct a time line. Direct groups to research their time period and select 10 important events to enter on the time line. Have group representatives write their selections on the time line along with annotations explaining each event. L1

*Use the **Reading Skills Handbook** for more reading strategies.*

representatives to a lawmaking body called Parliament. These representatives then choose an official called the **prime minister** to head the government. The British king or queen visits Canada only once in a while, so a Canadian official called the governor-general carries out most of the government's ceremonial duties.

Reading Check What was the result of Great Britain keeping the French and British areas separate?

A Bilingual Country

Canada's history of being colonized by both France and Great Britain means that two European languages and cultures exist together today. About one-fourth of the Canadians are descended from French-speaking settlers. (By comparison, in the United States, only 1 person out of 20 claims French ancestry.) Most of these people live in Quebec. There, the French, not the British, are the majority ethnic group.

The people of Quebec have long refused to give up their French language and customs. They did not want to "become English." As a result, Canada today is a **bilingual** country, with two official languages.

Primary Source

A DECLARATION OF FIRST NATIONS

"We the Original Peoples of this land know the Creator put us here.
The Creator gave us laws that govern all our relationships to live in harmony with nature and mankind.
The Laws of the Creator defined our rights and responsibilities.
The Creator gave us our spiritual beliefs, our languages, our culture, and a place on Mother Earth, which provided us with all our needs.
We have maintained our Freedom, our Languages, and our Traditions from time immemorial.
We continue to exercise the rights and fulfill the responsibilities and obligations given to us by the Creator for the land upon which we were placed.
The Creator has given us the right to govern ourselves and the right to self-determination.
The rights and responsibilities given to us by the Creator cannot be altered or taken away by any other Nation."

Analyzing Primary Sources

The U.S. Declaration of Independence states that ". . . all men are created equal, that they are endowed by their Creator with certain **unalienable** Rights. . ." Look up the meaning of *unalienable*. Then, identify the line in the Declaration of First Nations that expresses the same idea.

Differentiated Instruction

Meeting Special Needs: Logical/Mathematical Give students the following figures, which represent the population (in millions) of Canada's 10 provinces: Alberta—2.85; British Columbia—3.95; Manitoba—1.15; New Brunswick—.76; Newfoundland—.56; Nova Scotia—.95; Ontario—11.4; Prince Edward Island—.14; Quebec—7.42; Saskatchewan—1.0. (Note: The populations of the territories are much smaller and cannot be compared on the same graph.) Have them construct a chart or graph that displays this information. They could choose a circle or bar graph, a table, or some other form. Have students explain why they chose the kind of graphic they constructed. **L2**

Chapter 5

Section 2, pages 165–169

L1/ELL

Guided Reading Activity

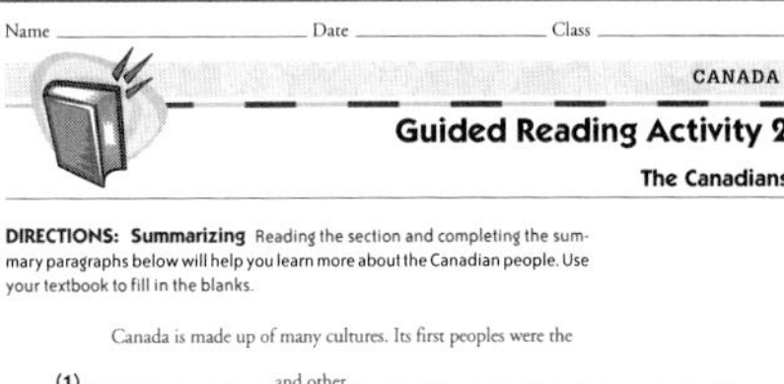

Name ______ Date ______ Class ______

CANADA

Guided Reading Activity 2

The Canadians

DIRECTIONS: Summarizing Reading the section and completing the summary paragraphs below will help you learn more about the Canadian people. Use your textbook to fill in the blanks.

Canada is made up of many cultures. Its first peoples were the **(1)** ______ and other ______. In about A.D. 1000, **(2)** ______ landed on the Newfoundland coast. In the 1500s and 1600s, both **(3)** ______ and **(4)** ______ claimed areas of Canada. For almost 230 years, France ruled the region and called it ______. After wars in the 1600s and 1700s,

Reading Check Answer

Each region had its own colonial government.

3 Assess

Assign Section 2 Assessment as homework or an in-class activity.

Have students use the Interactive Tutor Self-Assessment CD-ROM to review Section 2.

Primary Source

Answer *Unalienable* means "incapable of being surrendered." The rights and responsibilities given to us by the Creator cannot be altered or taken away by any other Nation.

Activity Have students organize into groups and stage a debate about whether the Native Americans of Canada should be given more control over land and resources. Give each group time to prepare its arguments.

Chapter 5

Section 2, pages 165–169

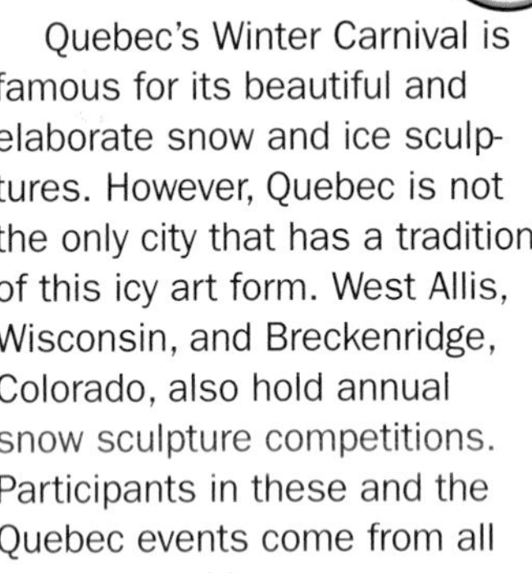

Did You Know?

Quebec's Winter Carnival is famous for its beautiful and elaborate snow and ice sculptures. However, Quebec is not the only city that has a tradition of this icy art form. West Allis, Wisconsin, and Breckenridge, Colorado, also hold annual snow sculpture competitions. Participants in these and the Quebec events come from all over the world.

Time to Play

Fifteen-year-old Natalie Menard has been playing ice hockey since she was five years old. Winters are long in Quebec, so Natalie enjoys plenty of time on the ice. Natalie also enjoys visiting her cousin Angela, who lives in Toronto, Ontario. More than 6 miles (10 km) of covered walkways and underground tunnels in downtown Toronto connect subways with shops, offices, hotels, and restaurants. Natalie and Angela walk from place to place without even thinking of the weather.

An official language is one that is recognized by the government as being a legal language for conducting government business. Government documents and publications in Canada are printed in English and French. Traffic signs are also printed in both languages. School students learn to speak both languages. Of course, some areas of the country favor one language over the other. What language do you think is more popular in Quebec?

For many years, many French-speaking people have wanted Quebec to secede, or withdraw, from Canada. They would like Quebec to become an independent country, apart from the rest of the Canadian provinces. They do not believe that French culture can be protected in a largely English-speaking country. So far, they have been defeated in two very important votes on this issue. However, Canada's future as a united country is still uncertain.

✓ Reading Check **What are Canada's two official languages?**

Nunavut, A New Territory

As you have already learned, the first peoples of Canada were Inuit and other Native Americans. In recent years, the Canadian government has given these peoples more control over their land. In 1999 the new territory of Nunavut was created for the Inuit. *Nunavut* is an Inuit word that means "our land." The Inuit now control the government and mineral rights in this new territory. In this way, most of the Inuit living in Canada have **autonomy**, or the right to govern themselves. When issues involve other nations, however, the national government of Canada still makes the decisions.

Nunavut is almost three times the size of the state of Texas. Part of it lies on the North American continent, but more than half of Nunavut is made up of hundreds of islands in the Arctic Ocean. As large as it is, Nunavut does not include all of Canada's Inuit people. Many live in Quebec, Newfoundland and Labrador, and the Northwest Territories.

The population of Nunavut is also different from the rest of Canada because of its age. More than 60 percent of the population is under the age of 25. Finding jobs to take care of the young population is difficult because there is not much industry in this region. The government is the largest employer, but there are not enough jobs. People often must hunt and fish to make sure they have enough food and warm clothes to stay alive. Nunavut must develop an economy that will grow along with its population so that its citizens will not have to depend on government welfare.

✓ Reading Check **For whom was Nunavut created?**

A Growing Ethnic Diversity

Like the United States, Canada has opened its doors to a great many immigrants. Ukrainians, for example, first settled in the Prairie Provinces about 100 years ago. Many other settlers came from Italy, Hungary, and other European countries.

✓ **Reading Check Answer**

English and French

L2

Section Quiz

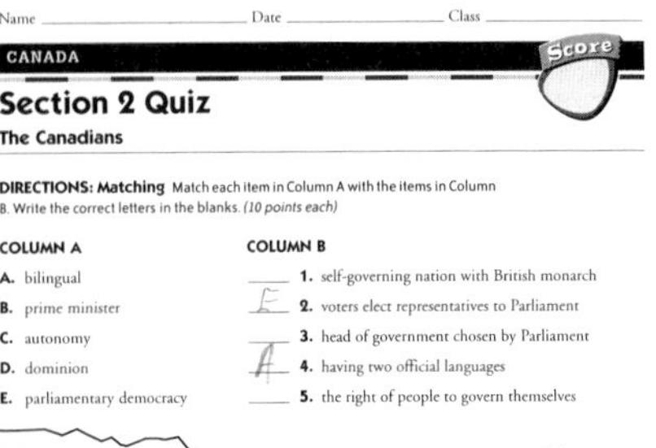

Name ____ Date ____ Class ____

CANADA

Score

Section 2 Quiz

The Canadians

DIRECTIONS: Matching Match each item in Column A with the items in Column B. Write the correct letters in the blanks. *(10 points each)*

COLUMN A	COLUMN B
A. bilingual	____ **1.** self-governing nation with British monarch
B. prime minister	E **2.** voters elect representatives to Parliament
C. autonomy	____ **3.** head of government chosen by Parliament
D. dominion	A **4.** having two official languages
E. parliamentary democracy	____ **5.** the right of people to govern themselves

✓ **Reading Check Answer**

the Inuit

Reading Strategy — Reading the Text

Predicting Organize students into groups and develop a list of consequences that might result if Quebec were indeed to separate from the rest of Canada. They should consider such issues as the impact on the economy of Quebec and of the other provinces, how transportation and communication across the new national borders would take place, how Canada's government would have to change, and what changes would affect people in their daily lives. Ask for representatives to offer the group's predictions. As a class, discuss which predictions are most likely to come true if Quebec does secede. **L1**

*Use the **Reading Skills Handbook** for more reading strategies.*

In the 1960s, Canada welcomed refugees and other people who lost their homes due to war or natural disasters. Many of these people came from Asia, especially China, Southeast Asia, and India. Cities such as Vancouver on the west coast have sizeable Asian populations. Many Africans have also migrated to Canada.

Canada has a long history of religious diversity as well. Most Canadians are Roman Catholic or Protestant. Many also follow Judaism, Buddhism, Hinduism, or Islam.

Food, Sports, and Recreation Since Canada has such ethnic diversity, people here enjoy a variety of tasty foods. People from many different groups have settled in cities such as Toronto. You can walk down the street and sample the foods of Ukraine, Greece, Italy, the Caribbean, and Asia all in the same day.

Canadians enjoy a variety of activities, especially outdoor sports. You will find local parks and national parks crowded with people exercising and having fun. Many young Canadians enjoy playing ice hockey. They also take part in other winter sports, including skiing, skating, curling, and snowboarding. During the summer, they might go sailing on Lake Ontario. Professional football and hockey are popular spectator sports. Many Canadian sports fans also flock to see the major league baseball games played in Toronto's and Montreal's large indoor stadiums.

Reading Check What groups make up Canada's diverse population?

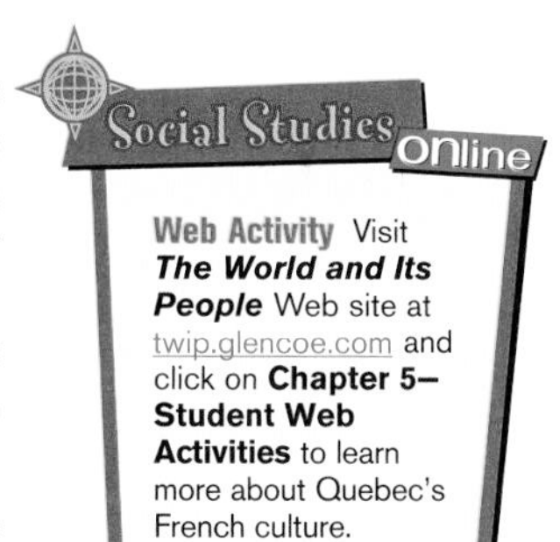

Social Studies Online

Web Activity Visit ***The World and Its People*** Web site at twip.glencoe.com and click on **Chapter 5—Student Web Activities** to learn more about Quebec's French culture.

Section 2 Assessment

Defining Terms

1. **Define** dominion, parliamentary democracy, prime minister, bilingual, autonomy.

Recalling Facts

2. **History** Who were the first peoples to live in Canada?
3. **Government** What is the new territory that was created in 1999, and what does its name mean?
4. **Culture** Name four activities enjoyed by Canadians.

Critical Thinking

5. **Analyzing Information** What is the link between Canada and Great Britain?
6. **Summarizing Information** What are two reasons for Canada's ethnic diversity?

Graphic Organizer

7. **Organizing Information** Create a diagram like this one. List two examples under each heading in the outer ovals.

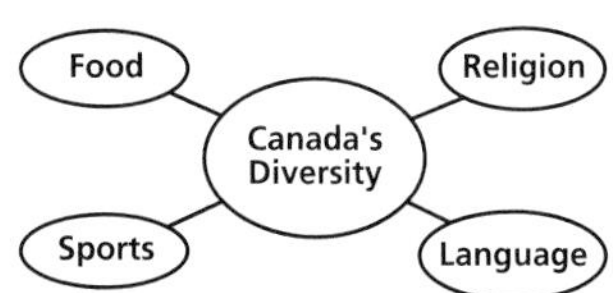

Applying Social Studies Skills

8. **Analyzing Graphs** Look at the bottom circle graph on page 121. What percentage of Canada's people are French? British? Other European?

Section 2 Assessment

1. The terms are defined in the Glossary.
2. Native Americans and Inuits
3. Nunavut, "our land"
4. Possible answers include ice hockey, skiing, skating, curling, snowboarding, sailing, attending spectator sports including football, hockey, and baseball.
5. The king or queen of the United Kingdom is also the king or queen of Canada but has no real power there.
6. early settlers, recent immigrants
7. Students' answers may vary. Check completed diagrams for accuracy.
8. 23 percent; 28 percent; 15 percent

Chapter 5

Section 2, pages 165–169

Social Studies Online

Objectives and answers to the Student Web Activity can be found in the Web Activity Lesson Plan at twip.glencoe.com

Reading Check Answer

people of British and French ancestry, Inuit and other Native Americans; recent immigrants include people from Ukraine, Italy, other European countries, Southeast Asia, India, and Africa

L1/ELL

Reading Essentials and Study Guide

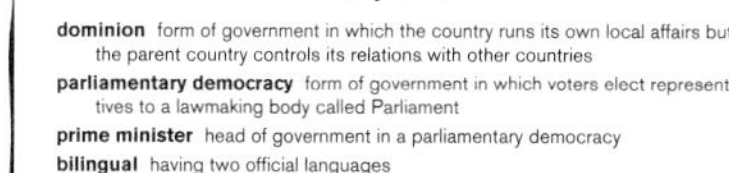

Name ______ Date ______ Class ______

CANADA

Reading Essentials and Study Guide 2

The Canadians

Key Terms

dominion form of government in which the country runs its own local affairs but the parent country controls its relations with other countries
parliamentary democracy form of government in which voters elect representatives to a lawmaking body called Parliament
prime minister head of government in a parliamentary democracy
bilingual having two official languages
autonomy the right of people to govern themselves

4 CLOSE

Canada celebrates its nationhood on July 1, a holiday called Canada Day. Have students assume the role of a Canadian political leader and write a Canada Day speech he or she might give honoring the country's history and diversity.

TEACH

Have students do a presentation on one of the indigenous groups of Canada. Students should research the history of the group, its traditions and culture, and its present political and economic situation, including examples of conflict and cooperation between these groups and the Canadian majority. Reports can be in the form of a poster or a multimedia presentation. L2

More About Matthew Coon Come

Matthew Coon Come didn't meet any white people until he was six, when he was taken away to a residential school. He was a 21-year-old law student when he was asked by Cree elders to run for election as the band's deputy chief.

Interdisciplinary Connections

Environment Many native peoples still follow traditional ways of life. One of their major concerns is the disappearance of forestland and, with it, the habitats of wildlife that these people depend on. Ask your students if they can think of examples of environmental issues that affect native peoples. *(Possible answers: destruction of the rain forest in Brazil, oil drilling in Alaska)*

Making Connections

ART | SCIENCE | CULTURE | TECHNOLOGY

Matthew Coon Come: Man With a Mission

Ne-Ha-Ba-Nus—"the one who wakes up with the sun"—is also known as Matthew Coon Come. A leader of his Cree people and the National Chief of the Assembly of First Nations, Matthew has worked to preserve the rights of Canada's native peoples.

A Proud Chief

In 1990 Matthew Coon Come led a fight against a proposed hydroelectric project, which would have flooded Cree lands in Quebec. He helped organize a canoe trip to get publicity for Cree leaders. The trip was from James Bay, across Lake Erie, down the Hudson River, and finally to New York City. The strategy was brilliantly effective. Coon Come gained much-needed worldwide attention and made his plea directly to New Yorkers, who cancelled their plans to buy power from the proposed project.

As Grand Chief of the Cree of northern Quebec, Coon Come became a foe of industry and politicians who want to separate Quebec from Canada. He stated that even if Quebec secedes from Canada, the Native Americans living there want to stay part of Canada. Coon Come spoke for only 12,000 Cree, Inuit, Nadkapi, and Innu people, but they live on two-thirds of the land area of Quebec.

What if these Native American peoples, who control two-thirds Quebec's land, would elect to rejoin Canada if Quebec seceded? Would this mean a problem for the newly formed Quebec nation? No one is really sure what would happen in that case.

For recognition of his leadership in environmental, human rights, and tribal communities, Matthew Coon Come has received numerous awards.

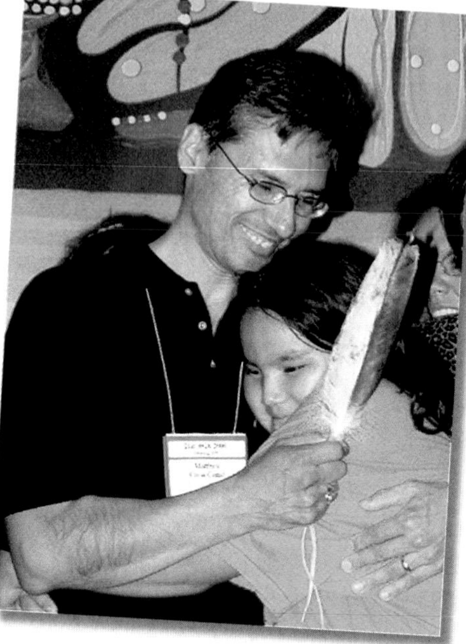

▲ Matthew Coon Come

Making the Connection

1. Why was Matthew Coon Come so opposed to the proposed hydroelectric project?
2. How will the Native Americans be affected if Quebec is successful in seceding from Canada?
3. **Synthesizing Information** Matthew Coon Come has his Christian name and his Cree name. They represent the two worlds he lives in. Develop a new name for yourself and explain what it represents.

Making the Connection

1. It would have flooded Cree lands in Quebec.
2. If native peoples were to stay part of Canada, they would be an unincorporated group within Quebec.
3. Answers will vary.

Chapter 5 Reading Review

Section 1 A Resource-Rich Country

Terms to Know
province
glacier
tundra
prairie
cordillera
newsprint

Main Idea

Canada is a vast country with many landforms and resources.

✓ Region Canada, the second-largest country in the world, is rich in natural resources.

✓ Economics Canada's economy is rich in fertile farmland, mineral resources, and skilled workers.

✓ Economics One of the best fishing grounds in the world is found in the Grand Banks off the coast of Newfoundland and Labrador.

✓ Place Quebec is the largest province.

✓ Culture Quebec and Ontario have Canada's largest cities and most of its people.

Section 2 The Canadians

Terms to Know
dominion
parliamentary democracy
prime minister
bilingual
autonomy

Main Idea

Canadians of many different backgrounds live in towns and cities close to the United States border.

✓ History Inuit and other Native Americans were the first Canadians. French and British settlers later built homes in Canada. Large numbers of immigrants have recently come from Asia and eastern Europe.

✓ Government Canada's government is a parliamentary democracy headed by a prime minister.

✓ Culture Some people in French-speaking Quebec want to separate from the rest of Canada.

✓ Culture Canada's native peoples have recently been given more autonomy to govern themselves.

Horseshoe Falls, Canada—one of the two waterfalls that makes up Niagara Falls ▶

Reading Review

Use the Chapter 5 Reading Review to preview, review, condense, or reteach the chapter.

Preview/Review

Use the Terms to Know lists to help students review and study.

Activity Have students create crossword puzzles for 10 of the terms from the chapter, exchange papers with another student, and try to complete their partner's puzzle.

Vocabulary PuzzleMaker CD-ROM reinforces the vocabulary terms used in Chapter 5.

The Interactive Tutor Self-Assessment CD-ROM allows students to review Chapter 5 content.

Condense

Have students read the Chapter 5 summary statements.

Guided Reading Activities

Audio Program

Reteach

Reteaching Activity

Reading Essentials and Study Guide

Reading Strategy Read to Write

Understanding Cause and Effect **Ask students:** How have climate and history affected the way Canadians live? Have students use the notes they took during their reading of Chapter 5 to help answer the question. Students can answer the question by creating a chart with two headings—"Effects of Climate" and "Effects of History." Have them write a list of effects under each column heading. L1

EE4 Human Systems: Standard 12

Assessment and Activities

GLENCOE TECHNOLOGY

MindJogger Videoquiz
Use MindJogger Videoquiz to review the Chapter 5 content.

Available in DVD and VHS

Using Key Terms

1. h
2. b
3. f
4. i
5. g
6. j
7. c
8. a
9. e
10. d

Reviewing the Main Ideas

11. free market economy
12. the Prairie Provinces of Manitoba, Saskatchewan, and Alberta
13. Ontario
14. The government provides health care and owns broadcasting, transportation, and electric power companies.
15. Appalachian and Laurentian Highlands, St. Lawrence River and Great Lakes region, Great Plains, Rocky Mountains
16. manufacturing, farming, and service industries
17. The waters have been overfished.
18. to protect Quebec's French culture in a largely English-speaking North America
19. Ottawa; Ontario
20. the Inuit and other Native Americans

Chapter 5 Assessment and Activities

Using Key Terms

Match the terms in Part A with their definitions in Part B.

A.

1. province
2. glacier
3. prairie
4. cordillera
5. newsprint
6. dominion
7. autonomy
8. bilingual
9. prime minister
10. parliamentary democracy

B.

- **a.** having or speaking two languages
- **b.** giant sheet of ice
- **c.** right of self-government
- **d.** voters elect representatives to a lawmaking body called Parliament
- **e.** government leader chosen by Parliament
- **f.** inland grassy area with fertile soil
- **g.** type of paper used for newspapers
- **h.** regional political division
- **i.** group of mountain ranges that run side by side
- **j.** nation that has its own government to run local affairs

Reviewing the Main Ideas

Section 1 A Resource-Rich Country

11. **Economics** What kind of economy does Canada have?
12. **Region** Which three provinces are good agricultural areas?
13. **Location** Which province is the most heavily populated?
14. **Government** Describe two ways in which Canada's government plays a role in the nation's economy.
15. **Geography** Which of Canada's landforms are shared with the United States?
16. **Economics** What are three economic activities of British Columbia?
17. **Human/Environment Interaction** Explain why Canada's government must regulate how many fish can be caught in the Grand Banks.

Section 2 The Canadians

18. **Culture** Why do some of Quebec's people want independence from Canada?
19. **Place** What is Canada's national capital, and in which province is it located?
20. **History** Who were the first people of Canada?

NATIONAL GEOGRAPHIC Canada

Place Location Activity

On a separate sheet of paper, match the letters on the map with the numbered places listed below.

1. Hudson Bay
2. Nunavut
3. British Columbia
4. Ottawa
5. Quebec (province)
6. St. Lawrence River
7. Rocky Mountains
8. Winnipeg
9. Ontario
10. Nova Scotia

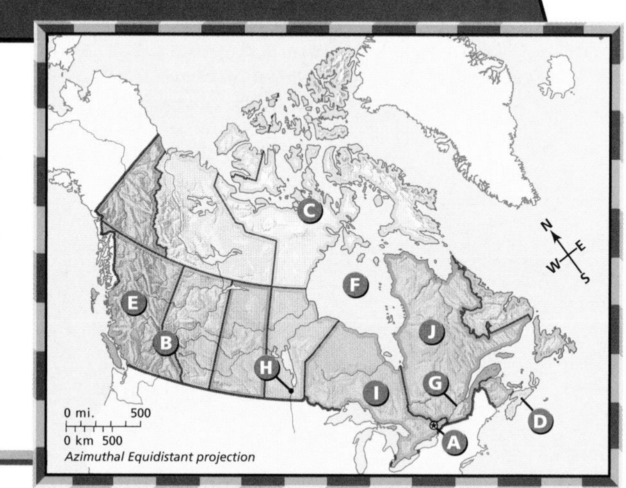

NATIONAL GEOGRAPHIC Place Location Activity

1. F
2. C
3. E
4. A
5. J
6. G
7. B
8. H
9. I
10. D

Critical Thinking

21. Northeast and northwest Canada have subarctic climates. The southeast is milder and humid. The southwest has the warmest temperatures along the coast, but the temperature varies in the highlands.
22. The climate is mildest along the southern border.
23. Answers will vary depending on the province or territory chosen.

Self-Check Quiz Visit ***The World and Its People*** Web site at twip.glencoe.com and click on **Chapter 5—Self-Check Quizzes** to prepare for the Chapter Test.

Critical Thinking

21. **Making Comparisons** Compare the climates of western and eastern Canada.
22. **Analyzing Information** Why do most Canadians live in southern Canada?
23. **Categorizing Information** Choose one of Canada's provinces or territories. Complete a chart like the one below with at least two facts or examples under each heading.

Province or Territory	Landforms	Resources
	Major Cities	Products

Comparing Regions Activity

24. **Culture** As you learned in this chapter, Canada is a bilingual country. India and Belgium are also bilingual nations. Make a chart to list these three countries and research to find the languages spoken there. Then research the histories of these nations to determine why each is bilingual. Compare your findings among nations.

Mental Mapping Activity

25. **Focusing on the Region** Create a simple outline map of Canada. Refer to the map on page 119, and then label the following:
- Arctic Ocean
- Quebec (province)
- Pacific Ocean
- Ontario
- Atlantic Ocean
- British Columbia
- Rocky Mountains
- Nunavut
- Hudson Bay
- Ottawa

Technology Skills Activity

26. **Using the Internet** Access the Internet and search for information on the Inuit and the new territory of Nunavut. Create an illustrated time line that shows the steps leading to the creation of the new territory.

Standardized Test Practice

Directions: Study the graph below, and then answer the questions that follow.

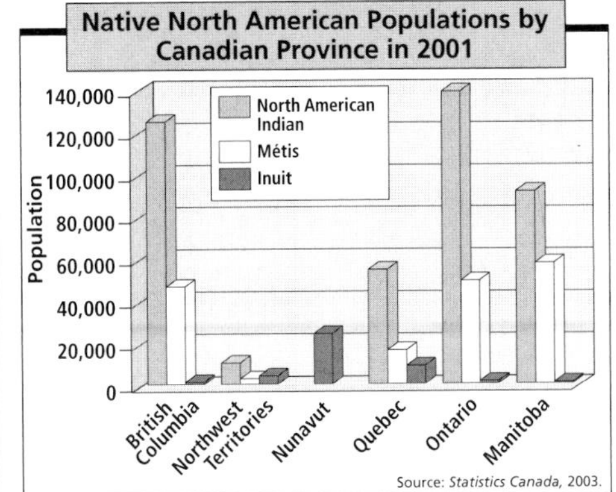

1. **Which of the following provinces has the largest North American Indian population?**
   A Northwest Territories
   B Manitoba
   C Ontario
   D British Columbia
2. **In what part of Canada does most of the Métis population live?**
   F The northern part of the country
   G The center of Canada
   H Near the Atlantic coast
   J In cities such as Toronto and Ontario

Test-Taking Tip: Sometimes you cannot answer a question directly from the information in a map or a graph. In these cases, you have to make an *inference,* or draw a conclusion, that is supported by information in the map or graph. The clues may also help you get rid of wrong choices.

173

Assessment and Activities

Standardized Test Practice

1. C
2. G

Tested Objectives: Reading a bar graph, interpreting information

Chapter Test Bonus Question

This question may be used for extra credit on the chapter test.

What is the capital of Nunavut? *(Iqaluit)*

Social Studies Online

Have students visit the Web site at twip.glencoe.com to review Chapter 5 and take the Self-Check Quiz.

FOLDABLES™ Study Organizer Dinah Zike's Foldables

Culminating Activity Have students use the notes they wrote on their foldables to write a one-page essay that compares and contrasts northern and southern Canada.

Comparing Regions Activity

24. Students should identify the languages spoken in these countries and explain why they are spoken there.

Mental Mapping Activity

25. This exercise helps students visualize Canada's geographic features and political boundaries. All attempts at freehand mapping should be accepted.

Technology Skills Activity

26. Students' time lines should show correct time scale and illustrations—perhaps with captions—that show the steps in the creation of Nunavut.

Unit 3 Planning Guide

- If you teach BOTH Eastern and Western world regions in one year, use the columns in red to help you pace your lessons.
- **If you teach ONLY Eastern or Western world regions in one year, use the columns in blue to help you pace your lessons.**

ALTERNATIVE PACING CHARTS

Unit 3		Chapter 6		Chapter 7		Chapter 8		Chapter 9	
Both East and West	Either East or West	Both East and West	Either East or West	Both East and West	Either East or West	Both East and West	Either East or West	Both East and West	Either East or West
Day 1 Unit Opener, Regional Atlas **Day 2** Regional Atlas	**Day 1** Unit Opener, Regional Atlas **Day 2** Regional Atlas **Day 3** Regional Atlas **Day 4** Regional Atlas	**Day 1** Chapter Opener, Section 1 **Day 2** Social Studies Skill, Section 2 **Day 3** Making Connections, Section 3 **Day 4** Section 3, Review **Day 5** Chapter Assessment	**Day 1** Chapter Opener, Section 1 **Day 2** Section 1 **Day 3** Section 1, Social Studies Skill **Day 4** Section 2 **Day 5** Section 2, Making Connections **Day 6** Section 3 **Day 7** Section 3 **Day 8** Review **Day 9** Chapter Assessment **Day 10** Chapter Assessment	**Day 1** Chapter Opener, Section 1 **Day 2** Making Connections, Section 2 **Day 3** Social Studies Skill, Review **Day 4** Chapter Assessment **Day 5** Geography and History	**Day 1** Chapter Opener, Section 1 **Day 2** Section 1 **Day 3** Section 1, Making Connections **Day 4** Section 2 **Day 5** Section 2, Social Studies Skill **Day 6** Review **Day 7** Chapter Assessment **Day 8** Chapter Assessment **Day 9** Geography and History	**Day 1** Chapter Opener, Section 1 **Day 2** Section 1, Critical Thinking Skill **Day 3** Section 2 **Day 4** Section 2, Making Connections, Review **Day 5** Chapter Assessment **Day 6** Eye on the Environment	**Day 1** Chapter Opener, Section 1 **Day 2** Section 1 **Day 3** Section 1 **Day 4** Critical Thinking Skill, Section 2 **Day 5** Section 2 **Day 6** Making Connections, Review **Day 7** Chapter Assessment **Day 8** Chapter Assessment **Day 9** Eye on the Environment	**Day 1** Chapter Opener, Section 1 **Day 2** Technology Skill, TIME Reports **Day 3** TIME Reports, Section 2 **Day 4** Section 2, Making Connections **Day 5** Section 3, Review **Day 6** Chapter Assessment	**Day 1** Chapter Opener, Section 1 **Day 2** Section 1, Technology Skill **Day 3** TIME Reports **Day 4** TIME Reports **Day 5** Section 2 **Day 6** Making Connections **Day 7** Section 3 **Day 8** Review **Day 9** Chapter Assessment

Note: The following materials may be used when teaching Unit 3.
Chapter level support materials can be found on the chapter resource pages.

TEACHING TRANSPARENCIES

Political Map Transparency L2

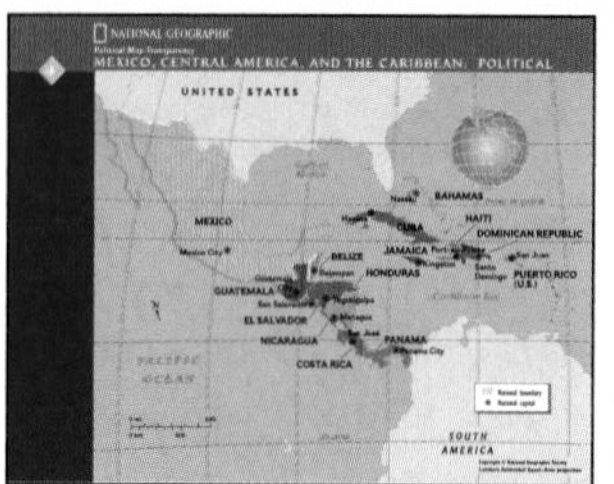

Map Overlay Transparencies L2

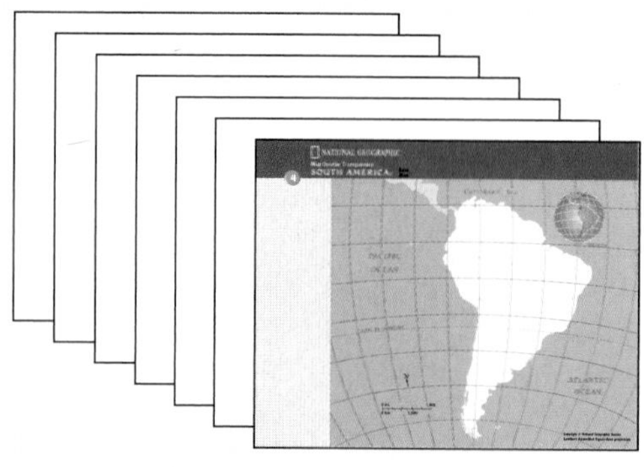

World Cultures Transparencies L2

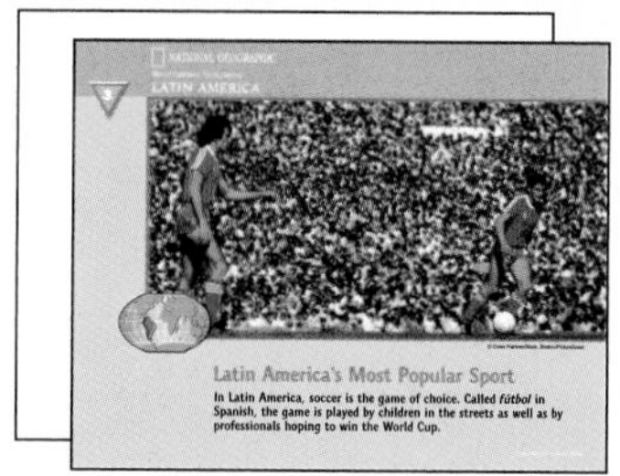

Unit 3 Resources

INTERDISCIPLINARY CONNECTIONS

World Literature Reading L2

Economics and Geography Activity L2

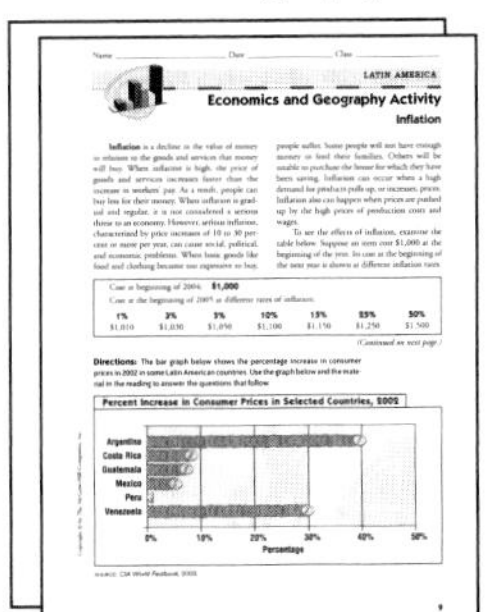

History and Geography Activity L2

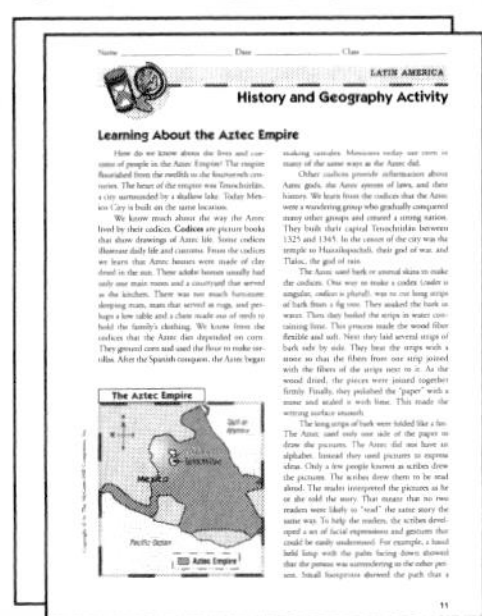

INTERDISCIPLINARY CONNECTIONS

Foods Around the World L1/ELL

World Music: A Cultural Legacy

CIVIC INVOLVEMENT

Citizenship Activity L1

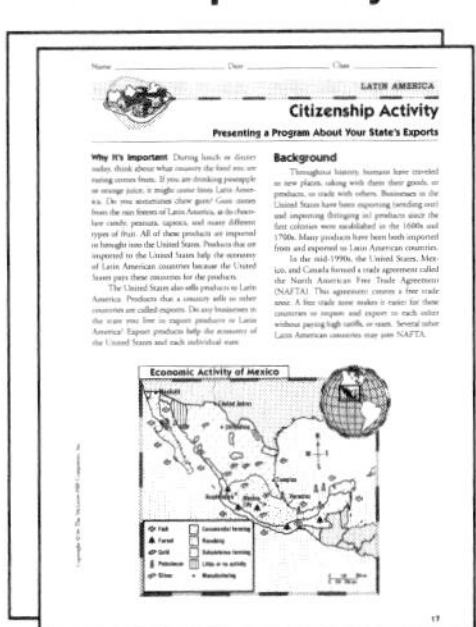

Environmental Case Study L2

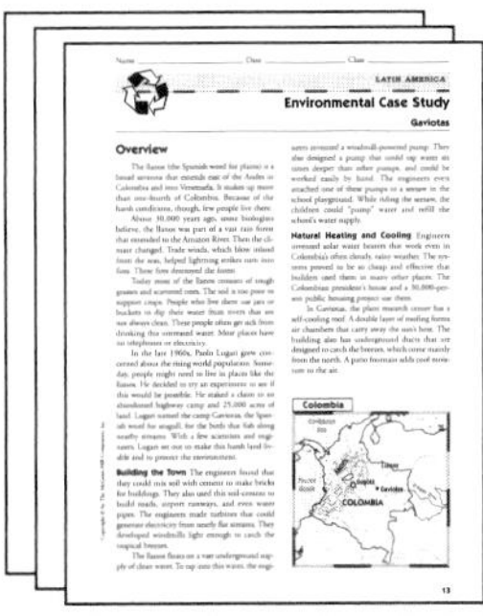

MAP AND GEOGRAPHY SKILLS

Building Geography Skills for Life

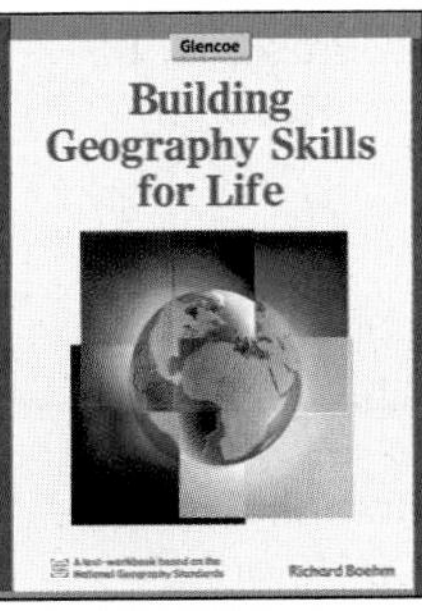

NGS Focus on Geography Literacy L2

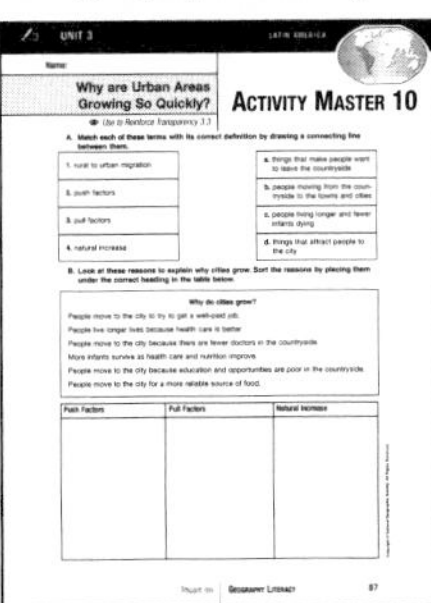

Regional Atlas Activity 3 L2

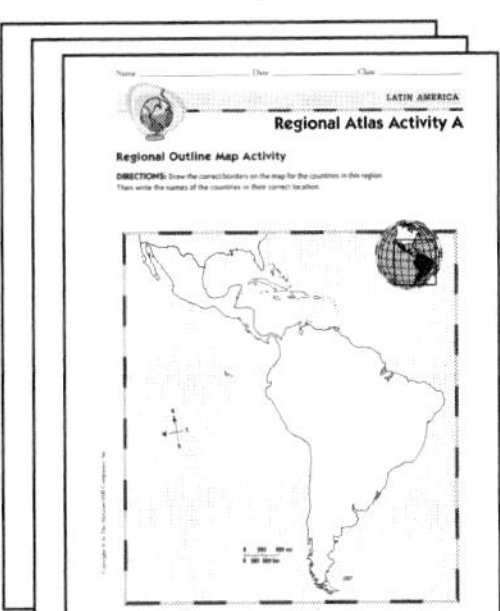

KEY TO ABILITY LEVELS

Teaching strategies have been coded for varying learning styles and abilities.

- L1 **BASIC** activities for all students
- L2 **AVERAGE** activities for average to above-average students
- L3 **CHALLENGING** activities for above-average students
- ELL **ENGLISH LANGUAGE LEARNER** activities

ASSESSMENT

Unit Pretests L2

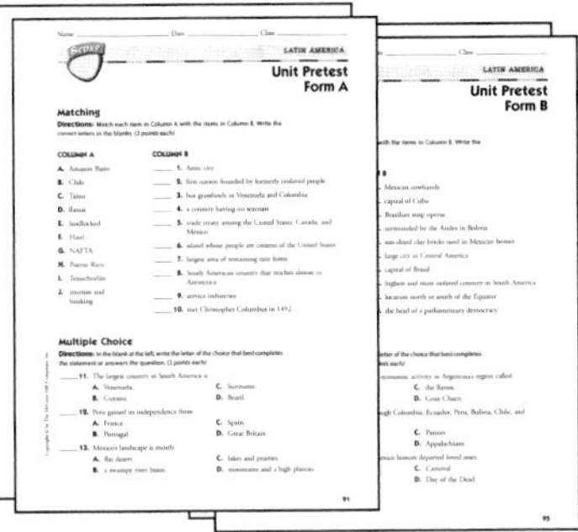

Unit Posttests L2

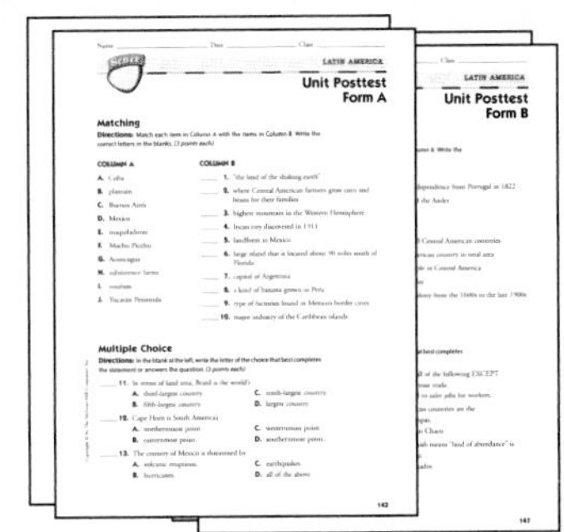

Glencoe Professional Development and Teacher Support Materials

- **Reading in the Content Area for the Middle School Classroom**
- **Inclusion Strategies for the Middle School Social Studies Classroom**
- **Character Education for the Middle School Classroom**
- **Teaching Strategies for the Social Studies Classroom**
- **Reproducible Lesson Plans**
- **Outline Map Resource Book**
- **Writing Process Transparencies for Middle School**
- **Social Studies: Reading Strategies**

Additional Unit 3 Resources

- **Timed Readings Plus in Social Studies** help students increase their reading rate and fluency while maintaining comprehension. The 400-word passages are similar to those found on state and national assessments.
- **Reading in the Content Area: Social Studies** concentrates on six essential reading skills that help students better comprehend what they read. The book includes 75 high-interest nonfiction passages written at increasing levels of difficulty.
- **Reading Fluency** helps students read smoothly, accurately, and expressively.
- **Jamestown's Reading Improvement,** by renowned reading expert Edward Fry, focuses on helping build your students' comprehension, vocabulary, and skimming and scanning skills.
- **Critical Reading Series** provides high-interest books, each written at three reading levels.

For more information about these products, see the Jamestown Education materials in the Classroom Solutions in the front of this Teacher Wraparound Edition. To order these products, call Glencoe at 1-800-334-7344.

The following videotape programs are available from Glencoe:

- **Evita: The Woman Behind the Myth** 0-7670-0029-3
- **Machu Picchu: City in the Sky** 0-7670-0143-5
- **Peru: Warriors and Treasure** 0-7670-1861-3

To order, call Glencoe at 1-800-334-7344. To find classroom resources to accompany many of these, check:

A&E Television: www.aetv.com

The History Channel: www.historychannel.com

Reading List Generator CD-ROM

Glencoe BookLink

The Glencoe BookLink CD-ROM is a database that allows you to search more than 15,000 titles to create a customized reading list for your students.

- Reading lists can be organized by students' reading level, author, genre, theme, or area of interest.
- The database provides Degrees of Reading Power™ (DRP) and Lexile™ readability scores for all selections.
- A brief summary of each selection is included.

Leveled reading suggestions for this unit:

For students at a Grade 5 reading level:

- ***Guatemala,*** by Michael Dahl.

For students at a Grade 6 reading level:

- ***Mexico,*** by Rob Alcraft and Sean Sprague.

For students at a Grade 7 reading level:

- ***Pyramid of the Sun, Pyramid of the Moon,*** by Leonard Everett Fisher.

To order this CD-ROM, call Glencoe at 1-800-334-7344.

Extending the Content

Readings for the Teacher

- ***The Cambridge Encyclopedia of Latin America and the Caribbean.*** New York: Cambridge University Press, 1992.
- ***Into the Amazon: The Struggle for the Rain Forest,*** by Augusta Dwyer. San Francisco, CA: Sierra Club Books, 1991.

Multimedia Resources

- ***Around South America.*** International Film and Video. Available through Social Studies School Service (800) 421-4246. VHS.
- ***Amazon Trail Third Edition: Rainforest Adventure.*** Novato, Calif.: Learning Company. Mac/Windows CD-ROM.

Service Learning Project

Connecting Classroom With Community

Have students work in groups to review current children's books about Latin America in the local library. Students should research to find new books to purchase. Alternatively, students could set up a story hour in which they read several of the books to young children. Have students complete a project summary report that includes such information as: How did this project help my community? What did I learn while completing this project?

Content Background Notes

Use this additional information as lecture notes or discussion prompts throughout the study of Unit 3.

Chapter 6 Mexico (pp. 188–209)

Desert Spring Water One of Mexico's most enchanting sites is *Quatro Ciénegas* (KWAH•troh see•AY•nay•gahs), or "Four Marshes." Although it is located in the middle of the burning Chihuahuan Desert, *Quatro Ciénegas* brims with life—waterborne life. The area holds several lakes, pools, and canals that are fed by underground springs. This surface water supports scores of plant and animal species, some of which are unique to the area. Local farmers tap the springwater for irrigation, but scientists say there is no evidence yet that the underground aquifers are being depleted. Still, they warn that human intervention does threaten this fragile area. The Mexican government has protected this unusual desert wetland by making it a biological reserve.

Chapter 7 Central America and the Caribbean Islands (pp. 210–227)

Volcanic Isle Montserrat was once home to recording studios used by world-famous rock stars and to million-dollar vacation homes with spectacular views. In 1995 life on this island in the Lesser Antilles changed dramatically, however. That year, the volcanic Soufriere Hills erupted, launching fire and ash into the sky. Two years later, new explosions triggered massive mudslides that led to the evacuation of more than half of the island's 11,000 people. The mudslides covered two-thirds of the island and completely buried its capital city. Many islanders remained, determined to rebuild their lives. They faced major challenges. Scientists have found that the ash spewed by the volcano contains a dangerous mineral that could cause a serious lung disease. Also, after several months of staying quiet, the volcano began erupting again in late 1999. Montserrat is not yet safe.

Chapter 8 Brazil and Its Neighbors (pp. 230–249)

One Step Forward . . . The effort to save Brazil's Amazon rain forest has moved in fits and starts in recent years. Brazil's government has made some moves to preserve the region:

- In 1998 the World Bank, the World Wide Fund for Nature, and the government announced a program in which the groups would provide funds to protect 61.8 million acres (25 million hectares) of rain forest. Brazil also passed a law setting harsh penalties for those who break environmental laws.
- In 1999 Brazil's government used army, navy, and air force personnel to prevent illegal logging in the rain forest. The government says that 80 percent of the logging there is illegal.
- In 2000 the government launched a new effort to improve monitoring of illegal logging by using satellites, radar, and airplanes.

However, in 2000 a special commission of Brazil's legislature recommended the easing of limits on rain forest logging. If approved, the move would allow landowners to clear up to 50 percent of their land instead of the current limit of 20 percent. This action alarmed environmentalists, especially in light of a 1999 study arguing that tree-cutting in the Amazon Basin is taking place two times faster than scientists had thought.

Chapter 9 The Andean Countries (pp. 252–277)

A Traditional Language Quechua is the name for a family of peoples that share a common language. The Quechua tribes became the most powerful and advanced element of the Incan empire. Before the arrival of Europeans in South America during the 16th century, the Quechua contributed artistic achievements as well as scientific advances in such areas as engineering and architecture. Even after the Spanish conquest of Peru, Quechua remained the dominant language of the region and is still spoken by several million people today in Peru, Bolivia, Ecuador, Chile, and Argentina. While the Spanish used the Quechua language to teach Christianity in South America, the Quechua Indians themselves resisted European influences on their culture and retain close ties to their heritage to this day. There is a sharp division in Peru, even today, among the highlander Indians and the coastal people of mixed Spanish and Indian descent.

00:00 Out of Time?

If time does not permit teaching each chapter in this unit, you may use the **Reading Essentials and Study Guide** for each chapter.

Unit Overview

The four chapters that comprise this unit introduce students to the geography and peoples of Latin America. The chapters detail the landforms, climate, economy, history, government, and lifestyles found in these countries. Before beginning to study the unit, point out to students that—although the countries of Latin America are diverse—most have the following features in common:

- a strong Spanish or Portuguese influence on language and culture
- a blend of Native American, African, and European heritages
- a mostly tropical or subtropical climate
- the world's largest zone of tropical rain forest

Glencoe Literature Library

As students study the unit, have them read *Barrio Boy* by Ernesto Galarzo from the **Glencoe Literature Library.** The Glencoe Literature Library consists of novels and other readings for middle school students, along with study guides that offer instructional support and student activities.

Unit 3

Peruvian Indian woman and child

Spanish colonial architecture in Guatemala

174

Using the Illustration

Visual Instruction The Maya flourished from about A.D. 250 to 900. They built pyramid-shaped temples that dominated their large city-states in Central America and southern Mexico. Around 1200, the Aztec built a mighty empire centered in Tenochtitlán, the site of modern Mexico City. The Inca also forged an empire, but theirs was based in Peru. Descendants of the Maya and Inca live in southern Mexico and Peru. **Ask: Why is there Spanish architecture in Guatemala?** *(In the late 1400s, European explorers set out to find new trade routes to Asia. These voyages led to exploration and conquest of the Americas. The Spanish built a colonial empire that included much of North, Central, and South America, and they brought the Roman Catholic Church with them.)*

NATIONAL GEOGRAPHIC

Latin America

Where can you find steamy tropical forests, frigid mountain peaks, thundering waterfalls, and peaceful island beaches? All of these contrasts can be found in Latin America—a huge part of the world made up of 33 nations on two continents. This region stretches from the Mexico–United States border, in North America, to the southernmost tip of South America.

NGS ONLINE
www.nationalgeographic.com/education

Spider monkey and Mayan ruins, Mexico ▲

Current Events Journal

After students have completed their study of the unit, have them choose one specific aspect of the physical geography or culture of Latin America that interests them. Students should then describe that feature in terms of taste, smell, feel, look, and sound. Have students illustrate their ideas using poster board and markers or paint. They might use cassette recorders to illustrate sounds. Display students' work on class bulletin boards. L1

NGS ONLINE
www.nationalgeographic.com/education

This online resource provides lesson plans, atlas updates, cartographic activities with interactive maps, an online map store, and geography links.

Unit Launch Activity

Why Study Latin America? Ask students to locate Latin America on a map. **Ask:** Where is Latin America? Why do you think the United States benefits from having good relations with its neighbors? How has the culture of Latin America affected the United States? Encourage students to keep a log in which they record information about Latin America that they hear on television and radio or read in newspapers or magazines. At the end of the unit, have student volunteers offer examples of the information they have collected. Then have the class answer this question: Why study Latin America?

EE1 The World in Spatial Terms: Standard 3

LESSON PLAN

Using the Regional Atlas
These features and activities may be used as an introduction to the unit or as teaching tools throughout the course of the unit.

FOCUS

Objectives
1. Describe the relative size and major physical features of Latin America.
2. Explain the different climates found in Latin America.
3. Outline the main features of the economy of Latin America.
4. Summarize what groups make up the people of Latin America.

5-Minute Precheck

Encourage students to discuss how geographic location affects their daily lives. For example, ask if their community is near a body of water. How does this affect what they eat or what leisure activities they enjoy? Is the climate where they live cold, moderate, or hot? Mostly wet or mostly dry? How do these factors influence what clothes they wear or how much time they spend outdoors? Have students make a list of the different ways that location and climate can affect people's lives. Have them refer to this list as they read about Latin America.

NATIONAL GEOGRAPHIC REGIONAL ATLAS

Focus on: Latin America

COMMON THREADS OF LANGUAGE AND RELIGION unite this region. Once claimed as European colonies, most Latin American countries still use either Spanish or Portuguese as the official language. These two languages are based on Latin, which is how the region gets its name. Most Latin Americans are Roman Catholic, another influence from colonial times.

The Land

Latin America stretches from the Rio Grande south to Tierra del Fuego, just 600 miles (966 km) from Antarctica's frozen shores. Three times larger than the continental United States, the region includes Mexico, Central America, the Caribbean islands, and South America.

Mountains Mountains are prominent features in many parts of Latin America. Some Caribbean islands are actually the exposed tops of ancient, submerged volcanoes. In Mexico, the branches of the Sierra Madre spread like welcoming arms to hug a central highland known as the Mexican Plateau. Mist-covered peaks stretch through the interior of Central America. The Andes, the longest series of mountain ranges in the world, follow the western coast of South America for 4,500 miles (7,242 km). Volcanic activity and earthquakes are common in these mountainous areas of Latin America.

Plains Narrow coastal plains line the edges of Mexico and Central America. South America has vast inland plains. These include the pampas of Argentina and the llanos of Colombia and Venezuela. The largest lowland area on this continent is the basin of the Amazon River, the longest river in the Western Hemisphere. Other rivers in Latin America are the Rio Grande, the Magdalena, the Orinoco, the Río de la Plata, and the São Francisco River in South America.

The Climate

Most of Latin America has a tropical climate. Daily showers drench the rain forests, which thrive in the lowlands. In Brazil, the Amazon River and its tributaries snake through the largest area of rain forest regions, which covers roughly one-third of South America.

The climate tends to be drier and cooler at higher elevations and farther away from the Equator. Under these conditions, tall grasses and scattered trees flourish. Drier still are parts of northern Mexico and southern Argentina. Here, rainfall is sparse and so is vegetation. Yet even these places are lush compared to the Atacama Desert, along Chile's coast. The barren Atacama is among the world's driest places.

Content Background

The Amazon The Amazon River is one of the world's great rivers. It begins high in the Andes, less than 100 miles (161 km) from the Pacific Ocean. The river flows nearly 4,000 miles (6,437 km) and empties into the Atlantic Ocean. Its length is about equal to the distance from New York City to Rome, Italy. This immense river carries a huge amount of water. Some scientists estimate that the Amazon River alone funnels about 20 percent of all the freshwater that flows over the earth. The Amazon discharges so much freshwater at its mouth that water up to 100 miles (161 km) offshore in the Atlantic Ocean still does not taste salty.

UNIT 3

Three-toed sloth in rain forest, Panama ▶

◀ Peaks of the Andes, Chile

177

Unit 3
Regional Atlas

2 TEACH

Making Comparisons Have students turn to the physical map of the world in the Reference Atlas. Ask them to compare the main landforms in western North and South America. *(North America: wide band of mountains in west with high plateaus between; South America: more narrow band of mountains along the Pacific coast)* **L1**

Current Events Journal

Encourage students to take notes on the information in the Regional Atlas, writing down the characteristics that make Latin America a culture region.

More About the Photos

Three-Toed Sloth The forests of Central and South America are home to the three-toed sloth and the five other species of tree sloth. Trees give these animals not only food but also safety. The leaves hide them, and the trees' height keeps them safe from jaguars, their main predator. The three-toed sloth is an endangered species.

The Andes The Andes are not one range but several, with high plateaus between them. They include the highest mountains in the Western Hemisphere.

Eyewitness to Geography

Galápagos Islands In 1831 Charles Darwin set off on a world voyage aboard HMS *Beagle,* a British naval ship. In this passage from *The Voyage of the* Beagle (1839), Darwin describes his travels in the Galápagos Islands: "As I was walking along I met two large tortoises, each of which must have weighed at least two hundred pounds; one was eating a piece of cactus, and as I approached, it stared at me and slowly walked away; the other gave a deep hiss, and drew in its head. These huge reptiles, surrounded by the black lava, the leafless shrubs, and large cacti, seemed to my fancy like some antediluvian animals. The few dull-colored birds cared no more for me than they did for the great tortoises."

NATIONAL GEOGRAPHIC **REGIONAL ATLAS**

Interdisciplinary Connections

History In 1804 Haiti became the first country in Latin America to win independence. The most recent was Saint Kitts and Nevis, a nation composed of two islands in the Caribbean, which won independence from the United Kingdom in 1983. Some islands are still possessions of European countries. Puerto Rico has its own government but is associated with the United States.

Cultural Kaleidoscope

Brazil Brazilians are such enthusiastic soccer fans that they close businesses and schools when the national team plays an important game.

More About the Photo

Roman Catholicism More than 95 percent of Mexico's people are Roman Catholic. The most important symbol of the Roman Catholic Church is the Virgin of Guadalupe.

The Economy

Latin America is rich in natural resources. Gold drew many of the first European conquerors. Copper, silver, iron ore, tin, and lead also are abundant in the region. Some Latin American countries are among the world's leading producers of oil and natural gas.

Agriculture plays an important role in the region's economy. Coffee, bananas, and sugarcane thrive in the moist, fertile lowlands. On higher ground, farmers grow grains and fruits, while cowhands known as gauchos drive huge herds of cattle across rolling grasslands.

Many countries in the Caribbean islands rely on tourism to support their economies. A warm, sunny climate and beautiful beaches attract millions of tourists a year.

Industrialization is increasing in Latin America. However, some countries are moving along this path more quickly than others. In recent years, Mexico, Brazil, and Chile have become major producers of manufactured goods. Lack of money, skilled labor, and reliable transportation have hindered industrial development in other parts of the region. Geographic barriers such as rugged mountains and thick forests have also been obstacles to development.

The People

Long before Europeans crossed the Atlantic Ocean, great Native American civilizations had developed in Latin America. The Olmec set up an early civilization along the Gulf of Mexico. The Maya later flourished in the Guatemalan lowlands and across Mexico's Yucatán Peninsula. The central highlands of Mexico were the site of the Aztec Empire. In South America, the Inca established an empire that stretched from southern Colombia to central Chile.

From Colonies to Nations Beginning in the 1500s, Spain and Portugal ruled most of Latin America. Explorers and settlers from these European countries destroyed the Native American civilizations. They also brought enslaved Africans to work alongside Native Americans on large farms called plantations.

Independence came for many Latin American countries in the early 1800s. Wealthy landowners and military officials controlled governments. They often ignored the needs of poor farmers and workers. During the mid-1900s, Latin America experienced dramatic economic, social, and political changes. Today a number of Latin American countries have democratic governments.

◀ Mexican boy carrying decorated cross for religious celebration

FUN FACTS

- **Chile** The *abrazo* is the most common greeting among relatives and friends in Chile. It consists of a handshake and a hug, sometimes followed by a kiss to the right cheek for women or family members.
- **Colombia** This country is the world's leading producer of emeralds. The value of the rich green gemstones depends on their color and lack of flaws. Perfect emeralds are more valuable than diamonds.
- **Peru** The Central Railway of Peru climbs from sea level to 15,800 feet (4,816 m). On its journey from Lima to Huancayo, the train crosses 59 bridges and goes through 66 tunnels.

Latin America Today

Latin America's countries remain a cultural mixture—Native Americans, Europeans, Africans, and others have all left their mark. Yet the region's cultures do maintain common threads. For example, the majority of Latin Americans practice the Roman Catholic faith brought by the Spanish and the Portuguese. In addition, most of them speak either the Spanish or Portuguese languages. Because these languages are based on the ancient Roman language Latin, the region became known as Latin America.

Most Latin Americans today live in urban areas along the coasts of South America or in a band reaching from Mexico into Central America. Some of the largest cities in the world are in Latin America, including Mexico City, Rio de Janeiro, and São Paulo.

Rio de Janeiro, Brazil ▼

Data Bits

Country	Automobiles per 1,000 people	Television sets per 1,000 people
Chile	88	240
Colombia	43	279
Ecuador	41	213
Mexico	102	272
Suriname	123	241
Venezuela	68	185

Population: Urban vs. Rural

Country	Urban	Rural
Chile	86%	14%
Colombia	76%	24%
Ecuador	63%	37%
Mexico	75%	25%
Suriname	75%	25%
Venezuela	87%	13%

Sources: *World Development Indicators*, 2002; *The World Almanac*, 2004.

Exploring the Region

1. What is Latin America's longest series of mountain ranges?
2. What type of climate is found across most of the region?
3. Which European countries once ruled Latin America?
4. Which Latin American countries are industrializing most rapidly?

Answers to Exploring the Region

1. the Andes
2. tropical
3. Spain and Portugal
4. Mexico, Brazil, and Chile

Unit 3 Regional Atlas

More About the Photo

Rio de Janeiro At the center of this photograph, you can see Sugar Loaf, which rises nearly 1,300 feet (396 m) above Rio's harbor. A fortress stands at its base, guarding the entrance to the harbor.

3 Assess

Assign the Exploring the Region questions as homework or as an in-class activity.

Reteach
On the board, create a four-column chart with the headings "The Land," "The Climate," "The Economy," and "The People." Ask students to offer statements about Latin America that belong under each heading.

Enrich
Have students research one of the major cities of Latin America, such as Rio de Janeiro, Mexico City, or Buenos Aires. Have each student present his or her findings orally or in written form.

4 Close

Reading Strategy

Writing a Paragraph Have students write a paragraph explaining why the countries of Latin America make up a culture region.

LESSON PLAN

Using the Regional Atlas
These features and activities may be used as an introduction to the unit or as teaching tools throughout the course of the unit.

FOCUS

Objectives
1. Describe the relative size and location of Latin America.
2. Name the major physical features of Latin America.
3. List the nations that make up Latin America.
4. Describe the population density of Latin America.

5-Minute Precheck
Ask students what facts they know about Latin America. On the board, write "Physical Geography" and "Human Geography." Prompt students to suggest which category each fact belongs to.

More About the Profile
In order to show a variety of physical features, this cross section begins at Lima, Peru, and ends at Salvador, Brazil, along 10°S latitude.

NATIONAL GEOGRAPHIC **REGIONAL ATLAS**

Latin America

Physical

UNITED STATES
Bermuda Is.
Baja California
Plateau of Mexico
SIERRA MADRE OCCIDENTAL
SIERRA MADRE ORIENTAL
Rio Grande
Gulf of Mexico
BAHAMAS
TROPIC OF CANCER
CUBA
Yucatán Peninsula
WEST INDIES
Greater Antilles
HAITI
DOM. REP.
MEXICO
Sierra Madre del Sur
BELIZE
JAMAICA
Puerto Rico
HONDURAS
ATLANTIC OCEAN
GUATEMALA
NICARAGUA
Caribbean Sea
Lesser Antilles
EL SALVADOR
Lake Maracaibo
COSTA RICA
Isthmus of Panama
PANAMA
VENEZUELA
Orinoco R.
GUYANA
SURINAME
FRENCH GUIANA
Llanos
Guiana Highlands
COLOMBIA
EQUATOR
Galápagos Islands
ECUADOR
AMAZON BASIN
Negro R.
Amazon R.
PERU
BRAZIL
ANDES
Madeira R.
Mato Grosso Plateau
BRAZILIAN HIGHLANDS
São Francisco R.
PACIFIC OCEAN
Lake Titicaca
BOLIVIA
Altiplano
Atacama Desert
PARAGUAY
Gran Chaco
Paraná R.
TROPIC OF CAPRICORN
▲ Mountain peak
CHILE
0 mi. 1,000
0 km 1,000
Lambert Azimuthal Equal-Area projection
Aconcagua 22,834 ft. (6,960 m)
ARGENTINA
Pampas
URUGUAY
Río de la Plata
ATLANTIC OCEAN
PATAGONIA
Strait of Magellan
Tierra del Fuego
Falkland Islands
Cape Horn
South Georgia I.
120°W 110°W 100°W 90°W 80°W 70°W 60°W 50°W
30°N 20°N 10°N 0° 10°S 20°S 30°S 40°S

26,247 ft. 8,000 m
19,685 ft. 6,000 m
13,123 ft. 4,000 m
6,562 ft. 2,000 m
0 mi. 500
0 km 500
ANDES
AMAZON BASIN
MATO GROSSO PLATEAU
BRAZILIAN HIGHLANDS
LIMA
Sea level
SALVADOR

180 UNIT 3

Regional Atlas Activity

Class Challenge Organize students into small groups to write at least five questions about the physical map of Latin America. Tell students to include direction, key, scale, or physical map questions, such as: **In what direction would you travel from the Yucatán Peninsula to Cuba?** *(east);* or **In the elevation profile, how do the Brazilian Highlands compare in elevation to the Andes?** *(The Andes, at about 15,000 feet, are about seven-and-one-half times higher than the Brazilian Highlands, at 2,000 feet.)* Allow time for groups to write questions and challenge one another. You may also want to repeat this activity at the end of the unit. **L1**

EE1 The World in Spatial Terms: Standard 1

UNIT 3

Political

MAP STUDY

1. What huge lowland area lies in northern Brazil?
2. What is the capital of Cuba?

Unit 3

Regional Atlas

2 TEACH

Interpreting a Map Have students look at the political map on this page. **Ask:** **What is different about the way the names French Guiana, Suriname, and Guyana are treated on the map?** *(French Guiana is followed by "Fr.")* **What does this difference mean?** *(French Guiana is not an independent country but a territory under another government.)* Have them find other similar places on the map. *(Cayman Islands; Virgin Islands; Puerto Rico; Bermuda; Guadeloupe; Martinique; Galápagos Islands; and Falkland Islands)* **L1**

Interpreting a Map **Ask:** **What continents form Latin America?** *(South America and part of North America)* **Why is part of Latin America called Central America?** *(It is geographically in the center between North America and South America.)* **L1**

MAP STUDY

Answers

1. Amazon Basin
2. Havana

Skills Practice

What is the largest South American country? *(Brazil)* **What are the only two countries in South America that do not share a border with Brazil?** *(Ecuador and Chile)*

Regional Atlas Activity

Analyzing Information Have students look at the physical map. **Ask:** **What islands seem to be an extension of continental landforms?** Students should recognize that Cuba seems to extend from the Yucatán Peninsula. Cuba and the other islands of the Greater Antilles are, in fact, the remnants of the same system of fault mountains that formed the Yucatán. Over millions of years, those mountains have eroded, and sea levels have risen, leaving the highest bits of land as isolated islands. Encourage students to research how the islands of the Lesser Antilles were formed. **L1**

EE3 Physical Systems: Standard 7

Regional Atlas

South America

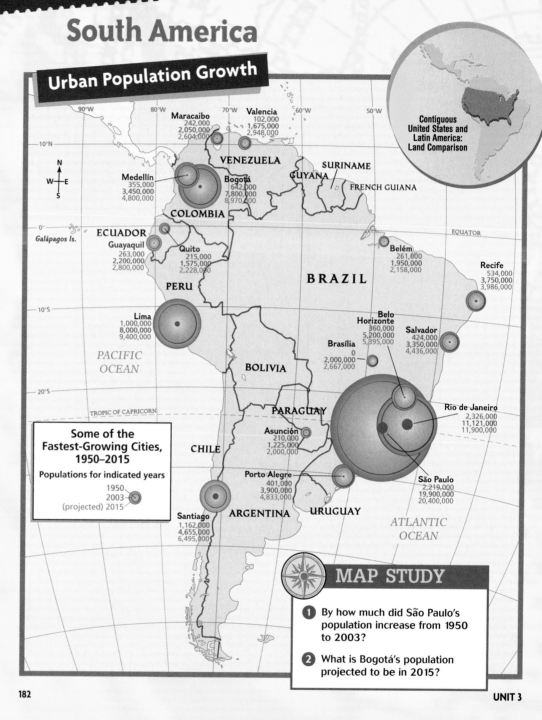

Urban Population Growth

Maracaibo
242,000
2,050,000
2,604,000

Valencia
102,000
1,675,000
2,948,000

Medellín
355,000
3,450,000
4,800,000

Bogotá
642,000
7,800,000
8,970,000

Guayaquil
263,000
2,200,000
2,800,000

Quito
215,000
1,575,000
2,228,000

Belém
261,000
1,950,000
2,158,000

Recife
534,000
3,750,000
3,986,000

Lima
1,000,000
8,000,000
9,400,000

Belo Horizonte
360,000
5,200,000
5,395,000

Salvador
424,000
3,350,000
4,436,000

Brasília
0
2,000,000
2,667,000

Rio de Janeiro
2,326,000
11,121,000
11,900,000

Asunción
210,000
1,225,000
2,000,000

Porto Alegre
401,000
3,900,000
4,833,000

São Paulo
2,219,000
19,900,000
20,400,000

Santiago
1,162,000
4,655,000
6,495,000

VENEZUELA
SURINAME
GUYANA
FRENCH GUIANA
COLOMBIA
ECUADOR
Galápagos Is.
PERU
BRAZIL
BOLIVIA
PARAGUAY
CHILE
ARGENTINA
URUGUAY
PACIFIC OCEAN
ATLANTIC OCEAN
EQUATOR
TROPIC OF CAPRICORN
90°W 80°W 70°W 60°W 50°W
10°N 0° 10°S 20°S

Contiguous United States and Latin America: Land Comparison

Some of the Fastest-Growing Cities, 1950–2015

Populations for indicated years

1950
2003
(projected) 2015

MAP STUDY

1. By how much did São Paulo's population increase from 1950 to 2003?
2. What is Bogotá's population projected to be in 2015?

Travel Guide

Among the main food crops in Brazil are white rice, black beans, and manioc. These ingredients are combined with steak, chicken, or fish. Traditional Brazilian dishes include *moqueca,* a seafood stew flavored with dendê oil and coconut milk; *caruru,* which is okra and other vegetables mixed with shrimp, onions, and peppers; and *feijoada,* a bean and meat stew.

Interdisciplinary Connections

Math Inform students that the distance overland from western Peru to eastern Brazil is about 47 degrees of longitude. Tell students that each degree of longitude corresponds to about 69 miles (111 km). Have them calculate the width of South America at this point. *(about 3,243 miles [47 × 69], or about 5,217 km [47 × 111])* **L1**

MAP STUDY

Answers

1. by 17,681,000
2. 8,970,000

Skills Practice

Which city has grown faster between 1950 and 2003—Medellín or Belo Horizonte? *(Belo Horizonte)*

Regional Atlas Activity

Unit Project Point out that some of South America's cities are among the fastest-growing cities in the world. **Ask: Why have many South Americans been moving to cities in recent years?** Have students investigate the answer to this question by identifying and researching the largest cities in South America. They should look at the cities' growth over time and determine what push-and-pull factors have motivated people to move into these cities. Students should research this question throughout their study of the unit. They can present their answers in the form of annotated graphs or oral presentations. **L3**

EE4 Human Systems: Standard 9

Unit 3

Unit 3
Regional Atlas

Geo Extremes

① HIGHEST POINT
Aconcagua (Argentina)
22,834 ft. (6,960 m) high

② LOWEST POINT
Valdés Peninsula (Argentina)
131 ft. (40 m) below sea level

③ LONGEST RIVER
Amazon River
(Brazil and Peru)
4,000 mi. (6,437 km) long

④ LARGEST LAKE
Lake Maracaibo (Venezuela)
5,217 sq. mi. (13,512 sq. km)

⑤ HIGHEST LARGE NAVIGABLE LAKE
Lake Titicaca
(Peru and Bolivia)
12,500 ft. (3,810 m) high

⑥ HIGHEST WATERFALL
Angel Falls (Venezuela)
3,212 ft. (979 m) high

⑦ DRIEST PLACE
Atacama Desert (Chile)
rainfall barely measurable

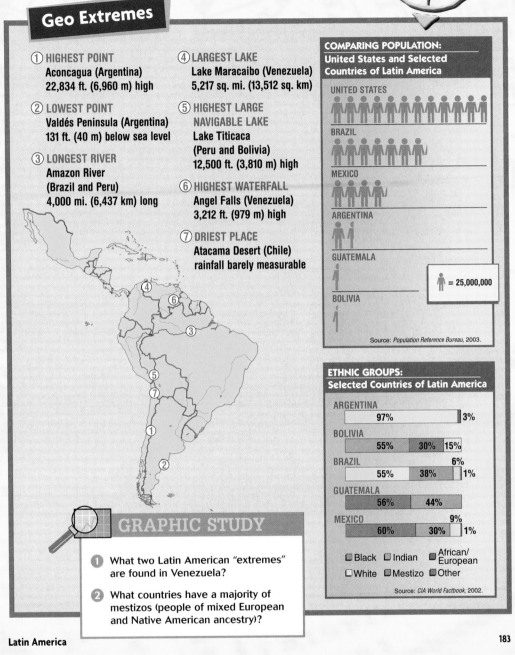

COMPARING POPULATION: United States and Selected Countries of Latin America

UNITED STATES
BRAZIL
MEXICO
ARGENTINA
GUATEMALA
BOLIVIA

(one figure) = 25,000,000

Source: *Population Reference Bureau*, 2003.

ETHNIC GROUPS: Selected Countries of Latin America

ARGENTINA: 97% | 3%
BOLIVIA: 55% | 30% | 15%
BRAZIL: 55% | 38% | 6% | 1%
GUATEMALA: 56% | 44%
MEXICO: 60% | 30% | 9% | 1%

Black, Indian, African/European, White, Mestizo, Other

Source: *CIA World Factbook*, 2002.

GRAPHIC STUDY

1. What two Latin American "extremes" are found in Venezuela?
2. What countries have a majority of mestizos (people of mixed European and Native American ancestry)?

Building Skills

Interpreting Graphs Remind students that when using pictograms like those on this page, they sometimes need to estimate the size of a fractional picture.

Reading Graphics Have students use the pictogram on this page to answer these questions: **How does the population of Brazil compare to that of the United States?** *(Brazil has just under two-thirds of the people the United States has—about 175 million compared to about 290 million.)* **With Mexico?** *(Mexico, with about 100 million, has just over one-third of the people of the United States.)* **L1**

Por puesto is a popular system of transportation in Venezuela. Taxi-like automobiles travel a regular route throughout a city, picking up and dropping off passengers at any point. The fare is more than a bus but less than a taxi.

GRAPHIC STUDY

Answers

1. largest lake; highest waterfall
2. Guatemala and Mexico

Skills Practice
What is the highest point in Latin America? *(Aconcagua in Argentina)*

Regional Atlas Activity

Predicting Consequences Have students choose one of the fastest-growing cities from the urban population growth map. Students should predict how continued growth will affect living and working conditions in the city and write their predictions in their notebooks. Then have students find three articles using the Internet that address these conditions to see if their predictions were accurate. Students should then note how the city is addressing the problems that arise from rapid population growth. Have students evaluate the solutions and discuss whether they think they will be effective. **L2**

EE5 Environment and Society: Standard 16

NATIONAL GEOGRAPHIC

REGIONAL ATLAS

Country Profiles

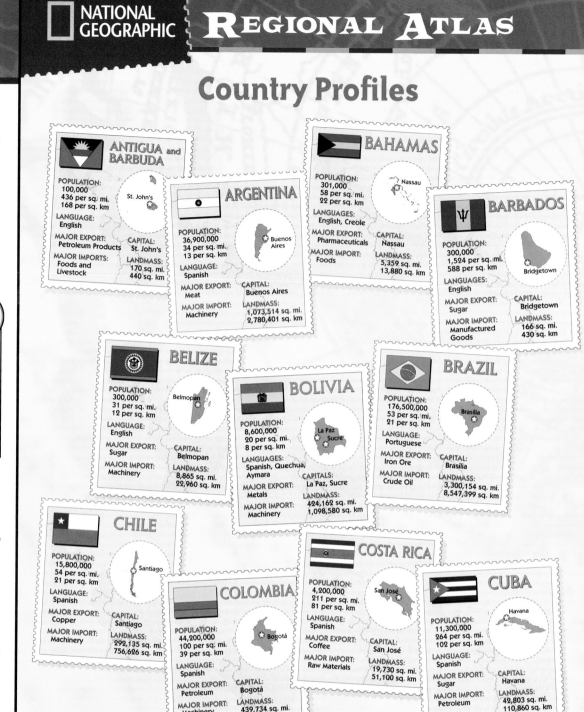

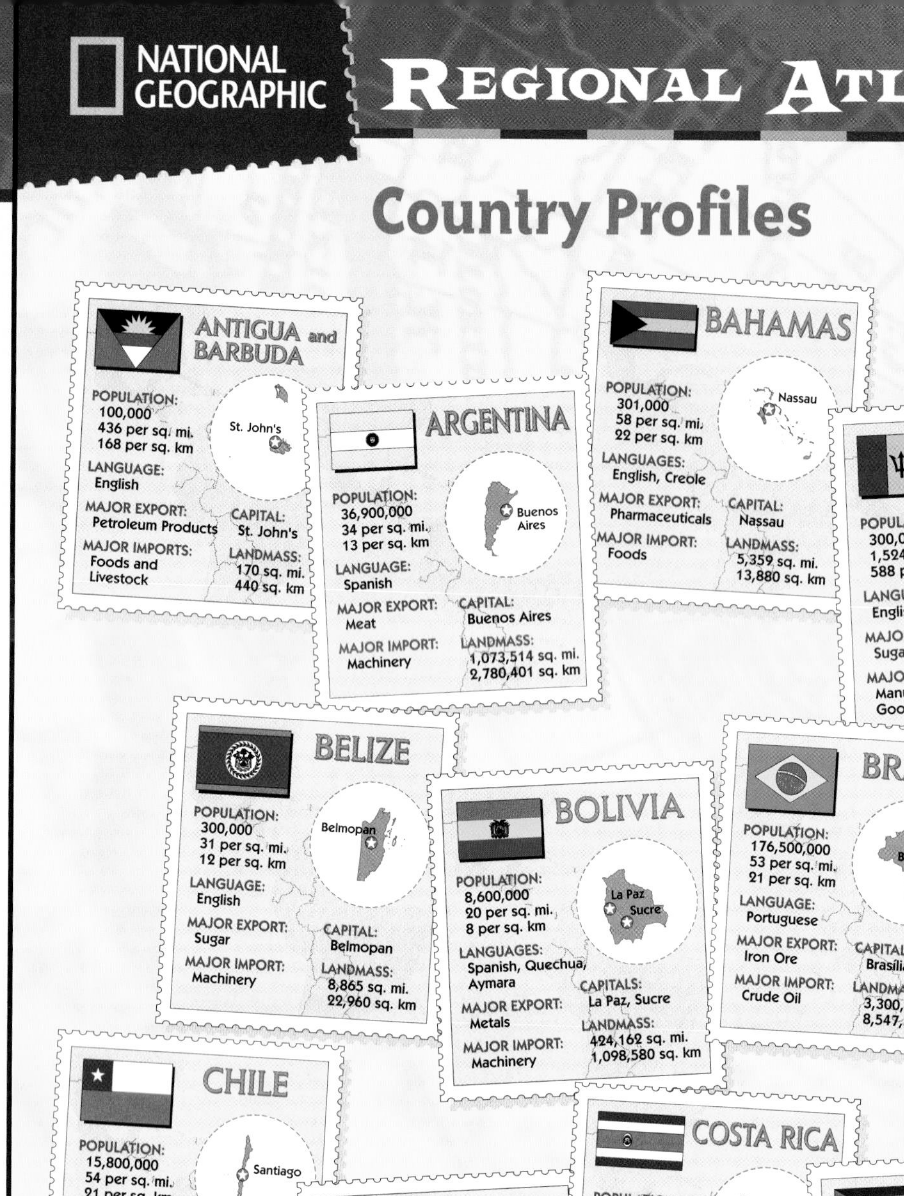

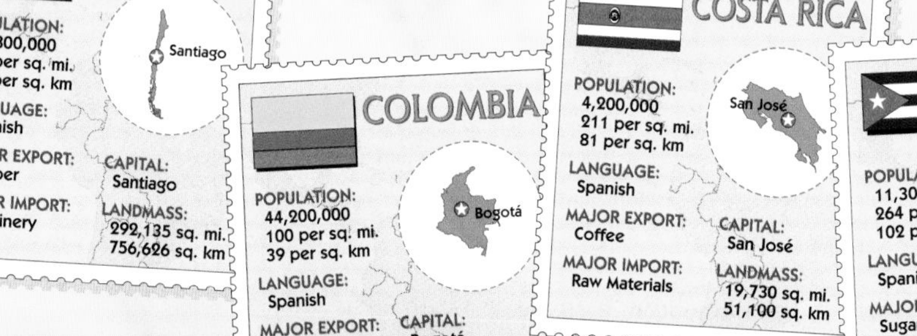

CHILE
POPULATION: 15,800,000 54 per sq. mi. 21 per sq. km
LANGUAGE: Spanish
MAJOR EXPORT: Copper
MAJOR IMPORT: Machinery
CAPITAL: Santiago
LANDMASS: 292,135 sq. mi. 756,626 sq. km
Santiago
COLOMBIA
POPULATION: 44,200,000 100 per sq. mi. 39 per sq. km
LANGUAGE: Spanish
MAJOR EXPORT: Petroleum
MAJOR IMPORT: Machinery
CAPITAL: Bogotá
LANDMASS: 439,734 sq. mi. 1,138,911 sq. km
Bogotá
COSTA RICA
POPULATION: 4,200,000 211 per sq. mi. 81 per sq. km
LANGUAGE: Spanish
MAJOR EXPORT: Coffee
MAJOR IMPORT: Raw Materials
CAPITAL: San José
LANDMASS: 19,730 sq. mi. 51,100 sq. km
San José
CUBA
POPULATION: 11,300,000 264 per sq. mi. 102 per sq. km
LANGUAGE: Spanish
MAJOR EXPORT: Sugar
MAJOR IMPORT: Petroleum
CAPITAL: Havana
LANDMASS: 42,803 sq. mi. 110,860 sq. km
Havana

Countries and flags not drawn to scale

184 UNIT 3

Using Maps and Charts
Assign a Latin American country to each student. Have students make up riddles about their country based on its location—in relation to bodies of water and other countries—or its characteristics as described in the Country Profile. Have students take turns reading their riddles and calling on classmates to identify their country. **L1**

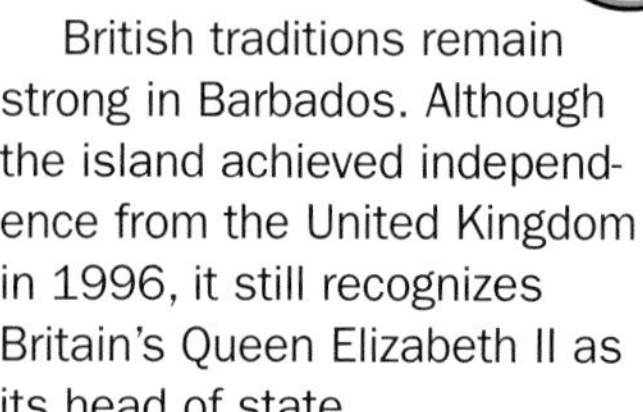

British traditions remain strong in Barbados. Although the island achieved independence from the United Kingdom in 1996, it still recognizes Britain's Queen Elizabeth II as its head of state.

 World Music: A Cultural Legacy

 World Art and Architecture Transparencies

 Focus on World Art Prints

Regional Atlas Activity

Categorizing Regions Tell students that South America can be divided into three areas: the Atlantic countries, the Andean countries, and the Caribbean countries. Each of these regions shares certain characteristics based on terrain, climate, and resources. Have students divide a sheet of paper into three columns labeled "Atlantic Countries," "Andean Countries," and "Caribbean Countries." Then have them group the nations of South America under the correct heading. *(Atlantic—Brazil, Uruguay, Paraguay, Argentina; Andean—Chile, Bolivia, Peru, Ecuador, Colombia; Caribbean—Venezuela, Guyana, Suriname, French Guiana)* **L1**

EE2 Places and Regions: Standard 5

UNIT 3

For more information on countries in this region, refer to the Nations of the World Data Bank in the Appendix.

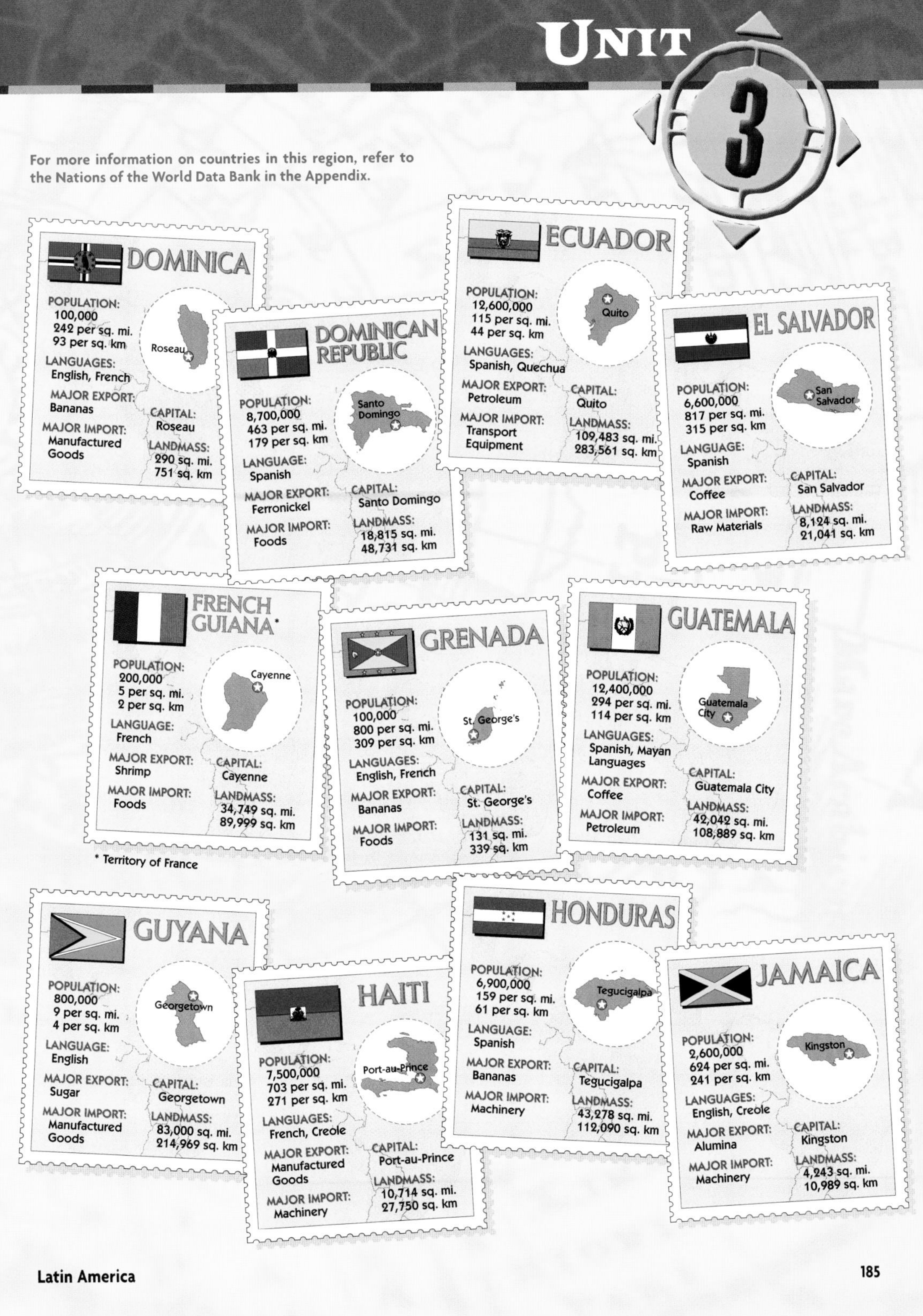

DOMINICA
POPULATION: 100,000 242 per sq. mi. 93 per sq. km
LANGUAGES: English, French
MAJOR EXPORT: Bananas
MAJOR IMPORT: Manufactured Goods
CAPITAL: Roseau
LANDMASS: 290 sq. mi. 751 sq. km
Roseau
DOMINICAN REPUBLIC
POPULATION: 8,700,000 463 per sq. mi. 179 per sq. km
LANGUAGE: Spanish
MAJOR EXPORT: Ferronickel
MAJOR IMPORT: Foods
CAPITAL: Santo Domingo
LANDMASS: 18,815 sq. mi. 48,731 sq. km
Santo Domingo
ECUADOR
POPULATION: 12,600,000 115 per sq. mi. 44 per sq. km
LANGUAGES: Spanish, Quechua
MAJOR EXPORT: Petroleum
MAJOR IMPORT: Transport Equipment
CAPITAL: Quito
LANDMASS: 109,483 sq. mi. 283,561 sq. km
Quito
EL SALVADOR
POPULATION: 6,600,000 817 per sq. mi. 315 per sq. km
LANGUAGE: Spanish
MAJOR EXPORT: Coffee
MAJOR IMPORT: Raw Materials
CAPITAL: San Salvador
LANDMASS: 8,124 sq. mi. 21,041 sq. km
San Salvador
FRENCH GUIANA*
POPULATION: 200,000 5 per sq. mi. 2 per sq. km
LANGUAGE: French
MAJOR EXPORT: Shrimp
MAJOR IMPORT: Foods
CAPITAL: Cayenne
LANDMASS: 34,749 sq. mi. 89,999 sq. km
Cayenne
* Territory of France
GRENADA
POPULATION: 100,000 800 per sq. mi. 309 per sq. km
LANGUAGES: English, French
MAJOR EXPORT: Bananas
MAJOR IMPORT: Foods
CAPITAL: St. George's
LANDMASS: 131 sq. mi. 339 sq. km
St. George's
GUATEMALA
POPULATION: 12,400,000 294 per sq. mi. 114 per sq. km
LANGUAGES: Spanish, Mayan Languages
MAJOR EXPORT: Coffee
MAJOR IMPORT: Petroleum
CAPITAL: Guatemala City
LANDMASS: 42,042 sq. mi. 108,889 sq. km
Guatemala City
GUYANA
POPULATION: 800,000 9 per sq. mi. 4 per sq. km
LANGUAGE: English
MAJOR EXPORT: Sugar
MAJOR IMPORT: Manufactured Goods
CAPITAL: Georgetown
LANDMASS: 83,000 sq. mi. 214,969 sq. km
Georgetown
HAITI
POPULATION: 7,500,000 703 per sq. mi. 271 per sq. km
LANGUAGES: French, Creole
MAJOR EXPORT: Manufactured Goods
MAJOR IMPORT: Machinery
CAPITAL: Port-au-Prince
LANDMASS: 10,714 sq. mi. 27,750 sq. km
Port-au-Prince
HONDURAS
POPULATION: 6,900,000 159 per sq. mi. 61 per sq. km
LANGUAGE: Spanish
MAJOR EXPORT: Bananas
MAJOR IMPORT: Machinery
CAPITAL: Tegucigalpa
LANDMASS: 43,278 sq. mi. 112,090 sq. km
Tegucigalpa
JAMAICA
POPULATION: 2,600,000 624 per sq. mi. 241 per sq. km
LANGUAGES: English, Creole
MAJOR EXPORT: Alumina
MAJOR IMPORT: Machinery
CAPITAL: Kingston
LANDMASS: 4,243 sq. mi. 10,989 sq. km
Kingston

Unit 3
Regional Atlas

Note-taking tip

Remind students that Spanish is the predominant language in the region. Suggest that they can more easily remember the languages of the different countries of Latin America by noting the *exceptions*—those in which Spanish is not the main language.

Cultural Kaleidoscope

Haiti Most of Haiti is mountainous. Its name comes from a Native American word meaning "high ground."

Did You Know

The Amazon River was named by Spanish explorer Francisco de Orellana for the Amazons, a band of female warriors in Greek mythology. Orellana supposedly chose the name after he was attacked by a group of female warriors.

Regional Atlas Activity

Making Charts Point out to students that all the nations of Latin America were once the colonies of European powers. **Ask: What information in the Country Profiles suggests which European country had the Latin American country as a colony?** *(language)* Have students create a chart with the headings Spain, Portugal, France, Britain, and Holland. Have them write the names of each Latin American country under the heading of the appropriate European colonial power. As an option, you could ask them to color in an outline map showing the extent of Latin America controlled by each European power. Have them refer to their chart or map as they read the unit to see if their suggestions were correct. **L2**

EE6 The Uses of Geography: Standard 18

REGIONAL ATLAS

Cultural Kaleidoscope

Brazil On New Year's Eve, some Brazilians traditionally honor *Iemanja,* the sea goddess. They dress in blue and white and place flowers and candles on the beach.

Dominican Republic Dominicans point with puckered lips rather than with a finger.

Venezuela Flowers are very important in Venezuelan festivities. During each holiday, statues of Simón Bolívar, the founder of Venezuela, are decorated with colorful wreaths.

Did You Know

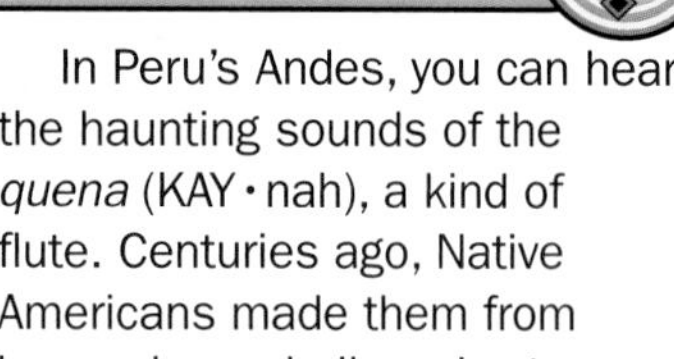

In Peru's Andes, you can hear the haunting sounds of the *quena* (KAY • nah), a kind of flute. Centuries ago, Native Americans made them from bone, clay, or hollowed-out gourds, but today they use cane.

ASSESS

Organize students into groups. Have groups use the maps and graphs from the Regional Atlas to quiz one another on the geography of Latin America.

Country Profiles

MEXICO
POPULATION: 104,900,000; 139 per sq. mi.; 54 per sq. km
LANGUAGES: Spanish, Native American Languages
MAJOR EXPORT: Crude Oil
MAJOR IMPORT: Machinery
CAPITAL: Mexico City
LANDMASS: 756,062 sq. mi.; 1,958,201 sq. km

NICARAGUA
POPULATION: 5,500,000; 109 per sq. mi.; 42 per sq. km
LANGUAGE: Spanish
MAJOR EXPORT: Coffee
MAJOR IMPORT: Manufactured Goods
CAPITAL: Managua
LANDMASS: 50,193 sq. mi.; 129,999 sq. km

PANAMA
POPULATION: 3,000,000; 102 per sq. mi.; 32 per sq. km
LANGUAGE: Spanish
MAJOR EXPORT: Bananas
MAJOR IMPORT: Machinery
CAPITAL: Panama City
LANDMASS: 29,158 sq. mi.; 75,519 sq. km

PARAGUAY
POPULATION: 6,200,000; 39 per sq. mi.; 15 per sq. km
LANGUAGES: Spanish, Guarani
MAJOR EXPORT: Cotton
MAJOR IMPORT: Machinery
CAPITAL: Asunción
LANDMASS: 157,046 sq. mi.; 406,749 sq. km

PERU
POPULATION: 27,100,000; 55 per sq. mi.; 21 per sq. km
LANGUAGES: Spanish, Quechua, Aymara
MAJOR EXPORT: Copper
MAJOR IMPORT: Machinery
CAPITAL: Lima
LANDMASS: 496,224 sq. mi.; 1,285,220 sq. km

PUERTO RICO*
POPULATION: 3,900,000; 1,123 per sq. mi.; 434 per sq. km
LANGUAGES: Spanish, English
MAJOR EXPORT: Pharmaceuticals
MAJOR IMPORT: Chemical Products
CAPITAL: San Juan
LANDMASS: 3,456 sq. mi.; 8,951 sq. km

* U.S. Commonwealth

ST. KITTS and NEVIS
POPULATION: 50,000; 339 per sq. mi.; 128 per sq. km
LANGUAGE: English
MAJOR EXPORT: Machinery
MAJOR IMPORT: Electronic Goods
CAPITAL: Basseterre
LANDMASS: 139 sq. mi.; 360 sq. km

ST. LUCIA
POPULATION: 200,000; 677 per sq. mi.; 261 per sq. km
LANGUAGES: English, French
MAJOR EXPORT: Bananas
MAJOR IMPORT: Foods
CAPITAL: Castries
LANDMASS: 239 sq. mi.; 619 sq. km

ST. VINCENT and the GRENADINES
POPULATION: 100,000; 731 per sq. mi.; 282 per sq. km
LANGUAGES: English, French
MAJOR EXPORT: Bananas
MAJOR IMPORT: Foods
CAPITAL: Kingstown
LANDMASS: 151 sq. mi.; 391 sq. km

SURINAME
POPULATION: 400,000; 6 per sq. mi.; 3 per sq. km
LANGUAGE: Dutch
MAJOR EXPORT: Bauxite
MAJOR IMPORT: Machinery
CAPITAL: Paramaribo
LANDMASS: 63,039 sq. mi.; 163,271 sq. km

TRINIDAD and TOBAGO
POPULATION: 1,300,000; 661 per sq. mi.; 255 per sq. km
LANGUAGE: English
MAJOR EXPORT: Petroleum
MAJOR IMPORT: Machinery
CAPITAL: Port-of-Spain
LANDMASS: 1,981 sq. mi.; 5,131 sq. km

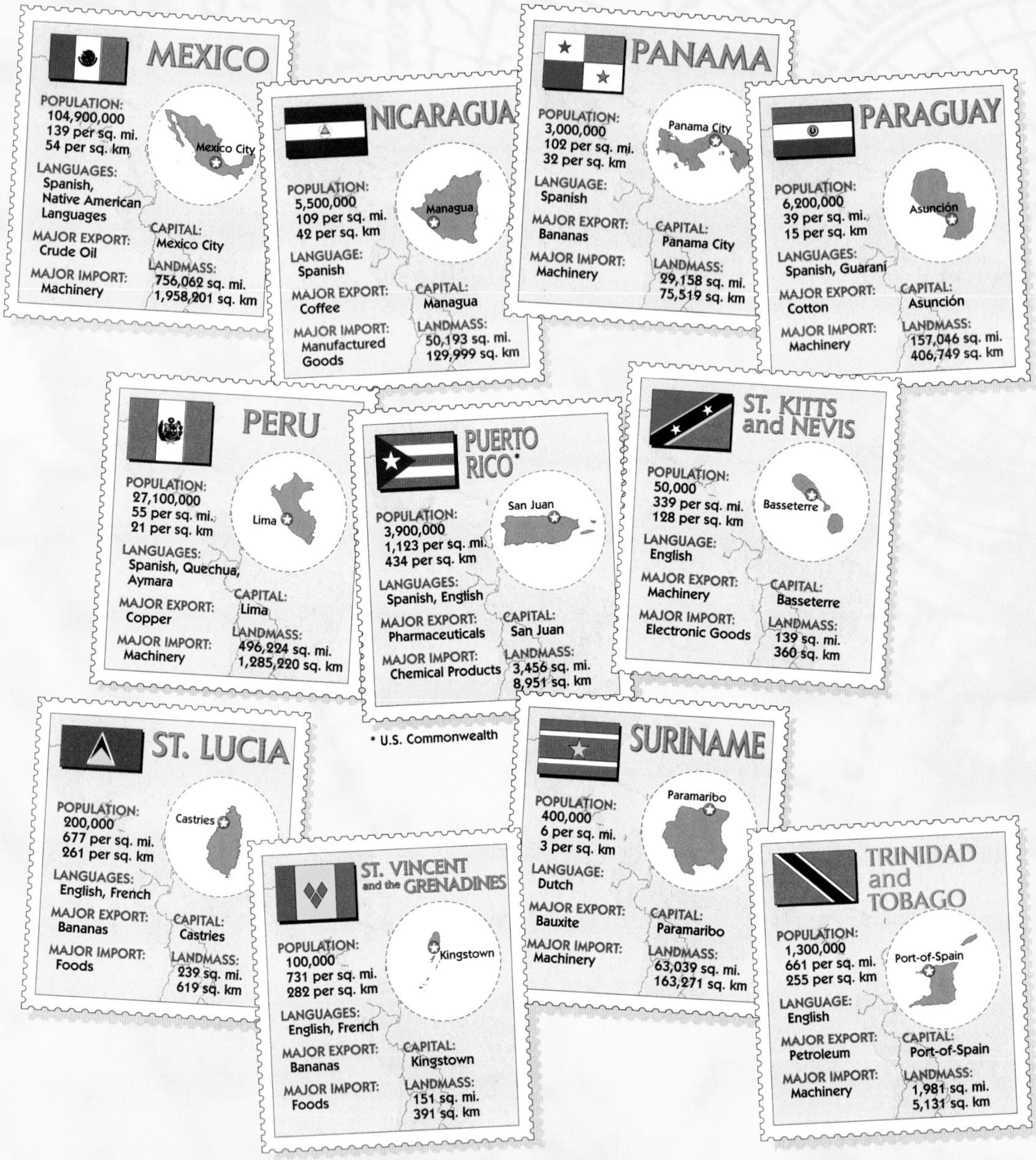

Countries and flags not drawn to scale

Country Profiles Activity

Classifying Exports Have students create a chart called "Chief Exports" with four columns headed "Food Product," "Mineral," "Petroleum," and "Manufactured Good." Have them look in the Country Profiles to find the chief export of each country in Latin America. Then have them write the name of each country in the appropriate column based on which category its chief export belongs. When they have completed their charts, have students analyze their results and make a generalization about the economies of Latin America. L1

 **EE2 Places and Regions: Standard 5**

UNIT 3

For more information on countries in this region, refer to the Nations of the World Data Bank in the Appendix.

URUGUAY
POPULATION:
3,400,000
49 per sq. mi.
19 per sq. km
LANGUAGE:
Spanish
MAJOR EXPORT:
Wool
MAJOR IMPORT:
Machinery
CAPITAL:
Montevideo
LANDMASS:
68,498 sq. mi.
177,410 sq. km
Montevideo
VENEZUELA
POPULATION:
25,700,000
73 per sq. mi.
28 per sq. km
LANGUAGE:
Spanish
MAJOR EXPORT:
Petroleum
MAJOR IMPORT:
Raw Materials
CAPITAL:
Caracas
LANDMASS:
352,143 sq. mi.
912,050 sq. km
Caracas
VIRGIN ISLANDS*
POPULATION:
123,498
922 per sq. mi.
356 per sq. km
LANGUAGE:
English
MAJOR EXPORT:
Chemical Products
MAJOR IMPORT:
Crude Oil
CAPITAL:
Charlotte Amalie
LANDMASS:
134 sq. mi.
347 sq. km
Charlotte Amalie
* Territory of U.S.

BUILDING CITIZENSHIP

Public and Private Needs More than one-third of the area of Brazil is covered by a rain forest. This fragile ecosystem is home to millions of plant, animal, and insect species. Some of the plants are important sources of medicines. According to scientists, more than 50 percent of the world's species live in the rain forest.

The rain forest is also a major source of timber, minerals, fruits, and vegetables. Building roads and clearing land to reach these resources has led to major destruction of the rain forest habitat. The government of Brazil has tried to set aside large portions of the rain forest as preserves. The government does allow development of its natural resources as income for its citizens, however.

Because of its effect on climate, the rain forest is important not just to Brazil but to the whole world. Who should have more say about how much of the rain forest is preserved—Brazil or the United Nations?

Imagine that a new golf course is being built in your city. The area where it is being built includes natural wetlands where birds and animals live. Write a letter to the city council outlining what steps you think the golf course developers should take to protect the wetlands.

Brazilian rain forest

BUILDING CITIZENSHIP

Answer Students will have a hard time pitting the ownership rights of Brazil against what is for the greater common good. Some interesting opinions and debates should arise from discussion of this question.

Write About It! Students' papers should recognize the potential conflict between the property rights of the golf course developers and the need to protect the environmental resources and endangered species. They should also realize that compromise is possible by incorporating the wetlands into the design of the golf course or by donating other land to compensate for damage to the wetlands.

Cultural Kaleidoscope

Tierra del Fuego Have students find the Strait of Magellan and Tierra del Fuego on the physical map of Latin America. Tell students that as he sailed past the island, Magellan named it *Tierra del Fuego*, or "Land of Fire," because he noticed large fires on the land.

4 CLOSE

Have students draw and label the countries of South America.

Content Background

Cash Crops Tell students that several of the agricultural products raised in Latin America are cash crops. Coffee, bananas, and sugarcane are all grown for export. Explain that the prices of these foods rise and fall with supply and demand. Also, severe weather can destroy most of a year's crop, hurting the country's ability to earn money from exports. In addition, countries must worry about competition from countries elsewhere in the world growing the same crops. In years with good harvests, the country's earnings from exports can rise.

Chapter 6 Resources

Note: The following materials may be used when teaching Chapter 6.
Section level support materials are shown at point of use in the margins of the Teacher Wraparound Edition.

Timesaving Tools

TeacherWorks™ All-In-One Planner and Resource Center

- **Interactive Teacher Edition** See the **Interactive Teacher Edition** CD-ROM to electronically integrate your Teacher Wraparound Edition and blackline masters.
- **Interactive Lesson Planner** Organize your week, month, semester, or year with all the lesson helps you need. The **Interactive Lesson Planner** CD-ROM contains all Chapter 6 resources.

Use Glencoe's **Presentation Plus!** multimedia teacher tool to easily present dynamic lessons that visually excite your students. Using Microsoft PowerPoint® you can customize the presentations to create your own personalized lessons.

TEACHING TRANSPARENCIES

Graphic Organizer Transparency 6 L2

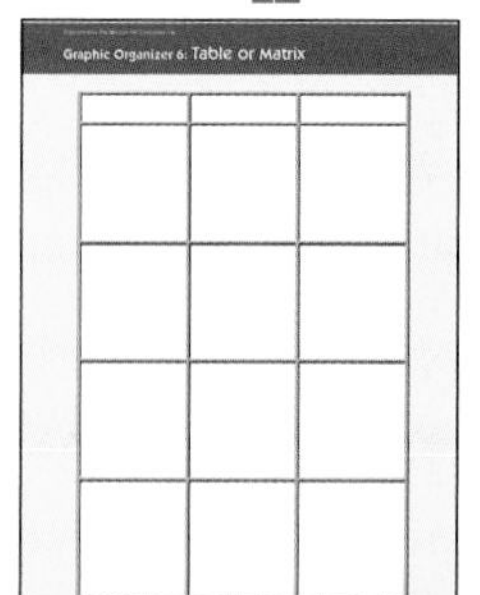

In-text Map Transparency L1

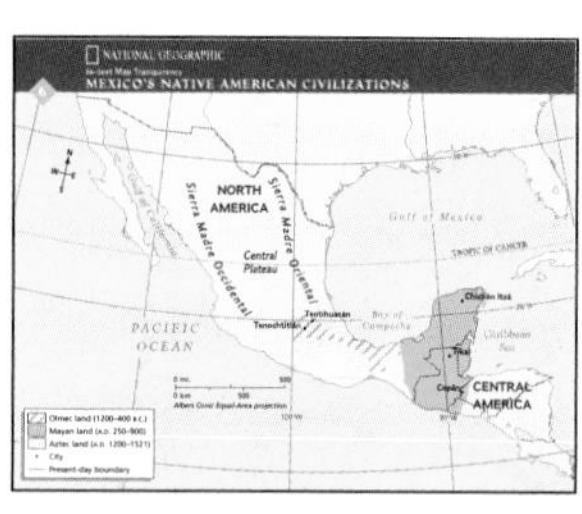

FOLDABLES™ Study Organizer

Dinah Zike's Foldables

Foldables are three-dimensional, interactive graphic organizers that help students practice basic writing skills, review key vocabulary terms, and identify main ideas. Additional chapter activities can be found in the ***Reading and Study Skills Foldables*** booklet.

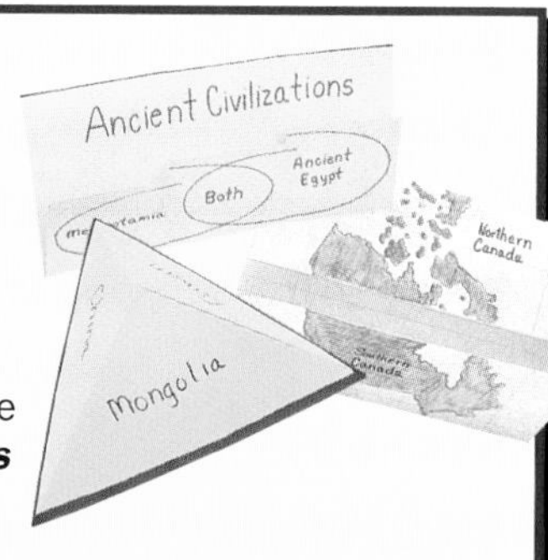

MAP AND GEOGRAPHY SKILLS

Chapter Map Activity L2

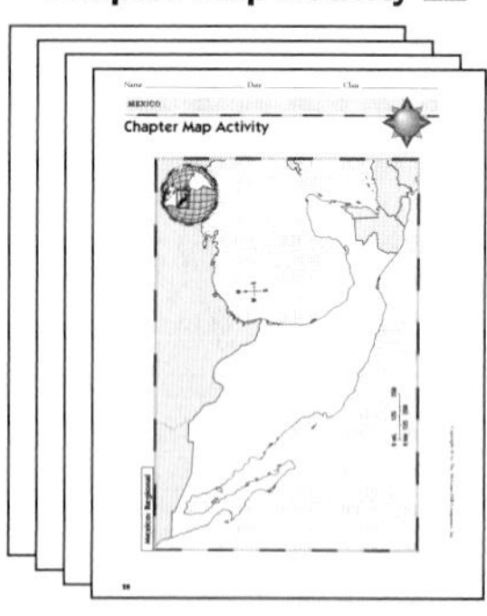

GeoLab Activity L2

READING SUPPORT

Vocabulary Activity L1

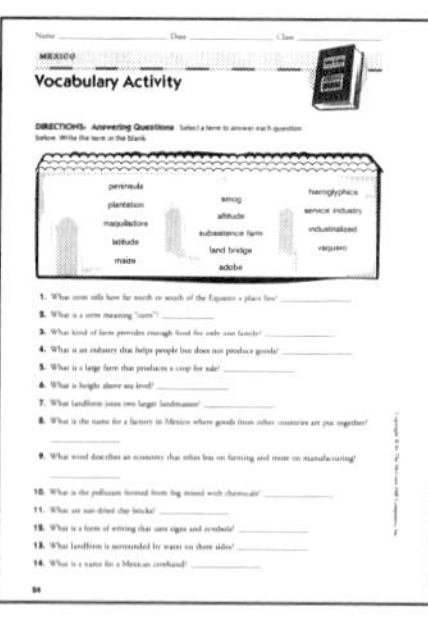

Workbook Activity L1

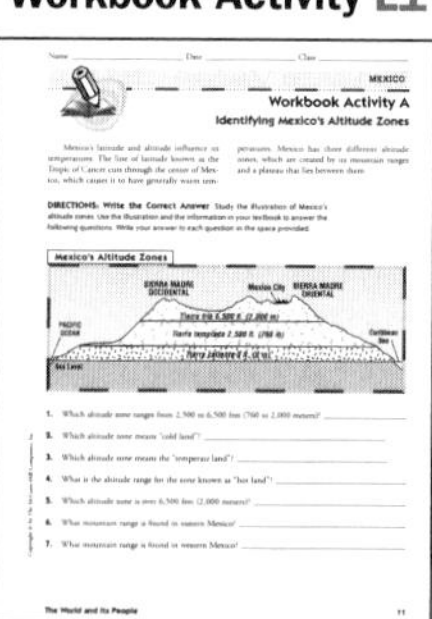

Reading and Writing Skills Activity L1/ELL

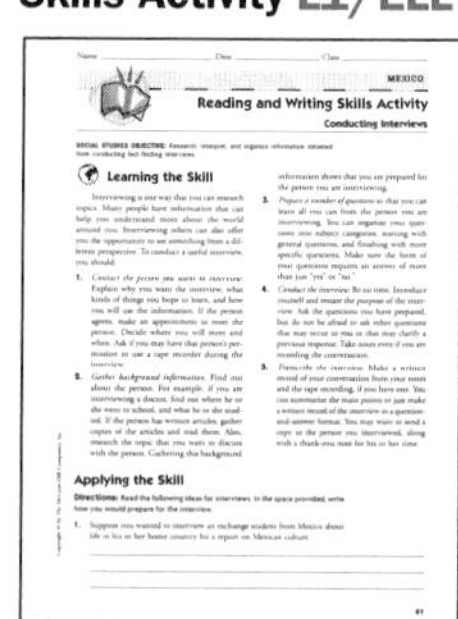

DIFFERENTIATED INSTRUCTION

Use these review and reinforcement materials to help less-proficient readers, English learners, and gifted and talented students.

Reteaching Activity L1

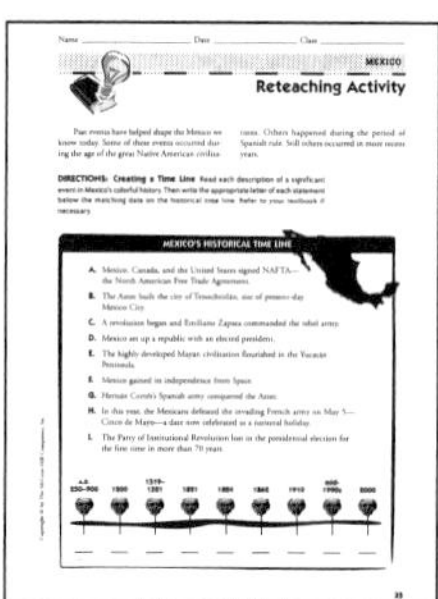

Chapter Skills Review L2

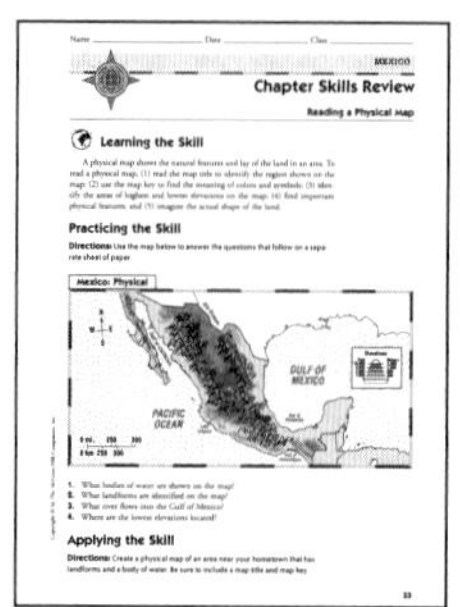

Cooperative Learning Activity L1/ELL

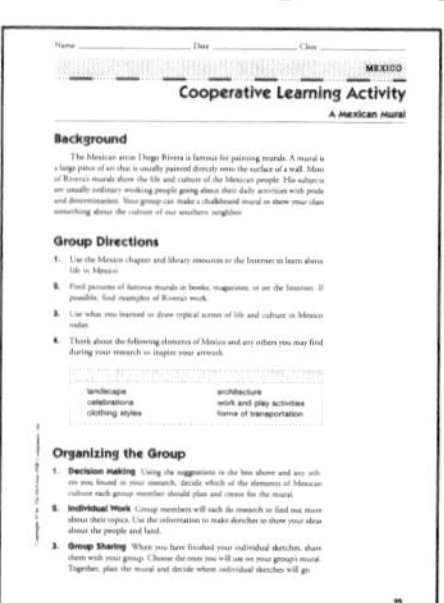

Enrichment Activity L3

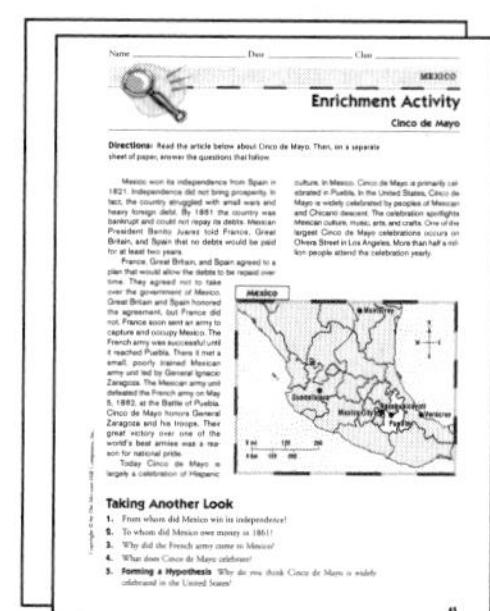

ASSESSMENT

Chapter Test, Form A L2

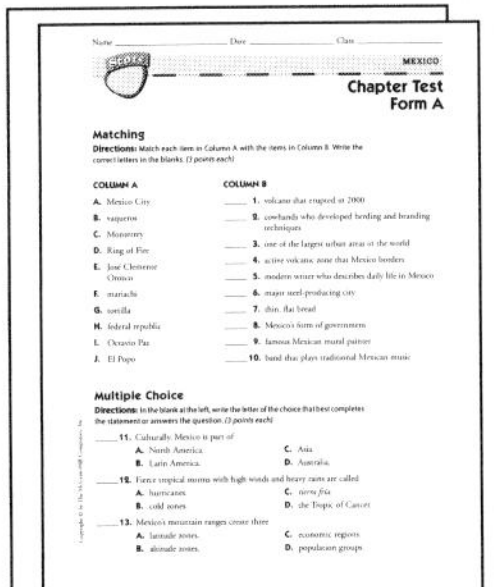

Chapter Test, Form B L2

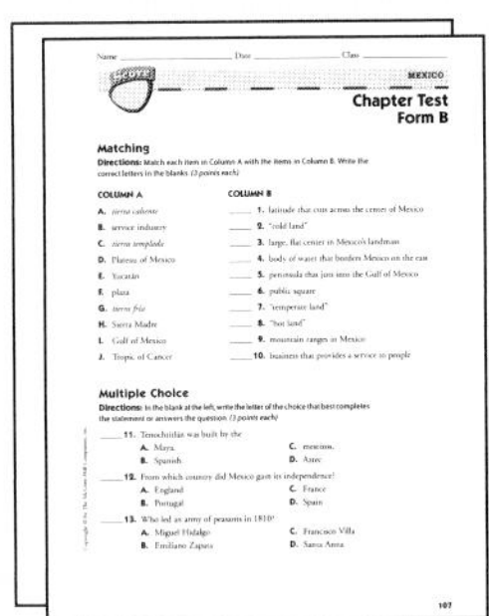

Performance Assessment Activity L1/ELL

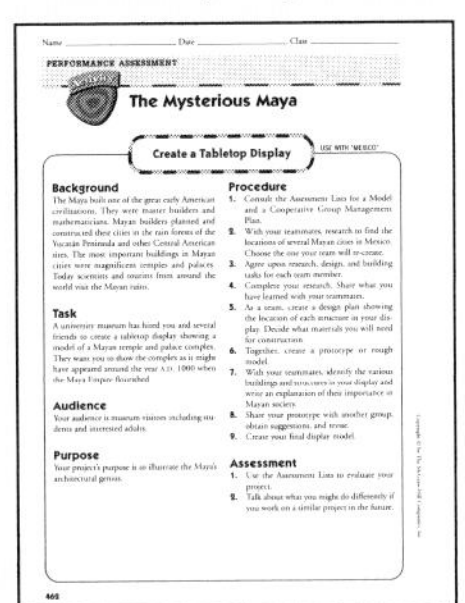

ExamView® Pro Testmaker CD-ROM

STANDARDIZED ASSESSMENT SKILLS

Critical Thinking Skills Activity L2

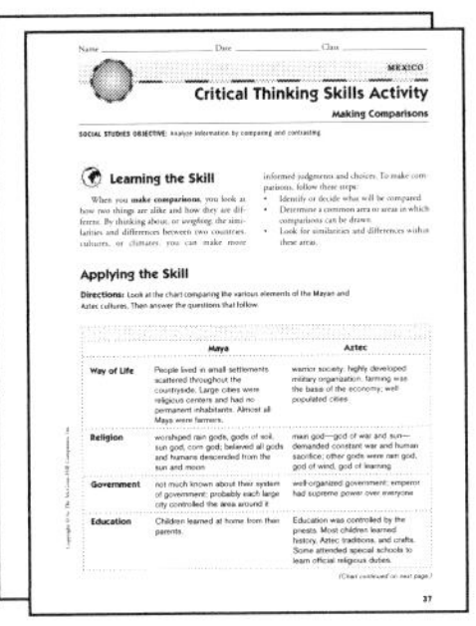

Map and Graph Skills Activity L2

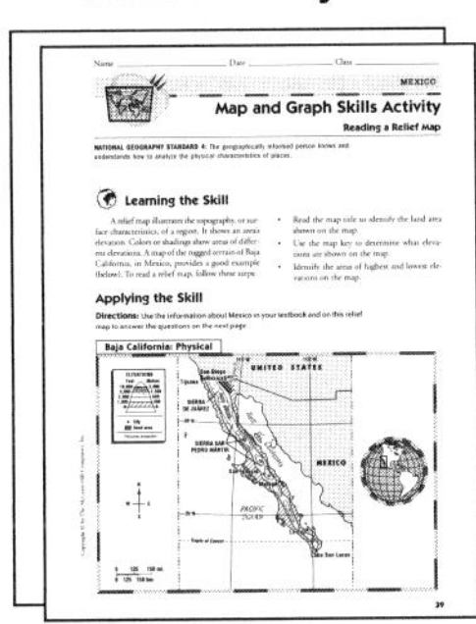

Standardized Test Skills Practice Workbook Activity L2

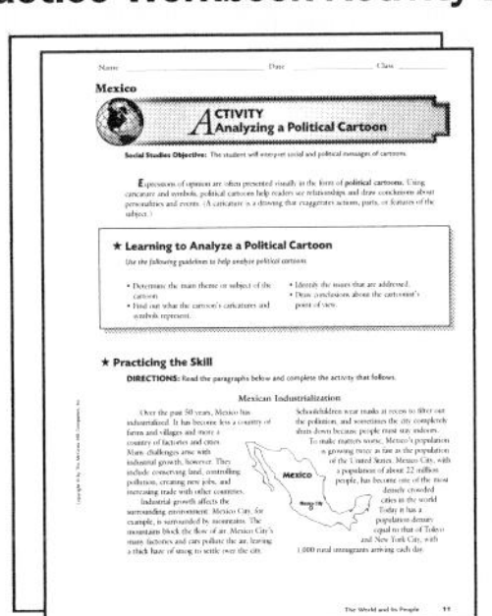

HOME INVOLVEMENT

Take-Home Review Activity L1

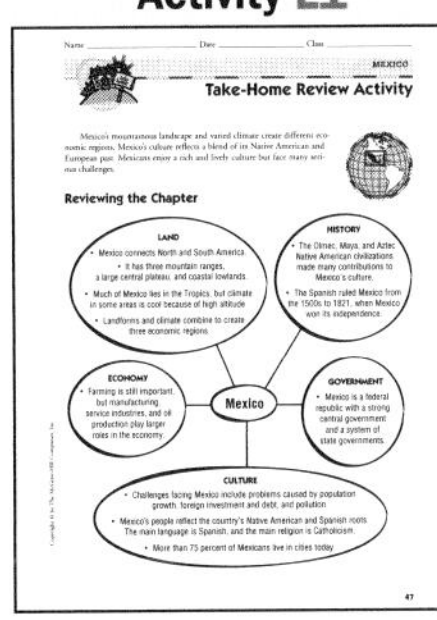

MULTIMEDIA

- National Geographic's The World and Its People
- MindJogger Videoquiz
- Vocabulary PuzzleMaker CD-ROM
- Interactive Tutor Self-Assessment CD-ROM
- ExamView® Pro Testmaker CD-ROM
- TeacherWorks CD-ROM
- StudentWorks CD-ROM
- Skillbuilder Interactive Workbook CD-ROM, Level 1
- Presentation Plus! CD-ROM
- Audio Program

SPANISH RESOURCES

The following Spanish language materials are available in the Spanish Resources binder:

- **Spanish Summaries**
- **Spanish Vocabulary Activities**
- **Spanish Guided Reading Activities**
- **Spanish Quizzes and Tests**
- **Spanish Take-Home Review Activities**
- **Spanish Reteaching Activities**

Meeting National Standards

Geography for Life

The following standards are covered in Chapter 6:

Section 1	**EE2 Places and Regions: Standards 4, 5**
	EE3 Physical Systems: Standards 7, 8
	EE5 Environment and Society: Standard 14
Section 2	**EE4 Human Systems: Standards 9, 10, 12, 13**
Section 3	**EE4 Human Systems: Standards 9, 11, 12, 13**
	EE5 Environment and Society: Standard 14

State and Local Objectives

____

____

____

Chapter 6 Planning Guide

SECTION RESOURCES

Daily Objectives	Reproducible Resources	Multimedia Resources
Section 1 **Mexico's Land and Economy** **1.** Describe the landforms found in Mexico. **2.** Describe how Mexico's climates vary with altitude. **3.** Compare the three economic zones of Mexico.	Reproducible Lesson Plan Daily Lecture and Discussion Notes Note-taking Guide Guided Reading Activity* Reading Essentials and Study Guide* Section Quiz*	Daily Focus Skills Transparency GeoQuiz Transparency Vocabulary PuzzleMaker CD-ROM Interactive Tutor Self-Assessment CD-ROM ExamView® Pro Testmaker CD-ROM Presentation Plus! CD-ROM
Section 2 **Mexico's History** **1.** Describe the groups that influenced Mexico's history. **2.** Discuss how Spaniards changed life in Mexico. **3.** Outline changes that took place in Mexico in the 1800s and 1900s.	Reproducible Lesson Plan Daily Lecture and Discussion Notes Note-taking Guide Guided Reading Activity* Reading Essentials and Study Guide* Section Quiz*	Daily Focus Skills Transparency In-text Map Transparency Vocabulary PuzzleMaker CD-ROM Interactive Tutor Self-Assessment CD-ROM ExamView® Pro Testmaker CD-ROM Presentation Plus! CD-ROM
Section 3 **Mexico Today** **1.** Describe life in the cities and villages of Mexico. **2.** Identify elements of Mexican culture. **3.** Discuss Mexico's government. **4.** Explain what challenges face Mexico.	Reproducible Lesson Plan Daily Lecture and Discussion Notes Note-taking Guide Guided Reading Activity* Reading Essentials and Study Guide* Section Quiz*	Daily Focus Skills Transparency Vocabulary PuzzleMaker CD-ROM Interactive Tutor Self-Assessment CD-ROM ExamView® Pro Testmaker CD-ROM Presentation Plus! CD-ROM MindJogger Videoquiz

00:00 **Out of Time?** Assign the **Reading Essentials and Study Guide*** for this chapter.

*Also available in Spanish

KEY TO ABILITY LEVELS

Teaching strategies have been coded for varying learning styles and abilities.

L1 **BASIC** activities for all students
L2 **AVERAGE** activities for average to above-average students
L3 **CHALLENGING** activities for above-average students
ELL **ENGLISH LANGUAGE LEARNER** activities

KEY TO TEACHING RESOURCES

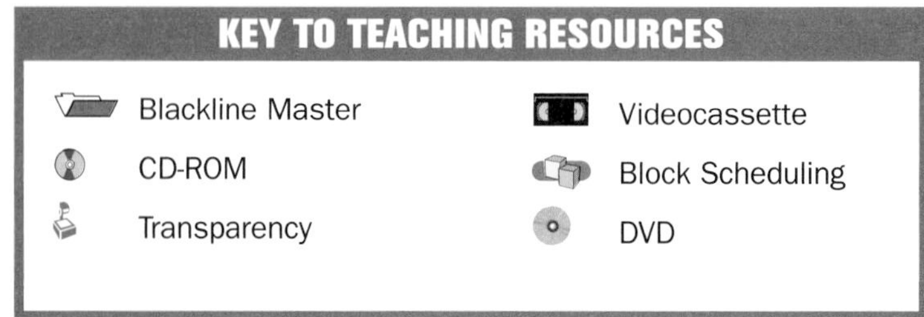

Catch the World!

Donna Jett
Powell Middle School
Powell, Tennessee

You need an inflatable globe for this activity. Every so often, perhaps after each chapter or unit of study, have a student write two categories on the board: "Land" and "Water." Take out the inflatable globe and toss it to a student, who reports what is located at his or her right thumb. Write the country or body of water under its correct category on the board. Then have the student tell something about the place: its location in latitude and longitude or hemisphere, physical characteristics of the place, climate, capital, and so on. The student should toss the globe to another student, who repeats the process.

Meeting Special Needs

In addition to the Differentiated Instruction strategies found in each section, the following resources are also suitable for your special needs students:

- ***ExamView® Pro Testmaker CD-ROM*** allows teachers to tailor tests by reducing answer choices.
- The ***Audio Program*** includes the entire narrative of the student edition so that less-proficient readers can listen to the words as they read them.
- The ***Reading Essentials and Study Guide*** provides the same content as the student edition but is written two grade levels below the textbook.
- ***Guided Reading Activities*** give less-proficient readers point-by-point instructions to increase comprehension as they read each textbook section.
- ***Enrichment Activities*** include a stimulating collection of readings and activities for gifted and talented students.

NATIONAL GEOGRAPHIC TEACHER'S CORNER

Index to National Geographic Magazine:

The following articles may be used for research relating to this chapter:

- "The Royal Crypts of Copán," by George E. Stuart, December 1997.
- *Mexico,* A National Geographic Special Edition, August 1996.
- "Tex-Mex Border," by Richard Conniff, February 1996.

National Geographic Society Products:

To order the following products for use with this chapter, call National Geographic Society at 1-800-368-2728:

- *Mexico: Nations of the World Series* (Videos)
- *Lost City of the Maya* (Video)
- *Maya Way of Death* (Video)
- *National Geographic Desk Reference* (Book)

NGS ONLINE

Access National Geographic's Web site for current events, activities, links, interactive features, and archives.
www.nationalgeographic.com

NATIONAL GEOGRAPHIC MapMachine

Find the latest coverage of geography in the news, atlas updates, cartographic activities with interactive maps, an online map store, and links at www.nationalgeographic.com/maps

SOCIAL STUDIES Online

Use our Web site for additional resources. All essential content is covered in the Student Edition.

You and your students can visit twip.glencoe.com, the Web site companion to *The World and Its People*. This innovative integration of electronic and print media offers your students a wealth of opportunities. The student text directs students to the Web site for the following options:

- Chapter Overviews
- Student Web Activities
- Self-Check Quizzes
- Textbook Updates

Answers are provided for you in the Web Activity Lesson Plan. Additional Web resources and Interactive Tutor puzzles are also available.

Introducing Chapter 6

Introduce students to chapter content and key terms by having them access Chapter Overview 6 at twip.glencoe.com

Chapter Objectives

1. Identify the location of Mexico and describe its physical features and climate.
2. Describe the economy of Mexico.
3. Outline the history and government of Mexico.
4. Describe the Mexican people and the challenges they face today.

GLENCOE TECHNOLOGY

NATIONAL GEOGRAPHIC

The World and Its People Video Program

Chapter 6 Mexico

The following segments enhance the study of this chapter:

- **Mexico City**
- **Agua Azul**
- **Hills of Michoacán**

MindJogger Videoquiz

Use MindJogger Videoquiz to preview the Chapter 6 content.

Both programs available in DVD and VHS

Chapter 6 Mexico

The World and Its People NATIONAL GEOGRAPHIC

To learn more about the people and places of Mexico, view ***The World and Its People* Chapter 6** video.

Social Studies Online

Chapter Overview Visit ***The World and Its People*** Web site at twip.glencoe.com and click on **Chapter 6—Chapter Overviews** to preview information about Mexico.

188

Reading Strategy Purpose for Reading

Use the **Think/Pair/Share** reading strategy to activate students' prior knowledge. **Think**—Ask students to think about how many products they use that are derived from corn (corn on the cob, corn tortillas, cornmeal, and so on). **Pair**—Have them share their answers with a partner and discuss their ideas. **Share**—Ask volunteers to share their answers with the class. To close the discussion, explain that corn was first cultivated in Mexico dating back to 4,700 years ago. L1

Categorizing Information

When you group information into categories on a table, it is easier to study characteristics of items. Make this foldable to help you describe Mexico's land, economy, and government—past and present.

Step 1 Fold a sheet of paper into thirds from top to bottom.

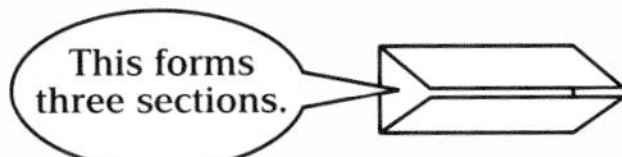

This forms three sections.

Step 2 Open the paper and refold it into fourths from side to side.

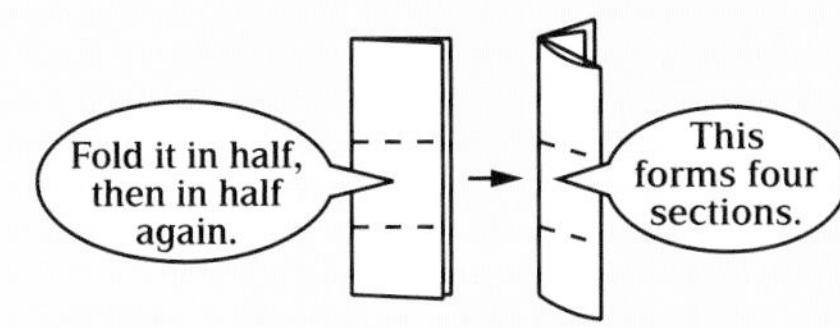

Fold it in half, then in half again.
This forms four sections.

Step 3 Unfold, turn the paper, and draw lines along the folds.

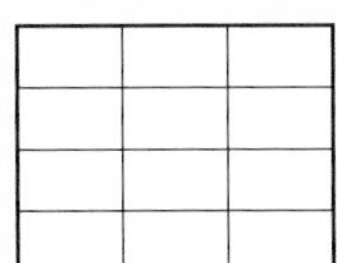

Step 4 Label your table as shown.

	Past	Present
Mexico's Land		
Mexico's Economy		
Mexico's Government		

Reading and Writing As you read the chapter, record key facts about Mexico's land, economy, and government in the appropriate places on your table foldable.

Why It Matters

Moving Forward

Mexico is a country working hard to catch up with the more industrialized countries of the world. Today Mexico is an important trading partner of the United States. However, a rapidly growing population and a developing economy have made it difficult for Mexico to support all of its people.

◀ **The Lighthouse of Commerce and the Cathedral of Monterrey, Monterrey, Mexico**

Dinah Zike's Foldables

Purpose This activity requires students to create a table and organize information from the chapter on it. Students group information from the chapter into categories, in effect comparing Mexico's land, economy, and government of the past to the land, economy, and government of the present.

Have students complete the ***Reading and Study Skills Foldables*** activity for this chapter.

Why It Matters

Have students imagine that they are editorial writers for a newspaper in Mexico. Using information in the chapter and from outside sources, have them write an editorial either supporting or criticizing Mexico's rapidly growing population and rapidly developing economy. Their editorials should include specific examples of how the growth in population and the expanding economy have affected daily life in Mexico.

About the Photo

Monterrey is a blend of old and new. The Cathedral of Monterrey was built in the 1600s and is a reminder of the city's beginnings as a Spanish colonial outpost. Today, modern skyscrapers reflect Monterrey's importance as a finance and industrial center. The city continues to prosper because of its proximity to the United States. Between 1995 and 1999, the number of maquiladoras—foreign-owned factories—in Monterrey's state of Nuevo León has grown from 5 to 124. More than 600 international firms have offices there. Workers, however, are very dependent on the American economy. When there is an economic slowdown in the United States, many workers lose their jobs. Since they work for low wages with no benefits, unemployment can lead to severe hardship.

Chapter 6

Section 1, pages 190–195

1 Focus

Section Objectives

1. Describe the landforms found in Mexico.
2. Describe how Mexico's climates vary with altitude.
3. Compare the three economic zones of Mexico.

BELLRINGER
Skillbuilder Activity

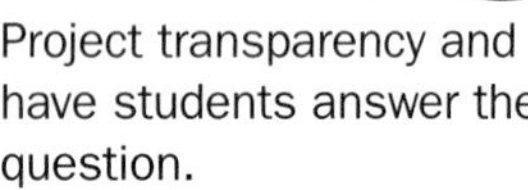

Project transparency and have students answer the question.

Daily Focus Skills Transparency

Interpreting Tables

During which month are the average temperatures in these two Mexican cities most similar?

A January
B March
C July
D December

Reading Preview

■ **Activating Prior Knowledge** Ask students what they know about Mexico. Have them write these ideas in their notebooks and refer to them after reading the chapter to see what they can add.

■ **Preteaching Vocabulary** The terms *latitude* and *altitude* are often confused. Have students find these words in a dictionary and use them in separate sentences.

Guide to Reading

Main Idea

Mexico's mountainous landscape and varied climate create different economic regions.

Terms to Know

- land bridge
- peninsula
- latitude
- altitude
- hurricane
- vaquero
- maquiladora
- subsistence farm
- plantation
- industrialize
- service industry

Reading Strategy

Create a chart of Mexico's economic regions like this one. List the main economic activity of each region.

Region of Mexico	Economic Activity
Northern	
Central	
Southern	

Section 1 Mexico's Land and Economy

NATIONAL GEOGRAPHIC **Exploring Our World**

Mexican farmer Dionisio Pulido was plowing his cornfield one day. Suddenly his son heard a rumble in the ground. Then white smoke began to spew into the air. When they awoke the next day, they saw a volcano 30 feet (9 m) high. Today, more than 50 years later, the volcano named Paricutín soars nearly 9,200 feet (2,800 m) above sea level.

Paricutín and other volcanoes are part of the rugged landscape of Mexico, which sits where three plates in the earth's crust collide. Sometimes the movement of these plates brings disastrous results. Hot magma, or melted rock, shoots through a volcano. The ground shifts violently in an earthquake. Do you see why Native Americans once called Mexico "the land of the shaking earth"?

Bridging Two Continents

Mexico forms part of a **land bridge,** or narrow strip of land that joins two larger landmasses. This land bridge connects North America and South America. Look at the map on page 191. You can see that Mexico borders the southern United States.

Physical geographers, or people who study continents and landforms, think of Mexico as part of North America. Cultural geographers, however, think of Mexico as being part of Latin America. For cultural

Section Resources

Reproducible Masters
- Reproducible Lesson Plan
- Daily Lecture and Discussion Notes
- Note-taking Guide
- Guided Reading Activity
- Reading Essentials and Study Guide
- Section Quiz

Transparencies
- Daily Focus Skills Transparency
- GeoQuiz Transparency

Multimedia
- Vocabulary PuzzleMaker CD-ROM
- Interactive Tutor Self-Assessment CD-ROM
- Presentation Plus! CD-ROM
- ExamView® Pro Testmaker CD-ROM

geographers, language, customs, religion, and history are important areas of study. Both groups are correct. Mexico is a Latin (Spanish-speaking) country on the continent of North America. Its location in North America makes it an important trading partner to the United States and Canada. Yet Mexico's culture is closely tied to Central and South America. It is a country that bridges two continents.

The Pacific Ocean borders Mexico on the west. Extending south along this western coast is **Baja** (BAH•hah) **California.** It is a long, narrow peninsula, or piece of land with water on three sides. On Mexico's eastern side, the **Gulf of Mexico** and the **Caribbean Sea** border the coasts. Between the Gulf and the Caribbean Sea is another peninsula—the **Yucatán** (YOO•kah•TAHN) **Peninsula.**

Mexico is a rugged land. If you were to see it from space, you might think that the country looked like a crumpled piece of paper with deep folds. Towering mountain ranges and a huge, high plateau occupy the center of the country.

The Sierra Madre Three different mountain ranges in Mexico make up the **Sierra Madre** (SYEHR•ah MAH•thray), or "mother range." Because of

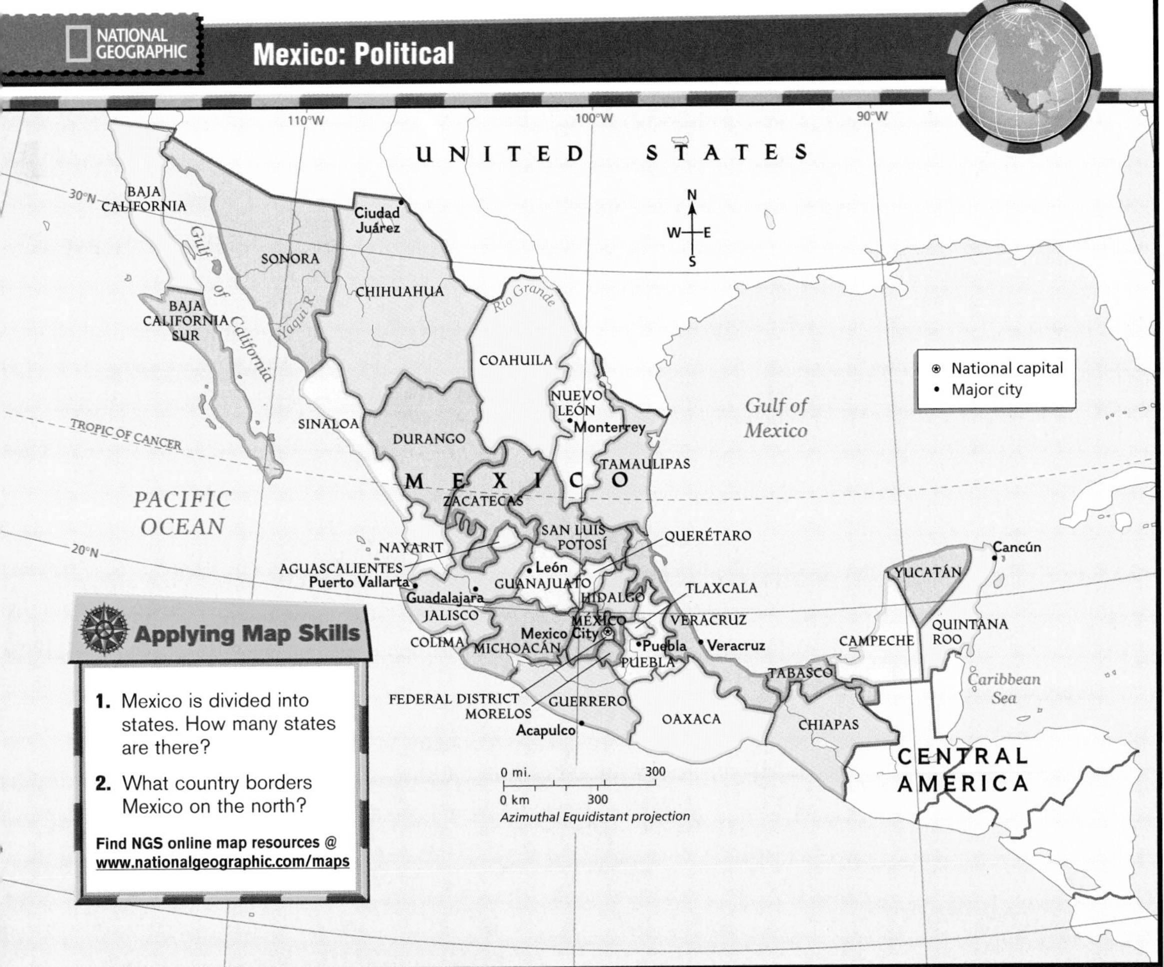

Applying Map Skills

1. Mexico is divided into states. How many states are there?
2. What country borders Mexico on the north?

Find NGS online map resources @ www.nationalgeographic.com/maps

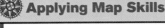

Reading Strategy Reading the Text

Using Word Parts Help students learn how suffixes can help them unlock the meaning of words. A suffix is a word part that comes after a base word or a root. It may change the meaning of the word or the way the word is used in the sentence. Provide students with these examples: *–less* means "without" (careless, powerless); *–ful,* "full of" (playful, thoughtful); *–ist,* "a person who" (biologist, artist); and *–ous,* "full of" (joyous, nervous). Have students find words with suffixes in the section and identify the root word's meaning. **L1**

*Use the **Reading Skills Handbook** for more reading strategies.*

TEACH

Reading a Map Remind students that the United States and Canada share some physical features. Point out that Mexico, too, is part of North America. Have students study physical maps of Mexico and the United States. **Ask:** **What landforms in Mexico seem to be similar to landforms in the United States?** *(Mountains in Baja California extend from Sierra Nevada in California; the Sierra Madre Occidental extend from the Rocky Mountains; the Plateau of Mexico is part of the high plains east of the Rockies; the Gulf Coastal Plain is shared.)* **L1**

Daily Lecture and Discussion Notes

MEXICO

Daily Lecture and Discussion Notes

Mexico's Land and Economy

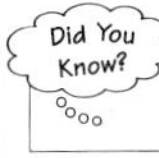

Mexico has a vast array of mineral resources, limited agricultural land, and a rapidly growing population. These factors are the basis for many of the country's present problems as well as opportunities for future development.

I. Bridging Two Continents

A. Mexico forms part of a **land bridge,** or narrow strip of land that joins two larger landmasses. This land bridge connects North America and South America.

B. Mexico is bordered by the Pacific Ocean on the west. Extending south along ... is Baja California. It is a **peninsula,** or piece of land with ... eastern side, the Gulf of Mexico and the

Applying Map Skills

Answers

1. 31 states and one Federal District
2. the United States

Skills Practice

What is the capital of Mexico? *(Mexico City)*

More About the Photo

Mexico City Mexico City is endangered by earthquakes. It lies on a fault, and much of the city rests on a former lake bed. As a result, the soil is soft, which means that buildings can move a great deal during a quake.

Caption Answer volcanoes and earthquakes

Interdisciplinary Connections

History In 1521 Spanish soldier Hernán Cortés conquered Mexico. When he returned to Spain, the Spanish king asked him to describe the land. Legend says that Cortés, to show the ruggedness of Mexico's land, crumpled a piece of paper and threw it on a table, saying, "This, your Majesty, is the land of Mexico."

Reading Check Answer

Ring of Fire

the rugged terrain, few people live in the Sierra Madre. The mountains are rich in resources, though. They hold copper, zinc, silver, and timber.

Many of Mexico's mountains are volcanoes. Popocatepetl (POH•puh•KA•tuh•PEH•tuhl), or "El Popo," as Mexicans call it, erupted violently centuries ago. In December 2000, El Popo erupted again, hurling molten rock into the sky. About 30,000 people from surrounding areas were forced to temporarily leave their homes. Tens of millions of people live 50 miles (80 km) or less from the mountain and could face even worse eruptions in the future.

Mexicans face another danger from the land. Earthquakes can destroy their cities and homes. A 1985 earthquake killed nearly 10,000 people in Mexico's capital, **Mexico City,** even though the earthquake's center was about 185 miles (298 km) away. Mexico experiences many earthquakes because it is one of the countries that border the "Ring of Fire." This name describes the active volcanic zone that forms the western, northern, and eastern edges of the Pacific Ocean. Earthquakes in the zone are common due to movement of the huge Pacific plate deep under the earth's crust.

Mexico City

Popocatepetl rises above Mexico City's hazy skyline.

Human/Environment Interaction **What two natural dangers do people in Mexico face?**

The Plateau of Mexico The map on page 196 shows that the Sierra Madre surround the large, flat center of the country, the Plateau of Mexico. You find mostly deserts and grassy plains in the northern part of the plateau. Broad, flat valleys that slice through the center hold many of the country's chief cities and most of its people. To the south, the plateau steadily rises until it meets the high, snowcapped mountains of the Sierra Madre del Sur.

Coastal Lowlands Mexico's lowland plains squeeze between the mountains and the sea. The Pacific Coastal Plain begins with a hot, largely empty desert in the north. As you move farther south, better soil and rainfall allow ranching and farming along this plain. On the other side of the country, the Gulf Coastal Plain has more rain and fertile soil for growing crops and raising animals.

✓ Reading Check **What is the volcanic zone called that affects Mexico?**

Land of Many Climates

Mexico has many different climates. Why? As you read in Chapter 2, latitude—or location north or south of the Equator—affects temperature. The Tropic of Cancer, which cuts across the center of Mexico at 23½°N latitude, marks the northern edge of the Tropics. Areas south of

Differentiated Instruction

Meeting Special Needs: Visual/Spatial Have students construct a chart comparing Mexico's altitude zones. Bases of comparison might include location, temperature range, and vegetation. Have them use the completed chart to analyze the relationship between climate and altitude. L2

Refer to *Inclusion for the Middle School Social Studies Classroom Strategies and Activities* in the TCR.

Mexico's Altitude Zones

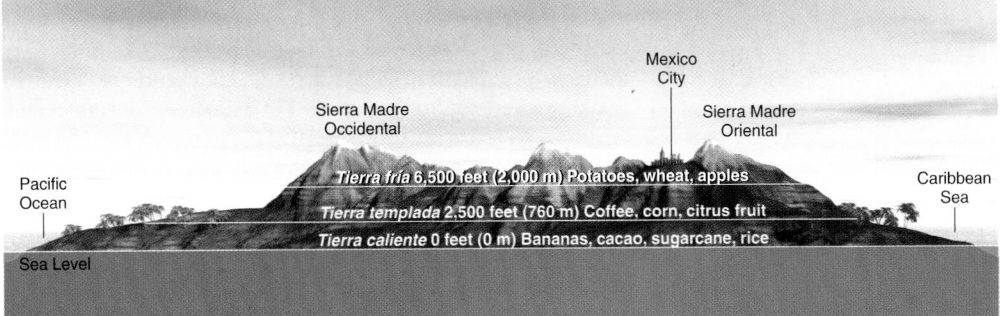

this line have warm temperatures throughout the year. Areas north of this line are warm in summer and cooler in winter.

Altitude, or height above sea level, also affects temperatures in Mexico. The higher the altitude, the cooler the temperatures are—even within the Tropics. The diagram above shows that Mexico's mountains and plateau create three altitude zones. You could travel through all of these zones in a day's trip across the Sierra Madre.

Because the coastal lowlands are near sea level, they have high temperatures. Mexicans call this altitude zone the *tierra caliente* (tee•EH•rah kah•lee•EHN•tay), or "hot land." Moving higher in altitude, you find the *tierra templada* (tehm•PLAH•dah), or "temperate land." Here the climate becomes more moderate. In the highest zone, the climate becomes even cooler. Mexicans call this the *tierra fría* (FREE•ah), or "cold land."

Rainfall varies throughout Mexico. Baja California and northern Mexico receive very little precipitation. Other regions receive more, mostly in the summer and early fall. From June to October, Mexico can be hit by **hurricanes.** These fierce tropical storms with high winds and heavy rains form over the warm waters of the Atlantic or Pacific Oceans. They can strike Mexico with fury.

Reading Check What is Mexico's warmest altitude zone?

Analyzing the Diagram

Mexico has zones of different climates that result from different altitudes.

Location In which altitude zone is Mexico City located?

Mexico's Economic Regions

Mexico's physical geography and climate together give the country three distinct economic regions: the North, Central Mexico, and the South. Large stretches of northern Mexico are too dry and rocky to farm without irrigation. By building canals to carry water to their fields, farmers can grow cotton, fruits, grains, and vegetables.

Northern Mexico Did you know that the skills used by American cowhands originated in Mexico? Mexican cowhands, called **vaqueros** (vah•KEHR•ohs), developed the tools and techniques for herding, roping, and branding cattle. Vaqueros carry on this work today.

Chapter 6

Section 1, pages 190–195

Analyzing the Diagram

Answer
tierra fría

Skills Practice
What products are grown in the *tierra templada?* (coffee, corn, and citrus fruit)

L1/ELL

Guided Reading Activity

Name ______ Date ______ Class ______

MEXICO

Guided Reading Activity 1

Mexico's Land and Economy

DIRECTIONS: Filling in the Blanks Reading the section and completing the summary paragraphs below will help you learn more about Mexico's land and economy. Refer to your textbook to fill in the blanks.

Mexico forms part of a land bridge between **(1)** ______ and **(2)** ______.
Mexico borders the southern **(3)** ______.
Mexico's two large peninsulas include **(4)** ______ on the west coast and the **(5)** ______ Peninsula

3 Assess

Assign Section 1 Assessment as homework or an in-class activity.

Have students use the Interactive Tutor Self-Assessment CD-ROM to review Section 1.

Reading Check Answer

the *tierra caliente* ("hot land")

Cooperative Learning Activity

Making Murals Point out to students that murals are popular vehicles for art in Mexico, dating back to the time of the Mayan civilization. In the twentieth century, artists such as Diego Rivera and José Clemente Orozco gained fame for their murals celebrating Mexico's past and present. Have students devise their own vehicle for celebrating the past of their community. Students should read about the history and development of the area, identifying famous individuals and significant events. They might also talk to older members of the community to gather stories about the past. Then have students work in groups to create a product—a mural, set of bulletin boards, or multimedia presentation—that describes the area's past. L2 

EE6 The Uses of Geography: Standard 17

Did You Know?

The clothing industry in Mexico experienced explosive growth after NAFTA was signed. Since then, Mexican clothing imports to Canada have quadrupled. The life of a maquiladora worker is not easy, however. Hours are long, wages are low, and conditions are sometimes very bad.

Reading Check Answer

Northern Mexico has seen a recent economic boom from growth in manufacturing; southern Mexico's economy is based on farming, and the region is poor.

Measure student knowledge of physical features.

GeoQuiz Transparency

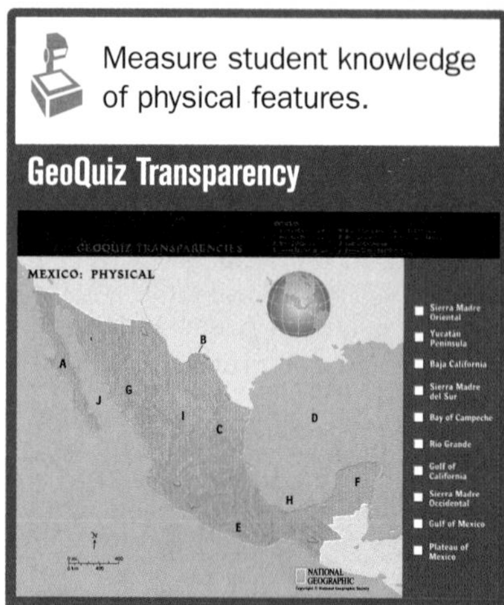

▲ A skilled seamstress makes clothing in a maquiladora in northern Mexico.

Northern Mexico has seen an economic boom. **Monterrey,** Mexico's main producer of steel and cement, has long been an important industrial city. In this and other cities, many companies from the United States and elsewhere have built **maquiladoras** (mah•KEEL•ah•DOHR•as), or factories that assemble parts made in other countries. As a result, thousands of Mexicans have flocked to cities such as **Tijuana** (tee•WAH•nah) and **Ciudad Juárez** (see•ooh•DAHD HWAH•rayz), located along the U.S.–Mexico border. The growth in these border cities has raised the standard of living in northern cities through factory work and increased trade. However, this quick growth has also brought concerns about damaging the environment, pollution, and dangers to the health and safety of workers.

Central Mexico More than half of Mexico's people live in the central region, the country's heartland. Why do they call this area home? The climate is one reason. Although central Mexico lies in the Tropics, its high elevation keeps it from being hot and humid. Temperatures are mild, and the climate is pleasant year-round. A second reason is the fertile soil. This soil was created by volcanic eruptions over the centuries and allows for productive farming.

Large industrial cities such as Mexico City and **Guadalajara** (GWAH•duhl•uh•HAHR•uh) also prosper in central Mexico. About 22 million people live in Mexico City and its suburbs, making it one of the largest cities in the world. Mexico City has been the largest city in the Americas since before the Spanish arrived in the early 1500s.

Southern Mexico The South is the poorest economic region of the country. The mountains towering in the center of this region have poor soil. **Subsistence farms,** or small plots where farmers grow only enough food to feed their families, are common here. In contrast, the coastal lowlands of this area have good soil and plentiful rain. Wealthy farmers grow sugarcane or bananas on **plantations,** large farms that raise a single crop for sale.

Both coasts of Mexico also have beautiful beaches and a warm climate. Tourists from all over the world flock to such resort cities as **Acapulco** and **Puerto Vallarta** on the Pacific coast and **Cancún** on the Yucatán Peninsula.

Reading Check How does the economic region of northern Mexico differ from that of southern Mexico?

Mexico's Economy Today

With many resources and workers, Mexico has a growing economy. Did you know that Mexico's economy ranks among the top 15 in the world? As in the past, agriculture is important. Farmers raise food to feed people at home—and also to ship around the world. Corn, beans, wheat, and rice are the main crops grown for food. Exports include coffee, cotton, vegetables, fruits, livestock, and tobacco.

Critical Thinking Activity

Identifying Alternatives Although NAFTA has created many jobs in Mexican border towns, the area remains poor. Millions live in "colonias"—communities of ramshackle homes. Many of the colonias have no water, electricity, sewer systems, paved roads, or streetlights. Volunteers from both Mexico and the United States help residents by teaching proper health care, digging septic systems for waste disposal, and providing small loans of $100 to $200 to set up small businesses like dress-making or tire repair. Larger bank loans help the communities build garbage dumps and water purifying plants. **Ask: If you ran the bank, for what large and small needs would you lend people in colonias money?** Students should think about larger problems like electricity and safety, but also smaller needs like school supplies and child care. **L1**

In recent years, Mexico has **industrialized,** or changed its economy to rely less on farming and more on manufacturing. Factories in Mexico now make cars, consumer goods, and steel. The labels on your clothing might even say "Made in Mexico."

Mexico has large deposits of petroleum and natural gas in the Gulf of Mexico and along the southern coast. As a result, Mexico is among the world's major oil-producing nations.

Mexico is also home to important service industries such as banking and tourism. **Service industries** are businesses that provide services to people rather than produce goods.

NAFTA As you learned in the last unit, Mexico, the United States, and Canada entered into NAFTA, the North American Free Trade Agreement, in 1994. Remember that under this agreement, most goods traded between these countries are free of tariffs, or special taxes. This means a homemaker in Canada would probably choose to buy a tablecloth made in Mexico rather than to pay more for a taxed tablecloth produced in Europe.

Some Americans have been afraid that belonging to NAFTA means American jobs will "go south." They fear that the lower rate of pay for labor in Mexico will encourage many manufacturers to move their businesses to Mexico rather than keep them in the United States. The debate about the overall effect of NAFTA is still going on.

Reading Check Why are some Americans afraid jobs will "go south"?

Section 1 Assessment

Defining Terms

1. **Define** land bridge, peninsula, latitude, altitude, hurricane, vaquero, maquiladora, subsistence farm, plantation, industrialize, service industry.

Recalling Facts

2. **History** How did the vaqueros of Mexico influence American ranching?
3. **Location** Why is Mexico a land bridge?
4. **Economics** Why have many Mexicans moved to the cities of the north?

Critical Thinking

5. **Understanding Cause and Effect** How has NAFTA affected the people in Canada and the people in Mexico? Do you think NAFTA has been good or bad for the people in border cities of the United States? Explain.
6. **Analyzing Information** Why is Mexico part of both North America and Latin America?

Graphic Organizer

7. **Organizing Information** Create a diagram like this one, and then list two facts that explain the large population of central Mexico.

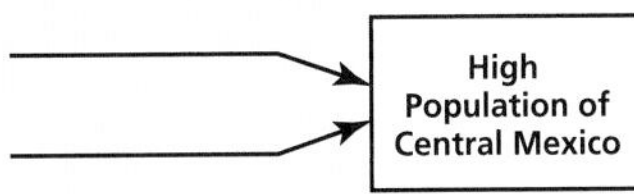

Applying Social Studies Skills

8. **Analyzing Diagrams** Study Mexico's altitude zones on page 193. At which elevation do you think most people live? Why do they live here?

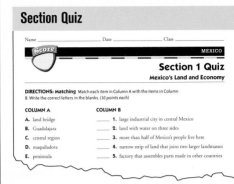

Section 1 Assessment

1. The terms are defined in the Glossary.
2. American cowhands use tools and techniques for herding, roping, and cattle branding developed by vaqueros.
3. It joins two larger land masses, namely North America and South America.
4. to work in factories there
5. Answers will vary but should be supported by facts.
6. Mexico is geographically part of North America and culturally part of Latin America.
7. pleasant climate and fertile soil for farming and ranching, and jobs in industrial cities like Mexico City and Guadalajara
8. 2,500 feet (760 m); moderate climate

Chapter 6

L2

Section Quiz

Name ______ Date ______ Class ______

Score MEXICO

Section 1 Quiz

Mexico's Land and Economy

DIRECTIONS: Matching Match each item in Column A with the items in Column B. Write the correct letters in the blanks. *(10 points each)*

COLUMN A	COLUMN B
A. land bridge	____ 1. large industrial city in central Mexico
B. Guadalajara	____ 2. land with water on three sides
C. central region	____ 3. more than half of Mexico's people live here
D. maquiladora	____ 4. narrow strip of land that joins two larger landmasses
E. peninsula	____ 5. factory that assembles parts made in other countries

Reading Check Answer

They fear that Mexico's low wages will lure American businesses away from the United States.

L1/ELL

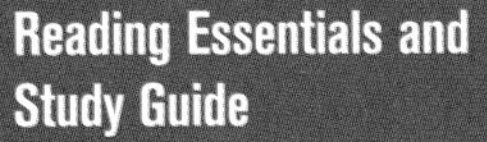

Reading Essentials and Study Guide

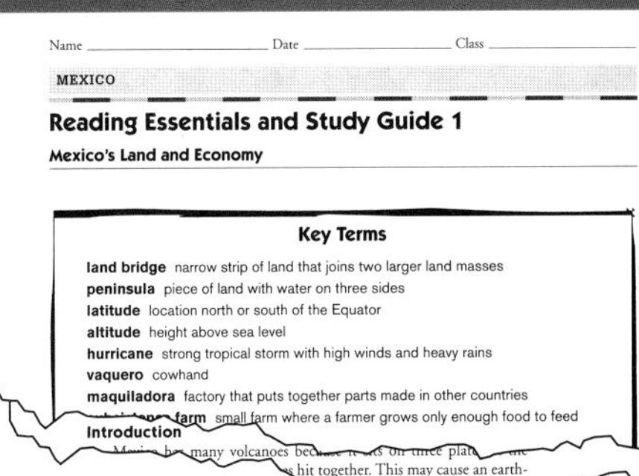

Name ______ Date ______ Class ______

MEXICO

Reading Essentials and Study Guide 1

Mexico's Land and Economy

Key Terms

land bridge narrow strip of land that joins two larger land masses
peninsula piece of land with water on three sides
latitude location north or south of the Equator
altitude height above sea level
hurricane strong tropical storm with high winds and heavy rains
vaquero cowhand
maquiladora factory that puts together parts made in other countries
subsistence farm small farm where a farmer grows only enough food to feed

Introduction

CLOSE

Reading Strategy

Making a Concept Map

Have students make a concept web for Mexico's geography and climates.

Social Studies Skill

TEACH

Display a photograph that shows mountains and lowlands. **Ask:** **How can geographers show the differences in the landforms?** If students are unable to answer, point to the physical map in the textbook on this page. Explain that the different colors indicate different elevations. Discuss the scale with the students so they can see how the color codes work. L1

Additional Skills Practice

1. **What elevation is represented by the color red?** *(5,000 to 10,000 feet, or 1,500 to 3,000 meters)*
2. **What does it mean when the land around some of the rivers is colored yellow or green?** *(Rivers cut valleys in the mountains.)*
3. **How would you describe Mexico in terms of elevation?** *(Most of the country is 2,000 to 10,000 feet [600 to 3000 m] above sea level.)*

Additional Skills Resources

 Chapter Skills Review

 Building Geography Skills for Life

GLENCOE TECHNOLOGY

 **Skillbuilder Interactive Workbook CD-ROM, Level 1**

This interactive CD-ROM reinforces student mastery of essential social studies skills.

Social Studies Skill

Reading a Physical Map

A map that shows the different heights of the land is called a **physical map.** Physical maps use colors and shading to show relief—or how flat or rugged the land surface is. Colors are also used to show the land's elevation—or height above sea level. Green often shows the lowest elevations (closest to sea level). Yellows, oranges, browns, and reds usually mean higher elevations. Sometimes the highest areas, such as mountain peaks, are white.

Learning the Skill

To read a physical map, apply these steps:

- Read the map title to identify the region shown on the map.
- Use the map key to find the meaning of colors and symbols.
- Identify the areas of highest and lowest elevation on the map.
- Find important physical features, including mountains, rivers, and coastlines.
- Mentally map the actual shape of the land.

Practicing the Skill

Look at the map to answer the following:

1. What country is shown on the map?
2. What mountain ranges are labeled?
3. What is the elevation of the green areas on the map (in feet and meters)?
4. What color on the map means 2,000–5,000 feet (600–1,500 m)?
5. Briefly describe the physical landscape of the area shown on the map, moving from west to east.

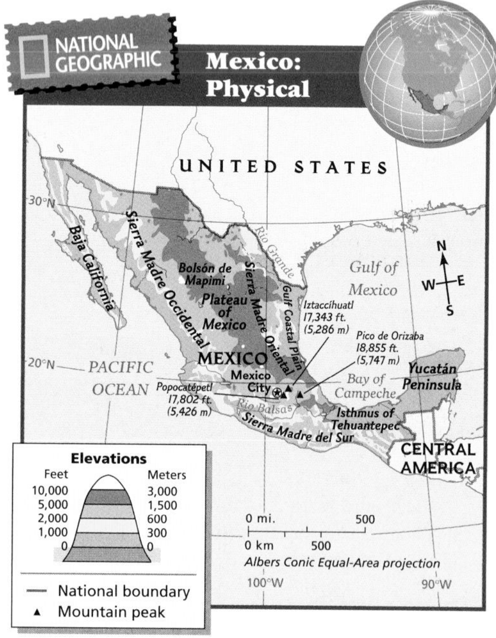

Applying the Skill

Look at the physical map of Latin America on page 180. Describe the physical landscape of the region, moving from east to west.

GO TO Practice key skills with **Glencoe Skillbuilder Interactive Workbook, Level 1.**

Practicing the Skill Answers

1. Mexico
2. Sierra Madre Occidental, Sierra Madre Oriental, Sierra Madre del Sur
3. 0–1000 feet (0–300 m)
4. orange
5. lowlands on the west coast, increasing to higher elevations in the center of the country, then lowlands on the east coast and Yucatán Peninsula

Applying the Skill

Possible answer: Brazilian Highlands in the east; Mato Grosso Plateau and Amazon Basin in central and northern regions; Andes mountain range in the west; to the north, the Sierra Madre Occidental, Sierra Madre Oriental, Sierra Madre del Sur, Plateau of Mexico

Mexico's History

Guide to Reading

Main Idea

Mexico's culture reflects a blend of its Native American and Spanish past.

Terms to Know

- jade
- obsidian
- maize
- hieroglyphics
- mural
- hacienda

Reading Strategy

Create a chart like this one, and then provide one example of how Native Americans and Europeans influenced Mexican culture.

Ethnic Groups	Influence on Mexican Culture
Native Americans	
Europeans	

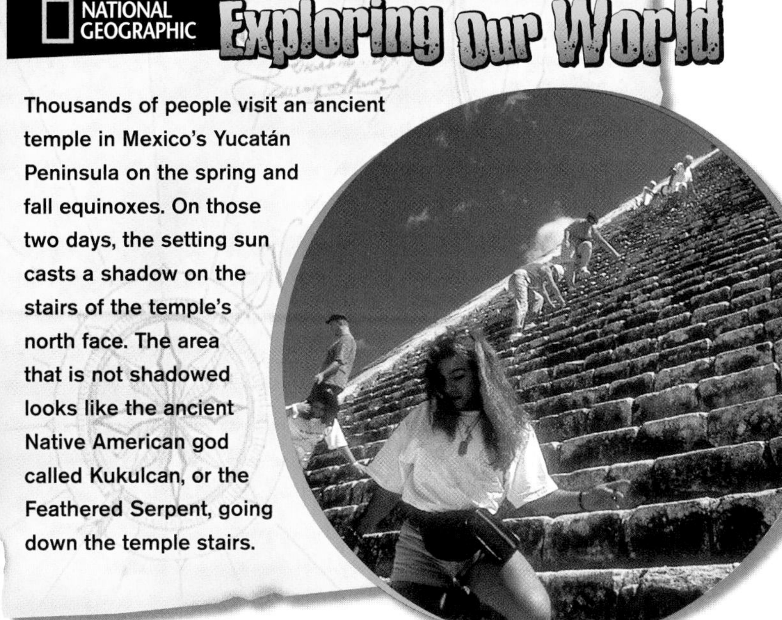

Thousands of people visit an ancient temple in Mexico's Yucatán Peninsula on the spring and fall equinoxes. On those two days, the setting sun casts a shadow on the stairs of the temple's north face. The area that is not shadowed looks like the ancient Native American god called Kukulcan, or the Feathered Serpent, going down the temple stairs.

The first people to arrive in Mexico were the ancestors of today's Native Americans. Mexico's Native American heritage has shaped the country's culture. So has Mexico's European heritage, brought by the Spaniards who conquered the area in the 1500s.

Native American Civilizations

Native Americans came to Mexico thousands of years ago. From about 1200 B.C. to the A.D. 1500s, these people built a series of brilliant, highly advanced civilizations on Mexican soil. Of these, the Olmec, Mayan, and Aztec civilizations are the best-known. Look at the map on page 198 to see where the Olmec, Mayan, and Aztec civilizations thrived.

The Olmecs The Olmecs built the first civilization in the Americas around 1200 B.C. They decorated their cities with large carved stone statues, some standing about 10 feet (3 m) high and weighing over 20 tons (18 t). They also carved smaller and more personal objects like jewelry out of jade, a local shiny stone that comes in many shades of

Section Objectives

1. Describe the groups that influenced Mexico's history.
2. Discuss how Spaniards changed life in Mexico.
3. Outline changes that took place in Mexico in the 1800s and 1900s.

Project transparency and have students answer the question.

Daily Focus Skills Transparency

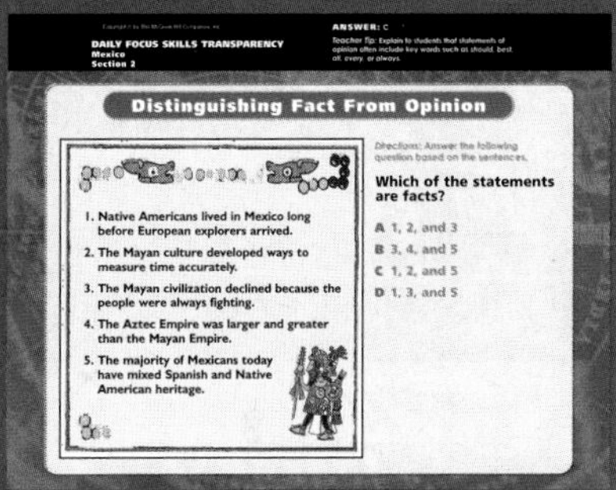

Reading Preview

- **Activating Prior Knowledge** **Ask:** What European group colonized Mexico and the southwestern United States? Give clues by mentioning Spanish place names such as Los Angeles and Santa Fe.
- **Preteaching Vocabulary** Have students find words with phonetic spellings and read these words aloud to a partner.

Section Resources

Reproducible Masters

- Reproducible Lesson Plan
- Daily Lecture and Discussion Notes
- Note-taking Guide
- Guided Reading Activity
- Reading Essentials and Study Guide
- Section Quiz

Transparencies

- Daily Focus Skills Transparency
- In-text Map Transparency

Multimedia

- Vocabulary PuzzleMaker CD-ROM
- Interactive Tutor Self-Assessment CD-ROM
- Presentation Plus! CD-ROM
- ExamView® Pro Testmaker CD-ROM

Chapter 6

Section 2, pages 197–200

TEACH

Reading Strategy

Identifying Main Ideas
Have students write each section subheading on a piece of paper. Under each subheading, have them identify the main idea of the subsection. L1

Daily Lecture and Discussion Notes

MEXICO

Daily Lecture and Discussion Notes
Mexico's History

Texas was once part of Mexico. In 1836 General Antonio López de Santa Anna defeated a Texas force in the Battle of the Alamo at San Antonio. But later that year, Texas forces defeated his army at San Jacinto and captured him. Santa Anna signed a treaty recognizing the independence of Texas. In addition to what is now the state of Texas, the new Republic of Texas included parts of present-day Colorado, Kansas, New Mexico, Oklahoma, and Wyoming.

...ve American Civilizations

...Native Americans came to Mexico thousands of years ago. These people built a ...eries of brilliant, highly advanced civilizations. The Olmecs built the first ... around 1200 B.C. It lasted longer (800 years) than

Applying Map Skills

Answers
1. the Maya
2. Tenochtitlán

In-text Map Transparency Activity Ask questions that require students to use the different types of information in the map key. **Ask**: **Which is the earliest Mexican civilization?** *(the Olmec)*

green as well as other colors. All these items were carved with **obsidian,** a hard, black glass created by the volcanoes in the area. Obsidian was used because the Olmecs had no metals.

The Olmecs were the first to grow **maize,** or corn, to feed their many people. In addition to cities and ceremonial centers, they built large drainage systems to direct rainwater away from their fields and settlements. The Olmecs lasted longer than any other Native American civilization, finally disappearing about 400 B.C.

The Maya The people called the Maya lived in the rain forests of the Yucatán Peninsula and surrounding areas from about A.D. 250 to 900. Religion held Mayan society together. Mayan priests needed to measure time accurately to hold religious ceremonies at the correct moment. They studied the heavens and developed a calendar of 365 days.

The Maya built huge stone temples in the shape of pyramids with steps. One of these structures, the temple of Kukulcan, showed careful planning. Each side of Kukulcan had 91 steps, totaling 364. The platform at the temple's top made one more step for a grand total of 365—just like the days in the year.

The Maya also developed **hieroglyphics,** a form of writing that uses signs and symbols. They had a complex number system. Artists decorated temples and tombs with elaborate **murals,** or wall paintings.

Around A.D. 900, Mayan civilization declined. Why? Historians do not know. Some suggest that the Maya overused the land and could not grow enough food. Others suggest that warfare or the spread of disease caused their decline. The Maya did not disappear, however. Their descendants still live in the same area and speak the Mayan language.

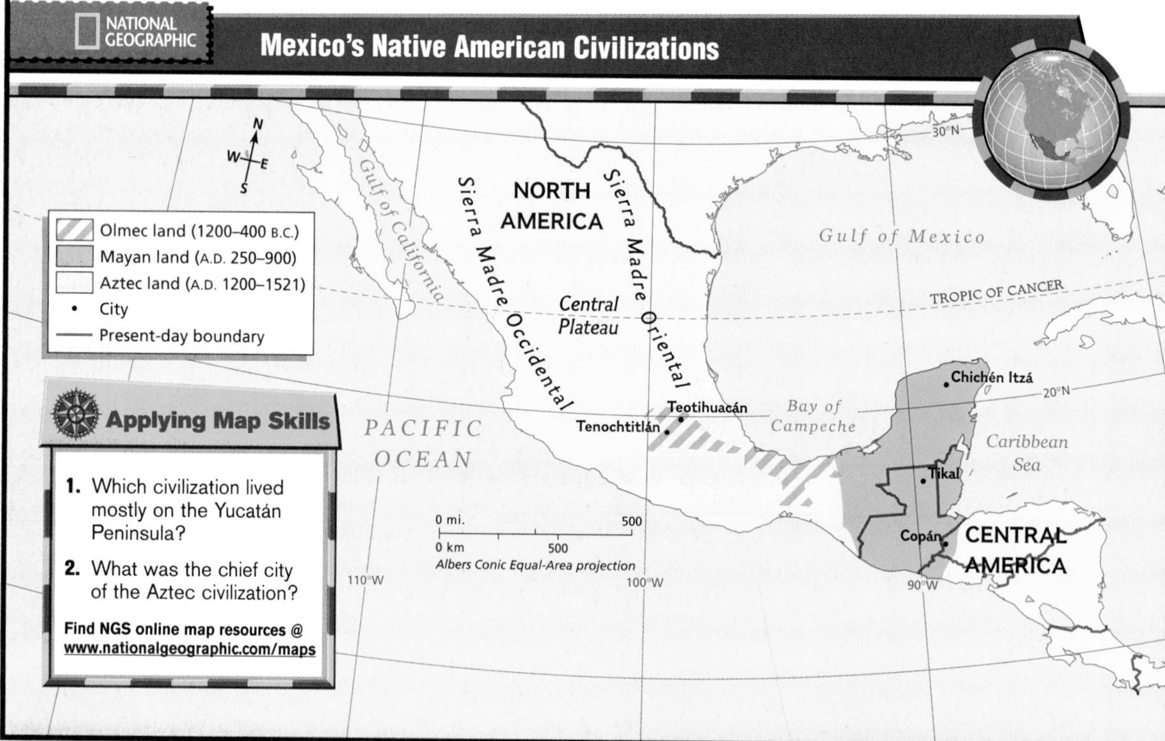

Reading Strategy — Reading the Text

Predicting Think/Pair/Share activities engage students in their subject matter through discussion. Have students think about how Mexico's politics, economy, and culture influence the United States today and write these ideas in their notebooks. Then pair students with partners and have them discuss their lists with each other. Students may add ideas to their lists based upon their discussions. Then, as a class, have students share their lists. L1

Use the ***Reading Skills Handbook*** *for more reading strategies.*

The Aztec Around A.D. 1200, a people called the Mexica moved into central Mexico from the north. The Spanish later called these people the Aztec. The Aztec conquered a large empire in central Mexico. Their capital, **Tenochtitlán** (tay•NAWCH•teet•LAHN), was magnificent. Mexico City—Mexico's capital—stands on this ancient site today.

Tenochtitlán was originally built on two islands in the middle of Lake Texcoco. Long dikes connected it to land. The city had huge stepped pyramids. Merchants traded gold, silver, and pottery in busy marketplaces. Farmers grew their crops in structures called "floating gardens," or rafts filled with mud. The rafts eventually sank to the lake bottom and piled up, forming fertile islands.

The Aztec people and many of their traditions survive today in Mexico. The food, crafts, and language of Mexico have roots in Aztec culture. Even the name of the country comes from the word the Aztec called themselves—the *Mexica*. The flag of modern Mexico honors this ancient civilization. In the center of the flag is the Aztec symbol of an eagle with a snake in its beak.

Reading Check What Native American cultures flourished in Mexico?

Spanish Mexico

In 1519 Mexico's history changed dramatically. A Spanish army led by Hernán Cortés landed on Mexico's Gulf coast. He and about 600 soldiers marched to Tenochtitlán, which they heard was filled with gold. Some Native Americans who opposed the harsh rule of the Aztec signed treaties with the Spanish and joined them. The Spanish had swords, muskets, cannons, and horses. This enabled them to defeat the Aztec Empire, which contained about 6 million people, within two years.

Spain made Mexico a colony, or an overseas territory, because Mexico's rocky land held rich deposits of gold and silver. Many Spanish settlers came to live in Mexico. Some raised cattle on large ranches called **haciendas** (ah•see•EHN•duhs). Others started gold and silver mines. The Spaniards made Native Americans work on the ranches and in the mines. Thousands of Native Americans died from mistreatment. Many thousands more died of diseases such as the common cold and smallpox, which they caught from Europeans. Spanish priests came to Mexico and in their own way tried to improve the lives of Native Americans. Because of their work, many Native Americans accepted the priests' teachings. Today about 90 percent of Mexico's people follow the Roman Catholic religion.

Reading Check Why was Mexico a valuable colony for Spain?

NATIONAL GEOGRAPHIC **On Location**

Teotihuacán

Hundreds of years before the appearance of the Aztec or the Spanish, Native Americans built monuments, such as the Temple of the Sun in the city of Teotihuacán. Teotihuacán was located near what is now Mexico City.

History **How was the small Spanish army able to defeat the Aztec?**

More About the Photo

Teotihuacán The city of *Teotihuacán* flourished as an important commerical and religious center in the area of the Valley of Mexico. *Teotihuacán* means "City of the Gods."

Caption Answer help from Native Americans opposed to the Aztec, superior weapons, and horses

Reading Check Answer

the Olmecs, the Maya, and the Aztec

3 Assess

Assign Section 2 Assessment as homework or an in-class activity.

Have students use the Interactive Tutor Self-Assessment CD-ROM to review Section 2.

L2

Section Quiz

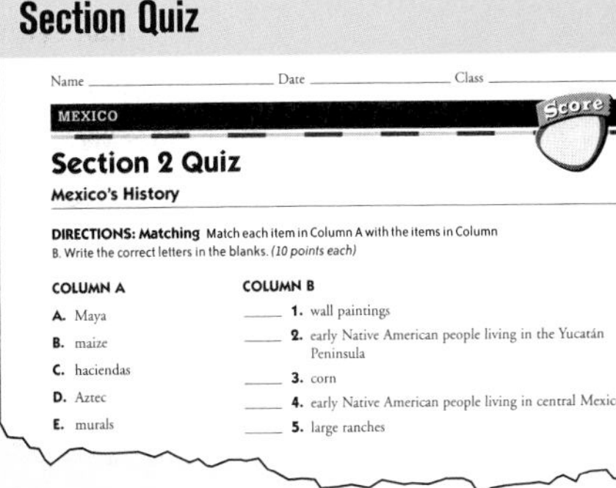

Name ______ Date ______ Class ______

MEXICO

Score

Section 2 Quiz

Mexico's History

DIRECTIONS: Matching Match each item in Column A with the items in Column B. Write the correct letters in the blanks. *(10 points each)*

COLUMN A	COLUMN B
A. Maya	____ **1.** wall paintings
B. maize	____ **2.** early Native American people living in the Yucatán Peninsula
C. haciendas	____ **3.** corn
D. Aztec	____ **4.** early Native American people living in central Mexico
E. murals	____ **5.** large ranches

Reading Check Answer

because it held rich deposits of gold and silver

Differentiated Instruction

Meeting Special Needs: Verbal/Linguistic Point out to students that some of the Terms to Know in this chapter are Spanish words. Remind them that the text often gives the pronunciations of these and other Spanish words. Have them follow the pronunciation guides and practice saying the Spanish words in this chapter aloud several times. **ELL**

Refer to *Inclusion for the Middle School Social Studies Classroom Strategies and Activities* in the TCR.

Objectives and answers to the Student Web Activity can be found in the Web Activity Lesson Plan at twip.glencoe.com

Emiliano Zapata

L1/ELL

Reading Essentials and Study Guide

Name ______ Date ______ Class ______

MEXICO

Reading Essentials and Study Guide 2

Mexico's History

Key Terms

jade a shiny stone that comes in many shades of green
obsidian a hard black glass created by volcanoes
maize corn
hieroglyphics form of writing that uses signs and symbols
mural wall painting
hacienda large ranch

Enrich

Have students learn more about Mayan culture, such as the calendar or hieroglyphics.

4 CLOSE

Reading Strategy

Sequencing Having students create an annotated time line of Mexican history.

Web Activity Visit ***The World and Its People*** Web site at twip.glencoe.com and click on **Chapter 6—Student Web Activities** to learn more about Mexico's history.

Independence and Revolution

The people of Mexico resented Spanish rule. In 1810 they rallied behind a Catholic priest, Miguel Hidalgo. He led an army of peasants in revolt. Spanish officials brought charges against Hidalgo and executed him, but the rebellion did not stop. Mexicans won their independence from Spain in 1821. In 1824 they set up a republic with an elected president.

Soon after independence, Mexico lost some valuable territory. Mexico's northern province of Texas fought for and won its own independence from Mexico and asked to join the United States. In 1846 the United States fought Mexico in a dispute over the southern boundary of Texas. In the treaty ending the war, Mexico gave up its claims to Texas. Mexico lost other valuable territory to the United States that included what are today the states of California, Utah, and Nevada.

For many decades, rich families, army officers, and Catholic Church leaders held most of the power and wealth in Mexico. In 1910 Mexican peasants revolted. Emiliano Zapata, who commanded a rebel army, stated the goals of this revolution. He wanted to give to the poor "the lands, woods, and water that the landlords or bosses have taken from us." Zapata's forces seized many large haciendas and divided the land among the poor. In Mexico's northwest area, Francisco "Pancho" Villa also tried to help the poor, mostly Native American peasants.

Reading Check Who led the 1910 revolution in Mexico?

Assessment

Defining Terms

1. **Define** jade, obsidian, maize, hieroglyphics, mural, hacienda.

Recalling Facts

2. **History** Describe three achievements of the ancient Maya.
3. **History** Which European country conquered and colonized Mexico?
4. **History** What were Emiliano Zapata's goals?

Critical Thinking

5. **Sequencing Information** Put the following events in the correct chronological order: Cortés conquers the Aztec, Mexico wins independence from Spain, the Mexica move into central Mexico, Zapata leads a revolution.
6. **Understanding Cause and Effect** How did the arrival of Europeans affect the Native Americans in Mexico?

Graphic Organizer

7. **Organizing Information** Create a chart like this one. In each column, list the major advancements of each civilization.

Olmec	Maya	Aztec

Applying Social Studies Skills

8. **Analyzing Maps** Refer to the map of Mexico's Native American civilizations on page 198. Which Native American group settled the farthest south?

Section 2 Assessment

1. The terms are defined in the Glossary.
2. *Any three:* a calendar of 365 days; pyramids; hieroglyphics; a number system; murals
3. Spain
4. to divide the lands of the rich among the poor
5. The Mexica move into central Mexico; Cortés conquers the Aztec; Mexico wins independence from Spain; Zapata leads a revolution.
6. Many Native Americans worked on ranches and in mines, died of mistreatment or disease, and accepted Catholicism.
7. Olmec: built first civilization in Americas, carved statues and jewelry, grew maize, built drainage systems; Maya: developed 365-day calendar, built pyramids, developed hieroglyphics, painted wall murals; Aztec: built a magnificent city, conquered an empire
8. the Maya

Making Connections

ART | SCIENCE | CULTURE | TECHNOLOGY

The Aztec Calendar Stone

It is hard to imagine how a huge stone filled with carved figures can serve as a calendar. Known commonly as the Sun Stone, the Aztec calendar is full of both scientific and religious information.

History

In 1790 workers in the heart of the *zócalo,* or main square, of Mexico City uncovered a massive circular stone. Mexico City sits on top of Tenochtitlán, the ancient capital of the Aztec Empire. Some 300 years earlier, the Aztec at Tenochtitlán had carved the 25-ton (23-t) basalt rock calendar. Using stone tools, they created a monument that measured 12 feet (3.6 m) in diameter and 3 feet (0.9 m) thick.

The face of the Aztec sun god appears at the center of the calendar stone. The sun god was thought to be one of the most important Aztec gods. Seven rings surround the sun god. In the closest ring are four squarelike spaces, each with a symbol that represents the four past ages of the world—the time that existed before humans appeared. Circling these symbols is a ring with signs representing the 20 days of the Aztec month.

Meaning of the Calendar

The Aztec calendar stone is actually two calendars in one. One calendar is a religious calendar based on a 260-day cycle. The Aztec believed that their lives depended on fulfilling their gods' demands. The calendar told Aztec priests when to make offerings and hold rituals for each god. It also divided the days among the gods. According to the Aztec view, this kept the universe in balance. An imbalance could lead to a power struggle among the gods and bring about the end of the world.

The second calendar is an agricultural calendar based on a 365-day solar cycle. The Aztec were very efficient farmers. They used this calendar to keep track of the seasons and ceremonies related to agricultural cycles.

Making the Connection

1. What does the Aztec agricultural calendar reveal about the scientific understanding of the Aztec?
2. Why was it important for the Aztec to divide the days among the gods?
3. **Making Comparisons** How do the two calendar systems of the Aztec differ?

◄ Today the Aztec calendar stone is displayed in the National Museum of Anthropology in Mexico City.

Making Connections

TEACH

The idea of two simultaneous calendar cycles may seem unusual to students or difficult to grasp. To make it more familiar, ask them: **When does the calendar year begin and end?** *(January 1, December 31)* **Does the school year begin and end at the same time?** *(no)* **What about sports seasons?** *(no)* **L1**

More About the Aztec Calendar

The two Aztec calendar cycles joined together every 52 years. The Aztec had two names for this occasion: the Binding Up of the Years and the New Fire Ceremony. All fires throughout the community were left to burn out before this day. Then, in a ritual of rebirth, a new fire was lit (on the chest of a person who was sacrificed for this purpose). The Aztec used the new flame to start their own home fires. As a result of this ceremony, the Aztec believed the world would not be destroyed.

Making the Connection

1. They understood that the year lasted 365 days. They were efficient and wise farmers who understood the cycle of seasons.
2. If the days were not evenly divided, the gods would fight and bring about the end of the world.
3. One year, of 260 days, is religious; the other, of 365 days, is agricultural.

Chapter 6

Section 3, pages 202–206

1 Focus

Section Objectives

1. Describe life in the cities and villages of Mexico.
2. Identify elements of Mexican culture.
3. Discuss Mexico's government.
4. Explain what challenges face Mexico.

BELLRINGER Skillbuilder Activity

Project transparency and have students answer the question.

Daily Focus Skills Transparency

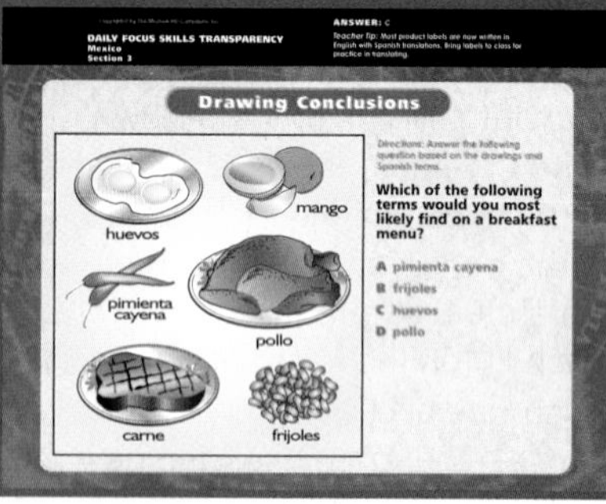

Reading Preview

■ **Activating Prior Knowledge** Have students predict what kinds of economic challenges they think Mexico might face based on what they know about Mexico's economy.

Reading Check Answer

plazas

Guide to Reading

Main Idea

Mexicans enjoy a rich and lively culture but face many serious challenges.

Terms to Know

- plaza
- adobe
- federal republic
- migrant worker
- national debt
- smog

Reading Strategy

Create a diagram like this one. In each of the smaller ovals, write a feature of Mexican culture. Add as many smaller ovals as you need.

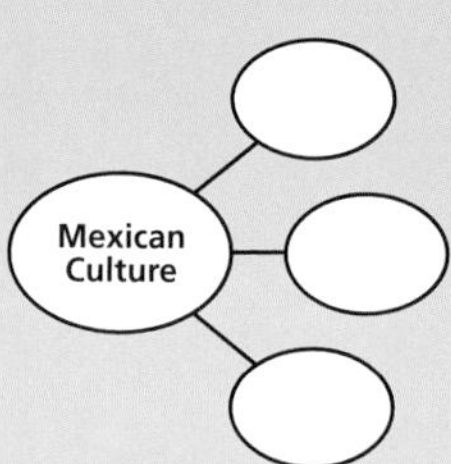

Section 3 Mexico Today

NATIONAL GEOGRAPHIC **Exploring Our World**

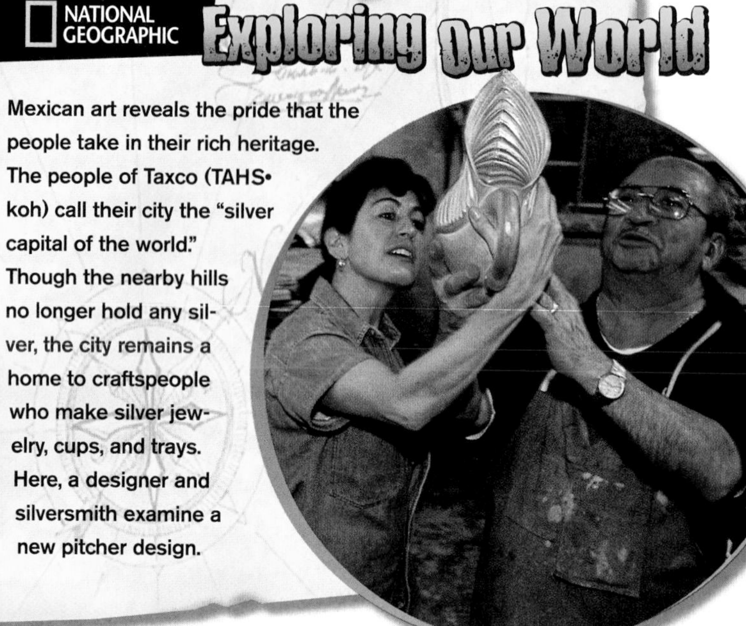

Mexican art reveals the pride that the people take in their rich heritage. The people of Taxco (TAHS•koh) call their city the "silver capital of the world." Though the nearby hills no longer hold any silver, the city remains a home to craftspeople who make silver jewelry, cups, and trays. Here, a designer and silversmith examine a new pitcher design.

Mexico—the third-largest country in area in Latin America, after Brazil and Argentina—has a large and dynamic population. About 75 percent of all Mexicans live in the country's bustling cities.

Mexico's Cities and Villages

In the center of Mexico's cities, you often find large **plazas**, or public squares. Around each city's plaza stand important buildings such as a church and a government center. When you look at the buildings, you can see the architectural style of Spanish colonial times. Newer sections of the cities have a mix of towering glass office buildings and modern houses. In the poorer sections of town, people build small homes out of whatever materials they can find. These materials may include boards, sheet metal, or even cardboard.

Rural villages also have central plazas. Streets lead from the plazas to residential areas. Many homes are made of **adobe** (uh•DOH•bee), or sun-dried clay bricks. The roofs might be made of straw or of colored tile, in the Spanish style.

Reading Check What do you find in the center of Mexico's cities and villages?

Section Resources

Reproducible Masters

- Reproducible Lesson Plan
- Daily Lecture and Discussion Notes
- Note-taking Guide
- Guided Reading Activity
- Reading Essentials and Study Guide
- Section Quiz

Transparencies

- Daily Focus Skills Transparency

Multimedia

- Vocabulary PuzzleMaker CD-ROM
- Interactive Tutor Self-Assessment CD-ROM
- Presentation Plus! CD-ROM
- ExamView® Pro Testmaker CD-ROM
-  MindJogger Videoquiz

Mexican Culture

Mexican artists and writers have created many national treasures. In the early 1900s, Mexican painters produced beautiful murals—just as Native American painters had done centuries before. Among the most famous of these mural painters were José Clemente Orozco, David Alfero Sequieros, and Diego Rivera. Rivera's wife, Frida Kahlo, became well-known for her paintings, which revealed her inner feelings. Modern writers such as Carlos Fuentes and Octavio Paz have written poems and stories that reflect the values of Mexico's people.

Food If you have tasted Mexican food, you know that it is a rich blend of flavors. Corn—first grown in Mexico—continues to be an important part of the Mexican diet. Chocolate, tomatoes, beans, squash, and chilies were all Native American foods as well. When the Spanish came, they brought beef, chicken, cheese, and olive oil, which Mexicans added to their cooking.

Today Mexicans use these different cooking traditions in popular foods such as tacos and enchiladas. Both dishes combine a flat bread called a tortilla with meat or beans, vegetables, cheese, and spicy chilies.

Celebrations Throughout the year, Mexicans enjoy celebrations called fiestas (fee•EHS•tuhs). These special days include parades, fireworks, music, and dancing. Mariachi (MAHR•ee•AH•chee) bands may play such traditional instruments as the violin, guitar, horn, and bass at fiestas. More likely, though, you will hear the fast-paced rhythms and singing of Latino bands, which have influenced the United States.

National holidays include Independence Day (September 16) and Cinco de Mayo (May 5). Cinco de Mayo celebrates the day in 1862 that Mexicans defeated an invading French army in battle. November 2 is a

Art

Mexican artist Diego Rivera is one of the most famous mural painters of the twentieth century. He believed that art belonged to the people. In Mexico City, Rivera's murals line the courtyard of the Ministry of Education building and cover the walls of the National Palace. With their characteristically vivid colors and distinctive style, Rivera's murals tell the story of the work, culture, and history of the Mexican people.

Looking Closer **How did Rivera's work support his belief that art belongs to the people?**

Mexico Through the Centuries ▶

Chapter 6

Section 3, pages 202–206

Making Comparisons Have students make a chart comparing Mexican culture to their culture. When they are done with their charts, have them discuss the similarities and differences. L1/ELL

Daily Lecture and Discussion Notes

MEXICO

Daily Lecture and Discussion Notes

Mexico Today

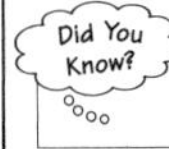

The Treaty of Tlatelolco was the first treaty to ban nuclear weapons in a geographic region. Under the leadership of Mexico, the countries of Latin America signed the treaty in 1967.

I. Mexico's Cities and Villages

A. In the center of Mexico's cities, large **plazas**—or public squares—are found. Around each city's plaza stand important buildings such as a church and a government center. These buildings have a Spanish colonial architecture style. Newer sections of the cities have large glass office buildings and modern homes.

B. ... homes are made of **adobe,** or sun-dried clay bricks.

Answer His work tells the story of Mexico's people and culture and is displayed in public places.

Ask students: **If you were to create a mural celebrating Mexican culture, what would you include?** Discuss the significance of the people, events, and cultural elements that students suggest.

Reading Strategy **Reading the Text**

Evaluating Have students use the Internet to find an article that addresses solving Mexico's population, foreign debt, or pollution problems. In a one-page essay, students should describe and evaluate the solution. Remind students as they evaluate the solution to think about the author's point of view and the facts that are cited to support it. L1

*Use the **Reading Skills Handbook** for more reading strategies.*

More About the Photo

Fiestas Independence Day celebrates Mexico's independence from Spain. People decorate streets, houses, buildings, and cars with Mexico's flag and national colors of green, white, and red. Lighted decorations are set up in every city, the most spectacular being those of the Zócalo, or main plaza, in Mexico City.

Caption Answer to celebrate special occasions in Mexico

Reading Check Answer

Independence Day, Cinco de Mayo, the Day of the Dead

L1/ELL

Guided Reading Activity

Name ________ Date ________ Class ________

MEXICO

Guided Reading Activity 3

Mexico Today

DIRECTIONS: Reading for Accuracy Reading the section and completing the activity below will help you learn more about Mexico today. Refer to your textbook to decide if a statement is true or false. Write **T** or **F**, and if a statement is false, rewrite it correctly.

____ 1. More than 70 percent of Mexicans live in rural areas.

____ 2. Carlos Fuentes and Octavio Paz are modern writers whose works reflect the values of Mexico's people.

____ 3. Corn is an important part of the Mexican diet.

Reading Check Answer

federal republic

NATIONAL GEOGRAPHIC **On Location**

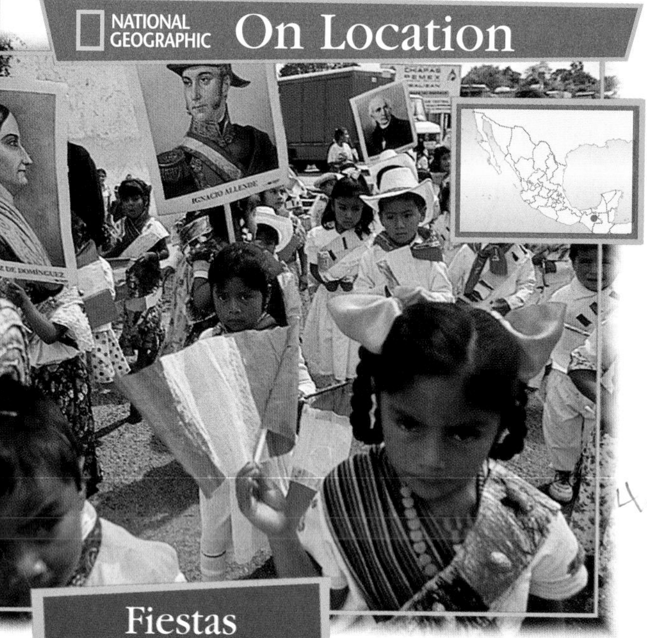

Fiestas

On September 16, Mexicans have parades to celebrate the women and men who helped win Mexican independence.

Culture What is the purpose of fiestas?

special religious celebration called the "Day of the Dead." On this day, families gather in cemeteries where they honor their departed loved ones by laying down food and flowers.

Reading Check What are some important celebrations in Mexico?

Mexico's Government

Mexico, like the United States, is a **federal republic,** where power is divided between national and state governments. A strong president leads the national government. Mexico's national government differs in that it has much more power than the state governments. The president of Mexico is head of the executive branch of government. He or she can serve only one six-year term but has more power than the legislative and judicial branches.

For many decades, one political party, called the Party of Institutional Revolution (PRI), led Mexico. All the presidents and most other elected officials came from this party. In recent years, economic troubles and the people's lack of political power led to growing frustration. In the year 2000, the newly elected president of Mexico, Vicente Fox, came from a different political party—for the first time in more than 70 years.

Mexico's government faces many difficult challenges. People in Mexico are demanding more political freedom to make decisions that affect their everyday lives. Traffic in illegal drugs is of concern to the government as well. Nearly 40 percent of Mexico's 100 million people live below the poverty line. To fight the country's pressing problems, from poverty to drugs, a strong central government is needed. To increase democracy in Mexico, however, Fox must give power back to local and state agencies. Fox will have to help his country find the balance between these two levels of government.

Reading Check What form of government does Mexico have?

Mexico's Challenges

Mexico has tried to use its resources to improve the lives of its people. These actions have had strong effects on Mexican life—and have created some challenges for the future.

Population Mexico's population has increased rapidly in recent decades. Because many people have moved to the cities to find jobs, the cities have grown quickly. A large number of people have had to

Differentiated Instruction

Meeting Special Needs: Auditory/Musical Locate recordings of Mexican *mariachi* and *ranchero* (ranch hand) music. Play the music for students and ask them to characterize the differences between these folk styles and other forms of music. They might comment on the rhythms used or the instrumentation. Students who are familiar with other forms of music from Latin America might bring examples to class to provide additional contrasts. L1/ELL

Refer to *Inclusion for the Middle School Social Studies Classroom Strategies and Activities* in the TCR.

take jobs that pay low wages. As a result, hundreds of thousands of people crowd together in slums, or poor sections of the cities.

Those Mexicans who cannot find any work in their country may become **migrant workers.** These are people who travel from place to place when extra workers are needed to plant or harvest crops. They legally and sometimes illegally cross Mexico's long border to work in the United States. Though the pay is low, the migrant workers can earn more in the United States than in Mexico.

Another challenge concerning Mexico's people involves the descendants of the ancient Maya Indians. The present-day Maya live in the southernmost state of Mexico called **Chiapas.** Turn to the map on page 191 to see where Chiapas is located. This state is one of the poorest states in Mexico. Over 75 percent of the people there live below the poverty level. Most of the wealth in Chiapas is concentrated in a very small number of ranching families who are of Spanish descent. Diseases and illness that result from poverty and lack of health care cause thousands of deaths every year. Many Maya are fighting for independence from the central government because they lost hope in the Mexican government.

Foreign Debt For decades, the Mexican government refused to let foreign companies build factories in Mexico. Leaders feared that the companies would take their profits to their own country, thus draining

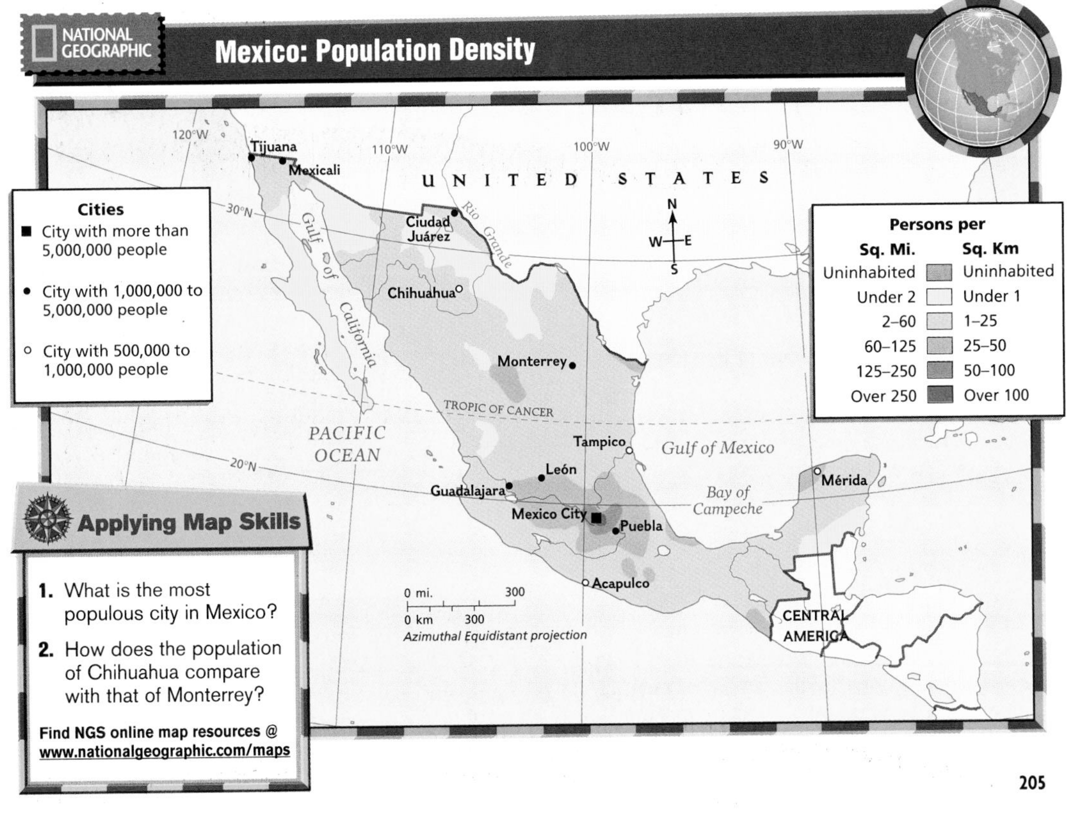

Applying Map Skills

1. What is the most populous city in Mexico?
2. How does the population of Chihuahua compare with that of Monterrey?

Find NGS online map resources @ www.nationalgeographic.com/maps

205

Chapter 6

Section 3, pages 202–206

3 ASSESS

Assign Section 3 Assessment as homework or an in-class activity.

Have students use the Interactive Tutor Self-Assessment CD-ROM to review Section 3.

L2

Section Quiz

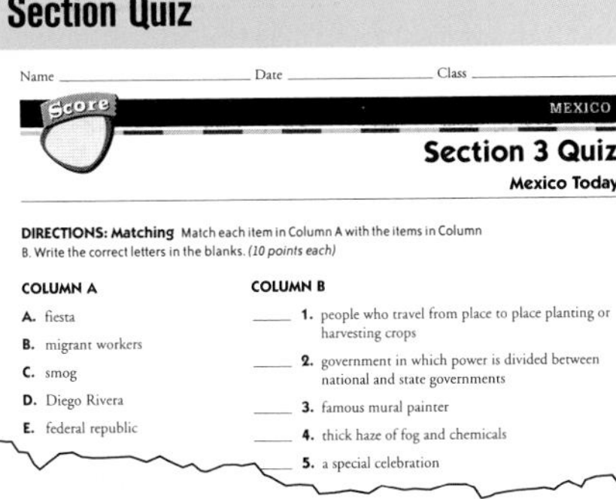

Name ______ Date ______ Class ______

Score | MEXICO

Section 3 Quiz

Mexico Today

DIRECTIONS: Matching Match each item in Column A with the items in Column B. Write the correct letters in the blanks. *(10 points each)*

COLUMN A	COLUMN B
A. fiesta	____ 1. people who travel from place to place planting or harvesting crops
B. migrant workers	____ 2. government in which power is divided between national and state governments
C. smog	____ 3. famous mural painter
D. Diego Rivera	____ 4. thick haze of fog and chemicals
E. federal republic	____ 5. a special celebration

Reteach

Have students work in pairs to quiz each other on the content of the text and map in this section.

Applying Map Skills

Answers

1. Mexico City
2. Chihuahua has 500,000 to 1 million people; Monterrey has 1 to 5 million people.

Skills Practice

Which part of Mexico has the lowest population density, the north or south? Why? *(north, because the climate and landscape are drier)*

Team-Teaching Activity

Economics Have a teacher with a background in economics discuss the issue of international debt in the developing world. Have the teacher talk about growing calls by leaders of developing countries for debt relief and explain why lenders and international bodies like the World Bank International Monetary Fund are reluctant to take that step without the countries involved taking additional actions to improve their internal financial systems. Then have students organize a debate on international lending. L3

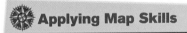

EE4 Human Systems: Standard 11

Chapter 6

Section 3, pages 202–206

TRAVEL GUIDE

Mexico offers sport to deep-sea fishers. Marlin, swordfish, and tarpon are among the game fish caught off Mexico's coast. Many fishers enjoy the waters off Cape San Lucas at the southern tip of Baja California.

✓ Reading Check Answer

need to find jobs and housing for growing population, diseases from poverty and lack of health care, repaying foreign debt, maintaining economic growth, pollution

L1/ELL

Reading Essentials and Study Guide

Name ________ Date ________ Class ________

MEXICO

Reading Essentials and Study Guide 3

Mexico Today

Key Terms

plaza public square
adobe sun-dried clay bricks
federal republic type of government in which power is divided between national and state governments and a strong president leads the national government
migrant worker worker who travels from place to place to plant or harvest crops when needed
national debt money owed by the government
smog haze of fog and chemicals in the air

Enrich

Have students research one aspect of Mexican culture, such as the food, music, or celebrations, and prepare a multimedia presentation of their findings.

4 CLOSE

Have students write a letter to a friend describing Mexican culture.

money out of Mexico. In the 1990s, the government changed this policy. Mexican officials were still concerned that money would be lost, but hoped that the new factories would create more jobs for Mexicans.

To help its economy grow, Mexico borrowed money from foreign banks. The government then had to use any money it earned in taxes to pay back the loans. As a result, Mexico's leaders did not have enough funds to spend on the Mexican people when the economy began to struggle. Many Mexicans grew angry. Yet, if the government did not make the loan payments, banks would refuse to lend more money for future plans. Because there are still loans to be repaid, Mexicans will face this situation for many years. The problem of repaying a **national debt,** or money owed by the government, is one that is being faced by many countries in the world today.

Pollution As Mexico's population boomed, its cities grew very large. At the same time, the economy industrialized. Both of these changes contributed to rising pollution in Mexico.

The mountains that surround Mexico City trap the exhaust fumes from hundreds of thousands of cars. People in this city wake each day to a thick haze of fog and chemicals called **smog.** Many people wear masks when they leave their homes to go to work or school. In northern Mexico, many factories release dangerous chemicals into the air or water. One environmental group says that the Rio Grande is now one of the most polluted rivers in North America.

✓ Reading Check What challenges does Mexico face?

Section 3 Assessment

Defining Terms

1. **Define** plaza, adobe, federal republic, migrant worker, national debt, smog.

Recalling Facts

2. **Culture** What percentage of Mexico's population lives in urban areas?
3. **Government** Explain how Mexico's government is similar to the government of the United States. How is it different?
4. **Government** Why did Mexico's government refuse to allow foreign factories in Mexico?

Critical Thinking

5. **Analyzing Information** What has resulted from the Mexican government's policy of borrowing from foreign banks?
6. **Summarizing Information** What problems have resulted from Mexico's expanding population?

Graphic Organizer

7. **Organizing Information** Create a diagram like this one. On the arrows, list three factors that have led to the smog problem of Mexico City. Be sure to consider physical characteristics of the area when listing the factors.

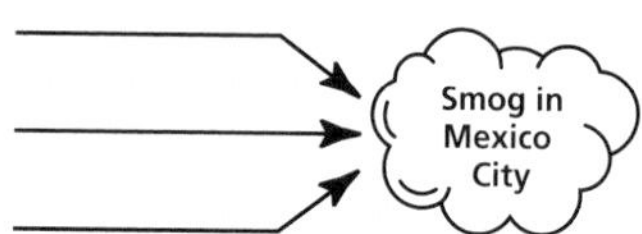

Applying Social Studies Skills

8. **Analyzing Maps** Look at the population density map on page 205. What is the population of Guadalajara? What is the population density of the area surrounding Mérida?

Section 3 Assessment

1. The terms are defined in the Glossary.
2. about 75 percent
3. similarities: federal republics, power divided between national and state governments, president head of executive branch; differences: president serves one six-year term; Mexico's national government has much more power than the states.
4. Leaders feared companies would take their profits to their own countries.
5. Mexico must use tax money to repay loans and cannot spend money on its people.
6. increased poverty in the cities, low-paying jobs, disease from poverty, conflict in Chiapas
7. growing population, industrialization, mountains trap smog
8. 1–5 million; 60–125 people per sq. mile (25–50 people per sq. km)

Reading Review

Section 1 Mexico's Land and Economy

Terms to Know
- land bridge
- peninsula
- latitude
- altitude
- hurricane
- vaquero
- maquiladora
- subsistence farm
- plantation
- industrialize
- service industry

Main Idea

Mexico's mountainous landscape and varied climate create different economic regions.

✓ Location Mexico is part of a land bridge that connects North and South America.

✓ Location Much of Mexico lies in the Tropics, but the climate in some areas is cool because of high elevation.

✓ Economics Landforms and climate combine to create three economic zones in Mexico.

✓ Movement Mexico's economy is growing, and many people are moving to the northern cities.

Section 2 Mexico's History

Terms to Know
- jade
- obsidian
- maize
- hieroglyphics
- mural
- hacienda

Main Idea

Mexico's culture reflects a blend of its Native American and Spanish past.

✓ History Mexico's Native American civilizations—the Olmec, Maya, and Aztec—made many contributions to Mexico's culture.

✓ Culture Mexico's people reflect the country's Native American and Spanish roots.

✓ History The Spanish ruled Mexico from the 1500s to 1821, when Mexico won its independence.

✓ History The poor people in Mexico revolted against the rich and powerful church and military leaders in 1910.

Section 3 Mexico Today

Terms to Know
- plaza
- adobe
- federal republic
- migrant worker
- national debt
- smog

Main Idea

Mexicans enjoy a rich and lively culture but face many serious challenges.

✓ Location About 75 percent of Mexicans live in cities today.

✓ Culture Mexicans enjoy celebrations called fiestas, which can include parades, fireworks, and music.

✓ Government Mexico's government is a federal republic.

✓ Economics Challenges facing Mexico include problems caused by population growth, foreign investment and debt, and pollution.

Reading Review

Use the Chapter 6 Reading Review to preview, review, condense, or reteach the chapter.

Preview/Review

Use the Terms to Know lists to help students review and study.

Activity Organize the class into teams and quiz students on the terms by offering the definition and asking them to supply the term.

Vocabulary PuzzleMaker CD-ROM reinforces the vocabulary terms used in Chapter 6.

The Interactive Tutor Self-Assessment CD-ROM allows students to review Chapter 6 content.

Condense

Have students read the Chapter 6 summary statements.

Guided Reading Activities

Audio Program

Reteach

Reteaching Activity

Reading Essentials and Study Guide

Reading Strategy Read to Write

Summarizing Information Have students complete the sentence "Mexico is a dynamic and diverse country because. . . ." Explain that students should present their answers in a written report. Remind students to include supporting details in their reports. Students may want to create outlines to organize their ideas before they write the reports. Their answers should address such issues as the country's geography, climate, economy, people, and culture. L1

EE6 The Uses of Geography: Standard 18

Assessment and Activities

GLENCOE TECHNOLOGY

MindJogger Videoquiz
Use MindJogger Videoquiz to review the Chapter 6 content.

Available in DVD and VHS

Using Key Terms

1.	e	6.	c
2.	h	7.	i
3.	b	8.	f
4.	a	9.	d
5.	j	10.	g

Reviewing the Main Ideas

11. The Tropic of Cancer (the northern edge of the Tropics) cuts across Mexico—areas south of the line have warm temperatures year-round, while areas north of the line are warm in summer and cooler in winter.
12. coffee, cotton, vegetables, fruit, livestock, tobacco, clothing, oil
13. They have caused an economic boom and attracted people looking for jobs. They have raised the standard of living in northern cities, but have also caused increased air and water pollution.
14. Tenochtitlán
15. Thousands died from mistreatment and diseases caught from Europeans; many were forced to work; many converted to Catholicism.
16. 1821
17. They are demanding more political freedom to make decisions that affect their everyday lives.
18. the day Mexico defeated an invading French army in 1862

Chapter 6 Assessment and Activities

Using Key Terms

Match the terms in Part A with their definitions in Part B.

A.

1. altitude
2. hurricane
3. vaquero
4. maquiladora
5. jade
6. adobe
7. plaza
8. smog
9. mural
10. subsistence farm

B.

a. factory that assembles parts from other countries
b. cowhand
c. sun-dried clay bricks
d. wall painting
e. height above sea level
f. fog mixed with smoke
g. produces only enough to support a family's needs
h. fierce tropical storm
i. public square
j. shiny stone that comes in many shades of green

Reviewing the Main Ideas

Section 1 Mexico's Land and Economy

11. **Location** How does Mexico's latitude affect its climate?
12. **Economics** What are Mexico's major exports?
13. **Movement** How have maquiladoras affected northern Mexico's cities?

Section 2 Mexico's History

14. **History** What was the capital city of the Aztec civilization?
15. **History** What effects did Spanish conquest have on Native Americans?
16. **History** When did Mexico win its independence from Spain?

Section 3 Mexico Today

17. **Government** What are people in Mexico demanding from the Mexican government?
18. **Culture** What does Cinco de Mayo celebrate?

NATIONAL GEOGRAPHIC Mexico

Place Location Activity

On a separate sheet of paper, match the letters on the map with the numbered places listed below.

1. Pacific Ocean
2. Mexico City
3. Plateau of Mexico
4. Yucatán Peninsula
5. Baja California
6. Rio Grande
7. Gulf of Mexico
8. Guadalajara
9. Monterrey
10. Caribbean Sea

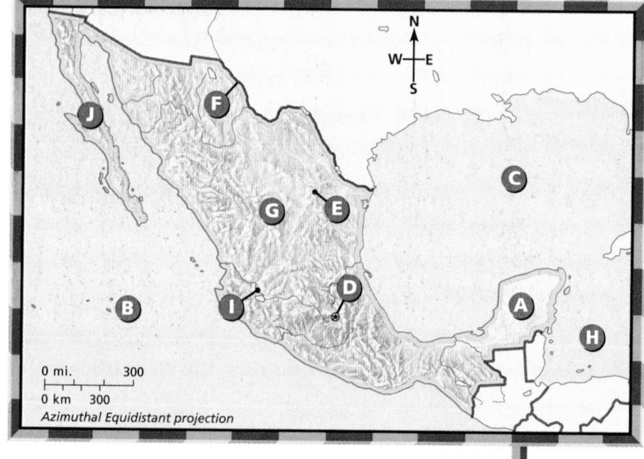

NATIONAL GEOGRAPHIC Place Location Activity

1.	B	6.	F
2.	D	7.	C
3.	G	8.	I
4.	A	9.	E
5.	J	10.	H

Critical Thinking

19. Leaders hope companies will open factories in Mexico, thus creating new jobs and economic growth.
20. Answers will vary but should be well-reasoned and be supported by facts and examples.

Self-Check Quiz Visit ***The World and Its People*** Web site at twip.glencoe.com and click on **Chapter 6—Self-Check Quizzes** to prepare for the Chapter Test.

Critical Thinking

19. **Understanding Cause and Effect** Why have Mexico's leaders encouraged free trade agreements with other countries?
20. **Problem Solving** If you were Mexico's president, what would you do to rid Mexico of the problems of illegal drugs and poverty?

Comparing Regions Activity

21. **Culture** People from different regions may have different ways of measuring time. The Aztec Stone, for example, was both a religious and an agricultural calendar. Compare the Aztec Stone to another region's calendar that is no longer in use, such as the ancient Egyptian or Roman calendar. How are they alike? How are they different?

Mental Mapping Activity

22. **Focusing on the Region** Create a simple outline map of Mexico. Refer to the physical map on page 196 and then label the following:
    - Pacific Ocean
    - Gulf of Mexico
    - Yucatán Peninsula
    - Baja California
    - Mexico City
    - Rio Grande
    - Sierra Madre Occidental

Technology Skills Activity

23. **Developing a Multimedia Presentation** Imagine that you work for Mexico's Economic Development Office. Create a multimedia presentation to present to a group of foreign investors. Use a software application such as PowerPoint® to showcase positive features like climate, resources, and labor supply. Your goal is to show investors that Mexico is a good place for them to invest their money.

Standardized Test Practice

Directions: Read the paragraph below, and then answer the question that follows.

The Aztec civilization was organized into classes. At the top was the emperor. His power came from his control of the army and the religious beliefs of the people. Next came the nobles, followed by commoners. Commoners included priests, merchants, and artists. Below commoners were the serfs, or workers who farmed the nobles' fields. Slaves, the lowest class, included criminals and people in debt, as well as female and child prisoners of war. Male prisoners of war were sacrificed to the Aztec gods. The Aztec believed that live human sacrifices were needed to keep the gods pleased and to prevent floods and other disasters.

1. **Which of the following statements is an opinion about the information given above?**
   - **F** The Aztec civilization was organized into classes.
   - **G** Male prisoners of war were sacrificed to the Aztec gods.
   - **H** Slaves included children.
   - **J** The Aztec should not have sacrificed people to the gods.

Test-Taking Tip: This question asks you to identify an opinion. An opinion is a person's belief. It is not a proven fact (such as answer F). Opinions often contain subjective words, such as *easier, best,* or *should.*

Assessment and Activities

Standardized Test Practice

1. J

Tested Objectives: Distinguishing between fact and opinion, analyzing information

Chapter Test Bonus Question

This question may be used for extra credit on the chapter test.

What industry is growing in the southern areas of Mexico? *(tourism)*

Have students visit the Web site at twip.glencoe.com to review Chapter 6 and take the Self-Check Quiz.

FOLDABLES™ Study Organizer **Dinah Zike's Foldables**

Culminating Activity Have students write a one-page essay that compares and contrasts Mexico's economy and government of today with its past economy and government.

Comparing Regions Activity

21. Calendar comparisons should include similarities and differences.

Mental Mapping Activity

22. This exercise helps students visualize the geographic and political features of Mexico. All attempts at freehand mapping should be accepted.

Technology Skills Activity

23. Students' multimedia presentations should include the requested information—climate, resources, and labor supply.

Chapter 7 Resources

Note: The following materials may be used when teaching Chapter 7.
Section level support materials are shown at point of use in the margins of the Teacher Wraparound Edition.

Timesaving Tools

TeacherWorks™ All-In-One Planner and Resource Center

- **Interactive Teacher Edition** See the **Interactive Teacher Edition** CD-ROM to electronically integrate your Teacher Wraparound Edition and blackline masters.
- **Interactive Lesson Planner** Organize your week, month, semester, or year with all the lesson helps you need. The **Interactive Lesson Planner** CD-ROM contains all Chapter 7 resources.

Use Glencoe's **Presentation Plus!** multimedia teacher tool to easily present dynamic lessons that visually excite your students. Using Microsoft PowerPoint® you can customize the presentations to create your own personalized lessons.

TEACHING TRANSPARENCIES

Graphic Organizer Transparency 5 L2

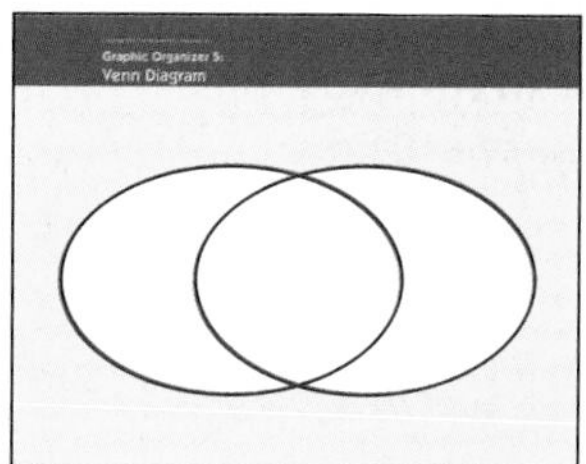

In-text Map Transparency L1

FOLDABLES™ Study Organizer

Dinah Zike's Foldables

Foldables are three-dimensional, interactive graphic organizers that help students practice basic writing skills, review key vocabulary terms, and identify main ideas. Additional chapter activities can be found in the ***Reading and Study Skills Foldables*** booklet.

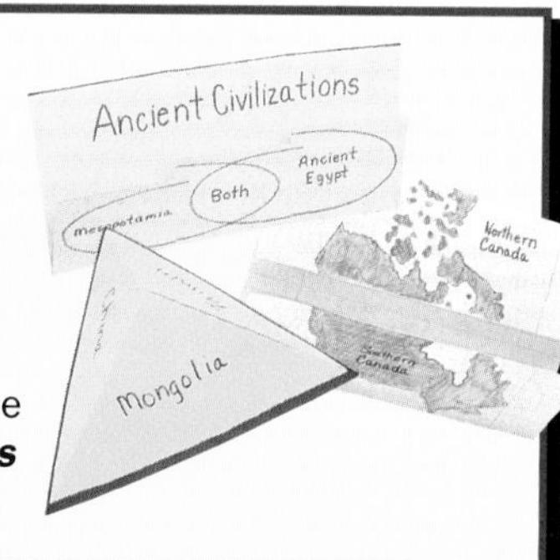

MAP AND GEOGRAPHY SKILLS

Chapter Map Activity L2

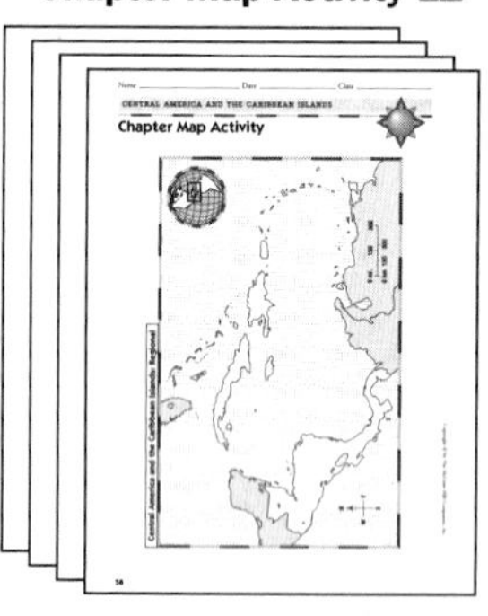

GeoLab Activity L2

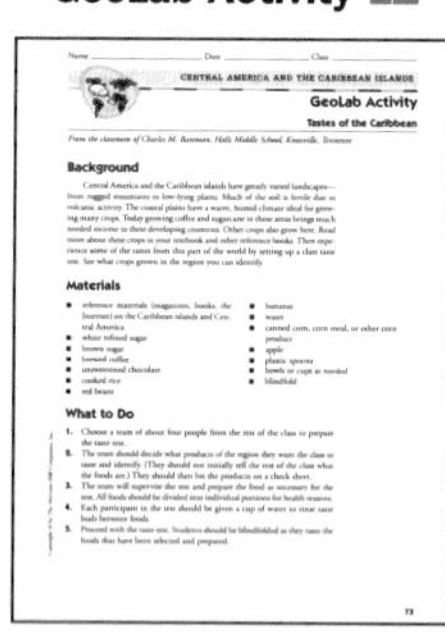

READING SUPPORT

Vocabulary Activity L1

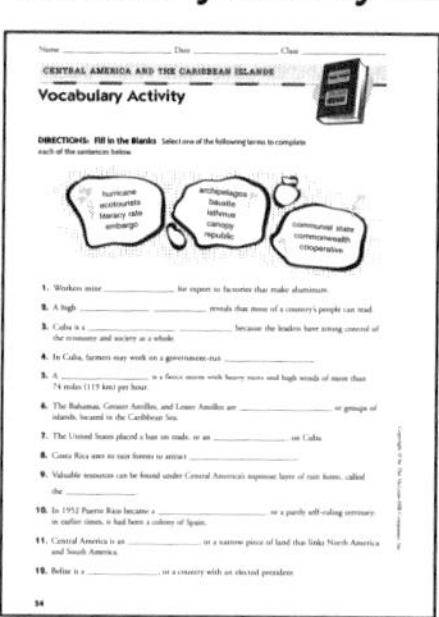

Workbook Activity L1

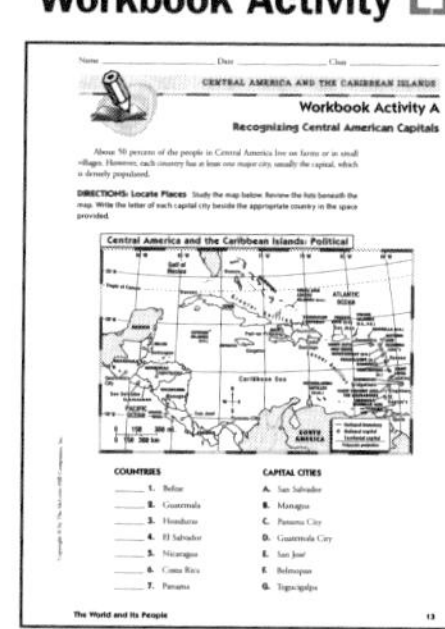

Reading and Writing Skills Activity L1/ELL

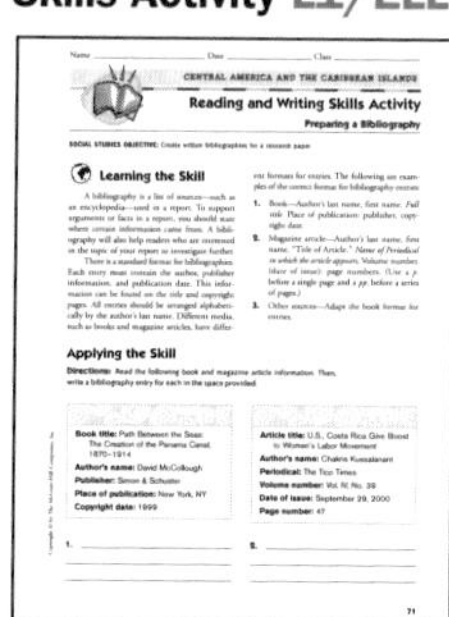

DIFFERENTIATED INSTRUCTION

Use these review and reinforcement materials to help less-proficient readers, English learners, and gifted and talented students.

Reteaching Activity L1

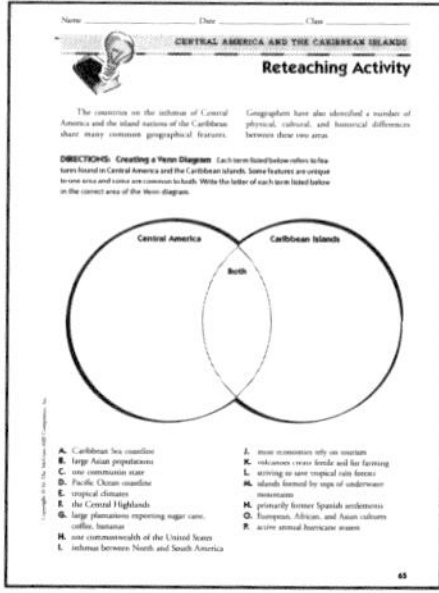

Chapter Skills Review L2

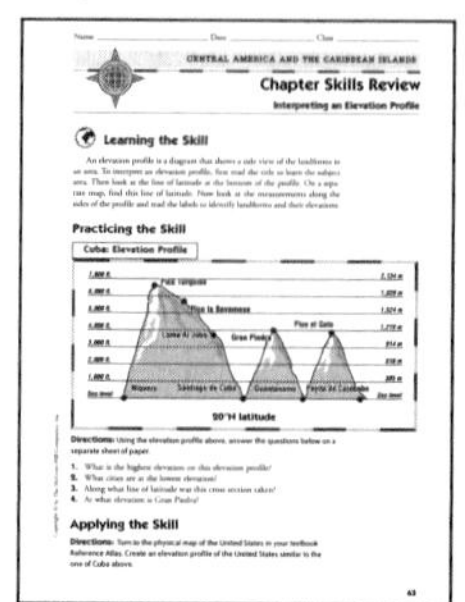

Cooperative Learning Activity L1/ELL

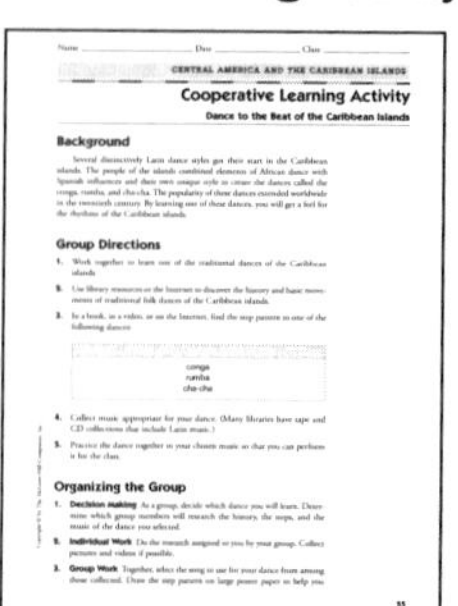

Enrichment Activity L3

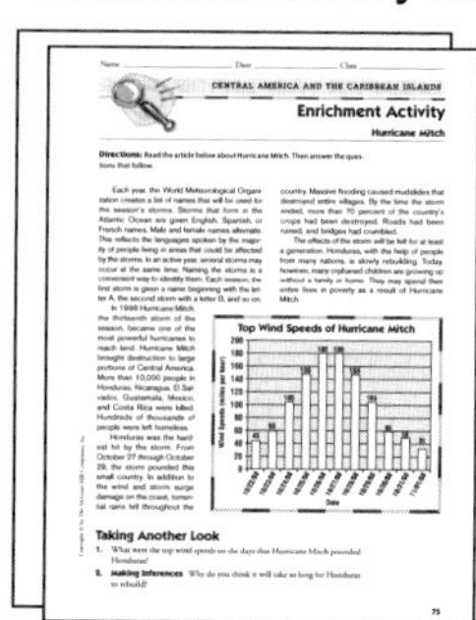

ASSESSMENT

Chapter Test, Form A L2

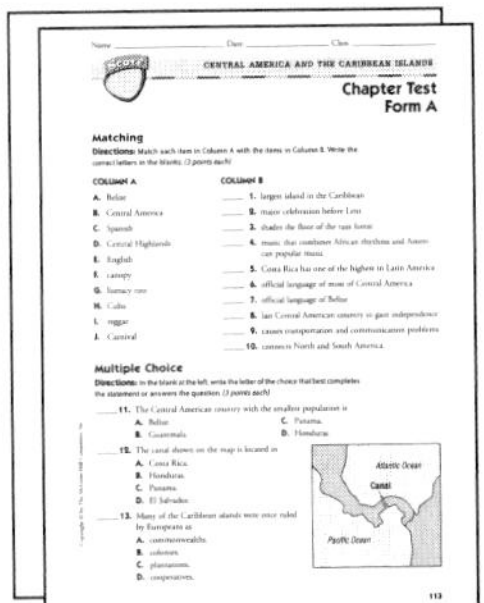

Chapter Test, Form B L2

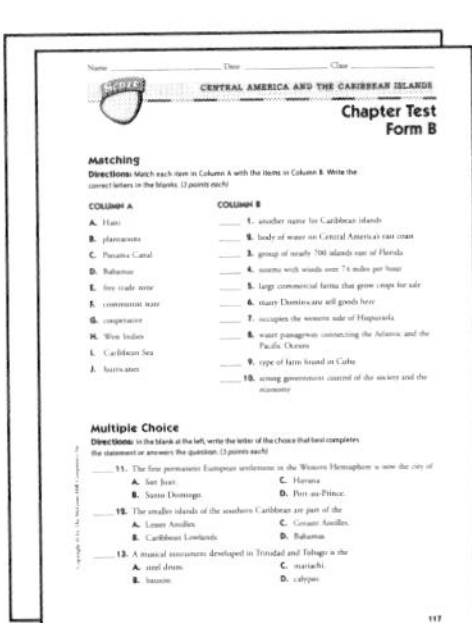

Performance Assessment Activity L1/ELL

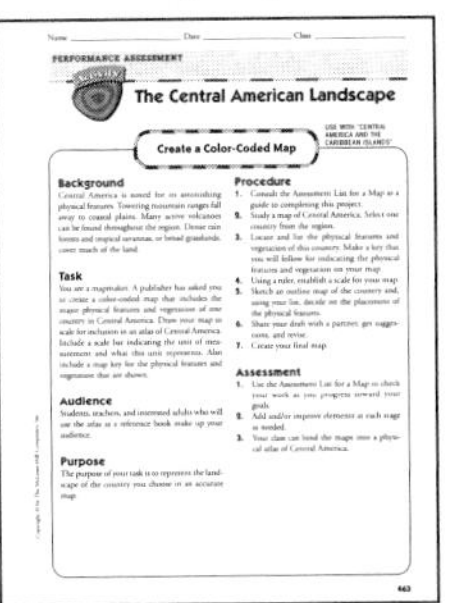

ExamView® Pro Testmaker CD-ROM

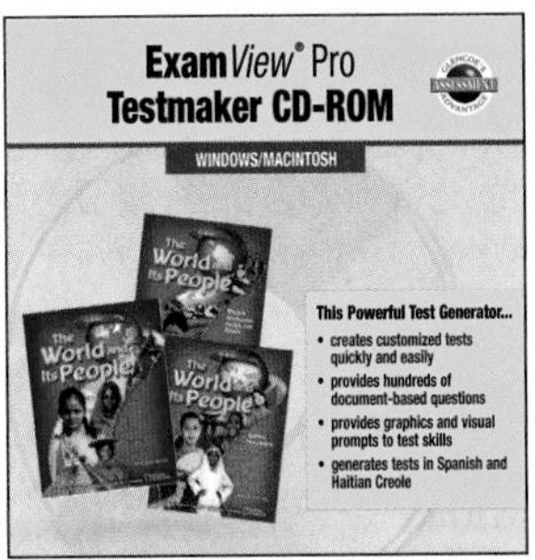

STANDARDIZED ASSESSMENT SKILLS

Critical Thinking Skills Activity L2

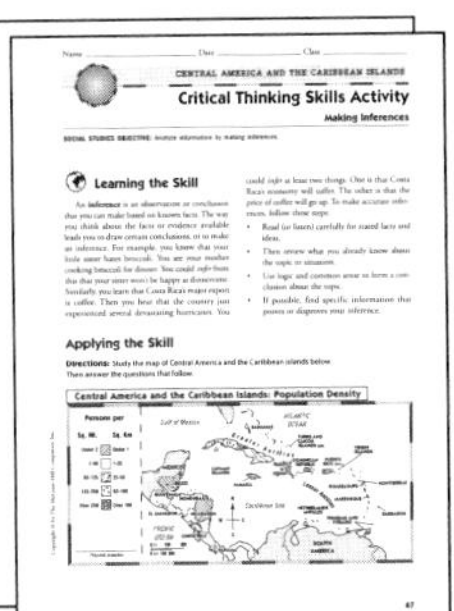

Map and Graph Skills Activity L2

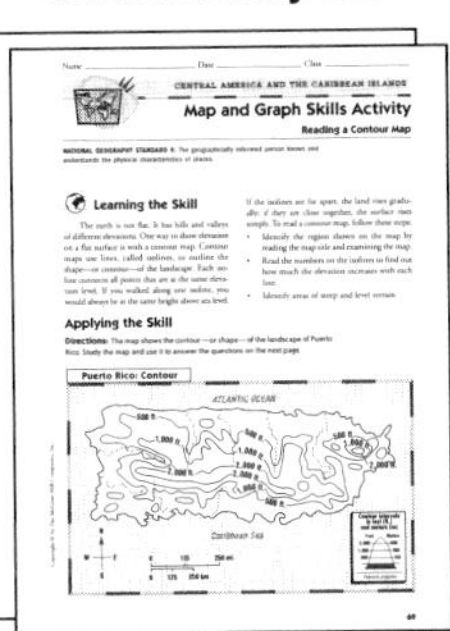

Standardized Test Skills Practice Workbook Activity L2

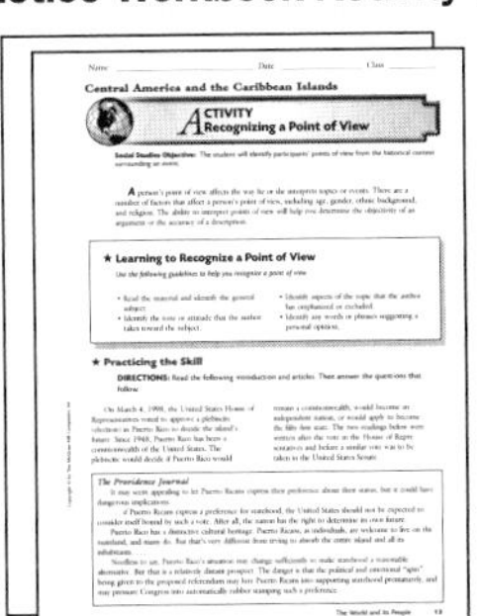

HOME INVOLVEMENT

Take-Home Review Activity L1

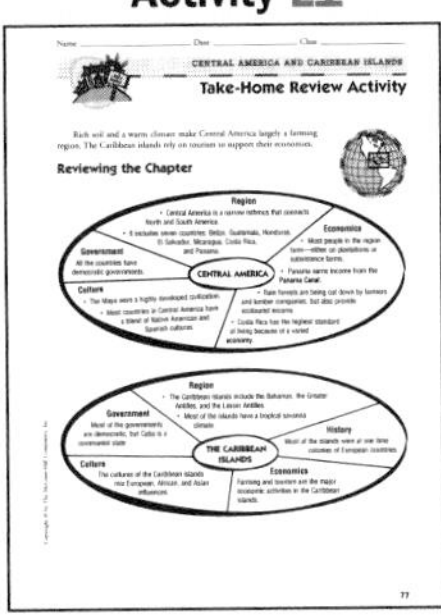

MULTIMEDIA

- National Geographic's The World and Its People
- MindJogger Videoquiz
- Vocabulary PuzzleMaker CD-ROM
- Interactive Tutor Self-Assessment CD-ROM
- ExamView® Pro Testmaker CD-ROM
- TeacherWorks CD-ROM
- StudentWorks CD-ROM
- Skillbuilder Interactive Workbook CD-ROM, Level 1
- Presentation Plus! CD-ROM
- Audio Program

SPANISH RESOURCES

The following Spanish language materials are available in the Spanish Resources binder:

- Spanish Summaries
- Spanish Vocabulary Activities
- Spanish Guided Reading Activities
- Spanish Quizzes and Tests
- Spanish Take-Home Review Activities
- Spanish Reteaching Activities

Meeting National Standards

Geography for Life

The following standards are covered in Chapter 7:

Section 1
- **EE2 Places and Regions: Standards 4, 5, 6**
- **EE3 Physical Systems: Standards 7, 8**
- **EE5 Environment and Society: Standards 14, 16**

Section 2
- **EE2 Places and Regions: Standards 4, 5, 6**
- **EE3 Physical Systems: Standards 7, 8**
- **EE5 Environment and Society: Standards 15, 16**

State and Local Objectives

___

___

___

Chapter 7 Planning Guide

SECTION RESOURCES		
Daily Objectives	**Reproducible Resources**	**Multimedia Resources**
Section 1 **Central America** **1.** Identify where Central America is and what nations make up this area. **2.** Describe the landforms and climate found in Central America. **3.** Explain the economy of Central America. **4.** Discuss the people and history of Central America's countries.	Reproducible Lesson Plan Daily Lecture and Discussion Notes Note-taking Guide Guided Reading Activity* Reading Essentials and Study Guide* Section Quiz*	Daily Focus Skills Transparency GeoQuiz Transparency In-text Map Transparency Vocabulary PuzzleMaker CD-ROM Interactive Tutor Self-Assessment CD-ROM ExamView® Pro Testmaker CD-ROM Presentation Plus! CD-ROM
Section 2 **Cultures of the Caribbean** **1.** Identify and compare the islands of the Caribbean. **2.** Describe the landforms and climates of the Caribbean islands. **3.** Explain the economic activities of the islands. **4.** Compare the cultures and history of the islands.	Reproducible Lesson Plan Daily Lecture and Discussion Notes Note-taking Guide Guided Reading Activity* Reading Essentials and Study Guide* Section Quiz*	Daily Focus Skills Transparency Vocabulary PuzzleMaker CD-ROM Interactive Tutor Self-Assessment CD-ROM ExamView® Pro Testmaker CD-ROM Presentation Plus! CD-ROM MindJogger Videoquiz

00:00 **Out of Time?** Assign the **Reading Essentials and Study Guide*** for this chapter.

*Also available in Spanish

KEY TO ABILITY LEVELS

Teaching strategies have been coded for varying learning styles and abilities.

L1 **BASIC** activities for all students
L2 **AVERAGE** activities for average to above-average students
L3 **CHALLENGING** activities for above-average students
ELL **ENGLISH LANGUAGE LEARNER** activities

KEY TO TEACHING RESOURCES

- Blackline Master
- CD-ROM
- Transparency
- Videocassette
- Block Scheduling
- DVD

Teacher to Teacher

Show Me the Money

Mary Ann Polve
Mesa High School
Mesa, Arizona

Gale Olp Ekiss
Powell Junior High School
Mesa, Arizona

You need a variety of foreign currency and coins for this activity. Inform students that they will be looking at a variety of money to find clues about the countries from which the money comes. Organize students into small groups and give each group a sample of coins and bills that you have collected. Students will examine the money to locate symbols and images. Then have them chart the information on a worksheet with the headings "Country of Origin," "Monetary Unit," "Year," "Watermarks or Authenticators," "People Pictured," "Buildings," "Natural Features," "Animals," "Symbols," and "Other." Have groups share their findings with the class. Finally, ask students to design the front and back of a bill for any country in this chapter.

Meeting Special Needs

In addition to the Differentiated Instruction strategies found in each section, the following resources are also suitable for your special needs students:

- ***ExamView® Pro Testmaker CD-ROM*** allows teachers to tailor tests by reducing answer choices.
- The ***Audio Program*** includes the entire narrative of the student edition so that less-proficient readers can listen to the words as they read them.
- The ***Reading Essentials and Study Guide*** provides the same content as the student edition but is written two grade levels below the textbook.
- ***Guided Reading Activities*** give less-proficient readers point-by-point instructions to increase comprehension as they read each textbook section.
- ***Enrichment Activities*** include a stimulating collection of readings and activities for gifted and talented students.

NATIONAL GEOGRAPHIC TEACHER'S CORNER

Index to National Geographic Magazine:

The following articles may be used for research relating to this chapter:

- "Cuba's Colonial Treasure," by A.R. Williams, October 1999.
- "Feast of the Tarpon," by David Doubilet, January 1996.
- "Treasure From the Silver Bank," by Tracy Bowden, July 1996.

National Geographic Society Products:

To order the following products for use with this chapter, call National Geographic Society at 1-800-368-2728:

- *Lost City of the Maya* (Video)
- *National Geographic Desk Reference* (Book)
- *National Geographic Atlas of the World, Seventh Edition* (Book)

NGS ONLINE

Access National Geographic's Web site for current events, activities, links, interactive features, and archives.
www.nationalgeographic.com

Find the latest coverage of geography in the news, atlas updates, cartographic activities with interactive maps, an online map store, and links at www.nationalgeographic.com/maps

SOCIAL STUDIES Online

Use our Web site for additional resources. All essential content is covered in the Student Edition.

You and your students can visit twip.glencoe.com, the Web site companion to *The World and Its People*. This innovative integration of electronic and print media offers your students a wealth of opportunities. The student text directs students to the Web site for the following options:

- Chapter Overviews
- Student Web Activities
- Self-Check Quizzes
- Textbook Updates

Answers are provided for you in the Web Activity Lesson Plan. Additional Web resources and Interactive Tutor puzzles are also available.

Introducing Chapter 7

Social Studies Online

Introduce students to chapter content and key terms by having them access Chapter Overview 7 at twip.glencoe.com

Chapter Objectives

1. Describe the physical and cultural geography of Central America.
2. Compare the major physical and cultural features of the Caribbean islands.

GLENCOE TECHNOLOGY

NATIONAL GEOGRAPHIC

The World and Its People Video Program

Chapter 7 Central America and the West Indies

The following segments enhance the study of this chapter:

- **Ancient Maya**
- **A Deadly Game**
- **Modern Maya**

MindJogger Videoquiz

Use MindJogger Videoquiz to preview the Chapter 7 content.

Both programs available in DVD and VHS

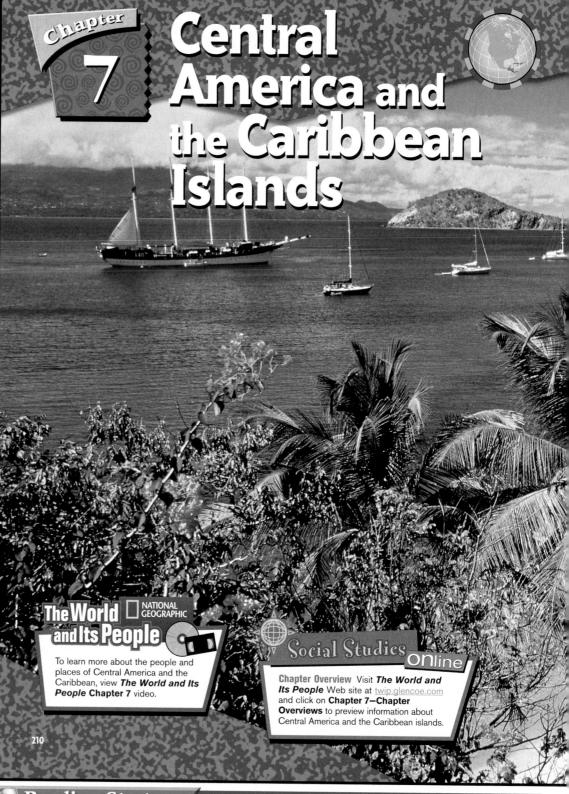

Chapter 7 Central America and the Caribbean Islands

The World and Its People NATIONAL GEOGRAPHIC

To learn more about the people and places of Central America and the Caribbean, view ***The World and Its People* Chapter 7** video.

Social Studies Online

Chapter Overview Visit ***The World and Its People*** Web site at twip.glencoe.com and click on **Chapter 7—Chapter Overviews** to preview information about Central America and the Caribbean islands.

210

Reading Strategy — Purpose for Reading

Anticipation Guides are a useful strategy to test student background knowledge (including stereotypes) and focus their investigations in a unit or lesson. On the board or on the overhead, brainstorm a list of items that students know (or think they know) about the islands in the Caribbean Sea. Have each student copy what he or she thinks are the most important 10 to 15 items. Have them decide whether they think each item is accurate or merely represents a stereotype seen in television or in movies. As students study the chapter, have them correct any stereotypes or incorrect information on their lists. L1

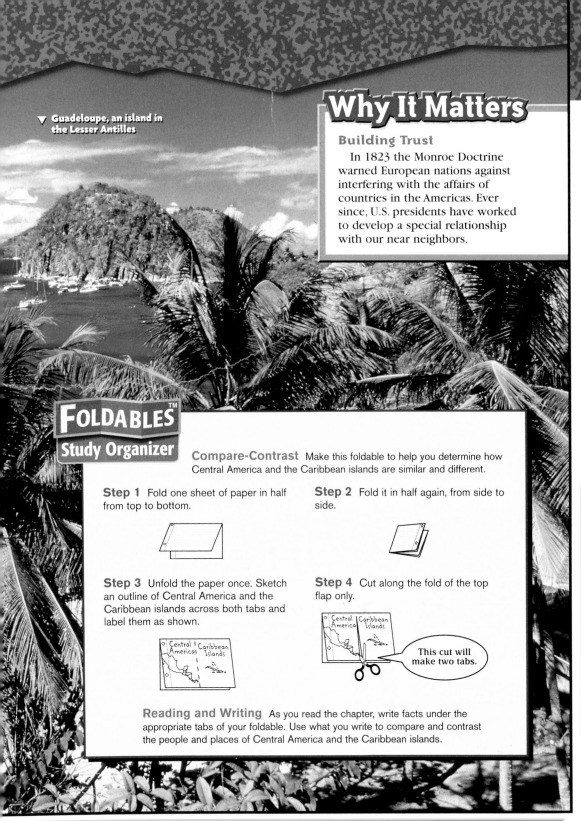

▼ Guadeloupe, an island in the Lesser Antilles

Why It Matters

Building Trust

In 1823 the Monroe Doctrine warned European nations against interfering with the affairs of countries in the Americas. Ever since, U.S. presidents have worked to develop a special relationship with our near neighbors.

FOLDABLES™ Study Organizer

Compare-Contrast Make this foldable to help you determine how Central America and the Caribbean islands are similar and different.

Step 1 Fold one sheet of paper in half from top to bottom.

Step 2 Fold it in half again, from side to side.

Step 3 Unfold the paper once. Sketch an outline of Central America and the Caribbean islands across both tabs and label them as shown.

Central America | Caribbean Islands

Step 4 Cut along the fold of the top flap only.

Central America | Caribbean Islands

This cut will make two tabs.

Reading and Writing As you read the chapter, write facts under the appropriate tabs of your foldable. Use what you write to compare and contrast the people and places of Central America and the Caribbean islands.

About the Photo

The Lesser Antilles, where Guadeloupe is located, extends from below Puerto Rico to Trinidad and Tobago. Unlike Central America, which was mostly colonized by Spain, the islands in this region were claimed by France, England, and the Netherlands. Today, some of the islands are independent, but many are still dependencies of their European colonizers. Although Guadeloupe has a popularly elected general council, the head of the government is a commissioner appointed by France. Citizens can vote in French elections and they are represented in the French Parliament.

FOLDABLES™ Study Organizer — Dinah Zike's Foldables

Purpose Students will make and use a foldable to help them organize the similarities and differences between Central America and the Caribbean islands. As students read the chapter and fill in information on their foldable, they analyze how the people and places of Central America and the islands of the Caribbean are similar and how they are different.

Have students complete the ***Reading and Study Skills Foldables*** activity for this chapter.

Why It Matters

Have students use outside sources and the Internet to research ways in which United States presidents became involved in the affairs of Central America and the Caribbean islands throughout history. Has the "special relationship" between the United States and its near neighbors always been a positive one? What is the relationship between the current United States president and our near neighbors?

Chapter 7

Section 1, pages 212–217

FOCUS

Section Objectives

1. Identify where Central America is and what nations make up this area.
2. Describe the landforms and climate found in Central America.
3. Explain the economy of Central America.
4. Discuss the people and history of Central America's countries.

BELLRINGER
Skillbuilder Activity

Project transparency and have students answer the question.

Daily Focus Skills Transparency

Reading a Bar Graph

LITERACY RATES IN CENTRAL AMERICA

Which country has the highest literacy rate in Central America?

A Belize
B Costa Rica
C Honduras
D Panama

Reading Preview

■ **Activating Prior Knowledge** Ask students what they know about hurricanes and their possible effect on an economy.

■ **Preteaching Vocabulary** Have students guess at the meaning of the word *ecotourist* from its prefix and root. Have them identify other words that begin with *eco-*. *(ecology, ecosphere, ecosystem)*

Guide to Reading

Main Idea

Central America is made up of seven nations that are home to a variety of peoples, exotic animals, and diverse landforms.

Terms to Know

- isthmus
- canopy
- ecotourist
- literacy rate
- republic
- parliamentary democracy

Reading Strategy

Create a chart like this one. List several countries in Central America, and write two key facts about each country.

Country	Key Facts

Section 1 Central America

NATIONAL GEOGRAPHIC Exploring Our World

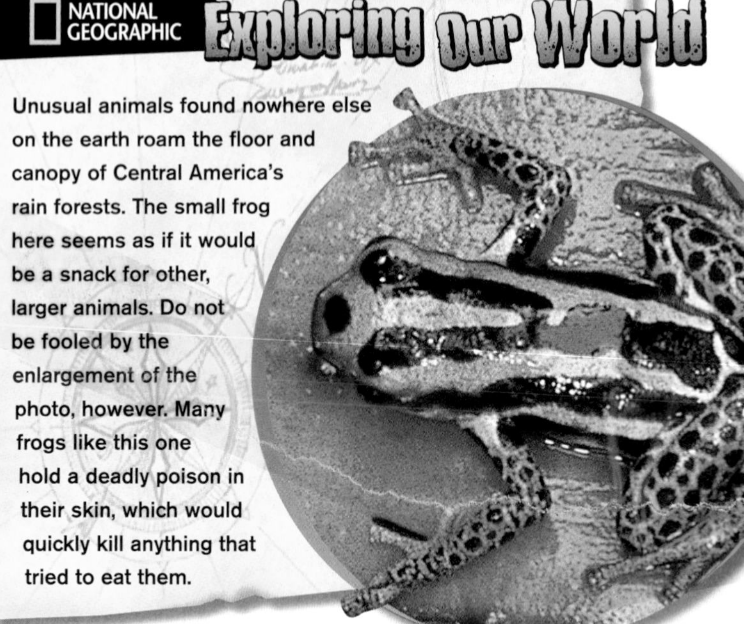

Unusual animals found nowhere else on the earth roam the floor and canopy of Central America's rain forests. The small frog here seems as if it would be a snack for other, larger animals. Do not be fooled by the enlargement of the photo, however. Many frogs like this one hold a deadly poison in their skin, which would quickly kill anything that tried to eat them.

Central America is an **isthmus,** or a narrow piece of land that links two larger areas of land—North America and South America. Most of the countries on the isthmus have two coastlines—one on the Pacific Ocean and one on the Caribbean Sea. This narrow region is actually part of North America. Seven countries make up Central America: **Belize, Guatemala, El Salvador, Honduras, Nicaragua, Costa Rica,** and **Panama.**

A Rugged Land

Like Mexico, Central America sits where plates in the earth's crust meet. The collision of these plates produces volcanoes and earthquakes in the region. The Central Highlands, which curve like a backbone through inland Central America, are actually a chain of volcanic mountains. Because of their ruggedness, the Central Highlands are difficult to cross. This causes serious problems for transportation and communication and has also kept many of the region's people isolated from one another. The volcanoes of the Central Highlands do bring some benefits to farmers, though. Volcanic material has made the soil very fertile.

Section Resources

Reproducible Masters

- Reproducible Lesson Plan
- Daily Lecture and Discussion Notes
- Note-taking Guide
- Guided Reading Activity
- Reading Essentials and Study Guide
- Section Quiz

Transparencies

- Daily Focus Skills Transparency
- GeoQuiz Transparency
- In-text Map Transparency

Multimedia

- Vocabulary PuzzleMaker CD-ROM
- Interactive Tutor Self-Assessment CD-ROM
- Presentation Plus! CD-ROM
- ExamView® Pro Testmaker CD-ROM

Central America is mostly tropical, although the mountains remain cool. Lowlands along the Caribbean side receive about 100 inches (254 cm) of rain year-round. Lowlands along the Pacific, however, are drier from December through April. Cooling breezes from the Caribbean Sea can become deadly hurricanes during the summer and fall. Remember that hurricanes are fierce storms with heavy rains and high winds of more than 74 miles (119 km) per hour.

Reading Check How have the volcanoes in Central America been helpful?

Central American Economies

The economies of the Central American countries depend on farming and harvesting wood from their rain forests. Central America has two kinds of farms. Wealthy people and companies own plantations, which, as you learned in Chapter 6, are commercial farms that grow crops for sale. Major crops include coffee, bananas, cotton, and sugarcane. Plantations export their harvest to the United States and other parts of the world. Farmers in Guatemala and Costa Rica also grow flowers and ornamental plants for export.

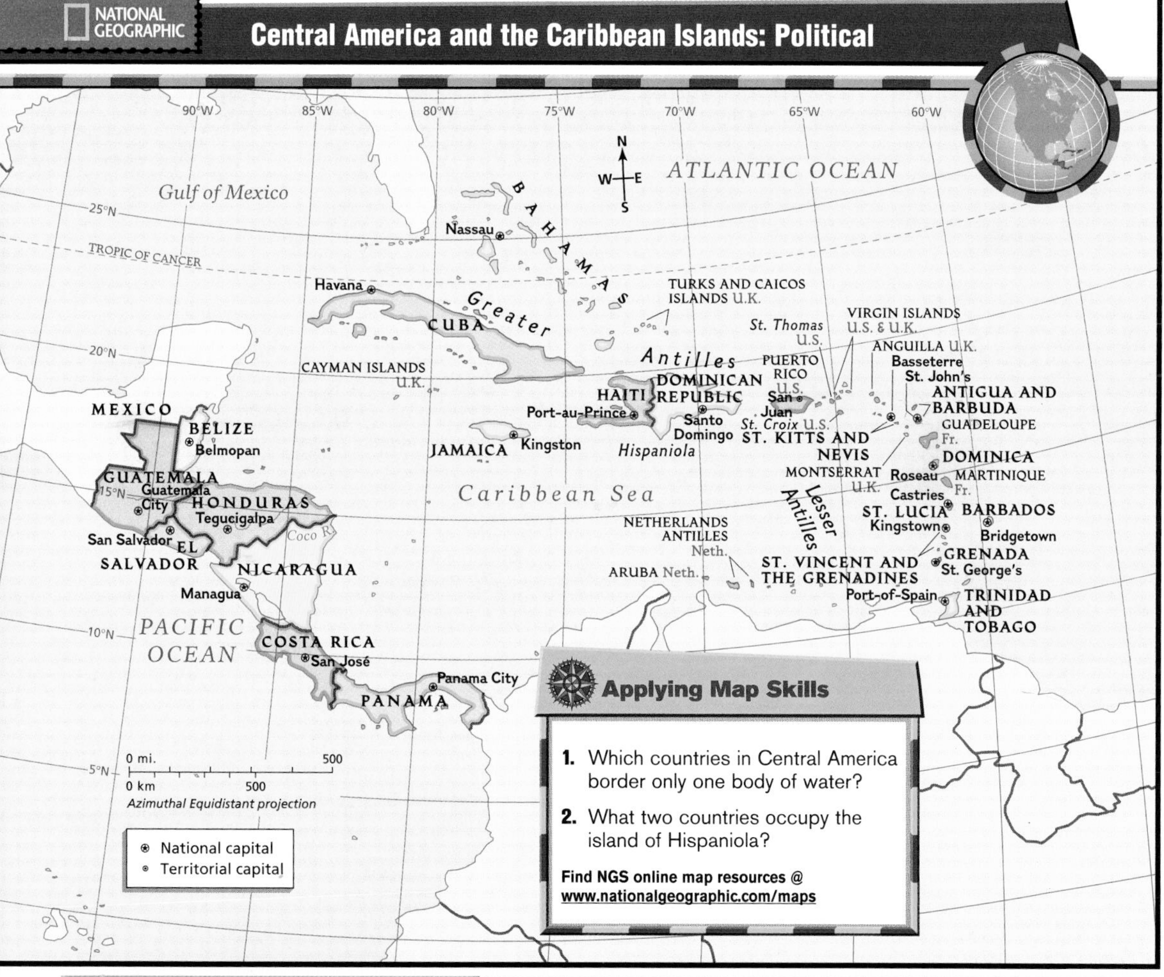

Applying Map Skills

1. Which countries in Central America border only one body of water?
2. What two countries occupy the island of Hispaniola?

Find NGS online map resources @ www.nationalgeographic.com/maps

Reading Strategy — Reading the Text

Categorizing Information Have students construct a classroom chart comparing the seven countries of Central America. Ask students to suggest topics for comparison. These might include physical geography, economic activities, history, government, or culture. Use the completed chart to prepare national profiles of the seven countries. L1

Use the ***Reading Skills Handbook*** *for more reading strategies.*

TEACH

Organizing Information
Have each student make up one riddle for each of the countries of Central America. Each riddle must be specific enough so that the country can be identified. Have students share and solve their riddles. L1

Daily Lecture and Discussion Notes

CENTRAL AMERICA AND THE CARIBBEAN ISLANDS

Daily Lecture and Discussion Notes
Central America

Did You Know? There are only a few places in the world where you can drive up to the edge of an active volcanic crater, and Poas National Park in Costa Rica is one of them. The eruption cycle of the Poas volcano is about 40 years, and the last eruption was in 1978. During heightened volcanic activity, the park may be closed.

I. A Rugged Land

A. Central America includes the countries of Belize, Guatemala, El Salvador, Honduras, Nicaragua, Costa Rica, and Panama.

B. Central America is an **isthmus**, or narrow piece of land that links two larger ... South America.

Reading Check Answer

Volcanic material has broken down to create fertile soil.

Applying Map Skills

Answers

1. El Salvador, Belize
2. Haiti, Dominican Republic

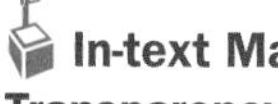

In-text Map Transparency Activity Have students explain how to estimate distance using the map scale. Then have a volunteer use the overhead transparency to find the shortest distance between Cuba and the southern tip of Florida. *(about 90 miles, or 145 km)*

Note-taking tip

Suggest that students write two questions and answers for each of the subheadings in the section. In writing them, they should aim to identify the main ideas of the subsections.

L1/ELL

Guided Reading Activity

Name ____________ Date ____________ Class ____________

CENTRAL AMERICA AND THE CARIBBEAN ISLANDS

Guided Reading Activity 1

Central America

DIRECTIONS: Answering Questions Reading the section and answering the questions below will help you learn more about Central America. Refer to your textbook to write answers to the questions.

1. What seven countries make up Central America?

2. What are the problems and benefits of the Central Highlands?

...does the economy of Central America depend?

Applying Map Skills

Answers

1. Belize, Guatemala, El Salvador, Honduras, Nicaragua, and Panama
2. growing sugarcane/subsistence farming

Skills Practice

What is the primary resource of Jamaica? *(bauxite)*

Many farms in Central America are not plantations but subsistence farms. These are small plots of land where poor farmers grow only enough food to feed their families. Subsistence farmers typically raise livestock and grow corn, beans, and rice.

Rain Forests Beneath Central America's green **canopy,** or topmost layer of the rain forest that shades the forest floor, lie many treasures. Ancient ruins of past empires can be found as well as valuable resources. The dense forests offer expensive woods—mahogany and rosewood, for example. Unusual animal and plant species also thrive here. Scientists research the plants to develop new medicines.

Both local and foreign-owned companies have set up large-scale operations in the rain forests. Lumber companies cut down and export the valuable trees. Other companies and local farmers also cut or burn the trees to clear land for farming. Without trees to hold the soil in place, rains wash the soil and its nutrients away. As a result, the land soon becomes poor. The businesses and farmers then move on, clearing trees from another piece of land.

Many Central Americans worry about the rapid destruction of the rain forests. Some countries are responding to this crisis by helping workers replant cleared areas. Costa Rica has set aside one-fourth of its

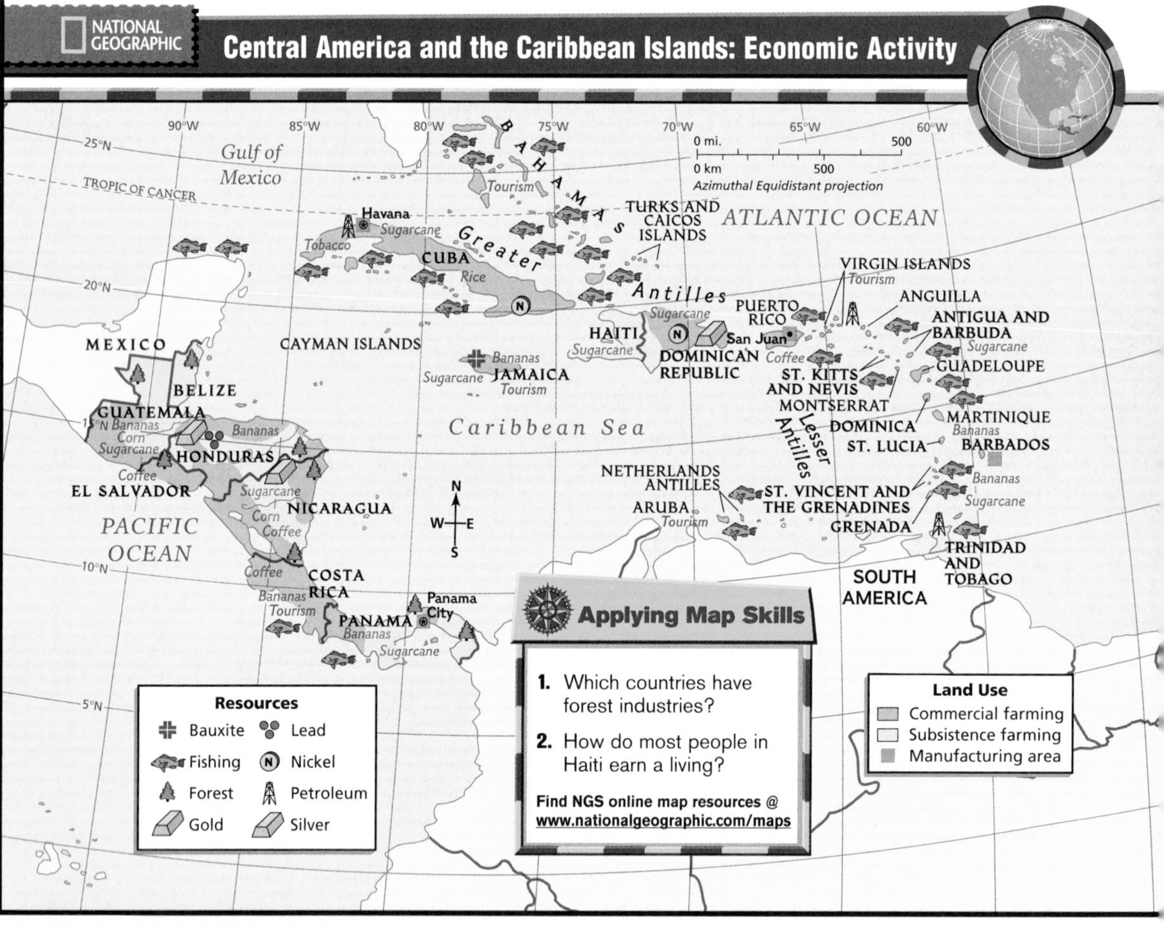

Differentiated Instruction

Meeting Special Needs: English Learners You can help learners keep track of the characteristics of the different countries of Central America by providing an outline map of the region. Have them write in the names and capitals of each country. Then suggest they annotate the map with information about the physical geography, climate, economy, and people, color coding their annotations by using a different color for each class of information (such as red for landforms, blue for climate, and so on). Students can use their completed maps as a study aid.

Refer to *Inclusion for the Middle School Social Studies Classroom Strategies and Activities* in the TCR.

forests as national parks. It uses the rain forests to attract **ecotourists,** or people who travel to other countries to enjoy natural wonders.

Industry Missing from the skylines of most major Central American cities are the smokestacks of industry. The few industries that exist generally focus on food processing. In Guatemala, Honduras, and Nicaragua, some factories produce clothing for export.

Guatemala, which has some oil reserves, exports crude oil. Costa Rica produces computer chips, other electronic goods, and medicines. With its varied economy, Costa Rica enjoys one of the highest standards of living in Latin America. It also has one of the highest **literacy rates,** or percentage of people who can read and write.

Tourism is of growing importance in Central America. If you like bird-watching, Costa Rica is the place to visit. The country has about 850 different kinds of birds. Guatemala and Honduras also draw many tourists to the magnificent ruins of their ancient Mayan culture.

The Panama Canal The economy in Panama—just like the other countries of Central America—is based on farming. Panama also earns money from its canal, however. The Panama Canal stretches across the narrow Isthmus of Panama. Ships pay a fee to use the canal to shorten travel time between the Atlantic and Pacific Oceans. Turn to page 218 to see how the canal works.

The United States built the canal and owned it for more than 80 years. Panama was given final control of the canal on December 31, 1999. Panama hopes to use this waterway to build its economy. Nearly half of Panama's 3 million people live and work in the canal area.

✓Reading Check What are the major crops grown on Central America's plantations?

Central Americans—Then and Now

Native Americans settled Central America thousands of years ago. The Olmecs were the first civilization in the area, from about 1200 B.C. to 400 B.C. The Maya flourished in the rain forests of the north from about A.D. 250 to 900. Look at the Native American civilizations map on

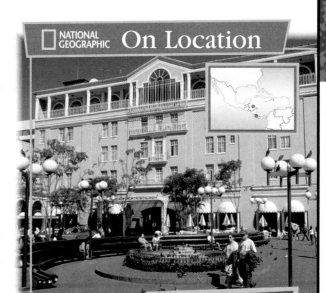

NATIONAL GEOGRAPHIC On Location

Economic Highs and Lows

San José, Costa Rica's capital (above), has shopping malls and fast-food chains like many North American cities. In 1998 Hurricane Mitch caused massive mudslides that buried whole villages and destroyed crops in Honduras (left).

Issues During what seasons do hurricanes strike Central America?

Chapter 7

Section 1, pages 212–217

More About the Photos

Hurricane Mitch The devastation wrought by Hurricane Mitch was extreme. The storm struck almost every country in the region (Costa Rica and Panama were spared) and left in its wake about 11,000 dead, about 2 million people without their homes, and about $10 billion in damages. Only the fierce "Great Hurricane" of 1780, which killed 22,000, was worse.

Caption Answer in the summer and fall

Travel Guide

A blending of Native American, African, and European—especially Spanish—cultures adds to the richness of Central American traditions. In each country, corn, beans, and rice are mixed with spices for a tasty variety of dishes. The music heard in these countries shares certain traits—rhythms, for instance—yet each country has its unique musical styles.

✓ Reading Check Answer

coffee, bananas, cotton, sugarcane

3 ASSESS

Assign Section 1 Assessment as homework or an in-class activity.

Have students use the Interactive Tutor Self-Assessment CD-ROM to review Section 1.

Team-Teaching Activity

Science Invite the science teacher to class to discuss the ecology of the rain forest. Ask the teacher to emphasize the biodiversity of rain forest flora and fauna, the fragility of this ecosystem, and why it is important to humans. Afterwards, have students create diagrams that describe and explain the physical processes that produce the fertile soil and the timber that grows in the rain forest. What happens if these processes are stopped due to deforestation? L2

EE3 Physical Systems: Standard 8

Measure student knowledge of physical features.

GeoQuiz Transparency

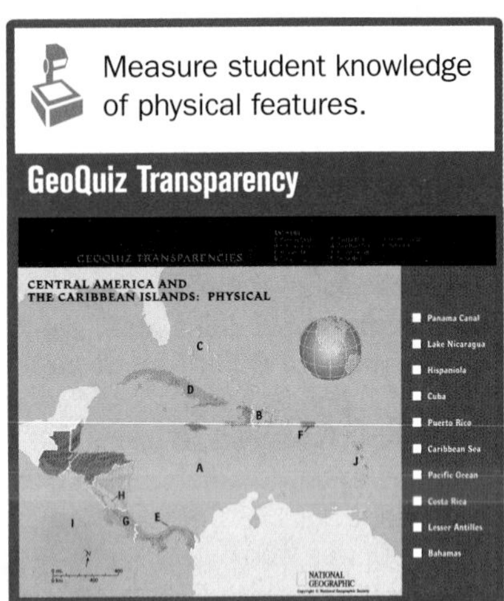

Building Skills

Research and Debate Have students research the Panama Canal treaties of 1977. Direct students to pay close attention to opinions that were for and against the transfer of control of the canal to Panama. Have volunteers debate the issue. Then poll the class to determine which viewpoint students favor.

L2

Section Quiz

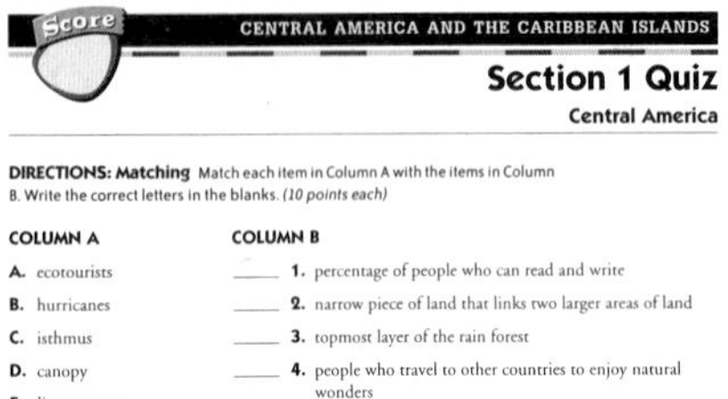

Name ______ Date ______ Class ______

CENTRAL AMERICA AND THE CARIBBEAN ISLANDS

Section 1 Quiz

Central America

DIRECTIONS: Matching Match each item in Column A with the items in Column B. Write the correct letters in the blanks. *(10 points each)*

COLUMN A	COLUMN B
A. ecotourists	____ 1. percentage of people who can read and write
B. hurricanes	____ 2. narrow piece of land that links two larger areas of land
C. isthmus	____ 3. topmost layer of the rain forest
D. canopy	____ 4. people who travel to other countries to enjoy natural wonders
E. literacy rate	____ 5. fierce storms with high winds

What a Catch!

The deep, blue waters of Lake Nicaragua are home to the world's only freshwater sharks and swordfish. Now the lake holds one less swordfish. Amadeo Robelo, who lives in Granada, Nicaragua, just spent three hours battling the powerful fish. Amadeo enjoys fishing with his father on weekends. His father wants Amadeo to become part of Nicaragua's middle class—something new in a region where you are either one of the few with wealth or one of the many who live in poverty.

page 198. In **Tikal** (tee•KAHL), Guatemala, and **Copán** (koh•PAHN), Honduras, the Maya created impressive temples and sculptures. Before Columbus arrived, Tikal was the site of the highest structure in the Americas, a 212-foot (64.6-m) temple rising from the floor of the rain forest. The Maya were a highly developed civilization. Their religion focused on the careful study of time and the stars, astronomy, and mathematics. The Maya developed a calendar and kept records on stone slabs. Then the Maya mysteriously left their cities. Many of their descendants still live in the area today.

In the 1500s, Spaniards established settlements in Central America. For the next 300 years, Spanish landowners forced Native Americans to work on plantations. The two cultures gradually blended. Native Americans started to speak the Spanish language and follow the Roman Catholic faith. Native Americans taught the Spanish about local plants for medicines and how to trap animals for food and hides.

Most Central American countries gained independence from Spain by 1821. The two exceptions are Panama and Belize. Panama was part of the South American country of Colombia for decades. In 1903 the United States helped Panama win its independence in exchange for the right to build the Panama Canal. Belize, a British colony until 1981, was the last Central American country to gain independence.

After Independence Most Central American countries faced constant conflict after they became independent. A small number of people in each country held most of the wealth and power. Rebel movements arose as poor farmers fought for changes that would give them land and better lives. Civil wars raged in Nicaragua, El Salvador, and Guatemala as recently as the 1980s and 1990s.

In Guatemala from 1960 to 1996, government military forces fought rebel groups living in the highlands. About 150,000 people died, and the civil war severely weakened Guatemala's economy. Tens of thousands of Guatemalans left the country to look for work in the United States.

In contrast, Costa Ricans have enjoyed peace. A stable democratic government rules, and the country has avoided conflict for most of its history. As a result of these peaceful relations, the country has no army—only a police force to maintain law and order.

Today each country in Central America has a democratic government, with voters choosing government officials. Six countries are also **republics,** with elected presidents as head of the government. Belize is a British-style **parliamentary democracy,** in which an elected legislature chooses a prime minister to head the government.

Daily Life Nearly 40 million people live in Central America. About one-third of this number live in Guatemala, the most heavily populated country in the region. In contrast, only about 300,000 people live in Belize, the region's least populous country. Spanish is the official language

216 CHAPTER 7

Reading Strategy — Reading the Text

Sequencing Organize students into seven groups and assign one of the countries of Central America to each group. Instruct groups to use the text and other references to find out their assigned country's political history. They should choose five or more important events to share with the class. Then have groups use these events to create annotated time lines. Call on groups to display and discuss their time lines. L1

*Use the **Reading Skills Handbook** for more reading strategies.*

throughout the region, except for English-speaking Belize. Many Central Americans also speak Native American languages, such as Mayan. Guatemala's population, for instance, is largely Native American and has more than 20 different Native American languages. Most Central Americans follow the Roman Catholic religion.

About 50 percent of all Central Americans live on farms or in small villages. At least one major city, usually the capital, is densely populated in each country. Guatemala's capital, **Guatemala City,** ranks with **San José,** Costa Rica, as one of the most populous cities in Central America. People living in urban areas hold manufacturing or service industry jobs, or they work on farms outside the cities. Those living in coastal areas may harvest shrimp, lobster, and other seafood to sell in city markets or for export.

Whether rural or urban, most people enjoy a major celebration called Carnival. This festival comes before Lent, a solemn period of prayer and soul-searching before the Christian celebration of Easter. During Carnival—and at other times—bands play salsa, a mixture of Latin American popular music, jazz, and rock. Do you like baseball? It is a national sport in Nicaragua and is very popular in Panama too. Most people throughout the region also enjoy *fútbol,* or soccer.

✓ Reading Check **Why is the government of Belize different from that of other countries in Central America?**

Section 1 Assessment

Defining Terms

1. Define isthmus, canopy, ecotourist, literacy rate, republic, parliamentary democracy.

Recalling Facts

2. Economics What is the difference between plantation and subsistence farming?

3. Culture What are the major religion and language of Central America?

4. Place Which country in Central America is the most heavily populated? The most sparsely populated?

Critical Thinking

5. Making Comparisons How have the differences in government stability affected the citizens of Guatemala and Costa Rica in the past and today?

6. Analyzing Cause and Effect Explain why rain forest soil does not keep its nutrients long after trees are cut down.

Graphic Organizer

7. Organizing Information Create a diagram like this one. On the lines, list the major products and industries of Central America.

Applying Social Studies Skills

8. Analyzing Maps Refer to the political map on page 213. Which countries of Central America border Mexico? Which border the Pacific Ocean?

Chapter 7

Section 1, pages 212–217

L1/ELL

Reading Essentials and Study Guide

Name ______ Date ______ Class ______

CENTRAL AMERICA AND THE CARIBBEAN ISLANDS

Reading Essentials and Study Guide 1

Central America

Key Terms

isthmus narrow piece of land that links two larger areas of land
canopy top layer of the rain forest that shades the forest floor
ecotourist person who travels to other countries to enjoy natural wonders
literacy rate percentage of people who can read and write
republic country with an elected president as head of the government
parliamentary democracy form of government in which an elected legislature chooses a prime minister to head the government

Reteach

Have students work in pairs to review the content of the section. Partners should take turns asking and answering questions based on the section text and maps.

✓ Reading Check Answer

Since it was once a British colony, and not a Spanish one, Belize has a British-style government.

Enrich

Have students research ecotourism or plantation farming in Central America. Have them present their findings in a report.

Close

Reading Strategy

Writing a Paragraph Have students write a paragraph comparing daily life in Central America with that in the United States.

Section 1 Assessment

1. The terms are defined in the Glossary.
2. Plantations: owned by wealthy people and companies, grow crops for sale; subsistence farms: poor farmers grow only enough to feed their families.
3. Roman Catholicism, Spanish
4. Guatemala; Belize
5. Civil war in Guatemala has weakened the economy, causing many people to seek work in the United States. Stability in Costa Rica has provided peace for its people.
6. Trees hold soil in place. Without trees, rains wash away soil and its nutrients.
7. Coffee, bananas, cotton, sugarcane, flowers, ornamental plants, clothing, oil, computer chips, medicine
8. Guatemala, Belize; Guatemala, El Salvador, Honduras, Nicaragua, Costa Rica, Panama

Making Connections

ART | SCIENCE | CULTURE | TECHNOLOGY

TEACH

Ask students what they know about canals. Use a map to show where the Panama Canal is and ask students to explain why this structure would be beneficial to shipping. L1

More About Panama Canal

Many people in the United States favored building the canal across Nicaragua, not Panama. Philippe Bunau-Varilla, a Panamanian who had invested in the French project, helped change their minds. Before the final vote, each senator received an envelope sent by Bunau-Varilla. The envelopes contained a Nicaraguan stamp that showed a volcano in Nicaragua in mid-eruption. The implication—that the volcano might destroy the canal—won the route for Panama.

Interdisciplinary Connections

Science Dr. Walter Reed had proved that mosquitoes carried yellow fever. Dr. William Gorgas was in charge of removing the threat of the mosquito-borne diseases in the canal. His work was so successful that yellow fever was completely wiped out of the isthmus of Panama in 1905.

The Panama Canal Locks

Before the Panama Canal was built, ships had to sail around the southern tip of South America to go from the Atlantic Ocean to the Pacific Ocean and vice versa. The canal provides a shortcut that reduces that trip by about 7,000 miles (11,270 km).

Digging the Canal

The first attempts to build a canal across Panama were begun in 1881 by a private French company. Huge expenses, poor planning, and the effects of diseases such as malaria and yellow fever stopped construction. In 1904 the United States government took over. Doctors had recently learned that bites from infected mosquitoes caused malaria and yellow fever. Workers drained swamps and cleared brush to remove the mosquitoes' breeding grounds. Then the digging began. The canal's course ran through hills of soft volcanic soil. Massive landslides regularly occurred before the 50-mile (80-km) canal was completed in 1914.

An Engineering Masterpiece

To move ships through the canal, engineers designed three sets of locks—the largest concrete structures on the earth. They allow ships to move from one water level to another by changing the amount of water in the locks. Together, the locks can raise or lower ships about 85 feet (26 m)—the height of a seven-story building. The diagram below shows you how these locks work.

Making the Connection

1. Why was a canal through Panama desirable?
2. What function do locks perform?
3. **Understanding Cause and Effect** How did medical advances affect the building of the Panama Canal?

Making the Connection

1. to cut travel time between the Atlantic and Pacific Oceans
2. Locks allow ships to move from one water level to another by changing the amount of water in the locks, thereby raising or lowering the ships.
3. The impact of diseases such as malaria and yellow fever stopped construction, and the curing and prevention of these diseases spurred construction.

Section 2 Cultures of the Caribbean

Guide to Reading

Main Idea

The Caribbean islands rely on tourism to support their economies.

Terms to Know

- archipelago
- bauxite
- communist state
- cooperative
- embargo
- free trade zone
- commonwealth

Reading Strategy

Create a diagram like this one. In the outer part of each oval, list a country in the Caribbean and features that are specific to it. Where the ovals overlap, list features that are true of both countries.

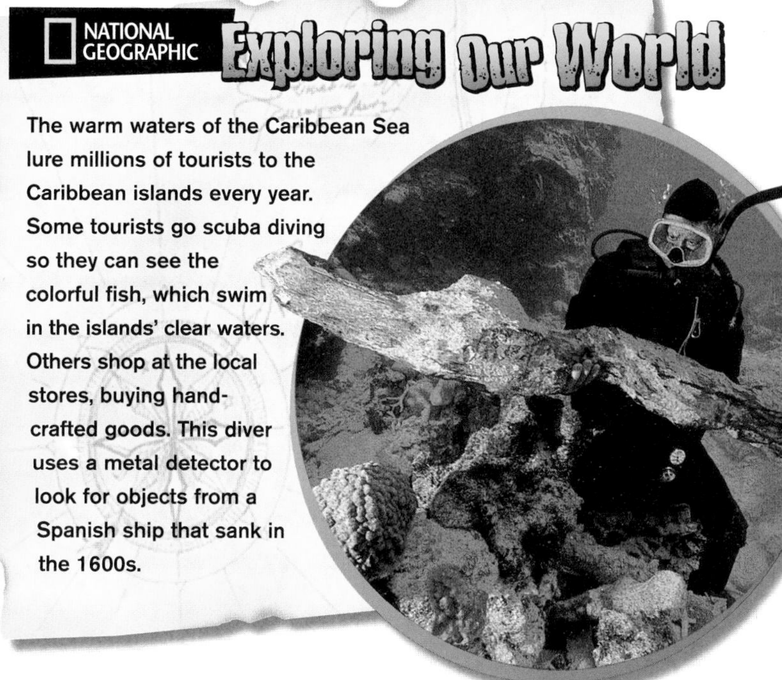

The warm waters of the Caribbean Sea lure millions of tourists to the Caribbean islands every year. Some tourists go scuba diving so they can see the colorful fish, which swim in the islands' clear waters. Others shop at the local stores, buying handcrafted goods. This diver uses a metal detector to look for objects from a Spanish ship that sank in the 1600s.

Several **archipelagos** (AHR•kuh•PEH•luh•GOHS), or groups of islands, dot the **Caribbean Sea.** East of Florida are the **Bahamas,** an archipelago of nearly 700 islands. South of Florida you find the **Greater Antilles.** This group includes the large islands of **Cuba, Jamaica, Hispaniola,** and **Puerto Rico.** To the southeast are smaller islands called the **Lesser Antilles.**

Mountaintop Islands

Many of the Caribbean islands (also known as the **West Indies**) are the tops of an underwater chain of mountains formed by volcanoes. A typical volcanic island has central highlands ringed by coastal plains. The volcanic soil in the highlands is rich. Other islands are limestone mountains that have been pushed up from the ocean floor by pressures under the earth's crust. Limestone islands are generally flatter than volcanic islands and have sandy soil that is not good for farming.

Section Resources

Reproducible Masters

- Reproducible Lesson Plan
- Daily Lecture and Discussion Notes
- Note-taking Guide
- Guided Reading Activity
- Reading Essentials and Study Guide
- Section Quiz

Transparencies

- Daily Focus Skills Transparency

Multimedia

- Vocabulary PuzzleMaker CD-ROM
- Interactive Tutor Self-Assessment CD-ROM
- Presentation Plus! CD-ROM
- ExamView® Pro Testmaker CD-ROM
- MindJogger Videoquiz

1 Focus

Section Objectives

1. Identify and compare the islands of the Caribbean.
2. Describe the landforms and climates of the Caribbean islands.
3. Explain the economic activities of the islands.
4. Compare the cultures and history of the islands.

BELLRINGER Skillbuilder Activity

Project transparency and have students answer the question.

Daily Focus Skills Transparency

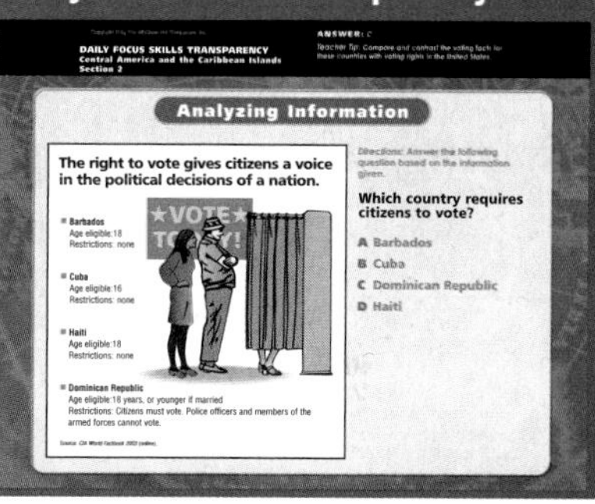

Reading Preview

- **Activating Prior Knowledge** Ask students to identify the citizenship of people born in Puerto Rico. *(They are citizens of the United States.)*
- **Preteaching Vocabulary** Have students try to determine the meaning of *cooperative* from its root *(cooperate)* and of *commonwealth* from the elements making up this compound *(common* and *wealth).*

TEACH

Synthesizing Information After students have read the section, organize them into two teams to take a quiz. Offer the first team a clue that will help them identify a Caribbean island country. If the team cannot answer correctly, offer a second clue to the second team. If that team cannot answer correctly, give a third clue and invite either team to answer. L1

Reading Check Answer

The islands are either mountains made by volcanoes or mountains composed of limestone that have been pushed up from the ocean floor.

Daily Lecture and Discussion Notes

CENTRAL AMERICA AND THE CARIBBEAN ISLANDS

Daily Lecture and Discussion Notes

Cultures of the Caribbean

The Caribbean now comprises more than 30 countries with a regional population of approximately 33 million people scattered over 2,000 square miles of ocean.

I. Mountaintop Islands

A. Three **archipelagos,** or groups of islands, make up the Caribbean: the Bahamas, the Greater Antilles (Cuba, Jamaica, Hispaniola, and Puerto Rico), and the Lesser Antilles.

B. Many Caribbean islands are the tops of an underwater chain of mountains ... by volcanoes. A typical volcanic island has central highlands with rich ... plains. Other islands are actually limestone ...

Reading Check Answer

tourism

Climate Most of the Caribbean islands have a fairly constant tropical savanna climate. Sea and wind, more than elevation, affect the climate here. Northeast breezes sweep across the Caribbean Sea and become the temperature of the cooler water beneath them. When the winds blow onshore, they keep temperatures pleasant. For half the year, however, hurricanes threaten the islands.

Reading Check What formed the Caribbean islands?

The Caribbean Economy

Tourism and farming are the most important economic activities in the Caribbean. The sunny climate and beautiful beaches attract millions of tourists each year. Tourism is the region's major industry. Airlines and cruise ships make regular stops at different islands.

Wealthy landowners grow sugarcane, bananas, coffee, and tobacco for export. Many laborers work on the plantations that grow these commercial crops. Some areas are used for subsistence farming. People may own or rent small plots of land. They grow rice and beans, which are basic parts of the diet in this region. They also grow fruits and vegetables.

Some countries in the Caribbean islands face an economic danger by depending on one commercial crop. If the crop fails, no income is earned. If too much of the crop is produced worldwide, overall prices fall and the economy is in serious trouble.

Look at the map on page 214. You can see that most of the islands do not have large amounts of minerals. Jamaica, however, mines bauxite, a mineral used to make aluminum. The country of Trinidad and Tobago exports oil products. In Puerto Rico, companies make chemicals and machinery. Haiti and the Dominican Republic have textile factories where workers make cloth. Several islands have banking and financial industries.

Reading Check What is the major industry in the Caribbean?

Caribbean History and Culture

When Christopher Columbus reached the island of San Salvador—now part of the Bahamas—in 1492, who met him? It was a Native American group—the Taíno. The Taíno and other Native Americans lived on the islands long before the coming of Europeans.

The Spaniards established the first permanent European settlement in the Western Hemisphere in 1496. That settlement is now the city of **Santo Domingo,** capital of the Dominican Republic. During the next 200 years, the Spaniards, the English, the French, and the Dutch also founded colonies, or overseas settlements, on many of the islands. They found the soil and climate perfect for growing sugarcane. During this time, new plants, animals, and other products were traded between the Americas and other parts of the world. Turn to page 228 to learn more about this so-called Columbian Exchange.

By the mid-1600s, most Native Americans had died from European diseases and harsh treatment. The Europeans then brought enslaved Africans to work on sugar plantations. When the slave trade ended in

Reading Strategy **Reading the Text**

Using Word Maps A word map can be any kind of graphic that is designed to show relationships between words or concepts. A commonly used word map or concept web map shows a central bubble containing a key word or idea. Bubbles that surround the center bubble may be used to show semantic relationships or to explain structure relationships. Choose a word or concept in the section and create a word map on the board. Have students complete the surrounding bubbles to clarify the relationships. L1

*Use the **Reading Skills Handbook** for more reading strategies.*

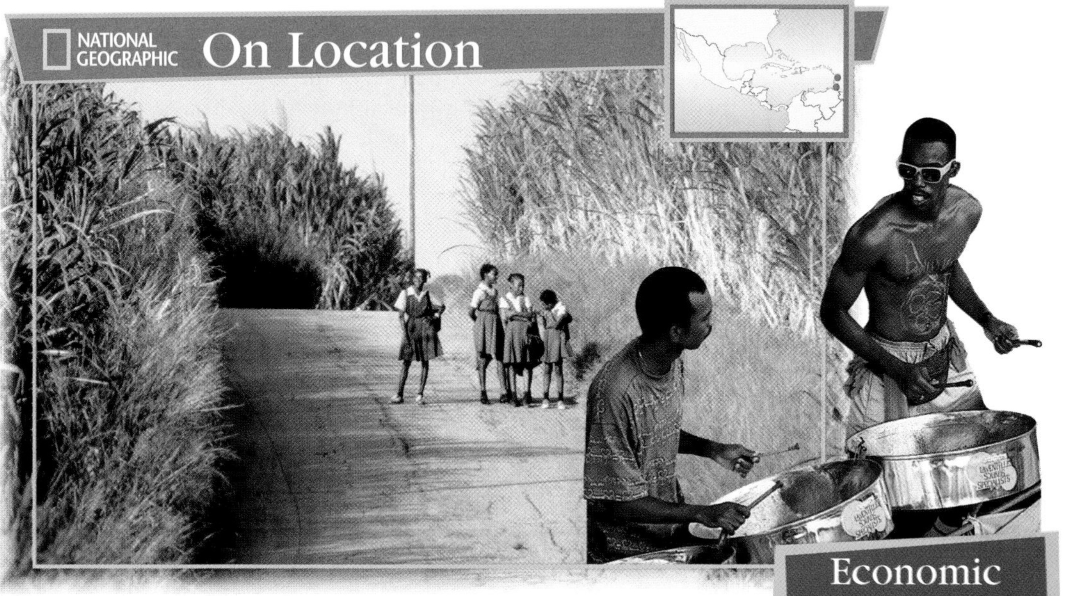

Economic Activities

Schoolgirls on Barbados walk past vast sugar plantations that European countries started in the colonial period (above left). A steel-drum band entertains tourists in Trinidad (above).

Region **What attracts so many tourists to the Caribbean islands?**

the early 1800s, plantation owners still in need of workers brought them from Asia, particularly India. Asians agreed to work a set number of years in return for free travel to the Caribbean and low wages.

Independence During the 1800s and 1900s, many Caribbean islands won their freedom from European rule. The first to become independent were the larger island countries, such as Haiti, the Dominican Republic, and Cuba. Later, smaller islands such as Barbados and Grenada became independent. Many countries—like Haiti and the Dominican Republic—are republics. Others—like Jamaica and the Bahamas—are British-style parliamentary democracies.

Cuba is the only country in the Western Hemisphere with a government based on communism. In a **communist state,** government leaders have strong control of the economy and society as a whole.

Some Caribbean islands are still not independent. Two large islands—Martinique and Guadeloupe—have ties to France. Puerto Rico and some of the Virgin Islands are linked to the United States. Other small islands are owned by the British or the Dutch.

Daily Life Many people in Central America have Native American ancestors. The peoples of the Caribbean, however, have African or mixed African and European ancestry. Large Asian populations live in Jamaica and Trinidad and Tobago as well.

More than 38 million people live in the Caribbean islands. Cuba, with about 11.3 million people, has the largest population in the region. Saint Kitts and Nevis has only about 50,000 people. Most people speak a European language and follow the Roman Catholic or Protestant religion.

L1/ELL

Guided Reading Activity

Name ________ Date ________ Class ________

CENTRAL AMERICA AND THE CARIBBEAN ISLANDS

Guided Reading Activity 2

Cultures of the Caribbean

DIRECTIONS: Filling in the Blanks Reading the section and completing the activity summary paragraphs below will help you learn more about the Caribbean islands. Refer to your textbook to fill in the blanks.

The Caribbean islands include **(1)** ________, the ________ ________, and the lesser Antilles. Many of the Caribbean islands are part of an underwater chain of mountains formed by **(2)** ________. Other islands are **(3)** ________ mountains. Most of the islands have a **(4)** ________ ________ climate. **(5)** ________ is the region's major industry. Many laborers work on ________. Most of the

More About the Photos

Steel Drums The idea of using steel drums as an instrument started in Trinidad. Ordinary metal drums used for shipping liquid cargo are cut and hammered to make a concave shape, which can play different notes. Steel drum bands can include anywhere from 4 to 100 members.

Caption Answer sunny climate and beautiful beaches

3 ASSESS

Assign Section 2 Assessment as homework or an in-class activity.

Have students use the Interactive Tutor Self-Assessment CD-ROM to review Section 2.

Differentiated Instruction

Meeting Special Needs: Less-proficient Readers Students who are not proficient readers benefit from having a specific purpose for reading. Point out the Guide to Reading at the beginning of the section. Demonstrate how to use this study guide to preview the lesson and to find main ideas in the section. As you complete each section, have students identify the Terms to Know and fill in a diagram like the one in the Reading Strategy. L1

Refer to *Inclusion for the Middle School Social Studies Classroom Strategies and Activities* in the TCR.

Reading Check Answer

the Spanish settlement that is now Santo Domingo, the capital of the Dominican Republic

L2

Section Quiz

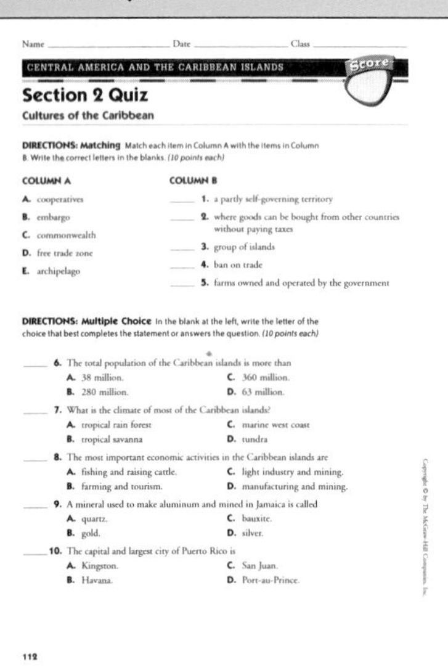
Name ______ Date ______ Class ______

CENTRAL AMERICA AND THE CARIBBEAN ISLANDS

Score

Section 2 Quiz

Cultures of the Caribbean

DIRECTIONS: Matching Match each item in Column A with the items in Column B. Write the correct letters in the blanks. *(10 points each)*

COLUMN A	COLUMN B
A. cooperatives	____ 1. a partly self-governing territory
B. embargo	____ 2. where goods can be bought from other countries without paying taxes
C. commonwealth	____ 3. group of islands
D. free trade zone	____ 4. ban on trade
E. archipelago	____ 5. farms owned and operated by the government

DIRECTIONS: Multiple Choice In the blank at the left, write the letter of the choice that best completes the statement or answers the question. *(10 points each)*

____ 6. The total population of the Caribbean islands is more than
A. 38 million. C. 360 million.
B. 280 million. D. 63 million.

____ 7. What is the climate of most of the Caribbean islands?
A. tropical rain forest C. marine west coast
B. tropical savanna D. tundra

____ 8. The most important economic activities in the Caribbean islands are
A. fishing and raising cattle. C. light industry and mining.
B. farming and tourism. D. manufacturing and mining.

____ 9. A mineral used to make aluminum and mined in Jamaica is called
A. quartz. C. bauxite.
B. gold. D. silver.

____ 10. The capital and largest city of Puerto Rico is
A. Kingston. C. San Juan.
B. Havana. D. Port-au-Prince.

112

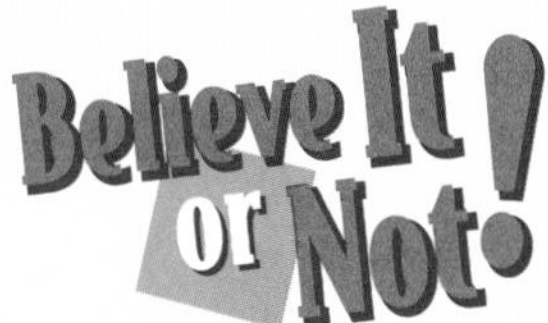

Bee Hummingbird

How small is this bird? The bee hummingbird of Cuba measures only 2 inches (5.1 cm) from head to tail. That is small enough to make it the tiniest bird in the world. The bird's wings move so fast—80 beats per second—that the human eye cannot see them. At two grams, the bee hummingbird weighs less than a penny.

About 60 percent of the people live in cities and villages. The other 40 percent live and work in the countryside. Many islanders have jobs in the hotels or restaurants that serve the tourist industry. If you visit the Caribbean, you are likely to hear lively music. The bell-like tones of the steel drum, developed in Trinidad and Tobago, are part of the rich musical heritage of the region. Jamaica's reggae music combines African rhythms and American popular music. Cuban salsa blends African rhythms, Spanish styles, and jazz.

On several islands, you will hear a different sound—the crack of a baseball bat. People in Puerto Rico, the Dominican Republic, and Cuba have a passion for baseball. Soccer is another popular sport.

Reading Check **Where was the first permanent European settlement in the Caribbean islands?**

Island Profiles

The Caribbean islands have many similarities, but they also have differences. Some of these differences can be seen in Cuba, Haiti, the Dominican Republic, and Puerto Rico.

Cuba One of the world's top sugar producers, Cuba lies about 90 miles (145 km) south of Florida. Most farmers work on cooperatives, or farms owned and operated by the government. In addition to growing sugarcane, they grow coffee, tobacco, rice, and fruits. In **Havana,** Cuba's capital and the largest city in the region, workers make food products, cigars, and household goods.

Cuba won its independence from Spain in 1898. The country had a democratic government, but in 1959 Fidel Castro led a revolution that took control of the government. Almost immediately, he set up a communist state and turned to the Soviet Union for support. When Castro seized property belonging to American companies, the United States government responded. It put in place an embargo, or a ban on trade, against Cuba.

Cuba relied on aid from the Soviet Union. When the Soviet Union broke apart in 1989, it stopped giving economic support to the island. The Cuban economy is struggling, and many Cubans live in poverty.

Haiti On the western half of the island of Hispaniola, you will find the country of **Haiti.** Led by a formerly enslaved man, Francois-Dominique Toussaint-Louverture, Haiti fought for and won its independence from France in 1804. It was the second independent republic in the Western Hemisphere (after the United States). It became the first nation in the history of the world to be founded by formerly enslaved persons. About 95 percent of Haiti's 7.5 million people are of African ancestry. Civil war has left Haiti's economy in ruins, and most Haitians are poor. Coffee and sugar, the main export crops, are shipped through **Port-au-Prince,** the country's capital.

Dominican Republic The **Dominican Republic** shares the island of Hispaniola with Haiti. The two countries have different histories and little contact, however. Haiti was a French colony. The Dominican

Critical Thinking Activity

Analyzing Information Pose the following question for students to consider: **Is tourism beneficial or harmful to the Caribbean islands? Why?** Provide time for students to reflect on the question and discuss it among themselves. Then ask several volunteers to present opposing viewpoints. *(Some may feel that tourism is beneficial because it helps local economies. Others may argue that countries that rely on tourism fail to develop other industries.)* Ask the entire class what steps a nation could take to address the problems raised by tourism. L2 

EE4 Human Systems: Standard 11

Republic was settled by Spaniards, who brought enslaved Africans to work on sugar plantations. Sugar is still an important crop. Tourism is growing too, and many Dominicans sell goods in the country's free trade zone. **Free trade zones** are areas where people can buy goods from other countries without paying taxes.

The government of the Dominican Republic hopes to build up the country's electrical power so the economy can grow more quickly. Poverty remains a problem. As a result, many Dominicans have left the country looking for work.

Puerto Rico To be or not to be a state in the United States? This is the question that Puerto Ricans ask themselves every few years. The last time they voted, they said no. How did Puerto Rico become part of the United States? The island was a Spanish colony from 1508 to 1898. After the Spanish-American War in 1898, the United States won control of Puerto Rico. Since 1952 the island has been a **commonwealth,** or a partly self-governing territory, under U.S. protection. By law, Puerto Ricans are U.S. citizens. They can come and go as they wish from the island to the United States.

Puerto Rico has a high standard of living compared to most other Caribbean islands. It boasts more industry, with factories producing chemicals, machinery, clothing, and more. **San Juan** is the capital and largest city. In rural areas, farmers grow sugarcane and coffee. Puerto Rico makes more money from tourism than any country in the region.

✓ Reading Check What is a commonwealth?

Web Activity Visit ***The World and Its People*** Web site at twip.glencoe.com and click on **Chapter 7—Student Web Activities** to learn more about Puerto Rico.

Section 2 Assessment

Defining Terms

1. **Define** archipelago, bauxite, communist state, cooperative, embargo, free trade zone, commonwealth.

Recalling Facts

2. **Region** What three archipelagos make up the Caribbean islands?
3. **History** Name four groups who have influenced the culture of the Caribbean region.
4. **Government** How is Cuba different from every other country in the Western Hemisphere?

Critical Thinking

5. **Drawing Conclusions** Explain why you think Puerto Ricans might be satisfied remaining a commonwealth.
6. **Making Predictions** What is the danger of a country's dependence on only one crop?

Graphic Organizer

7. **Organizing Information** Complete a chart like the one below with facts about Haiti and the Dominican Republic.

Facts	Haiti	Dominican Republic
Colonized by		
Economy		

Applying Social Studies Skills

8. **Analyzing Maps** Refer to the economic activity map on page 214. What resources are found in Cuba?

Section 2 Assessment

1. The terms are defined in the Glossary.
2. Bahamas, Greater Antilles, Lesser Antilles
3. Native Americans, Europeans, Africans, and Asians
4. It is a communist state.
5. People on the island are already U.S. citizens and are partly self-governing.
6. If the crop fails, no income is earned. Overproduction causes prices to fall, threatening the country's economy.
7. Haiti: France, coffee and sugar; Dominican Republic: Spain, sugar and tourism
8. fishing, petroleum, nickel

Objectives and answers to the Student Web Activity can be found in the Web Activity Lesson Plan at twip.glencoe.com

✓ Reading Check Answer

a partly self-governing territory

Reteach

Have students prepare an annotated map highlighting the cultural characteristics of the islands of the Caribbean.

L1/ELL

Reading Essentials and Study Guide

CENTRAL AMERICA AND THE CARIBBEAN ISLANDS

Reading Essentials and Study Guide 2

Cultures of the Caribbean

Key Terms

archipelago group of islands
bauxite a mineral used to make aluminum
communist state government in which the leaders have strong control of the economy and society
cooperative farm owned and operated by the government
embargo ban on trade
free trade zone area where people can buy goods from other countries without paying taxes

4 Close

Reading Strategy

Comparing and Contrasting Have students write a brief essay that explains what the island nations of the Caribbean have in common and how they differ.

Social Studies Skill

TEACH

Tell students that reading an elevation profile is similar to reading a line graph. The vertical scale corresponds to the *y*-axis. In some elevation profiles, a horizontal scale, corresponding to the *x*-axis, measures the length of the route, area, or landform in miles or kilometers. The profile, or top edge of the landscape shown, corresponds to the line in a line graph. This line shows elevation at specific points. Have students create a line graph using information in the elevation profile. **L2**

Additional Skills Practice

1. **What sea surrounds Jamaica?** *(Caribbean Sea)*
2. **Is Kingston on the coast? How can you tell?** *(You cannot tell, because although it is shown between landforms, the profile does not show a north-south cross section.)*
3. **How high are the Blue Mountains?** *(about 7,200 feet, or 2,200 m)*

Additional Skills Resources

 Chapter Skills Review

Building Geography Skills for Life

Social Studies Skill

Interpreting an Elevation Profile

You have learned that differences in land elevation are often shown on physical or relief maps. Another way to show elevation is on **elevation profiles.** When you view a person's profile, you see a side view. An elevation profile is a diagram that shows a side view of the landforms in an area.

Learning the Skill

Suppose you could slice right through a country from top to bottom and could look at the inside, or *cross section.* The cross section, or elevation profile, below pictures the island of Jamaica. It shows how far Jamaica's landforms extend above or below sea level.

Follow these steps to understand an elevation profile:

- Read the title of the profile to find out what country you are viewing.
- Look at the line of latitude written along the bottom of the profile. On a separate map, find the country and where this line of latitude runs through it.
- Look at the measurements along the sides of the profile. Note where sea level is located and the height in feet or meters.
- Now read the labels on the profile to identify the heights of the different landforms shown.
- Compare the highest and lowest points.

Practicing the Skill

Use the elevation profile below to answer the following questions.

1. At what elevation is Kingston?
2. What are the highest mountains, and where are they located?
3. Where are the lowest regions?
4. Along what line of latitude was this cross section taken?

Applying the Skill

Look at the elevation profile on page 118. What are the highest mountains? Where is the lowest point?

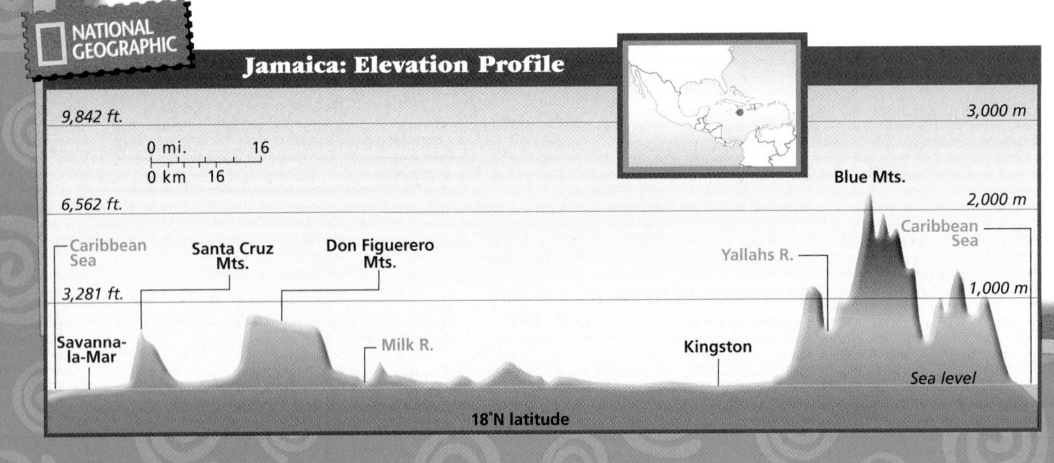

Practicing the Skill Answers

1. at about sea level
2. Blue Mountains, in the east
3. the Savanna-la-Mar in the west and the eastern valley where Kingston is located
4. 18°N

Applying the Skill

Highest mountains: Rocky Mountains; lowest point: Lake Superior

Reading Review

Section 1 Central America

Terms to Know
- isthmus
- canopy
- ecotourist
- literacy rate
- republic
- parliamentary democracy

Main Idea

Central America is made up of seven nations that are home to a variety of peoples, exotic animals, and diverse landforms.

✓Region Central America includes seven countries: Belize, Guatemala, Honduras, El Salvador, Nicaragua, Costa Rica, and Panama.

✓Region Volcanic mountains run down the center of Central America with coastal lowlands on either side.

✓Economics Most people in the region farm—either on plantations or on subsistence farms.

✓Culture Most countries in Central America have a blend of Native American and Spanish cultures.

The Panama Canal ▶

Section 2 Cultures of the Caribbean

Terms to Know
- archipelago
- bauxite
- communist state
- cooperative
- embargo
- free trade zone
- commonwealth

Main Idea

The Caribbean islands rely on tourism to support their economies.

✓History Christopher Columbus landed in this region in 1492.

✓History Most of the islands were at one time colonies of European countries.

✓Economics Farming and tourism are the major economic activities in the Caribbean region.

✓Culture The cultures of the Caribbean islands mix Native American, European, African, and Asian influences.

✓Government Most governments in the Caribbean islands are democratic, but a dictator rules Communist Cuba.

Reading Review

Use the Chapter 7 Reading Review to preview, review, condense, or reteach the chapter.

Preview/Review

Use the Terms to Know lists to help students review and study.

Activity Have students write the terms and definitions on index cards and group themselves into pairs. Have the pairs quiz each other on the terms.

Vocabulary PuzzleMaker CD-ROM reinforces the vocabulary terms used in Chapter 7.

The Interactive Tutor Self-Assessment CD-ROM allows students to review Chapter 7 content.

Condense

Have students read the Chapter 7 summary statements.

Guided Reading Activities

Audio Program

Reteach

Reteaching Activity

Reading Essentials and Study Guide

Reading Strategy — Read to Write

Writing a Letter Point out to students that life in the region has changed tremendously in the past 500 years or so since Christopher Columbus first landed in the region. Invite students to write a letter to Columbus describing these changes. Encourage them to include both positive and negative changes. They should use standard grammar, sentence structure, and punctuation. Call on volunteers to share their letters with the class. L1

EE6 The Uses of Geography: Standard 18

Assessment and Activities

GLENCOE TECHNOLOGY

MindJogger Videoquiz
Use MindJogger Videoquiz to review the Chapter 7 content.

Available in DVD and VHS

Using Key Terms

1.	d	6.	b
2.	h	7.	i
3.	a	8.	c
4.	f	9.	e
5.	j	10.	g

Reviewing the Main Ideas

11. Guatemala, Belize, Honduras, El Salvador, Nicaragua, Costa Rica, and Panama
12. Lumber companies cut down and export valuable trees; other companies and local farmers cut down or burn trees to clear land for farming. When the land loses its nutrients, the businesses and farmers clear trees from another piece of land.
13. Mexico, Guatemala, Belize, and Honduras
14. about 50 percent
15. farming and tourism
16. Cuba
17. steel drums, reggae, and salsa
18. Haiti
19. If the crop fails, no income is earned. Overproduction worldwide causes prices to fall, threatening the country's economy.

Assessment and Activities

Using Key Terms

Match the terms in Part A with their definitions in Part B.

A.

1. isthmus	6. bauxite
2. literacy rate	7. commonwealth
3. cooperative	8. embargo
4. ecotourist	9. free trade zone
5. archipelago	10. republic

B.

a. farm owned and operated by the government
b. mineral ore from which aluminum is made
c. ban on trade
d. narrow piece of land connecting two larger pieces of land
e. area where people can buy goods from other countries without paying taxes
f. person who travels to another country to enjoy its natural wonders
g. country with an elected president
h. percentage of adults who can read and write
i. partly self-governing territory
j. a group of islands

Reviewing the Main Ideas

Section 1 Central America

11. **Region** What seven countries make up Central America?
12. **Economics** Why are the Central American rain forests being destroyed?
13. **History** In what Central American countries did the Maya live?
14. **Culture** What percentage of Central Americans live on farms or in small villages?

Section 2 Cultures of the Caribbean

15. **Economics** What two activities form the basis of the Caribbean economies?
16. **Region** Which country has the largest population in the Caribbean?
17. **Culture** What types of music can you find in the Caribbean islands?
18. **History** What was the first nation in the world to be founded by formerly enslaved people?
19. **Economics** Why are commercial crops sometimes a risky business?

Central America and the Caribbean Islands

Place Location Activity

On a separate sheet of paper, match the letters on the map with the numbered places listed below.

1. Guatemala	6. Panama
2. Caribbean Sea	7. Bahamas
3. Cuba	8. Haiti
4. Puerto Rico	9. Jamaica
5. Costa Rica	10. Honduras

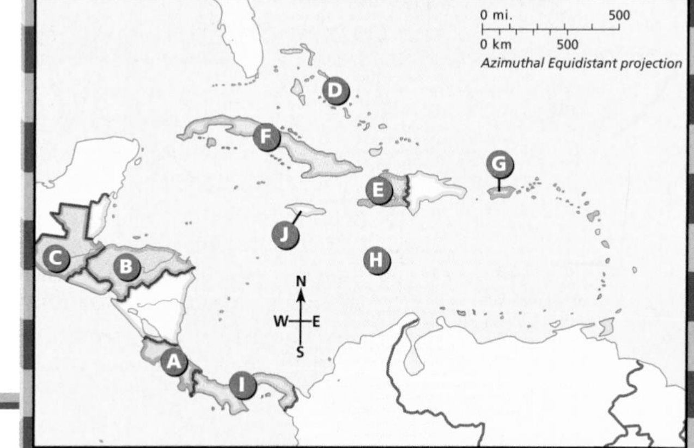

NATIONAL GEOGRAPHIC Place Location Activity

1.	C	6.	I
2.	H	7.	D
3.	F	8.	E
4.	G	9.	J
5.	A	10.	B

Critical Thinking

20. Because Cuba is only about 90 miles (145 km) from the United States, American officials keep a close watch on the island.
21. Answers will vary based on the country the student chooses. Check students' completed diagrams to be sure accurate facts are placed in appropriate places.

Self-Check Quiz Visit ***The World and Its People*** Web site at twip.glencoe.com and click on **Chapter 7—Self-Check Quizzes** to prepare for the Chapter Test.

Critical Thinking

20. **Analyzing Information** Explain why Cuba's location is an important factor in the United States's relationship with that nation.
21. **Categorizing Information** Create a diagram like this with details about the people, history, and economy of a country in this chapter.

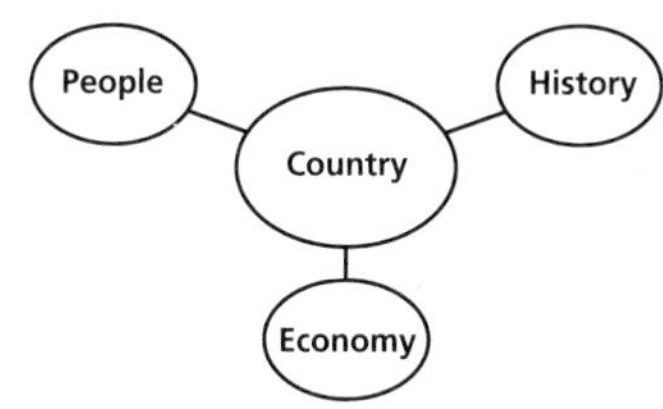

Comparing Regions Activity

22. **History** Compare the early Spanish settlements in Central America to the early British settlements in New Zealand. Use these examples to write a paragraph about what can happen when one country colonizes another.

Mental Mapping Activity

23. **Focusing on the Region** Create an outline map of Central America and the Caribbean islands, and then label the following:
    - Pacific Ocean
    - Cuba
    - Caribbean Sea
    - Puerto Rico
    - Guatemala
    - Dominican Republic
    - Panama
    - Bahamas

Technology Skills Activity

24. **Building a Database** Create a database about Central America, using the Country Profiles in the Unit 3 Regional Atlas as your information source. Make a record for each country. Each record should have a field for the following: population, landmass, and capital city. Sort the records from largest to smallest for population. What generalizations can you make based on these data?

Standardized Test Practice

Directions: Study the map below, and then answer the question that follows.

Contiguous U.S. and Latin America

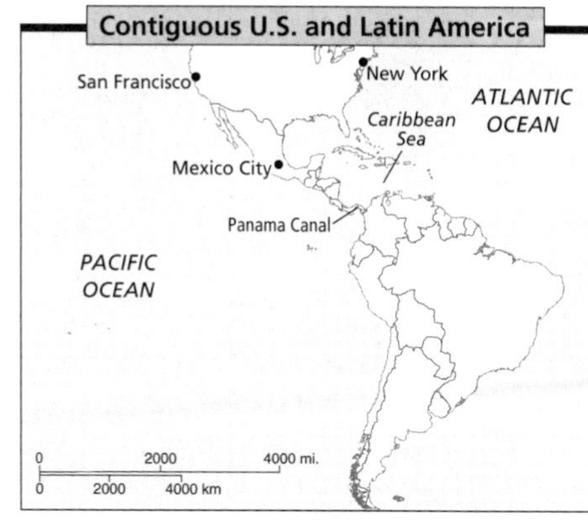

1. **Which of the following was true before the Panama Canal was completed?**
   - **A** A ship sailing from New York to San Francisco had to travel nearly 12,000 additional miles.
   - **B** A ship sailing from New York to San Francisco had to travel nearly 5,000 additional kilometers.
   - **C** The completion of the canal increased trade between Mexico City and San Francisco.
   - **D** Mexico City was extremely far away from New York City.

Test-Taking Tip: The scale shows you the actual distance between places on a map. Use your finger or a piece of paper to mark off the distance of the scale. Then use your finger or piece of paper to gauge the distance between two places on the map.

227

Assessment and Activities

Standardized Test Practice

1. A

Tested Objectives:
Reading a map, analyzing information

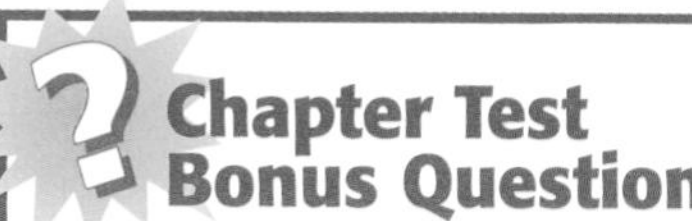

Chapter Test Bonus Question

This question may be used for extra credit on the chapter test.

Which country has taken steps to preserve its rain forests by declaring them national parks? *(Costa Rica)*

Have students visit the Web site at twip.glencoe.com to review Chapter 7 and take the Self-Check Quiz.

Dinah Zike's Foldables

Culminating Activity Have students write paragraphs that summarize the similarities and differences between the people and places of Central America and the Caribbean islands.

Comparing Regions Activity

22. Students may describe how the government, economy, and culture of one country might change when it is colonized by another country.

Mental Mapping Activity

23. This exercise helps students visualize the political boundaries and geographic features of Central America and the Caribbean islands. All attempts at freehand mapping should be accepted.

Technology Skills Activity

24. Students' databases should include the needed information: population, landmass, and capital city. In addition, the data should be organized according to population, and students should include a generalization about the data.

Ask students if they have ever traveled to another region or country. Have them think about how this different region or country looked. Were trees and plants the same? Was the sky more or less cloudy than they are used to at home? Point out that each region of the world has a unique combination of plants and animals that live there. The Columbian Exchange resulted when people from two widely different regions came together. L1

2 TEACH

Understanding Cause and Effect Ask students the following questions: **Why would Europeans bring plants and animals to the Americas? Why wouldn't they simply use the plants and animals that lived there?** *(because they wanted to raise the crops and animals with which they were familiar; also, the Americas did not have any large domesticated animals like cattle, sheep, and horses)* L1

Meeting National Standards

Geography for Life

The following standards are met in the Student Edition feature:

EE2 Places and Regions: Standards 5, 6

EE4 Human Systems: Standards 9, 10, 11, 12

EE5 Environment and Society: Standards 14, 15, 16

Columbus with King Ferdinand and Queen Isabella of Spain

The Columbian Exchange

The next time you eat a french fry, think about the long history of the lowly potato. The story begins high in the Andes mountain ranges of Bolivia and Peru (facing page), where thousands of years ago potatoes grew wild.

By the 1400s, the Inca, an early people who ruled a vast empire in western South America, had developed thousands of varieties of potatoes. The story of how potatoes came from such a faraway time and place is one that began even before the Inca. Now, potatoes are part of our everyday diet.

Two Separate Worlds

Before the 1400s, people living in the world's Eastern Hemisphere were unknown to those living in the Western Hemisphere. This changed on October 12, 1492, when explorer Christopher Columbus, who had sailed from Spain, landed in the Bahamas in the Americas. Believing he had reached the Indies of Asia, Columbus named the people on the islands "Indians" and claimed the land for Spain. Columbus returned to the Americas the following year, bringing more than a thousand men in 17 ships. With his second trip, Columbus began what became known as "the Columbian Exchange"—an exchange of people, animals, plants, and even diseases between the two hemispheres.

For Better and for Worse

The Europeans brought many new things to the Americas. Columbus brought horses, which helped the Native Americans with labor, hunting, and transportation. European farm animals such as sheep, pigs, and cattle created new sources of income. Explorers brought crops—oats, wheat, rye, and barley—that eventually covered North America's Great Plains. The sugarcane brought by Europeans flourished on plantations in Central and South America.

Some parts of the exchange were disastrous, however. Europeans brought diseases that killed millions of Native Americans. Plantation owners put enslaved Africans to work in their fields.

From the Americas, explorers returned home with a wide variety of plants. Spanish sailors carried potatoes to Europe. Nutritious and easy to grow, the potato became one of Europe's most important foods. (European immigrants then brought the potato to North America.) Corn from the Americas fed European cattle and pigs. Tobacco grown there became as valuable as gold. Peanuts, tomatoes, hot peppers, and cacao seeds (from which chocolate is made) changed the landscapes, eating habits, and cooking styles in Europe, Asia, and Africa.

QUESTIONS

1. **What is "the Columbian Exchange"?**
2. **Exchanges continue today. What are some present-day exchanges among the world's hemispheres?**

228

Women in Peru tend a potato field. ▶

Answers to the Questions

1. the exchange of people, animals, plants, and even diseases between the Western and Eastern Hemispheres as a result of the voyages of Christopher Columbus
2. *Possible answers:* movement of people from one hemisphere to another; movement of goods; transfer of ideas or culture

NATIONAL GEOGRAPHIC

The Spread of Plants and Animals

Time Line

- **8000 B.C.:** Bering Strait land bridge submerged; Eastern and Western Hemispheres begin to develop separately
- **1492:** Columbus lands in Americas
- **1493:** Columbus brings sugarcane to Americas
- **1500s:** Beans and maize (corn) brought from Americas to Europe
- **1500–1900:** Millions of Africans brought to Americas for slavery
- **1516:** Europeans bring bananas to Americas
- **1520–1600:** Millions of Native Americans die of disease
- **1521:** Cattle first brought to Americas
- **1700s:** Ireland begins widespread use of American potato
- **1820s–1930s:** Millions of Europeans emigrate to Americas

ASSESS

Have students answer the questions about the Columbian Exchange.

CLOSE

Reading Strategy

Organizing Information Have students create a graphic organizer that illustrates the "Columbian Exchange."

Geography and History Activity

Using Maps Have students study the map of The Spread of Plants and Animals above. Have them discuss exactly what the map is showing. **Ask:** What area first grew corn? Where were horses first raised? What items did Europe contribute to this exchange? Have students review the economic activity maps of the United States and Central America and the Caribbean islands. **Ask:** What products shown on the map above are important to the economies of these countries today? *(Cotton, tobacco, and ranching—originally from Central America and Europe—are important in the United States, while sugarcane and tobacco remain important in Central America and the Caribbean islands.)*

EE5 Environment and Society: Standard 16

Chapter 8 Resources

Note: The following materials may be used when teaching Chapter 8.
Section level support materials are shown at point of use in the margins of the Teacher Wraparound Edition.

Timesaving Tools

TeacherWorks™ All-In-One Planner and Resource Center

- **Interactive Teacher Edition** See the **Interactive Teacher Edition** CD-ROM to electronically integrate your Teacher Wraparound Edition and blackline masters.
- **Interactive Lesson Planner** Organize your week, month, semester, or year with all the lesson helps you need. The **Interactive Lesson Planner** CD-ROM contains all Chapter 8 resources.

Use Glencoe's **Presentation Plus!** multimedia teacher tool to easily present dynamic lessons that visually excite your students. Using Microsoft PowerPoint® you can customize the presentations to create your own personalized lessons.

TEACHING TRANSPARENCIES

Graphic Organizer Transparency 13 L2

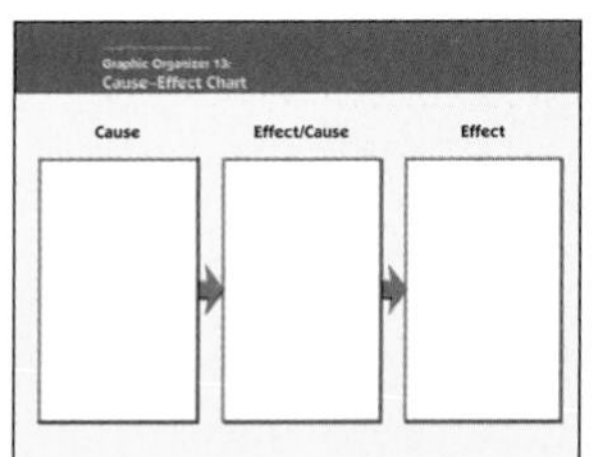

In-text Map Transparency L1

FOLDABLES™ Study Organizer

Dinah Zike's Foldables

Foldables are three-dimensional, interactive graphic organizers that help students practice basic writing skills, review key vocabulary terms, and identify main ideas. Additional chapter activities can be found in the ***Reading and Study Skills Foldables*** booklet.

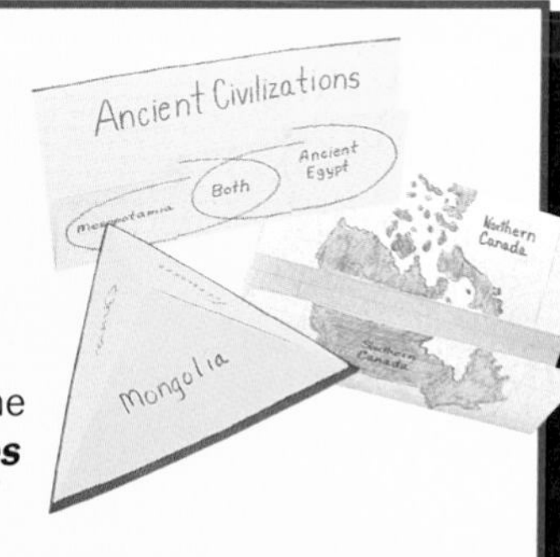

MAP AND GEOGRAPHY SKILLS

Chapter Map Activity L2

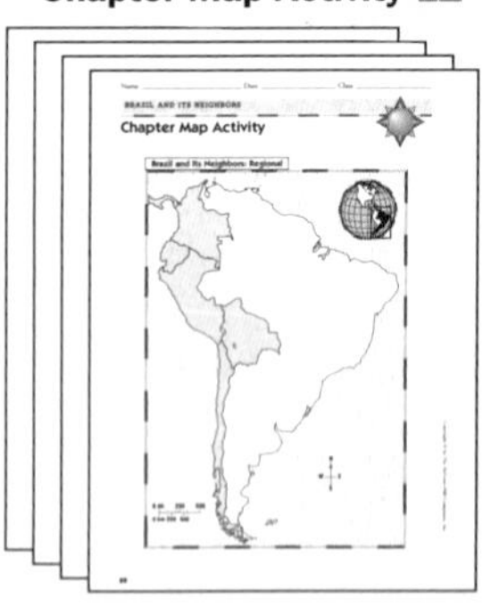

GeoLab Activity L2

READING SUPPORT

Vocabulary Activity L1

Workbook Activity L1

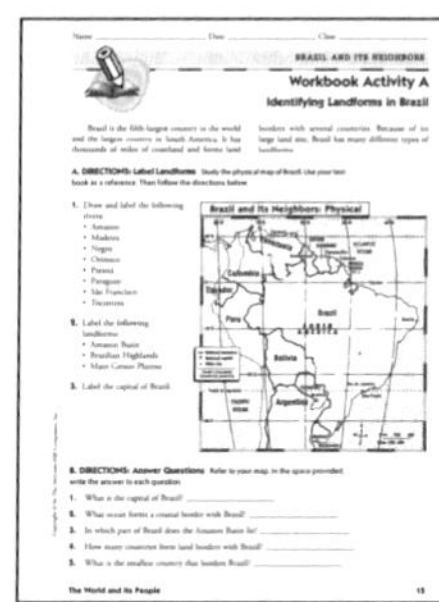

Reading and Writing Skills Activity L1/ELL

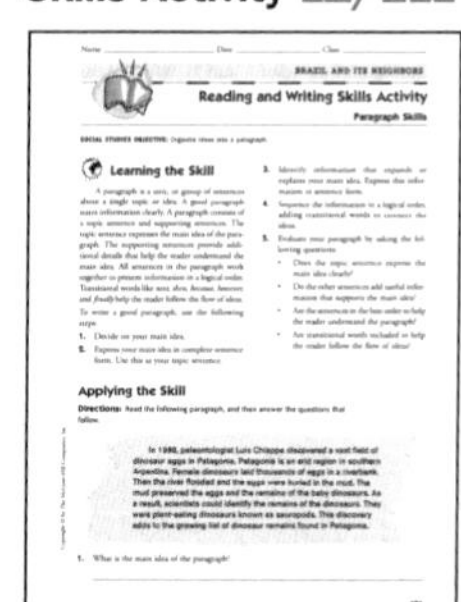

DIFFERENTIATED INSTRUCTION

Use these review and reinforcement materials to help less-proficient readers, English learners, and gifted and talented students.

Reteaching Activity L1

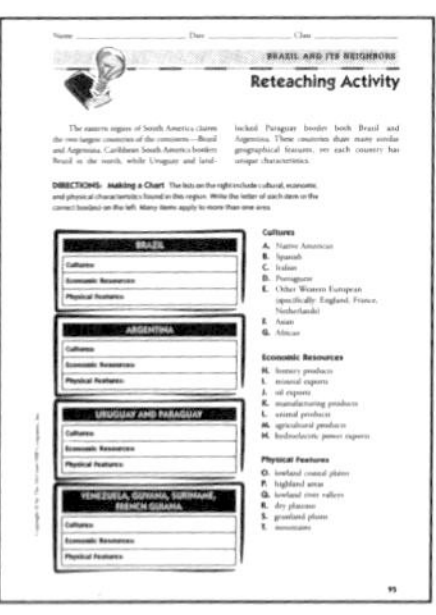

Chapter Skills Review L2

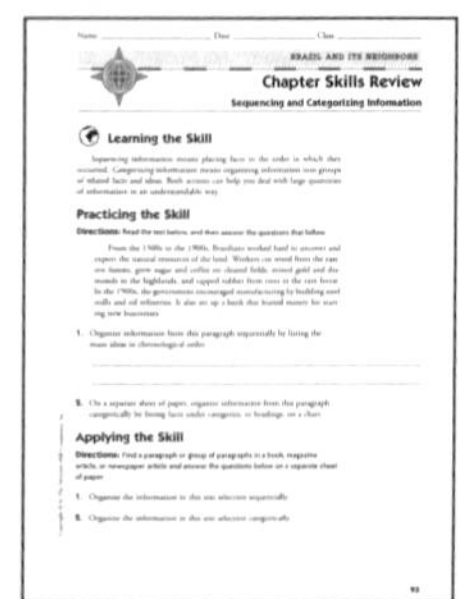

Cooperative Learning Activity L1/ELL

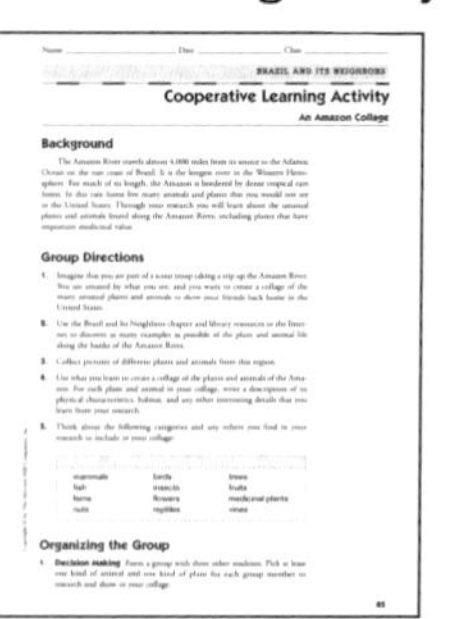

Enrichment Activity L3

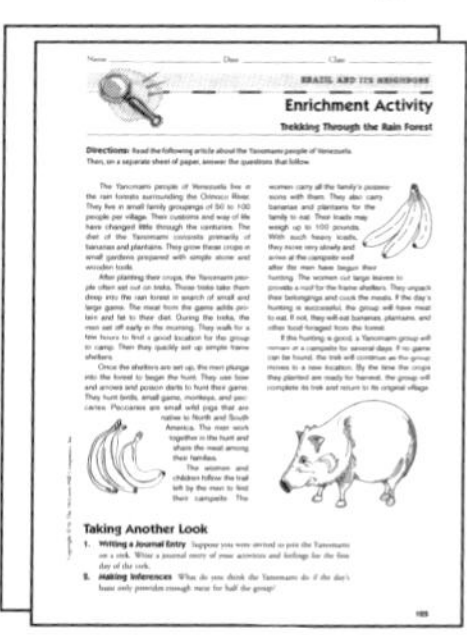

ASSESSMENT

Chapter Test, Form A L2

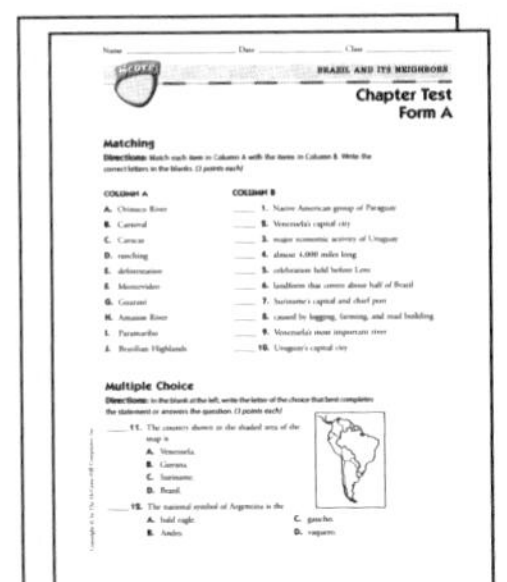

Chapter Test, Form B L2

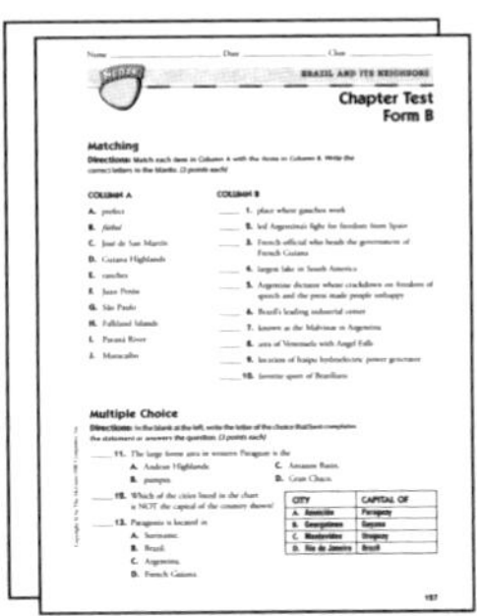

Performance Assessment Activity L1/ELL

ExamView® Pro Testmaker CD-ROM

STANDARDIZED ASSESSMENT SKILLS

GLENCOE'S ASSESSMENT ADVANTAGE

Critical Thinking Skills Activity L2

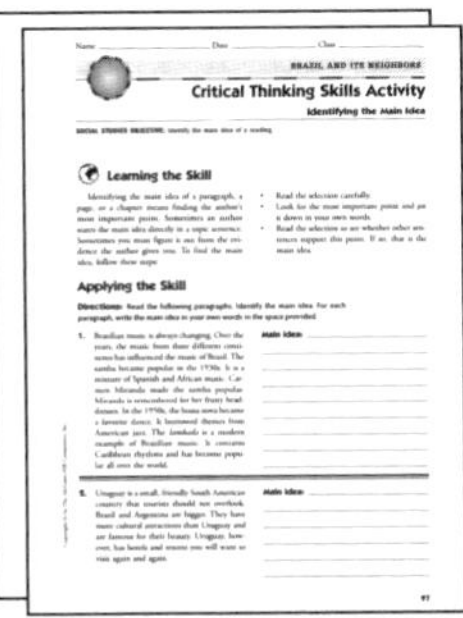

Map and Graph Skills Activity L2

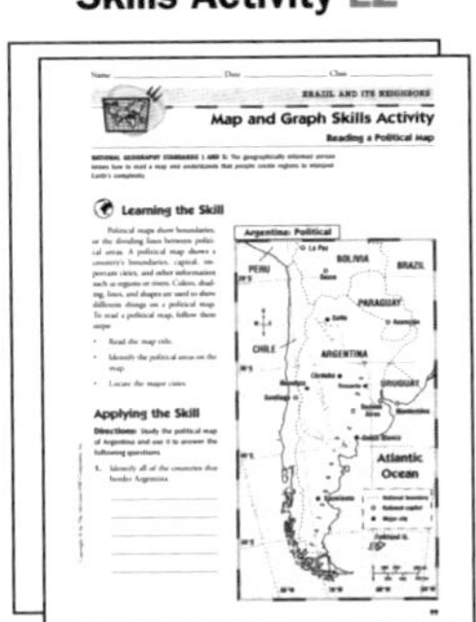

Standardized Test Skills Practice Workbook Activity L2

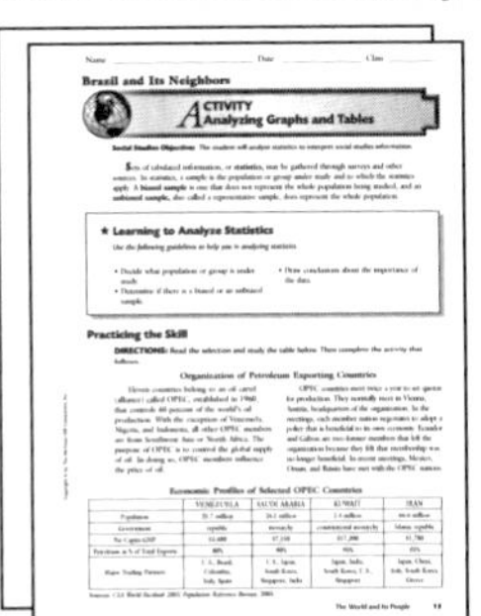

HOME INVOLVEMENT

Take-Home Review Activity L1

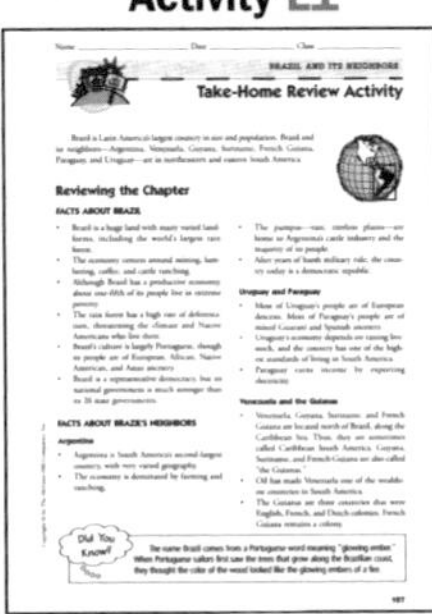

MULTIMEDIA

- **National Geographic's The World and Its People**
- **MindJogger Videoquiz**
- **Vocabulary PuzzleMaker CD-ROM**
- **Interactive Tutor Self-Assessment CD-ROM**
- **ExamView® Pro Testmaker CD-ROM**
- **TeacherWorks CD-ROM**
- **StudentWorks CD-ROM**
- **Skillbuilder Interactive Workbook CD-ROM, Level 1**
- **Presentation Plus! CD-ROM**
- **Audio Program**

SPANISH RESOURCES

The following Spanish language materials are available in the Spanish Resources binder:

- **Spanish Summaries**
- **Spanish Vocabulary Activities**
- **Spanish Guided Reading Activities**
- **Spanish Quizzes and Tests**
- **Spanish Take-Home Review Activities**
- **Spanish Reteaching Activities**

Meeting National Standards

Geography for Life

The following standards are covered in Chapter 8:

Section 1 **EE2 Places and Regions: Standards 4, 6**
EE3 Physical Systems: Standards 7, 8
EE4 Human Systems: Standard 13

Section 2 **EE1 The World in Spatial Terms: Standard 1**
EE2 Places and Regions: Standards 4, 5, 6
EE4 Human Systems: Standards 9, 10
EE5 Environment and Society: Standard 15

State and Local Objectives

Chapter 8 Planning Guide

SECTION RESOURCES

Daily Objectives	Reproducible Resources	Multimedia Resources
Section 1 **Brazil—Emerging Giant** 1. Describe Brazil's landforms and climates. 2. Identify the natural resources Brazil's economy depends on. 3. Discuss the people and culture of Brazil.	Reproducible Lesson Plan Daily Lecture and Discussion Notes Note-taking Guide Guided Reading Activity* Reading Essentials and Study Guide* Section Quiz*	Daily Focus Skills Transparency GeoQuiz Transparency In-text Map Transparency Vocabulary PuzzleMaker CD-ROM Interactive Tutor Self-Assessment CD-ROM ExamView® Pro Testmaker CD-ROM Presentation Plus! CD-ROM
Section 2 **Argentina to Venezuela** 1. Compare the landscapes and climates of Venezuela and Argentina. 2. Describe the economies of Brazil's northern and southern neighbors. 3. Discuss the histories of Brazil's neighboring countries.	Reproducible Lesson Plan Daily Lecture and Discussion Notes Note-taking Guide Guided Reading Activity* Reading Essentials and Study Guide* Section Quiz*	Daily Focus Skills Transparency Vocabulary PuzzleMaker CD-ROM Interactive Tutor Self-Assessment CD-ROM ExamView® Pro Testmaker CD-ROM Presentation Plus! CD-ROM MindJogger Videoquiz

00:00 **Out of Time?** Assign the **Reading Essentials and Study Guide*** for this chapter.

*Also available in Spanish

KEY TO ABILITY LEVELS

Teaching strategies have been coded for varying learning styles and abilities.

L1 **BASIC** activities for all students
L2 **AVERAGE** activities for average to above-average students
L3 **CHALLENGING** activities for above-average students
ELL **ENGLISH LANGUAGE LEARNER** activities

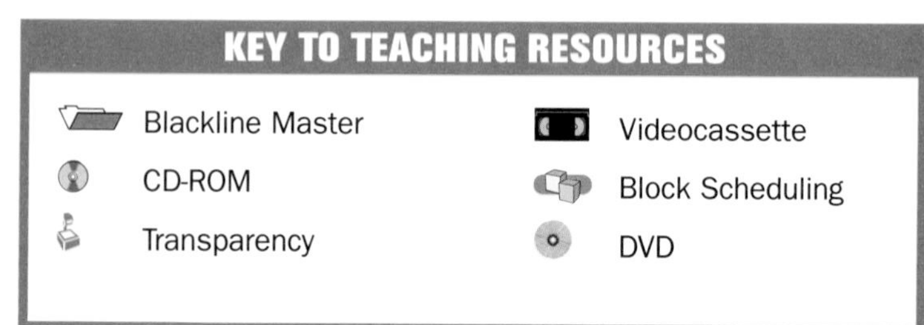

Teacher to Teacher

Lee Ann Burrow
Bob Courtway Middle School
Conway, Arkansas

Julie Hill
Bob Courtway Middle School
Conway, Arkansas

Travel Brochure

Have students create their own "South American Travel Brochure." Students can use the textbook, the Internet, travel agency brochures, or other sources to find information. Students' brochures should include information on climate, places to visit, interesting facts and information, currency, history, and landforms. Foods and recipes should also be added. Ask students to put their information on colored paper folded like a brochure and to use pictures, drawings, and attractive fonts.

Meeting Special Needs

In addition to the Differentiated Instruction strategies found in each section, the following resources are also suitable for your special needs students:

- ***ExamView® Pro Testmaker CD-ROM*** allows teachers to tailor tests by reducing answer choices.
- The ***Audio Program*** includes the entire narrative of the student edition so that less-proficient readers can listen to the words as they read them.
- The ***Reading Essentials and Study Guide*** provides the same content as the student edition but is written two grade levels below the textbook.
- ***Guided Reading Activities*** give less-proficient readers point-by-point instructions to increase comprehension as they read each textbook section.
- ***Enrichment Activities*** include a stimulating collection of readings and activities for gifted and talented students.

TEACHER'S CORNER

Index to National Geographic Magazine:

The following articles may be used for research relating to this chapter:

- "Feast of the Tarpon," by David Doubilet, January 1996.
- "Poison-Dart Frogs," by Mark W. Moffett, May 1995.
- "The Amazon," by Jere Van Dyk, February 1995.

National Geographic Society Products:

To order the following products for use with this chapter, call National Geographic Society at 1-800-368-2728:

- *South America* (Video)
- *National Geographic Atlas of the World, Seventh Edition* (Book)
- *Discovering the Inca Ice Maiden: My Adventures on Ampato* (Book)

NGS ONLINE

Access National Geographic's Web site for current events, activities, links, interactive features, and archives. www.nationalgeographic.com

NATIONAL GEOGRAPHIC MapMachine

Find the latest coverage of geography in the news, atlas updates, cartographic activities with interactive maps, an online map store, and links at www.nationalgeographic.com/maps

SOCIAL STUDIES Online

Use our Web site for additional resources. All essential content is covered in the Student Edition.

You and your students can visit twip.glencoe.com, the Web site companion to *The World and Its People*. This innovative integration of electronic and print media offers your students a wealth of opportunities. The student text directs students to the Web site for the following options:

- Chapter Overviews
- Student Web Activities
- Self-Check Quizzes
- Textbook Updates

Answers are provided for you in the Web Activity Lesson Plan. Additional Web resources and Interactive Tutor puzzles are also available.

Introducing
Chapter 8

Social Studies Online

Introduce students to chapter content and key terms by having them access Chapter Overview 8 at twip.glencoe.com

Chapter Objectives

1. Describe the major physical, economic, and cultural features of Brazil.
2. Compare and contrast the physical, economic, and cultural characteristics of Brazil's neighbors.

GLENCOE TECHNOLOGY

NATIONAL GEOGRAPHIC

The World and Its People Video Program

Chapter 8 Brazil and Its Neighbors

The following segments enhance the study of this chapter:

- **Samba**
- **Amazon Basin**
- **Jungle Countdown**

MindJogger Videoquiz

Use MindJogger Videoquiz to preview the Chapter 8 content.

Both programs available in DVD and VHS

Chapter 8

Brazil and Its Neighbors

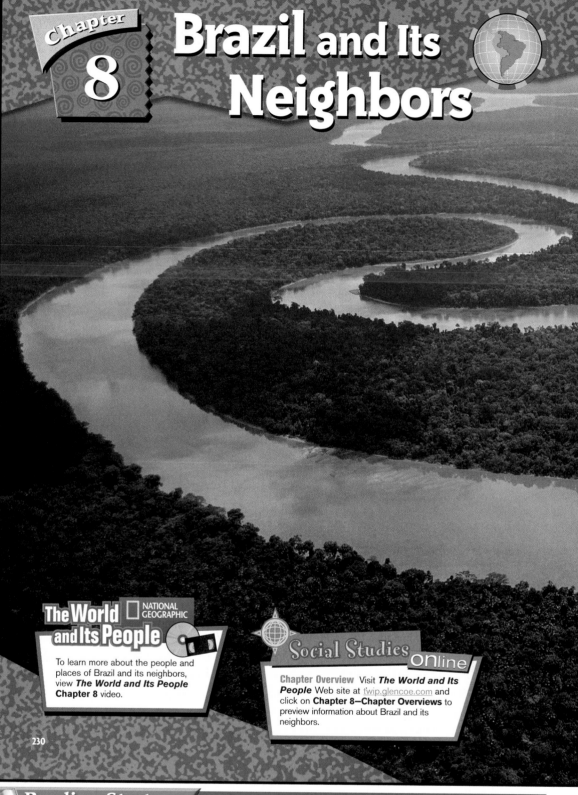

The World and Its People — National Geographic

To learn more about the people and places of Brazil and its neighbors, view ***The World and Its People*** **Chapter 8** video.

Social Studies Online

Chapter Overview Visit ***The World and Its People*** Web site at twip.glencoe.com and click on **Chapter 8—Chapter Overviews** to preview information about Brazil and its neighbors.

230

Reading Strategy — Purpose for Reading

Free Writes are used to explore student background knowledge and to engage students. For each section, ask students to examine the picture in the "Exploring Our World" feature. Ask them, for example, to write what they think is happening in the picture at the beginning of Section 1, such as, What is the man doing? What is he wearing? What might the boy be thinking? Emphasize that there are no wrong answers to the questions; it is important that all ideas are accepted. Have students discuss their answers as a class. Conclude the activity by explaining that students will be learning about the physical, economic, and cultural features of Brazil and its neighboring countries. L1

Summarizing Information Make this foldable and use it to organize note cards with information about the people and places of Brazil and its neighbors.

Step 1 Fold a 2-inch tab along the long edge of a sheet of paper.

Fold the left edge over 2 inches.

Step 2 Fold the paper in half so the tab is on the inside.

The tab can't be seen when the paper is folded.

Step 3 Open the paper pocket foldable, turn it, and glue the edges of the pockets together.

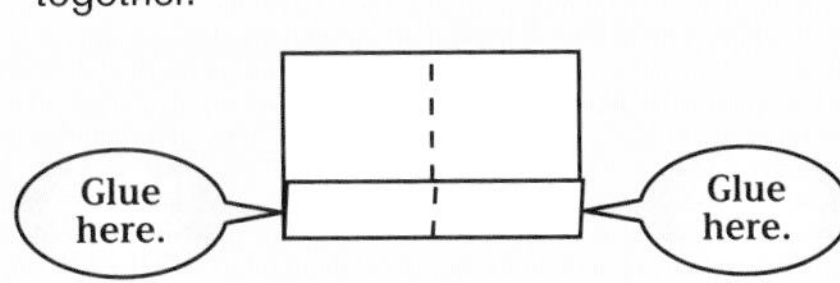

Step 4 Label the pockets as shown.

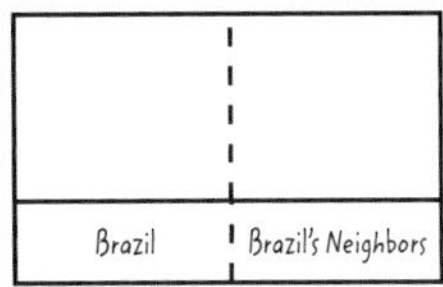

Reading and Writing As you read the chapter, summarize key facts about Brazil and its neighbors on note cards or on quarter sheets of notebook paper. Organize your notes by placing them in your pocket foldable inside the appropriate pockets. (Keep your pocket foldable to use with Chapter 9.)

Why It Matters

Preserving the Environment

The Amazon rain forest—sometimes called the "lungs of the planet" because of the huge amounts of oxygen given off by its trees—is home to up to 30 percent of the animal and plant life on Earth. Destroying these trees may cause the extinction of many wildlife species and damage to the earth's environment—on which we depend for our survival. This is just one of many issues facing the people and government of Brazil.

◀ The Amazon River, Brazil

About the Photo

Rivers are powerful forces that shape the earth's surface. Great civilizations sprang up along such rivers as the Tigris-Euphrates, the Nile, and the Indus. The Amazon is bordered by thick rain forest along much of its 4,000-mile (6,437 km) length. It is about 100 miles (120 km) shorter than the world's longest river, the Nile-Kagera in Africa, though the Amazon carries a much larger volume of water to the sea. The Amazon and the Congo carry the greatest volume of water of any of the world's rivers. Why so much water? Both rivers are located on the Equator, are fed by tropical rains, and have many tributaries, or smaller streams, feeding into them.

Dinah Zike's Foldables

Purpose This activity requires students to create note cards and a pocket foldable to organize information from the chapter. Students record key facts about the countries in the chapter and then group the information into categories, in effect, comparing the people and places of Brazil and its neighbors.

Have students complete the ***Reading and Study Skills Foldables*** activity for this chapter.

Why It Matters

Discuss the concept of "annual rainfall," and what the average annual rainfall is where they live. Provide a supply of 1" by 1" construction paper squares and a piece of butcher paper 12 feet long. (Some 1" by 10" strips will save time.) Create a chart with 11-foot columns for each location you choose to list. Ask volunteers to glue the correct number of squares in a straight line to represent inches of rainfall.

Annual Rainfall in Inches

Location	Inches
Your Town	??
Amazon Rain Forest	120
Mt. Waialeale, HI (world's highest)	460
Arica, Chile (world's lowest)	.03

Chapter 8

Section 1, pages 232–237

1 Focus

Section Objectives

1. Describe Brazil's landforms and climates.
2. Identify the natural resources Brazil's economy depends on.
3. Discuss the people and culture of Brazil.

BELLRINGER Skillbuilder Activity

Project transparency and have students answer the question.

Daily Focus Skills Transparency

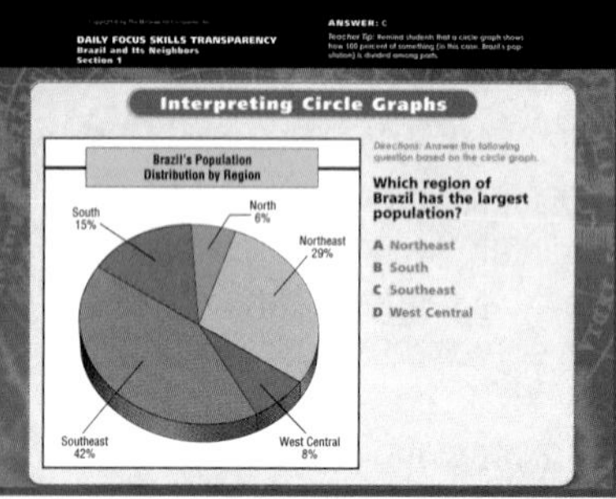

Interpreting Circle Graphs
Brazil's Population Distribution by Region
South 15%
North 6%
Northeast 29%
Southeast 42%
West Central 8%
Which region of Brazil has the largest population?
A Northeast
B South
C Southeast
D West Central

Reading Preview

- **Activating Prior Knowledge**
Ask: What do you know about Brazil? List students' responses. As they read, have students determine if the items on the list are true.

- **Preteaching Vocabulary**
Have students find or create illustrations for each landform word on the Terms to Know list.

Guide to Reading

Main Idea

Brazil is a large country with many resources, a lively culture, and serious economic challenges.

Terms to Know

- basin
- *selva*
- escarpment
- favela
- deforestation

Reading Strategy

Create a chart like the one below and fill in at least one key fact about Brazil in each category.

Brazil	
Land	
History	
Economy	
Government	
People	

Section 1 Brazil—Emerging Giant

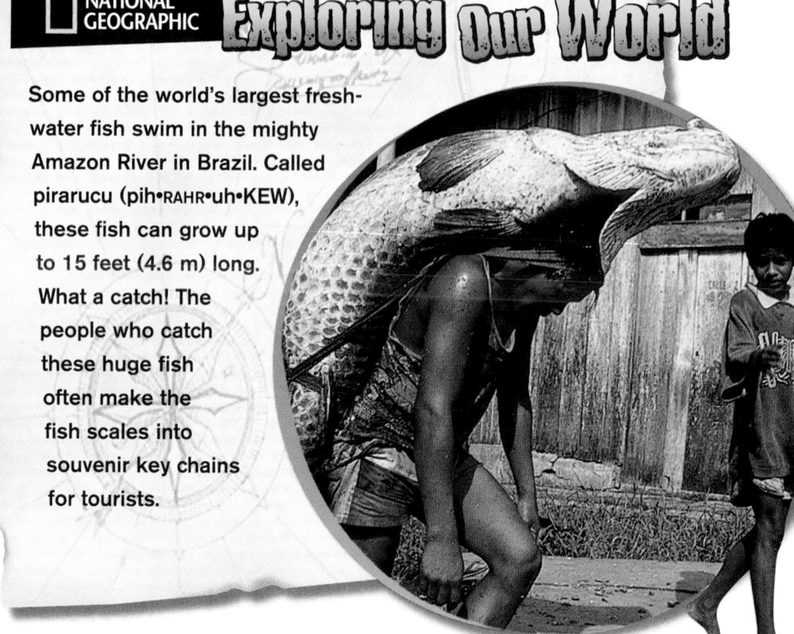

NATIONAL GEOGRAPHIC Exploring Our World

Some of the world's largest freshwater fish swim in the mighty Amazon River in Brazil. Called pirarucu (pih•RAHR•uh•KEW), these fish can grow up to 15 feet (4.6 m) long. What a catch! The people who catch these huge fish often make the fish scales into souvenir key chains for tourists.

Like the pirarucu, Brazil is large. It is the fifth-largest country in the world and the largest in South America. In fact, Brazil makes up almost half of South America.

Brazil's Rain Forests and Highlands

Brazil has many different types of landforms and climates. The map on page 233 shows you that Brazil has narrow coastal plains, highland areas, and lowland river valleys. The **Amazon River** is the world's second-longest river, winding almost 4,000 miles (6,437 km) from the **Andes** mountain ranges to the Atlantic Ocean. Its powerful current carries soil 60 miles (97 km) out to sea! On its journey to the Atlantic, the Amazon drains water from a wide, flat basin, or low area surrounded by higher land. In the **Amazon Basin,** rainfall can reach as much as 120 inches (305 cm) per year. These rains support the growth of thick rain forests, which Brazilians call *selvas.*

Section Resources

Reproducible Masters
- Reproducible Lesson Plan
- Daily Lecture and Discussion Notes
- Note-taking Guide
- Guided Reading Activity
- Reading Essentials and Study Guide
- Section Quiz

Transparencies
- Daily Focus Skills Transparency
- GeoQuiz Transparency
- In-text Map Transparency

Multimedia
- Vocabulary PuzzleMaker CD-ROM
- Interactive Tutor Self-Assessment CD-ROM
- Presentation Plus! CD-ROM
- ExamView® Pro Testmaker CD-ROM

Brazil has lowlands along the Paraná and the São Francisco Rivers. The **Brazilian Highlands** cover about half of the country, then drop sharply to the Atlantic Ocean. This drop is called the Great Escarpment. An escarpment is a steep cliff between higher and lower land.

✓ Reading Check **What is significant about the Amazon River?**

Brazil's Economy

How do Brazilians earn a living? Agriculture, mining, and forestry have been important for centuries. The Amazon Basin has been a mysterious region with secrets that were guarded by the Native Americans living there. This began to change in the mid-1800s. World demand skyrocketed for the rubber harvested from the basin's trees, and new

Applying Map Skills

1. Which area of Brazil—the north or the south—has the higher elevation?
2. Name two rivers that flow into the Amazon River.

Find NGS online map resources @ www.nationalgeographic.com/maps

TEACH

Brainstorming Point out that about half of Brazil's area is covered by a tropical rain forest. Explain that this rain forest covers 2.3 million square miles (nearly 6 million sq. km) and receives between 60 and 120 inches (152 to 305 cm) of rain a year. Have students explain how the rain forest might help or hurt Brazil's economic development. **L1**

✓ Reading Check Answer

It is the world's second-longest river.

Daily Lecture and Discussion Notes

BRAZIL AND ITS NEIGHBORS

Daily Lecture and Discussion Notes

Brazil—Emerging Giant

As naturalists catalog new species of freshwater fish, their findings suggest that there may be as many as 3,000 kinds of fish in the Amazon Basin's rivers and lakes. Among the fish found in the area are the pirarucu, said to be the largest freshwater fish in the world with specimens measuring up to 15 feet in length and weighing 275 pounds, and the tambaqui, a member of the fruit-eating characin family with teeth that can crack hard seeds.

I. Brazil's Rain Forests and Highlands

A. The second-longest river in the world, the Amazon River winds almost 4,000 miles and drains water from a wide, flat **basin.** Up to 120 inches of rainfall each ... growth of rain forests, known as *selvas,* in Brazil's Amazon Basin.

Applying Map Skills

Answers

1. the south
2. *Any two:* Negro River, Madeira River, Xingu River, Tocantins River

In-text Map Transparency Activity Ask: Where do you think most people in Brazil live? Why? *(along the coast; because inland areas are more difficult to reach)*

Reading Strategy — Reading the Text

Understanding Cause and Effect Have students create a chart to illustrate the cause-and-effect relationships that have influenced life in Brazil. For example, the government built roads in the Amazon Basin, leading more people to settle there. Also, the cool climate and rich soil of Brazil's highlands make it appropriate for growing coffee. Have students add other examples from the section to their charts. When students have completed their charts, ask for volunteers to read an example to the class. Discuss how landforms, climate, settlement patterns, and history all influence the way people live in Brazil. **L1**

Use the ***Reading Skills Handbook*** *for more reading strategies.*

Chapter 8

Section 1, pages 232–237

L1/ELL

Guided Reading Activity

Name ______ Date ______ Class ______

BRAZIL AND ITS NEIGHBORS

Guided Reading Activity 1

Brazil—Emerging Giant

DIRECTIONS: Reading for Accuracy Reading the section and completing the activity below will help you learn more about Brazil. Refer to your textbook to decide if a statement is true or false. Write **T** or **F**, and if a statement is false, rewrite it correctly.

____ 1. The Amazon River flows from the Andes to the Pacific Ocean.

____ 2. Rainfall in the Amazon Basin contributes to the growth of thick tropical rain forests.

____ 3. The Great Escarpment is where the highlands drop sharply to the Atlantic Ocean.

Interdisciplinary Connections

Science Brazilians are harnessing the power of their water resources to supply their energy needs. The Itaípu Dam on the Paraná River is a joint $20-billion project of Brazil and Paraguay. The dam is designed to supply one-fifth of Brazil's electricity.

Analyzing the Graph

Answer
Brazil and Colombia

Skills Practice
Which country is the leading coffee producer? *(Brazil)* **How much coffee does this country produce each year?** *(about 2 1/2 billion pounds per year)*

Leading Coffee-Producing Countries

Analyzing the Graph

Brazil's highlands have the right soil and climate to grow coffee.

Economics **Which leading coffee-producing countries are in South America?**

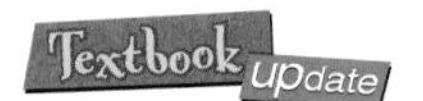

Visit twip.glencoe.com and click on **Chapter 8—Textbook Updates.**

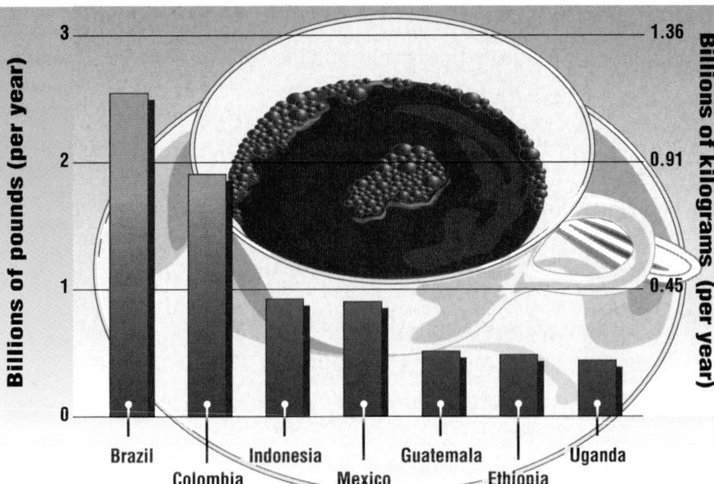

Source: Food and Agriculture Organization of the United Nations.

settlers streamed to Brazil's interior. Today mining companies dig for minerals such as bauxite, tin, and iron ore. Logging companies harvest mahogany and other woods from the rain forest. Farmers use the cleared land to grow soybeans and tobacco and to graze cattle.

South of the Amazon Basin are rich mineral resources and fertile farmland. The southern region of Brazil boasts one of the world's largest iron ore deposits. The highlands are perfect for growing coffee. As the graph above shows, Brazil produces far more coffee than other countries. It also has huge cattle ranches and exports beef all over the world.

Brazil's major cities are located in the south. Tourists flock to coastal **Rio de Janeiro,** which has more than 11.2 million people. **São Paulo,** home to more than 18.5 million people, is one of the fastest-growing urban areas in the world. It is also Brazil's leading trade and industrial center.

Brazil's Economic Challenges Today Brazil's economy is diverse and productive, yet the country still faces serious economic challenges. Brazil's economy has brought wealth to many Brazilians and created a large and strong middle class. Yet as many as one-fifth of Brazil's people live in extreme poverty. Many Brazilian cities are surrounded by favelas, or slum areas. Thousands of poor people move to cities looking for work in the factories. They live in crude shacks with neither running water nor sewage systems. City governments have tried to clean up these areas, but people continue to settle here because they have no money to pay for housing. Many children as young as 10 years old go to work to help earn money for their families.

Differentiated Instruction

Meeting Special Needs: Visual/Spatial Have students work in small groups to create an annotated map of Brazil's regions. Their maps should include illustrations and captions that identify the region's natural features, climates, major economic activities, cities, and environmental issues. Groups can be subdivided, with each smaller group researching a particular region. Then the small groups can reassemble to prepare their annotated map. Have groups present their maps to the class. L2

Refer to *Inclusion for the Middle School Social Studies Classroom Strategies and Activities* in the TCR.

Although Brazil has the largest area of remaining rain forest in the world, it also has the highest rate of deforestation. **Deforestation** is the destroying of large areas of forest. To increase jobs and products for export, the government has encouraged mining, logging, and farming in the rain forest. However, as you learned in Chapter 2, deforestation leads to soil erosion. It also harms the rain forest ecosystem and biodiversity. As deforestation takes place, roads are built, bringing companies, farmers, and change. Native Americans who live in the Amazon Basin find it difficult to follow their traditional cultures as this occurs. In addition, tropical forests give off huge amounts of oxygen and play a role in regulating the earth's climate. Thus, although the Amazon rain forest belongs to Brazil, the effects of deforestation are felt worldwide. Turn to page 250 to learn more about the vanishing rain forests.

✓ Reading Check **Why has the Brazilian government encouraged mining, logging, and farming in the rain forest?**

Brazil's History and Culture

With 176.5 million people, Brazil has the largest population of all Latin American nations. Brazil's culture is largely Portuguese. The Portuguese were the first and largest European group to colonize

Literature

BOTOQUE

Kayapo Indian Myth

In this myth of central Brazil, the hero brings fire to his people.

> ***"Botoque and the animals safely returned to their village with Jaguar's possessions. Everyone was delighted to eat grilled meat. They loved being able to warm themselves by the fire when the nights became cool. And they liked having the village fires provide protection from wild animals.***
>
> ***As for Jaguar, when he returned home and found that he had been robbed of his special possessions, his heart flooded with fury. 'So this is how Botoque has repaid me for adopting him as my son and teaching him the secret of the bow and arrow!' he exclaimed. 'Why, he did not even leave me fire. Well, no matter. In memory of this theft, from this time forth and evermore, I will eat my catch raw! This will keep the memory of my adopted son before my eyes and hatred for him—and all who walk the earth as he does—alive in my heart!'"***

Source: *"Botoque, Bringer of Fire"* excerpted from *Folklore, Myths, and Legends: A World Perspective.* Edited by Donna Rosenberg. NTC Publishing, 1997.

Analyzing Literature

Do you think the Kayapo Indians feared jaguars? Why or why not?

Chapter 8

Section 1, pages 232–237

Cultural Kaleidoscope

Brazil The name *Brazil* comes from a Portuguese word meaning "glowing ember." When Portuguese sailors first saw the trees that grow along the Brazilian coast, they thought the color of the wood looked like the glowing embers of a fire.

Literature

Answer Yes, because they portray the jaguar as being angry at Botoque and his people and keeping his hatred for Botoque alive in his heart.

Activity Read other Latin American myths to your class. Discuss the concepts the myths explain and how animals and humans are portrayed.

✓ Reading Check Answer

to increase jobs and products for export

3 Assess

Assign Section 1 Assessment as homework or an in-class activity.

Have students use the Interactive Tutor Self-Assessment CD-ROM to review Section 1.

Cooperative Learning Activity

Making Dioramas Have students work in groups to create a diorama of the Amazon rain forest. Individual students in each group can focus on specific topics for their diorama. For instance, one student can concentrate on trees; another on plants; and still others on birds, reptiles, mammals, or amphibians. Instruct members of each group to research their assigned topic. Then have them choose representative species to include in their group's diorama. Have students work in their groups to assemble the display. When it is complete, have students discuss the challenge of portraying the incredible variety of plant and animal life in this region. **ELL**

EE3 Physical Systems: Standard 8

Chapter 8

Section 1, pages 232–237

More About the Photos

Carnival Carnival is a four-day celebration that takes place before the Christian religious period called Lent. The famous Mardi Gras of New Orleans celebrates the same event.

Caption Answer people of European, African, Native American, Asian, or mixed ancestry

Measure student knowledge of physical features.

GeoQuiz Transparency

L2

Section Quiz

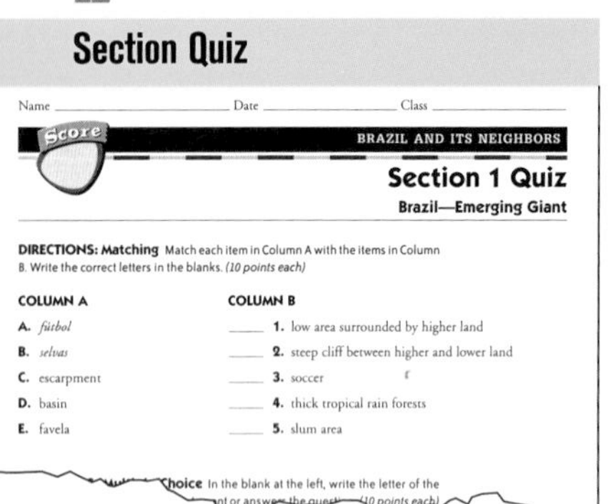
Name ______ Date ______ Class ______

Score

BRAZIL AND ITS NEIGHBORS

Section 1 Quiz

Brazil—Emerging Giant

DIRECTIONS: Matching Match each item in Column A with the items in Column B. Write the correct letters in the blanks. *(10 points each)*

COLUMN A	COLUMN B
A. *fútbol*	____ 1. low area surrounded by higher land
B. *selvas*	____ 2. steep cliff between higher and lower land
C. escarpment	____ 3. soccer
D. basin	____ 4. thick tropical rain forests
E. favela	____ 5. slum area

...Choice In the blank at the left, write the letter of the ... or answers the question. *(10 points each)*

Rio de Janeiro

A huge statue of Christ overlooks Rio de Janeiro (above right). Crowds of people in Rio de Janeiro celebrate Carnival wearing brightly colored costumes (above).

Culture What groups make up Brazil's population?

Brazil. Today Brazilians are of European, African, Native American, Asian, or mixed ancestry. Almost all of them speak a Brazilian form of Portuguese, which includes many words from Native American and African languages. Most of the population follow the Roman Catholic religion. Many Brazilians, however, combine Catholicism with beliefs and practices from African and Native American religions.

Influence of History Native Americans were the first people to live in Brazil. In the 1500s, the Portuguese forced Native Americans to work on large plantations that grew tobacco and, later, sugarcane. Many Native Americans died from disease or overwork. To replace them, early Portuguese settlers brought people from Africa and enslaved them. Slavery finally was banned in 1888, but Africans remained in Brazil, most of them living in the northeastern part of the country. Over the years, African traditions have influenced Brazilian religion, music, dance, and food.

Moving to the Cities Much of Brazil is sparsely populated. Millions of people have moved from rural areas to coastal cities to find better jobs. Now the government is encouraging people to move back to less populated inland areas to reduce city crowding. Highways now crisscross the country and reach many formerly remote regions. In 1960 Brazil moved its capital from coastal Rio de Janeiro 600 miles (966 km) inland to the newly built city of **Brasília.** With more than 2 million people, Brasília is a modern and rapidly growing city.

Content Background

Brazil's Economy For many centuries, Brazil swung between good and bad economic times because its economy was focused on producing only one or two commodities. When prices dropped or supplies were used up, the economy suffered. For most of that period, the economy centered on exploiting Brazil's resources. Lumber and sugar were the first main exports in the 1500s. By the 1700s, those seeking wealth mined Brazil's gold and diamonds. When easy-to-find supplies of these minerals were depleted, people built vast rubber plantations. Rubber was a major source of wealth in the late 1800s and early 1900s. Today Brazil's economy is more diverse. With its strong manufacturing and service industries, the country is somewhat better equipped to absorb price drops or falling demand for its minerals and export crops.

The Government Brazil declared independence from Portugal in 1822. At first the new nation was an empire, with emperors ruling until 1889. Then, like some other countries in Central and South America, Brazil was ruled by military dictators. Today Brazil is a democratic republic, where people elect a president and other leaders. In Brazil, though, citizens cannot choose whether to vote or not vote. People from ages 18 to 70 are required by law to vote. Brazil has more than a dozen political parties—not just two main ones, as in the United States.

The national government of Brazil is much stronger than its 26 state governments. Brazil's president has more power over the country than an American president does in the United States.

Leisure Time Brazilians enjoy soccer, which they call *fútbol.* Every village has a soccer field, and the larger cities have stadiums. Maracana Stadium in Rio de Janeiro seats 220,000 fans. Basketball is another popular sport.

Brazil is also famous for Carnival. This festival is celebrated just before the beginning of Lent, the Christian holy season that comes before Easter. The most spectacular Carnival is held each year in Rio de Janeiro. The celebration includes Brazilian music and showy parades.

Brazil has one of the largest television networks in the world. This network produces prime-time soap operas called *telenovelas.* These programs are wildly popular in Brazil—and viewers in more than 60 other nations enjoy them too.

✓ **Reading Check** **Why do most Brazilians speak a form of Portuguese?**

Assessment

Defining Terms

1. **Define** basin, *selva,* escarpment, favela, deforestation.

Recalling Facts

2. **History** Who was the first and largest group of Europeans to colonize Brazil?
3. **Economics** What resources attract companies to the Amazon Basin?
4. **Culture** What is the major religion of Brazil?

Critical Thinking

5. **Drawing Conclusions** In what way is deforestation threatening the Native Americans who live in the rain forest?
6. **Summarizing Information** What economic challenges face Brazilians?

Graphic Organizer

7. **Organizing Information** Create a diagram like this one. Beside the left arrow, write the cause of the government action. On the right, list three results of this action.

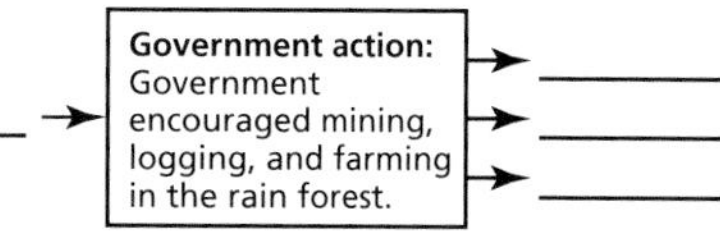

Applying Social Studies Skills

8. **Analyzing Maps** Look at the physical map on page 233. What large landform in Brazil surrounds the Amazon River?

Section 1 Assessment

1. The terms are defined in the Glossary.
2. the Portuguese
3. rubber, minerals, wood
4. Roman Catholicism
5. Native Americans find it difficult to follow traditional ways of life.
6. poverty, destruction of rain forest and Native American lands
7. Cause: desire to increase jobs and products for export; Effect: land is damaged, deforestation, Native Americans threatened
8. the Amazon Basin

Chapter 8

Section 1, pages 232–237

✓ Reading Check Answer

because Brazil was once a Portuguese colony

Reteach

Write false statements about Brazil. Ask for volunteers to correct the statements.

L1/ELL

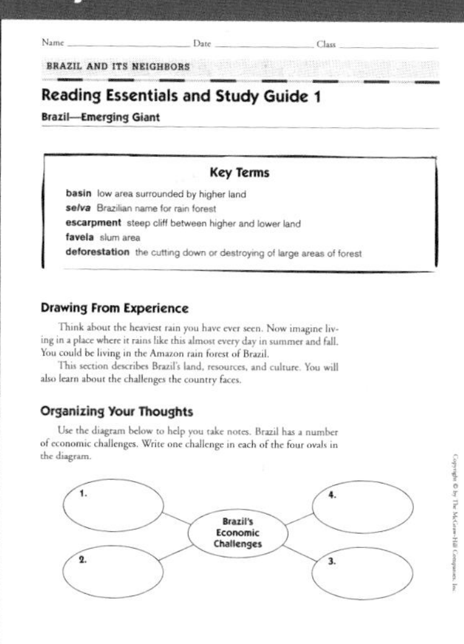
Reading Essentials and Study Guide

Name ______ Date ______ Class ______

BRAZIL AND ITS NEIGHBORS

Reading Essentials and Study Guide 1

Brazil—Emerging Giant

Key Terms

basin low area surrounded by higher land
selva Brazilian name for rain forest
escarpment steep cliff between higher and lower land
favela slum area
deforestation the cutting down or destroying of large areas of forest

Drawing From Experience

Think about the heaviest rain you have ever seen. Now imagine living in a place where it rains like this almost every day in summer and fall. You could be living in the Amazon rain forest of Brazil.

This section describes Brazil's land, resources, and culture. You will also learn about the challenges the country faces.

Organizing Your Thoughts

Use the diagram below to help you take notes. Brazil has a number of economic challenges. Write one challenge in each of the four ovals in the diagram.

96

CLOSE

Have each student list five facts about Brazil from this lesson. Then have students work in groups to create a summary of the lesson based on their lists.

Critical Thinking Skill

TEACH

To demonstrate the importance of sequencing information correctly, write the following three steps: "Put the two pieces of bread together," "Spread peanut butter on one piece of bread," "Spread jelly on the other piece of bread." Ask for volunteers to explain the problem with this sequence. *(Putting the bread together should be done last.)* L1

Additional Skills Practice

1. **Why are words like *first, then,* and *finally* useful in determining sequence?** *(They show the order in which things happened.)*
2. Have students read the subsection Brazil's Economy. **What categories could you use to group the information that you read?** *(Possible answers: crops and industries; economic successes and challenges)*

Additional Skills Resources

 Chapter Skills Review

 Building Geography Skills for Life

GLENCOE TECHNOLOGY

Skillbuilder Interactive Workbook CD-ROM, Level 1

This interactive CD-ROM reinforces student mastery of essential social studies skills.

Critical Thinking Skill

Sequencing and Categorizing Information

Sequencing means placing facts in the order in which they occurred. *Categorizing* means organizing information into groups of related facts and ideas. Both actions help you deal with large quantities of information in a manageable way.

Learning the Skill

Follow these steps to learn sequencing and categorizing skills:

- Look for dates or clue words that provide you with a chronological order: *in 2004, the late 1990s, first, then, finally, after the Great Depression,* and so on.
- If the sequence of events is not important, you may want to categorize the information instead. Categories might include economic activities or cultural traits.
- List these characteristics, or categories, as the headings on a chart.
- As you read, fill in details under the proper category on the chart.

Practicing the Skill

Read the paragraphs below, and then answer the questions that follow.

After Brazil's independence from Portugal in 1822, a bill was presented to build a new capital named Brasília. More than 100 years later, in 1955, a planning committee chose the site for the new capital. The first streets were paved in 1958. On April 20, 1960, the festivities to officially "open" the new capital started at 4:00 P.M.

Brasília has both positive and negative aspects. The positive include virtually no air pollution, no threat of natural disasters, many green areas, and a pleasant climate. The negative aspects of the capital include very high housing prices, inefficient public transportation, few parking spaces, and long distances between the various government buildings.

1. What information can be organized sequentially?
2. What information can be organized under these categories: "Positive Aspects" and "Negative Aspects"?

Brasília

Applying the Skill

Find two newspaper or magazine articles about Brazil or another South American country. Sequence or categorize the information in the articles on note cards or in a chart.

GO TO Practice key skills with **Glencoe Skillbuilder Interactive Workbook, Level 1.**

CHAPTER 8

Practicing the Skill Answers

1. The facts about the development of Brasília; 1822—proposal to build a new capital; 1955—site chosen; 1958—first streets paved; 1960—new city officially opened
2. Positive and negative aspects of Brasília; Positive—low pollution, low threat of natural disasters, presence of open space, pleasant climate; Negative—high housing prices, poor transportation and parking, need to travel long distances between government buildings

Applying the Skill

Students' cards or charts should show the information properly categorized or sequenced. You might wish to ask them to supply the original source along with their completed work.

Guide to Reading

Main Idea

Brazil's neighboring countries have a diverse array of landforms, climates, and cultures.

Terms to Know

- pampas
- *estancia*
- gaucho
- hydroelectric power
- llanos
- altitude
- caudillo

Reading Strategy

Create a diagram like this one. Fill in the names of Brazil's neighbors to the north and south, and then write at least one key fact about the people from each country.

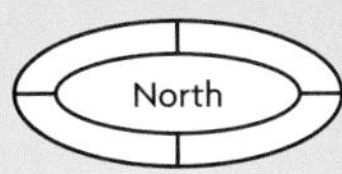

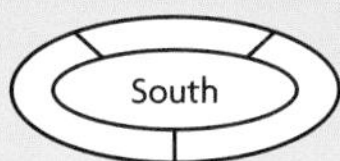

Argentina to Venezuela

The traditional music of Paraguay seems to be out of place with the rest of its culture. The harp is the country's national instrument, and Paraguayans are famous for their slow, mournful guitar playing. In contrast, the traditional dances are much livelier. Here, a woman performs the bottle dance—a difficult feat even though the bottles are attached to one another.

South of Brazil lie **Argentina, Uruguay,** and **Paraguay.** North of Brazil is Caribbean South America, which includes **Venezuela, Guyana, Suriname,** and **French Guiana.**

Argentina

Argentina is South America's second-largest country, after Brazil. Its southern tip reaches almost to the continent of Antarctica. Argentina is about the size of the United States east of the Mississippi River.

The Andes tower over the western part of Argentina. Snowcapped peaks and clear blue lakes attract tourists for skiing and hiking. **Aconcagua** (AH•kohn•KAH•gwah) soars to a height of 22,834 feet (6,960 m), making it the highest mountain in the Western Hemisphere.

South and east of the Andes lies a dry, windswept plateau called **Patagonia.** Most of Patagonia gets little rain and has poor soil. As a result, sheep raising is the only major economic activity there.

239

Focus

Section Objectives

1. Compare the landscapes and climates of Venezuela and Argentina.
2. Describe the economies of Brazil's northern and southern neighbors.
3. Discuss the histories of Brazil's neighboring countries.

BELLRINGER Skillbuilder Activity

Project transparency and have students answer the question.

Daily Focus Skills Transparency

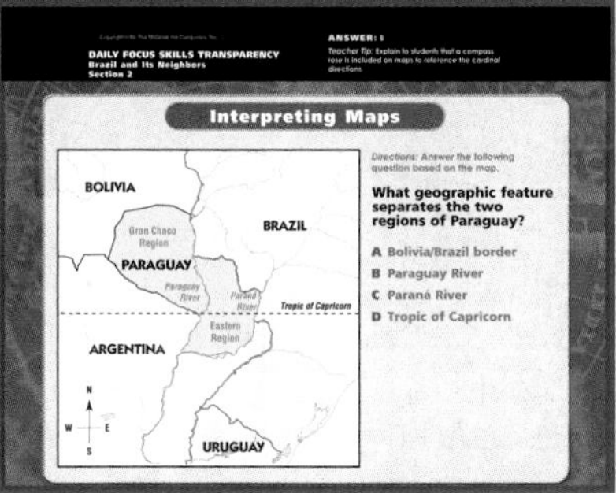

Reading Preview

■ **Activating Prior Knowledge** Ask students to describe the American West. *(large open spaces; ranches; cattle and sheep; grasslands)* Point out that these words apply to large parts of Argentina as well.

■ **Preteaching Vocabulary** Have students practice the pronunciation of *caudillo.* Note that the double *l* sounds like a *y.*

Section Resources

Reproducible Masters
- Reproducible Lesson Plan
- Daily Lecture and Discussion Notes
- Note-taking Guide
- Guided Reading Activity
- Reading Essentials and Study Guide
- Section Quiz

Transparencies
- Daily Focus Skills Transparency

Multimedia
- Vocabulary PuzzleMaker CD-ROM
- Interactive Tutor Self-Assessment CD-ROM
- Presentation Plus! CD-ROM
- ExamView® Pro Testmaker CD-ROM
- MindJogger Videoquiz

2 TEACH

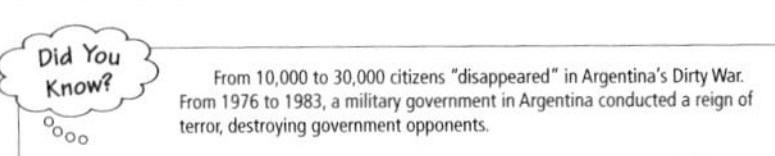

Reading Strategy

Outlining Have students create an outline for the section by writing down the headings and subheadings and then writing two summary statements under each subheading. L1

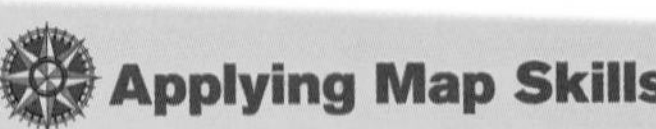

Daily Lecture and Discussion Notes

BRAZIL AND ITS NEIGHBORS

Daily Lecture and Discussion Notes

Argentina to Venezuela

Did You Know? From 10,000 to 30,000 citizens "disappeared" in Argentina's Dirty War. From 1976 to 1983, a military government in Argentina conducted a reign of terror, destroying government opponents.

I. Argentina

A. Nearly reaching the continent of Antarctica, Argentina is approximately the size of the United States east of the Mississippi River.

B. The Andes tower over the western part of Argentina. South and east of the Andes is Patagonia, a dry and windswept plateau.

Applying Map Skills

Answers

1. ranching, commercial farming
2. Venezuela, Guyana, Suriname, French Guiana, Brazil

Skills Practice

What are the major crops grown in Argentina? *(tobacco, fruit, grapes, and cotton)*

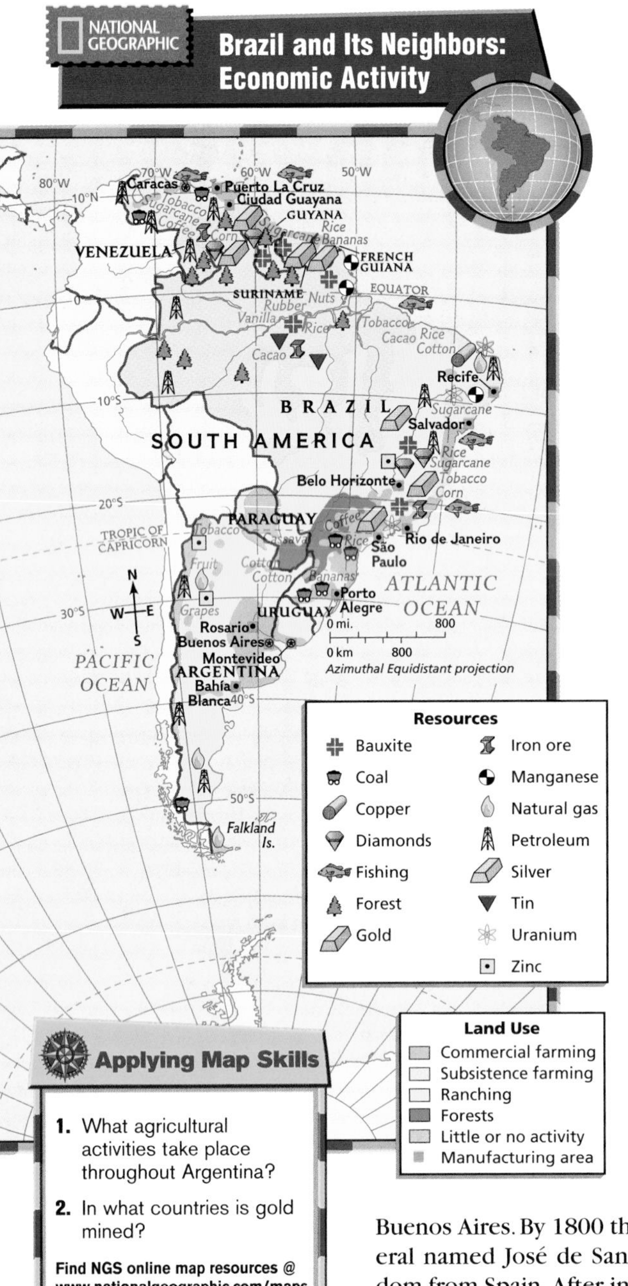

Applying Map Skills

1. What agricultural activities take place throughout Argentina?
2. In what countries is gold mined?

Find NGS online map resources @ www.nationalgeographic.com/maps

The center of Argentina has vast treeless plains known as the **pampas.** Similar to the Great Plains of the United States, the pampas are home to farmers who grow grains and ranchers who raise livestock. More than two-thirds of Argentina's people live in this region.

Argentina's Economy Argentina's economy depends heavily on farming and ranching. The country's major farm products include beef, sugarcane, wheat, soybeans, and corn. Huge ***estancias*** (ay•STAHN•see•ahs), or ranches, cover the pampas. **Gauchos** (GOW•chohs), or cowhands, take care of the livestock on the ranches. Gauchos are the national symbol of Argentina, admired for their independence and horse-riding skills. The livestock that the gauchos herd and tend are a vital part of the country's economy. Beef and food products are Argentina's chief exports. Turn to page 246 to read more about gauchos.

Argentina is one of the most industrialized countries in South America. Most of the country's factories are in or near **Buenos Aires,** Argentina's capital and largest city. The leading manufactured goods are food products, automobiles, chemicals, textiles, books, and magazines.

Petroleum is Argentina's most valuable mineral resource. The country's major oil fields are in Patagonia and the Andes. Other minerals, such as zinc, iron ore, copper, tin, and uranium, are mined in the Andes as well. Despite these resources, Argentina's economy has struggled during the early years of the twenty-first century.

Argentina's History In the late 1500s, Spaniards settled in the area that is now Buenos Aires. By 1800 the city was a flourishing port. In 1816 a general named José de San Martín led Argentina in its fight for freedom from Spain. After independence, the country was torn apart by civil war. By the mid-1850s, a strong national government had emerged, and Argentina entered a time of prosperity. During the first half of the 1900s, however, Argentina's elected leaders governed poorly. The economy suffered, and the military took over.

Reading Strategy — Reading the Text

Categorizing Information Have students work in pairs to organize this section's information in a chart. Have partners prepare a chart with the column headings "Landforms," "Climate," "Economy," "People," and "History." Then have both students in each pair write a list of 10 to 12 facts about Brazil's neighbors. Have students take turns reading their facts to each other. The partner then has the task of placing each fact in the correct category by writing it under the appropriate column heading. L1

*Use the **Reading Skills Handbook** for more reading strategies.*

One of these military leaders, Juan Perón, became a dictator in the late 1940s. With his popular wife, Eva, at his side, Perón tried to improve the economy and give more help to workers. His crackdown on freedom of speech and the press made people unhappy, however. In 1955 a revolt drove Perón from power, and democracy returned.

Military officers again took control of Argentina in the 1970s. They ruled harshly, and political violence resulted in the deaths of many people. In 1982 Argentina suffered defeat in a war with the United Kingdom for control of the **Falkland Islands.** The Falklands, known in Argentina as the Malvinas, lie in the Atlantic Ocean off the coast of Argentina. The military stepped down, and elected leaders regained control of the government when Argentina lost this war.

Today Argentina is a democratic republic. As in the United States, the national government is much stronger than the 23 provincial, or state, governments. A powerful elected president leads the nation for a four-year term. A legislature with two houses makes the laws.

Argentina's People About 85 percent of Argentina's people are of European ancestry. During the late 1800s, immigrants in large numbers came to Argentina from Spain and Italy. Their arrival greatly influenced Argentina's society and culture. Many more immigrants arrived from Europe after World War II. European ways of life are stronger in Argentina today than in most other Latin American countries.

The official language of Argentina is Spanish, although the language includes many Italian words. Most people are Roman Catholic. About 90 percent of Argentina's people live in cities and towns. More than 13 million people live in Buenos Aires and its suburbs. Buenos Aires has wide streets and European-style buildings. Its citizens call themselves *porteños* (pohr•TAY•nyohs), which means "people of the port." Many have a passion for the national dance of Argentina, the tango.

Reading Check Why does Argentina have a strong European culture?

Uruguay and Paraguay

Uruguay and Paraguay differ from each other in environment, population, and development. Uruguay has a mild climate, rolling hilly plains and rich grasslands. This nation is a buffer zone between the two powerful nations of Brazil and Argentina. Originally settled by the Portuguese, then taken over by Spain, Uruguay revolted against both countries and eventually became completely independent in 1828.

Immigration from Spain and Italy and the introduction of sheep are keys to Uruguay's development. The country's 3.4 million people, half of whom live in the capital city of **Montevideo,** are mostly of European descent. Uruguay's economy depends on raising sheep and cattle. In fact, sheep and cattle outnumber people by ten to one, and about 70 percent of the country is pasture. Animal products—meat, wool, and hides—top Uruguay's exports. The major industries—textiles, footwear, and leather goods—use the products of the vast animal herds. Large haciendas are complemented by many medium-sized and

Web Activity Visit ***The World and Its People*** Web site at twip.glencoe.com and click on **Chapter 8—Student Web Activities** to learn about Paraguay.

Chapter 8

Section 2, pages 239–245

Reading Check Answer

because about 85 percent of Argentina's people are of European ancestry

L1/ELL

Guided Reading Activity

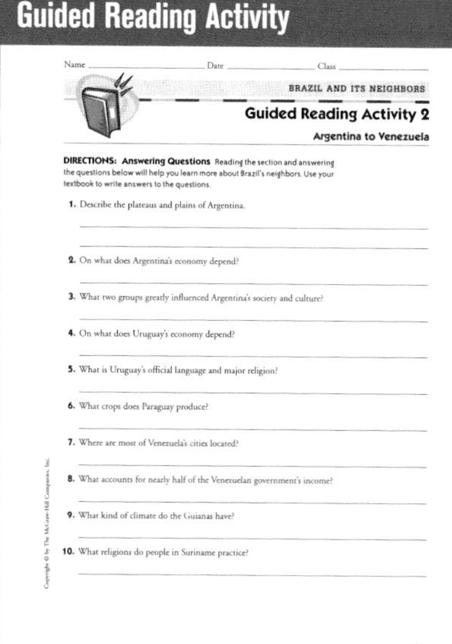
Name ______ Date ______ Class ______

BRAZIL AND ITS NEIGHBORS

Guided Reading Activity 2

Argentina to Venezuela

DIRECTIONS: Answering Questions Reading the section and answering the questions below will help you learn more about Brazil's neighbors. Use your textbook to write answers to the questions.

1. Describe the plateaus and plains of Argentina.
2. On what does Argentina's economy depend?
3. What two groups greatly influenced Argentina's society and culture?
4. On what does Uruguay's economy depend?
5. What is Uruguay's official language and major religion?
6. What crops does Paraguay produce?
7. Where are most of Venezuela's cities located?
8. What accounts for nearly half of the Venezuelan government's income?
9. What kind of climate do the Guianas have?
10. What religions do people in Suriname practice?

111

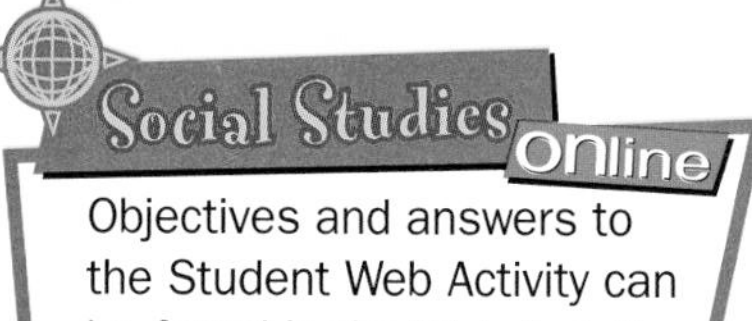

Objectives and answers to the Student Web Activity can be found in the Web Activity Lesson Plan at twip.glencoe.com

Differentiated Instruction

Meeting Special Needs: Verbal/Linguistic Have students organize into pairs and have each member of a pair write a set of fill-in-the-blank questions using information from this section. On a separate sheet of paper, have them prepare a list of answers for all the questions, but with the letters of the answer words scrambled. Have one student in each pair ask the other his or her questions, with the respondent student referring to the scrambled words to identify the answer. When the first student has asked all of his or her questions, have the students reverse roles. L1

Refer to *Inclusion for the Middle School Social Studies Classroom Strategies and Activities* in the TCR.

Paraguay's flag has a different design on each side. On one side is the country's coat of arms. On the other side is the seal of the national treasury.

3 Assess

Assign Section 2 Assessment as homework or an in-class activity.

Have students use the Interactive Tutor Self-Assessment CD-ROM to review Section 2.

Reading Check Answer

hydroelectric power

small farms. The Uruguayans have the highest literacy rate, the lowest population growth rate, the best diet, and one of the highest standards of living of any South American country. Spanish is the official language, and the Roman Catholic faith is the major religion.

Paraguay In Paraguay, the society and economy have followed quite a different course. The eastern third of Paraguay, with its rich soils and fertile grasslands, was settled by the Spanish. The western two-thirds of the country, a great forest area known as the **Gran Chaco,** was brought into the Spanish territory by Roman Catholic missionaries.

In the 1800s and 1900s, a series of wars severely hurt Paraguay, destroying the economy of the country. After the worst of these—the five-year war against Brazil, Argentina, and Uruguay in the 1860s—Paraguay's male population was cut in half. Experts estimate that Paraguay also lost 55,000 square miles of territory.

Forestry and farming are Paraguay's major economic activities. Large cattle ranches cover much of the country. Most farmers, however, grow grains, cotton, soybeans, and cassava on small plots. Cassava roots can be ground up to make tapioca. They can also be sliced and fried just like potatoes.

Paraguay also exports electricity. The country has the world's largest hydroelectric power generator at the Itaipu (ee•TY•poo) Dam, on the Paraná River. **Hydroelectric power** is electricity that is generated by flowing water. Paraguay sells nearly 90 percent of the electricity it produces to neighboring countries.

Paraguayans today are mostly of mixed Guaraní—a Native American group—and Spanish ancestry. Both Spanish and Guaraní are official languages, but more people speak Guaraní. Most people practice the Roman Catholic faith. About one-half of the people live in cities. **Asunción** (ah•SOON•see•OHN) is the capital and largest city.

Paraguayan arts are influenced by Guaraní culture. Guaraní lace is Paraguay's most famous handicraft. Like people in Uruguay, the people of Paraguay enjoy meat dishes and sip *yerba maté,* a tealike drink.

Reading Check What important export is generated at the Itaipu Dam?

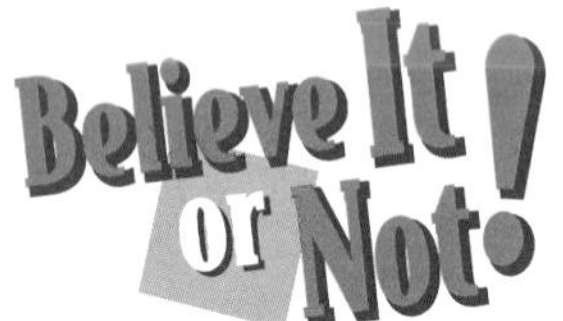

Roping a Capybara

Capybaras are the world's largest rodents. They can grow to be 2 feet tall and 4 feet long, and weigh more than 100 pounds. Found in Central and South America, capybaras (ka•pih•BAR•uhs) live along rivers and lakes and eat vegetation. Here, a gaucho ropes a dog-sized capybara in Venezuela. Some Venezuelans eat capybara during the Easter season.

Venezuela

Venezuela (VEH•nuh•ZWAY•luh) is the westernmost country of Caribbean South America. In the northwest lie the lowland coastal areas surrounding **Lake Maracaibo** (MAH•rah•KY•boh), the largest lake in South America. Swamps fill much of this area, and few people live here. The great number of towering oil wells, however, give you a clue that rich oil fields lie under the lake and along its shores. Venezuela has more oil reserves than any other country in the Americas.

The Andean highlands begin south of the lake and are part of the Andes mountain ranges. This area includes most of the nation's cities, including **Caracas** (kah•RAH•kahs), the capital and largest city. East of the highlands, you see grassy plains known as the **llanos** (LAH•nohs). The llanos have many ranches, farms, and oil fields. Venezuela's most

Team-Teaching Activity

Mathematics The Itaipu Dam is very large. In fact, it may be difficult for students to appreciate its size. Give students the following statistics: The dam has a reservoir capacity of 1.02 trillion cubic feet (28.9 billion cubic m). The waters of the Paraná River explode through a 400-yard-wide spillway at more than 90 miles per hour. The force of the water is transformed into 12,600 megawatts of electricity. One megawatt is equal to 1 million watts. Have students work with the math teacher to compare these figures to those of other structures so that they understand how large the dam is. L1 

EE5 Environment and Society: Standard 14

important river—the **Orinoco**—flows across the llanos. This river is a valuable source of hydroelectric power for Venezuela's cities.

South and east of the llanos rise the Guiana Highlands, which are deeply cut by rivers. **Angel Falls**—the world's highest waterfall—spills over a bluff in this region.

Because it is close to the Equator, Venezuela has a mostly tropical climate. In the Guiana Highlands to the south, you enter a steamy rain forest. As in Mexico, temperatures in Venezuela differ with **altitude,** or height above sea level. Higher altitudes have cooler climates.

Venezuela's Economy Venezuelans once depended on crops such as coffee and cacao to earn a living. Since the 1920s, petroleum has changed the country's economy. Venezuela is a world leader in oil production and one of the chief suppliers of oil to the United States. Because the government owns the oil industry, oil provides nearly half of the government's income. A two-month national oil strike from December 2002 to February 2003 temporarily halted Venezuela's economic activity. This shows how much the country relies on its oil production.

Iron ore, limestone, bauxite, gold, diamonds, and emeralds are also mined. Factories make steel, chemicals, and food products. About 10 percent of the people farm, growing sugarcane and bananas or raising cattle.

History and Government Originally settled by Native Americans, Venezuela became a Spanish colony in the early 1500s. With its many rivers, the land in South America reminded early Spanish explorers of Venice, Italy, which is full of canals. They named the area *Venezuela,* which means "Little Venice."

In the early 1800s, rebellion swept across the Spanish colonial empire. Simón Bolívar (see•MOHN boh•LEE•VAHR), who was born in Venezuela, became one of the leaders of this revolt. He and his soldiers freed Venezuela and neighboring regions from Spanish rule. In 1830 Venezuela became independent.

During most of the 1800s and 1900s, the country was governed by military rulers called **caudillos** (kow•THEE•yohz). Their rule was often harsh. Since 1958, Venezuela has been a democracy led by a president and a two-house legislature.

Rising oil prices during the 1970s benefited many Venezuelans. When oil prices fell in the 1990s, the country suffered. In 1998 voters

NATIONAL GEOGRAPHIC **On Location**

Angel Falls

Angel Falls—the highest waterfall in the world at 3,212 feet (979 m)—roars over a cliff in Venezuela. It would take 11 football fields stacked end-to-end to reach the top.

Economics **What is one of the rivers that provides Venezuela with hydroelectric power?**

Chapter 8

Section 2, pages 239–245

Cultural Kaleidoscope

Venezuela Most Venezuelan cities have a *Plaza Bolívar*—a public square honoring the South American liberator, Simón Bolívar. Venezuelans consider it rude to behave disrespectfully in one of these squares. They also take negative comments about Bolívar as an insult.

More About the Photo

Angel Falls The water at Angel Falls does not pour over the top of the mesa—which is named Auyán Tepui, or "Devil's Mountain." Rather, the river flows in underground streams beneath the mesa's surface and emerges 200 to 300 feet (61 to 91 m) below the top.

Caption Answer the Orinoco

Cooperative Learning Activity

Comparing Governments Organize students into four groups and assign one of the countries of Caribbean South America to each group. Direct groups to research the history and government of their assigned country. Have groups present their findings in an illustrated report. After all the reports have been presented, have students discuss the similarities and differences among the governments of these countries. L2

EE4 Human Systems: Standard 12

More About the Photo

Celebration Most Venezuelans follow the Roman Catholic faith, so many of the celebrations are associated with religious observances. While some celebrations involve dancing, music, costumes, and parades, many involve attending Mass, a type of worship service.

Caption Answer Roman Catholicism

Reading Check Answer

oil/petroleum

L2

Section Quiz

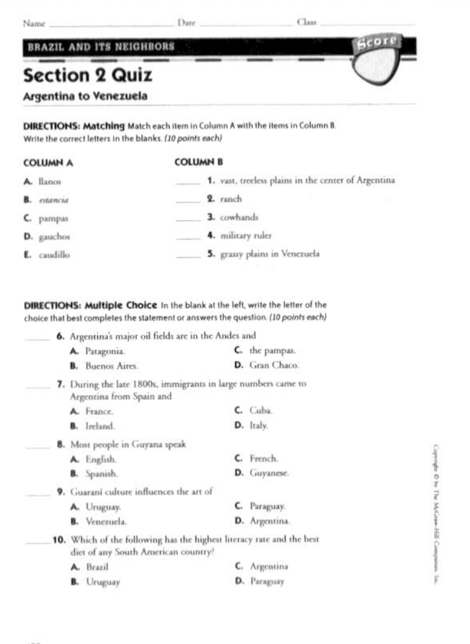

Name ____ Date ____ Class ____

BRAZIL AND ITS NEIGHBORS — Score

Section 2 Quiz

Argentina to Venezuela

DIRECTIONS: Matching Match each item in Column A with the items in Column B. Write the correct letters in the blanks. *(10 points each)*

COLUMN A	COLUMN B
A. llanos	____ 1. vast, treeless plains in the center of Argentina
B. *estancia*	____ 2. ranch
C. pampas	____ 3. cowhands
D. gauchos	____ 4. military ruler
E. caudillo	____ 5. grassy plains in Venezuela

DIRECTIONS: Multiple Choice In the blank at the left, write the letter of the choice that best completes the statement or answers the question. *(10 points each)*

____ 6. Argentina's major oil fields are in the Andes and
A. Patagonia. C. the pampas.
B. Buenos Aires. D. Gran Chaco.

____ 7. During the late 1800s, immigrants in large numbers came to Argentina from Spain and
A. France. C. Cuba.
B. Ireland. D. Italy.

____ 8. Most people in Guyana speak
A. English. C. French.
B. Spanish. D. Guyanese.

____ 9. Guaraní culture influences the art of
A. Uruguay. C. Paraguay.
B. Venezuela. D. Argentina.

____ 10. Which of the following has the highest literacy rate and the best diet of any South American country?
A. Brazil C. Argentina
B. Uruguay D. Paraguay

122

Celebration

Venezuelan dancers in costumes and playing maracas take part in Corpus Christi, a local Roman Catholic celebration.

Religion **What is the major religion in Venezuela?**

elected a former military leader, Hugo Chávez, as president. Chávez promised to solve Venezuela's problems, but his growing power split the country into opposing groups. In 2000 the military overthrew Chávez, but street protests put him back in office. Two years later, a nationwide strike also failed to remove Chávez from office. This strike lasted three months and damaged Venezuela's already weak economy.

Venezuela's People Most of the 25.7 million people in Venezuela have a mix of European, African, and Native American backgrounds. Spanish is the major language of the country, and the major religion is Roman Catholicism. About 90 percent of Venezuelans live in cities. Some 2.8 million people live in Caracas, the capital, which has skyscrapers surrounded by mountains.

Reading Check **What product changed Venezuela's economy?**

The Guianas

Caribbean South America also includes the countries of Guyana (gy•AH•nuh) and Suriname (SUR•uh•NAH•muh) and the territory of French Guiana (gee•A•nuh). Guyana was a British colony called British Guiana. Suriname, once a colony of the Netherlands, was called Dutch Guiana. As a result, these three lands are called "the Guianas."

The Guianas have similar landforms. Highlands in the interiors are covered by thick rain forests. Toward the Caribbean coast, the land descends to low coastal plains. The climate is hot and tropical. Most people live on the coastal plains because of the cooling ocean winds. Sugarcane grows in Guyana and French Guiana, while rice and bananas flourish in Suriname. Many people earn their living mining gold and bauxite.

Guyana In the early 1600s, the Dutch were the first Europeans to settle in Guyana. They forced Native Americans and Africans to work on tobacco, coffee, and cotton farms and, later, on sugarcane plantations. The United Kingdom won possession of the Dutch colonies in the early 1800s and ended slavery. Still needing workers, the British paid Indians from Asia to move here. Today people from India make up most of Guyana's population. Another one-third are of African ancestry. Small numbers of Native Americans and Europeans also live here. Christianity and Hinduism are the chief religions. Most people speak English. **Georgetown,** the capital, is the major city.

Guyana won its independence from Britain in 1966. Guyana remains a very poor country, however, and depends on aid from the United Kingdom and other countries.

Differentiated Instruction

Meeting Special Needs: Gifted and Talented Have students research the ethnic, political, and religious differences among major components of the population in Guyana and Suriname. Have students think about what problems might arise because of these differences. **Ask:** **How might these differences divide society? How could they hold back economic development? What steps could a government take to try to overcome these differences?** Have students discuss their answers to these questions as a class. **L3**

Refer to *Inclusion for the Middle School Social Studies Classroom Strategies and Activities* in the TCR.

Suriname The British were the first Europeans to settle Suriname, but the Dutch gained control in 1667. As in Guyana, the Dutch brought enslaved Africans to work on large sugarcane plantations. Because of harsh treatment, many Africans fled into the isolated interior of the country. Their descendants still live there today. Later the Dutch hired workers from the Asian lands of India and Indonesia.

Asians form a large part of Suriname's population. About half of Suriname's people practice Christianity. The rest follow Hinduism or Islam. The main language is Dutch. **Paramaribo** (PAH•rah•MAH•ree•boh) is the capital and chief port. In 1975 Suriname won its independence from the Dutch. The country is poor, however, so it still relies on aid from the Dutch government.

French Guiana French Guiana became a colony of France in the 1600s and remains one today. The country is headed by a French official called a *prefect,* who lives in the capital, **Cayenne** (ky•EHN). The French government provides jobs and aid to many of French Guiana's people.

Most people in French Guiana are of African or mixed African and European ancestry. They speak French and are Roman Catholic. In Cayenne, you see sidewalk cafés and police in French uniforms. Shoppers use euros, the French currency—just as they would in Paris, France. You also see local influences, such as Carnival, Native American woodcarving, and Caribbean music and dance.

Reading Check What European countries influenced the development of Guyana, Suriname, and French Guiana?

Section 2 Assessment

Defining Terms

1. **Define** pampas, *estancia,* gaucho, hydroelectric power, llanos, altitude, caudillo.

Recalling Facts

2. **Region** Describe two ways in which the pampas are similar to the Great Plains of the United States.
3. **Human/Environment Interaction** What is the significance of the Itaipu Dam?
4. **History** Who was Simón Bolívar?

Critical Thinking

5. **Analyzing Cause and Effect** Which of Juan Perón's policies led to his removal from office?
6. **Drawing Conclusions** Why is Hinduism one of the major religions of Guyana?

Graphic Organizer

7. **Organizing Information** Create a diagram like this one. In the top box, under the heading, list similarities about the Guianas. In the bottom boxes, under the headings, write facts about each country that show their differences.

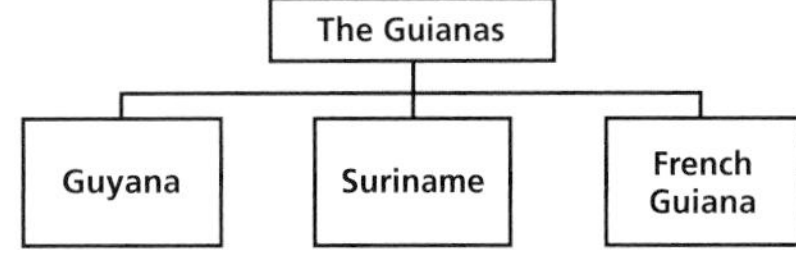

Applying Social Studies Skills

8. **Analyzing Maps** Look at the economic activity map on page 240. What agricultural activities take place in Venezuela?

Chapter 8

Section 2, pages 239–245

Reading Check Answer

Guyana—Great Britain; Suriname—Netherlands; French Guiana—France

L1/ELL

Reading Essentials and Study Guide

BRAZIL AND ITS NEIGHBORS

Reading Essentials and Study Guide 2
Argentina to Venezuela

Key Terms
pampas vast treeless plains
estancia huge ranches on the pampas
gaucho cowhand
hydroelectric power electricity generated by flowing water
llanos grassy plains
altitude height above sea level
caudillo military ruler

Reading Strategy

Enrich
Have students research the history of one of the countries in this region and create an annotated time line, complete with illustrations and captions.

Close

Give students an outline map of the region and have them label Brazil's seven neighboring countries, their capitals, major landforms, and economic activities.

Section 2 Assessment

1. The terms are defined in the Glossary.
2. They are home to farmers who grow grains and ranchers who raise livestock.
3. It is the world's largest hydroelectric power generator.
4. leader of the revolt against Spanish rule that gained independence for Venezuela and neighboring regions
5. cracking down on freedom of speech and the press
6. People from India make up most of Guyana's population.
7. Students should list similarities and differences as found in the textbook.
8. tobacco, sugarcane, coffee, corn

TEACH

Ask students if they are familiar with songs, books, or movies about the life of American cowboys. Ask volunteers to identify what values these works often portray. *(Possible answers include self-reliance, hard work, toughness, affection for animals, and respect for others.)* Suggest that they look for similar values in this poem. L1

More About José Hernández

Hernández was born in Buenos Aires, but he became acquainted with the life of the gaucho in his teens when he was sent to live in the countryside for his health. His poem aimed to celebrate the lost life of the gauchos to whom, Hernández felt, the people of Argentina owed much and who were threatened by modernization.

Interdisciplinary Connections

Literature *El Gaucho Martín Fierro* is now seen as the impassioned praise of a persecuted minority. Have students select a group that they feel is threatened by social changes and write a short poem celebrating that group's way of life. Ask for volunteers to read their poems to the class.

Making Connections

ART | SCIENCE | CULTURE | TECHNOLOGY

Poetry on the Pampas

As you learned in Section 2, gauchos herd cattle on the pampas. In 1872 José Hernández wrote the epic poem *El Gaucho Martín Fierro*. The poem tells the story of Martín Fierro, who recalls his life as a gaucho on the pampas. The following lines were translated from the poem.

El Gaucho Martín Fierro
by José Hernández (1834–1886)

A son am I of the rolling plain,
A gaucho born and bred;
For me the whole great world is small,
Believe me, my heart can hold it all;
The snake strikes not at my passing foot,
The sun burns not my head.

. . . .

Ah, my mind goes back and I see again
The gaucho I knew of old;
He picked his mount, and was ready aye,
To sing or fight, and for work or play,
And even the poorest one was rich
In the things not bought with gold.

The neediest gaucho in the land,
That had least of goods and gear,
Could show a troop of a single strain,
And rode with a silver-studded rein,
The plains were brown with the grazing herds,
And everywhere was cheer.

And when the time of the branding came,
It did one good to see
How the hand was quick and the eye was true,
When the steers they threw with the long lassoo [lasso],
And the merry band that the years have swept
Like leaves from the autumn tree.

Gauchos on Argentina's pampas ▲

Making the Connection

1. How does the poet describe the land on which the gaucho lives?
2. How can you tell from the poem that a gaucho is often on the move?
3. **Drawing Conclusions** What evidence does the poem give that the gaucho's way of life was a proud and happy one?

Making the Connection

1. Hernández describes the land as a rolling plain that has snakes and hot sun and is full of vast herds of cattle.
2. The poem mentions that snakes cannot strike at the passing gaucho; a gaucho picked his horse and was ready to ride.
3. The lines printed here mention that even the poorest gaucho was rich and rode with a silver-studded rein, and everywhere there was cheer.

Reading Review

Section 1 Brazil—Emerging Giant

Terms to Know
- basin
- *selva*
- escarpment
- favela
- deforestation

Main Idea

Brazil is a large country with many resources, a lively culture, and serious economic challenges.

✓ History Brazil declared independence in 1822 after centuries of colonial rule by Portugal.

✓ Economics Brazil is trying to reduce its number of poor people and balance the use of resources with the preservation of its rain forests.

✓ Culture Most Brazilians are of mixed Portuguese, African, Native American, and Asian ancestry.

Section 2 Argentina to Venezuela

Terms to Know
- pampas
- *estancia*
- gaucho
- hydroelectric power
- llanos
- altitude
- caudillo

Main Idea

Brazil's neighboring countries have a diverse array of landforms, climates, and cultures.

✓ Region Few people live in Argentina's Andes region or Patagonia. The most populous area is the vast grassland called the pampas.

✓ Culture Argentina's capital, Buenos Aires, is a huge city with European style.

✓ Economics Uruguay and Paraguay have large areas of grass-covered plains that support ranching and industries that depend on raising livestock.

✓ Culture Most Venezuelans are of mixed European, African, and Native American ancestry. Most live in cities in the central highlands.

✓ History Simón Bolívar led a revolt that freed Venezuela from Spain in 1830.

✓ Culture Guyana and Suriname have large numbers of people descended from workers who were brought from Africa and Asia.

This broad street in Buenos Aires is the Avenida 9 de Julio—or the Avenue of the Ninth of July. It is named in honor of the day Argentina won independence from Spain. ▶

Reading Review

Use the Chapter 8 Reading Review to preview, review, condense, or reteach the chapter.

Preview/Review

Use the Terms to Know lists to help students review and study.

Activity Have students group the terms according to the category to which they belong—physical geography, economics, human geography. Read the terms aloud, one at a time, and ask for volunteers to categorize each term.

Vocabulary PuzzleMaker CD-ROM reinforces the vocabulary terms used in Chapter 8.

The Interactive Tutor Self-Assessment CD-ROM allows students to review Chapter 8 content.

Condense

Have students read the Chapter 8 summary statements.

Guided Reading Activities

Audio Program

Reteach

Reteaching Activity

Reading Essentials and Study Guide

Reading Strategy — Read to Write

Creating a Photo Album Have students choose one of the countries studied in this chapter and imagine that they have visited there. Ask them to create a photo album that shows what they saw in the country. They should look for photographs that show the landscape, cities, places of interest, and people of their chosen country. With each photograph, have them write a brief caption that identifies the subject of the photo and gives additional information about it. L1

 **EE2 Places and Regions: Standard 4**

Assessment and Activities

GLENCOE TECHNOLOGY

MindJogger Videoquiz

Use MindJogger Videoquiz to review the Chapter 8 content.

 Available in DVD and VHS

Using Key Terms

1.	g	6.	b
2.	j	7.	i
3.	a	8.	c
4.	d	9.	e
5.	f	10.	h

Reviewing the Main Ideas

11. Millions of inland-dwellers have moved to coastal cities to find better jobs.
12. People from 18 to 70 are required by law to vote.
13. 1960; to encourage people to move inland to less crowded areas to reduce overcrowding in the cities
14. More than two-thirds of the population lives in this region. It is home to farmers and ranchers.
15. Spanish; Roman Catholicism
16. forestry, farming, and electricity
17. oil
18. Most live on the coastal plains because of the cooling ocean winds.
19. French Guiana

Chapter 8 Assessment and Activities

 Using Key Terms

Match the terms in Part A with their definitions in Part B.

A.

1.	basin	6.	gaucho
2.	*estancia*	7.	*selva*
3.	escarpment	8.	deforestation
4.	caudillo	9.	llanos
5.	altitude	10.	pampas

B.

a. steep cliff separating two flat land surfaces, one higher than the other
b. cowhand
c. cutting down large areas of forest
d. military ruler
e. large, grassy plains region with many ranches, farms, and oil fields
f. height above sea level
g. broad, flat lowland surrounded by higher land
h. vast treeless plains
i. tropical rain forest in Brazil
j. large ranch

 Reviewing the Main Ideas

Section 1 Brazil—Emerging Giant

11. **History** Why are Brazil's inland areas sparsely populated?
12. **Government** What are the voting requirements in Brazil?
13. **History** When and why did Brazil's government move the capital city to Brasília?

Section 2 Argentina to Venezuela

14. **Economics** Why are the pampas an important region of Argentina?
15. **Culture** What are the major language and religion of Uruguay?
16. **Economics** What are the major economic activities of Paraguay?
17. **Economics** Which of Venezuela's resources is its main source of income?
18. **Culture** Where do most of the people of the Guianas live? Why do they live there?
19. **History** Which of Brazil's neighbors has been a colony of France since the 1600s?

NATIONAL GEOGRAPHIC Brazil and Its Neighbors

Place Location Activity

On a separate sheet of paper, match the letters on the map with the numbered places listed below.

1.	Brazil	6.	Orinoco River
2.	Amazon River	7.	Uruguay
3.	Argentina	8.	Venezuela
4.	Rio de Janeiro	9.	Brasília
5.	Paraguay	10.	Suriname

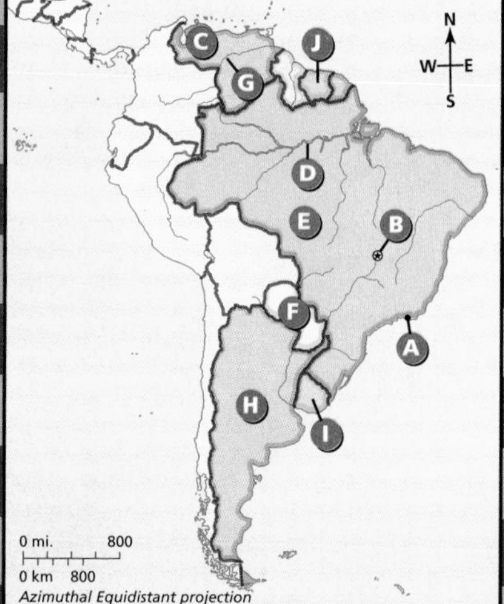

NATIONAL GEOGRAPHIC Place Location Activity

1.	E	6.	G
2.	D	7.	I
3.	H	8.	C
4.	A	9.	B
5.	F	10.	J

Critical Thinking

20. Argentina produces many manufactured goods, such as food products, automobiles, chemicals, textiles, books, and magazines.
21. Students' charts will vary. Possible answers: *For*—to help economy, provide jobs and products; *Against*—soil erosion, harms the ecosystem and biodiversity, traditional cultures of Native Americans threatened

Self-Check Quiz Visit ***The World and Its People*** Web site at twip.glencoe.com and click on **Chapter 8—Self-Check Quizzes** to prepare for the Chapter Test.

Critical Thinking

20. **Analyzing Information** What facts support the statement "Argentina is one of the most industrialized countries in South America"?

21. **Identifying Points of View** In a chart like the one below, identify arguments for and against the cutting down of the rain forest.

Cutting Down the Rain Forest	
For	Against

Comparing Regions Activity

22. **Geography** Rain forests of the Amazon have the highest rate of deforestation. Other regions in the world face similar challenges to their natural resources. Create a chart in your notebook that shows the current deforestation rates of five regions: Africa, Asia, Europe, Latin America, and North America. Find sample pictures of each region's forests to illustrate your chart.

Mental Mapping Activity

23. **Focusing on the Region** Create an outline map of South America. Refer to the map on page 233, and then label the following:

- Patagonia
- Brazil
- Atlantic Ocean
- Argentina
- Pacific Ocean
- Brazilian Highlands
- Amazon Basin
- Falkland Islands
- Venezuela
- Guiana Highlands

Technology Skills Activity

24. **Using the Internet** Conduct a search for information about the Amazon rain forest and create an annotated bibliography of five useful Web sites. Your bibliography should contain the Web address, a brief summary of the information found on the site, and a statement of why you think the site is useful.

Standardized Test Practice

Directions: Read the passage below, and then answer the question that follows.

The Amazon Basin is a gigantic system of rivers and rain forests, covering half of Brazil and extending into neighboring countries. Much of the Amazon is still unexplored, and the rain forest holds many secrets. Some of the animals found here include the jaguar, tapir, spider monkey, sloth, river dolphin, and boa constrictor. Forest birds include toucans, parrots, hummingbirds, and hawks. More than 1,800 species of butterflies and 200 species of mosquitoes give you an idea about the insect population. In addition, the fish—such as piranha, pirarucu, and electric eel—are very unusual. Biologists cannot identify much of the catch found in markets.

1. On the basis of this passage, which of the following generalizations is most accurate?

F The Amazon rain forest covers about one-third of the South American continent.

G Native Americans living in the rain forest are losing their old way of life.

H The Amazon Basin is huge, and its rain forests hold thousands of animal species.

J The Amazon Basin is located only in Brazil.

Test-Taking Tip: This question asks you to make a generalization about the Amazon Basin. A *generalization* is a broad statement. Look for facts and the main idea *in the passage* to support your answer. Do not rely only on your memory. The main idea can help you eliminate answers that do not fit. Also, look for the statement that is true and that is covered in the paragraph.

Assessment and Activities

Standardized Test Practice

1. H

Tested Objectives: Making generalizations, analyzing information

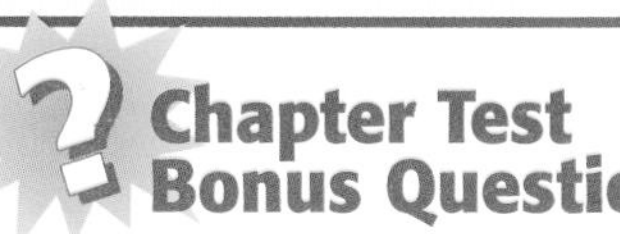

Chapter Test Bonus Question

This question may be used for extra credit on the chapter test.

This country is the only one in the region that was once a colony of Portugal. *(Brazil)*

Have students visit the Web site at twip.glencoe.com to review Chapter 8 and take the Self-Check Quiz.

Dinah Zike's Foldables

Culminating Activity Have students write ten questions based on facts collected for their foldables. Students should exchange their questions with a partner and answer them. Have students revise their questions if they are misleading or vague.

Comparing Regions Activity

22. Students' charts should include the deforestation rates and sample pictures for each region.

Mental Mapping Activity

23. This exercise helps students visualize the countries and geographic features of South America. All attempts at freehand mapping should be accepted.

Technology Skills Activity

24. Students' bibliographies should include at least five sites, each of which is evaluated in terms of its usefulness.

1 Focus

Ask students to imagine the following situation: A lake near their town is about to be filled in to allow a shopping mall to be built. The lake is the only place where gilded grumpfish are known to live. Would students vote for the mall plan to proceed, or would they vote to stop the project to protect the grumpfish? Why? After discussion, tell students that governments controlling rain forest areas face similar problems. L1

2 Teach

Designing Campaign Buttons Have students research animals that live in the rain forests of Brazil. Tell them to choose one animal and to use this animal as the basis of the slogan and design of a "Save the Rain Forest Wildlife" campaign button. Have students display their button designs. L1 ELL

Meeting National Standards

Geography for Life

The following standards are met in the Student Edition feature:

EE4 Human Systems: Standards 11, 12

EE5 Environment and Society: Standards 14, 15, 16

EE6 The Uses of Geography: Standard 18

EYE on the Environment

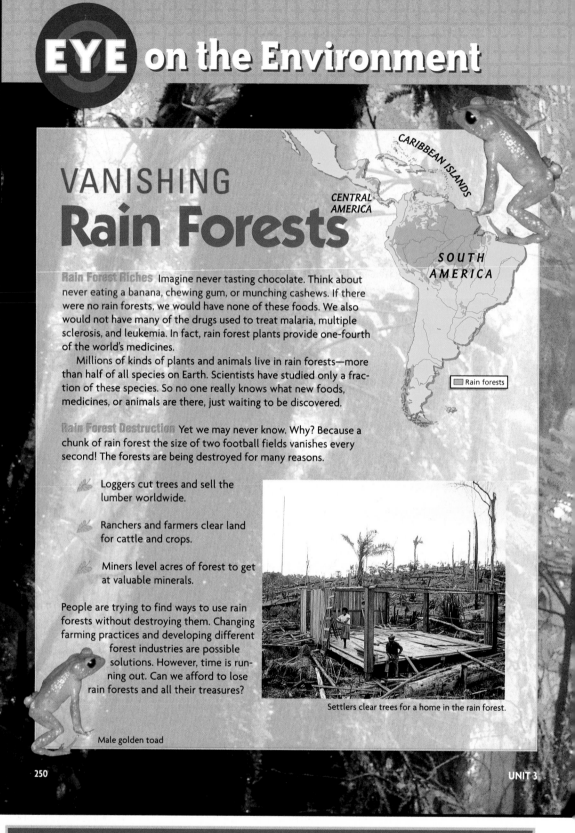

VANISHING Rain Forests

CARIBBEAN ISLANDS
CENTRAL AMERICA
SOUTH AMERICA
Rain forests

Rain Forest Riches Imagine never tasting chocolate. Think about never eating a banana, chewing gum, or munching cashews. If there were no rain forests, we would have none of these foods. We also would not have many of the drugs used to treat malaria, multiple sclerosis, and leukemia. In fact, rain forest plants provide one-fourth of the world's medicines.

Millions of kinds of plants and animals live in rain forests—more than half of all species on Earth. Scientists have studied only a fraction of these species. So no one really knows what new foods, medicines, or animals are there, just waiting to be discovered.

Rain Forest Destruction Yet we may never know. Why? Because a chunk of rain forest the size of two football fields vanishes every second! The forests are being destroyed for many reasons.

- Loggers cut trees and sell the lumber worldwide.
- Ranchers and farmers clear land for cattle and crops.
- Miners level acres of forest to get at valuable minerals.

People are trying to find ways to use rain forests without destroying them. Changing farming practices and developing different forest industries are possible solutions. However, time is running out. Can we afford to lose rain forests and all their treasures?

Settlers clear trees for a home in the rain forest.

Male golden toad

More About the Issues

Environment and Society One of the many problems resulting from the development of the rain forests is the displacement of indigenous peoples. These people, recognized by countries as an important resource, are as endangered as the plants and animals in the region. Throughout the Americas and beyond, local, national, and international organizations have begun to protest the displacement of these peoples and to work to secure their land and resource rights. See if students can identify similar examples of cultural conflicts and cooperation in the United States. L2

Making a Difference

New species *Callithrix humilis*, a dwarf marmoset

Discovering New Monkeys How would it feel to discover an animal that no one knew existed? Dutch scientist Marc van Roosmalen knows. He recently discovered a new species of monkey (photo, at right) in Brazil.

Van Roosmalen runs an orphanage for abandoned monkeys. One day, a man showed up with a tiny monkey van Roosmalen had never seen before. He spent about a year tracking down a wild population of the monkeys deep in the Amazon rain forest. Of some 250 kinds of monkeys known worldwide, about 80 live in Brazil. At least 7 new species have been discovered since 1990.

Rain Forest Field Trip With help from the Children's Environmental Trust Foundation, students from Millbrook, New York, traveled to Peru's Yarapa River region, deep in the Amazon rain forest. Students studied the forest from platforms built in the canopy, and they soared among the tall trees using ropes. The students met rain forest creatures at night, went bird-watching at dawn, and swam in the Yarapa River—home to crocodiles called caimans.

Back in Millbrook, the students educate others about saving rain forests. They also raise money to help support a Peruvian zoo that protects rain forest animals.

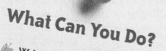

A Millbrook student traps insects for study.

What Can You Do?

Write a Note
Write to your government representatives and encourage them to support plans that help save rain forests.

Check Out Your Community
What environmental problems face your community? What can you do to help solve the problems? For example, does your community have problems with water pollution or water shortages? What steps does your community take to make sure you have clean water to drink?

251

GLOBAL ISSUES

Interdependence Many scientists believe that the medicinal applications of rain forest plants and animals have been only partially explored. Further experimentation might also help preserve the rain forest.

3 Assess

Have students work individually or in groups to complete the What Can You Do? activities.

4 Close

Discuss with students the What Can You Do? activities. Encourage them to find out more about the groups that are working to save the rain forest. Students might want to start their own local organization to help in this work.

For an additional regional case study, use the following:

Environmental Case Study

What Can You Do? Teacher Tips

Write a Note: Remind students who write to a public official to include statistics and rational arguments supporting their position. Remind them also to carefully proofread their work. You might research in advance to locate the addresses of your state's senators and members of the House of Representatives.

Check Out Your Community: Have students brainstorm possible sources of information on local environmental issues. The telephone book and the Internet might provide some suggestions if they are having difficulty generating ideas.

Chapter 9 Resources

Note: The following materials may be used when teaching Chapter 9.
Section level support materials are shown at point of use in the margins of the Teacher Wraparound Edition.

Timesaving Tools

TeacherWorks™ All-In-One Planner and Resource Center

- **Interactive Teacher Edition** See the **Interactive Teacher Edition** CD-ROM to electronically integrate your Teacher Wraparound Edition and blackline masters.
- **Interactive Lesson Planner** Organize your week, month, semester, or year with all the lesson helps you need. The **Interactive Lesson Planner** CD-ROM contains all Chapter 9 resources.

Use Glencoe's **Presentation Plus!** multimedia teacher tool to easily present dynamic lessons that visually excite your students. Using Microsoft PowerPoint® you can customize the presentations to create your own personalized lessons.

TEACHING TRANSPARENCIES

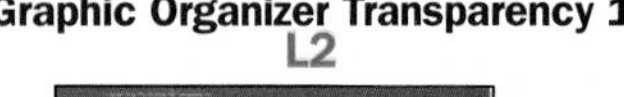

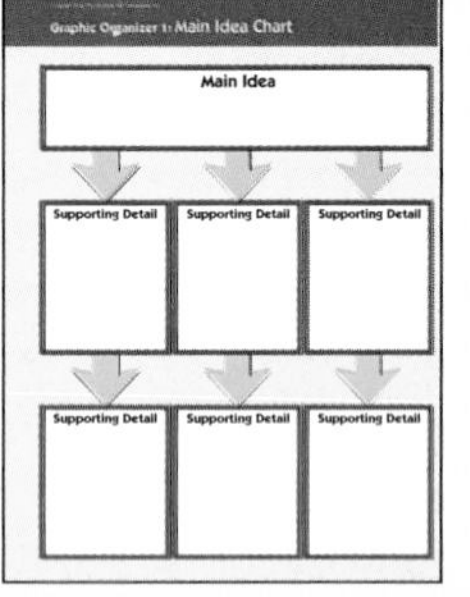

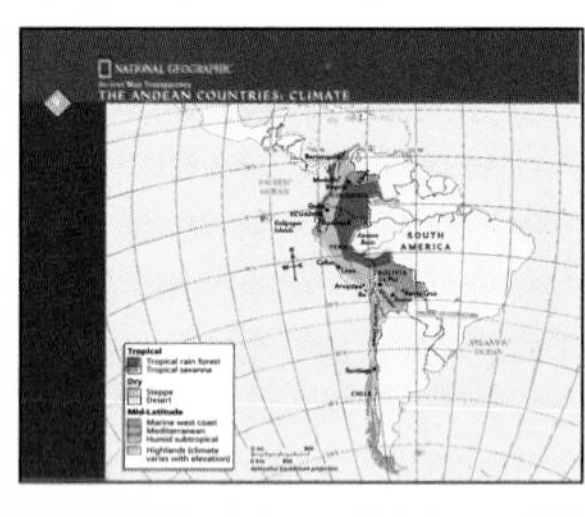

FOLDABLES™ Study Organizer

Dinah Zike's Foldables

Foldables are three-dimensional, interactive graphic organizers that help students practice basic writing skills, review key vocabulary terms, and identify main ideas. Additional chapter activities can be found in the ***Reading and Study Skills Foldables*** booklet.

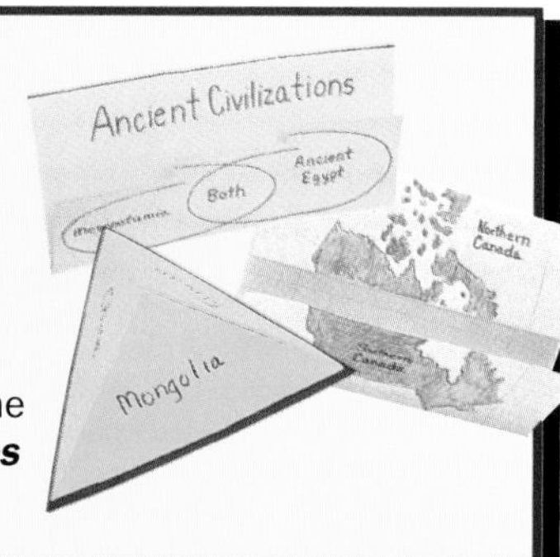

MAP AND GEOGRAPHY SKILLS

Chapter Map Activity L2

GeoLab Activity L2

READING SUPPORT

Vocabulary Activity L1

Workbook Activity L1

Reading and Writing Skills Activity L1/ELL

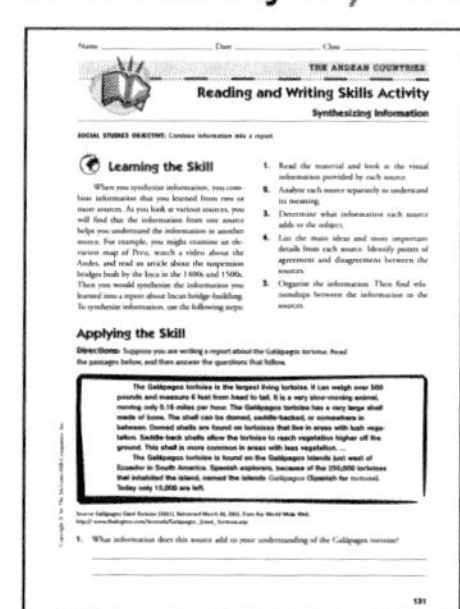

DIFFERENTIATED INSTRUCTION

Use these review and reinforcement materials to help less-proficient readers, English learners, and gifted and talented students.

Reteaching Activity L1

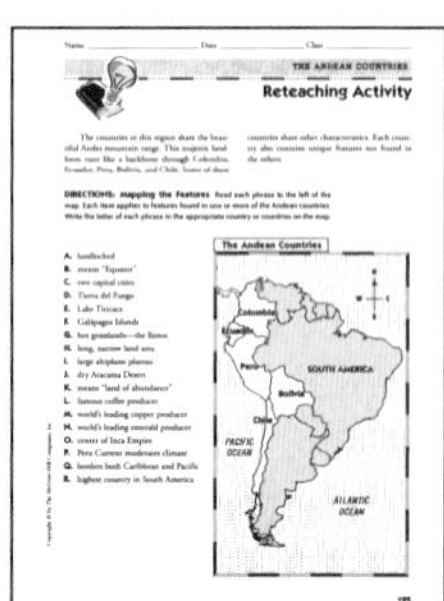

Chapter Skills Review L2

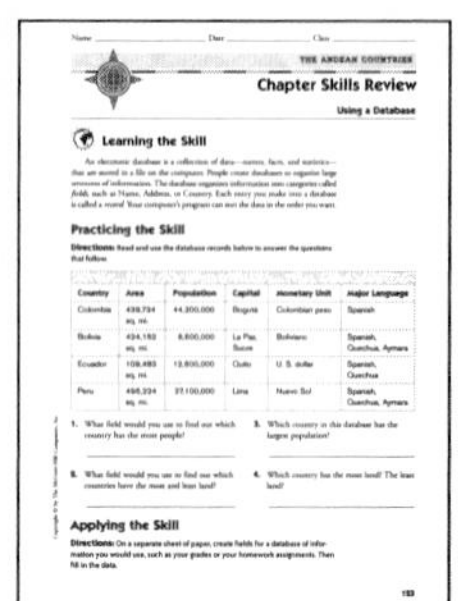

Cooperative Learning Activity L1/ELL

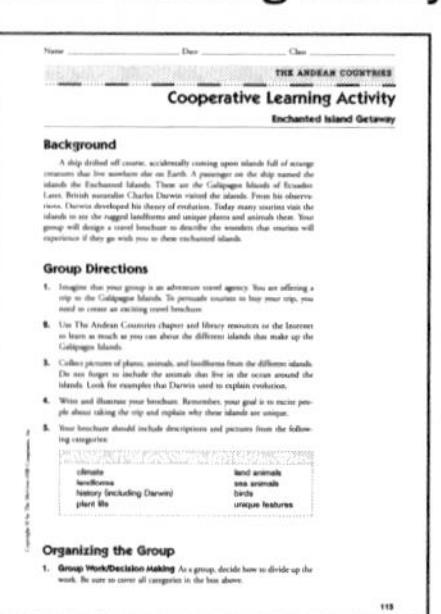

Enrichment Activity L3

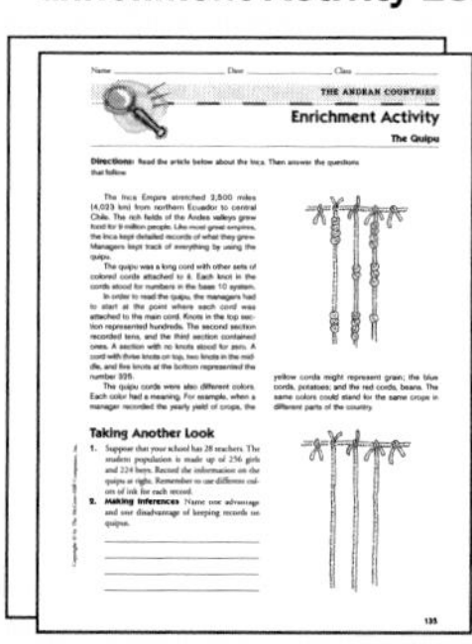

ASSESSMENT

Chapter Test, Form A L2

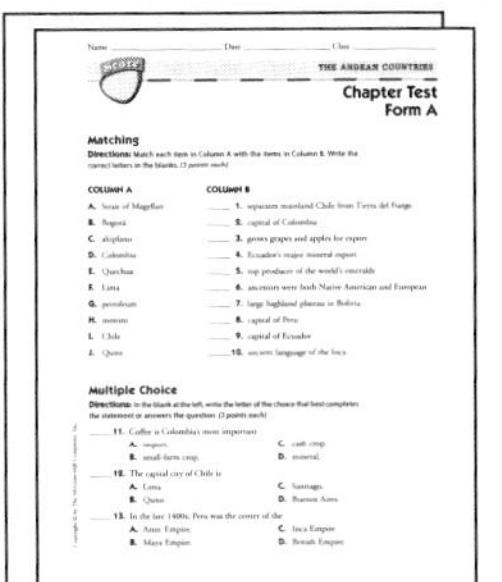

Chapter Test, Form B L2

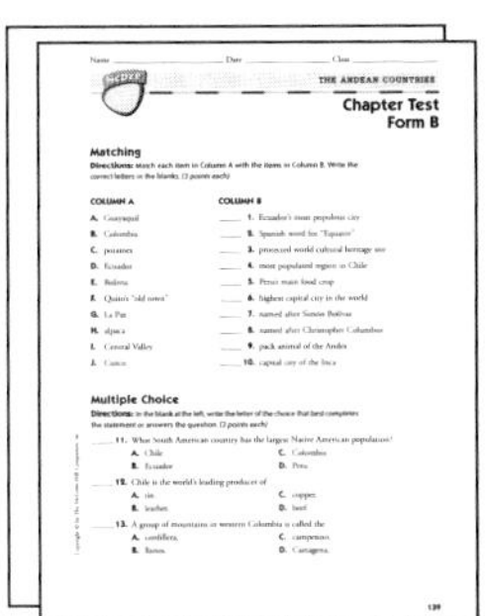

Performance Assessment Activity L1/ELL

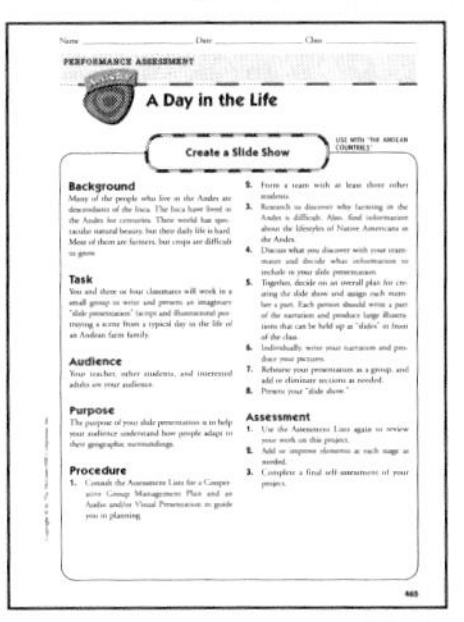

ExamView® Pro Testmaker CD-ROM

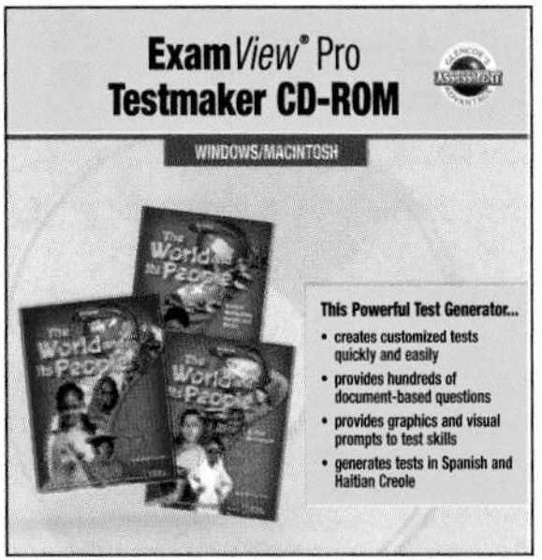

STANDARDIZED ASSESSMENT SKILLS

Critical Thinking Skills Activity L2

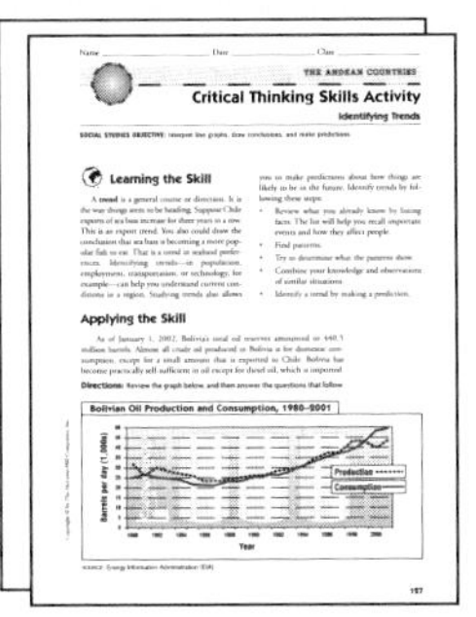

Map and Graph Skills Activity L2

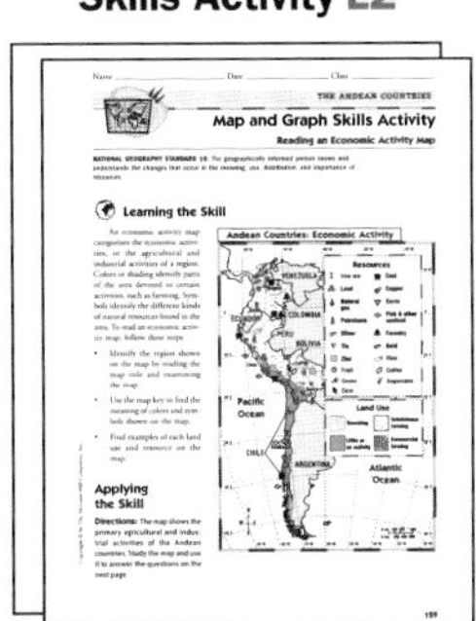

Standardized Test Skills Practice Workbook Activity L2

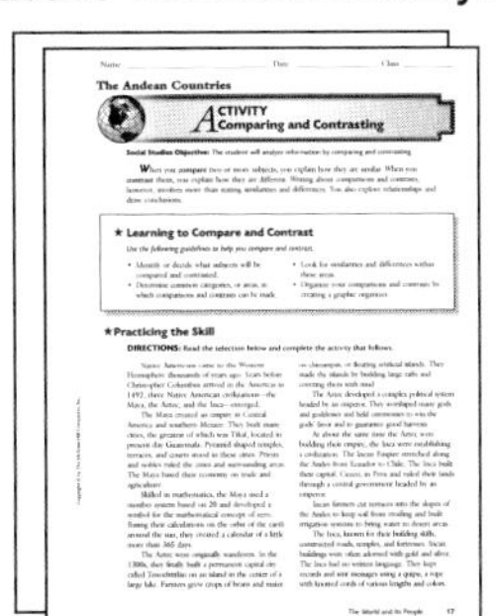

HOME INVOLVEMENT

Take-Home Review Activity L1

MULTIMEDIA

- **National Geographic's The World and Its People**
- **MindJogger Videoquiz**
- **Vocabulary PuzzleMaker CD-ROM**
- **Interactive Tutor Self-Assessment CD-ROM**
- **ExamView® Pro Testmaker CD-ROM**
- **TeacherWorks CD-ROM**
- **StudentWorks CD-ROM**
- **Skillbuilder Interactive Workbook CD-ROM, Level 1**
- **Presentation Plus! CD-ROM**
- **Audio Program**

SPANISH RESOURCES

The following Spanish language materials are available in the Spanish Resources binder:

- **Spanish Summaries**
- **Spanish Vocabulary Activities**
- **Spanish Guided Reading Activities**
- **Spanish Quizzes and Tests**
- **Spanish Take-Home Review Activities**
- **Spanish Reteaching Activities**

Meeting National Standards

Geography for Life

The following standards are covered in Chapter 9:

Section 1	**EE4 Human Systems: Standards 11, 12, 13**
Section 2	**EE4 Human Systems: Standards 9, 10**
	EE5 Environment and Society: Standards 14, 15
Section 3	**EE4 Human Systems: Standards 9, 10, 11, 12, 13**
	EE5 Environment and Society: Standards 14, 15, 16

State and Local Objectives

Chapter 9 Planning Guide

SECTION RESOURCES

Daily Objectives	Reproducible Resources	Multimedia Resources
Section 1 **Colombia's Culture and Challenges** **1.** Locate Colombia on a map or globe and describe its landforms. **2.** Discuss Colombia's economy and the challenges it faces. **3.** Describe Colombia's history and people.	Reproducible Lesson Plan Daily Lecture and Discussion Notes Note-taking Guide Guided Reading Activity* Reading Essentials and Study Guide* Section Quiz*	Daily Focus Skills Transparency GeoQuiz Transparency Vocabulary PuzzleMaker CD-ROM Interactive Tutor Self-Assessment CD-ROM ExamView® Pro Testmaker CD-ROM Presentation Plus! CD-ROM
Section 2 **Land and People of Peru and Ecuador** **1.** Describe the landforms and climates of Peru and Ecuador. **2.** Compare how the people of Peru and Ecuador earn a living. **3.** Discuss what the people of Peru and Ecuador are like.	Reproducible Lesson Plan Daily Lecture and Discussion Notes Note-taking Guide Guided Reading Activity* Reading Essentials and Study Guide* Section Quiz*	Daily Focus Skills Transparency Vocabulary PuzzleMaker CD-ROM Interactive Tutor Self-Assessment CD-ROM ExamView® Pro Testmaker CD-ROM Presentation Plus! CD-ROM
Section 3 **The Bolivians and Chileans** **1.** Identify where Bolivia and Chile are located. **2.** Describe the landforms and climates found in Bolivia and Chile. **3.** Compare the economies and people of Bolivia and Chile.	Reproducible Lesson Plan Daily Lecture and Discussion Notes Note-taking Guide Guided Reading Activity* Reading Essentials and Study Guide* Section Quiz*	Daily Focus Skills Transparency In-text Map Transparency Vocabulary PuzzleMaker CD-ROM Interactive Tutor Self-Assessment CD-ROM ExamView® Pro Testmaker CD-ROM Presentation Plus! CD-ROM MindJogger Videoquiz

00:00 **Out of Time?** Assign the **Reading Essentials and Study Guide*** for this chapter.

*Also available in Spanish

KEY TO ABILITY LEVELS

Teaching strategies have been coded for varying learning styles and abilities.

L1 **BASIC** activities for all students
L2 **AVERAGE** activities for average to above-average students
L3 **CHALLENGING** activities for above-average students
ELL **ENGLISH LANGUAGE LEARNER** activities

KEY TO TEACHING RESOURCES

- Blackline Master
- CD-ROM
- Transparency
- Videocassette
- Block Scheduling
- DVD

Teacher to Teacher

News Maps

Nora Austin
Chestnut Community School
Belchertown, Massachusetts

Jean Serafino
Chestnut Community School
Belchertown, Massachusetts

Provide students with an outline map of the world with the seven culture regions separated by a thick border: North America; South America; Europe; Russia; Africa south of the Sahara; North Africa, Southwest Asia, and Central Asia; and Australia, Oceania, and Antarctica. Ask students to find one newspaper article for each culture region. They are to read the article and write a summary of its main points. Students then glue their summary to its proper place on the map. Then they must highlight the name of the country within the summary that shows it belongs in that particular culture region.

Meeting Special Needs

In addition to the Differentiated Instruction strategies found in each section, the following resources are also suitable for your special needs students:

- ***ExamView® Pro Testmaker CD-ROM*** allows teachers to tailor tests by reducing answer choices.
- The ***Audio Program*** includes the entire narrative of the student edition so that less-proficient readers can listen to the words as they read them.
- The ***Reading Essentials and Study Guide*** provides the same content as the student edition but is written two grade levels below the textbook.
- ***Guided Reading Activities*** give less-proficient readers point-by-point instructions to increase comprehension as they read each textbook section.
- ***Enrichment Activities*** include a stimulating collection of readings and activities for gifted and talented students.

NATIONAL GEOGRAPHIC TEACHER'S CORNER

Index to National Geographic Magazine:

The following articles may be used for research relating to this chapter:

- "Lost Tombs of Peru," by Peter Lerche, September 2000.
- "Sierra Madre Pilgrimage," by Paul Salopek, June 2000.
- "Chiquibul Cave," by Thomas Miller, April 2000.

National Geographic Society Products:

To order the following products for use with this chapter, call National Geographic Society at 1-800-368-2728:

- *National Geographic Desk Reference* (Book)
- *PicturePack: Ancient Civilizations: South America* (Transparencies)
- *PictureShow: Ancient Civilizations: Middle and South America* (CD-ROM)

NGS ONLINE

Access National Geographic's Web site for current events, activities, links, interactive features, and archives. www.nationalgeographic.com

NATIONAL GEOGRAPHIC MapMachine

Find the latest coverage of geography in the news, atlas updates, cartographic activities with interactive maps, an online map store, and links at www.nationalgeographic.com/maps

SOCIAL STUDIES Online

Use our Web site for additional resources. All essential content is covered in the Student Edition.

You and your students can visit twip.glencoe.com, the Web site companion to *The World and Its People.* This innovative integration of electronic and print media offers your students a wealth of opportunities. The student text directs students to the Web site for the following options:

- Chapter Overviews
- Student Web Activities
- Self-Check Quizzes
- Textbook Updates

Answers are provided for you in the Web Activity Lesson Plan. Additional Web resources and Interactive Tutor puzzles are also available.

Introducing
Chapter 9

Social Studies Online

Introduce students to chapter content and key terms by having them access Chapter Overview 9 at twip.glencoe.com

Chapter Objectives

1. Describe the landforms and climates of the Andean countries.
2. Explain how the people of the Andean countries earn a living.
3. Discuss the culture of the Andean countries.

GLENCOE TECHNOLOGY

NATIONAL GEOGRAPHIC

The World and Its People Video Program

Chapter 9 The Andean Countries

The following segments enhance the study of this chapter:

- **Patagonia Puma**
- **Atacama Desert**

MindJogger Videoquiz

Use MindJogger Videoquiz to preview the Chapter 9 content.

Both programs available in DVD and VHS

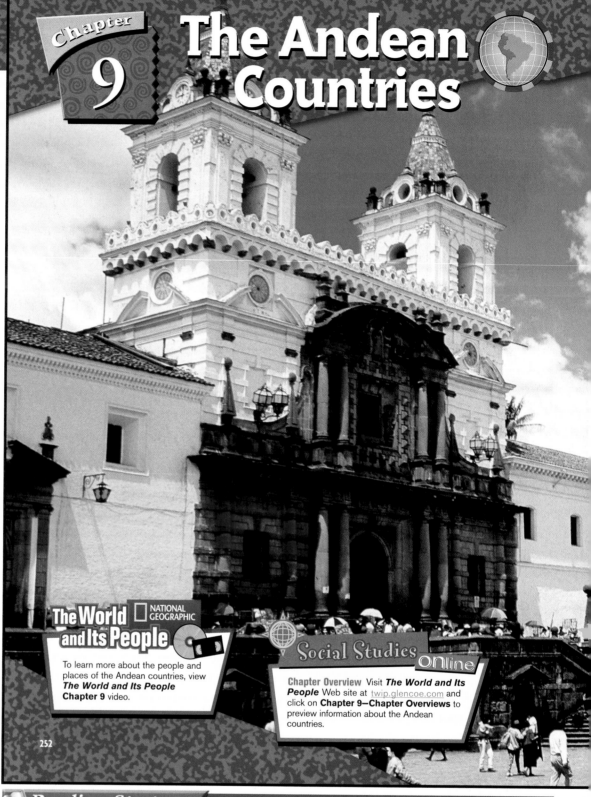

Chapter 9 The Andean Countries

The World and Its People NATIONAL GEOGRAPHIC

To learn more about the people and places of the Andean countries, view ***The World and Its People*** **Chapter 9** video.

Social Studies Online

Chapter Overview Visit ***The World and Its People*** Web site at twip.glencoe.com and click on **Chapter 9—Chapter Overviews** to preview information about the Andean countries.

252

Reading Strategy — Purpose for Reading

Capsule Vocabulary is a strategy that helps students use vocabulary that they encounter in their reading. This strategy also promotes comprehension of complex words and ideas. Write some of the chapter vocabulary words on the board or an overhead transparency. Organize students into pairs and start a "conversation," using as many of the words as possible. Ask students to write down some of these conversations. Conclude the activity by explaining that they will learn the correct definitions of these terms as they read the chapter. As they study the chapter, students can correct or enhance the information they received from the conversations. L1

Summarizing Information

Make this foldable and use it to organize note cards with information about the people and places of the Andean countries of South America.

Step 1 Fold a 2-inch tab along the long edge of a sheet of paper.

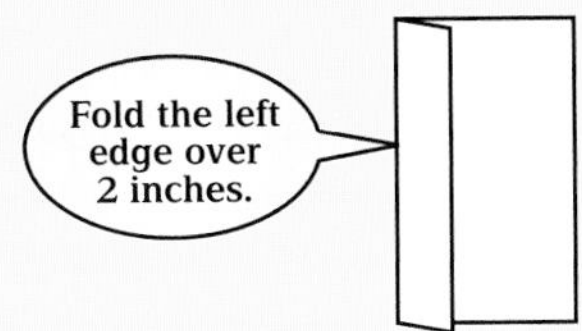

Fold the left edge over 2 inches.

Step 2 Fold the paper in half so the tab is on the inside.

The tab can't be seen when the paper is folded.

Step 3 Open the paper pocket foldable and glue the edges of the pockets together.

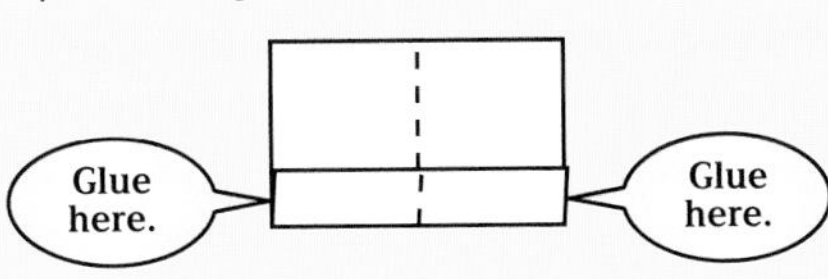

Step 4 Label the pockets as shown.

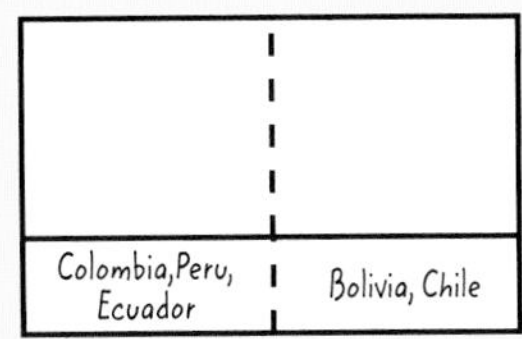

Reading and Writing As you read the chapter, summarize key facts about the Andean countries on note cards or on quarter sheets of notebook paper. Organize your notes by placing them in your pocket foldable inside the appropriate pockets. (Glue your foldable from Chapter 8 on the front cover of this foldable to form a four-pocket foldable on South America.)

Why It Matters

Wealth in the Andes

The Andes form the spine of South America and are the longest mountain chain on Earth. These high, rocky peaks are the source of some of the world's most highly desired substances, including oil, emeralds, gold, silver, coffee, and "Colombian Gold"—the illegal drug, cocaine. Worldwide demand for these products has caused corruption and instability in the countries of this region.

◀ Monastery of San Francisco, Quito, Ecuador

About the Photo

Quito, Ecuador, is the oldest capital city in South America. It was once settled by the Inca but was captured by the Spanish in 1534. Like many colonial cities, it has narrow streets and a large central plaza that is dominated by a cathedral. Quito is located in the Andes on the slopes of the volcano Pichincha. Although the city lies near the Equator, it has a moderate climate because of its high altitude.

Introducing Chapter 9

FOLDABLES™ Study Organizer Dinah Zike's Foldables

Purpose This activity requires students to create note cards and a pocket foldable to organize information from the chapter. Students record key facts and then group the information into categories to compare the people and places of the Andean countries.

Have students complete the ***Reading and Study Skills Foldables*** activity for this chapter.

Why It Matters

Explain that the Andes have benefits as well as disadvantages for the people of South America. Create a two-column chart labeled "The Andes," with one column labeled "Advantages" and the other column labeled "Disadvantages." Ask students to think of ways these mountains help people *(providing building stone, mineral wealth, and river sources)* and ways they challenge people *(isolation, difficulty of transportation, poor farming, danger from earthquakes and volcanoes)*. Have volunteers fill in the chart with their ideas.

Focus

Section Objectives

1. Locate Colombia on a map or globe and describe its landforms.
2. Discuss Colombia's economy and the challenges it faces.
3. Describe Colombia's history and people.

BELLRINGER Skillbuilder Activity

Project transparency and have students answer the question.

Daily Focus Skills Transparency

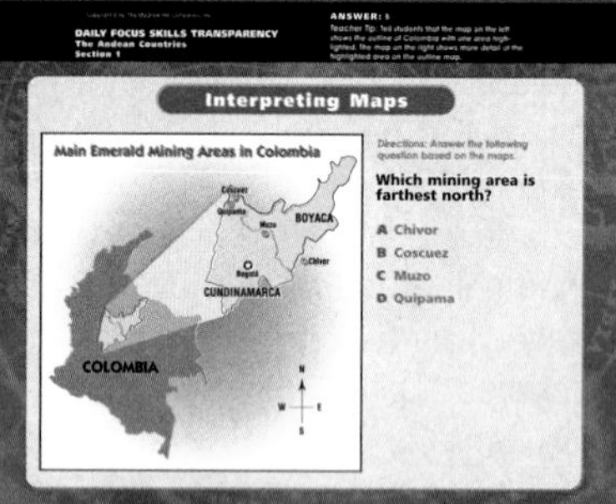

Reading Preview

■ **Activating Prior Knowledge** **Ask:** What famous person do you think Colombia is named for? *(Christopher Columbus)* Why do you think the country was named for him? *(because he launched the colonization of the Americas)*

■ **Preteaching Vocabulary** Have students skim the section to find the vocabulary words and their definitions. Tell students to write this information in their notebooks and refer to it as they read.

Guide to Reading

Main Idea

Although it has many resources, Colombia faces political and economic unrest.

Terms to Know

- cordillera
- cash crop
- mestizo
- campesino

Reading Strategy

Create a chart like the one below and list advantages that Colombia enjoys in the left column. In the right column, list the challenges that it faces.

Colombia	
Advantages	Challenges

Section 1

Colombia's Culture and Challenges

In a thin vein of black shale, a miner in Colombia spots a glistening green stone. He is not the first Colombian to mine the precious gemstones we call emeralds. The Colombian mine called Muzo has been producing top-quality emeralds for a thousand years. Early Native American rulers would offer these gems—more rare than diamonds—to their gods.

Colombia was named after Christopher Columbus. The lofty Andes mountain ranges at the northwestern edge of South America run through Colombia. These mountains continue south through five other countries—**Ecuador, Peru, Bolivia, Chile,** and **Argentina.**

Colombia's Landscape

Colombia—almost three times larger than Montana—has coasts on both the Caribbean Sea and the Pacific Ocean. The Andes rise in the western part of Colombia. Here they become a **cordillera**—mountain ranges that run side by side. Nearly 80 percent of Colombia's people live in the valleys and highland plateaus of the Andes. Thick forests spread over lowlands along the Pacific coast. Few people live there.

Only a few Native American groups live in the hot, steamy tropical rain forests of the southeast. In the northeast, ranchers drive cattle across the llanos, which, as you recall, are grassy plains.

Section Resources

Reproducible Masters
- Reproducible Lesson Plan
- Daily Lecture and Discussion Notes
- Note-taking Guide
- Guided Reading Activity
- Reading Essentials and Study Guide
- Section Quiz

Transparencies
- Daily Focus Skills Transparency
- GeoQuiz Transparency

Multimedia
- Vocabulary PuzzleMaker CD-ROM
- Interactive Tutor Self-Assessment CD-ROM
- Presentation Plus! CD-ROM
- ExamView® Pro Testmaker CD-ROM

Colombia lies within the Tropics. Temperatures are very hot, and heavy rains fall along the coasts and in the interior plains. In the high elevations of the Andes, temperatures are very cool for a tropical area. **Bogotá,** Colombia's capital and largest city, lies on an Andean plateau. High temperatures there average only 67°F (19°C).

Reading Check Where do most of Colombia's people live?

Colombia's Economic Resources

Colombia has many natural resources. The mountains hold valuable minerals and precious stones, and Colombia has more coal than any other country in South America. Second only to Brazil in its potential hydroelectric power, Colombia also has large petroleum reserves in

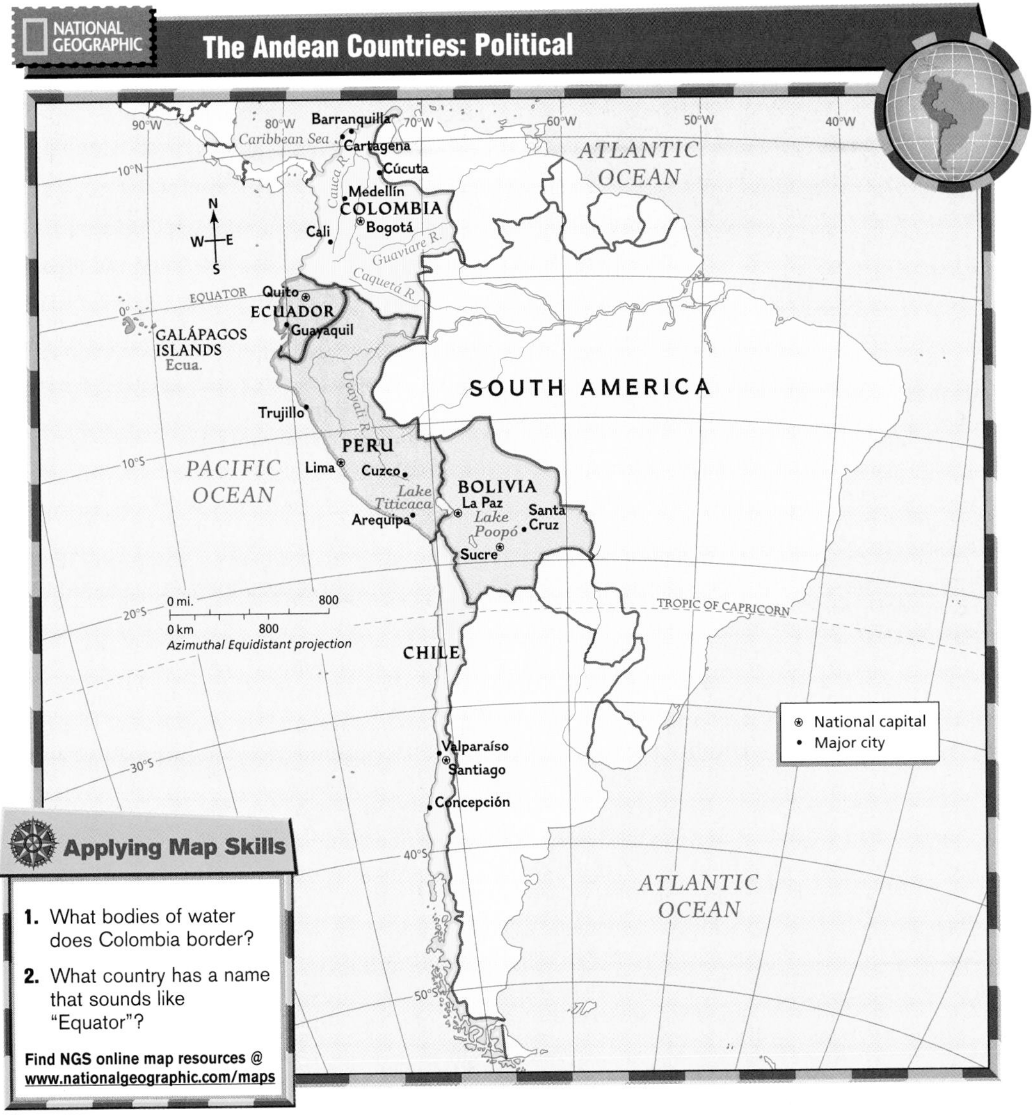

Applying Map Skills

1. What bodies of water does Colombia border?
2. What country has a name that sounds like "Equator"?

Find NGS online map resources @ www.nationalgeographic.com/maps

Chapter 9

Section 1, pages 254–257

2 TEACH

Reading Strategy

Identifying Main Ideas As students read each subsection, have them write one sentence that expresses the main idea in that subsection. Have volunteers offer their sentences and discuss whether they summarize the main idea of the subsection. **L1**

Reading Check Answer

in the valleys and highland plateaus of the Andes

Daily Lecture and Discussion Notes

THE ANDEAN COUNTRIES

Daily Lecture and Discussion Notes

Colombia's Culture and Challenges

Did You Know?

Colombia claims to have the highest number of species of plants and animals per unit area of any country in the world. Its animals include jaguars, ocelots, peccaries, tapirs, deer, armadillo, numerous species of monkeys, and the rare spectacled bear. Colombia's herbariums have classified more than 130,000 plants, including Victoria Amazonica, which is similar to a water lily and has leaves large and strong enough to support a child.

I. Colombia's Landscape

A. Colombia borders the Caribbean Sea and the Pacific Ocean. It is almost three times larger than Montana.

... western part of Colombia. Here they become a ...

Applying Map Skills

Answers

1. Caribbean Sea, Pacific Ocean
2. Ecuador

Skills Practice

What is unusual about Bolivia's capital? *(There are two—La Paz and Sucre.)*

Reading Strategy — Reading the Text

Responding and Reflecting Have students carefully review the information under the subheading Economic Challenges. After they have finished their reading, **Ask:** **What do you think is the most serious issue facing Colombia? Why?** Ask for volunteers to give their answers and explanations. After a few students have spoken, have the class discuss the different suggestions and the reasons given. **L1**

*Use the **Reading Skills Handbook** for more reading strategies.*

More About the Photo

Coffee Coffee was first cultivated in either Arabia or Ethiopia. Coffee growing spread to the Americas in the 1700s.

Caption Answer bananas, cacao, sugarcane, rice, and cotton

L1/ELL

Guided Reading Activity

Name ____ Date ____ Class ____

THE ANDEAN COUNTRIES

Guided Reading Activity 1

Colombia's Culture and Challenges

DIRECTIONS: Filling in the Blanks Reading the section and completing the summary paragraphs below will help you learn more about the country of Colombia. Refer to your textbook to fill in the blanks.

Colombia has a coast on both the (1) ____ and the (2) ____. A mountain range called the (3) ____ runs through the (4) ____ side of Colombia. The mountains become a (5) ____, which is where a group of mountain ranges run side

Reading Check Answer

coca; powerful drug dealers protect the illegal trade through violence and corruption

Measure student knowledge of physical features.

GeoQuiz Transparency

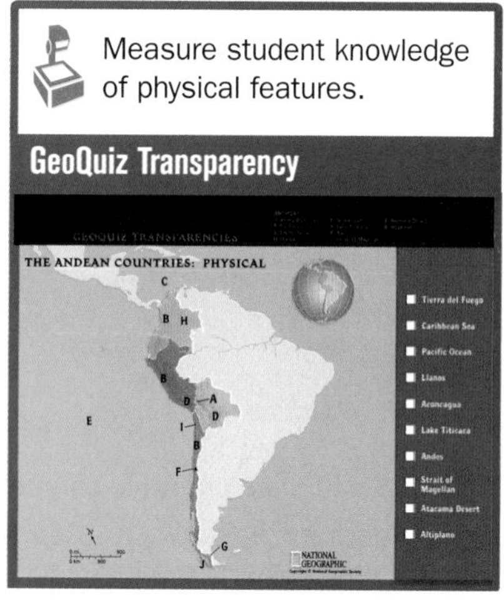

NATIONAL GEOGRAPHIC **On Location**

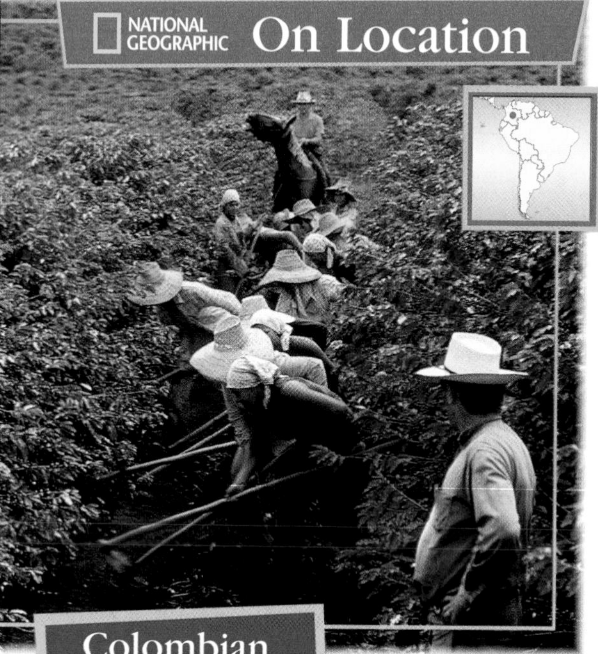

Colombian Coffee

Many historians believe that coffee was "discovered" in Ethiopia, Africa. Eventually, Spanish missionaries brought the first coffee plants to Colombia.

Economics What other crops does Colombia export?

the lowlands. In addition, the country is a major supplier of gold and the world's number one source of emeralds. Factories produce clothing, leather goods, food products, paper, chemicals, and iron and steel products.

Agriculture The coastal regions and the highlands have good soil for growing a variety of crops. Coffee is the country's major **cash crop**—a product sold for export. Colombian coffee is known all over the world for its rich flavor.

Colombia exports bananas as well as cacao, sugarcane, rice, and cotton. Huge herds of cattle roam large *estancias,* or ranches, in the llanos. The rain forests also supply a valuable resource—lumber.

Economic Challenges Despite many natural resources, Colombia faces economic challenges. Since the 1980s, drug dealers have been a major force in Colombia. The dealers pay farmers more to grow coca leaves—which are used to make the illegal drug cocaine—than the farmers earn growing coffee. Much of this cocaine is smuggled into the United States and western Europe. The drug dealers have used their immense profits to build private armies. They have threatened—and even killed—government officials who have tried to stop them.

With U.S. support, the government of Colombia has stepped up its efforts to break the power of the drug dealers. In addition, the government has tried to persuade thousands of farmers to switch back to growing other crops. See **TIME Perspectives: Exploring World Issues** on pages 259–265 for an in-depth study of the drug problem.

Reading Check What crop has been a problem in Colombia? Why?

Colombia's History and People

About 44.2 million people live in Colombia. Nearly all Colombians are **mestizos** (meh•STEE•zohs). This means they have mixed European and Native American backgrounds. Most speak Spanish and follow the Roman Catholic faith.

In 1810 Colombia was one of the first Spanish colonies in the Americas to declare independence. Simón Bolívar, whom you read about in Chapter 8, led this struggle for independence. In 1819 Colombia became part of New Granada, an independent country that included Venezuela, Ecuador, and Panama. Later, these other regions broke away and became separate countries.

Colombia today is a republic with an elected president. Political violence has scarred the country's history, though. During the late 1800s

Differentiated Instruction

Meeting Special Needs: Less-proficient Readers Help students determine the main idea by inviting them to read one paragraph. Then ask students: **What one idea are all the sentences in this paragraph about? How does that idea fit in with what I know about this topic? How this section is organized? What sentences add information to the most important idea?** L1

Refer to *Inclusion for the Middle School Social Studies Classroom Strategies and Activities* in the TCR.

alone, Colombia suffered through more than 50 revolts and 8 civil wars. Fighting broke out again in 1948. About 250,000 people died in this conflict, which ended in the late 1950s.

To prevent further unrest, the two main political parties agreed to govern the country together. Efforts were made to improve the lives of poor farmers by giving them more land. Factories and industrial jobs opened up. Still, a wide gap between rich and poor remained, causing further disturbances.

In the 1960s, rebels in the countryside began fighting the government. This latest civil war is still being fought. It has left more than 100,000 people dead. In 2003 the United States responded to the Colombian government's call for help. It sent U.S. special forces to Colombia to train Colombian soldiers and to protect an oil pipeline.

Web Activity Visit ***The World and Its People*** Web site at twip.glencoe.com and click on **Chapter 9—Student Web Activities** to learn more about Colombia.

A Diverse Culture Colombia has a rapidly growing urban population. Colombian farmers, or **campesinos,** and their families have journeyed to cities to look for work or to flee the fighting in the countryside. Thirty cities have more than 100,000 people each.

You can see Colombia's Spanish, Native American, and African heritages reflected in its culture. Native American skills in weaving and pottery date back before the arrival of Columbus. Caribbean African rhythms blend with Spanish-influenced music.

Reading Check What is a mestizo?

Section 1 Assessment

Defining Terms

1. **Define** cordillera, cash crop, mestizo, campesino.

Recalling Facts

2. **Economics** Colombia is the world's number one source of what resource?
3. **Culture** What language do most Colombians speak? What religion do they practice?
4. **History** Who led Colombia's struggle for independence from Spain?

Critical Thinking

5. **Analyzing Cause and Effect** Why does Bogotá, which is located in the Tropics, have an average temperature of only 67°F (19°C)?
6. **Drawing Conclusions** Why do you think it is so difficult for Colombian farmers to stop growing coca?

Graphic Organizer

7. **Organizing Information** Create a time line like this one. Then put the following events and their dates in the correct order on it: U.S. special forces sent to Colombia, groups of rebels fight the government, Colombia declares independence from Spain, Colombia suffers 50 revolts and 8 civil wars, Colombia becomes part of New Granada.

Applying Social Studies Skills

8. **Analyzing Maps** Study the political map on page 255. What rivers run through Colombia? What are Colombia's major cities?

Section 1 Assessment

1. The terms are defined in the Glossary.
2. emeralds
3. Spanish, Roman Catholicism
4. Simón Bolívar
5. because of its high elevation on an Andean plateau
6. Farmers can earn more money growing coca, which has increased the amount grown.
7. Colombia declares independence from Spain (1810); Colombia becomes part of New Granada (1819); Colombia suffers 50 revolts and 8 civil wars (late 1800s); groups of rebels fight the government (1960s); U.S. special forces sent to Colombia (2003)
8. Rivers: Cauca, Guaviare, Caquetá; Cities: Cartagena, Cúcuta, Medellín, Bogotá, Barranquilla

Objectives and answers to the Student Web Activity can be found in the Web Activity Lesson Plan at twip.glencoe.com

3 ASSESS

Assign Section 1 Assessment as homework or an in-class activity.

Have students use the Interactive Tutor Self-Assessment CD-ROM to review Section 1.

Reading Check Answer

a person of mixed European and Native American ancestry

L1/ELL

Reading Essentials and Study Guide

THE ANDEAN COUNTRIES

Reading Essentials and Study Guide 1

Colombia's Culture and Challenges

Key Terms

cordillera group of mountain ranges that run side by side
cash crop a farm product sold to other countries
mestizo person of mixed European and Native American background
campesino farmer

Drawing From Experience

4 CLOSE

Have students prepare a section quiz that tests mastery of the section content.

Technology Skill

TEACH

Begin discussion of this page by surveying the class to find out if any students have done computer database searches (as in a library's electronic card catalog). In discussing the construction of a database, refer to a phone directory. Give examples of *fields* (for example, name, phone number, and address); *records* (such as the specific names, phone numbers, and addresses of particular people); and *data files* (a collection of records). **L1**

Additional Skills Practice

1. **What is the difference between a field and a record?** *(A field is the category of information, whereas a record is a specific piece of information.)*
2. **What fields would you want in a database of a CD collection?** *(Possible answers: artist name, CD title, songs included, type of music)*
3. Look at the Country Profiles in the Regional Atlas for this unit. **What fields are included for each country in this database?** *(country name, population, languages, major exports, major imports, capital, landmass)*

Additional Skills Resources

Chapter Skills Review

Building Geography Skills for Life

Technology Skill

Using a Database

An electronic **database** is a collection of data—names, facts, and statistics—that is stored in a file on the computer. Databases are useful for organizing large amounts of information. The information in a database can be sorted and presented in different ways.

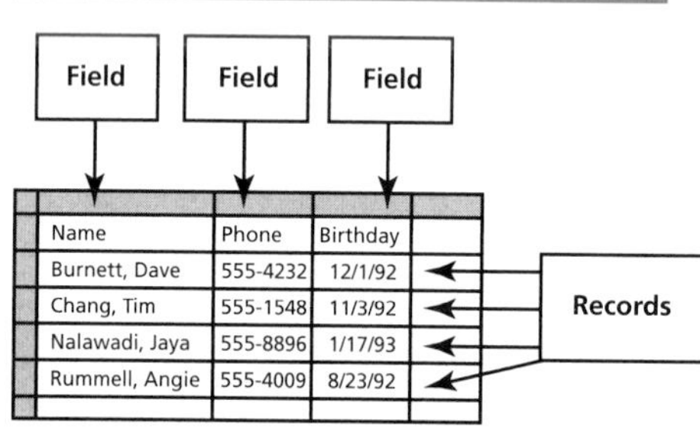

▲ **Using a database can help organize statistics, names and addresses, and even baseball card collections.**

Learning the Skill

The database organizes information in categories called fields. For example, as shown above, a database of your friends might include the fields **Name, Telephone Number,** and **Birthday.** Each person you enter into the database is called a record. After entering the records, you might create a list sorted by birthdays or use the records to create a personalized phonebook. Together, all the records make up the database.

Scientists use databases for many purposes. They often have large amounts of data that they need to analyze. For example, a sociologist might want to compare and contrast certain information about the people of the Andean countries. A database would be a good place to sort and compare information about the languages, religions, and ethnic groups of these countries.

Practicing the Skill

Follow these steps to build a database about the Andean countries.

1. Determine what facts you want to include in your database and research to collect that information.
2. Follow the instructions in the database that you are using to set up fields. Then enter each item of data in its assigned field.
3. Determine how you want to organize the facts in the database—chronologically by the date, alphabetically, or by some other method.
4. Follow the instructions in your computer program to sort the information.
5. Check that all the information in your database is correct. If necessary, add, delete, or change information or fields.

Applying the Skill

Research and build a database that organizes information about an Andean country of your choice. Explain why the database is organized the way it is.

Practicing the Skill Answers

1. *Possible answers:* country name, landforms, resources
2. Monitor students' performance at this step.
3. Suggest that for this database, students organize their information by country.
4. Monitor students' performance at this step.
5. Have students present printed copies of the different records.

Applying the Skill

Students' completed databases should include different categories of information.

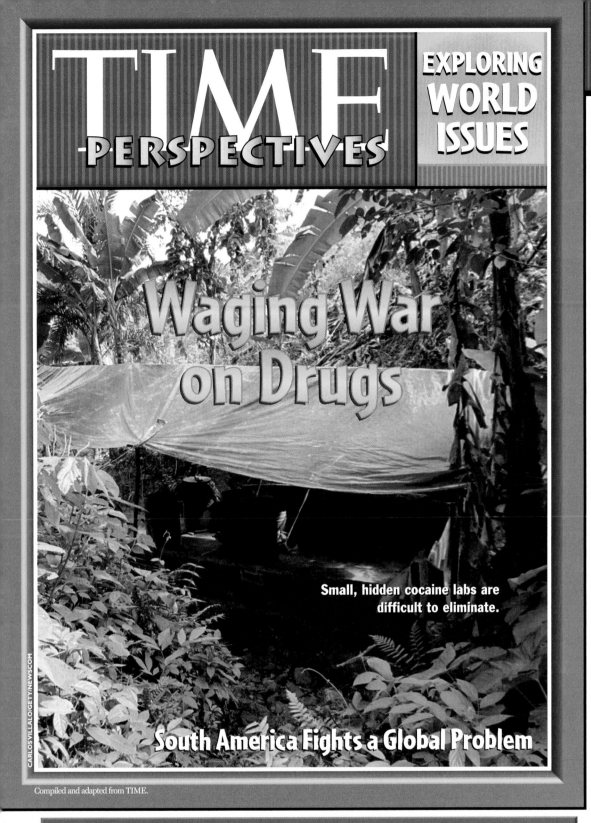

TIME PERSPECTIVES

EXPLORING WORLD ISSUES

Waging War on Drugs

Small, hidden cocaine labs are difficult to eliminate.

South America Fights a Global Problem

CARLOS VILLALO/GETTY/NEWSCOM

Compiled and adapted from TIME.

Making Connections

Drug Abuse **Ask students:** **How common do you think drug abuse is in our town? What kinds of drugs do you think are being abused?** Write students' answers. **Ask:** **How do young people get these drugs? Are the methods different for a legal drug (such as alcohol) than for an illegal drug (such as marijuana)? How does the use of illegal drugs affect your friends and our town?** Tell students that this article will discuss some of the things being done to reduce drug abuse.

TIME PERSPECTIVES

Exploring World Issues

Teacher Background

Until the 1960s, illegal drug use was seen as primarily a lower-class activity. Middle-class drug use grew in the 1960s. In response, the Bureau of Narcotics and Dangerous Drugs was founded in 1968, and the Drug Enforcement Administration (DEA) was founded in 1973.

TIME REPORTS

LATIN AMERICA

Waging War on Drugs

THEME: ECONOMICS AND GOVERNMENT

Guide To Teaching With This Unit

Inside This Unit Three activity masters are designed to help your students grasp some of the complexities of the cocaine trade, whose roots are in the Andes.

- Activity Master 1: A flow chart lets students trace key steps in the cocaine trade, from farmers to drug abusers.
- Activity Master 2: A graph on Colombia's legal exports is a reminder that

democratic government and a solid middle class. Yet leftist guerrillas have plagued the country for 40 years. Two guerrilla armies, together earning more than $1 million a day on the cocaine trade, promise to redistribute the nation's land to the poor. Not surprisingly, landowners have hired their own soldiers, paramilitary forces that act as if repression is the only answer to Colombia's problems. Ordinary people are caught in the crossfire. In the meantime, the cocaine trade continues to destabilize legal ... government. And as ... into the rain

that Colombia trades legal goods not just with other South American nations, but with Japan, European Union nations, the United States, and many others as well. After students complete the exercise, have them name specific items in each of the nine categories of exports that their families use. Why don't Americans make all those items in the U.S.? (Some items—coffee, for instance—don't grow easily in our climate. Many manufactured goods are far cheaper to make abroad, in low-wage countries like Colombia.)

Preparing the Student

The United States provides the world's largest market for commonly abused drugs. Some government agencies involved in the "war on drugs" include the Drug Enforcement Administration (DEA), the FBI, and U.S. Customs.

1 Focus

On the board, write the following recommendations from the Los Angeles Citizens' Commission on U.S. Drug Policy:

- The government should fund drug treatment programs for anyone who wants them.
- People who are arrested for drug use and then successfully take part in drug treatment should not be imprisoned.
- To protect children from drug dealers, we should find ways to take the profit out of drug sales.

Ask: Do you think these recommendations would reduce drug use? Explain.

Interpreting Maps and Charts

ANSWERS

1. The U.S. spent large amounts of money in Bolivia and Peru, where coca cultivation has decreased. Cultivation increased in Colombia, where little money was spent.
2. The line for Colombia would go down while the line(s) for Peru and/or Bolivia could go up if drug dealers moved back there.

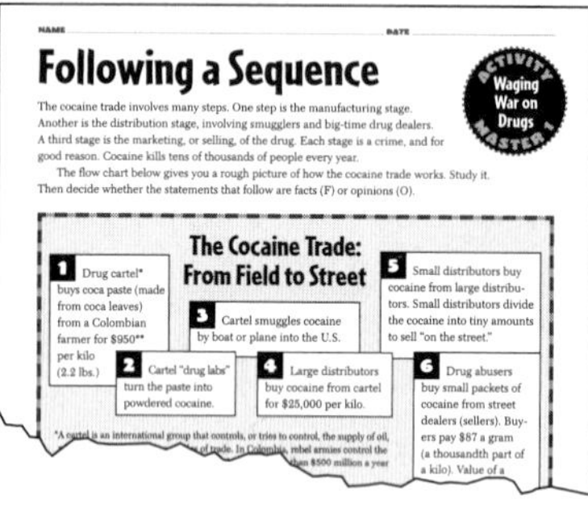

NAME DATE

Following a Sequence

ACTIVITY Waging War on Drugs MASTER 1

The cocaine trade involves many steps. One step is the manufacturing stage. Another is the distribution stage, involving smugglers and big-time drug dealers. A third stage is the marketing, or selling, of the drug. Each stage is a crime, and for good reason. Cocaine kills tens of thousands of people every year.

The flow chart below gives you a rough picture of how the cocaine trade works. Study it. Then decide whether the statements that follow are facts (F) or opinions (O).

The Cocaine Trade: From Field to Street

1. Drug cartel* buys coca paste (made from coca leaves) from a Colombian farmer for $950** per kilo (2.2 lbs.)
2. Cartel "drug labs" turn the paste into powdered cocaine.
3. Cartel smuggles cocaine by boat or plane into the U.S.
4. Large distributors buy cocaine from cartel for $25,000 per kilo.
5. Small distributors buy cocaine from large distributors. Small distributors divide the cocaine into tiny amounts to sell "on the street."
6. Drug abusers buy small packets of cocaine from street dealers (sellers). Buyers pay $87 a gram (a thousandth part of a kilo). Value of a

*A cartel is an international group that controls, or tries to control, the supply of oil, ... of trade. In Colombia, rebel armies control the ... than $500 million a year

TIME PERSPECTIVES

EXPLORING WORLD ISSUES

A war on many fronts: U.S. Navy Seals on patrol in Brazil. Police in Peru seize cocaine.

LUKE FRAZZA/AFP

MARIANA BAZO/REUTERS

The Drug Trade's Tragic Effect

Chris Farley lived every actor's dream. During the 1990s, the comic actor spent five successful years on television's hit series *Saturday Night Live.* Farley became so popular that in 1995 he left *SNL* to start a career in films.

Chris Farley's career was heading to the top.

CORBIS SYGMA

Hollywood quickly became a fan of Farley's and his fame grew. He played roles in movies such as *Tommy Boy* and *Black Sheep.* By 1997, a well-known talk-show host predicted Farley would be "a major motion picture star."

Farley played outrageous characters that battled the world with humor and a big heart. In real life, the actor also battled an addiction to alcohol and drugs like cocaine and heroin. **Cocaine** is a drug that can cause brain injuries if taken only once. In December 1997, Farley used cocaine and other drugs and died.

A Deadly Import

The cocaine that killed Chris Farley came from South America. And so did the 650 tons of cocaine smuggled into the United States in 2000. Every day Americans died as a result of using this drug.

Cocaine is made from the coca plant, which is grown in only three countries. Colombia is by far the biggest producer, followed by Peru and Bolivia.

In all three countries, coca is grown high up in the Andes. Cocaine "factories" there turn coca leaves into a white powder. **Smugglers** use boats and airplanes to slip that powder, cocaine, into countries around the world.

The Drug War in the Andes

INTERPRETING MAPS AND CHARTS

1. **Interpreting Data** What does this map tell you about the U.S. role in South America's drug war?
2. **Making Inferences** Suppose the war against drugs succeeds in Colombia. How might the lines on the graph change?

260

Team-Teaching Activity

Science Explain that Incans and their ancestors have been cultivating coca leaves for more than one thousand years. They chew coca leaves to relieve altitude sickness and hunger. South American Indians also use coca leaves as a mild stimulant, much like Americans use coffee. Invite a science teacher to class who can discuss the chemical makeup and medicinal uses of coca leaves. Have the teacher point out that the chemical used to make cocaine is just one component of the coca leaf and that cocaine has been used in medicines to alleviate pain, to treat skin diseases such as eczema and shingles, and to kill certain kinds of bacteria. Ask him or her to list the addictive and nonaddictive chemicals of the coca leaf.

Farley could have been a major star but drugs cost him his life.

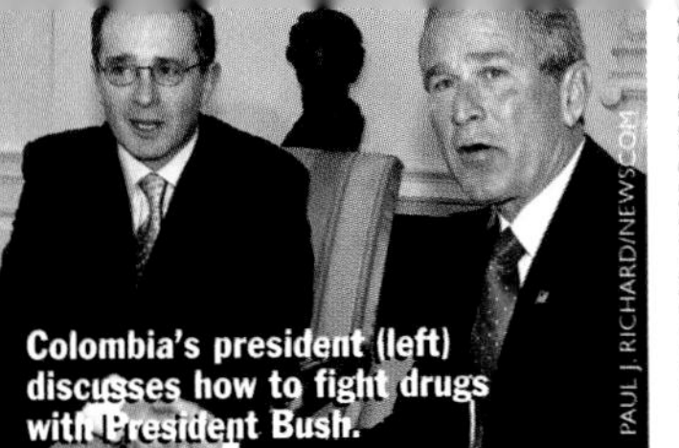
Colombia's president (left) discusses how to fight drugs with President Bush.

TIME PERSPECTIVES

▲ The beautiful poppy is harvested for deadly heroin.

Heroin, another deadly drug, is made from the poppy plant. In South America, poppies are turned into heroin only in Colombia.

Rebels' Businesses

Drugs have nearly brought Colombia to its knees. Colombia is a country about the size of Texas and California combined. Rebel armies based in Colombia's jungles have fought government troops for some 40 years. The rebels make and sell cocaine and heroin. Their drug business brings them more than $1 million a day. They spend a lot of that money on weapons.

Paramilitaries add to Colombia's woes. These are armed men that landowners and businesses hire to protect their workers. In 2000, rebels and paramilitaries kidnapped eight innocent civilians every day and murdered 80 more. The chaos has forced some 2 million Colombians to flee their homes.

U.S. money had helped Bolivia and Peru tackle drug problems during the 1990s. But many cocaine producers in those countries moved their operations to Colombia, where cocaine production doubled between 1995 and 2000.

In 2000, the U.S. decided to help Colombia rid itself of the drug trade. It gave Colombia's government $1.3 billion to equip and train its army to fight drugs.

Think, Laugh and Live

If no one bought drugs, no one would produce them. Chris Farley's death helped persuade many people to avoid cocaine. But millions still use it, so the cocaine business remains strong.

Farley's friends and family have created the Chris Farley Foundation to teach kids about the dangers of **drug abuse.** The Foundation encourages young people to "think, laugh and live" when peers try to get them to use drugs. And it does so—as Farley would have—with humor. ■

EXPLORING THE ISSUE

1. **Explaining** What comment does this article's title make about the trade in illegal drugs?
2. **Cause and Effect** Describe how Chris Farley's death could have persuaded millions of Americans to avoid cocaine.

261

2 TEACH

Reading Strategy

Identifying Main Ideas Have students write down the headings for the four sections in this report. After each heading have them write the main idea of the section. Next have them write down the subheadings in each section, with the main idea and three supporting statements under each. L1

More About the Photo

Chris Farley Ask: Why do you suppose Chris Farley took the cocaine that killed him?

EXPLORING THE ISSUE

ANSWERS

1. It suggests that the drug trade is as much a threat to our nation as an attack, and the government will take action to fight it if necessary.
2. Cocaine use killed the actor as he was rising to stardom, and it is dangerous to use cocaine.

Differentiated Instruction

Meeting Special Needs: Logical/Mathematical According to the Office of National Drug Control Policy, in 1990 there were approximately 7,786,000 cocaine users in the United States, who used 271 metric tons of cocaine and spent a total of $61.3 billion. In 2000 there were 7,480,000 cocaine users who used 269 metric tons and spent a total of $36.1 billion. Have students put these figures into a chart and then compare the results. **Ask:** How have the number of users, amount of cocaine, and total spent on cocaine changed in 10 years? How does this information relate to this report? Why is the change greater for the amount spent than the other two categories? *(fewer users and greater availability of the drug might have reduced the cost)* L2

Recommended Internet Sites

www.dea.gov/

The Web site of the Drug Enforcement Administration is a good source of information about drug use and drug deterrence programs.

www.pbs.org/wgbh/pages/ frontline/shows/drugs/

This PBS's Frontline Web site covers 30 years of the war on drugs, including candid accounts from people directly involved, such as DEA and FBI agents. It also includes a teacher's guide.

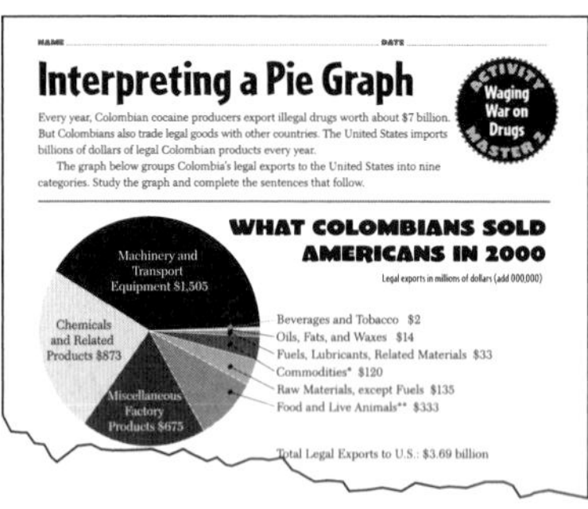

NAME ____ DATE ____

Interpreting a Pie Graph

Activity Master 2 — Waging War on Drugs

Every year, Colombian cocaine producers export illegal drugs worth about $7 billion. But Colombians also trade legal goods with other countries. The United States imports billions of dollars of legal Colombian products every year.

The graph below groups Colombia's legal exports to the United States into nine categories. Study the graph and complete the sentences that follow.

WHAT COLOMBIANS SOLD AMERICANS IN 2000

Legal exports in millions of dollars (add 000,000)

Machinery and Transport Equipment $1,505
Chemicals and Related Products $873
Miscellaneous Factory Products $675
Beverages and Tobacco $2
Oils, Fats, and Waxes $14
Fuels, Lubricants, Related Materials $33
Commodities* $120
Raw Materials, except Fuels $135
Food and Live Animals** $333

Total Legal Exports to U.S.: $3.69 billion

EXPLORING THE ISSUE

ANSWERS

1. As long as illegal drugs are being grown, suppliers will find ways to get them to those who will pay money for them.
2. About 80 percent of the cocaine that comes into the U.S. is from Colombia. If cocaine production is wiped out at the source, then it decreases the amount of cocaine even reaching the United States.

Targeting Drug Supplies

Pop works for the U.S. Customs Service in Hidalgo, Texas. He looks for illegal drugs in vehicles that cross into the United States from Mexico.

By any measure, Pop is good at his job. In 1998 he discovered 3,075 pounds of cocaine in a pineapple truck. In 1999 he found 50 pounds of marijuana hidden in an ice chest.

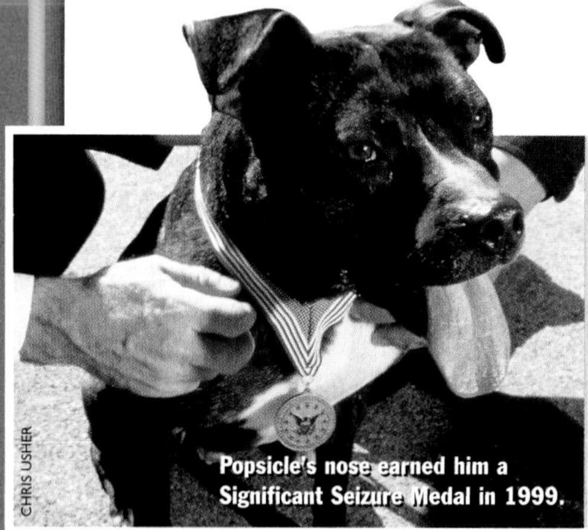

CHRIS USHER

Popsicle's nose earned him a Significant Seizure Medal in 1999.

What makes Pop so successful? His nose. Pop—short for Popsicle—is a pit bull. Like 500 other **customs dogs** in the U.S., he's been trained to sniff out drugs.

Popsicle plays a role in the worldwide effort to stop the flow of drugs. Many thousands of people are also part of that effort. Police officers, for example, arrest people who sell drugs on the street. Members of the U.S. Coast Guard head off smugglers at sea. Soldiers in Colombia destroy coca plants and cocaine factories.

U.S. Help

About 80 percent of the cocaine that reaches the United States comes from Colombia. That's why the U.S. has put more than $1.3 billion behind Colombia's fight against drugs. Colombia's armed forces use most of the money to train soldiers and buy equipment. Planes bought with U.S. dollars drop chemicals that kill growing coca plants. New helicopters rush soldiers to cocaine factories defended by heavily armed rebel troops.

Stopping cocaine at its source isn't just a military job. It's also an effort to change minds. Colombian officials are trying to persuade farmers to stop growing coca and poppies. They pay farmers to grow cocoa, coffee, palm hearts, and other crops instead.

Will those efforts work? Some experts think so. Others aren't so sure. "Those that profit from producing cocaine and heroin are not about to roll over and play dead," said one expert. "There is evidence that drug factories are moving into Brazil and Ecuador."

If she's right, Popsicle has a lot of work ahead of him.

EXPLORING THE ISSUE

1. **Explaining** Why is stopping cocaine at its source important to the war on drugs?
2. **Analyzing Information** Why might it be more effective to wipe out cocaine in Colombia than to stop it in the United States?

Critical Thinking Activity

Interpreting Points of View Tell students that according to the United Nations Development Program and the World Bank, 1.2 billion people live on less than a dollar a day. Point out that the farmers in Latin America are some of the poorest people in the world. Then ask students to imagine paying for food, shelter, clothing, education, transportation, fertilizer, and medicine with less than a dollar a day. Add that the price of coffee has fallen in recent years and that a cacao (the plant used to make cocoa) blight has wiped out many small cacao plantations in Latin America and Africa. **Ask:** What types of economic choices do poor Latin American farmers have? **L2**

262

Dealing With Demand

It's tragic but true: Someone somewhere is always going to want to buy illegal drugs. And someone else will be willing to **supply** them. Worldwide, about 14 million people use cocaine today. About 5.3 million of them live in the United States. Nine million people in the world use heroin. More than 650,000 of them are Americans.

Suppose those numbers were cut in half. Heroin and cocaine production would plunge. And illegal drugs would cause far less misery.

Inside Drug Court

Is slashing the **demand** for drugs by 50 percent an impossible dream? Not in Baltimore, Maryland. Baltimore has a Drug Treatment Court. The court's goal is to help people arrested for carrying illegal drugs to stop abusing them. "If you ask for help," a Drug Court judge said in 2001, "you'll get it. If you don't ask, you'll go to jail."

According to the Maryland courts, half the addicts placed in treatment by the Drug Court have stayed away from drugs. Copy that success rate throughout the nation, and the demand in the U.S. for illegal drugs would nose-dive.

Educating Americans

No war on drugs can be successful without such a drop in usage, experts say. U.S. president George W. Bush shares their view. "The main reason drugs are shipped . . . to the United States," he said in 2001, "is because United States citizens use drugs. Our nation must do a better job of educating our citizenry about the dangers and evils of drug use."

Yes, someone somewhere is always going to want to buy illegal drugs. But proper education and treatment will surely reduce the demand for drugs everywhere.

▲ Phoenix, Arizona, has a drug court like Baltimore's. Here a judge rewards a drug offender's good behavior with tickets to Phoenix's science museum.

EXPLORING THE ISSUE

1. **Analyzing Information** Which is more important—reducing the demand for illegal drugs or stopping criminals from producing them? Why?
2. **Problem Solving** What could schools do to lower the demand for illegal drugs?

More About the Photo

Rewards Ask: Do you think a reward such as the one given by this judge would affect whether a young person abuses drugs? Why or why not?

Did You Know

Money is no good if you cannot spend it. Drug traffickers often receive large cash payments. They must then get the money into the mainstream without arousing suspicion. This process is referred to as "money laundering."

Synthesizing Information Prescription drugs such as tranquilizers and amphetamines are also bought, sold, and used illegally. Have students research and write a report on the illegal use of prescription drugs and how drug enforcement agencies handle this problem. L2

EXPLORING THE ISSUE

ANSWERS

1. Answers will vary. Many people believe it is most important to reduce demand, because as long as there is a market, dealers will provide the desired product.
2. *Possible answers:* teach students about the dangers of drugs; provide in-school treatment and counseling

Interdisciplinary Activity

Journalism Have students research antidrug programs in your city, local area, or, if necessary, state. Then have them write a "pretend" newspaper article on these programs. If possible, they may want to talk to local enforcement agents. They might even include a question-and-answer style interview in their article. In addition, they should check out their state drug enforcement agency's Web site. They may want to pursue getting their article published in the school newspaper or elsewhere. L2

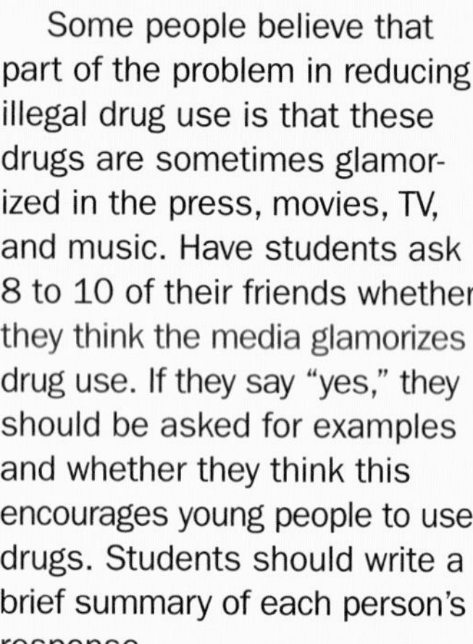

Current Events Journal

Some people believe that part of the problem in reducing illegal drug use is that these drugs are sometimes glamorized in the press, movies, TV, and music. Have students ask 8 to 10 of their friends whether they think the media glamorizes drug use. If they say "yes," they should be asked for examples and whether they think this encourages young people to use drugs. Students should write a brief summary of each person's response.

EXPLORING THE ISSUE

ANSWERS

1. Students should learn about the dangers of drugs before the sixth grade so that they are prepared with appropriate knowledge.
2. He is famous in a sport (skateboarding) that is popular with teenagers. This sport is sometimes associated with "outsiders," who may be more likely than the average student to abuse drugs.

TIME PERSPECTIVES

Fighting Drug Abuse: What Can One Person Do?

Andy McDonald is a man with a mission—helping kids stay away from drugs. Andy is a national spokesperson for the Partnership for a Drug-Free America. His message: "Kids don't need drugs to succeed."

Andy should know. He's one of the few top-ranked skateboarders in the world. He's so good, he once jumped over three SUVs and one car—all at the same time. That feat landed him in *The Guinness Book of World Records*. "That right there," he says of skateboarding, "is my idea of getting high."

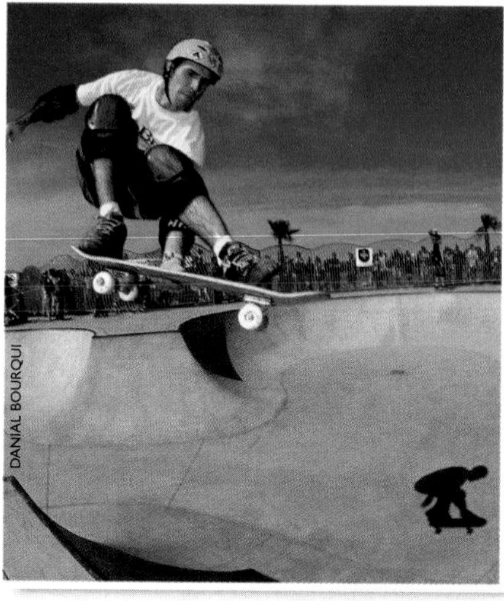

▲ **Andy McDonald: too active to do drugs**

Speaking Out

You don't have to be a champion athlete to fight drug abuse. Kaelin Weiler proved it. Between 1996 and 1998, heroin killed 11 teens in her hometown of Plano, Texas. The youngest victim was a seventh-grader.

Kaelin, 17, persuaded other kids to fight back. They tied white ribbons around traffic lights to remind people of the problem. They created a "memorial wall"—pictures of kids lost to drugs and the families they left behind. And they made videos about the dangers of drugs and showed them at assemblies.

You can work with school officials to start a similar program in your school and town. Learn as much as you can about the dangers of illegal drugs. Then design a program to teach what you learned to young students and their parents. Launch your program. Afterwards, describe the program and its results in a letter to your local newspaper's editor. E-mail a copy to the "In Your Own Words" Web site page of the Partnership for a Drug-Free America (**www.drugfreeamerica.org**).

EXPLORING THE ISSUE

1. **Making Inferences** Experts say that the risk for alcohol and other drug use skyrockets in the sixth grade. Assuming that's true, when—and why—should kids begin learning about the dangers of illegal drugs?
2. **Analyzing Information** What makes Andy McDonald an effective promoter of a drug-free life?

Your Government and You

Tell students that in December 2002 the House Government Reform Committee held a hearing on "America's Heroin Crisis, Colombian Heroin, and How We Can Improve Plan Colombia." Then read the following quote from Representative Dan Burton, a conservative Republican from Indiana: "I don't think they would be refining coca and heroin in Colombia if they couldn't make any money . . . . Don't just talk about education. Don't just talk about eradication. Don't just talk about killing people like Escobar [a Colombian drug lord], who is going to be replaced by somebody else. Let's talk about what would happen if we started addressing how to get the profit out of drugs." Have students brainstorm ideas for getting the profit out of drugs. Then ask them to send their ideas in a letter to their U.S. congressperson. L2

REVIEW AND ASSESS

UNDERSTANDING THE ISSUE

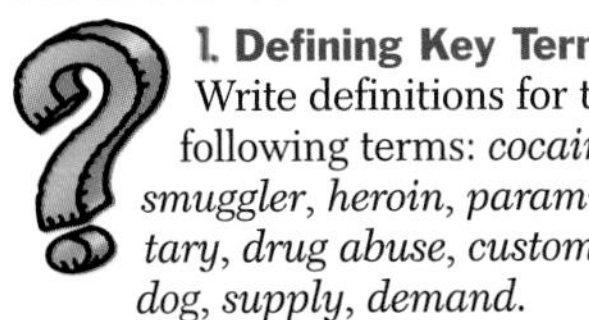

1. **Defining Key Terms** Write definitions for the following terms: *cocaine, smuggler, heroin, paramilitary, drug abuse, customs dog, supply, demand.*

2. **Writing to Inform** In a 300-word article, explain why the drug trade needs both buyers and suppliers for its survival. Use at least five of the key terms listed above.

3. **Writing to Persuade** In your view, can the war against drugs ever be won? Support your answer to that question in a brief essay.

INTERNET RESEARCH ACTIVITY

4. Since 1998 the U.S. government has funded ads designed to combat drug abuse among young people. How good are the ads? You be the judge. Browse the Internet or use copies of current magazines and newspapers to find ads designed to combat drug abuse. Choose two you think are effective and two you think are not effective. Either print copies off the Internet, or photocopy ads from magazines and newspapers. Attach a comment to each one explaining why it does or doesn't work well.

5. The No. 1 drug problem in America isn't cocaine or heroin. It's underage drinking. One organization that works to prevent underage drinking is Mothers Against Drunk Driving (MADD). Use Internet resources to learn more about this organization and report your findings to the class.

BEYOND THE CLASSROOM

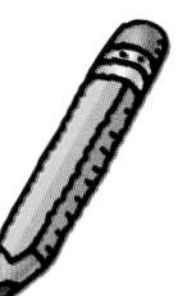

6. **Research the way farmers live in Colombia, Bolivia, or Peru.** In a short article, explain why those farmers might see growing poppies or coca as a way to improve their lives.

7. **Research the geography and people of Afghanistan and Myanmar.** Most of the world's heroin is produced in those two countries. Make a list of conditions—poverty, climate, and location, for example—that each country shares with Colombia. In class, explain what your list suggests about places in which drug production thrives.

▲ Venus and Serena Williams are at the top of their game—and far from drugs.

WHAT DRUG AND ALCOHOL ABUSE COST

Annual Cost of Alcohol Abuse in the U.S. $185 billion

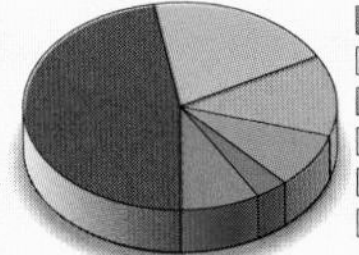

- Output[1] lost to alcohol-related illness: **$87.6 billion**
- Output lost to early deaths: **$36.5 billion**
- Healthcare: **$23.6 billion**
- Car-crash damage: **$15.7 billion**
- Alcohol-related crime: **$6.3 billion**
- Other costs: **$15.3 billion**

Annual Cost of Drug Abuse in the U.S. $143 billion

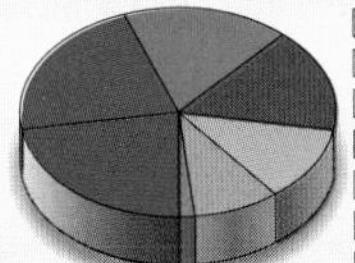

- Output[2] lost by crime victims: **$32.2 billion**
- Property damage, government expenses[3]: **$31.4 billion**
- Output lost to lives of crime: **$24.6 billion**
- Output lost to drug-related illness: **$23.1 billion**
- Output lost to early deaths: **$16.6 billion**
- Healthcare: **$12.8 billion**
- Other costs: **$2.3 billion**

[1]Output is the estimated amount of goods and services that workers would have produced if they had not died or gotten sick, injured, or jailed. [2]Includes output lost by victims of drug-related crimes and criminals jailed for those crimes. [3]Includes the cost of government anti-drug efforts, police, prisons, and other items.
Source: National Institutes of Health

BUILDING GRAPH READING SKILLS

1. **Explaining** A worker's "output" consists of the goods and services that he or she produces. The abuse of alcohol and other drugs costs the U.S. billions of dollars in lost output. How do these two graphs show that?

2. **Making Inferences** Suppose the U.S. Congress made cocaine and heroin as legal as alcohol. What might happen to the annual cost of drug abuse?

FOR UPDATES ON WORLD ISSUES GO TO www.timeclassroom.com/glencoe

3 ASSESS

Have students take the Time Reports Quiz or do the Alternative Assessment project for this unit provided in the Teacher's Classroom Resources.

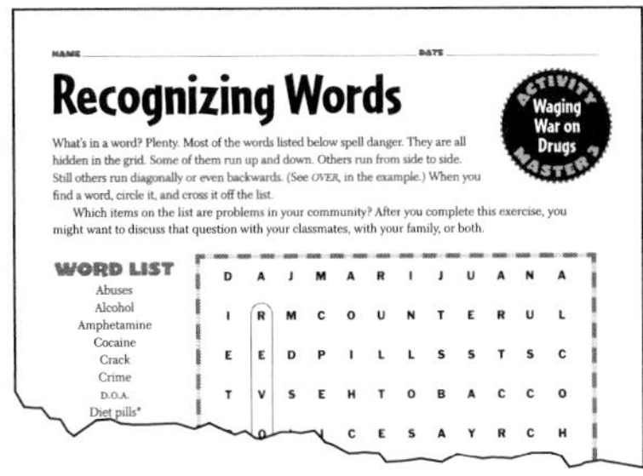

Recognizing Words

What's in a word? Plenty. Most of the words listed below spell danger. They are all hidden in the grid. Some of them run up and down. Others run from side to side. Still others run diagonally or even backwards. (See OVER, in the example.) When you find a word, circle it, and cross it off the list.

Which items on the list are problems in your community? After you complete this exercise, you might want to discuss that question with your classmates, with your family, or both.

WORD LIST: Abuses, Alcohol, Amphetamine, Cocaine, Crack, Crime, D.O.A., Diet pills

BUILDING GRAPH READING SKILLS

ANSWERS

1. Output lost to illness and early death from alcohol abuse costs $124.1 billion. Output lost by crime victims, output lost to lives of crime, illness, and early death due to drug abuse costs $96.5 billion.
2. *Possible answers:* The cost might drop because of lower drug prices and fewer related crimes. Also there would be fewer costs for sending people to jail. The cost might rise because of illnesses and accidents related to drug use.

4 CLOSE

Ask students to write a paragraph starting with this sentence: *The U.S. war on drugs would be more effective if . . . .*

Culminating Activity

To close this lesson, have students complete the Review and Assess section questions and activities above. Students should use classroom discussion, contextual clues, and their student dictionaries to write definitions for terms. Before assigning the Internet activities, it is recommended that you review your school district policy on student Internet use.

Focus on Debate

As a final activity to further student understanding of the issue, have students debate the pro and con position of the following topic: **As long as there is a demand for illegal drugs, suppliers will find a way to obtain them. L2**

 **EE4 Human Systems: Standard 11**

Focus

Section Objectives

1. Describe the landforms and climates of Peru and Ecuador.
2. Compare how the people of Peru and Ecuador earn a living.
3. Discuss what the people of Peru and Ecuador are like.

BELLRINGER
Skillbuilder Activity

Project transparency and have students answer the question.

Daily Focus Skills Transparency

Reading Preview

■ **Activating Prior Knowledge** Have students look at the photograph in Exploring Our World. Ask why they think this ancient site was not discovered until 1911.

■ **Preteaching Vocabulary** Have students check the definitions of the words in the Terms to Know. Direct them to use each term correctly in a sentence.

Guide to Reading

Main Idea

Peru and Ecuador share similar landscapes, climates, and history.

Terms to Know

- navigable
- foothills
- empire

Reading Strategy

Create two ovals like these. Under each heading, list facts about Peru and Ecuador in the outer parts of the ovals. Where the ovals overlap, write facts that apply to both countries.

Section 2

Land and People of Peru and Ecuador

NATIONAL GEOGRAPHIC **Exploring Our World**

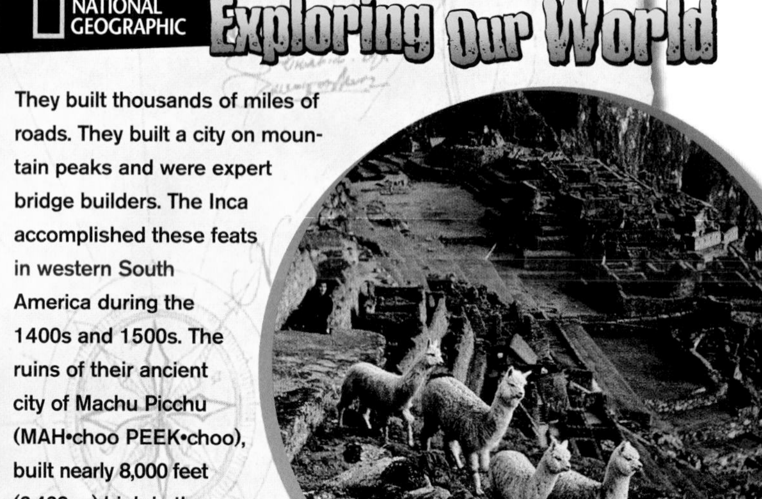

They built thousands of miles of roads. They built a city on mountain peaks and were expert bridge builders. The Inca accomplished these feats in western South America during the 1400s and 1500s. The ruins of their ancient city of Machu Picchu (MAH•choo PEEK•choo), built nearly 8,000 feet (2,438 m) high in the Andes, were not even known to modern people until 1911.

Peru and **Ecuador** lie along the Pacific coast of South America, west of Brazil and south of Colombia. The Andes form the spine of these countries. *Peru*—a Native American word that means "land of abundance"—is rich in mineral resources.

Peru

Dry deserts, the snowcapped Andes, and hot, humid rain forests greet you in Peru. Most of Peru's farms and cities lie on a narrow coastal strip of plains and deserts. The cold **Peru Current** in the Pacific Ocean keeps temperatures here fairly mild even though the area is very near the Equator. Find the Peru Current on the map on page 57.

The Andes, with their highland valleys and plateaus, sweep through the center of Peru. On Peru's border with Bolivia, you can see **Lake Titicaca** (TEE•tee•KAH•kah), the highest navigable lake in the world. Navigable means that a body of water is wide and deep enough to

Section Resources

Reproducible Masters
- Reproducible Lesson Plan
- Daily Lecture and Discussion Notes
- Note-taking Guide
- Guided Reading Activity
- Reading Essentials and Study Guide
- Section Quiz

Transparencies
- Daily Focus Skills Transparency

Multimedia
- Vocabulary PuzzleMaker CD-ROM
- Interactive Tutor Self-Assessment CD-ROM
- Presentation Plus! CD-ROM
- ExamView® Pro Testmaker CD-ROM

allow ships to travel in it. East of the Andes you descend to the foothills and flat plains of the **Amazon Basin.** Foothills are the low hills at the base of a mountain range. Rainfall is plentiful here, and thick, hot rain forests cover almost all of the plains area.

Mining, Fishing, and Farming Peru's economy relies on a variety of natural resources. The Andes contain many minerals, including copper, silver, gold, and iron ore. Peru's biggest export is copper. The second-largest export—fish—comes from the Peru Current.

About one-third of Peru's people farm the land. Some grow sugarcane, cotton, and coffee for export. Like Colombia, Peru grows coca leaves. Most people, however, work on subsistence farms, where they grow only enough food to meet their family's needs. Some of these farms are terraced, or stair-stepped, up the mountainsides of the Andes. The chief crops are rice, plantains (a kind of banana), and corn. Native Americans in the Andes were the first people ever to grow potatoes. Today potatoes are Peru's main food crop, and farmers grow hundreds of varieties in different colors and shapes. Refer back to page 228 to see how the potato was part of the Columbian Exchange.

From Empire to Republic During the 1400s, a Native American people called the Inca had a powerful civilization in the area that is now Peru. Their empire, or group of lands under one ruler, stretched more than 2,500 miles (4,023 km) along the Andes.

The Incan emperor developed courts, military posts, trade inspections, work rules, and a complex system of record keeping. Work crews built irrigation systems, roads, and suspension bridges that linked the regions of the empire to Cuzco, the capital city of the Inca. You can still see the remains of magnificent fortresses and buildings erected centuries ago by skilled Incan builders. The photograph on page 266 shows the ruins of one of the Inca's most famous cities—Machu Picchu.

In the early 1500s, Spaniards arrived in Peru. They desired the gold and silver found here. The Spaniards defeated the Inca and made Peru a Spanish territory. Peru gained its freedom from Spain in the 1820s. After independence, Peru fought wars with neighboring Chile and Ecuador over land.

Peru is now a republic with an elected president. In recent years, the country's economy has grown very rapidly. Many of Peru's people, however, still live in poverty and cannot find steady jobs.

Peru's Culture Peru's 27.1 million people live mostly along the Pacific coast. **Lima** (LEE•mah), with more than 7 million people, is the capital and largest city. In recent years, many people from the countryside have moved to Lima in search of work. Because of this sudden rise in population, the city has become overcrowded, noisy, and polluted.

About half of Peru's people are Native American. In fact, Peru has one of the largest Native American populations in the Western Hemisphere. Many live in the Andean highlands or eastern rain forests where they follow a traditional way of life. Most of them blend the Catholic faith, Peru's main religion, with beliefs of their ancestors.

The Quipu

The Inca did not have a written language. To keep records, they used a system of knotted strings called the quipu. The strings were of various lengths and colors, and each knot meant a different item or number. Men in charge of the quipu used the knots to record all the taxes brought each year to the Inca. They recorded the number of men who went to war and how many were born and died every year. In short, it might be said that they recorded on their quipu everything that could be counted.

Reading Strategy

Determining Cause and Effect Have students write down these key facts about Peru and Ecuador: "High altitude," "Peru Current nearby," "Ancient Native American culture," and "Once a colony of Spain." Tell students that each of these statements is a cause and that they are to identify the effects of these causes. Have volunteers read their suggestions to the class. L2

Daily Lecture and Discussion Notes

THE ANDEAN COUNTRIES

Daily Lecture and Discussion Notes
Land and People of Peru and Ecuador

Did You Know? Ecuador is home to some of the world's most extraordinary national parks. In a matter of 200 miles, a traveler can visit parks in all of the country's defining regions—the coastal lowlands in the west, the volcanic central highlands, and the rain forests of the east.

I. Peru

A. Most of Peru's farms and cities lie on a narrow coastal strip along the Pacific Ocean. The Andes run through the center of the country. Peru has many climates, including dry deserts, frigid mountains, and hot, humid rain forests. The cold Peru Current keeps temperatures mild along the coast.

... you can see Lake Titicaca, the highest navigable ...

Did You Know?

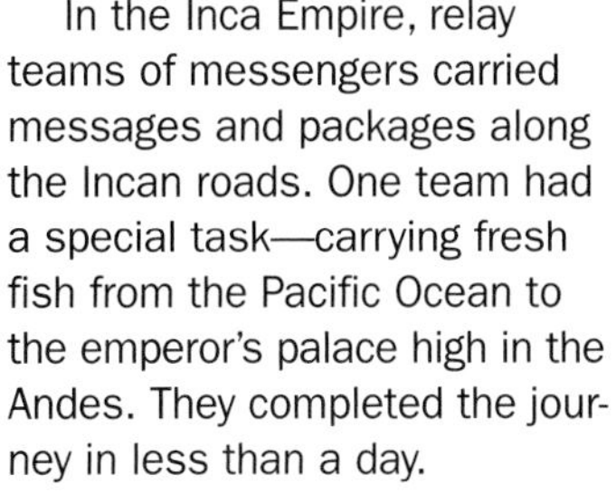

In the Inca Empire, relay teams of messengers carried messages and packages along the Incan roads. One team had a special task—carrying fresh fish from the Pacific Ocean to the emperor's palace high in the Andes. They completed the journey in less than a day.

Reading Strategy — Reading the Text

Outlining Students may want to use power notes to outline the section. Power notes are easy for students to use because main ideas and details are identified by numbers. Main ideas are power 1 ideas, and details can be power 2's, 3's, and so on. Power 3 supports power 2, and power 2 supports power 1. Have students outline the section using power notes. L1

*Use the **Reading Skills Handbook** for more reading strategies.*

Answer Answers will vary but may include: similarity—players wear uniforms; difference—called *fútbol* rather than soccer.

Sports Soccer was brought to the Andean region by British immigrants and first played in 1892.

✓ Reading Check Answer

the Inca

Assess

Assign Section 2 Assessment as homework or an in-class activity.

Have students use the Interactive Tutor Self-Assessment CD-ROM to review Section 2.

L2

Section Quiz

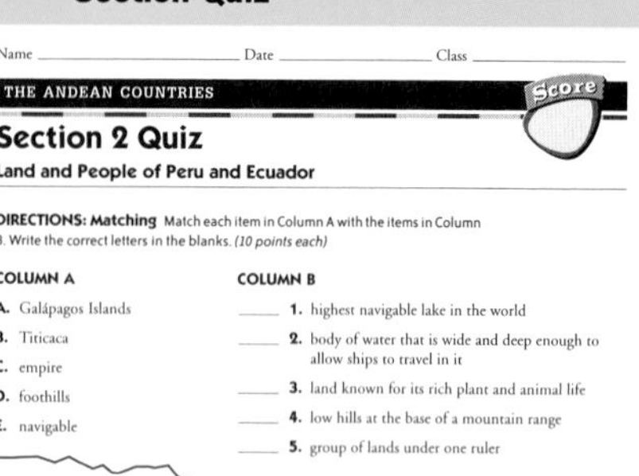

Name ______ Date ______ Class ______

THE ANDEAN COUNTRIES

Score

Section 2 Quiz

Land and People of Peru and Ecuador

DIRECTIONS: Matching Match each item in Column A with the items in Column B. Write the correct letters in the blanks. *(10 points each)*

COLUMN A	COLUMN B
A. Galápagos Islands	____ **1.** highest navigable lake in the world
B. Titicaca	____ **2.** body of water that is wide and deep enough to allow ships to travel in it
C. empire	____ **3.** land known for its rich plant and animal life
D. foothills	____ **4.** low hills at the base of a mountain range
E. navigable	____ **5.** group of lands under one ruler

Sports

Sports have been played in Peru for centuries. Ancient vases show the Inca playing early forms of badminton and basketball. Today soccer, called *fútbol*, is the national sport of Peru. Boys and girls learn the sport at a young age, and every village has a local soccer team. Peruvians also enjoy baseball and basketball. In addition, volleyball has become very popular since 1988. That was the year the women's volleyball team from Peru won an Olympic medal.

Looking Closer **How is the game shown here similar to and different from an American soccer game?**

Peruvians also include many people of mixed or European ancestry. People of Asian heritage form a small but important part of the population. Although a minority, Peruvians of European ancestry (mainly Spanish) control most of Peru's wealth and political power.

Spanish is Peru's official language, but about 70 Native American languages also are spoken. You can hear Quechua (KEH•chuh•wuh), the ancient language of the Inca, in many Native American villages. Another sound you may hear is the flutelike tones of the panpipe. An ancient instrument, panpipes are made from different lengths of bamboo stalks tied together.

✓ Reading Check **Who built a huge empire centered in Peru?**

Ecuador

Ecuador is one of the smallest countries in South America. Can you guess how it got its name? *Ecuador* is the Spanish word for "Equator," which runs right through Ecuador. West of Ecuador and also on the Equator are the **Galápagos Islands.** Owned by Ecuador since 1832, these scattered islands are known for their rich plant and animal life. Turn to page 270 to learn more about the unusual Galápagos Islands.

Ecuador's land and climate are similar to Peru's. Swamps and fertile plains stretch along Ecuador's Pacific coast. The Peru Current in the Pacific Ocean keeps coastal temperatures mild. The Andes run through the center of the country. The higher you climb up these mountains, the colder the climate gets. In contrast, hot, humid rain forests cover the lowlands of eastern Ecuador. Few people live in the rain forests.

An Agricultural Economy Agriculture is Ecuador's most important economic activity. Because of the mild climate, bananas, cacao, coffee,

Differentiated Instruction

Meeting Special Needs: Interpersonal Organize students into three groups and assign one of the following topics to each group: landforms, economy, or population. Group members should work together to prepare a map of Peru and Ecuador depicting their assigned topic. Display the completed maps and have student groups discuss how economic activities in these two countries are related to the landforms, climates, and resources found there. L2

Refer to *Inclusion for the Middle School Social Studies Classroom Strategies and Activities* in the TCR.

rice, sugarcane, and other export crops grow plentifully in the coastal lowlands. Farther inland, farms in the Andean highlands grow coffee, beans, corn, potatoes, and wheat. The eastern lowlands yield petroleum, Ecuador's major mineral export.

Ecuador's People Mestizos and Native Americans each make up about 40 percent of Ecuador's population. Spanish is the official language, but many Native Americans speak their traditional languages. About half of Ecuador's 12.6 million people live along the coast. The port of **Guayaquil** (GWY•ah•KEEL) is the most populous city. The other half of the population live in the valleys and plateaus of the Andes. **Quito** (KEE•toh), Ecuador's capital, lies more than 9,000 feet (2,743 m) above sea level. From the heart of Quito, you can see several snowcapped volcanoes. The city's historic center has Spanish colonial churches and old whitewashed houses with red-tiled roofs. These houses are built around central courtyards. You will not find flashing neon signs here because the construction of modern buildings has been strictly controlled since 1978. In that year, the United Nations Educational, Scientific, and Cultural Organization (UNESCO) declared the "old town" section of Quito a protected world cultural heritage site. Quito does have a "new town" section, though, in the north. This area has modern offices, embassies, and shopping centers.

✓ Reading Check Why are Ecuador's eastern lowlands important economically?

Section 2 Assessment

Defining Terms

1. **Define** navigable, foothills, empire.

Recalling Facts

2. **History** Who were the first people to grow potatoes?
3. **Culture** What has been the result of Lima's sudden population growth?
4. **Economics** What is Ecuador's major mineral export?

Critical Thinking

5. **Analyzing Information** Why is Peru's name, which means "land of abundance," appropriate? Why is it also inappropriate?
6. **Analyzing Cause and Effect** What effect does the Peru Current have on the coastal areas of Peru?

Graphic Organizer

7. **Organizing Information** Create two diagrams like this one, one for Peru and one for Ecuador. Under each heading, list facts about the countries.

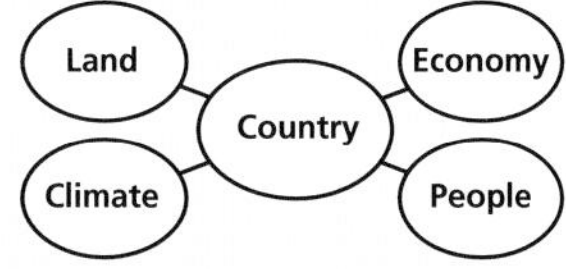

Applying Social Studies Skills

8. **Analyzing Maps** Turn to the political map on page 255. What Andean capital city lies closest to the Equator?

Chapter 9

Section 2, pages 266–269

✓ Reading Check Answer

They have petroleum, the major mineral export.

Reteach

Have students write five questions about Peru and Ecuador using the section text and chapter maps. Then put students in pairs and have them take turns asking and answering questions.

L1/ELL

Reading Essentials and Study Guide

Name ______ Date ______ Class ______

THE ANDEAN COUNTRIES

Reading Essentials and Study Guide 2

Land and People of Peru and Ecuador

Key Terms

navigable body of water wide and deep enough for ships to travel in it
foothills low hills at the base of mountains
empire group of lands under one ruler

Drawing From Experience

Enrich

Have students research and report on the animals of the Galápagos Islands.

Close

Have students choose a destination in Peru or Ecuador that they would like to visit. Have them prepare a brochure about the place.

Section 2 Assessment

1. The terms are defined in the Glossary.
2. Native Americans in the Andes
3. Lima has become overcrowded, noisy, and polluted.
4. petroleum
5. It is appropriate because Peru is rich in a variety of natural resources, including copper, silver, gold, iron ore, and fish. It is inappropriate because most people work on subsistence farms.
6. The Peru Current, which is cool, keeps the climate mild, even though the area is very near the Equator.
7. Students' organizers will vary. Check facts for accuracy.
8. Quito, Ecuador

TEACH

Point out to students that the Galápagos Islands were never connected to a larger body of land. **Ask:** **If that is true, how did plants and animals get there?** *(birds by flying; plants carried by the wind or in bird droppings; other animals by sea; plants and animals brought by humans)* **L1**

More About the Galápagos

Pirates used the islands as a base for attacking Spanish treasure ships. In the 1680s, the English pirate Ambrose Cowley first mapped the islands, giving them English names. Today most islands have Spanish names although one remains named for Cowley himself.

Interdisciplinary Connections

Science The Galápagos offer insight into the problems raised by introduced species—plants and animals that are not native to an area but brought there. Less than 20 years ago, Isabela Island had no wild goats. Today there are about 40,000 of these animals. Their efficient foraging of the island's vegetation threatens one species of tortoise and is causing deforestation.

Making Connections

ART | SCIENCE | CULTURE | TECHNOLOGY

The Galápagos Islands

The Galápagos Islands are located in the eastern Pacific Ocean about 600 miles (966 km) west of mainland Ecuador. Since 1959 about 95 percent of the islands has been maintained as a national park.

History of Exploration

From the first documented visit to the Galápagos Islands in 1535, people have commented on the islands' unusual wildlife. Sailors, including pirates and whalers, stopped on the islands to collect water and to trap the huge *galápagos*, or tortoises, found on the islands. Sailors valued the tortoises as a source of fresh meat because the giant tortoises could live on ships for months without food or water.

Charles Darwin

The most famous visitor to the Galápagos Islands was Charles Darwin, a scientist from England. He was studying animals all over the world. In 1835 Darwin spent five weeks visiting four of the biggest islands in the Galápagos. He carefully studied the volcanic landscape and the plant and animal life that he saw. He took notes on the differences among animals such as finches, mockingbirds, and iguanas from island to island. Darwin believed that these differences showed how populations of the same species change to fit their environment.

▲ Giant Galápagos tortoise

A Fragile Environment

Today the Galápagos Islands are still prized for their amazing variety of animal and plant life. Many of the species found here exist nowhere else on the earth. For instance, the marine iguana that lives here is the only seagoing lizard in the world.

Unfortunately, years of contact between the islands and humans have had serious effects. Three of the 14 types of tortoises are extinct, and others are seriously threatened. Populations of goats, pigs, dogs, rats, and some types of plants, brought by visitors, have grown so large that they threaten the survival of native plants and animals. Demand for exotic marine life, including sharks and sea cucumbers, has led to overfishing. The government of Ecuador, along with environmentalists worldwide, is now working to protect the islands.

Making the Connection

1. Why did sailors long ago stop at the islands?
2. What did Darwin observe about the islands?
3. **Drawing Conclusions** Why are environmentalists and the government of Ecuador working to protect the Galápagos Islands?

Making the Connection

1. to collect water and to trap the large tortoises found there
2. He used them to help understand how populations change to fit their environments.
3. because many species found there exist nowhere else on the earth and because many species are threatened with extinction

Section 3

The Bolivians and Chileans

Guide to Reading

Main Idea

Bolivia and Chile share the Andes, but their economies and people are different.

Terms to Know

- landlocked
- altiplano
- sodium nitrate

Reading Strategy

Create a chart like the one below. In each row, write at least one fact about Bolivia and one about Chile.

	Bolivia	Chile
Land		
Climate		
Economy		
People		

NATIONAL GEOGRAPHIC **Exploring Our World**

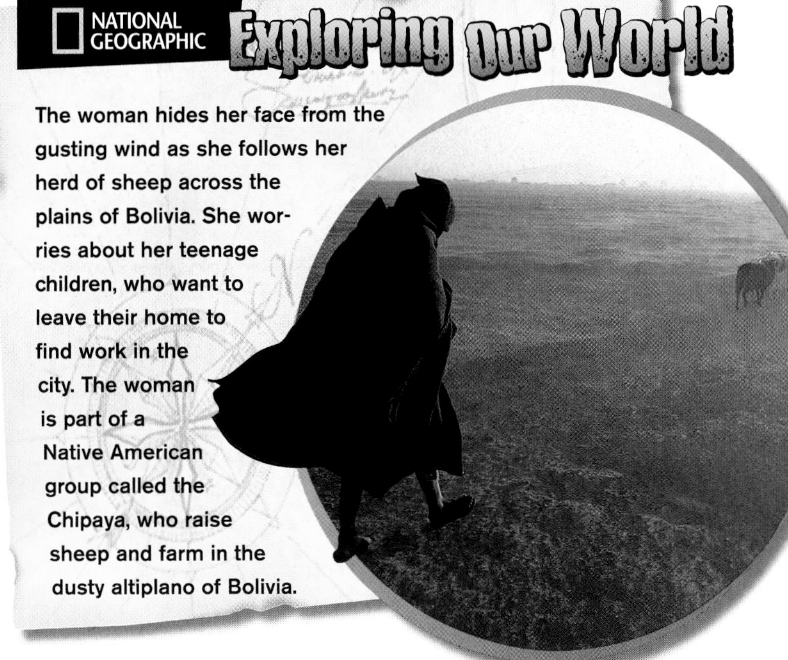

The woman hides her face from the gusting wind as she follows her herd of sheep across the plains of Bolivia. She worries about her teenage children, who want to leave their home to find work in the city. The woman is part of a Native American group called the Chipaya, who raise sheep and farm in the dusty altiplano of Bolivia.

At first glance, **Bolivia** and **Chile** seem very different. Bolivia lacks a seacoast, while Chile has a long coastline on the Pacific Ocean. The Andes, however, affect the climate and cultures of both countries.

Bolivia

Bolivia lies near the center of South America. It is a landlocked country, which means it has no sea or ocean that touches its land. Fortunately, in 1993 Peru agreed to give Bolivia a free trade zone in the port city of **Ilo.** This gave Bolivia better access to the free flow of people, goods, and ideas. Bolivia is the highest and most isolated country in South America. Why? The Andes dominate Bolivia's landscape. Look at the map on page 180. You see that in western Bolivia, the Andes surround a high plateau called the altiplano. Over one-third of Bolivia is a mile or more high. Unless you were born in this area, you would find that the cold, thin air makes it difficult to breathe. Few trees grow on

271

1 Focus

Section Objectives

1. Identify where Bolivia and Chile are located.
2. Describe the landforms and climates found in Bolivia and Chile.
3. Compare the economies and people of Bolivia and Chile.

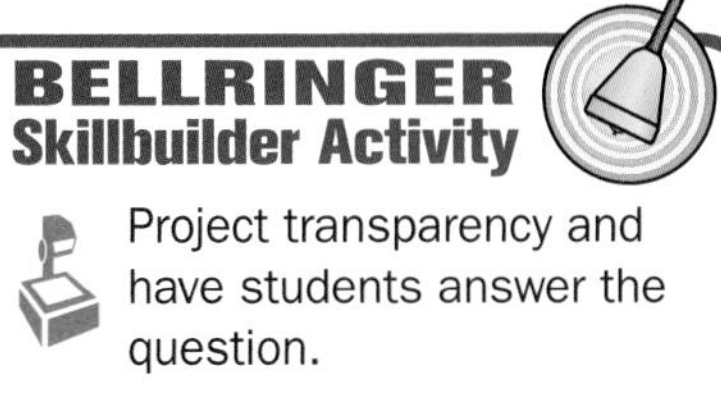

BELLRINGER Skillbuilder Activity

Project transparency and have students answer the question.

Daily Focus Skills Transparency

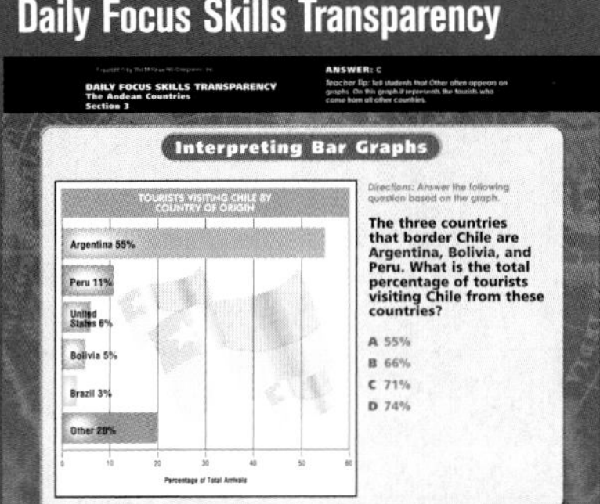

Reading Preview

■ **Activating Prior Knowledge** Have students look at the Exploring Our World photograph and discuss what they think life might be like in Bolivia.

■ **Preteaching Vocabulary** Have students look up the definition of *sodium nitrate.* Ask if they are aware of any other words in which *sodium* appears. *(sodium chloride, or salt)*

Section Resources

Reproducible Masters
- Reproducible Lesson Plan
- Daily Lecture and Discussion Notes
- Note-taking Guide
- Guided Reading Activity
- Reading Essentials and Study Guide
- Section Quiz

Transparencies
- Daily Focus Skills Transparency
- In-text Map Transparency

Multimedia
- Vocabulary PuzzleMaker CD-ROM
- Interactive Tutor Self-Assessment CD-ROM
- Presentation Plus! CD-ROM
- ExamView® Pro Testmaker CD-ROM
- MindJogger Videoquiz

TEACH

Drawing Conclusions Have students suggest challenges that Bolivia might face because of its high altitude, dry climate, and status as a landlocked country. L1

More About the Photos

Santiago Santiago was founded in 1541 by the Spanish. It became the capital of newly independent Chile in 1818. Today it is Chile's chief industrial city, main highway and railroad hub, and cultural center. Although the city is Chile's capital, the country's legislature meets in Valparaíso.

Caption Answer Tierra del Fuego

Daily Lecture and Discussion Notes

THE ANDEAN COUNTRIES

Daily Lecture and Discussion Notes

The Bolivians and Chileans

Chile stretches 2,652 miles (4,267 km) along the southwestern coast of South America, a distance roughly the same as that from San Francisco to New York City. At the same time, its width never exceeds 150 miles (241 km), making the country more than 18 times longer than its widest point. The most obvious factor in Chile's remarkable slenderness is the massive, virtually impassable wall of the Andes, a mountain range that contains more than 50 active volcanic peaks.

I. Bolivia

A. Bolivia is a **landlocked** country, having no land that touches a sea or an ocean. Bolivia is also the highest and most isolated country in Latin America. The [illegible] dominate Bolivia's landscape. In western Bolivia, the Andes surround a [illegible] **altiplano.** Most Bolivians live on the altiplano.

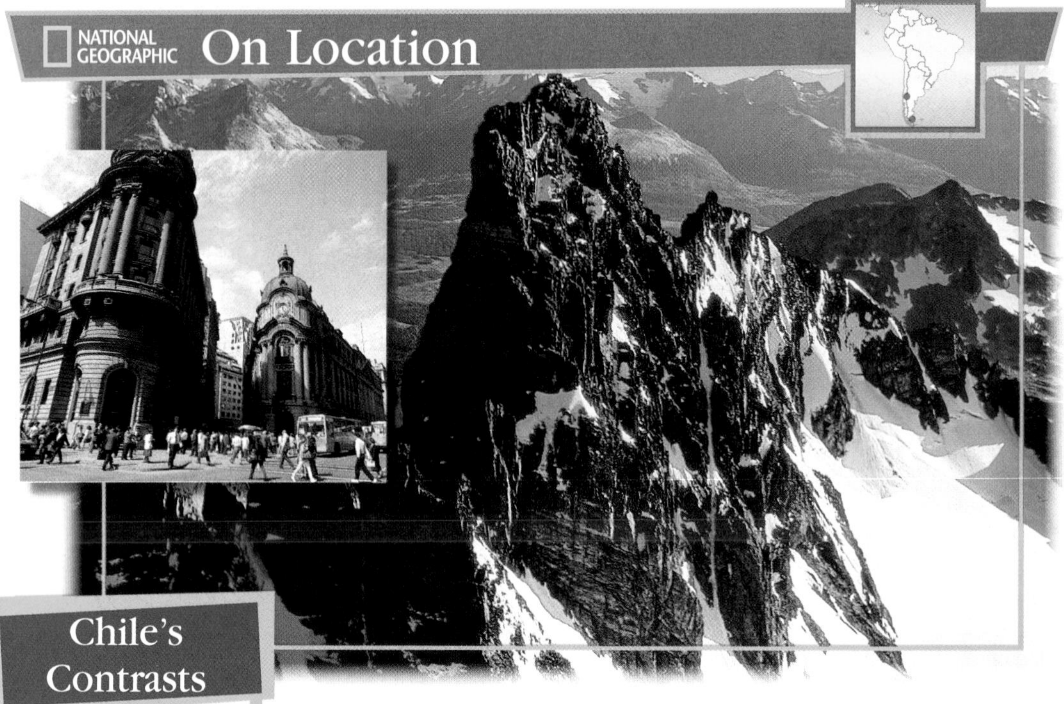

Chile's Contrasts

Chile has a wide variety of climates and landforms. The moderate capital city of Santiago in central Chile (above) contrasts sharply with the icy southern region (right).

Location **What group of islands lies at the southern tip of Chile?**

the altiplano, and most of the land is too dry to farm. Still, the vast majority of Bolivians live on this high plateau. Those areas that have water have been farmed for many centuries.

Bolivia also has lowland plains and tropical rain forests in the east and north. Most of this area has a hot, humid climate. South-central Bolivia, however, has more fertile land, and many farms dot this region.

A Struggling Economy Bolivia is rich in minerals such as tin, silver, and zinc. Miners remove these minerals from high in the Andes. Workers in the eastern lowlands draw out gold, petroleum, and natural gas.

Still, Bolivia is a poor country. About two-thirds of the people live in poverty. Throughout the highlands, many villagers practice subsistence farming. They struggle to grow wheat, potatoes, and barley. At higher elevations, herders raise animals such as alpacas and llamas for wool and for carrying goods. In the south, farmers plant soybeans, a growing export. Timber is another important export. Unfortunately, one crop that can be grown for sale is coca, which is made into cocaine.

Bolivia's People Bolivia was part of the Incan Empire until Spain conquered the Inca. The country won independence in 1825 and was named after Simón Bolívar. What is unusual about Bolivia's capital? There is not just one capital city, but two. The official capital is **Sucre** (SOO•kray). The administrative capital and largest city is **La Paz** (lah PAHZ). Both capital cities are located in the altiplano. La Paz—at 12,000 feet (3,658 m)—is the highest capital city in the world.

Reading Strategy — Reading the Text

Understanding Vocabulary Have students work in groups to create an illustrated dictionary of Latin American terms. They can begin with the term in this section—*altiplano*—but can add those from other sections (*cordillera, mestizo,* and *campesino* from the section on Colombia, for example). Assign a specific task to each group member, such as finding terms, writing definitions, illustrating the words, and collating pages. Make sure that all group members receive a copy of the dictionary. L1

*Use the **Reading Skills Handbook** for more reading strategies.*

Most of Bolivia's 8.6 million people live in the Andean highlands. About half are of Native American ancestry, and another 30 percent are mestizos. In the cities, most people follow modern ways of living. In the countryside, you may hear traditional sounds, such as music played with panpipes and other flutelike instruments.

✓Reading Check What is the altiplano?

Chile

Chile is almost twice the size of California. Although its average width is only 110 miles (177 km), Chile stretches 2,652 miles (4,267 km) along the Pacific Ocean.

About 80 percent of Chile's land is mountainous. The high Andes run along Chile's border with Bolivia and Argentina. Except in the altiplano area of Chile's north, very few Chileans live in the Andes.

Also in the north is the **Atacama Desert.** It is one of the driest places on the earth. Why? This area is in the rain shadow of the Andes. Winds from the Atlantic Ocean bring precipitation to regions east of the Andes, but they carry no moisture past them. In addition, the cold Peru Current in the Pacific Ocean does not evaporate as much as a warm current does. As a result, only dry air hits the coast.

A steppe climate zone lies just north of **Santiago,** Chile's capital. Most of Chile's people live in a central region called the Central Valley. With a mild Mediterranean climate, the fertile valleys here have the largest concentration of cities, industries, and farms.

The lake region, also known as "the south," has a marine west coast climate that supports thick forests. Chile's far south is a stormy, wind-swept region of snowcapped volcanoes, thick forests, and huge glaciers. The **Strait of Magellan** separates mainland Chile from a group of islands known as **Tierra del Fuego** (FWAY•goh)—or "Land of Fire." This region is shared by both Chile and Argentina. Cold ocean waters batter the rugged coast around **Cape Horn,** the southernmost point of South America.

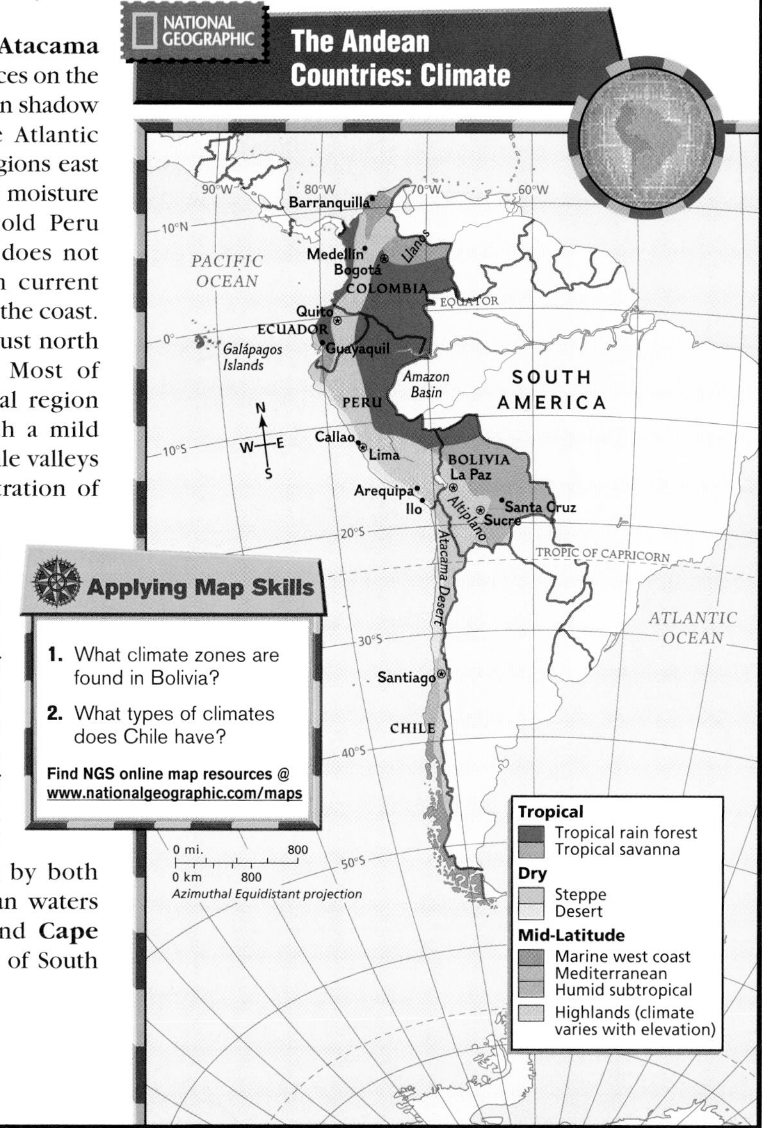

Applying Map Skills

1. What climate zones are found in Bolivia?
2. What types of climates does Chile have?

Find NGS online map resources @ www.nationalgeographic.com/maps

Chapter 9

Section 3, pages 271–274

✓ Reading Check Answer

a high plateau

L1/ELL

Guided Reading Activity

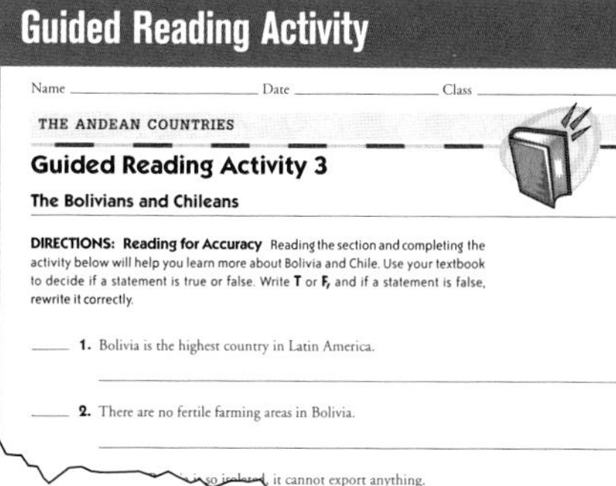
Name ______ Date ______ Class ______

THE ANDEAN COUNTRIES

Guided Reading Activity 3

The Bolivians and Chileans

DIRECTIONS: Reading for Accuracy Reading the section and completing the activity below will help you learn more about Bolivia and Chile. Use your textbook to decide if a statement is true or false. Write **T** or **F**, and if a statement is false, rewrite it correctly.

____ 1. Bolivia is the highest country in Latin America.

____ 2. There are no fertile farming areas in Bolivia.

... it cannot export anything.

3 ASSESS

Assign Section 3 Assessment as homework or an in-class activity.

Have students use the Interactive Tutor Self-Assessment CD-ROM to review Section 3.

Applying Map Skills

Answers

1. tropical savanna, tropical rain forest, highlands, steppe, and humid subtropical
2. highland, desert, steppe, Mediterranean, and marine west coast

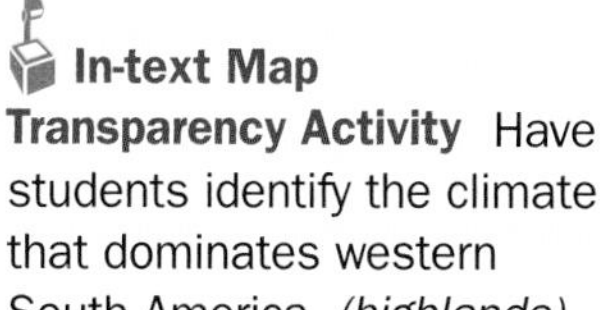

In-text Map Transparency Activity Have students identify the climate that dominates western South America. *(highlands)*

Differentiated Instruction

Meeting Special Needs: Visual/Spatial Point out to students that the altiplano of Bolivia and the mountains and deserts of Chile are very different environments. Remind them that a special community of plants and animals are suited to each of those environments. With the aid of the biology or other science teacher, have students research an environment found in Bolivia or Chile. Have them prepare dioramas that illustrate the plant and animal life found in those environments. Afterwards, have them compare the two countries using the dioramas. L1

EE3 Physical Systems: Standard 8

Chapter 9

Section 3, pages 271–274

L2

Section Quiz

Name ______ Date ______ Class ______

THE ANDEAN COUNTRIES

Score

Section 3 Quiz

The Bolivians and Chileans

DIRECTIONS: Matching Match each item in Column A with the items in Column B. Write the correct letters in the blanks. *(10 points each)*

COLUMN A	COLUMN B
A. Central Valley	____ 1. the southernmost point of South America
B. Atacama Desert	____ 2. group of islands separated from mainland Chile by the Strait of Magellan
C. Cape Horn	____ 3. mineral used to make fertilizer and explosives
D. sodium nitrate	____ 4. one of the world's driest places
E. Tierra del Fuego	____ 5. area of Chile with most of its cities, farms, and industries

✓ Reading Check Answer

mestizos, European descent, and Native Americans

L1/ELL

Reading Essentials and Study Guide

Name ______ Date ______ Class ______

THE ANDEAN COUNTRIES

Reading Essentials and Study Guide 3

The Bolivians and Chileans

Key Terms

landlocked land that does not touch the sea or ocean

altiplano a high plateau

sodium nitrate a mineral used in fertilizer and in explosives

Drawing From Experience

Have you ever run so long that you could not seem to get your breath? Did you stop and pant to draw in more air? Visitors in Bolivia sometimes ... Bolivia sits near the ... Bolivia is so high that the air is thin. If you ... the sea, Bolivia is the highest country in South America ... a high plateau called the **altiplano**. Because ...

Have students prepare an annotated map highlighting the key characteristics of Bolivia and Chile.

Chile's Economy In recent years, Chile has had high economic growth, and the number of people below the poverty line has fallen by half. Mining forms the backbone of Chile's economy. The Atacama region is rich in minerals. Chile ranks as the world's leading copper producer. The country also mines and exports gold, silver, iron ore, and **sodium nitrate**—a mineral used in fertilizer and explosives.

Agriculture is also a major economic activity. Farmers produce wheat, corn, beans, sugar, and potatoes. The grapes and apples you eat in winter may come from Chile's summer harvest. (Remember that the seasons here in the Southern Hemisphere are opposite of those you experience in the Northern Hemisphere.) Many people also raise cattle, sheep, and other livestock.

Chile has factories that process fish and other foods. Other workers manufacture wood products, iron, steel, vehicles, cement, and textiles. Service industries such as banking and tourism also thrive.

Chile's Culture Of the 15.8 million people in Chile, most are mestizos. A large minority are of European descent, and some Native American groups live in the altiplano and "the south." Nearly all the people speak Spanish, and most are Roman Catholic. Some 80 percent of Chile's population live in urban areas. Chile has been a democratic republic since the end of strict military rule in 1990.

✓ Reading Check What are the three cultural backgrounds of Chile's 15.8 million people?

Assessment

Defining Terms

1. **Define** landlocked, altiplano, sodium nitrate.

Recalling Facts

2. **Economics** What part of Bolivia's population lives in poverty?
3. **Geography** What makes La Paz unusual?
4. **Economics** Chile is the world's leading producer of what mineral?

Critical Thinking

5. **Analyzing Cause and Effect** Why is the Atacama Desert one of the world's driest places?
6. **Making Comparisons** What are differences and similarities between the economies of Bolivia and Chile?

Graphic Organizer

7. **Organizing Information** Create a diagram like this one. Under each arrow, list supporting facts for the main idea.

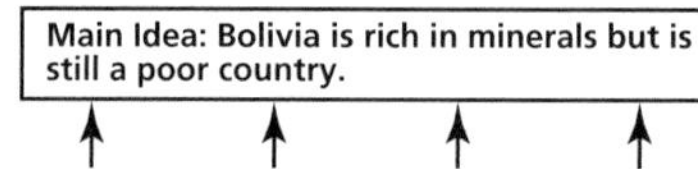
Main Idea: Bolivia is rich in minerals but is still a poor country.

Applying Social Studies Skills

8. **Analyzing Maps** Study the physical map on page 180. The southernmost tip of South America is part of what country? What is the name of the group of islands at the southern tip of South America? What does the name mean?

Section 3 Assessment

1. The terms are defined in the Glossary.
2. about two-thirds of the people
3. It is the world's highest capital city.
4. copper
5. Moist winds from the Atlantic do not reach past the Andes. Also, winds from the Pacific are dry because the current is cold.
6. *Differences:* Bolivia is mostly poor, Chile has more economic growth; Bolivians practice subsistence farming, Chilean farmers export products; Chile has factories and provides services. *Similarities:* Mining and agriculture are important.
7. minerals such as tin, silver, zinc, gold, petroleum, and natural gas; farmers struggle to grow food; two-thirds live in poverty.
8. Chile; Tierra del Fuego; "Land of Fire"

Reading Review

Section 1 Colombia's Culture and Challenges

Terms to Know
cordillera
cash crop
mestizo
campesino

Main Idea

Although it has many resources, Colombia faces political and economic unrest.

✓Economics Colombia is rich in hydroelectric power, gold, and emeralds.

✓Government The government of Colombia is struggling to combat the power of drug dealers who make huge fortunes from selling cocaine, which comes from the coca plant.

✓Culture Most Colombians speak Spanish and follow the Roman Catholic religion.

✓History Civil war in Colombia is still being fought today.

Section 2 Land and People of Peru and Ecuador

Terms to Know
navigable
foothills
empire

Main Idea

Peru and Ecuador share similar landscapes, climates, and history.

✓History The Inca had a powerful civilization in the area that is now Peru. They developed a complex system of record keeping.

✓Economics Peru's main exports are copper and fish. Many people farm. Ecuador's economy is focused on agriculture.

✓Culture Most people in Peru and Ecuador live along the coast.

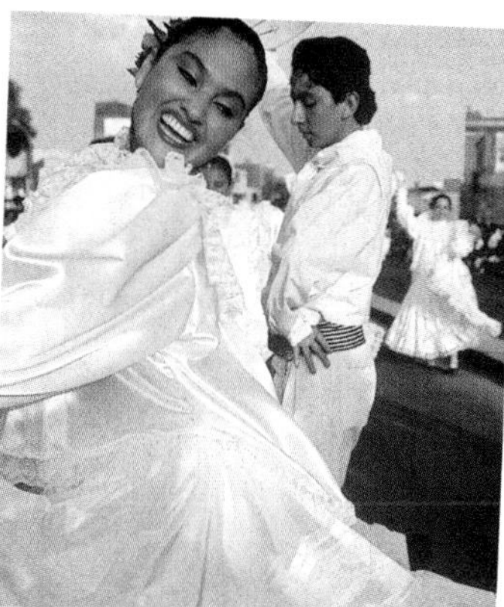

▲ Dancers in Peru

Section 3 The Bolivians and Chileans

Terms to Know
landlocked
altiplano
sodium nitrate

Main Idea

Bolivia and Chile share the Andes, but their economies and people are different.

✓Human/Environment Interaction Bolivia is a poor country consisting mainly of the towering Andes and a high plateau that is difficult to farm.

✓Culture Most of Chile's people speak Spanish and follow the Roman Catholic religion.

✓Economics Chile has a diverse economy that includes mining—especially copper and sodium nitrate—farming, and manufacturing.

Reading Review

Use the Chapter 9 Reading Review to preview, review, condense, or reteach the chapter.

Preview/Review

Use the Terms to Know lists to help students review and study.

Activity Have students form into teams and play a game in which teams have to provide the correct definitions for the terms from the chapter.

Vocabulary PuzzleMaker CD-ROM reinforces the vocabulary terms used in Chapter 9.

The Interactive Tutor Self-Assessment CD-ROM allows students to review Chapter 9 content.

Condense

Have students read the Chapter 9 summary statements.

Guided Reading Activities

Audio Program

Reteach

Reteaching Activity

Reading Essentials and Study Guide

Reading Strategy Read to Write

Identifying Cause and Effect **Ask students:** How do the Andes affect the lives of people in the countries from Colombia to Chile? Have them prepare a report that focuses on one area of life, such as earning a living, clothing, food, housing, and so on. Have them research life in each of the Andean countries in terms of this area and prepare an illustrated display that shows the impact of the Andes on at least three of the five countries. Displays should contain written text that describes the impact. L1

 **EE5 Environment and Society: Standard 15**

Assessment and Activities

GLENCOE TECHNOLOGY

MindJogger Videoquiz
Use MindJogger Videoquiz to review the Chapter 9 content.

 Available in DVD and VHS

Using Key Terms

1. e
2. i
3. b
4. j
5. f
6. h
7. d
8. c
9. g
10. a

Reviewing the Main Ideas

11. *Any four:* petroleum, gold, emeralds, coal, hydroelectric power, timber
12. mestizo
13. political violence (revolts and civil wars); drug trade
14. Lake Titicaca
15. the Inca
16. Ecuador
17. They are poor subsistence farmers or herders, living on the altiplano.
18. democratic republic
19. mestizo

Chapter 9 Assessment and Activities

Using Key Terms

Match the terms in Part A with their definitions in Part B.

A.

1. cordillera
2. campesino
3. cash crop
4. altiplano
5. navigable
6. foothills
7. empire
8. sodium nitrate
9. landlocked
10. mestizo

B.

a. person of mixed Native American and European ancestry
b. crop grown to be sold, often for export
c. mineral used in making fertilizer
d. group of lands under one ruler
e. group of mountain ranges that run side by side
f. when a body of water is wide and deep enough for ships to pass through
g. land that does not have a sea or an ocean touching it
h. low hills at the base of a mountain range
i. farmer in Colombia
j. large highland plateau

Reviewing the Main Ideas

Section 1 Colombia's Culture and Challenges

11. **Economics** List four of Colombia's natural resources.
12. **History** What is the heritage of most of Colombia's people?
13. **History** What type of activities have scarred Colombia's history?

Section 2 Land and People of Peru and Ecuador

14. **Place** What is the highest navigable lake in the world?
15. **History** What ancient Native American civilization of the Andes lived in Peru?
16. **Government** Which country owns the Galápagos Islands?

Section 3 The Bolivians and Chileans

17. **Culture** What is life like for about two-thirds of Bolivia's people?
18. **Government** What type of government does Chile have?
19. **Culture** What is the ethnic background of most Chileans?

The Andean Countries

Place Location Activity

On a separate sheet of paper, match the letters on the map with the numbered places listed below.

1. Colombia
2. Peru
3. Chile
4. Andes
5. Lake Titicaca
6. Quito
7. Bogotá
8. Strait of Magellan
9. Lima
10. Bolivia

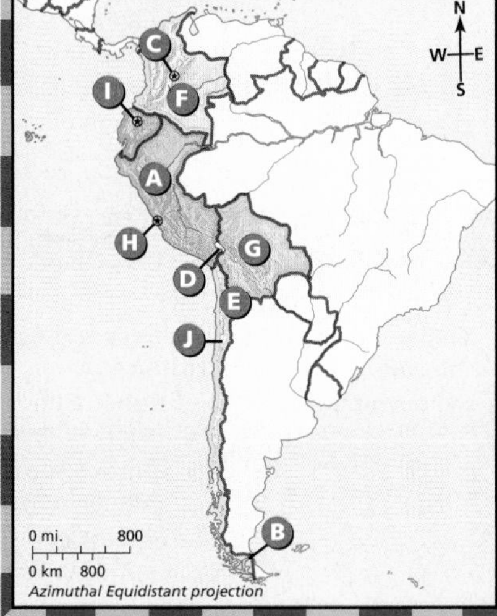

NATIONAL GEOGRAPHIC **Place Location Activity**

1. F
2. A
3. J
4. E
5. D
6. I
7. C
8. B
9. H
10. G

Critical Thinking

20. In isolated regions, these groups do not come into contact with more modern ways of doing things, so they are likely to follow traditional ways of life.
21. Factors should include drug wars, poverty (wide gap between rich and poor), and differences between major political parties.

Self-Check Quiz Visit ***The World and Its People*** Web site at twip.glencoe.com and click on **Chapter 9—Self-Check Quizzes** to prepare for the Chapter Test.

Critical Thinking

20. **Making Inferences** Why are Native Americans who live in the Andean highlands more likely to follow a traditional way of life than those who live in the cities?
21. **Analyzing Cause and Effect** On a diagram like the one below, list factors that have led to political violence during Colombia's history.

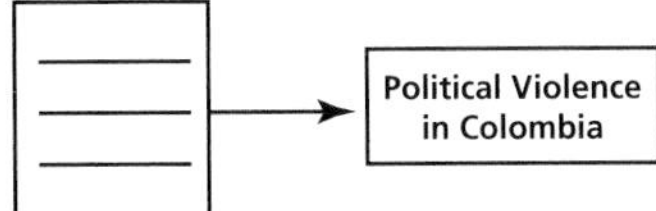

Comparing Regions Activity

22. **Geography** Compare the features of the Andes to the Himalaya in South Asia. Write a travel article for a mountain climbing magazine to tell potential climbers which region might be best for them to try.

Mental Mapping Activity

23. **Focusing on the Region** Create a simple outline map of South America, and then label the following:

- Pacific Ocean
- Peru
- Andes
- Colombia
- Atacama Desert
- Galápagos Islands
- Strait of Magellan
- Lake Titicaca
- Chile
- Ecuador

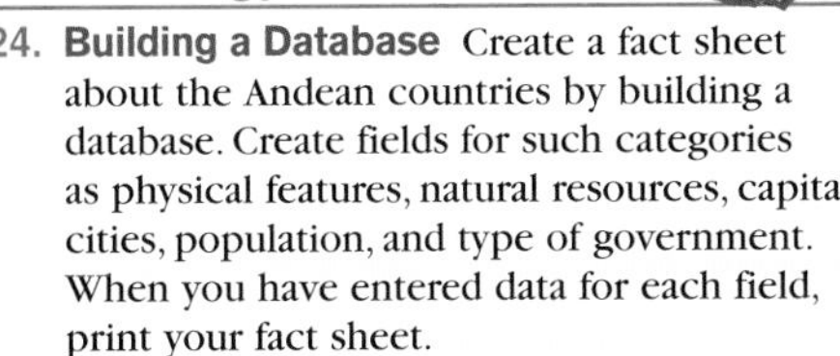

Technology Skills Activity

24. **Building a Database** Create a fact sheet about the Andean countries by building a database. Create fields for such categories as physical features, natural resources, capital cities, population, and type of government. When you have entered data for each field, print your fact sheet.

Standardized Test Practice

Directions: Read the paragraphs below, and then answer the question that follows.

Simón Bolívar, an aristocrat from Venezuela, led many of South America's lands to independence. He believed in equality and saw liberty as "the only object worth a man's life." Called "the Liberator," Bolívar devoted his life to freedom for Latin Americans.

Bolívar was the son of a rich family in New Granada, or what is today Colombia, Venezuela, Panama, and Ecuador. In 1805 he went to Europe. There he learned about the French Revolution and its ideas of democracy. He returned home, vowing to free his people from Spanish rule. In 1810 Bolívar started a revolt against the Spaniards in Venezuela. Spanish officials soon crushed the movement, but Bolívar escaped and trained an army. During the next 20 years, Bolívar and his forces won freedom for the present-day countries of Venezuela, Colombia, Panama, Bolivia, and Ecuador.

1. What is the main idea of the paragraphs above?

A Bolívar was the son of a rich family.
B Bolívar traveled to Europe and learned about democracy.
C Simón Bolívar was called "the Liberator."
D Bolívar devoted his life to freedom for Latin Americans.

Test-Taking Tip: This question asks you to find the main idea, or to make a generalization. Most of the answer choices provide specific details, not a general idea. Which of the answers is more of a general statement?

Assessment and Activities

Standardized Test Practice

1. D

Tested Objectives: Making generalizations, identifying the main idea

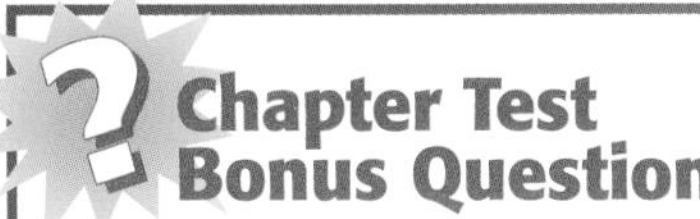

Chapter Test Bonus Question

This question may be used for extra credit on the chapter test.

Is Ecuador located in the Northern Hemisphere or the Southern Hemisphere? *(both)*

Have students visit the Web site at twip.glencoe.com to review Chapter 9 and take the Self-Check Quiz.

Dinah Zike's Foldables

Culminating Activity Have students write paragraphs that summarize the information they collected for their foldables. Students should revise their facts and their paragraphs if main ideas are missing.

Comparing Regions Activity

22. Articles should describe and compare the Andes and the Himalaya.

Mental Mapping Activity

23. This exercise helps students visualize the countries and geographic features of South America. All attempts at freehand mapping should be accepted.

Technology Skills Activity

24. Students' fact sheets should include all the required information for each of the countries covered in the chapter.

Unit 4 Planning Guide

- If you teach BOTH Eastern and Western world regions in one year, use the columns in red to help you pace your lessons.
- **If you teach ONLY Eastern or Western world regions in one year, use the columns in blue to help you pace your lessons.**

ALTERNATIVE PACING CHARTS

Unit 4		Chapter 10		Chapter 11		Chapter 12		Chapter 13	
Both East and West	Either East or West	Both East and West	Either East or West	Both East and West	Either East or West	Both East and West	Either East or West	Both East and West	Either East or West
Day 1 Unit Opener, Regional Atlas **Day 2** Regional Atlas	**Day 1** Unit Opener, Regional Atlas **Day 2** Regional Atlas **Day 3** Regional Atlas **Day 4** Regional Atlas	**Day 1** Chapter Opener, Section 1 **Day 2** Social Studies Skill, Section 2 **Day 3** Section 3 **Day 4** Making Connections, Review **Day 5** Chapter Assessment	**Day 1** Chapter Opener, Section 1 **Day 2** Section 1 **Day 3** Social Studies Skill, Section 2 **Day 4** Section 2 **Day 5** Section 3 **Day 6** Section 3, Making Connections **Day 7** Review **Day 8** Chapter Assessment	**Day 1** Chapter Opener, Section 1 **Day 2** Making Connections, Section 2 **Day 3** Section 3, TIME Reports **Day 4** TIME Reports, Social Studies Skill, Review **Day 5** Chapter Assessment	**Day 1** Chapter Opener, Section 1 **Day 2** Section 1, Making Connections **Day 3** Section 2 **Day 4** Section 3 **Day 5** TIME Reports **Day 6** TIME Reports, Social Studies Skill **Day 7** Review **Day 8** Chapter Assessment	**Day 1** Chapter Opener, Section 1 **Day 2** Making Connections, Section 2 **Day 3** Social Studies Skill, Section 3 **Day 4** Section 4 **Day 5** Section 5, Review **Day 6** Chapter Assessment	**Day 1** Chapter Opener, Section 1 **Day 2** Section 1 **Day 3** Making Connections, Section 2 **Day 4** Section 2 **Day 5** Social Studies Skill, Section 3 **Day 6** Section 3 **Day 7** Section 4 **Day 8** Section 5 **Day 9** Review **Day 10** Chapter Assessment	**Day 1** Chapter Opener, Section 1 **Day 2** Section 2, Study and Writing Skill **Day 3** Section 3, Making Connections **Day 4** Section 4, Review **Day 5** Chapter Assessment	**Day 1** Chapter Opener, Section 1 **Day 2** Section 1 **Day 3** Section 2, Study and Writing Skill **Day 4** Section 3 **Day 5** Section 3, Making Connections **Day 6** Section 4 **Day 7** Review **Day 8** Chapter Assessment

Note: The following materials may be used when teaching Unit 4.
Chapter level support materials can be found on the chapter resource pages.

TEACHING TRANSPARENCIES

Political Map Transparency L2

Map Overlay Transparencies L2

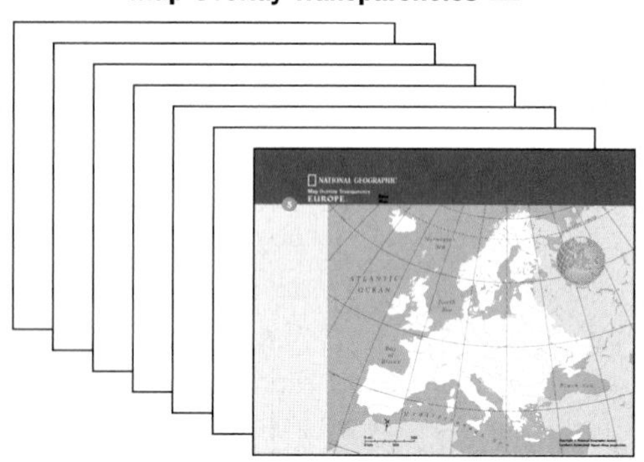

World Cultures Transparencies L2

Unit 4 Resources

INTERDISCIPLINARY CONNECTIONS

World Literature Reading L2

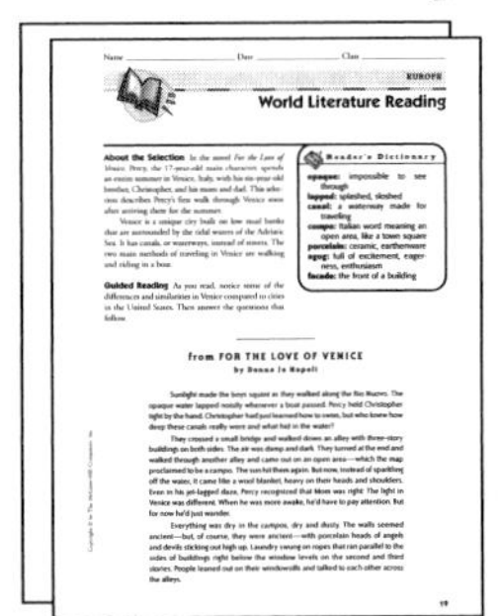

Economics and Geography Activity L2

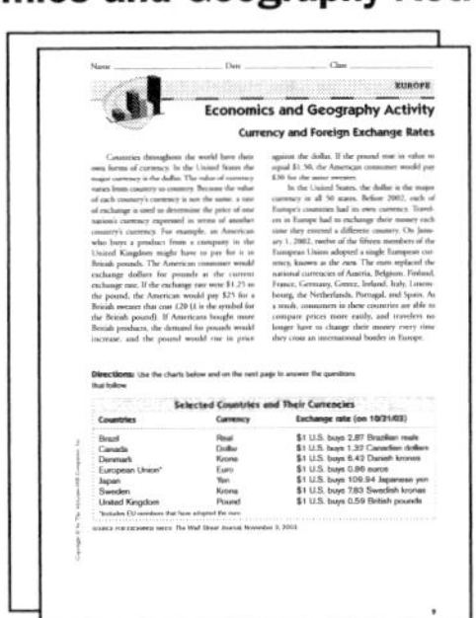

History and Geography Activity L2

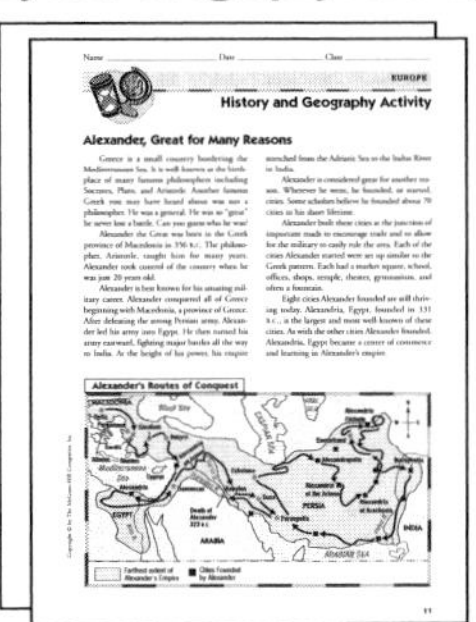

INTERDISCIPLINARY CONNECTIONS

Foods Around the World L1/ELL

World Music: A Cultural Legacy

CIVIC INVOLVEMENT

Citizenship Activity L1

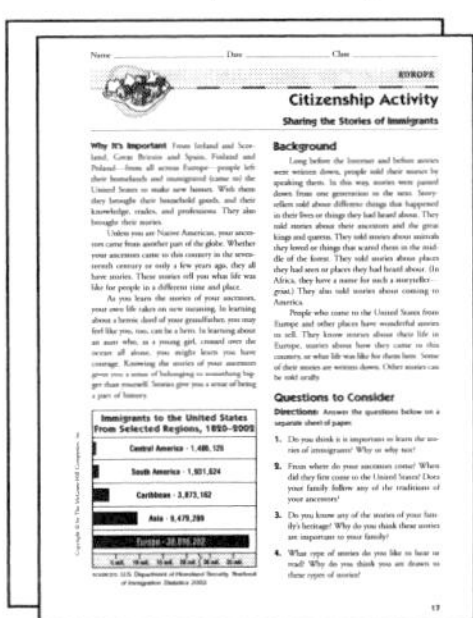

Environmental Case Study L2

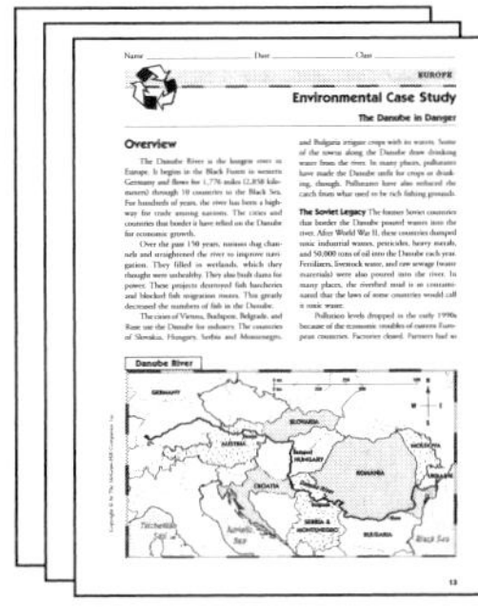

MAP AND GEOGRAPHY SKILLS

Building Geography Skills for Life

NGS Focus on Geography Literacy L2

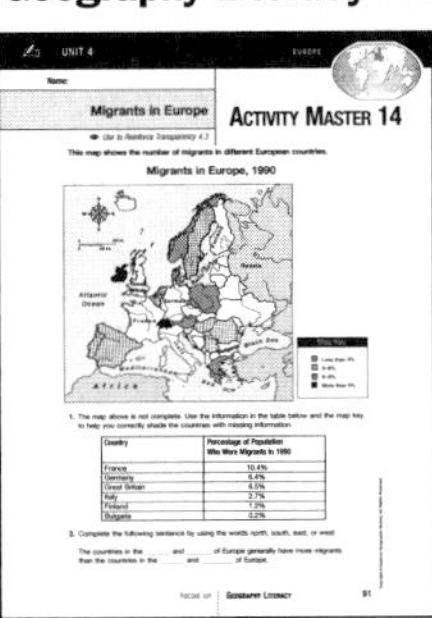

Regional Atlas Activity L2

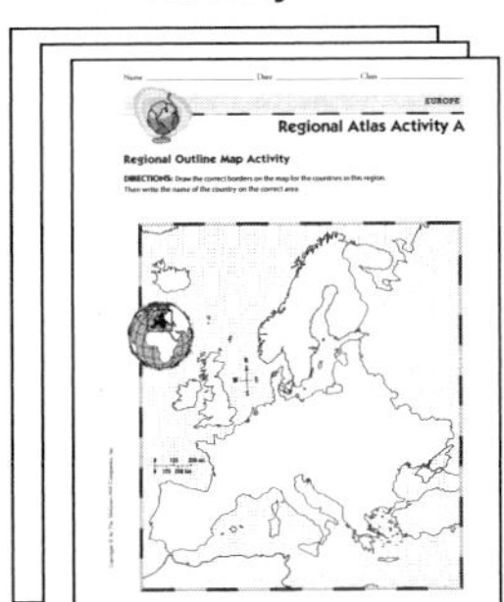

KEY TO ABILITY LEVELS

Teaching strategies have been coded for varying learning styles and abilities.

- **L1** **BASIC** activities for all students
- **L2** **AVERAGE** activities for average to above-average students
- **L3** **CHALLENGING** activities for above-average students
- **ELL** **ENGLISH LANGUAGE LEARNER** activities

ASSESSMENT

Unit Pretests L2

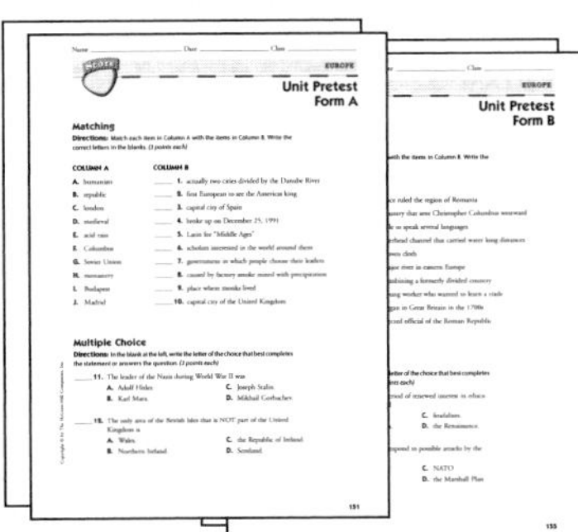

Unit Posttests L2

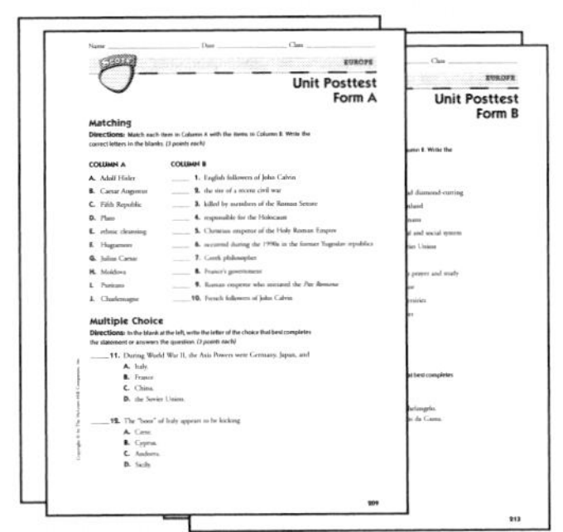

Glencoe Professional Development and Teacher Support Materials

- Reading in the Content Area for the Middle School Classroom
- Inclusion Strategies for the Middle School Social Studies Classroom
- Character Education for the Middle School Classroom
- Teaching Strategies for the Social Studies Classroom
- Reproducible Lesson Plans
- Outline Map Resource Book
- Writing Process Transparencies for Middle School
- Social Studies: Reading Strategies

Additional Unit 4 Resources

- **Timed Readings Plus in Social Studies** help students increase their reading rate and fluency while maintaining comprehension. The 400-word passages are similar to those found on state and national assessments.
- **Reading in the Content Area: Social Studies** concentrates on six essential reading skills that help students better comprehend what they read. The book includes 75 high-interest nonfiction passages written at increasing levels of difficulty.
- **Reading Fluency** helps students read smoothly, accurately, and expressively.
- **Jamestown's Reading Improvement,** by renowned reading expert Edward Fry, focuses on helping build your students' comprehension, vocabulary, and skimming and scanning skills.
- **Critical Reading Series** provides high-interest books, each written at three reading levels.

For more information about these products, see the Jamestown Education materials in the Classroom Solutions in the front of this Teacher Wraparound Edition. To order these products, call Glencoe at 1-800-334-7344.

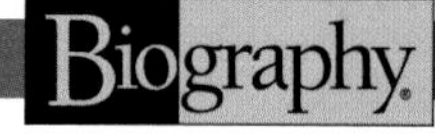

The following videotape programs are available from Glencoe:

- **Ancient Rome** 0-7670-1263-1
- **Mystical Monuments of Ancient Greece** 0-7670-0012-9
- **Constantine: The Christian Emperor** 0-7670-0577-5
- **Michelangelo** 1-56501-425-1
- **Napoleon Bonaparte: The Glory of France** 0-7670-1211-9
- **The War in Europe** 1-56501-993-8
- **Anne Frank** 0-7670-1409-X
- **Eiffel Tower** 1-56501-465-0

To order, call Glencoe at 1-800-334-7344. To find classroom resources to accompany many of these, check:

A&E Television: www.aetv.com

The History Channel: www.historychannel.com

Reading List Generator CD-ROM

GLENCOE BOOKLINK

The Glencoe BookLink CD-ROM is a database that allows you to search more than 15,000 titles to create a customized reading list for your students.

- Reading lists can be organized by students' reading level, author, genre, theme, or area of interest.
- The database provides Degrees of Reading Power™ (DRP) and Lexile™ readability scores for all selections.
- A brief summary of each selection is included.

Leveled reading suggestions for this unit:

For students at a Grade 5 reading level:

- ***I Remember Bosnia,*** by Anita Ganeri.

For students at a Grade 6 reading level:

- ***The Romans and Their Empire,*** by Trevor Cairns.

For students at a Grade 7 reading level:

- ***Food and Feasts in the Middle Ages,*** by Imogen Dawson.

To order this CD-ROM, call Glencoe at 1-800-334-7344.

Extending the Content

Readings for the Teacher

- ***The New Europe: Economy, Society, and Environment,*** ed. David Pinder. New York, NY: John Wiley & Son, 1998.
- ***A European Geography,*** by Tim Unwin. New York, NY: Addison-Wesley, 1998.

Multimedia Resources

- **Glencoe World History Primary Source Document Library CD-ROM**
- ***Making of the German Nation.*** Chicago, Ill.: Clearvue. Mac/Windows CD-ROM.

Service Learning Project

Connecting Classroom With Community

The opposing sides of the conflict in Northern Ireland overcame their differences with the aid of a mediator. Many schools have established peer mediation programs. The steps include creating ground rules for the mediation, having the parties express their views without interruption, encouraging the parties to identify and discuss possible resolutions, and leading the parties to settle on a solution. Have students set up a peer mediation program in their school.

Content Background Notes

Use this additional information as lecture notes or discussion prompts throughout the study of Unit 4.

Chapter 10 Europe—Early History (pp. 292–311)

Olive Oil Olives were first grown in the eastern Mediterranean region about 6,000 years ago. Phoenician sailors brought them to Greece and Spain. Greeks planted olives in their colonies in Italy. Today Spain, Italy, and Greece produce about 74 percent of the world's olive oil output—nearly 500 million gallons a year. In a friendly rivalry, producers in the three countries vigorously debate which nation has the best quality oil.

Olive oil has gained in popularity in the past few decades not only because of its flavor but for health reasons. A 1970 study linked olive oil in the diet of southern Europeans to the fact that these people had the lowest rate of heart disease of all western nations. Later studies connected olive oil to other health benefits, including a reduced risk of breast cancer among women. These studies and other trends have helped contribute to a fivefold increase in U.S. imports of olive oil from the early 1980s to the late 1990s. Among Mediterranean peoples, this sudden popularity is probably not surprising. An ancient Greek myth says that the goddess Athena won a contest in which she and other gods gave gifts to humankind. Her gift—the olive tree—won the contest because it was deemed the most useful gift.

Chapter 11 Europe—Modern History (pp. 312–337)

The Euro By 2001, fifteen European countries belonged to the economic and political organization called the European Union (EU). By 2020, the EU is expected to grow to 30 nations. Most members of the EU use a common currency, the euro. The euro was launched in 1999, although at first only for record-keeping and trading. By 2002, actual EU currency became available as the official currency in participating countries. After a brief transition period, member countries dropped their national currencies in favor of the euro. Thus, the French franc, the German deutschmark, the Italian lira, and other well-known European currencies ceased to function as a means of exchange.

The United Kingdom, Sweden, and Denmark decided to not join with other member countries in adopting the common currency. Danish participation was denied in 2000, when, in a national referendum, the Danish people voted against using the euro.

Chapter 12 Western Europe Today (pp. 338–365)

Iceland: The Gene Laboratory Iceland's status as an isolated land with a homogeneous population has made the country a focus of modern genetics research. The country's 300,000 people are largely descended from the Nordic immigrants who arrived on the island in the 800s and 900s. As a result, the variations in Iceland's gene pool are fairly narrow. At the same time, the country's tradition of accurately recording genealogies makes it possible to trace the ancestry of today's islanders. These combined factors have led to an ambitious study of human genetics.

A native Icelander started a company that is studying the DNA of Icelanders who suffer from the same diseases. Scientists hope to identify genetic causes for these diseases—a task made more simple because of the population's small degree of genetic variation. In 1998 the company signed an agreement with a major drug manufacturer. The deal gives the drugmaker the right to the genetic information as a basis for developing new medicines. Icelanders, in turn, will be given those new medicines for free.

Also in 1998, Iceland's parliament approved the creation of a vast national database containing genetic information on the country's people. The move has stirred some controversy. Critics fear that information in the database could be abused, but supporters hope that Iceland's unique status could be useful in helping science cure some serious diseases.

Chapter 13 The New Eastern Europe (pp. 366–389)

Chernobyl's Legacy The 1986 nuclear disaster at the Chernobyl power plant continues to haunt Ukraine. The rate of thyroid cancers among people in the nearby area has skyrocketed. The plant itself needs attention. The concrete shell surrounding the reactor that exploded is cracked and leaking. Rebuilding the shell and disposing of nuclear waste will cost hundreds of millions of dollars—money Ukraine does not have.

Some problems lurk in the future. Environmental scientists say that radiation in the Dneiper River, near Chernobyl, will peak 60 to 90 years from now, causing problems then.

In 2000, Ukraine—under pressure from other countries—finally decided to shut down the last reactors at Chernobyl. That may not be the end of the story, however. Many scientists are worried about the possibility of a similar disaster elsewhere. Fourteen other nuclear plants have the same flawed design as the Chernobyl works. They are located in Lithuania and Russia. In addition, 25 other Soviet-built plants in eastern Europe and Russia have designs that are considered less safe than those employed in western countries.

Introducing
Unit 4

00:00 OUT OF TIME?

If time does not permit teaching each chapter in this unit, you may use the **Reading Essentials and Study Guide** for each chapter.

Unit Overview

The four chapters that comprise this unit introduce students to the geography and peoples of Europe. The chapters describe the physical and human geography of these countries and explore their contributions to world culture. Point out to students that the countries of Europe share the following features:

- several related language families account for most of the languages spoken
- most people share one form of the Christian religion
- most countries are democratic
- most countries follow free market economies

Glencoe Literature Library

As students study the unit, have them read *Anne Frank Remembered* by Miep Gies with Alison Leslie Gold from the **Glencoe Literature Library.** The Glencoe Literature Library consists of novels and other readings for middle school students, along with study guides that offer instructional support and student activities.

Unit 4

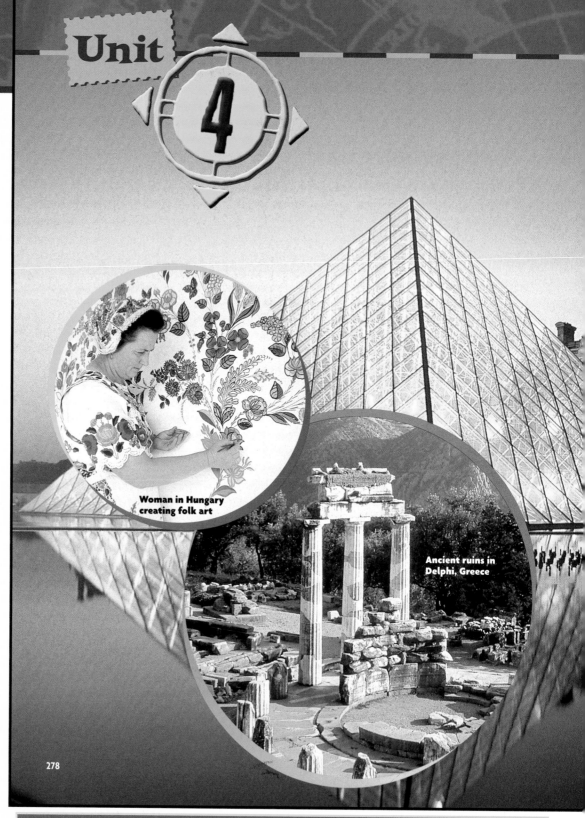

Woman in Hungary creating folk art

Ancient ruins in Delphi, Greece

278

Using the Illustration

Visual Instruction The Louvre is on the original site of a royal castle built by King Philip II of France in the late 1100s. In the 1540s, King Francis I tore down the castle and began the first phase of construction on the structure now known as the Louvre. It first became an art museum in 1793, after the French Revolution. In the 1980s and 1990s, the museum was updated and renovated. The glass pyramid—designed by renowned architect I.M. Pei—was part of this. **Ask: What can you tell about Europe from the photos on these pages?** *(Europe has ancient cultures, evident from the Greek ruins; cities with impressive modern structures; and a lively tradition of folk art.)*

Introducing
Unit 4

Current Events Journal

Have students look at a map of Europe and ask them what they notice. They should see that Europe is a small area with many countries. Have students list in their journals the effects that might result from this fact. *(conflicts over land, need to share resources)* Suggest that as they study the unit they look for details that show these effects.

NGS ONLINE
www.nationalgeographic.com/education

This online resource provides lesson plans, atlas updates, cartographic activities with interactive maps, an online map store, and geography links.

NATIONAL GEOGRAPHIC

Europe

You have learned about the Americas. Now let us spin the globe and travel to Europe. Relatively small as continents go, Europe is rich in history and culture. Like the United States, most nations in Europe are industrialized and have high standards of living. Unlike the United States, however, the people of Europe do not share a common language or government.

▲ The Louvre museum, Paris, France

NGS ONLINE
www.nationalgeographic.com/education

279

Unit Launch Activity

Why Study Europe? Point out that people have been living in Europe for many thousands of years and that they have significantly altered the environment. **Ask:** **How do countries in general use the environment?** Suggest that they think about resources, waterways, and recreational uses. **How do human actions harm the environment?** Suggest to students that they look for evidence of human use of the environment as they study this unit. Then have the class discuss the questions: **How do Europeans use the environment? What impact do those uses have?**

EE5 Environment and Society: Standard 14

Lesson Plan

Using the Regional Atlas
These features and activities may be used as an introduction to the unit or as teaching tools throughout the course of the unit.

Focus

Objectives

1. Identify the major physical features of Europe.
2. Describe the different types of climates of Europe.
3. Discuss the economies of Europe.
4. Explain what groups make up the people of Europe.

5-Minute Precheck

Ask students to identify as many countries of Europe as they can. Write the country names on the board. Then point to each entry and ask: **What do you know about this country?** Then explain that Europe is a diverse continent with many different countries, ethnic groups, languages, and customs but also with many common characteristics. Point out that in this unit, students will learn about both the similarities and the differences.

Focus on: Europe

BOTH A CONTINENT and a region, Europe has a wide range of cultures—and a history of conflict among its people. Recently, connections in trade, communication, and transportation have helped to create greater unity among European nations.

The Land

Jutting westward from Asia, Europe is a great peninsula that breaks into smaller peninsulas and is bordered by several large islands. Europe's long, jagged coastline is washed by many bodies of water, including the Arctic and Atlantic Oceans, and the North, Baltic, and Mediterranean Seas. Deep bays and well-protected inlets shelter fine harbors. Closeness to the sea has enabled Europeans to trade with other lands. Many Europeans also depend on the sea for food.

Mountains sweep across much of the continent. Those in the British Isles and large parts of northern Europe are low and rounded. Higher and more rugged are the Pyrenees, between France and Spain, and the Carpathians, in eastern Europe. The snow-capped Alps are Europe's highest mountains, towering over the central and southern parts of the continent.

Curving around these mountain ranges are broad, fertile plains. In the north, the North European Plain stretches from France to Russia. Cities, towns, and farms dot the gently rolling landscape.

Rivers For centuries, Europe's rivers have provided links between coastal ports and inland population centers. In western Europe, the Rhine flows northwest from the Alps until it empties into the North Sea. The Danube winds through eastern Europe on its way to the Black Sea.

The Climate

Despite its northern location, Europe enjoys a relatively mild climate. This is because of the region's closeness to the Atlantic Ocean. An ocean current known as the North Atlantic Current brings warm waters and winds to bathe Europe's western shores. As a result, northwestern Europe enjoys mild temperatures all year, along with plentiful rainfall. Farther south, countries along the Mediterranean Sea have hot, dry summers and mild winters. The region's northernmost countries have longer, colder winters than their southern neighbors. Winters are also cold in Europe's interior, which lies far from the influence of the North Atlantic Current.

Diverse Vegetation The vegetation varies from one climate zone to another.

Content Background

Continent or Region? Point out to students that *Europe* can mean two things. The *continent* of Europe extends from the Atlantic Ocean to the Ural Mountains in Russia. The *region* of Europe, discussed in this unit, does not include Russia. This distinction helps explain why Mont Blanc is the highest mountain in the *region* of Europe, but Mount Elbrus is the highest mountain in the *continent* of Europe. Mount Elbrus is in Russia, which is not considered part of the same cultural region.

UNIT 4

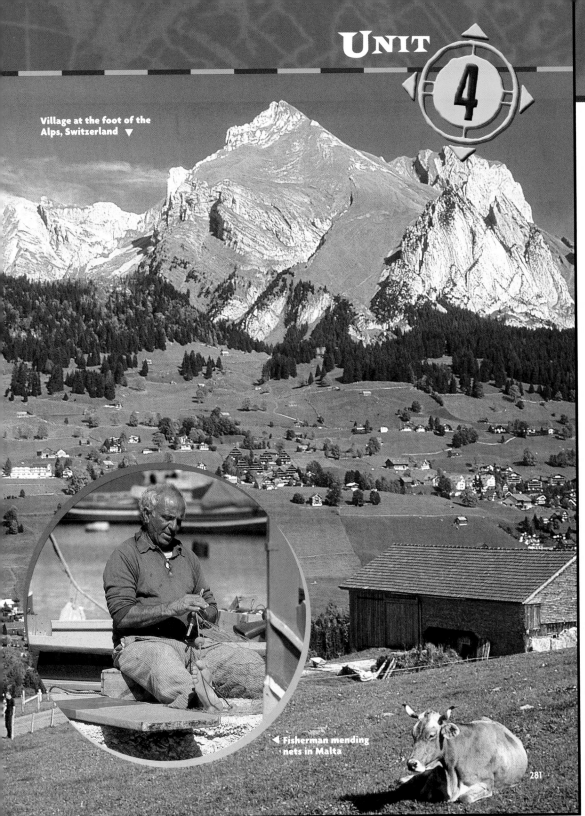

Village at the foot of the Alps, Switzerland ▼

◀ Fisherman mending nets in Malta

281

Eyewitness to Geography

Spain James Michener wrote *Iberia* (1968) to express his appreciation of the Spanish landscape and people. In this passage, he describes the harshness of one part of the Spanish environment: "In a hot bus that talked back to itself I was plodding through the vast region called Extremadura, that empty, rocky section of Spain lying southwest from Madrid along the Portuguese border. It was a day of intense heat, with the thermometer well above a hundred and ten. For as far as I could see there were no towns, no villages, only the brassy, shimmering heat rising up from the plains and the implacable sky without even a wisp of cloud. When dust rose, it hung in the motionless air and required minutes to fall back to the caked and burning earth. I saw no animals, no birds, no men, for they refused to venture forth in this remorseless heat."

2 TEACH

Making Predictions Before reading the section The Climate, have students look at the world physical map in the Reference Atlas. **Ask: Between what latitudes is the western coast of Europe located?** *(from about 30°N to about 70°N)* **How does this compare to the latitudes at which North America is located?** *(similar to the latitudes of the northeast United States and eastern Canada)* **What climate would you expect to find in this area of Europe?** *(cold, as in that part of North America)* Then have students read the section. **L1**

Note-taking tip

Suggest that, after students read each of the sections in the Regional Atlas, they write the heading of the section and a sentence expressing the main idea.

More About the Photos

The Alps The Alps stretch through nine countries—from the French-Swiss border east to Yugoslavia. Several of Europe's major rivers—the Po, Rhône, Rhine, and Danube—have their source in the Alps.

Malta Malta is an island republic in the central Mediterranean Sea. The country actually includes five islands, of which Malta is the largest.

NATIONAL GEOGRAPHIC

REGIONAL ATLAS

Interdisciplinary Connections

History The Netherlands—where Rotterdam is located—has prospered through the creation of a complex system of dikes and dams that have been used to hold back the waters of the North Sea. These dikes have resulted in more land for the Dutch people to utilize. Sometimes, however, the sea strikes back. In 1995 rivers swollen by heavy rain and melting snow broke through this system, causing a severe natural disaster that killed 1,600 people.

More About the Photo

Rotterdam Location is the key to Rotterdam's importance as a port. First, it sits in the midst of the heavily industrialized area that stretches from the United Kingdom to northern France and Germany. Second, the city is located at the mouths of two rivers—the Rhine and the Mosel—and opens to the North Sea, making it a key locale for shipping goods between the interior of Europe and the rest of the world.

In Scandinavia's far north, you would find mostly mosses and small shrubs blanketing a tundra-like landscape. In northwestern and eastern Europe, grasslands and forests cover the rolling land. Farther south, drought-resistant shrubs and small trees cover rugged hills.

The Economy

An abundance of key natural resources, waterways, and ports has helped make Europe a global economic power. Agriculture, manufacturing, and service industries dominate the region's economies.

Rich Farmland Some of the most productive farmland in the world can be found on the European continent. From the fertile black soil, farmers gather bountiful harvests of grains, fruits, and vegetables. Cattle and sheep graze through lush European pastures.

Resources and Industry Vast reserves of oil and natural gas lie offshore. Rich deposits of iron ore, coal, and other minerals have provided the raw materials for heavy industry and manufacturing. Europe was the birthplace of the Industrial Revolution, which transformed the region from an agricultural society into an industrial one. Today countries such as France, Germany, Italy, Poland, and the United Kingdom rank among the world's top manufacturing centers. These industrial countries produce steel, machinery, cars, textiles, electronic equipment, food products, and household goods. Service industries such as banking, insurance, and tourism are also important to Europe's market economies.

The People

After Asia, Europe is the most densely populated continent on the earth. In some European countries, such as Sweden, most people belong to the same ethnic group. The populations of other countries, however, are made up of several ethnic groups. Some ethnic groups live together peacefully. Other groups often face tension and conflict.

Artistic Treasures Europeans enjoy a rich cultural heritage that stretches back thousands of years. In fact, all Western cultures have their roots in the ancient periods of Classical Greece and Rome. If you walk through the heart of any large European city, you might see ancient Roman ruins, Gothic cathedrals built during the Middle Ages, and sculptures created by Renaissance masters, such as Michelangelo and Leonardo da Vinci.

◀ Cargo lining the docks of Rotterdam, a port city in the Netherlands

UNIT 4

FUN FACTS

- **France** The French take pride in the beauty of their language. Some want the purity of the language closely protected. For example, they want to ban the use of such foreign adaptations as *le weekend* and *le sandwich.*
- **Luxembourg** Going to the polls is compulsory for voters in this constitutional monarchy.
- **Liechtenstein** The government of tiny Liechtenstein earns one-tenth of its income from the sale of postage stamps.

Unit 4 Regional Atlas

Revolutions After the 1700s, political changes increased freedom for the common people. An interest in science and the invention of machines during the Industrial Revolution changed the economy and raised standards of living. In eastern Europe, once-powerful empires faced growing challenges from ethnic groups that wanted independence.

Global Influence Throughout their history, Europeans have explored and settled other lands. They have spread their culture around the world. Competition among European nations in the past led to two World Wars and a bitter division into communist and non-communist areas. Many European nations have recently joined the European Union to become a united economic force.

Children by road signs in Ireland ▼

Data Bits

Country	Automobiles per 1,000 people	Television sets per 1,000 people
Austria	495	526
Finland	403	643
France	469	620
Greece	254	480
Ireland	272	406

Population: Urban vs. Rural

Country	Urban	Rural
Austria	67%	33%
Finland	59%	41%
France	76%	24%
Greece	60%	40%
Ireland	59%	41%

Sources: *World Development Indicators, 2002; The World Almanac, 2004.*

Exploring the Region

1. What bodies of water border Europe?
2. Why is Europe's climate relatively mild?
3. What has helped make Europe a global economic power?
4. How did European culture spread to other parts of the world?

283

More About the Photo

Metric System The signs in this photograph use metric measures, which are employed throughout Europe. This system was invented during the French Revolution to supplant the measurements in use at that time—which were a confusing collection of local, rather than national, measures. The system became standardized internationally in 1875, when delegates met at an international conference in Paris.

3 Assess

Assign the Exploring the Region questions as homework or as an in-class activity.

Reteach
Have students create a concept web that contains key points about the land, climate, economy, and people of Europe.

Enrich
Have students research one of the cultural periods described in the section The People. Then have them prepare a bulletin board display that highlights the key features of that period.

4 Close

Reading Strategy

Writing a Paragraph Have students write a paragraph that completes the following sentence: "Europe is a cultural region because . . . ."

Answers to Exploring the Region

1. Atlantic Ocean, Arctic Ocean, North Sea, Mediterranean Sea, Baltic Sea; Students may also include Bay of Biscay, Norwegian Sea, Black Sea, Aegean Sea, Adriatic Sea, and the Strait of Gibraltar.
2. The North Atlantic Current brings warm waters and winds to Europe's western shores.
3. an abundance of key natural resources, waterways and ports; productive farmland; and mineral resources that helped fuel the Industrial Revolution
4. Europeans explored and settled other lands.

LESSON PLAN

Using the Regional Atlas
These features and activities may be used as an introduction to the unit or as teaching tools throughout the course of the unit.

FOCUS

Objectives

1. Describe the relative size and location of Europe.
2. Name the major physical features of Europe.
3. Identify the languages spoken in Europe.
4. Describe the population characteristics of Europe.

5-Minute Precheck

Have students look at the physical map of Europe on this page. Have them describe, in general terms, the landscape of Europe. *(mountains throughout the south; a vast lowland plain in the middle; some countries are islands and peninsulas)*

More About the Profile

In order to show a variety of physical features, this cross section begins at Lisbon, Portugal, and ends at Warsaw, Poland.

NATIONAL GEOGRAPHIC **REGIONAL ATLAS**

Europe

Physical

284 UNIT 4

Regional Atlas Activity

Analyzing Maps On the board, copy the puzzle shown at right, omitting the letters above the lines. Have students complete the acrostic with names of physical features from the map above. Provide hints, such as "Body of water east of Greece" or "River in northern Germany." L2

EE2 Places and Regions: Standard 4

A E **G** E A N S E A
E L B E R I V E R
P **O** R I V E R
H U N **G** A R I A N P L A I N
C A **R** P A T H I A N M O U N T A I N S
A L P S
A **P** E N N I N E S
R **H** I N E R I V E R
P **Y** R E N E E S

Unit 4

Political

● National capital

0 mi. 400
0 km 400
Lambert Azimuthal Equal-Area projection

MAP STUDY

1. What body of water lies between Scandinavia and Poland?
2. What is the capital of the United Kingdom?

2 TEACH

Making Comparisons Have students use the Nations of the World Databank to identify the countries that rank in the top 10 for Gross National Product (GNP). Have students analyze the geographic distribution. **Ask:** **What world regions are represented in this distribution? What regions are not represented?** Then have students pose and answer five questions comparing Europe to other world regions. **L3**

Europe is the only continent without a major desert.

MAP STUDY

Answers

1. Baltic Sea
2. London

Skills Practice

What body of water separates the Mediterranean Sea from the Atlantic Ocean? *(Strait of Gibraltar)*

Regional Atlas Activity

Analyzing Maps Have students study the physical maps of Europe, Asia, and North Africa in the Reference Atlas. Point out that Asia and Africa often have had a great deal of influence on European culture and history—and vice versa. **Ask:** **What features of physical geography would contribute to this fact?** *(Europe and Asia are connected; there are no major geographical barriers preventing people from moving to Europe from Asia, or in the opposite direction—in fact, the presence of lowland steppes make such movement easy; Europe lies near Africa and—through the Mediterranean Sea—has easy access to Africa.)* **L2**

EE1 The World in Spatial Terms: Standard 3

Creating a Graph Have students write down the population of Germany, found in the Country Profiles. Then have them choose three additional countries from different culture regions that have the largest populations for those regions. Have them copy that information on the same sheet. Finally, have them create a bar graph that compares the information on the four countries. L1

Cultural Kaleidoscope

Denmark Trolls originated in Danish legend. Folklore explains that trolls spend their nights burying treasure and their days guarding their loot.

Travel Guide

Hungarians usually greet each other by shaking hands. If their hands are dirty, they offer elbows.

MAP STUDY

Answers

1. Germanic
2. Spanish, Portuguese, Galician, Catalan, French, Italian, Sardinian, Romanian, and Moldavian

Skills Practice

From what language family do most eastern European languages come? *(Slavic)*

Regional Atlas

Europe

Languages

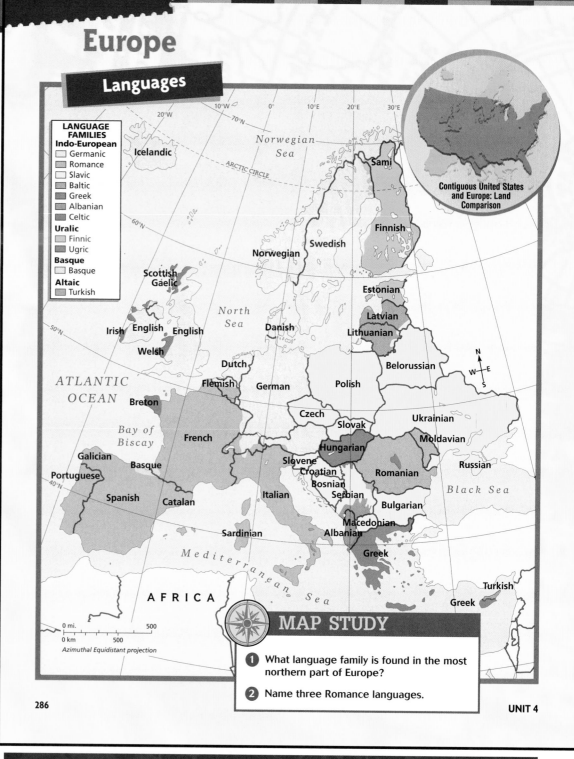

LANGUAGE FAMILIES

Indo-European
- Germanic
- Romance
- Slavic
- Baltic
- Greek
- Albanian
- Celtic

Uralic
- Finnic
- Ugric

Basque
- Basque

Altaic
- Turkish

Icelandic, Sami, Norwegian Sea, Arctic Circle, Finnish, Swedish, Norwegian, Scottish Gaelic, Estonian, North Sea, Latvian, Irish, English, English, Danish, Lithuanian, Welsh, Dutch, Belorussian, Atlantic Ocean, Flemish, German, Polish, Breton, Czech, Ukrainian, Slovak, Bay of Biscay, French, Moldavian, Hungarian, Galician, Slovene, Russian, Basque, Croatian, Romanian, Portuguese, Bosnian, Black Sea, Serbian, Spanish, Catalan, Italian, Bulgarian, Macedonian, Sardinian, Albanian, Greek, Mediterranean Sea, Turkish, Africa, Greek

0 mi. 500
0 km 500
Azimuthal Equidistant projection

Contiguous United States and Europe: Land Comparison

MAP STUDY

1. What language family is found in the most northern part of Europe?
2. Name three Romance languages.

286 UNIT 4

Regional Atlas Activity

Categorizing Regions Inform students that Europe is often divided into regions, in which several countries are grouped together according to common characteristics. Tell them that, for example, the countries of Spain, Italy, and Greece are often called the Mediterranean countries. **Ask: What characteristics do these countries share?** *(southern location, Mediterranean coastlines, generally high elevations, peninsular)* Ask them what the map of European languages above shows about how countries could be grouped together according to language or how languages cut across national boundaries. L1

EE2 Places and Regions: Standard 5

Unit 4
Regional Atlas

Making Comparisons Have students look at the countries identified in the chart that compares the population of the United States to selected European countries. Then have them look at the Country Profiles listings to see if the countries on the chart include Europe's *most* populous country and the *least* populous country. If not, have them list the names of those countries and their populations. Then have them draw a pictogram comparing the populations of the listed countries to that of the United States. L1

Geo Extremes

① **HIGHEST POINT**
Mont Blanc (France and Italy)
15,771 ft. (4,807 m) high

② **LOWEST POINT**
Nieuwerkerk aan den IJssel (Netherlands)
22 ft. (7 m) below sea level

③ **LONGEST RIVER**
Danube (central Europe)
1,776 mi. (2,858 km) long

④ **LARGEST LAKE**
Lake Vänern (Sweden)
2,156 sq. mi. (5,584 sq. km)

⑤ **HIGHEST WATERFALL**
Mardalsfossen, Southern (Norway)
2,149 ft. (655 m) high

⑥ **LARGEST ISLAND**
Great Britain
84,210 sq. mi. (218,103 sq. km)

COMPARING POPULATION: United States and Selected Countries of Europe

UNITED STATES
GERMANY
UKRAINE
SPAIN
BELGIUM

(figure) = 25,000,000

Source: Population Reference Bureau, 2003.

RELIGIONS: Selected Countries of Europe

BOSNIA AND HERZEGOVINA: 40% | 31% | 15% | 4% | 10%
GERMANY: 38% | 34% | 1.7% | 26.3%
MOLDOVA: 98.5% | 1.5%
SPAIN: 99% | 1%
UNITED KINGDOM: 72% | 23% | 2.5% | 2.5%

Eastern Orthodox, Jewish, Protestant, Roman Catholic, Muslim, Other

Source: *CIA World Factbook*, 2002.

GRAPHIC STUDY

1. Which two countries share the highest point in Europe?
2. Roughly what is the population of Germany? What percentage of the population is Protestant?

Building Skills

Making Inferences Tell students to read Geo Extremes. **Ask:** Based on this information, would you say Norway is generally flat or has high elevation? Why? *(high elevation; because it has a waterfall that is nearly 2,150 feet high)*

GRAPHIC STUDY

Answers

1. France and Italy
2. About 85 to 90 million people; about 38 percent

Skills Practice

Which country has the greatest percentage of Roman Catholic followers in the population? *(Spain)*

FUN FACTS

- **Bulgaria** Bulgarians shake their head from side to side to denote "yes" and nod up and down to denote "no."
- **Greece** The people of Greece are well known for their hospitality. The tradition of hospitality may stem from the ancient belief that one needed to treat strangers kindly in case they were gods in disguise. Indeed, ancient Greek myths include stories in which some mortals are rewarded for kindness to strangers, and others are punished for treating strangers inhospitably.
- **Czech Republic** Czechs give each other marzipan candies shaped like pigs for good luck in the New Year.

THE HUMANITIES CONNECTION

World Music: A Cultural Legacy

World Art and Architecture Transparencies

Building Skills

Using Decimals If students are taking notes on the areas or populations of Europe's countries, suggest that they use shorthand by converting the numbers into decimals. Thus, Austria's population of 8,200,000 becomes 8.2 million; Iceland's 300,000 is written as 0.3 million.

Cultural Kaleidoscope

Austria Dinner guests in Austria bring their host an odd number of flowers. To bring an even number would be considered unlucky. They also avoid bringing roses, which symbolize romantic love.

NATIONAL GEOGRAPHIC REGIONAL ATLAS

Country Profiles

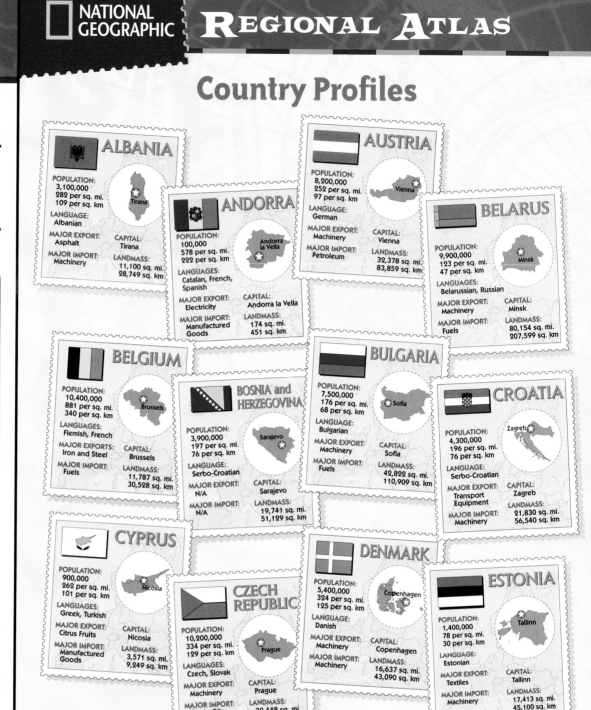

ALBANIA
POPULATION: 3,100,000; 282 per sq. mi.; 109 per sq. km
LANGUAGE: Albanian
MAJOR EXPORT: Asphalt
MAJOR IMPORT: Machinery
CAPITAL: Tirana
LANDMASS: 11,100 sq. mi.; 28,749 sq. km

ANDORRA
POPULATION: 100,000; 578 per sq. mi.; 222 per sq. km
LANGUAGES: Catalan, French, Spanish
MAJOR EXPORT: Electricity
MAJOR IMPORT: Manufactured Goods
CAPITAL: Andorra la Vella
LANDMASS: 174 sq. mi.; 451 sq. km

AUSTRIA
POPULATION: 8,200,000; 252 per sq. mi.; 97 per sq. km
LANGUAGE: German
MAJOR EXPORT: Machinery
MAJOR IMPORT: Petroleum
CAPITAL: Vienna
LANDMASS: 32,378 sq. mi.; 83,859 sq. km

BELARUS
POPULATION: 9,900,000; 123 per sq. mi.; 47 per sq. km
LANGUAGES: Belarussian, Russian
MAJOR EXPORT: Machinery
MAJOR IMPORT: Fuels
CAPITAL: Minsk
LANDMASS: 80,154 sq. mi.; 207,599 sq. km

BELGIUM
POPULATION: 10,400,000; 881 per sq. mi.; 340 per sq. km
LANGUAGES: Flemish, French
MAJOR EXPORTS: Iron and Steel
MAJOR IMPORT: Fuels
CAPITAL: Brussels
LANDMASS: 11,787 sq. mi.; 30,528 sq. km

BOSNIA and HERZEGOVINA
POPULATION: 3,900,000; 197 per sq. mi.; 76 per sq. km
LANGUAGE: Serbo-Croatian
MAJOR EXPORT: N/A
MAJOR IMPORT: N/A
CAPITAL: Sarajevo
LANDMASS: 19,741 sq. mi.; 51,129 sq. km

BULGARIA
POPULATION: 7,500,000; 176 per sq. mi.; 68 per sq. km
LANGUAGE: Bulgarian
MAJOR EXPORT: Machinery
MAJOR IMPORT: Fuels
CAPITAL: Sofia
LANDMASS: 42,822 sq. mi.; 110,909 sq. km

CROATIA
POPULATION: 4,300,000; 196 per sq. mi.; 76 per sq. km
LANGUAGE: Serbo-Croatian
MAJOR EXPORT: Transport Equipment
MAJOR IMPORT: Machinery
CAPITAL: Zagreb
LANDMASS: 21,830 sq. mi.; 56,540 sq. km

CYPRUS
POPULATION: 900,000; 262 per sq. mi.; 101 per sq. km
LANGUAGES: Greek, Turkish
MAJOR EXPORT: Citrus Fruits
MAJOR IMPORT: Manufactured Goods
CAPITAL: Nicosia
LANDMASS: 3,571 sq. mi.; 9,249 sq. km

CZECH REPUBLIC
POPULATION: 10,200,000; 334 per sq. mi.; 129 per sq. km
LANGUAGES: Czech, Slovak
MAJOR EXPORT: Machinery
MAJOR IMPORT: Crude Oil
CAPITAL: Prague
LANDMASS: 30,448 sq. mi.; 78,860 sq. km

DENMARK
POPULATION: 5,400,000; 324 per sq. mi.; 125 per sq. km
LANGUAGE: Danish
MAJOR EXPORT: Machinery
MAJOR IMPORT: Machinery
CAPITAL: Copenhagen
LANDMASS: 16,637 sq. mi.; 43,090 sq. km

ESTONIA
POPULATION: 1,400,000; 78 per sq. mi.; 30 per sq. km
LANGUAGE: Estonian
MAJOR EXPORT: Textiles
MAJOR IMPORT: Machinery
CAPITAL: Tallinn
LANDMASS: 17,413 sq. mi.; 45,100 sq. km

Countries and flags not drawn to scale

288 UNIT 4

Regional Atlas Activity

Drawing Conclusions Tell students that the Channel Tunnel (Chunnel) links the United Kingdom and France. Denmark's Storebaelt ("Great Belt") Bridge is the second-longest suspension bridge in the world. It connects the island on which Copenhagen is located to the mainland. This 1-mile (1.6-km) bridge is part of a much longer transportation system called the Oresund Fixed Link. The Fixed Link stretches 9.3 miles (14.9 km) across the North Sea from Copenhagen to Malmö, Sweden. It includes a bridge, a roadway built on an artificial island, and a tunnel. **Ask:** **Why would people in Europe invest in these elaborate structures?** *(to allow easier access from one place to another; to increase trade and communication between countries)* **L1**

 **EE4 Human Systems: Standard 11**

Unit 4

Regional Atlas

For more information on countries in this region, refer to the Nations of the World Data Bank in the Appendix.

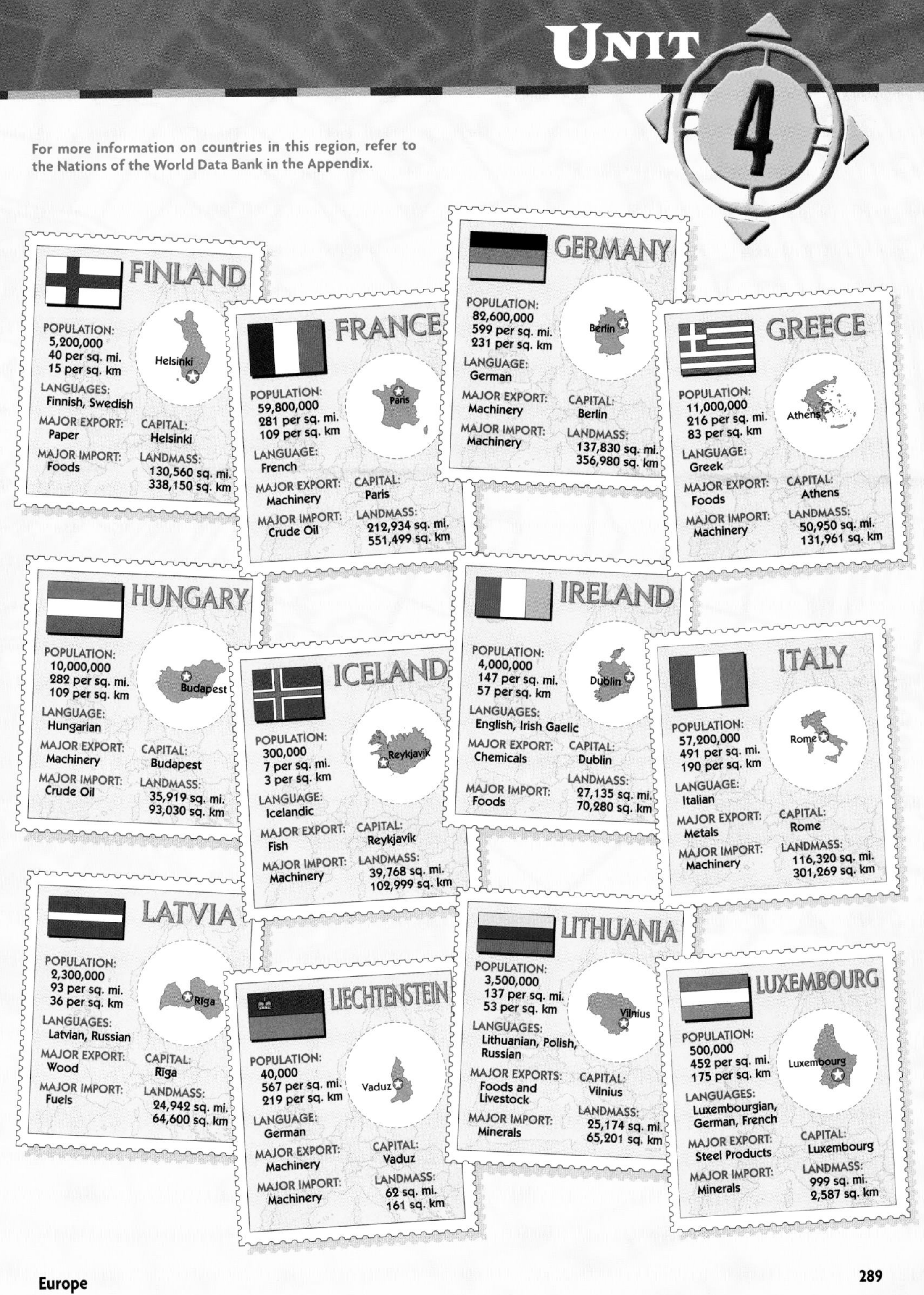

UNIT 4
FINLAND
POPULATION: 5,200,000 40 per sq. mi. 15 per sq. km
LANGUAGES: Finnish, Swedish
MAJOR EXPORT: Paper
CAPITAL: Helsinki
MAJOR IMPORT: Foods
LANDMASS: 130,560 sq. mi. 338,150 sq. km
Helsinki
FRANCE
POPULATION: 59,800,000 281 per sq. mi. 109 per sq. km
LANGUAGE: French
MAJOR EXPORT: Machinery
CAPITAL: Paris
MAJOR IMPORT: Crude Oil
LANDMASS: 212,934 sq. mi. 551,499 sq. km
Paris
GERMANY
POPULATION: 82,600,000 599 per sq. mi. 231 per sq. km
LANGUAGE: German
MAJOR EXPORT: Machinery
CAPITAL: Berlin
MAJOR IMPORT: Machinery
LANDMASS: 137,830 sq. mi. 356,980 sq. km
Berlin
GREECE
POPULATION: 11,000,000 216 per sq. mi. 83 per sq. km
LANGUAGE: Greek
MAJOR EXPORT: Foods
CAPITAL: Athens
MAJOR IMPORT: Machinery
LANDMASS: 50,950 sq. mi. 131,961 sq. km
Athens
HUNGARY
POPULATION: 10,000,000 282 per sq. mi. 109 per sq. km
LANGUAGE: Hungarian
MAJOR EXPORT: Machinery
CAPITAL: Budapest
MAJOR IMPORT: Crude Oil
LANDMASS: 35,919 sq. mi. 93,030 sq. km
Budapest
ICELAND
POPULATION: 300,000 7 per sq. mi. 3 per sq. km
LANGUAGE: Icelandic
MAJOR EXPORT: Fish
CAPITAL: Reykjavík
MAJOR IMPORT: Machinery
LANDMASS: 39,768 sq. mi. 102,999 sq. km
Reykjavík
IRELAND
POPULATION: 4,000,000 147 per sq. mi. 57 per sq. km
LANGUAGES: English, Irish Gaelic
MAJOR EXPORT: Chemicals
CAPITAL: Dublin
MAJOR IMPORT: Foods
LANDMASS: 27,135 sq. mi. 70,280 sq. km
Dublin
ITALY
POPULATION: 57,200,000 491 per sq. mi. 190 per sq. km
LANGUAGE: Italian
MAJOR EXPORT: Metals
CAPITAL: Rome
MAJOR IMPORT: Machinery
LANDMASS: 116,320 sq. mi. 301,269 sq. km
Rome
LATVIA
POPULATION: 2,300,000 93 per sq. mi. 36 per sq. km
LANGUAGES: Latvian, Russian
MAJOR EXPORT: Wood
CAPITAL: Riga
MAJOR IMPORT: Fuels
LANDMASS: 24,942 sq. mi. 64,600 sq. km
Riga
LIECHTENSTEIN
POPULATION: 40,000 567 per sq. mi. 219 per sq. km
LANGUAGE: German
MAJOR EXPORT: Machinery
CAPITAL: Vaduz
MAJOR IMPORT: Machinery
LANDMASS: 62 sq. mi. 161 sq. km
Vaduz
LITHUANIA
POPULATION: 3,500,000 137 per sq. mi. 53 per sq. km
LANGUAGES: Lithuanian, Polish, Russian
MAJOR EXPORTS: Foods and Livestock
CAPITAL: Vilnius
MAJOR IMPORT: Minerals
LANDMASS: 25,174 sq. mi. 65,201 sq. km
Vilnius
LUXEMBOURG
POPULATION: 500,000 452 per sq. mi. 175 per sq. km
LANGUAGES: Luxembourgian, German, French
MAJOR EXPORT: Steel Products
CAPITAL: Luxembourg
MAJOR IMPORT: Minerals
LANDMASS: 999 sq. mi. 2,587 sq. km
Luxembourg

Europe 289

Making Predictions About 30,000 years ago, bison and rhinoceroses wandered the land that is now France. Scientists know this because they have identified these animals in cave paintings found in France and dating from this period. **Ask:** **What probably happened to these animals?** *(They were probably overhunted or driven elsewhere.)* **L1**

Cultural Kaleidoscope

Rome, Italy Rome was the first area of Europe that had professional barbers. They first set up shop in 303 B.C. Early Romans prized dark hair as much as a good cut, and they used dyes made by boiling walnut shells and leeks to darken their hair. The dyes were so harsh, however, that they often made the Romans' hair fall out.

Making Inferences San Marino is the world's smallest republic and Europe's oldest existing country, with about 1,600 years of independent existence. Its inhabitants, however, do not have their own national language. Have students locate San Marino on the political map. **Ask:** **What language do its people probably speak?** *(Italian)* Then have them check their answer on the Country Profile "stamp." **L1**

Regional Atlas Activity

Mapping an Empire The achievements of ancient Rome can still be seen throughout Europe. In Rome itself are the Colosseum, Pantheon, and the Forum. Italy has the buried cities of Pompeii and Herculaneum and parts of the Roman road called the Appian Way. Southern France has the aqueduct called the Pont du Gard, and another impressive aqueduct is found in Segovia, Spain. Remains of Hadrian's Wall can be found in the United Kingdom. Give students an outline map of Europe and a list of Roman sites. Have them place the sites on the map so they can see the extent of the Roman Empire. **L2**

EE4 Human Systems: Standard 10

REGIONAL ATLAS

Favorite foods of the Dutch are chocolate spread on bread for breakfast and smoked eel for the main meal.

Current Events Journal

Suggest that students compare the countries of Europe in terms of size and population. Have them create a two-column chart in their notebooks with the column headings "Area" and "Population." Then have them find the five largest and five most populous countries and write the names under the appropriate heading.

Cultural  Kaleidoscope

Portugal Bakers in Sintra, Portugal, make delicious, bite-sized cheese tarts. Local legend says that a thirteenth-century king loved the tarts so much that he allowed his subjects to use them to pay their taxes.

3 ASSESS

Organize students into groups. Have groups use the maps and graphs from the Regional Atlas to quiz one another on the geography of Europe.

Country Profiles

MACEDONIA, Former Yugoslav Republic of

POPULATION: 2,100,000
207 per sq. mi.
80 per sq. km
LANGUAGES: Macedonian, Albanian
MAJOR EXPORT: Manufactured Goods
MAJOR IMPORT: Fuels
CAPITAL: Skopje
LANDMASS: 9,927 sq. mi. 25,711 sq. km

MOLDOVA

POPULATION: 4,300,000
327 per sq. mi.
128 per sq. km
LANGUAGES: Moldovan, Russian
MAJOR EXPORT: Foods
MAJOR IMPORT: Petroleum
CAPITAL: Chişinău
LANDMASS: 13,012 sq. mi. 33,701 sq. km

MALTA

POPULATION: 400,000
3,205 per sq. mi.
1,237 per sq. km
LANGUAGES: Maltese, English
MAJOR EXPORT: Machinery
MAJOR IMPORT: Foods
CAPITAL: Valletta
LANDMASS: 124 sq. mi. 321 sq. km

MONACO

POPULATION: 30,000
45,333 per sq. mi.
11,503 per sq. km
LANGUAGE: French
MAJOR EXPORT: N/A
MAJOR IMPORT: N/A
CAPITAL: Monaco
LANDMASS: 1.0 sq. mi. 2.6 sq. km

NETHERLANDS

POPULATION: 16,200,000
1,030 per sq. mi.
398 per sq. km
LANGUAGE: Dutch
MAJOR EXPORT: Manufactured Goods
MAJOR IMPORT: Raw Materials
CAPITAL: Amsterdam
LANDMASS: 15,768 sq. mi. 40,839 sq. km

POLAND

POPULATION: 38,600,000
309 per sq. mi.
119 per sq. km
LANGUAGE: Polish
MAJOR EXPORT: Manufactured Goods
MAJOR IMPORT: Machinery
CAPITAL: Warsaw
LANDMASS: 124,807 sq. mi. 323,250 sq. km

NORWAY

POPULATION: 4,600,000
37 per sq. mi.
14 per sq. km
LANGUAGE: Norwegian
MAJOR EXPORT: Petroleum
MAJOR IMPORT: Machinery
CAPITAL: Oslo
LANDMASS: 125,050 sq. mi. 323,880 sq. km

PORTUGAL

POPULATION: 10,400,000
294 per sq. mi.
114 per sq. km
LANGUAGE: Portuguese
MAJOR EXPORT: Clothing
MAJOR IMPORT: Machinery
CAPITAL: Lisbon
LANDMASS: 35,514 sq. mi. 91,981 sq. km

ROMANIA

POPULATION: 21,600,000
235 per sq. mi.
91 per sq. km
LANGUAGES: Romanian, Hungarian
MAJOR EXPORT: Textiles
MAJOR IMPORT: Fuels
CAPITAL: Bucharest
LANDMASS: 92,042 sq. mi. 238,389 sq. km

SERBIA AND MONTENEGRO

POPULATION: 10,700,000
271 per sq. mi.
105 per sq. km
LANGUAGES: Serbo-Croatian, Albanian
MAJOR EXPORT: Manufactured Goods
MAJOR IMPORT: Machinery
CAPITAL: Belgrade
LANDMASS: 39,448 sq. mi. 102,170 sq. km

SAN MARINO

POPULATION: 30,000
1,295 per sq. mi.
500 per sq. km
LANGUAGE: Italian
MAJOR EXPORT: Building Stone
MAJOR IMPORT: Manufactured Goods
CAPITAL: San Marino
LANDMASS: 23 sq. mi. 60 sq. km

SLOVAKIA

POPULATION: 5,400,000
283 per sq. mi.
110 per sq. km
LANGUAGES: Slovak, Hungarian
MAJOR EXPORT: Transport Equipment
MAJOR IMPORT: Machinery
CAPITAL: Bratislava
LANDMASS: 18,923 sq. mi. 49,011 sq. km

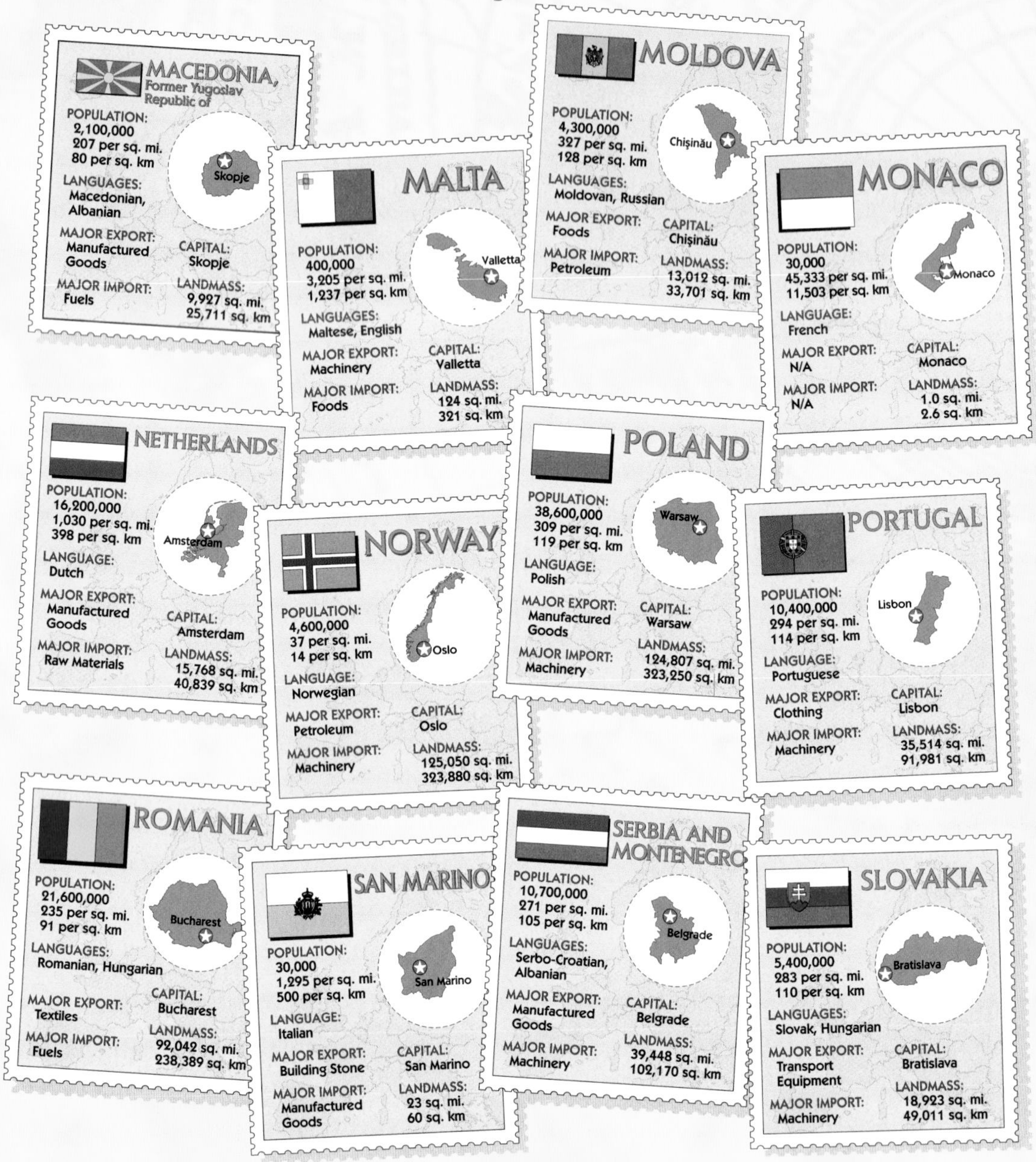

Countries and flags not drawn to scale

Regional Atlas Activity

Identifying Locations Have students locate the following cities on the map of Europe in the Reference Atlas: London and Edinburgh, (United Kingdom); Paris, Nantes, Bordeaux, and Marseilles (France); Barcelona and Madrid (Spain); Rome and Venice (Italy); Berlin and Hamburg, (Germany); Vienna (Austria); Warsaw (Poland); Stockholm (Sweden); and Oslo (Norway). **Ask:** What do almost all of these cities have in common? *(All but Madrid are located near water.)* What does this fact of location tell you about these cities? *(They probably arose as ports or along transportation routes.)* **L2**

EE6 The Uses of Geography: Standard 17

For more information on countries in this region, refer to the Nations of the World Data Bank in the Appendix.

UNIT 4
SLOVENIA
POPULATION: 2,100,000
256 per sq. mi.
99 per sq. km
LANGUAGES: Slovene, Serbo-Croatian
MAJOR EXPORT: Transport Equipment
MAJOR IMPORT: Machinery
CAPITAL: Ljubljana
LANDMASS: 7,819 sq. mi. 20,251 sq. km
Ljubljana
SPAIN
POPULATION: 41,300,000
212 per sq. mi.
82 per sq. km
LANGUAGES: Spanish, Catalan, Galician, Basque
MAJOR EXPORTS: Cars and Trucks
MAJOR IMPORT: Machinery
CAPITAL: Madrid
LANDMASS: 195,363 sq. mi. 505,990 sq. km
Madrid
SWEDEN
POPULATION: 9,000,000
52 per sq. mi.
20 per sq. km
LANGUAGE: Swedish
MAJOR EXPORT: Paper Products
MAJOR IMPORT: Crude Oil
CAPITAL: Stockholm
LANDMASS: 173,730 sq. mi. 449,961 sq. km
Stockholm
SWITZERLAND
POPULATION: 7,300,000
460 per sq. mi.
178 per sq. km
LANGUAGES: German, French, Italian
MAJOR EXPORT: Precision Instruments
MAJOR IMPORT: Machinery
CAPITAL: Bern
LANDMASS: 15,942 sq. mi. 41,290 sq. km
Bern
UKRAINE
POPULATION: 47,810,000
205 per sq. mi.
79 per sq. km
LANGUAGES: Ukrainian, Russian
MAJOR EXPORT: Metals
MAJOR IMPORT: Machinery
CAPITAL: Kiev
LANDMASS: 233,089 sq. mi. 603,701 sq. km
Kiev
UNITED KINGDOM
POPULATION: 59,200,000
626 per sq. mi.
242 per sq. km
LANGUAGES: English, Welsh, Scottish Gaelic
MAJOR EXPORT: Manufactured Goods
MAJOR IMPORT: Foods
CAPITAL: London
LANDMASS: 94,548 sq. mi. 244,879 sq. km
London
VATICAN CITY
POPULATION: 1,000
LANGUAGES: Italian, Latin
MAJOR EXPORT: N/A
MAJOR IMPORT: N/A
CAPITAL: N/A
LANDMASS: 0.2 sq. mi. 0.4 sq. km

BUILDING CITIZENSHIP

Participation All citizens are expected to obey the laws of their country. Sometimes, however, the right thing to do is not clear. During World War II, many people in Germany broke the law by helping Jews escape Nazi persecution. During Communist rule, many citizens in Eastern Europe bought and sold goods on the black market.

What do you think would have happened to people helping the Jews if they had been caught?

In the United States, we work to change laws we believe are unfair. Trying to influence the decisions of our elected leaders is an important part of being an active citizen. Write a letter to your school board explaining why you think students should or should not wear uniforms.

Should students have to wear uniforms? ▼

BUILDING CITIZENSHIP

Answer Even if a law appears to be wrong, people who break the law must accept the consequences. The people helping the Jews believed so strongly that what they were doing was right that they were willing to risk jail or death.

Write About It! Students should recognize the authority of the school board to make rules for student dress and conduct. Their letters should argue why uniforms will or will not improve the school. They may be asked to consider the trade-off between community and individual rights.

Enrich
Have students choose one of the countries profiled on these pages and prepare a display on the country's national symbols. The display should identify the meaning behind the symbols and colors on its flag.

4 CLOSE

Reading Strategy

Writing a Paragraph Tell students that Europe is sometimes called "a peninsula of peninsulas." Have them write a paragraph explaining why that statement is true.

Country Profiles Activity

Charting Major Exports Have students make a chart with three columns. The column headings should read "Food Products," "Manufactured Goods," and "Natural Resources." Have students look at the Major Exports entry in each Country Profile. Tell them to write each country name in the appropriate column based on what kind of export the country has. Have them compare the entries in each column to see whether the economies of Europe are primarily based on agriculture, industry, or natural resources. L1

Chapter 10 Resources

Note: The following materials may be used when teaching Chapter 10. Section level support materials are shown at point of use in the margins of the Teacher Wraparound Edition.

Timesaving Tools

TeacherWorks™ All-In-One Planner and Resource Center

- **Interactive Teacher Edition** See the **Interactive Teacher Edition** CD-ROM to electronically integrate your Teacher Wraparound Edition and blackline masters.
- **Interactive Lesson Planner** Organize your week, month, semester, or year with all the lesson helps you need. The **Interactive Lesson Planner** CD-ROM contains all Chapter 10 resources.

Use Glencoe's **Presentation Plus!** multimedia teacher tool to easily present dynamic lessons that visually excite your students. Using Microsoft PowerPoint® you can customize the presentations to create your own personalized lessons.

TEACHING TRANSPARENCIES

Graphic Organizer Transparency 1 L2

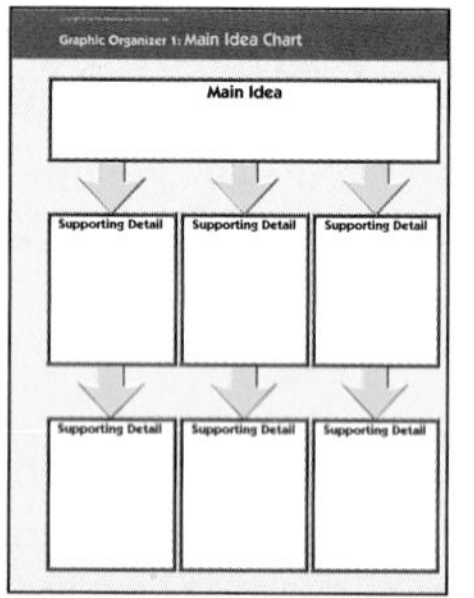

In-text Map Transparency L1

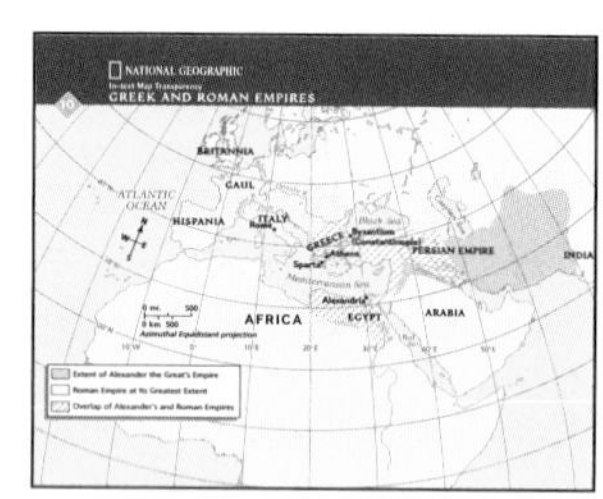

FOLDABLES™ Study Organizer

Dinah Zike's Foldables

Foldables are three-dimensional, interactive graphic organizers that help students practice basic writing skills, review key vocabulary terms, and identify main ideas. Additional chapter activities can be found in the ***Reading and Study Skills Foldables*** booklet.

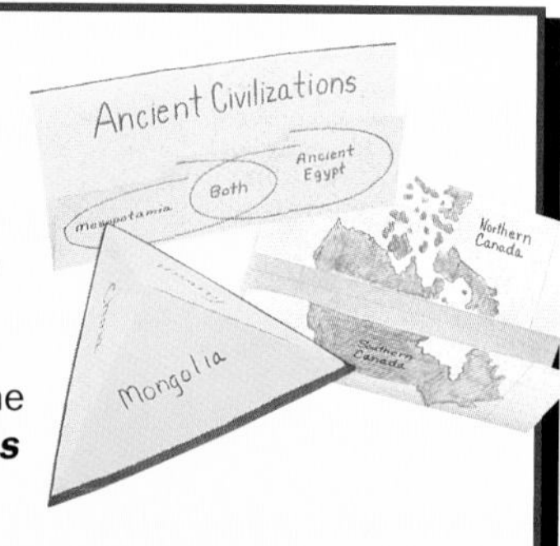

MAP AND GEOGRAPHY SKILLS

Chapter Map Activity L2

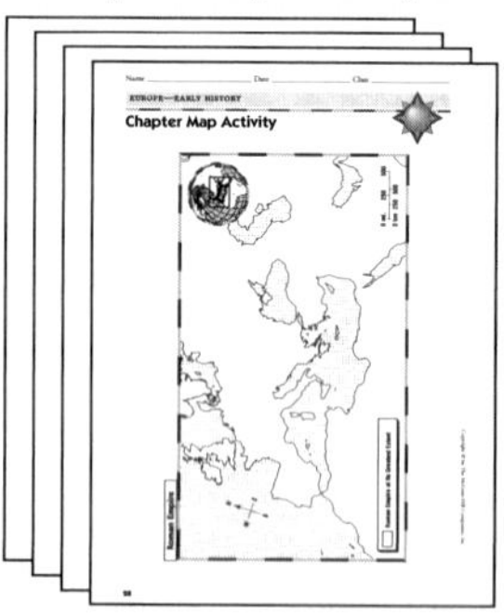

GeoLab Activity L2

READING SUPPORT

Vocabulary Activity L1

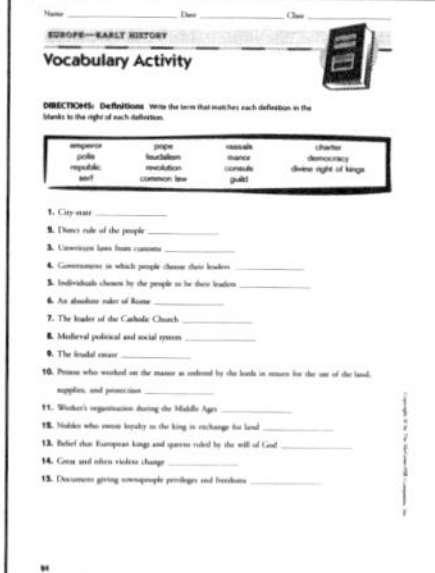

Workbook Activity L1

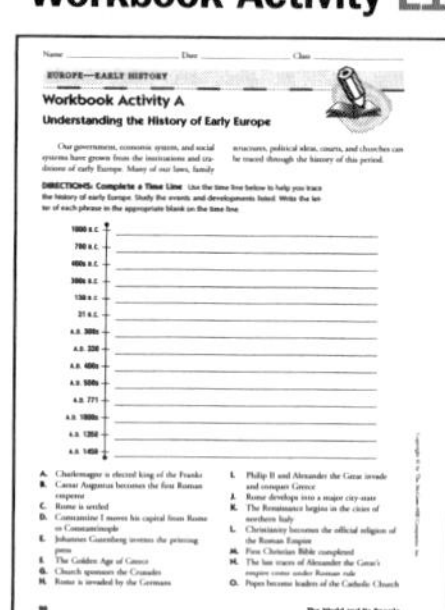

Reading and Writing Skills Activity L1/ELL

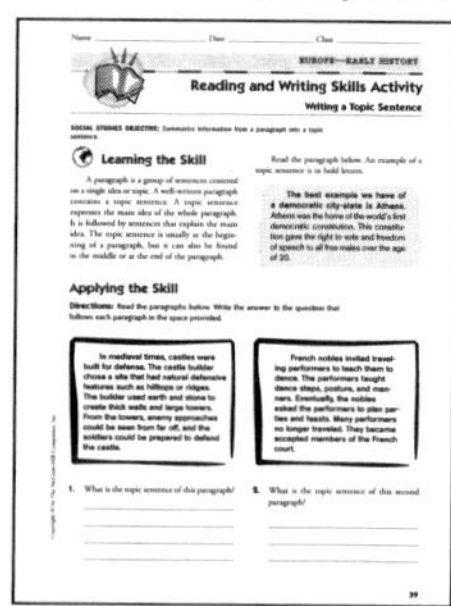

DIFFERENTIATED INSTRUCTION

Use these review and reinforcement materials to help less-proficient readers, English learners, and gifted and talented students.

Reteaching Activity L1

Chapter Skills Review L2

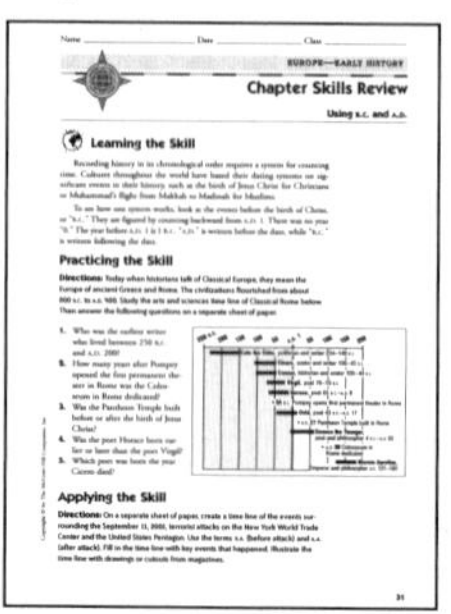

Cooperative Learning Activity L1/ELL

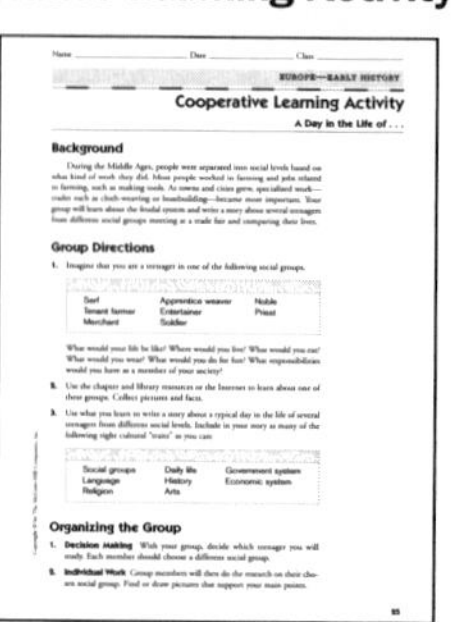

Enrichment Activity L3

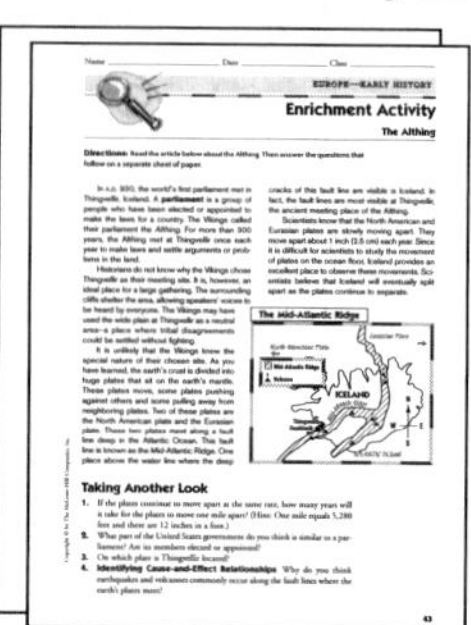

ASSESSMENT

Chapter Test, Form A L2

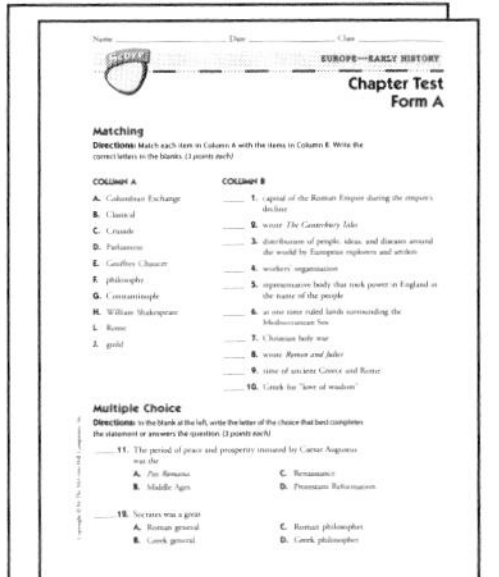

Chapter Test, Form B L2

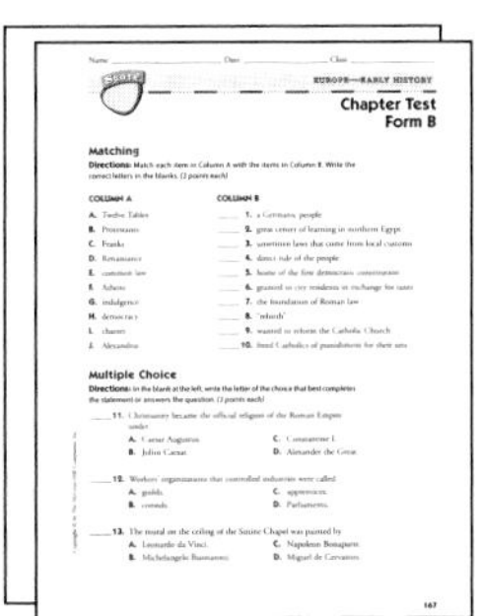

Performance Assessment Activity L1/ELL

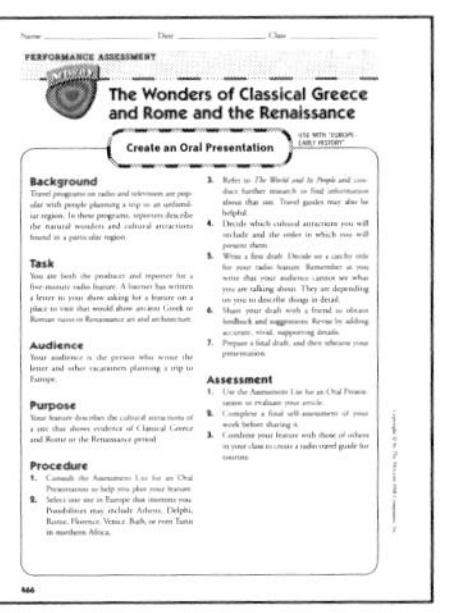

ExamView® Pro Testmaker CD-ROM

STANDARDIZED ASSESSMENT SKILLS

Critical Thinking Skills Activity L2

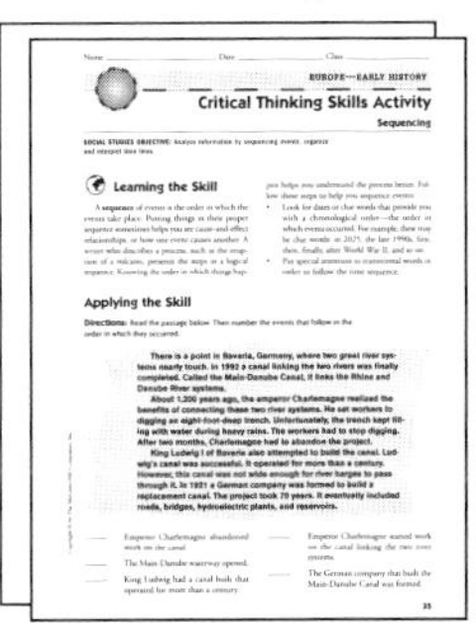

Map and Graph Skills Activity L2

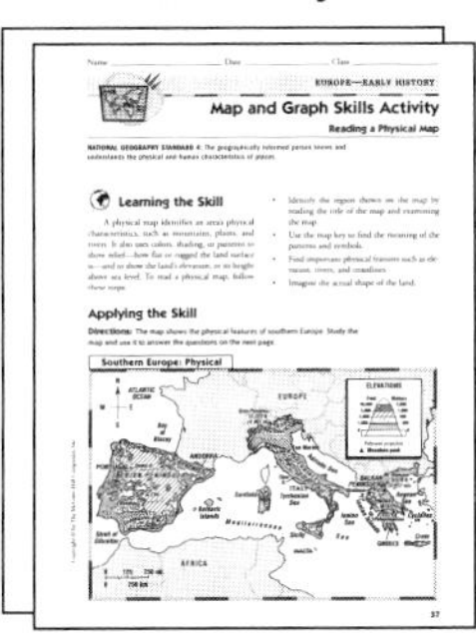

Standardized Test Skills Practice Workbook Activity L2

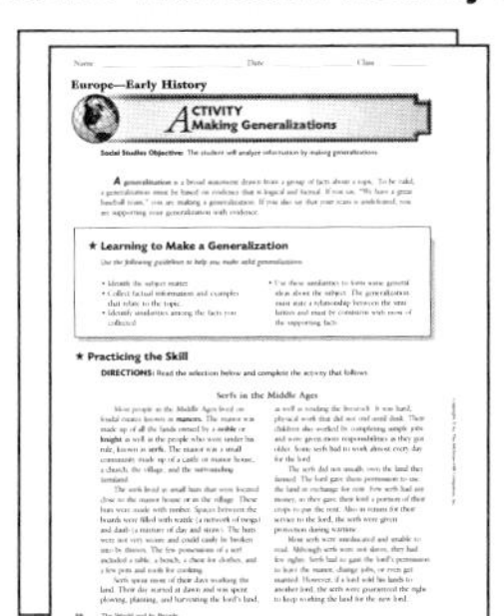

HOME INVOLVEMENT

Take-Home Review Activity L1

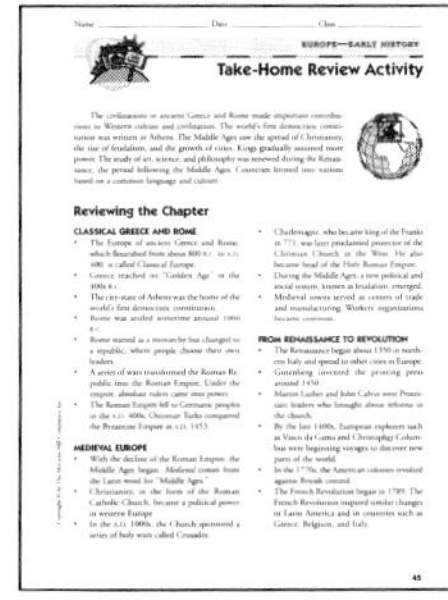

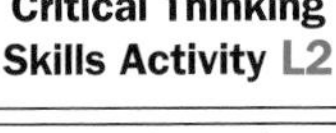

MULTIMEDIA

- National Geographic's The World and Its People
- MindJogger Videoquiz
- Vocabulary PuzzleMaker CD-ROM
- Interactive Tutor Self-Assessment CD-ROM
- ExamView® Pro Testmaker CD-ROM
- TeacherWorks CD-ROM
- StudentWorks CD-ROM
- Skillbuilder Interactive Workbook CD-ROM, Level 1
- Presentation Plus! CD-ROM
- Audio Program

SPANISH RESOURCES

The following Spanish language materials are available in the Spanish Resources binder:

- Spanish Summaries
- Spanish Vocabulary Activities
- Spanish Guided Reading Activities
- Spanish Quizzes and Tests
- Spanish Take-Home Review Activities
- Spanish Reteaching Activities

Meeting National Standards

Geography for Life

The following standards are covered in Chapter 10:

Section 1 **EE4 Human Systems: Standards 9, 10, 11, 12, 13**
EE6 The Uses of Geography: Standard 17

Section 2 **EE4 Human Systems: Standards 9, 10, 11, 12, 13**
EE5 Environment and Society: Standards 14, 15, 16

Section 3 **EE4 Human Systems: Standards 9, 10, 11, 12, 13**
EE5 Environment and Society: Standards 14, 15, 16
EE6 The Uses of Geography: Standards 17, 18

State and Local Objectives

Chapter 10 Planning Guide

SECTION RESOURCES

Daily Objectives	Reproducible Resources	Multimedia Resources
Section 1 **Classical Greece and Rome** **1.** Identify significant accomplishments of Greek culture. **2.** Explain how Alexander spread Greek culture. **3.** Describe the Roman system of government and law.	Reproducible Lesson Plan Daily Lecture and Discussion Notes Note-taking Guide Guided Reading Activity* Reading Essentials and Study Guide* Section Quiz*	Daily Focus Skills Transparency In-text Map Transparency Vocabulary PuzzleMaker CD-ROM Interactive Tutor Self-Assessment CD-ROM ExamView® Pro Testmaker CD-ROM Presentation Plus! CD-ROM
Section 2 **Medieval Europe** **1.** Explain the importance of Christianity as a political influence in Medieval Europe. **2.** Describe the medieval social and political systems.	Reproducible Lesson Plan Daily Lecture and Discussion Notes Note-taking Guide Guided Reading Activity* Reading Essentials and Study Guide* Section Quiz*	Daily Focus Skills Transparency Vocabulary PuzzleMaker CD-ROM Interactive Tutor Self-Assessment CD-ROM ExamView® Pro Testmaker CD-ROM Presentation Plus! CD-ROM
Section 3 **From Renaissance to Revolution** **1.** Explain advances in arts, science, and nationhood achieved during the Renaissance. **2.** Identify the causes of the Reformation. **3.** Compare the causes and results of revolutions in the Americas and Europe.	Reproducible Lesson Plan Daily Lecture and Discussion Notes Note-taking Guide Guided Reading Activity* Reading Essentials and Study Guide* Section Quiz*	Daily Focus Skills Transparency Vocabulary PuzzleMaker CD-ROM Interactive Tutor Self-Assessment CD-ROM ExamView® Pro Testmaker CD-ROM Presentation Plus! CD-ROM MindJogger Videoquiz

00:00 **Out of Time?** Assign the **Reading Essentials and Study Guide*** for this chapter.

*Also available in Spanish

KEY TO ABILITY LEVELS

Teaching strategies have been coded for varying learning styles and abilities.

L1 **BASIC** activities for all students
L2 **AVERAGE** activities for average to above-average students
L3 **CHALLENGING** activities for above-average students
ELL **ENGLISH LANGUAGE LEARNER** activities

KEY TO TEACHING RESOURCES

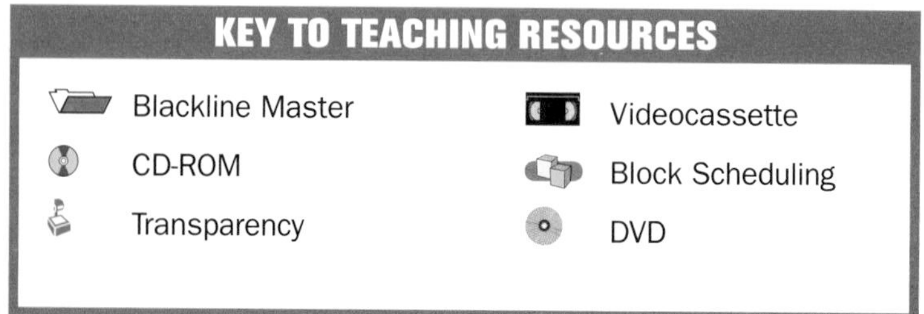

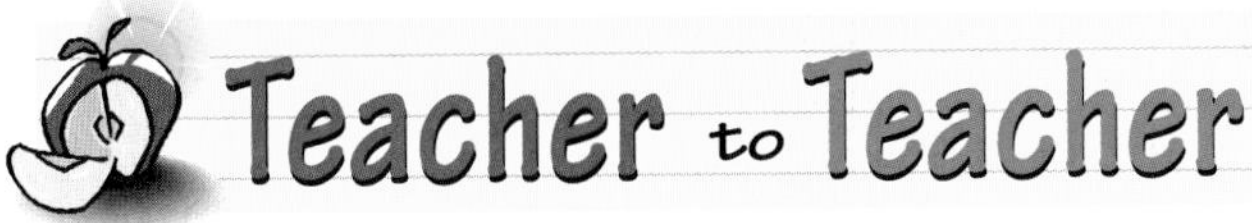

European Art—Phases and Schools

Camille King-Thompson
Williston Middle School
Williston, Florida

With the aid of the art teacher, have a class discussion about the progression that European art has made and its impact on art throughout the world. Have students look at examples of styles of European art from different periods, such as realism, pointilism, impressionism, cubism, and abstract expressionism. Then ask students to choose the style or piece of art they like the best and explain why they like it. Finally, ask students to do research and write a short report on their piece of art, explaining the relationship between the piece or style of art and the particular society it came from. Students should describe ways in which societal issues influenced the piece or style of art.

Meeting Special Needs

In addition to the Differentiated Instruction strategies found in each section, the following resources are also suitable for your special needs students:

- ***ExamView® Pro Testmaker CD-ROM*** allows teachers to tailor tests by reducing answer choices.
- The ***Audio Program*** includes the entire narrative of the student edition so that less-proficient readers can listen to the words as they read them.
- The ***Reading Essentials and Study Guide*** provides the same content as the student edition but is written two grade levels below the textbook.
- ***Guided Reading Activities*** give less-proficient readers point-by-point instructions to increase comprehension as they read each textbook section.
- ***Enrichment Activities*** include a stimulating collection of readings and activities for gifted and talented students.

NATIONAL GEOGRAPHIC TEACHER'S CORNER

Index to National Geographic Magazine:

The following articles may be used for research relating to this chapter:

- "Ancient Greece, Parts I, II, and III," by Caroline Alexander, December 1999, February and March 2000.
- "Italy's Endangered Art," by Erla Zwingle, August 1999.
- "Monaco," by Richard Conniff, May 1996.

National Geographic Society Products:

To order the following products for use with this chapter, call National Geographic Society at 1-800-368-2728:

- *PicturePack: The Middle Ages* (Transparencies)
- *PictureShow: Ancient Civilizations: Greece & Rome* (CD-ROM)
- *PictureShow: The Renaissance* (CD-ROM)

NGS ONLINE

Access National Geographic's Web site for current events, activities, links, interactive features, and archives.
www.nationalgeographic.com

NATIONAL GEOGRAPHIC MapMachine

Find the latest coverage of geography in the news, atlas updates, cartographic activities with interactive maps, an online map store, and links at www.nationalgeographic.com/maps

SOCIAL STUDIES Online

Use our Web site for additional resources. All essential content is covered in the Student Edition.

You and your students can visit twip.glencoe.com, the Web site companion to *The World and Its People*. This innovative integration of electronic and print media offers your students a wealth of opportunities. The student text directs students to the Web site for the following options:

- Chapter Overviews
- Student Web Activities
- Self-Check Quizzes
- Textbook Updates

Answers are provided for you in the Web Activity Lesson Plan. Additional Web resources and Interactive Tutor puzzles are also available.

Introducing Chapter 10

Social Studies online

Introduce students to chapter content and key terms by having them access Chapter Overview 10 at twip.glencoe.com

Chapter Objectives

1. Describe the governments and culture of ancient Greece and Rome.
2. Explain the importance of religion in European history.
3. Outline events that defined the beginnings of the Modern Age.

GLENCOE TECHNOLOGY

NATIONAL GEOGRAPHIC

The World and Its People Video Program

Chapters 10–13 Europe
The following segments enhance the study of this chapter:

- **Gondolas of Venice**
- **Dracula's Castle**
- **The New Forest**

MindJogger Videoquiz

Use MindJogger Videoquiz to preview the Chapter 10 content.

Both programs available in DVD and VHS

Chapter 10 Europe—Early History

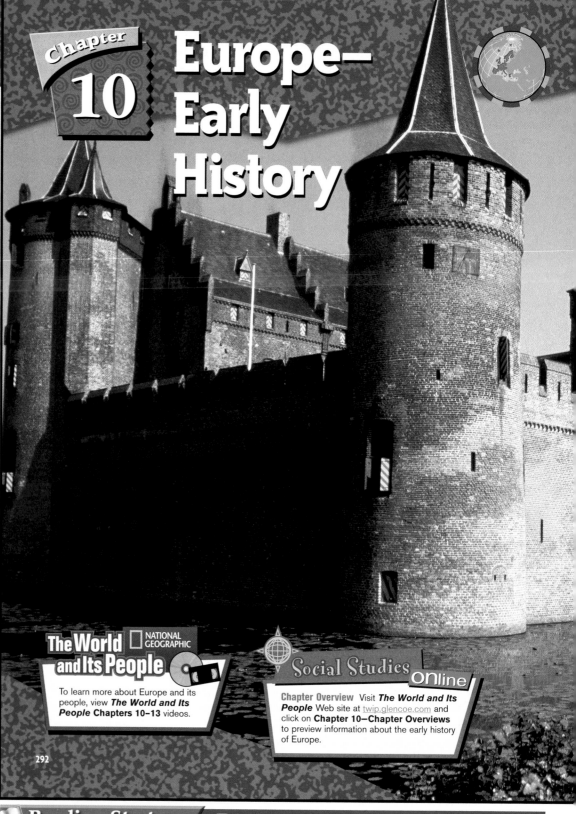

The World and Its People NATIONAL GEOGRAPHIC

To learn more about Europe and its people, view ***The World and Its People*** **Chapters 10–13** videos.

Social Studies online

Chapter Overview Visit ***The World and Its People*** Web site at twip.glencoe.com and click on **Chapter 10—Chapter Overviews** to preview information about the early history of Europe.

292

Reading Strategy — Purpose for Reading

The **Chapter Tour** is an important tool for generating student interest, previewing material to be covered, and identifying the Author's Craft. Have students skim the chapter and write about which section, pictures, and highlights are most interesting to them. Have them share the information with a partner and then with the entire class. Conclude by telling the students that they will study the early history of Europe in this chapter. L1

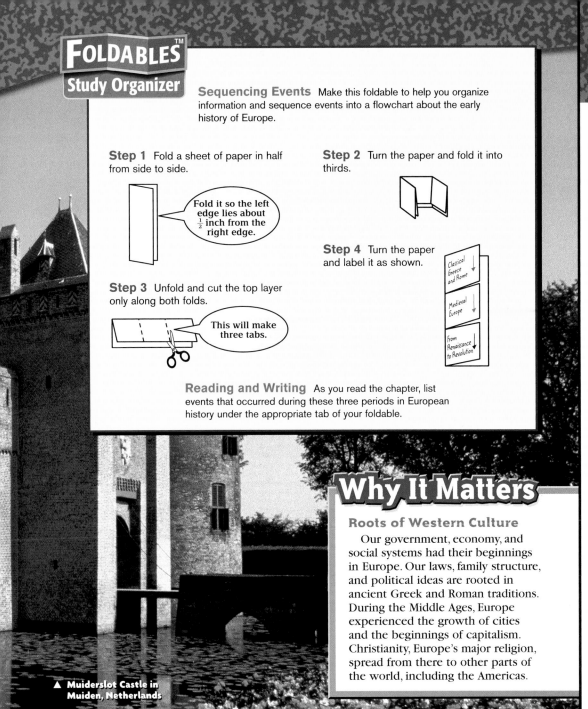

FOLDABLES™ Study Organizer

Sequencing Events Make this foldable to help you organize information and sequence events into a flowchart about the early history of Europe.

Step 1 Fold a sheet of paper in half from side to side.

Step 2 Turn the paper and fold it into thirds.

Step 3 Unfold and cut the top layer only along both folds.

Step 4 Turn the paper and label it as shown.

Reading and Writing As you read the chapter, list events that occurred during these three periods in European history under the appropriate tab of your foldable.

Why It Matters

Roots of Western Culture

Our government, economy, and social systems had their beginnings in Europe. Our laws, family structure, and political ideas are rooted in ancient Greek and Roman traditions. During the Middle Ages, Europe experienced the growth of cities and the beginnings of capitalism. Christianity, Europe's major religion, spread from there to other parts of the world, including the Americas.

▲ Muiderslot Castle in Muiden, Netherlands

About the Photo

Castles in medieval Europe were primarily defensive structures intended to extend control over adjacent territories. The walls and turrets were designed to withstand attacks and siege. Whenever possible, castles were built on hills or islands that provided natural defenses. When that wasn't possible, moats were dug to provide additional defense.

Introducing
Chapter 10

Dinah Zike's Foldables

Purpose Students will make and use a foldable to organize events from the early history of Europe. As students read the chapter, they are required to sequence and describe important events. When students have completed the activity, they should have a flowchart that outlines the events of classical, medieval, and pre-modern Europe.

Have students complete the ***Reading and Study Skills Foldables*** activity for this chapter.

Why It Matters

Have students create a chart with two columns. Label one column "European" and the other "American." In each column, have students list important characteristics of the modern United States that originated in each of the regions. Examples might include government, language, religion, cars, sports, computers, and so on. Ask for volunteers to present and discuss their charts.

Chapter 10

Section 1, pages 294–297

1 Focus

Section Objectives

1. Identify significant accomplishments of Greek culture.
2. Explain how Alexander spread Greek culture.
3. Describe the Roman system of government and law.

BELLRINGER Skillbuilder Activity

Project transparency and have students answer the question.

Daily Focus Skills Transparency

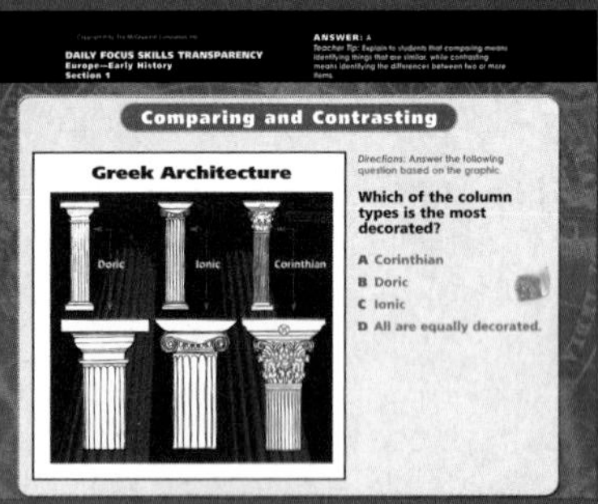

Reading Preview

■ **Activating Prior Knowledge** Have the class give examples of different forms of government.

■ **Preteaching Vocabulary** Have students find the meanings of *monarchy* and *republic.* Then have them identify synonyms, or words with the same meanings. *(monarchy—kingdom; republic—democracy)*

Guide to Reading

Main Idea

Ancient Greece and Rome made important contributions to Western culture and civilization.

Terms to Know

- Classical
- polis
- democracy
- republic
- consul
- emperor

Reading Strategy

Create a chart like the one below. Write one fact that you already know about each category in the "Know" column. After reading the section, write one fact that you have learned about each category in the "Learn" column.

Category	Know	Learn
Greece		
Rome		
Roman law		
Christianity		

Section 1 Classical Greece and Rome

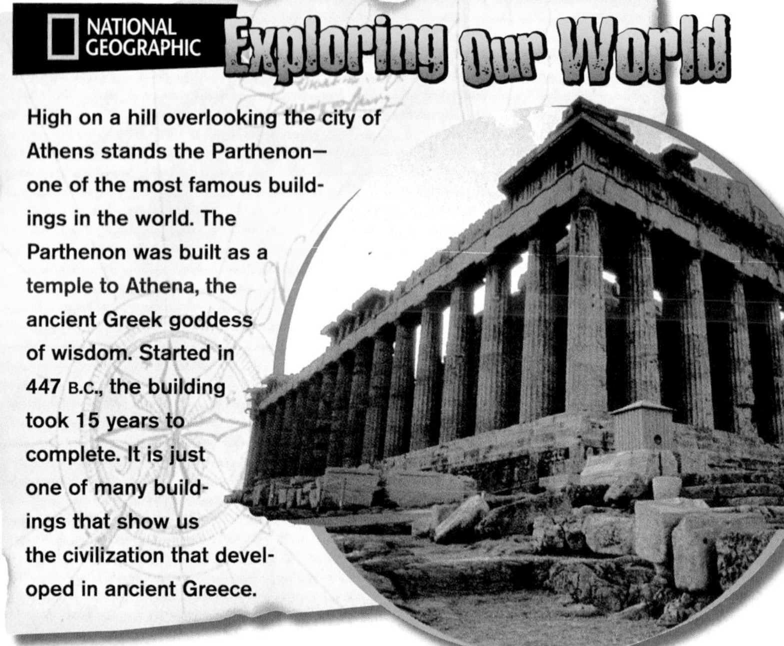

NATIONAL GEOGRAPHIC Exploring Our World

High on a hill overlooking the city of Athens stands the Parthenon—one of the most famous buildings in the world. The Parthenon was built as a temple to Athena, the ancient Greek goddess of wisdom. Started in 447 B.C., the building took 15 years to complete. It is just one of many buildings that show us the civilization that developed in ancient Greece.

When historians talk of **Classical** Europe, they mean ancient Greece and Rome. These civilizations flourished from about 800 B.C. to A.D. 400, and their achievements profoundly influenced Western culture.

The Golden Age of Greece

Greece reached its "Golden Age" in the 400s B.C. Before then, the city-state, or **polis,** had been ruled by a king. The Golden Age brought in direct rule of the people, or **democracy.** Classical Greece has been called the "cradle of democracy" because we trace the beginnings of our political system to this time.

Athens The city-state of **Athens** was the home of the world's first democratic constitution. All free males over the age of 20 had the right to vote and speak freely. Athenians also produced significant works of philosophy, literature, and drama. The word *philosophy* is Greek for

Section Resources

Reproducible Masters

- Reproducible Lesson Plan
- Daily Lecture and Discussion Notes
- Note-taking Guide
- Guided Reading Activity
- Reading Essentials and Study Guide
- Section Quiz

Transparencies

- Daily Focus Skills Transparency
- In-text Map Transparency

Multimedia

- Vocabulary PuzzleMaker CD-ROM
- Interactive Tutor Self-Assessment CD-ROM
- Presentation Plus! CD-ROM
- ExamView® Pro Testmaker CD-ROM

"love of wisdom." Two great philosophers, Socrates and his student Plato, sought to understand and explain human nature. Aristotle, a student of Plato's, wrote powerful works dealing with politics, literature, ethics, and philosophy. Greek writers and dramatists dealt with these timeless themes in their poems and plays.

Conflict Between the City-States During this period, the Greek city-states of Sparta and Athens wanted to expand their boundaries. **Sparta,** ruled by a few nobles, disliked change. Athens, as you learned, was open to democracy and new ideas. These two rivals often fought against each other. Sparta and Athens briefly united during the Persian Wars, when they prevented the Persians from taking over Greece. From 431 B.C. to 404 B.C., however, they fought each other again. Sparta finally defeated Athens in the Peloponnesian War, which further divided and weakened Greece.

▲ Greek theater comedy mask

Greek Culture Spreads In the 300s B.C., Philip II of Macedonia and his son Alexander the Great invaded the northern border of Greece. They easily conquered all of Greece. Alexander went on to create an empire that included Persia and Egypt and stretched eastward into India. Locate the extent of Alexander's empire on the map below. Although his empire barely survived his death, Alexander spread Greek culture everywhere he invaded. Over time, Greek customs mixed with Persian and Egyptian culture. The empire's important center was at Alexandria in northern Egypt. There, a great center of learning—a museum-library—was founded. The last traces of Alexander's empire came under Roman rule by about 130 B.C.

✓Reading Check **Why has Greece been called the "cradle of democracy"?**

NATIONAL GEOGRAPHIC

Greek and Roman Empires

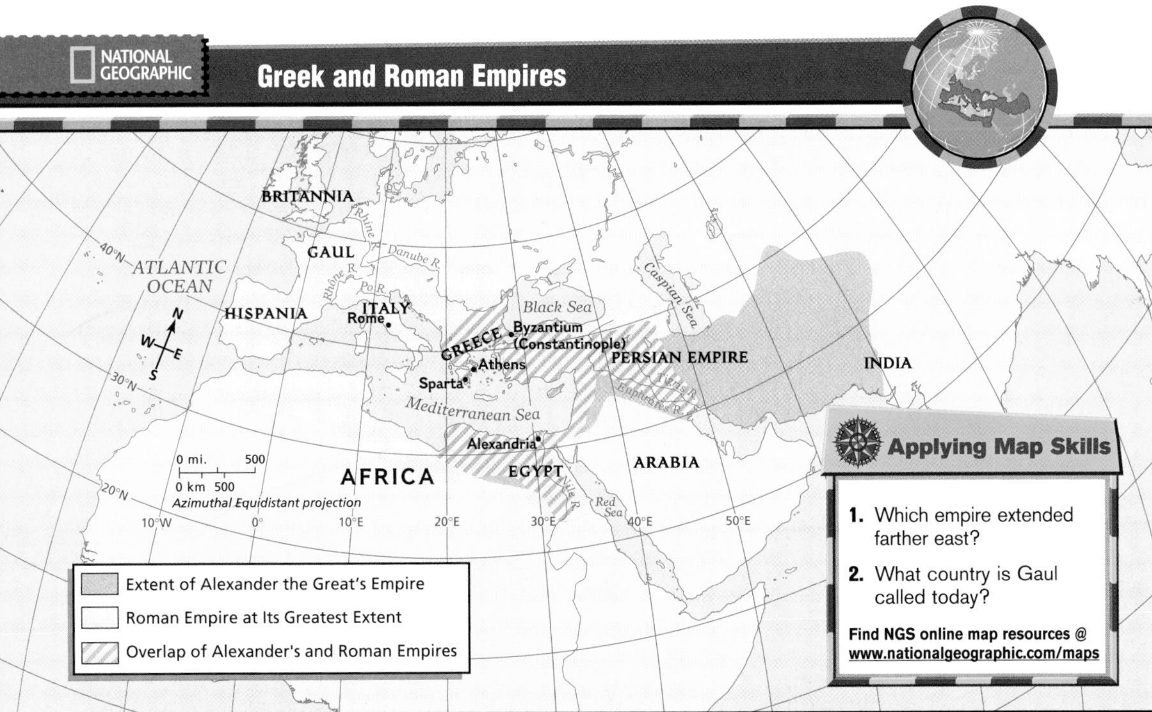

Applying Map Skills

1. Which empire extended farther east?
2. What country is Gaul called today?

Find NGS online map resources @ www.nationalgeographic.com/maps

Reading Strategy — Reading the Text

Using Word Parts Have students use prefixes to unlock the meanings of unknown words. A *prefix* is a word part that comes before a base word or a root and changes the meaning of the word. For example, *dis-* means "the opposite of" and is found in words such as *disobey, displease,* and *disown. In-* means "not." Have students provide examples of words that use this prefix *(inactive, incorrect, inability, incomplete).* L1

Use the ***Reading Skills Handbook*** *for more reading strategies.*

Chapter 10

Section 1, pages 294–297

2 TEACH

Reading Strategy

Sequencing Information
Have students create a time line covering the period 800 B.C. to A.D. 400. Have them show the approximate time of significant events in ancient Greece and Rome as well as the span of the Golden Age and the *Pax Romana.* L2

Daily Lecture and Discussion Notes

EUROPE—EARLY HISTORY

Daily Lecture and Discussion Notes
Classical Greece and Rome

Did You Know? The ancient Greek Olympics included boxing, footracing, and the pentathlon (wrestling, long jump, running, throwing the discus, and throwing the javelin), as well as chariot racing and an event called the pancratium—a brutal mixture of boxing and wrestling.

I. The Golden Age of Greece
A. When historians talk of **Classical** Europe, they mean ancient Greece and Rome.
B. The Classical period of Greece reached its "Golden Age" in the 400s B.C.
C. By that time, the city-state, or **polis,** had grown from being ruled by a king to the direct rule of the people, or **democracy.**

✓ Reading Check Answer

because we trace the beginnings of our political system to this time

Applying Map Skills

Answers
1. Roman
2. France

In-text Map Transparency Activity
Ask: **How do you think the Mediterranean Sea contributed to the growth of the Roman Empire?** *(The Mediterranean Sea allowed for better access to conquer and control lands.)*

Chapter 10

Section 1, pages 294–297

L1/ELL

Guided Reading Activity

Name ______ Date ______ Class ______

EUROPE—EARLY HISTORY

Guided Reading Activity 1

Classical Greece and Rome

DIRECTIONS: Summarizing Reading the section and completing the summary paragraphs below will help you learn more about ancient Greece and Rome. Use your textbook to fill in the blanks.

The achievements of Classical Greece and Rome profoundly influenced (1) ______ ______. In the 400s B.C., the Greek city-state, or (2) ______, came under the direct rule of the people, or (3) ______. (4) ______ had the world's first democratic constitution.

City-states like Athens and (5) ______ wanted to expand, so they often fought against each other. Sparta defeated Athens in the ______. It weakened all of Greece. In the

More About the Photo

The Colosseum The dedication ceremonies for the Colosseum in A.D. 80 included 100 days of games and competition. The Colosseum measures 620 by 530 feet (190 by 155 meters) and could seat 50,000 spectators.

Caption Answer Answers will vary but should include sports stadiums, convention centers, and concert auditoriums.

Reading Check Answer

provided a model for a republican government and established Roman law

ASSESS

Assign Section 1 Assessment as homework or an in-class activity.

Have students use the Interactive Tutor Self-Assessment CD-ROM to review Section 1.

NATIONAL GEOGRAPHIC **On Location**

Ancient Rome

The Colosseum was built as an arena for gladiator fights.

Place **Name some arenas where public events take place today.**

The Rise of Rome

According to legend, the city of **Rome** was founded by twin brothers Romulus and Remus. As infants, they had been left to die on the banks of the Tiber River. They were rescued by a she-wolf, who raised them as her cubs. When grown, the twins built the city on seven hills in central Italy.

Historical Rome What we know for fact is that Rome was settled sometime around 1000 B.C. By about 700 B.C., it had evolved into a major city-state that began to dominate much of the Italian peninsula. Italy was more easily invaded than mountainous Greece, so the Romans developed a strong army. The Romans borrowed the Latin alphabet from the Greeks, who also influenced Roman art, religion, and mythology.

The Roman Republic Rome started as a monarchy but changed to a republic. In a **republic,** people choose their leaders. Rome was led by two **consuls,** or individuals elected by the people of Rome to represent them. The consuls reported to the Senate. Members of the Senate were landowners who served for life. This was guaranteed by the system of Roman law. The foundation of Roman law was the Twelve Tables. The "tables" were actually bronze tablets on which laws regarding wills, courts, and property were recorded. Along with Greek democracy, republican government and Roman law were important contributions to Western civilization and the Modern Age.

Reading Check **How has Rome influenced Western civilization?**

From Republic to Empire

From 264 to 146 B.C., a series of wars transformed the Roman Republic into the **Roman Empire.** Eventually, the Mediterranean Sea became a "Roman lake" surrounded by the Roman Empire. The peoples conquered by Rome were given Roman citizenship and equality under the Roman law. Beyond the boundaries of its vast empire, Rome opened up trade with civilizations as far away as India and China.

Under the empire, senators lost power to **emperors,** or absolute rulers, of Rome. Supporters of the Senate killed the great Roman general Julius Caesar in 44 B.C. for trying to become the first emperor. This led to a civil war between Caesar's supporters and those of the Senate. In 31 B.C., Caesar's nephew Octavius became the first Roman emperor, Caesar Augustus. He initiated a period of peace and prosperity known as the *Pax Romana,* which lasted for almost 200 years.

Roman Achievements The Romans were skilled at building temples, stadiums, and baths. Their projects included the Colosseum and a domed temple called the Pantheon. Both still stand in Rome today.

Differentiated Instruction

Meeting Special Needs: Verbal/Linguistic Organize students into four groups. Have each of the groups research the functions of the Roman Senate. Have them consider such items as who the senators were, who they represented, the issues they debated, and the rules of debate. Have each group prepare a presentation of their findings. Then conduct a mock Senate debate. Combine the groups into two teams. Have the teams debate a current event issue following the rules of the Roman Senate and representing the interests of Roman Senators. L2

EE6 The Uses of Geography: Standard 17

Romans used the arch to build aqueducts, or overhead channels that carried water long distances. They also built roads to bring goods and people into Italy. This led to the growth of Rome's population and wealth.

Christianity and Rome Jesus of Nazareth was born in Palestine, which was under the rule of Caesar Augustus. Jesus carried out his teaching during the early *Pax Romana.* Two disciples, Peter and Paul, established the new Christian Church in Rome. Even though the early Christians were cruelly persecuted, Christianity spread over the Roman world. In the A.D. 300s, under the emperors Constantine I and Theodosius I, Christianity became the official religion of the Roman Empire.

▲ Roman soldier's breastplate

The Decline of the Empire After the period of the *Pax Romana,* the Roman Empire began to decline. In A.D. 330, Emperor Constantine I moved the capital from Rome in Italy eastward to the newly built city of **Constantinople,** near the Black Sea. Constantine tried to save the empire by reforming the government, but it was too late. Plagues that came in from Asia over trade routes killed numerous people.

Finally, in the A.D. 400s, the northern defenses crumbled. Rome was left open to invasion by various groups of Germanic peoples. The Germans came to rule over Rome and much of Italy and Europe. The Eastern Roman Empire, or Byzantine Empire, did not fall to the Germans but continued on for another 1,000 years until its conquest by the Ottoman Turks in 1453.

✓Reading Check What are aqueducts?

Section 1 Assessment

Defining Terms

1. **Define** Classical, polis, democracy, republic, consul, emperor.

Recalling Facts

2. **Government** In its democratic constitution, what two rights did Athens give all free males over the age of 20?
3. **Culture** Name four influences that Greece had on Roman culture.

Critical Thinking

4. **Analyzing Information** Why do you suppose some of Rome's citizens wanted absolute rulers instead of elected senators?
5. **Making Connections** What is one freedom that American democracy has today that was clearly not recognized in the Roman Empire?

Graphic Organizer

6. **Creating Time Lines** Create a time line like the one below. Place the letter of the event next to its date.
   A. Greek empire comes under Roman rule.
   B. Julius Caesar is killed.
   C. Germans invade Rome.
   D. Rome is settled.
   E. Octavius becomes the first Roman emperor.

1000 B.C. — 130 B.C. — 44 B.C. — 31 B.C. — A.D. 400s

Applying Social Studies Skills

7. **Making Inferences** Why do you think the story of Romulus and Remus was created?

Section 1 Assessment

1. The terms are defined in the Glossary.
2. the right to vote and to speak freely
3. art, religion, mythology, and the Latin alphabet
4. *Possible answer:* an absolute ruler can make decisions without having to discuss, debate, or compromise.
5. *Possible answer:* freedom of religion
6. **A.** 130 B.C. **B.** 44 B.C. **C.** A.D. 400s **D.** 1000 B.C. **E.** 31 B.C.
7. This exercise helps students understand the importance of mythology in preserving and relating history and the connection between myth and history. All reasonable attempts at answers should be accepted.

Chapter 10

Section 1, pages 294–297

L2

Section Quiz

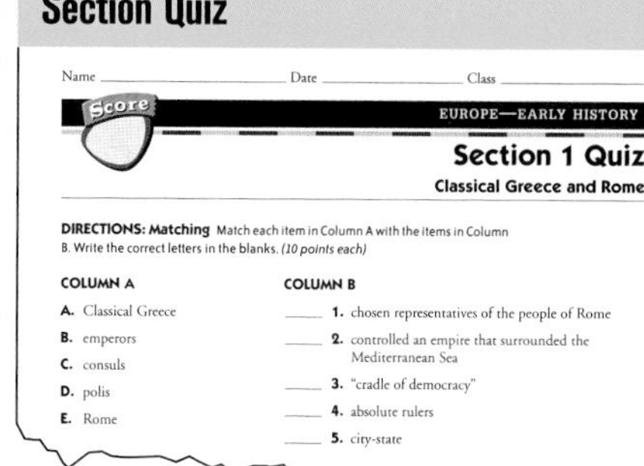

Name ______ Date ______ Class ______

Score

EUROPE—EARLY HISTORY

Section 1 Quiz

Classical Greece and Rome

DIRECTIONS: Matching Match each item in Column A with the items in Column B. Write the correct letters in the blanks. *(10 points each)*

COLUMN A	COLUMN B
A. Classical Greece	____ 1. chosen representatives of the people of Rome
B. emperors	____ 2. controlled an empire that surrounded the Mediterranean Sea
C. consuls	____ 3. "cradle of democracy"
D. polis	____ 4. absolute rulers
E. Rome	____ 5. city-state

✓ Reading Check Answer

overhead channels that carried water long distances

L1/ELL

Reading Essentials and Study Guide

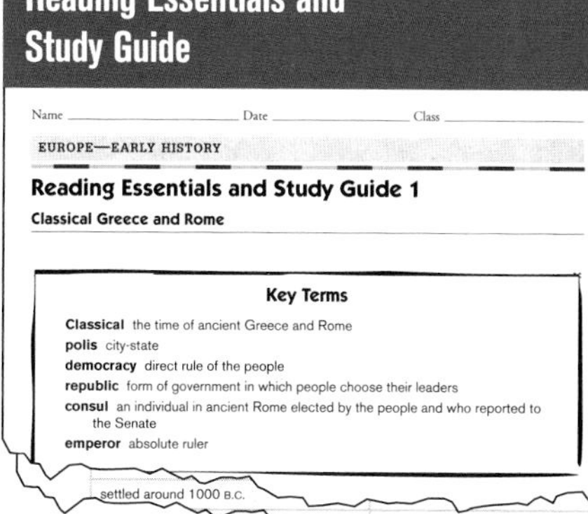

Name ______ Date ______ Class ______

EUROPE—EARLY HISTORY

Reading Essentials and Study Guide 1

Classical Greece and Rome

Key Terms

Classical the time of ancient Greece and Rome
polis city-state
democracy direct rule of the people
republic form of government in which people choose their leaders
consul an individual in ancient Rome elected by the people and who reported to the Senate
emperor absolute ruler

4 CLOSE

Reading Strategy

Writing a Paragraph Have students research the art of Greece and Rome. Have them write a paragraph that describes how social issues influenced the art of these civilizations.

TEACH

Compare the Western calendar with alternative dating methods, such as those found in the Hebrew, Chinese, and Muslim calendars. The conversion to the Western calendar's year 2005 is as follows:

	Beginning Date	Year 2005
Hebrew	3760 B.C.	5765
Chinese	2637 B.C.	4642
Muslim	A.D. 622	1383

Additional Skills Practice

1. **How is the number of years between two B.C. dates calculated?** *(The later date is subtracted from the earlier date.)*
2. **How is the number of years between two A.D. dates calculated?** *(The earlier date is subtracted from the later date.)*
3. **How is the number of years between a B.C. date and an A.D. date calculated?** *(The two dates are added together.)*

GLENCOE TECHNOLOGY

Skillbuilder Interactive Workbook CD-ROM, Level 1

This interactive CD-ROM reinforces student mastery of essential social studies skills.

Social Studies Skill

Using B.C. and A.D.

Cultures throughout the world have based their dating systems on significant events in their history. For example, Islamic countries use a dating system that begins with Muhammad's flight from Makkah to Madinah. For most Western cultures, the dating system is based on the birth of Jesus. Christians refer to Jesus as "Christ."

Learning the Skill

About 515, a Christian monk developed a system that begins dating from *anno Domini,* Latin for "the year of the Lord." Although some historians believe that the monk made a small mistake in his figuring of the exact year of Christ's birth, his system of dating has lasted. Events before the birth of Christ, or "B.C.," are figured by counting backward from A.D. 1. There was no year "0." The year before A.D. 1 is 1 B.C. Notice that "A.D." is written before the date, while "B.C." is written following the date.

Practicing the Skill

Study the time line of Classical Europe to answer the following questions.

1. How old was Plato when he became a student of Socrates?
2. For how long did Alexander the Great rule?
3. How old was Julius Caesar when he was assassinated?
4. Who was emperor nearly 500 years after the rule of Alexander the Great?

NATIONAL GEOGRAPHIC

Classical Europe

- 500 B.C.
- 470 B.C. Socrates born
- 427 B.C. Plato born
- 407 B.C. Plato becomes student of Socrates
- 400 B.C.
- 384 B.C. Aristotle born
- 343 B.C. Alexander the Great becomes student of Aristotle
- 336 B.C.–323 B.C. Alexander the Great rules
- 300 B.C.
- 200 B.C.
- 100 B.C.
- 100 B.C. Julius Caesar born
- 44 B.C. Julius Caesar assassinated
- 31 B.C.–A.D. 14 Octavius emperor
- B.C. / 1 B.C. / A.D.
- A.D. 47 Plutarch, Greek historian, born
- A.D. 100
- A.D. 161–A.D. 180 Marcus Aurelius emperor
- A.D. 200

Applying the Skill

Create a time line using the terms B.M.B. (before my birth) and A.M.B. (after my birth). Fill in the time line with key events that happened before and after you were born. Illustrate the time line with drawings or cutouts from magazines.

GO TO Practice key skills with Glencoe **Skillbuilder Interactive Workbook, Level 1.**

Practicing the Skill Answers

1. 20 years old
2. for 13 years
3. 56 years old
4. Marcus Aurelius

Applying the Skill
Students' time lines will vary.

Section 2

Medieval Europe

Guide to Reading

Main Idea

The Middle Ages saw the spread of Christianity, the growth of cities, and the growing powers of kings.

Key Terms

- pope
- missionary
- common law
- feudalism
- vassal
- manor
- serf
- guild
- charter

Reading Strategy

Create a chart like the one below. Fill in the chief duty or role of each of these members of society.

Lord	
Vassal	
Guild member	
Apprentice	
Serf	

NATIONAL GEOGRAPHIC **Exploring Our World**

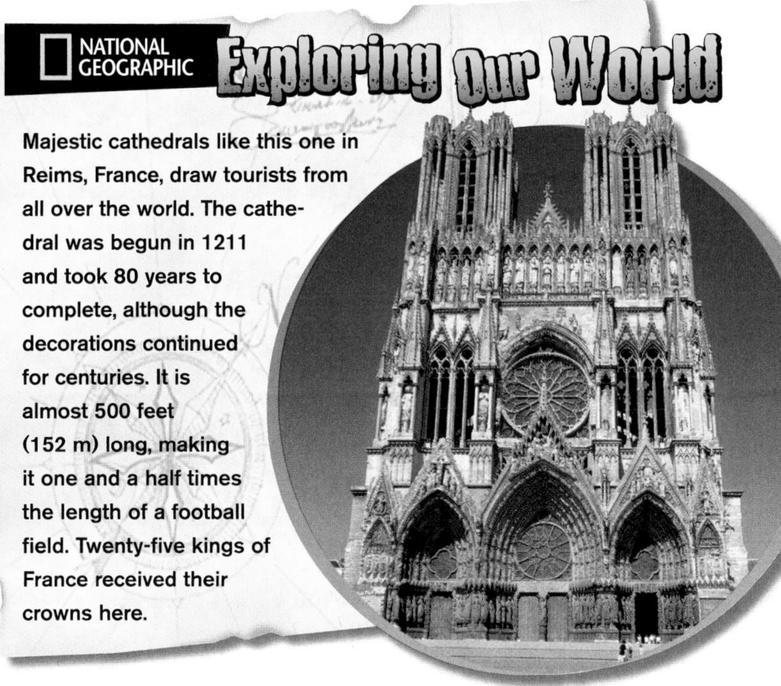

Majestic cathedrals like this one in Reims, France, draw tourists from all over the world. The cathedral was begun in 1211 and took 80 years to complete, although the decorations continued for centuries. It is almost 500 feet (152 m) long, making it one and a half times the length of a football field. Twenty-five kings of France received their crowns here.

With the decline of the Roman Empire, a new age began called the Middle Ages. *Medieval* is derived from a Latin word for "Middle Ages." It is a fitting name for the 1,000-year period that took place between Classical and modern times. Medieval Europe combined characteristics of the Roman Empire with practices of Christianity and other European traditions.

The Rise of Christianity

It was during the Middle Ages that Christianity, in the form of the Roman Catholic Church, became a political power in western Europe. A leader called a bishop headed each major Christian community. By the A.D. 500s, the bishops of Rome, now known as **popes**, became the leaders of the Catholic Church. The influence of the Church was so strong at this time that the popes also became important political figures.

In eastern Europe, the Byzantine Empire, started by Constantine I, continued. There, Christianity was known as Eastern Orthodoxy. It was not under the leadership of the popes in Rome, but rather under the emperors in Constantinople.

Section Resources

Reproducible Masters

- Reproducible Lesson Plan
- Daily Lecture and Discussion Notes
- Note-taking Guide
- Guided Reading Activity
- Reading Essentials and Study Guide
- Section Quiz

Transparencies

- Daily Focus Skills Transparency

Multimedia

- Vocabulary PuzzleMaker CD-ROM
- Interactive Tutor Self-Assessment CD-ROM
- Presentation Plus! CD-ROM
- ExamView® Pro Testmaker CD-ROM

1 Focus

Section Objectives

1. Explain the importance of Christianity as a political influence in Medieval Europe.
2. Describe the medieval social and political systems.

BELLRINGER Skillbuilder Activity

Project transparency and have students answer the question.

Daily Focus Skills Transparency

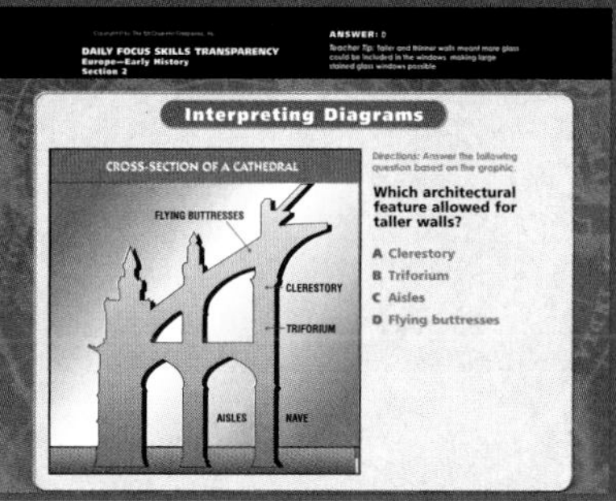

Reading Preview

Activating Prior Knowledge Have students brainstorm a list of words they think of when they hear the term *medieval.* As students read the section, have them look for those words, ideas, or concepts.

Preteaching Vocabulary Ask students to write definitions of *vassal* and *serf.* As they study the section, have students change the definition as they learn about the terms.

Chapter 10

Section 2, pages 299–302

2 TEACH

Analyzing Information Ask students to find a picture of a castle or cathedral from medieval Europe. Have them write a paragraph telling about the building and attach it to the picture. The pictures and reports can then be used to create a collage on a bulletin board.

Daily Lecture and Discussion Notes

EUROPE—EARLY HISTORY

Daily Lecture and Discussion Notes

Medieval Europe

In the Middle Ages, Christians made pilgrimages to Palestine to visit the places associated with Jesus Christ. To journey to these sites, European pilgrims might have to travel for years and put up with many hardships and frequent danger.

I. The Rise of Christianity

A. The 1,000-year period between Classical and modern times is called the medieval era, from a Latin word for "Middle Ages."

B. It was during the Middle Ages that Christianity in the form of the Roman Catholic Church became a political power in western Europe. By the A.D. 500s, ... the leaders of the Church.

Objectives and answers to the Student Web Activity can be found in the Web Activity Lesson Plan at twip.glencoe.com

✓ Reading Check Answer

They were sent to every part of Europe, spreading their religious views.

✓ Reading Check Answer

He was protector of the Christian Church of the West and head of the Holy Roman Empire.

Web Activity Visit ***The World and Its People*** Web site at twip.glencoe.com and click on **Chapter 10—Student Web Activities** to learn more about the Crusades.

Manor Economy

A medieval manor had a traditional economy in which jobs and skills were handed down generation after generation. For example, a tenant farmer's son became a farmer. The children of serfs had no choice but to learn the skills of their parents. Serfs were not always farmers, however. Some were millers who made flour out of grain, or coopers who made barrels and buckets. Some were blacksmiths and made tools, weapons, or horseshoes out of iron and other metals. Young women were usually married by age 14 and worked at home and in the fields.

Spreading the Faith By A.D. 500, the first Christian Bible was completed. The early popes sent **missionaries,** or those who spread their religious views, to every part of Europe. Many were monks and nuns. Monks were men who devoted their lives to prayer, study, and good works. They lived in monasteries. Women who chose a similar life were called nuns and lived in convents. Missionaries helped the poor and needy, and they were teachers as well. Through its schools, the Christian Church greatly advanced learning in Europe. In the 1100s, the Church also founded the first universities at Bologna in Italy and Oxford in England.

Crusades Beginning in the A.D. 1000s, the Church sponsored a series of holy wars called Crusades. The Church sent armies to capture Jerusalem in Palestine from the Islamic caliphs, or rulers. The Crusades led to centuries of distrust between Christians and Muslims. They also increased Christian mistreatment of the Jews in Europe. Yet the Crusades made Europeans aware of the rich cultures of the Byzantines and Muslims. Europeans began to demand more spices and woven cloth that the crusading armies brought home from the east. To meet these demands, European merchants opened up new trade routes. As trade grew, so did the towns of western Europe.

✓ Reading Check **How did missionaries help spread Christianity?**

The Holy Roman Empire

The Germans combined their **common law,** the unwritten laws that come from local customs, with Roman law and founded kingdoms all over Europe—from Spain to England to Germany and Italy. Many of these kingdoms soon became Christian. The early kings, like the German tribal chiefs before them, were elected by all nobles and knights. Over time, however, the kings became more independent and powerful. The crown was passed down to the next generation, usually the king's first-born son.

Charlemagne One of the most important German kingdoms was that of the Franks. By the A.D. 700s, the Franks controlled much of what would become France and Germany. In fact, the name "France" comes from the word *Franks.* In 771 Charlemagne was elected king of the Franks. Through war he added more of Germany and parts of Spain and Italy, including Rome, to the kingdom of the Franks.

On Christmas Day in the year 800, Charlemagne knelt before the pope in the Church of St. Peter in Rome. He was proclaimed the protector of the Christian Church in the West. He was also crowned the head of the Roman Empire in the West. That empire came to be known as the **Holy Roman Empire.**

After Charlemagne's death in 814, his empire was inherited by his son and grandsons and broken up into several kingdoms. These kingdoms were the foundations for modern Germany, Italy, France, and Spain. At about the same time, several Germanic groups like the Angles, Saxons, Jutes, and Danes helped found the first English kingdom. England gets its name from "Angle land."

✓ Reading Check **What was Charlemagne's role in the spread of Christianity?**

Reading Strategy — Reading the Text

Drawing Conclusions There was little privacy in the manor house. The cramped living quarters and the lack of heating did much to foster togetherness. It was not uncommon for nobles to have huge beds (12 feet wide) that allowed a noble, his wife, their children, some servants, and key members of the lord's "fellowship" (his knights) to sleep together in the dead of winter. Fortunately, medieval people liked being clean. During the warm weather, on one of the many religious holidays, you would easily find freshly bathed, cleanly dressed peasants. **Ask: How do you think medieval people heated their homes? Why might it be difficult for them to take baths? What would they do to stay clean in cold weather? L1**

*Use the **Reading Skills Handbook** for more reading strategies.*

Medieval Society

During the Middle Ages, a new political and social system known as **feudalism** emerged. Under this system, kings gave land to their loyal nobles or lords. In exchange for the land or feudal estate, the nobles provided military service and knights for the king's army. These nobles who swore loyalty to the king were known as **vassals.** The king's vassals, great lords themselves, might also have had their own vassals who would owe them military service in return for a grant of land.

The Manor The feudal estate was called the **manor.** At its heart was usually a manor house or a castle. Most of the population of the manor was made up of common people who farmed and performed other tasks. There were two types of farmers. Those who paid rent for their land and then worked the land as they pleased were known as tenants. The other much larger group was the **serfs.**

Serfs were not as free as tenant farmers and were usually poorer. In return for the use of land, seed, tools, and protection, serfs had to work as ordered by the lords of the manors, whether in the fields or elsewhere. Often the serfs worked on roads, walls, fortifications, and other hard jobs. In times of trouble, male serfs also became foot soldiers who served under the direction of the cavalry of knights.

These were often quite violent times, and the common people rarely strayed too far from the safety of the manor. On occasion, the manors might be visited by wanderers with special skills. For example, tinkers made a living by moving from estate to estate, patching pots or fixing other metal objects. Minstrels and other troubadours entertained by playing music, juggling, or acting as comedians or fools.

Reading Check What did a vassal receive for his service to a king or lord?

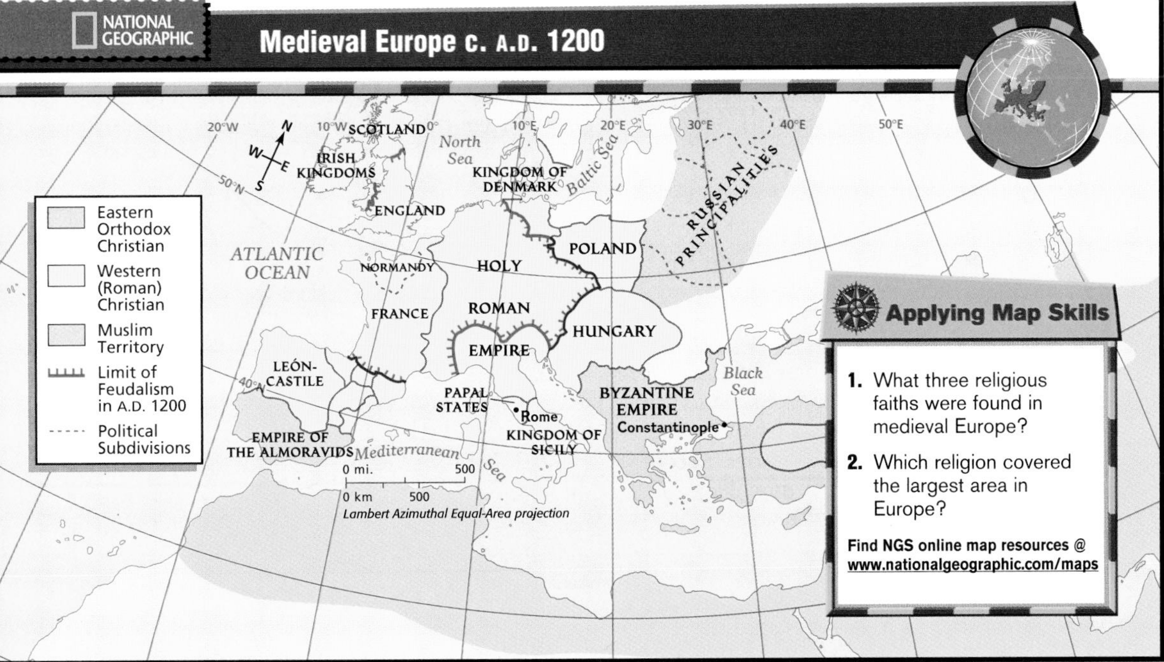

Applying Map Skills

1. What three religious faiths were found in medieval Europe?
2. Which religion covered the largest area in Europe?

Find NGS online map resources @ www.nationalgeographic.com/maps

Differentiated Instruction

Meeting Special Needs: Less-proficient Readers Have students create a concept web that illustrates the feudal system. In the center of the web, students may write the words *feudal system.* For the outer ovals, they may write *manor, serfs, vassals,* and so on. Students should write descriptions of each of these terms that will help them organize their thoughts concerning medieval society's economic system. L1

Refer to *Inclusion for the Middle School Social Studies Classroom Strategies and Activities* in the TCR.

L1/ELL

Guided Reading Activity

Name ____ Date ____ Class ____
EUROPE—EARLY HISTORY
Guided Reading Activity 2
Medieval Europe

DIRECTIONS: Answering Questions Reading the section and answering the questions below will help you learn more about Medieval Europe. Use your textbook to write answers to the questions.

1. What were the Middle Ages?
2. Who were the leaders in the Roman Catholic Church?
3. What was Eastern Orthodoxy, and who were its leaders?

Reading Check Answer

land

Applying Map Skills

Answers

1. Eastern Orthodox Christianity, Western (Roman) Christianity, and Islam
2. Western Christianity

Skills Practice

Was the Byzantine Empire within the limits of feudalism? *(no)*

3 ASSESS

Assign Section 2 Assessment as homework or an in-class activity.

Have students use the Interactive Tutor Self-Assessment CD-ROM to review Section 2.

Chapter 10

Section 2, pages 299–302

L2

Section Quiz

Name ______________ Date ______________ Class ______________

EUROPE—EARLY HISTORY

Score

Section 2 Quiz

Medieval Europe

DIRECTIONS: Matching Match each item in Column A with the items in Column B. Write the correct letters in the blanks. *(10 points each)*

COLUMN A	COLUMN B
A. pope	____ 1. those who spread their religious views
B. vassals	____ 2. feudal estates
C. missionaries	____ 3. poor people who were not free but had to do whatever work their feudal lord required
D. serfs	____ 4. leader of the Catholic Church
E. manors	____ 5. nobles who swore loyalty to the king

Reading Check Answer

for protection against powerful nobles

L1/ELL

Reading Essentials and Study Guide

Name ______________ Date ______________ Class ______________

EUROPE—EARLY HISTORY

Reading Essentials and Study Guide 2

Medieval Europe

Key Terms

pope leader of the Catholic Church
missionary person who spreads his or her religious views
common law unwritten laws that come from local customs
feudalism medieval political and social system based on an exchange of land for military service
vassal person who swore loyalty to a higher lord in exchange for a grant of land
manor feudal estate
serf a type of farmer who was not as free as a tenant farmer and was usually

CLOSE

Have students create a display of a manor and its lands.

▲ Stained glass showing a craftsman at work

The Growth of Cities

Towns in the Middle Ages were fairly independent and wanted to be free of the feudal lords' control. Towns served as centers of trade and manufacturing. Their importance increased during the Crusades because the Christian armies needed supplies. By the twelfth century, towns hosted great trade fairs, where merchants from far and wide came together to do business.

Manufacturing came under the control of workers' organizations known as **guilds.** Different guilds controlled industries such as brewing, cloth making, boat building, and many others. Young workers, called apprentices, spent years learning a trade so that they could join a guild. With experience, the apprentices became journeymen and eventually master craftsmen.

Over time, some towns grew into cities and became political and religious centers as well. The new, more powerful kings and churchmen understood the importance of cities. They built great cathedrals and granted the residents privileges and freedoms in written documents called **charters.** By doing this, the kings won the support of the townspeople. This support was useful in times of war and for protection against powerful nobles. The kings also raised money by collecting taxes from the towns in return for granting charters. Now, with an economy based on money, kings could pay their soldiers instead of giving them feudal estates. Serfs could buy their freedom. Thus, feudalism and the power of the nobles began to decline.

✓Reading Check **Why did kings want the support of large cities?**

Assessment

Defining Terms

1. **Define** pope, missionary, common law, feudalism, vassal, manor, serf, guild, charter.

Recalling Facts

2. **History** When was the first Christian Bible completed?
3. **History** What kind of work were most people involved in during the Middle Ages?

Critical Thinking

4. **Evaluating Information** Common laws were unwritten laws that came from local customs. What are the possible difficulties that can arise from having such unwritten laws?
5. **Understanding Cause and Effect** How did the Crusades affect the growth of towns in western Europe?

Graphic Organizer

6. **Organizing Information** Create a pyramid like the one below. On the lines, list serfs, vassals, and tenants in the order they would be ranked under a king in the feudal system.

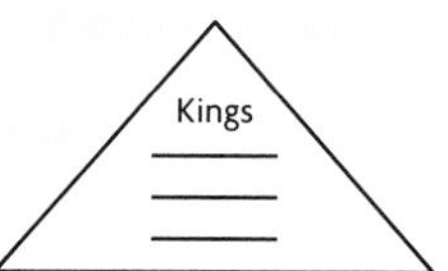

Applying Social Studies Skills

7. **Summarizing Information** In a few sentences, describe life on the manor for a common person. Use as many adjectives as possible.

302

Section 2 Assessment

1. The terms are defined in the Glossary.
2. by A.D. 500
3. farming
4. *Possible answers:* laws are open to interpretation and may not be uniformly applied; different customs may conflict; as conditions change, common law may no longer apply.
5. Christian armies needed supplies that were made and traded in towns.
6. kings, vassals, tenants, serfs
7. This exercise helps students visualize and articulate conditions during medieval times. All reasonable attempts at realistic descriptions should be accepted.

Guide to Reading

Main Idea

The study of science, art, and education was renewed in the period following the Middle Ages.

Key Terms

- indulgences
- revolution
- divine right of kings

Reading Strategy

Create a time line like the one below. As you read the section, add the following events to the line in the correct order.

Protestant Reformation
Age of Exploration
American Revolution
Renaissance
French Revolution

Section 3

From Renaissance to Revolution

From the 1300s to the 1600s, important cultural achievements in the arts and learning spread throughout Europe. Merchant families used their wealth to help artists and scholars explore new ways of thinking. Michelangelo's statue of David, shown here, is one of the many masterpieces from this period we call the Renaissance.

The growth of cities and trade and the gradual breakup of feudalism led to the end of the Middle Ages. Around 1350 interest in education, art, and science peaked in several parts of Europe, especially in the cities and towns. The result was the Renaissance—a French word meaning "rebirth."

The Renaissance

To many people, the Renaissance was the beginning of a new golden age like that of ancient Greece and Rome. The Renaissance began in the cities of northern Italy and spread to other cities of Europe.

Humanism During the Renaissance, scholars became less concerned about the mysteries of heaven and more interested in the world and humans around them. Because of this, Renaissance scholars

303

Chapter 10

Section 3, pages 303–307

1 Focus

Section Objectives

1. Explain advances in arts, science, and nationhood achieved during the Renaissance.
2. Identify the causes of the Reformation.
3. Compare the causes and results of revolutions in the Americas and Europe.

BELLRINGER Skillbuilder Activity

Project transparency and have students answer the question.

Daily Focus Skills Transparency

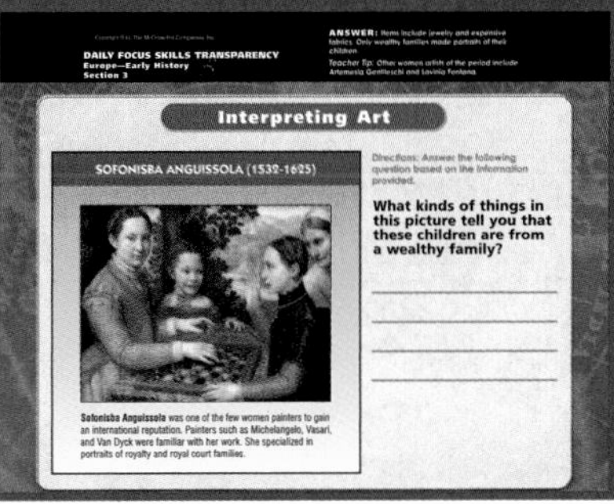

Reading Preview

■ **Activating Prior Knowledge** Ask students to identify any revolutions they know of. Ask who fights in a revolution and why.

■ **Preteaching Vocabulary** Have students explain the differences between and similarities of the words *reformation* and *revolution.*

Section Resources

Reproducible Masters

- Reproducible Lesson Plan
- Daily Lecture and Discussion Notes
- Note-taking Guide
- Guided Reading Activity
- Reading Essentials and Study Guide
- Section Quiz

Transparencies

- Daily Focus Skills Transparency

Multimedia

- Vocabulary PuzzleMaker CD-ROM
- Interactive Tutor Self-Assessment CD-ROM
- Presentation Plus! CD-ROM
- ExamView® Pro Testmaker CD-ROM
- MindJogger Videoquiz

2 TEACH

Reading Strategy

Making Inferences On a world map, locate Europe and India. Ask students why the Portuguese explorers may have tried to reach India by sailing around Africa. *(They could stay near land.)* Why didn't explorers want to try to reach India by sailing west across the ocean? *(They would have to navigate unknown oceans without landmarks.)* **L2**

Daily Lecture and Discussion Notes

EUROPE—EARLY HISTORY

Daily Lecture and Discussion Notes

From Renaissance to Revolution

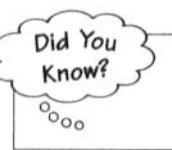

Many of the crops grown in the world today were originally from the Americas and introduced to Europe during the Age of Exploration. These crops include corn, potatoes, tomatoes, and chocolate.

I. The Renaissance

A. The growth of cities and trade and the gradual breakup of feudalism led to the end of the Middle Ages.

B. The Renaissance—sparked by an interest in education, art, and science—began around 1350 in cities of northern Italy and spread to other cities of Europe.

...lars were called humanists because they were interested more ... around them than in religious ideas.

Reading Check Answer

It made books more numerous and less expensive.

L1/ELL

Guided Reading Activity

Name ______ Date ______ Class ______

EUROPE—EARLY HISTORY

Guided Reading Activity 3

From Renaissance to Revolution

DIRECTIONS: Outlining Reading the section and completing the outline below will help you learn more about the time following the Middle Ages. Refer to your textbook to fill in the blanks.

I. The ______, a French word meaning "rebirth," emerged around 1350.

A. Italian artists such as ______ ______ and ______ expressed the spirit of the Renaissance.

B. Writers during this time were also inspired by the ideas of the Renaissance.

1. ______ ______ wrote the *Canterbury Tales*.

2. ______ ______ wrote plays like *Romeo and Juliet*.

3. ______ ______ wrote *Don Quixote*.

______ was the movement to change the Catholic Church.

were called humanists. Humanist ideas—the right of people to learn and think for themselves—broke with medieval thinking and helped bring about the rise of the modern world.

Renaissance Artists Like the ancient Greeks and Romans, Renaissance artists appreciated the beauty in human beings and nature. They developed new ways to make their works true to life and full of color and action. They painted and sculpted not only religious images but also people and creatures from myths. Above all, they were more interested in the human qualities than the religious qualities of their subjects. Two of the many outstanding Renaissance artists were Leonardo da Vinci and Michelangelo Buonarotti. (See page 308 to learn more about the achievements of Leonardo da Vinci.)

The painter and sculptor Michelangelo expressed human emotions such as anger, sorrow, and strength in his paintings and sculptures. His most famous work is the mural on the ceiling of the Sistine Chapel in the Vatican Palace in Rome. It is made up of 145 separate paintings and took nearly five years to complete.

▲ The Sistine Chapel, painted by Michelangelo

Renaissance Writers Writers were also inspired by the ideas of the Renaissance. Until this time, most literature was written in Medieval Latin. To reach a wider audience, writers began to use the language they spoke every day instead of Latin or French, the languages of the educated. Geoffrey Chaucer wrote *The Canterbury Tales* and William Shakespeare wrote plays such as *Hamlet* and *Romeo and Juliet* in English. Miguel de Cervantes wrote his novel *Don Quixote* in Spanish.

These works were reproduced in many copies for the first time by the printing press, which was invented by Johannes Gutenberg around 1450. Although the Chinese had developed a printing process, Gutenberg developed the idea of movable type. The printing press made books more numerous and less expensive, thereby encouraging more people to learn to read and write.

Rise of Nations During the Renaissance, western European rulers became more powerful. They used their power to unite their peoples, creating nations based on a common language and culture. England was strengthened by the first Tudor king, Henry VII, and his famous granddaughter Elizabeth I. King Ferdinand and Queen Isabella united Spain by driving out the last of the Muslims and Jews. By the 1450s, the kings of France finally liberated their country from the English.

Reading Check How did the printing press make it easier for people to learn to read and write?

The Protestant Reformation

Many of the new ideas of the Renaissance led to questions about religion. Some people believed that Church leaders were more interested in wealth than religion. Others disagreed with corrupt practices of the Church. One of these practices was the selling of documents called

Reading Strategy — Reading the Text

Using Word Parts A *root* is the part of the word that contains its basic meaning. Unlike a base word, a root is not a word by itself. Many roots come from Greek or Latin. For example, *bio* means "life" (biology, biography); *tele* means "distant" (television, telescope); *dent* means "tooth" (dentist, trident). Have students find root words in their study of the section and find their meanings using a dictionary. **L1**

*Use the **Reading Skills Handbook** for more reading strategies.*

indulgences, which freed their owners of punishment for sins they had committed. The Christians who "protested" corrupt Church practices and wanted to return to basic Christian teachings came to be called Protestants. The movement to reform, or change, the Catholic Church was called the Protestant Reformation.

One of the first Protestant leaders to challenge the Catholic Church was Martin Luther, a German monk and scholar. In 1520 the pope banished Luther from the Catholic Church for his criticism. Luther organized his own new Christian church, which taught in German, not Latin, from a Bible that Luther himself had translated into German. This split between the Catholics and Protestants led to many long years of religious wars in Europe.

Another early Protestant leader was John Calvin. His followers in France were called Huguenots, and in England they were called Puritans. Many came to the Protestant cause seeking not only greater religious freedom, but also political, economic, and intellectual freedom. The Puritans eventually sought freedom in the Americas to practice their own religion.

✓Reading Check **What was the Protestant Reformation?**

The Age of Exploration

By the mid-1400s, Europe began to reach out beyond its boundaries in a great age of discovery and exploration. The Portuguese began to sail southward in the Atlantic, down the West African coast. They were seeking a route to the profitable spice trade in Asia. In 1488 Bartholomeu Dias reached the Cape of Good Hope at the southern tip of Africa. Ten years later, Vasco da Gama sailed around it to India.

While the Portuguese were searching for a way around Africa, King Ferdinand and Queen Isabella of Spain were trying to find another way to Asia. In 1492 they sent an Italian navigator, Christopher Columbus, with three small ships—the *Niña,* the *Pinta,* and the *Santa María*—westward across the Atlantic. Although he never realized it, Columbus had landed in a part of the world unknown to Europeans at that time. He called its people "Indians" because he believed he was in the East Indies in Asia.

▲ **Luther criticized Catholic Church officials for selling indulgences.**

The Dutch, English, and French soon joined the Spanish and Portuguese in exploring and settling and trading with the Americas, Asia, and Africa. Eventually—in addition to trade goods—people, diseases, and ideas were distributed around the world in a process called the Columbian Exchange. You read about this on page 228. Europeans unknowingly brought to the Americas diseases such as measles and smallpox, which infected and killed millions of Native Americans. These natives had been used as laborers on plantations and in mines. In their place, traders eventually transported more than 20 million Africans to the Americas as enslaved persons, until the slave trade was outlawed in the early 1800s.

✓Reading Check **Which European nation first explored the coast of Africa?**

✓ Reading Check Answer

the movement to reform, or change, the Catholic Church

Interdisciplinary Connections

Religion Martin Luther dealt the symbolic blow that began the Reformation when he nailed his Ninety-Five Theses to the door of the church in Wittenberg. That document contained an attack on papal abuses and the sale of indulgences by Church officials. Luther defended his position before the Emperor at the Diet of Worms. When Luther was asked to recant his views, it was said that he replied, "Here I stand. I cannot do otherwise."

✓ Reading Check Answer

Portugal

3 Assess

Assign Section 3 Assessment as homework or an in-class activity.

Have students use the Interactive Tutor Self-Assessment CD-ROM to review Section 3.

Differentiated Instruction

Meeting Special Needs: Visual/ Spatial To reinforce the verbal descriptions in this chapter, have students collect pictures and photographs that illustrate the cultures and events described. They can clip pictures from travel brochures or magazines, can make copies from books, or can download images from the Internet. Organize the students into groups and give each group a selection of pictures. Have the groups discuss each picture and determine what it depicts and what time period it illustrates. **L1**

Refer to *Inclusion for the Middle School Social Studies Classroom Strategies and Activities* in the TCR.

Literature

The Scarlet Pimpernel was written in 1905, more than 100 years after the events it describes. It tells of a brave band of Englishmen who risk their lives to rescue the intended victims of the guillotine. Their leader is an enigmatic hero known only by his calling card: the red, star-shaped wildflower known as the Scarlet Pimpernel.

Answer These questions can be used to start a class discussion on the roles and motives of people during revolutions. Not everyone is involved in the conflict, and not everyone involved is motivated by revolutionary zeal.

L2

Section Quiz

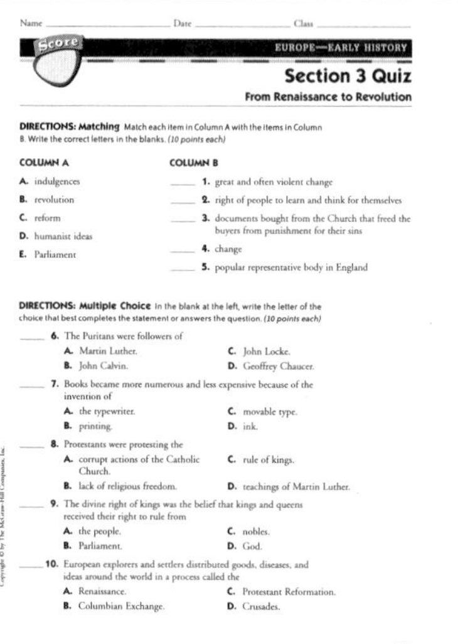

Name ____________ Date ____________ Class ____________

Score

EUROPE—EARLY HISTORY

Section 3 Quiz

From Renaissance to Revolution

DIRECTIONS: Matching Match each item in Column A with the items in Column B. Write the correct letters in the blanks. *(10 points each)*

COLUMN A	COLUMN B
A. indulgences	____ **1.** great and often violent change
B. revolution	____ **2.** right of people to learn and think for themselves
C. reform	____ **3.** documents bought from the Church that freed the buyers from punishment for their sins
D. humanist ideas	____ **4.** change
E. Parliament	____ **5.** popular representative body in England

DIRECTIONS: Multiple Choice In the blank at the left, write the letter of the choice that best completes the statement or answers the question. *(10 points each)*

____ **6.** The Puritans were followers of
A. Martin Luther. **C.** John Locke.
B. John Calvin. **D.** Geoffrey Chaucer.

____ **7.** Books became more numerous and less expensive because of the invention of
A. the typewriter. **C.** movable type.
B. printing. **D.** ink.

____ **8.** Protestants were protesting the
A. corrupt actions of the Catholic Church. **C.** rule of kings.
B. lack of religious freedom. **D.** teachings of Martin Luther.

____ **9.** The divine right of kings was the belief that kings and queens received their right to rule from
A. the people. **C.** nobles.
B. Parliament. **D.** God.

____ **10.** European explorers and settlers distributed goods, diseases, and ideas around the world in a process called the
A. Renaissance. **C.** Protestant Reformation.
B. Columbian Exchange. **D.** Crusades.

161

The Age of Revolution

A revolution is a great and often violent change. In the Americas, the colonies won freedom from the European countries that ruled them. In Europe, people fought for freedom from their kings, queens, and nobles.

The Rule of the People The eighteenth century ended with great changes to Europe and many of its American colonies. The belief in the divine right of kings—that European kings and queens ruled by the will of God—was fading. In learning about the examples from ancient Greece and Rome, people came to feel that they should play a greater, more direct role in government. Philosophers such as John Locke and Jean Jacques Rousseau looked at the nature of man and government. They believed that government should serve and protect citizens and their freedom. However, this also meant that citizens had to take more responsibility for themselves and their own actions.

British Democracy Revolutionary changes came more peacefully in some countries than in others. Over many centuries, Great Britain had slowly developed a system of shared power and responsibility. The king ruled with the Parliament, a popular representative body that gradually took power in the name of the people. Eventually, British

Literature

THE SCARLET PIMPERNEL

by Baroness Orczy

During and after the French Revolution, many nobles were executed by the lower classes that had rebelled against them. The number of these executions shocked the people of Europe. *The Scarlet Pimpernel* is a novel about an English nobleman who helps aristocrats escape from France.

"It had all occurred in such a miraculous way. She and her husband had understood that they had been placed on the list of 'suspected persons,' which meant that their trial and death was but a matter of days—of hours, perhaps. Then came the hope of salvation: the mysterious [letter], signed with the scarlet device; . . . the flight with her two children; the covered cart; . . . Every moment under that cart she expected recognition, arrest. [These young Englishmen] . . . had risked their lives to save them all, as they had already saved scores of other innocent people. And all only for sport? Impossible!"

Analyzing Literature

1. Do you think that the Scarlet Pimpernel's actions were really just for sport? Why or why not?
2. Do you think the Englishmen were right to try to save the French nobility? Explain.

Content Background

Christopher Columbus Few people thought the world was flat when Columbus set out on his voyage for India. What was in doubt was the exact circumference of the earth and, therefore, the westward distance from Europe to India. Columbus relied on thousand-year-old maps made by Ptolemy that both underestimated the earth's diameter and overestimated the eastward extent of Asia. This had the effect of making the westward distance from Europe to Asia seem much smaller than it actually is and made Columbus believe, erroneously, that India could be reached by sailing west.

kings and queens were forced to accept a constitution that shared power but gave most of it to the Parliament.

Democracy in the Americas In the 1770s, the American colonies, beginning with the thirteen British colonies in North America, revolted against British control. The new United States, with its Declaration of Independence, Constitution, and representative Congress, became a model for many other revolutions. By the 1830s, most of the Spanish, Portuguese, and British colonies in the Americas south of Canada had also gained their independence.

The French Revolution In the 1780s, revolution erupted in Europe as well, starting with France. The French Revolution began in 1789 and went through several stages. When King Louis XVI and Queen Marie Antoinette opposed the revolution and tried to aid the nobility, they were executed. By 1799, Napoleon Bonaparte, a military hero of the French Revolution, became the dictator of France. He declared himself emperor of a new French Empire in 1804. Eventually, people almost everywhere in Europe reacted against Napoleon and went to war against France. Napoleon was finally defeated in 1815.

The revolution in France stimulated Latin Americans and other European peoples to demand more personal and political control over their lives. Countries such as Greece, Belgium, Italy, and Germany also experienced revolutions.

✓Reading Check How was the growth of democracy in Great Britain different from that in France?

Assessment

Defining Terms

1. **Define** indulgences, revolution, divine right of kings.

Recalling Facts

2. **History** What was the movement to reform the Catholic Church called?
3. **People** Why were Renaissance scholars known as humanists?

Critical Thinking

4. **Examining Results** Describe the effects of the Columbian Exchange.
5. **Making Connections** How might a revolution in one country encourage political changes around the world?

Graphic Organizer

6. **Identifying People** Create a table like the one below. In the left column, list ten people from this section. Then explain why they are considered significant.

Person	Significance

Applying Social Studies Skills

7. **Drawing Conclusions** Why do you suppose the period known as the Renaissance was considered a rebirth?

Section 3 Assessment

1. The terms are defined in the Glossary.
2. the Reformation
3. They were concerned less with the mysteries of heaven and more with the world and humans.
4. The movement of goods and ideas also brought diseases, which killed Native Americans. To replace their labor, Africans were brought to America as enslaved persons.
5. The success of a revolution in one country may encourage revolutionary changes elsewhere.
6. Students may describe the significance of people such as Michelangelo, Johannes Gutenberg, Martin Luther, Christopher Columbus, and Napoleon Bonaparte.
7. Interest in arts, science, and culture were "reborn" after being in decline during the Middle Ages.

Cultural Kaleidoscope

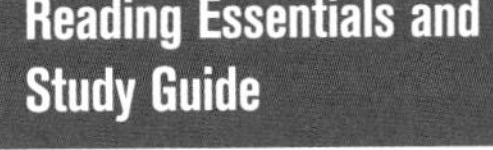

Great Britain does not celebrate an Independence Day like the Fourth of July. However, Guy Fawkes Day, November 5, is celebrated in England with fireworks and bonfires. It marks the anniversary of an unsuccessful plot to blow up the British parliament in 1605.

L1/ELL

Reading Essentials and Study Guide

Name ____ Date ____ Class ____

EUROPE—EARLY HISTORY

Reading Essentials and Study Guide 3

From Renaissance to Revolution

Key Terms

indulgences documents that people bought from the Catholic Church to become free from punishment for their sins

revolution a great and often violent change

divine right of kings the belief that European kings and queens ruled by the will of God

Drawing From Experience

The king and queen of France ... were executed.

Reading Check Answer

In Great Britain the change occurred more peacefully and over a long period of time.

4 CLOSE

Have students create a three-column chart with the headings "Renaissance," "Reform," and "Revolution." Have them fill in the chart with important events and people from this section.

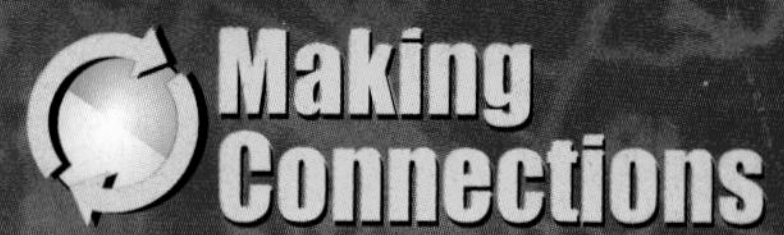

Teach

Ask students if they have ever heard the phrase "Renaissance person." Explain that the words refer to someone who has talents and interests in many different areas. **Ask:** **Can you think of anyone to whom this term could be applied? Why? L1**

More About Leonardo

One of Leonardo's works was completed 500 years late. In 1482 Leonardo designed an equestrian statue for his patron, the duke of Milan. Soon after, the French invaded the city, and Leonardo had to abandon the work. In the 1970s, an American art collector decided to create the statue as a tribute to him. The final piece, a bronze horse that stands 24 feet (7 m) high and was based on Leonardo's designs, was completed in September 1999 in Milan.

Interdisciplinary Connections

Art One of the hallmarks of Renaissance painting is the use of linear perspective to create the illusion of three dimensions. Architect Filippo Brunelleschi developed the first principles of perspective in the early 1400s. Show some examples of medieval and Renaissance art so that students can see the contrast.

Making Connections

ART | SCIENCE | CULTURE | TECHNOLOGY

Leonardo da Vinci

The Italian Leonardo da Vinci is considered to be one of the greatest artists of the Renaissance. He painted the *Mona Lisa* and the *Last Supper*, two of the world's best-known paintings. He was also a talented architect, engineer, and inventor.

The Artist

Leonardo da Vinci was born in 1452 in a small town near Florence, Italy. As the son of a wealthy man, he received the best education that Florence could offer. Leonardo became known for his ability to create sculptures and paintings that looked almost lifelike. Much of his success in this area came from his keen interest in nature. He also studied human anatomy and used this knowledge to make his figures realistic.

The Inventor

As a child, Leonardo was fascinated with machines and began to draw his own inventions. The first successful parachute jump was made from the top of a French tower in 1783—but Leonardo had sketched a parachute in 1485. He designed flying machines, armored tanks, and aircraft landing gear. He even drew a diver's suit that used tubes and air chambers to allow a swimmer to remain underwater for long periods of time.

Leonardo's Notebooks

Much of what we know about Leonardo comes from the thousands of pages of notes and sketches he kept in his notebooks. He used mirror, or reverse, writing, starting at the right side of the page and moving across to the left. No one is sure why Leonardo wrote this way. Some think he was trying to keep people from reading and stealing his ideas. He may also have been trying to hide his thoughts from the Roman Catholic Church, whose teachings sometimes conflicted with his ideas. From a practical standpoint, writing in reverse probably helped him avoid smearing wet ink, since he was left-handed.

▲ Leonardo da Vinci, self-portrait

▲ The *Mona Lisa*

Making the Connection

1. What are two of Leonardo's best-known works?
2. Why might Leonardo have written his notebooks in mirror writing?
3. **Understanding Cause and Effect** In what way did Leonardo's interest in the world around him influence his work?

Making the Connection

1. the *Mona Lisa* and the *Last Supper*
2. perhaps to keep others from stealing his ideas, to hide them from the Church, or to keep the pages neat and unsoiled by smeared ink
3. He used knowledge gained from his study of nature to make his paintings more realistic.

Reading Review

Section 1 Classical Greece and Rome

Terms to Know
- Classical
- polis
- democracy
- republic
- consul
- emperor

Main Idea

Ancient Greece and Rome made important contributions to Western culture and civilization.

✓ Government The world's first democratic constitution was written in Athens.

✓ History Alexander the Great conquered all of Greece and spread Greek culture everywhere he invaded.

✓ History Rome grew from a republic on the Italian Peninsula to an empire that included western Europe, northern Africa, and southwest Asia.

✓ Religion Christianity spread throughout the Roman world.

✓ History The Roman Empire was invaded by Germanic peoples and declined.

Section 2 Medieval Europe

Terms to Know
- pope
- missionary
- common law
- feudalism
- vassal
- manor
- serf
- guild
- charter

Main Idea

The Middle Ages saw the spread of Christianity, the growth of cities, and the growing powers of kings.

✓ Religion The Roman Catholic Church became a political power in western Europe.

✓ History The first Christian Bible was completed by A.D. 500.

✓ History Charlemagne was crowned head of the Roman Empire and proclaimed Protector of the Christian Church in the West.

✓ Government Feudalism, the medieval political and social system, was an exchange of land from the king to nobles who provided military service.

Section 3 From Renaissance to Revolution

Terms to Know
- indulgences
- revolution
- divine right of kings

Main Idea

The study of science, art, and education was renewed in the period following the Middle Ages.

✓ Culture Important cultural achievements in the arts and learning spread throughout Europe in the period known as the Renaissance.

✓ History Johannes Gutenberg invented the printing press.

✓ Government Countries formed into nations based on a common language and culture.

✓ Religion The Protestant faith emerged in protest to the corrupt practices of the Roman Catholic Church.

✓ History Christopher Columbus sailed across the Atlantic.

✓ Government Revolution erupted in the Americas and Europe.

Reading Review

Use the Chapter 10 Reading Review to preview, review, condense, or reteach the chapter.

Preview/Review

Use the Terms to Know lists to help students review and study.

Activity Have students identify the time period for which each term is relevant. Read the terms aloud, one at a time, and ask for volunteers to categorize each. Note that some terms may apply to more than one country.

Vocabulary PuzzleMaker CD-ROM reinforces the vocabulary terms used in Chapter 10.

The Interactive Tutor Self-Assessment CD-ROM allows students to review Chapter 10 content.

Condense

Have students read the Chapter 10 summary statements.

Guided Reading Activities

Audio Program

Reteach

Reteaching Activity

Reading Essentials and Study Guide

Reading Strategy Read to Write

Writing a Travel Brochure Tell students to imagine they work for the "U-R-There" time-travel agency. Have them create a four-page travel brochure that highlights the attractions for one of the periods in this chapter. Explain that the travel brochure should include both physical and cultural features that visitors would want to see. Advise students that an effective brochure includes appealing visuals as well as brief, engaging text. L1

EE2 Places and Regions: Standard 6

Chapter 10 Assessment and Activities

Using Key Terms

Match the terms in Part A with their definitions in Part B.

A.

1. emperor
2. common law
3. feudalism
4. democracy
5. indulgences
6. serf
7. polis
8. charter
9. missionary
10. guild

B.

a. unwritten laws from customs
b. poor people who were controlled by the lords of the manor
c. freed owners from punishment for sins
d. medieval political and social system
e. absolute ruler
f. direct rule of the people
g. person who spreads his or her religious views
h. documents giving townspeople privileges and freedoms
i. workers' organization
j. city-state

Reviewing the Main Ideas

Section 1 Classical Greece and Rome

11. **Government** Where was the first democratic constitution written?
12. **History** Who conquered all of Greece?
13. **Religion** Which religion spread all over the Roman world?
14. **History** Who invaded the Roman Empire?

Section 2 Medieval Europe

15. **Religion** Which religious group became a political power in western Europe?
16. **Economics** Explain the difference between vassals and serfs.
17. **Government** Name the political and social system in medieval Europe.

Section 3 From Renaissance to Revolution

18. **History** What did Johannes Gutenberg invent?
19. **Religion** Which faith emerged out of protest to the Catholic Church?
20. **History** For what is Christopher Columbus historically known?
21. **Government** Where were revolutions taking place in the eighteenth century?

Classical Europe

Place Location Activity

On a separate sheet of paper, match the letters on the map with the numbered places listed below.

1. Alexandria
2. North Africa
3. Mediterranean Sea
4. Constantinople
5. Black Sea
6. Greece
7. Athens
8. Rome
9. Tiber River
10. Sparta

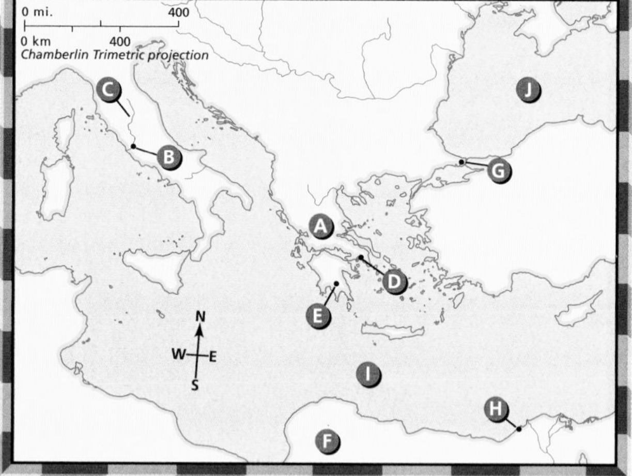

Assessment and Activities

GLENCOE TECHNOLOGY

MindJogger Videoquiz
Use MindJogger Videoquiz to review the Chapter 10 content.

Available in DVD and VHS

Using Key Terms

1. e
2. a
3. d
4. f
5. c
6. b
7. j
8. h
9. g
10. i

Reviewing the Main Ideas

11. Greece
12. Phillip II and his son, Alexander the Great
13. Christianity
14. various groups of German peoples
15. Roman Catholic Church
16. Vassals were knights or nobles who received land and swore loyalty to a lord; serfs were poor farmers who in return for use of land, seeds, tools, and protection had to work as ordered by the lords of the manor.
17. feudalism
18. a printing press with movable type
19. Protestant
20. being the first to "discover" America
21. in the Americas and in Europe

Critical Thinking

22. Answers may include the following: The beginnings of our political system can be traced to Greece; the Greeks developed the first democratic constitution; republican government and codified law were developed by the Romans; Greece and Rome developed art, philosophy, and an alphabet.
23. The power of the state and the church were combined in one person so there were no checks on abuse.

NATIONAL GEOGRAPHIC Place Location Activity

1. H
2. F
3. I
4. G
5. J
6. A
7. D
8. B
9. C
10. E

Self-Check Quiz Visit ***The World and Its People*** Web site at twip.glencoe.com and click on **Chapter 10—Self-Check Quizzes** to prepare for the Chapter Test.

Critical Thinking

22. **Making Connections** In what ways have our political and social lives today been influenced by ancient Greek and Roman customs?
23. **Drawing Conclusions** Eastern Orthodoxy was ruled by emperors rather than by popes. This made the emperors very powerful. What kinds of problems might have occurred because of this?

Comparing Regions Activity

24. **Culture** Research to find information on an American artist from the nineteenth century. Write a paragraph with information about the artist's life and contributions. Compare this information to what you learned about Renaissance artists.

Mental Mapping Activity

25. **Identifying People and Places** Create a simple outline map of Europe that includes Germany, Italy, France, Rome, and Greece. Place the letter of the individual's name next to the place from which he originated.

a. Michelangelo Buonarotti	**f.** Leonardo da Vinci
b. Alexander the Great	**g.** Christopher Columbus
c. Julius Caesar	**h.** Napoleon Bonaparte
d. Socrates	**i.** Martin Luther
e. Charlemagne	**j.** Plato

Technology Skills Activity

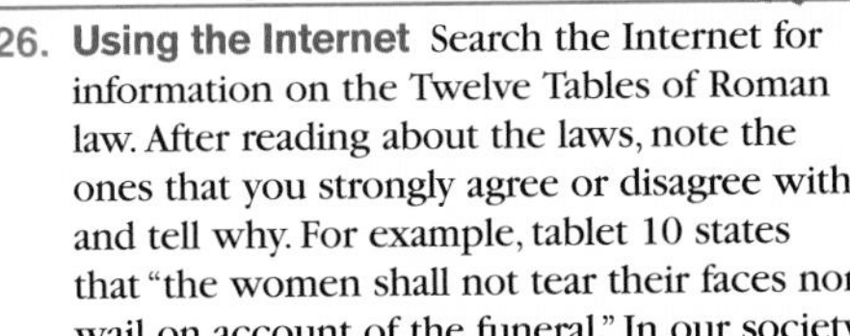

26. **Using the Internet** Search the Internet for information on the Twelve Tables of Roman law. After reading about the laws, note the ones that you strongly agree or disagree with and tell why. For example, tablet 10 states that "the women shall not tear their faces nor wail on account of the funeral." In our society, we are not punished for expressing grief.

Standardized Test Practice

Directions: Read the paragraphs below, and then answer the question that follows.

The ancient Greeks held the Olympic Games in Olympia every four years. The games were a religious festival in honor of Zeus, the Greeks' chief god. Trading and wars stopped while the games took place. The first Greek calendar began with the supposed date of the first Olympic Games in 776 B.C.

Athletes came from all over the Greek-speaking world to compete. Only male athletes, however, were allowed to take part, and women were not permitted even as spectators. Olympic events at first consisted only of a footrace. Later the broad jump, the discus throw, boxing, and wrestling were added. The Greeks crowned Olympic winners with wreaths of olive leaves and held parades in their honor.

1. From the paragraphs, which of the following statements about Greek culture is correct?

F The Greeks stressed group effort over individual achievement.
G The Greeks believed in one God.
H The Greeks were not religious.
J The Greeks encouraged individual glory.

Test-Taking Tip: Read all the choices carefully before choosing the one that correctly describes Greek culture. Eliminate answers that you know are incorrect. For example, all the Olympic events were performed by individuals, not by teams. Therefore, answer F does not describe Greek culture. The question is asking for the statement that DOES describe Greek culture.

311

Assessment and Activities

Standardized Test Practice

1. J

Tested Objectives:
Analyzing information, synthesizing information

Have students visit the Web site at twip.glencoe.com to review Chapter 10 and take the Self-Check Quiz.

Chapter Test Bonus Question

This question may be used for extra credit on the chapter test.

The revolution in this country began in 1789 and stimulated revolutionary change in Latin America and Europe.

What country is it? *(France)*

Dinah Zike's Foldables

Culminating Activity Have students describe the information they wrote in their foldables. Students should use transitional words to describe the sequence of events in Europe.

Comparing Regions Activity

24. Students should describe the contributions of an American artist from the nineteenth century and describe how these contributions are similar to or different from Renaissance artists.

Mental Mapping Activity

25. This exercise helps students visualize the areas they have been studying and how cultures interacted to spread new ideas and achievements. Accept all reasonable attempts at freehand mapping.

Technology Skills Activity

26. Students' answers will vary. They should compare Roman law to the laws or accepted norms of today.

Chapter 11 Resources

Note: The following materials may be used when teaching Chapter 11.
Section level support materials are shown at point of use in the margins of the Teacher Wraparound Edition.

Timesaving Tools

TeacherWorks™ All-In-One Planner and Resource Center

- **Interactive Teacher Edition** See the **Interactive Teacher Edition** CD-ROM to electronically integrate your Teacher Wraparound Edition and blackline masters.
- **Interactive Lesson Planner** Organize your week, month, semester, or year with all the lesson helps you need. The **Interactive Lesson Planner** CD-ROM contains all Chapter 11 resources.

Use Glencoe's **Presentation Plus!** multimedia teacher tool to easily present dynamic lessons that visually excite your students. Using Microsoft PowerPoint® you can customize the presentations to create your own personalized lessons.

TEACHING TRANSPARENCIES

Graphic Organizer Transparency 9 L2

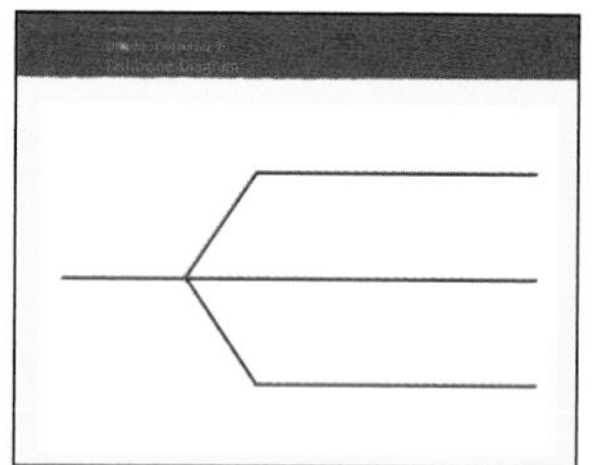

In-text Map Transparency L1

FOLDABLES™ Study Organizer

Dinah Zike's Foldables

Foldables are three-dimensional, interactive graphic organizers that help students practice basic writing skills, review key vocabulary terms, and identify main ideas. Additional chapter activities can be found in the ***Reading and Study Skills Foldables*** booklet.

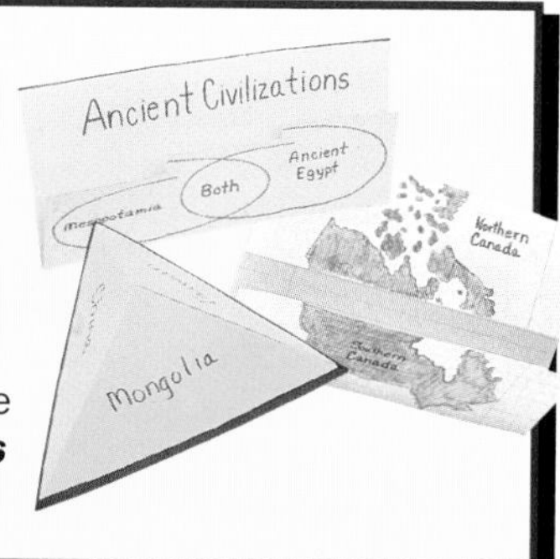

MAP AND GEOGRAPHY SKILLS

Chapter Map Activity L2

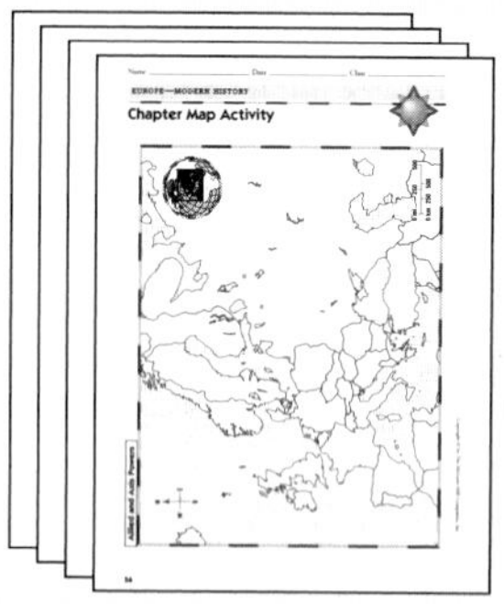

GeoLab Activity L2

READING SUPPORT

Vocabulary Activity L1

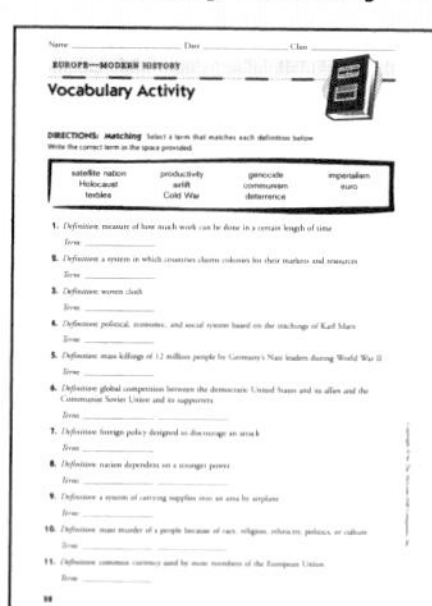

Workbook Activity L1

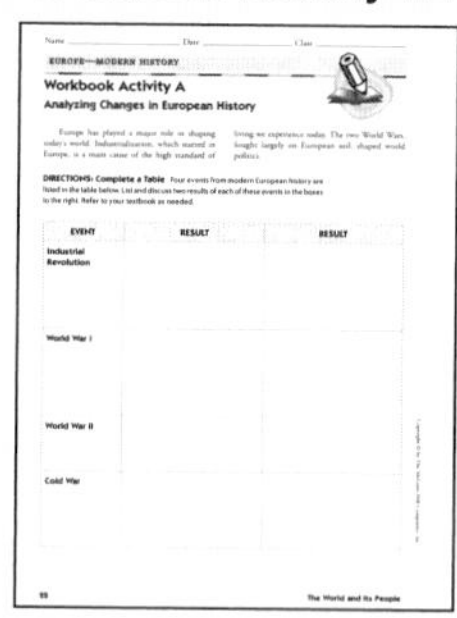

Reading and Writing Skills Activity L1/ELL

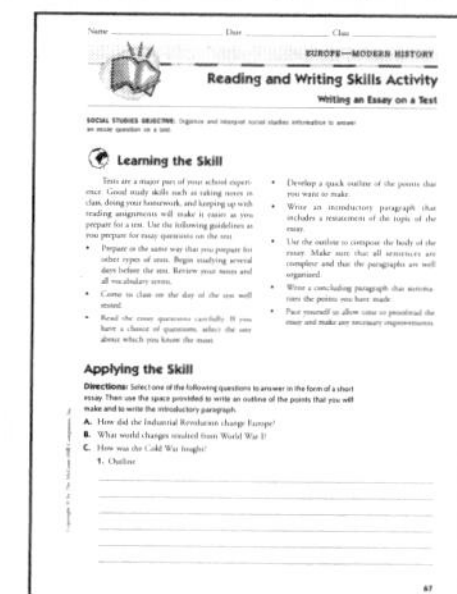

DIFFERENTIATED INSTRUCTION

Use these review and reinforcement materials to help less-proficient readers, English learners, and gifted and talented students.

Reteaching Activity L1

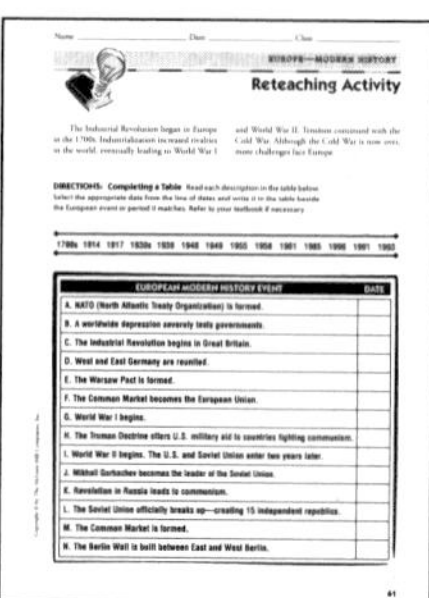

Chapter Skills Review L2

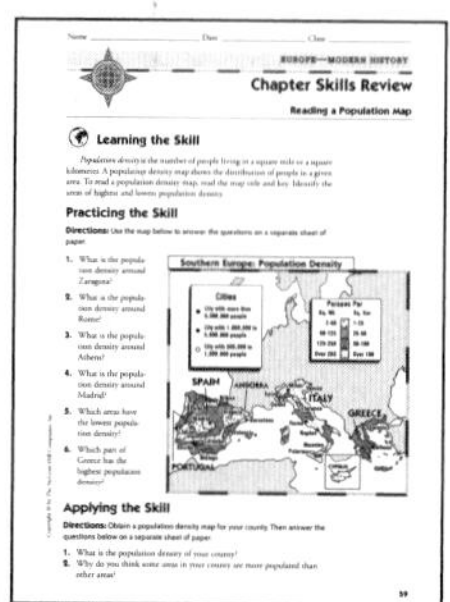

Cooperative Learning Activity L1/ELL

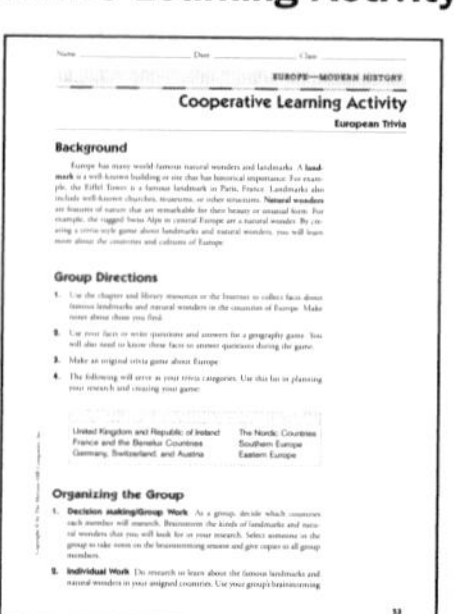

Enrichment Activity L3

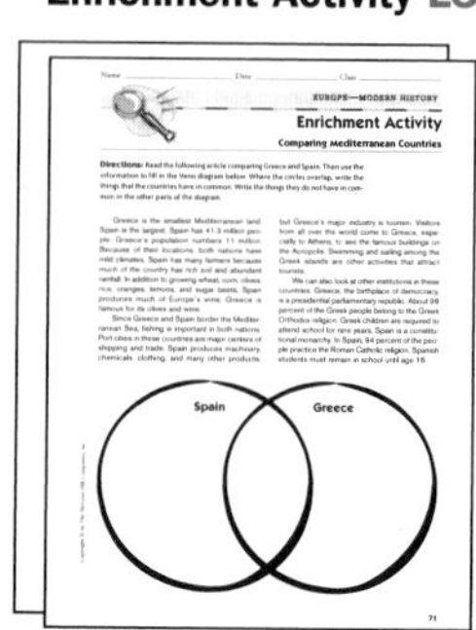

ASSESSMENT

Chapter Test, Form A L2

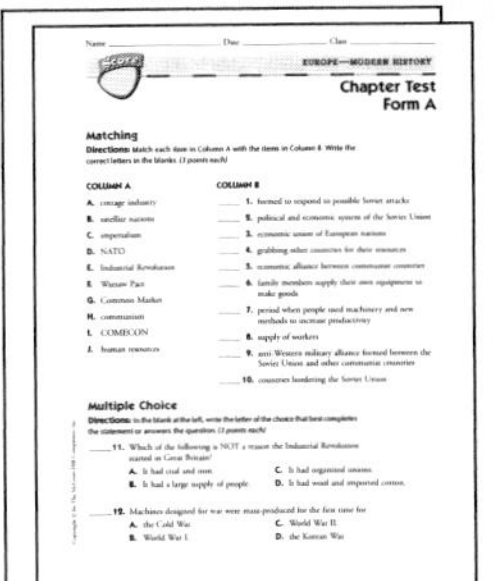

Chapter Test, Form B L2

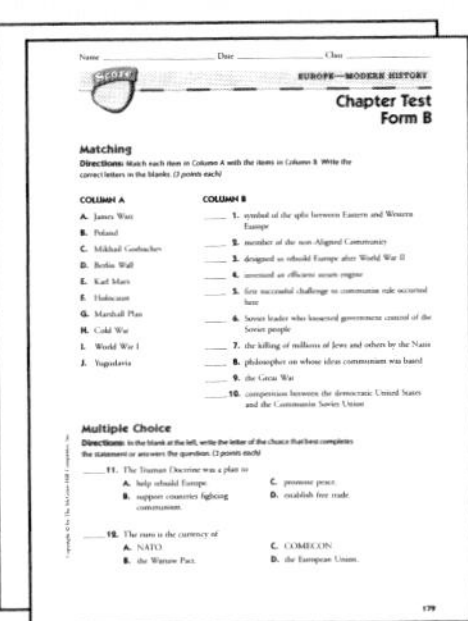

Performance Assessment Activity L1/ELL

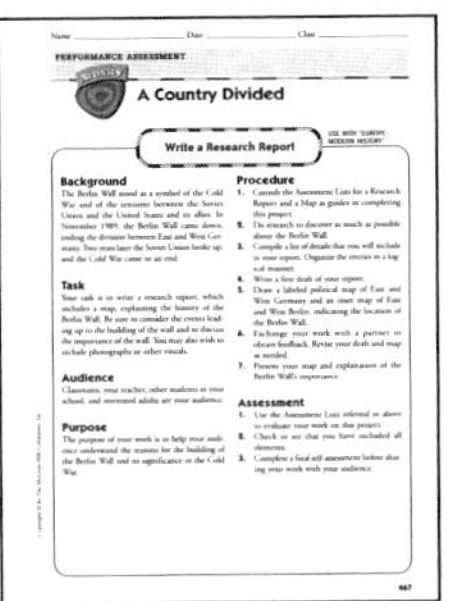

ExamView® Pro Testmaker CD-ROM

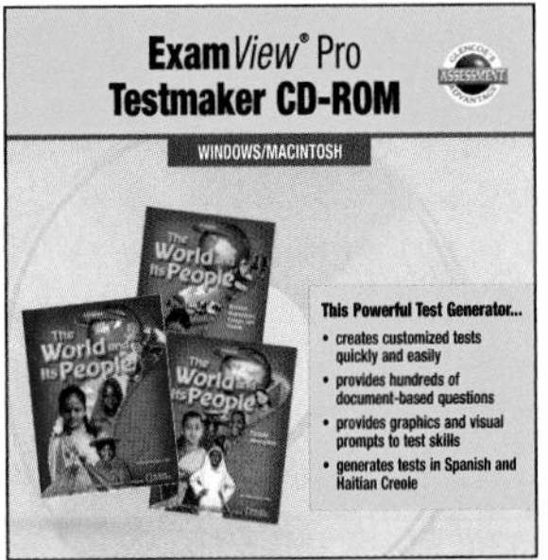

STANDARDIZED ASSESSMENT SKILLS

Critical Thinking Skills Activity L2

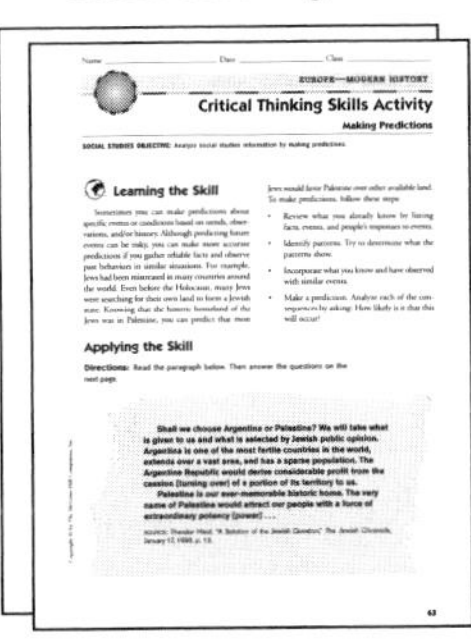

Map and Graph Skills Activity L2

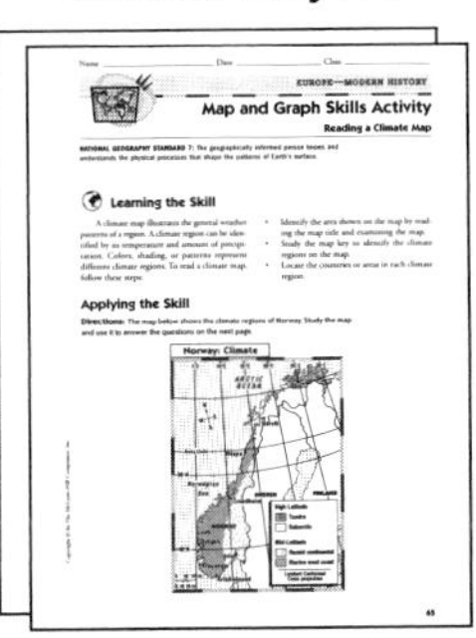

Standardized Test Skills Practice Workbook Activity L2

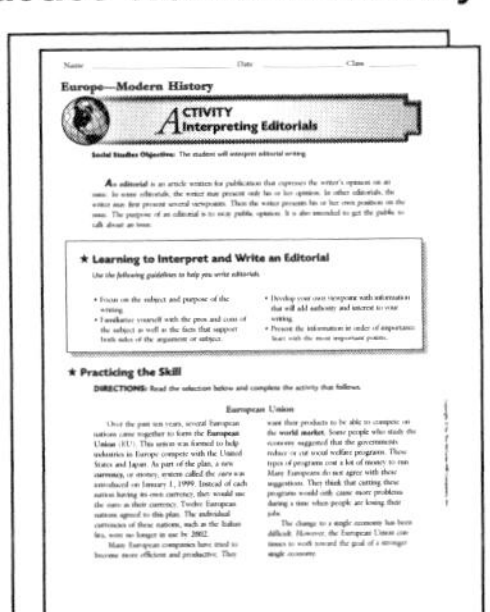

HOME INVOLVEMENT

Take-Home Review Activity L1

MULTIMEDIA

- National Geographic's The World and Its People
- MindJogger Videoquiz
- Vocabulary PuzzleMaker CD-ROM
- Interactive Tutor Self-Assessment CD-ROM
- ExamView® Pro Testmaker CD-ROM
- TeacherWorks CD-ROM
- StudentWorks CD-ROM
- Skillbuilder Interactive Workbook CD-ROM, Level 1
- Presentation Plus! CD-ROM
- Audio Program

SPANISH RESOURCES

The following Spanish language materials are available in the Spanish Resources binder:

- Spanish Summaries
- Spanish Vocabulary Activities
- Spanish Guided Reading Activities
- Spanish Quizzes and Tests
- Spanish Take-Home Review Activities
- Spanish Reteaching Activities

Meeting National Standards

Geography for Life

The following standards are covered in Chapter 11:

Section 1 — **EE4 Human Systems: Standards 12, 13**
EE5 Environment and Society: Standard 14, 15, 16

Section 2 — **EE2 Places and Regions: Standards 4, 5, 6**
EE6 The Uses of Geography: Standards 17, 18

Section 3 — **EE1 The World in Spatial Terms: Standards 1, 2, 3**
EE4 Human Systems: Standards 11, 13
EE6 The Uses of Geography: Standards 17, 18

State and Local Objectives

____

____

Chapter 11 Planning Guide

SECTION RESOURCES

Daily Objectives	Reproducible Resources	Multimedia Resources
Section 1 **The Modern Era Emerges** 1. Discuss the Industrial Revolution and the changes it created. 2. Explain how industrialization created new rivalries between European countries. 3. Explain how the two World Wars changed the balance of power in the world.	Reproducible Lesson Plan Daily Lecture and Discussion Notes Note-taking Guide Guided Reading Activity* Reading Essentials and Study Guide* Section Quiz*	Daily Focus Skills Transparency Vocabulary PuzzleMaker CD-ROM Interactive Tutor Self-Assessment CD-ROM ExamView® Pro Testmaker CD-ROM Presentation Plus! CD-ROM
Section 2 **A Divided Continent** 1. Explain the circumstances that created the Cold War. 2. Discuss the events that led to the end of the Cold War.	Reproducible Lesson Plan Daily Lecture and Discussion Notes Note-taking Guide Guided Reading Activity* Reading Essentials and Study Guide* Section Quiz*	Daily Focus Skills Transparency In-text Map Transparency Vocabulary PuzzleMaker CD-ROM Interactive Tutor Self-Assessment CD-ROM ExamView® Pro Testmaker CD-ROM Presentation Plus! CD-ROM
Section 3 **Moving Toward Unity** 1. Discuss the outcome of the breakup of the Soviet Union. 2. Explain how Europe has become more united. 3. Explain the challenges facing Europe today.	Reproducible Lesson Plan Daily Lecture and Discussion Notes Note-taking Guide Guided Reading Activity* Reading Essentials and Study Guide* Section Quiz*	Daily Focus Skills Transparency Vocabulary PuzzleMaker CD-ROM Interactive Tutor Self-Assessment CD-ROM ExamView® Pro Testmaker CD-ROM Presentation Plus! CD-ROM MindJogger Videoquiz

00:00 **Out of Time?** Assign the **Reading Essentials and Study Guide*** for this chapter.

*Also available in Spanish

KEY TO ABILITY LEVELS

Teaching strategies have been coded for varying learning styles and abilities.

L1 **BASIC** activities for all students
L2 **AVERAGE** activities for average to above-average students
L3 **CHALLENGING** activities for above-average students
ELL **ENGLISH LANGUAGE LEARNER** activities

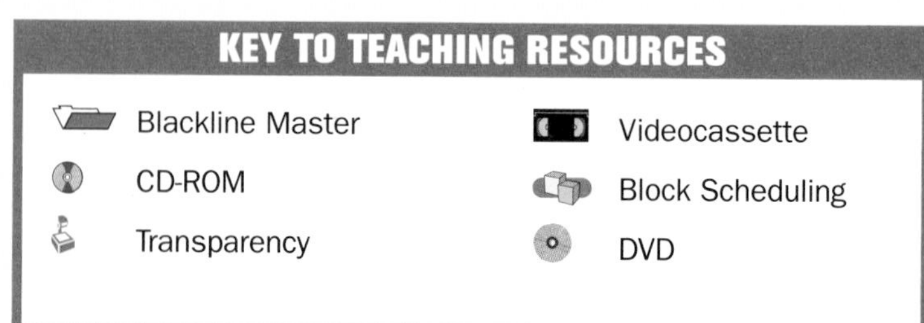

Teacher to Teacher

Passport Portfolios

Kristine Louise Edwards
Dodge Intermediate School
Twinsburg, Ohio

Create a contract for students to work independently on preparing a "portfolio" of a selected country. Assign points for each of the following activities they complete: (A) Utilize five resources for research=10 points. (B) Make a landforms map of your selected country=15 points. (C) Design a portfolio cover with the selected country's flag=5 points. (D) Create a Venn diagram comparing the culture of the selected country with that of the United States=15 points. (E) Orally present an art project, music, or a recipe from your selected country=25 points. (F) Complete a written report on your selected country=30 points. Then have students share their portfolios with one another.

Meeting Special Needs

In addition to the Differentiated Instruction strategies found in each section, the following resources are also suitable for your special needs students:

- ***ExamView® Pro Testmaker CD-ROM*** allows teachers to tailor tests by reducing answer choices.
- The ***Audio Program*** includes the entire narrative of the student edition so that less-proficient readers can listen to the words as they read them.
- The ***Reading Essentials and Study Guide*** provides the same content as the student edition but is written two grade levels below the textbook.
- ***Guided Reading Activities*** give less-proficient readers point-by-point instructions to increase comprehension as they read each textbook section.
- ***Enrichment Activities*** include a stimulating collection of readings and activities for gifted and talented students.

TEACHER'S CORNER

Index to National Geographic Magazine:

The following articles may be used for research relating to this chapter:

- "In Search of Vikings," by Priit J. Vesilind, May 2000.
- "Mystery Ships From a Danish Bog," by Michael Klesius, May 2000.
- "Civilized Denmark," by Garrison Keillor, July 1998.

National Geographic Society Products:

To order the following products for use with this chapter, call National Geographic Society at 1-800-368-2728:

- *Europe: The Road to Unity* (Video)
- *PicturePack: World War I Era* (Transparencies)
- *PicturePack: World War II Era* (Transparencies)

NGS ONLINE

Access National Geographic's Web site for current events, activities, links, interactive features, and archives. www.nationalgeographic.com

Find the latest coverage of geography in the news, atlas updates, cartographic activities with interactive maps, an online map store, and links at www.nationalgeographic.com/maps

SOCIAL STUDIES Online

Use our Web site for additional resources. All essential content is covered in the Student Edition.

You and your students can visit twip.glencoe.com, the Web site companion to *The World and Its People*. This innovative integration of electronic and print media offers your students a wealth of opportunities. The student text directs students to the Web site for the following options:

- Chapter Overviews
- Student Web Activities
- Self-Check Quizzes
- Textbook Updates

Answers are provided for you in the Web Activity Lesson Plan. Additional Web resources and Interactive Tutor puzzles are also available.

Introducing Chapter 11

Social Studies online

Introduce students to chapter content and key terms by having them access Chapter Overview 11 at twip.glencoe.com

Chapter Objectives

1. Discuss the Industrial Revolution and the social changes it created.
2. Explain how industrialization led to greater rivalry among nations.
3. Discuss the events that contributed to the Cold War.
4. Explain the breakup of the Soviet Union and its aftereffects on Europe.

GLENCOE TECHNOLOGY

NATIONAL GEOGRAPHIC

The World and Its People Video Program

Chapters 10–13 Europe
The following segments enhance the study of this chapter:

- **Avalanche!**
- **Shipwreck**
- **Fire and Ice**

MindJogger Videoquiz
Use MindJogger Videoquiz to preview the Chapter 11 content.

Both programs available in DVD and VHS

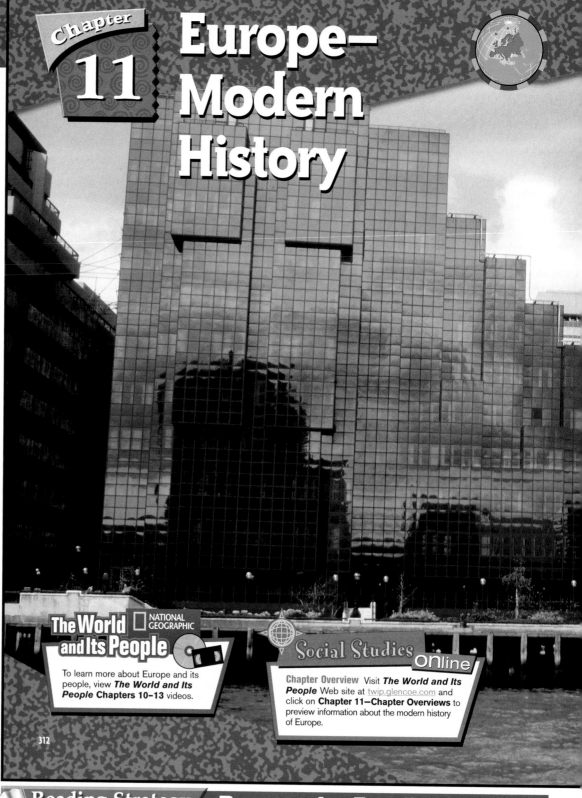

Chapter 11 Europe—Modern History

The World and Its People NATIONAL GEOGRAPHIC

To learn more about Europe and its people, view ***The World and Its People*** **Chapters 10–13** videos.

Social Studies online

Chapter Overview Visit ***The World and Its People*** Web site at twip.glencoe.com and click on **Chapter 11—Chapter Overviews** to preview information about the modern history of Europe.

312

Reading Strategy: Purpose for Reading

Pre and Post Responses is a strategy to tap background knowledge and engage students before starting a unit or lesson. Have your students copy several of the main topics from this chapter (World War I, World War II, the Holocaust, the Cold War, the European Union) on a piece of paper. They should then brainstorm a list of four or five ideas that they have heard or read about for each topic. Students should then discuss with a partner what they wrote. Finally discuss the ideas as a class. Students can then add to and modify their lists as they study the chapter. L1

FOLDABLES™ Study Organizer

Summarizing Information Make the following foldable to help you organize and summarize information about historic events and modern events in Europe, and how they are related.

Step 1 Fold a sheet of paper from side to side, leaving a 2-inch tab uncovered along the side.

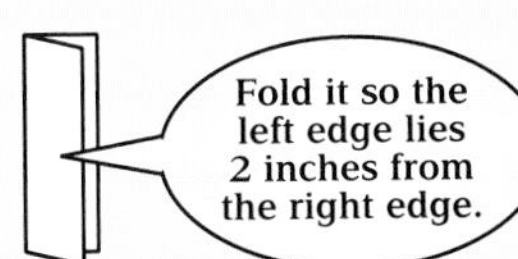

Fold it so the left edge lies 2 inches from the right edge.

Step 2 Turn the paper and fold it into thirds.

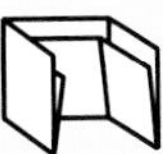

Step 3 Unfold and cut along the two inside fold lines.

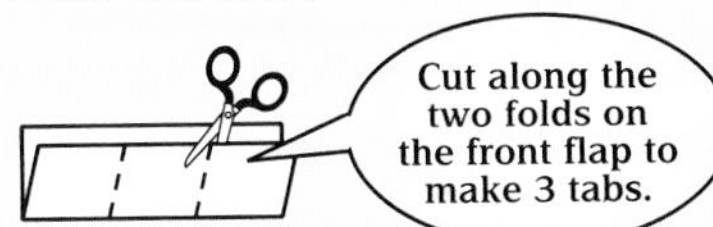

Cut along the two folds on the front flap to make 3 tabs.

Step 4 Label the foldable as shown.

Reading and Writing As you read about the modern history of Europe, write important facts under each appropriate tab of your foldable.

◀ A modern office building stands next to Billingsgate Fish Market in London, England.

Why It Matters

The Modern Era

Europe has played a major role in shaping today's world. Industrialization, which started in Europe, is one of the reasons for the high standard of living we experience today. The two World Wars, fought largely on European soil, shaped world politics and preserved democracy.

About the Photo

For much of the eighteenth century, Great Britain was known as the workshop of the world. By the nineteenth century, industry began to spread to other countries in Europe, as well as the United States. When these countries began to industrialize, they could use Great Britain as a model. Often they would change existing British techniques to meet the needs of their own country. As more countries industrialized around the world, there were new Industrial Revolutions that varied according to the time and place they occurred.

Introducing Chapter 11

FOLDABLES™ Study Organizer Dinah Zike's Foldables

Purpose Students are required to group information from the chapter into categories and then evaluate how the facts are related.

Have students complete the ***Reading and Study Skills Foldables*** activity for this chapter.

Why It Matters

Use this activity to demonstrate how industrial practices can lead to rivalry and even war between nations. Organize students into four groups. Propose the following scenario to each group.

1. They manufacture woolen hats.
2. They buy wool from the same place: the Island of Sheep.
3. They have become rich from making hats and can afford armies and navies.
4. The Island of Sheep has such a demand for its wool that it can charge more, and it favors the groups that will pay more.
5. There are so many woolen hats that customers want to pay less.
6. There's too much competition among groups for the same wool and the same hat customers.

Have groups write proposals that ensure their supply of wool and their position as the only hat supplier in the world. Make sure each group explains the possible consequences of their proposals.

Focus

Section Objectives

1. Discuss the Industrial Revolution and the changes it created.
2. Explain how industrialization created new rivalries between European countries.
3. Explain how the two World Wars changed the balance of power in the world.

BELLRINGER Skillbuilder Activity

Project transparency and have students answer the question.

Daily Focus Skills Transparency

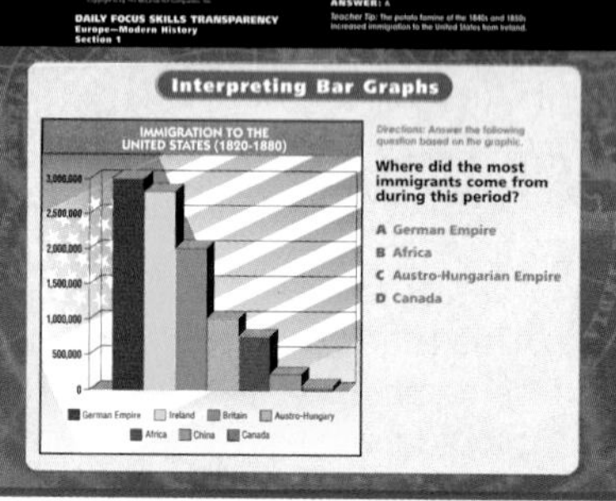

Reading Preview

■ **Activating Prior Knowledge** Ask students to think about how their clothing is made. How do they think it was made before automated factories were created?

■ **Preteaching Vocabulary** Have students look for words or phrases that signal cause/effect relationships, such as *as a result, because,* or *therefore.*

Guide to Reading

Main Idea

Industrialization led not only to a higher standard of living for some, but also to increased tensions in the world.

Terms to Know

- productivity
- human resources
- textiles
- cottage industry
- union
- strike
- imperialism
- communism
- Holocaust
- genocide

Reading Strategy

Create a chart like the one below. Write three statements of fact under the Fact column. In the Opinion column, write how you feel about each fact statement.

Fact	Opinion

Section 1

The Modern Era Emerges

NATIONAL GEOGRAPHIC Exploring Our World

From the beginning of the Industrial Revolution, factories required a new system of labor. It involved regular hours and shifts to keep the machinery producing. This arrangement was different from that in rural areas, where farmers worked hard during some periods but had little work to do at other times. Life in a British factory town ran on a regular schedule.

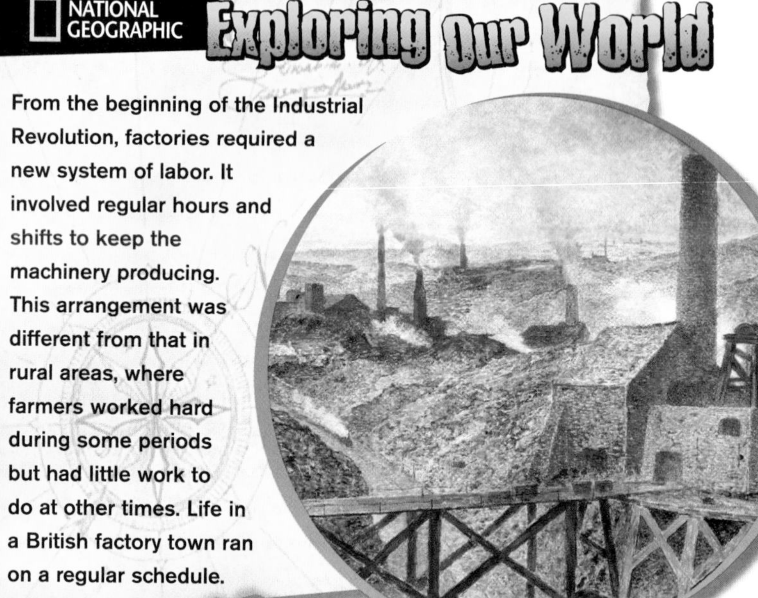

The Industrial Revolution began in Great Britain in the 1700s. It was a time when people used machinery and new methods to increase **productivity.** Productivity is a measure of how much work can be done in a certain length of time. The changes these machines brought led to a revolution in the way work was done and in how people lived.

A Rapidly Changing World

The Industrial Revolution started in Great Britain for several reasons. Great Britain had a ready supply of natural resources such as coal and iron. These were needed to make and run machinery. There was also a plentiful supply of raw materials such as wool and imported cotton, used to make cloth. In addition, there was a supply of people—**human resources**—who could run the machines. As farmers relied more on machines to plant and harvest crops, fewer people were

Section Resources

Reproducible Masters
- Reproducible Lesson Plan
- Daily Lecture and Discussion Notes
- Note-taking Guide
- Guided Reading Activity
- Reading Essentials and Study Guide
- Section Quiz

Transparencies
- Daily Focus Skills Transparency

Multimedia
- Vocabulary PuzzleMaker CD-ROM
- Interactive Tutor Self-Assessment CD-ROM
- Presentation Plus! CD-ROM
- ExamView® Pro Testmaker CD-ROM

needed in the fields. Many people who used to work on the farms went to the cities to find work in factories and shops.

Major Industries Textiles, or woven cloth, was the first industry to be moved to factories. Before that, spinning and cloth weaving had been a cottage industry, in which family members supplied their own equipment to make goods. With industrialization, huge quantities of cloth could be produced in factories that employed many workers. Textile mills became even more productive when steam replaced waterpower for running the machinery.

The steam engine was invented by Thomas Newcomen in the early 1700s and was first used to pump water out of coal mines. In 1769 James Watt invented a more efficient steam engine, which was used for textile mills, riverboats, and locomotives. Inventions like the railroad improved transportation and stimulated the growth of more industries. By the early 1800s, the Industrial Revolution had spread from Great Britain to much of western Europe and North America.

✓Reading Check **How did machinery affect the textile industry?**

Changing Lifestyles

As towns and cities grew, people's lives changed dramatically. At first, industrial workers, including women and children, had to work hard for long hours often under dangerous conditions. Eventually, the workers formed groups called unions. A union spoke for all the workers in a factory or industry and bargained for better working conditions, higher pay, and a shorter working day. If a factory owner refused these demands, union members often went on strike. That is, they refused to work until their demands were met.

Overall, the Industrial Revolution made life more difficult for people in the short term but easier in the long run. For example, because manufactured cotton clothing was better and cheaper, people could afford more. They could change their clothes and wash them more often. This new cleanliness reduced sickness and disease, so people generally lived healthier and longer lives.

The Industrial Revolution also resulted in strong economies in western Europe. It was because of this economic strength that Europe was able to dominate the world in the 1800s and early 1900s.

✓Reading Check **How did the Industrial Revolution improve people's lives?**

NATIONAL GEOGRAPHIC On Location

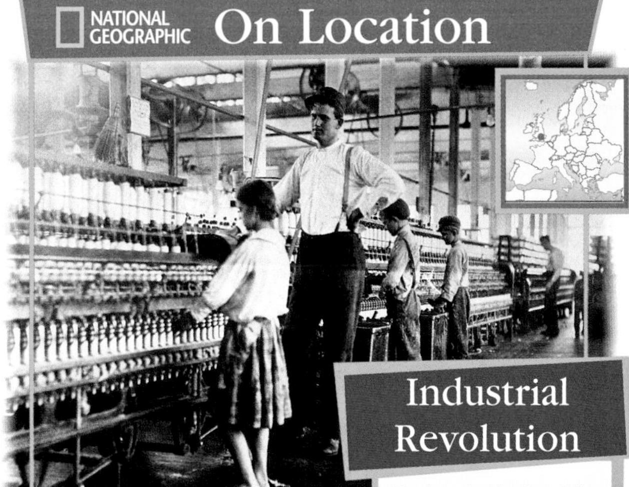

Industrial Revolution

During the Industrial Revolution, children as young as age seven worked 12 to 15 hours per day, six days a week.

Economics **How did new machinery affect production?**

Chapter 11

Section 1, pages 314–317

2 TEACH

Brainstorming Ask students to look around the room and think of how it would be different if there were no factories or mass manufacturing. *(Possible answers: limited supplies of books, paper, pencils, and so on; fewer windows; wearing the same clothes every day)* **L1**

Daily Lecture and Discussion Notes

EUROPE—MODERN HISTORY

Daily Lecture and Discussion Notes

The Modern Era Emerges

Did You Know? Much of the technology we can't live without today was invented in the last 100 years, including the computer, TV, compact discs, photocopiers, and Scotch tape.

I. A Rapidly Changing World

A. The Industrial Revolution began in Great Britain in the 1700s. It was a time when people used machinery and new methods to increase **productivity,** or the measure of how much work can be done in a certain period of time.

B. Great Britain had a ready supply of natural resources, plentiful raw materials, ... supply of **human resources,** or people to work.

✓ **Reading Check Answer**

Huge quantities of cloth could be produced.

More About the Photo

Technology Although seldom used today, the steam engine made it possible to develop other sources of power, such as the gasoline engine.

Caption Answer Goods could be produced faster and more cheaply.

✓ **Reading Check Answer**

Clothing was cheaper, making it easier for people to stay clean. This reduced disease.

Reading Strategy **Reading the Text**

Making Inferences Have students research the European languages spoken by the countries in Africa. They can use an almanac or find the information on the Internet. *(They should find that the main European languages are French, English, and Portuguese.)* Using their findings, have students group the African countries according to the European language they speak, then have them locate the countries on a map. Ask them why these African countries speak European languages. *(They were once European colonies.)* **L1**

*Use the **Reading Skills Handbook** for more reading strategies.*

Chapter 11

Section 1, pages 314–317

More About the Photos

The Germans launched a massive offensive against Verdun in February 1916. The French rallied with the battle cry "They shall not pass!" By December, the French had recovered much of the land that had been lost.

Caption Answer *Possible answers:* London, England; Berlin, Germany; Hiroshima, Japan

L1/ELL

Guided Reading Activity

Name ______ Date ______ Class ______

EUROPE—MODERN HISTORY

Guided Reading Activity 1

The Modern Era Emerges

DIRECTIONS: Reading for Accuracy Reading the section and completing the activity below will help you learn more about industrialization and the conflicts in the world. Refer to your textbook to decide if a statement is true or false. Write **T** or **F**, and if a statement is false, rewrite it correctly.

____ 1. During the Industrial Revolution, people used machinery and new methods to increase productivity.

____ 2. The Industrial Revolution started in Britain because that nation did not have enough natural resources, such as coal and iron.

ASSESS

Assign Section 1 Assessment as homework or an in-class activity.

Have students use the Interactive Tutor Assessment CD-ROM to review Section 1.

NATIONAL GEOGRAPHIC **On Location**

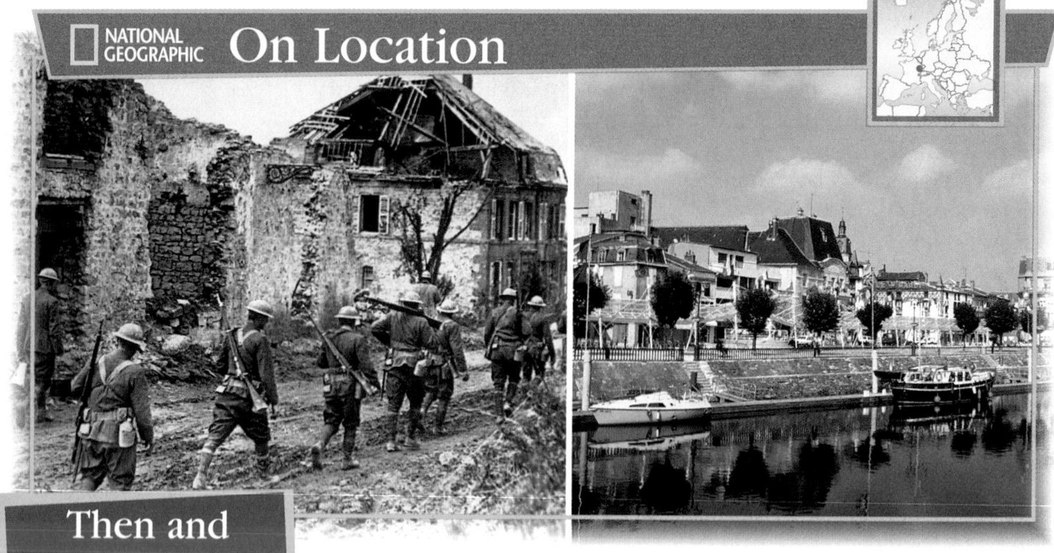

Then and Now

The town of Verdun, France, was nearly destroyed during World War I (above). Today it is a thriving commercial center and tourist attraction (above right).

Place Name another city that has been rebuilt since World War I.

Rivalry Between Nations

Industrialization created new rivalries among the countries of Europe. Great Britain, France, Germany, and other European countries competed around the world for markets and resources for their factories. Under a system called **imperialism,** European countries claimed colonies in Africa and Asia in the late 1800s. European nations built up armies and navies to protect themselves and their empires. Different alliances were formed, whereby various countries agreed to support one another in times of war.

World War I In 1914 a war broke out in Europe that quickly spread to the European colonies and other areas of the world. It was known as the Great War, and later called World War I. This war was not like any earlier wars. With the techniques learned in the Industrial Revolution, machines designed for war were mass-produced. Tanks, heavy artillery, machine guns, and airplanes helped make the war more violent than any before it. In the four years of the war, millions of people were killed or wounded, and many European cities and villages were destroyed.

New Problems Arise As a result of the war, Europe faced political and social turmoil. Millions were homeless and hungry. Germany was blamed for starting the war and was asked to pay for much of it. The United States and Japan became great powers. A revolution in Russia in 1917 led to a new political, economic, and social system called **communism.** Communism was based on the teachings of a German philosopher named Karl Marx. Marx believed that industrialization had created two classes of people. One class owned the means of producing goods and the other worked to produce the goods. He wrote that this system was unfair and needed to be overthrown.

Differentiated Instruction

Meeting Special Needs: Less-proficient Readers England went through great changes because of the Industrial Revolution, particularly in the following areas: pollution, health, working conditions, social classes, and transportation. Organize your class into groups. Have each group research one of those topics as it pertains to nineteenth-century England. Have each group make a poster that illustrates important points or examples and use it as part of a presentation. Have the class discuss how their various topics might have connections to one another. L1

Refer to *Inclusion for the Middle School Social Studies Classroom Strategies and Activities* in the TCR.

World War II In the 1930s, a worldwide depression severely tested the ability of many governments to provide for their citizens. The problems that were not solved after World War I eventually led to new alliances in Europe. Germany became a dictatorship under Adolf Hitler and his National Socialist German Workers' Party. Its members, called Nazis, believed in German superiority. By 1939 Germany, Italy, and Japan (the Axis Powers) were at war with Great Britain, France, and China (the Allies). In 1941 the United States and Soviet Union joined the Allies in the war that became known as World War II.

During the war, Hitler and the Nazis carried out the **Holocaust,** in which over 12 million people were killed. Over 6 million of the victims were Jews. Other persecuted groups included the Roma people (called Gypsies), Poles, individuals with disabilities, and many other groups that were classified as "undesirable" by the Nazi leaders. The Holocaust is an example of the war crime of **genocide,** or the mass murder of a people because of race, religion, ethnicity, politics, or culture.

Italy surrendered in 1943. Germany was finally defeated in May 1945, but the Japanese continued to fight. In August, the United States—in an effort to end the war in Asia—dropped two atomic bombs on the Japanese cities of Hiroshima and Nagasaki. From this global conflict, the United States and the Soviet Union emerged as superpowers.

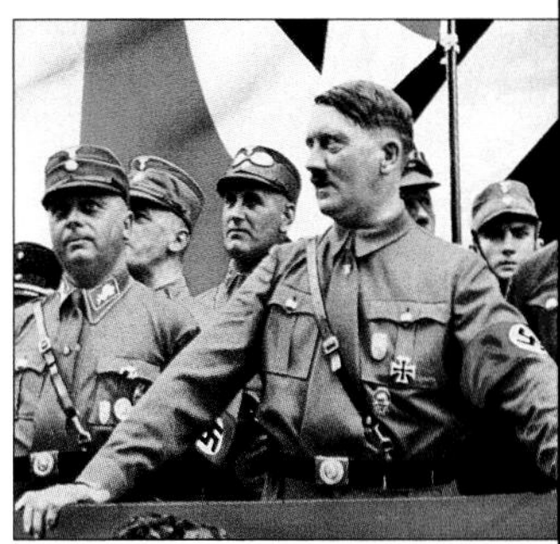

▲ Hitler at a Nazi rally, Dortmund, Germany

✓Reading Check What was the Holocaust?

Section 1 Assessment

Defining Terms

1. **Define** productivity, human resources, textiles, cottage industry, union, strike, imperialism, communism, Holocaust, genocide.

Recalling Facts

2. **History** Where did the Industrial Revolution begin?
3. **Government** Name the political, economic, and social system that was based on the teachings of Karl Marx.

Critical Thinking

4. **Comparing and Contrasting** How did people's living habits change after the introduction of factories? Do you think people were generally better off? Explain.
5. **Evaluating Information** Why did the new military equipment introduced in World War I change the way wars were fought?

Graphic Organizer

6. **Organizing Information** Create a diagram like the one below. Then fill in the names of the countries that made up the two powers fighting each other in World War II.

Axis Powers	Allies

Applying Social Studies Skills

7. **Analyzing Maps** Refer to the **Reference Atlas** map of the world on pages RA2–RA3. Which of the Allies was located nearest to Japan?

Section 1 Assessment

1. The terms are defined in the Glossary.
2. England
3. communism
4. They moved to cities to be closer to factories; they worked long hours under dangerous conditions until unions were formed; clothing was more affordable; they could stay cleaner and live healthier lives. Students' opinions will likely vary.
5. They made the war more violent than any war before it.
6. Axis: Germany, Italy, Japan; Allies: Britain, France, China, United States, Soviet Union
7. China

Chapter 11

Section 1, pages 314–317

L2

Section Quiz

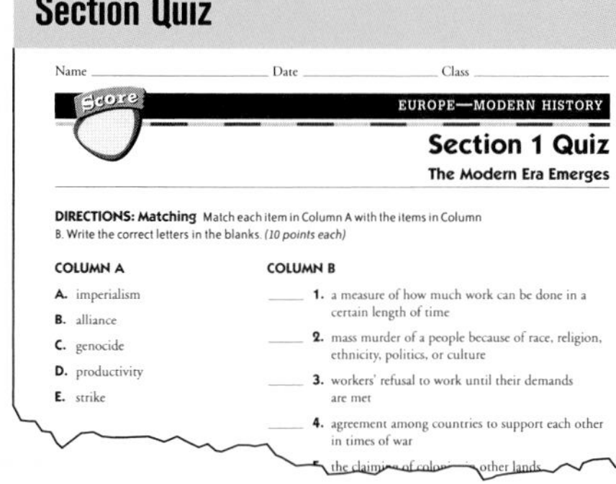
Name ______ Date ______ Class ______

Score

EUROPE—MODERN HISTORY

Section 1 Quiz

The Modern Era Emerges

DIRECTIONS: Matching Match each item in Column A with the items in Column B. Write the correct letters in the blanks. (10 points each)

COLUMN A	COLUMN B
A. imperialism	____ 1. a measure of how much work can be done in a certain length of time
B. alliance	____ 2. mass murder of a people because of race, religion, ethnicity, politics, or culture
C. genocide	____ 3. workers' refusal to work until their demands are met
D. productivity	____ 4. agreement among countries to support each other in times of war
E. strike	

✓ Reading Check Answer

the Nazi genocide of over 12 million people

L1/ELL

Reading Essentials and Study Guide

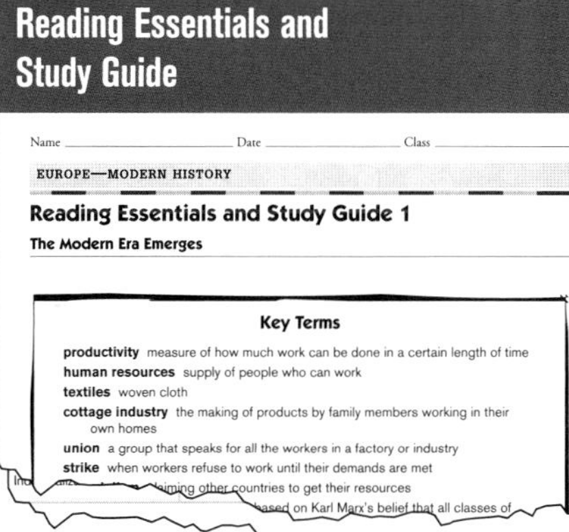
Name ______ Date ______ Class ______

EUROPE—MODERN HISTORY

Reading Essentials and Study Guide 1

The Modern Era Emerges

Key Terms

productivity measure of how much work can be done in a certain length of time
human resources supply of people who can work
textiles woven cloth
cottage industry the making of products by family members working in their own homes
union a group that speaks for all the workers in a factory or industry
strike when workers refuse to work until their demands are met

4 Close

Reading Strategy

Synthesizing Have students research daily life in the eighteenth century and write an essay about what life was like before the Industrial Revolution.

TEACH

Explain to students that often prejudice and intolerance come from ignorance and fear. Ask the class to name groups (religious, ethnic, social, political) that they think might often be the victims of prejudice. Have each student write a question asking for specific information about one of the groups they know little about. Collect their questions and give them to other students to answer. Answers might have to be researched, but they should be unbiased and supported with examples. Share responses with the class and discuss how recent current events have led to some prejudice. L1

More About the Holocaust

Unfortunately, events like the Holocaust were not limited to World War II. In the early 20th century, over half the Armenian population of Turkey was massacred. Mass murder is still happening around the world today. In eastern Europe and Africa, ethnic conflicts have led to the deaths of many innocent people.

Making Connections

ART | SCIENCE | CULTURE | TECHNOLOGY

The Holocaust

The Holocaust is one of the most horrifying events in human history. *Holocaust* is a word that means complete and total destruction. Learning about the Holocaust is important so that such crimes against humanity can be prevented in the future.

The Final Solution

Adolf Hitler, chancellor of Germany, believed that the Germanic peoples of the world, called Aryans, were a superior race. His goal was to populate Europe with one "master" race of people. In the years before and during World War II, Hitler's government persecuted many racial, religious, and ethnic groups that he considered "undesirable." These groups included the Roma (Gypsies), Jehovah's Witnesses, people with disabilities, and political protesters of all backgrounds.

The chief target of Hitler's plan—which he called his "Final Solution"—was the Jews. Jewish communities throughout Germany and German-controlled territory suffered terribly. Jews, forced to wear identification badges, were blamed for all of Germany's economic and social problems.

Between 1939 and 1945, Hitler's Nazi forces attempted to kill the Jews in every country Germany invaded, as well as in those countries that were Nazi allies. Jews from Germany, Poland, the Soviet Union, France, Belgium, the Netherlands, Greece, and Hungary were among those killed during the Holocaust.

▲ Auschwitz Nazi concentration camp in Oswiecim, Poland

Mass Murder

In the early years of the war, Jewish people in Eastern Europe were rounded up, gathered together, shot by machine guns, and buried in mass graves. Later, millions of Jews were uprooted and forced into concentration camps. Few people survived these. Those who were too young, sick, or elderly for heavy labor were executed in gas chambers. In all, more than 6 million Jews and about 6 million Roma (Gypsies), Poles, Soviet prisoners of war, and others were murdered.

Making the Connection

1. What was the Holocaust?
2. Why did Hitler want to rid Europe of its Jewish people?
3. **Understanding Cause and Effect** How can studying about the Holocaust today help prevent another genocide from happening in the future?

318 CHAPTER 11

Making the Connection

1. the organized murder of Jews and other ethnic, religious, or political groups by the Nazis during World War II
2. He wanted to eliminate any group that he considered undesirable and he particularly targeted Jews.
3. Answers will vary. One possible response is that showing the horrors forced upon a people simply because of race and beliefs will help people see the inhuman results of hatred and intolerance.

A Divided Continent

Guide to Reading

Main Idea

After World War II, the democratic United States and the Communist Soviet Union worked to bring their forms of government to the war-torn nations of Europe.

Terms to Know

- Cold War
- nuclear weapon
- deterrence
- satellite nation
- blockade
- airlift

Reading Strategy

As you read the section, fill in a time line like the one below with an event that occurred during that year.

1948 ______
1955 ______
1961 ______
1985 ______
1989 ______

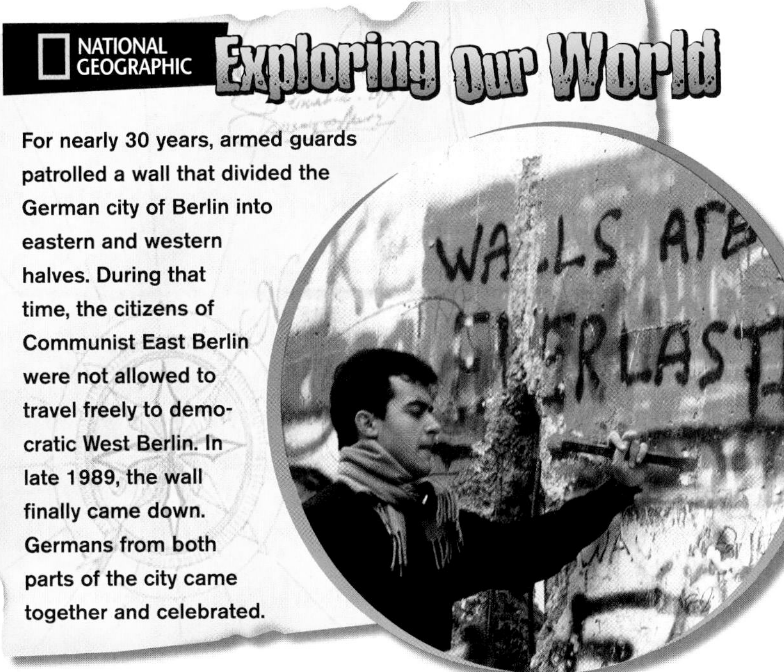

For nearly 30 years, armed guards patrolled a wall that divided the German city of Berlin into eastern and western halves. During that time, the citizens of Communist East Berlin were not allowed to travel freely to democratic West Berlin. In late 1989, the wall finally came down. Germans from both parts of the city came together and celebrated.

After World War II, much of Europe was in ruins. The total defeat of Germany, Italy, and Japan left a power gap that would be filled by two rivals—the United States and the Soviet Union.

The Cold War

The global competition between the democratic United States and its allies and the Communist Soviet Union and its supporters came to be called the **Cold War**. It was a dangerous time because by 1950 both sides had **nuclear weapons**. Nuclear weapons use atomic reactions to release enormous power and can cause mass destruction. It was a "cold" war because countries never mobilized armies in an official war.

The Cold War began in Europe. In 1948 the United States started a loan program called the Marshall Plan. The goals were to help rebuild Europe and try to stop the spread of communism. Under the Marshall Plan, factories were rebuilt, mines were reopened, and roads were

1 Focus

Section Objectives

1. Explain the circumstances that created the Cold War.
2. Discuss the events that led to the end of the Cold War.

BELLRINGER Skillbuilder Activity

Project transparency and have students answer the question.

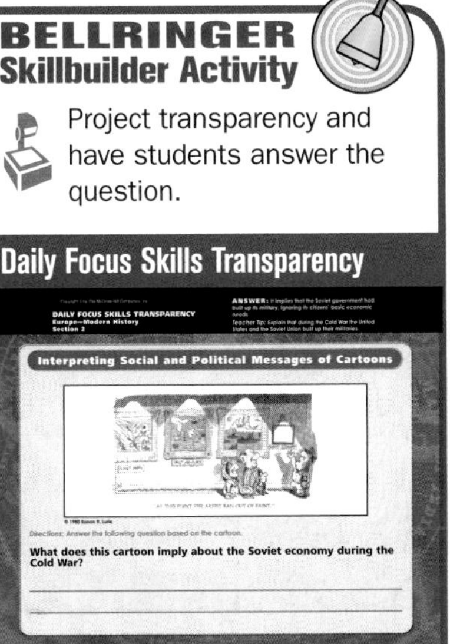
Daily Focus Skills Transparency

Reading Preview

■ **Activating Prior Knowledge** Have students explain why countries form alliances with other countries. Ask them if they think alliances provide stability among nations.

■ **Preteaching Vocabulary** Ask students why the term *cold war* was used to describe the conflict between the United States and the Soviet Union.

Section Resources

Reproducible Masters
- Reproducible Lesson Plan
- Daily Lecture and Discussion Notes
- Note-taking Guide
- Guided Reading Activity
- Reading Essentials and Study Guide
- Section Quiz

Transparencies
- Daily Focus Skills Transparency
- In-text Map Transparency

Multimedia
- Vocabulary PuzzleMaker CD-ROM
- Interactive Tutor Self-Assessment CD-ROM
- Presentation Plus! CD-ROM
- ExamView® Pro Testmaker CD-ROM

TEACH

Reading Strategy

Sequencing Events Write the following events on the board, overhead projector, or PowerPoint® presentation and have your class date them and place them in the correct order: NATO is formed, World War II ends in Europe, Mikhail Gorbachev becomes the leader of the Soviet Union, the Berlin Wall is built, the Marshall Plan is started. *(1945: WWII ends; 1948: Marshall Plan; 1949: NATO; 1961: Berlin Wall; 1985: Gorbachev)* L2

Reading Check Answer

a global competition between the United States and the Soviet Union

Applying Map Skills

Answers

1. Western
2. Soviet Union, German Democratic Republic, Czechoslovakia, Hungary, Romania, Bulgaria

In-text Map Transparency Activity
Ask students: Which Eastern European countries are landlocked? *(Czechoslovakia, Hungary)* Outline the borders of these countries as students identify them.

repaired and replaced. Western European countries that were liberated by the United States and Great Britain during World War II began to develop prosperous economies.

Reading Check What was the Cold War?

Western Europe Cooperates

In 1948 under the Truman Doctrine, the United States offered military aid to countries such as Greece and Turkey that were fighting communism inside their borders. In 1949 the North Atlantic Treaty Organization (NATO) was formed to respond to possible attacks by the Soviet Union. Each country in NATO agreed to treat an attack on any other member as an attack on itself. The NATO countries believed that the Soviet Union would not attack Western Europe if Soviet leaders thought such an attack would trigger nuclear war with the United States. This policy is known as deterrence, because it is designed to deter, or discourage, an attack.

Eventually, Western European countries began to cooperate economically with one another. The small countries of Belgium, the Netherlands, and Luxembourg joined together in 1948 to form the Benelux trade union, an arrangement for the free movement of money, goods, and people among these nations. West Germany, France, and

NATIONAL GEOGRAPHIC **Western and Eastern Europe (c. 1950)**

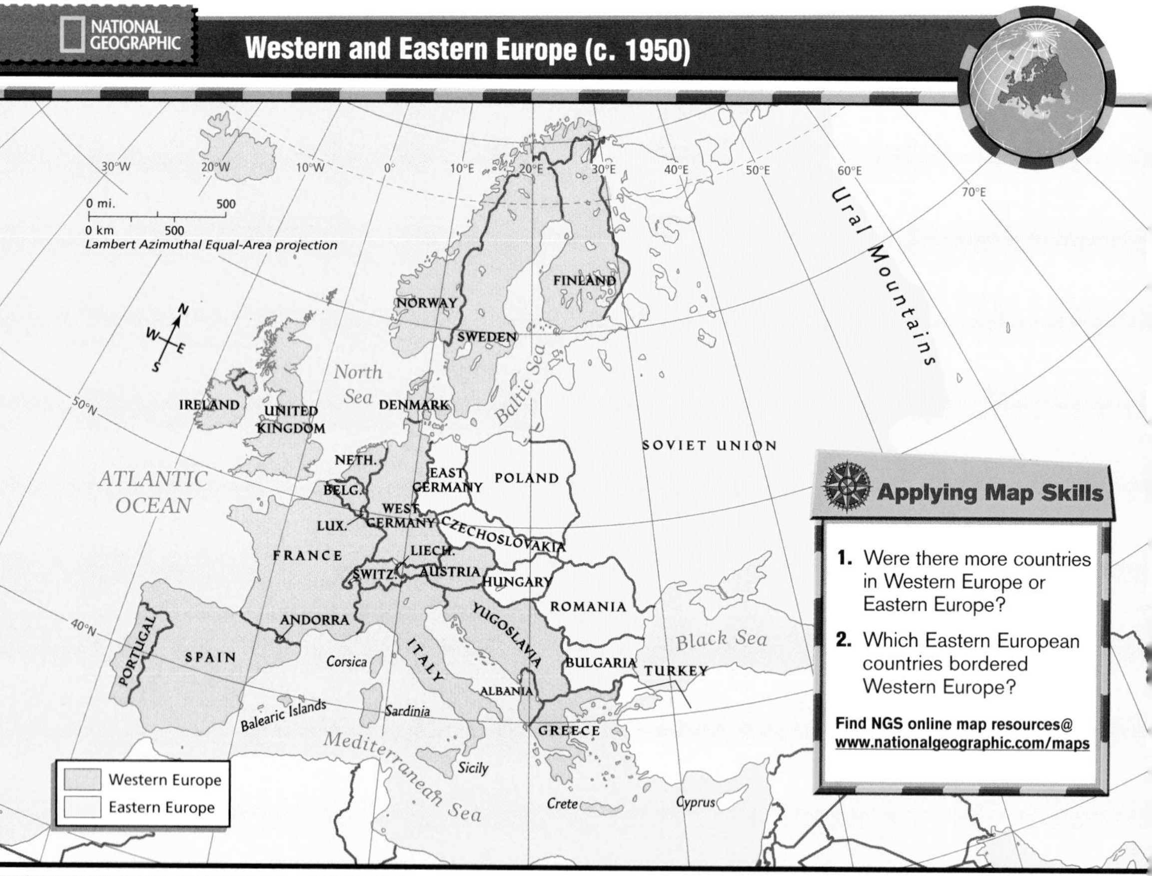

Applying Map Skills

1. Were there more countries in Western Europe or Eastern Europe?
2. Which Eastern European countries bordered Western Europe?

Find NGS online map resources@ www.nationalgeographic.com/maps

Reading Strategy — Reading the Text

Responding and Reflecting Have your students research the North Atlantic Treaty Organization (NATO) to find out when and why it was started, who the members are, and what its current role in the world is. Organize the class into groups, each representing one of the members of NATO. Have each group identify three reasons it is important that their country belongs to NATO. Afterwards, have groups share their reasons and see if there are any similarities or differences between countries. L1

*Use the **Reading Skills Handbook** for more reading strategies.*

Italy joined with the Benelux countries to form the European Coal and Steel Community. In 1958 this became the European Economic Community, also called the Common Market. The members agreed to free trade amongst themselves. This meant that no tariffs blocked trade and that workers from one country could get jobs in any of the other member countries. Between 1958 and 1986, Denmark, the United Kingdom, Ireland, Spain, Portugal, and Greece also joined the Common Market. Now known as the European Union, its goal is greater cooperation and economic development.

Reading Check **Why did the countries of Western Europe join NATO?**

Soviets Control Eastern Europe

In Eastern Europe, the Soviet Union made **satellite nations** of those countries bordering it. Satellite nations are dependent upon a stronger power. Bulgaria, Romania, Czechoslovakia, Hungary, Poland, and East Germany became communist. They were strictly controlled by the Soviet Union. With these countries, the Soviet Union created the Council for Mutual Economic Assistance, or COMECON, primarily for its own economic benefit.

To counter NATO, the Soviet Union formed its satellites into an anti-Western military alliance known as the Warsaw Pact in 1955. It was named after the Polish capital city of Warsaw, where the treaty of alliance was signed.

Yugoslavia and Albania also became communist but refused to be placed under Soviet control. During the Cold War, Yugoslavia joined a number of Asian and African countries to form the Non-Aligned Community. Its members tried to stay neutral—to not support either side—during the Cold War.

Reading Check **In what way was the Warsaw Pact like NATO?**

A Clash in Berlin

During the Cold War, there were many "hot spots," or areas of tension and conflict. Some of these were China, Korea, Cuba, and Vietnam. The earliest clash, however, took place in Berlin, Germany.

Divided Berlin At the end of World War II, the Allies (the United States, the Soviet Union, Great Britain, and France) occupied Germany. Germany was divided into four occupation zones. The Soviet Union controlled the eastern part of the country, while the other three Allies divided and controlled the western part. Turn to the map on page 337 to see the four occupation zones. The German capital of Berlin, located deep within Soviet-controlled East Germany, was also divided among the four nations. In 1948, to promote peace and German recovery, the United States, Great Britain, and France united their occupation zones. The Soviet Union was against any plan that would strengthen Germany, its historical enemy. In June 1948, the Soviets **blockaded,** or closed off, all land and water traffic into the western part of Berlin. They hoped this would force the other three powers to leave the city.

Restructuring

Under Soviet control, the satellite nations had command economies. This meant that the government owned all resources. A communist central planning committee decided what goods and services to produce, and how and for whom they would be produced. When the Soviet Union fell in 1991, the Eastern European satellites tried to restructure to a free market economy. This was not easy. Why? Imagine a family-owned business in which the head of the family makes all the decisions. Then suddenly the head of the family disappears. Family members must now make the business decisions, even though they have had no experience doing so. In a similar way, moving from a command economy to a free market economy has been a difficult change.

Reading Check Answer

to form an alliance in order to respond to possible attacks by the Soviet Union

Daily Lecture and Discussion Notes

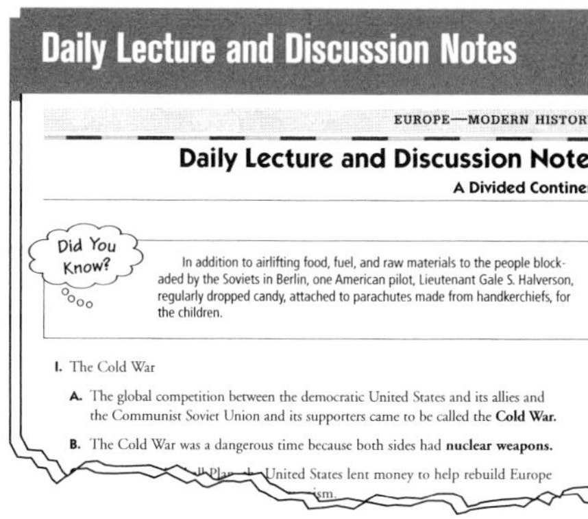
EUROPE—MODERN HISTORY

Daily Lecture and Discussion Notes

A Divided Continent

Did You Know? In addition to airlifting food, fuel, and raw materials to the people blockaded by the Soviets in Berlin, one American pilot, Lieutenant Gale S. Halverson, regularly dropped candy, attached to parachutes made from handkerchiefs, for the children.

I. The Cold War

A. The global competition between the democratic United States and its allies and the Communist Soviet Union and its supporters came to be called the **Cold War.**

B. The Cold War was a dangerous time because both sides had **nuclear weapons.**

Reading Check Answer

It was also a military alliance, but against the West.

L1/ELL

Guided Reading Activity

Name ______ Date ______ Class ______

EUROPE—MODERN HISTORY

Guided Reading Activity 2

A Divided Continent

DIRECTIONS: Answering Questions Reading the section and answering the questions below will help you learn more about the conflict between the United States and the Soviet Union. Use your textbook to write answers to the questions.

1. What was the Cold War?
2. Why did the United States set up the Marshall Plan?
3. Why did the NATO countries follow a policy known as deterrence?
4. How did Western European countries begin to cooperate with one another after World War II?
5. Which nations did the Soviet Union force to become satellite nations?
6. How was Germany divided after World War II?
7. How did the Soviet Union try to stop people in East Berlin from escaping to West Berlin?
8. Who became the Soviet leader in 1985?
9. How did the Soviet Union change in 1991?

77

Differentiated Instruction

Meeting Special Needs: Interpersonal Draw a line down the middle of the room with a piece of chalk or masking tape. Half of your students should be on the side with the door. The other half should have limited or no access to "the outside world." Tell your students that they should imagine a wall where the line is. From now on, they can't communicate with their friends on the other side of the line. Those on the side with the door will have free access to the rest of the school. Those on the other side of the line will have to get permission to leave and are stuck with the supplies they have on hand. Have the class discuss the consequences of dividing the classroom. L1

 **EE4 Human Systems: Standard 13**

Chapter 11

Section 2, pages 319–323

More About the Photos

Berlin After the airlift ended in 1949, Berlin remained divided into East and West. It wasn't until 1990 that the city reunited and again became Germany's capital.

Caption Answer Even though the Soviets closed off land and water routes into Berlin, the West was able to maintain its hold there by bringing in supplies by airplane.

✓ Reading Check Answer

the split between Eastern and Western Europe

3 ASSESS

Assign Section 2 Assessment as homework or an in-class activity.

Have students use the Interactive Tutor Self-Assessment CD-ROM to review Section 2.

L2

Section Quiz

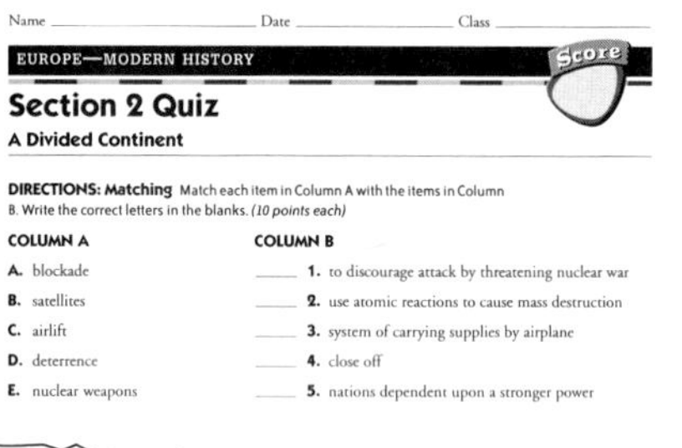

Name ______ Date ______ Class ______

EUROPE—MODERN HISTORY — Score

Section 2 Quiz

A Divided Continent

DIRECTIONS: Matching Match each item in Column A with the items in Column B. Write the correct letters in the blanks. *(10 points each)*

COLUMN A	COLUMN B
A. blockade	____ 1. to discourage attack by threatening nuclear war
B. satellites	____ 2. use atomic reactions to cause mass destruction
C. airlift	____ 3. system of carrying supplies by airplane
D. deterrence	____ 4. close off
E. nuclear weapons	____ 5. nations dependent upon a stronger power

oice In the blank at the left, write the letter of the

NATIONAL GEOGRAPHIC On Location

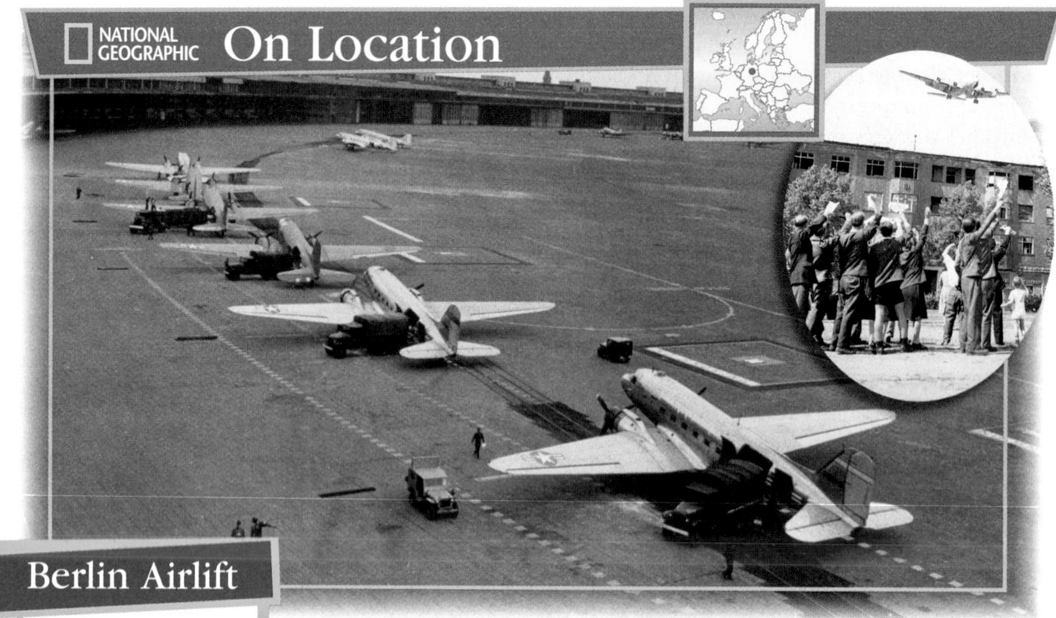

Berlin Airlift

People in West Berlin (above right) wave to an American airlift plane. A line of planes (above) waits to be unloaded at a Berlin airfield.

Technology **How did airplane technology affect Soviet military plans in Germany?**

In response, the United States and Great Britain began an **airlift**, or a system of carrying supplies into West Berlin by airplane. Day and night, the planes flew tons of food, fuel, and raw materials into the city. This heroic effort caused the Soviets to finally end the 11-month blockade of West Berlin. That same year, two separate governments were set up. Bonn became the capital of West Germany, which was democratic. East Berlin, in the Soviet zone, became the capital of East Germany, which was communist. West Berlin remained a democratic stronghold surrounded by communism.

The Berlin Wall Many people in East Germany were unhappy under communist rule. About 3 million people fled to West Berlin in search of political freedom and better living conditions. The East German government wanted to stop this movement. In August 1961, the government built a 103-mile (166-km) wall between East and West Berlin. The wall, with Soviet soldiers guarding it, became a symbol of the split between Eastern and Western Europe. Many East Germans continued to risk their lives trying to escape over or under the wall.

✓ **Reading Check** **What did the Berlin Wall symbolize?**

Freedom for Eastern Europe

During the Cold War, the Soviet Union spent large sums of money on military and space ventures. In spite of plans to improve consumer housing and agriculture, the economies of the Soviet Union and its satellites kept falling further and further behind the United States and its Western European allies.

Team-Teaching Activity

Economics Invite a teacher with a background in economics to class to discuss how business is run under communism and capitalism. Then make a chart on the board, with a heading for the Soviet Union and one for the United States. Have students answer the following questions for each column: *Who determines what new businesses should begin? How do people get jobs? How are salaries determined? Who controls the prices of consumer goods? Who gets the business profits?* Afterwards, discuss the advantages and disadvantages of each system. **L2** 

EE4 Human Systems: Standard 12

In 1985 Mikhail Gorbachev became the leader of the Soviet Union. To encourage economic growth, he introduced reforms that loosened government control over the Soviet people and the satellite nations. These reforms unleashed a powerful desire for independence. Soon, the satellite nations in Eastern Europe began to demand their freedom. The first successful challenge to communist rule came in Poland. In 1989 the Polish communists lost power as a result of a democratic election. In East Germany, massive protests caused the country's communist government to resign. The Berlin Wall came down, and West Germany and East Germany reunited in October 1990. By 1991 all of the Soviet-controlled nations in Eastern Europe had thrown off communist rule in favor of democracy.

The Soviet Union officially broke up on December 25, 1991. It separated into Russia and a number of other independent republics. Yugoslavia and Czechoslovakia also broke up. After much fighting and a number of civil wars, Yugoslavia became the independent republics of Slovenia, Croatia, Bosnia and Herzegovina, Macedonia, and Serbia and Montenegro. Czechoslovakia peacefully became the Czech Republic and Slovakia. All of these countries today struggle with poor economies, ethnic tensions, and a lack of understanding of democracy. You will read more about the countries of Eastern Europe in Chapter 13.

✓ Reading Check **Which Russian leader moved the Soviet Union and Eastern Europe toward democracy?**

Web Activity Visit ***The World and Its People*** Web site at twip.glencoe.com and click on **Chapter 11–Student Web Activities** to learn more about the Cold War.

Section 2 Assessment

Defining Terms

1. **Define** Cold War, nuclear weapon, deterrence, satellite nation, blockade, airlift.

Recalling Facts

2. **History** What was the purpose of the Marshall Plan?
3. **Place** Which countries were considered satellites of the Soviet Union?

Critical Thinking

4. **Making Inferences** What are the similarities and differences between a "cold" war and a "hot" war?
5. **Analyzing Information** How did the city of Berlin reflect tensions between the United States and the Soviet Union?

Graphic Organizer

6. **Organizing Information** Create a chart like this. Explain how each of the following events intensified the Cold War.

Marshall Plan	
Truman Doctrine	
NATO	
Warsaw Pact	

Applying Social Studies Skills

7. **Analyzing Maps** Look at the map of Western and Eastern Europe on page 320. Name the Western European countries that shared a border with countries in Eastern Europe.

Social Studies Online

Objectives and answers to the Student Web Activity can be found in the Web Activity Lesson Plan at twip.glencoe.com

✓ Reading Check Answer

Mikhail Gorbachev

L1/ELL

Reading Essentials and Study Guide

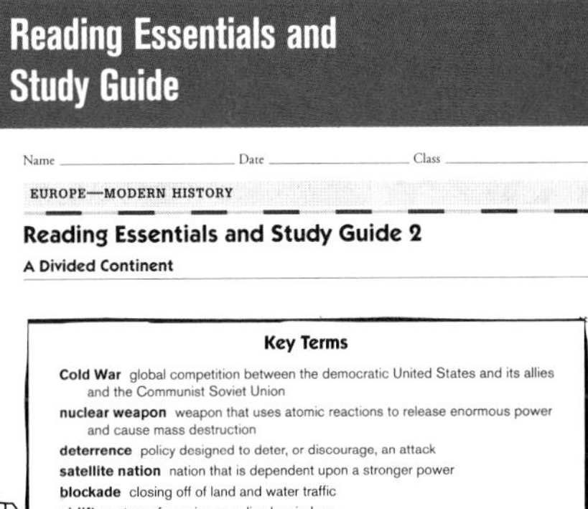
Name ______ Date ______ Class ______

EUROPE—MODERN HISTORY

Reading Essentials and Study Guide 2
A Divided Continent

Key Terms

Cold War global competition between the democratic United States and its allies and the Communist Soviet Union
nuclear weapon weapon that uses atomic reactions to release enormous power and cause mass destruction
deterrence policy designed to deter, or discourage, an attack
satellite nation nation that is dependent upon a stronger power
blockade closing off of land and water traffic
airlift system of carrying supplies by airplane

4 Close

Have students look up the Russian term *perestroika* to find out its English translation. *("restructuring")* Ask students why they think that term was used to describe Gorbachev's policies. *(He restructured Russia's economy to allow more free enterprise.)*

Section 2 Assessment

1. The terms are defined in the Glossary.
2. to help rebuild Europe after WWII
3. Bulgaria, Romania, Czechoslovakia, Hungary, Poland, East Germany
4. In a cold war there's no official declaration of war or direct military confrontation.
5. It had separate democratic and communist governments and was divided by the Berlin Wall.
6. *Marshall Plan:* improved economies of Western Europe to stop spread of communism; *Truman Doctrine:* military aid to countries fighting communism; *NATO:* military alliance of Western nations against Soviets; *Warsaw Pact:* anti-Western military alliance between the Soviet Union and its satellites
7. Finland, Federal Republic of Germany, Austria, Yugoslavia, Greece, Turkey

1 Focus

Section Objectives

1. Discuss the outcome of the breakup of the Soviet Union.
2. Explain how Europe has become more united.
3. Explain the challenges facing Europe today.

BELLRINGER
Skillbuilder Activity

Project transparency and have students answer the question.

Daily Focus Skills Transparency

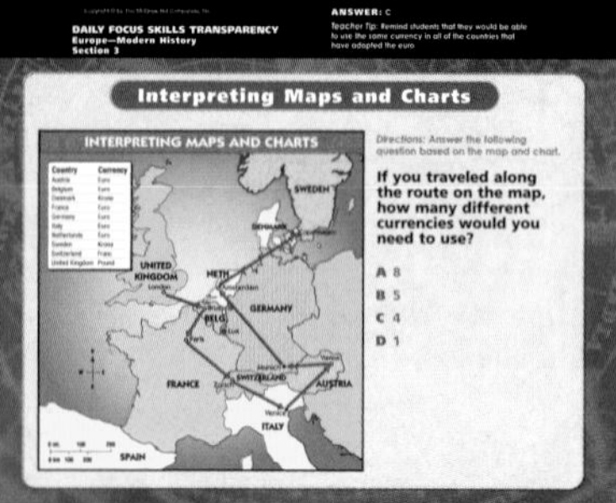

Reading Preview

■ **Activating Prior Knowledge** Have students think about the consequences if the United States were 50 separate small countries. How would this affect its political and economic power?

■ **Preteaching Vocabulary** Have students brainstorm a list of what they know or have heard about Europe. Have them evaluate the accuracy of this list after they have read the section.

Guide to Reading

Main Idea

Although the Cold War is over, many challenges still face the old and new nations of Europe.

Term to Know

- euro

Reading Strategy

Create a chart like the one below and write one key fact about each topic.

European Union	
NATO	
Chunnel	
Pollution	

Section 3 Moving Toward Unity

NATIONAL GEOGRAPHIC Exploring Our World

The end of communist rule in 1989 brought many changes to Eastern Europe and the Soviet Union. Factory workers now labor to convert weapons no longer needed to new uses. In this factory, workers remove the cannons from tanks, make other changes, and paint the vehicles red and white. Why? They are creating radio-controlled fire-fighting vehicles.

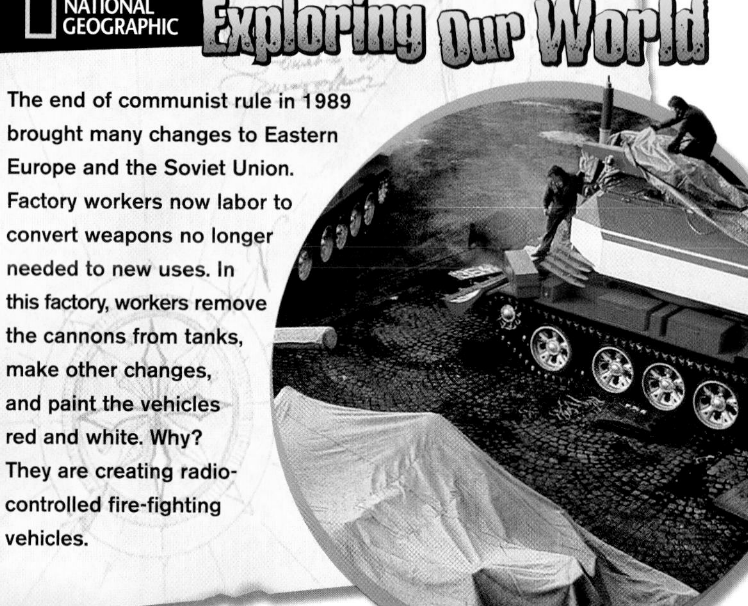

Since the fall of communism and the Soviet Union, there is no longer a political division between western and eastern Europe. Cultural and economic differences remain, however. As a result of cooperation though, Europe is becoming an economic powerhouse in the world.

The New Europe

As you learned in Section 2, many European countries joined together for economic reasons after World War II. One of the economic alliances was the Common Market, which became the European Union (EU) in 1993. At that time, the twelve members included the United Kingdom, Ireland, France, Luxembourg, Spain, Portugal, Denmark, the Netherlands, Belgium, Germany, Italy, and Greece. Austria, Finland, and Sweden joined in 1995. In 2004, ten additional countries, including many from eastern Europe, joined the EU. Three other nations have begun preparations to join the EU.

Section Resources

Reproducible Masters

- Reproducible Lesson Plan
- Daily Lecture and Discussion Notes
- Note-taking Guide
- Guided Reading Activity
- Reading Essentials and Study Guide
- Section Quiz

Transparencies

- Daily Focus Skills Transparency

Multimedia

- Vocabulary PuzzleMaker CD-ROM
- Interactive Tutor Self-Assessment CD-ROM
- Presentation Plus! CD-ROM
- ExamView® Pro Testmaker CD-ROM
- MindJogger Videoquiz

The European Union is moving toward even greater unity today. Some Europeans would eventually like to see it become a United States of Europe that would include all European countries. Citizens of EU countries hold common passports and can travel anywhere in the EU to work, shop, save, and invest. In January 2002, most EU members began using a common currency, the **euro,** to replace their national currencies. This means that citizens of countries in the EU are using the same type of money to buy goods and services. You can read more about the European Union and its significance in **Time Perspectives: Exploring World Issues** on pages 327–333.

Continued Cooperation European countries have cooperated in science and technology as well as economics. Europe had one of the first treaties on nuclear energy. The European Atomic Energy Community (EURATOM) has wide powers. These include the right to enter into contracts, obtain raw materials, and establish standards to protect workers and the general population from nuclear radiation.

Technology has also brought Europe's countries closer. A high-speed rail system links London in the British Isles with Paris and Brussels on the European mainland. The rail line passes beneath the English Channel through the Chunnel, or Channel Tunnel. In 2000 Denmark and Sweden were connected for the first time when they opened a bridge and tunnel system linking the two countries.

NATO's New Role In recent years, the once-communist eastern European countries have joined NATO. Russia, at first, was opposed to NATO's growth toward its borders. Now it cooperates with NATO as a limited partner. With more members, NATO is moving beyond its original role as Europe's protector from communism. It has taken on

The Euro

Ten different national sides of the one euro coin are shown, along with the front image (above) that does not change.

Place **How many nations can you identify by the images chosen to represent the country?**

Chapter 11

Section 3, pages 324–326

TEACH

Analyzing Information For many Europeans, the use of the euro is a major change after centuries of separate monetary systems defined by distinctive notes and coins. Have students use the Internet and library sources to learn more about how the euro works. Have students research the economic risks a common currency may entail as well as the probable benefits. Students should organize the information in a chart and present their findings to the class. L3

More About the Photos

The Euro In January 2002, euro notes and coins began replacing the currencies of the 12 members of the European Monetary Union (EMU).

Caption Answer *Top row:* Austria (Mozart), Belgium (King Albert), Finland (two swans over a lake), France (Tree of Life), Germany (Federal Eagle); *bottom row:* Ireland (Irish harp), Italy (Leonardo da Vinci drawing), Netherlands (Queen Beatrix), Portugal (seal with castles and coats of arms), Spain (King Juan Carlos). Luxembourg and the United Kingdom are not represented here.

Reading Strategy — Reading the Text

Making Inferences When students make inferences, they use their reason and their experience to take educated guesses about what an author implies or suggests. To help students learn how to make inferences, guide them to look for text clues. Encourage them to notice descriptions, events, or relationships that might signal information a writer is suggesting. Ask students to think about what they already know, either from prior text clues or from their own experiences. L1

*Use the **Reading Skills Handbook** for more reading strategies.*

Assess

Assign Section 3 Assessment as homework or an in-class activity.

Have students use the Interactive Tutor Self-Assessment CD-ROM to review Section 3.

Reading Check Answer

the euro

Reading Check Answer

Rivers transfer waste from country to country.

L1/ELL

Reading Essentials and Study Guide

Name ______ Date ______ Class ______

EUROPE—MODERN HISTORY

Reading Essentials and Study Guide 3

Moving Toward Unity

Key Term

euro common currency used by most European Union members

Drawing From Experience

Have you ever had to solve a problem by yourself or when others were working against you? Have you ever worked on a problem with other peo- ... as interested as you were in solving it? Which way allowed ... the easiest way? Cooperation among coun-

Close

Have students use the Internet and other sources to create a chart showing the countries that are members of the EU along with the year they joined.

peacekeeping tasks in the former Yugoslav republics. Its forces are also now being trained to respond quickly to terrorist threats that may arise in areas far beyond NATO's borders. NATO's success, however, depends on close ties among its members. In 2003 these ties were strained as a result of the United States-led war on Iraq. Several member countries, such as France and Germany, opposed the conflict.

Reading Check What is the name of the new European Union currency?

Facing the Region's Challenges

Several challenges face Europe, which Europeans are actively trying to solve. The income gap between the rich and poor nations of Europe needs to be lessened. The increasing food and health needs of the people of these countries must also be met.

Environmental Issues Another important challenge for Europe concerns the environment. In France, rivers like the Seine and the Loire are polluted, as are the major canals. Nowhere is the problem worse than in the Rhine River. As the river flows north, it passes through a continuous bank of cities and industrial regions. By the time it reaches the Netherlands, it is carrying a staggering 25 million tons of industrial waste per year. This is all dumped into the North Sea. Air pollution is another environmental issue in the region. You will learn more about these and other challenges in Chapters 12 and 13.

Reading Check Why is water pollution a problem in Europe?

Section 3 Assessment

Defining Terms

1. **Define** euro.

Recalling Facts

2. **History** List three of the original twelve members of the European Union.
3. **Economics** What is the European Union trying to achieve?

Critical Thinking

4. **Making Inferences** What allowed the construction of the Chunnel?
5. **Making Predictions** Do you think Russia will join the European Union? Why or why not?

Graphic Organizer

6. **Organizing Information** Create a diagram like the one below. Then write three of Europe's challenges in the ovals.

Applying Social Studies Skills

7. **Summarizing** Write a paragraph that summarizes the changing role of NATO. In your summary, be sure to include NATO's original role, why that role has changed, and any issues surrounding its new role.

Section 3 Assessment

1. The terms are defined in the Glossary.
2. *Any three:* United Kingdom, Ireland, France, Luxembourg, Spain, Portugal, Denmark, the Netherlands, Belgium, Germany, Italy, Greece
3. greater economic unity between European countries
4. technology and cooperation among European countries
5. *Possible answers:* It will join for more economic power and easier trade. It won't join to maintain its independence.
6. gap between rich and poor, rising health and food needs, air pollution
7. Paragraphs should summarize NATO's role and the challenges it faces.

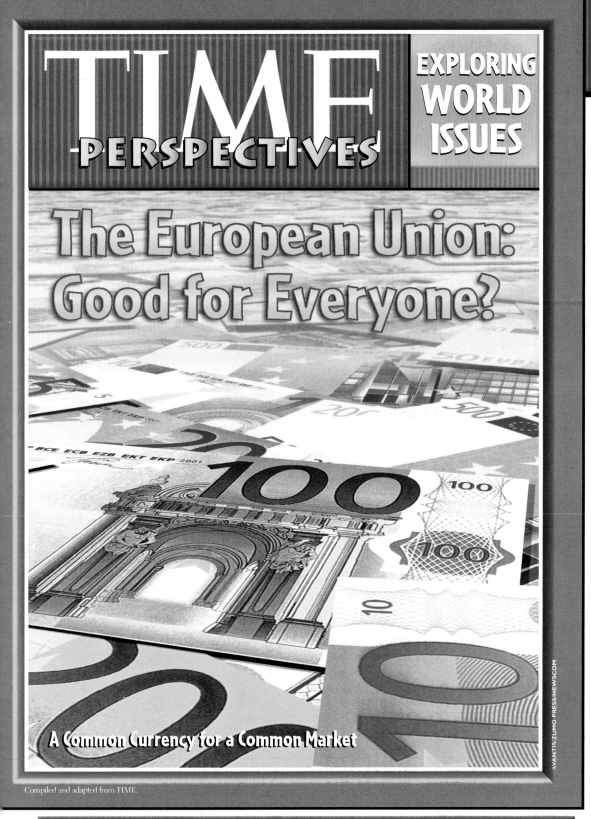

TIME PERSPECTIVES

EXPLORING WORLD ISSUES

The European Union: Good for Everyone?

A Common Currency for a Common Market

AVANTIS/ZUMO PRESS/NEWSCOM

Compiled and adapted from TIME.

Making Connections

Free Trade Organize students into groups. Tell each group to imagine what the United States would be like if we did not have free trade among the states. Students should assume that each state prints its own currency, controls who can enter that state, and charges tariffs (taxes) on items coming from other states. Have the groups discuss the disadvantages of this system. Can they think of any advantages? Have groups discuss this topic and then present their advantages and disadvantages to the class as a whole. After students have completed their presentations, explain that these are the kinds of problems that Europe is working to solve. L2

TIME PERSPECTIVES

Exploring World Issues

Teacher Background

With increasing globalization, it has become more difficult for individual European countries to compete in the world marketplace. In addition, since the breakup of the Soviet Union, the nations of eastern Europe have needed support in implementing democratic governments and marketplace economies. The European Union has played an increasingly important role in tackling these problems.

The concept of a unified Europe gained strength after World War II. The 1951 establishment of the European Coal and Steel Community (ECSC) and the 1957 establishment of the European Economic Community (EEC) were both major milestones along the way. In 1992, the Treaty on European Union was signed in the Netherlands.

Preparing the Student

Remind students that both Western and Eastern Europe have traditionally been composed of small, autonomous countries, each with its own currency, tariffs, and security forces. Over the centuries, numerous major wars have been fought, resulting in loss of life, regional and ethnic hostilities, and shifting national boundaries.

Europeans began using new currency in January 2002. The impact was gigantic—like this mocked-up coin.

1 Focus

Ask students the following question: **What services do you think a democratic government should provide for its people?** Encourage students to think about this in the very broadest sense. Some items might include free trade, a common currency, free elections, individual rights, an army, and free public education. Then tell students that if a country is small and must interact with many other countries, providing economic and political security can be difficult. The European Union is designed to simplify these activities.

Have students examine the "Europe in 2004" map. Be sure to discuss any changes that have taken place in EU membership since this map was created. L2

Europe in 2004

ANSWERS

1. Current EU members are in Western Europe. Nations that want to join are in Eastern Europe.
2. *Possible answers:* The nations of Eastern Europe do not have as long a history of democratic government as those in Western Europe. In addition, they tend to be less stable and not as well off economically. These differences could cause disagreement on economic and political issues.

Building a United Europe

Damien Barry had a problem. In 2001 he wanted to work in Paris, France. The trouble was, the French were fussy. French people could work in France. And so could people from 14 other loosely united European nations. All 15 nations belonged to the **European Union**, or the EU. Barry wasn't from an EU nation. He was from Brooklyn, New York.

But that didn't stop him. Ireland is an EU nation. It grants citizenship to anyone with an Irish parent or grandparent. Barry had Irish grandparents. He applied for an Irish passport and got one. Soon after that he had a job in a French bank.

A Big Story for Americans

Barry would never give up his U.S. citizenship. Yet he's not letting go of his Irish passport, either. "It's worth a million dollars to me," he said.

Barry's story suggests how much the EU matters to Americans. The EU nations form the world's largest trading group. That gives them awesome power to control jobs and the price of many things you buy.

That's not all. The EU is expanding. In 2004, ten new countries—including Poland and Estonia—joined the Union. In the past, the U.S. dealt one-on-one with those countries. Now it has to deal with them through the EU. By 2020, the EU plans to grow to 30 nations.

What's more, the EU is piecing together a small army. That army will change the U.S. military's role in Europe. "In the next 10 years," TIME magazine said in 2001, "there may be no bigger story than the EU."

Europe in 2004

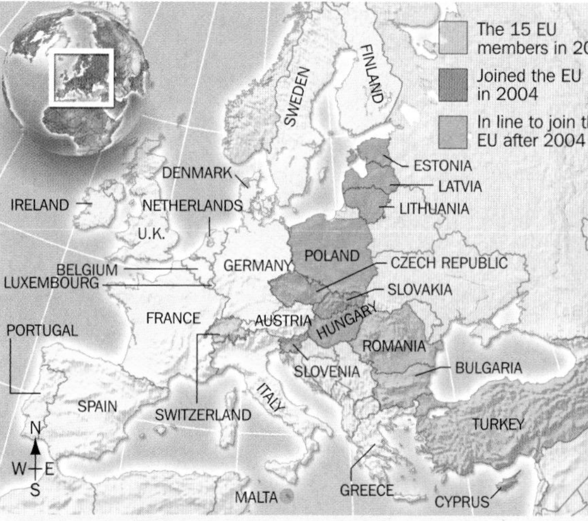

INTERPRETING MAPS

1. **Categorizing** In which part of Europe—east or west—are most current EU members? In which part are nations that want to join?
2. **Making Inferences** Why might it be hard for all these nations to agree on important issues?

328

Team-Teaching Activity

Economics Ask a teacher with a background in economics to discuss the significance of the EU's having a single currency, the euro. Have the teacher emphasize the role of a common currency in the establishment of free trade. Ask the teacher to lead a class discussion about why some countries might not want to adopt the common currency. Some reasons might be that some countries (especially those in Eastern Europe) have weaker economies than others. Other countries associate their currency with their national identity. L2

 **EE4 Human Systems: Standard 11**

The new euro is exchanged for bread.

Farm animals' health is a big EU concern.

This Dutchman is one of hundreds of pro soccer players in the EU.

CENTRAL AUDIOVISUAL LIBRARY, EUROPEAN COMMISSION

Common Problems

What is the EU? Simply put, it is a group of nations that have joined forces to solve common problems. Finding a safe way to recycle used batteries is one problem. Convincing Europeans to stop smoking is another. Making sure goods flow freely within Europe is still another. The EU is a **free trade zone**. That means EU nations don't tax goods they import from each other.

The EU hopes to help its members prosper. But it has another goal—bringing peace to a continent with a long history of conflict.

A Heavy Load

To get the euro to shoppers by January 2002, the EU sent 56 billion coins to banks in 12 nations. The coins weighed 168,000 tons—24 times more than the Eiffel Tower in Paris, France!

Weak Government

Some people compare the EU with the United States around 1785. The U.S. government had little muscle then. It had no president, no army, no power to raise money. The states had all the money and almost all the power.

In many ways, the EU is like that. Officials at EU offices in Brussels, Belgium, make a lot of decisions, but they have no **authority** to force member nations to give up their armies. They can't even make them stop printing money.

In 1789 America's original 13 states agreed to give up some powers. They did it by approving the U.S. Constitution.

The EU doesn't have a constitution. Its members are joined by treaties, or written agreements. Without a constitution to guide them, it's hard to get all of the nations to agree on anything.

New Money

One thing most EU members have agreed on is a common currency, the **euro**. In January 2002, most EU nations replaced their own money with the euro. Three nations—the United Kingdom, Denmark, and Sweden—chose not to make the switch immediately.

In 2001 Damien Barry got paid in French francs. Now he gets paid in euros. When he goes to Italy and Holland, he no longer carries Italian lira and Dutch guilders. Like his Irish passport, the euro has made his life easier. And it's done the same for the more than 300 million Europeans who use the euro every day.

CENTRAL AUDIOVISUAL LIBRARY, EUROPEAN COMMISSION

EXPLORING THE ISSUE

1. **Making Generalizations** Three EU nations refused to replace their currencies with the euro. Why might a nation want to keep its own currency?
2. **Cause and Effect** How might the EU affect your life—today, and in the future?

329

TIME REPORTS

2 TEACH

Reading Strategy

Identifying Main Ideas
Have students read the subsection titled "Common Problems." Ask them to state the main idea presented in this section. Write their answers. Then have them find examples in the text that support this idea. L1

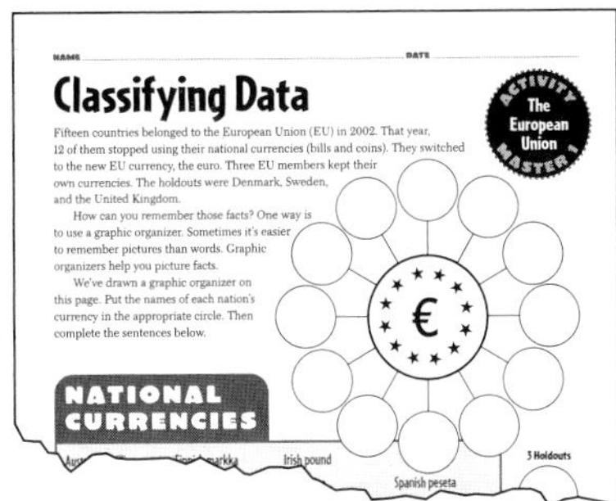

EXPLORING THE ISSUE

ANSWERS

1. *Possible answers:* Some countries feel that having their own currency is vital to their identity and that being able to control interest rates and exchange rates is vital for a stable economy.
2. *Possible answers:* It simplifies travel within Europe. It may make it more difficult for a U.S. citizen to get a job in Europe. Increased trade between European countries could reduce Europe's trade with the United States.

Differentiated Instruction

Meeting Special Needs: Auditory/Musical Have students use the Internet to find the anthem of the European Union. Students should then listen to the anthem. Then have students respond to the following questions: **Can you identify the music?** *(the last movement of Beethoven's Ninth Symphony)* **How does the anthem make you feel? How do you think these feelings match the goals of the European Union? Why are symbols such as anthems important to the EU?** L1

Refer to *Inclusion for the Middle School Social Studies Classroom Strategies and Activities* in the TCR.

TIME PERSPECTIVES

Reading Strategy

Comparing and Contrasting Canada, the United States, and Mexico have joined together under NAFTA, the North American Free Trade Agreement. Have students research NAFTA and write a paragraph about how it is similar to the EU and how it differs. L3

More About the Photo

Jean Monnet Ask: Why would reducing an individual country's supply of coal and steel decrease the chance of war?

EXPLORING THE ISSUE

ANSWERS

1. International control of steel and energy production makes it more difficult for individual countries to wage war. Free trade, a common currency, open borders, and a European security force make people feel more united.
2. Businesses no longer have to worry about paying tariffs when exporting goods to another EU country. Time and money is saved in not having to perform currency exchanges.

TIME PERSPECTIVES

From Peace to Prosperity

World War II ended in 1945. It was the third time in 75 years that Germany and France had fought each other.

Could another war be prevented? A Frenchman named Jean Monnet thought so. He proposed taking coal and steel production out of the hands of individual countries. Without fuel and steel, he said, nations couldn't wage war.

UPI/CORBIS-BETTMANN

U.S. President John F. Kennedy shares a smile with Jean Monnet.

In 1951 six nations accepted Monnet's proposal. They were Belgium, West Germany, Italy, Luxembourg, the Netherlands, and France. They set up an organization that told each nation how much coal and steel it could produce.

A Free Trade Zone

That was a big step. Next, in 1957, all six nations agreed to stop taxing goods they imported from each other. Those **import taxes** acted like walls, stopping goods from moving between nations. By removing those walls, these nations created a **common market**.

How the EU Grew

1951: France, Germany, Italy, the Netherlands, Belgium, and Luxembourg agree to pool their coal, iron ore, and steel industries.

1973: Denmark, Ireland, and the United Kingdom join.

1981: Greece joins.

1986: Spain and Portugal join.

1995: Austria, Finland, and Sweden join.

2004: Cyprus, the Czech Republic, Estonia, Hungary, Latvia, Lithuania, Malta, Poland, Slovakia, and Slovenia join.

Common markets were nothing new. The United States had had one for more than 150 years. California never taxed beef "imported" from Texas, for instance. Free trade was new for Europe, however. And it helped businesses there grow.

Growing Pains

By 1995, nine nations had joined the original six, and ten countries became new members in 2004. Looking ahead, the EU expects to let other nations join by 2020.

Getting so many nations to work together won't be easy. But no one doubts that the EU's impact on the world is going to grow. ■

EXPLORING THE ISSUE

1. **Explaining** In what ways might the simple fact of the EU's existence promote peace?
2. **Cause and Effect** How might a common market help businesses grow?

330

Critical Thinking Activity

Drawing Conclusions Briefly remind students about the importance of Sir Winston Churchill who led Britain through World War II. Then tell the students that Churchill made the statement "But we have our own dream and our own task. We are with Europe but not of it. We are linked but not combined. We are interested and associated but not absorbed." **Ask students:** Do you think Winston Churchill would be in favor of or against the European Union? Why? Have students do some research to find out about the United Kingdom's role in the EU and why people there might feel separate from the rest of Europe. L2

 **EE4 Human Systems: Standard 13**

A Model for Change

Hungary had a bumpy 50 years after World War II. This East European nation suffered under Communist rule from 1948 to 1990. Now Hungarians have a democratic government. Individuals there can own their own businesses again. Those changes put Hungary on track to join the EU in 2004.

Qualifying for entry wasn't easy. Hungary's government had to budget its spending. It had to sell factories and land it owned to private citizens. Thousands of workers lost their jobs.

Creating Jobs

Hungarians were willing to make the sacrifices, because they wanted to join the EU. Once in, they would be able to sell what they made to other EU members. Those sales would create jobs at home and make lives easier for Hungarians.

Would Hungary have changed if the EU didn't exist? Certainly. But chances are it wouldn't have changed so fast—and so completely. The EU has served as a model for Hungary and other former Communist nations to follow.

The Top Two **Output of goods and services in 2001, in trillions of dollars**

Analyzing information
One of every 10 people in the world lives in the U.S. or in EU nations. But every year U.S. and EU workers together create more than half the world's goods and services. Why do you think this is so?

CENTRAL AUDIOVISUAL LIBRARY, EUROPEAN COMMISSION

▲ U.S. President George W. Bush confers with an EU official.

The EU has been especially good for the United States. Every day the U.S. and the EU nations sell each other goods worth $2 billion. In 2000 EU citizens bought nearly $41 billion worth of goods from Texas and California alone. That money paid the salaries of at least 696,000 Texans and Californians.

Democracy

The U.S. and the EU compete with each other. They often disagree on major issues. But they are firm friends, and both advocate democracy and free trade. The prospect of joining their "club" spurred Hungary and other nations to change—and to change quickly. ■

EXPLORING THE ISSUE

1. **Comparing** How are the U.S. and the EU alike?
2. **Making Inferences** Why might a Hungarian worker be both for and against change?

Recommended Internet Sites

www.eurunion.org
The official Web site of the Delegation of the European Commission to the United States contains a wealth of information on the EU. Within this site is the "A-Z Index of European Union Web sites."

The Top Two

ANSWER
The United States and Europe are more technologically advanced, and their citizens use more consumer goods than most countries.

NAME ______ DATE ______

Interpreting Tables

ACTIVITY MASTER 1 — The European Union

Although the European Union (EU) isn't a single nation, the table below treats it as one. That's because the EU's 15 member nations form a single economic bloc. That bloc is big enough to challenge the world's strongest economy—that of the United States. The table suggests why. Read it. Then react to the statements that follow.

The United States and the European Union in 2000*

	European Union	United States
Area (in 1,000 square miles; add 000)	1,249	3,718
Population (in millions; add 000,000)	378	284
People per square mile	302	77
GDP** (in billions; add 000,000,000)	$7,837	$9,896
Value of all imports (in billions)	$959	$1,258
Value of all exports (in billions)	$855	$782
People with jobs (in millions; add 000,000)	171	139
[illegible] benefits	$26	$22

EXPLORING THE ISSUE

ANSWERS

1. *Possible answers:* Like most countries of the EU, U.S. states have a common currency, no tariffs, and open borders between them.
2. *For:* They will be able to freely sell to other EU countries, hopefully increasing the number of available jobs. *Against:* Some workers lost jobs when the government sold industries that it owned.

Interdisciplinary Activity

Language Arts Have students write lyrics for the European Union anthem. The lyrics should be written in English and should emphasize the EU's goals, such as strength through solidarity, peace, and democracy. Have students work individually or in small groups. When they are finished, have them share their results. Discuss the problem with having the anthem lyrics in a single language, such as English. L1

 **EE4 Human Systems: Standard 10**

Current Events Journal

Have students create a chart that lists issues that face the European Union and how they are trying to be resolved. Issues may include ethnic differences among people, weak economies of countries planning to join the EU, and political divisions among governments. Have students watch for news reports about these issues throughout the year and update their charts to show how the issues are being resolved.

EXPLORING THE ISSUE

ANSWERS

1. In all four disputes, at least one side believes that the other is trying to unfairly control it.
2. They all involve controversial subjects that at least one side believes are of global importance. For example, global warming and food safety could affect everyone.

Resolving Differences: What Can One Person Do?

The EU and the United States are good friends. But friends have their differences. Here are four:

1. The U.S. doesn't trade with Libya, Iran, and Cuba. It tried to get EU nations to do the same, but the EU refused. Companies in EU nations want to be free to sell goods to anyone.

2. The EU puts limits on some U.S. companies that do business in Europe. Some Americans don't think the EU should be able to tell U.S. companies how to run their businesses.

3. Another dispute involved food. U.S. food companies wanted to grow **genetically altered crops** that resisted disease. So their scientists invented new types of crops. Many Europeans are afraid that those crops might pose health risks. Some EU countries won't even allow those products inside their borders.

4. Global warming is another sticking point. Scientists fear that gases from factories and automobiles keep the earth's heat from escaping into space. EU nations and the U.S. can't agree on the best way to solve the problem.

Choose one of the four problems. Research each side's argument. Then create a solution to the problem—one you think both sides might accept.

Make your views public. Put them in a letter. Send the letter to your representatives in Congress. You might even want to send a copy to the European Union's ambassador to the United States. Address: Ambassador, Delegation of the European Commission to the United States, 2300 M Street, NW, Washington, D.C., 20037. 

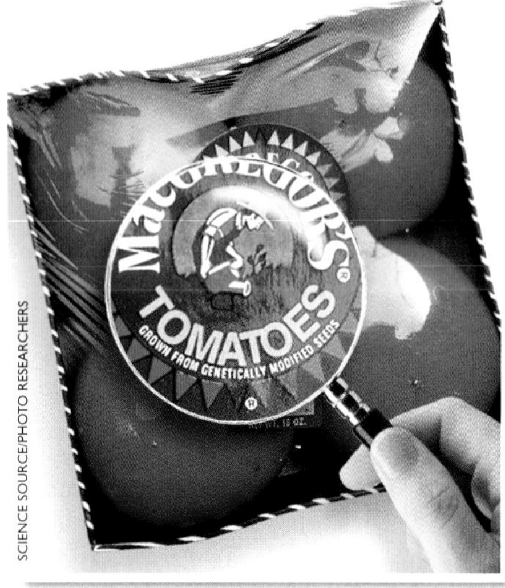

SCIENCE SOURCE/PHOTO RESEARCHERS

▲ Genetically altered foods are creating an EU controversy.

EXPLORING THE ISSUE

1. **Analyzing Information** What might all four disputes have to do with each side's view of its "rights"?
2. **Making Predictions** How might these disputes affect parts of the world outside the U.S. and the EU?

332

Your Government and You

While the United States and Europe have long been friends, there are many ongoing differences between the two countries. Twice a year, an EU-U.S. summit is held. Areas of concern are discussed along with proposed solutions. Students can read about some of these issues at the Web site www.eurunion.org/partner/summit.htm

Have students explain one difference they've read about to the rest of the class. Then ask students their opinions about whom they agree with on the issue and why. L2

EE4 Human Systems: Standard 13

REVIEW AND ASSESS

UNDERSTANDING THE ISSUE

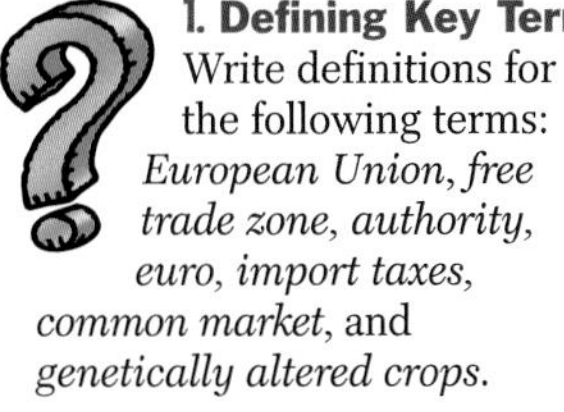

1. Defining Key Terms Write definitions for the following terms: *European Union, free trade zone, authority, euro, import taxes, common market,* and *genetically altered crops.*

2. Writing to Inform Write a short article about the European Union, explaining how it could affect you and other students. Use as many words as you can from the above list.

3. Writing to Persuade Write a letter to an imaginary friend in Denmark. Convince your friend that all European countries should use the euro.

INTERNET RESEARCH ACTIVITY

4. Use Internet resources to find information about the European Union. Read about the EU's three main governing bodies. Choose one and write a brief description of it in your own words. Then decide, with your classmates, how those bodies work together and which ones have the most power.

5. With your teacher's help, use Internet resources to research the symbols of the European Union: the flag, the anthem, and Europe Day. How is the EU's flag like—and different from—the first U.S. flag? Download the EU anthem. Why do you think the EU chose it? How is Europe Day like Independence Day in the U.S.? Put your answers in a 250-word essay.

BEYOND THE CLASSROOM

6. Research the history of the U.S. dollar. How hard was it to get Americans to accept U.S. currency in 1792? Ask your parents about the U.S. $2.00 bill. How did they react to its introduction? How is the dollar like the euro? Explain your answers in an article appropriate for a school newspaper.

7. Organize the class into three teams. Debate this resolution: "It is unfair for the EU to let only European citizens work in EU countries." A panel of student judges will decide which team has the most convincing arguments.

CENTRAL AUDIOVISUAL LIBRARY, EUROPEAN COMMISSION

The EU flag's gold stars represent solidarity and harmony among European peoples.

It's All About Jobs!

Where U.S. Exports Create Jobs
(Top ten states with jobs supported by exports to Europe)

State	Number of Jobs
1 California	490,300
2 New York	281,100
3 Washington	221,500
4 Texas	206,200
5 Mass.	141,400
6 Illinois	127,200
7 New Jersey	114,100
8 Michigan	88,800
9 Ohio	88,300
10 Penn.	83,200

Where Europe's Money Creates Jobs
(Top ten states with jobs supported by European companies)

State	Number of Jobs
1 California	336,300
2 New York	268,500
3 Texas	260,600
4 N. Carolina	200,000
5 Penn.	188,200
6 Illinois	185,000
7 Florida	183,800
8 Michigan	176,900
9 New Jersey	173,400
10 Ohio	162,200

Source: European-American Business Council. Note: "Europe" refers to the 15 EU members in 2003 plus four members of a related group, the European Free Trade Association (Iceland, Liechtenstein, Norway, and Switzerland).

BUILDING SKILLS FOR READING TABLES

1. **Analyzing Data** Using an almanac, find the 10 states with the largest populations. How many of those states are listed among the top 10 on each graph? What relationships do you see between state populations and jobs supported by exports? How might state populations influence the number of jobs European companies create in the U.S.? Put your answers in a short report.

2. **Making Inferences** European companies create more jobs in Florida and North Carolina than exports do. How might you explain this?

FOR UPDATES ON WORLD ISSUES GO TO www.timeclassroom.com/glencoe

3 ASSESS

Have students take the Time Reports Quiz or do the Alternative Assessment project for this unit provided in the Teacher's Classroom Resources.

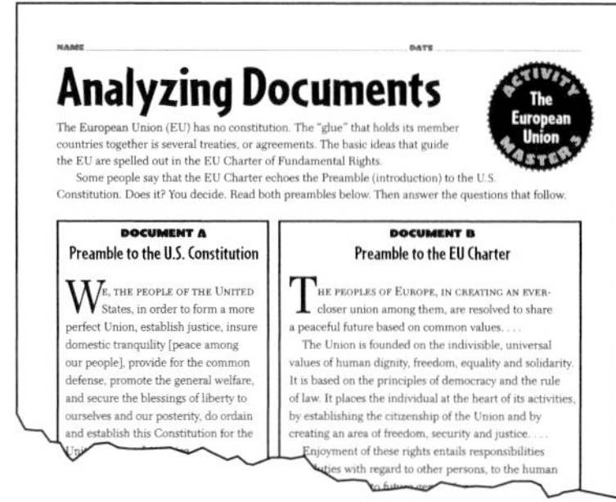

Analyzing Documents

Activity: The European Union

The European Union (EU) has no constitution. The "glue" that holds its member countries together is several treaties, or agreements. The basic ideas that guide the EU are spelled out in the EU Charter of Fundamental Rights.
Some people say that the EU Charter echoes the Preamble (introduction) to the U.S. Constitution. Does it? You decide. Read both preambles below. Then answer the questions that follow.

DOCUMENT A — Preamble to the U.S. Constitution

We, the people of the United States, in order to form a more perfect Union, establish justice, insure domestic tranquility [peace among our people], provide for the common defense, promote the general welfare, and secure the blessings of liberty to ourselves and our posterity, do ordain and establish this Constitution for the

DOCUMENT B — Preamble to the EU Charter

The peoples of Europe, in creating an ever-closer union among them, are resolved to share a peaceful future based on common values. . . .
The Union is founded on the indivisible, universal values of human dignity, freedom, equality and solidarity. It is based on the principles of democracy and the rule of law. It places the individual at the heart of its activities, by establishing the citizenship of the Union and by creating an area of freedom, security and justice. . . .
Enjoyment of these rights entails responsibilities . . . with regard to other persons, to the human

BUILDING SKILLS FOR READING TABLES

ANSWERS

1. Students should use an almanac to write their reports.
2. *Possible answer:* Florida and North Carolina have a desirable location and work force that attracts European companies with a U.S. market.

4 CLOSE

Reading Strategy

Synthesizing Ask students to write a paragraph starting with this topic sentence: *The European Union has had a positive effect on the world because . . . .*

Culminating Activity

To close this lesson, have students complete the Review and Assess section questions and activities above. Students should use classroom discussion, contextual clues, and their student dictionaries to write definitions for terms. Before assigning the Internet activities, it is recommended that you review your school district policy on student Internet use.

Focus on Debate

As a final activity for further student understanding of the issue, have students debate the pro and con positions of the following topic: **NAFTA has promoted economic growth in North America. L2**

 **EE4 Human Systems: Standard 11**

TEACH

Display a map of your city or county. Have students draw a freehand copy of the map. Ask them to mark on the map those areas where they think many people live and those where they think few people live. Point out that geographers express these differences as population density. Ask students what impact the population density of their city or county has on their lives. **L1**

Additional Skills Practice

1. **How is population density expressed?** *(as the number of people living in every square mile or square kilometer of an area)*
2. **How is population density shown on maps?** *(Distinct colors represent different ranges of population density.)*
3. **How is the population size of different cities shown on maps?** *(Different symbols represent different levels of population.)*

Additional Skills Resources

 Chapter Skills Review

 Building Geography Skills for Life

GLENCOE TECHNOLOGY

 **Skillbuilder Interactive Workbook CD-ROM, Level 1**

This interactive CD-ROM reinforces student mastery of essential social studies skills.

Social Studies Skill

Reading a Population Map

Population density is the number of people living in a square mile or square kilometer. A **population density map** shows you where people live in a given region. Mapmakers use different colors to represent different population densities. The darker the color, the more dense, or crowded, the population is in that particular area. Cities that are shown by dots or squares also represent different population sizes.

Learning the Skill

To read a population density map, follow these steps:

- Read the title of the map.
- Study the map key to determine what the colors mean.
- On the map, find the areas that have the lowest and highest population density.
- Identify what symbols are used to show how heavily populated the cities are.

Practicing the Skill

Look at the map below to answer the following questions.

1. Which color stands for 125–250 people per square mile (50–100 per sq. km)?
2. Which cities have more than 1 million people?
3. Which areas have the lowest population density? Why?

Applying the Skill

Obtain a population density map of your state. What is the population density of your area? What is the nearest city with 1 million people?

GO TO Practice key skills with **Glencoe Skillbuilder Interactive Workbook, Level 1.**

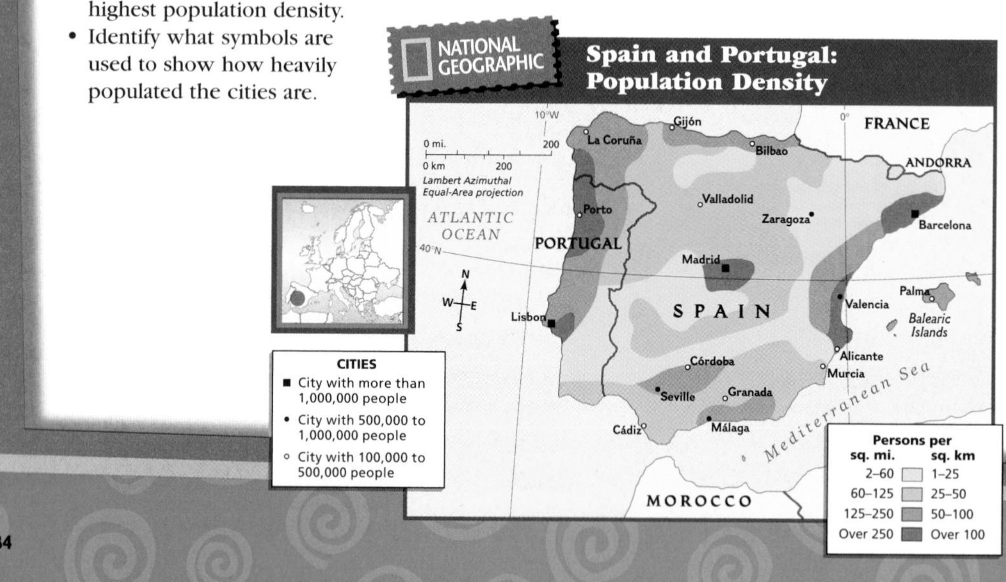

334

Practicing the Skill Answers

1. dark orange
2. Barcelona, Lisbon, Madrid
3. north central Spain, the interior of eastern Spain, and the interior of southern and southwestern Spain; these tend to be highland areas and may be too dry to support much farming.

Applying the Skill

Verify students' answers for accuracy.

Reading Review

Section 1 The Modern Era Emerges

Terms to Know
productivity
human resources
textiles
cottage industry
union
strike
imperialism
communism
Holocaust
genocide

Main Idea

Industrialization led not only to a higher standard of living for some, but also to increased tensions in the world.

✓Economics Machinery made it possible to increase productivity, leading to the Industrial Revolution.

✓Culture Industry changed the way people worked and lived.

✓Economics Competition for markets and resources led to imperialism and friction among European countries.

✓History The two World Wars changed the way wars were fought and created new political power for the United States and the Soviet Union.

Section 2 A Divided Continent

Terms to Know
Cold War
nuclear weapon
deterrence
satellite nation
blockade
airlift

Main Idea

After World War II, the democratic United States and the Communist Soviet Union worked to bring their forms of government to the war-torn nations of Europe.

✓History Competition between the United States and the Soviet Union started the Cold War.

✓Economics Western European countries joined together to form the European Common Market, which moved toward greater cooperation and economic development.

✓Government The Soviet Union made satellites of its surrounding nations.

✓History Berlin became a "hot spot" for conflict between the superpowers, symbolized by the Berlin Wall.

✓Government By 1991 countries in Eastern Europe had thrown off communist rule in favor of democracy.

Section 3 Moving Toward Unity

Term to Know
euro

Main Idea

Although the Cold War is over, many challenges still face the old and new nations of Europe.

✓Economics The European Union is moving much of Europe toward greater economic and political unity. It has expanded to include many eastern European countries.

✓Economics In 2002 most EU member countries began using a common currency.

✓Human/Environment Interaction Problems still remain in Europe, including poverty and pollution.

Reading Review

Use the Chapter 11 Reading Review to preview, review, condense, or reteach the chapter.

Preview/Review

Use the Terms to Know lists to help students review and study.

Activity Have students group the terms according to one of the following categories: industry, war, economics, politics. Some words may go under more than one category. Read a term out loud and ask for volunteers to categorize it and explain why they chose that category.

Vocabulary PuzzleMaker CD-ROM reinforces the vocabulary terms used in Chapter 11.

The Interactive Tutor Self-Assessment CD-ROM allows students to review Chapter 11 content.

Condense

Have students read the Chapter 11 summary statements.

Guided Reading Activities

Audio Program

Reteach

Reteaching Activity

Reading Essentials and Study Guide

Reading Strategy Read to Write

Understanding Perspective Have students do more research about Mikhail Gorbachev's policies of glasnost and perestroika. Discuss with the class how these policies might have changed life for Russians. Then, have your students write two letters as if they were a Russian citizen writing to a friend in the United States. The first letter should describe the writer's life before these policies were implemented (around 1985). The second should be dated a year later and describe how life has changed. L1

EE4 Human Systems: Standard 12

Assessment and Activities

GLENCOE TECHNOLOGY

MindJogger Videoquiz
Use MindJogger Videoquiz to review the Chapter 11 content.

Available in DVD and VHS

Using Key Terms
1. g
2. a
3. f
4. i
5. c
6. h
7. j
8. b
9. e
10. d

Reviewing the Main Ideas
11. People had to work on a regular schedule. Living conditions improved because manufactured goods were less expensive.
12. so they could have markets and resources for their factories
13. *Possible answers:* a worldwide depression; new alliances after WWI; Hitler became dictator of Germany.
14. The U.S. offered military aid to countries that were engaged in fighting communism inside their borders. The doctrine intensified the Cold War.
15. the European Union
16. an alliance of countries that wished to remain neutral during the Cold War; Yugoslavia
17. to prevent people from fleeing to West Berlin from East Berlin
18. Eastern Europe countries demanded independence and democracy.
19. hold common passports; travel anywhere in the EU to work, shop, save, invest; use a common currency to buy goods and services
20. a common currency used by most EU members
21. water and air pollution

Chapter 11 Assessment and Activities

Using Key Terms

Match the terms in Part A with their definitions in Part B.

A.
1. productivity
2. union
3. imperialism
4. communism
5. genocide
6. Cold War
7. deterrence
8. textiles
9. cottage industry
10. euro

B.
- **a.** group that bargains for better working conditions
- **b.** woven cloth
- **c.** mass murder of a people because of race, religion, ethnicity, politics, or culture
- **d.** European Union common currency
- **e.** work carried out in homes rather than in factories
- **f.** countries claim colonies for their resources and markets
- **g.** how much work can be done in a certain length of time
- **h.** conflict between the United States and the Soviet Union
- **i.** political system that called for the overthrow of the industrialized system
- **j.** designed to discourage a first attack

Reviewing the Main Ideas

Section 1 The Modern Era Emerges
11. **History** How did the Industrial Revolution change working and living conditions?
12. **Economics** Why did European countries find it necessary to have colonies?
13. **History** What were some of the problems that led to World War II?

Section 2 A Divided Continent
14. **History** What was the Truman Doctrine, and why was it important?
15. **History** What is the Common Market known as today?
16. **Government** What was the Non-Aligned Community, and which European nation belonged to it?
17. **History** Why did the Soviet Union build the Berlin Wall?
18. **Government** How did the policies of Mikhail Gorbachev affect Eastern Europe?

Section 3 Moving Toward Unity
19. **Economics** What are the advantages to citizens of EU member countries?
20. **Economics** What is the euro?
21. **Human/Environment Interaction** What environmental issues does Europe face?

NATIONAL GEOGRAPHIC — The Allies and Axis Powers

Place Location Activity

On a separate sheet of paper, match the letters on the map with the numbered places listed below.

1. Germany
2. Italy
3. United Kingdom
4. France
5. China
6. Soviet Union
7. Japan
8. United States

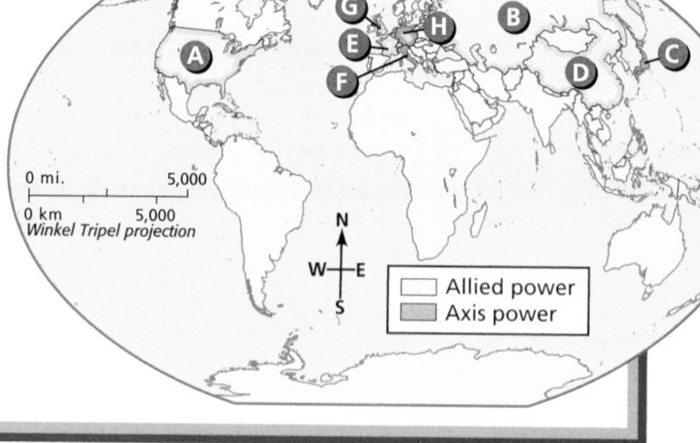

NATIONAL GEOGRAPHIC Place Location Activity

1. H
2. F
3. G
4. E
5. D
6. B
7. C
8. A

Critical Thinking
22. *Possible answers:* Western Europe could become stronger economically; Russia and/or its former satellites could become part of a European trade agreement.
23. *Possible answers:* Marshall Plan; Truman Doctrine; formation of NATO, Benelux, and European Union; Warsaw Pact; Berlin Wall

Self-Check Quiz Visit ***The World and Its People*** Web site at twip.glencoe.com and click on **Chapter 11—Self-Check Quizzes** to prepare for the Chapter Test.

Critical Thinking

22. **Predicting Consequences** What further changes will occur in Europe as a result of the European Union and the collapse of the Soviet Union?
23. **Sequencing Events** List five events that made the Cold War "colder."

1. ____________________
2. ____________________
3. ____________________
4. ____________________
5. ____________________

Comparing Regions Activity

24. **History** Like Europe after World War II, the Korean Peninsula was comprised of Communist and non-Communist countries. Eastern Europe had much in common with North Korea during the Cold War. Create a chart and list the similarities between Communist Eastern Europe and North Korea. On another chart, list the similarities between non-Communist Western Europe and South Korea.

Mental Mapping

25. **Focusing on the Region** Draw a simple outline map of Europe and label the following:

- United Kingdom
- Germany
- Italy
- France
- Russia
- Spain
- Greece

Technology Skills Activity

26. **Using the Internet** Research the national currencies that are being used in at least three European countries that have not yet adopted the euro. Note what each country's currency is called and when the country plans to phase it out. Research to find how the transition to the euro works.

Standardized Test Practice

Directions: Study the map, and then answer the question that follows.

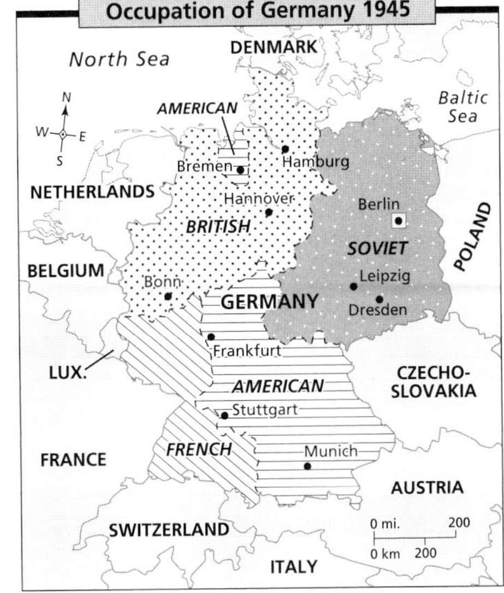

1. **In 1945, which country controlled the land surrounding Berlin, Germany's capital?**
   - **F** the United Kingdom
   - **G** the Soviet Union
   - **H** the United States
   - **J** France

Test-Taking Tip: This question asks you to synthesize information on the map with prior knowledge. Notice that the map does not specifically state that the United Kingdom, for example, controlled a portion of Germany. Instead, it refers to this area as "British."

337

Assessment and Activities

Standardized Test Practice

1. G

Tested Objectives: Reading a map, analyzing information

Social Studies Online

Have students visit the Web site at twip.glencoe.com to review Chapter 11 and take the Self-Check Quiz.

Chapter Test Bonus Question

This question may be used for extra credit on the chapter test.

What was it called when European nations claimed colonies in Africa and Asia? *(imperialism)*

FOLDABLES™ Study Organizer **Dinah Zike's Foldables**

Culminating Activity Have students use their foldables to write a one-page essay that describes how historical events have influenced Europe. Students should use words that identify cause-and-effect relationships.

Comparing Regions Activity

24. Students' charts should identify political, economic, and social similarities between the countries under each type of economic system.

Mental Mapping Activity

25. This exercise helps students visualize the region they have been studying and understand the relationships of various points. Accept all attempts at freehand mapping that show places in correct relation to one another.

Technology Skills Activity

26. Students' reports should include information about the transition to the euro and citations of Internet Web sites that were used.

Chapter 12 Resources

Note: The following materials may be used when teaching Chapter 12.
Section level support materials are shown at point of use in the margins of the Teacher Wraparound Edition.

Timesaving Tools

TeacherWorks™ All-In-One Planner and Resource Center

- **Interactive Teacher Edition** See the **Interactive Teacher Edition** CD-ROM to electronically integrate your Teacher Wraparound Edition and blackline masters.
- **Interactive Lesson Planner** Organize your week, month, semester, or year with all the lesson helps you need. The **Interactive Lesson Planner** CD-ROM contains all Chapter 12 resources.

Use Glencoe's **Presentation Plus!** multimedia teacher tool to easily present dynamic lessons that visually excite your students. Using Microsoft PowerPoint® you can customize the presentations to create your own personalized lessons.

TEACHING TRANSPARENCIES

Graphic Organizer Transparency 3 L2

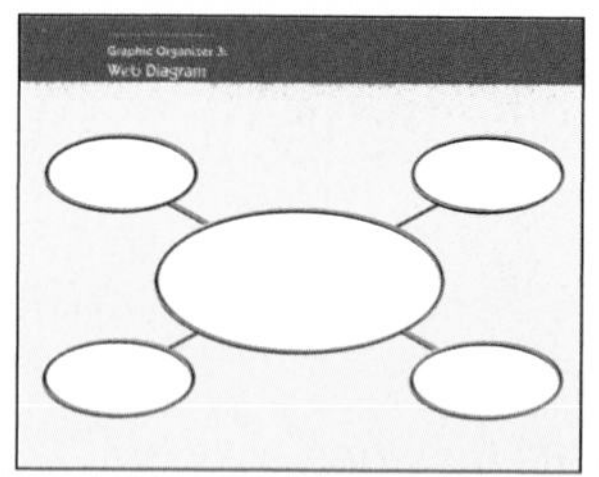

In-text Map Transparency L1

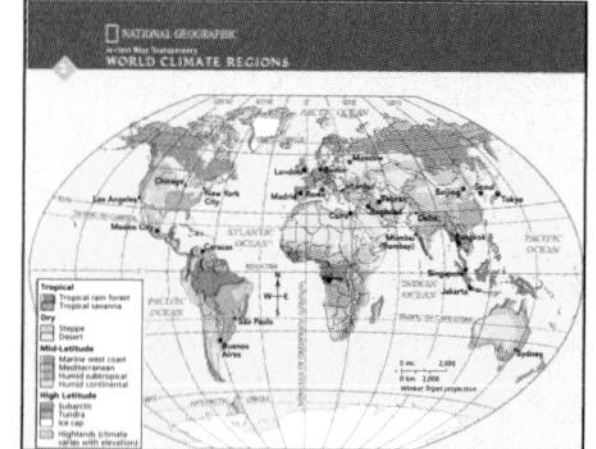

FOLDABLES™ Study Organizer

Dinah Zike's Foldables

Foldables are three-dimensional, interactive graphic organizers that help students practice basic writing skills, review key vocabulary terms, and identify main ideas. Additional chapter activities can be found in the ***Reading and Study Skills Foldables*** booklet.

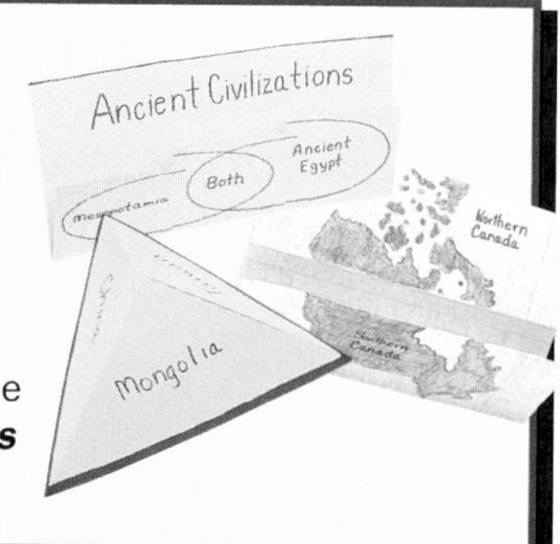

MAP AND GEOGRAPHY SKILLS

Chapter Map Activity L2

GeoLab Activity L2

READING SUPPORT

Vocabulary Activity L1

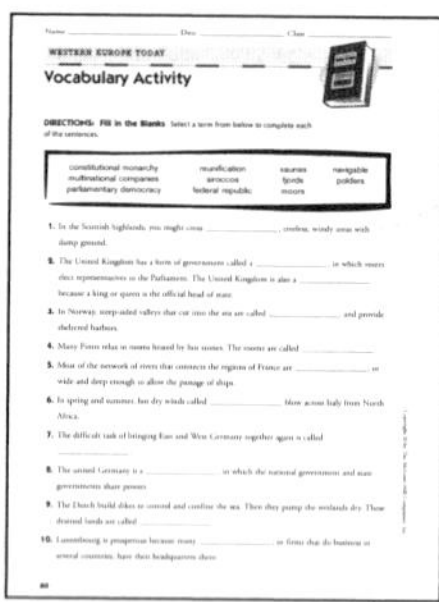

Workbook Activity L1

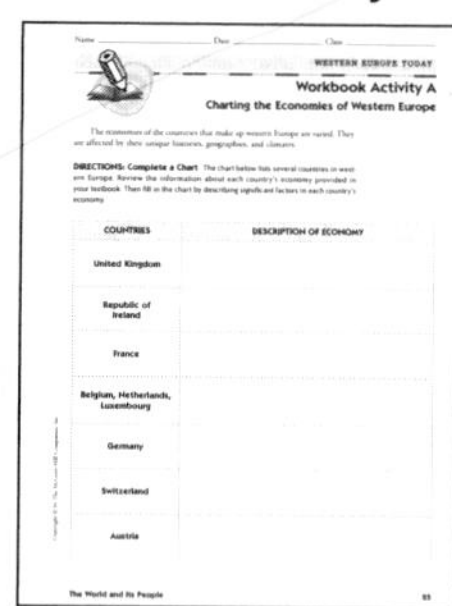

Reading and Writing Skills Activity L1/ELL

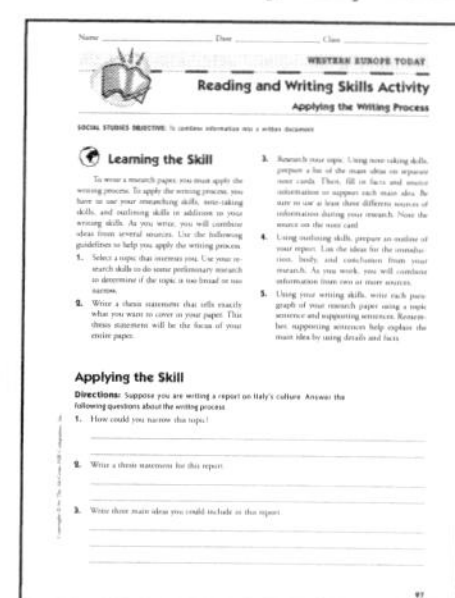

DIFFERENTIATED INSTRUCTION

Use these review and reinforcement materials to help less-proficient readers, English learners, and gifted and talented students.

Reteaching Activity L1

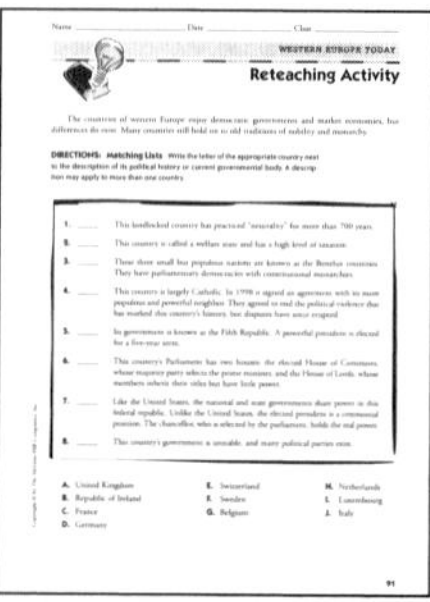

Chapter Skills Review L2

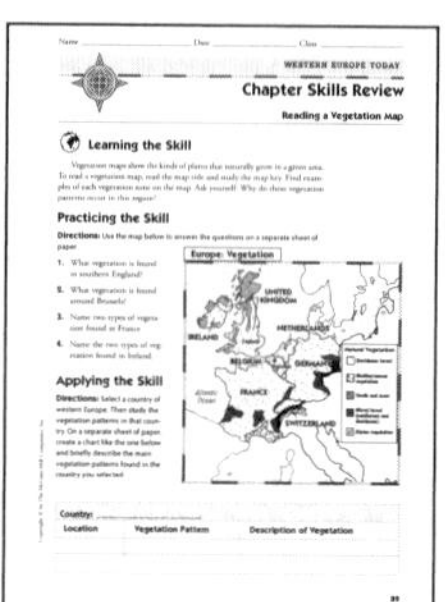

Cooperative Learning Activity L1/ELL

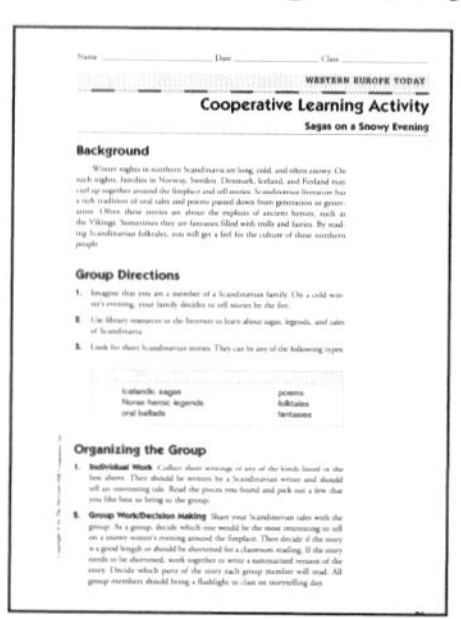

Enrichment Activity L3

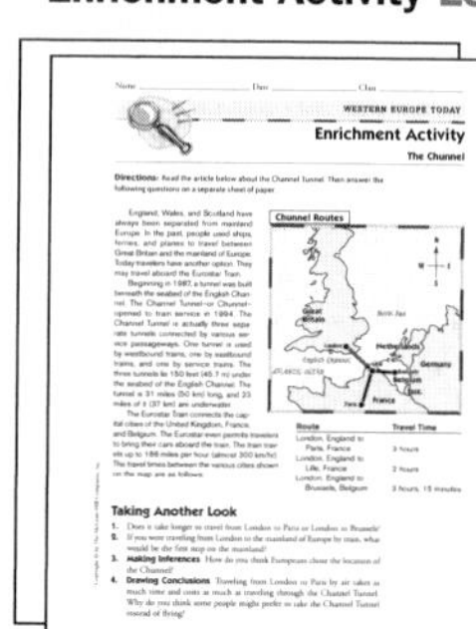

ASSESSMENT

Chapter Test, Form A L2

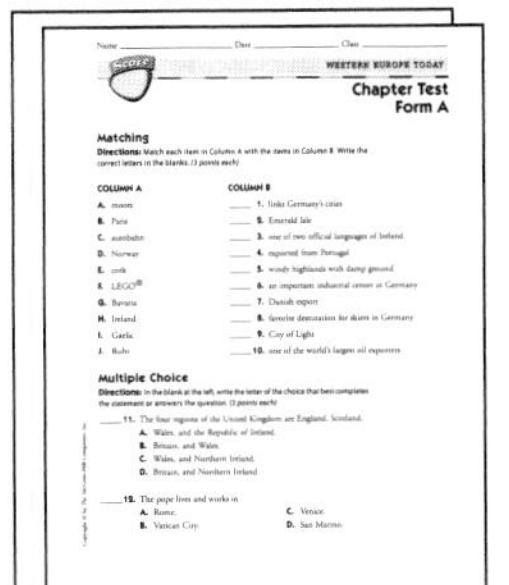

Chapter Test, Form B L2

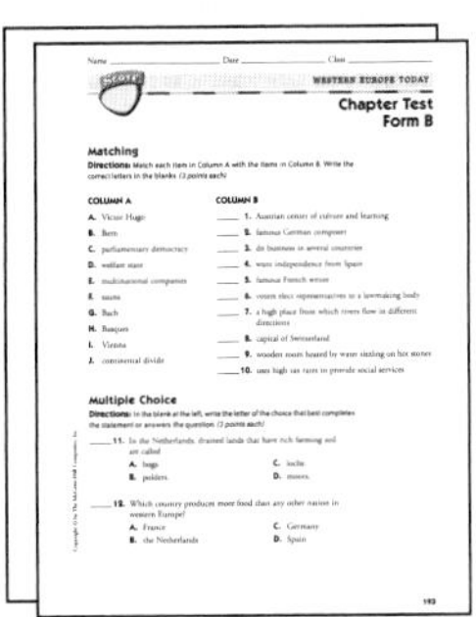

Performance Assessment Activity L1/ELL

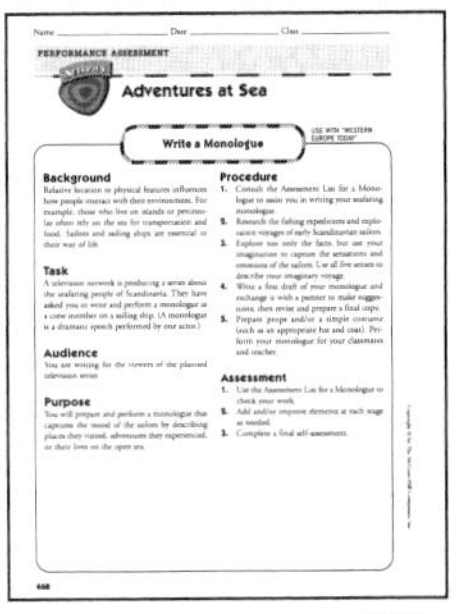

ExamView® Pro Testmaker CD-ROM

STANDARDIZED ASSESSMENT SKILLS

Critical Thinking Skills Activity L2

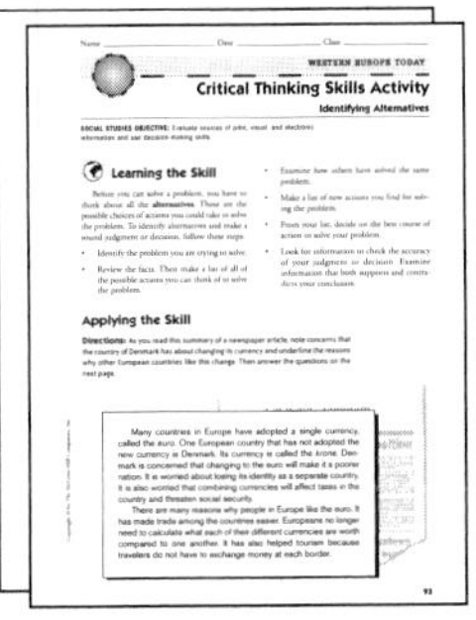

Map and Graph Skills Activity L2

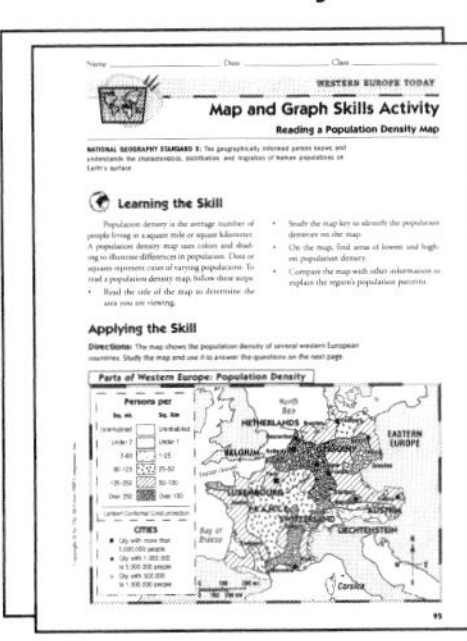

Standardized Test Skills Practice Workbook Activity L2

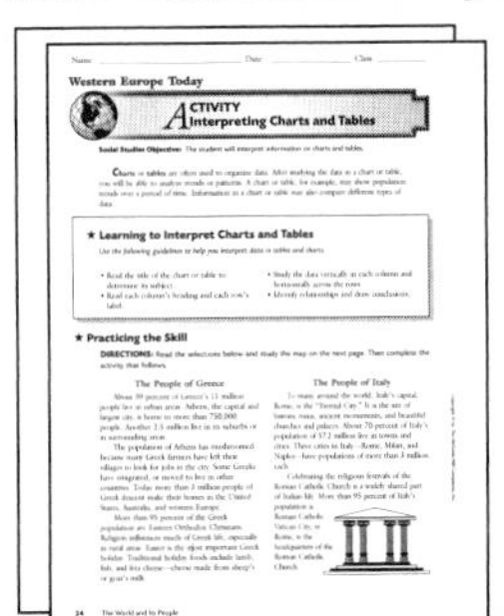

HOME INVOLVEMENT

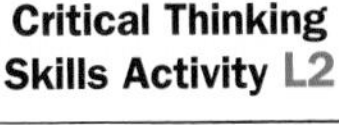

Take-Home Review Activity L1

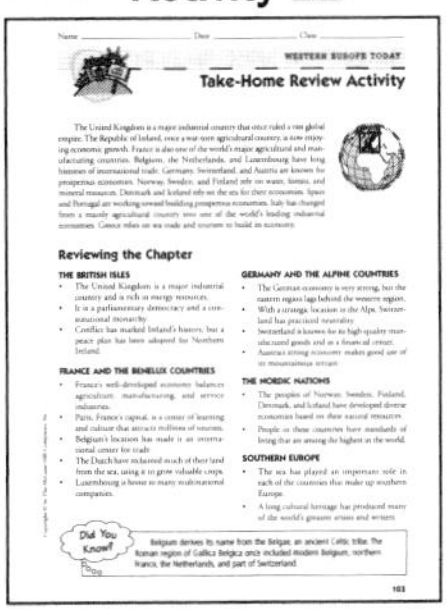

MULTIMEDIA

- National Geographic's The World and Its People
- MindJogger Videoquiz
- Vocabulary PuzzleMaker CD-ROM
- Interactive Tutor Self-Assessment CD-ROM
- ExamView® Pro Testmaker CD-ROM
- TeacherWorks CD-ROM
- StudentWorks CD-ROM
- Skillbuilder Interactive Workbook CD-ROM, Level 1
- Presentation Plus! CD-ROM
- Audio Program

SPANISH RESOURCES

The following Spanish language materials are available in the Spanish Resources binder:

- Spanish Summaries
- Spanish Vocabulary Activities
- Spanish Guided Reading Activities
- Spanish Quizzes and Tests
- Spanish Take-Home Review Activities
- Spanish Reteaching Activities

Meeting National Standards

Geography for Life

The following standards are covered in Chapter 12:

Section 1	EE1 The World in Spatial Terms: Standards 1, 2, 3
	EE6 The Uses of Geography: Standard 17
Section 2	EE4 Human Systems: Standards 9, 10, 11, 12, 13
Section 3	EE2 Places and Regions: Standards 4, 5, 6
Section 4	EE4 Human Systems: Standards 9, 11, 12, 13
Section 5	EE1 The World in Spatial Terms: Standards 1, 2, 3
	EE2 Places and Regions: Standard 4

State and Local Objectives

____

____

Chapter 12 Planning Guide

SECTION RESOURCES

Daily Objectives	Reproducible Resources	Multimedia Resources
Section 1 **The British Isles** 1. Discuss the economies and governments of the United Kingdom and Ireland. 2. Explain the history and culture of the United Kingdom and Ireland.	Reproducible Lesson Plan Daily Lecture and Discussion Notes Note-taking Guide Guided Reading Activity* Reading Essentials and Study Guide* Section Quiz*	Daily Focus Skills Transparency GeoQuiz Transparency In-text Map Transparency Vocabulary PuzzleMaker CD-ROM Interactive Tutor Self-Assessment CD-ROM ExamView® Pro Testmaker CD-ROM Presentation Plus! CD-ROM
Section 2 **France and the Benelux Countries** 1. Discuss the economy and people of France. 2. Compare the cultures and economies of the Benelux countries.	Reproducible Lesson Plan Daily Lecture and Discussion Notes Note-taking Guide Guided Reading Activity* Reading Essentials and Study Guide* Section Quiz*	Daily Focus Skills Transparency Vocabulary PuzzleMaker CD-ROM Interactive Tutor Self-Assessment CD-ROM ExamView® Pro Testmaker CD-ROM Presentation Plus! CD-ROM
Section 3 **Germany and the Alpine Countries** 1. Discuss the economy and government of Germany. 2. Compare the geography and economies of Switzerland and Austria.	Reproducible Lesson Plan Daily Lecture and Discussion Notes Note-taking Guide Guided Reading Activity* Reading Essentials and Study Guide* Section Quiz*	Daily Focus Skills Transparency Vocabulary PuzzleMaker CD-ROM Interactive Tutor Self-Assessment CD-ROM ExamView® Pro Testmaker CD-ROM Presentation Plus! CD-ROM
Section 4 **The Nordic Nations** 1. Describe the landscapes and climates of the Nordic nations. 2. Compare the economies and people of this region.	Reproducible Lesson Plan Daily Lecture and Discussion Notes Note-taking Guide Guided Reading Activity* Reading Essentials and Study Guide* Section Quiz*	Daily Focus Skills Transparency Vocabulary PuzzleMaker CD-ROM Interactive Tutor Self-Assessment CD-ROM ExamView® Pro Testmaker CD-ROM Presentation Plus! CD-ROM
Section 5 **Southern Europe** 1. Compare the geography and people of Spain and Portugal. 2. Summarize the history and cultural contributions of Italy. 3. Explain how physical geography has shaped life and history in Greece.	Reproducible Lesson Plan Daily Lecture and Discussion Notes Note-taking Guide Guided Reading Activity* Reading Essentials and Study Guide* Section Quiz*	Daily Focus Skills Transparency GeoQuiz Transparency Vocabulary PuzzleMaker CD-ROM Interactive Tutor Self-Assessment CD-ROM ExamView® Pro Testmaker CD-ROM Presentation Plus! CD-ROM MindJogger Videoquiz

00:00 **Out of Time?** Assign the **Reading Essentials and Study Guide*** for this chapter.

*Also available in Spanish

Teacher to Teacher

Europe in a Box

Phillip G. Hays
Conrad Weiser Middle School
Robesonia, Pennsylvania

Students create a cereal box showing the culture of their chosen country. Each student brings in an empty cereal box and chooses one country from Europe. Students use drawings, photos from magazines, and other visual aids to design their boxes. On the front panel of the box, students should show a map of the country and visuals of the land. The back panel should show photos of the people. On the side panels, students should create charts and graphs to illustrate the economy. The box top lists statistics about the country. The name of the cereal should reflect the country's name or a part of its culture—Ukraine Krispies, Londonberry Loops. Three items representing the land, the people, and the economy are placed inside the box (for example, a wool scarf to represent sheep raising). Students then incorporate main and supporting ideas to create a 30-second commercial to advertise their "cereal."

Meeting Special Needs

In addition to the Differentiated Instruction strategies found in each section, the following resources are also suitable for your special needs students:

- ***ExamView® Pro Testmaker CD-ROM*** allows teachers to tailor tests by reducing answer choices.
- The ***Audio Program*** includes the entire narrative of the student edition so that less-proficient readers can listen to the words as they read them.
- The ***Reading Essentials and Study Guide*** provides the same content as the student edition but is written two grade levels below the textbook.
- ***Guided Reading Activities*** give less-proficient readers point-by-point instructions to increase comprehension as they read each textbook section.
- ***Enrichment Activities*** include a stimulating collection of readings and activities for gifted and talented students.

NATIONAL GEOGRAPHIC TEACHER'S CORNER

Index to National Geographic Magazine:

The following articles may be used for research relating to this chapter:

- "London," by Simon Worrall, June 2000.
- "Tale of Three Cities," by Joel L. Swerdlow, August 1999.
- *Biodiversity,* a National Geographic Special Edition, February 1999.

National Geographic Society Products:

To order the following products for use with this chapter, call National Geographic Society at 1-800-368-2728:

- *GeoKit: Pollution* (Kit)
- *Europe: The Road to Unity* (Video)
- *Capitalism, Communism, Socialism Series* (3 Videos)

NGS ONLINE

Access National Geographic's Web site for current events, activities, links, interactive features, and archives.
www.nationalgeographic.com

NATIONAL GEOGRAPHIC MapMachine

Find the latest coverage of geography in the news, atlas updates, cartographic activities with interactive maps, an online map store, and links at www.nationalgeographic.com/maps

SOCIAL STUDIES Online

Use our Web site for additional resources. All essential content is covered in the Student Edition.

You and your students can visit twip.glencoe.com, the Web site companion to *The World and Its People.* This innovative integration of electronic and print media offers your students a wealth of opportunities. The student text directs students to the Web site for the following options:

- Chapter Overviews
- Student Web Activities
- Self-Check Quizzes
- Textbook Updates

Answers are provided for you in the Web Activity Lesson Plan. Additional Web resources and Interactive Tutor puzzles are also available.

Introducing Chapter 12

Social Studies online

Introduce students to chapter content and key terms by having them access Chapter Overview 12 at twip.glencoe.com

Chapter Objectives

1. Describe the government and economy of the United Kingdom and its relationship with Ireland.
2. Compare the economies and cultures of France and the Benelux countries.
3. Discuss the economies of Germany, Switzerland, and Austria.
4. Explain how physical geography affects life in the Nordic nations.
5. Describe the cultural contributions of southern Europe.

GLENCOE TECHNOLOGY

NATIONAL GEOGRAPHIC

The World and Its People Video Program

Chapters 10–12 Western Europe

The following segments enhance the study of this chapter:

- **Crazy for Tulips**
- **Bears of Svalbard**
- **Gran Paradiso**

MindJogger Videoquiz

Use MindJogger Videoquiz to preview the Chapter 12 content.

Both programs available in DVD and VHS

Chapter 12 Western Europe Today

The World and Its People NATIONAL GEOGRAPHIC

To learn more about the people and places of western Europe, view ***The World and Its People* Chapters 10–12** videos.

Social Studies online

Chapter Overview Visit ***The World and Its People*** Web site at twip.glencoe.com and click on **Chapter 12—Chapter Overviews** to preview information about western Europe.

338

Reading Strategy — Purpose for Reading

Have students use the **Think/Pair/Share** reading strategy before they read the chapter. **Think**—Quickly review information about what students have already learned about European history. Focus students' attention on what they have learned about ancient Greece and Rome, the two World Wars, and the European Union. Ask the students to think about how Europe's past has influenced it today. **Pair**—Have students discuss their ideas with a partner. **Share**—Ask students to share their responses and discuss them as a class. Talk about how western European countries have affected American history and culture. As students read the chapter, have them think about how Europe might affect the United States in the future. L1

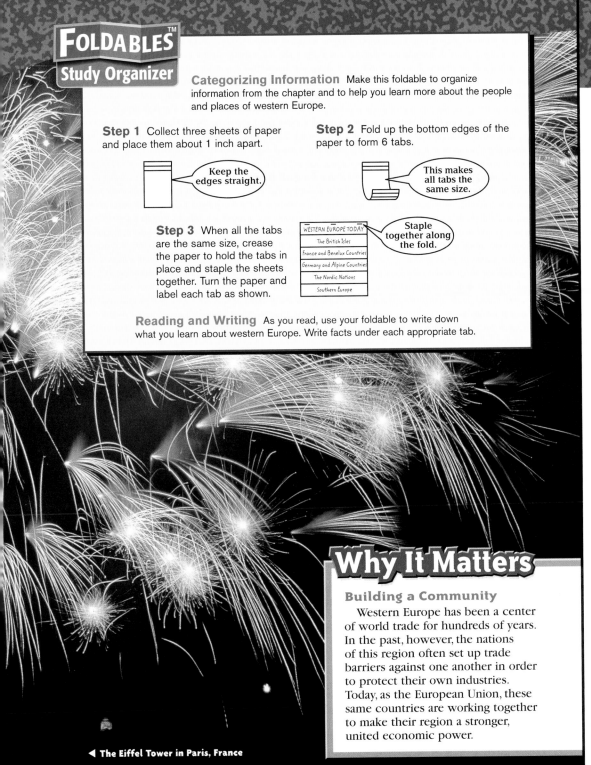

FOLDABLES™ Study Organizer

Categorizing Information Make this foldable to organize information from the chapter and to help you learn more about the people and places of western Europe.

Step 1 Collect three sheets of paper and place them about 1 inch apart.

Keep the edges straight.

Step 2 Fold up the bottom edges of the paper to form 6 tabs.

This makes all tabs the same size.

Step 3 When all the tabs are the same size, crease the paper to hold the tabs in place and staple the sheets together. Turn the paper and label each tab as shown.

WESTERN EUROPE TODAY
The British Isles
France and Benelux Countries
Germany and Alpine Countries
The Nordic Nations
Southern Europe

Staple together along the fold.

Reading and Writing As you read, use your foldable to write down what you learn about western Europe. Write facts under each appropriate tab.

Why It Matters

Building a Community

Western Europe has been a center of world trade for hundreds of years. In the past, however, the nations of this region often set up trade barriers against one another in order to protect their own industries. Today, as the European Union, these same countries are working together to make their region a stronger, united economic power.

◀ The Eiffel Tower in Paris, France

About the Photo

Bastille Day, July 14, is a national holiday in France celebrated with parades, speeches, and fireworks. It commemorates the 1789 "storming of the Bastille," an infamous Paris prison, in the opening days of the French Revolution. Ask students to compare Bastille Day with the Fourth of July. Why are these holidays important to the people of France and the United States?

FOLDABLES™ Study Organizer — Dinah Zike's Foldables

Purpose This activity requires students to create a table and organize information from the chapter on it. Students group information from the chapter into categories, in effect comparing the people and places of the countries of western Europe.

Have students complete the ***Reading and Study Skills Foldables*** activity for this chapter.

Why It Matters

The European Union's mission is to organize relations between the Member States and between their peoples in a coherent manner and on the basis of solidarity. However, there are many difficulties in trying to unite different countries and cultures. Organize students into five groups and assign one of the following topics to each group: *money, language, laws, defense, social programs.* Have students prepare a brief presentation on how their topic presents barriers to unification and what they think could be done to overcome the barriers.

1 Focus

Section Objectives

1. Discuss the economies and governments of the United Kingdom and Ireland.
2. Explain the history and culture of the United Kingdom and Ireland.

BELLRINGER
Skillbuilder Activity

Project transparency and have students answer the question.

Daily Focus Skills Transparency

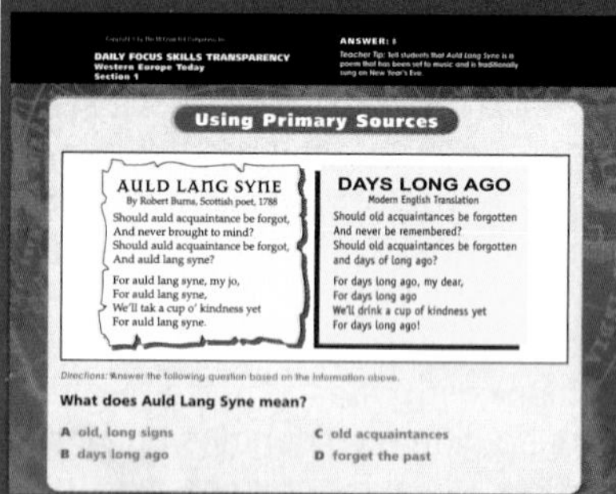

Using Primary Sources

AULD LANG SYNE
By Robert Burns, Scottish poet, 1788
Should auld acquaintance be forgot,
And never brought to mind?
Should auld acquaintance be forgot,
And auld lang syne?
For auld lang syne, my jo,
For auld lang syne,
We'll tak a cup o' kindness yet
For auld lang syne.

DAYS LONG AGO
Modern English Translation
Should old acquaintances be forgotten
And never be remembered?
Should old acquaintances be forgotten
and days of long ago?
For days long ago, my dear,
For days long ago
We'll drink a cup of kindness yet
For days long ago!

What does Auld Lang Syne mean?

A old, long signs
B days long ago
C old acquaintances
D forget the past

Reading Preview

■ **Activating Prior Knowledge** American law and government are based on practices followed in one of the countries of western Europe. Ask them to identify that country. *(United Kingdom or England or Great Britain)*

■ **Preteaching Vocabulary** Have students find the words *democracy* and *monarchy* in the section. Have them explain the differences between these two forms of government.

Guide to Reading

Main Idea

The United Kingdom and Ireland are small in size, but their people have had a great impact on the rest of the world.

Terms to Know

- moor
- parliamentary democracy
- constitutional monarchy
- peat
- bog

Reading Strategy

Create a diagram like this one. Fill in the names of the four regions that make up the United Kingdom and one fact about each. Create a second diagram for Ireland and include one fact about it.

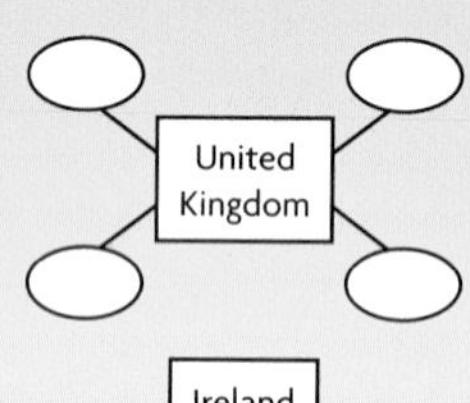

Section 1 The British Isles

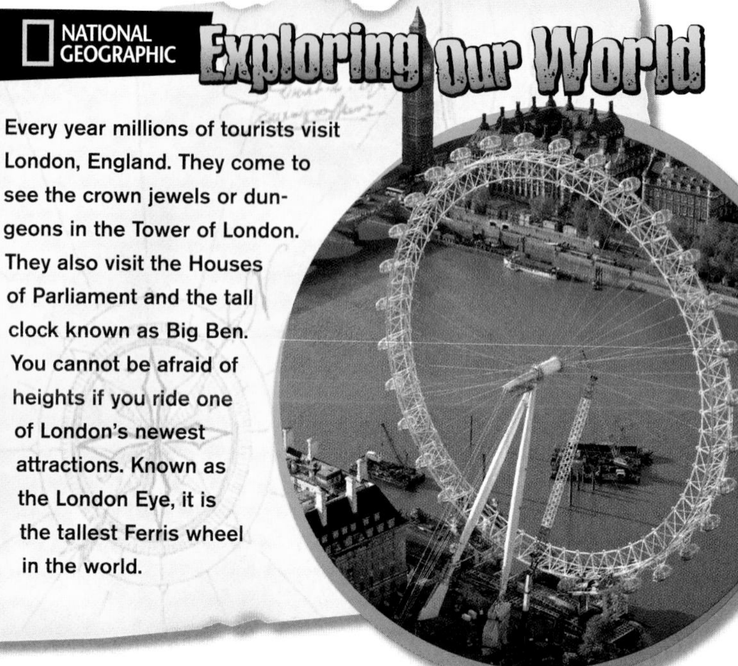

Every year millions of tourists visit London, England. They come to see the crown jewels or dungeons in the Tower of London. They also visit the Houses of Parliament and the tall clock known as Big Ben. You cannot be afraid of heights if you ride one of London's newest attractions. Known as the London Eye, it is the tallest Ferris wheel in the world.

The countries of the **United Kingdom** and the **Republic of Ireland** are known as the British Isles. They lie in the North Atlantic Ocean, west of the European continent. These two countries share similar physical characteristics but are different culturally.

The United Kingdom

About the size of Oregon, the United Kingdom is made up of four regions. **England** dominates the United Kingdom, in population and economic strength. However, **Scotland** and **Wales** are important parts of the United Kingdom. Both were conquered by England centuries ago. Today, movements for independence have grown in both countries. In 1999 Scotland and Wales set up legislatures to run their local affairs. The people of Scotland and Wales also take pride in their ancient languages—Scottish Gaelic in Scotland and Welsh in Wales. These languages are taught in schools to keep the old cultures and traditions alive.

In northern England, Scotland, and Wales, you find rugged hills and low mountain ranges. You also cross moors—treeless, windy highland

Section Resources

Reproducible Masters

- Reproducible Lesson Plan
- Daily Lecture and Discussion Notes
- Note-taking Guide
- Guided Reading Activity
- Reading Essentials and Study Guide
- Section Quiz

Transparencies

- Daily Focus Skills Transparency
- GeoQuiz Transparency
- In-text Map Transparency

Multimedia

- Vocabulary PuzzleMaker CD-ROM
- Interactive Tutor Self-Assessment CD-ROM
- Presentation Plus! CD-ROM
- ExamView® Pro Testmaker CD-ROM

areas with damp ground. The United Kingdom's fourth region—**Northern Ireland**—shares the island of Ireland with the Republic of Ireland. In Northern Ireland, you see a landscape of gentle mountains, valleys, and fertile lowlands.

The Economy Over 250 years ago, inventors and scientists here sparked the Industrial Revolution. Today, the United Kingdom is still a major industrial and trading country. Manufactured goods and machinery are the leading exports. New computer and electronic industries, however, are gradually replacing older industries. Service industries such as banking, insurance, communications, and health care employ most of the country's people.

Farming is very efficient here. Still, the United Kingdom must import about one-third of its food. Why? A lack of farmland and a limited growing season make it impossible to feed the large population.

The Government The United Kingdom is a **parliamentary democracy.** In this form of government, voters elect representatives to a lawmaking body called Parliament. It has two houses—the House of Commons and the House of Lords. The political party that has the largest number of members in the House of Commons chooses the government's leader, the prime minister. The House of Lords has little

Applying Map Skills

1. What four regions make up the United Kingdom?
2. What capital in western Europe is farthest north?

Find NGS online map resources @ www.nationalgeographic.com/maps

Reading Strategy — Reading the Text

Understanding Vocabulary Possible Sentences is a strategy that allows students to speculate about word meanings. Write the vocabulary terms on the board, using the words either correctly or incorrectly. Then ask students to comment on whether the sentences are "possible." As students encounter the key vocabulary during the reading, they note each term's usage in the selection's context. After reading, students should reread the sentences. Revise the sentences using the students' suggestions. L1

Use the ***Reading Skills Handbook*** *for more reading strategies.*

2 TEACH

Reading Strategy

Predicting Give students a map of Ireland. Ask why the island of Ireland is divided between two countries. Write down answers and ask again after students have read the chapter. L1

Daily Lecture and Discussion Notes

WESTERN EUROPE TODAY

Daily Lecture and Discussion Notes

The British Isles

Did You Know? The BBC (British Broadcasting Corporation), founded in 1922, is known and respected throughout the world. It runs two television channels and five radio channels that provide a public news service for the United Kingdom. The BBC World Service supplies the news in over 40 languages to countries around the world.

I. The United Kingdom

A. The British Isles include the countries of the United Kingdom and the Republic of Ireland. The United Kingdom has four regions—England, Wales, Scotland, and Northern Ireland.

...d Wales have rugged hills, low mountain

Applying Map Skills

Answers

1. England, Scotland, Wales, and Northern Ireland
2. Reykjavík, Iceland

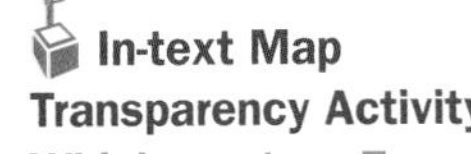

In-text Map Transparency Activity **Which western European countries are islands?** *(United Kingdom, Ireland)* **Do you think the cultures of these countries might be similar to or different from those found in continental Europe?** *(Students may note that their cultures are probably different from those on the continent as a result of their location.)*

Chapter 12

Section 1, pages 340–343

More About the Photo

London The Romans withdrew from London in the fifth century. Celts, Saxons, and Danes fought over its general area, but it was not until 886 that London became an important town. The town came under the control of King Alfred who established a city government and rebuilt its defenses for protection against the Danes.

Caption Answer about 90 percent

Reading Check Answer

parliamentary democracy and a constitutional monarchy

Measure student knowledge of physical features.

GeoQuiz Transparency

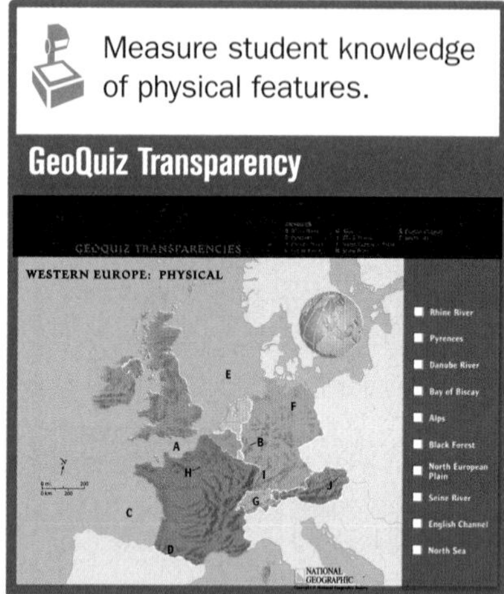

ASSESS

Assign Section 1 Assessment as homework or an in-class activity.

Have students use the Interactive Tutor Self-Assessment CD-ROM to review Section 1.

NATIONAL GEOGRAPHIC On Location

London

People get around London by riding colorful double-decker buses or by using the subway, which the British call "the Tube."

Place **What percentage of the United Kingdom's people live in towns and cities, such as London?**

power. Most members of the House of Lords are nobles who have inherited their titles or who have been given titles by the queen.

The United Kingdom's government is also a **constitutional monarchy,** in which a queen or king is the official head of state. Although the monarch represents the country at public events, he or she has little power.

The People and Culture About 60 million people live in the United Kingdom. The British people speak English, although Welsh and Scottish Gaelic are spoken in some areas. Most people are Protestant Christians, although immigrants practice Islam and other religions.

About 90 percent of the United Kingdom's people live in cities and towns. With more than 7 million people, the capital city of **London** is one of Europe's most heavily populated cities.

For centuries, the people of the United Kingdom have left their mark on world culture. Visitors see prehistoric stone monuments, ruins of Roman forts, and medieval churches and castles. Famous writers, such as William Shakespeare, have also made an impact on the world.

Reading Check **What form of government does the United Kingdom have?**

The Republic of Ireland

Surrounded by the blue waters of the Atlantic Ocean and the Irish Sea, Ireland has lush green meadows and tree-covered hills. It is called the Emerald Isle because of its landscape. At Ireland's center lies a wide, rolling plain covered with forests and farmland. The area is rich in **peat,** or plants partly decayed in water which can be dried and used for fuel. Peat is dug from **bogs,** or low swampy lands.

The Economy Potatoes, barley, wheat, sugar beets, and turnips are Ireland's major crops. Farmers raise sheep, as well as beef and dairy cattle. Manufacturing employs more people than farming and contributes more to the country's economy. Ireland joined the European Union so that it could market its products more widely. The Irish work in many manufacturing industries. These include processing foods and beverages and making textiles, clothing, pharmaceuticals, and computer equipment.

The Northern Ireland Conflict Ireland has suffered hundreds of years of unrest under British rule. The southern, mostly Catholic, counties of Ireland won independence from Britain in 1921. They later

Differentiated Instruction

Meeting Special Needs: Interpersonal Organize the class into six groups numbered 1 through 6. Have each group split up into four subgroups called A, B, C, and D. Have all students in the four subgroups meet together. (That is, groups 1A through 6A get together, as do groups 1B through 6B, and so on.) Assign each subgroup one of the following topics: land and climate; economy; history; and culture. Have the students in each subgroup develop ways of teaching information about their topic in relation to the United Kingdom. Then send students back to the original groups. Have the subgroups take turns teaching other group members about their topic. **L1**

Refer to *Inclusion for the Middle School Social Studies Classroom Strategies and Activities* in the TCR.

became a republic. The northern counties, where many British Protestants had settled, remained part of the United Kingdom. Peace still did not come to the island. The Nationalists, who are typically Catholic, want the six counties of Northern Ireland to be reunited with the Republic of Ireland. The Loyalists, who are typically Protestant, prefer that Northern Ireland remain under British rule. The fighting between these two groups, which the Irish refer to as "the troubles," has led to many deaths.

In 1998 officials of the United Kingdom and the Republic of Ireland met with leaders of both sides in Northern Ireland. They signed an agreement to end the violence, but disputes have since erupted.

The People The Irish trace their ancestry to the Celts (KEHLTS) who settled Ireland around 500 B.C. Gaelic, a Celtic language, and English are Ireland's two official languages.

Today, Ireland is an urban nation. About 58 percent of the country's people live in cities or towns. Nearly one-third live in or around **Dublin,** the capital. Life often centers on the neighborhood church.

Irish music and folk dancing are performed around the world. Of all the arts, however, the Irish have had the greatest influence on literature. Playwright George Bernard Shaw, poet William Butler Yeats, and novelist James Joyce are some of the country's best-known writers.

▲ The Irish countryside

Reading Check How are Northern Ireland and the Republic of Ireland different?

Section 1 Assessment

Defining Terms

1. **Define** moor, parliamentary democracy, constitutional monarchy, peat, bog.

Recalling Facts

2. **Region** What are the four regions of the United Kingdom?
3. **Economics** What are the two leading exports of the United Kingdom?
4. **Economics** Why did Ireland join the European Union?

Critical Thinking

5. **Analyzing Information** Why does the House of Lords have little power in the United Kingdom's Parliament?
6. **Understanding Cause and Effect** What disagreement has led to fighting in Northern Ireland?

Graphic Organizer

7. **Organizing Information** Create two diagrams like this one, one for the United Kingdom and one for the Republic of Ireland. Under each heading, list as many facts as you can for both countries.

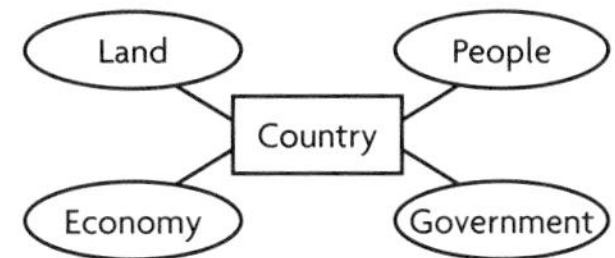

Applying Social Studies Skills

8. **Analyzing Maps** Look at the political map on page 341. What is the capital of the United Kingdom? Of the Republic of Ireland?

Section 1 Assessment

1. The terms are defined in the Glossary.
2. England, Scotland, Wales, and Northern Ireland
3. manufactured goods and machinery
4. to market its products more widely
5. Members inherit their titles; they have not been elected and so do not have the support of a political constituency.
6. The mainly Protestant Northern Ireland wishes to remain part of the United Kingdom while the Catholic Republic of Ireland wants a united Ireland.
7. Students should list facts from the text under the appropriate category.
8. London; Dublin

Chapter 12

Section 1, pages 340–343

L2

Section Quiz

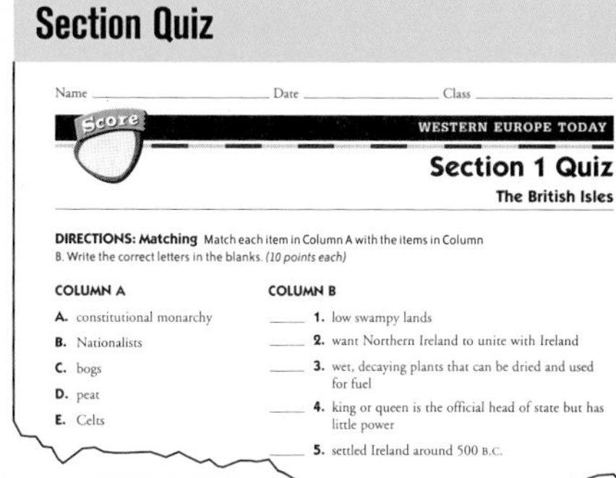

Name ______ Date ______ Class ______

Score

WESTERN EUROPE TODAY

Section 1 Quiz

The British Isles

DIRECTIONS: Matching Match each item in Column A with the items in Column B. Write the correct letters in the blanks. (10 points each)

COLUMN A	COLUMN B
A. constitutional monarchy	____ 1. low swampy lands
B. Nationalists	____ 2. want Northern Ireland to unite with Ireland
C. bogs	____ 3. wet, decaying plants that can be dried and used for fuel
D. peat	____ 4. king or queen is the official head of state but has little power
E. Celts	____ 5. settled Ireland around 500 B.C.

Reading Check Answer

Northern Ireland is still part of the United Kingdom. The Republic of Ireland is an independent country.

L1/ELL

Reading Essentials and Study Guide

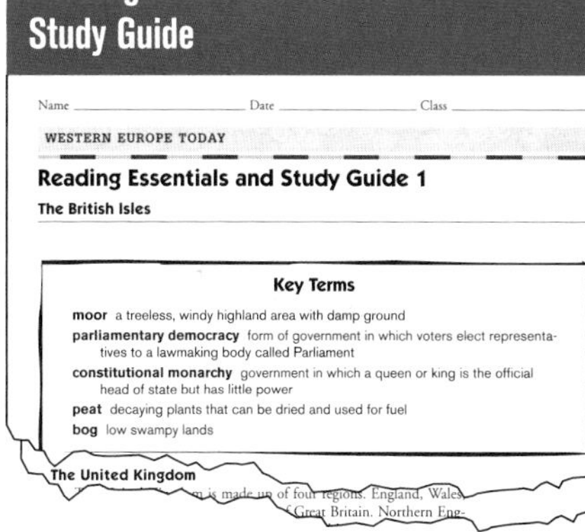

Name ______ Date ______ Class ______

WESTERN EUROPE TODAY

Reading Essentials and Study Guide 1

The British Isles

Key Terms

moor a treeless, windy highland area with damp ground
parliamentary democracy form of government in which voters elect representatives to a lawmaking body called Parliament
constitutional monarchy government in which a queen or king is the official head of state but has little power
peat decaying plants that can be dried and used for fuel
bog low swampy lands

The United Kingdom

 CLOSE

Have students research the history of Northern Ireland and prepare an oral presentation describing characteristics of the society today that resulted from historical factors such as invasion and colonization.

TEACH

Although many different societies and cultures exist in the world, they often build structures that serve the same purposes—for shelter, as meeting places for government or religious purposes, for transportation, and even as tombs and monuments. Ask students for examples of each. *(any home; the Capitol building; churches and temples; bridges, roads, and tunnels; the pyramids and Washington Monument)* Have students consider the relationships that exist between societies and their architecture as they read about Stonehenge. **L1**

More About Mysterious Monuments

Nature has recently revealed a structure similar to Stonehenge. For centuries, a layer of peat covered a circle made of logs along Great Britain's North Sea coast. Recently the sea washed the peat away, exposing the wooden posts in a circle 22 feet (6.7 m) wide. Archaeologists have dated the structure reminiscent of Stonehenge as about 4,000 years old. Ask students how this society's belief system affected their building technology.

Making Connections

ART | SCIENCE | CULTURE | TECHNOLOGY

Stonehenge

Stonehenge, one of the world's best-known and most puzzling ancient monuments, stands in southern England.

History of Stonehenge

The most noticeable part of Stonehenge is its huge stones set up in four circular patterns. A circular ditch and mound form a border around the site. Shallow dirt holes also circle the stones.

Stonehenge was built over a period of more than 2,000 years. The earliest construction, that of the circular ditch and mound, probably began about 3100 B.C. The outer ring of large pillars, topped with horizontal rocks, was built about 2000 B.C. An inner ring of stone pillars also supports horizontal stones.

There was no local source of stone, so workers carried it from an area that was about 20 miles (32 km) north. The stones are huge—up to 30 feet (9 m) long and 50 tons (45 t) in weight. Before setting the stones in place, workers smoothed and shaped them. They carved joints into the stones so that they would fit together perfectly. Then the builders probably used levers and wooden supports to raise the stones into position.

About 500 years later, builders added the third and fourth rings of stones. This time they used bluestone, which an earlier group of people had transported 240 miles (386 km) from the Preseli Mountains of Wales.

What Does It Mean?

Experts do not agree on who built Stonehenge. In 2003, however, archaeologists uncovered the 4,500-year-old remains of seven people near Stonehenge. The people are believed to have lived during the building of the monument.

An even greater mystery is why Stonehenge was built. Most experts agree that Stonehenge was probably used as a place of worship. Some believe that the series of holes, stones, and archways were used as a calendar. By lining up particular holes and stones, people could note the summer and winter solstices. They could also keep track of the months. Some scientists think that early people used the site to predict solar and lunar eclipses.

▲ Stonehenge

Making the Connection

1. About how old is Stonehenge?
2. From where did the stones used at Stonehenge come?
3. **Sequencing Information** Describe the order in which Stonehenge was built.

Making the Connection

1. about 5,100 years old
2. Some came from 20 miles (32 km) away; others came from 240 miles (386 km) away.
3. The circular ditch and mound were built about 3100 B.C.; the outer ring of pillars was built about 2000 B.C., as was an inner ring; two more rings were added about 1500 B.C.

Guide to Reading

Main Idea

France and the Benelux countries are important cultural, agricultural, and manufacturing centers of Europe.

Terms to Know

- navigable
- polder
- multinational company
- multilingual

Reading Strategy

Create a diagram like this one. Then list two countries that have major products in these categories. List two products for each country.

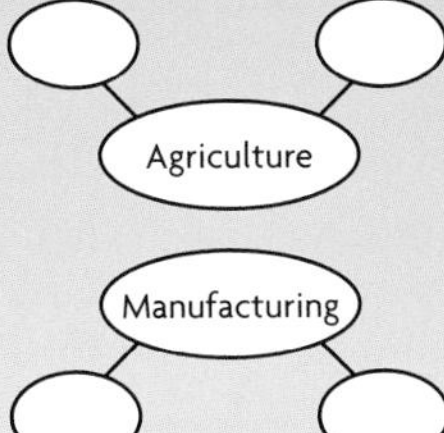

France and the Benelux Countries

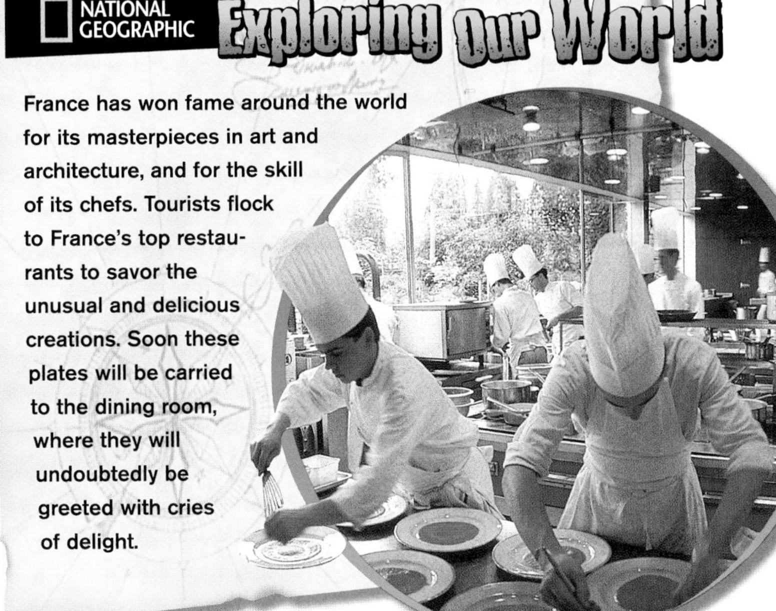

NATIONAL GEOGRAPHIC Exploring Our World

France has won fame around the world for its masterpieces in art and architecture, and for the skill of its chefs. Tourists flock to France's top restaurants to savor the unusual and delicious creations. Soon these plates will be carried to the dining room, where they will undoubtedly be greeted with cries of delight.

France and its Benelux neighbors rank as major economic and cultural centers of the world. The word *Benelux* comes from combining the first letters of three countries' names: **Belgium,** the **Netherlands,** and **Luxembourg.**

France

The largest country in western Europe, **France** is slightly smaller than the state of Texas. France's landscape includes high mountain ranges that separate the country from Spain, Italy, and Switzerland. In contrast, most of northern France is part of the vast North European Plain. A network of rivers, including the **Seine** (SAYN) and the **Loire** (LWAHR), connects the different regions of France. Most of these rivers are **navigable,** or wide and deep enough to allow the passage of ships.

Most of France has a climate that is ideal for agriculture. The rich soil in the North European Plain makes France an important food

345

1 Focus

Section Objectives

1. Discuss the economy and people of France.
2. Compare the cultures and economies of the Benelux countries.

BELLRINGER Skillbuilder Activity

Project transparency and have students answer the question.

Daily Focus Skills Transparency

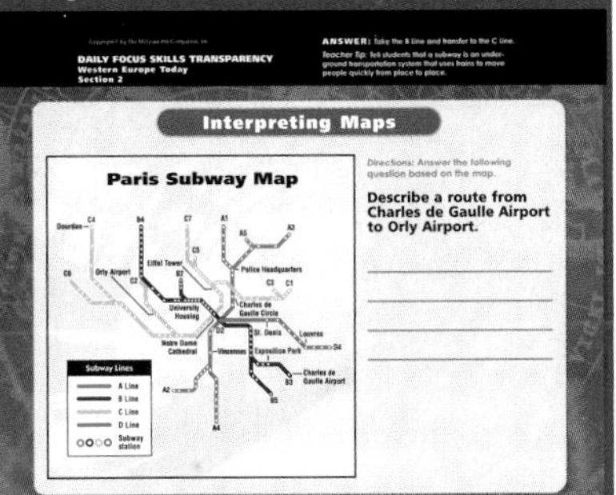

Reading Preview

- **Activating Prior Knowledge** **Ask:** What characteristics would you expect a country to have that was productive in agriculture? *(good soil, mild climate, and efficient agricultural practices)*
- **Preteaching Vocabulary** The suffix *–or* means "one who," *–ation* means "act of," and *–able* means "can be." Point out that a *navigator* is "one who sails," and *navigation* is "the act of sailing." Ask students to explain what *navigable* means. *(can be sailed)*

Section Resources

Reproducible Masters

- Reproducible Lesson Plan
- Daily Lecture and Discussion Notes
- Note-taking Guide
- Guided Reading Activity
- Reading Essentials and Study Guide
- Section Quiz

Transparencies

- Daily Focus Skills Transparency

Multimedia

- Vocabulary PuzzleMaker CD-ROM
- Interactive Tutor Self-Assessment CD-ROM
- Presentation Plus! CD-ROM
- ExamView® Pro Testmaker CD-ROM

TEACH

Reading Strategy

Summarizing Information Have students create a summary of the section by listing the subheadings and, under each subheading, writing the main idea. Then have them write two supporting details for each main idea. Suggest that they use this summary as a study guide for the section. **L1**

Daily Lecture and Discussion Notes

WESTERN EUROPE TODAY

Daily Lecture and Discussion Notes

France and the Benelux Countries

People in France own more second homes than people in any other country in the world.

I. France

A. The largest country in western Europe, France is slightly smaller than the state of Texas. It has high mountains, a large flat plain, and several rivers, including the Seine and the Loire. Most rivers are **navigable.**

B. France's economy depends on agriculture and manufacturing. Most people, however, work in service industries. Tourism is also important.

More About the Photos

Notre Dame Cathedral Notre Dame is an example of early Gothic architecture in France. It is located on the Île de la Cité, a small island in the Seine River. The cornerstone was laid in 1163 by Pope Alexander III.

Caption Answer *Possible answers:* sunny weather, green vegetation, lush grapevines

NATIONAL GEOGRAPHIC **On Location**

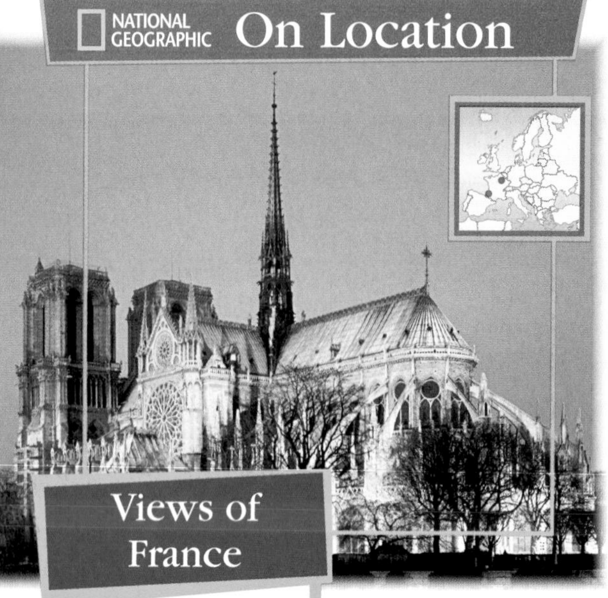

Views of France

Tourists in Paris, France, enjoy the grandeur of Notre Dame, a cathedral built in the 1100s (above). Wine grapes are harvested in one of France's grape-growing valleys (below).

Place What details in the photos suggest that France has a mild climate?

producer. In many French towns, you can find open-air markets displaying an abundance of fresh farm produce.

France's Economy France's well-developed economy relies on agriculture and manufacturing. Most people, however, work in service industries such as banking, commerce, communications, and tourism. Tourists from all over the world visit France's historic and cultural sites, such as palaces and museums. They also come to enjoy the blue skies, rocky cliffs, and lovely beaches of France's Mediterranean coast.

France produces more food than any other nation in western Europe. It ranks as the second-largest food exporter in the world, after the United States. Yet only 5 percent of French workers labor on farms. Their success is partly due to France's fertile soil, mild climate, and modern farming methods.

French farmers grow grains, sugar beets, fruits, and vegetables. They also raise beef and dairy cattle. In addition, vineyards are a common sight. The grapes are used to make famous French wines. Olives are grown along the warm, dry Mediterranean coast.

France's natural resources include bauxite, iron ore, and coal. France has small petroleum reserves and little hydroelectric power. How does the nation power its industries? About 80 percent of France's electricity comes from nuclear power plants.

Workers produce a variety of manufactured goods, including steel, chemicals, textiles, airplanes, cars, and computers. France is a leading center of commerce, with an international reputation in fashion.

The French People "Liberté . . . Egalité . . . Fraternité" (Liberty, Equality, Fraternity)—France's national motto—describes the spirit of the French people. The French share a strong national loyalty. Most French trace their ancestry to the Celts, Romans, and Franks of early Europe. They speak French, and about 90 percent of them are Roman Catholic.

France's government is known as the Fifth Republic. A republic is a strong national government headed by elected leaders. A powerful president, elected for a five-year term, leads the nation. The French president manages the country's foreign affairs. He or she appoints a prime minister to run the day-to-day affairs of government.

About three-fourths of France's 59.8 million people live in cities and towns. **Paris,** the capital and largest city, has a population of more than 10 million people, which includes its suburbs. The city is home

Reading Strategy — Reading the Text

Comparing and Contrasting Have the class discuss the government of France, comparing it to the United States government. Focus on issues such as the different relative powers of the national and regional governments, the relative powers of the presidents, and the role of the prime minister in France. Have students form groups and create Venn diagrams that place characteristics of American government in one circle, traits of French government in the other circle, and characteristics of both in the area where the circles overlap. **L1**

*Use the **Reading Skills Handbook** for more reading strategies.*

to many universities, museums, and other cultural sites. Outstanding cultural figures who lived in Paris include the writer Victor Hugo and the painters Claude Monet and Pierre-Auguste Renoir. Each year, millions of tourists go to the City of Light, as Paris is called. They visit such sites as the Eiffel Tower, the cathedral of Notre Dame, and the Louvre (LOOV), one of the world's most famous art museums.

Reading Check What is the main religion in France?

The Benelux Countries

The small Benelux countries of Belgium, the Netherlands, and Luxembourg have much in common. Their lands are low, flat, and densely populated. Most people live in cities, work in businesses or factories, and enjoy a high standard of living. All three nations are members of the European Union. They are also parliamentary democracies with constitutional monarchies.

Belgium About the size of Maryland, Belgium touches France, Luxembourg, Germany, and the Netherlands. Lying near major industrial regions, Belgium has long been a trade and manufacturing center. Belgian lace, chocolate, and diamond-cutting all have a worldwide reputation for excellence. With few natural resources of their own, the Belgian people import metals, fuels, and raw materials from less-developed countries. They use these materials to make and export vehicles, chemicals, and textiles.

Most Belgians are Roman Catholic. The country has two main cultural and language groups. The Flemings in the north speak Flemish, a language based on Dutch. The south is home to the French-speaking Walloons. Tensions sometimes arise between the two groups, especially because there is more wealth and industry in the north than in the south. Most Belgians live in crowded urban areas. **Brussels,** the capital and largest city, is an international center for trade.

▲ A tulip field in the Netherlands

The Netherlands The Netherlands—about half the size of Maine—is one of the most densely populated countries in the world. Sometimes called Holland, its people are known as the Dutch.

Netherlands means "lowlands." Nearly half of this small, flat country lies below sea level. Without defenses against the sea, high tides would flood much of the country twice a day. The Dutch build dikes, or banks of soil, to control and confine the sea. Then they drain and pump the wetlands dry. Once run by windmills, pumps are now driven by steam or electricity. These drained lands, called **polders,** have rich farming soil. The Dutch build factories, airports, and even towns on them. The Delta Plan Project, completed in 1986, consists of huge barriers that keep the North Sea from overflowing the countryside during storms.

High technology makes small farms so productive that the Dutch can export cheese, vegetables, and flowers. The Netherlands ranks third in the world—after the United States and France—in the value of its agricultural exports. Because machines make farming more productive, most people work in service industries, manufacturing, and trade.

Social Studies Online
Web Activity Visit The World and Its People Web site at twip.glencoe.com and click on Chapter 12—Student Web Activities to learn more about the Delta Plan Project.

Chapter 12

Section 2, pages 345–348

Reading Check Answer

Roman Catholic

L1/ELL

Guided Reading Activity

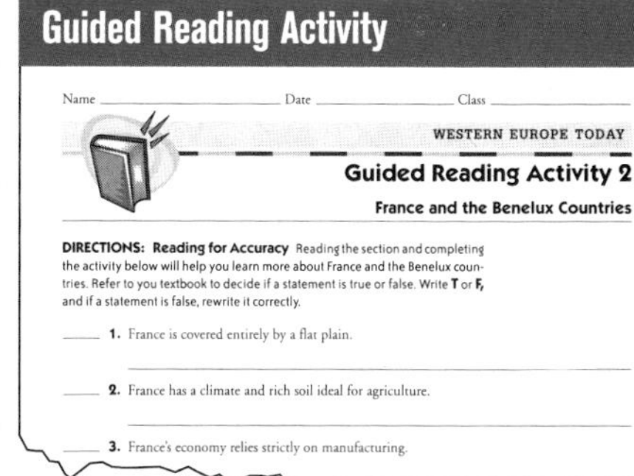
Name ______ Date ______ Class ______

WESTERN EUROPE TODAY

Guided Reading Activity 2

France and the Benelux Countries

DIRECTIONS: Reading for Accuracy Reading the section and completing the activity below will help you learn more about France and the Benelux countries. Refer to you textbook to decide if a statement is true or false. Write **T** or **F**, and if a statement is false, rewrite it correctly.

____ 1. France is covered entirely by a flat plain.

____ 2. France has a climate and rich soil ideal for agriculture.

____ 3. France's economy relies strictly on manufacturing.

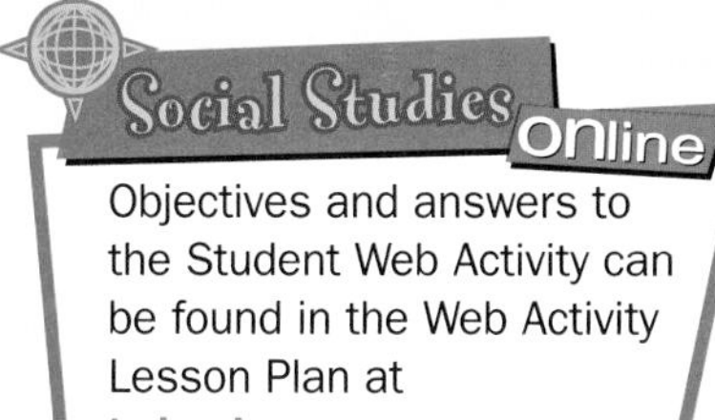

Social Studies Online
Objectives and answers to the Student Web Activity can be found in the Web Activity Lesson Plan at twip.glencoe.com

3 ASSESS

Assign Section 2 Assessment as homework or an in-class activity.

Have students use the Interactive Tutor Self-Assessment CD-ROM to review Section 2.

Differentiated Instruction

Meeting Special Needs: Verbal/Linguistic Verbal learners can use puzzles as a way of remembering key facts about France. Write the word *FRANCE* on the board, and have students copy it in their notebooks. Tell them that you will give them clues to a characteristic of France. The solution to each clue will begin with one of the letters of the country's name. Then proceed with these clues: (1) Major economic activity *(Food producer)*; (2) Type of government *(Republic)*; (3) Mountains in southeast *(Alps)*; (4) Characteristic of rivers *(Navigable)*; (5) Area in which France is a leader *(Culture)*; and (6) Organization of which France is a member *(European Union)*. L1

Refer to *Inclusion for the Middle School Social Studies Classroom Strategies and Activities* in the TCR.

Chapter 12

Section 2, pages 345–348

L2

Section Quiz

Name ______ Date ______ Class ______

WESTERN EUROPE TODAY

Score

Section 2 Quiz

France and the Benelux Countries

DIRECTIONS: Matching Match each item in Column A with the items in Column B. Write the correct letters in the blanks. *(10 points each)*

COLUMN A	COLUMN B
A. navigable	____ 1. capital city of France
B. Paris	____ 2. wide and deep enough to allow the passage of ships
C. Brussels	____ 3. area of drained land reclaimed from the sea
D. polder	____ 4. capital city of the Netherlands
E. Amsterdam	____ 5. capital city of Belgium

✓ Reading Check Answer

steel and banking

L1/ELL

Reading Essentials and Study Guide

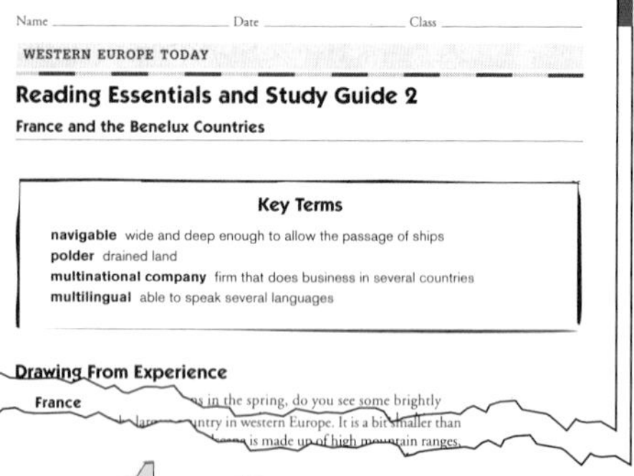
Name ______ Date ______ Class ______

WESTERN EUROPE TODAY

Reading Essentials and Study Guide 2

France and the Benelux Countries

Key Terms

navigable wide and deep enough to allow the passage of ships
polder drained land
multinational company firm that does business in several countries
multilingual able to speak several languages

Drawing From Experience

4 CLOSE

Reading Strategy

Using Primary and Secondary Sources Have students use a variety of primary and secondary sources to identify and explain the following issues: ethnic conflict and cooperation in Belgium, reclaiming land from the sea in the Netherlands, or the factors that influence the economy of Luxembourg.

About 90 percent of the Dutch live in cities and towns. **Amsterdam** is the capital and largest city. Living in a densely populated country, the Dutch make good use of their space. Houses are narrow but tall, and apartments are often built on canals and over highways. Some of Amsterdam's most famous people are the painters Rembrandt van Rijn and Vincent van Gogh. You may have read *The Diary of Anne Frank.* This Dutch teenager's autobiography tells how she and her family tried to hide from the German Nazis during World War II.

About two-thirds of the Dutch people are Christian. A small number of immigrants are Muslims. The people of the Netherlands speak Dutch, but most also speak English.

Luxembourg Southeast of Belgium lies Luxembourg, one of Europe's smallest countries. The entire country is only about 55 miles (89 km) long and about 35 miles (56 km) wide.

Despite its size, Luxembourg is prosperous. Many **multinational companies,** or firms that do business in several countries, have their headquarters here. It is home to the second-largest steel-producing company in Europe and is a major banking center as well.

Why is Luxembourg so attractive to foreign companies? First, the country is centrally located. Second, most people in this tiny land are **multilingual,** or able to speak several languages. They speak Luxembourgian, a blend of old German and French; French, the official language of the law; and German, used in most newspapers.

✓ Reading Check What industries are important in Luxembourg?

Assessment

Defining Terms

1. **Define** navigable, polder, multinational company, multilingual.

Recalling Facts

2. **Economics** Name five of France's agricultural products.
3. **Culture** What are the two major cultures and languages of Belgium?
4. **Human/Environment Interaction** How do the Dutch protect their land from the sea?

Critical Thinking

5. **Drawing Conclusions** France is the second-largest food exporter in the world. Why is that remarkable?
6. **Analyzing Information** Why do foreign companies come to Luxembourg?

Graphic Organizer

7. **Organizing Information** Create a diagram like this one. In the center circle, list three characteristics that are shared by these countries.

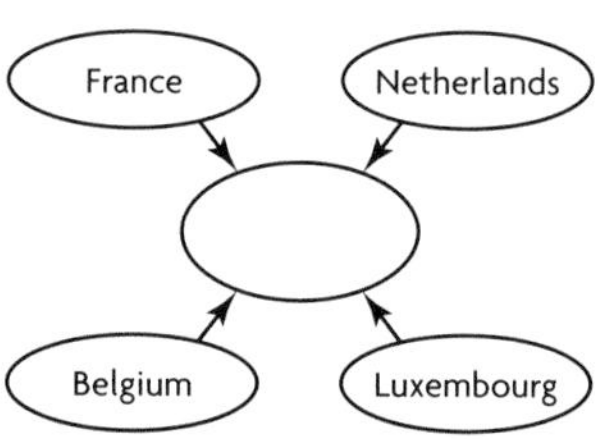

Applying Social Studies Skills

8. **Analyzing Maps** Turn to the political map on page 341. Which country borders France, Belgium, the Netherlands, and Luxembourg?

Section 2 Assessment

1. The terms are defined in the Glossary.
2. *Any five:* grains, sugar beets, fruits, vegetables, beef, dairy cattle, grapes, olives
3. Flemings speak Flemish; Walloons speak French.
4. by building dikes and pumping the water out; Delta Plan Project consists of barriers to prevent flooding of the countryside.
5. because only 5 percent of French workers are involved in agriculture
6. It is centrally located and most people are multilingual.
7. *Any three:* European; border Germany; at least some people speak French; industrialized; prosperous
8. Germany

Social Studies Skill

Reading a Vegetation Map

Vegetation maps show the kinds of plants that naturally grow in a given area. Climate largely determines the vegetation of an area. For example, evergreen trees with cones and needle-shaped leaves (also called conifers) such as firs and spruces grow in cool climates. In the year-round warmth of the Tropics, evergreens with broad leaves, such as palm trees and rubber trees, can grow. Between these two extremes, deciduous trees are common. Deciduous trees have broad leaves, but they shed them in autumn. In dry or Mediterranean climates, grasses and shrubs are found because there is not enough water to support tree growth. Highland climates may have alpine vegetation—small shrubs and wildflowers. Extremely cold or dry climates may have little or no vegetation.

Learning the Skill

To read a vegetation map, follow these steps:

- Read the title of the map.
- Study the map key.
- Find examples of each vegetation zone on the map.
- Look at other aspects of the area's geography, such as rivers, oceans, and landforms to explain the vegetation patterns.

NATIONAL GEOGRAPHIC

France: Vegetation

Natural Vegetation
- Deciduous forest
- Coniferous forest
- Mixed forest (coniferous and deciduous)
- Mediterranean vegetation
- Alpine vegetation

UNITED KINGDOM, English Channel, ATLANTIC OCEAN, BELGIUM, GERMANY, LUXEMBOURG, Paris, Strasbourg, Nantes, Bay of Biscay, FRANCE, LIECH., SWITZERLAND, Lyon, ITALY, Bordeaux, Toulouse, Montpellier, Marseille, Nice, MONACO, SPAIN, ANDORRA, Mediterranean Sea, Corsica

0 mi. 200 / 0 km 200 / Lambert Azimuthal Equal-Area projection

Practicing the Skill

Look at the map above to answer the following questions.

1. What vegetation covers most of France?
2. What type of vegetation is found along France's Mediterranean coast?
3. From the map, what conclusions can you draw about the amount of rain the regions of France receive?

Applying the Skill

Find a vegetation map of your state. What types of vegetation are common in your part of the country?

TEACH

Display photographs of different types of vegetation. For each photo, ask students to identify the vegetation type and locations where that type might be found. Call on a volunteer to explain why different kinds of vegetation grow in different regions. *(varied soils and amounts of sunlight, warmth, and rainfall)* **L1**

Additional Skills Practice

1. **Based on this map alone, which area of France probably has the highest elevation? Why?** *(along the border with Italy; because it is the only area with alpine vegetation)*
2. **If you traveled due north from Montpellier to Paris, what vegetation zones would you pass through?** *(Mediterranean vegetation, mixed forest, coniferous forest, and deciduous forest)*

Additional Skills Resources

- Chapter Skills Review
- Building Geography Skills for Life

GLENCOE TECHNOLOGY

Skillbuilder Interactive Workbook CD-ROM, Level 1

This interactive CD-ROM reinforces student mastery of essential social studies skills.

Practicing the Skill Answers

1. deciduous forest
2. Mediterranean vegetation
3. Because deciduous and mixed forest vegetation grows throughout most of France, and these types of vegetation need plentiful rainfall, France must have a relatively wet climate.

Applying the Skill

Answers will vary. Check students' answers for accuracy.

1 Focus

Section Objectives

1. Discuss the economy and government of Germany.
2. Compare the geography and economies of Switzerland and Austria.

BELLRINGER Skillbuilder Activity

Project transparency and have students answer the question.

Daily Focus Skills Transparency

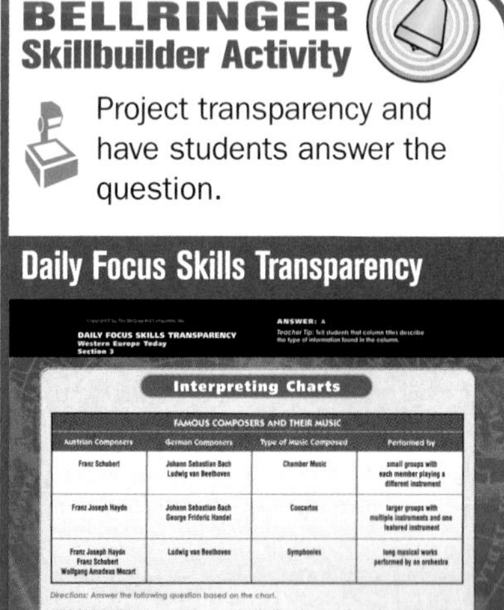

DAILY FOCUS SKILLS TRANSPARENCY
Western Europe Today
Section 3

ANSWER: A

Teacher Tip: Tell students that column titles describe the type of information found in the column.

Interpreting Charts

FAMOUS COMPOSERS AND THEIR MUSIC			
Austrian Composers	German Composers	Type of Music Composed	Performed by
Franz Schubert	Johann Sebastian Bach Ludwig van Beethoven	Chamber Music	small groups with each member playing a different instrument
Franz Joseph Haydn	Johann Sebastian Bach George Frideric Handel	Concertos	larger groups with multiple instruments and one featured instrument
Franz Joseph Haydn Franz Schubert Wolfgang Amadeus Mozart	Ludwig van Beethoven	Symphonies	long musical works performed by an orchestra

Directions: Answer the following question based on the chart.

Which Austrian composer wrote both chamber music and symphonies?

A Franz Schubert
B Franz Joseph Haydn
C Ludwig van Beethoven
D Wolfgang Amadeus Mozart

Reading Preview

■ **Activating Prior Knowledge**
Ask: What effect might a mountainous landscape be likely to have on people's lives? *(cool climate, mineral resources, isolation, opportunities for recreation)*

■ **Preteaching Vocabulary**
Write the following definitions on the board: "not joining either side in a fight" and "to rejoin separated parts." Have students identify the correct terms. *(neutrality, reunification)*

Guide to Reading

Main Idea

Germany, Switzerland, and Austria are known for their mountain scenery and prosperous economies.

Terms to Know

- autobahn
- federal republic
- reunification
- neutrality
- continental divide

Reading Strategy

Create a diagram like this one. Under the headings, fill each oval with facts about each country. Put statements that are true of all three countries where the ovals overlap.

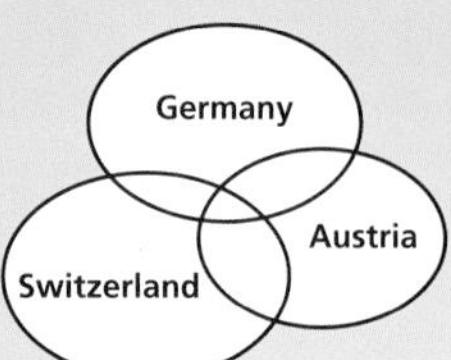

Section 3

Germany and the Alpine Countries

NATIONAL GEOGRAPHIC **Exploring Our World**

Bavaria, the beauty spot of Germany, was the home of King Ludwig II, who became the king of Bavaria at the age of 18. Disappointed after a lost war with the Prussians, Ludwig lost all interest in politics and became increasingly eccentric. Ludwig built three "fairy tale castles" at tremendous expense before dying a mysterious—and some say not accidental—death.

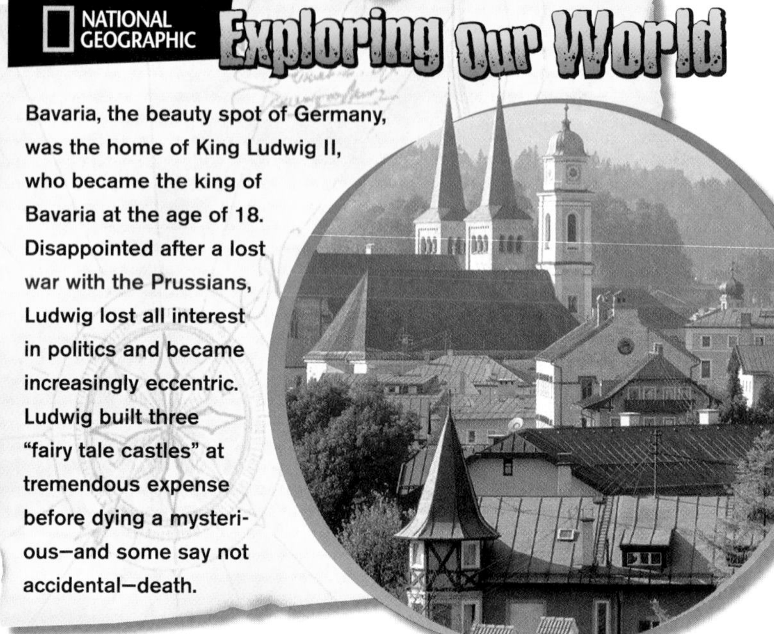

The people of **Germany** and the Alpine countries—**Switzerland, Austria,** and **Liechtenstein**—are adjusting to the changes sweeping Europe since the fall of communism. Fortunately, these countries have strong market economies, so their people enjoy high standards of living.

Germany

About the size of Montana, Germany lies in the heart of Europe. The North European Plain forms the northern landscape. The Alps rise in the southern German state of **Bavaria.** The lower slopes of these mountains—a favorite destination for skiers—are covered with forests.

One of Europe's most important waterways originates in the Alps. The **Danube River** winds eastward across southern Germany. Rivers are also important in northern Germany, where they are used to transport raw materials and manufactured goods. The **Rhine River,** in the west, forms part of the border with France.

Section Resources

Reproducible Masters

- Reproducible Lesson Plan
- Daily Lecture and Discussion Notes
- Note-taking Guide
- Guided Reading Activity
- Reading Essentials and Study Guide
- Section Quiz

Transparencies

- Daily Focus Skills Transparency

Multimedia

- Vocabulary PuzzleMaker CD-ROM
- Interactive Tutor Self-Assessment CD-ROM
- Presentation Plus! CD-ROM
- ExamView® Pro Testmaker CD-ROM

Because of the rivers and fertile land, Germany's northern plain has many cities and towns. **Berlin,** the capital, is the major center of the northeast. To the west lies **Hamburg,** Germany's largest port city, located on the Elbe River.

An Economic and Industrial Power Germany is a global economic power and a leader in the European Union. An area in western Germany called the Ruhr ranks as one of the world's most important industrial centers. The Ruhr developed around rich deposits of coal and iron ore. Europe's leaders have fought for control of this productive area. Factories here produce high-quality steel, ships, cars, machinery, chemicals, and electrical equipment.

The growth of factories, service industries, and high technology in the last decade has used up the supply of workers. Thus, a growing number of immigrant workers have come from Turkey, Italy, Greece, and the former Yugoslav republics. Sometimes they are the targets of racist attacks. When the economy takes a downturn and jobs are scarce, native-born people sometimes resent foreign laborers.

Germany imports about one-third of its food, although it is a leading producer of beer, wine, and cheese. Farmers raise livestock and grow grains, vegetables, and fruits. Superhighways called **autobahns,** along with railroads, rivers, and canals, link Germany's cities.

Lying just north of the Alps, Germany's Black Forest is famous for its beautiful scenery and for its wood products. The forest is not really black, but in places the trees grow so close together that it appears this way. The Black Forest has suffered severe damage from acid rain. Much of the pollution comes from industries in other countries. The Germans have to work together with other Europeans to find a solution to this acid rain problem.

Germany's Government Like the United States, Germany is a **federal republic** in which a national government and state governments share powers. An elected president serves as Germany's head of state, but he or she carries out only ceremonial duties. The country's chancellor, chosen by one of the two houses of parliament, is the real head of the government.

One of the challenges of the current government has been **reunification**—bringing together Germany's two parts under one government. Remember that Germany was divided into East and West Germany after World War II. Workers in East Germany had less experience and training in modern technology than workers in West Germany. After reunification, many old and inefficient factories in the east could not compete with the more advanced industries in the west and were forced to close.

▲ A cuckoo clock from the Black Forest region of Germany

The Germans Most of Germany's 82.6 million people trace their ancestry to groups who settled in Europe from about the A.D. 100s to 400s. The people speak German, a language that is related to English.

In Chapter 10, you learned that a German priest named Martin Luther began a new form of Christianity known as Protestantism.

Teach

Reading Strategy

Organizing Information Have students create graphic organizers that identify the main ideas about Germany, Switzerland, and Austria. Graphic organizers may include charts or web diagrams. Check students' graphic organizers to be sure that students have included all of the main ideas for each section of text. L1

Daily Lecture and Discussion Notes

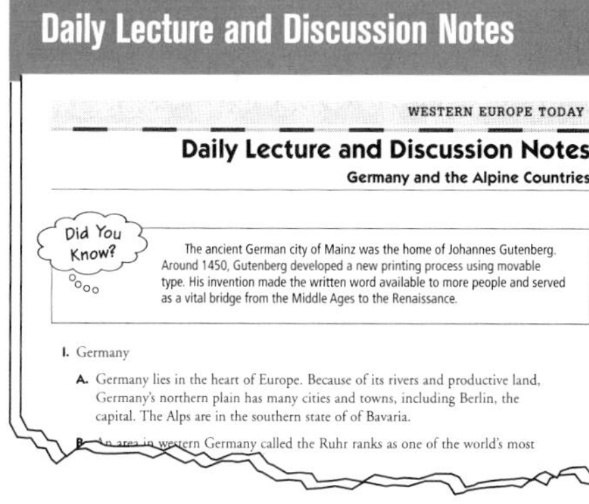

WESTERN EUROPE TODAY

Daily Lecture and Discussion Notes

Germany and the Alpine Countries

Did You Know? The ancient German city of Mainz was the home of Johannes Gutenberg. Around 1450, Gutenberg developed a new printing process using movable type. His invention made the written word available to more people and served as a vital bridge from the Middle Ages to the Renaissance.

I. Germany

A. Germany lies in the heart of Europe. Because of its rivers and productive land, Germany's northern plain has many cities and towns, including Berlin, the capital. The Alps are in the southern state of of Bavaria.

B. An area in western Germany called the Ruhr ranks as one of the world's most

L1/ELL

Guided Reading Activity

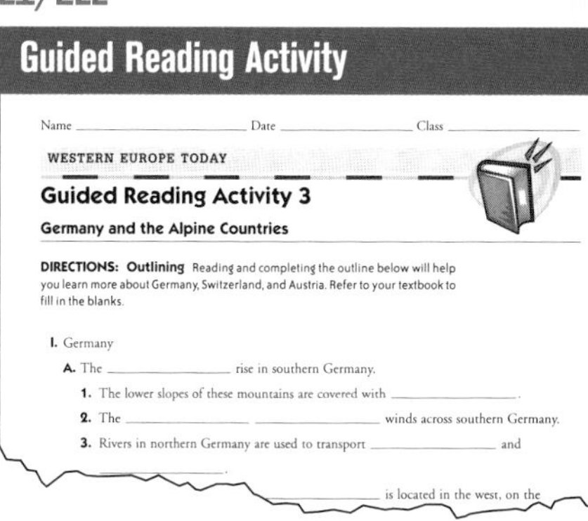

Name ______ Date ______ Class ______

WESTERN EUROPE TODAY

Guided Reading Activity 3

Germany and the Alpine Countries

DIRECTIONS: Outlining Reading and completing the outline below will help you learn more about Germany, Switzerland, and Austria. Refer to your textbook to fill in the blanks.

I. Germany

A. The ______ rise in southern Germany.

1. The lower slopes of these mountains are covered with ______.

2. The ______ ______ winds across southern Germany.

3. Rivers in northern Germany are used to transport ______ and ______.

______ is located in the west, on the

Reading Strategy: Reading the Text

Evaluating Information As students have access to increasingly larger amounts of information, they need to be able to evaluate what they read. Evaluating requires making a judgment or forming an opinion. To help students learn how to evaluate information, pose the following questions: Is the author qualified to write on this subject? Is the point of view biased? Is there another point of view not expressed here? Are opinions backed with facts, statistics, and examples? Remind students to ask themselves these questions as they read. L1

*Use the **Reading Skills Handbook** for more reading strategies.*

Chapter 12

Section 3, pages 350–353

Interdisciplinary Connections

Science Switzerland's Alpine forests have been under stress in recent years, just as Germany's Black Forest has suffered. Growing levels of acid rain and higher levels of ozone are damaging the needles of these evergreens. Weakened trees become susceptible to bark beetles and other pests, which eventually kill the trees and then spread to others.

Reading Check Answer

autobahns, railroads, rivers, and canals

More About the Photo

Swiss Economy Just three companies account for about 90 percent of foreign sales funneling into Switzerland. One of these companies is a chocolate manufacturer. The others make metals and pharmaceuticals.

Caption Answer electronic equipment, clocks, watches, chemicals, cheese

3 ASSESS

Assign Section 3 Assessment as homework or an in-class activity.

Have students use the Interactive Tutor Self-Assessment CD-ROM to review Section 3.

NATIONAL GEOGRAPHIC **On Location**

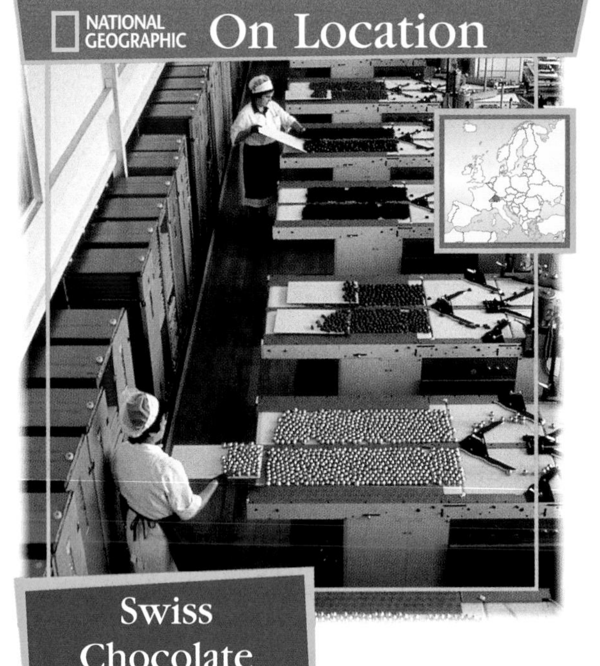

Swiss Chocolate

Switzerland's factories produce some of the best chocolate in the world.

Economics What other products are made in Switzerland?

Today Protestants and Catholics are fairly evenly represented in Germany. Germans have made important contributions to music and culture. Johann Sebastian Bach and Ludwig van Beethoven composed some of the world's greatest classical music. **Munich** (MYOO•nihk), the largest city in southern Germany, is known for its theaters, museums, and concert halls. Berlin has also emerged as a cultural center.

Reading Check What links Germany's cities?

The Alpine Countries

The **Alps** form most of the landscape in Switzerland, Austria, and Liechtenstein. That is why they are called the Alpine countries. Liechtenstein is a tiny country—only 60 square miles (155 sq. km)—sandwiched between Switzerland and Austria. The rugged Swiss Alps prevent easy travel between northern and southern Europe. For centuries, landlocked Switzerland guarded the few routes that cut through this barrier.

Switzerland The Swiss have enjoyed a stable democratic government for more than 700 years. Because of its location in the center of Europe, Switzerland has practiced **neutrality**—refusing to take sides in disagreements and wars between countries. As a result of this peaceful history, the Swiss city of **Geneva** is today the center of many international organizations. Switzerland's policy of neutrality is likely to be tested in the years ahead. It is building closer ties to the European Union and has joined the United Nations.

The Alps in Switzerland are the continental divide of central Europe. A **continental divide** is a high place from which rivers flow in different directions. Several rivers, including the **Rhine** and the **Rhône,** begin in the Swiss Alps. Dams built on Switzerland's rivers produce great amounts of hydroelectric power. Most of Switzerland's industries and its richest farmlands are found on a high plateau between two mountain ranges. **Bern,** Switzerland's capital, and **Zurich,** its largest city, are also located on this plateau.

Although it has few natural resources, Switzerland is a thriving industrial nation. Using imported materials, Swiss workers make high-quality goods such as electronic equipment, clocks, and watches. They also produce chemicals and gourmet foods such as chocolate and cheese. Tourism is an important industry, as are banking and insurance. Zurich and Geneva are important centers of international finance.

Given its geographic location, Switzerland has many different ethnic groups and religions. Did you know that the country has four national

Differentiated Instruction

Meeting Special Needs: Auditory/Musical Bring to class recordings of the work of Bach and Beethoven. Choose contrasting works, such as Bach's *Brandenburg Concertos* and Beethoven's *Ninth Symphony.* Have students listen to brief excerpts of the two compositions and contrast the styles of the two composers. For Bach, they might point out that the instrumentation is less varied, the music complex, and the dynamics (loudness and softness of sounds) less varied. Beethoven, on the other hand, uses the full orchestra to great effect and employs great dynamic range. **L3**

Refer to *Inclusion for the Middle School Social Studies Classroom Strategies and Activities* in the TCR.

languages? They are German, French, Italian, and Romansch. Most Swiss speak German, and many speak more than one language.

Austria Austria is a landlocked country located south of Germany. The Alps cover three-fourths of Austria. In fact, Austria is one of the most mountainous countries in the world. Have you ever seen the movie *The Sound of Music*? It was set in Austria's spectacular mountains. The country's climate is similar to Switzerland's. In winter, lowland areas receive rain, and mountainous regions have snow. Summers are cooler in Austria than they are in Switzerland.

Austria's economy is strong and varied. Its rivers generate hydroelectric power, and the mountains provide valuable timber. Millions of tourists come to enjoy hiking and skiing. Factories produce machinery, chemicals, metals, and vehicles. Farmers raise dairy cattle and other livestock, sugar beets, grains, potatoes, and fruits.

Most of Austria's 8.2 million people live in cities and towns and work in manufacturing or service jobs. The majority of people speak German. About 80 percent of the people are Roman Catholic.

Vienna, on the Danube River, is the capital and largest city. It has a rich history as a center of culture and learning. Some of the world's greatest composers, including Mozart, Schubert, and Haydn, lived or performed in Vienna. The city's concert halls, historic palaces and churches, and grand architecture continue to draw musicians today.

▲ Young people dance in one of Vienna's many ballrooms.

✓Reading Check What economic benefits do Austria's mountains provide?

Section 3 Assessment

Defining Terms

1. Define autobahn, federal republic, reunification, neutrality, continental divide.

Recalling Facts

2. Human/Environment Interaction What has damaged the Black Forest?
3. Culture Name Switzerland's four languages.
4. Economics What types of jobs do most Austrians have?

Critical Thinking

5. Understanding Cause and Effect What problems have emerged as a result of German reunification?
6. Analyzing Information Why has Switzerland maintained a policy of neutrality?

Graphic Organizer

7. Organizing Information Create a diagram like the one below. On the lines list two facts about Austria's physical features, two facts about Austria's people, and four facts about Austria's economy.

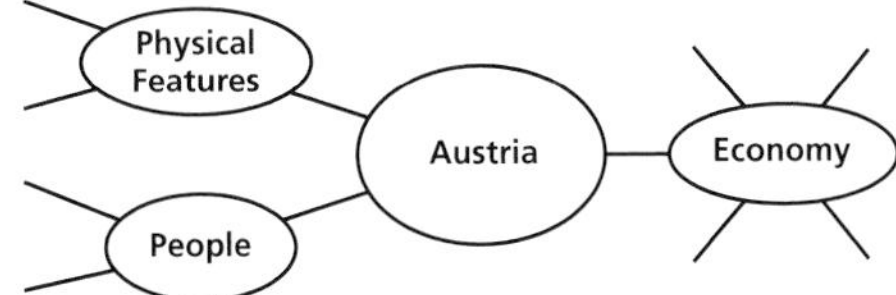

Applying Social Studies Skills

8. Analyzing Maps Look at the political map on page 341. The city of Berlin, Germany, is located at what degree of latitude?

Section 3 Assessment

1. The terms are defined in the Glossary.
2. acid rain
3. German, French, Italian, Romansch
4. manufacturing or service jobs
5. East German workers were not as well-trained in modern technology, and factories were old and inefficient and could not compete with those in the west, forcing them to close.
6. because it is in the center of Europe
7. Students' diagrams will vary.
8. about 54°N

Chapter 12

Section 3, pages 350–353

L2

Section Quiz

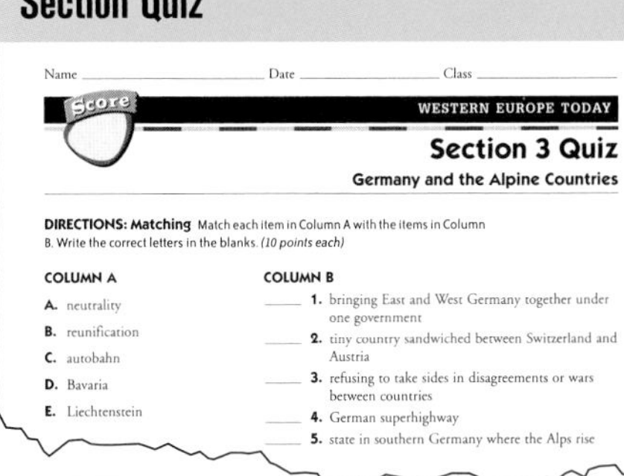

Name ______ Date ______ Class ______

Score

WESTERN EUROPE TODAY

Section 3 Quiz

Germany and the Alpine Countries

DIRECTIONS: Matching Match each item in Column A with the items in Column B. Write the correct letters in the blanks. *(10 points each)*

COLUMN A	COLUMN B
A. neutrality	___ 1. bringing East and West Germany together under one government
B. reunification	___ 2. tiny country sandwiched between Switzerland and Austria
C. autobahn	___ 3. refusing to take sides in disagreements or wars between countries
D. Bavaria	___ 4. German superhighway
E. Liechtenstein	___ 5. state in southern Germany where the Alps rise

✓ Reading Check Answer

timber, hydroelectric power, and tourist attractions

L1/ELL

Reading Essentials and Study Guide

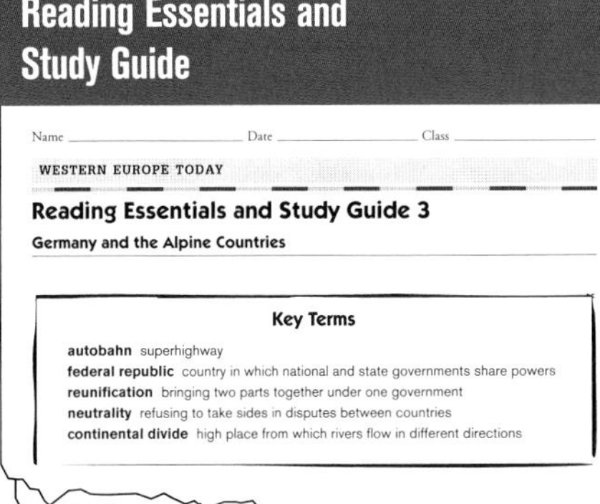

Name ______ Date ______ Class ______

WESTERN EUROPE TODAY

Reading Essentials and Study Guide 3

Germany and the Alpine Countries

Key Terms

autobahn superhighway
federal republic country in which national and state governments share powers
reunification bringing two parts together under one government
neutrality refusing to take sides in disputes between countries
continental divide high place from which rivers flow in different directions

4 CLOSE

Reading Strategy

Writing a Paragraph Have students write a paragraph contrasting the economies of Germany and Switzerland.

Chapter 12

Section 4, pages 354–357

Focus

Section Objectives

1. Describe the landscapes and climates of the Nordic nations.
2. Compare the economies and people of this region.

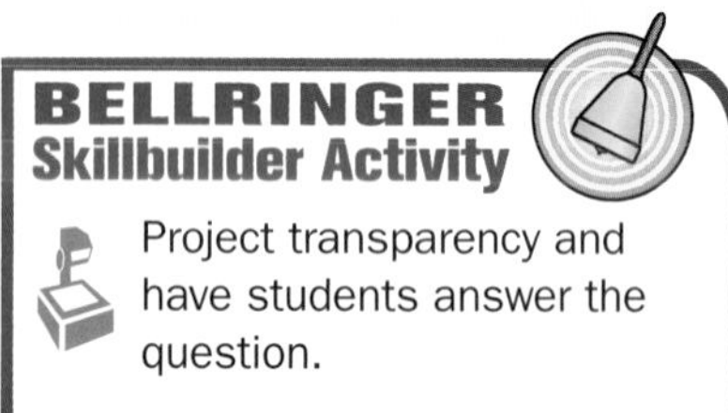

BELLRINGER Skillbuilder Activity

Project transparency and have students answer the question.

Daily Focus Skills Transparency

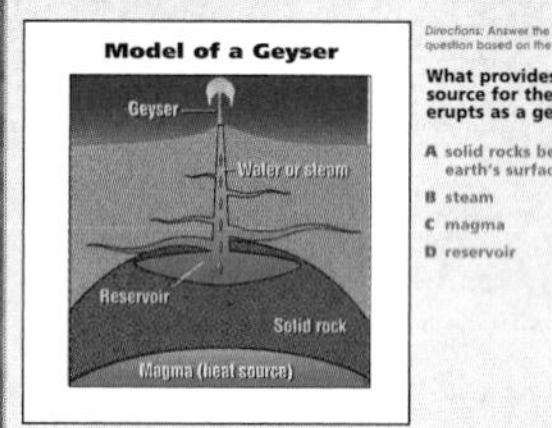

Reading Preview

- **Activating Prior Knowledge** Ask students if they are familiar with stories of the Vikings. Have them recount the stories. In this section they will read about people descended from the Vikings.
- **Preteaching Vocabulary** Inform students that two of the Terms to Know are Nordic words. *(fjord, sauna)* Ask them to find their definitions.

Guide to Reading

Main Idea

The Nordic countries have developed diverse economies, and their people enjoy a high standard of living.

Terms to Know

- fjord
- welfare state
- heavy industry
- sauna
- geyser
- geothermal energy

Reading Strategy

Create a chart like this one for each of the following countries: Norway, Sweden, Finland, Denmark, and Iceland. Fill in at least two key facts for (1) the land, (2) the economy, and (3) the people of each country.

Country	(1)
	(2)
	(3)

Section 4 The Nordic Nations

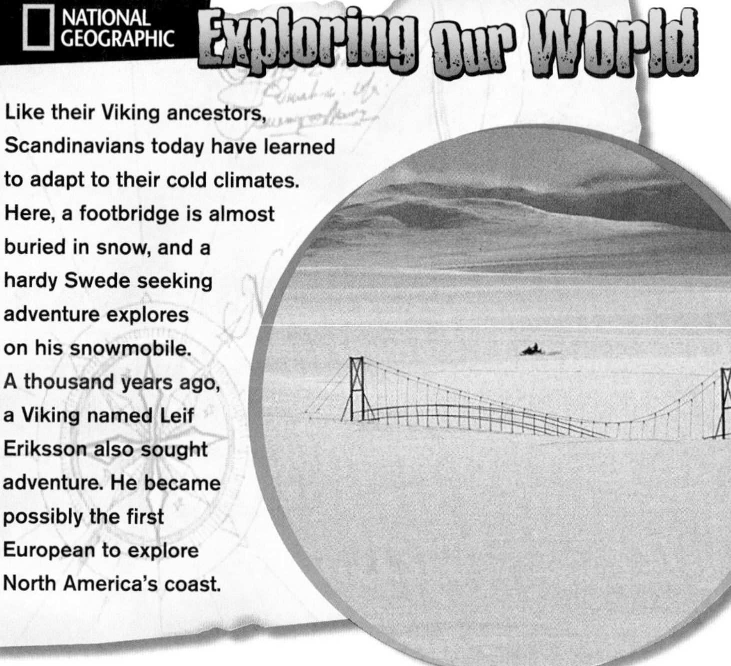

Like their Viking ancestors, Scandinavians today have learned to adapt to their cold climates. Here, a footbridge is almost buried in snow, and a hardy Swede seeking adventure explores on his snowmobile. A thousand years ago, a Viking named Leif Eriksson also sought adventure. He became possibly the first European to explore North America's coast.

The northernmost part of Europe—also known as Scandinavia or the Nordic countries—is made up of five nations: **Norway, Sweden, Finland, Denmark,** and **Iceland.** Scandinavians have standards of living that are among the world's highest.

Norway

Norway's far northern location results in a mostly cold climate. About one-third of Norway lies north of the Arctic Circle. This rugged area is often called Land of the Midnight Sun. Here the sun never sets in the midsummer months. In the midwinter months, the sun never rises. A mild climate, however, is found along Norway's southern and western coasts. This is due to warm winds from the North Atlantic Current. Most of Norway's 4.6 million people live near these coasts.

Norway's long, jagged coastline on the Atlantic Ocean includes many **fjords** (fee•AWRDS), or steep-sided valleys that are inlets of the sea. Thousands of years ago, glaciers carved these deep valleys that became flooded when the glacial ice melted. Today the fjords provide sheltered harbors and beautiful scenery that is popular with tourists.

Section Resources

Reproducible Masters
- Reproducible Lesson Plan
- Daily Lecture and Discussion Notes
- Note-taking Guide
- Guided Reading Activity
- Reading Essentials and Study Guide
- Section Quiz

Transparencies
- Daily Focus Skills Transparency

Multimedia
- Vocabulary PuzzleMaker CD-ROM
- Interactive Tutor Self-Assessment CD-ROM
- Presentation Plus! CD-ROM
- ExamView® Pro Testmaker CD-ROM

Norway is a wealthy country, partly because of oil and natural gas pumped from beneath the North Sea. It is one of the world's largest oil exporters. The seas themselves provide an important export—fish. Warm ocean currents keep most of Norway's harbors ice-free all year—a great plus for the country's commercial and cruise ships.

Norway is a parliamentary democracy. It has a monarchy but is governed by an elected prime minister. In 1994 Norway voted not to join the European Union (EU) so that it could keep control of its own economy. EU membership is still hotly debated, however.

The people of Norway greatly value their cultural traditions. Elaborate folk dress is often seen at weddings and village festivals. Norwegians are a very modern people, though. Three-fourths of the population live in urban centers like the capital, **Oslo.** About half of the Norwegians own computers. For recreation, they enjoy skiing and riding snowmobiles.

✓ Reading Check **What type of government does Norway have?**

Sweden

Like Norway, Sweden is a wealthy, industrial country. Its prosperity comes from abundant natural resources, including iron ore deposits and extensive pine forests. Exports include machinery, motor vehicles, paper products, wood, and electronic products. Only about 8 percent of Sweden's land can be used for farming. Swedish farmers have developed efficient ways to grow crops, and their farms supply most of the nation's food.

Sweden's wealth enabled it to become a **welfare state**—a country that uses high rates of taxation to provide services to people who are sick, needy, jobless, or retired. Sweden is a constitutional monarchy and a member of the European Union.

NATIONAL GEOGRAPHIC **On Location**

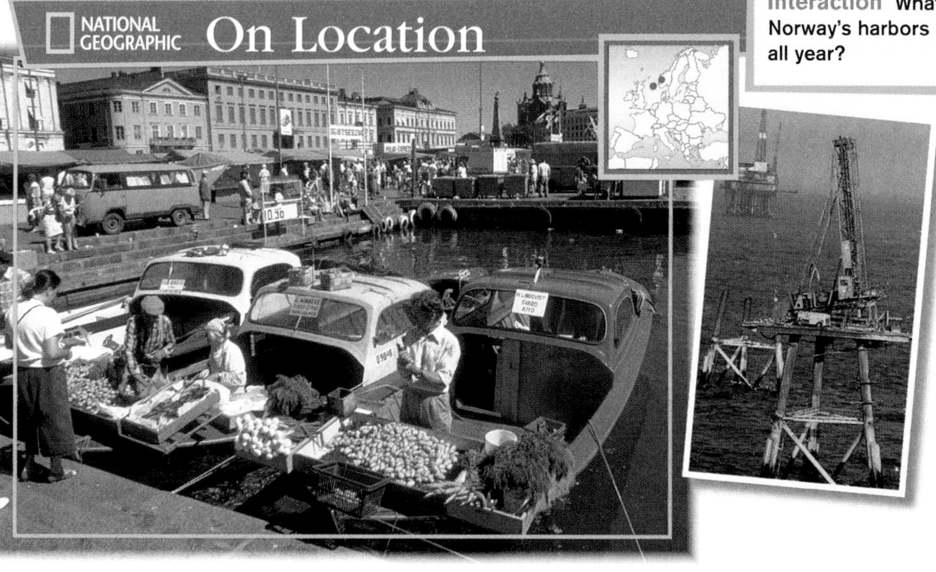

Norway's Economy

A shopper goes from boat to boat looking for bargains in Bergen, Norway's water market (below left). Europe's richest oil and natural gas fields are found in the North Sea (below right).

Human/Environment Interaction **What keeps Norway's harbors ice-free all year?**

355

Chapter 12

Section 4, pages 354–357

2 TEACH

Reading Strategy

Outlining Have students create a concept web with one of the Nordic countries in the center. The web should have five secondary areas—"Land," "Climate," "Economy," "History," and "People." Then tell students to add details related to each of these areas. L1

Daily Lecture and Discussion Notes

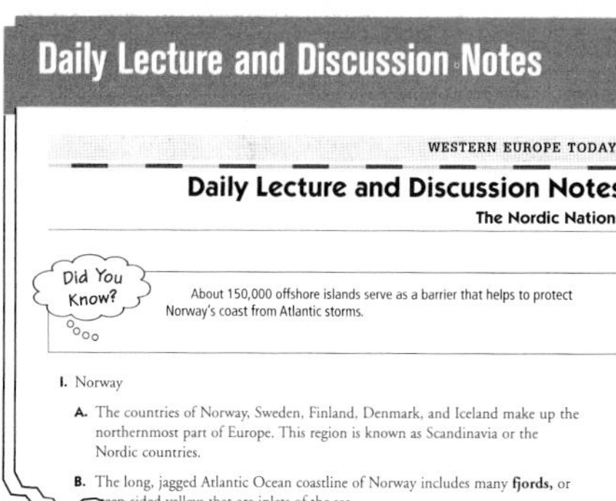
WESTERN EUROPE TODAY

Daily Lecture and Discussion Notes

The Nordic Nations

Did You Know? About 150,000 offshore islands serve as a barrier that helps to protect Norway's coast from Atlantic storms.

I. Norway

A. The countries of Norway, Sweden, Finland, Denmark, and Iceland make up the northernmost part of Europe. This region is known as Scandinavia or the Nordic countries.

B. The long, jagged Atlantic Ocean coastline of Norway includes many **fjords**, or ... valleys that are inlets of the sea.

✓ Reading Check Answer

parliamentary democracy

More About the Photos

The North Sea Pollution has become a problem in the North Sea as a result of heavy shipping activity. Countries bordering this sea have reached several agreements aimed at cutting this pollution, but enforcement has been spotty.

Caption Answer warm ocean currents

Reading Strategy — Reading the Text

Identifying Main Ideas Have students copy the subheads in this section onto a piece of paper. Tell them to leave ample space beneath each heading to write in additional information. After their outline is completed, have them read the section and write the sentence from the section that they think best summarizes the main idea. If students cannot identify a summarizing sentence, then they should construct one that does. L1

*Use the **Reading Skills Handbook** for more reading strategies.*

Most of Sweden's 9 million people live in cities in the southern lowlands. **Stockholm** is the country's capital and largest city. Sweden's high standard of living has attracted more than 1 million immigrants from nearby Norway and Denmark and distant Turkey and Vietnam.

✓Reading Check What resources have helped make Sweden wealthy?

Finland

Finland holds some of the largest unspoiled wilderness in Europe. Most of Finland's wealth comes from its huge forests of spruce, pine, and birch. Paper and wood products are important exports. In recent years, heavy industry—or industry that produces manufactured goods such as machinery—has driven Finland's economy. The Finns are also leaders in the electronic communications industry. In 1995 Finland joined the European Union.

The ancestors of the Finns settled in the region thousands of years ago, probably coming from what is now Siberia in Russia. As a result, Finnish language and culture differ from those of other Nordic countries.

Most of Finland's 5.2 million people live in towns and cities on the southern coast. **Helsinki,** the capital, has more than 1 million people, but the city has still kept a small-town atmosphere. For example, there are no high-rise buildings. With snow on the ground for about half of the year, Finns enjoy cross-country skiing. They also like to relax in saunas, or wooden rooms heated by water sizzling on hot stones.

✓Reading Check Where did the ancestors of the Finns come from?

Denmark and Iceland

Denmark and Iceland are countries whose histories are closely tied to the sea. For centuries, Iceland was ruled by Denmark so Danish is still widely spoken and understood in Iceland.

Most of Denmark is made up of a peninsula known as Jutland. Denmark also includes nearly 500 islands, only about 100 of which have people living on them. Denmark also rules the large island of Greenland. Throughout history, Denmark's location has made it a link for people and goods between the Nordic countries and the rest of Europe. Ferries and bridges connect Jutland and the islands. A bridge and tunnel now join Denmark's Zealand Island to Sweden.

Denmark has some of the richest farmland in northern Europe. Danish farm products include butter, cheese, bacon, and ham. Royal Copenhagen porcelain, a famous Danish export, is among the finest in the world. The Danes also invented and export the world-famous LEGO® toy building blocks.

The 5.4 million Danes enjoy a high standard of living. Instead of noisy, traditional festivals, many Danes prefer quiet evenings at home or spending time with friends at small cafés. The country has a parliamentary democracy, with a king or queen as head of state. Elected officials run the government. Denmark joined the European Union in 1993. **Copenhagen,** Denmark's capital, is the largest of the Nordic cities.

Cozy Ballet?

Helle Oelkers (far right) is a member of one of Europe's finest ballet companies—the Royal Danish Ballet. Helle likes to think that her performance encourages audience members to feel *hygge. Hygge* means feeling cozy and snug. She explains, "The greatest compliment a Dane can give is to thank someone for a cozy evening."

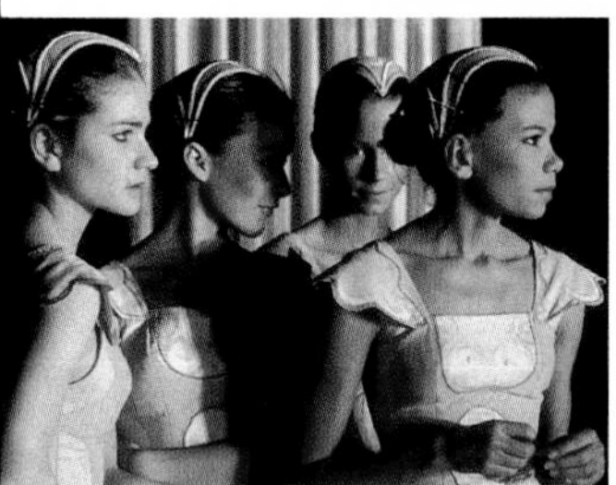

✓ Reading Check Answer

iron ore and pine forests

L1/ELL

Guided Reading Activity

Name ____ Date ____ Class ____

WESTERN EUROPE TODAY

Guided Reading Activity 4

The Nordic Nations

DIRECTIONS: Answering Questions Reading the section and answering the questions below will help you learn more about the Nordic countries. Use your textbook to write answers to the questions.

1. Why does Norway have a mostly cold climate?
2. Why is Norway wealthy?
3. What type of government exists in Norway today?

✓ Reading Check Answer

Siberia

ASSESS

Assign Section 4 Assessment as homework or an in-class activity.

Have students use the Interactive Tutor Self-Assessment CD-ROM to review Section 4.

L2

Section Quiz

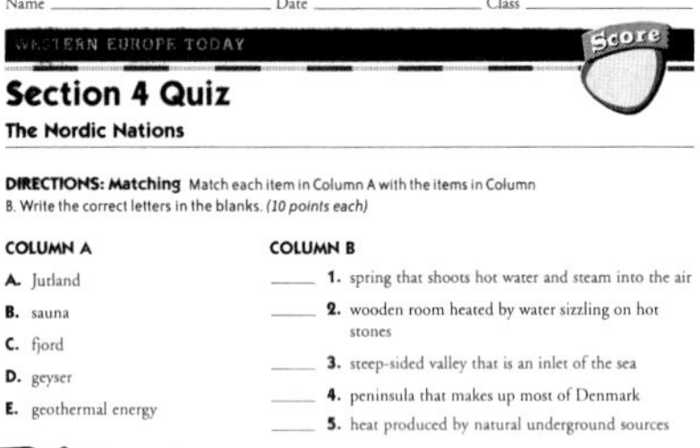
Name ____ Date ____ Class ____

WESTERN EUROPE TODAY

Score

Section 4 Quiz

The Nordic Nations

DIRECTIONS: Matching Match each item in Column A with the items in Column B. Write the correct letters in the blanks. (10 points each)

COLUMN A	COLUMN B
A. Jutland	____ 1. spring that shoots hot water and steam into the air
B. sauna	____ 2. wooden room heated by water sizzling on hot stones
C. fjord	____ 3. steep-sided valley that is an inlet of the sea
D. geyser	____ 4. peninsula that makes up most of Denmark
E. geothermal energy	____ 5. heat produced by natural underground sources

Differentiated Instruction

Meeting Special Needs: Kinesthetic Have students research and create a model of the landscape of one of the countries in this section. They can use clay, dough made from flour and water, or other materials. Students should paint their models to show different elevation levels and prepare a key explaining the colors used. Have them also create an accompanying sheet that shows the vegetation and economic activities found at different elevations. **L2**

Refer to *Inclusion for the Middle School Social Studies Classroom Strategies and Activities* in the TCR.

In Copenhagen's harbor is a famous attraction: a statue of the Little Mermaid. She is a character from a story by the Danish author Hans Christian Andersen. Andersen, who lived and wrote during the 1800s, is one of Denmark's most famous writers.

Iceland Iceland, an island in the North Atlantic, is a land of glaciers and **geysers**—springs that shoot hot water and steam into the air. The people of Iceland make the most of this unusual environment. They use **geothermal energy**, or heat produced by natural underground sources, to heat most of their homes, buildings, and swimming pools.

What makes such natural wonders possible? Sitting on top of a fault line, Iceland is at the mercy of constant volcanic activity. Every few years, one of the country's 200 volcanoes erupts. The volcanoes heat hot springs that appear across the length of Iceland.

Iceland's economy depends heavily on fishing. Fish exports provide the money to buy food and consumer goods from other countries. Iceland is concerned that overfishing will reduce the amount of fish available. To reduce its dependence on the fishing industry, Iceland has introduced new manufacturing and service industries.

More than 90 percent of the nearly 300,000 Icelanders live in urban areas. More than half the people live in the capital city of **Reykjavík** (RAY•kyah•VEEK). The people have a passion for books, magazines, and newspapers. In fact, the literacy rate in Iceland is 100 percent.

▲ The Little Mermaid statue in Copenhagen

Reading Check How do the people of Iceland take advantage of the country's geysers?

Assessment

Defining Terms

1. **Define** fjord, welfare state, heavy industry, sauna, geyser, geothermal energy.

Recalling Facts

2. **Location** Name the five Nordic countries.
3. **Economics** What resource produces most of Norway's wealth?
4. **History** Why do some Icelanders speak Danish?

Critical Thinking

5. **Analyzing Information** How has Denmark's location affected its relationship with the rest of Europe?
6. **Understanding Cause and Effect** Why is Finnish culture different from the rest of the Nordic countries?

Graphic Organizer

7. **Organizing Information** Create a diagram like the one below. Explain three effects on Iceland that result because of its location on a fault line.

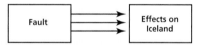

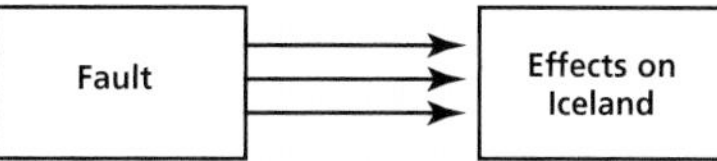

Applying Social Studies Skills

8. **Analyzing Maps** Study the political map on page 341. Which Nordic capital lies the farthest north? Which Nordic capital lies the farthest south?

Chapter 12

Section 4, pages 354–357

Reteach

Write the name of a country and a category of information on a flash card, such as "Denmark—climate" or "Iceland—people." Show the flash cards to the class and ask for volunteers to supply a piece of information that fits that country and category.

Reading Check Answer

They use them to generate geothermal energy to heat homes, buildings, and swimming pools.

L1/ELL

Reading Essentials and Study Guide

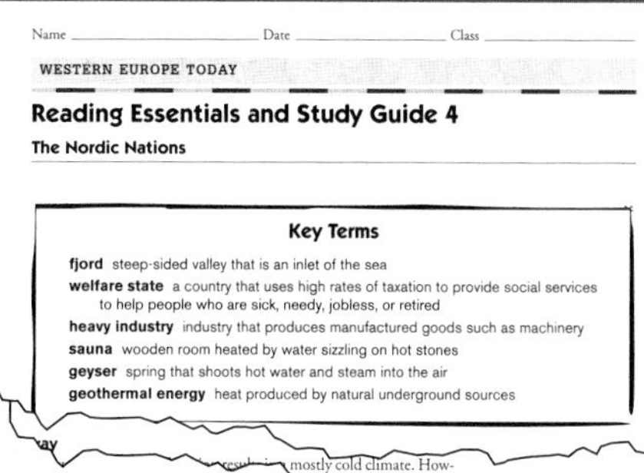

Name ______ Date ______ Class ______

WESTERN EUROPE TODAY

Reading Essentials and Study Guide 4

The Nordic Nations

Key Terms

fjord steep-sided valley that is an inlet of the sea
welfare state a country that uses high rates of taxation to provide social services to help people who are sick, needy, jobless, or retired
heavy industry industry that produces manufactured goods such as machinery
sauna wooden room heated by water sizzling on hot stones
geyser spring that shoots hot water and steam into the air
geothermal energy heat produced by natural underground sources

Close

Have students create a bulletin board display about one of the countries in this section with images and captions that highlight important features of the country.

Section 4 Assessment

1. The terms are defined in the Glossary.
2. Norway, Sweden, Finland, Denmark, Iceland
3. oil
4. Denmark ruled Iceland for centuries.
5. It has been a link between mainland Europe and the Nordic countries.
6. Finland was probably originally settled by people from Siberia in eastern Russia.
7. presence of geysers and hot springs; geothermal energy; volcanic activity
8. Reykjavík; Copenhagen

Chapter 12

Section 5, pages 358–362

1 Focus

Section Objectives

1. Compare the geography and people of Spain and Portugal.
2. Summarize the history and cultural contributions of Italy.
3. Explain how physical geography has shaped life and history in Greece.

BELLRINGER Skillbuilder Activity

Project transparency and have students answer the question.

Daily Focus Skills Transparency

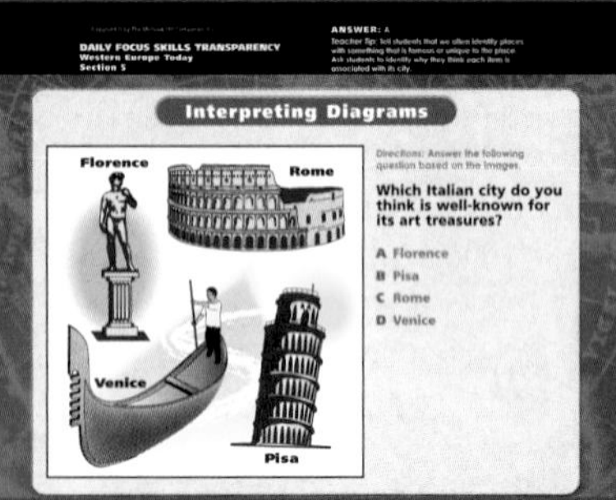

Reading Preview

■ **Activating Prior Knowledge** Remind students that most of the countries of Latin America were once colonies of Spain and Portugal. **Ask:** **What does this suggest about the histories of these two countries?** *(They once were powerful empires.)*

■ **Preteaching Vocabulary** Have students look up the meanings of the Terms to Know and then use each in a sentence.

Guide to Reading

Main Idea

The sea has played an important role in southern European countries.

Terms to Know

- dry farming
- sirocco
- coalition government

Reading Strategy

Create a chart like this one for each of the following countries: Spain, Portugal, Italy, and Greece. Fill in at least one key fact about each country for each category listed.

Country	
Land	
Economy	
Government	
People	

Section 5 Southern Europe

NATIONAL GEOGRAPHIC Exploring Our World

The "running of the bulls" is an annual and controversial event in Pamplona, a city in northern Spain. Although animal rights groups object to it, each morning during the weeklong Festival of San Fermín, a half dozen bulls are released to run along the city's narrow streets. People risk their lives by running ahead of the bulls. Their goal is to stay in the race as long as possible.

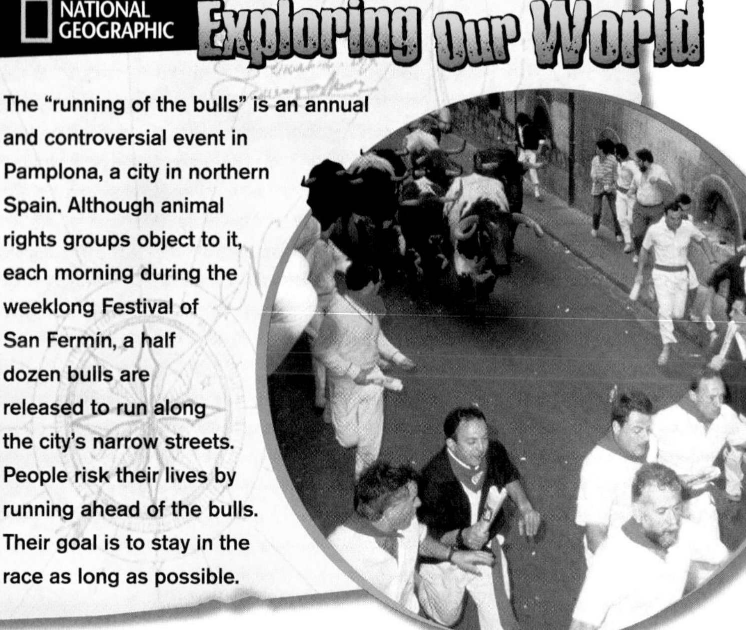

Spain, Portugal, Italy, and **Greece**—along with several tiny countries—make up southern Europe. A rich cultural heritage has produced many of the world's greatest writers, artists, and musicians. As you read in Chapter 10, it was the people of ancient Greece and Rome who played an especially important role in the development of Western civilization.

The Iberian Peninsula

Spain and its neighbors, Portugal and **Andorra,** make up the **Iberian Peninsula.** Tiny Andorra, with only 174 square miles (451 sq. km), perches high in the **Pyrenees** mountain range near Spain's border with France.

Portugal and most of Spain have mild winters and hot summers. Much of the interior of the peninsula is a dry plateau. In many areas the reddish-yellow soil is poor, and the land is dry-farmed to grow crops such as wheat and vegetables. In **dry farming,** irrigation is not used. Instead, the land is left unplanted every few years so that it can store moisture.

Section Resources

Reproducible Masters
- Reproducible Lesson Plan
- Daily Lecture and Discussion Notes
- Note-taking Guide
- Guided Reading Activity
- Reading Essentials and Study Guide
- Section Quiz

Transparencies
- Daily Focus Skills Transparency
- GeoQuiz Transparency

Multimedia
- Vocabulary PuzzleMaker CD-ROM
- Interactive Tutor Self-Assessment CD-ROM
- Presentation Plus! CD-ROM
- ExamView® Pro Testmaker CD-ROM
- MindJogger Videoquiz

Growing Economies Spain and Portugal both belong to the European Union. The two countries were once slow in developing manufacturing. In recent years, however, they have worked hard to catch up economically with other European Union nations.

Spain is one of the world's leading producers of olive oil. Portuguese farmers grow potatoes, grains, fruits, olives, and grapes. Portugal is also the world's leading exporter of cork. The cork comes from the bark of certain oak trees, which grow well in central Portugal.

People travel to the Iberian Peninsula to enjoy the sunny climate, beautiful beaches, and ancient castles and cathedrals. Andorra draws millions of tourists each year to its duty-free shops. Spain and Portugal also depend on the tourist industry.

Manufacturing industries benefit both countries' economies as well. Spanish workers mine rich deposits of iron ore and make processed foods, clothing, footwear, steel, and automobiles.

Democratic Governments Spain and Portugal are modern democracies. Spain is a constitutional monarchy, in which a king or queen is head of state, but elected officials run the government. Portugal is a parliamentary republic, with a president as head of state. A prime minister, chosen by the legislature, is the head of government. Andorra is a parliamentary democracy that is a semi-independent principality—it is governed by both Spain and France.

Spanish and Portuguese Cultures Most people in Spain and Portugal are Roman Catholic. Despite similar histories, the people of Spain and Portugal have cultural differences. Portugal developed a unified culture based on the Portuguese language. Spain remained a "country of different countries." The Spanish people do not all speak the same language or even have a single culture.

The Basque people in the Pyrenees see themselves as completely separate from Spain. They speak Basque, a language unlike any other in the world. Having lived in Spain longer than any other group, many Basques want independence in order to preserve their way of life. Some Basque groups have used violence against the Spanish government.

Lisbon is Portugal's busy capital, but Portugal is mostly rural. In contrast, more than three-fourths of Spain's people live in cities and towns. **Madrid,** Spain's capital, has nearly 5 million people and ranks as one of Europe's leading cultural centers. Madrid faces the usual urban challenges of heavy traffic and air pollution. Fast-paced **Barcelona** is Spain's leading seaport and industrial center.

You find some centuries-old traditions even in the modern cities. For example, most Spanish families usually do not eat dinner until 9 or 10 o'clock at night. On special occasions, Spaniards enjoy *paella* (pah•AY•yuh), a traditional dish of shrimp, lobster, chicken, ham, and vegetables mixed with seasoned rice.

Rock and jazz music are popular with young Spaniards and Portuguese. The people of each region have their own traditional songs, dances, and instruments as well. Spanish musicians often

Believe It or Not!

Islamic Art

The Muslims brought scientific knowledge to Spain. They introduced methods of irrigation and new crops. They also brought literature, music, and art.

Islam discourages art that includes human forms. As a result, Muslim artists create complex patterns and elaborate designs. The tile below is an example of the beautiful mosaics seen today throughout the world.

Chapter 12

Section 5, pages 358–362

2 Teach

Reading Strategy

Making Comparisons Make a table with three columns. List the characteristics of people living in the Iberian Peninsula, Italy, and Greece. Have students determine the similarities and differences of the people in these countries. L1

Daily Lecture and Discussion Notes

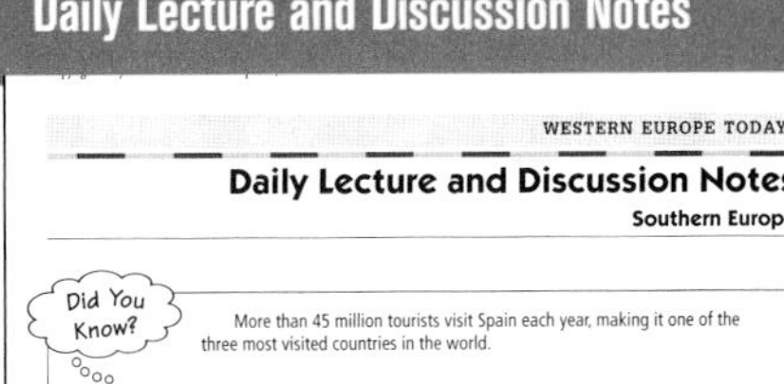

WESTERN EUROPE TODAY

Daily Lecture and Discussion Notes

Southern Europe

Did You Know? More than 45 million tourists visit Spain each year, making it one of the three most visited countries in the world.

I. The Iberian Peninsula

A. Spain and Portugal share the Iberian Peninsula. Tiny Andorra perches high in the Pyrenees mountain range near Spain's border with France.

B. Portugal and most of Spain have mild winters and hot summers.

C. Since much of the soil is poor, **dry farming** is practiced, in which the land is ... so that it can store moisture.

Measure student knowledge of physical features.

GeoQuiz Transparency

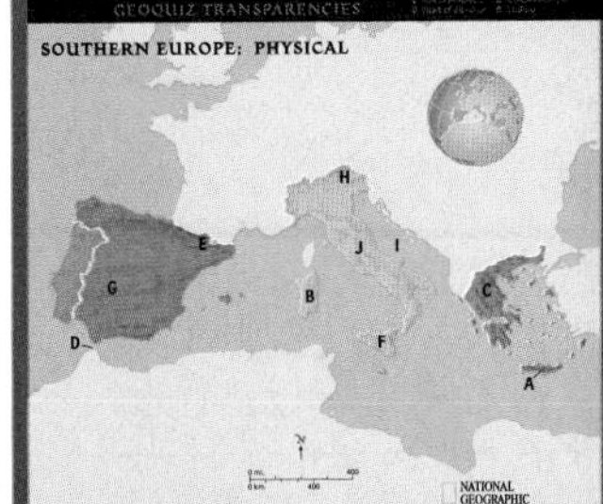

Reading Strategy **Reading the Text**

Varying Reading Rate Teach students to adjust their reading rate as they work through the section. They need to slow down when they encounter difficult concepts, connections to previous ideas, new vocabulary, or text that contains a great deal of information. L1

*Use the **Reading Skills Handbook** for more reading strategies.*

More About the Photos

Gondolas Gondolas are to Venice what taxis are to New York City. Each boat carries up to six passengers, costs about $30,000, and lasts over 20 years. Because of their unique design, gondolas are easily maneuvered through crowded canals, even when fully loaded.

Caption Answer from a mainly agricultural economy to a leading industrial economy

Reading Check Answer

cork

L1/ELL

Guided Reading Activity

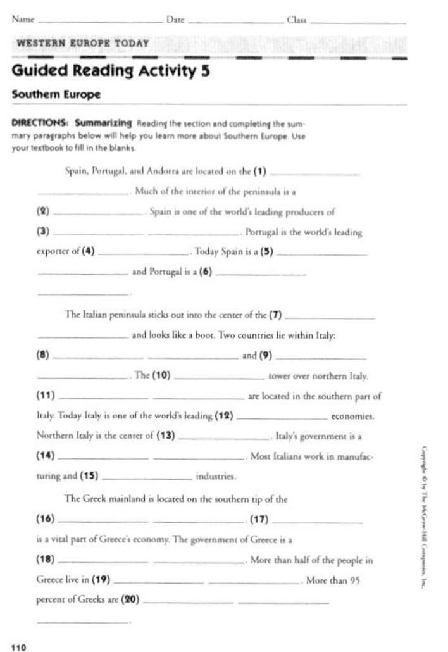

Name ______ Date ______ Class ______

WESTERN EUROPE TODAY

Guided Reading Activity 5

Southern Europe

DIRECTIONS: Summarizing Reading the section and completing the summary paragraphs below will help you learn more about Southern Europe. Use your textbook to fill in the blanks.

Spain, Portugal, and Andorra are located on the **(1)** ______ ______. Much of the interior of the peninsula is a **(2)** ______. Spain is one of the world's leading producers of **(3)** ______ ______. Portugal is the world's leading exporter of **(4)** ______. Today Spain is a **(5)** ______ ______ and Portugal is a **(6)** ______ ______.

The Italian peninsula sticks out into the center of the **(7)** ______ ______ and looks like a boot. Two countries lie within Italy: **(8)** ______ ______ and **(9)** ______ ______. The **(10)** ______ tower over northern Italy. **(11)** ______ ______ are located in the southern part of Italy. Today Italy is one of the world's leading **(12)** ______ economies. Northern Italy is the center of **(13)** ______. Italy's government is a **(14)** ______ ______. Most Italians work in manufacturing and **(15)** ______ industries.

The Greek mainland is located on the southern tip of the **(16)** ______ ______. **(17)** ______ is a vital part of Greece's economy. The government of Greece is a **(18)** ______ ______. More than half of the people in Greece live in **(19)** ______ ______. More than 95 percent of Greeks are **(20)** ______ ______ ______.

110

Copyright © by The McGraw-Hill Companies, Inc.

NATIONAL GEOGRAPHIC On Location

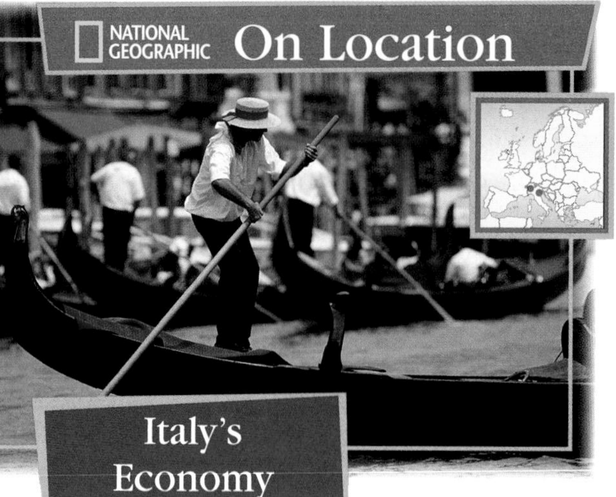

Italy's Economy

The canals of Venice draw thousands of tourists (above). The city of Milan boasts a fashion industry with stylish models (below).

Economics **How has Italy's economy changed in the past 50 years?**

accompany singers and dancers on guitars, castanets, and tambourines. Spanish dances, such as the *bolero* and *flamenco,* and soulful Portuguese folk songs known as *fado* have spread throughout the world.

Reading Check Portugal leads the world in what export?

Italy

The Italian peninsula sticks out from Europe into the center of the **Mediterranean Sea.** The peninsula looks like a boot about to kick a triangular football. The "football" is **Sicily,** an island that belongs to Italy. Two tiny countries—**San Marino** and **Vatican City**—lie within the Italian "boot."

The Alps tower over northern Italy, while the rumbling of volcanic mountains echoes through the southern part of the peninsula and the island of Sicily. Throughout history, southern Italy has experienced volcanic eruptions and earthquakes.

Most of Italy has a mild climate of sunny summers and rainy winters. In spring and summer, hot dry winds called siroccos blow across Italy from North Africa.

Italy's Economy In the past 50 years, Italy has changed from a mainly agricultural country into one of the world's leading industrial economies. Many products are manufactured by small, family-owned businesses rather than by large corporations. Italian businesses are known for creating new designs and methods for making products. Italy is a member of the European Union.

Most of the country's manufacturing takes place in northern Italy. Tourism is also important in northern and central Italy. Resorts in the Alps attract skiers. **Venice,** to the northeast, is built on 117 islands. You find no cars in this city, which is crisscrossed by canals and relies on boats for transportation. In central Italy lies **Rome,** Italy's capital and largest city. In Classical times, Rome was the seat of the Roman Empire. In Rome, you can still see ancient Roman ruins and magnificent Renaissance churches and palaces.

Southern Italy is poorer and less industrialized than northern and central Italy. Unemployment and poverty are common. Many southern Italians have moved to northern Italy or to other parts of Europe.

Italy's Government After World War II, Italy became a democratic republic. Yet democracy did not bring a stable government. Rivalry between the wealthy north and the poorer south has caused political tensions. In addition, many political parties exist, and no single party has been strong enough to gain control. Instead, Italy has seen many coalition governments, where two or more political parties work together to run the country.

Differentiated Instruction

Meeting Special Needs: Visual/Spatial Organize students into five or six groups and supply each group with 10 large index cards. Inform groups that their task is to create a set of 10 information cards on the Iberian Peninsula. First, have group members spend time discussing what they think are the 10 most important features of the region. Then direct groups to create their cards. Some group members could design visuals to illustrate the features on the fronts of the cards. Others could research the features and write brief descriptions of them for the backs of the cards. Call on the groups to present their cards to the class. Have them explain why they selected the features they chose. L1

Italy's People About 70 percent of Italy's 57.2 million people live in towns and cities. More than 90 percent of Italians work in manufacturing and service industries. Most Italians—more than 95 percent—are Roman Catholic. Celebrating the Church's religious festivals is a widely shared part of Italian life. Vatican City, surrounded by Rome, is the headquarters of the Roman Catholic Church. The pope, who is the head of the Church, lives and works here. Vatican City has many art treasures as well as the world's largest church, St. Peter's Basilica.

The people of Italy speak Italian, which developed from Latin, the language of ancient Rome. Italian is closely related to French and Spanish. Pasta, made from flour and water, is the basic dish in Italy. Some pasta dishes are spaghetti, lasagna, and ravioli.

✓ Reading Check **Why have coalition governments been necessary in Italy?**

Greece

The Greek mainland sits on the southern tip of the **Balkan Peninsula,** which juts out from Europe into the Mediterranean Sea. Greece also includes 2,000 islands around the mainland. Like other Mediterranean areas, Greece is often shaken by earthquakes. Mountain ranges divide Greece into many separate regions. Historically, this has kept people in one region isolated from people in other regions.

Of the 2,000 Greek islands, only about 170 have people living on them. The largest Greek island, covering more than 3,000 square miles (7,770 sq. km), is **Crete.** Farther east in the Mediterranean is the island country of **Cyprus.** Once under Turkish and then British rule, Cyprus became independent in 1960. For centuries Greeks and Turks have lived on Cyprus, but fighting between the two groups has resulted in a divided country.

Architecture

For more than 800 years the Leaning Tower of Pisa in Italy has stood as a monument to construction mistakes. Begun in 1173, the tower began to tilt even before it was finished. Over time the tower moved even more, until by 1990, it leaned 15 feet (4.5 m) to the south. Fearing the tower would fall over, experts closed it. They added 800 tons (726 t) of lead weights to its base. They also removed 30 tons (27 t) of subsoil from underneath the north side of the tower in hopes that it would sink the opposite way. Visitors have again returned to the tower.

Looking Closer **Why do you think experts fixed the tower's problem but still left it leaning?**

Chapter 12

Section 5, pages 358–362

✓ Reading Check Answer

There are many political parties and no single party has been strong enough to gain control.

Did You Know

The name *Greece* comes from the Latin word *Graeci,* the name that the Romans gave to the people who lived in what is today northern Greece.

Answer to continue to attract tourists to the famed tower

Ask students: **Do you think people should act to preserve and protect old buildings? Why or why not?**

Assign Section 5 Assessment as homework or an in-class activity.

Have students use the Interactive Tutor Self-Assessment CD-ROM to review Section 5.

Cooperative Learning Activity

Celebrating Ethnic Diversity The people of southern Europe have many festivals and holidays. Some might be celebrated in your community if immigrants from these lands settled there. Other groups living in your community have their own special occasions. Have students investigate which ethnic groups are in your community, learn what special days these groups observe, and find out how they celebrate these days. Then have students create posters or brochures that celebrate the ethnic diversity in the community by illustrating one of the festivals.

EE5 Human Systems: Standards 9, 10

L2

Section Quiz

Name ______ Date ______ Class ______

Score | WESTERN EUROPE TODAY

Section 5 Quiz
Southern Europe

DIRECTIONS: Matching Match each item in Column A with the items in Column B. Write the correct letters in the blanks. (10 points each)

COLUMN A	COLUMN B
A. Vatican City	____ 1. shared by Spain and Portugal
B. Balkan Peninsula	____ 2. land is left unplanted every few years
C. dry farming	____ 3. Greece lies on its southern tip
D. siroccos	____ 4. headquarters of the Roman Catholic Church
E. Iberian Peninsula	____ 5. hot, dry winds from North Africa

Reading Check Answer

shipping and tourism

L1/ELL

Reading Essentials and Study Guide

Name ______ Date ______ Class ______

WESTERN EUROPE TODAY

Reading Essentials and Study Guide 5
Southern Europe

Key Terms

dry farming method in which the land is left unplanted every few years so that it can store moisture
sirocco hot, dry winds from North Africa that blow in spring and summer
coalition government where two or more political parties work together to run a country

4 Close

Reading Strategy

Writing a Letter Tell students to imagine they are on a vacation in southern Europe. Have them write a letter home describing the things that they have seen, using standard grammar, spelling, sentence structure, and punctuation.

▲ Greek folk dancers

Greece's Economy Greece belongs to the European Union but has one of the least industrialized economies in Europe. Because of the poor, stony soil, most people living in the highlands must graze sheep and goats. Greece must import food, fuels, and many manufactured goods. Farmers cultivate sugar beets, grains, citrus fruits, and tobacco. The major crops of Greece are olives, used for olive oil, and grapes, used for wine.

No part of Greece is more than 85 miles (137 km) from the sea. Shipping is vital to the economy. Greece has one of the largest shipping fleets in the world, including oil tankers, cargo ships, fishing boats, and passenger vessels.

Tourism is another key industry. Each year millions of visitors come to Greece to visit historic sites, such as the Parthenon in the capital city of **Athens** and the temple of Apollo at Delphi. Others come to relax on beaches and to enjoy the beautiful island scenery.

The Greeks Today Greece is a parliamentary republic. About 60 percent of Greece's 11 million people live in urban areas. The Greeks today have much in common with their ancestors. They debate political issues with great enthusiasm, and they value the art of storytelling.

More than 95 percent of Greeks are Greek Orthodox Christians. Religion influences much of Greek life, especially in rural areas. Easter is the most important Greek holiday. Traditional holiday foods include lamb, fish, and feta cheese—made from sheep's or goat's milk.

✓Reading Check **What are two key industries in Greece?**

Section 5 Assessment

Defining Terms

1. **Define** dry farming, sirocco, coalition government.

Recalling Facts

2. **Location** What three countries are located on the Iberian Peninsula?
3. **Economics** Which is the more prosperous region in Italy—north or south?
4. **Culture** List four things tourists see in Italy.

Critical Thinking

5. **Analyzing Information** Why is it expected that Greece's economy would be dependent upon the sea?
6. **Understanding Cause and Effect** Why do the Basque people feel separate from the rest of Spain?

Graphic Organizer

7. **Organizing Information** Draw a diagram like this one. Choose two countries from this section and compare them. Write statements that are true of both countries where the ovals overlap. List information unique to each country in the outer parts of the ovals.

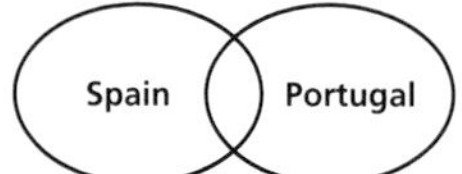

Applying Social Studies Skills

8. **Analyzing Maps** Turn to the political map on page 341. What body of water touches most of the southern countries of Europe?

362

Section 5 Assessment

1. The terms are defined in the Glossary.
2. Spain, Portugal, and Andorra
3. North
4. *Possible answers:* the Alps, Venice, Rome, Vatican City
5. No part of Greece is more than 85 miles from the sea, and the soil is poor and stony.
6. The Basques live in an isolated region of northern Spain, and they have a totally separate language and culture from the Spanish.
7. Students' diagrams should contain information from the section.
8. the Mediterranean Sea

Chapter 12 Reading Review

Section 1 The British Isles

Terms to Know
- moor
- peat
- parliamentary democracy
- bog
- constitutional monarchy

Main Idea

The United Kingdom and Ireland are small in size, but their people have had a great impact on the rest of the world.

✓Geography Ireland is called the Emerald Isle because of its landscape.

✓Economics The United Kingdom is a major industrial and trading country.

✓History After years of conflict, a peace plan was adopted in Northern Ireland.

Section 2 France and the Benelux Countries

Terms to Know
- navigable
- polder
- multinational company
- multilingual

Main Idea

France and the Benelux countries are important cultural, agricultural, and manufacturing centers of Europe.

✓Culture Paris is a world center of art, learning, and culture.

✓Location Belgium's location has made it an international center for trade.

✓Economics Luxembourg is home to many multinational companies.

Section 3 Germany and the Alpine Countries

Terms to Know
- autobahn
- federal republic
- reunification
- neutrality
- continental divide

Main Idea

Germany, Switzerland, and Austria are known for their mountain scenery and prosperous economies.

✓Economics The German economy is very strong.

✓Economics Switzerland produces high-quality manufactured goods.

✓Economics Austria's economy makes use of the mountainous terrain.

Section 4 The Nordic Nations

Terms to Know
- fjord
- welfare state
- heavy industry
- sauna
- geyser
- geothermal energy

Main Idea

The Nordic countries have developed diverse economies, and their people enjoy a high standard of living.

✓Region The Nordic countries include Norway, Sweden, Finland, Denmark, and Iceland.

✓Culture Finnish culture differs from other Nordic countries.

✓Economics Sweden's prosperity comes from forests and iron ore.

Section 5 Southern Europe

Terms to Know
- dry farming
- sirocco
- coalition government

Main Idea

The sea has played an important role in southern European countries.

✓Location Spain, Portugal, and Andorra occupy the Iberian Peninsula.

✓Economics Italy is one of the world's leading industrial economies.

✓Place Greece consists of a mountainous mainland and 2,000 islands.

Reading Review

Use the Chapter 12 Reading Review to preview, review, condense, or reteach the chapter.

Preview/Review

Use the Terms to Know lists to help students review and study.

Activity Give students a quiz of the chapter's terms by reading a definition and having them identify the correct word.

Vocabulary PuzzleMaker CD-ROM reinforces the vocabulary terms used in Chapter 12.

The Interactive Tutor Self-Assessment CD-ROM allows students to review Chapter 12 content.

Condense

Have students read the Chapter 12 summary statements.

Guided Reading Activities

Audio Program

Reteach

Reteaching Activity

Reading Essentials and Study Guide

Reading Strategy — Read to Write

Sequencing Information Have students choose one of the countries profiled in this chapter and create an illustrated time line of that country's history. Advise them to include events from ancient as well as modern times and to address the country's cultural contributions as well as political events. They can prepare their time lines as bulletin board displays or as multimedia presentations. L1

EE4 Human Systems: Standards 9, 10, 12

Assessment and Activities

GLENCOE TECHNOLOGY

MindJogger Videoquiz
Use MindJogger Videoquiz to review the Chapter 12 content.

Available in DVD and VHS

Using Key Terms

1. h
2. j
3. i
4. c
5. b
6. d
7. a
8. g
9. f
10. e

Reviewing the Main Ideas

11. England, Scotland, Wales, and Northern Ireland
12. Gaelic and English
13. the name of the current government in France
14. They have such high population density that they need more land.
15. Eastern Germany has old and inefficient factories that cannot compete with the more advanced industries in the west, and it does not have well-trained workers.
16. because of Switzerland's heritage of neutrality, which is a result of its location in the Alps
17. because of oil and natural gas and fish exports
18. 100 percent
19. The Basque people see their culture as separate from Spain's and want to preserve their way of life.
20. The soil is too poor and rocky for farming. Shipping and sea-related activities are more dominant economic activities.

Chapter 12 Assessment and Activities

Using Key Terms

Match the terms in Part A with their definitions in Part B.

A.

1. multilingual
2. heavy industry
3. coalition government
4. neutrality
5. dry farming
6. welfare state
7. polder
8. autobahn
9. constitutional monarchy
10. multinational company

B.

a. land reclaimed from the sea
b. leaving land unplanted to store moisture
c. refusing to take sides
d. country that uses tax money to help people in need
e. company that has offices in several countries
f. government that has a king or queen but is run by elected officials
g. superhighway
h. able to speak several languages
i. two or more political parties working together to run a country
j. production of industrial goods

Reviewing the Main Ideas

Section 1 The British Isles

11. **Region** What regions make up the United Kingdom?
12. **Culture** Name the two official languages of the Republic of Ireland.

Section 2 France and the Benelux Countries

13. **Government** What is the Fifth Republic?
14. **Location** Why do the Dutch have to protect their land from the sea?

Section 3 Germany and the Alpine Countries

15. **Government** What challenges does the reunification of Germany bring?
16. **Location** Why is Geneva the center of many international organizations?

Section 4 The Nordic Nations

17. **Economics** What makes Norway wealthy?
18. **Culture** What is Iceland's literacy rate?

Section 5 Southern Europe

19. **Culture** Why do the Basque people want independence from Spain?
20. **Economics** How does the rocky landscape influence Greece's economy?

Western Europe

Place Location Activity

On a separate sheet of paper, match the letters on the map with the numbered places listed below.

1. Ireland
2. North Sea
3. Belgium
4. Austria
5. Switzerland
6. Spain
7. Norway
8. Portugal
9. Sweden
10. Iceland

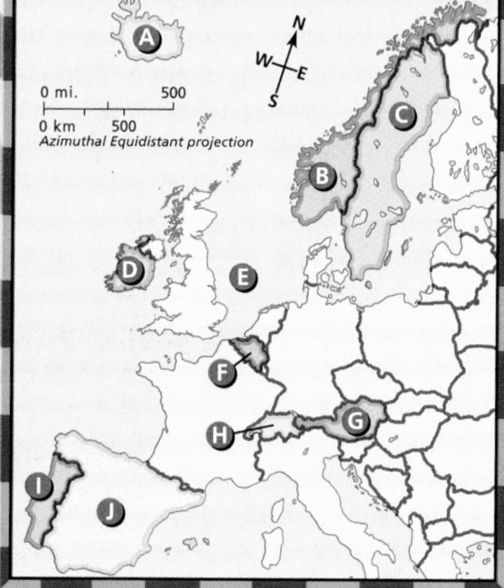

Place Location Activity

1. D
2. E
3. F
4. G
5. H
6. J
7. B
8. I
9. C
10. A

Critical Thinking

21. "Fire" is appropriate because the island experiences geysers and volcanoes due to its location along a fault line. "Ice" is appropriate because many areas are covered by ice due to its northern latitude.
22. Students' outlines will vary.

Self-Check Quiz Visit ***The World and Its People*** Web site at twip.glencoe.com and click on **Chapter 12—Self-Check Quizzes** to prepare for the Chapter Test.

Critical Thinking

21. **Analyzing Information** Why is the name Land of Fire and Ice appropriate for Iceland?
22. **Organizing Information** Create an outline for each country in Section 5. Use the following guide as your base outline.
    - **I.** Name of Country
        - **A.** Land
        - **B.** Economy
        - **C.** People

Comparing Regions Activity

23. **Culture** Visit a newsstand or library to find a magazine published for European teens. Does it have the same look and feel as a magazine you read? What common features or advertisements do you see?

Mental Mapping Activity

24. **Focusing on the Region** Create a simple outline map of western Europe, and then label the following:

- United Kingdom
- France
- Germany
- Sweden
- Italy
- Spain
- Switzerland
- Iceland

Technology Skills Activity

25. **Using a Spreadsheet** List the names of the western European countries in a spreadsheet, beginning with cell A2 and continuing down the column. Find each country's population and record the figures in column B. In column C list each country's area in square miles. Title column D "Population Density," then divide column B by column C to find the population density. Print and share your spreadsheet with the class.

Standardized Test Practice

Directions: Study the graph below, and then answer the question that follows.

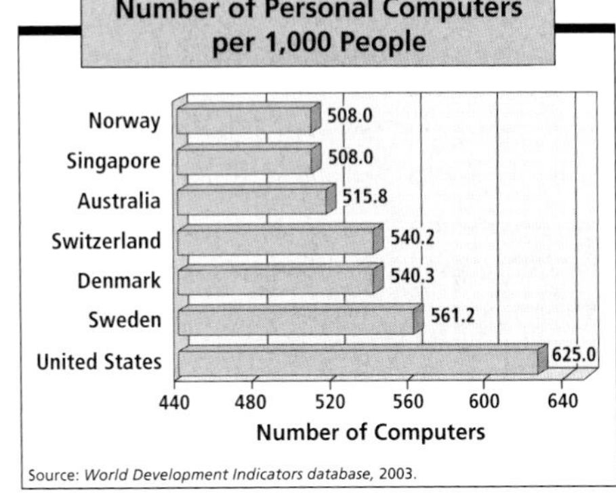

1. Which Nordic country has the highest number of personal computers per 1,000 people?

- **A** United States
- **B** Switzerland
- **C** Denmark
- **D** Sweden

Test-Taking Tip: Use the information on the graph to help you answer this question. Look carefully at the information on the bottom and the side of a bar graph to understand what the bars represent. The important word in the question is *Nordic.* Other countries may have more personal computers, but which Nordic country listed on the graph has the most personal computers per 1,000 people?

Assessment and Activities

Standardized Test Practice

1. D

Tested Objectives:
Reading a bar graph, analyzing information

Chapter Test Bonus Question

This question may be used for extra credit on the chapter test.

The country in which you plan to vacation: (1) has coastal areas on the Mediterranean and the Atlantic; (2) is famous for its wine; (3) is a world center of art and learning. **Where will you be taking your vacation?** *(France)*

Social Studies Online

Have students visit the Web site at twip.glencoe.com to review Chapter 12 and take the Self-Check Quiz.

FOLDABLES™ Study Organizer **Dinah Zike's Foldables**

Culminating Activity Organize students into groups to create a collage that illustrates the facts and information they collected from the chapter.

Comparing Regions Activity

23. Have students discuss their observations as a class. Students may want to show both American and European magazines to the class during the discussion.

Mental Mapping Activity

24. This exercise helps students visualize the countries they have been studying in this chapter. Accept all attempts at freehand mapping.

Technology Skills Activity

25. Students' spreadsheets or databases should have clearly defined fields and accurate records with no typographical or other errors. Encourage students to create bar graphs or other means of showing comparative information.

Chapter 13 Resources

Note: The following materials may be used when teaching Chapter 13.
Section level support materials are shown at point of use in the margins of the Teacher Wraparound Edition.

Timesaving Tools

TeacherWorks™ All-In-One Planner and Resource Center

- **Interactive Teacher Edition** See the **Interactive Teacher Edition** CD-ROM to electronically integrate your Teacher Wraparound Edition and blackline masters.
- **Interactive Lesson Planner** Organize your week, month, semester, or year with all the lesson helps you need. The **Interactive Lesson Planner** CD-ROM contains all Chapter 13 resources.

Use Glencoe's **Presentation Plus!** multimedia teacher tool to easily present dynamic lessons that visually excite your students. Using Microsoft PowerPoint® you can customize the presentations to create your own personalized lessons.

TEACHING TRANSPARENCIES

Graphic Organizer Transparency 6 L2

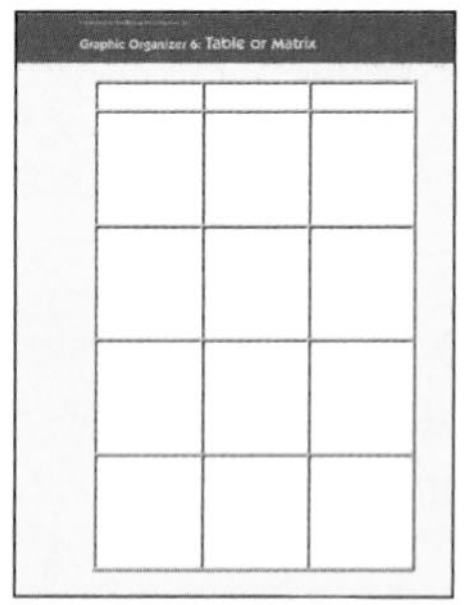

In-text Map Transparency L1

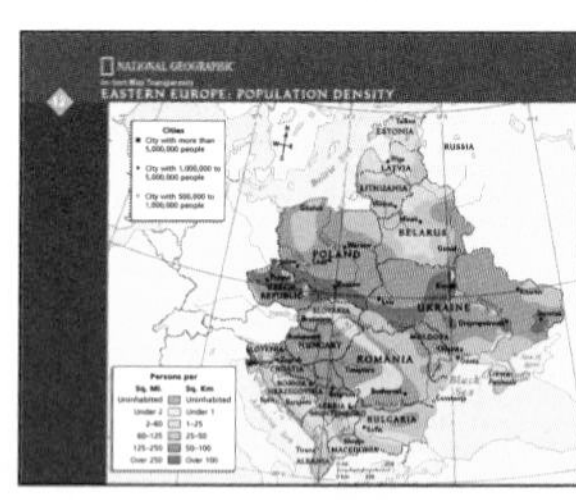

FOLDABLES™ Study Organizer **Dinah Zike's Foldables**

Foldables are three-dimensional, interactive graphic organizers that help students practice basic writing skills, review key vocabulary terms, and identify main ideas. Additional chapter activities can be found in the ***Reading and Study Skills Foldables*** booklet.

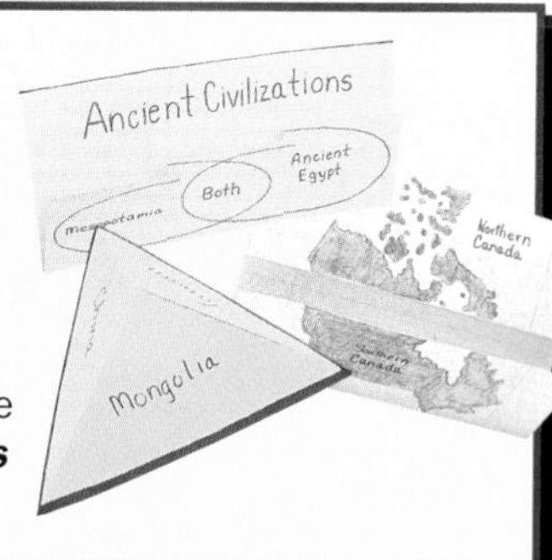

MAP AND GEOGRAPHY SKILLS

Chapter Map Activity L2

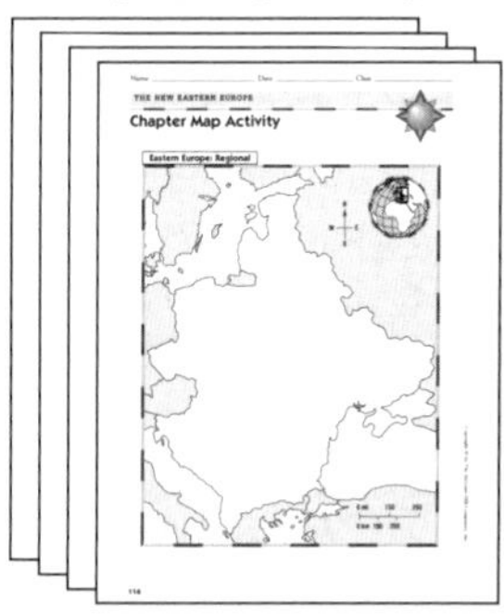

GeoLab Activity L2

READING SUPPORT

Vocabulary Activity L1

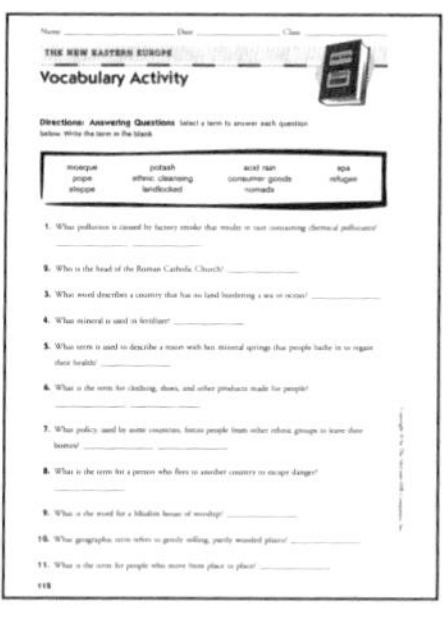

Workbook Activity L1

Reading and Writing Skills Activity L1/ELL

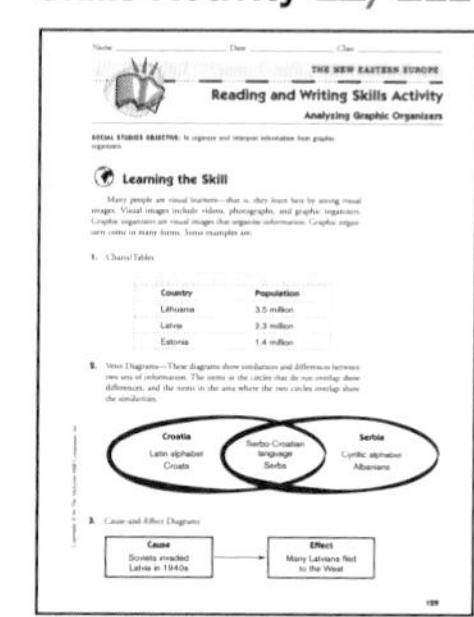

DIFFERENTIATED INSTRUCTION

Use these review and reinforcement materials to help less-proficient readers, English learners, and gifted and talented students.

Reteaching Activity L1

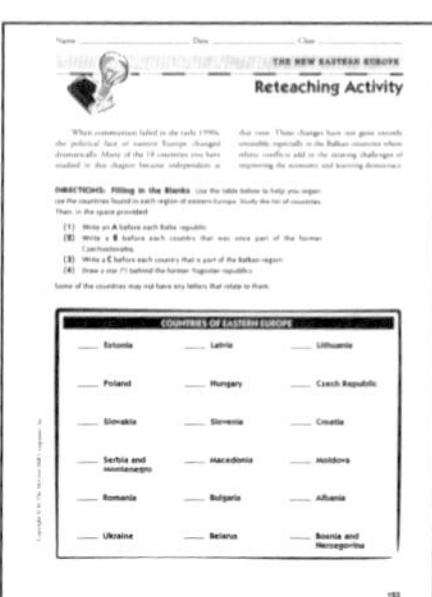

Chapter Skills Review L2

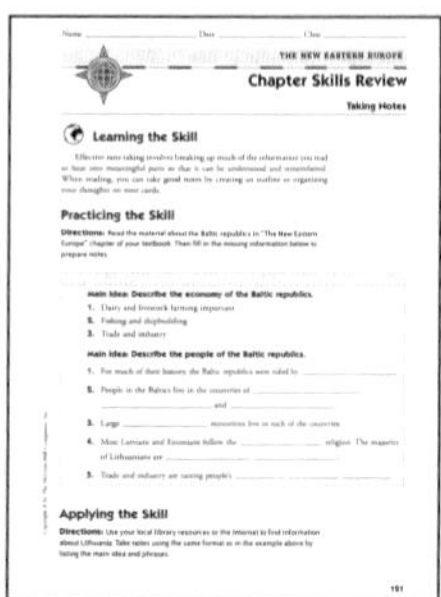

Cooperative Learning Activity L1/ELL

Enrichment Activity L3

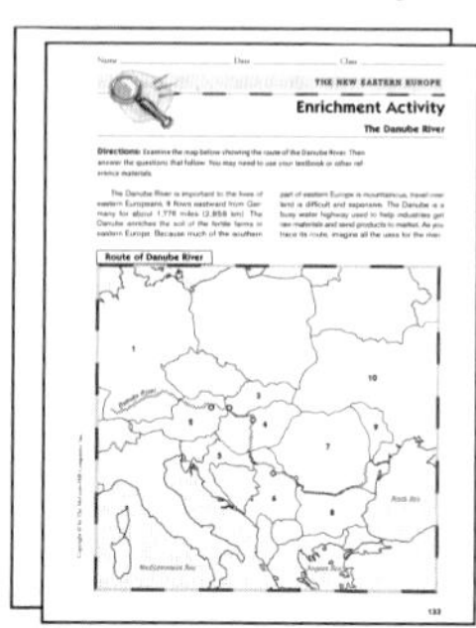

ASSESSMENT

Chapter Test, Form A L2

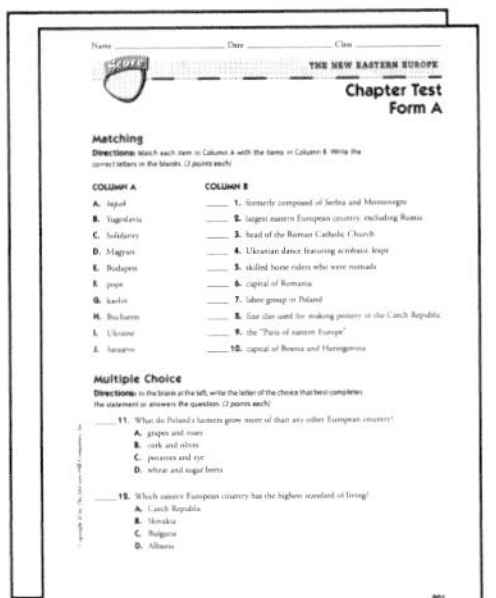

Chapter Test, Form B L2

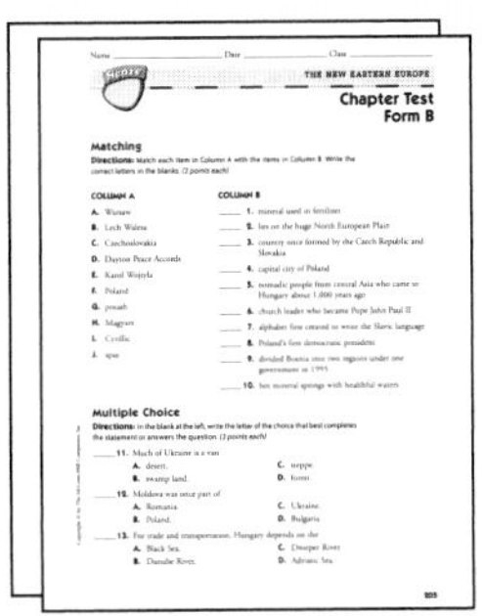

Performance Assessment Activity L1/ELL

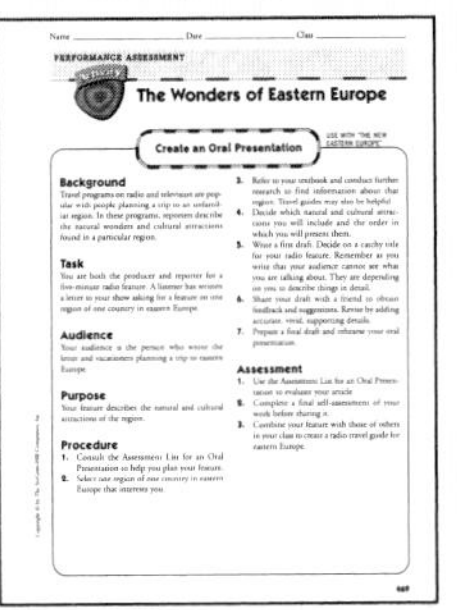

ExamView® Pro Testmaker CD-ROM

STANDARDIZED ASSESSMENT SKILLS

Critical Thinking Skills Activity L2

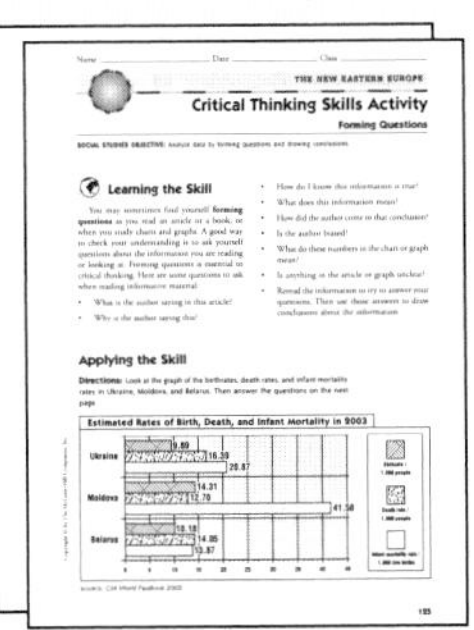

Map and Graph Skills Activity L2

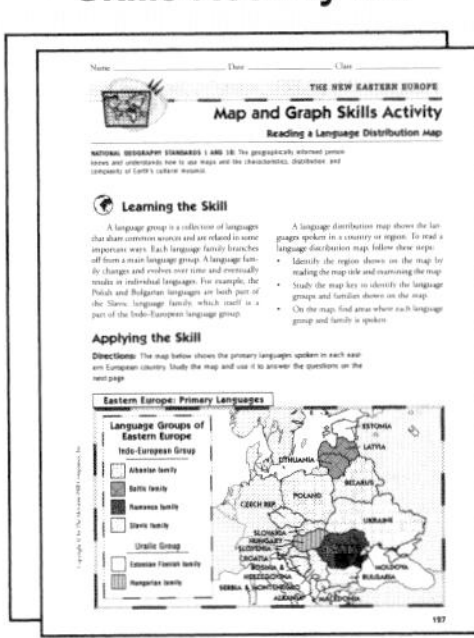

Standardized Test Skills Practice Workbook Activity L2

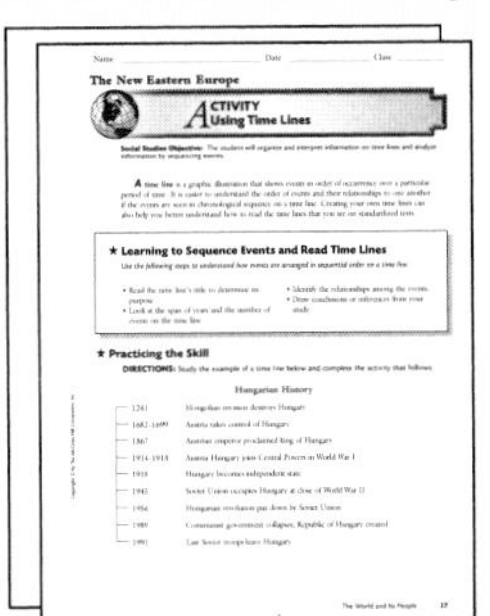

HOME INVOLVEMENT

Take-Home Review Activity L1

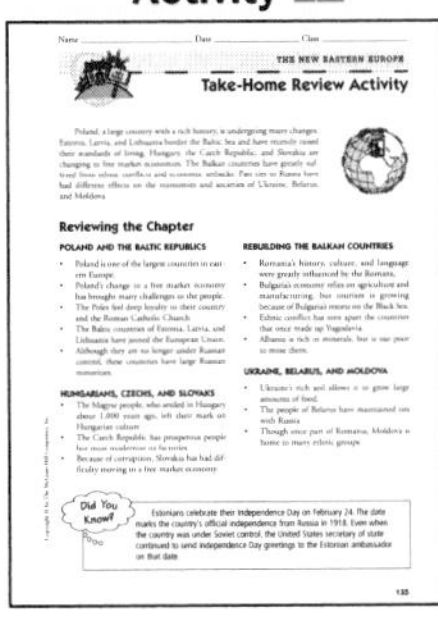

MULTIMEDIA

- National Geographic's The World and Its People
- MindJogger Videoquiz
- Vocabulary PuzzleMaker CD-ROM
- Interactive Tutor Self-Assessment CD-ROM
- ExamView® Pro Testmaker CD-ROM
- TeacherWorks CD-ROM
- StudentWorks CD-ROM
- Skillbuilder Interactive Workbook CD-ROM, Level 1
- Presentation Plus! CD-ROM
- Audio Program

SPANISH RESOURCES

The following Spanish language materials are available in the Spanish Resources binder:

- Spanish Summaries
- Spanish Vocabulary Activities
- Spanish Guided Reading Activities
- Spanish Quizzes and Tests
- Spanish Take-Home Review Activities
- Spanish Reteaching Activities

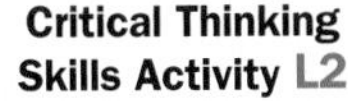

Meeting National Standards

Geography for Life

The following standards are covered in Chapter 13:

Section 1
- **EE3 Physical Systems: Standards 7, 8**
- **EE4 Human Systems: Standards 10, 11, 12**
- **EE5 Environment and Society: Standards 14, 15, 16**

Section 2
- **EE4 Human Systems: Standards 9, 10, 13**

Section 3
- **EE4 Human Systems: Standards 9, 10, 11, 12, 13**
- **EE5 Environment and Society: Standards 14, 15, 16**

Section 4
- **EE3 Places and Regions: Standards 4, 5**
- **EE4 Human Systems: Standards 9, 10, 13**

Chapter 13 Planning Guide

SECTION RESOURCES

Daily Objectives	Reproducible Resources	Multimedia Resources
Section 1 **Poland and the Baltic Republics** 1. Explain how the economy of Poland has changed in recent years. 2. Discuss the people and economies of the Baltic Republics.	Reproducible Lesson Plan Daily Lecture and Discussion Notes Note-taking Guide Guided Reading Activity* Reading Essentials and Study Guide* Section Quiz*	Daily Focus Skills Transparency Vocabulary PuzzleMaker CD-ROM Interactive Tutor Self-Assessment CD-ROM ExamView® Pro Testmaker CD-ROM Presentation Plus! CD-ROM
Section 2 **Hungarians, Czechs, and Slovaks** 1. Discuss the history and peoples of Hungary, the Czech Republic, and Slovakia. 2. Describe the changing economies of Hungary, the Czech Republic, and Slovakia.	Reproducible Lesson Plan Daily Lecture and Discussion Notes Note-taking Guide Guided Reading Activity* Reading Essentials and Study Guide* Section Quiz*	Daily Focus Skills Transparency Vocabulary PuzzleMaker CD-ROM Interactive Tutor Self-Assessment CD-ROM ExamView® Pro Testmaker CD-ROM Presentation Plus! CD-ROM
Section 3 **Rebuilding the Balkan Countries** 1. Compare the economies and the peoples of the Balkan countries. 2. Explain why Yugoslavia broke into separate countries.	Reproducible Lesson Plan Daily Lecture and Discussion Notes Note-taking Guide Guided Reading Activity* Reading Essentials and Study Guide* Section Quiz*	Daily Focus Skills Transparency Vocabulary PuzzleMaker CD-ROM Interactive Tutor Self-Assessment CD-ROM ExamView® Pro Testmaker CD-ROM Presentation Plus! CD-ROM
Section 4 **Ukraine, Belarus, and Moldova** 1. Describe the landforms of Ukraine, Belarus, and Moldova. 2. Compare the economies, history, and culture of Ukraine, Belarus, and Moldova.	Reproducible Lesson Plan Daily Lecture and Discussion Notes Note-taking Guide Guided Reading Activity* Reading Essentials and Study Guide* Section Quiz*	Daily Focus Skills Transparency In-text Map Transparency Vocabulary PuzzleMaker CD-ROM Interactive Tutor Self-Assessment CD-ROM ExamView® Pro Testmaker CD-ROM Presentation Plus! CD-ROM MindJogger Videoquiz

00:00 **Out of Time?** Assign the **Reading Essentials and Study Guide*** for this chapter.

*Also available in Spanish

KEY TO ABILITY LEVELS

Teaching strategies have been coded for varying learning styles and abilities.

L1 **BASIC** activities for all students
L2 **AVERAGE** activities for average to above-average students
L3 **CHALLENGING** activities for above-average students
ELL **ENGLISH LANGUAGE LEARNER** activities

KEY TO TEACHING RESOURCES

Blackline Master
CD-ROM
Transparency
Videocassette
Block Scheduling
DVD

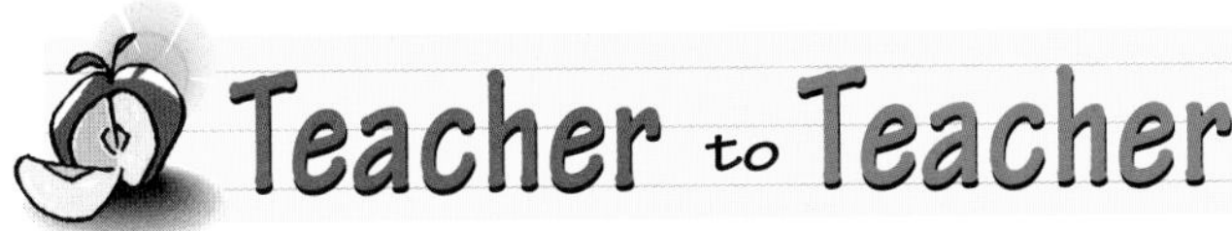

Ten Clues

Sue Brinkley
Hampshire Unit School
Hampshire, Tennessee

Give each student a 4" × 6" note card and a specific country of Europe. Then have each student draw an outline of the country he or she has been assigned. On the back of their cards, students should write 10 clues to help with the identification of their country. Then have students exchange cards and work in pairs to quiz each other on the countries' identifications.

Meeting Special Needs

In addition to the Differentiated Instruction strategies found in each section, the following resources are also suitable for your special needs students:

- ***ExamView® Pro Testmaker CD-ROM*** allows teachers to tailor tests by reducing answer choices.
- The ***Audio Program*** includes the entire narrative of the student edition so that less-proficient readers can listen to the words as they read them.
- The ***Reading Essentials and Study Guide*** provides the same content as the student edition but is written two grade levels below the textbook.
- ***Guided Reading Activities*** give less-proficient readers point-by-point instructions to increase comprehension as they read each textbook section.
- ***Enrichment Activities*** include a stimulating collection of readings and activities for gifted and talented students.

NATIONAL GEOGRAPHIC TEACHER'S CORNER

Index to National Geographic Magazine:

The following articles may be used for research relating to this chapter:

- "Albanians: A People Undone," by Priit J. Vesilind, February 2000.
- "Eyewitness Kosovo," by Alexandra Boulat, February 2000.
- "Romania's New Day," by Ed Vuilliamy, September 1998.

National Geographic Society Products:

To order the following products for use with this chapter, call National Geographic Society at 1-800-368-2728:

- *GeoKit: Pollution* (Kit)
- *Europe: The Road to Unity* (Video)
- *Communism* (Video)

NGS ONLINE

Access National Geographic's Web site for current events, activities, links, interactive features, and archives. www.nationalgeographic.com

Find the latest coverage of geography in the news, atlas updates, cartographic activities with interactive maps, an online map store, and links at www.nationalgeographic.com/maps

SOCIAL STUDIES Online

Use our Web site for additional resources. All essential content is covered in the Student Edition.

You and your students can visit twip.glencoe.com, the Web site companion to *The World and Its People.* This innovative integration of electronic and print media offers your students a wealth of opportunities. The student text directs students to the Web site for the following options:

- Chapter Overviews
- Student Web Activities
- Self-Check Quizzes
- Textbook Updates

Answers are provided for you in the Web Activity Lesson Plan. Additional Web resources and Interactive Tutor puzzles are also available.

Social Studies Online

Introduce students to chapter content and key terms by having them access Chapter Overview 13 at twip.glencoe.com

Chapter Objectives

1. Discuss the land, economies, and cultures of Poland and the Baltic Republics.
2. Compare the economies and cultures of Hungary, the Czech Republic and Slovakia.
3. Identify similarities and differences among the Balkan countries.
4. Describe the economies and people of Ukraine, Belarus, and Moldova.

GLENCOE TECHNOLOGY

NATIONAL GEOGRAPHIC

The World and Its People Video Program

Chapter 13 Eastern Europe
The following segments enhance the study of this chapter:

- **Down the Dunajec**
- **Poland's Storks**
- **Dracula's Castle**

MindJogger Videoquiz

Use MindJogger Videoquiz to preview the Chapter 13 content.

Both programs available in DVD and VHS

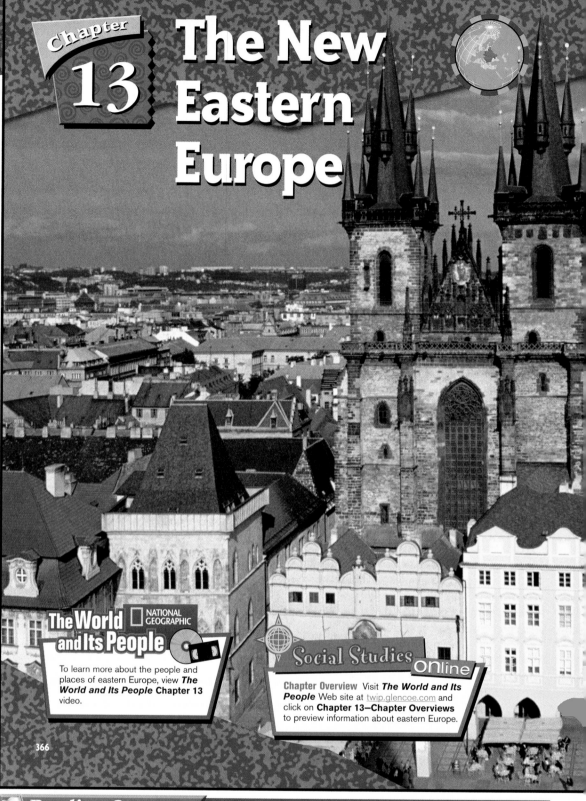

Chapter 13 The New Eastern Europe

The World and Its People NATIONAL GEOGRAPHIC

To learn more about the people and places of eastern Europe, view ***The World and Its People*** Chapter 13 video.

Social Studies Online

Chapter Overview Visit ***The World and Its People*** Web site at twip.glencoe.com and click on **Chapter 13—Chapter Overviews** to preview information about eastern Europe.

366

Reading Strategy — Purpose for Reading

Use the **K-W-L** reading strategy to draw on students' prior knowledge of eastern Europe. Have students divide notebook paper into three columns. In the first column, have them write "What Do I Know About the Countries of Eastern Europe?" In the middle column, have them write "What Do I Want to Know?" In the last column, have them write "What Have I Learned?" Ask them to complete the first two columns. You may want them to discuss what they wrote with a partner and then have partners share their responses with the class. Finally, ask students to add information to the last column as they study the chapter. **L1**

Compare-Contrast Make the following foldable to help you compare and contrast what you learn about western Europe and eastern Europe.

Step 1 Fold a sheet of paper in half from side to side.

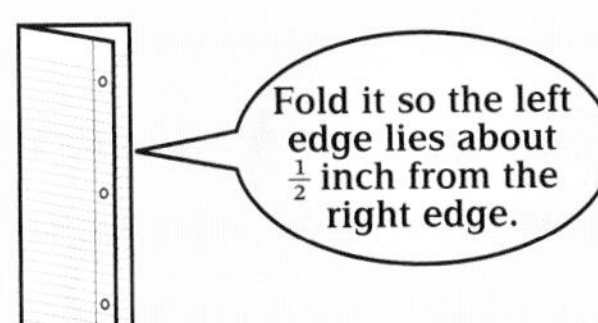

Fold it so the left edge lies about ½ inch from the right edge.

Step 2 Turn the paper and fold it into thirds.

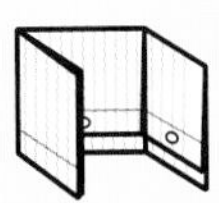

Step 3 Unfold and cut the top layer only along both folds.

This will make three tabs.

Step 4 Label as shown.

Reading and Writing Before you read Chapter 13, record what you learned about western Europe in Chapter 12 under the "Western Europe" tab of your foldable. As you read Chapter 13, write what you learn about eastern Europe under the correct tab. Then list ways these two regions are similar under the middle tab.

Why It Matters

From Communism to Democracy

Since the fall of communism, the countries of eastern Europe have continued to change. The formation of new democratic governments has led to closer ties with other free nations in Europe. The economic influence of eastern Europe grows as the region becomes a new market for western goods. The changes are not occurring smoothly, however, and many challenges have to be met.

◀ Starometske Namesti and Tyn Church in Prague, Czech Republic

About the Photo

Cherished as one of the most beautiful cities in the world, Prague lies in the center of Europe in the Czech Republic. Sometimes called the "City of One Hundred Spires," Prague is alive with towers and other beautiful buildings that reflect a rich and unique architectural heritage. The city is also known for being one of the cultural centers of eastern Europe. Museums and galleries are plentiful as are concerts and theater performances. Musical events in Prague today offer a variety of styles including classical, Dixieland jazz, folk and world music, and pop.

Introducing Chapter 13

Dinah Zike's Foldables

Purpose Students make and use a foldable to collect and organize information about western Europe and eastern Europe. Students will compare and contrast characteristics of the two regions by using a foldable that is a Venn diagram.

Have students complete the ***Reading and Study Skills Foldables*** activity for this chapter.

Why It Matters

Compare free market and command economic systems. Help students understand the difficulty of changing from a communist to free market system for the countries in this chapter. Ask students to recall a time in their lives when they moved from a familiar, comfortable way of life to something different. Point out that even if the change was for the better, they still may have had difficulty adjusting. Have students write a paragraph describing the difficulties they felt during this transition. **Ask:** **How difficult do you think it might be if an entire society were undergoing such change?**

Chapter 13

Section 1, pages 368–371

1 Focus

Section Objectives

1. Explain how the economy of Poland has changed in recent years.
2. Discuss the people and economies of the Baltic Republics.

BELLRINGER
Skillbuilder Activity

Project transparency and have students answer the question.

Daily Focus Skills Transparency

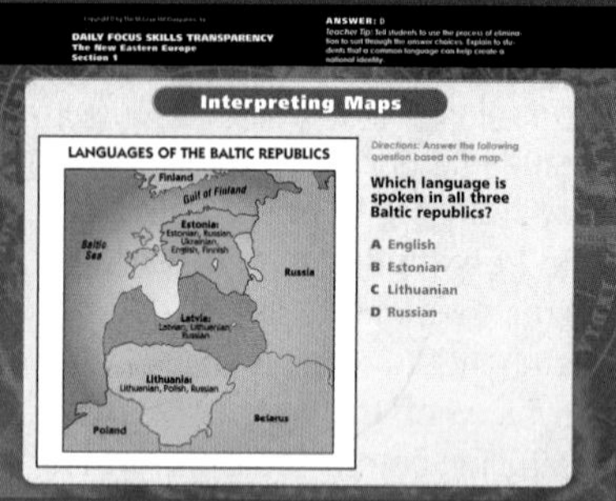

Reading Preview

■ Activating Prior Knowledge
Have students use the map in this section to find the Baltic Sea.
Ask: What characteristics would you expect in countries that border the sea? *(importance of shipbuilding, sea travel, and fishing; influences on climate)*

■ Preteaching Vocabulary
Encourage students to use a dictionary to find the origins of the word *pope*.

Guide to Reading

Main Idea

Poland and the Baltic republics have undergone many changes to their political and economic systems.

Terms to Know

- bog
- communist state
- acid rain
- pope

Reading Strategy

Create a chart like this one, and then write one fact about the people of Poland and the Baltic republics.

Country	People
Poland	
Estonia	
Latvia	
Lithuania	

Section 1

Poland and the Baltic Republics

NATIONAL GEOGRAPHIC Exploring Our World

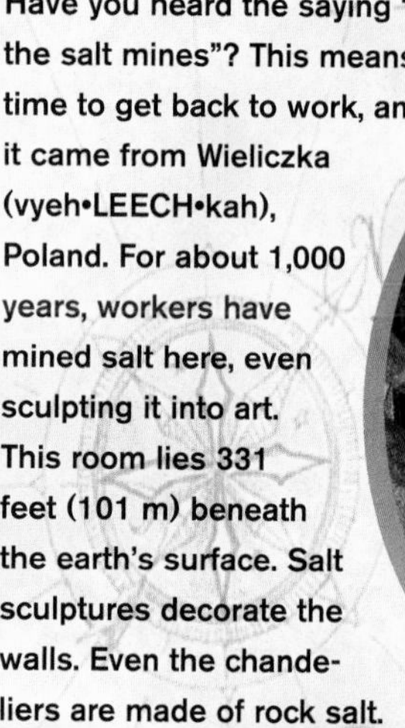

Have you heard the saying "Back to the salt mines"? This means it is time to get back to work, and it came from Wieliczka (vyeh•LEECH•kah), Poland. For about 1,000 years, workers have mined salt here, even sculpting it into art. This room lies 331 feet (101 m) beneath the earth's surface. Salt sculptures decorate the walls. Even the chandeliers are made of rock salt.

Along the southern shores of the Baltic Sea lie **Poland** and the Baltic republics of **Estonia, Latvia,** and **Lithuania.** Although they are neighboring countries, they have distinct histories and cultures.

Poland

Poland is one of the largest countries in Europe. About the size of New Mexico, Poland lies on the huge North European Plain. This plain stretches from France to Russia. Rivers such as the Vistula (VIHSH•chuh•luh) and the Oder flow through Poland's flat lowlands. Many Polish people live in this fertile central region.

North toward the Baltic Sea, you find lakes, forests, and bogs, or low swampy lands. In the south, the **Carpathian** (kahr•PAY•thee•uhn) **Mountains** stretch along Poland's border with Slovakia. Poland's location and lack of mountains on its eastern and western borders have made the country an easy target for invading armies.

Section Resources

Reproducible Masters
- Reproducible Lesson Plan
- Daily Lecture and Discussion Notes
- Note-taking Guide
- Guided Reading Activity
- Reading Essentials and Study Guide
- Section Quiz

Transparencies
- Daily Focus Skills Transparency

Multimedia
- Vocabulary PuzzleMaker CD-ROM
- Interactive Tutor Self-Assessment CD-ROM
- Presentation Plus! CD-ROM
- ExamView® Pro Testmaker CD-ROM

Warm winds blowing across Europe from the Atlantic Ocean bring year-round mild weather to western Poland. Cooler weather can be found in eastern Poland. It has cool summers and cold winters.

A Changing Economy In the past, Poland was a communist state, or a country in which the government has strong control over the economy and society. The Polish government decided what, how, and for whom goods would be produced. In 1989 Poland started moving toward a market economy. The change has been difficult. In their communist state, workers had jobs for life, even if business was slow. Today businesses lay off workers if they cannot afford to keep a large staff. Poland is adjusting to meet economic challenges. Many people have started businesses, and Poles no longer suffer from shortages of goods.

Poland is dotted with thousands of small farms, on which about 25 percent of Poles work. Polish farmers grow more potatoes and rye than farmers in any other European country. Other crops include wheat,

NATIONAL GEOGRAPHIC **Eastern Europe: Political**

Applying Map Skills

1. What is the capital of Poland?
2. Which eastern European countries border the Adriatic Sea?

Find NGS online map resources @ www.nationalgeographic.com/maps

Chapter 13

Section 1, pages 368–371

2 TEACH

Reading Strategy

Sequencing Events Have students research Poland's transition from a communist command economy to a democracy and free market system. Have them create an annotated time line showing the changes in Poland's government and economy. L2

Daily Lecture and Discussion Notes

THE NEW EASTERN EUROPE

Daily Lecture and Discussion Notes

Poland and the Baltic Republics

Did You Know? Toruń, 200 kilometers south of the city of Gdańsk, Poland, is the birthplace of Nicolaus Copernicus. He is the mathematician who, in 1513, developed the theory that the earth revolves around the sun.

I. Poland

A. Poland is one of the largest countries in Europe and lies on the vast North European Plain.

B. In northern Poland, forests, lakes, and **bogs**, or low swampy lands, dot the countryside.

...untains stretch along Poland's border with

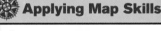

Applying Map Skills

Answers

1. Warsaw
2. Slovenia, Croatia, Bosnia and Herzegovina, Serbia and Montenegro, Albania

Skills Practice

Which rivers travel through Poland? *(Oder River, Warta River, and Vistula River)*

Reading Strategy — Reading the Text

Previewing and Skimming Before students begin to read the section, have them skim the heads to learn what the section will be about. One way of determining the main idea of each subsection is to turn the heads into questions. For example, the title "Poland" might become "Where is Poland?" Students should then expect to find that information in the subsection. Have students practice this strategy as they read the chapter. L1

*Use the **Reading Skills Handbook** for more reading strategies.*

L1/ELL

Guided Reading Activity

Name ________ Date ________ Class ________

THE NEW EASTERN EUROPE

Guided Reading Activity 1

Poland and the Baltic Republics

DIRECTIONS: Answering Questions Reading the section and answering the questions below will help you learn more about Poland. Use your textbook to write answers to the questions.

1. What is the landscape of Poland like?

2. Why is the economy changing?

...that have come from the changing economy.

More About the Photo

Poland's Economy Poland moved from a command economy to a market economy by undergoing what was called "shock therapy." The steps included freezing wages, lifting price controls, gradually removing subsidies paid to state-owned industries, and privatizing those industries. This helped to hold down inflation.

Caption Answer foods, machinery, transportation equipment, chemicals, ships

ASSESS

Assign Section 1 Assessment as homework or an in-class activity.

Have students use the Interactive Tutor Self-Assessment CD-ROM to review Section 1.

NATIONAL GEOGRAPHIC **On Location**

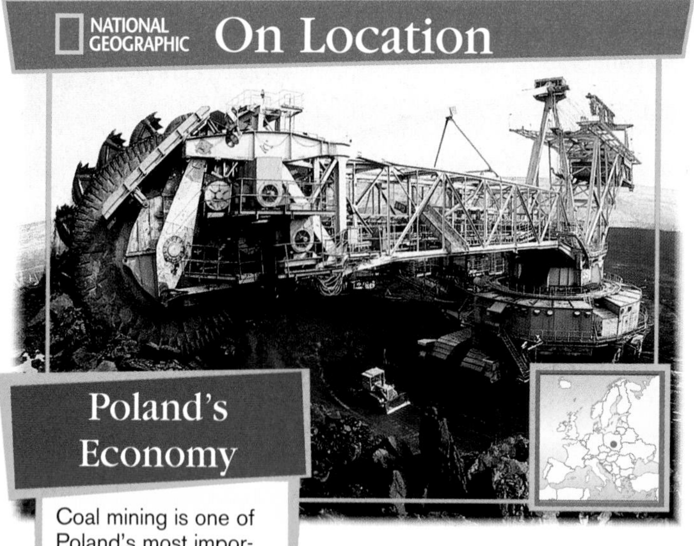

Poland's Economy

Coal mining is one of Poland's most important industries and is concentrated near the Czech Republic.

Economics **What are some products manufactured in Poland?**

sugar beets, fruits, and vegetables. Some farmers raise cattle, pigs, and chickens.

Most mining and manufacturing take place in central and southern Poland. Coal mining is one of Poland's major industries. The mountains also hold copper, zinc, and lead. Petroleum and natural gas are found here as well. The country produces hydroelectric power, or electric power produced by moving water.

Polish factories process foods and make machinery, transportation equipment, and chemicals. The city of **Gdańsk** (guh•DAHNSK), a Baltic seaport, is an important shipbuilding center. Under Communist rule, Polish factories caused some of the worst water and air pollution in Europe. Since 1989 there has been a decline in heavy industry and the government is more concerned with the environment. Still, problems continue because Polish factories rely on burning coal. Factory smoke causes **acid rain**, or rain containing chemicals that pollute water, air, and land.

Struggle for Freedom Founded in the A.D. 900s, Poland was a powerful kingdom during the Middle Ages. By the 1800s, it had fallen victim to stronger neighbors—Germany, Russia, and Austria. In 1939 German troops overran western Poland, starting World War II. Poles suffered greatly during the war. **Warsaw,** the capital, was bombed to ashes. Some 6 million European Jews and 6 million others were murdered in brutal prison camps set up by the Germans in Poland and elsewhere. After the war, the Soviet Union swallowed up lands in eastern Poland. In exchange, the Poles gained western areas belonging to defeated Germany.

In 1947 a communist government came to power in Poland. Resisting its rule, workers and farmers in 1980 formed Solidarity, a labor group that struggled peacefully for democratic change. The communist government finally allowed free elections in 1989, and a new democratic government was formed. A year later, Solidarity leader Lech Walesa (LEHK vah•LEHN•suh) was elected Poland's first democratic president. Today Poland is a democratic republic, or government headed by elected leaders. Drawing closer to western Europe, Poland joined the European Union in 2004.

Daily Life About 38.6 million people live in Poland. Almost all are ethnic Poles who belong to a larger ethnic group called Slavs. They speak Polish, which is a Slavic language. Poland is more rural than

Content Background

Polish Hero Irena Sendler received Poland's highest award in November 2003 for saving approximately 2,500 children during the Holocaust. Sendler worked in a Polish underground movement that rescued Jews during World War II. She posed as a nurse and visited the Warsaw Ghetto, persuading parents that their children would more likely survive if they lived outside its walls. Sendler, along with 20 helpers, smuggled children out of the ghetto between 1942 and 1943 and placed them in the homes of Polish families. Sendler was arrested in 1943 and suffered severe beatings by the Nazis. Polish President Aleksander Kwasniewski said at the awards ceremony, "Thanks to people like you, we believe that good can triumph...."

nations in other parts of Europe. About one-third of the people live in the countryside. As Poland's economy changes, more people are moving to cities such as Warsaw and Kraków.

Poles feel a deep loyalty to their country. Religion unites Poles as well. Most are Roman Catholic, and religion has a strong influence on daily life. The Polish people were very proud in 1978 when Karol Wojtyla (voy•TEE•wah) was named pope, or head of the Roman Catholic Church. Taking the name John Paul II, he was the first Pole to become pope.

▲ Fish caught in the nearby Baltic Sea are sold in Rīga's Central Market.

✓Reading Check **What two beliefs or attitudes unite the Polish people?**

The Baltic Republics

The small Baltic republics of Estonia, Latvia, and Lithuania lie on the shores of the **Baltic Sea.** For much of their history, the Baltic republics were under Russian control. With the fall of the Soviet Union in 1991, Estonia, Latvia, and Lithuania became independent. All three countries still have large Russian minority populations. Most people in Estonia and Latvia are Protestants, while Roman Catholics make up the majority in Lithuania.

The Baltic republics are located on poor, swampy land. Even so, their well-developed economies are based mainly on dairy farming, beef production, fishing, and shipbuilding. In recent years, increased trade and industry have raised standards of living in this region.

✓Reading Check **Which two major religions are practiced in the Baltic republics?**

Section 1 Assessment

Defining Terms

1. Define bog, communist state, acid rain, pope.

Recalling Facts

2. Human/Environment Interaction Why does pollution continue to be a problem in Poland?

3. Economics Why is Gdańsk important?

4. Region Which three countries are considered the Baltic republics?

Graphic Organizer

5. Organizing Information On a time line like this one, label five important events and their dates in Poland's history.

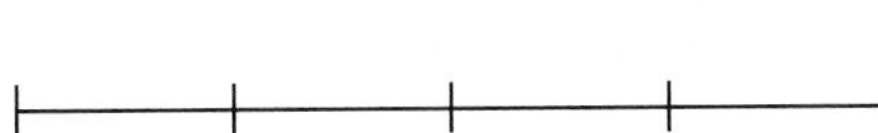

Critical Thinking

6. Understanding Cause and Effect Which of Poland's physical features has made it an easy target for invading armies? Why?

7. Making Comparisons What is the difference in job security under a communist state and a free market economy?

Applying Social Studies Skills

8. Analyzing Maps Refer to the political map on page 369. The Vistula River empties into what body of water? Now turn to the population density map on page 384. What is the population density of the area surrounding Kraków?

Section 1 Assessment

1. The terms are defined in the Glossary.
2. Factories continue to rely on coal, which creates smoke, causing acid rain.
3. It is a seaport and a shipbuilding center.
4. Estonia, Latvia, Lithuania
5. *Any five: 900s:* Poland founded; *1800s:* Poland victimized by neighbors; *1939:* Nazis invade Poland; *1947:* Communists come to power; *1980:* Solidarity union formed; *1989:* free elections held; *1990:* Walesa elected president; *2004:* joins European Union
6. location and lack of mountains on eastern and western borders
7. Under a communist state, people had jobs for life. In the free market, they could lose their jobs.
8. Baltic Sea; over 250 people per square mile (over 100 people per sq. km)

L2

Section Quiz

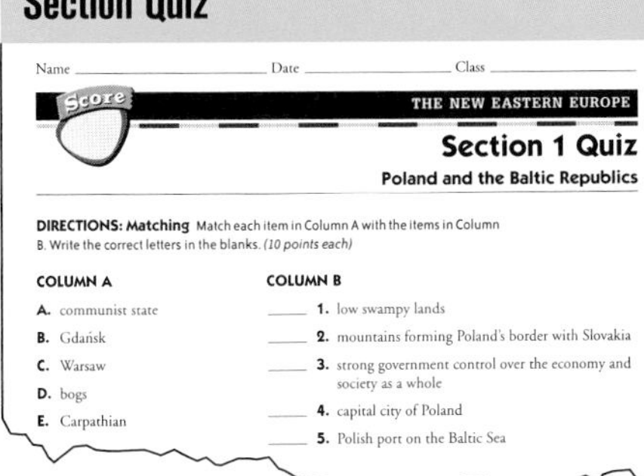

Name ______ Date ______ Class ______

Score

THE NEW EASTERN EUROPE

Section 1 Quiz

Poland and the Baltic Republics

DIRECTIONS: Matching Match each item in Column A with the items in Column B. Write the correct letters in the blanks. *(10 points each)*

COLUMN A	COLUMN B
A. communist state	____ 1. low swampy lands
B. Gdańsk	____ 2. mountains forming Poland's border with Slovakia
C. Warsaw	____ 3. strong government control over the economy and society as a whole
D. bogs	____ 4. capital city of Poland
E. Carpathian	____ 5. Polish port on the Baltic Sea

✓ Reading Check Answer

love of country and religion

L1/ELL

Reading Essentials and Study Guide

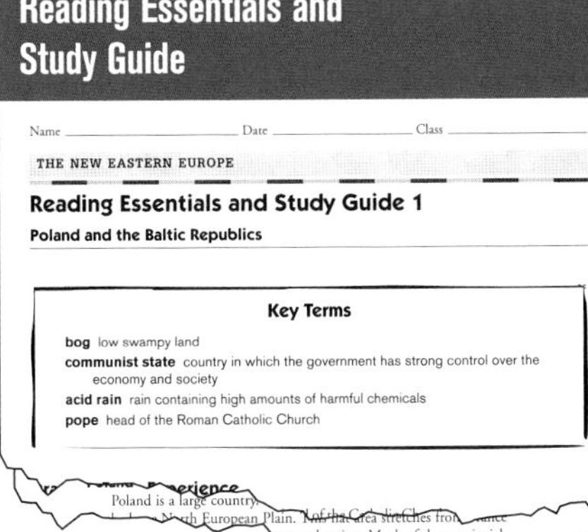

Name ______ Date ______ Class ______

THE NEW EASTERN EUROPE

Reading Essentials and Study Guide 1

Poland and the Baltic Republics

Key Terms

bog low swampy land
communist state country in which the government has strong control over the economy and society
acid rain rain containing high amounts of harmful chemicals
pope head of the Roman Catholic Church

✓ Reading Check Answer

Protestantism and Roman Catholicism

4 CLOSE

Have students create a poster that highlights important features of the economies and people of Poland or one of the Baltic Republics.

1 Focus

Section Objectives

1. Discuss the history and peoples of Hungary, the Czech Republic, and Slovakia.
2. Describe the changing economies of Hungary, the Czech Republic, and Slovakia.

BELLRINGER Skillbuilder Activity

Project transparency and have students answer the question.

Daily Focus Skills Transparency

DAILY FOCUS SKILLS TRANSPARENCY
The New Eastern Europe
Section 2

ANSWER: Alike: government and voting age. Different: all other categories
Teacher Tip: Urban population percentage is the percentage of the population that lives in cities

Comparing and Contrasting

	CZECH REPUBLIC	SLOVAKIA
Landmass	30,448 sq. mi. (78,860 sq. km)	18,923 sq. mi. (49,011 sq. km)
Population	10,200,000	5,400,000
Urban Population Percentage	75%	58%
Type of Government	Parliamentary democracy	Parliamentary democracy
Voting Age	18 years old	18 years old
Monetary Unit	Czech Koruna	Slovak Koruna
Languages	Czech, Slovak	Slovak, Hungarian

Directions: Answer the following question based on the chart.

In which categories are the two countries alike? In which categories are the two countries different?

Reading Preview

■ **Activating Prior Knowledge** Ask students to describe how location might affect the cultures of the eastern European countries.

■ **Preteaching Vocabulary** Have students define *landlocked* from the meanings of the words that form this compound.

Guide to Reading

Main Idea

Hungary, the Czech Republic, and Slovakia are changing to free market economies.

Terms to Know

- landlocked
- nomad
- spa
- privatize

Reading Strategy

Fill in a chart like the one below with facts about the past and present of Hungary, the Czech Republic, and Slovakia.

Country	Past	Present
Hungary		
Czech Republic		
Slovakia		

Section 2

Hungarians, Czechs, and Slovaks

Prague, the capital of the Czech Republic, is often called "the city of a hundred spires" because of its many church steeples. You won't hear just religious music here, however. Musical contributions range from classical to punk. More recently, the Czech Republic has become a leading European center of jazz.

In the center of eastern Europe are **Hungary,** the **Czech Republic,** and **Slovakia.** All three countries became communist under Soviet control after World War II. In 1989 they all became independent democracies with free market economies.

Hungary—Land of the Magyars

Hungary, almost the size of Indiana, is landlocked, meaning that its land does not border a sea or an ocean. Hungary depends on the mighty **Danube River** for trade and transportation. Its vast waters flow 1,776 miles (2,858 km) before emptying into the Black Sea.

The Hungarian Plain runs through eastern Hungary. This vast lowland area has excellent soil for farming and grazing animals. The Danube River separates the plain from Transdanubia, a region in western Hungary. Rolling hills, forests, and lakes are found there. Many Hungarians vacation near Lake Balaton—one of Europe's largest lakes.

Section Resources

Reproducible Masters

- Reproducible Lesson Plan
- Daily Lecture and Discussion Notes
- Note-taking Guide
- Guided Reading Activity
- Reading Essentials and Study Guide
- Section Quiz

Transparencies

- Daily Focus Skills Transparency

Multimedia

- Vocabulary PuzzleMaker CD-ROM
- Interactive Tutor Self-Assessment CD-ROM
- Presentation Plus! CD-ROM
- ExamView® Pro Testmaker CD-ROM

The Carpathian Mountains rise in northern Hungary. In this scenic area, you can wander through thick forests, find strange rock formations, and explore underground caves.

The Economy Hungary's farmers grow corn, sugar beets, wheat, and potatoes in the country's rich soil. Grapes, used to make wine, are also grown here. Hungary's natural resources include coal, petroleum, and natural gas. Foods, beverages, and tobacco products are manufactured along with machines, chemicals, and metals. Service industries, such as financial services and tourism, also thrive.

The Hungarians Magyars came to the Danube area from Central Asia about 1,000 years ago. They were nomads, or people who move from place to place, often with herds of animals. The Magyars were skilled horse riders who used the grassy plains to feed their animals. Eventually they set up a large kingdom and adopted Christianity.

Beginning in the 1500s, the Ottoman Turks and later the Austrians ruled most or all of Hungary. In 1867 Hungary and Austria became partners in a large empire. After being defeated in World War I, Hungary lost territory and became the landlocked nation it is today.

About 90 percent of Hungary's 10.1 million people are descended from the Magyars. Almost all speak the Hungarian language. About two-thirds are Roman Catholic, while another one-fourth is Protestant. **Budapest** (BOO•duh•PEHST), the capital and largest city, is called "the Paris of eastern Europe." It is actually two cities divided by the Danube River. On the western bank lies the old city of Buda, full of beautiful churches and palaces. Bridges link this older settlement to the newer city of Pest, which has factories and tall, modern buildings.

✓ **Reading Check** What river is important to Hungary, and why?

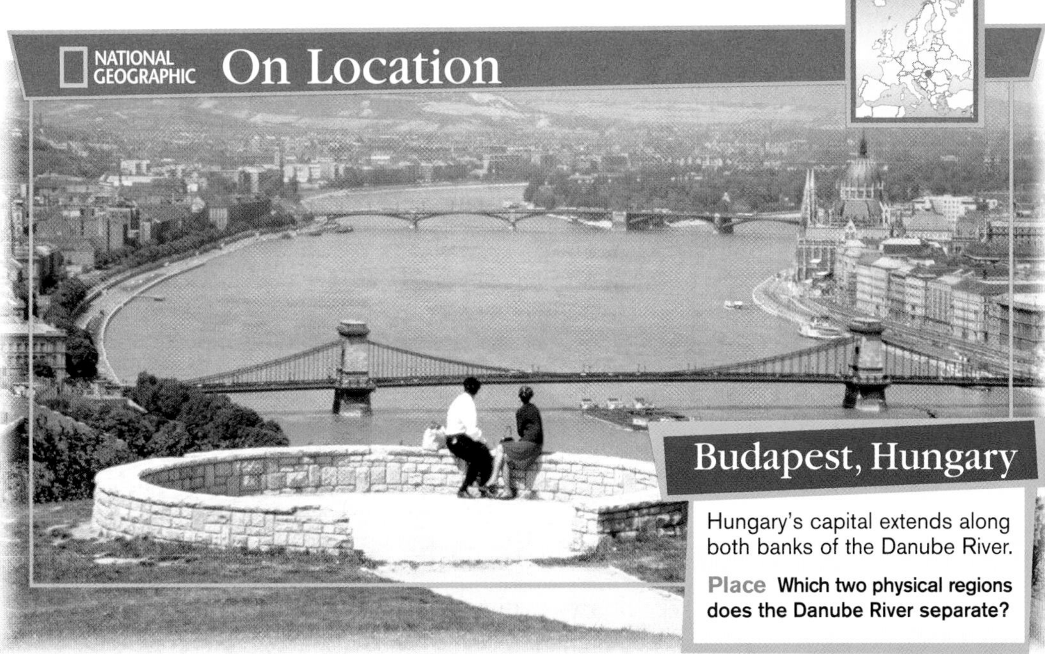

Budapest, Hungary

Hungary's capital extends along both banks of the Danube River.

Place Which two physical regions does the Danube River separate?

Chapter 13

Section 2, pages 372–375

TEACH

Reading Strategy

Determining Cause and Effect Write the following statements on the board and have students copy them into their notebooks: Hungary is landlocked. Many factories in the Czech Republic are harmful to the environment. Some government officials in Slovakia acted corruptly when businesses were privatized. As students read the section, have them write what has happened as a result of these causes. L1

More About the Photo

Budapest Many Europeans travel to Budapest to soak in the city's many baths. These baths are fed by more than 120 hot springs around the city.

Caption Answer Hungarian Plain to the east and hilly, forested Transdanubia to the west

✓ Reading Check Answer

Since Hungary is landlocked, it relies on the Danube River for transportation and trade.

Reading Strategy — Reading the Text

Summarizing Information To help students learn how to summarize, teach them the following strategies. Have students describe what the selection is about. Remind them that only the main ideas should be included in a summary but that all the main ideas should be included. Tell students that to determine whether they have included all the main ideas in the summary, they should ask themselves: Can my summary be easily understood by someone who has not read the selection? Have students summarize the section after they have read it. L1

*Use the **Reading Skills Handbook** for more reading strategies.*

Answer Answers will vary. Some students probably will consider the Thanksgiving turkey as the national dish. Others may mention hot dogs and/or hamburgers.

Food Spices used commonly in Czech dishes include caraway seed, bacon, and salt. Slovak food is usually more spicy, much like Hungarian dishes.

L1/ELL

Guided Reading Activity

Name ______ Date ______ Class ______

THE NEW EASTERN EUROPE

Guided Reading Activity 2

Hungarians, Czechs, and Slovaks

DIRECTIONS: Summarizing Reading the section and completing the summary below will help you learn more about the countries of Hungary, the Czech Republic, and Slovakia. Use your textbook to fill in the blanks.

In 1989 Hungary, the Czech Republic, and Slovakia became independent (1) ______. Hungary is (2) ______ because it does not border water. Therefore it depends on the (3) ______ ______ for trade and transportation. Eastern Hungary is a (4) ______ with excellent soil for farming and (5) ______ ...de of Hungary is called (6) ______

Reading Check Answer

the Austrian Empire

ASSESS

Assign Section 2 Assessment as homework or an in-class activity.

Have students use the Interactive Tutor Self-Assessment CD-ROM to review Section 2.

Food

In Slovakia and the Czech Republic, lunch is the main meal of the day. It commonly includes roast pork; dumplings, potatoes, or rice covered with a thick sauce; and sauerkraut or another heavily cooked vegetable. Czech dumplings are not like American dumplings, however. They are made with either potatoes or stale bread rolls, mixed with flour and milk, and then boiled. The Slovak national dish is *bryndzové halušky*—sheep's cheese with pasta.

Looking Closer **What would you consider the national dish of the United States?**

The Czech Republic

The Czech Republic is also a landlocked country. Many areas are known for their natural beauty. In the mountains to the north and south, you can hike trails and visit spas, or health resorts with hot mineral springs. The Czechs enjoy a high standard of living compared to other eastern Europeans. Large fertile areas make the Czech Republic a major agricultural producer. Manufacturing forms the backbone of the country's economy, however. Factories make machinery, vehicles, metals, and textiles. Minerals include limestone, coal, and kaolin, a fine clay used for pottery.

Prague, the capital, is a center of service industries, tourism, and high-tech companies. Although manufacturing provides consumer products, many factories are old, inefficient, and harmful to the environment. The Czechs are trying to modernize their factories and move toward nuclear energy.

The Czechs Slavic groups settled in the Czech region in the A.D. 400s and 500s. By 900 the Czechs had adopted Christianity and formed a kingdom called Bohemia. It became part of the Austrian Empire, which ruled from the 1500s until 1918. In that year, the Czechs and their Slovak neighbors formed Czechoslovakia, which came under Soviet rule. In 1993 the Czechs and Slovaks agreed to split into the Czech Republic and the Republic of Slovakia. Today the Czech Republic is a parliamentary democracy with a president and a prime minister.

Two-thirds of the 10.2 million Czechs live in cities, many in crowded apartment buildings. The country is famous for the splendor of its historic buildings and monuments. The Czechs have also produced great literature, including plays written by the Czech Republic's first president.

Reading Check **What country ruled the Czechs from the 1500s to 1918?**

Differentiated Instruction

Meeting Special Needs: Less-proficient Readers Students who do not read efficiently benefit from having a specific purpose for reading. Point out the Guide to Reading at the beginning of the section. Demonstrate how to use this study guide to preview the lesson and to find the main ideas in the section. **L1**

Refer to *Inclusion for the Middle School Social Studies Classroom Strategies and Activities* in the TCR.

Slovakia

The Carpathian Mountains tower over the northern region of Slovakia. They are rich in iron ore, lead, zinc, and copper. Factories use these minerals to produce iron and steel products. Under communist rule, factories were built for heavy industry. Although communism is now gone, the push to develop industries continues. Workers also make cement, plastics, textiles, and processed foods. Rugged peaks, thick forests, and blue lakes make this area a popular vacation spot. Farther south, vineyards and farms spread across fertile lowlands. Farmers grow barley, corn, potatoes, sugar beets, and grapes.

Slovakia has had difficulty changing to a free market economy. After the fall of communism, Slovak leaders set out to privatize businesses. This means that factory ownership transfers from the government to individual citizens. Some government officials acted corruptly, giving advantages to themselves or to their friends. This made few foreign companies willing to start new businesses here. Slovak factories also suffer from outdated technology, which contributes to pollution.

The Slovaks have a language and culture different from the Czechs. Most Slovaks are Roman Catholics. Nearly 60 percent of Slovakia's 5.4 million people live in modern towns and cities. **Bratislava,** a port on the Danube, is Slovakia's capital and largest city. Tourists visit village festivals to see people dress in traditional clothes and to hear musicians play folk music on shepherds' flutes and bagpipes.

✓ Reading Check What contributes to pollution in Slovakia?

Assessment

Defining Terms

1. **Define** landlocked, nomad, spa, privatize.

Recalling Facts

2. **Culture** To what ethnic group do most Hungarians belong?
3. **Geography** What are three of the Czech Republic's natural resources?
4. **Economics** Why has Slovakia had difficulty changing to a free market economy?

Critical Thinking

5. **Analyzing Information** Why do the Czechs have a high standard of living?
6. **Understanding Cause and Effect** Why do you think the Magyars settled in the Danube area?

Graphic Organizer

7. **Organizing Information** Draw a diagram like the one below. Then add at least two facts under the headings in each outer oval.

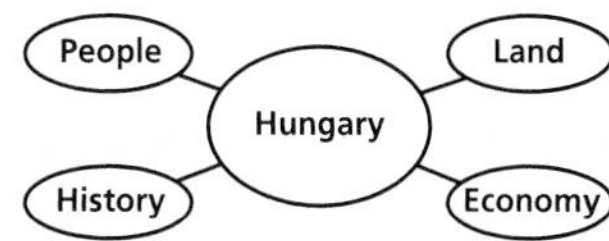

Applying Social Studies Skills

8. **Analyzing Maps** Turn to the political map on page 369. What countries border Hungary to the north? To the east?

Chapter 13

Section 2, pages 372–375

L2

Section Quiz

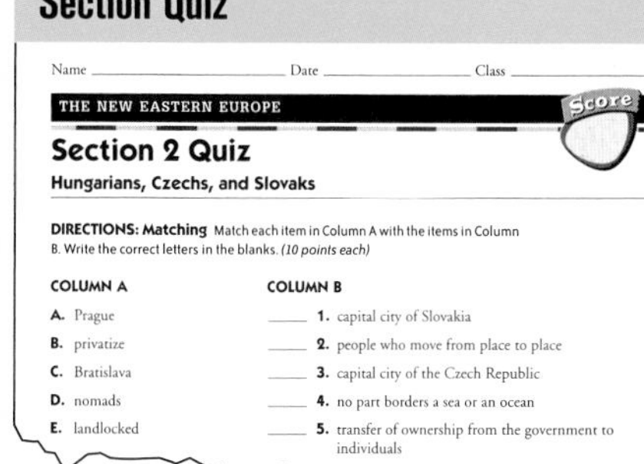
Name ______ Date ______ Class ______

THE NEW EASTERN EUROPE

Score

Section 2 Quiz

Hungarians, Czechs, and Slovaks

DIRECTIONS: Matching Match each item in Column A with the items in Column B. Write the correct letters in the blanks. *(10 points each)*

COLUMN A	COLUMN B
A. Prague	____ 1. capital city of Slovakia
B. privatize	____ 2. people who move from place to place
C. Bratislava	____ 3. capital city of the Czech Republic
D. nomads	____ 4. no part borders a sea or an ocean
E. landlocked	____ 5. transfer of ownership from the government to individuals

Reading Check Answer

Factories have outdated technology.

L1/ELL

Reading Essentials and Study Guide

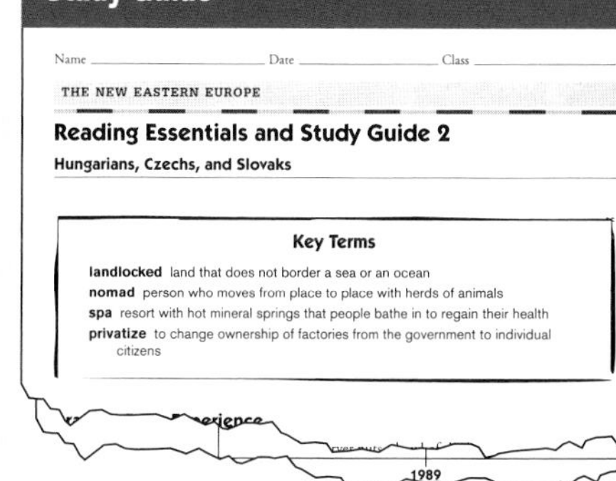
Name ______ Date ______ Class ______

THE NEW EASTERN EUROPE

Reading Essentials and Study Guide 2

Hungarians, Czechs, and Slovaks

Key Terms

landlocked land that does not border a sea or an ocean
nomad person who moves from place to place with herds of animals
spa resort with hot mineral springs that people bathe in to regain their health
privatize to change ownership of factories from the government to individual citizens

Close

Have students create an advertisement that encourages people to travel to Hungary, the Czech Republic, or Slovakia.

Section 2 Assessment

1. The terms are defined in the Glossary.
2. Magyars
3. limestone, coal, and kaolin
4. Official corruption discouraged investment by foreign companies, and older technology causes pollution.
5. Fertile areas make the Czech Republic a food producer; factories produce manufactured goods; mountains and spas attract tourists; and the country has important resources.
6. They were nomadic and used the grassy plains to feed their animals.
7. Students' diagrams will vary.
8. Slovakia (and Austria); Romania, Ukraine

TEACH

Have students read and take notes on the material under the Poland heading in Section 1. Remind them that notes should be written as phrases. When students are done, have volunteers exchange notes with another student. Then have the second student try to re-create the key facts in the section by reading the notes. Have the class compare what the student says to what is written in the textbook. You should be able to explain that effective note-taking is a skill that students can use to re-create a lesson or their reading. L1

Additional Skills Practice

1. **What questions would you ask to find the main ideas on the subject of Poland's environmental challenges?** *(What types of pollution are found in Poland? How is Poland trying to solve its pollution problems?)*
2. **Why is it necessary to record information about the source on note cards for a research paper?** *(so that the source can be cited when writing the research paper, and the source can be rechecked if necessary)*

Additional Skills Resources

 Chapter Skills Review

Building Geography Skills for Life

Study and Writing Skill

Taking Notes

Effective note taking involves more than just writing facts in short phrases. It involves breaking up information into meaningful parts so that it can be remembered.

Learning the Skill

To take good notes, follow these steps:

- Write key points and important facts and figures quickly and neatly. Use abbreviations and phrases.
- Copy words, statements, or diagrams from the board or your research.
- Ask the teacher to repeat important points you do not understand.
- When studying textbook material, organize your notes into an outline or a concept map that links important information.
- For a research report, take notes on cards. Note cards should include the title, author, and page number of sources.

Practicing the Skill

Suppose you are writing a research report on eastern Europe. First, identify main idea questions about this topic, such as "Who has ruled Poland?" or "What economic activities are found in the Czech Republic?" Then research each question.

Using this textbook as a source, read the material on pages 369–370 and 374 and prepare notes as shown below. The first few have been started for you.

Main Idea: What economic activities are found in Poland?
1. Agriculture: potatoes, rye . . .
2. Mining: coal, copper, zinc . . .
3. Manufacturing: foods, machines . . .
Main Idea: What economic activities are found in the Czech Republic?
1.
2.
3.

Applying the Skill

In an encyclopedia or on the Internet, find information about Poland's coal industry and the environmental consequences of burning coal. Take notes by writing the main idea and supporting facts. Then rewrite the article using only your notes.

◀ A Czech teenager displays Soviet souvenirs for tourists who visit Prague.

Practicing the Skill Answers

Poland: agriculture—wheat, sugar beets, fruits, vegetables; mining—lead, petroleum, natural gas, hydroelectric power; manufacturing—transportation equipment, chemicals; Czech Republic: agricultural products; manufacturing—machinery, vehicles, metals, textiles; minerals such as limestone, coal and kaolin; service industries: tourism and high-tech companies

Applying the Skill

Have students print out the pages of the Web sites they visit for information on Poland's coal industry and environmental consequences. Check their notes against the original information to be sure that they identified the key points correctly.

Guide to Reading

Main Idea

The Balkan countries have suffered greatly from ethnic conflicts and economic setbacks.

Terms to Know

- consumer goods
- ethnic cleansing
- refugee
- mosque

Reading Strategy

Create a chart like this one. For each Balkan country, choose an event that occurred. Write the cause of the event in the left box. Then write an effect in the right box.

Cause → Effect

Rebuilding the Balkan Countries

NATIONAL GEOGRAPHIC **Exploring Our World**

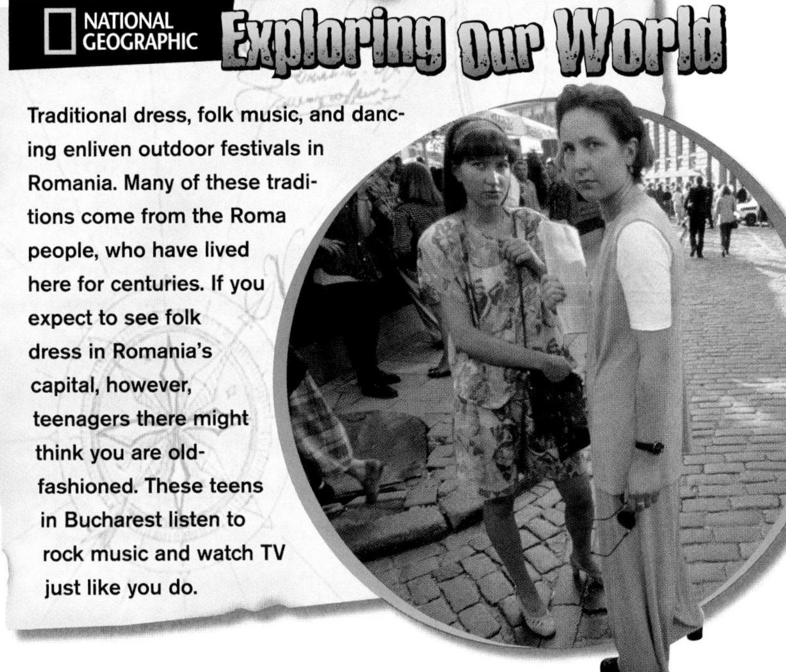

Traditional dress, folk music, and dancing enliven outdoor festivals in Romania. Many of these traditions come from the Roma people, who have lived here for centuries. If you expect to see folk dress in Romania's capital, however, teenagers there might think you are old-fashioned. These teens in Bucharest listen to rock music and watch TV just like you do.

Europe's **Balkan Peninsula** lies between the Adriatic Sea and the Black Sea. The physical map on page 284 shows you that several countries make up this Balkan region. They are **Romania, Bulgaria,** the former **Yugoslav republics,** and **Albania.**

Romania

Romania sits on the northeastern edge of the Balkan Peninsula. The Carpathian Mountains take up about one-third of the country's land area. A vast plateau covers central Romania. A coastal region along the Black Sea includes the mouth of the Danube River. Winters can be very cold and foggy, with much snow. Summers are hot and sunny, but rainfall is abundant.

Romania's economic activities include farming, manufacturing, and mining. The forested mountains and central plateau contain deposits of coal, petroleum, and natural gas. Oil derricks rise in the

1 Focus

Section Objectives

1. Compare the economies and the peoples of the Balkan countries.
2. Explain why Yugoslavia broke into separate countries.

BELLRINGER Skillbuilder Activity

Project transparency and have students answer the question.

Daily Focus Skills Transparency

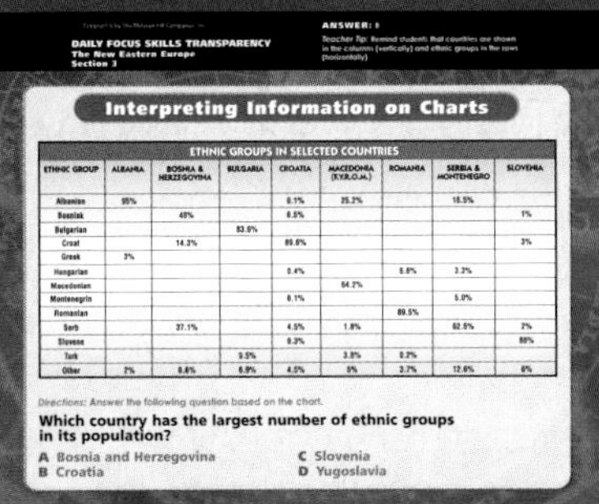
Interpreting Information on Charts

Which country has the largest number of ethnic groups in its population?
A Bosnia and Herzegovina
B Croatia
C Slovenia
D Yugoslavia

Reading Preview

■ **Activating Prior Knowledge** Ask students to describe the ethnic and religious makeup of their community. Have them discuss how people there cooperate and work together despite diversity.

■ **Preteaching Vocabulary** Tell students that when they shop, they act as consumers. Ask students to list the kinds of goods they and their families buy regularly. Tell them that these goods are *consumer goods.*

Section Resources

Reproducible Masters

- Reproducible Lesson Plan
- Daily Lecture and Discussion Notes
- Note-taking Guide
- Guided Reading Activity
- Reading Essentials and Study Guide
- Section Quiz

Transparencies

- Daily Focus Skills Transparency

Multimedia

- Vocabulary PuzzleMaker CD-ROM
- Interactive Tutor Self-Assessment CD-ROM
- Presentation Plus! CD-ROM
- ExamView® Pro Testmaker CD-ROM

2 TEACH

Drawing Conclusions On the board, write the following headings: "Country," "Ethnic Groups," and "Religions." Call on volunteers to list details about each country in the Balkans under the appropriate headings. Then have students use the information in the chart to determine which countries have similar ethnic groups, which have similar religions, and which are different from their neighbors. L1

Daily Lecture and Discussion Notes

THE NEW EASTERN EUROPE

Daily Lecture and Discussion Notes

Rebuilding the Balkan Countries

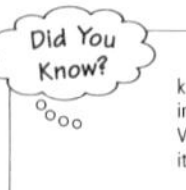

The legend of Dracula is based on a historical figure, Vlad Tepes, who was known as Dracula. *Dracula* means "son of a devil." The main tourist attraction in Romania, Bran Castle is popularly known as "Dracula's Castle." Although Vlad Tepes, the original Dracula, did not live in the castle, he may have visited it. With its fairy-tale turrets and whitewashed walls, it is not exactly menacing.

I. Romania

A. Romania is on the northeastern edge of the Balkan Peninsula. The Carpathian Mountains cover about one-third of Romania.

B. Under communism, Romania's factories produced steel, chemicals, and ... **consumer goods**—clothing, shoes, and other products made ...

Reading Check Answer

French, Italian, Spanish

Reading Check Answer

the Cyrillic alphabet

south. Orchards and vineyards stretch along Romania's western, eastern, and southern borders. Farmers also grow grains, vegetables, and herbs here.

Despite abundant resources, Romania's economy has been held back by the communist policies of the past. Under communism, Romania's factories produced steel, chemicals, and machinery. Few **consumer goods**—clothing, shoes, and other goods that people use—were manufactured. Romania now has a free market economy to supply these goods, but aging factories need to be updated for Romania's economy to grow. In addition, the country needs to heal an environment widely damaged by air and water pollution.

The Romanians About 56 percent of Romania's 21.6 million people live in towns and cities. **Bucharest,** the capital and largest city, has more than 2 million people. What does Romania's name tell you about its history? If you guessed that the Romans once ruled this region, you are correct. Romania's history and culture were greatly influenced by the Romans. The Romanian language is closer to French, Italian, and Spanish—all based on Latin—than it is to other eastern European languages. In other ways, the Romanians are more like their Slavic neighbors. Many Romanians are Eastern Orthodox Christians.

Reading Check To what other languages is Romanian related?

Believe It or Not!

Transylvania

The region of central Romania known as Transylvania was the setting for English author Bram Stoker's vampire novel *Dracula*. Recently, a doctor noticed that many myths about vampires matched the symptoms of rabies, including pain from bright lights. He found that rabies had spread through the region at the same time that the vampire tales began.

Bulgaria

Mountainous Bulgaria lies south of Romania. Fertile valleys and plains are tucked among the Balkan Mountains and the Rhodope Mountains, which span most of the country. The coast along the Black Sea has warmer year-round temperatures than the mountainous inland areas.

Bulgaria's economy relies on both agriculture and manufacturing. Wheat, corn, and sugar beets grow in the fertile valleys. Roses are grown in the central Valley of the Roses. Their sweet-smelling oil is used in perfumes. Manufacturing depends on the country's deposits of zinc and coal. Factories produce machinery, metals, textiles, and processed foods. Tourism is growing as visitors seek out Bulgaria's scenic resorts on the Black Sea.

Daily Life Most of Bulgaria's 7.5 million people trace their ancestry to the Slavs, Turks, and other groups from Central Asia. Most Slavic people use the Cyrillic (suh•RIH•lihk) alphabet, which was first created to write the Slavic language. The Bulgarian language, similar to Russian, is also written in this Cyrillic alphabet. Most Bulgarians are Eastern Orthodox Christians. About 13 percent of the people are Muslims, or followers of the Islamic religion.

Sofia, with over 1 million people, is the capital and largest city. During the summer, Bulgarians join vacationers from other countries at resorts on the Black Sea coast. Here, modern hotels line wide, sandy beaches.

Reading Check What alphabet is used in many Slavic languages?

Reading Strategy — Reading the Text

Categorizing Information Have students work in pairs to organize Section 3's information in a chart. Have each student prepare a chart with the column headings "Landforms," "Economy," "People," and "History." Then have both students in each pair draw up a list of two or three facts about each country in the section. Have students take turns reading their facts to each other. The partner then has the task of placing each one in the correct category by writing it under the appropriate column heading. L1

Use the ***Reading Skills Handbook*** *for more reading strategies.*

Former Yugoslav Republics

The former Yugoslav republics used to be one large country called **Yugoslavia.** In the early 1990s, long-simmering disputes among ethnic groups boiled to the surface and tore the country apart. Five countries eventually emerged: **Slovenia, Croatia, Bosnia and Herzegovina** (HEHRT•seh•GAW•vee•nah), **Serbia and Montenegro,** and **Macedonia,** also known as the Former Yugoslav Republic of Macedonia (or **F.Y.R.O.M.**).

After the breakup, Serbia and Montenegro kept the name of Yugoslavia. Serbia wanted to control the other former Yugoslav republics and to protect the Serbs living in them. As a result, wars erupted throughout the 1990s. Some countries listed above forced people of other ethnic groups to leave their homes, a policy called ethnic cleansing. Tens of thousands died or were murdered. Thousands more became refugees, or people who flee to another country to escape danger or disaster. These wars left the region badly scarred. By 2002 Serbia's hope of one Yugoslavia had ended. Serbia and Montenegro formed a looser union and dropped the Yugoslav name.

Slovenia Slovenia is located in the northwest of the Balkans region. It has rugged mountains and fertile, densely populated valleys. Of all the countries of the old Yugoslavia, Slovenia is the most peaceful and prosperous. With many factories and service industries, it also has the region's highest standard of living. About 52 percent of the 2 million Slovenians live in towns and cities. Most are Roman Catholic.

Croatia Croatia spreads along the island-studded coast of the Adriatic Sea. Inland, Croatia has rugged mountains and a fertile plain. **Zagreb,** the capital and largest city, lies in this inland area. A republic, Croatia supports agriculture as well as industry. Tourists once crowded Croatia's beautiful Adriatic beaches, but war has since damaged many of these places.

The Croats, a Slavic group, make up 78 percent of Croatia's 4.3 million people. Another 12 percent are Serbs. Both Croats and Serbs speak the same Serbo-Croatian language, but they use different alphabets. The Croats use the Latin alphabet, the same one that you use for English. The Serbs write with the Cyrillic alphabet. Religion also divides Croats and Serbs. Croats are mainly Roman Catholic, while Serbs are Eastern Orthodox Christians.

NATIONAL GEOGRAPHIC **On Location**

Vukovar, Croatia

In 1991 Serbs attacked Vukovar in a revolt against Croatian independence. The revolt became a war, which lasted many years and took many lives.

Place What are some ways the war affected Croatia?

Chapter 13

Section 3, pages 377–381

More About the Photo

Croatia The war in the former Yugoslav republics lasted from 1991 to 1995. During these four years, nearly 1 million refugees from Bosnia and Herzegovina flooded into Croatia, prompting Croatia's government to ask for international humanitarian and financial aid.

Caption Answer Buildings were destroyed, many lives were lost, and tourism suffered.

L1/ELL

Guided Reading Activity

THE NEW EASTERN EUROPE

Guided Reading Activity 3

Rebuilding the Balkan Countries

Differentiated Instruction

Meeting Special Needs: Interpersonal Organize students into several groups. Have each group create a board game that people in the Balkan countries could use to learn about the free market economy. Suggest that groups use board games as models but that they name the squares after streets in a Balkan city. They can check maps of cities in travel guides for street names. Help groups create cards that reflect situations in a free market economy, such as "You priced your product too high for the market. Lose 1 turn" or "Your investment paid off. Win $500." Give groups a chance to explain their games to the other students. L3

Chapter 13

Section 3, pages 377–381

Primary Source

Answer Answers will vary.

Activity Have students research information about the refugees from the former Yugoslav republics. Ask them to imagine that they are among those refugees. Have the students write a diary entry about the day they were forced to leave home. Ask them to use their senses of sight, smell, and hearing to describe in detail the events that are taking place around them. Ask them to describe their feelings.

Assess

Assign Section 3 Assessment as homework or an in-class activity.

Have students use the Interactive Tutor Self-Assessment CD-ROM to review Section 3.

L2

Section Quiz

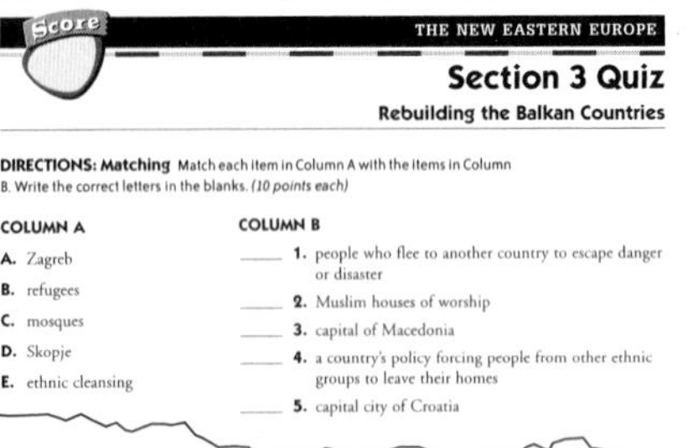

Name ______ Date ______ Class ______

Score

THE NEW EASTERN EUROPE

Section 3 Quiz

Rebuilding the Balkan Countries

DIRECTIONS: Matching Match each item in Column A with the items in Column B. Write the correct letters in the blanks. *(10 points each)*

COLUMN A	COLUMN B
A. Zagreb	____ 1. people who flee to another country to escape danger or disaster
B. refugees	____ 2. Muslim houses of worship
C. mosques	____ 3. capital of Macedonia
D. Skopje	____ 4. a country's policy forcing people from other ethnic groups to leave their homes
E. ethnic cleansing	____ 5. capital city of Croatia

Reading Check Answer

Slovenia, Croatia, Bosnia and Herzegovina, Serbia and Montenegro, and Macedonia

Primary Source

ZLATA'S DIARY

by Zlata Filipović

Young Zlata Filipović kept a diary about her experiences in Sarajevo.

"BOREDOM!!! SHOOTING!!! SHELLING!!! PEOPLE BEING KILLED!!! DESPAIR!!! HUNGER!!! MISERY!!! FEAR!!! That's my life! The life of an innocent eleven-year-old schoolgirl!!! A schoolgirl without a school. A child without games, without friends, without the sun, without birds, without nature, without fruit, without chocolate or sweets, with just a little powdered milk. In short, a child without a childhood. A wartime child. . . . I once heard that childhood is the most wonderful time of your life. And it is. I loved it, and now an ugly war is taking it all away from me. Why? I feel sad. I feel like crying. I am crying."

Taken from *Zlata's Diary: A Child's Life in Sarajevo*, © 1994 by Viking Penguin. Translation copyright Fixotet editions Robert Laffont, 1994.

Analyzing Primary Sources

Making Inferences What things do you think you would miss the most if war or another tragedy took them from you?

Bosnia and Herzegovina Mountainous and poor, the country of Bosnia and Herzegovina has an economy based mainly on crops and livestock. **Sarajevo** (SAR•uh•YAY•voh), the capital, has the look of an Asian city, with its marketplaces and mosques, or Muslim houses of worship. Many of the Bosnian people are Muslims. Others are Eastern Orthodox Serbs or Roman Catholic Croats. Serbs in the region began a bitter war after Bosnia's independence in 1992. The Dayton Peace Accords divided Bosnia into two regions under one government in 1995. American soldiers and other troops came as peacekeepers.

Serbia and Montenegro Since 2002 Serbia and its reluctant partner Montenegro have formed a loose union. In 2003 an agreement was reached to vote for independence in each republic in 2006. The economies of these two republics are based on agriculture and industry. The region's largest city is **Belgrade.** Most of the 10.7 million Serbs and Montenegrins practice the Eastern Orthodox faith.

Serbia has faced growing unrest in some of its local provinces. Muslim Albanians living in the province of **Kosovo** want independence from Serbia. Also living in Kosovo is a smaller group of Eastern Orthodox Serbs. For centuries, Albanians and Serbs have felt a deep anger toward each other. In 1999 Serb forces tried to push the Albanians out of Kosovo. The United States and other nations bombed Serbia to force it to withdraw its troops. Even with the help of United Nations peacekeeping troops, peace in Kosovo remains shaky.

Macedonia (F.Y.R.O.M.) Macedonia's 2.1 million people are a mix of different ethnic groups from the Balkans. In **Skopje** (SKAW•pyeh), Macedonia's capital, there is an amazing mix of ancient Christian churches, age-old Turkish markets, and modern shopping centers. Close to Kosovo, Macedonia handled a huge wave of ethnic Albanian refugees from Kosovo who fled Serb forces in 1999.

Reading Check What nations were formed from the former Yugoslavia?

Team-Teaching Activity

Language Arts Invite a foreign language teacher to class to discuss the different language families in Europe. Have the teacher point out the language chart in Section 4. (The teacher might mention that the chart shows only national languages and does not include those spoken by smaller groups, such as Basque and Catalan in Spain or Sami in the Nordic countries.) Suggest that the teacher offer students examples of common words from the Germanic, Romance, or Slavic languages that show the similarities among languages in that family. Then have students identify which language groups are represented in eastern Europe. L1

EE4 Human Systems: Standard 10

Albania

Bordering the Adriatic Sea, Albania is slightly smaller than the state of Maryland. Mountains cover most of Albania, contributing to its isolation from neighboring countries. Albania is a very poor nation. Although the country has valuable mineral resources, it lacks the money to mine them. Most Albanians farm—growing corn, grapes, olives, potatoes, sugar beets, and wheat—in mountain valleys.

Almost two-thirds of Albanians live in the countryside. The capital and largest city, **Tirana,** and its suburbs have a population of about 270,000. Although 3.1 million people live in Albania, another 3.2 million Albanians live in nearby countries. These refugees fled Albania to escape the violence that occurred in the 1990s.

About 70 percent of Albanians are Muslim. The rest are Christian. The Communists that once ruled Albania opposed religion, but Albania's current democratic government has allowed people to practice their faith. A famous Albanian, the Catholic nun Mother Teresa, served the poor in India.

Reading Check What is the main religion in Albania?

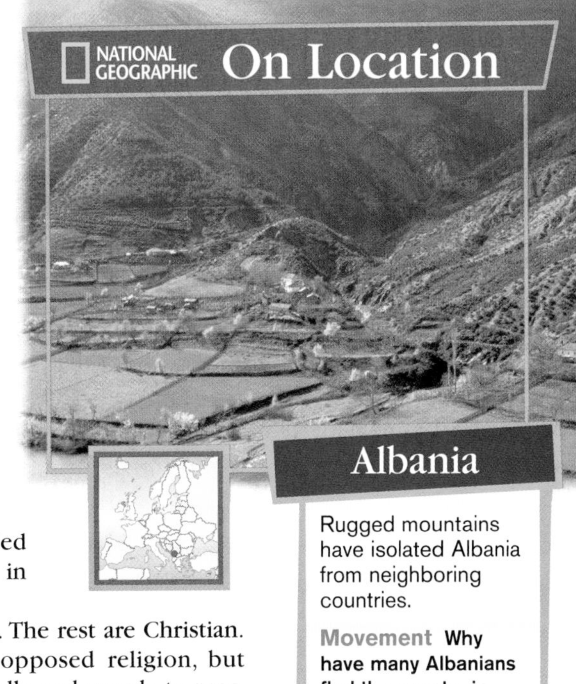

Albania

Rugged mountains have isolated Albania from neighboring countries.

Movement **Why have many Albanians fled the country in recent years?**

Section 3 Assessment

Defining Terms

1. **Define** consumer goods, ethnic cleansing, refugee, mosque.

Recalling Facts

2. **Place** What is the capital of Romania?
3. **Economics** How are roses used in Bulgaria?
4. **Economics** Which of the former Yugoslav republics is most prosperous?

Critical Thinking

5. **Drawing Conclusions** How do you think people in the Balkans feel about the recent changes in their countries?
6. **Understanding Cause and Effect** What effect did the policy of ethnic cleansing have on the people of Serbia?

Graphic Organizer

7. **Organizing Information** Create a chart like the one below and complete it by filling in two facts under each country's name.

Romania	Bulgaria	Slovenia	Croatia
Bosnia and Herzegovina	Serbia and Montenegro	Macedonia	Albania

Applying Social Studies Skills

8. **Analyzing Maps** Study the political map on page 369. What countries are found on the east coast of the Adriatic Sea?

Section 3 Assessment

1. The terms are defined in the Glossary.
2. Bucharest
3. Roses are grown so that their sweet-smelling oils can be used in perfume.
4. Slovenia
5. Students' answers will vary but should suggest that people's feelings will depend on the situation in each particular country. Some countries have fared well since the fall of communism, and others have not.
6. Many people lost their lives and many became refugees.
7. Students' charts will vary.
8. Slovenia, Croatia, Serbia and Montenegro, Albania, Bosnia and Herzegovina

Chapter 13

Section 3, pages 377–381

Reteach

Have students write two key facts about each country in the Balkan region.

L1/ELL

Reading Essentials and Study Guide

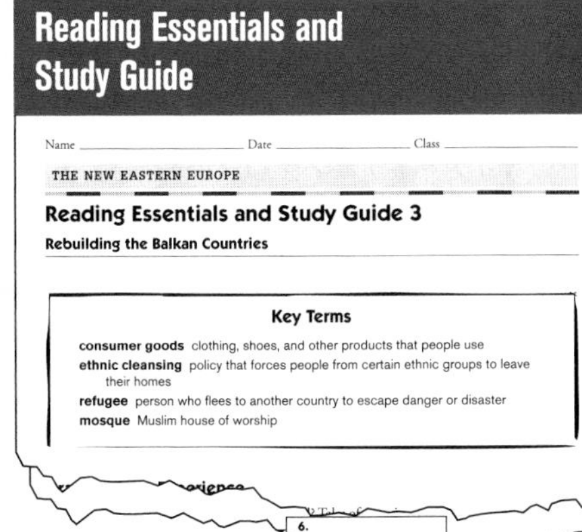
Name ______ Date ______ Class ______

THE NEW EASTERN EUROPE

Reading Essentials and Study Guide 3

Rebuilding the Balkan Countries

Key Terms

consumer goods clothing, shoes, and other products that people use
ethnic cleansing policy that forces people from certain ethnic groups to leave their homes
refugee person who flees to another country to escape danger or disaster
mosque Muslim house of worship

Reading Check Answer

Islam

Enrich

Have students research the traditional culture of one of the countries in the region, such as Hungarian dances or folk costumes in Slovenia. Have them report their findings to the class.

4 Close

Give students an outline map of the Balkans and have them fill in the names of the countries and capitals.

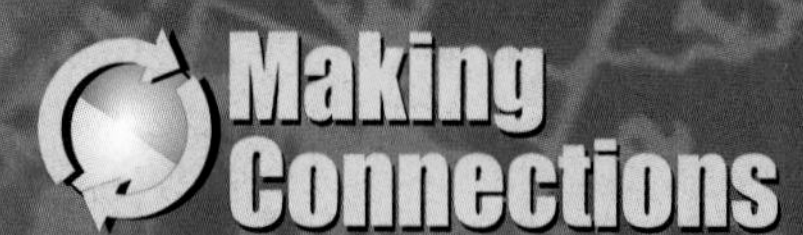

TEACH

Name or show some examples of folk art—such as quilts, pottery, wood carvings, or dolls. **Ask:** **What functions do folk arts serve for their societies?** *(as decoration; as an expression of cultural values; as a celebration of a group's identity)* **What aspect of Ukrainian culture influences their folk art?** *(early myths and Christianity)* **L2**

More About Ukrainian Legends

Pysanky also plays a role in maintaining the world, according to Ukrainian legend. Stories say that a serpentlike monster lives in a cave, chained to the walls. Each year, he sends out agents to see if eggs are still being decorated. If not, the chains are loosened and he is released to do mischief and evil. If they are, the monster remains in chains.

Interdisciplinary Connections

Art The most famous decorated Easter eggs are the handiwork of the Russian jeweler Peter Carl Fabergé. He created gold-and-jewel-encrusted objects that were the artistic height of decorated eggs. The eggs, produced for the family of Russia's ruling czars, were made for special occasions. Each egg opened to reveal a surprise inside. Forty of the original 50 imperial eggs still exist.

Making Connections

ART | SCIENCE | CULTURE | TECHNOLOGY

Ukrainian Easter Eggs

Ukrainians have a rich folk art tradition that dates back thousands of years. It includes pottery, textiles, and woodworking. The best-known Ukrainian art form, however, is that of *pysanky,* or decorated eggs.

History

Ukrainian Easter eggs are known worldwide for their beauty and skillful designs. Many of the designs date back to a time when people in the region worshiped a sun god. According to legend, the sun god preferred birds over all other creatures. Birds' eggs became a symbol of birth and new life, and people believed the eggs could ward off evil and bring good luck. Eggs were decorated with sun symbols and used in ceremonies that marked the beginning of spring.

When Christianity took hold in Ukraine in A.D. 988, the tradition of making decorative eggs continued. The egg came to represent religious rebirth and new life. People decorated eggs in the days before Easter and then gave them as gifts on Easter morning.

Technique

The word *pysanky* comes from Ukrainian words meaning "things that are written upon." This phrase helps explain the wax process used to decorate the eggs. An artist uses a pin or a tool called a *kistka* to "write" a design in hot wax onto the egg. The egg is then dipped into yellow dye, leaving the wax-covered portion of the eggshell white. After removing the egg from the dye, the artist writes with hot wax over another section of the egg. This portion stays yellow as the egg is dipped into a second dye color. The process continues, with the artist adding wax and dipping the egg into a darker and darker color. At the end, the artist removes the wax layers to reveal the multicolored design.

Making the Connection

1. What is *pysanky,* and when did it originate?
2. What role does placing wax onto the eggshell play in creating a decorative egg?
3. **Drawing Conclusions** What purposes, other than entertainment, might folk art accomplish?

◄ Ukrainian Easter eggs

382 CHAPTER 13

Making the Connection

1. *Pysanky* is the art of decorating eggs. The first eggs were made thousands of years ago when people from the region worshiped a sun god.
2. Areas covered by wax retain the color underneath when the egg is plunged into dye.
3. *Possible answers:* to build a sense of pride and identity; to embody legends and traditions

Section 4

Ukraine, Belarus, and Moldova

Guide to Reading

Main Idea

Past ties to Russia have had different effects on the economies and societies of Ukraine, Belarus, and Moldova.

Terms to Know

- steppe
- potash

Reading Strategy

Create a diagram like this one. Under the country's name, list at least one fact that shows the Soviet Union's effect on these countries.

NATIONAL GEOGRAPHIC Exploring Our World

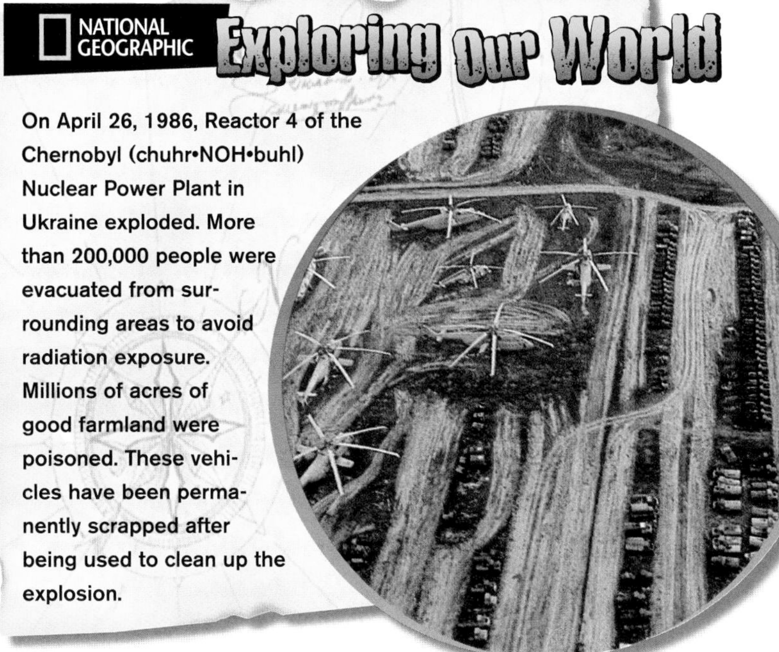

On April 26, 1986, Reactor 4 of the Chernobyl (chuhr•NOH•buhl) Nuclear Power Plant in Ukraine exploded. More than 200,000 people were evacuated from surrounding areas to avoid radiation exposure. Millions of acres of good farmland were poisoned. These vehicles have been permanently scrapped after being used to clean up the explosion.

Ukraine, Belarus (BEE•luh•ROOS), and **Moldova** (mawl•DAW•vuh) once belonged to the Soviet Union. When the Soviet Union broke apart in late 1991, Ukraine, Belarus, and Moldova became independent. Since then, they have struggled to build new economies.

Ukraine

Slightly smaller than Texas, Ukraine is by far the largest eastern European country (excluding Russia). The Carpathian Mountains rise along its southwestern border. Farther east, a vast steppe, or gently rolling, partly wooded plain, makes up the country. Numerous rivers, most of which are too shallow for ships, twist across the steppe. The most important waterway, the **Dnieper** (NEE•puhr) **River,** has been made navigable so that ships can carry goods to distant markets. The **Crimean Peninsula** juts into the Black Sea. Most of Ukraine has cold winters and warm summers.

1 Focus

Section Objectives

1. Describe the landforms of Ukraine, Belarus, and Moldova.
2. Compare the economies, history, and culture of Ukraine, Belarus, and Moldova.

BELLRINGER Skillbuilder Activity

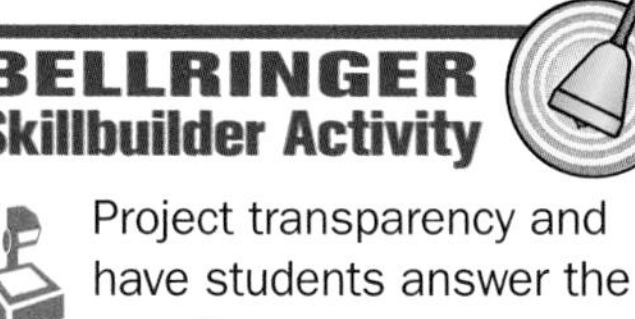

Project transparency and have students answer the question.

Daily Focus Skills Transparency

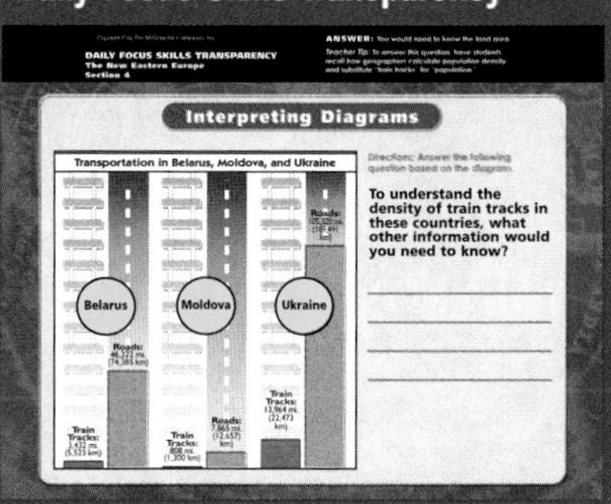

Reading Preview

■ **Activating Prior Knowledge** **Ask:** What do you think of when you hear a region called a "breadbasket"? *(that it produces large quantities of grain)* Inform students that in this section, they will read about such a region.

■ **Preteaching Vocabulary** Have students find the definitions of *steppe* and *potash* and restate them in their own words.

Section Resources

Reproducible Masters

- Reproducible Lesson Plan
- Daily Lecture and Discussion Notes
- Note-taking Guide
- Guided Reading Activity
- Reading Essentials and Study Guide
- Section Quiz

Transparencies

- Daily Focus Skills Transparency
- In-text Map Transparency

Multimedia

- Vocabulary PuzzleMaker CD-ROM
- Interactive Tutor Self-Assessment CD-ROM
- Presentation Plus! CD-ROM
- ExamView® Pro Testmaker CD-ROM
- MindJogger Videoquiz

Chapter 13

Section 4, pages 383–386

TEACH

Reading Strategy

Making Comparisons Have students scan the section for names of crops and manufactured goods produced in Ukraine, Belarus, and Moldova. Then have them copy the information and add it to a chart with the headings "Country," "Crops," and "Manufactured Goods." Remind them to use their charts as study aids. L1

Daily Lecture and Discussion Notes

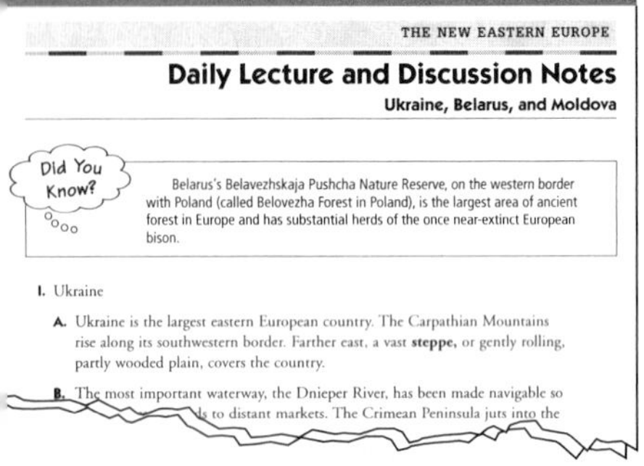

THE NEW EASTERN EUROPE

Daily Lecture and Discussion Notes

Ukraine, Belarus, and Moldova

Did You Know? Belarus's Belavezhskaja Pushcha Nature Reserve, on the western border with Poland (called Belovezha Forest in Poland), is the largest area of ancient forest in Europe and has substantial herds of the once near-extinct European bison.

I. Ukraine

A. Ukraine is the largest eastern European country. The Carpathian Mountains rise along its southwestern border. Farther east, a vast **steppe**, or gently rolling, partly wooded plain, covers the country.

B. The most important waterway, the Dnieper River, has been made navigable so ...ls to distant markets. The Crimean Peninsula juts into the

Applying Map Skills

Answers

1. Kiev
2. 60–125 people per sq. mi (25–50 per square km)

In-text Map Transparency Activity Outline the border of Ukraine. **Ask:** **What cities of over 1 million people are found in Ukraine?** *(Kiev, Kharkiv, Dnipropetrovsk, Donetsk, Lviv, and Odesa)*

Rich, dark soil covers nearly two-thirds of Ukraine. Farms are very productive, earning the country the name "breadbasket of Europe." Farmers grow sugar beets, potatoes, and grains and raise cattle and sheep. Factories make machinery, processed foods, and chemicals.

The Ukrainians Early Slavic groups settled and traded along the rivers of the region. During the A.D. 800s, warriors from Nordic countries united these groups into a large state centered on the city of Kiev (KEE•ihf). A century later, the people of Kiev accepted the Eastern Orthodox faith. They built one of Europe's most prosperous civilizations. After 300 years of freedom, the people of Kiev were conquered by Mongols, then Lithuanians and Poles, and finally the Russians.

In the 1930s, Soviet dictator Joseph Stalin brought Ukraine's farms under government control. Millions were murdered or starved in the famine that followed. Millions more died when Germans invaded

NATIONAL GEOGRAPHIC

Eastern Europe: Population Density

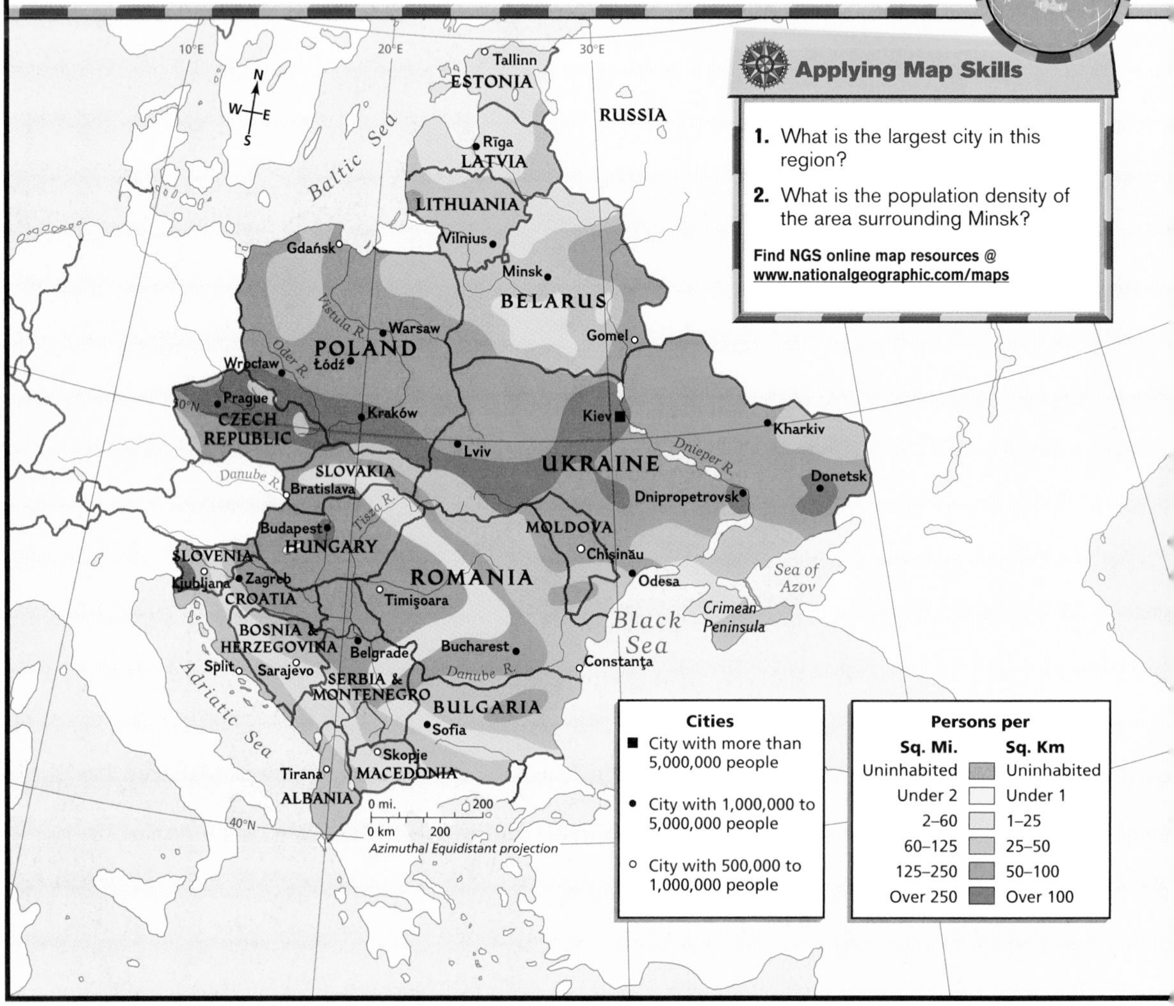

Applying Map Skills

1. What is the largest city in this region?
2. What is the population density of the area surrounding Minsk?

Find NGS online map resources @ www.nationalgeographic.com/maps

Cities

■ City with more than 5,000,000 people

• City with 1,000,000 to 5,000,000 people

○ City with 500,000 to 1,000,000 people

Persons per

Sq. Mi.	Sq. Km
Uninhabited	Uninhabited
Under 2	Under 1
2–60	1–25
60–125	25–50
125–250	50–100
Over 250	Over 100

Azimuthal Equidistant projection

Reading Strategy — Reading the Text

Reading Charts Before students read the *Language Families of Europe* chart, be sure that they read the title. Direct them to the names of the two major language families. Then have students list the subcategories under these families. Remind students as they read the chart to identify the broad general categories first and then examine the information within these categories for more detailed facts. L1

Use the ***Reading Skills Handbook*** *for more reading strategies.*

Language Families of Europe

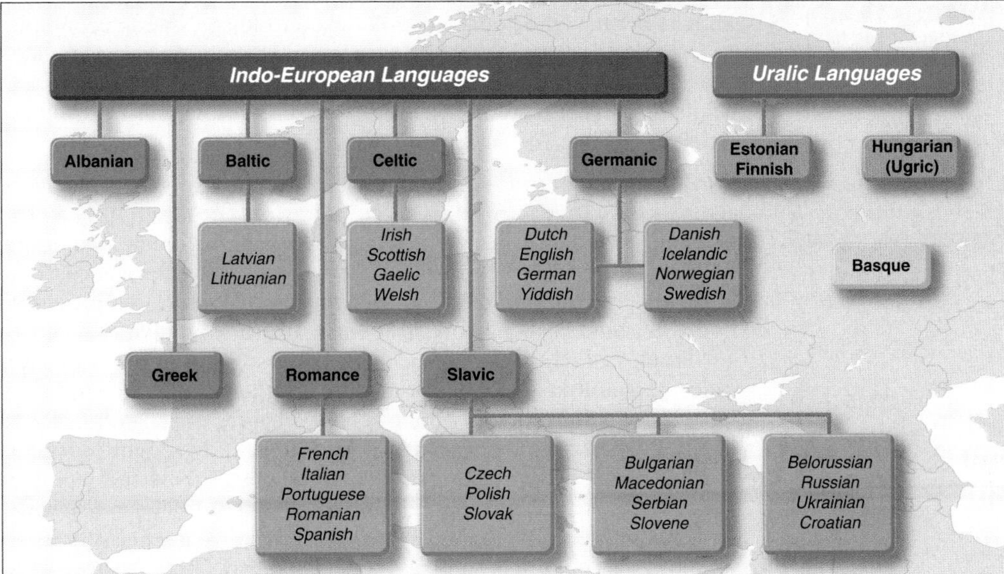

Ukraine during World War II. Finally in 1991, with the decline of Soviet power, Ukraine once again became a free nation.

Ukraine has about 48 million people. Nearly 75 percent are ethnic Ukrainians. About 22 percent are Russians, who live mainly in eastern areas. Most of the people follow the Eastern Orthodox religion and speak Ukrainian, a Slavic language closely related to Russian.

More than 70 percent of the people live in cities. **Kiev,** the capital, has more than 2.6 million people. Modern Ukrainians, even teenagers, enjoy listening to folk music played on a stringed instrument called a bandura and watching the acrobatic leaps of the *hopak* dance.

Reading Check **Why is Ukraine called the "breadbasket of Europe"?**

Analyzing the Chart

Seven main language families stem from Indo-European origins. Compare this chart with the locations of the languages on the map on page 286.

History **From what language family did Ukrainian develop?**

Belarus and Moldova

Belarus, slightly smaller than Kansas, is largely lowlands. If you visited Belarus, you would see wide stretches of birch tree groves, vast forested marshlands, and wooden villages surrounded by fields. Summers are cool and wet, and winters are cold.

Farmers grow potatoes, grains, vegetables, sugar beets, and fruits. Factory workers make equipment, chemicals, and construction materials. Food processing is another important industry. In addition to having petroleum and natural gas, Belarus has **potash,** a mineral used in fertilizer.

Slavic groups first settled the area that is today Belarus in the A.D. 500s. Surrounded by larger countries, Belarus was under foreign rule

Chapter 13

Section 4, pages 383–386

Analyzing the Chart

Answer
Slavic

L1/ELL

Guided Reading Activity

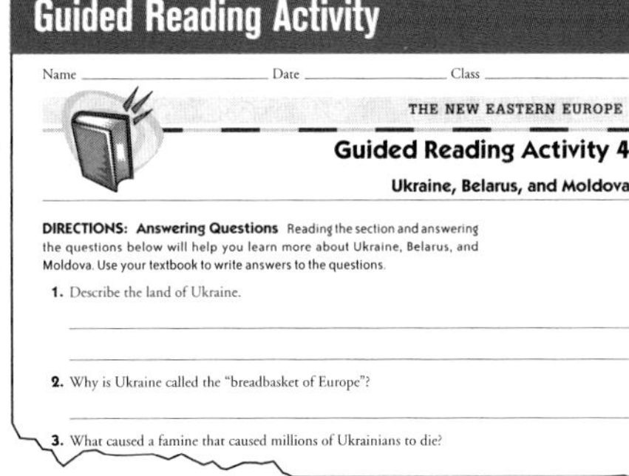
Name ____________ Date ____________ Class ____________

THE NEW EASTERN EUROPE

Guided Reading Activity 4

Ukraine, Belarus, and Moldova

DIRECTIONS: Answering Questions Reading the section and answering the questions below will help you learn more about Ukraine, Belarus, and Moldova. Use your textbook to write answers to the questions.

1. Describe the land of Ukraine.
2. Why is Ukraine called the "breadbasket of Europe"?
3. What caused a famine that caused millions of Ukrainians to die?

Reading Check Answer

Rich, dark soil covers most of the country, and its farms are very productive.

3 Assess

Assign Section 4 Assessment as homework or an in-class activity.

Have students use the Interactive Tutor Self-Assessment CD-ROM to review Section 4.

L2

Section Quiz

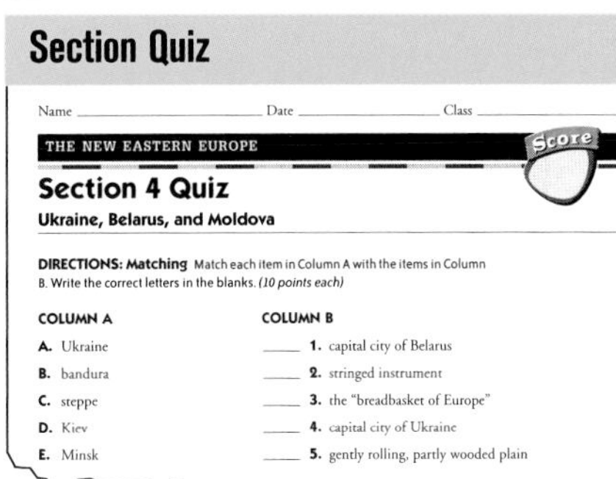
Name ____________ Date ____________ Class ____________

THE NEW EASTERN EUROPE

Section 4 Quiz

Ukraine, Belarus, and Moldova

Score

DIRECTIONS: Matching Match each item in Column A with the items in Column B. Write the correct letters in the blanks. *(10 points each)*

COLUMN A	COLUMN B
A. Ukraine	____ 1. capital city of Belarus
B. bandura	____ 2. stringed instrument
C. steppe	____ 3. the "breadbasket of Europe"
D. Kiev	____ 4. capital city of Ukraine
E. Minsk	____ 5. gently rolling, partly wooded plain

Differentiated Instruction

Meeting Special Needs: Visual/Spatial Organize students into four groups and provide each with a large outline map of Ukraine. Assign each group one of the following topics to research: landforms, crops, mineral resources, and industrial centers. Have the groups create pictures or symbols representing their topic. Then have them place these pictures or symbols on the map. Remind them to create a key to explain the meaning of their pictures and symbols. **L1/ELL**

Refer to *Inclusion for the Middle School Social Studies Classroom Strategies and Activities* in the TCR.

Objectives and answers to the Student Web Activity can be found in the Web Activity Lesson Plan at twip.glencoe.com

Reading Check Answer

Russia

L1/ELL

Reading Essentials and Study Guide

Name ______ Date ______ Class ______

THE NEW EASTERN EUROPE

Reading Essentials and Study Guide 4

Ukraine, Belarus, and Moldova

Key Terms

steppe gently rolling, partly wooded plain
potash mineral used in fertilizer

Drawing From Experience

Do your dances require a lot of energy? Imagine a dance that requires you to leap high and then drop to a squat. From the squat, you kick your ... This lively dance is the Ukrainian *hopak*. ... To the east is a large **steppe**. ... They wind through the steppe. ...

Close

Have students imagine they are visiting these three countries. Ask them to write three postcards to a friend back home. Each postcard should describe what they see in each of these countries.

Web Activity Visit ***The World and Its People*** Web site at twip.glencoe.com and click on **Chapter 13—Student Web Activities** to learn more about the effects of Chernobyl's nuclear disaster.

for most of its history. Communist Party leaders still control Belarus's government, which is a republic, and have maintained close ties with Russia. Foreign companies have been unwilling to do business in Belarus, in part because the country is still linked to Russia's weak economy.

The 9.9 million people of Belarus are mostly Eastern Orthodox Slavs. Their Belorussian language is closely related to Russian and Ukrainian and is written in Cyrillic. Two-thirds of Belarus's people live in cities. **Minsk,** the largest city, is the capital.

Moldova Moldova is mostly a rolling, hilly plain sliced by rivers. These waterways form valleys that hold rich, fertile soil. Due to this soil and a favorable climate, Moldova can support much agriculture. Farmers grow sugar beets, grains, potatoes, apples, and tobacco. Some grow grapes that are used to make wine. Factories turn out processed foods, machinery, metals, construction materials, and textiles.

Moldova's flag looks similar to Romania's flag. Why? Moldova was once part of Romania. About two-thirds of the people trace their language and culture to that country. Moldova's eastern region, home to many Russians, Ukrainians, and Turks, has recently sought independence. After a violent civil war, Russian troops entered the region as peacekeepers. Despite talks, no lasting settlement has been reached.

Moldova has 4.3 million people. About half live in cities, but much of Moldova's culture is still based on a rural way of life. Villagers celebrate special occasions with lamb, cornmeal pudding, and goat's milk cheese. The main city is the capital, **Chişinău** (KEE•shee•NOW).

Reading Check With what nation does Belarus have close ties?

Section 4 Assessment

Defining Terms

1. Define steppe, potash.

Recalling Facts

2. Location Where is the Crimean Peninsula located?
3. Government What type of government does Belarus have?
4. Economics Name three of Moldova's agricultural products.

Critical Thinking

5. Categorizing Information List four agricultural products and three manufactured products of Ukraine.
6. Understanding Cause and Effect Why is the culture of Moldova similar to that of Romania?

Graphic Organizer

7. Organizing Information Create a time line like this one. Then label five important periods or events in Ukraine's history.

Applying Social Studies Skills

8. Analyzing Maps Compare the political and population maps on pages 369 and 384. What is the population density around Ukraine's Dniester River?

Section 4 Assessment

1. The terms are defined in the Glossary.
2. in southern Ukraine extending into the Black Sea
3. republic
4. *Any three:* sugar beets, grains, potatoes, apples, tobacco, grapes
5. *Agriculture*—sugar beets, potatoes, grains, cattle, sheep; *Products*—machinery, processed foods, chemicals
6. because Moldova was once part of Romania
7. *800s*—Nordic warriors create a state in Kiev; *900s*—Kievans take Orthodox faith; *1200s*—Mongol conquest; *1930s*—farms brought under Soviet control; *1991*—Ukraine becomes independent
8. over 250 people per sq. mi (over 100 people per sq. km)

Chapter 13 Reading Review

Section 1 Poland and the Baltic Republics

Terms to Know
bog
communist state
acid rain
pope

Main Idea
Poland and the Baltic republics have undergone many changes to their political and economic systems.

✓Place Poland is a large country with southern mountains and northern plains.
✓Economics The change to a free market economy has brought challenges.
✓Culture The Poles feel deep loyalty to their country and the Catholic Church.
✓Place The countries of Estonia, Latvia, and Lithuania border the Baltic Sea and have recently raised their standards of living.

Section 2 Hungarians, Czechs, and Slovaks

Terms to Know
landlocked
nomad
spa
privatize

Main Idea
Hungary, the Czech Republic, and Slovakia are changing to free market economies.

✓Geography The Danube River separates the fertile Hungarian Plain from Transdanubia's rolling hills and forests.
✓Economics The Czech Republic is prosperous but must modernize its factories.
✓Economics Slovakia has had difficulty moving to a free market economy.

Section 3 Rebuilding the Balkan Countries

Terms to Know
consumer goods
ethnic cleansing
refugee
mosque

Main Idea
The Balkan countries have suffered greatly from ethnic conflicts and economic setbacks.

✓Culture The people of Romania are not related to the Slavic peoples who form the populations of most eastern European countries.
✓History Ethnic conflicts have torn apart the former Yugoslav republics.
✓Economics Albania is rich in minerals but is too poor to develop them.

Section 4 Ukraine, Belarus, and Moldova

Terms to Know
steppe
potash

Main Idea
Past ties to Russia have had different effects on the economies and societies of Ukraine, Belarus, and Moldova.

✓Geography Ukraine's rich soil allows it to grow large amounts of food.
✓Economics Belarus maintains close economic ties to Russia.
✓Economics Moldova's eastern region has tried to seek independence, but even after a civil war, no lasting settlement has been reached.

Reading Review

Use the Chapter 13 Reading Review to preview, review, condense, or reteach the chapter.

Preview/Review

Use the Terms to Know lists to help students review and study.

Activity Have students draw up a matching quiz of ten terms and their definitions from the chapter. Then have them exchange quizzes with another student and take the quiz their partner prepared.

Vocabulary PuzzleMaker CD-ROM reinforces the vocabulary terms used in Chapter 13.

The Interactive Tutor Self-Assessment CD-ROM allows students to review Chapter 13 content.

Condense

Have students read the Chapter 13 summary statements.

Guided Reading Activities

Audio Program

Reteach

Reteaching Activity

Reading Essentials and Study Guide

Reading Strategy — Read to Write

Making Predictions Have students choose one of the countries discussed in this chapter and find information using the Internet about the country's transition from its past economic system to a free market economy. Using this information, students should then make predictions about the country's future economic growth. Students should present the information and their predictions in a written report. L1

Assessment and Activities

GLENCOE TECHNOLOGY

MindJogger Videoquiz
Use MindJogger Videoquiz to review the Chapter 13 content.

 Available in DVD and VHS

Using Key Terms

1.	b	6.	d
2.	h	7.	f
3.	g	8.	e
4.	a	9.	i
5.	j	10.	c

Reviewing the Main Ideas

11. coal mining
12. increased trade and industry
13. the Danube
14. Prague
15. inexperience with manufacturing consumer goods, inefficient factories, and environmental damage
16. Eastern Orthodox Christianity
17. disputes among ethnic groups
18. Kiev
19. Russian and Ukrainian
20. Moldova once was part of Romania.

Critical Thinking

21. Muslim Albanians living in Kosovo want independence from Serbia. Serb forces tried to push the Albanians out of Kosovo.
22. Students should explain why they listed certain countries in each category.

Chapter 13 Assessment and Activities

Using Key Terms

Match the terms in Part A with their definitions in Part B.

A.

1. spa	6. landlocked
2. ethnic cleansing	7. mosque
3. acid rain	8. consumer goods
4. pope	9. refugee
5. steppe	10. potash

B.

a. head of the Roman Catholic Church
b. health resort with hot mineral springs
c. mineral used in fertilizer
d. having no access to the sea
e. products made for people to use themselves
f. Muslim house of worship
g. rain containing chemical pollutants
h. forcing people from other ethnic groups to leave their homes
i. person who must flee to another country to escape danger or disaster
j. gently rolling, partly wooded plain

Reviewing the Main Ideas

Section 1 Poland and the Baltic Republics

11. **Economics** What is one of Poland's most important industries?
12. **History** What has raised standards of living in the Baltic republics?

Section 2 Hungarians, Czechs, and Slovaks

13. **Place** What river divides Hungary?
14. **Place** What is the Czech Republic's capital?

Section 3 Rebuilding The Balkan Countries

15. **Economics** What factors are holding back Romania's economy?
16. **Culture** What is the main religion of Bulgaria?
17. **History** What caused Yugoslavia to fall apart?

Section 4 Ukraine, Belarus, and Moldova

18. **Place** What is the capital of Ukraine?
19. **Culture** To what languages is Belorussian similar?
20. **History** Why does Moldova's flag look similar to Romania's flag?

Eastern Europe

Place Location Activity

On a separate sheet of paper, match the letters on the map with the numbered places listed below.

1. Danube River	6. Hungary
2. Black Sea	7. Warsaw
3. Croatia	8. Carpathian Mountains
4. Albania	9. Baltic Sea
5. Latvia	10. Ukraine

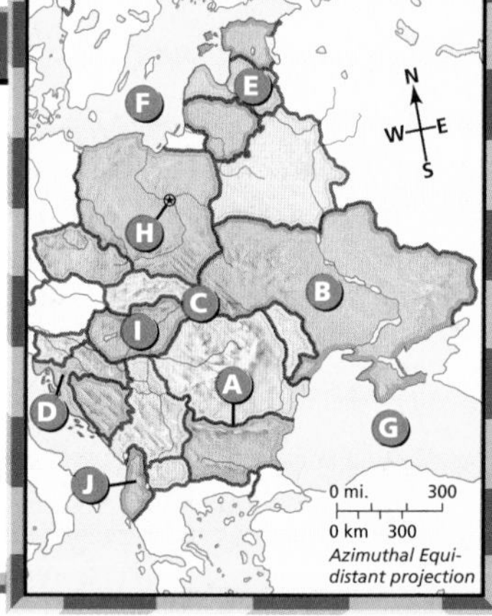

NATIONAL GEOGRAPHIC Place Location Activity

1. A	6. I
2. G	7. H
3. D	8. C
4. J	9. F
5. E	10. B

Comparing Regions Activity

23. Students' conversations might include topics about homesickness, fear, and anger.

Self-Check Quiz Visit ***The World and Its People*** Web site at twip.glencoe.com and click on **Chapter 13—Self-Check Quizzes** to prepare for the Chapter Test.

Critical Thinking

21. **Understanding Cause and Effect** What has led to the unrest in parts of Serbia and Montenegro?
22. **Categorizing Information** In a chart like the one below, identify eastern European countries that are succeeding economically and ones that continue to struggle.

Countries That Are Succeeding	Countries That Are Struggling

Comparing Regions Activity

23. **Culture** People in eastern Europe have experienced much conflict over ethnic identity. This conflict has produced a large number of refugees from countries such as Bosnia and Croatia. There are large numbers of refugees in parts of Africa due to conflict as well. With a partner, research to find information about refugees in eastern European and African countries. Write a conversation that an eastern European refugee and an African refugee might have.

Mental Mapping Activity

24. **Focusing on the Region** Create a map of eastern Europe, and then label the following:

- Poland
- Albania
- Czech Republic
- Serbia & Montenegro
- Hungary
- Lithuania
- Black Sea
- Danube River
- Ukraine
- Adriatic Sea

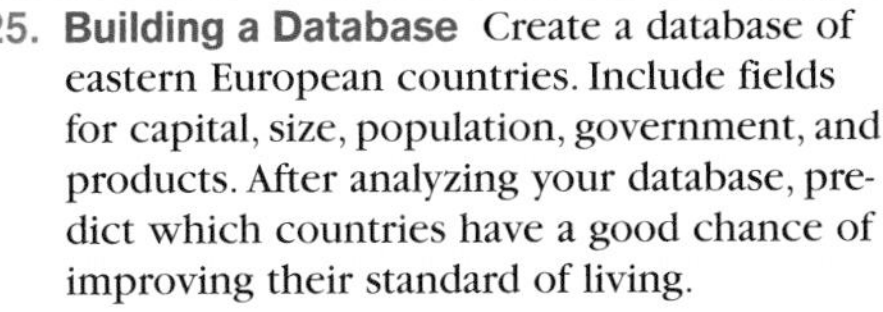

Technology Skills Activity

25. **Building a Database** Create a database of eastern European countries. Include fields for capital, size, population, government, and products. After analyzing your database, predict which countries have a good chance of improving their standard of living.

Standardized Test Practice

Directions: Study the map below, and then answer the question that follows.

1. Which of the following nations in eastern Europe has applied for membership in the European Union?

A Bulgaria
B Spain
C Ireland
D Germany

Test-Taking Tip: Notice that the question asks you to base your answer on location. Three of the choices are countries in western Europe. You should use the process of elimination to find the correct answer.

Assessment and Activities

Standardized Test Practice

1. A

Tested Objectives: Analyzing information, reading a map

Chapter Test Bonus Question

This question may be used for extra credit on the chapter test.

This country is well-known for its rich folk art tradition of creating elaborate and beautiful Easter eggs. What is this country? *(Ukraine)*

Social Studies Online

Have students visit the Web site at twip.glencoe.com to review Chapter 13 and take the Self-Check Quiz.

FOLDABLES Study Organizer Dinah Zike's Foldables

Culminating Activity Have students use their foldables to write a one-page essay summarizing the similarities and differences between western Europe and eastern Europe.

Mental Mapping Activity

24. This exercise helps students visualize the countries and geographic features of eastern Europe. Accept all attempts at freehand mapping that show places in a correct relationship to one another.

Technology Skills Activity

25. After completing this activity, students should discuss all the different factors that help a country succeed in taking care of its people and improving the standard of living.

Unit 5 Planning Guide

- If you teach BOTH Eastern and Western world regions in one year, use the columns in red to help you pace your lessons.
- **If you teach ONLY Eastern or Western world regions in one year, use the columns in blue to help you pace your lessons.**

ALTERNATIVE PACING CHARTS

Unit 5		Chapter 14		Chapter 15	
Both East and West	**Either East or West**	**Both East and West**	**Either East or West**	**Both East and West**	**Either East or West**
Day 1 Unit Opener, Regional Atlas **Day 2** Regional Atlas	**Day 1** Unit Opener, Regional Atlas **Day 2** Regional Atlas **Day 3** Regional Atlas	**Day 1** Chapter Opener, Section 1 **Day 2** Section 1, Making Connections **Day 3** Section 2 **Day 4** Section 2, Critical Thinking Skill, Review **Day 5** Chapter Assessment **Day 6** NGS Geography and History	**Day 1** Chapter Opener, Section 1 **Day 2** Section 1 **Day 3** Section 1, Making Connections **Day 4** Section 2 **Day 5** Section 2, Critical Thinking Skill **Day 6** Review **Day 7** Chapter Assessment **Day 8** NGS Geography and History	**Day 1** Chapter Opener, Section 1 **Day 2** Section 2 **Day 3** Section 2, Making Connections **Day 4** Section 3 **Day 5** TIME Reports **Day 6** TIME Reports, Critical Thinking Skill, Review **Day 7** Chapter Assessment	**Day 1** Chapter Opener, Section 1 **Day 2** Section 1 **Day 3** Section 2 **Day 4** Making Connections, Section 3 **Day 5** Section 3 **Day 6** TIME Reports **Day 7** Critical Thinking Skill **Day 8** Review **Day 9** Chapter Assessment

Note: The following materials may be used when teaching Unit 5.
Chapter level support materials can be found on the chapter resource pages.

TEACHING TRANSPARENCIES

Political Map Transparency L2

Map Overlay Transparencies L2

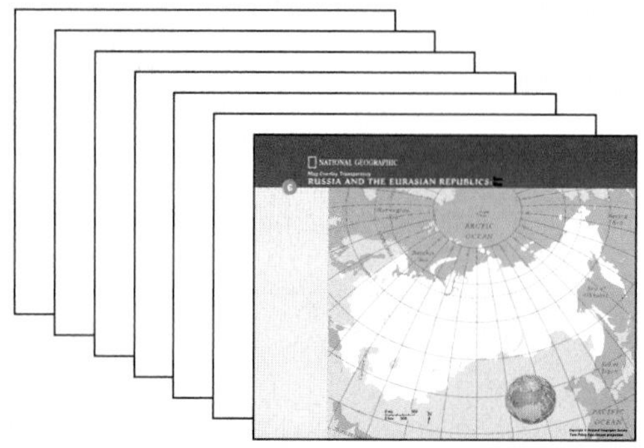

World Cultures Transparencies L2

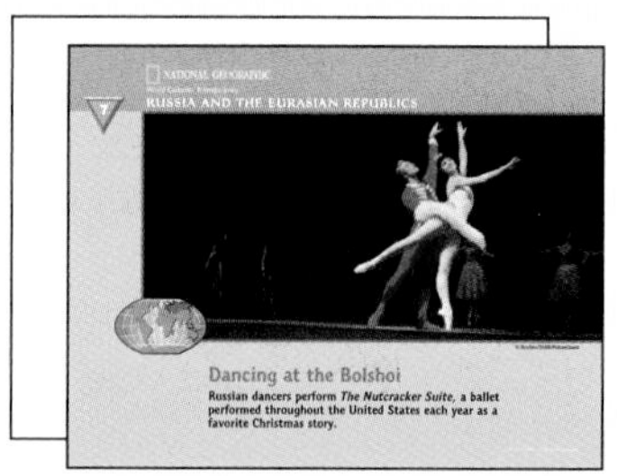

Unit 5 Resources

INTERDISCIPLINARY CONNECTIONS

World Literature Reading L2

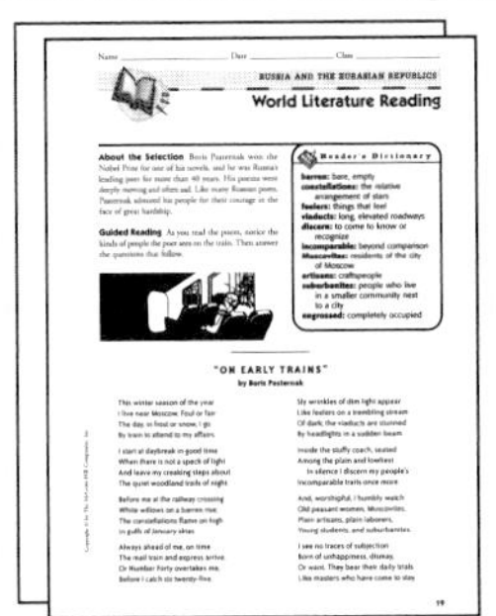

Economics and Geography Activity L2

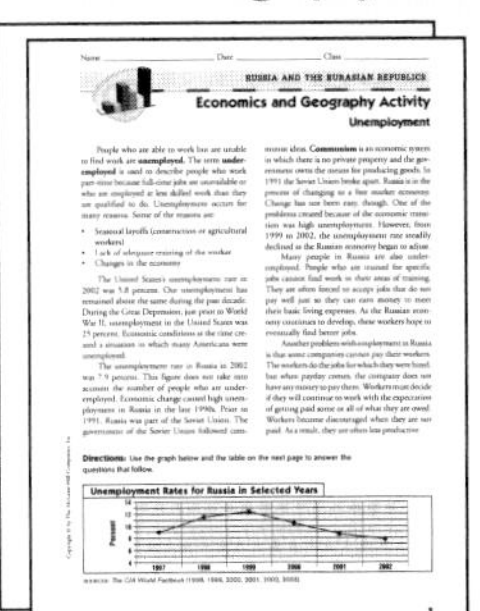

History and Geography Activity L2

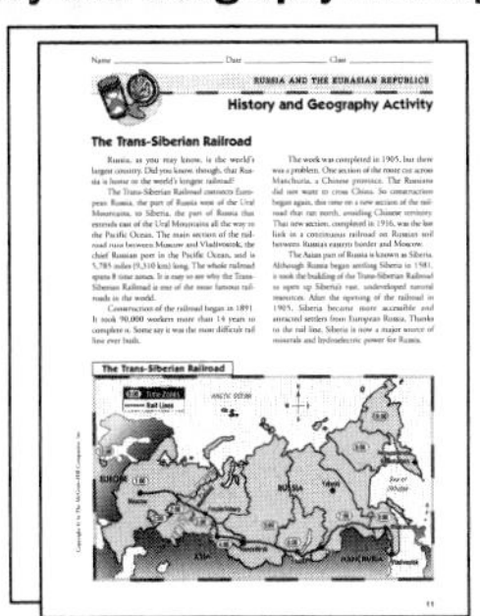

INTERDISCIPLINARY CONNECTIONS

Foods Around the World L1/ELL

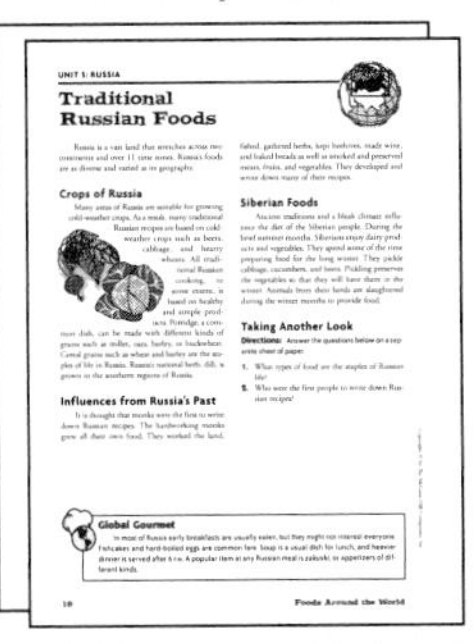

World Music: A Cultural Legacy

CIVIC INVOLVEMENT

Citizenship Activity L1

Environmental Case Study L2

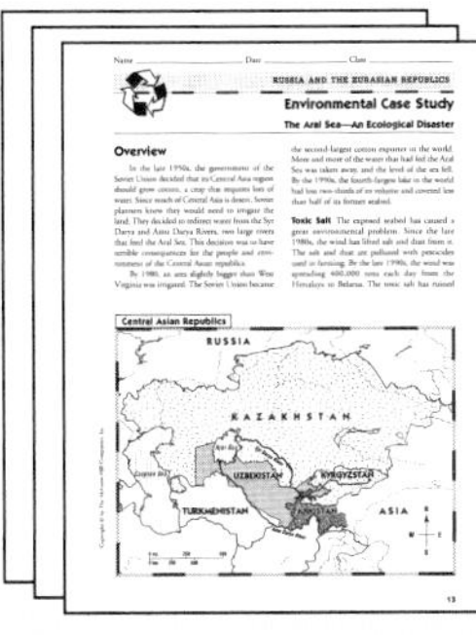

MAP AND GEOGRAPHY SKILLS

Building Geography Skills for Life

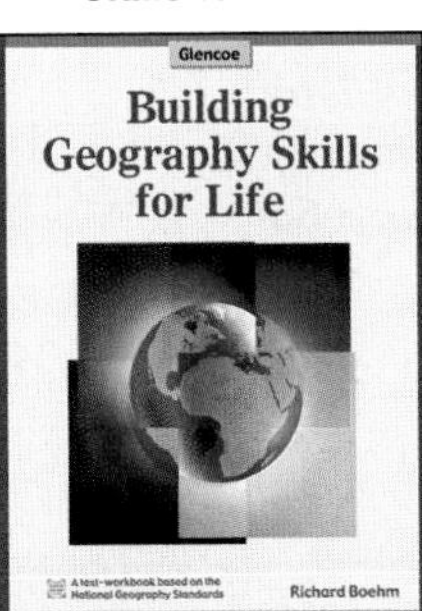

NGS Focus on Geography Literacy L2

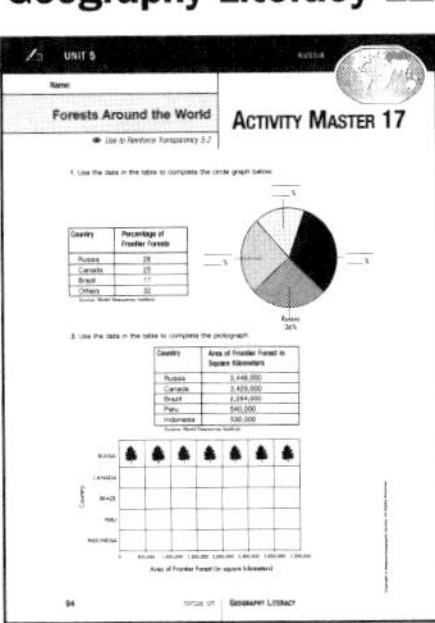

Regional Atlas Activity L2

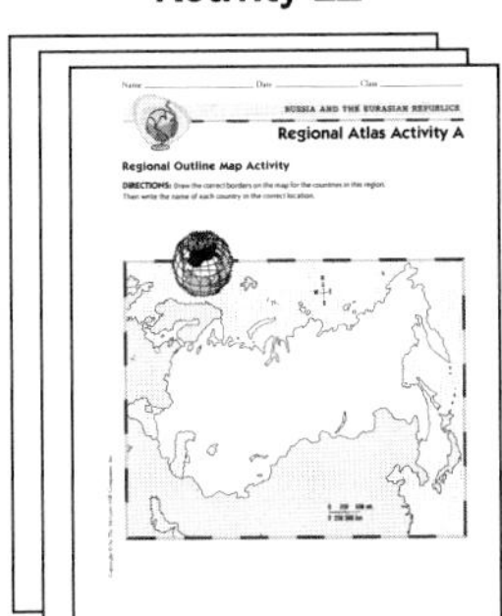

KEY TO ABILITY LEVELS

Teaching strategies have been coded for varying learning styles and abilities.

L1 **BASIC** activities for all students

L2 **AVERAGE** activities for average to above-average students

L3 **CHALLENGING** activities for above-average students

ELL **ENGLISH LANGUAGE LEARNER** activities

ASSESSMENT

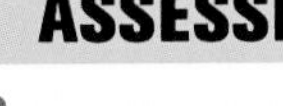

Unit Pretests L2

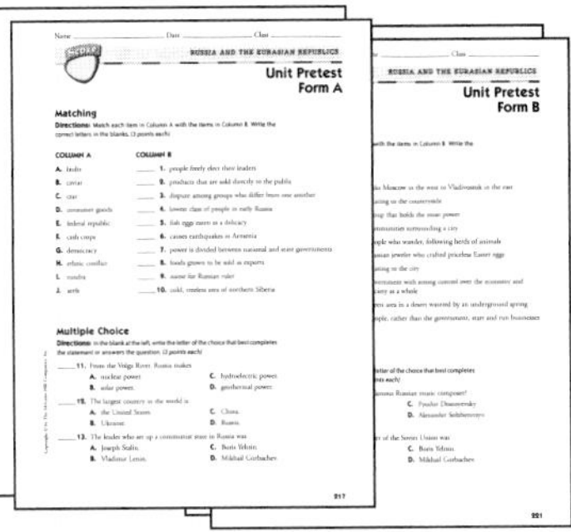

Unit Posttests L2

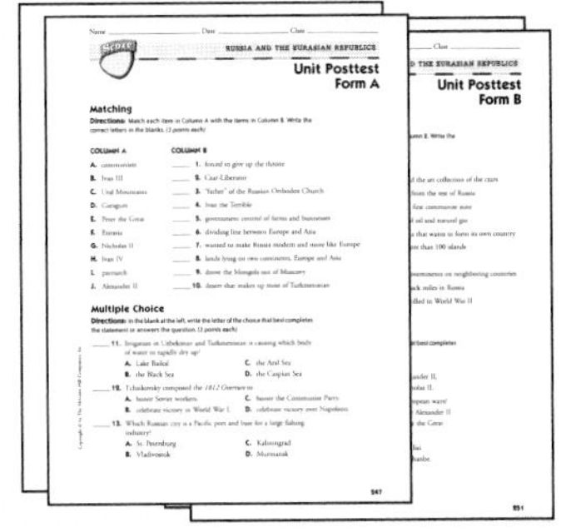

Glencoe Professional Development and Teacher Support Materials

- **Reading in the Content Area for the Middle School Classroom**
- **Inclusion Strategies for the Middle School Social Studies Classroom**
- **Character Education for the Middle School Classroom**
- **Teaching Strategies for the Social Studies Classroom**
- **Reproducible Lesson Plans**
- **Outline Map Resource Book**
- **Writing Process Transparencies for Middle School**
- **Social Studies: Reading Strategies**

Additional Unit 5 Resources

- **Timed Readings Plus in Social Studies** help students increase their reading rate and fluency while maintaining comprehension. The 400-word passages are similar to those found on state and national assessments.
- **Reading in the Content Area: Social Studies** concentrates on six essential reading skills that help students better comprehend what they read. The book includes 75 high-interest nonfiction passages written at increasing levels of difficulty.
- **Reading Fluency** helps students read smoothly, accurately, and expressively.
- **Jamestown's Reading Improvement,** by renowned reading expert Edward Fry, focuses on helping build your students' comprehension, vocabulary, and skimming and scanning skills.
- **Critical Reading Series** provides high-interest books, each written at three reading levels.

For more information about these products, see the Jamestown Education materials in the Classroom Solutions in the front of this Teacher Wraparound Edition. To order these products, call Glencoe at 1-800-334-7344.

The following videotape programs are available from Glencoe:

- **Fabergé: Imperial Jeweler** 1-56501-878-8
- **Ivan the Terrible** 0-7670-0517-1
- **Joseph Stalin** 1-56501-820-6

To order, call Glencoe at 1-800-334-7344. To find classroom resources to accompany many of these, check:

A&E Television: www.aetv.com

The History Channel: www.historychannel.com

Reading List Generator CD-ROM

GLENCOE **BOOKLINK**

The Glencoe BookLink CD-ROM is a database that allows you to search more than 15,000 titles to create a customized reading list for your students.

- Reading lists can be organized by students' reading level, author, genre, theme, or area of interest.
- The database provides Degrees of Reading Power™ (DRP) and Lexile™ readability scores for all selections.
- A brief summary of each selection is included.

Leveled reading suggestions for this unit:

For students at a Grade 5 reading level:
- ***Russia,*** by Kristin Thoennes.

For students at a Grade 6 reading level:
- ***Russia 1812: from The Expiation,*** by Victor Hugo.

For students at a Grade 7 reading level:
- ***Stalin: Russia's Man of Steel,*** by Albert Marrin.

To order this CD-ROM, call Glencoe at 1-800-334-7344.

Extending the Content

Readings for the Teacher
- ***CIS and Eastern Europe on File.*** New York: Facts on File, 1993.
- ***Teaching About the Former Soviet Union: History, Language, Culture, Art,*** rev. ed. By Patricia Winpenny, et al. Denver: Center for Teaching International Relations, 1994.

Multimedia Resources
- **Glencoe World History Primary Source Document Library CD-ROM**
- ***The Rise and Fall of the Soviet Union.*** Tapeworm, 1992. 2 videocassettes, 124 minutes.

Service Learning Project

Connecting Classroom With Community

Pollution is a very serious problem in Russia. Have students investigate a pollution-related issue that interests them, such as waste disposal, water pollution, or ozone depletion. Then have them identify ways that they can do something to try to alleviate this problem. They could participate in fund-raising or letter-writing campaigns, join an environmental group that works toward a goal that they share, or begin their own local clean-up effort.

Content Background Notes

Use this additional information as lecture notes or discussion prompts throughout the study of Unit 5.

Chapter 14 Russia's Landscape and History (pp. 402–419)

The Sky Is Falling One June morning in 1908, the stillness in remote central Siberia was shattered by a massive explosion in the air. Scientists estimate the blast was as strong as 10 to 15 megatons of dynamite—as powerful as many atomic bombs. The power of the blast was enough to flatten about 2,000 square miles (5,180 sq. km) of trees in the forest—an area more than half the size of Rhode Island. It was strong enough that the resulting shaking of the earth registered on seismographs in western Europe. Yet this massive explosion left no crater on the ground. What caused the "Tunguska Event," named for the river near where the explosion occurred?

Various explanations have been offered for this event, from the appearance of a black hole to the explosion of a power plant in a spaceship piloted by extraterrestrials. Today most scientists believe that the blast was the result of either an asteroid or a comet tumbling to Earth and burning up in the atmosphere. Comets—made of ice and dust—are more likely than rocky asteroids to burn up in the atmosphere, explaining why no crater has been found. However, some metallic fragments have been found in tree resin in the area, suggesting that the object was an asteroid. Whether asteroid or comet, the fragment must have been huge; scientists suggest a weight anywhere from 100,000 to 1 million tons (90,719 to 907,185 metric tons). Research at Tunguska continues, as scientists hope to learn more about Earth's explosive visitor.

A Mammoth Project Siberia is home to another fascinating research project—one attempting to reach not out in space but back in time. About 20,000 years ago, woolly mammoths lumbered across Siberia. These massive creatures—which measured up to 8.5 feet (2.6 m) across at the shoulders and weighed about 14,000 pounds (6,350 kg)—thrived in the cold Ice Age climate. One mammoth—47 years old—died and was later frozen in ice. Scientists used jackhammers to chisel a huge block of ice holding its remains. Then they used a helicopter to carry that block of ice to a nearby cave, where they are defrosting the animal so they can study it. Because they want to be sure not to destroy any evidence, the scientists have to defrost their sample very carefully—using hand-held hair dryers. By studying the mammoth and remains of other plants and animals trapped in the ice, scientists believe they can learn a wealth of information about the biology of the Ice Age world.

Chapter 15 The New Russia and Independent Republics (pp. 422–451)

The Kremlin One of the most familiar sites from Russia is Moscow's famous Kremlin, the fortress that was the center of the old city. The name *Kremlin* means "fortified town" in Russian, and this collection of buildings standing behind stout walls is precisely that—a walled city within a city. Full of palaces, churches, and military facilities, the Kremlin speaks of Russia's imperial past.

Construction of the Kremlin first began in 1147, when Moscow was founded, and the original citadel walls were finished 10 years later. By the 1300s, Moscow had become the center of the Russian Orthodox faith, and from then on, the Kremlin became home to some of Russia's most magnificent churches. Today five cathedrals rise within the walls of this enclave. The oldest is the Cathedral of the Assumption, built in the 1400s. The Cathedral of the Archangel Michael holds the burial tombs of all of Russia's czars over a period of hundreds of years.

The Kremlin also has armories, palaces from the days of the czars, the massive 40-ton (36–metric ton) Tsar Cannon (built in the 1580s and unworkable), and the 200-ton (181–metric ton) Tsar Bell (also unworkable). The complex is still in use. The ornate Senate building, built during the reign of Catherine the Great, today serves as the official residence of Russia's president.

Icons One of the hallmarks of the Russian Orthodox Church is the veneration of icons. Icons are painted images of Jesus and Mary, the archangels and apostles, church fathers, and important figures from the Old Testament. The style of icon painting is distinctive, drawing from ancient Greek, Roman, and Egyptian practices. Icon art looks different from western painting because it does not attempt to portray physical features in a realistic manner. Figures are less three-dimensional, and the relative sizes of figures are determined not by the actual size of the people represented or their placement nearer or farther from the viewer (as in western art) but according to their spiritual importance. The more significant the figure, the larger the size. The colors used by icon painters are distinctive as well and, again, aim to convey spiritual meaning, not physical reality. Icon painting originated in the Eastern Orthodox Church of the Byzantine Empire. Russian icon painters adapted the art but developed a distinctly Russian style that included darker colors and a more forgiving portrayal of Jesus than was often found in Byzantine art.

Introducing Unit 5

00:00 Out of Time?

If time does not permit teaching each chapter in this unit, you may use the **Reading Essentials and Study Guide** for each chapter.

Unit Overview

The two chapters in this unit introduce students to the geography, culture, and history of Russia and its neighbors. Before beginning to study the unit, point out to students the following characteristics of this region:

- physical features that have a historical and economic impact
- recent changes that have dramatically altered political and economic life
- distinctive, rich cultural traditions
- environmental problems due to development

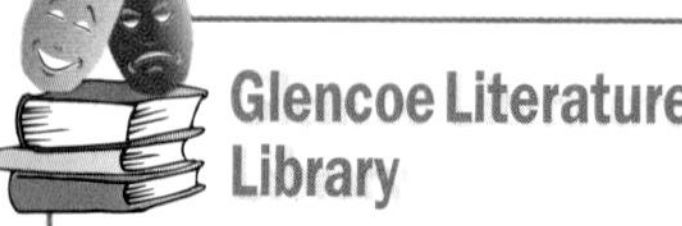

Glencoe Literature Library

As students study the unit, have them read *Letters from Rifka* by Karen Hesse from the **Glencoe Literature Library.** The Glencoe Literature Library consists of novels and other readings for middle school students, along with study guides that offer instructional support and student activities.

Unit 5

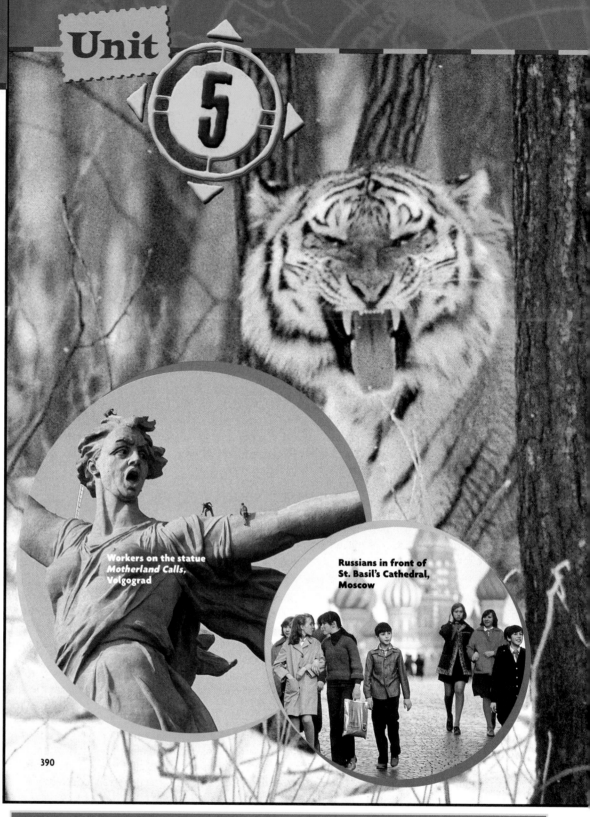

Workers on the statue *Motherland Calls,* Volgograd

Russians in front of St. Basil's Cathedral, Moscow

390

Using the Illustration

Visual Instruction Siberian tigers are in great danger of extinction. They once roamed a huge territory that included not only Siberia but China and the Korean Peninsula. The disorder that followed the collapse of the Soviet Union resulted in funding cuts for conservation activity and left the borders more porous, opening the way for a surge in illegal hunting. A single Siberian tiger is worth $15,000—far beyond the typical income of people in the region. As a result of this surge in hunting, today there are fewer than 500 of these animals in the wild. Have students research more about Siberia. They can do individual or group presentations on one of the following aspects of Siberia: physical features and climate, resources, ecology, history, economics, people. L1

NATIONAL GEOGRAPHIC

Russia and the Eurasian Republics

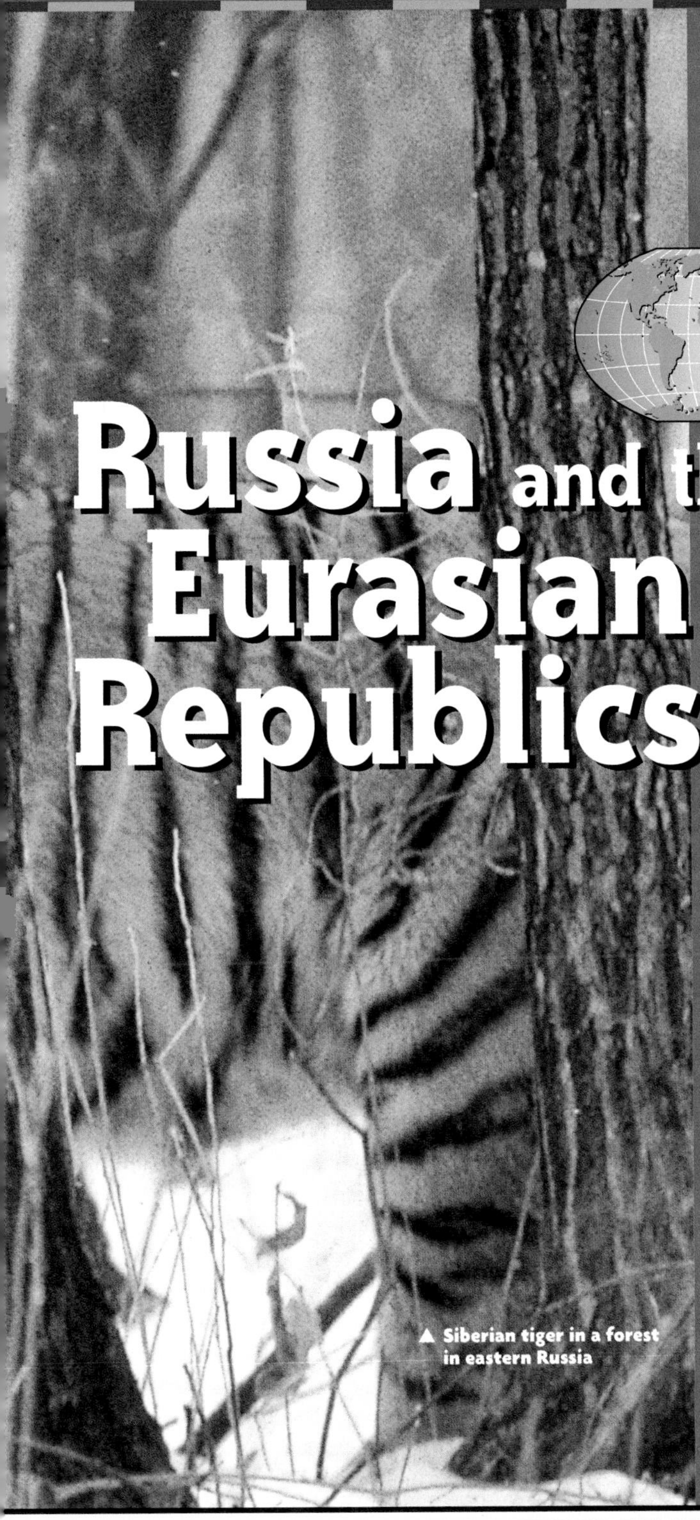

If you had to describe Russia in one word, that word would be BIG! Russia is the largest country in the world in area. Its almost 6.6 million square miles (17 million sq. km) are spread across two continents—Europe and Asia. As you can imagine, such a large country faces equally large challenges. In 1991 Russia emerged from the Soviet Union as an independent country. Since then it has been struggling to unite its many ethnic groups, set up a democratic government, and build a stable economy.

▲ Siberian tiger in a forest in eastern Russia

NGS ONLINE
www.nationalgeographic.com/education

391

Current Events Journal

Have students find Russia on the world political map in the Reference Atlas. **Ask:** **How would you describe Russia's size compared to other countries'?** *(very large)* Have students consider what impact this great size has on life in Russia. Ask them to write about such issues as transportation, communication, and government control over all regions.

NGS ONLINE
www.nationalgeographic.com/education

This online resource provides lesson plans, atlas updates, cartographic activities with interactive maps, an online map store, and geography links.

Unit Launch Activity

What Challenges Do Russians Face? In recent years, Russia has undergone many major changes: the end of Communist rule and the adoption of democratic government, the shrinking of the Russian Empire and the rise of ethnic conflict, and the transformation from a command to a market economy. Organize students into groups, and have each research one of the challenges facing the Russian people. Then have each group use problem-solving techniques to identify which challenge they think is the most important and design a three-part presentation: an explanation of what that challenge is, reasons that it is so difficult, and how to implement a solution to overcome those difficulties. Have each group present its findings to the class and be prepared to debate the effectiveness of the solution. L3

NATIONAL GEOGRAPHIC

REGIONAL ATLAS

LESSON PLAN

Using the Regional Atlas
These features and activities may be used as an introduction to the unit or as teaching tools throughout the course of the unit.

FOCUS

Objectives

1. Locate Russia and describe its landforms.
2. Discuss the impact that climate has on Russian life.
3. Describe the Russian economy.
4. Identify the chief characteristics of the Russian people.

5-Minute Precheck

Have students look at the physical map of Russia in the Reference Atlas. **Ask:** **Is Russia in Europe or in Asia?** *(both, because the Ural Mountains, which divide Europe and Asia, are inside Russia)* Ask if there are any other countries that are located on more than one continent. *(Turkey, which has a very small European section)*

Focus on:

Russia and the Eurasian Republics

THIS REGION spans the continents of Europe and Asia. It includes Russia—the world's largest country—and the neighboring independent republics of Armenia, Georgia, Azerbaijan, Kazakhstan, Uzbekistan, Turkmenistan, Kyrgyzstan, and Tajikistan. Russia and the Eurasian republics cover about 8 million square miles (20.7 million sq. km). This is greater than the size of Canada, the United States, and Mexico combined.

The Land

The region of Russia and the Eurasian republics stretches nearly halfway around the globe and includes many different landscapes. The Ural Mountains run north to south, dividing Russia into a European region and a much larger Asian region. West of the Urals is the fertile North European Plain—home to three-fourths of the country's population. East of the Urals lies Siberia, which means "sleeping land." Immense and sparsely populated, Siberia is an area of harsh, forbidding landscapes.

In the southern part of the region, the Caucasus Mountains rise along the borders of Russia, Georgia, and Azerbaijan. Mountains also pass through several republics in Central Asia. The Pamirs in Tajikistan have some of the region's highest peaks. The Tian Shan range in Kyrgyzstan holds some of the world's largest glaciers.

The Caspian Sea is actually a salt lake that lies at the base of the Caucasus Mountains in Russia's southwest. Farther east is Lake Baikal, the world's deepest lake. Many rivers wind through Russia and the Eurasian republics. Some of the rivers flow eastward, like the Amur, which forms Russia's border with China. Others, like the Volga, flow south through plains. The Lena, Yenisey, and Ob Rivers all flow north to the Arctic Ocean.

The Climate

Russia's far north is dominated by tundra, a treeless plain. Winters on the tundra are long, dark, and fiercely cold. During the brief summers, only the top few inches of soil thaw out. Deeper down is permafrost—permanently frozen ground.

South of the tundra are vast evergreen forests. This vast woodland area, known as the

Content Background

The Volga River Russia's Volga River is the longest river in Europe and the chief river of western Russia. From its source northwest of Moscow, the Volga flows nearly 2,200 miles (3,541 km) to the Caspian Sea. The area drained by the river holds a large part of Russia's population and for centuries has been a vital part of Russian agriculture. The river—navigable for most of its length—has long been one of the chief modes of transporting goods in Russia. Today river transport is hampered by strings of dams and reservoirs built along the river to provide cities with water and hydroelectric power. Still, the river and its tributaries carry more than half of the freight moved along Russia's inland waterways. Russians call the Volga River *"Volga Matushka,"* or "Mother Volga."

UNIT 5

Unit 5
Regional Atlas

Wildflowers and wooden churches on the North European Plain, in northwestern Russia ▼

◀ Young people strolling and singing in St. Petersburg

393

2 TEACH

Making Generalizations
Have students look at the photographs of Russia in the Regional Atlas. **Ask:** **How would you describe Russia?** *(both urban and rural)* **L1**

More About the Photos

Russian Churches The Russian Orthodox faith was based on the Eastern Orthodox Church of the ancient Byzantine Empire. As a result, Russian churches adopted the form and style of Byzantine churches. Over time, however, they took on their own unique style, particularly the bulbous "onion domes" evident in this photograph and the multicolored decorations that can be seen on the exterior of St. Basil's in Moscow.

Music in Russia Russian folk music—especially that played on the lutelike stringed instrument called the balalaika—has been heard throughout the world. Russia has gained its greatest fame, however, for the skill and artistry of its work in ballet.

Eyewitness to Geography

Siberia Writer Fen Montaigne recently completed a trek through north central Siberia and wrote about the contrasts between an industrialized city and the harsh but beautiful natural landscape there: "From the air Norilsk looks like a city on fire, with plumes of brown and gray smoke belching forth from dozens of smokestacks, merging into a thick pall that blots out the sun and can be seen from 50 miles away. . . . In Norilsk the air fills your mouth with the taste of burnt matches. . . ."

"After a two-hour flight we arrived at [our camp]. . . . Stepping out of the helicopter, we inhaled the cool, sweet air. A stone's throw away a waterfall rumbled; all around plateaus rose to nearly 5,000 feet, partly covered in verdant larch. . . . I was struck by the same feeling [my companion] had felt—the unsettling thrill of being dumped into a true wilderness."

Note-taking tip

Have students practice using abbreviations and symbols so that they can take notes more quickly. For instance, the first paragraph under The People could be written as "Pop. about 220 million, majority W of Urals (mildest climate, most fertile land)." Assign students another paragraph in the Regional Atlas to use for practicing this skill. Ask volunteers to write their abbreviated notes on the board, and have the class discuss which abbreviations are useful and which should be avoided because they obscure or confuse the original meaning.

More About the Photo

Russian Factories For several years in the 1990s, foreign companies were reluctant to invest in Russia because of uncertain political and economic conditions and corruption. In recent years, however, such companies as BMW, Ford, Caterpillar, Ikea, and Gillette have begun investing in new works there.

taiga, is the largest continuous stretch of forest on the earth. Snow blankets the taiga for as many as eight months of the year. Even farther south, the taiga gives way to flat grass-covered plains, or steppes. Here the climate is less harsh, and the soil is quite rich. For centuries, routes across these plains brought invading armies. Today the plains make up Russia's most important farming and industrial area.

The Economy

For many years, Russia and the Eurasian republics formed one state called the Soviet Union. It had an economy planned and run by Communist leaders. Wheat and other crops were grown on huge government-owned farms. The top economic priority was heavy industry, or the manufacturing of goods such as machinery and military equipment. Rich deposits of minerals, coal, and oil supplied the raw materials and energy for many industries. The Soviet push to industrialize, however, led to widespread pollution of the air, soil, and water.

Industrial growth was also more important than the needs of the people. Shortages of consumer goods—clothing and household products, for example—were common.

In the 1990s, when Russia and the other republics of the Soviet Union became independent countries, each took charge of its own economy. Today Russia and the Eurasian republics are struggling to make the change to a free market system, in which people run their own businesses and farms.

The People

About 220 million people live in Russia and the Eurasian republics. Russia has the region's largest population with about 145.5 million people. Climate and landscape affect where people live in Russia and the Eurasian republics. Most people in Russia live west of the Ural Mountains, where the climate is mildest and the land is most fertile.

Ethnic Groups Each of the republics has a major ethnic group, language, and culture. There are also many smaller groups in each republic. More than 100 different ethnic groups live throughout the region. Most Russians are descendants of Slavic peoples, or Slavs. They speak Russian and practice Eastern Orthodox Christianity. Various ethnic groups inhabit Armenia and Georgia. They practice their own forms of Christianity. Turkic ethnic groups (Uzbeks, Kazakhs, Turkmenis, and Azeris) are dominant in Central Asia. They have their own languages and practice the religion of Islam.

◀ Russian worker inspecting tractors in a factory

FUN FACTS

- **Moscow** Moscow's Metro carries more than 7 million passengers a day. Its 140 miles (225 km) of track link about 140 stations. These subway stations, which are the fanciest in the world, are decorated with chandeliers, marble panels, stained glass, paintings, and statues.
- **Taiga** Fully one-third of the world's forests lie across northern Russia in a huge expanse known as the taiga. It covers an area roughly 33 times larger than the Amazon rain forest.
- **Siberia** In northern Siberia, the permafrost layer is about 5,250 feet (1,600 m) thick.

The Arts The arts of Russia and the Eurasian republics include architecture, painting, music, and dance. Each republic has its own rich heritage. You have probably seen pictures of Russia's onion-domed churches and heard the classical music of Peter Tchaikovsky and other Russian composers. Ancient churches with drumlike tops and bells are scattered across the rugged countryside of Armenia and Georgia. In the Central Asian republics, beautiful tiles in swirling patterns decorate Islamic mosques.

▼ Church of the Resurrection in St. Petersburg, Russia

Russia

Data Bits

Automobiles per 1,000 people	120
Television sets per 1,000 people	421
Democratic elections	Yes

Ethnic Makeup

World Ranking

Population: Urban vs. Rural

Sources: *World Desk Reference*, 2000; *World Development Indicators*, 2002; *The World Almanac*, 2004.

Exploring the Region

1. Why might Russia's north-flowing rivers be difficult to travel in winter?
2. Why would it be hard to grow crops on the tundra?
3. What was the top economic priority of Communist leaders?
4. To which ethnic group do most Russians belong?

3 ASSESS

Assign the Exploring the Region questions as homework or as an in-class activity.

Reteach
Have students work in small groups to write 10 questions about the content in the Regional Atlas. Then have groups use their questions to quiz other groups.

Enrich
Have students research and report on the current state of the Russian transition to the free enterprise system.

4 CLOSE

Reading Strategy

Outlining Have students prepare an outline of the Regional Atlas by writing the headings in their notebooks and listing key facts under each heading.

Answers to Exploring the Region

1. Because the climate is so cold, the rivers freeze over.
2. Because even in summers, only the top few inches of soil thaw.
3. heavy industry
4. Slavic peoples

Lesson Plan

Using the Regional Atlas

These features and activities may be used as an introduction to the unit or as teaching tools throughout the course of the unit.

Focus

Objectives

1. Locate Russia and describe its landforms and climates.
2. Explain where people live in Russia.

5-Minute Precheck

Have students use their fingers to trace on the physical map the course of the following rivers and identify the bodies of water into which they empty: Volga *(Caspian Sea)*, Ob *(Kara Sea)*, N. Dvina *(Berents Sea)*, Don *(Black Sea)*, Lena *(Laptev Sea)*.

More About the Profile

In order to show a variety of physical features, this cross section begins at the Belarus-Russia border and ends at the Kamchatka Peninsula along 55°N latitude.

NATIONAL GEOGRAPHIC

Regional Atlas

Russia and the Eurasian Republics

Physical

National capital
Mountain peak

0 mi. 1,000
0 km 1,000
Two-Point Equidistant projection

Regional Atlas Activity

Analyzing Population Write the following information on the board:

	Russia	World Average
Birthrate per 1,000 people	9.3	25.0
Death rate per 1,000 people	15.0	9.3
Rate of natural increase per 1,000 people	–5.7	15.7

Ask: **What can you conclude about the population of Russia from these statistics? Why?** *(It is declining because there are fewer births per 1,000 people than deaths.)* **How does this compare to the world in general?** *(The Russian population is declining, but the population of the world in general is increasing—birthrate far exceeds death rate.)* **L2**

EE4 Human Systems: Standards 9, 13, 14

UNIT 5

Political

⊛ National capital
▲ Mountain peak

0 mi. 1,000
0 km 1,000
Two-Point Equidistant projection

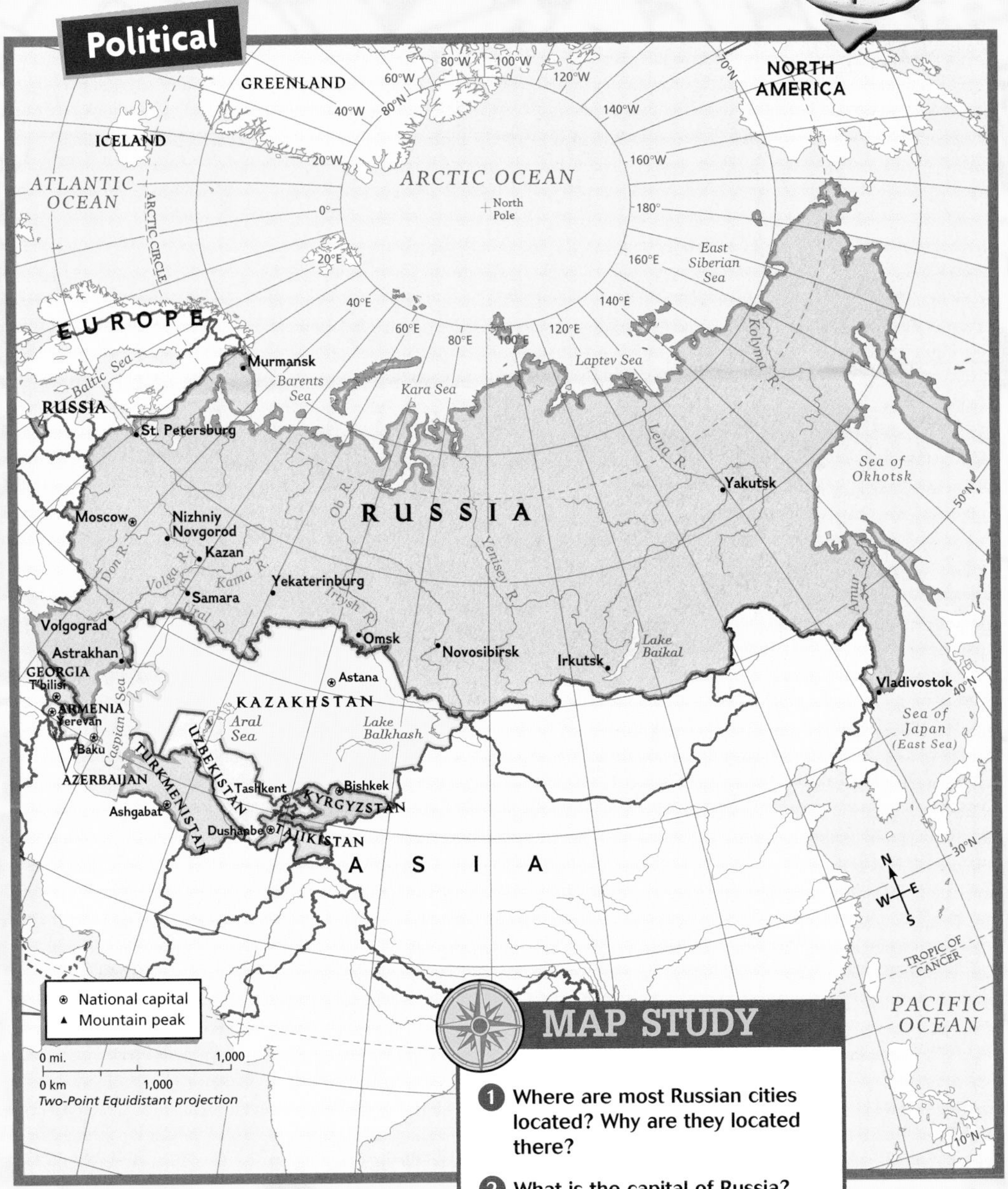

MAP STUDY

1. Where are most Russian cities located? Why are they located there?
2. What is the capital of Russia?

Unit 5

2 TEACH

Making Comparisons Have students look at the Russian political map and the map of the Russian winter in this Regional Atlas. Have them compare the Russian winter in four different Russian cities. Then have them speculate on the impact that these differences might have on life in the different cities. **L1**

Interdisciplinary Connections

History The name *Russia* comes from *Rus*—the name that people gave to the Vikings who started invading the area in the A.D. 800s. *Rus* is probably a mispronunciation of what the Vikings called themselves—*rothsmen,* or "rowers."

MAP STUDY

Answers

1. the south of Russia; the climate is warmer
2. Moscow

Skills Practice

On what body of water is Russia's largest coastline? *(Arctic Ocean)*

Regional Atlas Activity

Researching Features Organize students into groups and assign each group one of the landforms or bodies of water in Russia. For example, one group could be assigned the Ural Mountains, another the Volga River, and so on. Have each group conduct research about their physical feature with the goal of explaining how that feature affects the lives of Russians. They can look at the economic and cultural benefits of the feature or the obstacles to development that the feature offers. Have the groups also find information about how the people of Russia affect that geographical feature through their actions. After concluding their research, have each group prepare a bulletin board display about their feature. **L2**

EE5 Environment and Society: Standards 15, 16

NATIONAL GEOGRAPHIC REGIONAL ATLAS

Russia

The Russian Winter

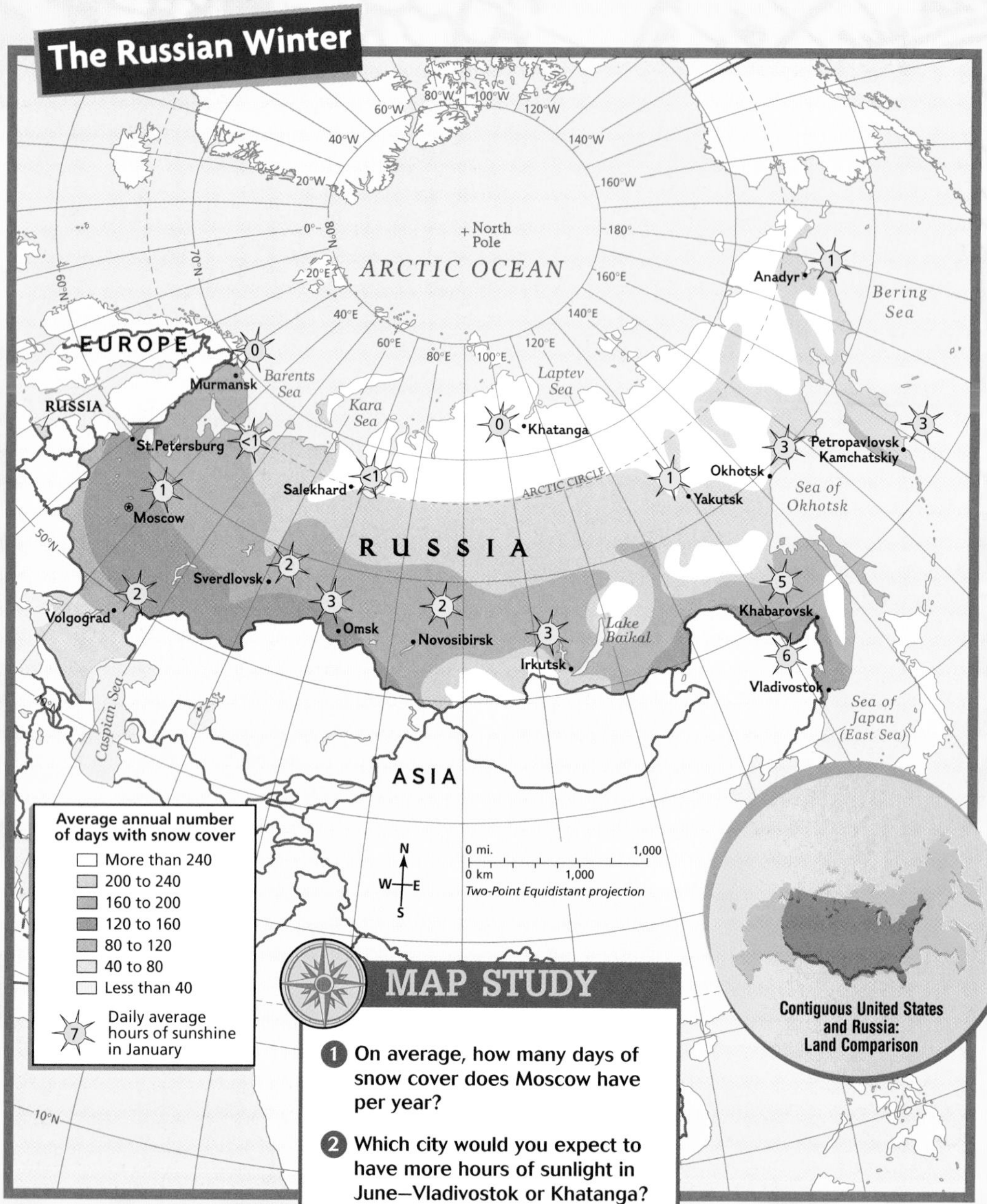

ARCTIC OCEAN
North Pole
EUROPE
RUSSIA
Barents Sea
Kara Sea
Laptev Sea
Bering Sea
Sea of Okhotsk
Sea of Japan (East Sea)
Caspian Sea
Lake Baikal
ARCTIC CIRCLE
R U S S I A
ASIA
Murmansk 0
St. Petersburg <1
Moscow 1
Volgograd 2
Sverdlovsk 2
Salekhard <1
Omsk 3
Novosibirsk 2
Irkutsk 3
Khatanga 0
Yakutsk 1
Okhotsk 3
Petropavlovsk Kamchatskiy 3
Anadyr 1
Khabarovsk 5
Vladivostok 6

Average annual number of days with snow cover
- More than 240
- 200 to 240
- 160 to 200
- 120 to 160
- 80 to 120
- 40 to 80
- Less than 40
- Daily average hours of sunshine in January

0 mi. 1,000
0 km 1,000
Two-Point Equidistant projection

Contiguous United States and Russia: Land Comparison

MAP STUDY

1. On average, how many days of snow cover does Moscow have per year?
2. Which city would you expect to have more hours of sunlight in June—Vladivostok or Khatanga?

Did You Know 

The potato is a staple of the Russian diet. It was not always so popular, however. When the government ordered peasants to plant potatoes on common ground in 1840, "anti-potato" riots broke out in 10 Russian provinces.

Travel Guide 

Guests in Russia often bring gifts of flowers to their hosts. They always give an odd number of flowers, however, since an even number of flowers is used for funerals.

MAP STUDY

Answers

1. 120 to 160 days
2. Khatanga

Skills Practice

How many hours of sunshine does Moscow have daily in January? *(1 hour)*

Regional Atlas Activity

Making Comparisons Have your students identify the Russian cities located above latitude 60°N on this map. Then have them look at other maps in the Reference Atlas to find at least five other cities around the world located above 60°N. Afterwards, students should use the Internet to find out what today's temperature is in each city. Have your students organize their information into a chart that lists the cities (and their countries), their latitude and longitude, and their temperatures. **Ask: Which city has the lowest and which has the highest temperature? How does it compare to the temperature in your own location? What factors might cause the differences in temperatures? L2**

EE1 The World in Spatial Terms: Standards 1, 2, 3

Unit 5

Russia's Geo Extremes

1. **HIGHEST POINT** Mount Elbrus 18,510 ft. (5,642 m) high
2. **LOWEST POINT** Caspian Sea 92 ft. (28 m) below sea level
3. **LONGEST RIVER** Ob-Irtysh 3,362 mi. (5,411 km) long
4. **LARGEST LAKE** Caspian Sea 143,244 sq. mi. (371,000 sq. km)
5. **DEEPEST LAKE** Lake Baikal 5,315 ft. (1,620 m) deep
6. **LARGEST ISLAND** Sakhalin 29,500 sq.mi. (76,405 sq. km)

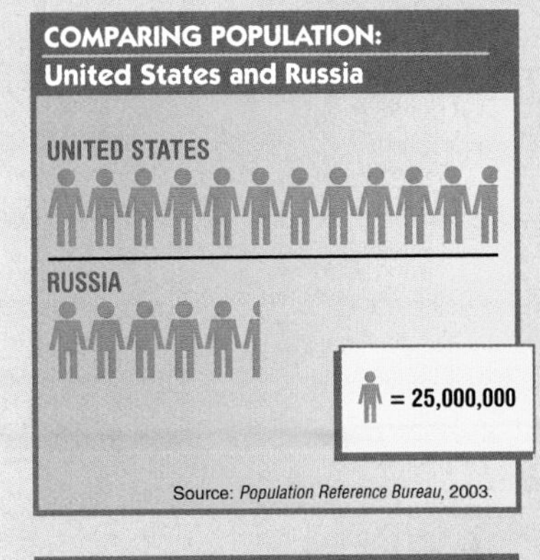

Source: *Population Reference Bureau*, 2003.

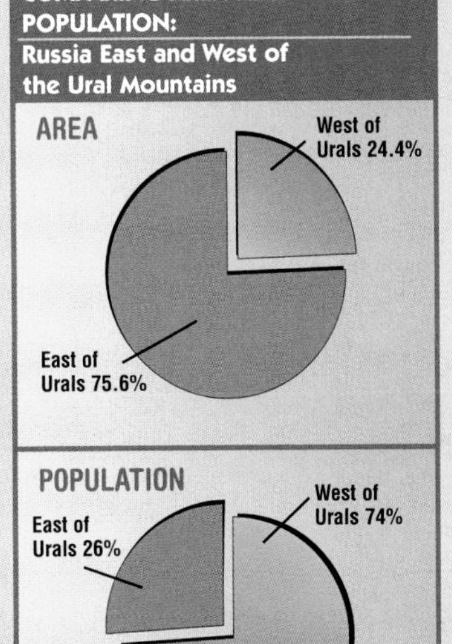

Source: *The Hammond Citation World Atlas*, 1999.

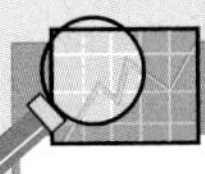

GRAPHIC STUDY

1. What two "extremes" does the Caspian Sea lay claim to?
2. What percentage of Russia's people live west of the Ural Mountains?

Unit 5
Regional Atlas

GRAPHIC STUDY

Answers

1. lowest point and largest lake
2. 74 percent

Skills Practice

How does Russia compare to the United States in terms of size? *(Russia is much larger.)* How does Russia compare to the United States in terms of population? *(Russia has about half the population of the United States.)*

Did You Know?

Lake Baikal is so deep that it would take an entire year for the volume of water from all the rivers on the earth to fill it.

Regional Atlas Activity

Ethnic Distribution Write the following information on the board: Belarus—11.4 percent; Estonia—28.1 percent; Kazakhstan—34.7 percent; Kyrgyzstan—12.5 percent; Latvia—29.6 percent; Lithuania—8.2 percent; Moldova—12.9 percent; Ukraine—20 percent. Point out that the percentages reflect the proportion of ethnic Russians living in each of these countries. Have students rank the countries according to these percentages, from highest to lowest. *(Kazakhstan, Latvia, Estonia, Ukraine, Moldova, Kyrgyzstan, Belarus, Lithuania)* **Ask:** What problems might be caused by having a high proportion of Russians in a country? *(possible tension with other ethnic groups within the country)* L1

EE4 Human Systems: Standards 9, 13, 14

Regional Atlas

Did You Know

Georgia has been controlled by many different peoples. The Byzantine Empire and Persia fought over this land, and in A.D. 645 it was conquered by the Arabs. Later, Georgia was part of the Mongol and Ottoman Empires and the Soviet Union.

Interdisciplinary Connections

Literature The folklore of Kyrgyzstan is preserved in the *Manas,* the longest oral chronicle of its kind in the world. It tells the adventures of the hero Manas the Strong.

Cultural Kaleidoscope

Kazakhstan The Kazakhs preserve many ancient traditions. Families sit on carpets and eat from low tables. Almost everyone can play the domras—a two-stringed musical instrument.

Assess

Organize students into groups. Have groups use the maps and graphs from this unit's Regional Atlas to quiz one another about Russia and the Eurasian Republics.

Country Profiles

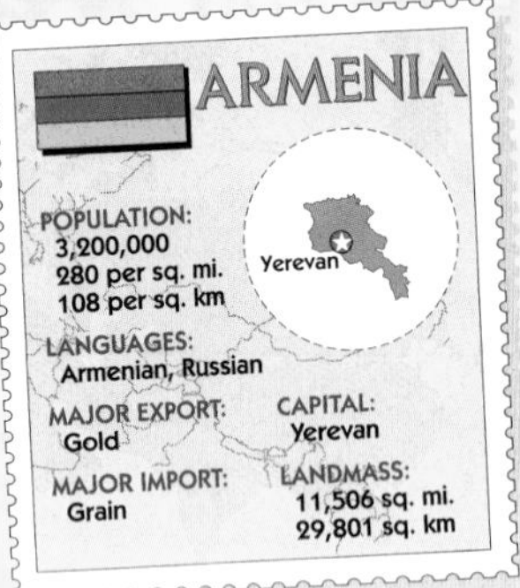

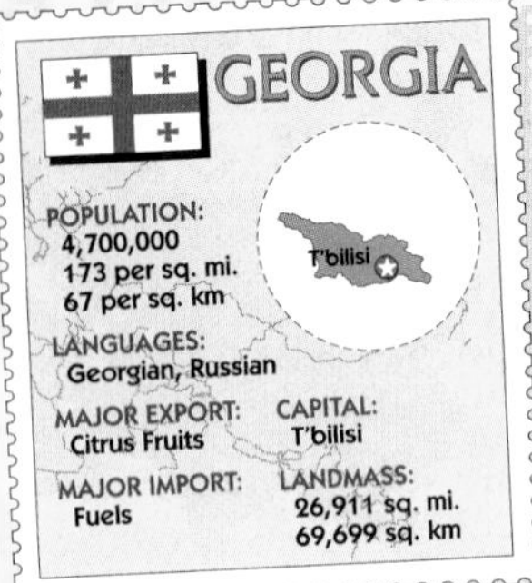

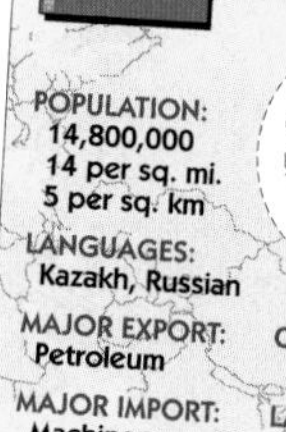

KYRGYZSTAN
POPULATION:
5,000,000
66 per sq. mi.
25 per sq. km
Bishkek
LANGUAGES:
Kirghiz, Russian
MAJOR EXPORT:
Cotton
CAPITAL:
Bishkek
MAJOR IMPORT:
Grain
LANDMASS:
76,641 sq. mi.
198,500 sq. km

▼ **Reindeer pulling sled across the tundra, Siberia**

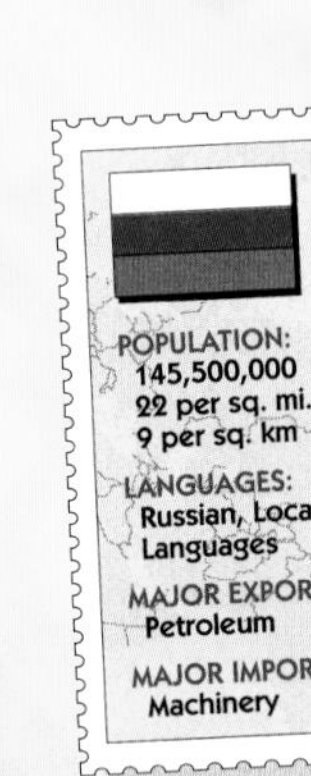

RUSSIA
POPULATION:
145,500,000
22 per sq. mi.
9 per sq. km
Moscow
LANGUAGES:
Russian, Local Languages
MAJOR EXPORT:
Petroleum
CAPITAL:
Moscow
MAJOR IMPORT:
Machinery
LANDMASS:
6,592,819 sq. mi.
17,075,401 sq. km

Countries and flags not drawn to scale

Fun Facts

- **Russia** Russian names often end in "ov" or "vich." *Ov* simply means "son of." The name *Ivanov* means "son of Ivan." The suffix "vich" also refers to the father's name, but it was originally restricted to only those in the upper class. So someone with the last name of *Ivanovich* might have an ancestor who was a dignitary named Ivan.
- **Georgia** After a wedding ceremony in Georgia, the bride and groom traditionally return to the groom's house. When the couple crosses the threshold, they stomp on a ceramic plate. The one who breaks the plate first will be the "boss" in the marriage. The number of broken pieces represents the number of problems the couple may later face together.

For more information on countries in this region, refer to the Nations of the World Data Bank in the Appendix.

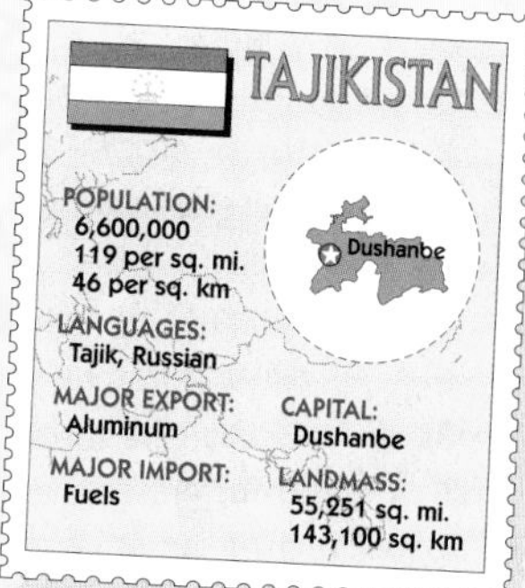

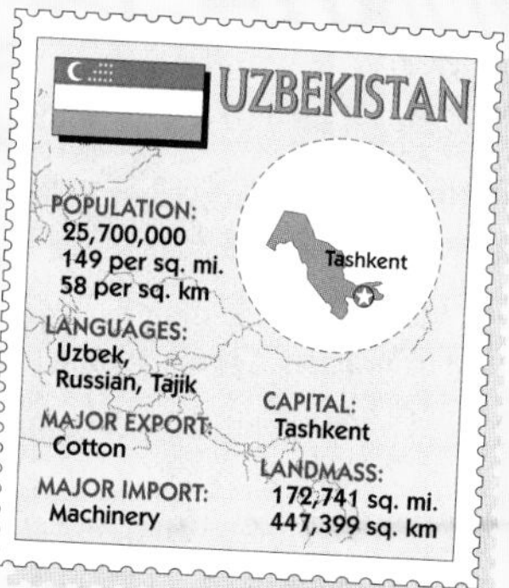

BUILDING CITIZENSHIP

Initiative Under communism, the government is the main employer. Many people no longer had a steady income when the Soviet Union broke apart. The government could no longer take care of them. People had to figure out on their own how to solve the problem of making enough money to feed their families. In other words, they had to show initiative.

Describe a time when you showed initiative to solve a challenge you faced.

You can develop initiative with practice. Use the problem-solving process to identify a business you could start alone or with friends. Gather information, list and consider your options, and consider the advantages and disadvantages. Then write a paragraph about the business you chose.

Teens washing cars to earn money ▼

BUILDING CITIZENSHIP

Answer Student answers will vary. You can explain that in order to have initiative, it helps to have a stable environment in which to start. When the Soviet Union collapsed and switched to a free market economy, there were no laws or government administration in place to help people who wanted to take advantage of the new economic climate. Without that support, it has been difficult for Russians to solve their financial problems.

Write About It! Students can work in groups to decide on a business. They should research what finances they would need to start it, if they would need to contact government or private agencies, who their competition would be, where they would locate, and to whom they would market.

4 CLOSE

Reading Strategy

Organizing Information Have students make a two-column chart in their notebooks. Have them write the headings "European Russia" and "Asian Russia" at the top of each column. Then have them study the text, maps, and graphs in the Regional Atlas and fill in information about each part of Russia under the appropriate heading. They might include such details as climate and landforms, cities, cultural information, populations, economics, and so on.

Regional Atlas Activity

Drawing Conclusions Uzbekistan, Turkmenistan, and Tajikistan were countries that few people knew about until they suddenly became critical players in the worldwide crisis caused by terrorist actions in New York and Washington, D.C., on September 11, 2001. The three countries all share a border with Afghanistan, a key target in the fight against the terrorists. Until they were thrust into the spotlight, these Islamic countries were trying to overcome their own problems. Like other former Soviet republics, their economies have suffered since independence, and they are also troubled by ethnic and religious conflicts. **Ask:** **What event has changed Americans' opinions of the importance of Uzbekistan, Turkmenistan, and Tajikistan? Why has the geographic location of these countries become important since the September 11 attacks?** L2

Chapter 14 Resources

Note: The following materials may be used when teaching Chapter 14.
Section level support materials are shown at point of use in the margins of the Teacher Wraparound Edition.

Timesaving Tools

TeacherWorks™ All-In-One Planner and Resource Center

- **Interactive Teacher Edition** See the **Interactive Teacher Edition** CD-ROM to electronically integrate your Teacher Wraparound Edition and blackline masters.
- **Interactive Lesson Planner** Organize your week, month, semester, or year with all the lesson helps you need. The **Interactive Lesson Planner** CD-ROM contains all Chapter 14 resources.

Use Glencoe's **Presentation Plus!** multimedia teacher tool to easily present dynamic lessons that visually excite your students. Using Microsoft PowerPoint® you can customize the presentations to create your own personalized lessons.

TEACHING TRANSPARENCIES

Graphic Organizer Transparency 2 L2

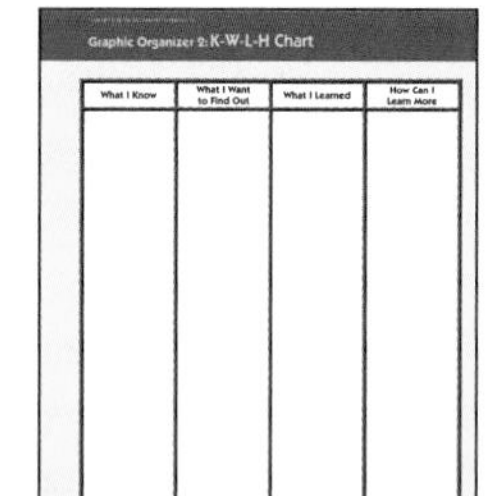

In-text Map Transparency L1

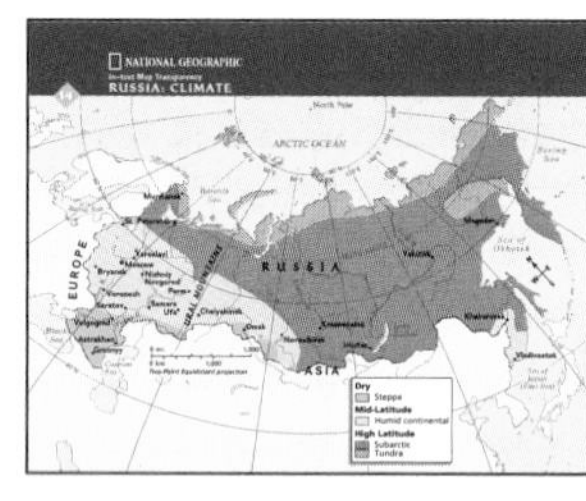

FOLDABLES™ Study Organizer

Dinah Zike's Foldables

Foldables are three-dimensional, interactive graphic organizers that help students practice basic writing skills, review key vocabulary terms, and identify main ideas. Additional chapter activities can be found in the ***Reading and Study Skills Foldables*** booklet.

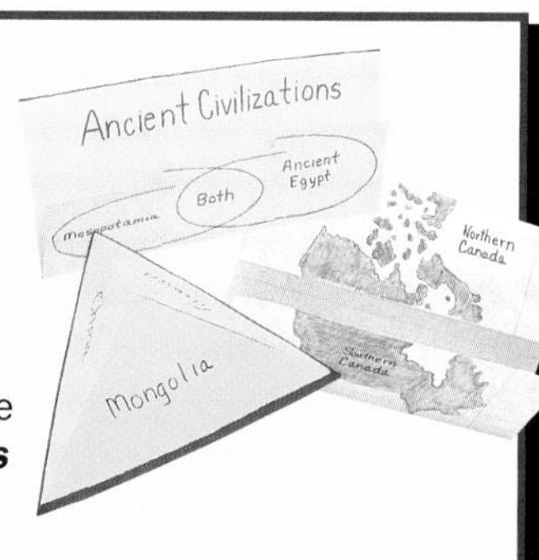

MAP AND GEOGRAPHY SKILLS

Chapter Map Activity L2

GeoLab Activity L2

READING SUPPORT

Vocabulary Activity L1

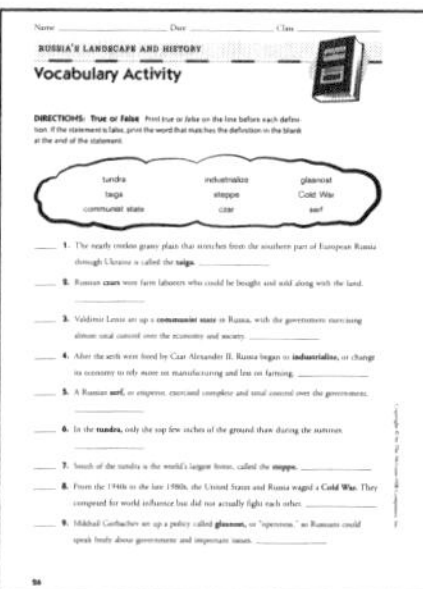

Workbook Activity L1

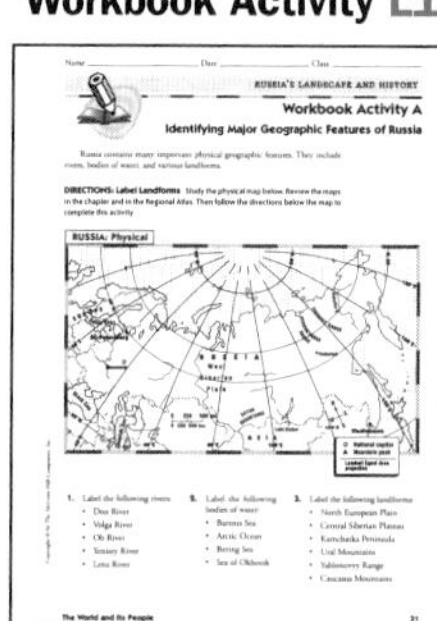

Reading and Writing Skills Activity L1

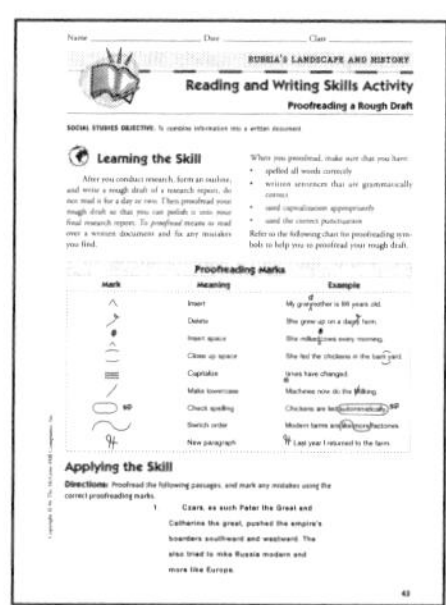

DIFFERENTIATED INSTRUCTION

Use these review and reinforcement materials to help less-proficient readers, English learners, and gifted and talented students.

Reteaching Activity L1

Chapter Skills Review L2

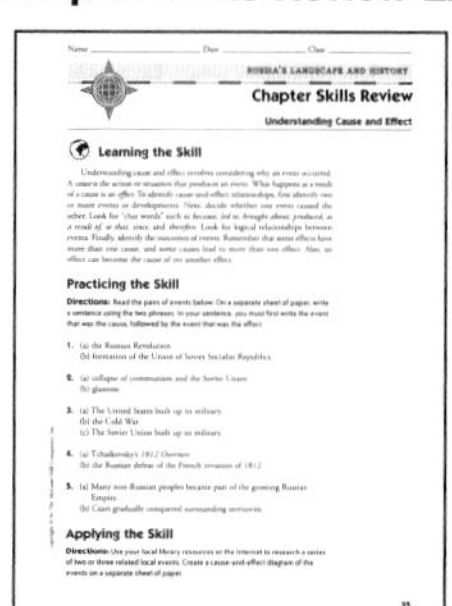

Cooperative Learning Activity L1/ELL

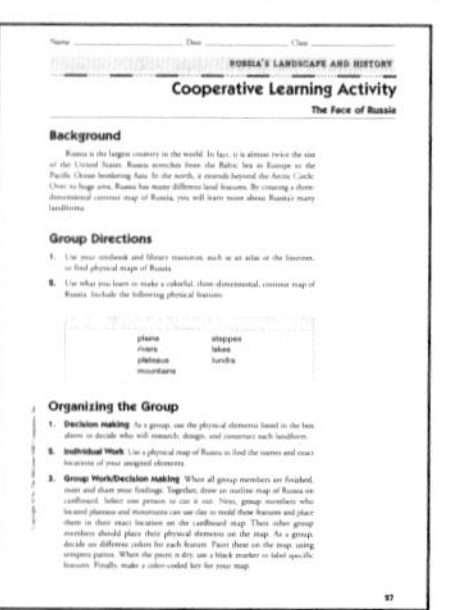

Enrichment Activity L3

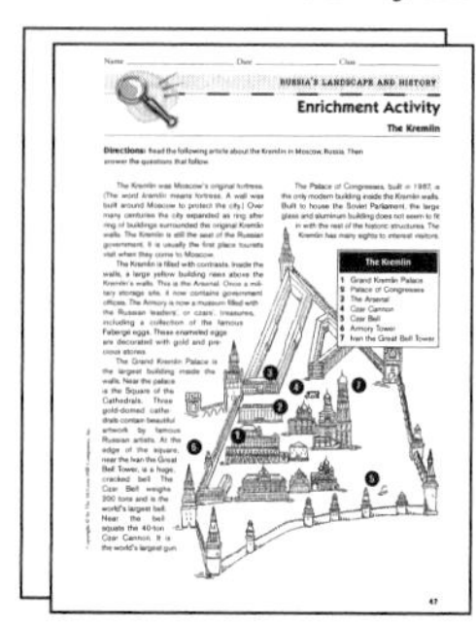

ASSESSMENT

Chapter Test, Form A L2

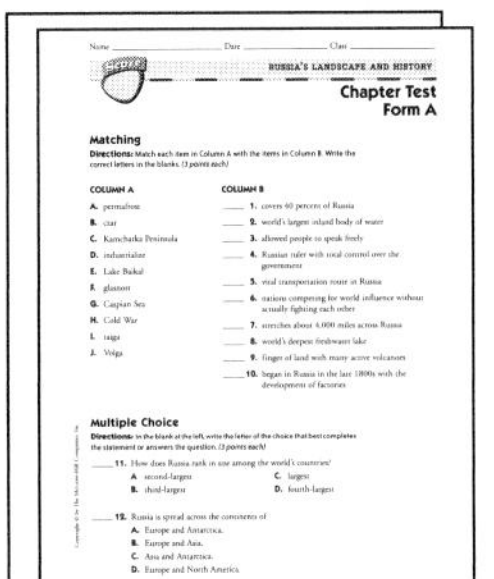

Chapter Test, Form B L2

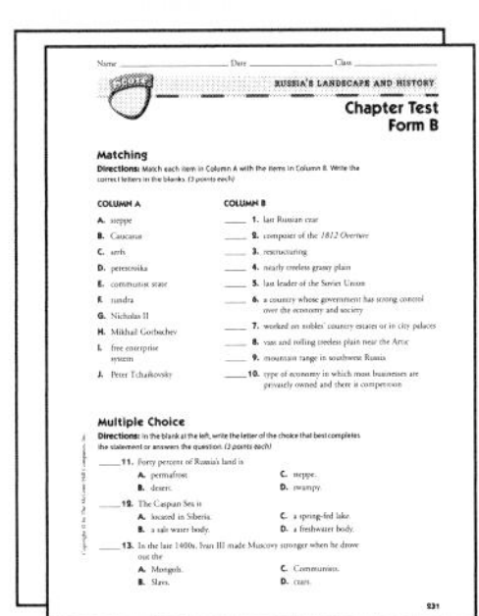

Performance Assessment Activity L1/ELL

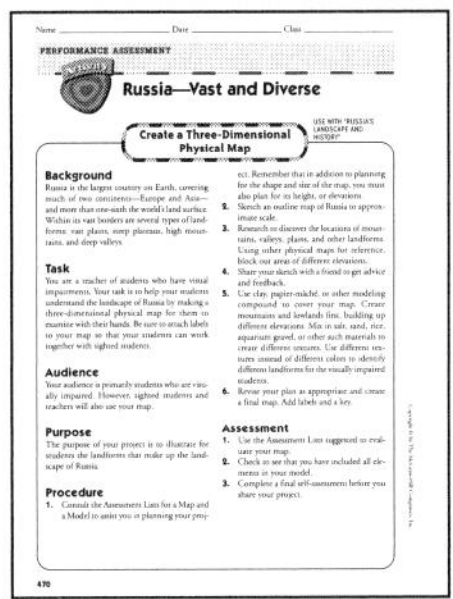

ExamView® Pro Testmaker CD-ROM

STANDARDIZED ASSESSMENT SKILLS

Critical Thinking Skills Activity L2

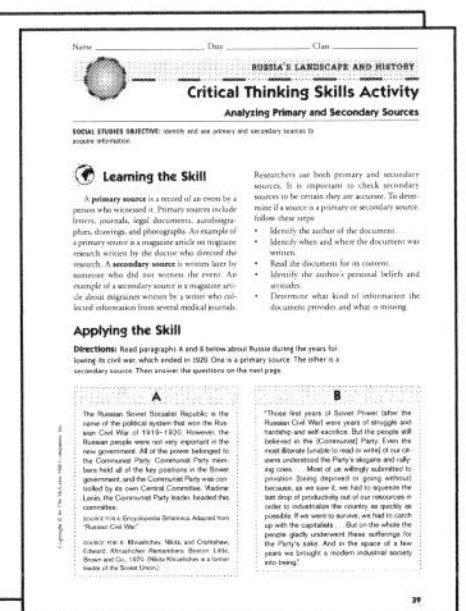

Map and Graph Skills Activity L2

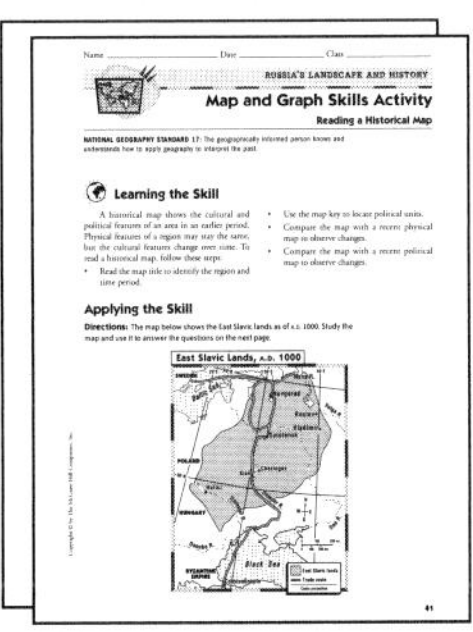

Standardized Test Skills Practice Workbook Activity L2

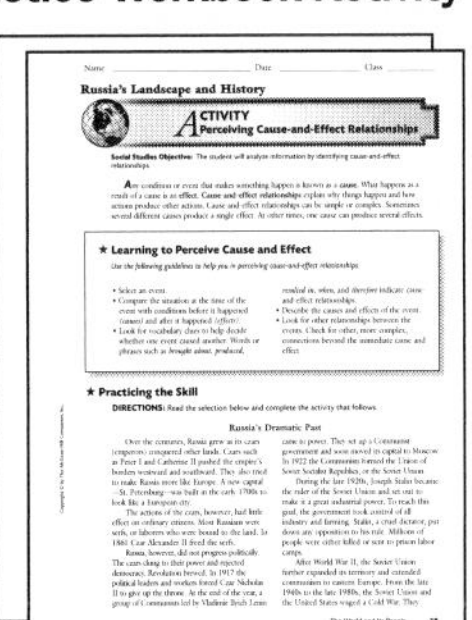

HOME INVOLVEMENT

Take-Home Review Activity L1

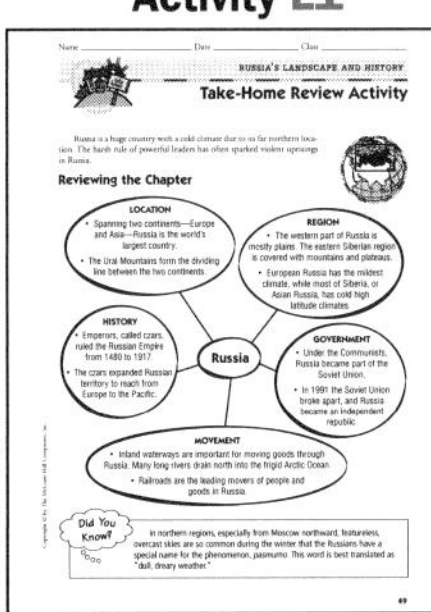

MULTIMEDIA

- National Geographic's The World and Its People
- MindJogger Videoquiz
- Vocabulary PuzzleMaker CD-ROM
- Interactive Tutor Self-Assessment CD-ROM
- ExamView® Pro Testmaker CD-ROM
- TeacherWorks CD-ROM
- StudentWorks CD-ROM
- Skillbuilder Interactive Workbook CD-ROM, Level 1
- Presentation Plus! CD-ROM
- Audio Program

SPANISH RESOURCES

The following Spanish language materials are available in the Spanish Resources binder:

- Spanish Summaries
- Spanish Vocabulary Activities
- Spanish Guided Reading Activities
- Spanish Quizzes and Tests
- Spanish Take-Home Review Activities
- Spanish Reteaching Activities

Meeting National Standards

Geography for Life

The following standards are covered in Chapter 14:

Section 1 **EE1 The World in Spatial Terms: Standards 1, 2, 3**

EE2 Places and Regions: Standards 4, 5, 6, 7, 8

EE5 Environment and Society: Standards 15, 16

Section 2 **EE4 Human Systems: Standards 9, 10, 12, 13, 14**

State and Local Objectives

Chapter 14 Planning Guide

SECTION RESOURCES

Daily Objectives	Reproducible Resources	Multimedia Resources
Section 1 **A Vast Land** 1. Describe the landforms and climates found in Russia. 2. Compare the geography of European Russia to that of Russia east of the Urals.	Reproducible Lesson Plan Daily Lecture and Discussion Notes Note-taking Guide Guided Reading Activity* Reading Essentials and Study Guide* Section Quiz*	Daily Focus Skills Transparency In-text Map Transparency Vocabulary PuzzleMaker CD-ROM Interactive Tutor Self-Assessment CD-ROM ExamView® Pro Testmaker CD-ROM Presentation Plus! CD-ROM
Section 2 **A Troubled History** 1. Describe life in Russia under the czars. 2. Discuss life in Russia under Communist rule. 3. Explain why the Soviet Union collapsed.	Reproducible Lesson Plan Daily Lecture and Discussion Notes Note-taking Guide Guided Reading Activity* Reading Essentials and Study Guide* Section Quiz*	Daily Focus Skills Transparency GeoQuiz Transparency Vocabulary PuzzleMaker CD-ROM Interactive Tutor Self-Assessment CD-ROM ExamView® Pro Testmaker CD-ROM Presentation Plus! CD-ROM MindJogger Videoquiz

00:00 **Out of Time?** Assign the **Reading Essentials and Study Guide*** for this chapter.

*Also available in Spanish

KEY TO ABILITY LEVELS

Teaching strategies have been coded for varying learning styles and abilities.

L1 **BASIC** activities for all students
L2 **AVERAGE** activities for average to above-average students
L3 **CHALLENGING** activities for above-average students
ELL **ENGLISH LANGUAGE LEARNER** activities

KEY TO TEACHING RESOURCES

Blackline Master
CD-ROM
Transparency
Videocassette
Block Scheduling
DVD

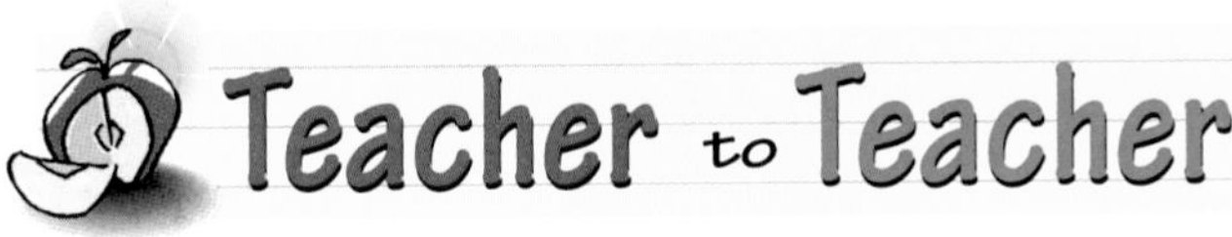

ABC's of Russia

Wanda J. Petersen
Landrum Middle School
Ponte Vedra, Florida

With a partner, have students create an ABC book on Russia. Students should match the letters of the alphabet to a particular aspect of Russia. For example, *K* could stand for *Kremlin,* followed by a sentence or two describing the Kremlin. Each item should be accompanied by an illustration, whether a photograph or drawing. Students should use standard grammar, spelling, sentence structure, and punctuation in the written portions of their booklets. Students can compile the booklets on a computer, including a title page and front and back covers. The booklets can be bound and the title pages laminated and then donated to an elementary school library.

Meeting Special Needs

In addition to the Differentiated Instruction strategies found in each section, the following resources are also suitable for your special needs students:

- ***ExamView*® *Pro Testmaker CD-ROM*** allows teachers to tailor tests by reducing answer choices.
- The ***Audio Program*** includes the entire narrative of the student edition so that less-proficient readers can listen to the words as they read them.
- The ***Reading Essentials and Study Guide*** provides the same content as the student edition but is written two grade levels below the textbook.
- ***Guided Reading Activities*** give less-proficient readers point-by-point instructions to increase comprehension as they read each textbook section.
- ***Enrichment Activities*** include a stimulating collection of readings and activities for gifted and talented students.

NATIONAL GEOGRAPHIC TEACHER'S CORNER

Index to National Geographic Magazine:

The following articles may be used for research relating to this chapter:

- "Remote Russia: Expedition to the Putorana Plateau," by Fen Montaigne, November 2000.
- "The Caspian Sea," by Robert Cullen, May 1999.
- "Russia's Iron Road," by Fen Montaigne, June 1998.

National Geographic Society Products:

To order the following products for use with this chapter, call National Geographic Society at 1-800-368-2728:

- *Rise and Fall of the Soviet Union* (Video)
- *Russia: After the U.S.S.R.* (Video)
- *1917: Revolution in Russia* (Video)

NGS ONLINE

Access National Geographic's Web site for current events, activities, links, interactive features, and archives.
www.nationalgeographic.com

Find the latest coverage of geography in the news, atlas updates, cartographic activities with interactive maps, an online map store, and links at www.nationalgeographic.com/maps

Use our Web site for additional resources. All essential content is covered in the Student Edition.

You and your students can visit twip.glencoe.com, the Web site companion to *The World and Its People.* This innovative integration of electronic and print media offers your students a wealth of opportunities. The student text directs students to the Web site for the following options:

- Chapter Overviews
- Student Web Activities
- Self-Check Quizzes
- Textbook Updates

Answers are provided for you in the Web Activity Lesson Plan. Additional Web resources and Interactive Tutor puzzles are also available.

Social Studies Online

Introduce students to chapter content and key terms by having them access Chapter Overview 14 at twip.glencoe.com

Chapter Objectives

1. Identify the location and the landforms of Russia.
2. Compare Russia under the czars and the Communists.
3. Explain why the Soviet Union collapsed.

GLENCOE TECHNOLOGY

NATIONAL GEOGRAPHIC

The World and Its People Video Program

Chapter 15 Russia—Past and Present

The following segments enhance the study of this chapter:

- **Return to Russia**
- **Circus School**

MindJogger Videoquiz

Use MindJogger Videoquiz to preview the Chapter 14 content.

Both programs available in DVD and VHS

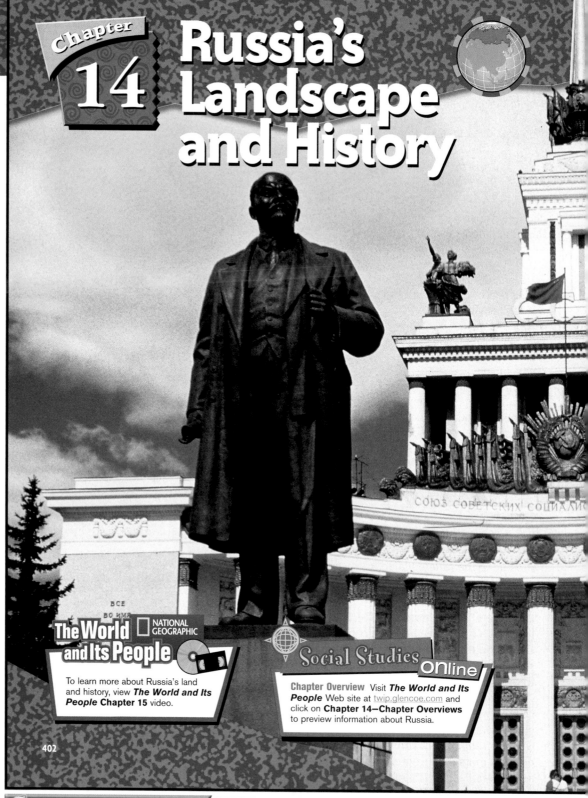

Chapter 14 Russia's Landscape and History

The World and Its People NATIONAL GEOGRAPHIC

To learn more about Russia's land and history, view ***The World and Its People*** **Chapter 15** video.

Social Studies Online

Chapter Overview Visit ***The World and Its People*** Web site at twip.glencoe.com and click on **Chapter 14–Chapter Overviews** to preview information about Russia.

402

Reading Strategy Purpose for Reading

Free Writes are used to explore student background knowledge and engage students. Have students look at the photographs in the chapter. **Ask:** **Based on these photographs, how does life in Russia look similar to life in your country? What aspects of life look different?** Suggest that students write their responses to these questions in their notebooks. Emphasize that there are no wrong answers to this activity. Conclude the activity by explaining that students will learn about Russia's geography and history in this chapter. **L1**

Categorizing Information When you group information into categories, it is easier to make sense of what you are learning. Make this foldable to help you learn about Russia's past and present.

Step 1 Fold one sheet of paper in half from top to bottom.

Step 2 Fold it in half again from side to side.

Step 3 Unfold the paper once. Cut up the inside fold of the top flap only.

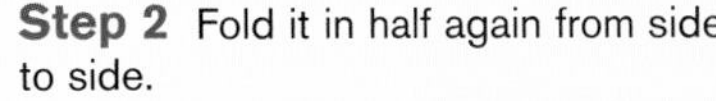

This cut will make two tabs.

Step 4 Turn the paper and sketch a map of the Soviet Union and Russia on the front tabs. Label your foldable as shown.

Reading and Writing As you read the chapter, write under the appropriate flaps of your foldable what you learn about the former Soviet Union and present-day Russia.

Why It Matters

A New Government

Russia is a land rich in natural resources but has a troubled political history. The various peoples in Russia have had little experience with hands-on government. This experience is needed for a stable democracy to work. On the other hand, a strong central government is needed to create policies to prevent continued air and water pollution and to build up the economy. How will Russia meet both of these aims? The answer is important to us all.

Statue of Vladimir Lenin at the Exhibition of Economic Achievement, Moscow, Russia

About the Photo

Although the Soviet Union collapsed in 1991, statues of Vladimir Lenin—the leader of the Russian Revolution and founder of the communist Soviet state—are still very common in Russia, as are other monuments to communism honoring everything from leaders and war heroes to farmers and their equipment. The Exhibition of Economic Achievement was originally used in 1939 as an agricultural exposition, celebrating the triumphs of Russia under the rule of Joseph Stalin. Have your students think of statues or monuments in your town. Whom do these memorials commemorate and why? What are the similarities and differences in the ways the two societies use monuments?

Dinah Zike's Foldables

Purpose This foldable will help students organize information about Russia's past and present. When grouping information from the chapter into two categories—*Past:* Soviet Union and *Present:* Russia—students are required to determine what is relevant factual information and group this data into the appropriate categories.

Have students complete the ***Reading and Study Skills Foldables*** activity for this chapter.

Why It Matters

Organize students into groups to investigate the following environmental issues in Russia: air pollution, water pollution, and land pollution. Have each group conduct research to identify what caused the problem, the extent of the problem, what steps the Russian government is taking to address the problem, what help Russia is receiving from outside organizations and countries, and the prospects for improving the situation. Have each group create a display showing the results of their findings.

1 Focus

Section Objectives

1. Describe the landforms and climates found in Russia.
2. Compare the geography of European Russia to that of Russia east of the Urals.

BELLRINGER Skillbuilder Activity

Project transparency and have students answer the question.

Daily Focus Skills Transparency

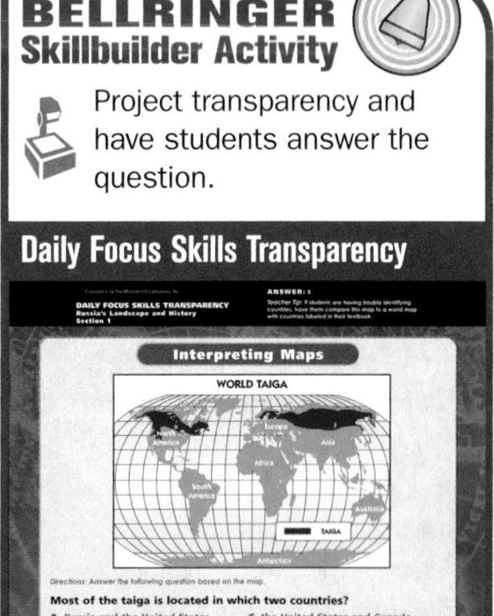

Reading Preview

■ **Activating Prior Knowledge** Before students look at this section, ask them what animals they think live in Russia. Then have them read the Exploring Our World feature. **Ask:** **Are you surprised that tigers live in Russia?** Have them write other facts about Russia that surprise them.

■ **Preteaching Vocabulary** Have students speculate on the meaning of *tundra.* Then ask them to find the term in the text to check the definition.

Guide to Reading

Main Idea

Russia is a huge country with a cold climate due to its far northern location.

Terms to Know

- steppe
- tundra
- permafrost
- taiga

Reading Strategy

Create a chart like this one. Give a specific name for each type of physical feature listed.

Russia	
Plains	
Mountains	
Rivers	

Section 1 A Vast Land

NATIONAL GEOGRAPHIC Exploring Our World

Siberian tigers hunt in the eastern forests of Russia—sometimes even climbing trees to find food. Only a few hundred now live in the wild, though. The animals they hunt—elk, deer, and wild boar—are dwindling, and the tigers are hunted by people. Poachers who kill the tigers illegally can sell a skin for $15,000. Russia is trying to enforce laws to save these animals.

Russia is the world's largest country. Nearly twice as big as the United States, Russia is called a Eurasian country because its lands lie on two continents—Europe and Asia. The **Ural Mountains** form the dividing line between the two continents. The European or western part of Russia borders countries such as Finland, Belarus, and Ukraine. The much larger eastern part of Russia stretches across Asia to the Pacific Ocean. The Chukchi Peninsula, on Russia's far eastern border, is separated from Alaska by only about 50 miles (80 km).

Russia is so wide that it shares borders with 14 other countries. It also includes 11 time zones from east to west. When it is 12:00 P.M. (noon) in eastern Russia and people are eating lunch, people in western Russia are still sound asleep at 1:00 A.M.

Russia's Climate

As you can see from the climate map on page 405, Russia's southern border is in the middle latitudes, but the north reaches past the Arctic Circle. Most of the western part of Russia has a humid continental climate. Summers are warm and rainy, while winters are cold

Section Resources

Reproducible Masters
- Reproducible Lesson Plan
- Daily Lecture and Discussion Notes
- Note-taking Guide
- Guided Reading Activity
- Reading Essentials and Study Guide
- Section Quiz

Transparencies
- Daily Focus Skills Transparency
- In-text Map Transparency

Multimedia
- Vocabulary PuzzleMaker CD-ROM
- Interactive Tutor Self-Assessment CD-ROM
- Presentation Plus! CD-ROM
- ExamView® Pro Testmaker CD-ROM

and snowy. In contrast, eastern Russia experiences short, cool summers and long, snowy winters. Russia has a long coastline along the Arctic Ocean, which is frozen most of the year. Ice makes shipping difficult or impossible. Many of Russia's ports on the Baltic Sea and Pacific Ocean are also closed because of ice part of the year.

Russia's gigantic size and harsh climates make transportation difficult within the country as well. If you visited Russia, you would discover that, unlike in the United States, railroads, rivers, and canals are still important means of getting around. With about 54,000 miles (about 87,000 km) of track, railroads are the leading movers of people and goods in Russia.

✓Reading Check **How does Russia's climate affect shipping?**

European Russia

Find the Ural Mountains on the physical map on page 396. The ancient Urals, worn by years of erosion, are not very tall. Their length is extensive, though, running from the Arctic Ocean to Russia's southern

Applying Map Skills

1. What high latitude climate zones cover much of Russia?
2. What type of climate does Moscow have?

Find NGS online map resources @ www.nationalgeographic.com/maps

Chapter 14

Section 1, pages 404–408

TEACH

Making Predictions Have students look at the climate map. Have them identify the kinds of climates found in Russia. *(steppe, humid continental, subarctic, and tundra)* Ask them to speculate on how each type of climate might affect ways of life in Russia. Call on volunteers to offer their suggestions to the class and give their reasons for their ideas. L1

✓ Reading Check Answer

Since Russia has a long coastline along the Arctic Ocean, which is frozen most of the year, ice makes shipping difficult or impossible.

Applying Map Skills

Answers

1. subarctic and tundra
2. humid continental

In-text Map Transparency Activity Point to the pattern for the tundra in the key and describe where the tundra appears on the map. Ask students to identify the pattern for steppes and describe where steppe climate zones are found. *(in the southwest, near the Caspian Sea, and the south central regions)*

Reading Strategy — Reading the Text

Previewing and Skimming Remind students to look at titles of sections, subsections, and maps, graphs, and charts before they read. When students read the section's title, have them ask themselves, "What is the main idea of this section?" Have them read the section's subtitles and ask themselves, "What will I be learning about this main idea?" Remind students to look at the photographs, graphs, charts, and maps to learn more clues as to what they will be reading. L1

Use the ***Reading Skills Handbook*** *for more reading strategies.*

Chapter 14

Section 1, pages 404–408

Daily Lecture and Discussion Notes

RUSSIA'S LANDSCAPE AND HISTORY

Daily Lecture and Discussion Notes

A Vast Land

Russia's most identifiable architectural feature is its onion-domed churches, which evolved when the wooden churches of the north were translated into brick and colorful tilework. Religious icons, futurism, and revolutionary graphic art are instantly recognizable Russian forms in the world of art.

I. Russia's Climate

- A. Russia is the world's largest country. It is called a Eurasian country because it lies on two continents—Europe and Asia. Russia's southern border is in the middle latitudes, while the north reaches past the Arctic Circle.
- B. The Ural Mountains form the geographical boundary between the continents of Europe and Asia.
- C. Russia shares borders with 14 other countries and includes 11 time zones.
- D. Most of western Russia has warm, rainy summers and cold, snowy winters. Eastern Russia has short, cool summers and long, snowy winters.
- E. Many of Russia's ports on the Baltic Sea and Pacific Ocean are closed by ice part of the year.
- F. Russia's gigantic size and harsh climates make transportation difficult within the country. Railroads, rivers, and canals are still important for getting around.

DISCUSSION QUESTION

How is the climate of western Russia different from the climate of eastern Russia? *(Western Russia has warm, rainy summers and cold, snowy winters, whereas eastern Russia has short, cool summers and long, snowy winters.)*

II. European Russia

- A. About 75 percent of Russia's people live west of the Ural Mountains, along the North European Plain. Fertile ground and the mildest climate are found there.

103

Reading Check Answer

the nearly treeless, grassy plain that stretches through Ukraine

More About the Photo

Siberia In Siberia, buildings rest on pilings 6 to 8 feet (1.8–2.4 m) off the ground so that heat from within does not melt the permafrost. Melting permafrost can cause building foundations to shift and crack.

Caption Answer fishing, hunting seals and walruses, herding reindeer

boundary. West of the Urals lies the **North European Plain.** This fertile plain has Russia's mildest climate, and about 75 percent of the population live here. This region holds Russia's capital, **Moscow,** and other important cities, such as **St. Petersburg** and **Volgograd.** Much of Russia's agriculture and industry is found on the North European Plain.

Good farmland also lies south of the North European Plain, along the Don and Volga Rivers. This area is part of the steppe, the nearly treeless grassy plain that stretches through Ukraine. To the far south of European Russia lay the high, rugged **Caucasus** (KAW•kuh•suhs) **Mountains.** Thickly covered with pines and other trees, the Caucasus are much taller than the Urals.

Reading Check What is the steppe?

East of the Urals

The huge Asian part of Russia lies east of the Ural Mountains and is known as **Siberia.** Northern Siberia has one of the coldest climates in the world. Not even hardy evergreens can grow here. Instead, you find tundra, a vast and rolling treeless plain in which only the top few inches of the ground thaw during the summer. The permanently frozen lower layers of soil are called permafrost and cover 40 percent of Russia.

The few people who live in the tundra make their living by fishing, hunting seals and walruses, or herding reindeer. With so few trees, many of the houses are made of walrus skins. Because the distances are so great and the land is usually covered in ice and snow, people may use helicopters for travel.

The Taiga South of the tundra is the world's largest forest, the taiga (TY•guh). Here, evergreen trees stretch about 4,000 miles (6,436 km) across the country in a belt 1,000 to 2,000 miles (1,609 to 3,218 km) wide. As with the tundra, few people live in this area. Those who do support themselves by lumbering or hunting. This area is so sparsely populated that forest fires sometimes burn for weeks before anyone notices.

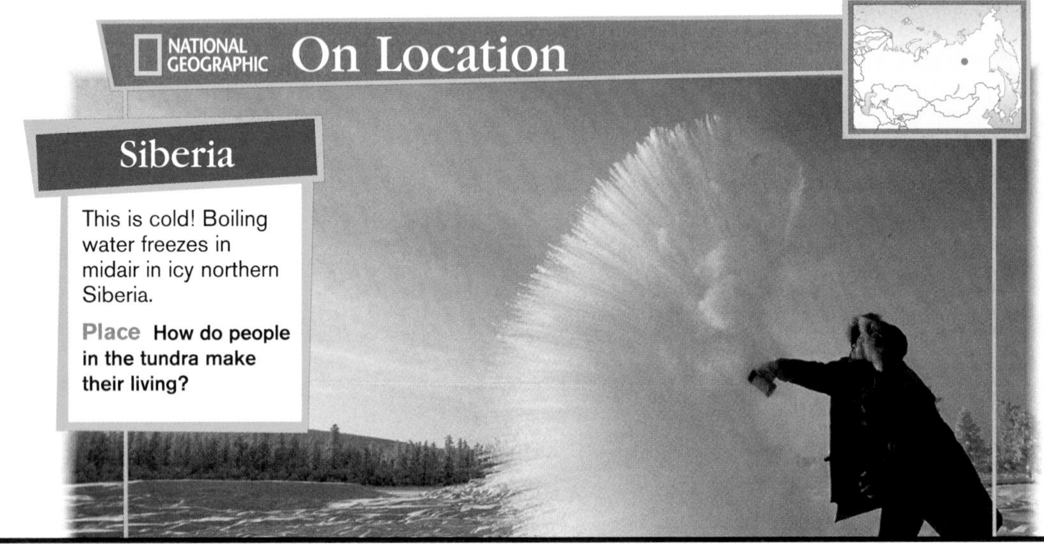

NATIONAL GEOGRAPHIC **On Location**

Siberia

This is cold! Boiling water freezes in midair in icy northern Siberia.

Place How do people in the tundra make their living?

Differentiated Instruction

Meeting Special Needs: Visual/Spatial Have students demonstrate their understanding of the landforms of Russia in one of several ways. Students could research and draw an elevation profile to show the different elevations across the country. As an alternative, they could create a clay model that shows the country's landforms. Another option would be to create a collage of photographs that illustrates Russia's physical diversity. **L2**

Refer to *Inclusion for the Middle School Social Studies Classroom Strategies and Activities* in the TCR.

NATIONAL GEOGRAPHIC On Location

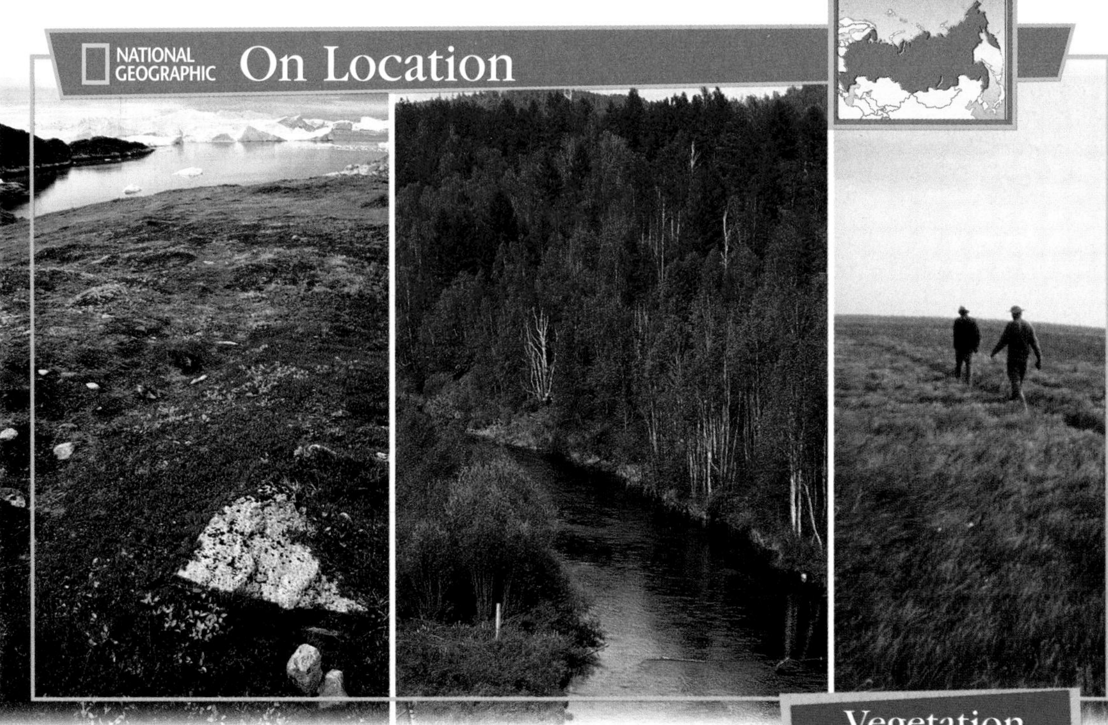

Vegetation in Russia

The tundra (left) is found in northern Russia. South of the tundra is the huge expanse of the taiga (center). The steppes dominate southwest Russia (right).

Place **What type of vegetation grows on the taiga?**

Southern Siberia Plains, plateaus, and mountain ranges cover the southern part of Siberia. Southeastern Siberia is home to the majestic Siberian tiger, now an endangered species. Other wildlife found here include bear, reindeer, lynx, wolf, wildcat, elk, and wild boar.

The Kamchatka Peninsula Mountains also rise on the far eastern Kamchatka (kam•CHAHT•kuh) Peninsula. Many of these mountains are part of the Ring of Fire. This name is used to describe the active volcanic zone that forms the western, northern, and eastern edges of the Pacific Ocean. Volcanic eruptions and earthquakes sometimes occur on this peninsula.

✓Reading Check **What is the Ring of Fire?**

Inland Water Areas

Russia touches many inland bodies of water. In the southwest, it borders the **Black Sea.** Through the Black Sea, Russian ships can reach the Mediterranean Sea. Look at the physical map on page 396 to find another large sea in southwestern Russia—the **Caspian Sea.** About the size of California, the Caspian Sea is actually the largest inland body of water in the world. Like the Great Salt Lake in Utah, the Caspian Sea has salt water, not freshwater. Russia shares this sea

L1/ELL

Guided Reading Activity

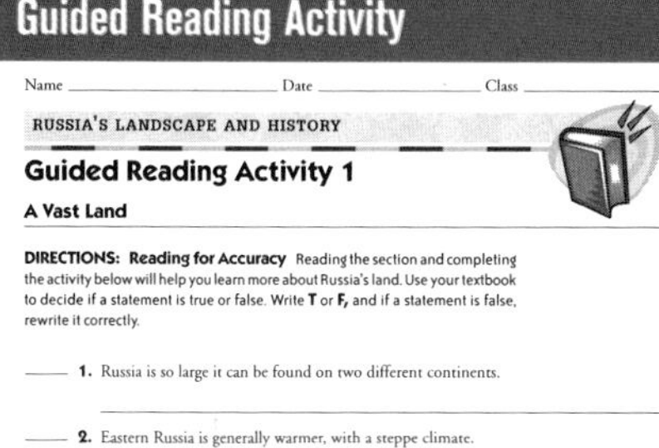

Name ____ Date ____ Class ____

RUSSIA'S LANDSCAPE AND HISTORY

Guided Reading Activity 1

A Vast Land

DIRECTIONS: Reading for Accuracy Reading the section and completing the activity below will help you learn more about Russia's land. Use your textbook to decide if a statement is true or false. Write **T** or **F**, and if a statement is false, rewrite it correctly.

____ 1. Russia is so large it can be found on two different continents.

____ 2. Eastern Russia is generally warmer, with a steppe climate.

____ 3. Transportation in Russia is much like that in the United States.

More About the Photos

The Steppes The soil on the steppes has a 3-foot (91-cm) thick top layer of humus, which is why it is so fertile.

Caption Answer evergreen trees

✓ Reading Check Answer

the active volcanic zone located along the western, northern, and eastern edges of the Pacific Ocean

3 ASSESS

Assign Section 1 Assessment as homework or an in-class activity.

Have students use the Interactive Tutor Self-Assessment CD-ROM to review Section 1.

Critical Thinking Activity

Interpreting Information Have students research the Trans-Siberian Railroad and create a display about it. Students' projects should address the physical and economic aspects of the railroad. The display should include a map of the route the railroad follows, images revealing the landscape through which the train passes, and text or visual information that describes the economic regions that the railroad traverses. Students should explain why the route goes through particular towns and regions. L1

EE1 The World in Spatial Terms: Standard 3

Chapter 14

Section 1, pages 404–408

L2

Section Quiz

Name ______ Date ______ Class ______

Score — RUSSIA'S LANDSCAPE AND HISTORY

Section 1 Quiz

A Vast Land

DIRECTIONS: Matching Match each item in Column A with the items in Column B. Write the correct letters in the blanks. *(10 points each)*

COLUMN A	COLUMN B
A. Volga	____ **1.** huge forests of evergreen trees
B. North European Plain	____ **2.** permanently frozen lower layers of soil
C. permafrost	____ **3.** landform on which 75 percent of Russia's people live
D. Ural Mountains	____ **4.** longest river in Europe
E. taiga	____ **5.** landform marking the boundary between Europe and Asia

Reading Check Answer

to save the lake from pollution and keep a needed industry

L1/ELL

Reading Essentials and Study Guide

Name ______ Date ______ Class ______

RUSSIA'S LANDSCAPE AND HISTORY

Reading Essentials and Study Guide 1

A Vast Land

Key Terms

steppe nearly treeless grassy plain
tundra large treeless plain in which only the top few inches of ground thaw in summer
permafrost permanently frozen lower layers of soil
taiga huge forests of evergreen trees that grow in cold climates

Drawing From Experience

... most terrible prison in the United States?

CLOSE

Reading Strategy

Visualizing Have students write a description of the landforms and climates they would see on a journey across Russia from east to west. Then ask them to trace the route of the journey on an outline map of Russia.

with four other countries—Azerbaijan, Iran, Turkmenistan, and Kazakhstan.

High in the Central Siberian Plateau is **Lake Baikal**—the world's deepest freshwater lake. In fact, Lake Baikal holds almost 20 percent of the world's supply of unfrozen freshwater. It is also the world's oldest lake, dating back nearly 30 million years. Some of the plant and fish species in the lake can be traced to prehistoric times. Scientists come from all over the world to study its rare and unusual species. Tourists travel by train to see the lake's shimmering blue waters.

Unfortunately, a large paper mill nearby has polluted the Lake Baikal region. The paper mill is a major source of jobs and wealth. An important issue for this region is to try to save both the lake and the badly needed industry.

Russia has several major rivers. The **Volga**—the longest river in Europe—is a vital transportation route. Canals connect it and other rivers of European Russia. Boats use the canals to transport people and goods from one city to another. Many rivers also flow through the Asian side of Russia. Most of these rivers begin in the mountains of southern Siberia and flow north across the marshy lowlands to empty into the frigid Arctic Ocean. The Lena (LEE•nuh), the Yenisey (YIH•nih•SAY), and the Ob (AHB) are among the longest rivers in the world.

Reading Check **What is an important issue for the Lake Baikal region?**

Section 1 Assessment

Defining Terms

1. Define steppe, tundra, permafrost, taiga.

Recalling Facts

2. Location What mountain range separates Europe and Asia?

3. Region How many countries does Russia border?

4. Place What is unique about Lake Baikal?

Critical Thinking

5. Analyzing Information Why do you think trains are more important than other kinds of vehicles for moving people and goods across Russia?

6. Making Comparisons How do the waters of the Caspian Sea and Lake Baikal differ?

Graphic Organizer

7. Categorizing Information Create a chart like this one. Then place each of the following items into the column in which it is located: Moscow, Lake Baikal, Kamchatka Peninsula, St. Petersburg, Volga River, Volgograd, taiga.

European Russia	Asian Russia

Applying Social Studies Skills

8. Analyzing Maps Turn to the climate map on page 405. Select a Russian city. Now look at the map of "The Russian Winter" on page 398. On average, how many days of snow cover does your selected city have per year?

Section 1 Assessment

1. The terms are defined in the Glossary.
2. the Ural Mountains
3. 14
4. It is the world's deepest freshwater lake.
5. *Possible answers:* Maintaining fueling stations for trucks across these great distances would be difficult; trains can haul heavier freight than trucks.
6. The Caspian Sea has salt water while Lake Baikal has freshwater.
7. European Russia: Moscow, St. Petersburg, Volga River, Volgograd; Asian Russia: Lake Baikal, Kamchatka Peninsula, taiga
8. Answers will vary.

Making Connections

ART SCIENCE CULTURE TECHNOLOGY

Cooperative Space Ventures

The space age officially began in 1957 when Russia launched *Sputnik I.* It was the first artificial satellite to orbit the earth.

The Space Race

The Russians sent the first person into space in 1961, when cosmonaut Yuri Gagarin orbited the earth. A few weeks later, Alan Shepard made the United States's first spaceflight. John Glenn was the first astronaut to orbit the earth in 1962. After this, the "space race" between the United States and Russia was of global importance. It was feared that one country could dominate the world if it had the right equipment in space.

Over the years, both Russia and the United States launched many spacecraft. In 1986 the Russian space station *Mir,* which means "peace," began to orbit the earth. This was the first permanently staffed laboratory in space. Astronauts from more than a dozen countries were invited to participate on the space station *Mir.* The astronauts and Russian cosmonauts performed many experiments on the effects of weightlessness.

In 1993 the United States and Russia decided to work jointly to build the International Space Station. In July 2000, the Russian space module *Zvezda* ("star") linked up with the rest of the station. Four months later, the International Space Station had its first permanent human inhabitants. The crew was made up of both Russian cosmonauts and American astronauts.

Making the Connection

1. What country launched the space age?
2. How have the United States and Russia cooperated on space ventures?
3. **Making Predictions** What space technology do you think we will see in the future? What social consequences might result from this?

NATIONAL GEOGRAPHIC

International Space Station

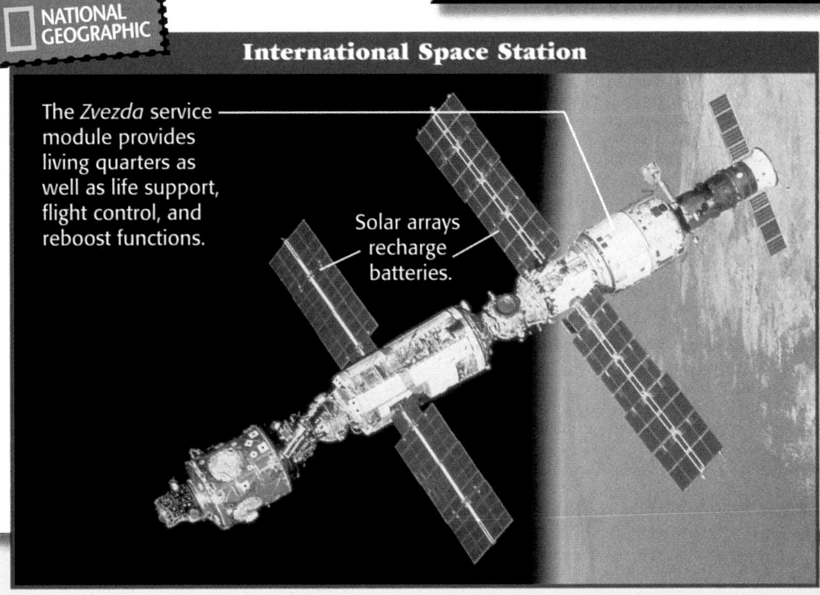
The *Zvezda* service module provides living quarters as well as life support, flight control, and reboost functions.
Solar arrays recharge batteries.

Making the Connection

1. Russia
2. They jointly built the International Space Station and its first crew was American and Russian.
3. Answers will vary. *Possible predictions:* a bigger and better space station, passenger shuttles to the moon, crewed missions to Mars; *Possible consequences:* new settlements outside of Earth, new energy or mineral resources from space, new technologies and discoveries

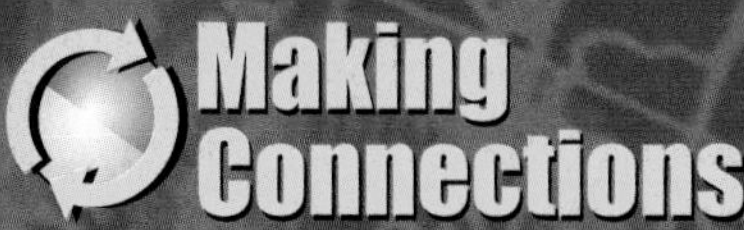

TEACH

Tell students to imagine that they must spend all day every day for two months in a space the size of the classroom with small compartments on the side for sleeping. Tell them that they must live and work in this space with the same two people every day. **Ask: What characteristics must a person have to live in these circumstances?** *(patience, tolerance, discipline)* Point out that this is how cosmonauts who served on *Mir* actually lived. L1

More About *Mir*

The living area of *Mir* was divided into crews' quarters (with a chair, a sleeping bag, and a porthole); bathroom facilities (with a toilet, sink, and shower); and a galley (with a table, cooking areas, and facilities for storing trash). The space station also had a stationary bike to use for exercise.

Interdisciplinary Connections

Science Students can visit the NASA Web site *(spaceflight.nasa.gov)* for information about the International Space Station. Included are a virtual reality tour of the station, a tracking map that shows the location of the station in real time, and a way of identifying when you can see the space station fly overhead.

1 Focus

Section Objectives

1. Describe life in Russia under the czars.
2. Discuss life in Russia under Communist rule.
3. Explain why the Soviet Union collapsed.

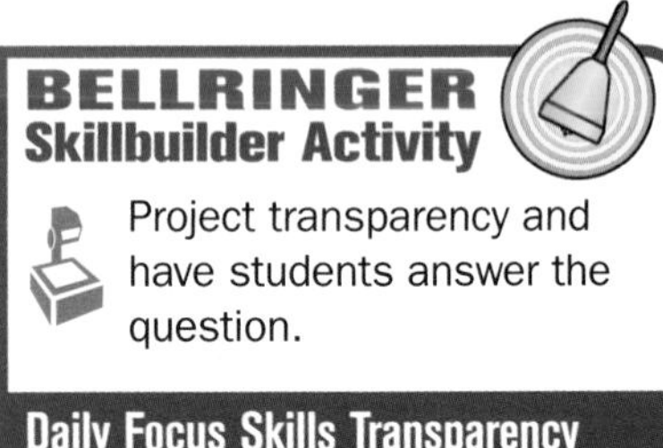

BELLRINGER
Skillbuilder Activity

Project transparency and have students answer the question.

Daily Focus Skills Transparency

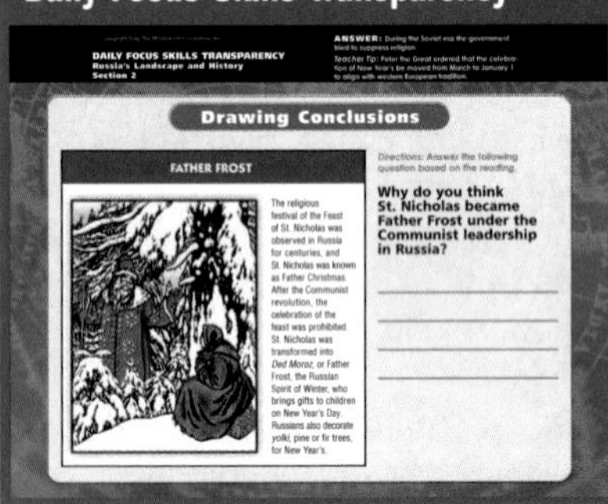

Reading Preview

- **Activating Prior Knowledge** Have the class discuss what a revolution is and how it can transform a society.
- **Preteaching Vocabulary** Have students find the meanings of the words *czar* and *serf*. Then have them identify synonyms, or words that have the same meanings. *(czar—emperor; serf—enslaved person, servant)*

Guide to Reading

Main Idea

The harsh rule of powerful leaders has often sparked violent uprisings in Russia.

Terms to Know

- czar
- serf
- industrialize
- communist state
- Cold War
- perestroika
- free enterprise system
- glasnost

Reading Strategy

Create a chart like this one. List three main czars and important facts to remember about them.

Czar	Importance

Section 2

A Troubled History

NATIONAL GEOGRAPHIC Exploring Our World

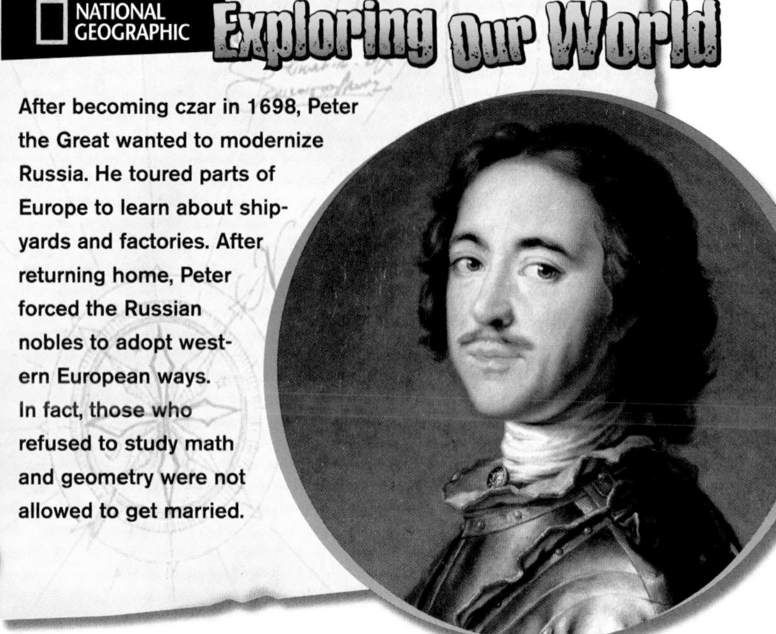

After becoming czar in 1698, Peter the Great wanted to modernize Russia. He toured parts of Europe to learn about shipyards and factories. After returning home, Peter forced the Russian nobles to adopt western European ways. In fact, those who refused to study math and geometry were not allowed to get married.

Today Russia is the world's largest country. Early in its history, however, it was a small territory on the edge of Europe. Strong rulers gradually expanded Russia's borders. Their harsh rule led to unrest, eventually leading to two major upheavals—one in 1917, the other in 1991.

Early Russia

To understand the challenges facing Russia today, let us go back through Russia's history. Modern Russians descend from early groups of Slavs who settled along the rivers of what are today Ukraine and Russia. During the A.D. 800s, these early Slavs built a civilization around the city of **Kiev,** today the capital of Ukraine. This civilization was called Kievan Rus (KEE•EH•vuhn ROOS). By the A.D. 1000s, the ruler and people of Kievan Rus had accepted Eastern Orthodox Christianity. They prospered from trade with the Mediterranean world and western Europe.

In the 1200s, the Mongols swept in from Central Asia and conquered Kiev. Under their 200-year-rule, Kiev lost much of its wealth and power. Meanwhile, Moscow became the center of a new Slavic

Section Resources

Reproducible Masters
- Reproducible Lesson Plan
- Daily Lecture and Discussion Notes
- Note-taking Guide
- Guided Reading Activity
- Reading Essentials and Study Guide
- Section Quiz

Transparencies
- Daily Focus Skills Transparency
- GeoQuiz Transparency

Multimedia
- Vocabulary PuzzleMaker CD-ROM
- Interactive Tutor Self-Assessment CD-ROM
- Presentation Plus! CD-ROM
- ExamView® Pro Testmaker CD-ROM

- MindJogger Videoquiz

territory called Muscovy (muh•SKOH•vee). In 1480 Ivan III, a prince of Muscovy, drove out the Mongols and made Muscovy independent. Ivan III was known as "Ivan the Great."

Rise of the Czars Muscovy slowly developed into the country we know today as Russia. Russian rulers expanded their power, built up armies, and seized land and other resources. They called themselves **czars,** or emperors. They had total control over the government. As a citizen of Muscovy, you would have feared Czar Ivan IV, who ruled during the 1500s. Known as "Ivan the Terrible," he used a secret police force to tighten his iron grip on the people and control their lives.

As the map on page 412 shows, the czars gradually conquered surrounding territories. As a result, many non-Russian peoples became part of the growing Russian Empire. (Russia still suffers from ethnic tensions caused by these early conquests.) Czars such as Peter the Great and Catherine the Great pushed the empire's borders southward and westward. They also tried to make Russia modern and more like Europe. Peter built a new capital—St. Petersburg—in the early 1700s. Built close to Europe near the Baltic coast, St. Petersburg was designed like a European city with elegant palaces, public squares, and canals. If you had been a Russian noble at this time, you would have spoken French as well as Russian. You also would have put aside traditional Russian dress, worn European clothes, and attended fancy balls and parties.

NATIONAL GEOGRAPHIC On Location

Early Czars

Ivan III, or "Ivan the Great," (left) ruled Muscovy until 1505. His grandson, Ivan IV, also known as "Ivan the Terrible," (right) used a secret police force to control the people of Muscovy.

History **Who drove the Mongols out of Kiev?**

Chapter 14

Section 2, pages 410–415

2 TEACH

Reading Strategy

Making Generalizations
Have students create a chart of Russian history with four major periods: early Russia, Russia under the czars, Communist Russia, and Russia after 1991. Have them write facts about each period under the appropriate heading. Then ask them to make a generalization about life in Russia in each period. L1

Daily Lecture and Discussion Notes

RUSSIA'S LANDSCAPE AND HISTORY

Daily Lecture and Discussion Notes

A Troubled History

Did You Know?

For those who travel for the pleasure of the journey, and those who believe that getting there is as much fun as being there, Russia's Trans-Siberian Railway has long been an almost mythic experience. It is the longest continuous rail line on Earth, each run clattering along in an epic journey of almost 6,000 miles (or about 10,000 km) over one-third of the globe.

I. Early Russia

A. During the A.D. 800s, early Slavs built a civilization around the city of Kiev, today the capital of Ukraine. This civilization was called Kievan Rus.

B. Mongols swept in during the 1200s and greatly reduced Kiev's wealth and ... 200 years.

More About the Photos

Early Czars Ivan III was the first czar of Russia, but Ivan IV was its most powerful. Under his rule, Russia expanded its territory and increased contact with Europe.

Caption Answer Ivan III

Reading Strategy — Reading the Text

Using Context Clues Help students learn to define words by using context clues. Ask for volunteers to identify a word that is unfamiliar to them. Help them guess at the meaning of the word by understanding the context in which it is used. Suggest that students write these words on a note card and check their guesses against the dictionary. That way they can be sure that they correctly understand new words they encounter in reading.

Use the ***Reading Skills Handbook*** *for more reading strategies.*

Chapter 14

Section 2, pages 410–415

Applying Map Skills

Answers

1. 1524–1689
2. 1945

Skills Practice

What lines of longitude does present-day Russia lie within? *(approximately 30°E and 170°W)*

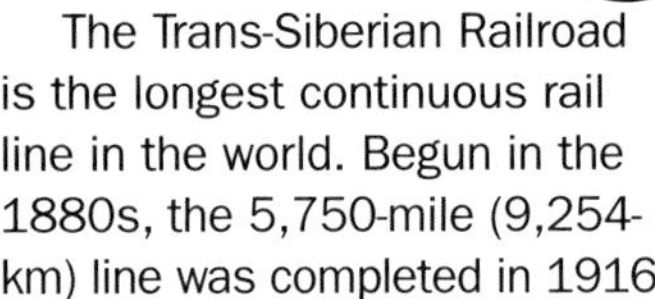

Did You Know

The Trans-Siberian Railroad is the longest continuous rail line in the world. Begun in the 1880s, the 5,750-mile (9,254-km) line was completed in 1916.

L1/ELL

Guided Reading Activity

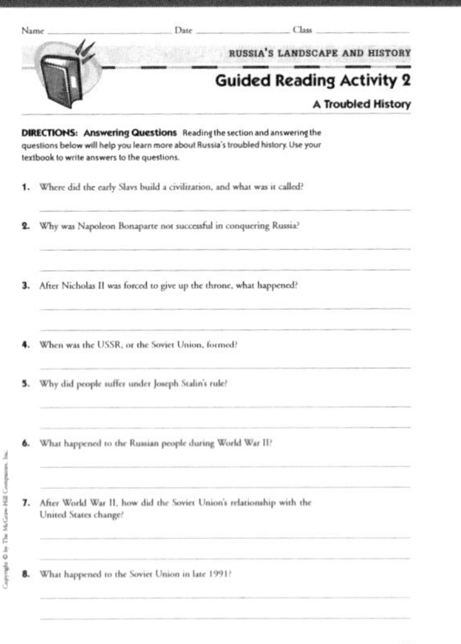

Name ______ Date ______ Class ______

RUSSIA'S LANDSCAPE AND HISTORY

Guided Reading Activity 2

A Troubled History

DIRECTIONS: Answering Questions Reading the section and answering the questions below will help you learn more about Russia's troubled history. Use your textbook to write answers to the questions.

1. Where did the early Slavs build a civilization, and what was it called?
2. Why was Napoleon Bonaparte not successful in conquering Russia?
3. After Nicholas II was forced to give up the throne, what happened?
4. When was the USSR, or the Soviet Union, formed?
5. Why did people suffer under Joseph Stalin's rule?
6. What happened to the Russian people during World War II?
7. After World War II, how did the Soviet Union's relationship with the United States change?
8. What happened to the Soviet Union in late 1991?

Copyright © by The McGraw-Hill Companies, Inc.

53

Applying Map Skills

1. During which time period was the most land added to Russia?
2. Was Russia's land area larger in 1945, or is it larger today?

Find NGS online map resources @ www.nationalgeographic.com/maps

The czars and nobles enjoyed rich, comfortable lives. At the bottom of society, however, were the great masses of people. Most were **serfs,** or farm laborers, who could be bought and sold along with the land. These people lived hard lives, working on the nobles' country estates or in city palaces. Few could read or write. They did not follow Western customs, but kept the Russian traditions.

Dramatic Changes In 1812 a French army led by Napoleon Bonaparte invaded Russia. Brave Russian soldiers and the fierce winter weather finally forced the French to retreat. Have you ever heard the *1812 Overture,* with its dramatic ending that includes ringing bells and bursts of cannon fire? Written by the Russian composer Peter Tchaikovsky (chy•KAWF•skee), this musical masterpiece celebrates the Russian victory over Napoleon. Turn to page 420 to read more about Napoleon's defeat.

In the late 1800s, Russia entered a period of economic and social change. The Russian Empire expanded southward into the Caucasus Mountains and eastward toward the Pacific Ocean. In 1861 Czar Alexander II, known as the Czar-Liberator, freed the serfs from being tied to the land. His new law did little to lift them out of poverty, though. Russia began to **industrialize,** or change its economy to rely

Differentiated Instruction

Meeting Special Needs: Auditory/Musical Obtain a recording of Tchaikovsky's *1812 Overture.* Explain that the work was written to commemorate Russia's victory over Napoleon. (The initial performance was outdoors, one reason that Tchaikovsky was able to include the famous cannons.) Point out that in the central section of the piece, Tchaikovsky uses the French and Russian national anthems ("La Marseillaise" and "God Save the Czar") to clash against each other, representing the clash of the French and Russian armies. Play the ending so students can hear the cannons roar, the triumph of the Russian anthem, and the church bells. After listening, have them discuss how such a piece of music would make Russians feel about their country and why it appeals to societies all over the world. **L1 ELL** 

more on manufacturing and less on farming. Railroads, including the famous Trans-Siberian Railroad, spread across the country. It linked Moscow in the west with Vladivostok on Russia's Pacific coast.

✓Reading Check **What civilization did early Slavs build in Ukraine?**

The Soviet Era

In 1914 World War I broke out in Europe. Russian and German armies met and fought bloody battles in eastern Europe. Unprepared for war, Russia suffered many defeats and had few victories. As the fighting dragged on, shortages of food in Russian cities caused starvation. The Russian people blamed the czars for their troubles.

The Russian Revolution In 1917 political leaders, soldiers, and factory workers forced Czar Nicholas II to give up the throne. Later that year, a political revolutionary named Vladimir Lenin led a second revolt and seized control. He and his followers set up a **communist state.** This means the country's government has strong control over the economy and society as a whole. Fearing invasion, the Communists moved Russia's capital from coastal St. Petersburg inland to Moscow.

Growth of Soviet Power By 1922, after a brutal civil war, Russia's Communist leaders were securely in power. In that year, they formed the Union of Soviet Socialist Republics (USSR), or the Soviet Union. This vast territory included the republic of Russia and 14 other republics—most of the conquered territories of the old Russian Empire. After Lenin died in 1924, Communist Party officials disagreed over who was to lead the country.

Within a few years, Joseph Stalin had won out over the others and became the Soviet Union's leader. Under Stalin's orders, the government took complete control of the economy. Stalin ended private ownership of farms and businesses, and he set up five-year plans to industrialize the country. Under this type of system, called a command economy, factory managers were told what to make and how to make it. Those who opposed Stalin's actions were killed or sent to remote prison camps deep in the vast forests of icy Siberia. Millions of people were brutally murdered or forced into slave labor under Stalin's rule.

In 1941 Nazi Germany invaded the Soviet Union, drawing the country into World War II. During the conflict, the Soviets joined with Great Britain and the United States to defeat the Germans. About 20 million Russian soldiers and civilians died in what Russians call the Great Patriotic Fatherland War.

Superpowers Wage the Cold War When World War II ended, Stalin wanted to protect the Soviet Union from any more invasions. He set up Communist governments in the neighboring Eastern European countries of Poland, East Germany, Czechoslovakia, Hungary, Romania, and Bulgaria. They became satellite nations, or countries controlled by another, more powerful nation. The Soviet government cut off these countries from contact with the rest of the world. As a result, they

Social Studies Online

Web Activity Visit ***The World and Its People*** Web site at twip.glencoe.com and click on **Chapter 14—Student Web Activities** to learn more about the Russian Revolution.

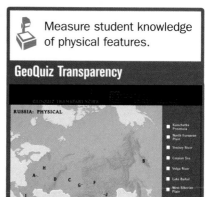

Critical Thinking Activity

Understanding Cause and Effect Write a list of statements on the board, such as "Serfs freed but remain poor," "Opponents killed or sent to prison camps," and "Czars expand Russia's borders." Have students identify the period in Russian history in which it belongs. When the exercise is complete, ask students to evaluate the relationships between past conflicts and current conditions in Russia. What common themes do they see in Russian history? L2

EE4 Human Systems: Standard 12

✓ Reading Check Answer

Kievan Rus

Objectives and answers to the Student Web Activity can be found in the Web Activity Lesson Plan at **twip.glencoe.com**

Measure student knowledge of physical features.

GeoQuiz Transparency

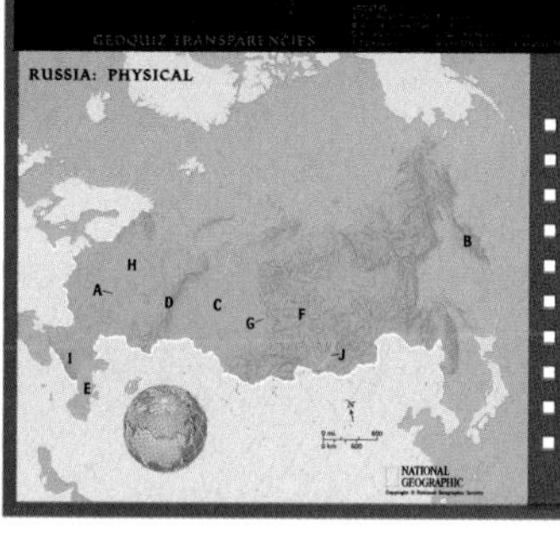

More About the Photo

Soviet Control The Soviet Union also sent troops to crush a rebellion against Communist rule in Hungary in 1956. In 1989 Mikhail Gorbachev refused to act similarly when anti-Communist movements swept across Eastern Europe. This decision allowed the reformers to seize control of several different governments.

Caption Answer to protect the Soviet Union from further invasions

ASSESS

Assign Section 2 Assessment as homework or an in-class activity.

Have students use the interactive Tutor Self-Assessment CD-ROM to review Section 2.

L2

Section Quiz

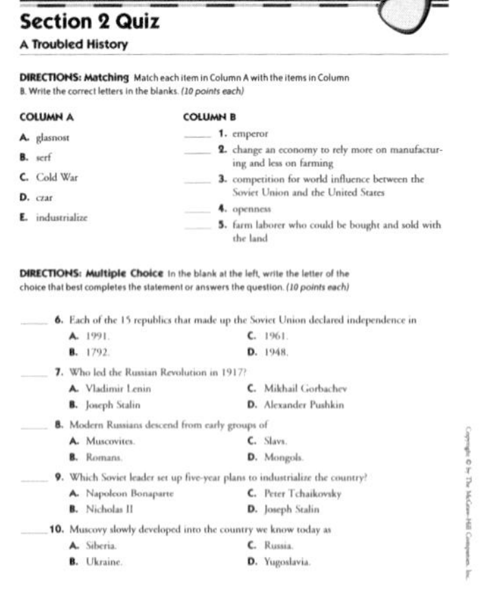

Name ______ Date ______ Class ______

RUSSIA'S LANDSCAPE AND HISTORY

Score

Section 2 Quiz

A Troubled History

DIRECTIONS: Matching Match each item in Column A with the items in Column B. Write the correct letters in the blanks. *(10 points each)*

COLUMN A	COLUMN B
A. glasnost	____ **1.** emperor
B. serf	____ **2.** change an economy to rely more on manufacturing and less on farming
C. Cold War	____ **3.** competition for world influence between the Soviet Union and the United States
D. czar	____ **4.** openness
E. industrialize	____ **5.** farm laborer who could be bought and sold with the land

DIRECTIONS: Multiple Choice In the blank at the left, write the letter of the choice that best completes the statement or answers the question. *(10 points each)*

____ **6.** Each of the 15 republics that made up the Soviet Union declared independence in
A. 1991. **C.** 1961.
B. 1792. **D.** 1948.

____ **7.** Who led the Russian Revolution in 1917?
A. Vladimir Lenin **C.** Mikhail Gorbachev
B. Joseph Stalin **D.** Alexander Pushkin

____ **8.** Modern Russians descend from early groups of
A. Muscovites. **C.** Slavs.
B. Romans. **D.** Mongols.

____ **9.** Which Soviet leader set up five-year plans to industrialize the country?
A. Napoleon Bonaparte **C.** Peter Tchaikovsky
B. Nicholas II **D.** Joseph Stalin

____ **10.** Muscovy slowly developed into the country we know today as
A. Siberia. **C.** Russia.
B. Ukraine. **D.** Yugoslavia.

226

NATIONAL GEOGRAPHIC **On Location**

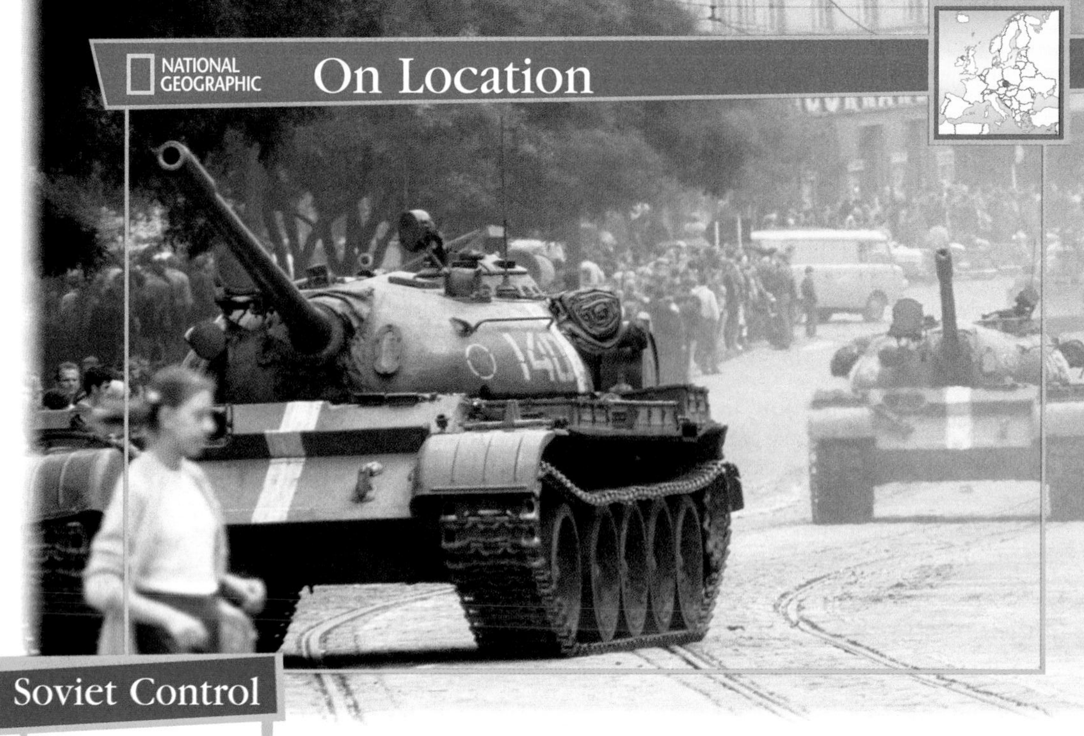

Soviet Control

Czechoslovakia tried to throw off Soviet control in 1968. Soviet tanks and troops poured into Bratislava to crush the revolt.

Movement **Why did Stalin set up Communist governments in Eastern European countries?**

were said to lie behind an "iron curtain." Any satellite nations that opposed Soviet rule were brutally put down.

Stalin and the leaders who followed him spent large amounts of money on the military and weapons. The Soviet Union became one of the two most powerful nations in the world. The other superpower—the United States—opposed Soviet actions. These two nations engaged in the **Cold War**, competing for world influence without breaking out in actual fighting. They even competed in space. Both the Soviet Union and the United States launched rockets in a bid to be first in outer space. Turn to page 409 to learn more about the space race.

During the Cold War years—from 1940 to the late 1980s—the Soviet economy faced many problems. With no competition, government-owned factories became inefficient and produced poor-quality goods. The government cared more about making tanks and airplanes for military purposes than consumer goods, such as cars and refrigerators. As a result, people had few goods to buy. Food often became scarce, and people waited in long lines to buy bread, milk, and other necessary items.

The Soviet Union had another challenge. This vast empire included not only Russians but also people from many other ethnic groups. Non-Russians in the Soviet republics resented the control of the government in Moscow, which they believed favored ethnic Russians. They wanted to leave the Soviet Union and form their own countries.

Cooperative Learning Activity

Illustrated Time Line Organize students into five groups and assign each group one of the following historical periods: 900s–1400s, 1400s–1800s, 1800s–1917, 1920–1990, and 1991–present. Have each group research its assigned time period and choose events to include on an illustrated time line of Russian history. Ask the history teacher to supply resource materials that students can use. On the classroom wall, attach a long strip of paper on which the dates are written. Have groups place annotated illustrations of their selected events in appropriate places along the time line. Suggest that they use yarn to connect each illustration with its correct date. L2

EE4 Human Systems: Standard 9

Soviet Collapse Despite plans to improve housing and agriculture, the Soviet economy fell even further behind the economy of the United States. In 1985 Mikhail Gorbachev (GAWR•buh•CHAWF) became the leader of the Soviet Union. He introduced changes to get the Soviet economy moving. Under his policy of **perestroika,** or "restructuring," Gorbachev allowed farmers and factory managers to make many of their own decisions. By loosening government control, Gorbachev moved the economy toward a **free enterprise system.** In this type of economy, most businesses are privately owned, and there is competition—resulting in better products at lower prices.

Gorbachev also allowed people to speak freely about the government and important issues, a policy called **glasnost,** or "openness." Instead of strengthening the country, however, Gorbachev's policies made the people doubt communism even more. Some people thought Gorbachev was moving too quickly with reforms. Others thought he was not moving fast enough. People's demands for more and more changes eventually led to the collapse of both communism and the Soviet Union.

In the late 1980s, massive protests against Soviet control erupted in the satellite nations. By 1991, all of the Soviet satellites had thrown off communist rule in favor of democracy. By the end of that year, each of the 15 republics that made up the Soviet Union also declared their independence. The Soviet Union no longer existed. Russia emerged as the largest and most powerful of those republics.

▲ Mikhail Gorbachev tried to lessen the Russian government's control of the economy and society.

✓Reading Check **Who helped move the Soviet Union toward democracy?**

Section 2 Assessment

Defining Terms

1. **Define** czar, serf, industrialize, communist state, Cold War, perestroika, free enterprise system, glasnost.

Recalling Facts

2. **History** Why did Peter the Great build a new capital of Russia?
3. **History** Who led the 1917 revolution in Russia?
4. **History** What happened to the Soviet Union in 1991?

Critical Thinking

5. **Understanding Cause and Effect** How did the Soviet economy change under perestroika?
6. **Analyzing Information** How did glasnost weaken the communist system?

Graphic Organizer

7. **Organizing Information** In a chart like this one, write facts that show the contrast between the nobles and the serfs of Russia.

Nobles	Serfs

Applying Social Studies Skills

8. **Creating Mental Maps** Create your own map of early Russian territory. Label where Kievan Rus was located. Then label where Peter the Great moved the capital.

Section 2 Assessment

1. The terms are defined in the Glossary.
2. He wanted it to be more European and closer to Europe.
3. Vladimir Lenin
4. It became 15 independent republics.
5. Farmers and factory managers made many of their own decisions.
6. People demanded more changes.
7. Nobles: spoke French and Russian; wore European clothes; attended fancy parties; enjoyed rich, comfortable lives; Serfs: were laborers; could be bought and sold; lived hard lives; could not read or write; followed Russian traditions
8. This exercise helps students visualize historic Russia. All attempts at freehand mapping should be accepted.

✓ Reading Check Answer

Mikhail Gorbachev

L1/ELL

Reading Essentials and Study Guide

Name ________ Date ________ Class ________

RUSSIA'S LANDSCAPE AND HISTORY

Reading Essentials and Study Guide 2

A Troubled History

Key Terms

czar emperor
serf farm laborer who could be bought and sold along with the land
industrialize to change an economy to rely more on manufacturing and less on farming
communist state country whose government has strong control over the economy and society
Cold War competing for world influence without actually fighting
perestroika restructuring the economy by allowing farmers and factory workers to make many of their own decisions
free enterprise system economy in which businesses are privately owned and there is competition
glasnost policy of allowing people to speak freely about the government and important issues

Drawing From Experience

Have you ever heard the phrase "duck and cover"? If you had lived during the Cold War, this phrase would have scared you. In school, students learned to duck under their desks and cover their heads at the sound of an alarm. The alarm meant that Soviet bombs were falling on the United States. Luckily, it never happened. Still, people of both countries lived in fear of each other during those years.

This section describes the history of Russia and its rise to world power. You will also learn how Russia grew out of the breakup of the Soviet Union.

192

193

CLOSE

Have students create a display that illustrates the Communist period in Russian history.

Critical Thinking Skill

TEACH

Write the following sentences on the board: (A) José ate dinner. (B) José was hungry. (C) José brushed his teeth. Ask students to put the sentences in a logical order. *(B, A, C)* Ask for volunteers to explain why this is a sensible order. *(José's hunger caused him to eat, and eating caused him to need to brush his teeth.)* Explain that these three sentences are a simple example of cause and effect. Then have them read the feature and practice the skill. L1

Additional Skills Practice

1. **Which is the cause and effect in this pair of facts? (A) Resources in Siberia have not been well developed. (B) Siberia is a remote region with a harsh environment.** *(Cause—B; Effect—A)*
2. **How can one event be both a cause and an effect?** *(It can result from one event but cause yet another—like José eating dinner in the TEACH activity.)*

Additional Skills Resources

 Chapter Skills Review

 Building Geography Skills for Life

GLENCOE TECHNOLOGY

 **Skillbuilder Interactive Workbook CD-ROM, Level 1**

This interactive CD-ROM reinforces student mastery of essential social studies skills.

Critical Thinking Skill

Understanding Cause and Effect

Understanding cause and effect involves considering *why* an event occurred. A *cause* is the action or situation that produces an event. What happens as a result of a cause is an *effect*.

▲ Revolutionary leaders and philosophers Lenin, Engels, and Marx

Learning the Skill

To identify cause-and-effect relationships, follow these steps:

- Identify two or more events or developments.
- Decide whether one event caused the other. Look for "clue words" such as *because, led to, brought about, produced, as a result of, so that, since,* and *therefore*.
- Look for logical relationships between events, such as "She overslept, and then she missed her bus."
- Identify the outcomes of events. Remember that some effects have more than one cause, and some causes lead to more than one effect. Also, an effect can become the cause of yet another effect.

Practicing the Skill

For each number below, identify which statement is the cause and which is the effect.

1. (A) Russia's capital was moved from coastal St. Petersburg to Moscow in the heart of the country.
   (B) The capital of Russia was threatened by an outside invasion.
2. (A) Revolutionary leaders seized control of the Russian government.
   (B) During World War I, shortages of food in Russian cities caused much starvation.
   (C) Discontent grew among the Russian people.
3. (A) The Soviet government kept prices for goods and services very low.
   (B) Many goods and services were in short supply in the Soviet Union.

Applying the Skill

In your local newspaper, read an article describing a current event. Determine at least one cause and one effect of that event. Show the cause-and-effect relationship in a diagram like the one here:

GO TO Practice key skills with Glencoe **Skillbuilder Interactive Workbook, Level 1.**

Practicing the Skill Answers

1. *Cause*—B; *Effect*—A
2. *Cause*—B; *First Effect*—C; *Second Effect*—A
3. *Cause*—A; *Effect*—B

Applying the Skill
Have students submit a copy of the newspaper article along with their diagrams. Check their responses for correct interpretation of the cause-and-effect relationship.

Chapter 14 Reading Review

Section 1 A Vast Land

Terms to Know
- steppe
- tundra
- permafrost
- taiga

Main Idea

Russia is a huge country with a cold climate due to its far northern location.

✓ Location Spanning two continents—Europe and Asia—Russia is the world's largest country.

✓ Region The western part of Russia is mostly plains. The eastern Siberian region is covered with mountains and plateaus.

✓ Region European Russia has the mildest climate, while most of Siberia, or Asian Russia, has cold high-latitude climate zones.

✓ Movement Inland waterways are important for moving goods through Russia, but many long rivers drain north into the frigid Arctic Ocean and freeze in winter.

Section 2 A Troubled History

Terms to Know
- czar
- serf
- industrialize
- communist state
- Cold War
- perestroika
- free enterprise system
- glasnost

Main Idea

The harsh rule of powerful leaders has often sparked violent uprisings in Russia.

✓ History Emperors known as czars ruled the Russian Empire from 1480 to 1917.

✓ History The czars expanded Russian territory to reach from Europe to the Pacific.

✓ Government Under the Communists, Russia became part of the Soviet Union.

✓ History In 1991 the Soviet Union broke apart into 15 independent republics.

◄ A train on the Trans-Siberian Railroad runs along Lake Baikal.

Reading Review

Use the Chapter 14 Reading Review to preview, review, condense, or reteach the chapter.

Preview/Review

Use the Terms to Know lists to help students review and study.

Activity Have students write the terms and definitions on index cards and group themselves into pairs. Have the pairs quiz each other on the terms.

Vocabulary PuzzleMaker CD-ROM reinforces the vocabulary terms used in Chapter 14.

The Interactive Tutor Self-Assessment CD-ROM allows students to review Chapter 14 content.

Condense

Have students read the Chapter 14 summary statements.

Guided Reading Activities

Audio Program

Reteach

Reteaching Activity

Reading Essentials and Study Guide

Reading Strategy Read to Write

Creating a Web Site Have students write an outline for their own Web site that summarizes Russian history. Students' outlines should show what the topic and main idea will be on each Web page. The outline might also suggest illustrations that they could include on each page. If students have time and interest, suggest that they design the opening page for the Web site or show how one of the detailed pages would look. L1

Assessment and Activities

GLENCOE TECHNOLOGY

MindJogger Videoquiz
Use MindJogger Videoquiz to review the Chapter 14 content.

Available in DVD and VHS

Using Key Terms

1.	d	6.	a
2.	f	7.	g
3.	i	8.	j
4.	c	9.	h
5.	e	10.	b

Reviewing the Main Ideas

11. The Arctic coast is blocked by ice for most of the year.
12. North European Plain
13. trains, rivers, and canals
14. It suffers from volcanic eruptions and earthquakes.
15. the Volga
16. Kiev
17. Ivan IV
18. 1922
19. because they opposed his actions
20. by allowing farmers and factory managers to make many of their own decisions

Chapter 14 Assessment and Activities

Using Key Terms

Match the terms in Part A with their definitions in Part B.

A.

1. permafrost
2. czar
3. perestroika
4. steppe
5. serf
6. taiga
7. glasnost
8. communist state
9. industrialize
10. tundra

B.

a. huge, subarctic evergreen forests
b. dry, treeless plains in the high latitudes
c. dry, treeless grasslands
d. permanently frozen lower layers of soil
e. farm laborer
f. former emperor of Russia
g. openness
h. rely more on manufacturing and less on farming
i. restructuring
j. government controls the economy

Reviewing the Main Ideas

Section 1 A Vast Land

11. **Human/Environment Interaction** Why is Russia unable to use ports along its Arctic coast for most of the year?
12. **Location** Which area of Russia has the mildest climate?
13. **Movement** What is an important means of transportation for people in Russia?
14. **Region** Why is the Kamchatka Peninsula considered part of the Ring of Fire?
15. **Place** What is the longest river in Europe?

Section 2 A Troubled History

16. **Location** Where was the earliest center of Russian civilization?
17. **History** Which czar used secret police to maintain strict control over the people?
18. **History** When was the Union of Soviet Socialist Republics formed?
19. **Government** Why did Stalin send people to Siberia?
20. **Economics** How did Gorbachev try to change the Soviet economy?

NATIONAL GEOGRAPHIC Russia's Landscape and History

Place Location Activity

On a separate sheet of paper, match the letters on the map with the numbered places listed below.

1. Ural Mountains
2. Kamchatka Peninsula
3. Lake Baikal
4. Volga River
5. Moscow
6. Don River
7. Siberia
8. Caspian Sea
9. Caucasus Mountains
10. St. Petersburg

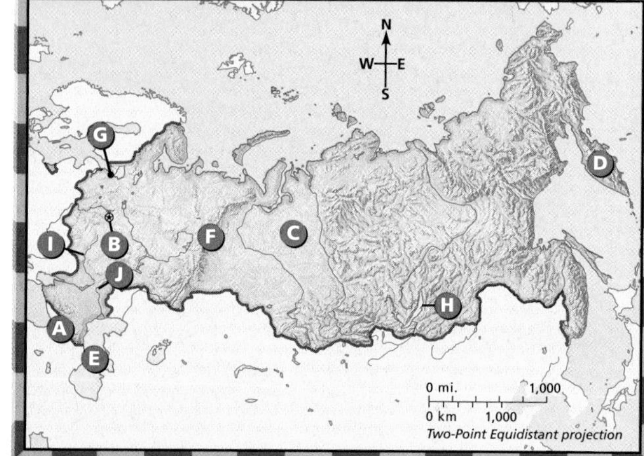

NATIONAL GEOGRAPHIC Place Location Activity

1.	F	6.	I
2.	D	7.	C
3.	H	8.	E
4.	J	9.	A
5.	B	10.	G

Critical Thinking

21. Because Russia was unprepared for war, its people suffered from food shortages and other deprivations. People blamed the czar for their troubles and discontent grew.
22. Possible answers: tundra, permafrost, taiga, mountains, Ring of Fire

Self-Check Quiz Visit ***The World and Its People*** Web site at twip.glencoe.com and click on **Chapter 14—Self-Check Quizzes** to prepare for the Chapter Test.

Critical Thinking

21. **Understanding Cause and Effect** How did World War I help lead to the Russian Revolution?
22. **Organizing Information** Create a diagram like this one. Complete it with four physical features in Siberia.

Comparing Regions Activity

23. **History** Catherine the Great expanded Russia's territory when she was czar in the eighteenth century. There are many other powerful women who have shaped the world's history. Create a list of five influential women, and include the region where they had influence. What do these women have in common?

Mental Mapping Activity

24. **Focusing on the Region** Create a simple outline map of Russia and label the following:
    - Arctic Ocean
    - Pacific Ocean
    - Vladivostok
    - Moscow
    - Ural Mountains
    - St. Petersburg
    - Siberia
    - Baltic Sea

Technology Skills Activity

25. **Developing Multimedia Presentations** Choose an ethnic or political problem that the Russian people have faced in the last 10 years. Research your choice and create a multimedia presentation on this problem. Include information on when, what, and where. Use pictures, maps, and time lines to make your presentation more visual.

Standardized Test Practice

Directions: Read the paragraph below, and then answer the question that follows.

You may be surprised to know that the former Soviet republic of Kazakhstan was—and still is—important to the exploration of outer space. The Russian space center Baikonur (by•kuh•NOOR) lies in south-central Kazakhstan. During the Soviet period, Baikonur was used for many space launches. Several historic "firsts in space" occurred here. For example, the first satellite was launched in 1957. The first crewed flight took place when cosmonaut Yuri Gagarin orbited the earth in 1961. In addition, the flight of the first woman in space, Valentina Tereshkova, was launched in 1963. After the Soviet collapse, the Russian-owned center remained in independent Kazakh territory.

1. The Soviet space program at Baikonur holds great importance, mostly because

F it is located in south-central Kazakhstan.

G it provides jobs for the people who live near the launch site.

H many "firsts in space" flights were launched from it.

J Valentina Tereshkova was the first woman in space.

Test-Taking Tip: When a question uses the word *most* or *mostly,* it means that more than one answer may be correct. Your job is to pick the *best* answer. For example, Baikonur's location in Kazakhstan may be important to the people who live near it, which is answer G. Another answer, however, provides a more general reason for Baikonur's importance.

Assessment and Activities

Standardized Test Practice

1. H

Tested Objectives: Analyzing information, drawing conclusions

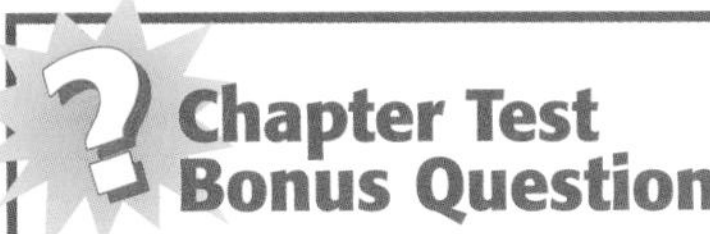

Chapter Test Bonus Question

This question may be used for extra credit on the chapter test.

What city was once the capital of Russia under the czars? *(St. Petersburg)*

Have students visit the Web site at twip.glencoe.com to review Chapter 14 and take the Self-Check Quiz.

Dinah Zike's Foldables

Culminating Activity Have students write a paragraph that explains whether they would like to live in the Soviet Union or present-day Russia, using the facts from their foldables.

Comparing Regions Activity

23. Students might also describe how the women influenced the regions.

Mental Mapping Activity

24. This exercise helps students visualize Russia and its physical features. All attempts at freehand mapping should be accepted.

Technology Skills Activity

25. After students have completed their presentations, have them discuss whether there are similar problems in the United States.

Ask students if they have ever experienced severe winter weather. Have volunteers describe the difficulty people and machines have in functioning under these conditions. Point out that armies can have the same problems, especially large armies of hundreds of thousands of troops (as in the cases of the French and German invasions). Then have students read the feature describing the history-changing effects of Russia's climate. L1

2 Teach

Synthesizing Information

Tell students that physical features—like weather—can have a major impact on an army's success or failure in battle. Give students a list of physical features—such as forests, swamps, hills, deserts, or islands—and ask how armies could benefit or face difficulties from having to fight or move through that feature. L1

Meeting National Standards

Geography for Life

The following standards are met in the Student Edition feature:

EE5 Environment and Society: Standard 15

EE6 The Uses of Geography: Standard 17

Napoleon and troops retreat from Russia.

RUSSIA'S STRATEGY: Freeze Your Foes

Winter weather can cancel school and stop traffic. It can even change history. Such was the case when French ruler Napoleon Bonaparte thought he had conquered the Russian Empire.

In fact, Napoleon did not want to conquer Russia. His real enemy was Great Britain. Napoleon wanted Russia and other countries to stop trading with Great Britain. Yet Russia's czar, Alexander I, refused. By 1812, Napoleon was determined to change Alexander's mind. In June, leading an army of more than half a million soldiers, Napoleon invaded Russia. To reach Moscow and the czar, Napoleon had to fight his way across the Russian countryside.

By the time Napoleon's battle-weary forces reached Moscow, supplies were scarce. All along the route, Russians had burned villages as they retreated, leaving no food or shelter. Reaching Moscow, Napoleon found the city in flames and nearly empty of people. The czar had moved to St. Petersburg. Napoleon took Moscow without a fight, but most of the city was in ashes.

Winter Wins a War

With winter approaching, Napoleon waited in Moscow for Alexander I to offer peace. The czar remained silent, however. With dwindling supplies and many of his troops lacking winter clothes, Napoleon was forced to retreat. He tried to take a new way back, but the Russians made Napoleon use the same ruined route he had used before. Armed bands of Russians attacked at every turn. Starving and desperate to escape the bitter cold, several of Napoleon's soldiers threw themselves into burning buildings. Most of Napoleon's troops never made it out of Russia.

History Repeats

More than a century later, during World War II, Russia's winter was again a mighty foe. On June 22, 1941, Adolf Hitler's German army invaded Russia, then part of the Soviet Union. As the German army fought its way to Moscow, Soviet leader Joseph Stalin issued his own "scorched-earth policy." Soviet citizens burned anything of use to the invaders. By December, German troops were within sight of the Kremlin, Moscow's government center, when winter struck.

Snow buried the invaders. Temperatures fell below freezing. Grease in guns and oil in vehicles froze solid. German soldiers suffered frostbite and died. The Soviets were better clothed and had winterized their tanks and trucks. Stalin's troops pushed back the German army. Once again the Russians triumphed with help from "General Winter."

QUESTIONS

1. After Napoleon conquered Moscow in 1812, why did he retreat?
2. How did Russia's winter affect fighting in World War II?

420

German prisoners of Russia's winter ▶

Answers to the Questions

1. He was waiting for the czar to offer peace, but the czar never did. Napoleon's army was without food and supplies, so it could not stay any longer in Moscow.
2. Snow stopped the equipment and the soldiers; bitter cold prevented vehicles from working and froze the German soldiers.

NATIONAL GEOGRAPHIC

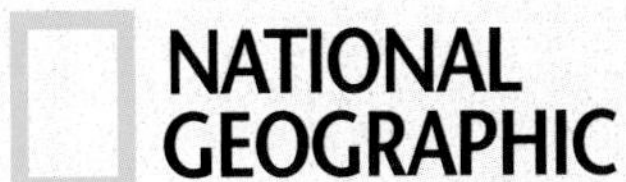

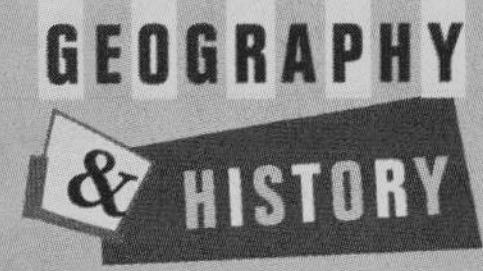

Average Winter Temperatures
EUROPE
Moscow
RUSSIA
ASIA
N
W
E
S
Napoleon's Advance, June–October 1812
German Forces Front Line, December 1941
< -40°F
-40° to -31°F
-30° to -21°F
-20° to -11°F
-10° to 0°F
0° to 10°F
11° to 20°F
21° to 30°F
> 30°F

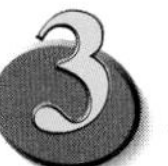

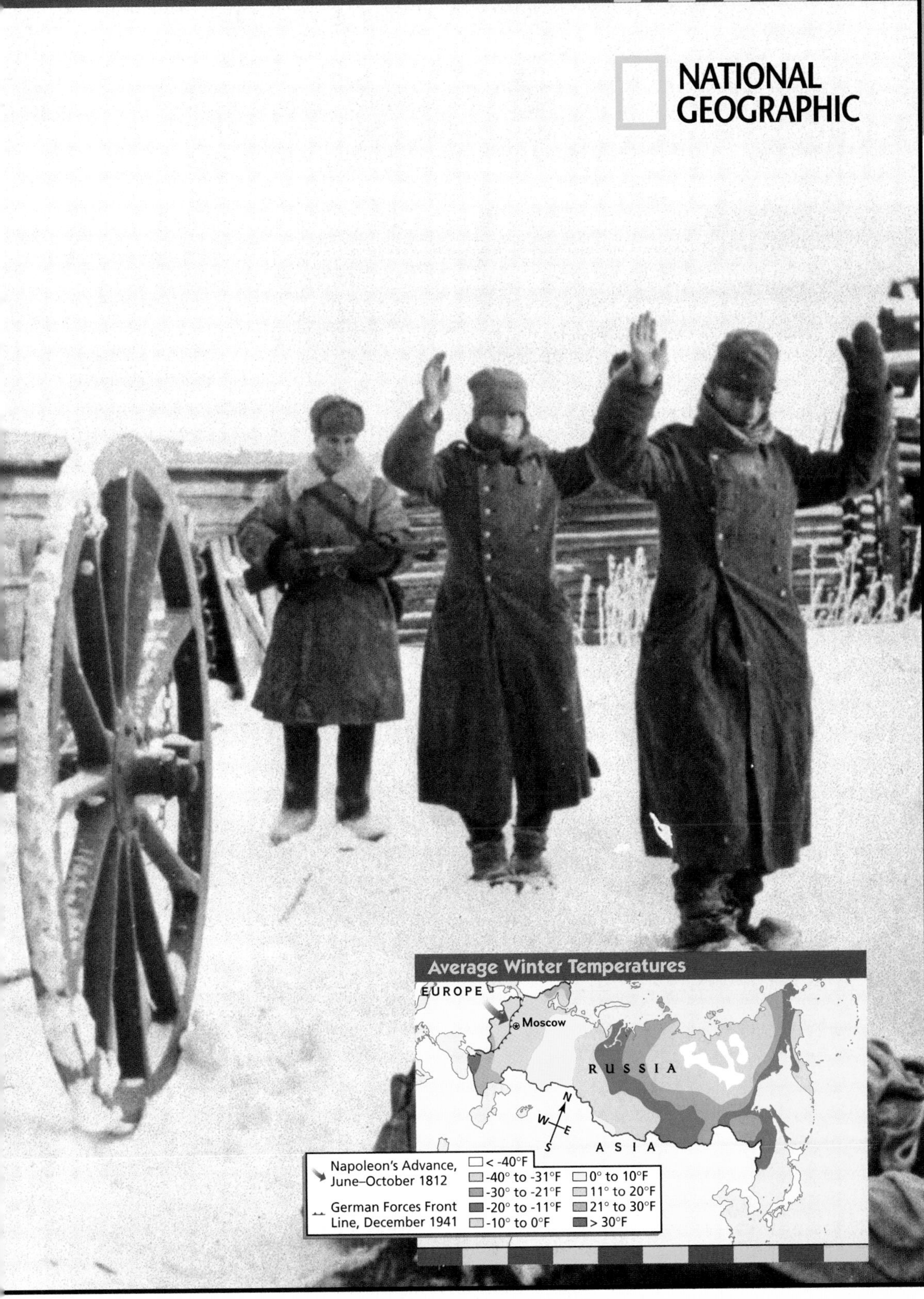

Geography and History Activity

Annotated Maps Have students conduct further research about Napoleon's or Hitler's invasions of Russia. Have them prepare an annotated map that highlights key events and places in these two conflicts. L2

GEOGRAPHY & HISTORY

Time Line

- **June 1812:** Napoleon's army invades Russia
- **Sept 1812:** Napoleon takes Moscow
- **Nov 1812:** Retreat finished
- **June 1941:** German army invades Russia
- **July 1941:** German army reaches 400 miles into Russia
- **Oct 1941:** German army advances on Moscow
- **Dec 1941:** Advance on Moscow slowed by winter
- **Dec 1941:** Soviet counter-attack begins to drive Germans back

3 Assess

Have students answer the questions on the previous page.

4 Close

Have students take the role of a Russian in either 1812 during Napoleon's invasion or in 1941 during Hitler's invasion. Have them write a poem, essay, or song in praise of "General Winter."

Chapter 15 Resources

Note: The following materials may be used when teaching Chapter 15. Section level support materials are shown at point of use in the margins of the Teacher Wraparound Edition.

Timesaving Tools

TeacherWorks™ **All-In-One Planner and Resource Center**

- **Interactive Teacher Edition** See the **Interactive Teacher Edition** CD-ROM to electronically integrate your Teacher Wraparound Edition and blackline masters.
- **Interactive Lesson Planner** Organize your week, month, semester, or year with all the lesson helps you need. The **Interactive Lesson Planner** CD-ROM contains all Chapter 15 resources.

Use Glencoe's **Presentation Plus!** multimedia teacher tool to easily present dynamic lessons that visually excite your students. Using Microsoft PowerPoint® you can customize the presentations to create your own personalized lessons.

TEACHING TRANSPARENCIES

Graphic Organizer Transparency 13 L2

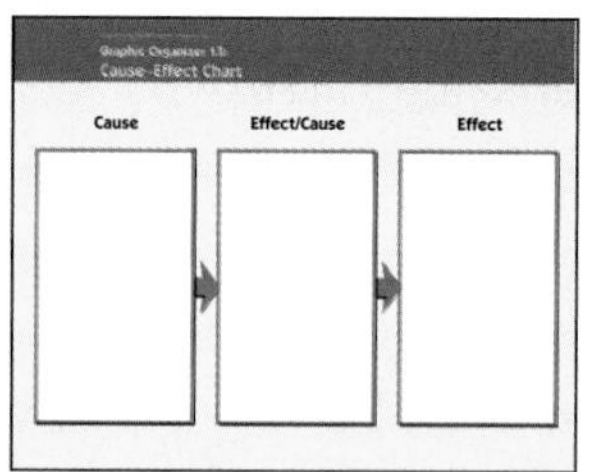

In-text Map Transparency L1

FOLDABLES™ Study Organizer

Dinah Zike's Foldables

Foldables are three-dimensional, interactive graphic organizers that help students practice basic writing skills, review key vocabulary terms, and identify main ideas. Additional chapter activities can be found in the ***Reading and Study Skills Foldables*** booklet.

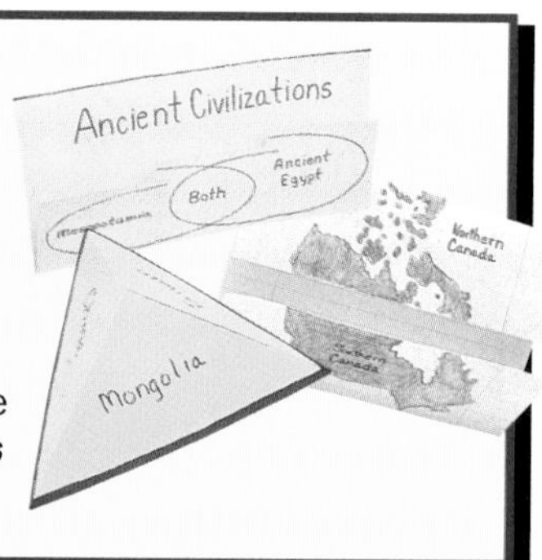

MAP AND GEOGRAPHY SKILLS

Chapter Map Activity L2

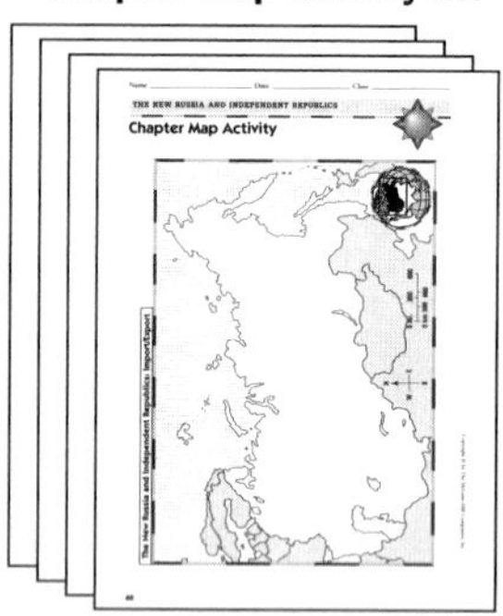

GeoLab Activity L2

READING SUPPORT

Vocabulary Activity L1

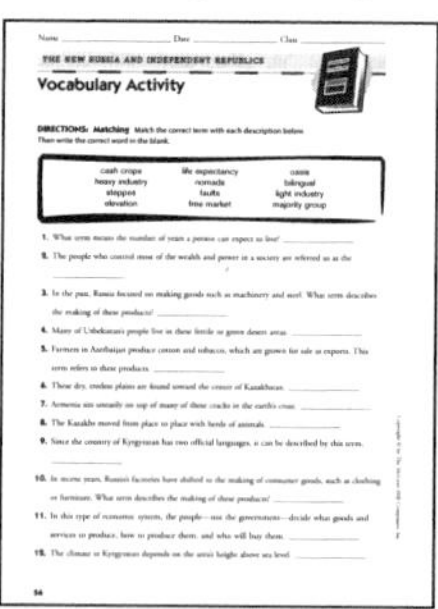

Workbook Activity L1

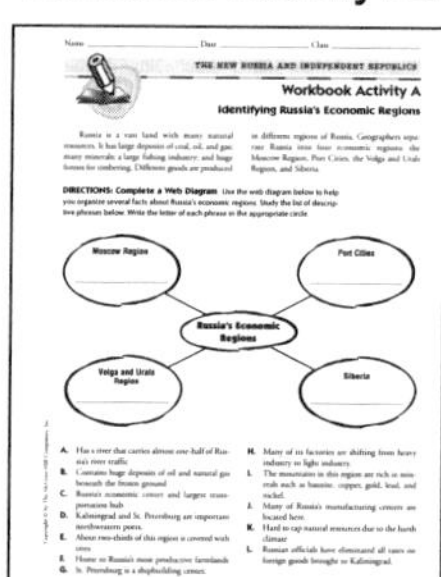

Reading and Writing Skills Activity L1/ELL

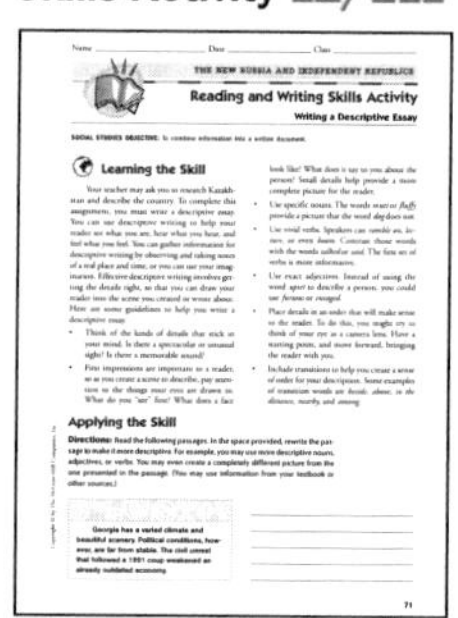

DIFFERENTIATED INSTRUCTION

Use these review and reinforcement materials to help less-proficient readers, English learners, and gifted and talented students.

Reteaching Activity L1

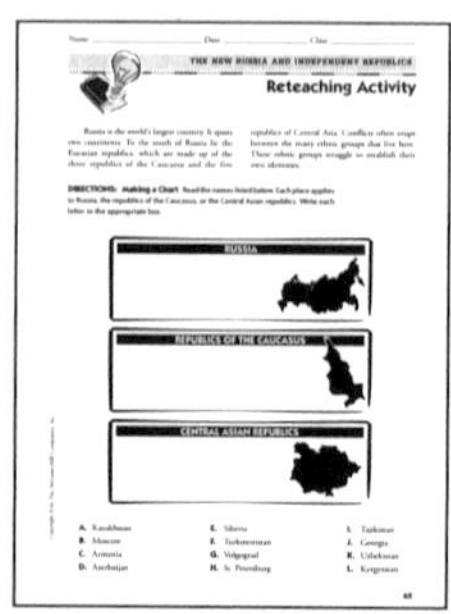

Chapter Skills Review L2

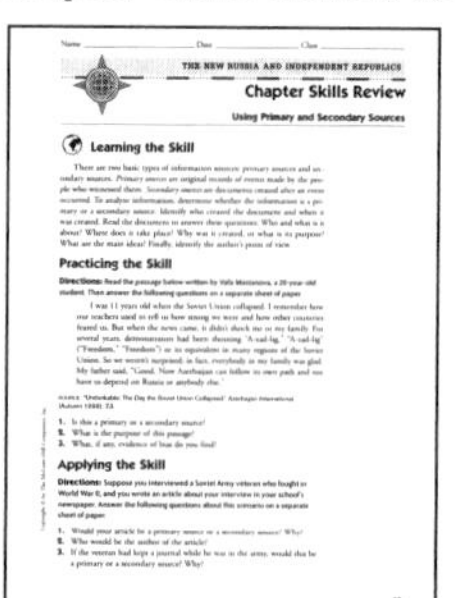

Cooperative Learning Activity L1/ELL

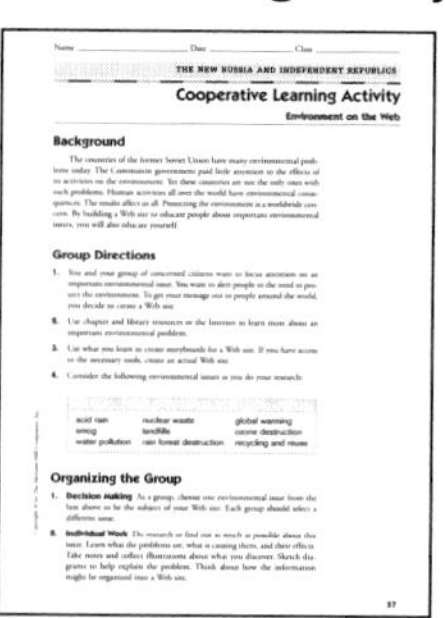

Enrichment Activity L3

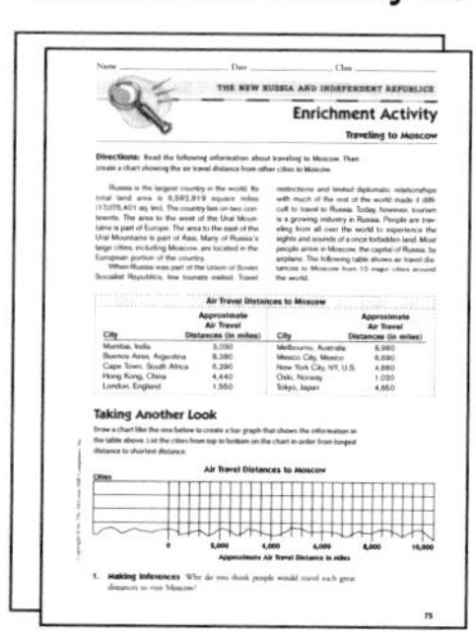

ASSESSMENT

Chapter Test, Form A L2

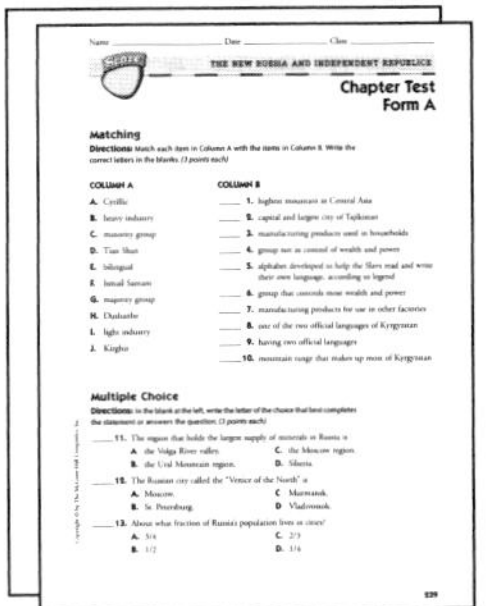

Chapter Test, Form B L2

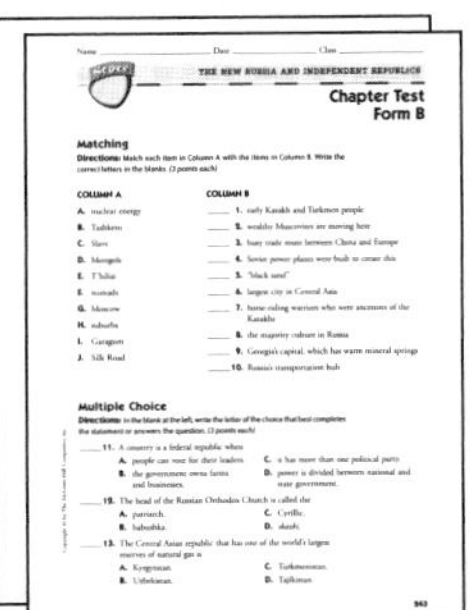

Performance Assessment Activity L1/ELL

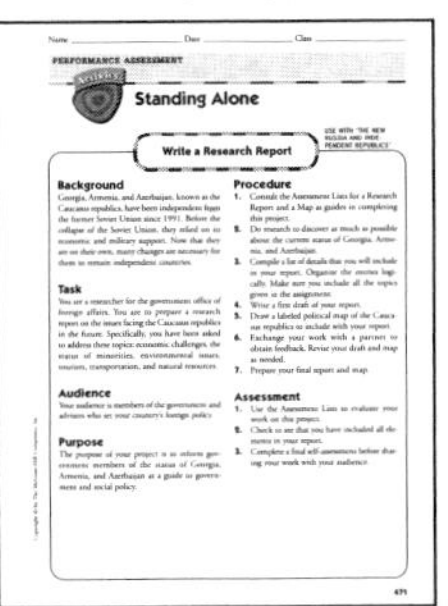

ExamView® Pro Testmaker CD-ROM

STANDARDIZED ASSESSMENT SKILLS

Critical Thinking Skills Activity L2

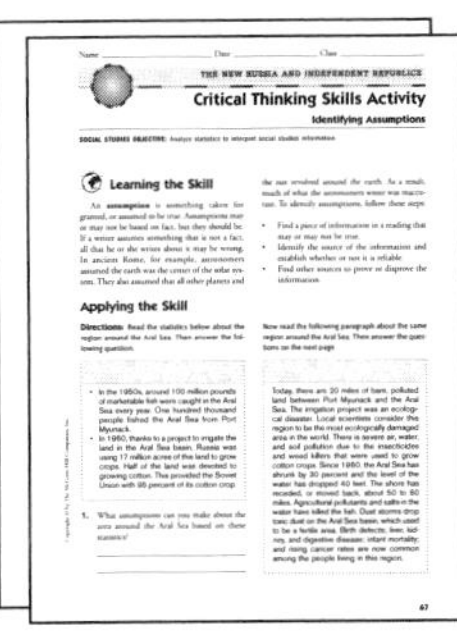

Map and Graph Skills Activity L2

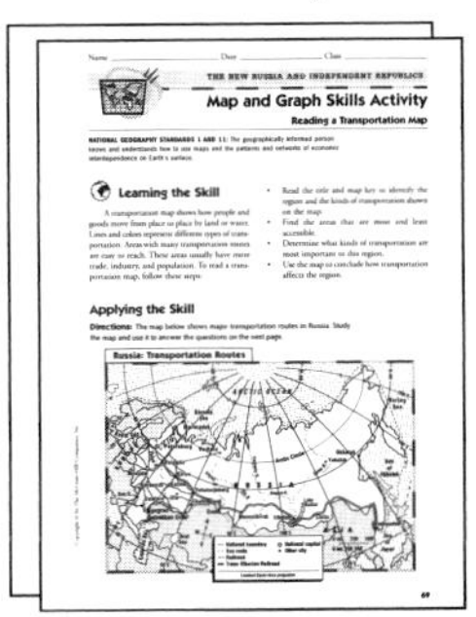

Standardized Test Skills Practice Workbook Activity L2

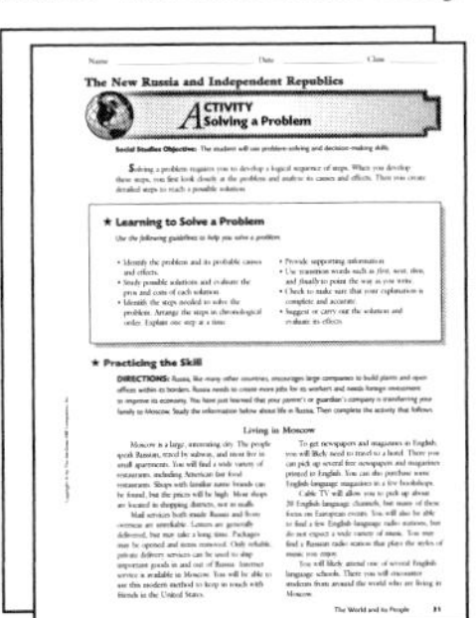

HOME INVOLVEMENT

Take-Home Review Activity L1

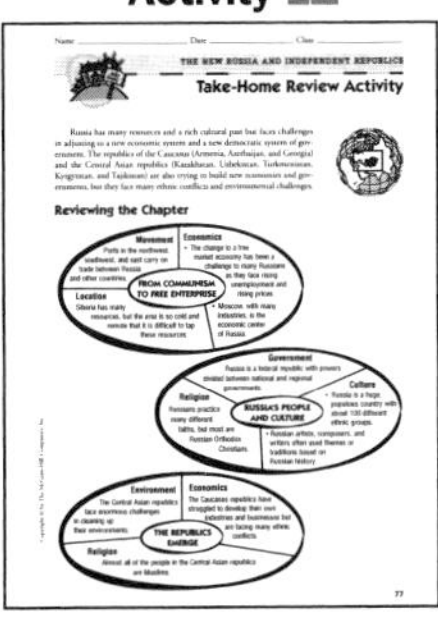

MULTIMEDIA

- National Geographic's The World and Its People
- MindJogger Videoquiz
- Vocabulary PuzzleMaker CD-ROM
- Interactive Tutor Self-Assessment CD-ROM
- ExamView® Pro Testmaker CD-ROM
- TeacherWorks CD-ROM
- StudentWorks CD-ROM
- Skillbuilder Interactive Workbook CD-ROM, Level 1
- Presentation Plus! CD-ROM
- Audio Program

SPANISH RESOURCES

The following Spanish language materials are available in the Spanish Resources binder:

- Spanish Summaries
- Spanish Vocabulary Activities
- Spanish Guided Reading Activities
- Spanish Quizzes and Tests
- Spanish Take-Home Review Activities
- Spanish Reteaching Activities

Meeting National Standards

Geography for Life

The following standards are covered in Chapter 15:

Section 1 EE1 The World in Spatial Terms: Standards 1, 2, 3
EE2 Places and Regions: Standards 4, 5
EE4 Human Systems: Standards 10, 11
EE5 Environment and Society: Standards 14, 15, 16

Section 2 EE4 Human Systems: Standards 9, 10, 12, 13

Section 3 EE1 The World in Spatial Terms: Standards 1, 2, 3
EE4 Human Systems: Standards 9, 10, 13
EE6 The Uses of Geography: Standards 17, 18

State and Local Objectives

Chapter 15 Planning Guide

SECTION RESOURCES

Daily Objectives	Reproducible Resources	Multimedia Resources
Section 1 **From Communism to Free Enterprise** 1. Describe changes in Russia's economy. 2. Compare Russia's economic regions. 3. Discuss Russia's environmental issues.	Reproducible Lesson Plan Daily Lecture and Discussion Notes Note-taking Guide Guided Reading Activity* Reading Essentials and Study Guide* Section Quiz*	Daily Focus Skills Transparency Vocabulary PuzzleMaker CD-ROM Interactive Tutor Self-Assessment CD-ROM ExamView® Pro Testmaker CD-ROM Presentation Plus! CD-ROM
Section 2 **Russia's People and Culture** 1. Discuss Russia's political and ethnic challenges. 2. Describe daily life in Russia. 3. Examine Russia's cultural traditions.	Reproducible Lesson Plan Daily Lecture and Discussion Notes Note-taking Guide Guided Reading Activity* Reading Essentials and Study Guide* Section Quiz*	Daily Focus Skills Transparency Vocabulary PuzzleMaker CD-ROM Interactive Tutor Self-Assessment CD-ROM ExamView® Pro Testmaker CD-ROM Presentation Plus! CD-ROM
Section 3 **The Republics Emerge** 1. Describe how the people in the Caucasus Republics earn their living. 2. Explain how Soviet rule affected the Central Asian Republics.	Reproducible Lesson Plan Daily Lecture and Discussion Notes Note-taking Guide Guided Reading Activity* Reading Essentials and Study Guide* Section Quiz*	Daily Focus Skills Transparency GeoQuiz Transparency In-text Map Transparency Vocabulary PuzzleMaker CD-ROM Interactive Tutor Self-Assessment CD-ROM ExamView® Pro Testmaker CD-ROM Presentation Plus! CD-ROM MindJogger Videoquiz

00:00 **Out of Time?** Assign the **Reading Essentials and Study Guide*** for this chapter.

*Also available in Spanish

KEY TO ABILITY LEVELS

Teaching strategies have been coded for varying learning styles and abilities.

L1 **BASIC** activities for all students

L2 **AVERAGE** activities for average to above-average students

L3 **CHALLENGING** activities for above-average students

ELL **ENGLISH LANGUAGE LEARNER** activities

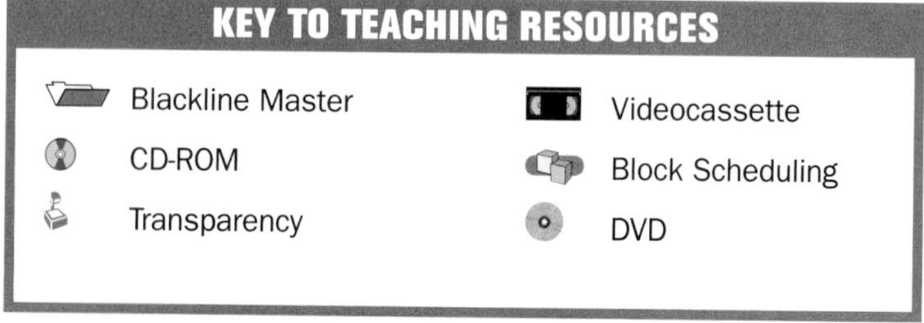

Teacher to Teacher

A Geographic Coat of Arms

April Robinson
Baxter Elementary School
Baxter, Tennessee

Have students interview family members to find out the countries of origin and careers of early family members. After plotting a family tree, students should design a coat of arms on a large piece of poster board. A map of the world should be the background. Draw the routes that family members took to arrive in the United States. Include drawings of ships, planes, and other types of transportation used. Embellish the coats of arms with samples of items that portray the careers of ancestors as they migrated toward your home city or town (slivers of wood to portray lumbering or shipbuilding, seeds to portray farming, and so on). Then have students carefully paint their final product.

Meeting Special Needs

In addition to the Differentiated Instruction strategies found in each section, the following resources are also suitable for your special needs students:

- ***ExamView® Pro Testmaker CD-ROM*** allows teachers to tailor tests by reducing answer choices.
- The ***Audio Program*** includes the entire narrative of the student edition so that less-proficient readers can listen to the words as they read them.
- The ***Reading Essentials and Study Guide*** provides the same content as the student edition but is written two grade levels below the textbook.
- ***Guided Reading Activities*** give less-proficient readers point-by-point instructions to increase comprehension as they read each textbook section.
- ***Enrichment Activities*** include a stimulating collection of readings and activities for gifted and talented students.

NATIONAL GEOGRAPHIC TEACHER'S CORNER

Index to National Geographic Magazine:

The following articles may be used for research relating to this chapter:

- "Stellar's Sea-Eagles," by Klaus Nigge, March 1999.
- *Biodiversity,* a National Geographic Special Edition, February 1999.
- "A Comeback for the Cossacks," by Mike Edwards, November 1998.

National Geographic Society Products:

To order the following products for use with this chapter, call National Geographic Society at 1-800-368-2728:

- *Russia: Then and Now Series* (Video)
- *Capitalism, Communism, Socialism Series* (3 Videos)
- *National Geographic Desk Reference* (Book)

NGS ONLINE

Access National Geographic's Web site for current events, activities, links, interactive features, and archives.
www.nationalgeographic.com

MapMachine

Find the latest coverage of geography in the news, atlas updates, cartographic activities with interactive maps, an online map store, and links at www.nationalgeographic.com/maps

SOCIAL STUDIES Online

Use our Web site for additional resources. All essential content is covered in the Student Edition.

You and your students can visit twip.glencoe.com, the Web site companion to *The World and Its People*. This innovative integration of electronic and print media offers your students a wealth of opportunities. The student text directs students to the Web site for the following options:

- Chapter Overviews
- Student Web Activities
- Self-Check Quizzes
- Textbook Updates

Answers are provided for you in the Web Activity Lesson Plan. Additional Web resources and Interactive Tutor puzzles are also available.

Introducing Chapter 15

Social Studies Online

Introduce students to chapter content and key terms by having them access Chapter Overview 15 at twip.glencoe.com

Chapter Objectives

1. Describe the economy of Russia.
2. Discuss the cultural aspects of Russia.
3. Explain how Russia's newly independent neighbors have recently changed.

GLENCOE TECHNOLOGY

NATIONAL GEOGRAPHIC

The World and Its People Video Program

Chapters 14 and 18 Russia and Its Neighbors

The following segments enhance the study of this chapter:

- **The Biggest Cat**
- **Lake Baikal**
- **Oil Boom**

MindJogger Videoquiz

Use MindJogger Videoquiz to preview the Chapter 15 content.

Both programs available in DVD and VHS

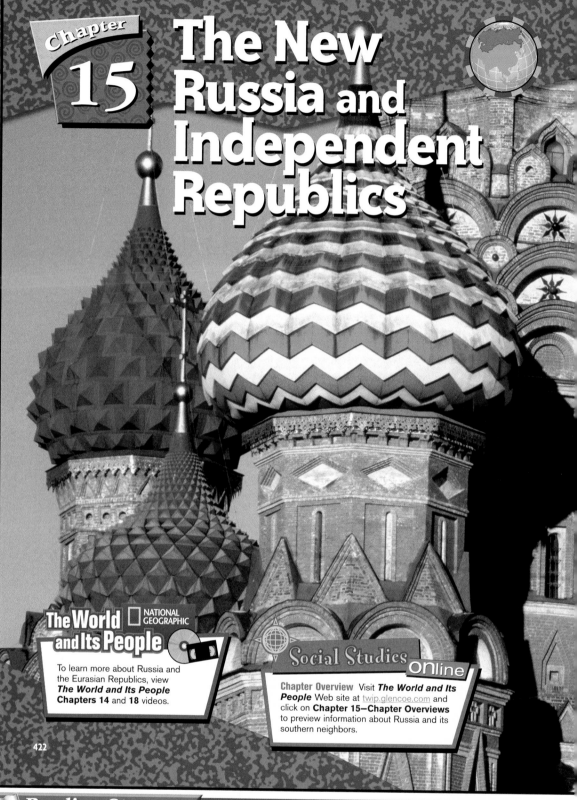

Chapter 15 The New Russia and Independent Republics

The World and Its People NATIONAL GEOGRAPHIC

To learn more about Russia and the Eurasian Republics, view ***The World and Its People*** **Chapters 14** and **18** videos.

Social Studies Online

Chapter Overview Visit ***The World and Its People*** Web site at twip.glencoe.com and click on **Chapter 15—Chapter Overviews** to preview information about Russia and its southern neighbors.

422

Reading Strategy — Purpose for Reading

A **Venn diagram** is an excellent graphic organizer for teaching students to identify similarities and differences between two or more ideas. Draw two overlapping circles on the board. Above the left circle, write "Old Russia (Soviet Union)." Above the right circle, write "New Russia and Independent States." Write above where the two circles overlap "Both." Have students copy the Venn diagram in their notebooks. Students should take notes as they read and write these notes under the appropriate categories. Have students discuss their Venn diagrams with partners. Students should add and correct information to their diagrams as needed. L1

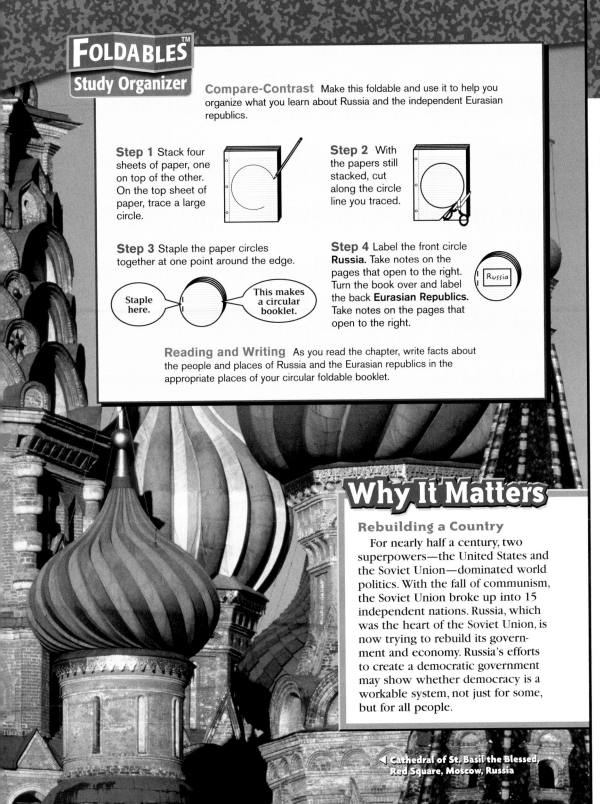

FOLDABLES™ Study Organizer

Compare-Contrast Make this foldable and use it to help you organize what you learn about Russia and the independent Eurasian republics.

Step 1 Stack four sheets of paper, one on top of the other. On the top sheet of paper, trace a large circle.

Step 2 With the papers still stacked, cut along the circle line you traced.

Step 3 Staple the paper circles together at one point around the edge.

Staple here.

This makes a circular booklet.

Step 4 Label the front circle **Russia.** Take notes on the pages that open to the right. Turn the book over and label the back **Eurasian Republics.** Take notes on the pages that open to the right.

Russia

Reading and Writing As you read the chapter, write facts about the people and places of Russia and the Eurasian republics in the appropriate places of your circular foldable booklet.

Why It Matters

Rebuilding a Country

For nearly half a century, two superpowers—the United States and the Soviet Union—dominated world politics. With the fall of communism, the Soviet Union broke up into 15 independent nations. Russia, which was the heart of the Soviet Union, is now trying to rebuild its government and economy. Russia's efforts to create a democratic government may show whether democracy is a workable system, not just for some, but for all people.

◀ Cathedral of St. Basil the Blessed, Red Square, Moscow, Russia

Dinah Zike's Foldables

Purpose Students make and use a foldable to help them organize the similarities and differences between Russia and the Eurasian republics—Russia's southern neighbors. As students read the chapter and fill in information on their foldables, they analyze the similarities and the differences of the people, places, and economies of Russia and its southern neighbors.

Have students complete the ***Reading and Study Skills Foldables*** activity for this chapter.

Why It Matters

On the board write: Armenia, Georgia, Azerbaijan, Kazakhstan, Kyrgyzstan, Tajikistan, Uzbekistan, and Turkmenistan. Ask students what they know about these countries. There will probably be little response. Assign a group of students to each country. Have each group locate its country on a map and find out information about the country's economy, government, and social issues since becoming independent from the Soviet Union.

About the Photo

Ask your students if anyone can identify the building in the photo, what it might be used for, and what is special about its features. The cathedral was built by Ivan the Terrible in the sixteenth century to commemorate a Russian victory. It is actually eight churches built around a ninth, all on the same foundation. A tenth church was added later over the grave of Basil the Blessed, and that is how the cathedral got its present name. The cathedral is located in Red Square, a vast open space that has been the site of military parades and celebrations, as well as demonstrations. **Ask: What makes this cathedral unique to Russia? What are the similarities and differences between it and other cathedrals found in Europe and the United States?**

Focus

Section Objectives

1. Describe changes in Russia's economy.
2. Compare Russia's economic regions.
3. Discuss Russia's environmental issues.

BELLRINGER
Skillbuilder Activity

Project transparency and have students answer the question.

Daily Focus Skills Transparency

DAILY FOCUS SKILLS TRANSPARENCY
The New Russia and Independent Republics
Section 1

ANSWER: People have more choices but may be unemployed and unable to afford goods.
Teacher Tip: Explain to students that freedom to choose can have positive and negative consequences.

Comparing and Contrasting

COMMUNISM	FREE ENTERPRISE SYSTEM
Government decides what products to make.	Business managers decide what products to make.
All people have jobs.	People can be unemployed.
People work in assigned jobs.	People can choose their jobs.
Limited goods and services available.	Wide choice of goods and services available.
Prices of goods and services kept low.	Prices of goods and services rise and fall with supply and demand.

Directions: Answer the following question based on the information given.

How has the move from communism to a free enterprise system given Russian people more choices but less certainty?

Reading Preview

- **Activating Prior Knowledge** Ask students to identify economic problems that some Americans face. As students read, have them note if Russians have similar problems.

- **Preteaching Vocabulary** Remind students to slow down their reading when they encounter difficult vocabulary terms.

From Communism to Free Enterprise

Guide to Reading

Main Idea

Russia has many resources but faces challenges in adjusting to a new economic system.

Terms to Know

- free market economy
- heavy industry
- light industry
- nuclear energy
- life expectancy

Reading Strategy

Create a chart like this one. Then list at least two facts about the economy of each region.

Region	Facts
Moscow	
Port Cities	
Siberia	
Volga and Urals	

NATIONAL GEOGRAPHIC Exploring Our World

Do you see people selling food on the street where you live? Many older Russians are poor. To earn extra money, these resourceful people grow food or bake bread. Then they sell their goods in busy areas, often using baby carriages as food carts. Russians today are slowly changing the way they earn their livings.

The fall of communism turned the economies of Russia, the other Soviet republics, and the Soviet satellite nations upside down. All of the new governments turned to a free market economy (also called a free enterprise economy or capitalism). In a **free market economy**, the people—not the government—decide what goods and services to produce, how to produce them, and who will buy them.

Difficult Changes in Russia

Changing to a free market economy has not been easy. In Chapter 13, you read about the economic challenges facing many eastern European countries. Most of these nations were either Soviet republics or satellites. Some, such as Ukraine and the Czech Republic, have been able to prosper from capitalism faster than other countries, such as Slovakia or Romania. All, however, have had to learn how to make changes. In this section, we will focus on the changes in the economy of Russia.

Section Resources

Reproducible Masters

- Reproducible Lesson Plan
- Daily Lecture and Discussion Notes
- Note-taking Guide
- Guided Reading Activity
- Reading Essentials and Study Guide
- Section Quiz

Transparencies

- Daily Focus Skills Transparency

Multimedia

- Vocabulary PuzzleMaker CD-ROM
- Interactive Tutor Self-Assessment CD-ROM
- Presentation Plus! CD-ROM
- ExamView® Pro Testmaker CD-ROM

The map below shows that Russia has many resources and manufacturing areas. Factory managers can decide what products to make from these resources. People can choose their own careers and open businesses—such as restaurants, stores, or computer companies. People now can make their own decisions, but those decisions do not always lead to success. Businesses can fail. People may become unemployed. Under communism, everybody had jobs. Workers today can lose their jobs if business is poor.

In addition, the government no longer sets prices for food and other goods. When prices were set low, the Russian people could afford the goods, but they often faced shortages. Without government controls, prices have risen. Higher prices make it harder to buy necessities such as food and clothing. Eventually, however, the higher prices and profits will encourage more manufacturers to start producing goods and services. The competition among producers will increase supplies and drive prices down.

In the meantime, though, a large number of Russians remain poor. These people lack the money to buy the consumer goods that are

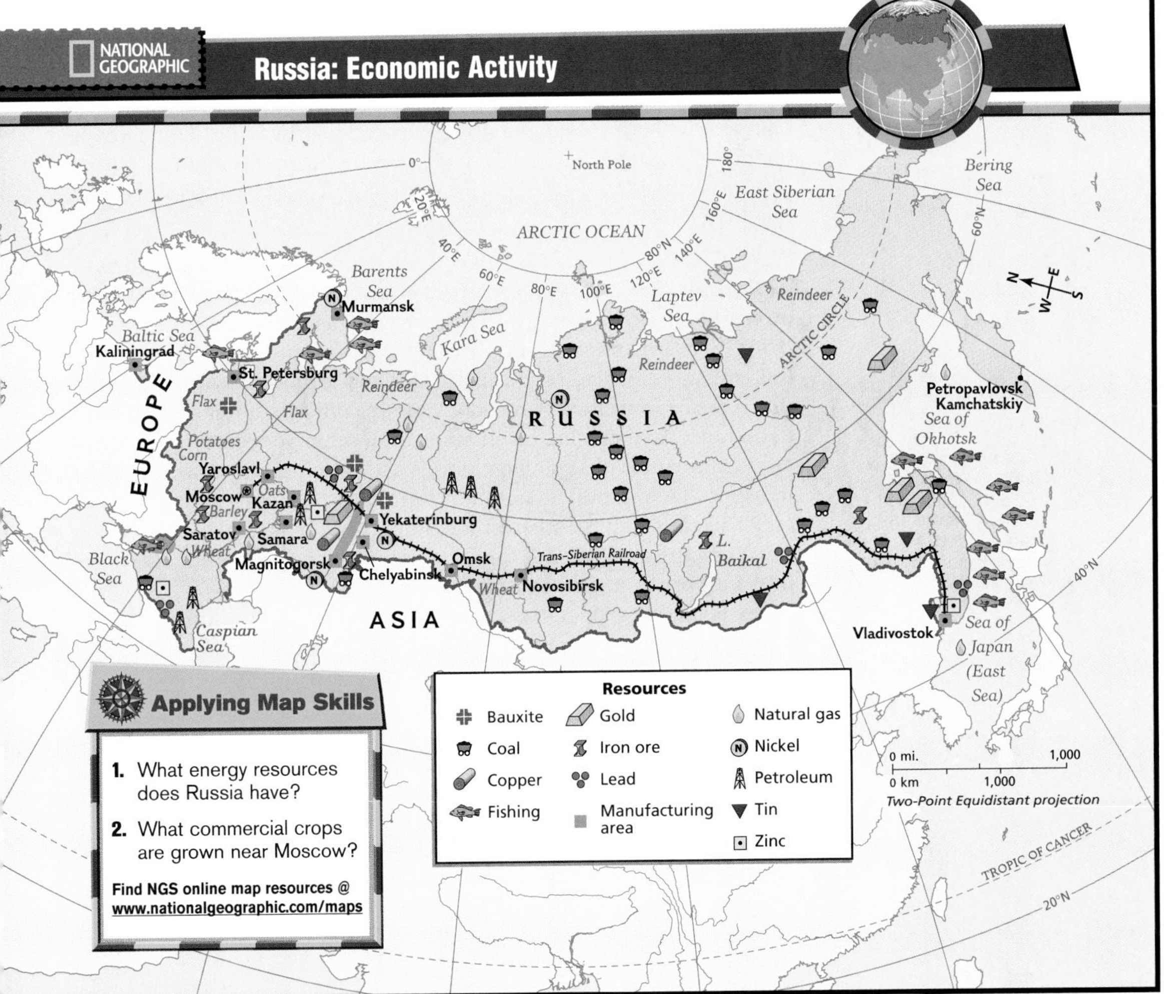

Applying Map Skills

1. What energy resources does Russia have?
2. What commercial crops are grown near Moscow?

Find NGS online map resources @ www.nationalgeographic.com/maps

Chapter 15
Section 1, pages 424–428

2 TEACH

Reading Strategy

Organizing Information
Have students create a chart with the economic regions as column headings. Have them write these row labels: "Location," "Resources," "Industry," and "Agriculture." As they read, have them fill in the chart with information from the text. **L1**

Daily Lecture and Discussion Notes

THE NEW RUSSIA AND INDEPENDENT REPUBLICS

Daily Lecture and Discussion Notes
From Communism to Free Enterprise

Did You Know? Murmansk, located halfway between Moscow and the North Pole, is surrounded by tundra. The people of Murmansk live with 24 hours of darkness during all of December and most of January. The city is home to Russia's nuclear-powered ships known as ice-breakers.

I. Difficult Changes in Russia

A. The fall of communism turned Russia's economy upside down. The new Russian government turned to a **free market economy,** the system followed in the United States. Under a free market economy, the people, not the government, decide what businesses to start and run.

...my has not been easy. Under communism,

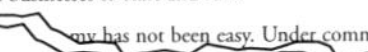

Applying Map Skills

Answers
1. coal, petroleum, natural gas
2. barley and oats

Skills Practice
Where are most of Russia's mineral resources found? *(Siberia)*

Reading Strategy — Reading the Text

Understanding Vocabulary Students should use a dictionary or the Glossary to help them understand words if they are having difficulty understanding the textbook's definition. Tell students that a dictionary provides the pronunciation and meaning(s) of words. They also give other forms of the word, their parts of speech, and synonyms. A glossary provides pronunciations and definitions of words found only in the textbook. Have students find the vocabulary terms in a dictionary and the Glossary and discuss their similarities and differences. **L1**

*Use the **Reading Skills Handbook** for more reading strategies.*

Chapter 15

Section 1, pages 424–428

Reading Check Answer

Supplies increase and drive prices down.

Objectives and answers to the Student Web Activity can be found in the Web Activity Lesson Plan at twip.glencoe.com

L1/ELL

Guided Reading Activity

Name ________ Date ________ Class ________

THE NEW RUSSIA AND INDEPENDENT REPUBLICS

Guided Reading Activity 1

From Communism to Free Enterprise

DIRECTIONS: Outlining Reading the section and completing the outline below will help you learn more about Russia's economy. Refer to your textbook to fill in the blanks.

I. Difficult Changes in Russia
   A. After the fall of communism, Russia turned to a ________ economy.
   B. Without government controls, ________ have risen.
   C. Eventually, the competition among producers will increase ________ and drive prices ________.

Did You Know?

In the past, Russian and Soviet governments banished criminals and political prisoners to the frigid lands of Siberia. Prisoners were forced to work in factories and mines. Today the Russian government offers high salaries and long vacations to attract workers to the region.

slowly becoming available. Many survive by standing in long lines to receive food given away by government agencies. Turn to the TIME Perspectives on page 441 to learn more about the challenges that Russians are facing in their shift to a free market economy.

Reading Check How does competition among producers affect supplies and prices?

Russia's Economic Regions

Russia is rich in resources and depends on them for economic growth. Russia is divided into four different economic regions: the Moscow region, Port Cities, Siberia, and the Volga and Urals region.

The Moscow Region About 800 years old, **Moscow** is the political and cultural center of Russia. Moscow is also the largest city, the country's economic center, and the largest transportation hub. Many of Russia's manufacturing centers are located in or near Moscow. In the past, most of the country's factories focused on heavy industry, or the production of goods such as machinery, mining equipment, and steel. In recent years, more factories have shifted to light industry, or the production of consumer goods such as clothing, shoes, furniture, and household products. High-technology services and electronics industries also have emerged in Moscow.

Farming takes place in the Moscow region as well. Farmers raise dairy cattle, barley, oats, potatoes, corn, and sugar beets. Other crops include flax, which is used to make textiles. Railroads and canals that crisscross the Moscow region are used to transport farm products and raw materials.

Web Activity Visit ***The World and Its People*** Web site at twip.glencoe.com and click on **Chapter 15–Student Web Activities** to learn more about St. Petersburg.

Port Cities Russia has two important northwestern ports—**Kaliningrad** and **St. Petersburg.** Look at the economic activity map on page 425. Do you see that Russia owns a small piece of land on the Baltic Sea separated from the rest of the country? The port of Kaliningrad is located on this land. This city is Russia's only Baltic port that remains free of ice year-round. Russian officials, hoping to increase trade here, have eliminated all taxes on foreign goods brought to this city. Companies that deliver goods to Kaliningrad, however, must transport their products another 200 miles (322 km) through other countries to reach the nearest inland part of Russia. In summer, when St. Petersburg's port is not frozen, ships must travel another 500 miles (805 km) north to reach that city.

St. Petersburg, once the capital of Russia, is a vital port and a cultural center. Czar Peter the Great built this city in the early 1700s on a group of more than 100 islands connected by bridges. Large palaces stand gracefully on public squares. Factories in St. Petersburg make light machinery, textiles, and scientific and medical equipment. Located on the Neva River near the Gulf of Finland, the city is also a shipbuilding center.

Murmansk, in Russia's far north, and **Vladivostok,** in the east, are other important port cities. Vladivostok is Russia's largest port on the

Differentiated Instruction

Meeting Special Needs: Interpersonal Organize the class into five groups numbered 1 through 5. Have each group split up into five subgroups called A, B, C, D, and E. Have all students in the five subgroups meet together. (That is, groups 1A through 5A get together, as do groups 1B through 5B, and so on.) Assign each subgroup one of the following topics: the Moscow region; port cities; the Volga region; the Urals region; and Siberia. Have the students in each subgroup develop ways of teaching information about the economy in their assigned region. Then send students back to the original groups. Have the subgroups take turns teaching other group members about their topic. L2

Refer to *Inclusion for the Middle School Social Studies Classroom Strategies and Activities* in the TCR.

NATIONAL GEOGRAPHIC On Location

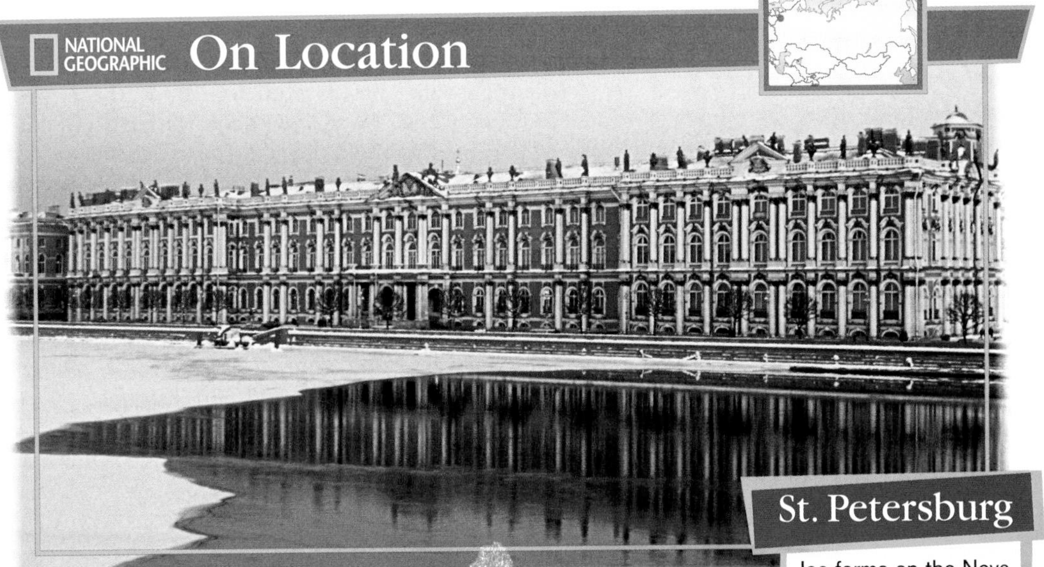

St. Petersburg

Ice forms on the Neva River in the heart of St. Petersburg. The Hermitage Museum in the background is Russia's best gallery of art and the main tourist attraction in St. Petersburg.

Economics **Name an economic activity that takes place in St. Petersburg.**

Pacific Ocean. Trade in these port cities brings needed goods to the Russian people. Vladivostok is also a base for Russia's huge fishing industry.

Siberia As you learned in Chapter 14, Siberia is the Asian part of Russia. It has the largest supply of minerals in Russia, including iron ore, uranium, gold, diamonds, and coal. Huge deposits of oil and natural gas lie beneath the frozen ground of northern Siberia. About two-thirds of Siberia is covered with forests that could support a lumber industry.

Tapping all of these resources is very difficult, however. Siberia is mostly undeveloped because of its harsh, cold climate. Another problem is size—it can take eight or more days to travel across all of Russia by train. Finding a way to develop the remote resources of Siberia is very important for Russia's economic future. Many of the minerals and fuels of western Russia have been used up. The industrial centers there need the resources from Siberia.

The Volga and Urals Region Tucked between the Moscow region and Siberia lies the industrial region of the Volga River and Ural Mountains. The **Volga River** carries almost one-half of Russia's river traffic. It provides water for irrigation and for hydroelectric power—the power generated by fast-flowing water. The region is also home to Russia's most productive farmlands.

The Ural Mountains are rich in minerals. Workers here mine copper, gold, lead, nickel, and bauxite, a mineral used to make aluminum. The mountains also have energy resources such as coal, oil, and natural gas.

✓ Reading Check **Why are Siberia's mineral resources important?**

More About the Photo

St. Petersburg The Hermitage Museum is the former czars' Winter Palace.

Caption Answer Answers may include manufacturing of light machinery, textlies, scientific and medical equipment, and shipbuilding.

✓ Reading Check Answer

Siberia's mineral resources are needed in western Russia since many of the fuels and minerals of this region have been used up.

3 ASSESS

Assign Section 1 Assessment as homework or an in-class activity.

Have students use the Interactive Tutor Self-Assessment CD-ROM to review Section 1.

L2

Section Quiz

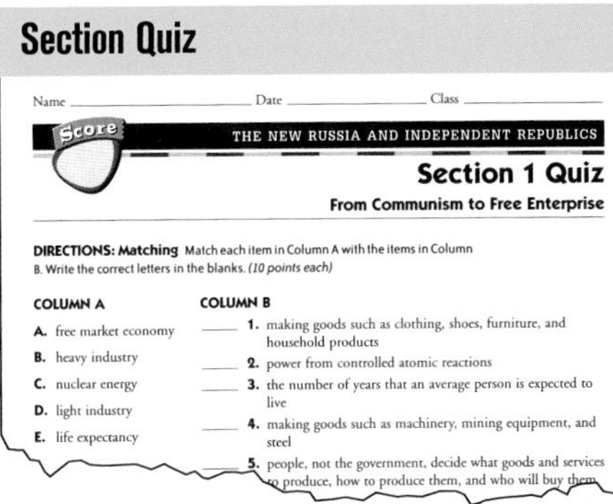

Name ______ Date ______ Class ______

Score

THE NEW RUSSIA AND INDEPENDENT REPUBLICS

Section 1 Quiz

From Communism to Free Enterprise

DIRECTIONS: Matching Match each item in Column A with the items in Column B. Write the correct letters in the blanks. *(10 points each)*

COLUMN A	COLUMN B
A. free market economy	____ **1.** making goods such as clothing, shoes, furniture, and household products
B. heavy industry	____ **2.** power from controlled atomic reactions
C. nuclear energy	____ **3.** the number of years that an average person is expected to live
D. light industry	____ **4.** making goods such as machinery, mining equipment, and steel
E. life expectancy	____ **5.** people, not the government, decide what goods and services to produce, how to produce them, and who will buy them

Content Background

Pollution The pollution in Russia has had devastating effects on people's lives. From 1973 to 1994, 90 children born in Moscow were missing part of a limb. More than half of them came from a few neighborhoods where pollution was particularly strong. While there is no clear evidence that the pollution caused these birth defects, the rate is higher than elsewhere in Russia. One-third of the people living in Magnitogorsk suffer from asthma or other respiratory problems, the result of heavy air pollution from the city's steel mills. In the southern Russian village of Seitovka, residents have gas masks that they must wear from time to time when smoke from a nearby sulfur plant grows too intense.

Reading Check Answer

soil erosion and land, air, and water pollution

L1/ELL

Reading Essentials and Study Guide

Name ______ Date ______ Class ______

THE NEW RUSSIA AND INDEPENDENT REPUBLICS

Reading Essentials and Study Guide 1

From Communism to Free Enterprise

Key Terms

free market economy economy in which people start and run businesses with little goverment involvement
heavy industry production of goods such as machines and steel for use by other factories
light industry production of goods such as clothes and furniture for use by people
nuclear energy power made by creating a controlled atomic reaction
life expectancy number of years an average person is expected to live

Drawing From Experience

What food do you love but save for special times because it costs a lot? Fishing boats collect a food that is special to Russians—caviar. Caviar is salted fish eggs. Sound tasty?

In the last chapter, you learned about the climates and land areas of Russia. You also learned about the troubled history of the Russian people. This section discusses the goods produced in different regions of Russia today.

Organizing Your Thoughts

Use the chart on the next page to help you take notes. The chart lists several sources of income for Russians. For each one, give one fact. Also, name the regions where these sources of income occur or are found.

196

197

CLOSE

Have students create an annotated map that describes the resources and products of Russia's different economic regions.

Fighting Pollution

The United States government passes laws to prevent or limit pollution. However, some companies fight the laws because making their factories pollution-free is very expensive. Fortunately, our government is strong and is able to enforce the anti-pollution laws. In Russia, the new government is not strong enough to enforce the anti-pollution laws that it has passed. Many companies are still polluting areas such as Lake Baikal.

Environmental Issues

Although Russians are moving toward a free market economy, they must learn to balance making profits with protecting the environment. Forests have been cut down, and seedlings have not been planted to replace the trees and hold the soil. This is causing soil erosion in some areas. Chemical fertilizers have been heavily used to increase crop production. These chemicals have built up in the soil over time, destroying its ability to grow food. In addition, the Soviet government built power plants to make **nuclear energy**, or energy from controlled atomic reactions. Many of these nuclear power plants are in decay, which can lead to dangerous nuclear waste.

Air Pollution Smog cloaks many of Russia's large cities. Pollution from heavy industry is particularly bad. Smoke and gases are given off by coal-fired electric plants, vehicles, and other forms of transportation. Many Russians suffer from lung diseases, and rising numbers of people have cancer. **Life expectancy**, or the number of years that an average person is expected to live, has fallen in Russia.

Water Pollution Chemicals used in agriculture and industry often end up in rivers and lakes. Poor sewer systems pollute waterways in Russia as well. Water pollution is also caused by the chemical weapons that were developed by the Soviet Union during the Cold War. Many of these weapons are buried in dumps throughout Russia and the former Soviet republics. Containers that hold the chemicals are deteriorating, and some of the chemicals leak into groundwater.

Reading Check What are some environmental effects of the Soviet era?

Assessment

Defining Terms

1. **Define** free market economy, heavy industry, light industry, nuclear energy, life expectancy.

Recalling Facts

2. **Place** What is the political and cultural center of Russia?
3. **Location** Why is Kaliningrad such an important city in Russia?
4. **Economics** List five mineral resources found in the Ural Mountains.

Critical Thinking

5. **Drawing Conclusions** Why would consumers want the Russian economy to change from relying on heavy industry to a greater emphasis on light industry?
6. **Understanding Cause and Effect** How have economic changes affected the Russian people?

Graphic Organizer

7. **Organizing Information** Draw a chart like the one below. Fill in at least two causes of soil, air, and water pollution in Russia.

Soil Pollution	Air Pollution	Water Pollution

Applying Social Studies Skills

8. **Analyzing Maps** Turn to the economic activity map on page 425. Which manufacturing areas are connected by the Trans-Siberian Railroad?

Section 1 Assessment

1. The terms are defined in the Glossary.
2. Moscow
3. It is the only Baltic port that is free of ice year round.
4. copper, gold, lead, nickel, and bauxite
5. Russian consumers need and want clothing, shoes, furniture, and household products.
6. Factory managers can choose what to make; people can choose careers and start businesses; Russia has higher unemployment and higher prices.
7. Soil pollution: chemical fertilizers, nuclear waste; air pollution: coal-fired electric plants, vehicles; water pollution: agricultural and industrial chemicals, poor sewer systems, chemical weapons
8. Moscow, Siberia, and the Volga and Urals regions

Guide to Reading

Main Idea

Russians have a rich cultural past and are learning to live in a democracy.

Terms to Know

- democracy
- federal republic
- majority group
- minority group

Reading Strategy

Create a chart like this one. Under each heading, list two political challenges and two ethnic challenges of Russia today.

Political Challenges	Ethnic Challenges

Section 2

Russia's People and Culture

NATIONAL GEOGRAPHIC **Exploring Our World**

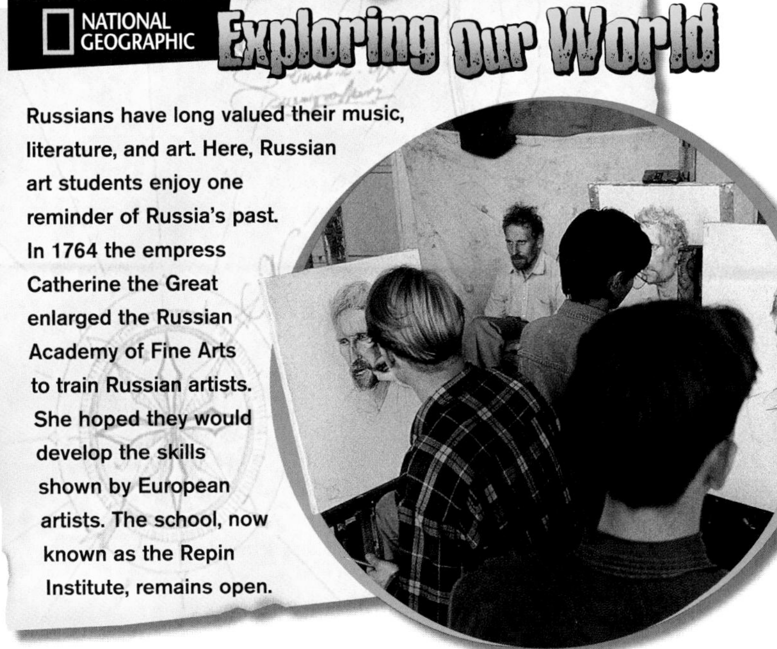

Russians have long valued their music, literature, and art. Here, Russian art students enjoy one reminder of Russia's past. In 1764 the empress Catherine the Great enlarged the Russian Academy of Fine Arts to train Russian artists. She hoped they would develop the skills shown by European artists. The school, now known as the Repin Institute, remains open.

Russia is one of the most populous countries in the world, with 145.5 million people. Since the breakup of the Soviet Union in 1991, the Russian people have seen not only their economy change, but also their political structure and daily lives.

Political Challenges

Under communism, members of the Communist Party controlled Russia's government and told people how to vote. Today Russia is a **democracy,** a government in which people freely elect their leaders. Russia is also a **federal republic.** This means that power is divided between national and state governments with a president who leads the nation.

A Russian president has stronger powers than an American president. For example, the Russian president can issue orders that become laws even if they are not passed by the legislature. Russia's first two

1 Focus

Section Objectives

1. Discuss Russia's political and ethnic challenges.
2. Describe daily life in Russia.
3. Examine Russia's cultural traditions.

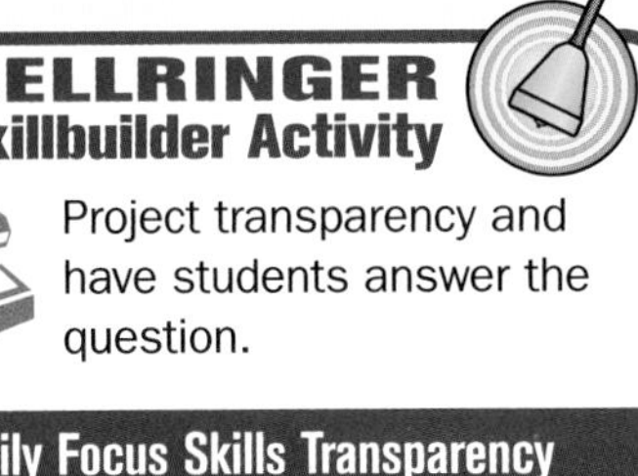

BELLRINGER
Skillbuilder Activity

Project transparency and have students answer the question.

Daily Focus Skills Transparency

ANSWER: concert (kontsert)

Teacher Tip: Explain to students that most Russian words are completely different from English words, but some words are the same, just spelled with different letters.

DAILY FOCUS SKILLS TRANSPARENCY
The New Russia and Independent Republics
Section 2

Interpreting Information on Tables

RUSSIAN (CYRILLIC) ALPHABET AND ENGLISH ALPHABET EQUIVALENT

Russian (Cyrillic) Letter	English Equivalent	Russian (Cyrillic) Letter	English Equivalent	Russian (Cyrillic) Letter	English Equivalent
А	A	К	K	Х	H
Б	B	Л	L	Ц	Ts
В	V	М	M	Ч	Ch
Г	G	Н	N	Ш	Sh
Д	D	О	O	Щ	Shch
Е	E	П	P	Ъ	"
Ё	Ë	Р	R	Ы	Y
Ж	Zh	С	S	Ь	'
З	Z	Т	T	Э	E
И	I	У	U	Ю	Yu
Й	J	Ф	F	Я	Ya

Directions: Answer the following question based on the table.

What is the English equivalent of the Russian word КОНЦЕРТ?

Reading Preview

Activating Prior Knowledge
Ask students to describe ethnic groups in their community and the contributions they have made.

Preteaching Vocabulary
Have students predict the definitions for *majority group* and *minority group.* Have them find the words in the text to check their predictions.

Section Resources

Reproducible Masters

- Reproducible Lesson Plan
- Daily Lecture and Discussion Notes
- Note-taking Guide
- Guided Reading Activity
- Reading Essentials and Study Guide
- Section Quiz

Transparencies

- Daily Focus Skills Transparency

Multimedia

- Vocabulary PuzzleMaker CD-ROM
- Interactive Tutor Self-Assessment CD-ROM
- Presentation Plus! CD-ROM
- ExamView® Pro Testmaker CD-ROM

TEACH

Reading Strategy

Identifying Main Ideas
Have students write down the headings in this section. Under each heading, have them write three facts that they learned from their reading. L1

Daily Lecture and Discussion Notes

THE NEW RUSSIA AND INDEPENDENT REPUBLICS

Daily Lecture and Discussion Notes

Russia's People and Culture

Russians originally believed in a variety of major and minor gods. According to tradition, Christianity was first introduced in Russia in A.D. 988, by Prince Vladimir whose grandmother Olga was converted to the Eastern Orthodox faith in Constantinople. The religion in Constantinople at the time was Eastern Catholicism or Orthodoxy (from Greek *orthos doxos* 'true faith'); hence the Russian Church is Orthodox rather than Roman Catholic.

I. Political Challenges

A. Today Russia is a **democracy,** a government in which people freely elect their leaders. Russia also is a **federal republic.** This means that power is divided ... national and state governments, with a president who leads the nation.

More About the Photo

Standing for Democracy In August 1991, leaders from the government and military tried to seize power and return control to the Communist Party. Yeltsin and thousands of Russians resisted the rebels.

Caption Answer They punished people who criticized their decisions.

Reading Check Answer

Laws govern not just ordinary people but also government officials.

Reading Check Answer

Slavs

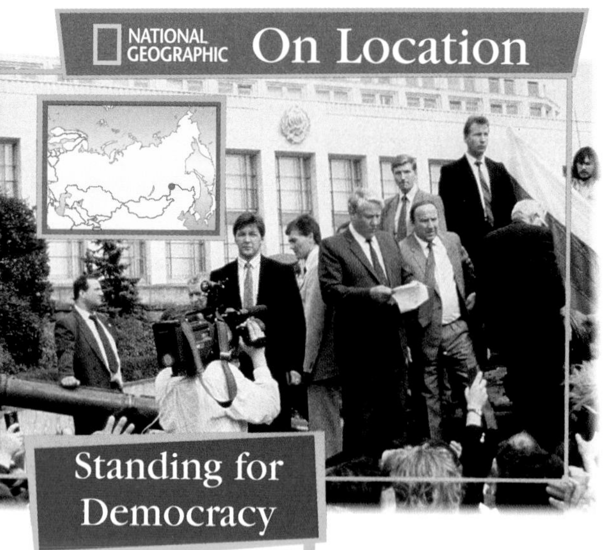

Standing for Democracy

In 1991 Russia's first president, Boris Yeltsin (holding paper), stood on a tank in defiance of a communist group who wanted to stop Russia's move to democracy.

Government **How did Russian government officials deal with criticism in the past?**

presidents—Boris Yeltsin and Vladimir Putin—used their powers to help develop and strengthen Russia's economy and democracy.

In adjusting to a new form of government, Russians face important political challenges. They have to learn how to function in a democracy. Democracy is built on the idea of the rule of law. This means that laws govern not just ordinary people but also government officials. In the past, Russian leaders did what they wanted. In the new system, they must learn to follow the law. Also, past governments punished people who criticized their decisions. Now officials have to learn to accept disagreements over government policies.

✓Reading Check **What is the rule of law?**

Ethnic Challenges

A large challenge facing the new government results from the fact that Russia is home to many different ethnic groups. Russians, along with Ukrainians and Belorussians, are part of a larger group of people called Slavs. Hundreds of years ago, the Slavs migrated from northeastern Europe to western Russia. In Russia today, more than 80 percent of the people are Slavs who speak Russian. Slavs are the **majority group,** or the group that controls most of the wealth and power.

About 100 other ethnic groups also live in Russia. Each group has its own distinctive language and culture. These peoples are known as **minority groups** because they are not the group that controls most of the wealth and power in the society.

When the Soviet Union existed, the central government kept tight control over its majority and minority groups. After the Soviet Union fell apart, many old feuds and remembered wrongs came to the surface. Fighting broke out among many of the ethnic groups who had been enemies in the past and whose differences had never been resolved. The Russian government today faces the task of protecting people in minority groups as well as promoting cooperation among the ethnic groups.

However, some of the minority groups want to form their own countries. Among them are the Chechens (CHEH•chehnz), who live in **Chechnya** (CHEHCH•nee•uh) near the Caspian Sea and Caucasus Mountains in southern Russia. Find Chechnya on the map on page 451. This region has oil reserves, and many oil pipelines crisscross Chechnya transporting fuel to major Russian cities. Russian troops have fought Chechen forces to keep Chechnya a part of Russia.

✓Reading Check **What is the largest, most powerful ethnic group in Russia?**

Reading Strategy Reading the Text

Identifying the Main Idea Point out to students that the main idea of a paragraph often appears in the first sentence and that the remainder of the paragraph often supplies supporting details. Have them read the second paragraph on this page to see whether it follows this model. Ask volunteers, using their own words, to express the paragraph's main idea and supporting details. Then have them practice this skill with other paragraphs in this section. L1

*Use the **Reading Skills Handbook** for more reading strategies.*

Chapter 15

Section 2, pages 429–434

Daily Life

As you learned in Chapter 14, the most densely populated area of Russia is the region west of the Ural Mountains—particularly around Moscow. About 75 percent of Russians live clustered in cities.

Urban and Rural Life Russia's urban, or city, areas are large and modern, with stone and concrete buildings and wide streets. Tall buildings hold apartments for hundreds of families. Many of these apartments are small and cramped, however. A typical Russian apartment has one bedroom, living room, kitchen, and bathroom for a family of four. The living room may also be used as a bedroom.

It is very hard to find housing in the cities. For this reason, many generations may share the same home. This can be helpful because many Russian mothers work outside of the home. The grandmother, or babushka, may cook, clean, shop, and care for young children. Shopping for food can take a long time because it often means waiting in long lines. When people in cities relax, they take walks through parks or attend concerts, movies, and the circus.

Russian cities have changed in recent years. Some people have benefited from the economic changes sweeping the country. Many of

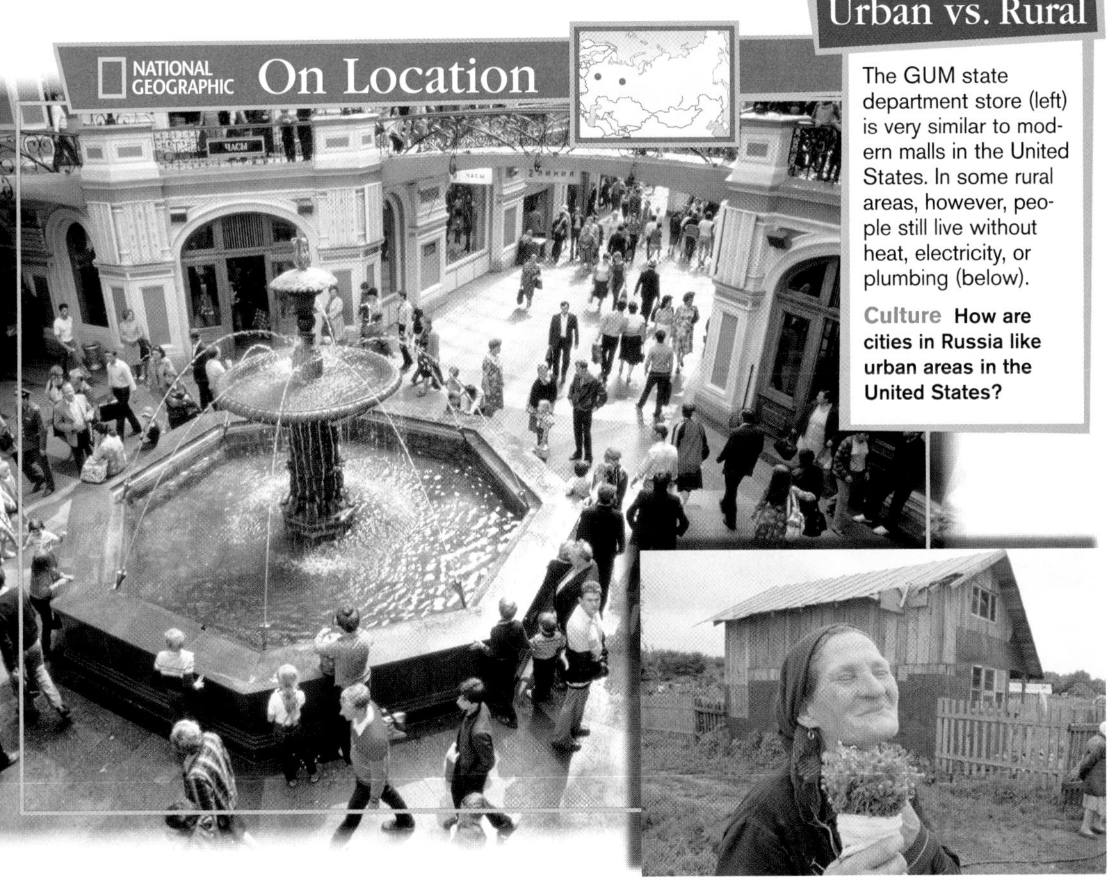

NATIONAL GEOGRAPHIC On Location

Urban vs. Rural

The GUM state department store (left) is very similar to modern malls in the United States. In some rural areas, however, people still live without heat, electricity, or plumbing (below).

Culture **How are cities in Russia like urban areas in the United States?**

More About the Photos

The GUM The largest department store in Moscow is referred to by its acronym *GUM,* taken from the three Russian words that mean "state department store." The store sells everything from coats to caviar.

Caption Answer They are large and modern, with tall buildings, wide streets, and many people.

L1/ELL

Guided Reading Activity

Name ______ Date ______ Class ______

THE NEW RUSSIA AND INDEPENDENT REPUBLICS

Guided Reading Activity 2

Russia's People and Culture

DIRECTIONS: Summarizing Reading the section and completing the summary paragraphs below will help you learn more about the people of Russia. Use your textbook to fill in the blanks.

Russia's government is now a **(1)** ______. It is also a **(2)** ______ ______, in which power is divided between national and state governments.

Russians are part of a larger group of people called **(3)** ______. They make up more than 80 percent of Russia's people and are the **(4)** ______ ______. About 100 other ethnic groups also live in Russia. These peoples are the **(5)** ______ ______.

About 75 percent of Russians live in **(6)** ______. Although Communists tried to stop religious practices, the **(7)** ______ ______ is very popular in Russia today. Russian Orthodoxy started a special alphabet called **(8)** ______.

The most festive nonreligous holiday is **(9)** ______ ______. Many Russians enjoy eating *borscht,* a **(10)** ______ made from beets.

The city of **(11)** ______ ______ is an important Russian cultural center. One of Russia's top **(12)** ______ ______ dances in the Mariinsky Theater in St. Petersburg. **(13)** ______ ______ wrote some of the world's favorite ballets. **(14)** ______ ______ novel *War and Peace* is about the Russian defeat of Napoleon. **(15)** ______ ______ wrote about Russian life during the late 1800s. **(16)** ______ ______ wrote novels about the harsh conditions under communism.

81

Differentiated Instruction

Meeting Special Needs: Visual/Spatial To help students understand the recent changes in Europe, it can be helpful for them to look at a map. Find an old map of the Soviet Union. Have students compare it to a recent map of eastern Europe. **Ask:** How many independent republics were formed when the Soviet Union broke up in 1991? What are the names of these new countries? **L1**

EE1 The World in Spatial Terms: Standard 3

Primary Source

Answers

1. Solzhenitsyn believes that a good writer can describe a physical or emotional experience in a way that allows readers to feel, or at least understand, the experience as if they had lived it themselves. Students would probably prefer reading Solzhenitsyn's experiences rather than living them—he wrote about the terrible times he endured in a Soviet prison.
2. Answers will vary, but students should describe why they felt differently from other times they read a book or watched a movie.

these prosperous people have clustered near Moscow. They are building large houses outside the city limits, where few people lived before. As a result, Russia is developing its first suburbs, or smaller communities that surround a city.

In Russia's rural areas, or countryside, most people live in houses built of wood. As in the United States, the quality of health care and education is often lower in rural areas than in the cities. Over the years, many people have left rural areas to find work in Russia's cities.

Religion in Russia Despite Communist laws in the past forbidding the practice of religion, the Russian Orthodox Church is very popular. Russian Orthodox is a Christian faith. It is headed by a figure called the patriarch—the Greek term for "father." Russian Orthodoxy was responsible for a special alphabet called Cyrillic. According to legend, St. Cyril, an Orthodox priest, developed the Cyrillic alphabet to help the Slavs read and write their own language. He invented new letters for sounds in the Slavic language that were not present in Greek or Latin languages.

Although more than 70 percent of the Russian population is Russian Orthodox, this is by no means the only religion in Russia. Many Muslims (followers of Islam), Roman Catholics, Protestants, and Buddhists live within Russia's boundaries. However, many of the Jews

Primary Source

ALEXANDER SOLZHENITSYN

(1918–)

For many years, Russian author Alexander Solzhenitsyn was the voice of protest for his people, speaking out through his novels about injustices in the Soviet Union's Communist system. Since the people could not "see" freedom for themselves, he used his great literary talent to bring truth to as many people as possible.

"*The sole substitute for an experience which we have not ourselves lived through is art and literature,*" **he wrote.** "*Wherever else it fails, art always has won its fight against lies, and it always will.*"

Source: *Nobel Lecture, 1972* by Alexander Isayevich Solzhenitsyn.

Analyzing Primary Sources

1. What does Solzhenitsyn mean when he says that literature can substitute for an experience we have not had? Do you agree?
2. Describe an event you "experienced" through art. This might include a scary story or a powerful scene from a film.

Team-Teaching Activity

Literature Invite a literature teacher to class to describe Nikolai Gogol's play *The Government Inspector* (often called *The Inspector General*). In this play, written in the 1830s during czarist times, corrupt town officials fear the upcoming arrival of a government inspector who is to enter their midst in disguise. When a stranger enters the town, the officials assume he is the inspector and treat him with overwhelming courtesy, which the clever stranger takes full advantage of. After he leaves, the officials are shocked when the real inspector shows up. Have the teacher explain the use of irony and satire in this and other works of Russian literature. Then have students give examples of Russian life and explain why they would be appropriate for satire. **L2** 

EE2 Places and Regions: Standard 6

Art

Peter Carl Fabergé was no ordinary Russian jeweler. His successful workshop designed extravagant jeweled flowers, figures, and animals. He is most famous for crafting priceless gold Easter eggs for the czar of Russia and other royalty in Europe and Asia. Each egg was unique and took nearly a year to create. Lifting the lid of the egg revealed a tiny surprise. One egg Fabergé created (shown here) held an intricate ship inside.

Looking Closer **Why do you think Fabergé's workshop closed after the Russian Revolution of 1917?**

Fabergé egg ▲

that at one time lived in Russia have emigrated to other areas. Fewer than 1 million Jews live in Russia today.

Celebrations, Foods, and Sports Russians enjoy small family get-togethers as well as national holidays. New Year's Eve is the most festive nonreligious holiday. Russian children decorate a fir tree and exchange presents with others in their families. Russians also celebrate May 1 with parades and speeches. May Day honors Russian workers.

If you were to have dinner with a Russian family, you might begin with a big bowl of *borscht,* a soup made from beets, or *shchi,* a soup made from cabbage. Next, you might have meat turnovers called *piroshki.* For the main course, you are likely to eat meat, poultry, or fish with boiled potatoes. On special occasions, Russians like to eat caviar. This delicacy is made from eggs of the sturgeon, a fish from the Caspian Sea.

Have you ever watched the Olympics? If so, you probably have seen Russian hockey players, figure skaters, and gymnasts. Due to Russia's cold climate, winter and indoor sports are popular. Russians also enjoy soccer, tennis, hiking, camping, and mountain climbing.

✓ Reading Check **How have Russia's cities changed in recent years?**

Rich Cultural Traditions

Russia has a rich tradition of literature, art, and music. The Russian storytelling tradition is one of the oldest and richest in the world. These stories, or *skazki,* were passed down orally from generation to generation, until finally they were recorded in print. Beasts and creatures with magical powers are common in these tales that grew out of a land with dark forests and long, cold winters.

Answer Russian royalty lived extravagantly. The post-revolutionary government did not tolerate such excesses.

Activity Have students design an egg using sequins or glitter.

✓ Reading Check Answer

Russia is developing its first suburbs.

Assign Section 2 Assessment as homework or an in-class activity.

Have students use the Interactive Tutor Self-Assessment CD-ROM to review Section 2.

L2

Section Quiz

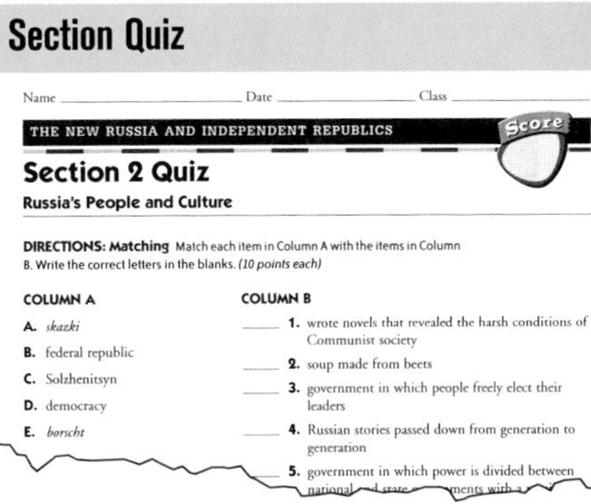
Name ________ Date ________ Class ________

THE NEW RUSSIA AND INDEPENDENT REPUBLICS

Score

Section 2 Quiz

Russia's People and Culture

DIRECTIONS: Matching Match each item in Column A with the items in Column B. Write the correct letters in the blanks. *(10 points each)*

COLUMN A	COLUMN B
A. *skazki*	____ **1.** wrote novels that revealed the harsh conditions of Communist society
B. federal republic	____ **2.** soup made from beets
C. Solzhenitsyn	____ **3.** government in which people freely elect their leaders
D. democracy	____ **4.** Russian stories passed down from generation to generation
E. *borscht*	____ **5.** government in which power is divided between

Cooperative Learning Activity

Writing a Petition Have students form small groups, each representing a different city in Russia. Ask them to imagine that they are Russian citizens and they must draw up a petition to make one change in their city. Students should use a problem-solving process to create their petitions, including identifying the problem they want to change, gathering information, considering options, advantages or disadvantages, and deciding on a solution. Possible topics include poor housing and lack of consumer goods. Their petitions should incorporate the main and supporting ideas they need to make their point. Afterwards, the groups should orally present their petitions to the rest of the class. L2

EE6 The Uses of Geography: Standard 18

Reading Check Answer

Alexander Solzhenitsyn

L1/ELL

Reading Essentials and Study Guide

Name ______ Date ______ Class ______

THE NEW RUSSIA AND INDEPENDENT REPUBLICS

Reading Essentials and Study Guide 2

Russia's People and Culture

Key Terms

democracy a government in which people freely elect their leaders
federal republic a country in which power is divided between national and state governments
majority group the ethnic group that controls most of the wealth and power in a society
minority group ethnic group different from the majority group in a region

CLOSE

Have students create a group of picture postcards showing images of Russia today. They should have a picture on one side and text about the picture on the other.

▲ Ballet in Russia dates back to 1738 with the founding of the first dancing school in St. Petersburg.

The great novels and plays of Russia reflect mostly historical political themes. Leo Tolstoy's novel *War and Peace* recounts how Russians rallied to defeat the French emperor Napoleon Bonaparte. Fyodor Dostoyevsky (FEE•uh•dor DAHS•tuh•YEHF•skee) wrote many novels that explored Russian life during the late 1800s. In the 1970s, Alexander Solzhenitsyn (SOHL•zhuh•NEET•suhn) wrote novels that revealed the harsh conditions of Communist society.

Art and Music St. Petersburg has many beautiful museums and statues. This is why it is called "Venice of the North" after the cultural center of Italy. One of Russia's top ballet companies dances in the Mariinsky (MAH•ree•IHN•skee) Theater in St. Petersburg. Russian ballet dancers are famous around the world. Composer Peter Tchaikovsky (chy•KAWF•skee) wrote some of the world's favorite ballets, including *Sleeping Beauty* and *The Nutcracker.* Nikolay Rimsky-Korsakov used Russian folktales and tunes in his operas and other works. Igor Stravinsky's *Firebird Suite* is based on a Russian legend.

If you enjoy painting, you would definitely want to stroll through St. Petersburg's Hermitage Museum. It was originally built to hold the art collection of the czars, including the famous Fabergé (fa•behr•zhay) eggs. The museum now publicly displays these and other works by Russian and European painters and sculptors.

Reading Check Which Russian author wrote about the harsh conditions of Communist society?

Section 2 Assessment

Defining Terms

1. **Define** democracy, federal republic, majority group, minority group.

Recalling Facts

2. **Government** Why has the Russian government sent troops to Chechnya?
3. **Culture** What is the major religion of Russia?
4. **Culture** Which Russian composer wrote the world famous ballet *The Nutcracker?*

Critical Thinking

5. **Analyzing Information** Describe the problems Russians face living in a democracy after years of Communist rule.
6. **Making Predictions** Art ideas are frequently drawn from life. What themes do you think you will see in future Russian arts?

Graphic Organizer

7. **Organizing Information** Create a diagram like this one, and list two facts for each topic in the four outer ovals.

Applying Social Studies Skills

8. **Synthesizing Information** Write a paragraph describing ways in which Russian and American cultures are different and similar. Then describe how your family's living conditions would change if you lived in a typical Russian apartment.

Section 2 Assessment

1. The terms are defined in the Glossary.
2. to fight Chechen forces and keep Chechnya part of Russia
3. Russian Orthodox
4. Tchaikovsky
5. Russian leaders had to learn to follow the law and to accept disagreements over government policies.
6. *Possible answer*: Art might address the difficulties Russians experience in making the transition to a free market economy and to democracy.
7. Students' diagrams should include facts from the section.
8. Answers will vary.

Making Connections

ART | SCIENCE | CULTURE | TECHNOLOGY

Count Leo Tolstoy

Count Leo Tolstoy (1828–1910) was a famous Russian novelist. Two of his epic works are *War and Peace* and *Anna Karenina.* What is not generally known is that Tolstoy also wrote for children. He wrote: "[These writings] will be used to teach generations of all Russian children, from the czar's to the peasant's, and from these readers they will receive their first poetic impressions, and having written these books, I can now die in peace."

Russian literature, even stories for children, contains more suffering and tragedy than American children would appreciate. The stories also celebrate qualities such as helpfulness, compassion, mercy, and justice. These values are needed to survive difficult times. This story is an example of just such literature.

▲ Russian grandfather

The Grandfather and His Little Grandson

by Count Leo Tolstoy (1828–1910)

The grandfather had become very old. His legs would not carry him, his eyes could not see, his ears could not hear, and he was toothless. And when he ate, he was untidy. His son and the son's wife no longer allowed him to eat with them at the table and had him take his meals near the stove. They gave him his food in a cup. Once he tried to move the cup closer to him and it fell to the floor and broke. The daughter-in-law scolded the old man, saying that he damaged everything around the house and broke their cups, and she warned him that from that day on she would give him his food in a wooden dish. The old man sighed and said nothing.

One day the old man's son and his wife were sitting in their hut, resting. Their little son was playing on the floor. He was putting together something out of small bits of wood. His father asked him: "What are you making, Misha?" And Misha said: "I'm making a wooden bucket. When you and Mommie get old, I'll feed you out of this wooden bucket."

The young peasant and his wife looked at each other and tears appeared in their eyes. They were shamed to have treated the old man so unkindly, and from that day they again ate with him at the table and took better care of him.

Source: "The Grandfather and His Little Grandson" from *A Harvest of Russian Children's Literature,* edited by Miriam Morton.

Making the Connection

1. What reasons did Tolstoy give for writing stories for children?
2. What do you think the young peasant and his wife learned from their son?
3. **Making Comparisons** Compare this story with one you have learned. How are they different? How are they the same?

Teach

Tolstoy once wrote: "Happy families are all alike. Every unhappy family is unhappy in its own way." Ask your students if they agree or disagree with Tolstoy and why. Do they think this story is a good example of Tolstoy's statement? Why or why not? L2

More About Leo Tolstoy

Tolstoy's family were aristocratic landowners, but even with his privileged background, he was determined to improve conditions for peasants. Many of his writings address moral and social issues, and they have had a strong influence on many writers and leaders, including Mohandas Gandhi.

Interdisciplinary Connections

Psychology Tolstoy is famous for the psychological realism in his work. Discuss the realistic elements of this story with your students. What emotions and issues does Tolstoy examine? Ask your students (or find a story in a magazine or newspaper) about how older people are treated today. What parallels and what differences are there to the story?

Making the Connection

1. He wanted to teach children and give them their first introduction to literature.
2. that if they treat the old man unkindly their son will learn from their actions and treat them the same way someday
3. Student answers will vary, but the selected stories should teach a moral lesson.

Focus

Section Objectives

1. Describe how the people living in the Caucasus Republics earn their living.
2. Explain how Soviet rule affected the Central Asian Republics.

BELLRINGER Skillbuilder Activity

Project transparency and have students answer the question.

Daily Focus Skills Transparency

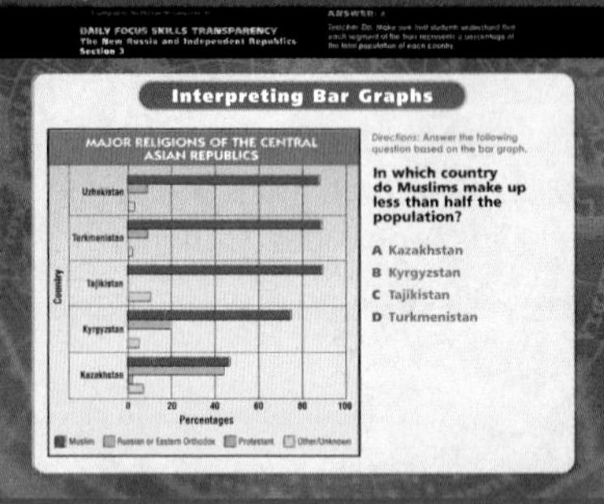

Reading Preview

■ **Activating Prior Knowledge** Have students locate the Caucasus Republics in the Reference Atlas. **Ask:** **What effect do you think having larger neighbors might have on these countries?** *(They might have been threatened by them.)*

■ **Preteaching Vocabulary** Have students look up the words *steppe* and *nomad* and use them in a sentence.

Guide to Reading

Main Idea

The Eurasian republics of the Caucasus and Central Asia are trying to build new economies and governments.

Terms to Know

- fault
- cash crop
- steppe
- nomad
- oasis
- elevation
- bilingual

Reading Strategy

In a chart like this, write two facts about each republic in the Caucasus and Central Asia.

Country	Facts
Armenia	
Azerbaijan	
Georgia	
Kazakhstan	
Uzbekistan	
Turkmenistan	
Kyrgyzstan	
Tajikistan	

Section 3

The Republics Emerge

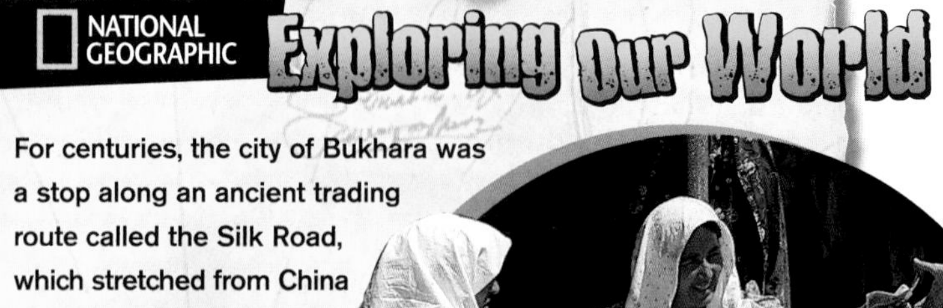

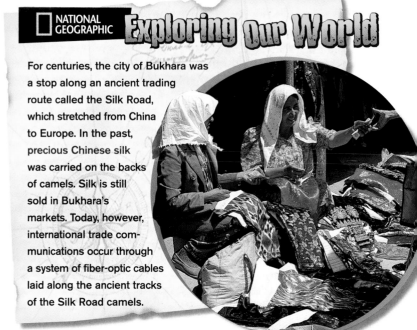

NATIONAL GEOGRAPHIC Exploring Our World

For centuries, the city of Bukhara was a stop along an ancient trading route called the Silk Road, which stretched from China to Europe. In the past, precious Chinese silk was carried on the backs of camels. Silk is still sold in Bukhara's markets. Today, however, international trade communications occur through a system of fiber-optic cables laid along the ancient tracks of the Silk Road camels.

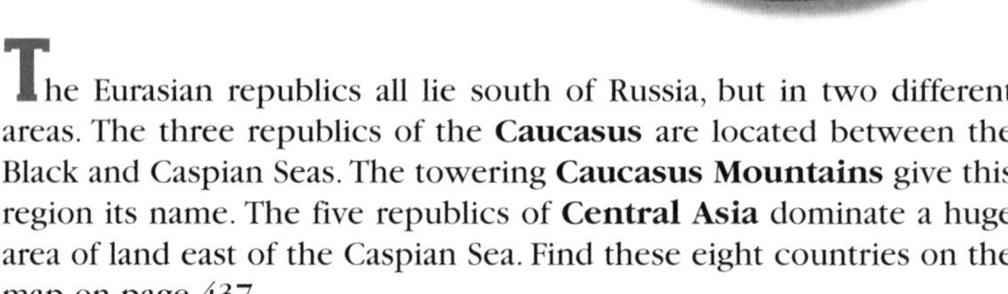

The Eurasian republics all lie south of Russia, but in two different areas. The three republics of the **Caucasus** are located between the Black and Caspian Seas. The towering **Caucasus Mountains** give this region its name. The five republics of **Central Asia** dominate a huge area of land east of the Caspian Sea. Find these eight countries on the map on page 437.

Arabs, Turks, Persians, and Russians have ruled these countries at one time or another. Many of these people stayed, making up the different ethnic groups living in the Eurasian republics today. Disagreements among some of these groups have sparked violent conflicts.

The Eurasian republics were once part of the Soviet Union. When the Soviet Union collapsed in 1991, they became independent—some for the first time in centuries. Since then, they have struggled to move to a free market economy and democracy. What makes this struggle even more difficult is the enormous challenge of cleaning up the

Section Resources

Reproducible Masters
- Reproducible Lesson Plan
- Daily Lecture and Discussion Notes
- Note-taking Guide
- Guided Reading Activity
- Reading Essentials and Study Guide
- Section Quiz

Transparencies
- Daily Focus Skills Transparency
- GeoQuiz Transparency
- In-text Map Transparency

Multimedia
- Vocabulary PuzzleMaker CD-ROM
- Interactive Tutor Self-Assessment CD-ROM
- Presentation Plus! CD-ROM
- ExamView® Pro Testmaker CD-ROM
- MindJogger Videoquiz

environment. Rapid industrialization during the Soviet era polluted the air and water. Diverting water for irrigation has drained rivers, and chemical fertilizers have badly damaged the soil.

Republics of the Caucasus

The Caucasus republics are **Armenia, Georgia,** and **Azerbaijan** (A•zuhr•by•JAHN). You may think that having the Caucasus Mountains so near would result in a cold climate. In fact, these three countries experience mostly a mild Mediterranean climate or dry steppe climate. The economic activity map below shows you that these favorable climates have resulted in much commercial farming. Farmers grow wheat, fruits, vegetables, and tea in river valleys.

Armenia Armenia's 3.2 million people are mostly ethnic Armenians who share a unique language and culture. In A.D. 301, an Armenian king made Christianity the official religion—the first country to do so. About 94 percent of the nation's people belong to the Armenian Orthodox Church. Many Christian Armenians also live in a small territory claimed by neighboring Azerbaijan. Fighting over this land has hurt the economies of both countries.

Nearly 70 percent of Armenians live in cities. Founded in 782 B.C., **Yerevan**—the capital—is one of the world's most ancient cities.

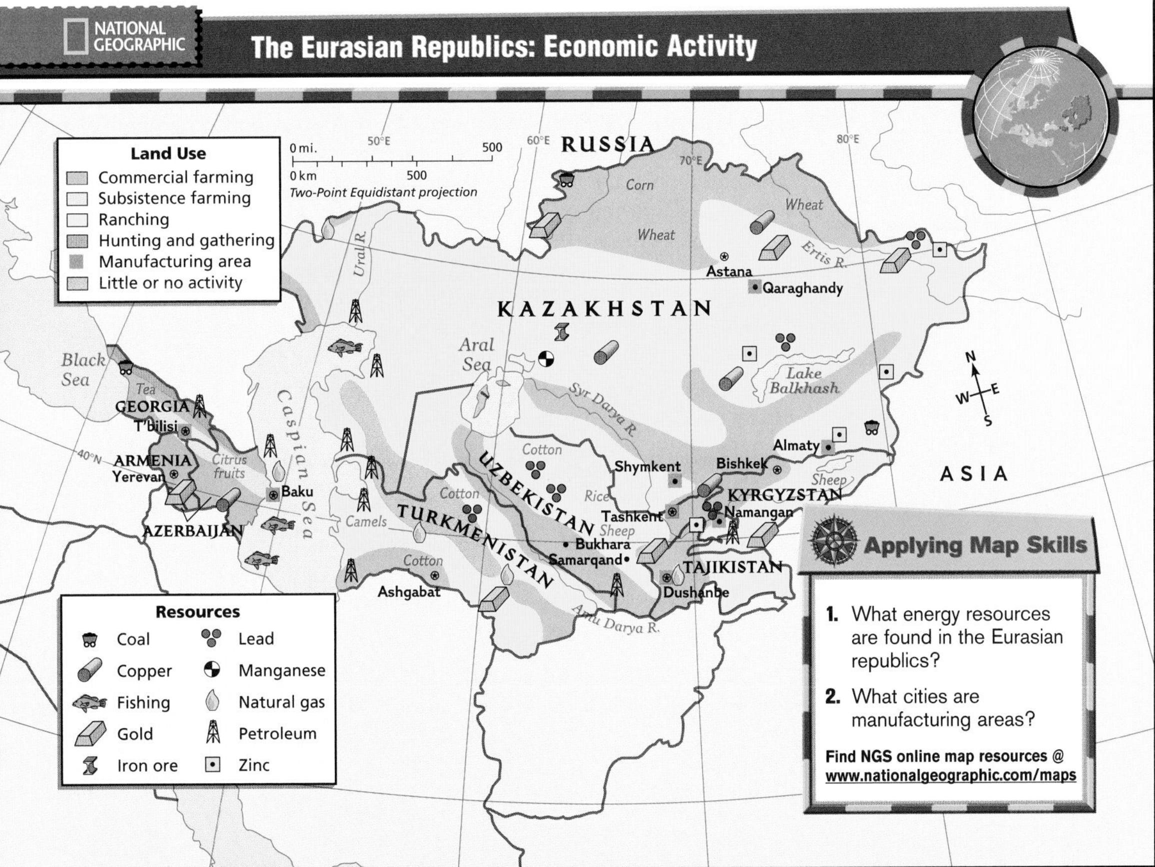

Applying Map Skills

1. What energy resources are found in the Eurasian republics?
2. What cities are manufacturing areas?

Find NGS online map resources @ www.nationalgeographic.com/maps

Reading Strategy Reading the Text

Making Comparisons Have students create a chart that compares the Eurasian republics in terms of resources, economic activities, population, ethnic mix, and most important challenges. When they have finished their work, have them write a brief essay describing the factors necessary for a free market economy, identifying which country they think is most likely to succeed in achieving one and explaining why they believe this. Organize the class into groups based on the country chosen, and have the class debate the selections based on the reasons provided by students. L1

Use the ***Reading Skills Handbook*** *for more reading strategies.*

Chapter 15

Section 3, pages 436–440

Teach

Using a Map Have students look at the physical map of Asia in the Reference Atlas. Have them locate the five countries discussed in this section. **Ask: Why are these countries called "Central Asian Republics"?** *(because they are located in the center of Asia)* L1

Daily Lecture and Discussion Notes

THE NEW RUSSIA AND INDEPENDENT REPUBLICS

Daily Lecture and Discussion Notes

The Republics Emerge

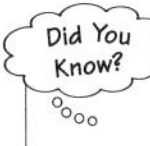

Armenians place great importance on hospitality and on close family ties. Often, more than two generations of a family live together. In the cities, many women hold jobs outside the home, but they still do most of the housework and shopping.

I. The Republics of the Caucasus

A. The republics of the Caucasus include Armenia, Georgia, and Azerbaijan. The towering Caucasus Mountains give this region its name. The countries have mostly a mild climate or dry steppe climate. These republics became independent in 1991 for the first time in centuries.

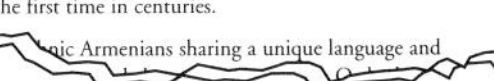

Applying Map Skills

Answers

1. coal, natural gas, and oil
2. T'bilisi, Baku, Shymkent, Tashkent, Dushanbe, Almaty, Namangan, Qaraghandy

In-text Map Transparency Activity Point to the color for commercial farming in the key at the top of the map and list the kinds of cash crops grown in the Caucasus and Central Asia—tea, citrus fruits, cotton, rice, wheat, and corn. Ask students to identify the crops grown in Kazakhstan. *(wheat and corn)*

L1/ELL

Guided Reading Activity

Name ______ Date ______ Class ______

THE NEW RUSSIA AND INDEPENDENT REPUBLICS

Guided Reading Activity 3

The Republics Emerge

DIRECTIONS: Reading for Accuracy Reading the section and completing the activity below will help you learn more about the Eurasian republics. Refer to your textbook to decide if a statement is true or false. Write **T** or **F**, and if a statement is false, rewrite it correctly.

____ **1.** Armenia, Georgia, and Azerbaijan make up the republics of the Caucasus.

____ **2.** Conflicts have developed between Christian Armenians and Georgia.

____ **3.** Under Soviet Communist rule, the people of Kazakhstan flourished and prospered.

____ **4.** Uzbekistan is one of the world's largest cotton producers.

____ **5.** Uzbekistan is a desert region with no large cities.

____ **6.** Turkmenistan has so few people because it is so small.

____ **7.** More than one half of Turkmenistan's people live in villages near oases.

____ **8.** The climate of Kyrgyzstan is mild throughout the republic.

____ **9.** Kyrgyzstan has one official language.

____ **10.** Tajikistan is mountainous, but farmers still grow cotton, rice, and fruits.

____ **11.** Most of Tajikistan's people are Uzbeks.

82

More About the Photo

Yurts A wheel called a *shaneraq* is used to pull together the yurt frame. It is considered a national symbol of Kazakhstan in celebration of the nomadic way of life.

Caption Answer because they were nomads who frequently moved

Reading Check Answer

Most Azeris are Muslims while most Armenians and Georgians are Christians.

NATIONAL GEOGRAPHIC On Location

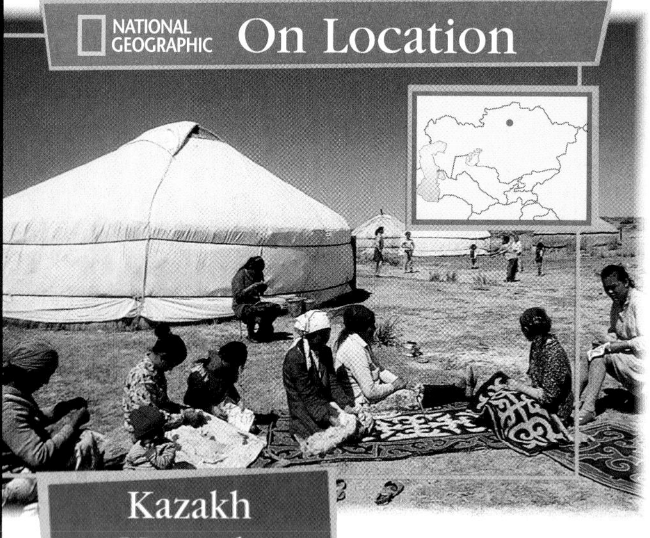

Kazakh Nomads

The traditional home of Kazakhs—called a yurt—can be easily taken apart and moved.

Culture **Why would the Mongols and early Kazakh people need a house that could be moved?**

Armenians are proud of its wide streets, attractive fountains, and colorful buildings made of volcanic stone. Although volcanoes no longer erupt here, Armenia sits uneasily on top of many **faults,** or cracks in the earth's crust. It often suffers serious earthquakes.

Azerbaijan Azerbaijan is split in two by the country of Armenia. Most people belong to a group called Azeris and speak the Azeri language. They follow the Islamic religion.

More than half of the country's 8.2 million people live in cities. The capital, **Baku** (bah•KOO), is a port on the Caspian Sea. The center of the country's oil industry and manufacturing, Baku is known for the strong winds that blow through the city. The oil and natural gas deposits under the Caspian Sea are the most promising for the future of Azerbaijan's economy. The country has made agreements with foreign companies to develop these resources. Agriculture is important too. Farmers in dry areas use irrigation to grow cotton and tobacco as **cash crops,** or products grown for sale as exports.

Georgia About 70 percent of Georgia's 4.7 million people are ethnic Georgians who are proud of their distinctive language, alphabet, and Christian heritage. Like Armenia, Georgia accepted Christianity in the A.D. 300s. Within the past 10 years, conflict has broken out between Georgians and the other ethnic groups in the country who want to set up their own countries.

T'bilisi (tuh•bih•LEE•see), Georgia's capital, is located near the mountains. The city has warm mineral springs heated by high temperatures inside the earth. Resorts along the mild Black Sea coast draw thousands of tourists each year. Georgia has many natural resources, such as copper, coal, manganese, and some oil. Swift rivers provide hydroelectric power for Georgia's industries. Skilled farmers produce nearly one-third of all the country's foods.

✓Reading Check **How does Azerbaijan's religion differ from that in Armenia and Georgia?**

The Central Asian Republics

The republics in Central Asia include **Kazakhstan** (kuh•ZAHK•STAHN), **Uzbekistan, Turkmenistan, Kyrgyzstan** (KIHR•gih•STAHN), and **Tajikistan.** All five countries follow the Islamic religion.

Kazakhstan The largest of the Central Asian republics, Kazakhstan is almost four times the size of Texas. Toward the center of the country lie the Steppes. A **steppe** is a dry, treeless plain (similar to the Great

Differentiated Instruction

Meeting Special Needs: Visual/Spatial Students who are visual learners might need visual cues to help them grasp the information explained in the section. Suggest that they refer to the different maps as they read the subsections on each country. It will be more meaningful for them to see the large stretches of steppe and desert climate regions in Kazakhstan than simply to read that steppes are found on the edges of deserts. Similarly, seeing the high elevations of the Tian Shan mountains on the physical map will convey more than the text description for these learners. Remind them to use the photographs in the chapter in similar ways. **L1**

Refer to *Inclusion for the Middle School Social Studies Classroom Strategies and Activities* in the TCR.

Plains in the United States). Farming is difficult in the harsh climate, but raising livestock on ranches is an important industry. Kazakhstan's mineral resources include copper, manganese, gold, zinc, and petroleum. Factories make machinery and chemicals and process foods.

About half of Kazakhstan's 14.8 million people are ethnic Kazakhs, whose ancestors were horse-riding warriors called the Mongols. Like the Mongols, the Kazakhs were mostly **nomads,** or people who move from place to place with herds of animals. Under Soviet rule, Kazakh nomads were forced to settle in one place. The Soviet government set up factories here, and Russian workers poured into the country. Today, Russians form Kazakhstan's second-largest ethnic group.

Uzbekistan South of Kazakhstan lies Uzbekistan, which is slightly larger than California. Most of the country's 25.7 million people are Uzbeks who generally live in fertile valleys and oases. An **oasis** is a fertile or green area in a desert watered by an underground spring. **Tashkent,** the capital, is the largest city and industrial center in Central Asia. About 2,000 years ago, the oases of Tashkent, Bukhara, and Samarqand were part of the busy trade route called the Silk Road that linked China and Europe.

This country is one of the world's largest cotton producers. This boom in cotton, unfortunately, has had disastrous effects on the environment. Large farms needing irrigation have nearly drained away the rivers flowing into the **Aral Sea.** Uzbek leaders are now trying to add more variety to the economy. They want to use newly discovered deposits of oil, gas, and gold.

Turkmenistan Turkmenistan is larger than neighboring Uzbekistan, but it has far fewer people. Why? Most of this vast country is part of a huge desert called the **Garagum** (GAHR•uh•GOOM). Look at the economic activity map on page 437. The Garagum, which means "black sand," is located in Turkmenistan's northern and central areas that have "little or no economic activity." Despite the harshness of the land, growing cotton and raising livestock are the leading economic activities. Not enough food is grown to feed everyone, however, and much food has to be imported.

Turkmenistan is important to world energy markets because it contains one of the world's largest reserves of natural gas. The country is hoping that its oil and natural gas will give it a brighter future.

Ashgabat, the capital, is Turkmenistan's largest city and leading economic and cultural center. Yet more than half of the country's 5.7 million people live in villages near oases. The Turkmen people used to be nomads who raised camels and other livestock in the desert. Like the Kazahks, the Turkmen were forced by the Soviets to settle on farms.

Kyrgyzstan The lofty **Tian Shan** (tee•AHN SHAHN) mountain range makes up most of Kyrgyzstan. The climate here depends on an area's

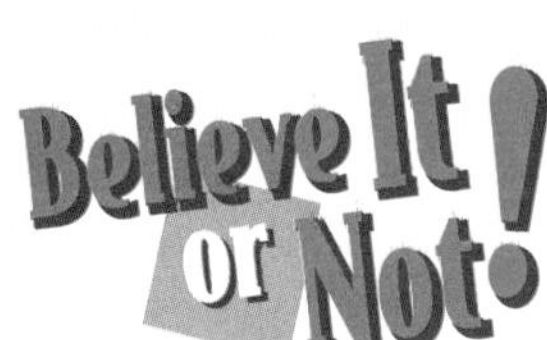

The Aral Sea

This ship once moved along the waters of the Aral Sea. The sea was huge—the fourth-largest inland body of water in the world. To irrigate fields of cotton, Soviet leaders took water from the rivers that flowed into the Aral Sea. The sea shrank to one-half its former size in just 40 years. Now camels walk where fish once swam.

Chapter 15

Section 3, pages 436–440

Assign Section 3 Assessment as homework or an in-class activity.

Have students use the Interactive Tutor Self-Assessment CD-ROM to review Section 3.

L2

Section Quiz

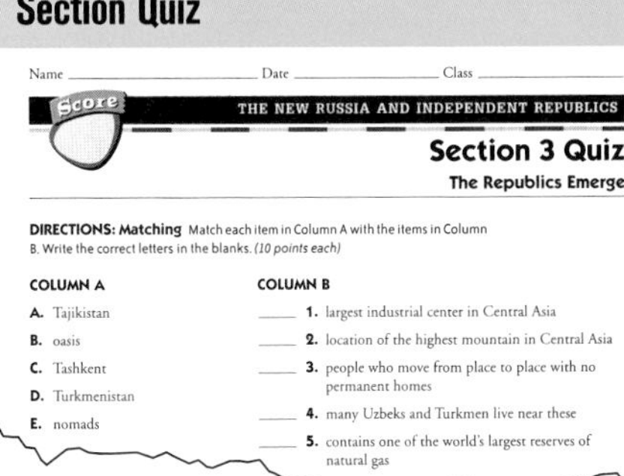

Name ______ Date ______ Class ______

Score

THE NEW RUSSIA AND INDEPENDENT REPUBLICS

Section 3 Quiz

The Republics Emerge

DIRECTIONS: Matching Match each item in Column A with the items in Column B. Write the correct letters in the blanks. *(10 points each)*

COLUMN A	COLUMN B
A. Tajikistan	____ 1. largest industrial center in Central Asia
B. oasis	____ 2. location of the highest mountain in Central Asia
C. Tashkent	____ 3. people who move from place to place with no permanent homes
D. Turkmenistan	____ 4. many Uzbeks and Turkmen live near these
E. nomads	____ 5. contains one of the world's largest reserves of natural gas

Measure student knowledge of physical features.

GeoQuiz Transparency

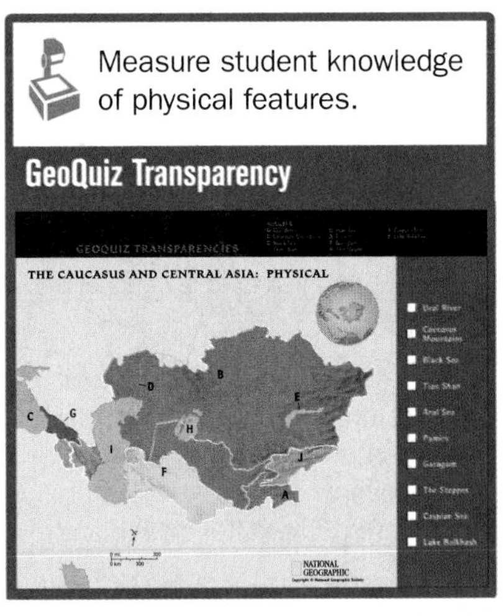

Team-Teaching Activity

History Invite a teacher with a background in world history to class to discuss the sufferings of Armenians under the Ottomans and the Turks. Severe persecution began in the 1890s when Ottoman soldiers killed hundreds of thousands of Armenians. Attacks continued in the 1910s when as many as a million Armenians may have been killed in what some call "the Armenian Holocaust." When the presentation is completed, have students discuss whether they think international bodies such as the United Nations or independent alliances of nations should intervene in such conflicts. L2

EE4 Human Systems: Standard 13

✓ Reading Check Answer

Kazakhstan, Uzbekistan, Turkmenistan, Kyrgyzstan, and Tajikistan

L1/ELL

Reading Essentials and Study Guide

Name ______ Date ______ Class ______

THE NEW RUSSIA AND INDEPENDENT REPUBLICS

Reading Essentials and Study Guide 3

The Republics Emerge

Key Terms

fault a crack in the earth's crust that can cause an earthquake
cash crop a product grown for sale as an export
steppe dry, treeless plain
nomad person who moves from place to place with a herd of animals
oasis fertile or green area in a desert watered by an underground spring
elevation an area's height above sea level
bilingual having or knowing two languages

Drawing From Experience

Have you ever felt silk? Centuries ago people did not have many soft fabrics. Silk was a welcome change from the rough clothing of the day. Traders brought silk to Europe from China. The Silk Road took them through Central Asia.

The last section discussed Russia's cultural achievements. This section discusses former Soviet lands and the challenges they face as new nations.

Organizing Your Thoughts

Use the chart below to help you take notes. For each country, give one fact about its land and one about its people.

Country	Fact About Land	Fact About People
Armenia	1.	2.
Azerbaijan	3.	4.
Georgia	5.	6.
Kazakhstan	7.	8.
Uzbekistan	9.	10.
Turkmenistan	11.	12.
Kyrgyzstan	13.	14.
Tajikistan	15.	16.

206 207

Give students an outline map of the Central Asian Republics. Have them create an annotated map that describes the resources and products of the different regions.

height above sea level, or **elevation.** Lower valleys and plains have warm, dry summers and chilly winters. Higher areas have cool summers and bitterly cold winters. A lack of fertile soil hinders farmers, but they manage to grow cotton, vegetables, and fruits. Many also raise sheep or cattle. Although the country has few industries, it does have valuable deposits of mercury and gold.

More than half of the people belong to the Kyrgyz ethnic group. Differences among clans, or family groups, often separate one part of the country from another. Kyrgyzstan is a **bilingual** country—one that has two official languages. These are Kirghiz, related to Turkish, and Russian. About 35 percent of the country's 5 million people live in cities, such as the capital, **Bishkek.**

Tajikistan Mountainous Tajikistan lies south of Kyrgyzstan. The highest mountain in Central Asia—**Ismail Samani Peak**—is located here. Mountain streams irrigate cotton, rice, and fruits grown in fertile river valleys. These streams also provide water for hydroelectric power.

The largest city is **Dushanbe** (doo•SHAM•buh), the capital. Most of Tajikistan's 6.6 million people are Tajiks, who are related to the Persians. Another 25 percent are Uzbeks, a group related to the Turks. In 1992 a bitter civil war broke out between rival clans. Many people were killed, and the economy was severely damaged. Despite a peace agreement in 1997, tensions still remain high.

✓ Reading Check Name the five Central Asian republics.

Section 3 Assessment

Defining Terms

1. **Define** fault, cash crop, steppe, nomad, oasis, elevation, bilingual.

Recalling Facts

2. **Region** What common characteristics make the countries of Armenia, Azerbaijan, and Georgia a region?
3. **Economics** What is the most promising part of Azerbaijan's economy?
4. **Culture** Who were ancestors of the Kazakhs?

Critical Thinking

5. **Making Inferences** Why do most Turkmen live along the southern border of Turkmenistan?
6. **Understanding Cause and Effect** Why has the Aral Sea shrunk in size?

Graphic Organizer

7. **Organizing Information** Create a chart like the one shown below. Fill in the chart with information about Georgia and Uzbekistan that you learned in this section.

	Georgia	Uzbekistan
Ethnic group		
Natural resources		
Economic activities		

Applying Social Studies Skills

8. **Analyzing Maps** Look at the political map on page 397 in the **Regional Atlas.** Which of the Eurasian republics do not border Russia?

Section 3 Assessment

1. The terms are defined in the Glossary.
2. All three countries are near the Caucasus Mountains, enjoy mild climates, and have commercial farming.
3. oil and gas deposits under the Caspian Sea
4. Mongols
5. because most of the northern and central areas are part of the desert called Garagum, which supports little economic activity
6. The Aral Sea receives less freshwater because the rivers that fed into it have been diverted for irrigation.
7. Students' diagrams should include facts from the section.
8. Armenia, Turkmenistan, Uzbekistan, Kyrgyzstan, Tajikistan

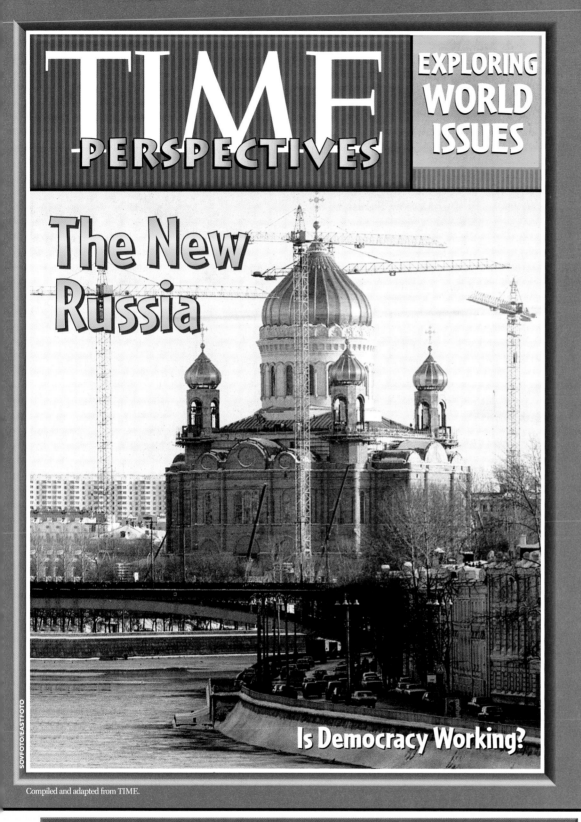

TIME PERSPECTIVES

EXPLORING WORLD ISSUES

The New Russia

Is Democracy Working?

SOVFOTO/EASTFOTO

Compiled and adapted from TIME.

Making Connections

Democracy **Ask students:** **How does U.S. society prepare young people to participate in democracy?** List the students' ideas on the board. Ideas might include taking government and civics courses in school, reading and hearing about politics in newspapers and on television, and watching adults vote. **Ask:** **How is this different from what happened in 1991 when the Soviet Union suddenly broke up? Why do you think it has been difficult for the Russian people to establish a stable democratic government?** **L1**

TIME PERSPECTIVES

Exploring World Issues

Teacher Background

The Communists seized control of the Russian government in 1917, eventually taking over the entire territory that became the Soviet Union. Because of the government's repressive policies, the economy performed poorly. From 1985 to 1991, Mikhail Gorbachev attempted to modernize communism by making the economy less centralized. However, this attempt ultimately failed, leading to the December 1991 breakup of the Soviet Union.

TIME REPORTS

RUSSIA AND THE EURASIAN REPUBLICS

The New Russia

THEME: CONTINUITY AND CHANGE

Guide To Teaching With This Unit

Preparing the Student

Explain to students that the breakup of the Soviet Union resulted in 15 independent nations, with Russia being the largest. Without any preparation, Russia went from being a highly restrictive, totalitarian government to a democracy. This report discusses the problems Russians continue to encounter because of this sudden transition.

1 Focus

Point to Russia on a world map and mention that it is the world's largest country. **Ask:** **What have you heard about life in Russia today?** *(Students might mention that Russians can now vote and own businesses. However, most of them are poor and there is a great deal of corruption, even among government officials.)* **L1**

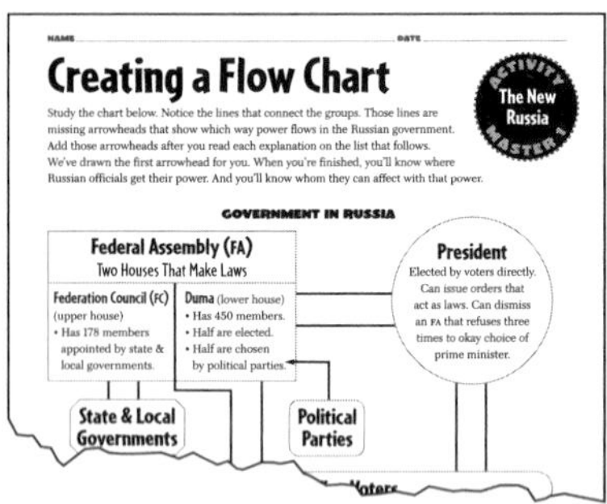

NAME DATE

Creating a Flow Chart

Activity Master 1 — The New Russia

Study the chart below. Notice the lines that connect the groups. Those lines are missing arrowheads that show which way power flows in the Russian government. Add those arrowheads after you read each explanation on the list that follows. We've drawn the first arrowhead for you. When you're finished, you'll know where Russian officials get their power. And you'll know whom they can affect with that power.

Did You Know?

Twenty-five percent of Russians live below the poverty level.

SOVFOTO/EASTFOTO

CHRISTOPHER ... / BLACK STAR

In Moscow a cathedral destroyed by the Communists has been rebuilt. Older Russians are especially pleased.

A New Nation and Economy

Daniel Strigin lives in Moscow, the capital of Russia. There he shares a tiny, three-room apartment with his mother, his grandmother, his wife—and the parts of a one-seat airplane. Strigin, 30, is what Russians call a ***kulibini***—a part-time inventor. By day he works as a computer technician. In his free time, he works on his dream of flying a plane he built himself.

Strigin is one of tens of thousands of *kulibini* in Russia. "There is something in the Russian man's soul," he says, "that pushes him to invent."

Housing goes up in Provideniya, a port city west of Alaska in Russia's Far East.

WOLFGANG KAEHLER/CORBIS

The impulse to invent is something Russia needs badly today. Its Communist government collapsed in 1991. Since then, the country of 146 million people has been struggling to remake itself as a democracy with a **free market economy**.

Remarkable Gains

The **Russian Federation,** the official name of Russia, has made great strides:

- Russians now elect their leaders, something they had never been allowed to do before.
- Reforms have turned Russia's state-controlled economy into a free market system that grew steadily from 1999 to 2003.
- Russia has shrunk its borders. Once it had been the Soviet Union's leading power. But that union fell to pieces. Now all 15 of the former republics, including Russia, are independent nations.

Russia still has a long way to go. Its elected leaders sometimes act illegally to silence their critics. Steel and other manufacturing companies are old and controlled by a few powerful people. There aren't enough privately owned **enterprises,** or businesses. Criminal gangs and corruption thrive. And in Chechnya, part of the Russian Federation, rebels have been at war with the government since 1994.

442

Team-Teaching Activity

Government Have a teacher with a background in political science talk about the Russian government today. He or she should talk about how government policies affect the average Russian and what the government is doing to try to improve citizens' lives. If possible, the teacher should discuss how the average Russian lives, the types of schools children attend, and the kinds of jobs people have. Efforts by foreign governments and the international community to stabilize the government and economy should also be discussed. Have students discuss how the new Russian government compares to the United States government. **L2**

 **EE4 Human Systems: Standard 10**

A man votes near a statue of Vladimir Lenin, the first Communist dictator.

A man dressed as a bear advertises a new restaurant in St. Petersburg.

Billboards near St. Basil Cathedral are evidence of the new Russian economy.

TIME REPORTS

2 TEACH

Reading Strategy

Identifying Main Ideas
As students finish reading each subsection, have them write a one-sentence summary of that subsection. Ask volunteers to share their sentences.

After the students have finished reading the report, ask them to state its main idea. **Ask:** **What message does Russia's experience send to all of us?** One important point is that citizens must be carefully prepared to take part in a democracy. L1

From Misery to Stability

The reforms caused great hardship. Under communism the state owned all businesses. In the shift to privately owned enterprises, thousands of farms and factories failed. Millions lost their jobs, and the government had no money. In 1999, 55 million people—one out of every three Russians—scraped by on less than $6 a month.

Reforms were introduced to create a stronger free market economy. More Russians now own factories, shops and other businesses. In 1999, 61% of Russians worked for private companies, compared to only 16% in 1991. By 2003, Russia had experienced four years of relative economic and political stability.

Where Russians Work

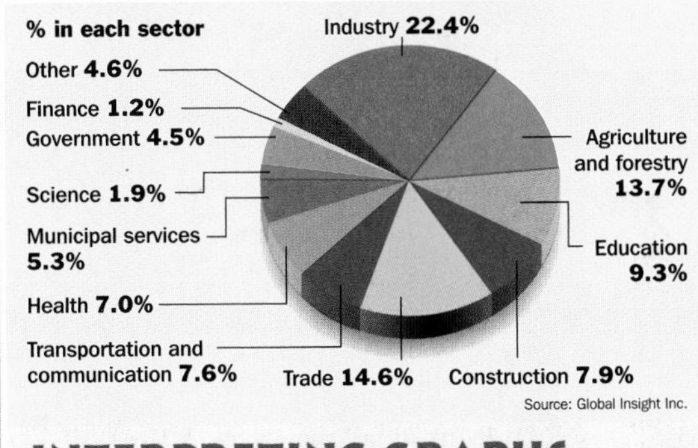

INTERPRETING GRAPHS

Explaining How does this graph tell you that about one in four Russians makes or sells industrial products?

EXPLORING THE ISSUE

1. **Analyzing** The rule of law means that everyone—including government officials—must follow the law. Why might this concept be difficult for Russians to accept?
2. **Compare and Contrast** Suppose all the states in the United States became independent nations. How might that situation be like—and unlike—what happened to the Soviet Union?

Uncertain Change

Russia and the world are waiting to see just how permanent the reforms will be. Establishing a lasting democracy with a market economy will take a lot of work. Important steps include forming reliable government institutions and an acceptance of the rule of law by Russian society.

Russia has many strengths. It is the world's largest country, and its people are well educated. Russia's natural resources—oil, lumber, and minerals—are plentiful. And many of its privately owned factories have figured out how to make first-rate products.

"A Russian is **inventive,**" says one of Daniel Strigin's *kulibini* friends, "because he has to find solutions in bad conditions."

Uncertain conditions haunt today's Russia. Time will tell whether its people will continue to have the will—and inventiveness—to overcome them. ■

EXPLORING THE ISSUE

ANSWERS

1. Before 1991 Russian officials were above the law and ran the country the way they saw fit rather than according to the law.
2. *Like:* Each state would have its own government, laws, army, taxes, currency. *Unlike:* American states have a number of things in common, such as a common language and a democratic government.

Where Russians Work

ANSWER

It shows that 22.4% work in industry.

Differentiated Instruction

Meeting Special Needs: Auditory/Musical Have a group of 6 to 8 students research Russian folk music and dance. Books and tapes on folk music and dance are available at the public library. The students may want to see if they can find a local person, such as a person of Russian descent, who would be able to help them learn about Russian music and dance. The students should practice one or more folk dances and then present them to the class. If facilities allow, perhaps they can teach the dance to the entire class. Afterwards, discuss how the music and dances reflect Russian culture. L1

Refer to *Inclusion for the Middle School Social Studies Classroom Strategies and Activities* in the TCR.

TIME
PERSPECTIVES

Recommended Internet Sites

news.bbc.co.uk
Enter "Collapse of USSR" in the Search box to find a time line and the latest news from Russia.

pbs.org/weta/faceofrussia/
This site has information on Russian culture and what it was like to live in a Communist society. It also has lesson plans.

More About the Photo

Stalin Ask: What do you think this veteran liked about life under Stalin's rule?

EXPLORING THE ISSUE

ANSWERS

1. Younger Russians have not lived for many years (or maybe not at all) under a totalitarian regime that told them where to work, provided housing, and took care of their health care and other needs.
2. If voters find out that these officials are mistreating people, they will not be reelected.

NAME ______ DATE ______

Analyzing a Table

ACTIVITY The New Russia MASTER 2

How can you get a sharper picture of life in Russia? One way is to compare numbers that describe Russia with those that describe other countries. The table on this page does just that. Read it. Then decide whether statements about the chart are true or false.

How Five Nations Measure Up

	China	D. R. Congo*	France	Russia	U.S.
People (in millions; add 000,000)	1,288	57	60	146	291
% of population who live in cities	30%	29%	73%	76%	75%
Years a person can expect to live	70	51	76	67	72
% of population with jobs	58%	36%	43%	50%	50%
% of pop. age 15+ who are able to read	82%	77%	99%	98%	97%
Calories eaten by one person per day	2,741	1,879	3,588	2,928	3,603
Corruption ranking**	57	Not avail.	23	79	16
Freedom compared with other nations***	7.6	6.5	1.2	4.5	1.1

* Democratic Republic of the Congo
** Out of [illegible] countries. Corruption occurs when government officials [illegible] them gifts. Researchers
*** Based on the amount of rights each nation allows. Rights include freedom to vote, speak out, worship as one wants, live where one wants, etc. Scoring: 1.0–2.5 (Free), 3.0–5.5 (Partly Free), 5.5–7.0 (Not Free). Source: Freedom House (2001).

Are Russians Better Off?

Valentina Fedotova cries when she tells her story. In 1946 she was a student nurse in the Ukrainian city of Kiev. One day the secret police arrested her. They never told her why. After a four-minute "trial," she was shipped off to Russia's brutally cold Siberia. There she spent 10 years in a labor camp, working year-round mining gold. After 10 years, she was freed. But her sentence required her to stay in Siberia for 10 more years. By the time those years were up, Fedotova was a broken woman. She never left the far east, where she now lives alone.

▼ **Many older Russians long for earlier times. This war veteran's hero is Joseph Stalin, a brutal dictator.**

CHRISTOPHER MORRIS/BLACK STAR

444

EXPLORING THE ISSUE

1. **Making Inferences** Why might younger Russians find it easier than older Russians to learn to rely on themselves?
2. **Contrasting** Elected leaders are less likely than dictators to arrest and imprison people without cause. Why do you think this is so?

Millions of people who lived through the Soviet era, from 1917 to 1991, have similar stories. The Communist government headed by Joseph Stalin between 1924 and 1953 imprisoned, executed, or starved to death millions of people. Prisoners in labor camps built canals, railroads, hydroelectric stations, mines, and other industries.

A New Self-Reliance

With the freedom that followed the Soviet Union's collapse in 1991, people had to take responsibility for their lives. "In today's Russia," a businessman says, "you have to rely on yourself."

Russians are becoming more self-reliant. Thanks to reforms and private enterprise, Russia's economy is growing. Wages are rising and companies are buying materials to help them grow in the future. Growing political and economic stability, most Russians believe, make them better off today than ever. ■

Critical Thinking Activity

Identifying Alternatives A major problem in Russia today is corruption at every level of government. Bribery is commonplace. Students may have little understanding of how this makes it difficult to conduct even ordinary business. Ask them how they would feel if they had to pay a bribe to get a driver's license or to avoid a speeding ticket. A major problem is that the world's stable governments may be reluctant to help such a government. Other governments may be afraid their aid will reach only corrupt officials. Have students brainstorm about how the United States might attempt to help the Russian people overcome this current situation, reduce corruption, and create a more stable society. L2

 **EE6 The Uses of Geography: Standard 18**

The Road to Somewhere

As the Soviet Union was ending in 1991, protesters gathered in Moscow's Red Square. One man held a sign that said, "70 Years to Nowhere." The sign spoke of the past—the years of Communist rule that had led to a dead end.

What about the next 70 years? They should bring fairer courts, for one thing. Russian judges are used to taking the government's side. Soon juries will be deciding many cases, making courts more even-handed.

Health and Jobs

Tomorrow's Russians will probably be wealthier and healthier than today's. Now, hospital patients must supply their own food, sheets, and medicine. Life expectancy for men is only 59 years—down from 64 in 1989.

But Russia's healthcare system is getting stronger, along with the nation's economy. A stronger economy will mean more jobs and less poverty. Steady jobs should persuade Russian men to stop abusing alcohol. That drug is shortening their lives.

How quickly will these changes come? It all depends on how quickly Russians change the way they think. Russians don't yet have democracy in their hearts. They are not used to voting or taking part in community affairs, either as volunteers or as elected officials. They tend to think it is more important to help themselves than their neighbors.

EAST NEWS/GETTY IMAGES/NEWSCOM

▲ Russian students hope to enjoy freedoms their parents never knew.

Self-Serve Government

Government workers think the same way. Few see themselves as **public servants.** Many of them serve themselves first. People must pay money "under the table" to get driver's licenses, fair treatment by police, and permits to build houses.

Today "70 Years to Somewhere" could be Russia's slogan. It's just far too early to say what that somewhere will be like.

EXPLORING THE ISSUE

1. **Explaining** Why might a stronger Russian economy lead to better health?
2. **Problem Solving** What could the United States do to help Russians learn to put "democracy in their hearts"?

445

Interpreting Information

Have students research the lives of average Russian citizens. **Ask:** **What kinds of jobs do they have? Where do they live? Do they own cars, washing machines, TVs, and stereos? What do teenagers do for recreation?** Then have them write a report titled "A Day in the Life of . . ." in which they describe a day in the life of an average teenager in Russia. **L2**

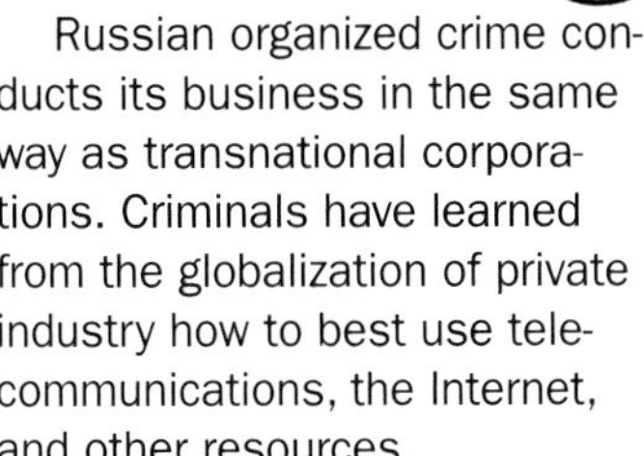

Russian organized crime conducts its business in the same way as transnational corporations. Criminals have learned from the globalization of private industry how to best use telecommunications, the Internet, and other resources.

EXPLORING THE ISSUE

ANSWERS

1. *Possible answers:* Health care will be better because of better training and facilities; people will eat better and therefore be healthier; people who can work and support their families are less likely to abuse alcohol.
2. *Possible answers:* show Russians that citizens' participation in government is good for individuals and the country as a whole; teach them that with rights come responsibilities.

Interdisciplinary Activity

Health Ask students about the type of health care they expect to get in the United States. What do they do when they get sick? How is their care paid for? What kind of treatment would they get if they were ill or in an accident? Tell them that in Russia under the Communist government, Russians had free health care, but it was not always the best. Have them research the Russian health care system to see how it has changed in the new free economy. **Ask:** **How does it compare to the American system as far as providing health care to all citizens and giving the best and most up-to-date treatment?** Have students debate the pros and cons of the two systems. **L3**

EE4 Human Systems: Standard 11

Making Comparisons
It is important to remember that 15 nations were created when the Soviet Union dissolved. Instruct students to research the government and economy of one of the other 14 countries. They should then write a report briefly comparing this nation to Russia. The report should discuss the stability of the government and how well the average citizen is doing. L2

Current Events Journal

Have students divide a piece of paper into two columns. They should label one column *Former Soviet Union* and the second column *Russia Today.* In the *Former Soviet Union* column, they should list the advantages of life in the Soviet Union. Below this list, they should list the disadvantages of life in the Soviet Union. This process should be repeated for the *Russia Today* column.

Making Generalizations
As shown in the map, Russia spans 11 time zones. In fact, it is 1.8 times the size of the United States. **Ask:** **Do you think it is easier to have a democracy in a large country or a small country? Why?** L2

Helping Russia Rebuild: What Can One Person Do?

In July 2000, former hockey star Mike Gartner made boys in two Russian hockey clubs very happy. One club was in Penza, a town outside Moscow. The other club was far to the east in Novokuznetsk, a city in Siberia. Gartner gave each club something it couldn't afford—hockey equipment worth thousands of dollars.

Goals & Dreams

Gartner heads the Goals & Dreams program of the National Hockey League Players' Association (NHLPA). "We're not doing this to try to make future NHL hockey players," Gartner said. "The goal is to try to make kids better people."

That's also the goal of the head of Novokuznetsk's hockey. "We are working toward a healthier lifestyle for our youth," he said.

That's not easy in a nation as hard-pressed as Russia. The Novokuznetsk club gives its members free food and medical care. But it has no money left over to buy equipment.

▲ **Former pro hockey star Mike Gartner meets members of a Russian hockey club.**

Encouraging Words

You can help Russians simply by supporting efforts like the NHLPA's. You don't have to send sports equipment. You don't have to send money. Just send those groups a letter, letting them know how much you appreciate their efforts. Groups that provide assistance to others gain strength just from knowing that others care.

Many groups are helping Russia today. One is the Eurasia Foundation, based in Washington, D.C. The World Wildlife Federation is another.

And don't forget Goals & Dreams. "We have stacks of letters from kids and families thanking us," Mike Gartner said. "This is a great job—kind of like being Santa Claus." ■

446

Your Government and You

The Center for Strategic and International Studies (CSIS) provides world leaders with insights into a variety of global issues. Students can visit its Web site (www.csis.org) to learn more about the Center's Russia/Eurasia Program. One of the issues the program addresses is HIV/AIDS. According to the CSIS, Russia and Eurasia are experiencing the highest rate of growth of HIV in the world. The World Bank estimates that in 2020, 21,000 Russians will die each month from AIDS and 5.4 million Russians will be infected with HIV. The CSIS urges preventative measures now because they will be cheaper than dealing with the costs incurred by AIDS in 2020. **Ask:** **What would be the social and economic costs of having millions of people sick and dying of AIDS?** L2

 **EE4 Human Systems: Standard 9**

REVIEW AND ASSESS

UNDERSTANDING THE ISSUE

1. **Defining Key Terms** Write definitions for the following terms: *kulibini, free market economy, Russian Federation, enterprise, inventive, public servant.*

2. **Writing to Inform** Imagine you are in a Russian middle school. Write a letter to an American friend explaining Russia's challenges. Use at least five of the key terms listed above.

3. **Writing to Persuade** "In today's Russia, you have to learn to rely on yourself." Write a letter to an imaginary Russian friend. Explain why self-reliance is a good thing.

INTERNET RESEARCH ACTIVITY

4. Russian army units have "adopted" a few thousand of the 1 million to 2 million Russian kids who have no home. Children as young as 11 live on army bases, wear uniforms, and attend school. They are not sent to war. Elsewhere children do fight wars. To learn about them, with your teacher's help, browse the Internet for information. List ways that real child soldiers seem like, and are different from, Russian kids in uniform. Compare your list with those of your classmates.

5. Since 1999, the Library of Congress has brought Russian officials to the United States to see democracy at work. Browse the Internet to find out more about this Library of Congress program. In a 250-word essay, describe the program and explain how it might benefit both Russians and Americans. Can you think of additional programs that would guide Russia?

The old and new reflect Russia's future. ▶

SERGEI GUNEYEV/TIMEPIX

BEYOND THE CLASSROOM

6. **Visit your school or local library** to learn about the Soviet Union. Working in groups, find out what it was like to live under a Communist government. What basic freedoms did Russians not have? Discuss your findings with your classmates.

7. **Research another nation** that has exchanged one-party rule for democracy. What might Russians learn from the other nation's experience? Put your findings in a report.

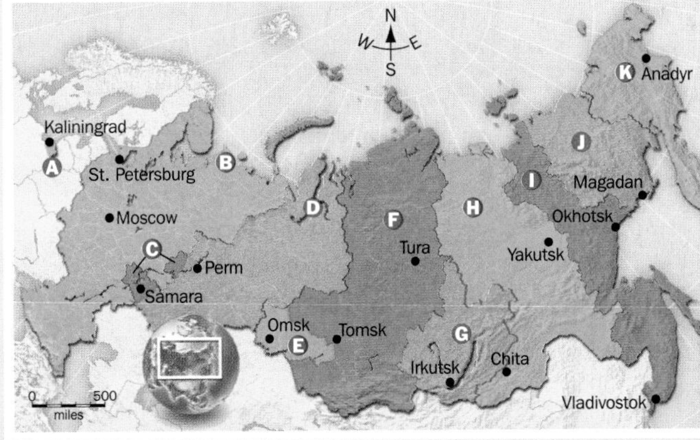

RUSSIA'S 11 TIME ZONES

The earth is divided into 24 time zones, one for each hour of the day. Russia spans 11 time zones, stretching nearly halfway around the globe. We've labeled Russia's time zones from A to K. There's an hour's difference between each zone. It's always later in the East, where the sun rises, than in the West.

BUILDING MAP READING SKILLS

1. **Interpreting Maps** If it's 9:00 A.M. in Kaliningrad, what time is it in Moscow? What time is it in Tura, Chita, Vladivostok, and Magadan? Suppose it is 2:00 A.M., January 20, in Tomsk. What time and day is it in Samara?

2. **Transferring Data** Across the top of a sheet of paper, write the name of one city in each time zone, from Kaliningrad to Anadyr. Draw a clock beneath each name. Set the sixth clock at midnight. Draw the correct time on the 10 other clocks.

FOR UPDATES ON WORLD ISSUES GO TO www.timeclassroom.com/glencoe

3 ASSESS

Have students take the TIME Reports Quiz or do the Alternative Assessment project for this unit provided in the Teacher's Classroom Resources.

NAME ______ DATE ______

Organizing Data

ACTIVITY MASTER 3 — The New Russia

If you lived in Russia, you'd get to celebrate many holidays. Some are new ones, added after 1991 to celebrate Russia's new democracy. Others, such as White Nights, are old ones. Still others, such as religious holidays, have been brought back to life. All of them provide you with a glimpse of Russia's values—what Russians find important.

Listed below are ten Russian holidays and the dates on which they were celebrated in 2004. Match them with the correct description on the right.

10 Russian Holidays	Holiday History
____ 1. January 1–2, New Year's	a. This holiday replaces Red Army Day, a celebration of the military might of the Soviet Union, which collapsed in 1991.
____ 2. January 7, Russian Orthodox Christmas	b. Hooray for the 1993 document that lays down the law on what Russia's government can and can't do.
____ 3. February 23, Defender's Day	c. This early May holiday replaces a Communist holiday called International Workers' Solidarity Day.
____ 4. March 8, International Women's Day	d. World War II in Europe ended on this day in 1945, and the Allies won. Russians use the day to remember the millions who died.
	...day good children open presents from Father

BUILDING MAP READING SKILLS

ANSWERS

1. Moscow: 10:00 A.M.; Tura: 2:00 P.M.; Chita: 4:00 P.M.; Vladivostok: 5:00 P.M.; Magadan: 6:00 P.M.; 11:00 P.M., January 19
2. From left (Kaliningrad) to right (Anadyr), the times will range from 7:00 P.M. to 5:00 A.M.

4 CLOSE

Reading Strategy

Writing a Paragraph Ask students to write a paragraph starting with this topic sentence: *Some of the ways the Russian government could encourage its citizens to participate in democracy are . . . .*

Culminating Activity

To close this lesson, have students complete the Review and Assess section questions and activities above. Students should use classroom discussion, contextual clues, and their student dictionaries to write definitions for terms. Before assigning the Internet activities, it is recommended that you review your school district policy on student Internet use.

Focus on Debate

Have students debate the pro and con position of the following topic: **The average Russian citizen was better off under the Communist government of the Soviet Union than he or she is today. L2**

 **EE6 The Uses of Geography: Standard 18**

TEACH

Have students think of reviews they have heard or read about a movie, CD, or book. **Ask: How did the reviewer reveal his or her point of view?** *(through the words chosen to praise or criticize the work being reviewed)* Explain that in this feature, they will learn how to evaluate a source for bias that might distort what is being said. **L1**

Additional Skills Practice

1. **Is a diary a primary or a secondary source?** *(primary)*
2. **If a television reporter interviews a member of Congress about a bill being considered, is the interview a primary or secondary source?** *(primary)*
3. **What biases might be shown in the interview described in question 2?** *(bias of the member of Congress, bias of the reporter)*

Additional Skills Resources

 Chapter Skills Review

 Building Geography Skills for Life

GLENCOE TECHNOLOGY

 **Skillbuilder Interactive Workbook CD-ROM, Level 1**

This interactive CD-ROM reinforces student mastery of essential social studies skills.

Study and Writing Skill

Using Primary and Secondary Sources

So much information comes our way in today's world. How can you analyze it to decide what is truly useful and accurate?

Learning the Skill

There are two basic types of information sources. *Primary sources* are original records of events made by the people who witnessed them. They include letters, photographs, and artifacts. *Secondary sources* are documents created after an event occurred. They report an event.

When reading sources, try to learn more about the person who wrote the information. Most people have a point of view, or bias. This bias influences the way they write about events.

To analyze information, follow these steps:

- Identify who created the document and when it was created.
- Determine whether the information is a primary or secondary source.
- Read the document. Who and what is it about? What are its purpose and main ideas?
- Determine how the author's point of view, or bias, is reflected in the work.

▼ **A polluted playground in Azerbaijan**

Practicing the Skill

Read the passage below, and then answer the questions that follow.

> I went south to Kazakhstan and, at 4:45 A.M., stumbled off a train in Aral and went to the hospital. Beginning in the 1970s the people became ill with hepatitis, typhus, and other diseases. They drank from the rivers, as always, but now the shrunken rivers ran with sewage, industrial metals, and poisons such as DDT. "It wasn't possible to mix infant formula with that water," said a doctor. "It made goo, like soft cheese."
>
> Dust storms often blow for days, sweeping up tons of salts and fertilizers. Doctors brace then to receive children with breathing problems. Kazakhstan, declared a Kazakh writer, was the Soviet Union's "junk heap."

Adapted from "The U.S.S.R.'s Lethal Legacy" by Mike Edwards, *National Geographic,* August 1994.

1. Is this a primary or secondary source?
2. Who is the author of this passage?
3. What is the document about?
4. Where does it take place?
5. What is the purpose of this passage?
6. What, if any, evidence of bias do you find?

Applying the Skill

Analyze one of the letters to the editor in your local newspaper. Summarize the main idea, the writer's purpose, and any primary sources the writer may refer to.

GO TO Practice key skills with **Glencoe Skillbuilder Interactive Workbook, Level 1.**

Practicing the Skill Answers

1. a primary source, although the author reports actions that took place in the past but not observed by him
2. Mike Edwards
3. effects of pollution
4. Kazakhstan
5. to reveal the health problems suffered by the people of Kazakhstan due to pollution
6. the statement of the Kazakh writer about Kazakhstan being the Soviet Union's "junk heap"

Applying the Skill

Have students hand in the original letter along with their analysis to enable you to assess their mastery of the skill.

Reading Review

Section 1 From Communism to Free Enterprise

Terms to Know
- free market economy
- heavy industry
- light industry
- nuclear energy
- life expectancy

Main Idea

Russia has many resources but faces challenges in adjusting to a new economic system.

✓ Economics The change to a free market economy has been a challenge to many Russians as they face rising unemployment and rising prices.

✓ Economics Moscow, with many industries, is the economic center of Russia.

✓ Movement Ports in the northwest, southwest, and east carry on trade between Russia and other countries.

✓ Location Siberia has many resources, but the area is so cold and remote that it is difficult to tap these resources.

Section 2 Russia's People and Culture

Terms to Know
- democracy
- federal republic
- majority group
- minority group

Main Idea

Russians have a rich cultural past and are learning to live in a democracy.

✓ Government Russia is a federal republic with powers divided between national and regional governments.

✓ Culture Russia is a huge, populous country with about 100 different ethnic groups.

✓ Religion Russians practice many different faiths, but most are Russian Orthodox Christians.

✓ Culture Russian artists, composers, and writers often used themes or traditions based on Russian history.

Section 3 The Republics Emerge

Terms to Know
- fault
- cash crop
- steppe
- nomad
- oasis
- elevation
- bilingual

Main Idea

The republics of the Caucasus and Central Asia are trying to build new economies and governments.

✓ Economics The Caucasus republics have struggled to develop their own industries and businesses but are facing many ethnic conflicts.

✓ Environment The Central Asian republics face enormous challenges in cleaning up their environments.

✓ Culture Almost all of the people in the five Central Asian republics are Muslims.

Republic Square in Yerevan, Armenia ▶

Reading Review

Use the Chapter 15 Reading Review to preview, review, condense, or reteach the chapter.

Preview/Review

Use the Terms to Know lists to help students review and study.

Activity Assign students a selection of terms from each section and have them write sentences using the assigned words. Have volunteers read their sentences aloud.

Vocabulary PuzzleMaker CD-ROM reinforces the vocabulary terms used in Chapter 15.

The Interactive Tutor Self-Assessment CD-ROM allows students to review Chapter 15 content.

Condense

Have students read the Chapter 15 summary statements.

- Guided Reading Activities
- Audio Program

Reteach

- Reteaching Activity
- Reading Essentials and Study Guide

Reading Strategy Read to Write

Writing an Editorial Have students review the chapter and identify an issue that challenges Russia and the Eurasian Republics. Issues may include pollution, ethnic conflict, or economic growth. Students should research the issue and identify ways that people are trying to resolve it. Have students write an editorial that describes the issue, what steps they think should be taken to resolve it, and opposing arguments for specific resolutions. Students should use persuasive writing and correct grammar, punctuation, and sentence structure in their editorials. Have students read their editorials to the class. L3

Assessment and Activities

GLENCOE TECHNOLOGY

MindJogger Videoquiz
Use MindJogger Videoquiz to review the Chapter 15 content.

Available in DVD and VHS

Using Key Terms

1.	d	6.	a
2.	f	7.	g
3.	b	8.	e
4.	c	9.	h
5.	j	10.	i

Reviewing the Main Ideas

11. free market economy
12. the Volga and Urals region
13. the Volga
14. Siberia's climate and size make developing its resources difficult.
15. Russia's leaders must follow the law and accept disagreements over government policies.
16. St. Petersburg
17. The Communists created laws forbidding its practice.
18. Baku
19. Garagum
20. Islam

Chapter 15 Assessment and Activities

Using Key Terms

Match the terms in Part A with their definitions in Part B.

A.

1. majority group
2. light industry
3. nuclear energy
4. steppe
5. bilingual
6. democracy
7. nomad
8. oasis
9. heavy industry
10. federal republic

B.

a. government in which people freely elect their leaders
b. energy from controlled atomic reactions
c. dry, treeless plain
d. group that controls the wealth and power
e. green area in a desert
f. production of consumer goods
g. person who moves from place to place
h. production of industrial goods
i. government in which national and state governments share powers
j. having two official languages

Reviewing the Main Ideas

Section 1 From Communism to Free Enterprise

11. **Economics** What type of economic system has Russia adopted?
12. **Economics** Where are Russia's most productive farmlands?
13. **Movement** What river carries almost half of Russia's river traffic?
14. **Location** Why is it difficult to tap Siberia's resources?

Section 2 Russia's People and Culture

15. **Government** What political challenges face Russians and their officials?
16. **Culture** In which city would you find the Hermitage Museum?
17. **History** What happened to religion during the Communist rule of Russia?

Section 3 The Republics Emerge

18. **Place** What is the capital of Azerbaijan?
19. **Place** What desert occupies most of Turkmenistan?
20. **Culture** What religion do the people of the Central Asian republics follow?

The Eurasian Republics

Place Location Activity

On a separate sheet of paper, match the letters on the map with the numbered places listed below.

1. Kazakhstan
2. Aral Sea
3. Caspian Sea
4. Turkmenistan
5. Azerbaijan
6. Armenia
7. Tajikistan
8. Baku

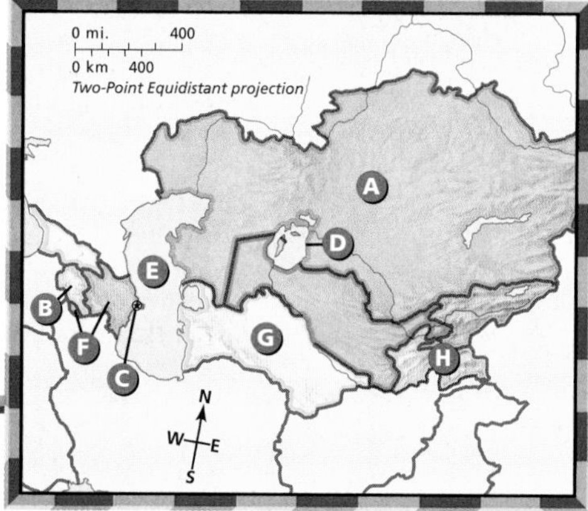

NATIONAL GEOGRAPHIC Place Location Activity

1.	A	5.	F
2.	D	6.	B
3.	E	7.	H
4.	G	8.	C

Critical Thinking

21. Changes have made it weaker because the government no longer has a strong control, and the Russian people do not have much experience creating jobs, starting businesses, or making money.
22. Students' charts will vary but should contain information from the chapter.

Self-Check Quiz Visit ***The World and Its People*** Web site at twip.glencoe.com and click on **Chapter 15—Self-Check Quizzes** to prepare for the Chapter Test.

Critical Thinking

21. **Making Generalizations** How have recent changes in Russia affected its economy?

22. **Organizing Information** Create a chart like this one. Then list the similarities and differences between the economies of two Central Asian republics.

Country	Similarities	Differences

Comparing Regions Activity

23. **Culture** Look at the circle graph on page 443 titled "Where Russians Work." Create your own circle graph and title it "Where Americans Work." Find information in your textbook and on the Internet to show the jobs people in the United States hold. Do you think the Russian graph will someday look more like the U.S. graph? Why or why not?

Mental Mapping Activity

24. **Focus on the Region** Create a simple outline map of Russia and the Eurasian republics, and then label the following:

- Black Sea
- Caspian Sea
- Aral Sea
- Volga River
- Ural Mountains
- Kazakhstan
- Armenia
- Lake Baikal

Technology Skills Activity

25. **Using the Internet** Search the Internet for information on the problems facing the Aral Sea. Find out what distinctive creatures live in the Aral Sea that cannot be found anywhere else in the world. Find a map that shows what countries border the Aral Sea.

Standardized Test Practice

Directions: Study the map below, and then answer the question that follows.

1. Which of the following statements about this map is NOT true?

F Chechnya lies along Russia's southern border.

G Chechnya is situated between the Black and Caspian Seas.

H Chechnya's landscape is mostly flat, fertile farmland.

J Chechnya's nearest neighbor is Georgia.

Test-Taking Tip: Be careful when you see the words NOT or EXCEPT in a question. Read all the answer choices and choose the one that *does not* fit with the question. Quickly eliminate answers that are true. Make sure that your answer choice is supported by information on the map.

Assessment and Activities

Standardized Test Practice

1. H

Tested Objectives: Reading a map, analyzing information

Chapter Test Bonus Question

This question may be used for extra credit on the chapter test.

What cultural feature of Georgia and Armenia is different from all the other countries covered in the Eurasian Republics? *(Religion—they are Orthodox Christian, and all the other countries are Muslim.)*

Have students visit the Web site at twip.glencoe.com to review Chapter 15 and take the Self-Check Quiz.

FOLDABLES Study Organizer Dinah Zike's Foldables

Culminating Activity Have students quiz each other using the information they collected for their foldables.

Comparing Regions Activity

23. Students should provide sound reasons and factual evidence for their predictions.

Mental Mapping Activity

24. This exercise helps students visualize the countries and geographic features they have been studying. All attempts at freehand mapping should be accepted.

Technology Skills Activity

25. Students may want to create posters that identify and discuss Aral Sea wildlife and the problems affecting it.

Unit 6 Planning Guide

- If you teach BOTH Eastern and Western world regions in one year, use the columns in red to help you pace your lessons.
- **If you teach ONLY Eastern or Western world regions in one year, use the columns in blue to help you pace your lessons.**

ALTERNATIVE PACING CHARTS

Unit 3		Chapter 16		Chapter 17		Chapter 18	
Both East and West	Either East or West	Both East and West	Either East or West	Both East and West	Either East or West	Both East and West	Either East or West
Day 1 Unit Opener, Regional Atlas **Day 2** Regional Atlas	**Day 1** Unit Opener, Regional Atlas **Day 2** Regional Atlas **Day 3** Regional Atlas	**Day 1** Chapter Opener, Section 1 **Day 2** Section 1, Making Connections **Day 3** Section 2 **Day 4** Study and Writing Skill, Review **Day 5** Chapter Assessment	**Day 1** Chapter Opener, Section 1 **Day 2** Section 1 **Day 3** Section 1 **Day 4** Making Connections, Section 2 **Day 5** Section 2 **Day 6** Section 2, Study and Writing Skill **Day 7** Review **Day 8** Chapter Assessment **Day 9** Chapter Assessment	**Day 1** Chapter Opener, Section 1 **Day 2** Section 1, Making Connections **Day 3** Section 2 **Day 4** Technology Skill, Review **Day 5** Chapter Assessment **Day 6** NGS Eye on the Environment	**Day 1** Chapter Opener, Section 1 **Day 2** Section 1 **Day 3** Section 1, Making Connections **Day 4** Section 2 **Day 5** Section 2, Technology Skill **Day 6** Review **Day 7** Chapter Assessment **Day 8** NGS Eye on the Environment	**Day 1** Chapter Opener, Section 1 **Day 2** Section 1, Making Connections **Day 3** Section 2 **Day 4** Section 3 **Day 5** Section 4 **Day 6** TIME Reports **Day 7** TIME Reports, Technology Skill, Review **Day 8** Chapter Assessment	**Day 1** Chapter Opener, Section 1 **Day 2** Section 1 **Day 3** Making Connections, Section 2 **Day 4** Section 2 **Day 5** Section 3 **Day 6** Section 4 **Day 7** TIME Reports **Day 8** TIME Reports, Technology Skill **Day 9** Review **Day 10** Chapter Assessment

Note: The following materials may be used when teaching Unit 6.
Chapter level support materials can be found on the chapter resource pages.

TEACHING TRANSPARENCIES

Political Map Transparency L2

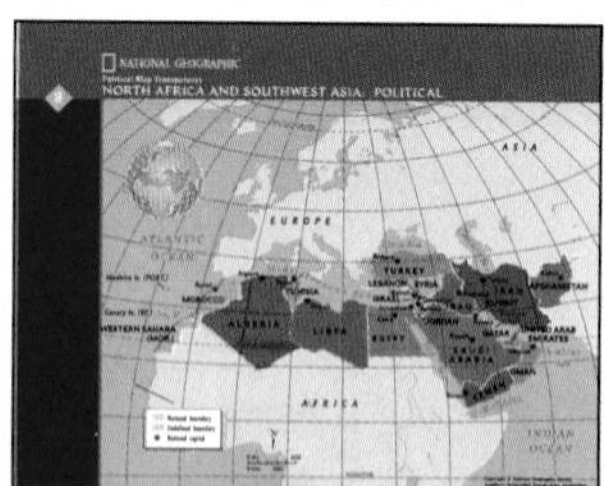

Map Overlay Transparencies L2

World Cultures Transparencies L2

Unit 6 Resources

INTERDISCIPLINARY CONNECTIONS

World Literature Reading L2

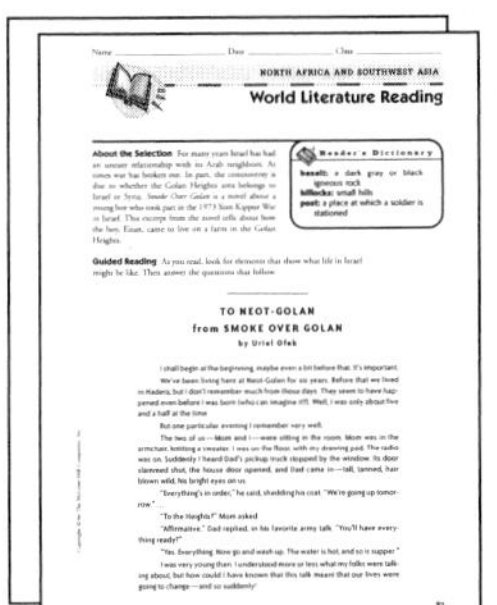

Economics and Geography Activity L2

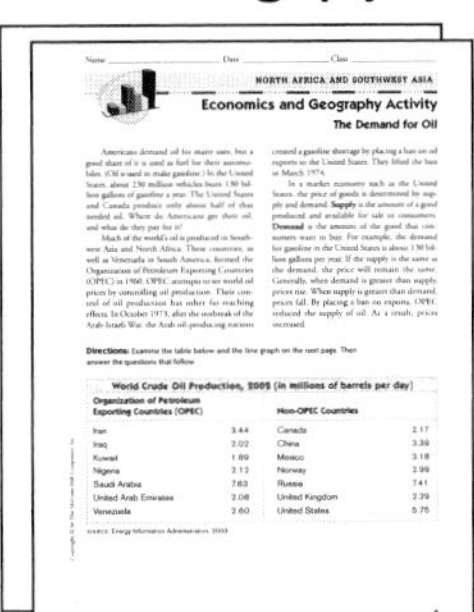

History and Geography Activity L2

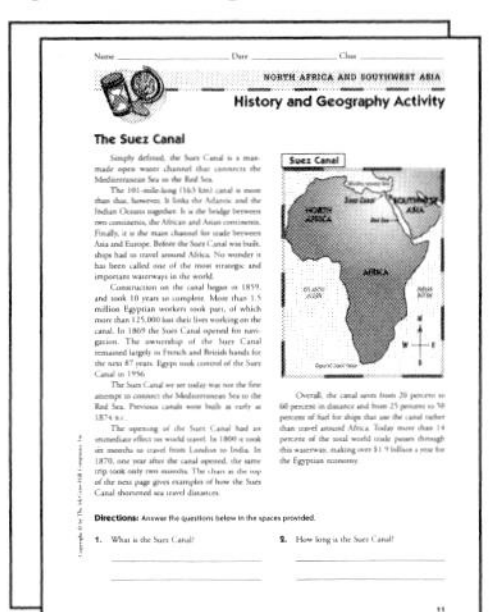

INTERDISCIPLINARY CONNECTIONS

Foods Around the World L1/ELL

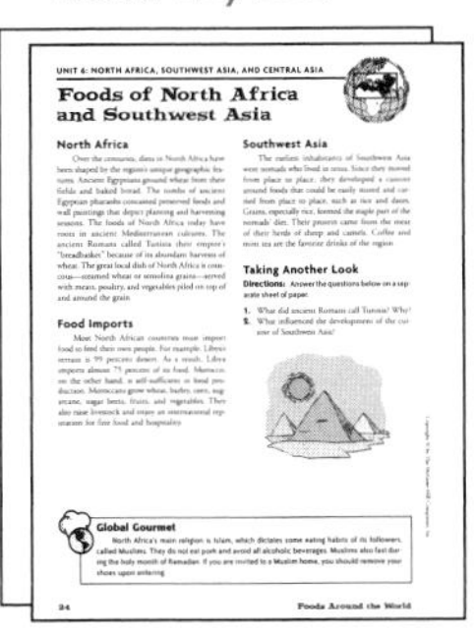

World Music: A Cultural Legacy

CIVIC INVOLVEMENT

Citizenship Activity L1

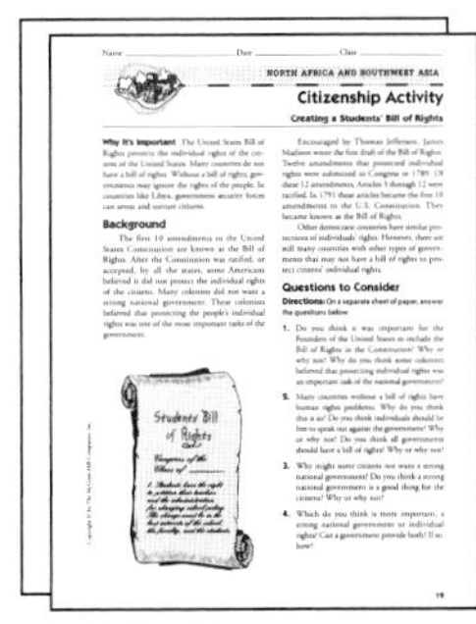

Environmental Case Study L2

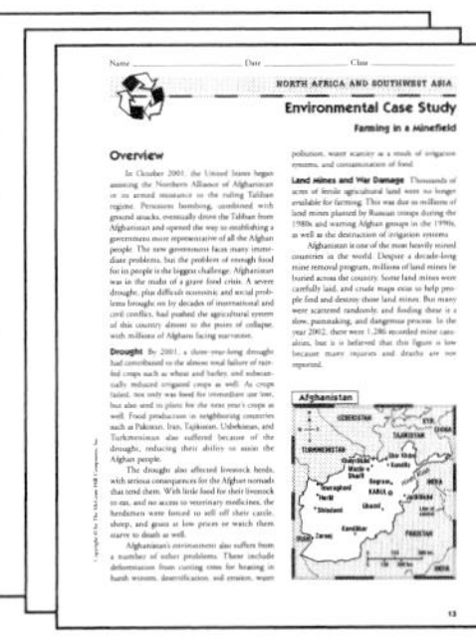

MAP AND GEOGRAPHY SKILLS

Building Geography Skills for Life

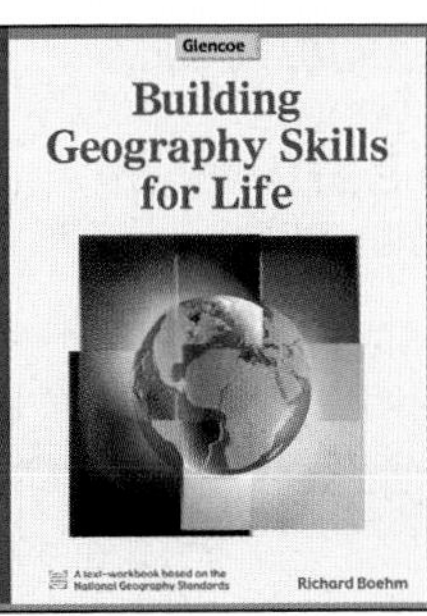

NGS Focus on Geography Literacy L2

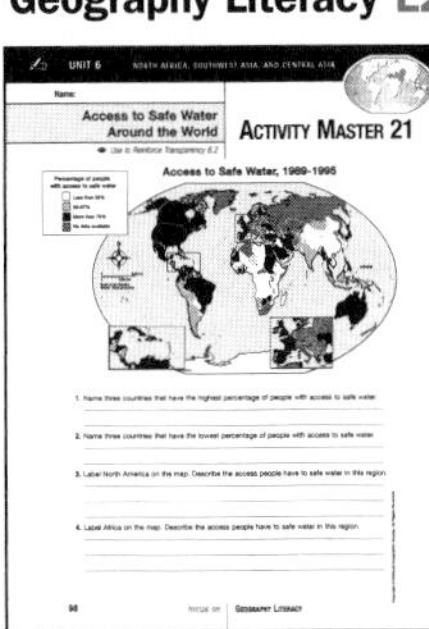

Regional Atlas Activity L2

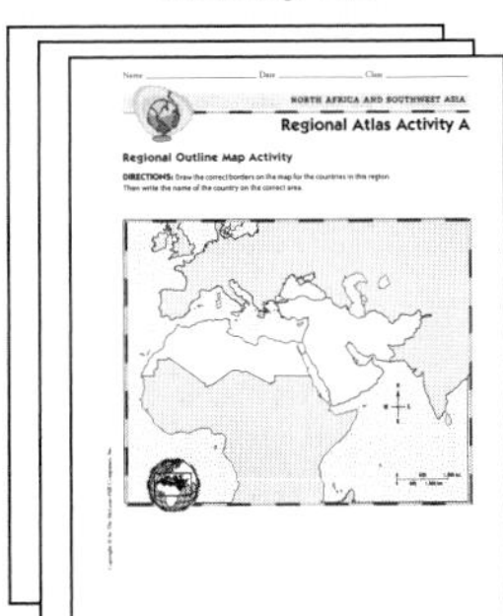

KEY TO ABILITY LEVELS

Teaching strategies have been coded for varying learning styles and abilities.

L1 **BASIC** activities for all students
L2 **AVERAGE** activities for average to above-average students
L3 **CHALLENGING** activities for above-average students
ELL **ENGLISH LANGUAGE LEARNER** activities

ASSESSMENT

Unit Pretests L2

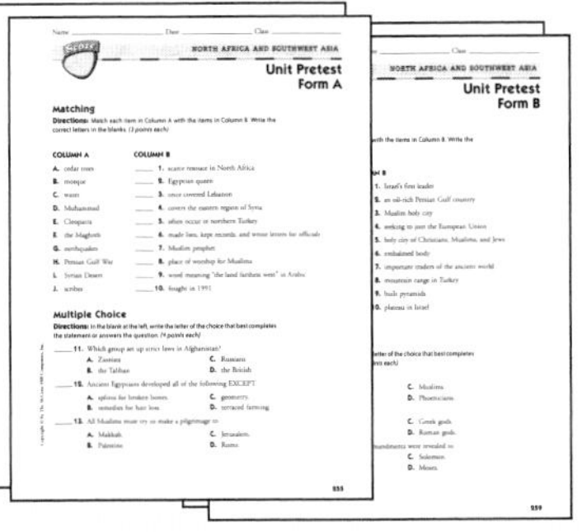

Unit Posttests L2

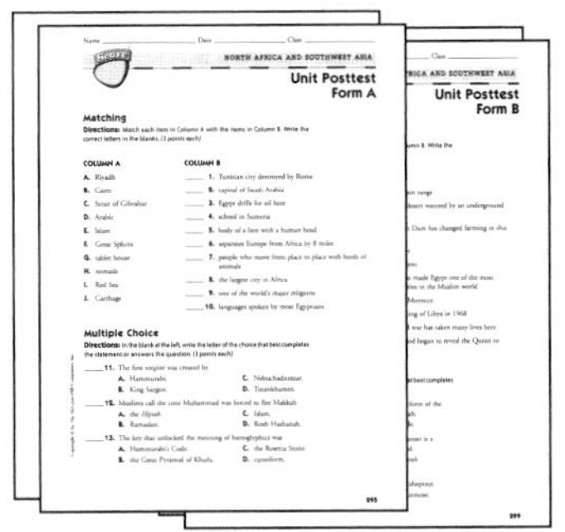

Glencoe Professional Development and Teacher Support Materials

- Reading in the Content Area for the Middle School Classroom
- Inclusion Strategies for the Middle School Social Studies Classroom
- Character Education for the Middle School Classroom
- Teaching Strategies for the Social Studies Classroom
- Reproducible Lesson Plans
- Outline Map Resource Book
- Writing Process Transparencies for Middle School
- Social Studies: Reading Strategies

- **Timed Readings Plus in Social Studies** help students increase their reading rate and fluency while maintaining comprehension. The 400-word passages are similar to those found on state and national assessments.
- **Reading in the Content Area: Social Studies** concentrates on six essential reading skills that help students better comprehend what they read. The book includes 75 high-interest nonfiction passages written at increasing levels of difficulty.
- **Reading Fluency** helps students read smoothly, accurately, and expressively.
- **Jamestown's Reading Improvement,** by renowned reading expert Edward Fry, focuses on helping build your students' comprehension, vocabulary, and skimming and scanning skills.
- **Critical Reading Series** provides high-interest books, each written at three reading levels.

For more information about these products, see the Jamestown Education materials in the Classroom Solutions in the front of this Teacher Wraparound Edition. To order these products, call Glencoe at 1-800-334-7344.

The following videotape programs are available from Glencoe:

- **Great Pyramids of Giza and Other Pyramids** 0-7670-0207-5
- **Mummies and the Wonders of Ancient Egypt** 1-56501-773-0
- **King Tut: The Face of Tutankhamen** 1-56501-159-7
- **Seven Wonders of the Ancient World** 0-7670-0401-9
- **Cleopatra: Destiny's Queen** 1-56501-454-5
- **Tomb of the Gods: The Great Pyramid** 0-7670-0081-1
- **The Great Pharaohs of Egypt** 0-7670-0273-3

To order, call Glencoe at 1-800-334-7344. To find classroom resources to accompany many of these, check:

A&E Television: www.aetv.com

The History Channel: www.historychannel.com

Reading List Generator CD-ROM

GLENCOE BOOKLINK

The Glencoe BookLink CD-ROM is a database that allows you to search more than 15,000 titles to create a customized reading list for your students.

- Reading lists can be organized by students' reading level, author, genre, theme, or area of interest.
- The database provides Degrees of Reading Power™ (DRP) and Lexile™ readability scores for all selections.
- A brief summary of each selection is included.

Leveled reading suggestions for this unit:

For students at a Grade 5 reading level:
- ***Israel,*** by Kristin Thoennes.

For students at a Grade 6 reading level:
- ***The Nile,*** by Aaron W. Percefull.

For students at a Grade 7 reading level:
- ***Into the Mummy's Tomb: The Real-Life Discovery of Tutankhamen's Treasures,*** by Nicholas Reeves.

To order this CD-ROM, call Glencoe at 1-800-334-7344.

Extending the Content

Readings for the Teacher
- ***Israel/Palestine: How to End the War of 1948,*** by Tanya Reinhart. New York: Seven Stories Press, 2002.
- ***Understanding the Contemporary Middle East,*** by Deborah J. Gerner, ed. London, UK: Lynne Rienner, 2000.

Multimedia Resources
- **Glencoe World History Primary Source Document Library CD-ROM**
- ***Shifting Sands: A History of the Middle East.*** Chatsworth, CA: Aims Multimedia. CD-ROM, Win/Mac.

Service Learning Project

Connecting Classroom With Community

One of the Five Pillars of Islam is that believers have a responsibility to give a portion of their wealth to the needy. Students can show a similar concern for others in their community by making an effort to help the homeless. They might, for example, collect such useful items as blankets and towels or volunteer to work in a soup kitchen that offers meals to homeless people. Hold a class discussion asking students to identify and explain the importance of voluntary civic participation in our society.

Content Background Notes

Use this additional information as lecture notes or discussion prompts throughout the study of Unit 6.

Chapter 16 Birthplace of Civilization (pp. 464–481)

The Great Flood Dr. Robert Ballard has led a series of National Geographic expeditions to investigate the theory that the Black Sea may be the site of a great flood discussed in sources such as the *Gilgamesh* epic. According to the theory, the Black Sea was once a much smaller and lower freshwater lake. Then the waters of the Mediterranean rose so high that they spilled through the Bosporus and flooded a huge region. These waters destroyed cities on the lake's shores and expanded the body of water to its current size. The catastrophe was so great that people remembered it in their legends.

In 1999 Ballard and his team made two important finds. Underwater scans revealed what looked like the contours of an ancient shoreline for the lake—which was found nearly 23 miles (37 km) into the Black Sea. Another key piece of evidence came from a sample of soil from the seabed. The sample included the preserved shells of mussels that were thousands of years old—some of which were freshwater species.

People Great pyramids, built as tombs for Egyptian rulers, rise above desert sands. They are a reminder that some of the world's oldest civilizations developed in this region. Roughly 5,000 years ago, the ancient Egyptians built a kingdom along the life-giving Nile River. The Sumerian civilization, an even older society, flourished in the fertile valley between the Tigris and Euphrates Rivers.

Water still dictates where people settle in this region. Most cities lie along seacoasts or rivers or near desert oases. Among the largest cities are Cairo, Egypt; Istanbul, Turkey; and Tehran, Iran.

In North Africa and Southwest Asia, most of the people are Arabs. Many other ethnic groups also live in the region. Despite the ethnic diversity, many who live here are united by religion. Most people practice Islam, which developed in this region centuries ago. Two other major religions, Judaism and Christianity, also began here. The country of Israel, the Jewish national homeland, is in this region.

Chapter 17 North Africa Today (pp. 482–497)

The Nile Delta The delta of the Nile River—for thousands of years one of the most productive agricultural regions on the earth—is suffering for many reasons. The Aswan High Dam, which controls flooding on the Nile, also blocks sediment from flowing downstream. As a result, the delta no longer receives a rich supply of nutrients, as it used to during the annual floods. Farmers must now add fertilizer to the soil, and the salinity of the land is increasing. Delta cities are growing, and concrete is covering larger and larger chunks of land. Finally, the Mediterranean Sea is reaching farther inland, covering parts of the low-lying delta.

At least one positive step has been taken. In the past, delta dwellers cut blocks of soil from the rich earth and then baked them to make bricks for building, reducing valuable farmland. Today laws in Egypt prevent this use of vital farmland for building.

Chapter 18 Southwest Asia (pp. 500–531)

Economy Like water, natural resources are distributed unevenly across the region. This helps create great differences in living standards. The region includes some of the world's wealthiest nations—and some of its poorest. Enormous reserves of oil and natural gas lie in countries such as Saudi Arabia and Kuwait. These countries export petroleum products to fuel-hungry societies and generally enjoy high standards of living.

On the other hand, those countries with economies based on agriculture have much lower standards of living. Only a small percentage of the region's land is suitable for growing crops. In river valleys and along the coasts, where there is water and fertile soil, farmers raise citrus fruits, grapes, dates, grains, and cotton. Nomadic herding is common across the large expanses of this region that are too dry for crops.

The Kurds The Kurds are a people without a country. This distinct ethnic group occupies a region called Kurdistan that extends from eastern Turkey through northern Iraq to western Iran.

The exact number of Kurds is unknown, although some estimates put them as high as 15 million. The Kurds have long struggled to achieve their own independent state—a right that was recognized in a treaty signed after World War I but which was later replaced by another treaty omitting reference of Kurdish rights. A powerful nationalist movement has arisen in Turkey, where some Kurds have fought and used terrorism to try to win independence. Along with the appeal of nationalism, these Kurds gain support by pointing to their people's poverty. In the wake of Iraqi attacks on Kurds after the Persian Gulf War of 1991, the United Nations offered protection to the Kurds living in that country. Kurds consider it unlikely that they will be granted independence, however, because Turkey is unwilling to give similar treatment to the Kurds living within its boundaries.

Introducing
Unit 6

00:00 Out of Time?

If time does not permit teaching each chapter in this unit, you may use the **Reading Essentials and Study Guide** for each chapter.

Unit Overview

The three chapters of this unit introduce students to two distinct but related cultural regions that stretch from the Atlantic coast of Africa through the eastern shores of the Mediterranean to the vast spaces of Southwest Asia. The countries in this area share the following features:

- rugged landscape that creates many difficulties for human life
- a harsh, dry climate that makes farming difficult
- important deposits of valuable resources
- rich cultures with long histories
- animosity between some religious and ethnic groups

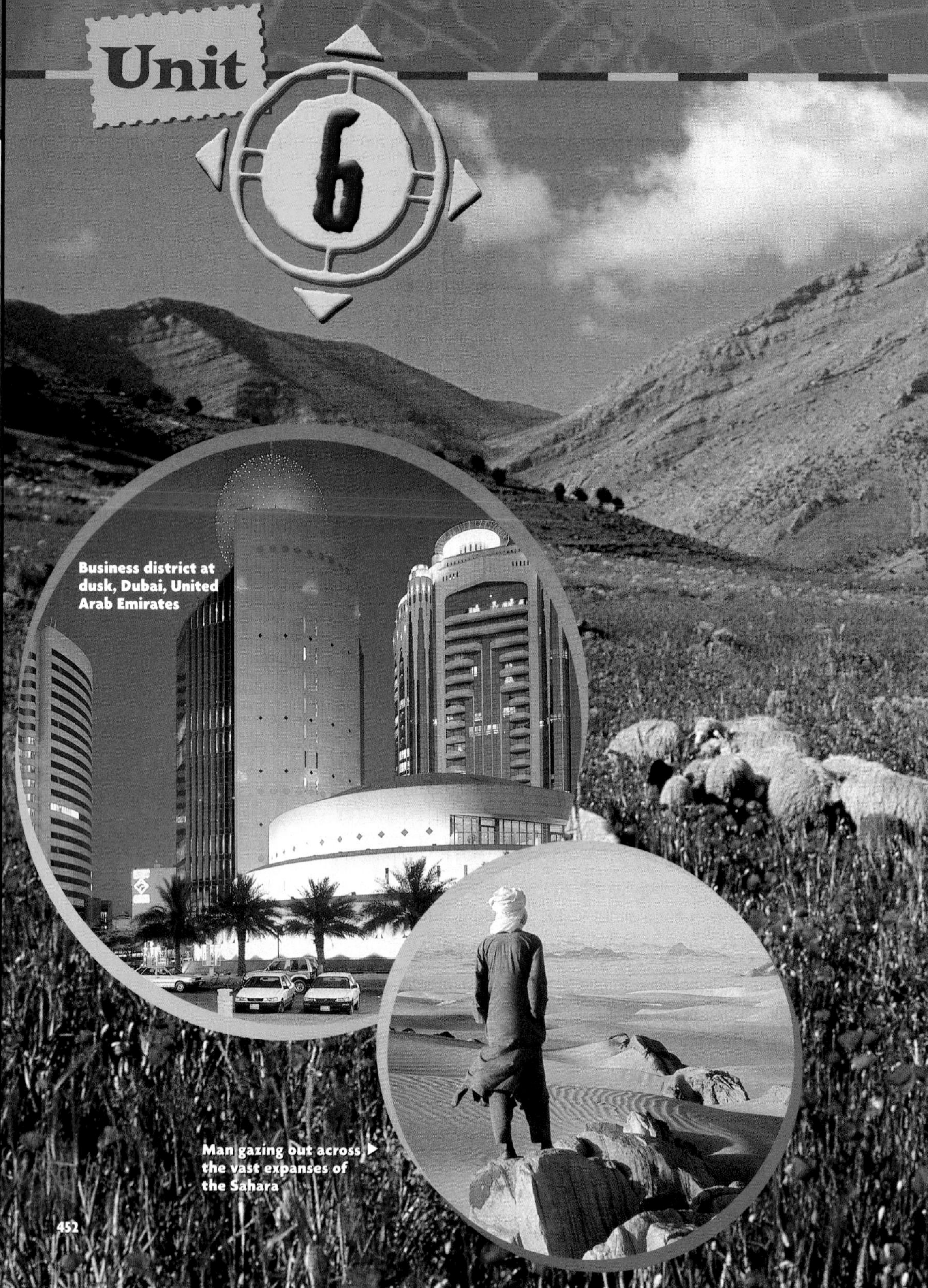

Business district at dusk, Dubai, United Arab Emirates

Man gazing out across the vast expanses of the Sahara ▶

Using the Illustration

Visual Instruction There are many contrasts in North Africa and Southwest Asia, where modern innovations often clash with ancient traditions. One of the reasons for these huge differences is the discovery of oil in the region. Oil production has made a great difference in the economies of many countries in Southwest Asia and North Africa. Using the maps in this unit, have students determine which countries produce and export oil. Then have them research to find out how this affects these countries' economies and standards of living as well as their foreign policies. L3

NATIONAL GEOGRAPHIC

North Africa and Southwest Asia

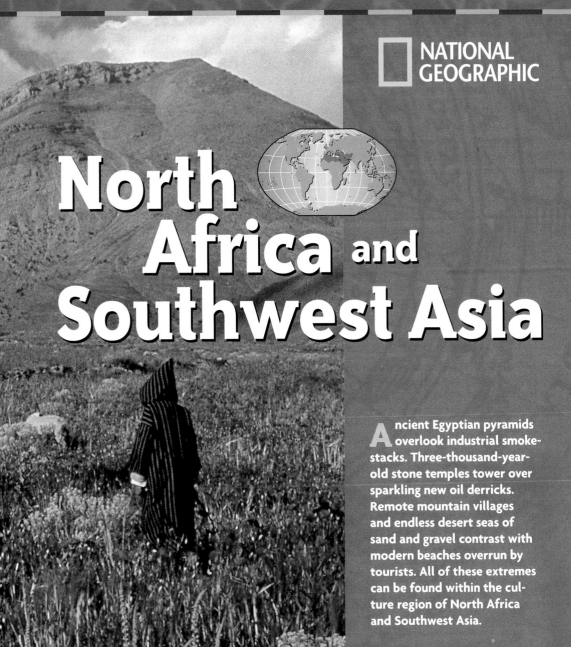

Ancient Egyptian pyramids overlook industrial smokestacks. Three-thousand-year-old stone temples tower over sparkling new oil derricks. Remote mountain villages and endless desert seas of sand and gravel contrast with modern beaches overrun by tourists. All of these extremes can be found within the culture region of North Africa and Southwest Asia.

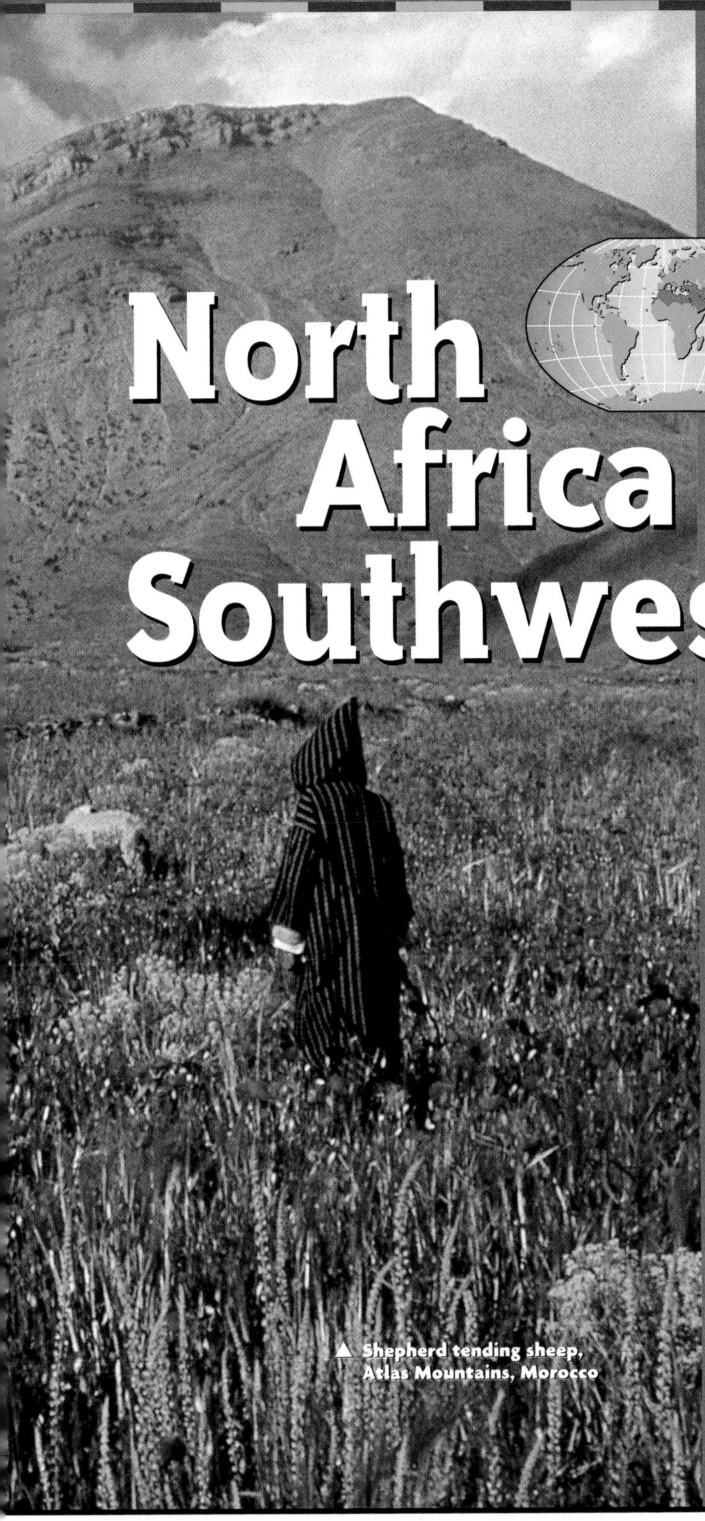

▲ Shepherd tending sheep, Atlas Mountains, Morocco

NGS ONLINE
www.nationalgeographic.com/education

453

Current Events Journal

Have students find the countries covered in this unit on the political map of the world in the Reference Atlas. Have them notice the great distance from the western to eastern edges of this region. **Ask:** **On what continents are these countries located?** *(Africa, Asia)* **What characteristics could these countries have in common that would tend to unite them? What characteristics would cause conflicts?** Have students write their answers in their notebooks. They can refer to these first thoughts later, as they study the unit.

NGS ONLINE
www.nationalgeographic.com/education

This online resource provides lesson plans, atlas updates, cartographic activities with interactive maps, an online map store, and geography links.

Unit Launch Activity

Why Is There Conflict in This Region? Many of the countries in North Africa and Southwest Asia are plagued by conflict. Some have bitter relations with neighbors. Others are torn by divisions within their own societies. Have students study these conflicts to try to determine the causes. *(Possibilities include religion, ethnic differences, and the struggle to control vital resources.)* Then have them discuss which kind of conflict they think is easiest to resolve and which they think would be the most difficult. L2

EE4 Human Systems: Standard 13

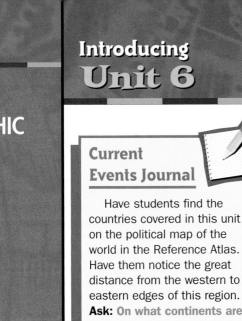

Lesson Plan

Using the Regional Atlas
These features and activities may be used as an introduction to the unit or as teaching tools throughout the course of the unit.

Focus

Objectives

1. Identify the major landforms in the region.
2. Explain how climate affects life in this region.
3. Describe the chief resources and economic activities of the region.
4. Discuss the different peoples who live in the region.

5-Minute Precheck

Have students look at the physical map of the world in the Reference Atlas and locate the countries in the unit. Have them also locate the following bodies of water: Atlantic Ocean, Mediterranean Sea, Black Sea, Red Sea, Arabian Sea, and Persian Gulf. **Ask: How could the location of these countries affect trade along these waterways?** *(Several countries—Morocco, Turkey, Egypt, and the Persian Gulf states—control narrow passages between two or more bodies of water, so they can control trade.)*

Focus on:

North Africa and Southwest Asia

LYING AT THE INTERSECTION of Europe, Asia, and Africa, this sprawling region has long been a meeting place for diverse peoples and cultures. Troubled by bitter conflicts and plagued by a scarcity of water, the region is also extremely rich in oil and other natural resources.

The Land

Glance at a physical map of North Africa and Southwest Asia and you will see a jumble of mountain chains. In the west, the Atlas Mountains—Africa's longest range—run through Morocco and Algeria. Slanting southeast through Turkey and Iran are the Zagros Mountains, where earthquakes often occur. Farther east in Afghanistan are the Hindu Kush—a lofty mountain range that is shared with neighboring Pakistan to the east. The Khyber Pass cuts through the Hindu Kush. The Pass has been used for centuries as a trade route linking Southwest Asia to other parts of Asia.

Seas of Sand Mountains block moist winds, helping to create vast deserts across much of the region. The Sahara, in North Africa, is the world's largest hot desert. It covers an area about the size of the continental United States. The Rub' al Khali, or Empty Quarter, covers about one-fourth of the Arabian Peninsula. The Empty Quarter has mountains of sand that reach heights of more than 1,000 feet (305 m).

Vital Waterways Through these very dry landscapes flow great rivers that bring life-giving water. The world's longest river, the Nile, runs 4,160 miles (6,693 km) through Egypt to the Mediterranean Sea. The Tigris and Euphrates Rivers flow southeast through Turkey, Syria, and Iraq. The earliest civilizations arose near these rivers.

The Climate

Water is precious in much of this region. Most areas receive a meager 10 inches (25 cm) or less of rainfall each year. In such dry lands, agriculture is only possible in limited areas. Crops grow along rivers and irrigation canals or in places where natural springs bubble to the surface to create lush but isolated oases.

In areas with a steppe climate, where enough rain falls to support grasses, people raise livestock such as sheep, camels, and goats. Steppes cover parts of many Southwest Asian countries. A narrow band of steppe runs along the northern edge of the Sahara too.

Content Background

Religion The chief religion in Israel is Judaism. All the other countries in the region are predominantly Muslim. Saudi Arabia is where Islam originated, and it is home to Islam's two holiest cities. This religion has five central beliefs, which are called the "Pillars of Islam": (1) publicly stating the belief in only one god and in Mohammed as the Prophet; (2) saying prayers five times every day; (3) giving charity to the poor; (4) fasting during the month of Ramadan; and (5) if possible, making a pilgrimage to the holy city of Makkah once in a lifetime.

Unit 6

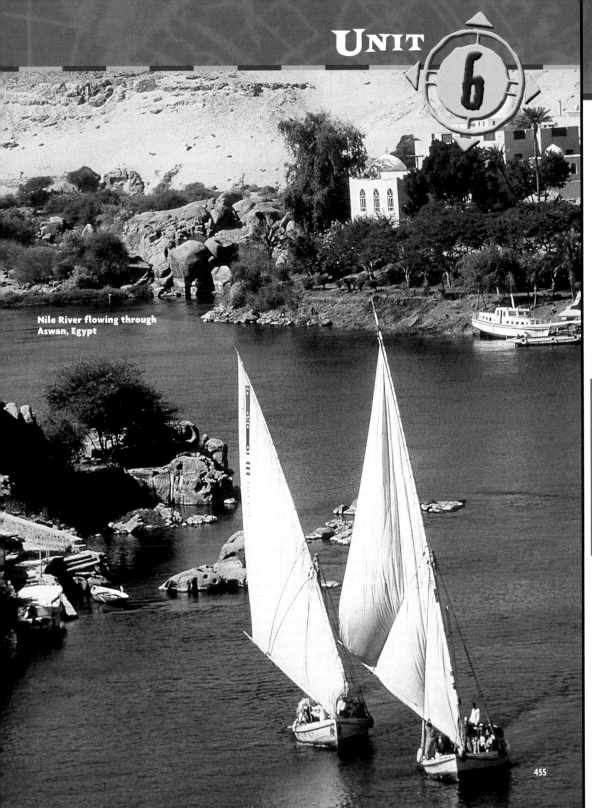

Nile River flowing through Aswan, Egypt

455

Eyewitness to Geography

The Nile Writer Peter Theroux, writing in *National Geographic,* vividly summarized the miracle created by the Nile River: "An ocean of yellow sand covers Egypt, divided by the dark green vein of the Nile River. The river injects life into the bright green fan at its mouth, while the gray, man-made mass of Cairo eats away at the fan's delicate stem.

"The black soil of the Nile Delta has made it the foundation stone of seven millennia of human history. By 5000 B.C. an increasingly arid climate had seared the grazing lands of Egypt, turning them into desert and forcing nomads to settle closer to the Nile. The resulting lifestyle in the Nile River Valley and the delta—growing crops, raising domesticated animals, and fishing—sustained settlements that evolved into the ancient world's first nation-state."

Unit 6

2 TEACH

Making Generalizations
Have students look at the physical map in the Regional Atlas. Ask them to state three generalizations about the countries in this region. *(Examples include: Most countries border a body of water; many of the countries have mountain ranges or plateaus; deserts cover large stretches of several countries.)* **L1**

Current Events Journal

Have students prepare a chart that groups the countries into two areas: North Africa and Southwest Asia. Then have them use the chart to compare the main economic activities in the different countries.

More About the Photo

The Nile River Although it flows through the desert in Egypt, the Nile begins in the humid tropical regions of East Africa. Heavy rains falling in the rain forests of Burundi and the highlands of Ethiopia feed the tributaries of the Blue Nile and White Nile, which eventually join near Khartoum, Sudan, to form the Nile.

NATIONAL GEOGRAPHIC

REGIONAL ATLAS

THE HUMANITIES CONNECTION

World Music: A Cultural Legacy

World Art and Architecture Transparencies

World Art Prints

More About the Photo

Oil The following countries in Southwest Asia are members of the Organization of Petroleum Exporting Countries (OPEC): Algeria, Iran, Iraq, Kuwait, Libya, Qatar, Saudi Arabia, and United Arab Emirates. OPEC members from outside the region include Ecuador, Gabon, Indonesia, Nigeria, and Venezuela.

The areas that border the Mediterranean, Black, and Caspian Seas enjoy a milder Mediterranean climate. Although summers are hot and dry, the winter months bring enough precipitation to turn coastal lowlands into green landscapes.

The Economy

Like water, natural resources are distributed unevenly across North Africa and Southwest Asia. This helps to create great differences in living standards. The region includes some of the world's wealthiest nations—and some of the world's poorest.

An Oil-Rich Region Enormous reserves of oil and natural gas lie in certain areas, including lands in central North Africa, along the Persian Gulf, and around the Caspian Sea. Countries such as Saudi Arabia and Kuwait, which export petroleum products to fuel-hungry societies, generally enjoy high standards of living. Money from oil exports has helped to build skyscrapers, modern freeways, schools, and hospitals.

Farming and Herding In contrast, those countries with economies based on agriculture have much lower standards of living. Only a small percentage of the region's land is suitable for growing crops. In river valleys and along the coasts, where there is water and fertile soil, farmers raise citrus fruits, grapes, dates, grains, and cotton. Nomadic herding is common across the large expanses of this region that are too dry for crops.

The People

Great pyramids, built as tombs for Egyptian rulers, rise above desert sands. They are a reminder that some of the world's oldest civilizations developed in this region. Roughly 5,000 years ago, the ancient Egyptians built a kingdom along the life-giving Nile River. The Sumerian civilization, an even older society, flourished in the fertile valley between the Tigris and Euphrates Rivers. Persians, Greeks, Romans, and Arabs all have left their mark on the cultures of North Africa and Southwest Asia.

Ancient Cities–Modern Challenges Water still dictates where people settle in this region. Most cities lie along seacoasts or rivers, or near desert oases. Among the largest cities are Cairo, Egypt; Istanbul, Turkey; and Tehran, Iran. These cities and others have been growing rapidly as

◀ Construction of an oil pipeline across a desert, Yemen

UNIT 6

FUN FACTS

- **Saudi Arabia** Islamic prayer rugs feature a pointed or arch-shaped pattern. During prayer, Muslims kneel on their rug with the arch pointed toward Makkah, Saudi Arabia.
- **Oman** This country is one of the hottest in the world. Temperatures here often reach 130°F (54°C).
- **Egypt** Ancient Egyptian women dyed their hair, wore red lip powder, and painted their fingernails. They used gray, black, or green paint to outline their eyes and color their eyebrows. Men often wore as much makeup as women.

UNIT 6

villagers move to them in search of a better life. As a result, governments must work to find solutions to the problems of overcrowding, poverty, and pollution.

Ethnic and Religious Rivalries In North Africa and Southwest Asia, most of the people are Arabs. Many other ethnic groups also live in the region. This situation has sparked violent clashes. Despite the ethnic rivalries, many who live here are united by religion. Most people practice Islam, which developed in this region centuries ago. Two other major religions, Judaism and Christianity, also began here. The country of Israel is the Jewish national homeland. Differences among religions, however, have contributed to conflicts in places such as Israel and the West Bank, Lebanon, and Iraq.

Desert dwellers sharing a meal, Saudi Arabia ▼

Data Bits

Country	Automobiles per 1,000 people	Television sets per 1,000 people
Jordan	50	83
Kuwait	317	480
Lebanon	313	355
Morocco	41	165
Yemen	15	286

Population: Urban vs. Rural

Country	Urban	Rural
Jordan	79%	21%
Kuwait	96%	4%
Lebanon	90%	10%
Morocco	56%	44%
Yemen	25%	75%

Sources: *World Development Indicators, 2002; The World Almanac, 2004.*

Exploring the Region

1. **How do mountains help create deserts across much of the region?**
2. **What parts of the region receive the most rainfall?**
3. **Why do some countries in this region have high standards of living?**
4. **What religion do most people in the region practice?**

Unit 6
Regional Atlas

More About the Photo

Meals Traditionally, Arab peoples eat meals with their hands. At the beginning of the meal, each diner washes his or her hands in water. Then the food is scooped up with the fingers. An ancient folk saying explains that it is best to use three fingers: "To eat with one finger is a sign of hatred; to eat with two shows pride; to eat with three accords with the Prophet; to eat with four or five is a sign of gluttony."

3 ASSESS

Assign the Exploring the Region questions as homework or an in-class activity.

Reteach
Have students create an outline of the Regional Atlas. They can use the four subheadings in the text as the main divisions of their outlines. Suggest that they include at least four facts under each heading.

Enrich
Have students research the spread of Islam from its origins in Saudi Arabia. They can create an annotated map with illustrations to show how and when Islam reached different areas of the world.

4 CLOSE

Have students write a paragraph explaining what the countries in this region have in common and what major differences they have.

Answers to Exploring the Region

1. They block moist winds, preventing rainfall from falling on the desert areas.
2. areas that border the Mediterranean, Black, and Caspian Seas
3. Some countries earn great wealth by exporting oil. Poorer countries are based on farming or herding.
4. Islam

LESSON PLAN

Using the Regional Atlas
These features and activities may be used as an introduction to the unit or as teaching tools throughout the course of the unit.

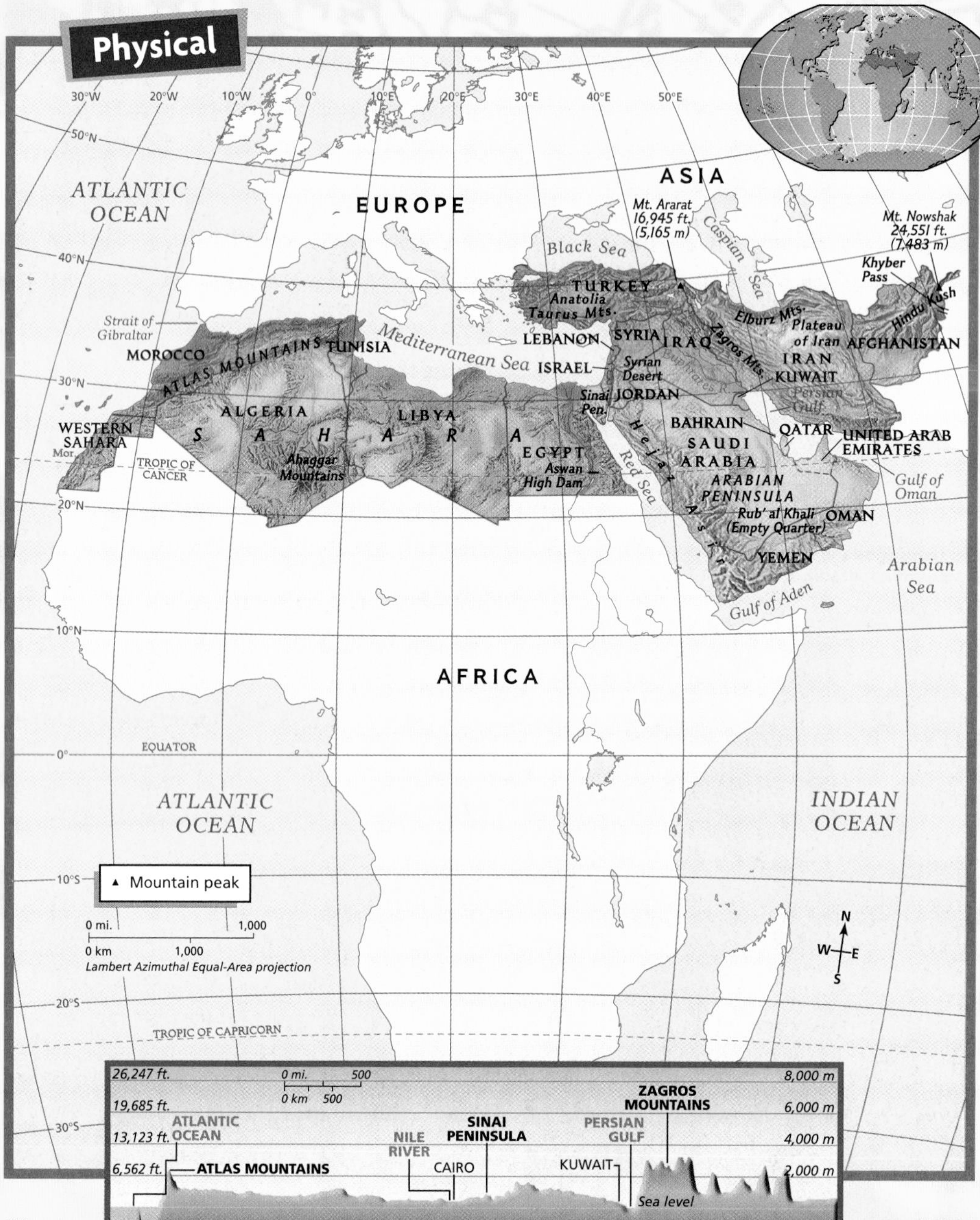

1 FOCUS

Objectives

1. Locate the major landforms of North Africa and Southwest Asia.
2. Identify the countries and capitals of this region.
3. Discuss the chief economic products of this region.
4. Compare the populations of the countries in this region.

5-Minute Precheck

Have students look at the physical map on this page. Have them identify the names and locations of all the deserts shown on the map. *(Sahara in North Africa, Empty Quarter in Saudi Arabia, Syrian Desert in Syria)*

More About the Profile

In order to show a variety of physical features, this cross section begins in Morocco and ends at the Afghanistan/Pakistan border along 30°N latitude.

NATIONAL GEOGRAPHIC

REGIONAL ATLAS

North Africa and Southwest Asia

Physical

ATLANTIC OCEAN
EUROPE
ASIA
AFRICA
ATLANTIC OCEAN
INDIAN OCEAN
Mt. Ararat 16,945 ft. (5,165 m)
Mt. Nowshak 24,551 ft. (7,483 m)
Khyber Pass
Hindu Kush
Black Sea
Caspian Sea
TURKEY
Anatolia
Taurus Mts.
Elburz Mts.
Plateau of Iran
AFGHANISTAN
Strait of Gibraltar
MOROCCO
ATLAS MOUNTAINS
TUNISIA
Mediterranean Sea
LEBANON
SYRIA
IRAQ
Zagros Mts.
IRAN
ISRAEL
Syrian Desert
KUWAIT
Sinai Pen.
JORDAN
Persian Gulf
WESTERN SAHARA
Mor.
ALGERIA
LIBYA
S A H A R A
BAHRAIN
QATAR
UNITED ARAB EMIRATES
SAUDI ARABIA
EGYPT
Aswan High Dam
Red Sea
Hejaz
Asir
TROPIC OF CANCER
Ahaggar Mountains
ARABIAN PENINSULA
Rub' al Khali (Empty Quarter)
OMAN
Gulf of Oman
YEMEN
Arabian Sea
Gulf of Aden
EQUATOR
TROPIC OF CAPRICORN
▲ Mountain peak
0 mi. 1,000
0 km 1,000
Lambert Azimuthal Equal-Area projection

26,247 ft. 19,685 ft. 13,123 ft. 6,562 ft.
8,000 m 6,000 m 4,000 m 2,000 m
0 mi. 500
0 km 500
ATLANTIC OCEAN
ATLAS MOUNTAINS
NILE RIVER
CAIRO
SINAI PENINSULA
PERSIAN GULF
KUWAIT
ZAGROS MOUNTAINS
Sea level

458 UNIT 6

Regional Atlas Activity

Researching Location The greatest population densities in this region tend to be found near bodies of water. The Nile River valley, for example, is one of the world's most heavily populated areas, and the Tigris and Euphrates Rivers are still—as they were millennia ago—home to many cities. Major cities in North Africa and the eastern Mediterranean are located along the Atlantic or Mediterranean coasts. Istanbul sits astride a major waterway. Have students choose one of the cities of the region and research its past. Have them prepare a report explaining why it is located where it is. Suggest that they consider economic and cultural factors as well as geographic factors. **L2**

 **EE4 Human Systems: Standards 9, 12**

Unit 6

Unit 6 Regional Atlas

Political

National capital

0 mi. 1,000
0 km 1,000
Lambert Azimuthal Equal-Area projection

EUROPE
ASIA
AFRICA
ATLANTIC OCEAN
INDIAN OCEAN
Mediterranean Sea
Black Sea
Caspian Sea
Red Sea
Persian Gulf
Gulf of Oman
Arabian Sea
Gulf of Aden
MOROCCO
ALGERIA
TUNISIA
LIBYA
EGYPT
WESTERN SAHARA
TURKEY
SYRIA
LEBANON
ISRAEL
JORDAN
IRAQ
IRAN
KUWAIT
BAHRAIN
QATAR
SAUDI ARABIA
UNITED ARAB EMIRATES
OMAN
YEMEN
AFGHANISTAN
Boundary claimed by Sudan

MAP STUDY

1. What physical feature covers much of North Africa?
2. What is the capital of Saudi Arabia?

TEACH

Making Predictions Have students study the physical features of this region and then predict which parts of the region might be used for farming. Then ask students to write generalizations about the relationship between physical geography and land use. L1

TRAVEL GUIDE

Syria Many of the marketplaces in Damascus—the capital of Syria—are in the old section of the city on narrow, winding streets. Merchants sell food and objects made of leather, brass, silver, and gold. People go to the marketplaces not only to shop but also to discuss business and to socialize. Here, as in other markets throughout the region, shoppers haggle or bargain with sellers over the price of goods.

MAP STUDY

Answers

1. Sahara
2. Riyadh

Skills Practice

What countries border Iraq? *(Iran, Turkey, Syria, Jordan, Saudi Arabia, Kuwait)* What is the capital of Turkey? *(Ankara)*

Regional Atlas Activity

Researching Irrigation The earliest cities that archaeologists have uncovered so far lie in the valley of the Tigris and Euphrates Rivers in Southwest Asia and date to about 3500 B.C. Civilizations arose here because the land and rivers provided rich soil for farming. Along these two rivers and the Nile, annual flooding brought nutrients to the soil, allowing farmers to grow crops. Since the floods came at certain times of the year, they were predictable, making farming more reliable. Still, farmers had to retain the water to use later in the year, when there was no rain. Have students research the irrigation methods used in ancient times and report on their findings. L2

EE4 Human Systems: Standard 12

Building Skills

Formulating Questions
Challenge students to generate a list of questions and answers based on the map on this page. They might focus on such issues as the economic benefit of the oil and gas reserves shown on the map, the environmental costs of obtaining these resources, relations between countries with and without these resources, or the reasons for the creation of the different transportation routes. After they have written their questions, ask volunteers to read some aloud. Then have the class discuss them.

MAP STUDY

Answers

1. Europe, North America, Russia, Southern Africa, and Asia
2. Southwest Asia and Caspian Sea

Skills Practice
What generalization can you make about the location of oil and natural gas deposits? *(Oil and natural gas deposits are generally located in the same area.)*

North Africa and Southwest Asia

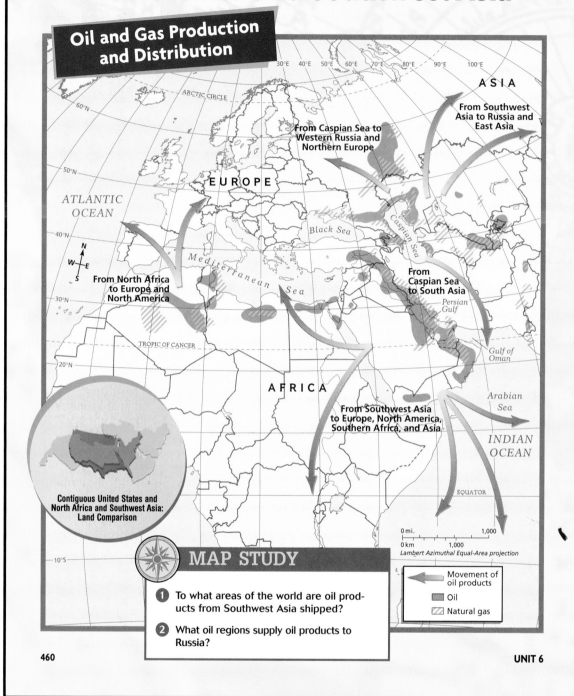

Oil and Gas Production and Distribution

From Caspian Sea to Western Russia and Northern Europe

From Southwest Asia to Russia and East Asia

From North Africa to Europe and North America

From Caspian Sea to South Asia

From Southwest Asia to Europe, North America, Southern Africa, and Asia

Contiguous United States and North Africa and Southwest Asia: Land Comparison

Lambert Azimuthal Equal-Area projection

Movement of oil products
Oil
Natural gas

MAP STUDY

1. To what areas of the world are oil products from Southwest Asia shipped?
2. What oil regions supply oil products to Russia?

FUN FACTS

- **Algeria** Algerians are complimented if a guest leaves some food on the plate at the end of a meal. This indicates that the host has provided more than enough to eat.
- **Egypt** Alexander the Great had Alexandria built in 332 B.C. Capital of Egypt in the days of Queen Cleopatra (69–30 B.C.), ancient Alexandria was the site of the largest library in the world at that time, housing nearly 500,000 books.

Unit 6

Regional Atlas

Geo Extremes

① HIGHEST POINT
Mt. Nowshak
(Afghanistan–Pakistan border)
24,551 ft. (7,483 m) high

② LOWEST POINT
Dead Sea
(Israel and Jordan)
1,349 ft. (411 m)
below sea level

③ LONGEST RIVER
Nile River
4,160 mi.
(6,693 km) long

④ LARGEST LAKE
Caspian Sea
143,244 sq. mi.
(371,000 sq. km)

⑤ LARGEST DESERT
Sahara (northern Africa)
3,475,000 sq. mi.
(9,000,208 sq. km)

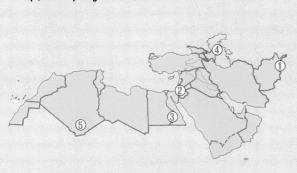

COMPARING POPULATION: United States and Selected Countries of North Africa and Southwest Asia

UNITED STATES

EGYPT

ALGERIA

SAUDI ARABIA

ISRAEL

= 20,000,000

Source: *Population Reference Bureau*, 2003.

URBAN POPULATIONS: Selected Cities of North Africa and Southwest Asia

ISTANBUL, TURKEY

TEHRAN, IRAN

CAIRO, EGYPT

ALEXANDRIA, EGYPT

ANKARA, TURKEY

= 500,000

Source: *World Gazetteer*, 2003.

GRAPHIC STUDY

1. The lowest point on the earth is found in this region. Where is it?
2. How does the population of Cairo compare to that of Tehran? How does the population of Ankara compare to that of Cairo?

TRAVEL GUIDE

Southwest Asia The pomegranate is a popular food in Southwest Asia. A picture of the fruit appeared on the pillars of Solomon's temple in Jerusalem. People in the region use the fruit's crimson-colored pulp to make drinks.

Cultural Kaleidoscope

Lebanon In Lebanon, people enjoy eating a salad called *tabbouleh*. This refreshing dish is made with cracked wheat, parsley, mint, minced onions, finely diced tomatoes, lemon juice, and olive oil.

GRAPHIC STUDY

Answers

1. the Dead Sea in Israel and Jordan
2. Tehran has a larger population than Cairo. The population of Ankara is about half the population of Cairo.

Skills Practice
What is the most populous country in the region? *(Egypt)*

Regional Atlas Activity

Passages Khyber Pass through the Hindu Kush of Afghanistan has been a major route for movement between Southwest Asia and South Asia. Centuries ago, invading armies took the pass to reach India. Merchants leading camel caravans used it to carry goods between Asia and the Mediterranean world. Other key passages—such as the Turkish Straits near Istanbul, the Strait of Gibraltar north of Morocco, the Suez Canal in Egypt, and the Strait of Hormuz along the Persian Gulf—are found in this region as well. Organize students into groups and have each group research one of these famous passageways. Have each group present its findings to the class. **L2**

EE1 The World in Spatial Terms: Standard 3

3 ASSESS

Organize students into groups. Have groups use the maps and graphs from the Regional Atlas to quiz one another on North Africa and Southwest Asia.

Current Events Journal

Have students prepare a chart that groups the countries profiled here into two areas: North Africa and Southwest Asia. Their chart might include the name of the country, the capital, the population, and the chief products. Then have them compare the main economic activities in the different areas.

THE HUMANITIES CONNECTION

World Music: A Cultural Legacy

World Art and Architecture Transparencies

REGIONAL ATLAS

Country Profiles

Country	Population	Language(s)	Major Export(s)	Major Import	Capital	Landmass
AFGHANISTAN	28,700,000; 114 per sq. mi.; 44 per sq. km	Pashto, Dari	Fruits and Nuts	Foods	Kabul	251,772 sq. mi.; 652,090 sq. km
ALGERIA	31,700,000; 35 per sq. mi.; 14 per sq. km	Arabic, French, Berber	Petroleum	Machinery	Algiers	919,591 sq. mi.; 2,381,741 sq. km
BAHRAIN	700,000; 2,545 per sq. mi.; 983 per sq. km	Arabic	Petroleum	Machinery	Manama	266 sq. mi.; 698 sq. km
EGYPT	72,100,000; 186 per sq. mi.; 72 per sq. km	Arabic	Crude Oil	Machinery	Cairo	386,660 sq. mi.; 1,001,449 sq. km
IRAN	66,600,000; 106 per sq. mi.; 41 per sq. km	Persian, Kurdish	Petroleum	Machinery	Tehran	630,575 sq. mi.; 1,633,189 sq. km
IRAQ	24,200,000; 143 per sq. mi.; 55 per sq. km	Arabic, Kurdish	Crude Oil	Machinery	Baghdad	169,236 sq. mi.; 438,321 sq. km
ISRAEL	6,700,000; 825 per sq. mi.; 319 per sq. km	Hebrew, Arabic	Polished Diamonds	Chemicals	Jerusalem*	8,131 sq. mi.; 21,059 sq. km
JORDAN	5,500,000; 159 per sq. mi.; 61 per sq. km	Arabic	Phosphates	Crude Oil	Amman	34,444 sq. mi.; 89,210 sq. km
KUWAIT	2,400,000; 346 per sq. mi.; 134 per sq. km	Arabic	Petroleum	Foods	Kuwait	6,880 sq. mi.; 17,819 sq. km
LEBANON	4,200,000; 1,045 per sq. mi.; 403 per sq. km	Arabic, French	Paper	Machinery	Beirut	4,015 sq. mi.; 10,399 sq. km
LIBYA	5,500,000; 8 per sq. mi.; 3 per sq. km	Arabic	Crude Oil	Machinery	Tripoli	679,359 sq. mi.; 1,759,540 sq. km
MOROCCO*	30,700,000; 178 per sq. mi.; 69 per sq. km	Arabic, French, Berber	Foods	Manufactured Goods	Rabat	269,757 sq. mi.; 698,671 sq. km

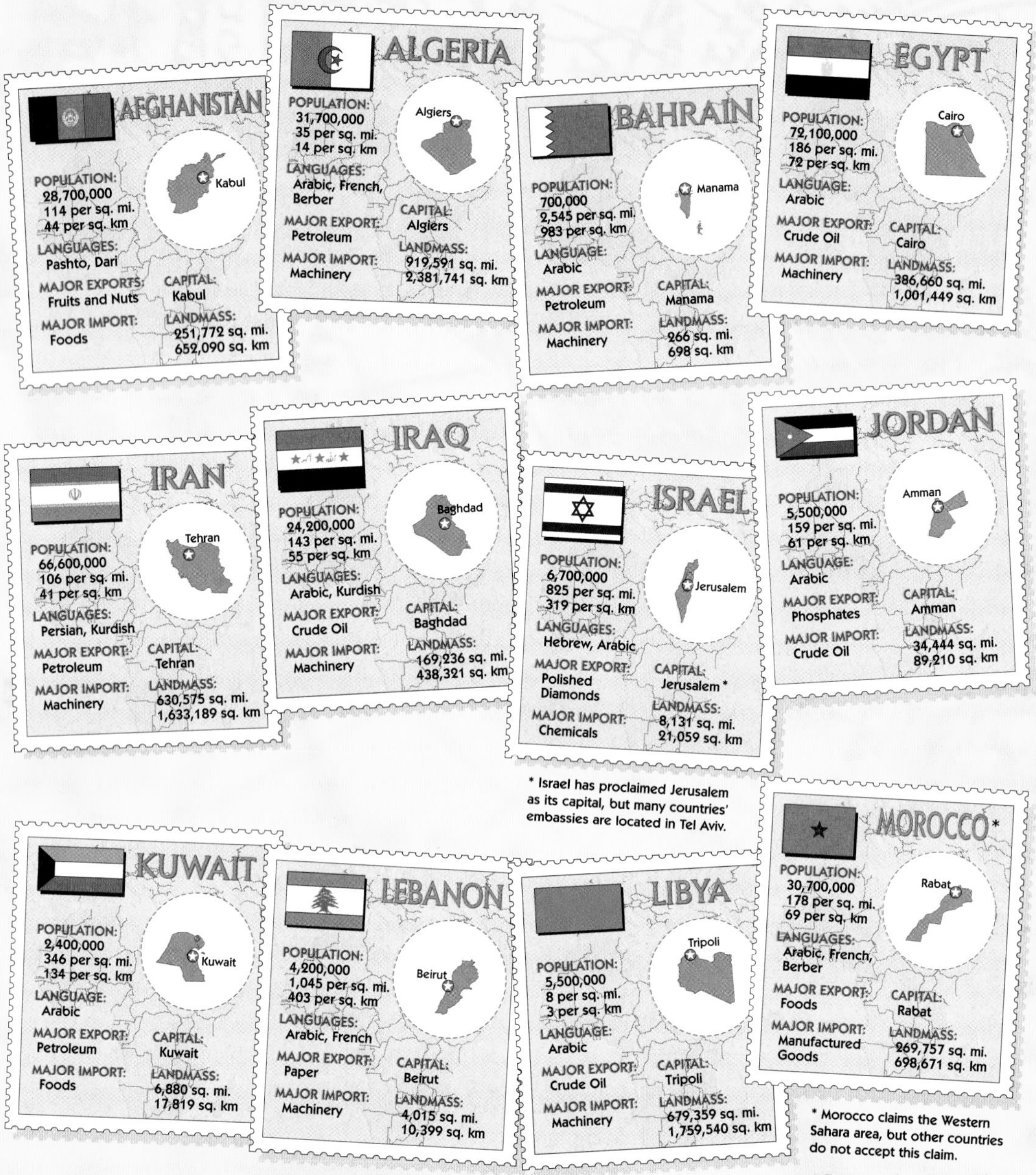

* Israel has proclaimed Jerusalem as its capital, but many countries' embassies are located in Tel Aviv.

* Morocco claims the Western Sahara area, but other countries do not accept this claim.

Countries and flags not drawn to scale

FUN FACTS

- **Saudi Arabia** Frankincense and myrrh are fragrant materials that come from trees that grow in this country. Since ancient times, people have burned these materials as incense or used them in perfumes.
- **Egypt** Ancient Egyptians buried their kings in a secret chamber inside or beneath a pyramid. They filled the chamber with gold and other treasures as well as practical, everyday items. Egyptians believed that the king would need these things in the afterlife.
- **Egypt** A team of archaeologists re-created the bread of ancient Egypt. For the flour, they used emmer wheat—the kind grown in ancient times—and ground it. They created a sourdough starter so the bread would rise.

UNIT 6

For more information on countries in this region, refer to the Nations of the World Data Bank in the Appendix.

BUILDING CITIZENSHIP

Religious Tolerance In Southwest Asia, there are holy places of many religions, including temples, shrines, tombs, and mosques. Because Muslims are forbidden to worship statues or images, in some Islamic countries officials have destroyed ancient shrines and statues revered by Hindus or Buddhists.

1. **Who owns religious properties in the United States?**
2. **Do you think government officials have a responsibility to protect valuable and sacred objects of all religions?**

Write a short script that could be read by a television news broadcaster. The script should report on the destruction of a holy site by members of another religion. Present both points of view.

▲ **Destroyed Buddhist statue in Afghanistan**

Unit 6
Regional Atlas

BUILDING CITIZENSHIP

The U.S. Constitution separates church and state but guarantees the right of everyone to worship in their own way. In some other countries, government and religion are combined, and followers of other religions and their holy sites may not be given the same rights and protection.

Answers
1. the religious organizations
2. Answers will vary but should include that the U.S. Constitution prohibits the government from favoring one religion over another.

Write About It! Students' scripts should reflect the fact that the people destroying the statues believe they are following the commands of their own religion. They should also point out what happens when there is no protection for minority religions.

4 CLOSE

Writing a Paragraph Have students write a paragraph explaining what physical, economic, and cultural features the countries of this region share.

Country Profiles Activity

Economics Assign a country to each student or pair of students. Direct students to use the Country Profiles and library resources to discover their assigned country's major imports, exports, and trading partners. Create a wall chart by pinning a sheet of butcher paper to the bulletin board. Have students enter their findings on the chart. Then call on volunteers to use information on the wall chart to make generalizations about the region's economic activities. L2

EE4 Human Systems: Standard 11

Chapter 16 Resources

Note: The following materials may be used when teaching Chapter 16.
Section level support materials are shown at point of use in the margins of the Teacher Wraparound Edition.

Timesaving Tools

TeacherWorks™ All-In-One Planner and Resource Center

- **Interactive Teacher Edition** See the **Interactive Teacher Edition** CD-ROM to electronically integrate your Teacher Wraparound Edition and blackline masters.
- **Interactive Lesson Planner** Organize your week, month, semester, or year with all the lesson helps you need. The **Interactive Lesson Planner** CD-ROM contains all Chapter 16 resources.

Use Glencoe's **Presentation Plus!** multimedia teacher tool to easily present dynamic lessons that visually excite your students. Using Microsoft PowerPoint® you can customize the presentations to create your own personalized lessons.

TEACHING TRANSPARENCIES

Graphic Organizer Transparency 11 L2

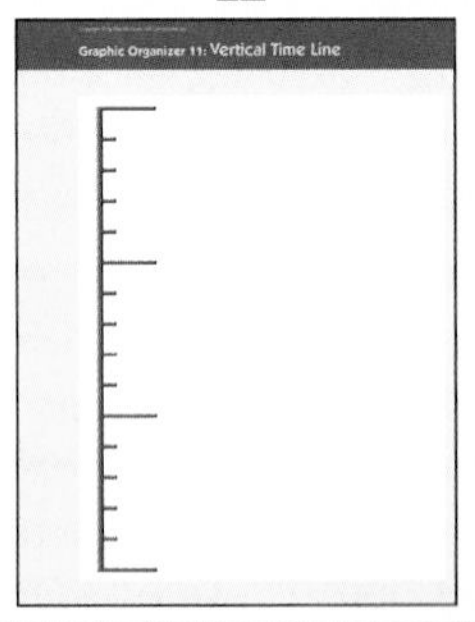

In-text Map Transparency L1

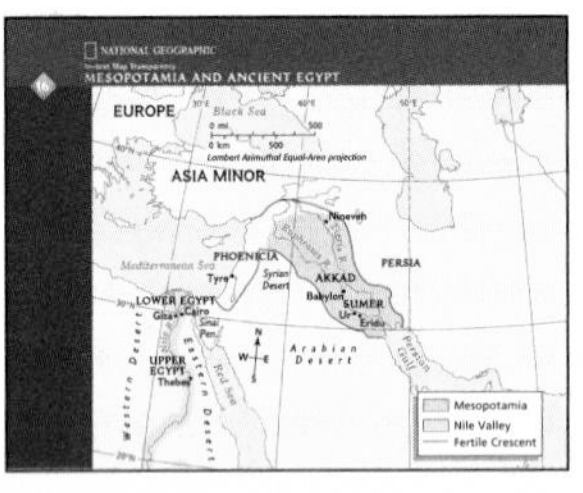

FOLDABLES™ Study Organizer

Dinah Zike's Foldables

Foldables are three-dimensional, interactive graphic organizers that help students practice basic writing skills, review key vocabulary terms, and identify main ideas. Additional chapter activities can be found in the ***Reading and Study Skills Foldables*** booklet.

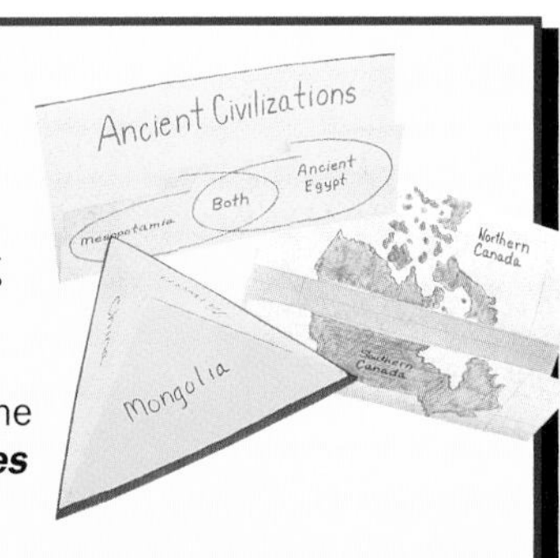

MAP AND GEOGRAPHY SKILLS

Chapter Map Activity L2

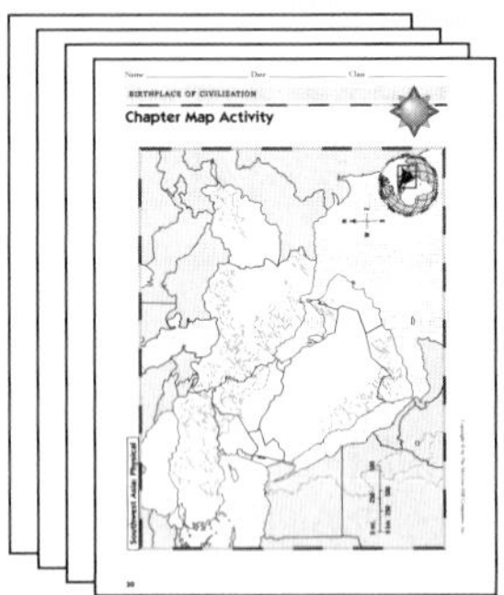

GeoLab Activity L2

READING SUPPORT

Vocabulary Activity L1

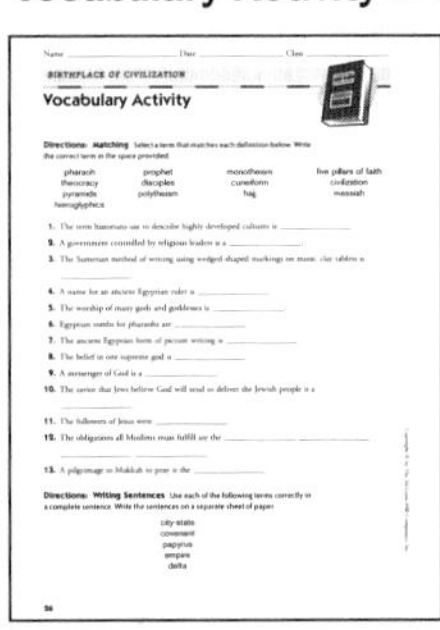

Workbook Activity L1

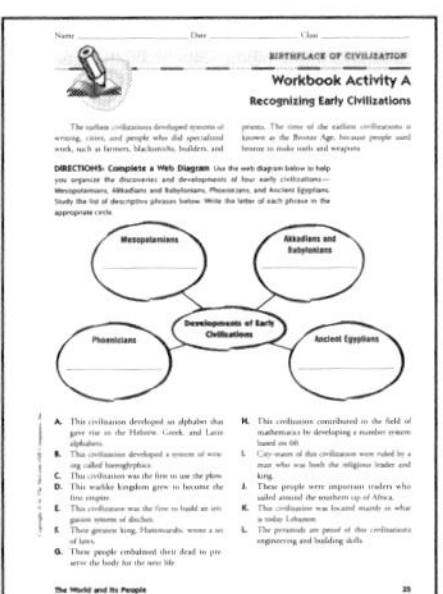

Reading and Writing Skills Activity L1/ELL

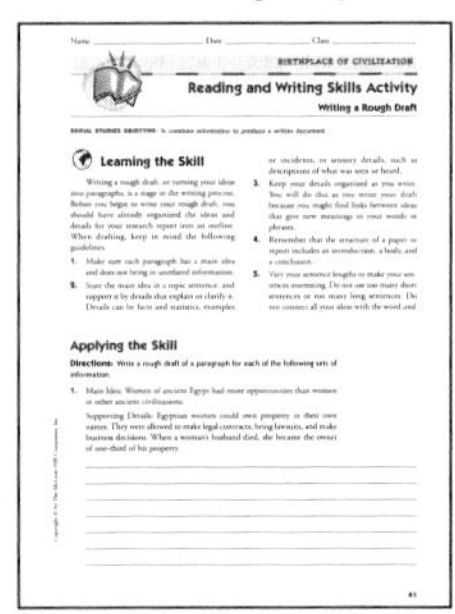

DIFFERENTIATED INSTRUCTION

Use these review and reinforcement materials to help less-proficient readers, English learners, and gifted and talented students.

Reteaching Activity L1

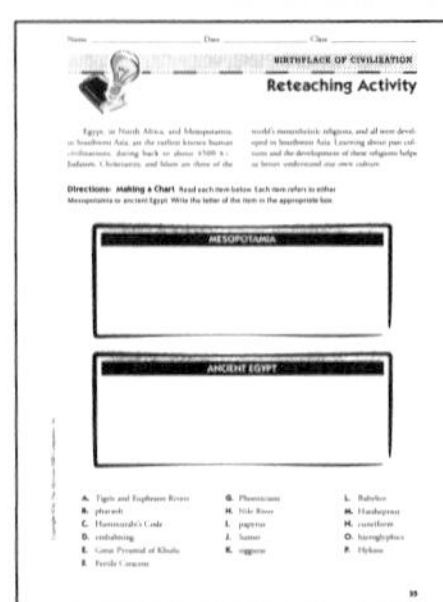

Chapter Skills Review L2

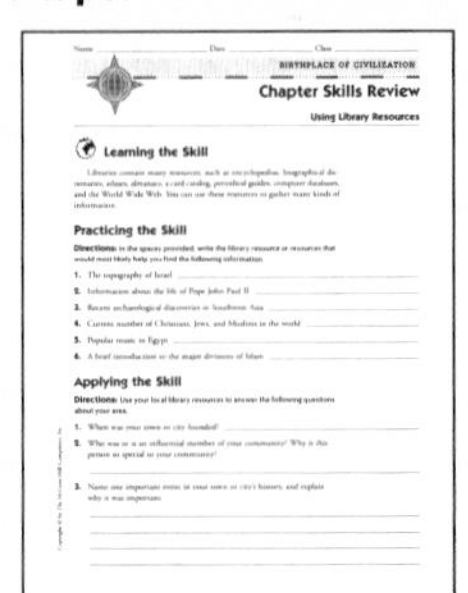

Cooperative Learning Activity L1/ELL

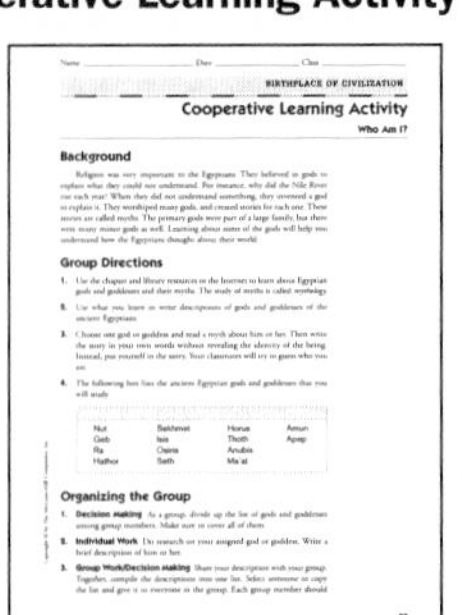

Enrichment Activity L3

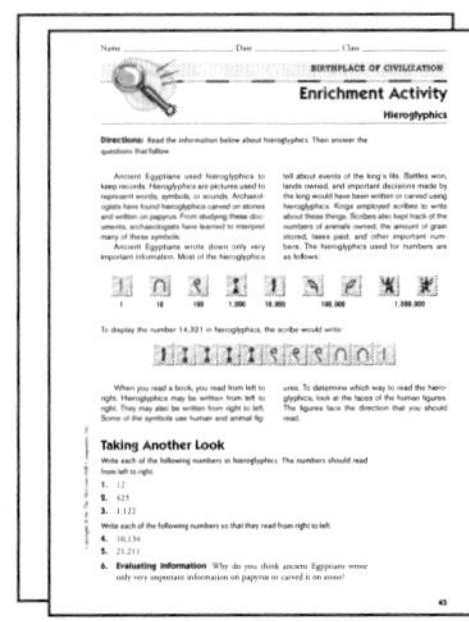

ASSESSMENT

Chapter Test, Form A L2

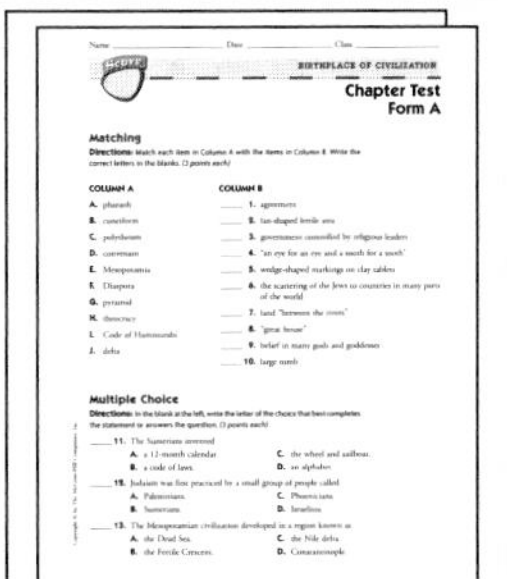
BIRTHPLACE OF CIVILIZATION
Chapter Test
Form A

Chapter Test, Form B L2

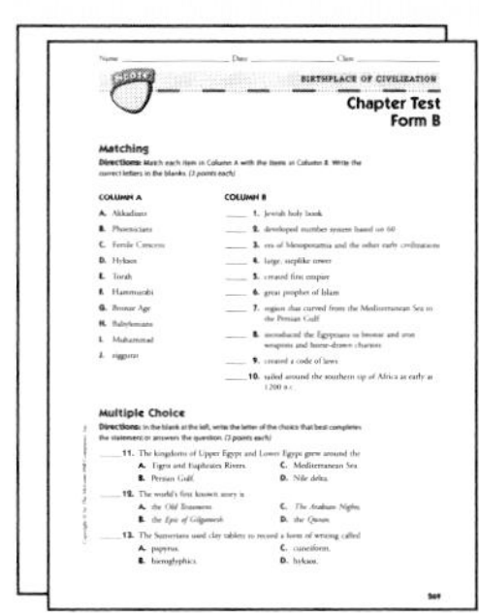
BIRTHPLACE OF CIVILIZATION
Chapter Test
Form B

Performance Assessment Activity L1/ELL

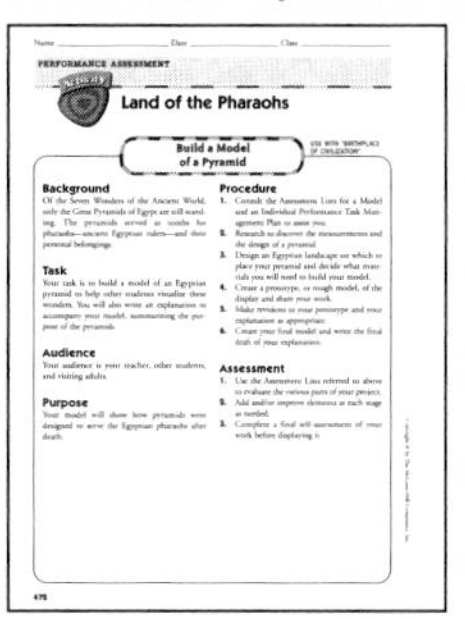
Land of the Pharaohs

ExamView® Pro Testmaker CD-ROM

STANDARDIZED ASSESSMENT SKILLS

Critical Thinking Skills Activity L2

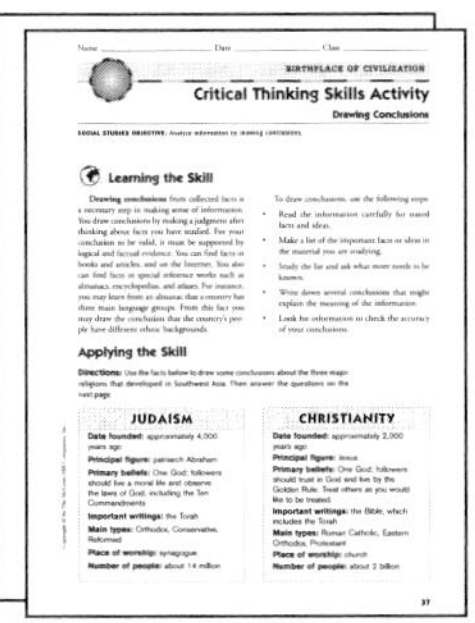
Critical Thinking Skills Activity

Map and Graph Skills Activity L2

Map and Graph Skills Activity

Standardized Test Skills Practice Workbook Activity L2

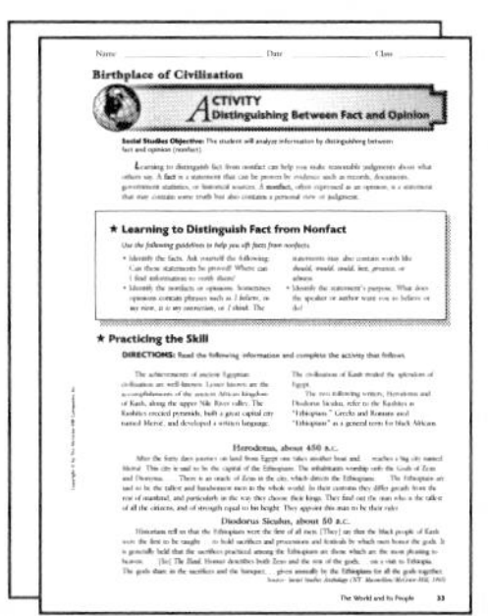
Birthplace of Civilization
Distinguishing Between Fact and Opinion

HOME INVOLVEMENT

Take-Home Review Activity L1

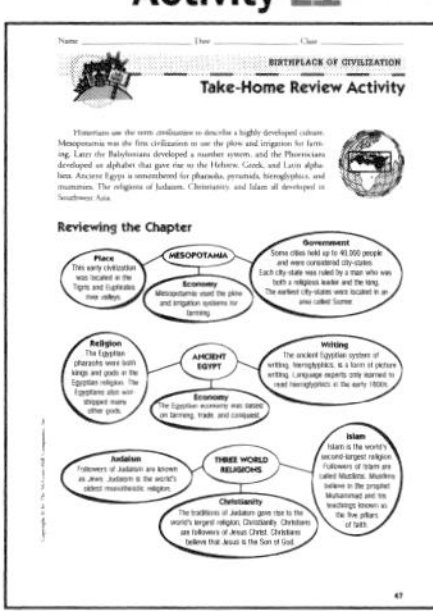
Take-Home Review Activity

MULTIMEDIA

- **National Geographic's The World and Its People**
- **MindJogger Videoquiz**
- **Vocabulary PuzzleMaker CD-ROM**
- **Interactive Tutor Self-Assessment CD-ROM**
- **ExamView® Pro Testmaker CD-ROM**
- **TeacherWorks CD-ROM**
- **StudentWorks CD-ROM**
- **Skillbuilder Interactive Workbook CD-ROM, Level 1**
- **Presentation Plus! CD-ROM**
- **Audio Program**

SPANISH RESOURCES

The following Spanish language materials are available in the Spanish Resources binder:

- **Spanish Summaries**
- **Spanish Vocabulary Activities**
- **Spanish Guided Reading Activities**
- **Spanish Quizzes and Tests**
- **Spanish Take-Home Review Activities**
- **Spanish Reteaching Activities**

Meeting National Standards

Geography for Life

The following standards are covered in Chapter 16:

Section 1 **EE2 Places and Regions: Standards 4, 5, 6**
EE4 Human Systems: Standards 9, 10, 11, 12, 13

Section 2 **EE2 Places and Regions: Standards 4, 5, 6**
EE4 Human Systems: Standards 9, 10, 12, 13

State and Local Objectives

Chapter 16 Planning Guide

SECTION RESOURCES

Daily Objectives	Reproducible Resources	Multimedia Resources
Section 1 **Mesopotamia and Ancient Egypt** **1.** Explain the early advancements in Mesopotamia. **2.** Discuss the ancient Egyptians' achievements.	Reproducible Lesson Plan Daily Lecture and Discussion Notes Note-taking Guide Guided Reading Activity* Reading Essentials and Study Guide* Section Quiz*	Daily Focus Skills Transparency GeoQuiz Transparency In-text Map Transparency Vocabulary PuzzleMaker CD-ROM Interactive Tutor Self-Assessment CD-ROM ExamView® Pro Testmaker CD-ROM Presentation Plus! CD-ROM
Section 2 **Three World Religions** **1.** Describe the world's three largest monotheistic religions. **2.** Explain similarities and differences among Judaism, Christianity, and Islam.	Reproducible Lesson Plan Daily Lecture and Discussion Notes Note-taking Guide Guided Reading Activity* Reading Essentials and Study Guide* Section Quiz*	Daily Focus Skills Transparency Vocabulary PuzzleMaker CD-ROM Interactive Tutor Self-Assessment CD-ROM ExamView® Pro Testmaker CD-ROM Presentation Plus! CD-ROM MindJogger Videoquiz

00:00 **Out of Time?** Assign the **Reading Essentials and Study Guide*** for this chapter.

*Also available in Spanish

KEY TO ABILITY LEVELS

Teaching strategies have been coded for varying learning styles and abilities.

L1 **BASIC** activities for all students
L2 **AVERAGE** activities for average to above-average students
L3 **CHALLENGING** activities for above-average students
ELL **ENGLISH LANGUAGE LEARNER** activities

KEY TO TEACHING RESOURCES

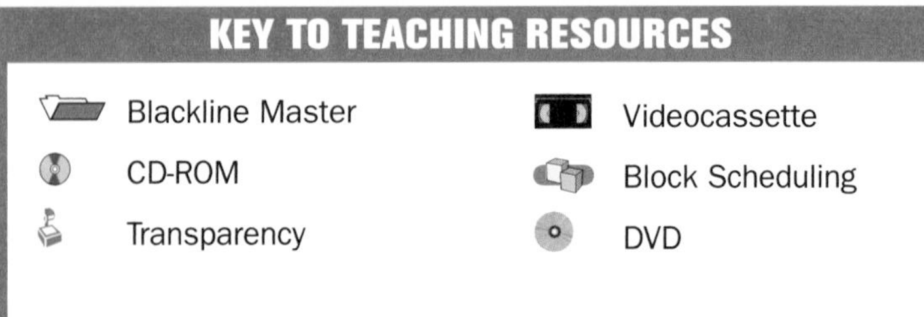

Teacher to Teacher

Building a Pyramid of Facts

Paula Gordon
Nettleton Intermediate Center
Jonesboro, Arkansas

During the study of this chapter, have students record important facts about Egypt on individual construction paper triangles. Use one piece of paper per triangle, and make all triangles the same size. After students use a large marker to record their facts, have them arrange and tape the triangles into a large pyramid on the wall. (NOTE: About half of the fact statements must be written on upside-down triangles so that readability is not an issue when the triangles are taped on the wall.) Students are usually eager to finish the pyramid, and they often do research on their own to find more facts.

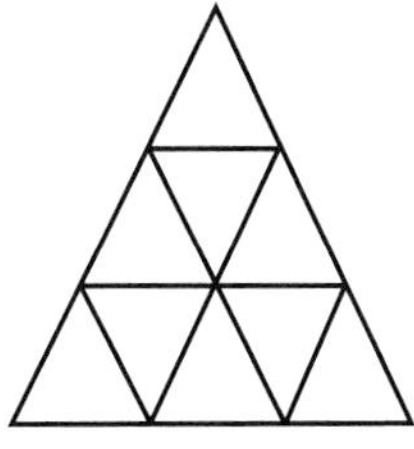

Meeting Special Needs

In addition to the Differentiated Instruction strategies found in each section, the following resources are also suitable for your special needs students:

- ***ExamView® Pro Testmaker CD-ROM*** allows teachers to tailor tests by reducing answer choices.
- The ***Audio Program*** includes the entire narrative of the student edition so that less-proficient readers can listen to the words as they read them.
- The ***Reading Essentials and Study Guide*** provides the same content as the student edition but is written two grade levels below the textbook.
- ***Guided Reading Activities*** give less-proficient readers point-by-point instructions to increase comprehension as they read each textbook section.
- ***Enrichment Activities*** include a stimulating collection of readings and activities for gifted and talented students.

TEACHER'S CORNER

Index to National Geographic Magazine:

The following articles may be used for research relating to this chapter:

- *"Libya: An End to Isolation?"* by Andrew Cockburn, November 2000.
- *"Valley of the Mummies,"* by Donovan Webster, October 1999.
- *"Abusir Tombs,"* by Zahi Hawass, November 1998.

National Geographic Society Products:

To order the following products for use with this chapter, call National Geographic Society at 1-800-368-2728:

- *Who Built the Pyramids?* (Video)
- *PicturePack: The Fertile Crescent* (Transparencies)
- *PictureShow: Ancient Civilizations: Egypt and the Fertile Crescent* (CD-ROM)

NGS ONLINE

Access National Geographic's Web site for current events, activities, links, interactive features, and archives.
www.nationalgeographic.com

Find the latest coverage of geography in the news, atlas updates, cartographic activities with interactive maps, an online map store, and links at www.nationalgeographic.com/maps

SOCIAL STUDIES Online

Use our Web site for additional resources. All essential content is covered in the Student Edition.

You and your students can visit twip.glencoe.com, the Web site companion to *The World and Its People*. This innovative integration of electronic and print media offers your students a wealth of opportunities. The student text directs students to the Web site for the following options:

- Chapter Overviews
- Student Web Activities
- Self-Check Quizzes
- Textbook Updates

Answers are provided for you in the Web Activity Lesson Plan. Additional Web resources and Interactive Tutor puzzles are also available.

Introducing
Chapter 16

Social Studies Online

Introduce students to chapter content and key terms by having them access Chapter Overview 16 at twip.glencoe.com

Chapter Objectives

1. Explain how farming, writing, and government developed in Mesopotamia.
2. Examine the artifacts of ancient Egypt.
3. Explain the basic beliefs of Judaism, Christianity, and Islam.
4. Discuss how past civilizations have contributed to our own culture.

GLENCOE TECHNOLOGY

NATIONAL GEOGRAPHIC

The World and Its People Video Program

Chapters 16 and 17 North Africa and Southwest Asia

The following segments enhance the study of this chapter:

- **Mummy of Abusir**
- **The Longest River**
- **Pyramids of Giza**

MindJogger Videoquiz

Use MindJogger Videoquiz to preview the Chapter 16 content.

Both programs available in DVD and VHS

Chapter 16 Birthplace of Civilization

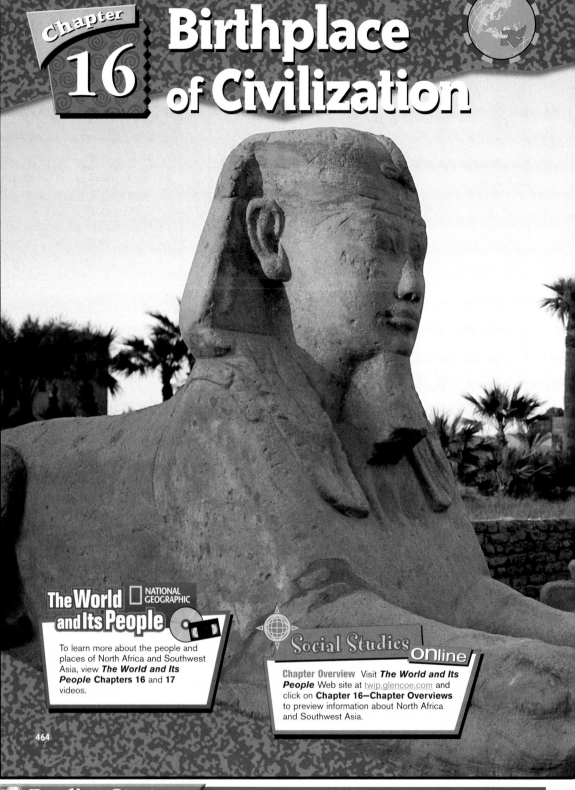

The World and Its People NATIONAL GEOGRAPHIC

To learn more about the people and places of North Africa and Southwest Asia, view ***The World and Its People*** **Chapters 16** and **17** videos.

Social Studies Online

Chapter Overview Visit ***The World and Its People*** Web site at twip.glencoe.com and click on **Chapter 16—Chapter Overviews** to preview information about North Africa and Southwest Asia.

464

Reading Strategy: Purpose for Reading

Use **Mindstreaming** to activate students' prior knowledge. Organize students into pairs. Have Student A talk to a partner for one minute about Egypt, telling everything he or she knows. Student B listens and encourages the responses. Have students reverse the roles and allow the discussion to continue for about another minute. You may ask the students to write some of the information from their discussions in their notebooks. Finally, discuss what the pairs talked about as a class. Conclude the discussion by telling the students that they will be studying ancient Egypt and the origins of civilization. **L1**

FOLDABLES™ Study Organizer

Compare-Contrast Make and use this foldable to help you determine how Mesopotamia and ancient Egypt were similar and different.

Step 1 Fold a sheet of paper from side to side, leaving a 2-inch tab uncovered along the side.

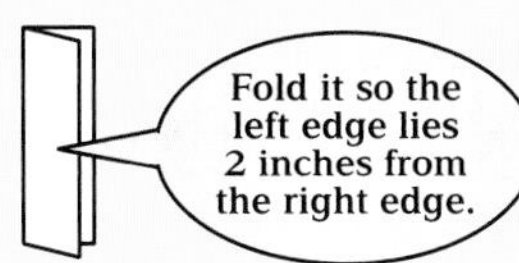

Fold it so the left edge lies 2 inches from the right edge.

Step 2 Turn the paper and fold it into thirds.

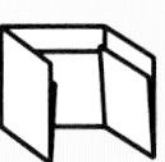

Step 3 Unfold and cut along the two inside fold lines.

Cut along the two folds on the front flap to make 3 tabs.

Step 4 Label your foldable as shown.

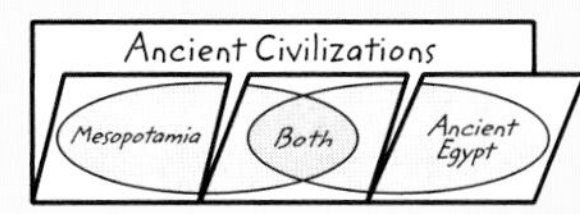

Reading and Writing As you read the chapter, write what you learn about these ancient civilizations under the tabs. Be sure to list similarities and differences under the appropriate tabs.

Why It Matters

Civilizations and Religions Emerge

Two of the world's first civilizations arose in Southwest Asia and North Africa about 5,000 years ago. The development of cities led to governments, laws, and trade. Organized religions emerged. These religions had the power to unite people, but also to create terrible conflict. The events that occurred centuries ago in the "birthplace of civilization" still influence our lives today.

▲ Avenue of the Sphinxes, Luxor, Egypt

About the Photo

A sphinx is a being with the head of a human and the body of a lion. In ancient Egypt, the head might assume the face of the reigning pharaoh who, along with the sphinx, was the earthly representation of the sky-god, Horus. In addition, the lion symbolizes kingship and courage. Most people first associate "sphinx" with the Great Sphinx of Egypt, which was "rediscovered" by the western world when Napoleon's soldiers encountered it in 1798. There are, however, other sphinxes in Egypt as well. This Avenue of Sphinxes leads to Luxor Temple. They were the guardians of the temple gates and the underworld.

FOLDABLES™ Study Organizer — Dinah Zike's Foldables

Purpose Students will make and use a foldable to collect and organize information to compare Mesopotamia and ancient Egypt. Students will write what they learn about these ancient civilizations and then will list similarities and differences that they find on their foldables.

Have students complete the ***Reading and Study Skills Foldables*** activity for this chapter.

Why It Matters

Egypt's dry climate helped preserve the achievements of this ancient land. The lack of humidity not only meant that mud-brick structures remained standing but also allowed softer materials like wood, textiles, and papyrus scrolls to remain recoverable after thousands of years.

Ask students to write a paragraph in which they agree or disagree with the following sentence: "The Nile gave life to the civilization of ancient Egypt, but the dry climate preserved that civilization." Then have students discuss their answers.

Chapter 16

Section 1, pages 466–471

Focus

Section Objectives

1. Explain the early advancements in Mesopotamia.
2. Discuss the ancient Egyptians' achievements.

BELLRINGER
Skillbuilder Activity

Project transparency and have students answer the question.

Daily Focus Skills Transparency

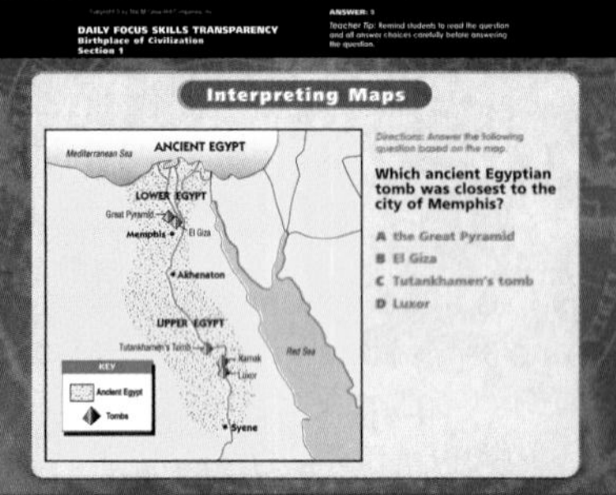

Reading Preview

- **Activating Prior Knowledge**
Ask: Have you ever heard of the pyramids? Where are they? *(Egypt)* What are they? *(tombs for the great rulers of Egypt)* For what purpose were they used? *(as tombs for the rich and pharaohs)*

- **Preteaching Vocabulary**
Inform students that the word *pharaoh* means "great house."

Guide to Reading

Main Idea

The peoples of Mesopotamia and Egypt were among the first to build civilizations.

Terms to Know

- civilization
- city-state
- polytheism
- theocracy
- cuneiform
- empire
- delta
- pharaoh
- pyramid
- hieroglyphics
- papyrus

Reading Strategy

In a chart like the one below, write facts about Mesopotamia in the M column and facts about ancient Egypt in the E column.

	M	E
Religion		
Trade		
Achievements		

Section 1

Mesopotamia and Ancient Egypt

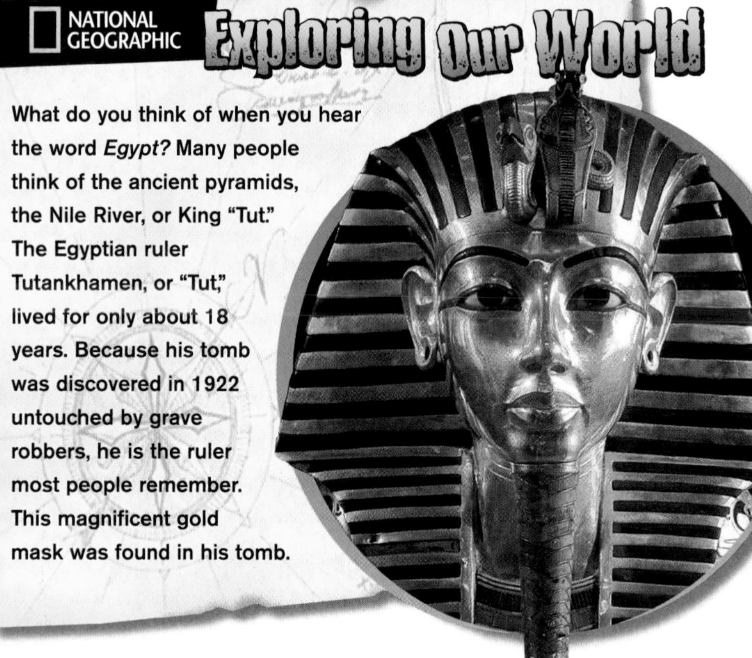

What do you think of when you hear the word *Egypt?* Many people think of the ancient pyramids, the Nile River, or King "Tut." The Egyptian ruler Tutankhamen, or "Tut," lived for only about 18 years. Because his tomb was discovered in 1922 untouched by grave robbers, he is the ruler most people remember. This magnificent gold mask was found in his tomb.

Egypt, in North Africa, and **Mesopotamia** (MEH•suh•puh•TAY•mee•uh), in Southwest Asia, were the earliest known civilizations. Historians use the term **civilization** to describe highly developed cultures. Civilizations include cities, organized governments and religions, and systems of writing. They have specialized workers, such as blacksmiths, builders, and teachers. Civilizations also use technology and metals. The time of the earliest civilizations is known as the Bronze Age, because people relied on the metal bronze, a mixture of copper and tin, to make tools and weapons.

Mesopotamia

Where were the first cities located? Where was the first school? These developments took place in Mesopotamia, a word that means "between the rivers." As the map on page 467 shows, Mesopotamia was located between the **Tigris River** and the **Euphrates River.** This

Section Resources

Reproducible Masters
- Reproducible Lesson Plan
- Daily Lecture and Discussion Notes
- Note-taking Guide
- Guided Reading Activity
- Reading Essentials and Study Guide
- Section Quiz

Transparencies
- Daily Focus Skills Transparency
- GeoQuiz Transparency
- In-text Map Transparency

Multimedia
- Vocabulary PuzzleMaker CD-ROM
- Interactive Tutor Self-Assessment CD-ROM
- Presentation Plus! CD-ROM
- ExamView® Pro Testmaker CD-ROM

region was part of the Fertile Crescent, a crescent-shaped area of rich soil that curved from the **Mediterranean Sea** to the **Persian Gulf.**

Around 4500 B.C., wandering peoples began settling along the Tigris and Euphrates Rivers. There they farmed the fertile soil left behind by yearly floods. To help control the floods, farmers built dirt walls and an irrigation system of ditches to channel the water to their fields of barley, wheat, and fruit trees. A 12-month calendar, based on phases of the moon, was developed to better predict the coming of the floodwaters. The plow was used for the first time, which made it possible to grow more food with less effort. With a steady food supply, the population grew larger.

Sumer In time, the Mesopotamians built cities, some of which eventually held up to 40,000 people. Each city was considered a small state, or nation. The city-state of this time was made up of the city and the farmland around it. Walls made from sun-dried bricks surrounded and protected the cities.

The earliest city-states arose in an area called **Sumer,** where the Tigris and Euphrates Rivers flowed closest to each other. The Sumerians grew wealthy from trade. They exchanged dried fish, wool, barley, wheat, and metal goods for copper, tin, and timber. They invented many things, including the wheel, which helped transportation. The Sumerians also invented the sailboat, which replaced muscle power with wind power. Sumerian traders traveled by land to the Mediterranean in the west and by sea to India in the east.

Applying Map Skills

1. What two major rivers are located in the Fertile Crescent?
2. Which is located farther north—Upper Egypt or Lower Egypt?

Find NGS online map resources@ www.nationalgeographic.com/maps

Religion and Government At the center of each city was a large, steplike tower called a ziggurat (ZIH•guh•RAT). Long stairways on the outside of the ziggurat led to a temple at the top. The temple was believed to be the home of the city's chief god or goddess. Only priests and priestesses were allowed to enter the temple.

Mesopotamia's religion was based on polytheism, or the worship of many gods and goddesses instead of just one god. At first, each city-state was a theocracy, or a government controlled by religious leaders. Mesopotamians believed that their priest-rulers received the right to rule from the gods. As the city-states grew, however, they fought one another over land and water. Military leaders became powerful and soon took the place of priests as permanent kings.

First Systems of Writing The Sumerians were the first people to write down laws and keep lists and records. They created a form of writing known as cuneiform (kyoo•NEE•uh•FAWRM). It was made

2 TEACH

Reading Strategy

Synthesizing Information
Help students create a diagram that shows each stage of the development of Mesopotamia from hunter-gatherers to the first empire. Have students list advancements associated with each of the stages. Discuss how the advancements contributed to the next stage of development. L3

Daily Lecture and Discussion Notes

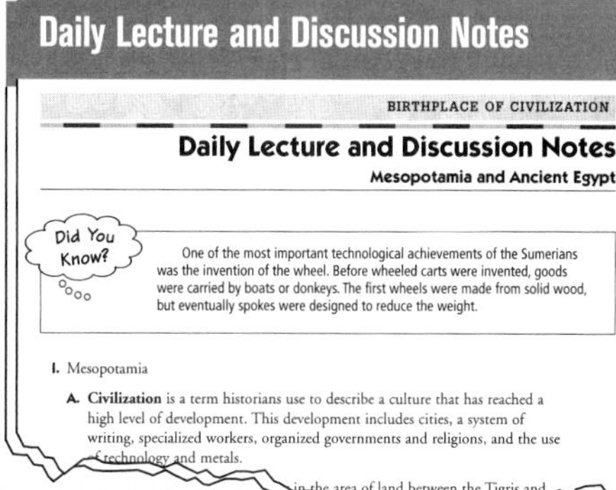
BIRTHPLACE OF CIVILIZATION

Daily Lecture and Discussion Notes

Mesopotamia and Ancient Egypt

Did You Know?

One of the most important technological achievements of the Sumerians was the invention of the wheel. Before wheeled carts were invented, goods were carried by boats or donkeys. The first wheels were made from solid wood, but eventually spokes were designed to reduce the weight.

I. Mesopotamia

A. **Civilization** is a term historians use to describe a culture that has reached a high level of development. This development includes cities, a system of writing, specialized workers, organized governments and religions, and the use of technology and metals.

in the area of land between the Tigris and

Applying Map Skills

Answers

1. Tigris and Euphrates
2. Lower Egypt

In-text Map Transparency Activity Point to the symbol in the key that represents the boundary line of the Fertile Crescent. Ask students to locate the Tigris River within the crescent and to name the city located along the river. *(Nineveh)*

Reading Strategy — Reading the Text

Organizing Information Remind students to create graphic organizers to help them organize and remember the information in the section. For example, Venn diagrams help when two ideas or subjects are being compared and contrasted. Time lines can be used when events are presented chronologically. After students have read the section, ask them what type of graphic organizer they think would work best for the type of information presented. Have them create the graphic organizers and explain them to the class. L1

*Use the **Reading Skills Handbook** for more reading strategies.*

L1/ELL

Guided Reading Activity

Did You Know

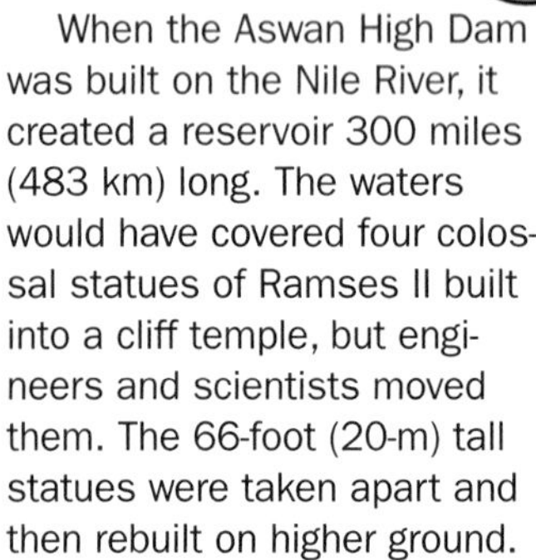

When the Aswan High Dam was built on the Nile River, it created a reservoir 300 miles (483 km) long. The waters would have covered four colossal statues of Ramses II built into a cliff temple, but engineers and scientists moved them. The 66-foot (20-m) tall statues were taken apart and then rebuilt on higher ground.

up of hundreds of markings shaped like wedges. The Sumerians wrote with sharp-ended reeds on moist, clay tablets. These records became permanent after the tablets were baked in the sun.

The Sumerians taught writing in schools called tablet houses. Only the wealthy could afford to send their sons—and sometimes daughters—to these schools. There, students trained to become scribes, or writers who made lists, kept records, and wrote letters for officials.

Sumerian scribes are believed to have written the world's first known story—the *Epic of Gilgamesh.* In this story, a king named Gilgamesh and his friend travel the world performing great acts of bravery. When his friend dies, Gilgamesh searches for a way to live forever. He learns that only the gods can live forever. Part of the Gilgamesh story tells of a great flood that covered the earth. The account of the flood is very much like the story of Noah's ark in the Bible.

Akkad and Babylon About 2300 B.C., the warlike kingdom of **Akkad** conquered Sumer and several other city-states. Akkad's King Sargon created the first empire, or group of states under one ruler. Over time, the Akkadian Empire weakened. It finally fell to the kingdom of **Babylon** in about 1800 B.C.

Babylon's greatest king was Hammurabi (HA•muh•RAH•bee). A great conqueror, Hammurabi pushed the boundaries of his empire to the Mediterranean Sea. He built temples and irrigation canals. He also encouraged trade and new ideas. During this golden age, the Babylonians developed a number system based on 60. From them, we borrowed the 60-minute hour, 60-second minute, and 360-degree circle.

Hammurabi's Code Before Hammurabi's rule, each city-state in Mesopotamia had its own codes, or collections of laws. Hammurabi took what he believed were the best laws from each code. He put these together and then issued one code that would apply to everyone in the empire. The Code of Hammurabi covered almost every aspect of daily life, including trade, debts, property, and family. Its basic idea was "an eye for an eye and a tooth for a tooth." This meant that if one person wronged another, he or she would be punished in the same way. Hammurabi had his laws carved in stone and placed where people could read them. Thus, everyone knew the rules and the punishments. The Code of Hammurabi served as a basis for future codes of law.

A New Babylon After Hammurabi's death, his empire split into smaller territories. Centuries later, during the 500s B.C., a new Babylonian empire rose and fell. It was ruled by a warrior people called the Chaldeans. Nebuchadnezzar (NEH•buh•kuhd•NEH•zuhr), the greatest Chaldean king, rebuilt the city of Babylon and made it a center of trade and culture. Magnificent palaces and temples emerged. The royal palace was known for its "hanging gardens." These were layered beds of earth with large trees and flowering vines that seemed to hang in mid-air. According to legend, Nebuchadnezzar built the gardens to please his wife, who missed the mountains and plants of her native land.

Exploring Economics

Centers of Trade

Why did some cities develop into rich centers of trade? Since water is the easiest way to transport goods, cities located nearest rivers and seas became important trading centers. To succeed at trade, however, there must be a demand for products. The people of Mesopotamia produced extra food, but they lacked trees for construction and mineral resources to make metals. They were able to trade extra food for these raw materials.

Differentiated Instruction

Meeting Special Needs: Interpersonal Many ancient sites in Southwest Asia contain artifacts from simple pottery and carved stone to elaborate and beautiful works of wrought gold or silver. The governments of Southwest Asia work to preserve these remains of their heritage. Encourage students to help preserve the heritage of their own community and to discuss the importance of voluntary civic participation in doing so. By volunteering at a local museum, library, or historical society, they can work to keep the past alive. Their work could range from preparing informational materials to cataloging materials or acting as a tour guide. L1

Refer to *Inclusion for the Middle School Social Studies Classroom Strategies and Activities* in the TCR.

NATIONAL GEOGRAPHIC On Location

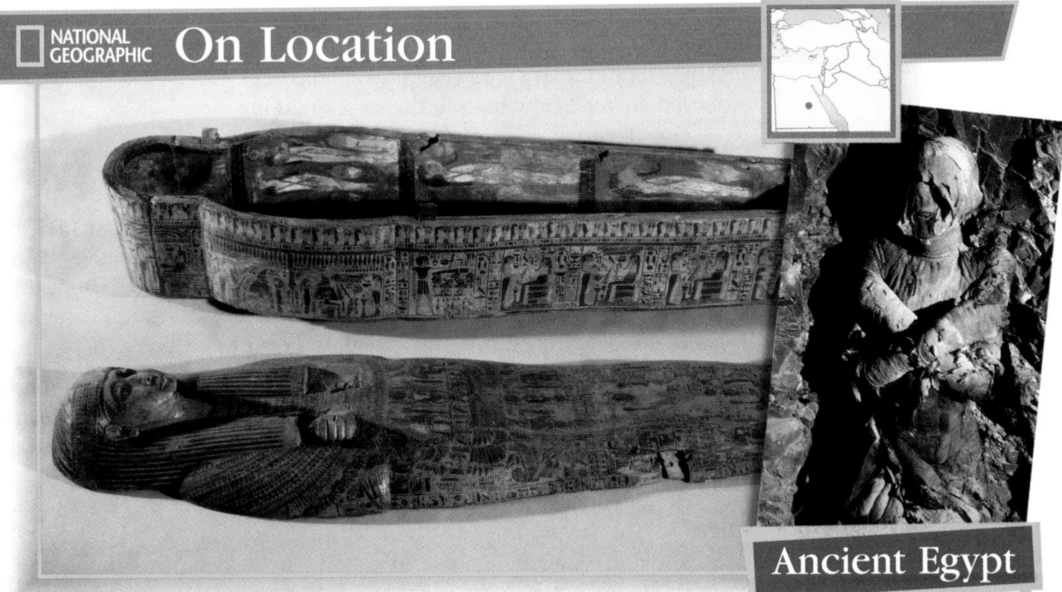

Ancient Egypt

This mummy (above right) was uncovered in the Valley of the Kings, Egypt. The coffin, or sarcophagus (above left), held a mummy and was created around 1000 B.C.

History **What were the biggest tombs called?**

Phoenicians As the peoples of Mesopotamia warred with neighboring states, they also traded. This helped to spread ideas and cultures. Among the most important traders were the Phoenicians, who were located mainly in what is today **Lebanon.** By about 1200 B.C., the Phoenicians had sailed as far as southern Europe and around the southern tip of Africa. They also became known for their alphabet, a set of symbols that represents the sounds of a language. To keep trade records, the Phoenicians made use of symbols, or letters, from which any number of words could be formed. The Phoenician alphabet eventually gave rise to the Hebrew, Greek, and Latin alphabets still in use today.

✓ Reading Check **Where was Mesopotamia located?**

Egypt—Gift of the Nile

Like Mesopotamia, Egypt developed in a river valley. Egyptian civilization arose along the **Nile River** in northeast Africa. The Nile is the world's longest river. It flows north 4,160 miles (6,693 km) from the mountains of East Africa to the Mediterranean Sea. The last 600 miles (960 km) are in Egypt. There the river cuts a narrow, green valley through the desert. Most ancient Egyptians lived near the river and its delta, or a fan-shaped fertile area, near the Mediterranean. For centuries, they farmed and were protected from invaders by the desert, the sea, and the Nile's waterfalls called cataracts.

Egyptian civilization was in many ways "the gift of the Nile." Egyptians depended on the Nile for their livelihood. Every year, about the middle of July, the Nile overflowed its banks. The floodwaters went down but left behind large amounts of rich soil good for growing crops.

Social Studies Online

Web Activity Visit ***The World and Its People*** Web site at twip.glencoe.com and click on **Chapter 16—Student Web Activities** to learn more about the Phoenicians.

More About the Photos

Ancient Egypt Mummification was the process of slowly drying a dead body to prevent it from rotting. The process consisted of removing certain internal organs, including the brain, then covering the corpse with a natural salt to absorb the body's water. The body was then filled with spices and wrapped with layers of linen soaked in resin.

Caption Answer pyramids

✓ Reading Check Answer

between the Tigris and Euphrates Rivers

Objectives and answers to the Student Web Activity can be found in the Web Activity Lesson Plan at twip.glencoe.com

Content Background

Ancient Mathematics The ancient civilizations of this region developed sophisticated mathematics—some of which still influence our number systems today. The mathematicians of Babylonia had a number system with a base of 60. Their method of counting is still found today in the way we count time—60 seconds in a minute and 60 minutes in an hour—and in measuring circles—360 degrees make a complete circle. Ancient Egyptian mathematicians used a decimal system, or a method of counting in groups of 10. They also had formulas for finding the area and volume of geometric figures, which they used when building the pyramids.

Chapter 16

Section 1, pages 466–471

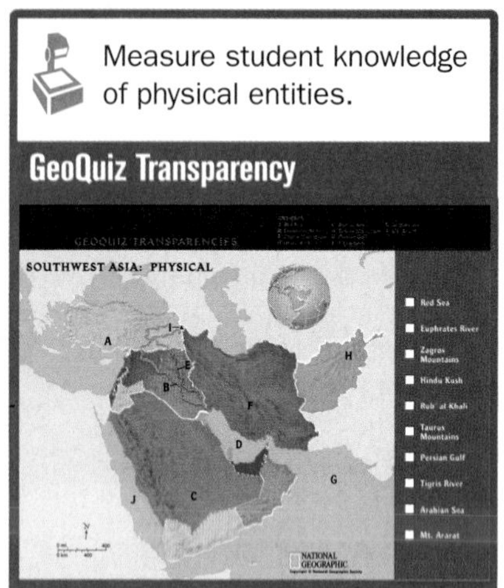

Assign Section 1 Assessment as homework or an in-class activity.

Have students use the Interactive Tutor Self-Assessment CD-ROM to review Section 1.

L2

Section Quiz

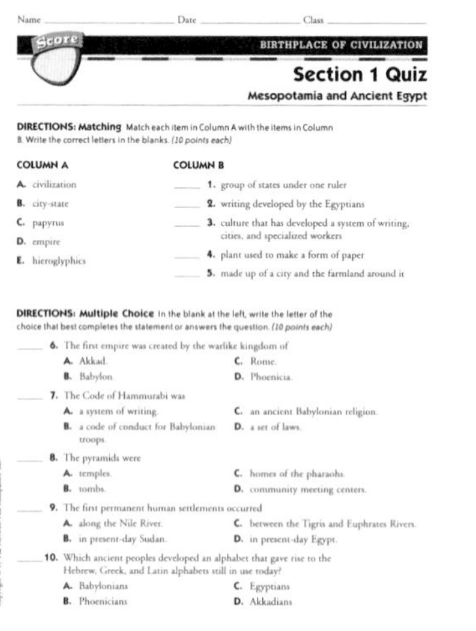

Name ______ Date ______ Class ______

BIRTHPLACE OF CIVILIZATION

Section 1 Quiz

Mesopotamia and Ancient Egypt

DIRECTIONS: Matching Match each item in Column A with the items in Column B. Write the correct letters in the blanks. *(10 points each)*

COLUMN A	COLUMN B
A. civilization	____ 1. group of states under one ruler
B. city-state	____ 2. writing developed by the Egyptians
C. papyrus	____ 3. culture that has developed a system of writing, cities, and specialized workers
D. empire	____ 4. plant used to make a form of paper
E. hieroglyphics	____ 5. made up of a city and the farmland around it

DIRECTIONS: Multiple Choice In the blank at the left, write the letter of the choice that best completes the statement or answers the question. *(10 points each)*

____ 6. The first empire was created by the warlike kingdom of
A. Akkad. C. Rome.
B. Babylon. D. Phoenicia.

____ 7. The Code of Hammurabi was
A. a system of writing. C. an ancient Babylonian religion.
B. a code of conduct for Babylonian troops. D. a set of laws.

____ 8. The pyramids were
A. temples. C. homes of the pharaohs.
B. tombs. D. community meeting centers.

____ 9. The first permanent human settlements occurred
A. along the Nile River. C. between the Tigris and Euphrates Rivers.
B. in present-day Sudan. D. in present-day Egypt.

____ 10. Which ancient peoples developed an alphabet that gave rise to the Hebrew, Greek, and Latin alphabets still in use today?
A. Babylonians C. Egyptians
B. Phoenicians D. Akkadians

Copyright © by The McGraw-Hill Companies, Inc.

263

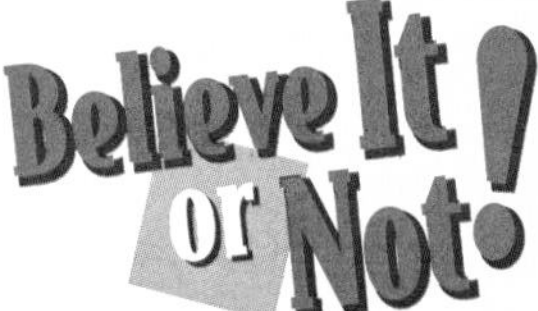

The Rosetta Stone

Language experts only learned to read hieroglyphics in the early 1800s. During the French ruler Napoleon's invasion of Egypt, a French soldier found what seemed to be a very old stone tablet near the town of Rosetta. This stone tablet provided the key that cracked the code for hieroglyphics. The Rosetta Stone had the same message written three times—in a form of Egyptian writing called Demotic, in Greek, and in hieroglyphics. Because both the Demotic and Greek could be read, scientists in 1821 were finally able to put meanings to the symbols used in hieroglyphics.

Hieroglyphics ▼

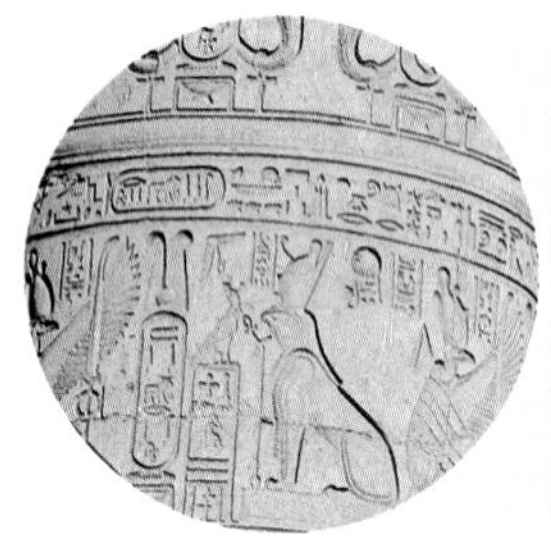

The Pharaoh Eventually, two kingdoms formed along the Nile—**Upper Egypt** to the south and **Lower Egypt** around the delta. About 3100 B.C., a king of Upper Egypt called Narmer moved north and conquered Lower Egypt, uniting the two kingdoms.

The Egyptian ruler had the title of **pharaoh** (FEHR•oh), which means "great house." Like Mesopotamia, Egypt was a theocracy. Egyptians believed that their pharaoh was a god, however, as well as a ruler and priest. The pharaoh was the center of Egyptian life. He owned all the land in Egypt, and he gave gifts of land to rich Egyptians and priests. The pharaoh had dams and irrigation canals built and repaired. He chose government officials to gather taxes and carry out his orders. The pharaoh also commanded Egypt's armies.

Religion Egyptians believed in many gods and goddesses. Each stood for some part of nature. The most important gods were the sun god Re, the river god Hapi, and the sky god Horus. Another important god was Osiris, the god of the harvest and eternal life.

The Egyptians believed in a form of life after death. They thought that the soul could not exist without the body, however. To preserve the body after death, it was embalmed. This was a process in which priests first removed certain organs from the body. Then they slowly dried the body to prevent it from decaying. Next, the embalmed body was wrapped in long strips of linen. The wrapped body was known as a mummy. The mummies of poor people were usually buried in caves or the desert sand. Those of rich people were placed in coffins, often in very elaborate tombs along with fabulous treasures.

The largest tombs belonged to the pharaohs and were called **pyramids.** These massive tombs were designed to protect the pharaohs' bodies from floods, wild animals, and robbers. Turn to page 472 to read about the largest pyramid—the Great Pyramid of Khufu. Great pharaohs—such as Khufu, Thutmose, and Ramses II—also were glorified with large monuments and statues. One such statue is the colossal Great Sphinx at Giza, which has the body of a lion and a human head.

Trade and Conquest Egypt conquered many lands during its long history. It also suffered defeats. In the 1700s B.C., invaders from Asia known as the Hyksos conquered Egypt. The Hyksos ruled for about 150 years until they were overthrown. From the Hyksos, the Egyptians learned to use bronze and iron weapons and horse-drawn chariots.

With this new military and transportation technology, Egypt sought gold and gems in the African kingdom of Kush, near present-day **Sudan.** The first female pharaoh, Hatsheptsut, expanded trade even further. During her rule, Egyptian traders sailed along the coast of East Africa to the land of Punt (near present-day **Somalia**). There, they exchanged beads, metal tools, and weapons for hardwoods, incense, ivory, and other products. To the north, Egypt traded across the eastern Mediterranean with the Phoenicians and the Greeks. As they traded, the Egyptians spread ideas and accomplishments.

Cooperative Learning Activity

Early Peoples Organize students into groups and assign one of the following peoples to each group: Sumerians, Egyptians, and Phoenicians. Have group members investigate the ways of life of each civilization or empire, concentrating on how people adapted to the environment of the region. Provide time for sharing insights. Lead a discussion on how these civilizations influenced students' present culture.

EE4 Human Systems: Standards 9, 10, 12

Egyptian Writing The ancient Egyptians wrote using **hieroglyphics.** This was a form of writing in which pictures were used for words or sounds. The Egyptians carved and painted hieroglyphic characters on their monuments or on **papyrus** (puh•PY•ruhs). Papyrus is a plant that grows along the Nile. It was used to make a form of paper, and it is the root word for *paper.* In order to write on papyrus, the Egyptians also developed ink. The dry climate of Egypt preserved some writings so well that they can still be read today.

Mathematics and Medicine The Egyptians made many other contributions to civilization. They used a number system based on ten. They also used fractions and whole numbers. They developed geometry to survey, or measure, land. The Nile's regular cycle of flooding helped the Egyptians create a calendar.

In the field of medicine, the Egyptians were the first to use splints, bandages, and compresses. They were skilled at sewing up cuts and setting broken bones. They even had remedies for hair loss and indigestion.

Decline Egypt eventually grew weak. The priests began to struggle with the pharaohs for power. In addition, much energy and money was spent trying to keep neighboring countries under Egyptian control. Egypt was eventually conquered by even greater empires—those of Greece and Rome.

✓ Reading Check How did the Egyptians view the pharaoh?

Assessment

Defining Terms

1. **Define** civilization, city-state, polytheism, theocracy, cuneiform, empire, delta, pharaoh, pyramid, hieroglyphics, papyrus.

Recalling Facts

2. **History** What were two early forms of writing, and where did they develop?
3. **Geography** Where did most Egyptians live? Why?
4. **Math** What mathematical contributions did Egyptians make to civilization?

Critical Thinking

5. **Drawing Conclusions** Why were the inventions of the wheel and the sailboat important to Sumer?
6. **Understanding Cause and Effect** Why was Hammurabi's code of laws an important development?

Graphic Organizer

7. **Organizing Information** On a diagram like this one, list ways that the Nile River influenced Egypt.

Applying Social Studies Skills

8. **Analyzing Maps** Look at the map on page 467. What do the locations of the towns have in common?

as a god, ruler, and priest

L1/ELL

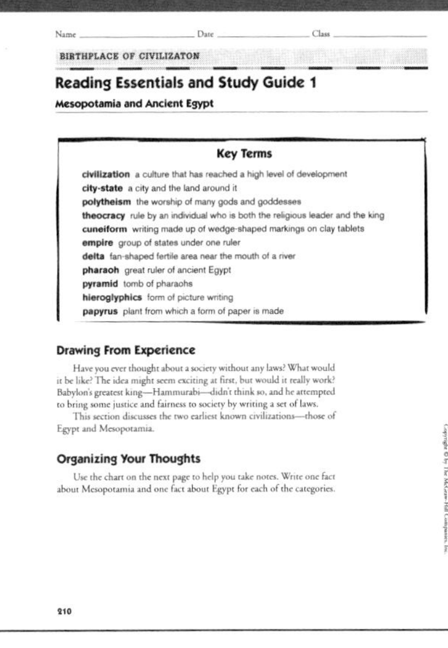

Name ______ Date ______ Class ______

BIRTHPLACE OF CIVILIZATON

Reading Essentials and Study Guide 1

Mesopotamia and Ancient Egypt

Key Terms

civilization a culture that has reached a high level of development
city-state a city and the land around it
polytheism the worship of many gods and goddesses
theocracy rule by an individual who is both the religious leader and the king
cuneiform writing made up of wedge-shaped markings on clay tablets
empire group of states under one ruler
delta fan-shaped fertile area near the mouth of a river
pharaoh great ruler of ancient Egypt
pyramid tomb of pharaohs
hieroglyphics form of picture writing
papyrus plant from which a form of paper is made

Drawing From Experience

Have you ever thought about a society without any laws? What would it be like? The idea might seem exciting at first, but would it really work? Babylon's greatest king—Hammurabi—didn't think so, and he attempted to bring some justice and fairness to society by writing a set of laws.

This section discusses the two earliest known civilizations—those of Egypt and Mesopotamia.

Organizing Your Thoughts

Use the chart on the next page to help you take notes. Write one fact about Mesopotamia and one fact about Egypt for each of the categories.

210

211

CLOSE

Have students create a bulletin board display about ancient Egypt with images and captions that highlight important features of the country and its people.

Section 1 Assessment

1. The terms are defined in the Glossary.
2. Sumerian cuneiform and the Phoenician alphabet
3. Most ancient Egyptians lived near the Nile River and its delta because the soil there was fertile.
4. a number system based on 10, fractions, whole numbers, and geometry
5. The wheel helped transportation and the sailboat replaced muscle power with wind power.
6. The Code of Hammurabi served as a basis for future laws.
7. Students' diagrams should be supported by facts from the section.
8. They are located along bodies of water.

Making Connections

ART | SCIENCE | CULTURE | TECHNOLOGY

TEACH

Have students suggest modern ways that important people are honored. *(by building structures like the Washington Monument; by naming structures for a person; by making a statue)* Explain that pyramids were built to honor the pharaohs, or rulers of ancient Egypt. L1

More About the Great Pyramid

To underscore the immense size of the Great Pyramid, give students the following height comparisons:

305 feet (93 m) Statue of Liberty

320 ft (98 m) Big Ben

555 ft (169 m) Washington Monument

Interdisciplinary Connections

Mathematics The pyramids show the mathematical skill of the ancient Egyptians. The four sides of the Great Pyramid measure, in feet, 755.43, 756.08, 755.88, and 755.77. Have students calculate the amount of deviation in the four sides. *(756.08 – 755.43, or 0.65 feet—less than 8 inches)* L1

The Egyptian Pyramids

The ancient Egyptians viewed the pharaoh, or king, as the most important person on the earth. They believed he was a god who would continue to guide them after his death. A pyramid served as a tomb for the pharaoh and provided a place where the body would safely pass into the afterlife. Rooms inside the pyramid held food, clothing, weapons, furniture, jewels, and everything else the pharaoh might need in the afterlife.

The Great Pyramid at Giza

The largest of Egypt's pyramids is the Great Pyramid of Khufu, built nearly 4,500 years ago. When the pyramid was new, it stood 482 feet (147 m) high. The square base of the pyramid covers 13 acres (about 5 ha). More than 2 million limestone and granite blocks were used in building it. These are no ordinary-sized blocks, however. The huge stones weigh an average of 2.5 tons (2.3 t) each.

Construction

For thousands of years, people have wondered how the Egyptians built the pyramids without modern tools or machinery. In the fifth century B.C., a Greek historian thought it took 100,000 people to build the Great Pyramid. Today archaeologists believe a workforce of about 20,000 did the job in about 20 years. Barges carried supplies and building materials for the pyramid down the Nile River. Nearby quarries supplied most of the stone. Skilled stonecutters carved the stones into the precise size and shape so that no mortar, or cementing material, was needed to hold the stones together.

Engineers think that workers built ramps and used papyrus twine to drag the huge stones to the pyramid. They formed ramps up all four sides of the pyramid and made the ramps higher and longer as the pyramid rose. They then dragged the stones up the ramps. Once finished, the ramps were cleared away. Then stonemasons smoothed and polished the stone, and the finished pyramid towered over the surrounding desert.

Making the Connection

1. Why did the Egyptians build the pyramids?
2. How many workers did ancient historians and modern archaeologists each estimate it took to build the Great Pyramid?
3. **Sequencing Information** Describe the process experts think Egyptians used to build the pyramids.

◄ The Great Pyramid at Giza, Egypt

Making the Connection

1. to provide a tomb for the pharaoh and a safe place for the pharaoh to pass into the afterlife
2. In the fifth century B.C., Greeks thought it took 100,000 people to build the Great Pyramid. Now experts think it took about 20,000.
3. Workers cut stones from nearby quarries, carved them into shape, and pulled them up ramps to the pyramid site. Builders extended the ramps up the sides of the pyramid to carry rocks to the top. After they reached the top, the ramps were cleared away. Stonemasons smoothed and polished the stones.

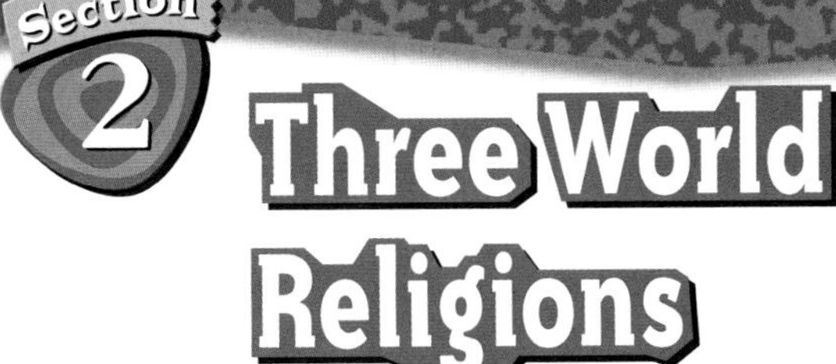

Three World Religions

Guide to Reading

Main Idea

Three of the world's monotheistic religions—Judaism, Christianity, and Islam—developed in Southwest Asia.

Terms to Know

- monotheism
- covenant
- prophet
- messiah
- disciple
- five pillars of faith
- hajj

Reading Strategy

Create and complete a chart like this one. List important beliefs of each religion.

Religion	Beliefs
Judaism	
Christianity	
Islam	

NATIONAL GEOGRAPHIC **Exploring Our World**

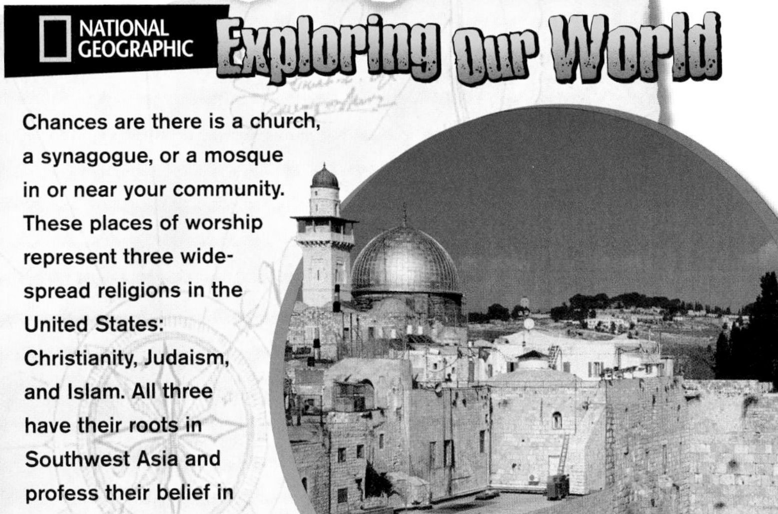

Chances are there is a church, a synagogue, or a mosque in or near your community. These places of worship represent three widespread religions in the United States: Christianity, Judaism, and Islam. All three have their roots in Southwest Asia and profess their belief in one god. All three view the ancient city of Jerusalem as a holy site.

Judaism, Christianity, and Islam have become major world faiths. All three religions are examples of **monotheism**, or the belief in one supreme god.

Judaism

Judaism is the oldest of these three world religions. It was first practiced by a small group of people in Southwest Asia called the Israelites. The followers of Judaism today are known as Jews. We know about the early history of the Jewish people and their religion from their holy book—the Torah.

According to Jewish belief, the Jews are descended from Abraham and Sarah, who first worshipped the one God, or Yahweh. Abraham was a herder who lived at least 3,700 years ago in what is now Iraq. The Torah states that God made a **covenant**, or agreement, with Abraham. If Abraham moved to the land of Canaan (Palestine), he

Chapter 16

Section 2, pages 473–477

1 Focus

Section Objectives

1. Describe the world's three largest monotheistic religions.
2. Explain similarities and differences among Judaism, Christianity, and Islam.

BELLRINGER Skillbuilder Activity

Project transparency and have students answer the question.

Daily Focus Skills Transparency

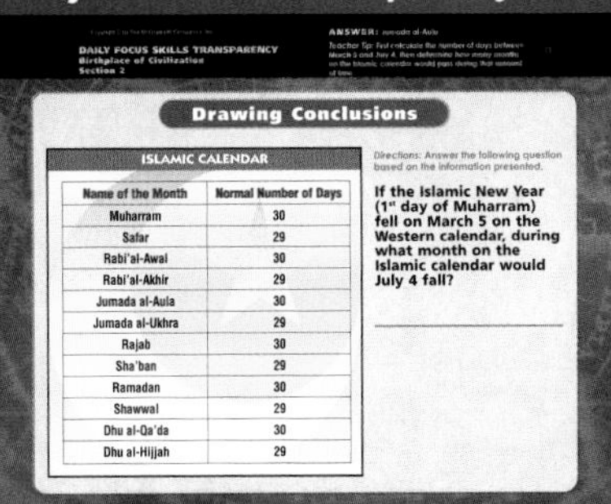

DAILY FOCUS SKILLS TRANSPARENCY

Drawing Conclusions

ISLAMIC CALENDAR

Name of the Month	Normal Number of Days
Muharram	30
Safar	29
Rabi'al-Awal	30
Rabi'al-Akhir	29
Jumada al-Aula	30
Jumada al-Ukhra	29
Rajab	30
Sha'ban	29
Ramadan	30
Shawwal	29
Dhu al-Qa'da	30
Dhu al-Hijjah	29

Directions: Answer the following question based on the information presented.

If the Islamic New Year (1st day of Muharram) fell on March 5 on the Western calendar, during what month on the Islamic calendar would July 4 fall?

Reading Preview

■ **Activating Prior Knowledge**
Ask: Have you ever heard the phrase "Holy Land"? To what place does it refer? *(Israel, which is holy to Jews, Christians, and Muslims)* Point out that students will learn more about the main religions of the Holy Land in this section.

■ **Preteaching Vocabulary**
Inform students that *mono* is Greek for *one*, and *theism* is from *theos*, which is the Greek word for *god*.

Section Resources

Reproducible Masters

- Reproducible Lesson Plan
- Daily Lecture and Discussion Notes
- Note-taking Guide
- Guided Reading Activity
- Reading Essentials and Study Guide
- Section Quiz

Transparencies

- Daily Focus Skills Transparency

Multimedia

- Vocabulary PuzzleMaker CD-ROM
- Interactive Tutor Self-Assessment CD-ROM
- Presentation Plus! CD-ROM
- ExamView® Pro Testmaker CD-ROM
- MindJogger Videoquiz

2 TEACH

Reading Strategy

Organizing Information Have students create a four-column chart with the names of the three religions in this section across columns 2, 3, and 4. In the first column, have them list the row's labels: "prophet," "holy book," and "holy days." Then have them fill in the information as they read the section. L1

Daily Lecture and Discussion Notes

BIRTHPLACE OF CIVILIZATION

Daily Lecture and Discussion Notes
Three World Religions

Did You Know? The Quran, the holy book of Islam, is believed to be the exact and precise word of God, revealed to Muhammad by the angel Gabriel over a period of approximately 23 years. Although the Quran has been translated into many languages, only the original Arabic is considered the literal word of Allah.

I. Judaism

A. Judaism, Christianity, and Islam are major faiths that are examples of **monotheism**, or belief in one supreme god.

B. Judaism was first practiced by a small group of people in Southwest Asia called the Israelites. The followers of Judaism today are known as Jews. Their holy

Analyzing the Map

Answer
Muslim

Skills Practice
What important religious site is outside the Old City? *(Tomb of David)*

Reading Check Answer

the Ten Commandments

NATIONAL GEOGRAPHIC

Jerusalem

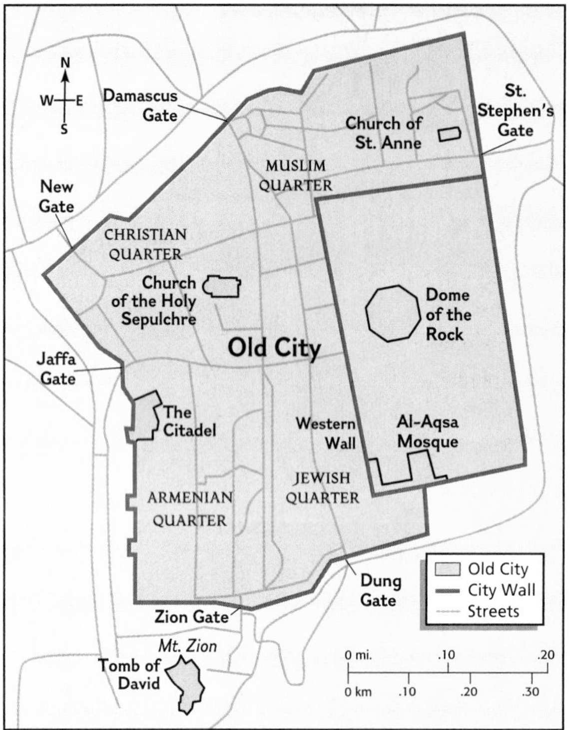

Analyzing the Map

The city of Jerusalem is divided into four quarters.

Place What quarter is located in the northeast part of the city?

would be blessed, and all nations would be blessed through him. Because of this covenant, Abraham's Israelite descendants believed that they were God's "chosen people" and would remain so as long as they followed God's laws.

The Ten Commandments The most important of these laws are the Ten Commandments. Jews believe that God revealed the Ten Commandments to a **prophet,** or messenger of God, called Moses. According to the Torah, Moses led the Israelites from slavery in Egypt. At the top of Mt. Sinai in the desert, Moses received the Ten Commandments. These rules differed from the laws of neighboring peoples because they were based on the worship of one god. The Israelites were to give their loyalty only to Yahweh. They were not to worship other gods or human-made images. Also, all people—whether rich or poor—were to be treated fairly.

The Jews About 1000 B.C., the Israelites under King David created a kingdom in the area of present-day **Israel.** The kingdom's capital was **Jerusalem.** By 922 B.C., the kingdom had split into two states—Israel and Judah. The people of Judah came to be called Jews. In later centuries, the Jews would be conquered and forced to leave their homeland many times. Eventually, the Jewish people spread to countries in many parts of the world. This scattering of the Jews was called the Diaspora. In many areas, the Jews were cruelly treated. In some areas, they were treated with tolerance and understanding. Wherever they lived, Jewish thinkers, writers, artists, and scientists increased the world's knowledge.

Judaism Today Despite hardships, the Jews have remained faithful to their religious heritage. They observe several important holy days. Every year during the festival of Passover, Jews retell the story of the exodus, or departure, of the Israelites from Egypt. Rosh Hashanah (RAHSH huh•SHAH•nuh) is New Year's Day on the Jewish calendar and is marked by prayer and solemn thoughts. Following Rosh Hashanah is Yom Kippur (YOHM kih•PUR), the holiest day in Judaism. Also called the Day of Atonement, Yom Kippur is observed by a 24-hour period of prayer and fasting.

Reading Check What are the basic laws revealed to Moses known as?

Reading Strategy — Reading the Text

Identifying Main Ideas Have students copy the subheads in this section on a piece of paper. Tell them to leave ample space beneath each heading to write additional information. After their outline is copied, have them read the section and write the main idea under the appropriate heading. After students have completed their exercise, ask for volunteers to read their main ideas aloud. As a class, discuss the different suggestions. L1

*Use the **Reading Skills Handbook** for more reading strategies.*

Christianity

The traditions of Judaism gave rise to the monotheistic religion known as Christianity. Christianity started in Southwest Asia among the Jews. Later, it spread to non-Jews and became one of the major influences in Western civilization.

Jesus Centuries after the rise of Judaism, a Jew named Jesus began preaching in what today is Israel, the West Bank, and Jordan. Jesus taught that God loved all people, even those who have sinned. He told people that if they placed their trust in God, they would be forgiven.

During Jesus' lifetime, many Jews were opposed to the Romans who ruled their land. Some believed that God would send a **messiah,** or savior, to deliver them. In A.D. 30, Jesus and his **disciples,** or followers, went to Jerusalem to celebrate Passover, a Jewish holiday. Some Jews there greeted him as the messiah. This worried other Jews and Romans alike. Jesus was convicted of treason under Roman law and was crucified, or executed on a cross, outside Jerusalem. Soon afterward, the disciples proclaimed that Jesus had risen from the dead and had appeared to them. They began preaching that Jesus was the Son of God and that

Primary Source

COMPARING SCRIPTURE

Although there are many differences between the world's major religions, there are also many similarities. These quotes from Judaism, Christianity, and Islam illustrate the belief in good deeds.

When the holy one loves a man, He sends him a present in the shape of a poor man, so that he should perform some good deed to him, through the merit of which he may draw a cord of grace. The Torah; Genesis 104a

He who has two coats, let him share with him who has none: and he who has food, let him do likewise. The Bible; Luke 3:11

Every person's every joint must perform a charity every day the sun comes up: to act justly between two people is a charity. . . . a good word is a charity; every step you take in prayers is a charity. . . . Saying of the Prophet Muhammad

Analyzing Primary Sources

All three religions share the message of helping others. Why do you suppose there has been such conflict among them?

Chapter 16

Section 2, pages 473–477

L1/ELL

Guided Reading Activity

Name ____ Date ____ Class ____

BIRTHPLACE OF CIVILIZATION

Guided Reading Activity 2

Three World Religions

DIRECTIONS: Answering Questions Reading the section and answering the questions below will help you learn more about three religions that developed in Southwest Asia. Use your textbook to write answers to the questions.

1. What do the religions of Judaism, Christianity, and Islam have in common?
2. What is the holy book of the Jews?
3. What are some beliefs of Judaism?
4. What are some beliefs of Christianity?
5. What items are included in the New Testament?
6. What major groups make up Christianity today?
7. What are the followers of Islam called?
8. What does the Quran, the Muslim holy book, describe?
9. Why is Ramadan an important holiday on the Muslim calendar?

51

Primary Source

Answer This question should prompt some lively discussion about why sometimes conflict exists among people of different religions.

Activity The Golden Rule of the ethic of reciprocity is found in the scriptures of nearly every religion. It is often regarded as the most concise and general principle of ethics. Basically it states that each person should treat others as they would themselves like to be treated. Ask students to discuss which principles they live by regarding their treatment of others.

Differentiated Instruction

Meeting Special Needs: Less-proficient Readers Suggest that before they read the section, students should read the questions in the Section Assessment. Point out that by reading the questions first, they can see what concepts and information in the section are most important. L1

Refer to *Inclusion for the Middle School Social Studies Classroom Strategies and Activities* in the TCR.

Chapter 16

3 Assess

Assign Section 2 Assessment as homework or an in-class activity.

Have students use the Interactive Tutor Self-Assessment CD-ROM to review Section 2.

L2

Section Quiz

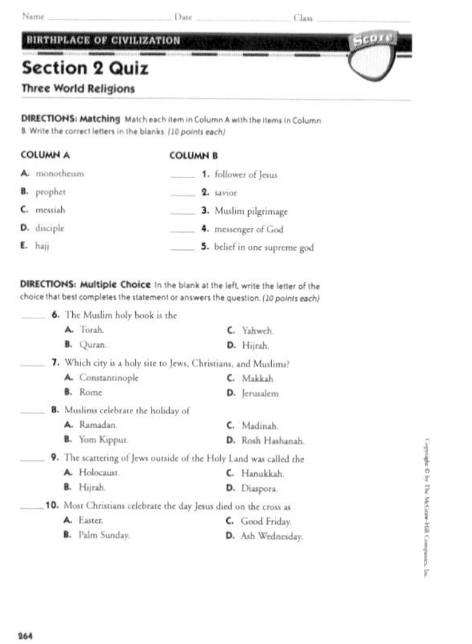

Name ______ Date ______ Class ______

BIRTHPLACE OF CIVILIZATION

Score

Section 2 Quiz

Three World Religions

DIRECTIONS: Matching Match each item in Column A with the items in Column B. Write the correct letters in the blanks. *(10 points each)*

COLUMN A	COLUMN B
A. monotheism	____ 1. follower of Jesus
B. prophet	____ 2. savior
C. messiah	____ 3. Muslim pilgrimage
D. disciple	____ 4. messenger of God
E. hajj	____ 5. belief in one supreme god

DIRECTIONS: Multiple Choice In the blank at the left, write the letter of the choice that best completes the statement or answers the question. *(10 points each)*

____ 6. The Muslim holy book is the
A. Torah. C. Yahweh.
B. Quran. D. Hijrah.

____ 7. Which city is a holy site to Jews, Christians, and Muslims?
A. Constantinople C. Makkah
B. Rome D. Jerusalem

____ 8. Muslims celebrate the holiday of
A. Ramadan. C. Madinah.
B. Yom Kippur. D. Rosh Hashanah.

____ 9. The scattering of Jews outside of the Holy Land was called the
A. Holocaust. C. Hanukkah.
B. Hijrah. D. Diaspora.

____ 10. Most Christians celebrate the day Jesus died on the cross as
A. Easter. C. Good Friday.
B. Palm Sunday. D. Ash Wednesday.

264

He legalized Christianity.

anyone who believed in him and lived by his teachings would know eternal life after death. From then on, the disciples called him Christ, after the Greek word *Christos* (krees•TOS), meaning "messiah."

Spread of Christianity The disciples spread the message of Jesus throughout the Mediterranean area and beyond. Jews and non-Jews who accepted this message became known as Christians. Stories about Jesus and early Christian writings—known as the New Testament—became part of the Christian Bible.

Until about A.D. 300, Christians faced persecution in the Roman Empire. Then the Roman emperor Constantine proclaimed that Christianity was to be a lawful religion. By A.D. 600, large areas of Southwest Asia, North Africa, and Europe were Christian. Disputes soon divided Christians into two major groups—Roman Catholics led by the pope in Italy, and Eastern Orthodox Christians who looked to the patriarch in Constantinople.

Christianity Today Christianity has more followers than any other religion. Three major groups—Roman Catholics, Eastern Orthodox, and Protestants—make up the Christian religion today. Christians mark important events in the life of Jesus. Christmas is the celebration of his birth. In the spring, Christians remember the last days of Jesus' life on Earth. Good Friday is the day of Jesus' crucifixion. Easter, believed to be the day Jesus rose from the dead, is the most important Christian holy day.

✓Reading Check **Why was Constantine important to Christianity?**

Islam

The third monotheistic religion from Southwest Asia is Islam. It began in the A.D. 600s in the Arabian Peninsula. In the Arabic language, *Islam* means "surrender" to the will of God, or Allah. The followers of Islam are called Muslims. They believe that Muhammad is the last and greatest prophet of Islam—following Abraham, Moses, and Jesus.

Muhammad Muhammad was born about A.D. 570 in **Makkah** (Mecca), a trading city and religious center in western Arabia. Arab pilgrims came to worship at the Kaaba, a shrine that housed a sacred black stone. According to Islamic teachings, in A.D. 610 Muhammad heard the voice of the angel Gabriel calling him to preach about God. He told the people of Makkah that there is only one God, Allah, before whom all believers are equal. He urged the rich to share with the poor. Muhammad saw life as preparation for the Day of Judgment, or the day when God would punish evildoers and reward the just.

Muhammad's message angered Makkah's rich merchants. They began to make threats against Muhammad. In A.D. 622, Muhammad and several hundred followers traveled to Yathrib (now known as Madinah), a small town north of Makkah. Muhammad's departure to Yathrib is known as the *Hijrah* (HIHJRUH), or migration.

In Madinah, Muhammad united the people politically and made them proud of their new faith. Armies from Makkah tried to capture

Critical Thinking Activity

Drawing Conclusions Religion has been a source of conflict in the Middle East for centuries. In the United States, however, many different religions coexist without conflict. Ask students what is different between the Middle East and the United States that allows religions in the United States to exist without conflict. The discussion will vary, but students should realize that a major difference is the separation of church and state. In the United States, the government has no control over its citizens' beliefs or type of worship. **L1**

Madinah, but Muhammad's forces were eventually able to defeat them. Muhammad made Makkah the center of Islam and dedicated the Kaaba to the worship of Allah. By the time of Muhammad's death in A.D. 632, all of Arabia had accepted Islam. Muslim armies, merchants, and scholars began to spread Islam outside of Arabia. Over several centuries, a series of empires based on Islam ruled vast areas of Asia, North Africa, and parts of Europe.

As Islam spread, the religion branched into two main groups—Sunnis (SU•NEEZ) and Shiites (SHEE•EYETS). Most of the world's Muslims are Sunni. In the countries of Iran and Iraq, however, most people are Shiites. Sunnis and Shiites differ on which leaders should rule in the Islamic community.

The Quran At the heart of Islam is the Quran (kuh•RAN), or the Muslim holy book. Muslims believe that the Quran is the direct word of Allah as given to Muhammad. The Quran presents the **five pillars of faith,** or the five obligations all Muslims must fulfill. The first duty is the confession, or statement, of faith: "There is no god but Allah, and Muhammad is his messenger." Second, Muslims must pray five times each day, facing the holy city of Makkah. The third duty is to give charity to people in need or to institutions that are involved in education or social services. The fourth duty is to fast. This means not eating or drinking during the daylight hours of the holy month of Ramadan (RAH•muh•DAHN). This is the month, according to Muslim beliefs, in which God began to reveal the Quran to Muhammad.

The last pillar of faith is a pilgrimage. Once in each Muslim's life, he or she must, if able, journey to Makkah to pray. This journey is called the **hajj.** The reward for fulfilling all these religious duties is paradise.

Reading Check What is the Islamic pilgrimage to Makkah called?

Assessment

Defining Terms

1. **Define** monotheism, covenant, prophet, messiah, disciple, five pillars of faith, hajj.

Recalling Facts

2. **Religion** What are the world's three largest monotheistic religions?
3. **History** What was the Diaspora?

Critical Thinking

4. **Making Comparisons** How did the Ten Commandments differ from the religious laws of neighboring regions?
5. **Summarizing Information** What are the main holy days for each of the religions discussed in this section?

Graphic Organizer

6. **Organizing Information** Create a time line like the one below. List four key events in the foundation of Islam and their dates.

Applying Social Studies Skills

7. **Analyzing Primary Sources** Read the quotes in the Primary Source feature on page 475. Summarize each quote in your own words.

Section 2 Assessment

1. The terms are defined in the Glossary.
2. Judaism, Christianity, and Islam
3. the scattering of Jews to different parts of the world
4. Unlike the laws of neighboring regions, they were based on the worship of one God.
5. Judaism: Passover, Rosh Hashanah, Yom Kippur; Christianity: Christmas, Good Friday, Easter; Islam: Ramadan
6. Students' time lines should highlight the dates of key events in the foundation of Islam.
7. Summaries for each religion should reflect the belief in good deeds.

a hajj

L1/ELL

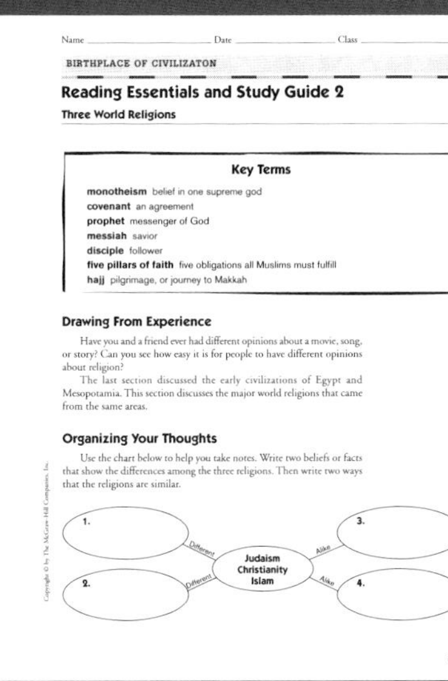

Reading Essentials and Study Guide

Name ______ Date ______ Class ______

BIRTHPLACE OF CIVILIZATON

Reading Essentials and Study Guide 2

Three World Religions

Key Terms

monotheism belief in one supreme god
covenant an agreement
prophet messenger of God
messiah savior
disciple follower
five pillars of faith five obligations all Muslims must fulfill
hajj pilgrimage, or journey to Makkah

Drawing From Experience

Have you and a friend ever had different opinions about a movie, song, or story? Can you see how easy it is for people to have different opinions about religion?

The last section discussed the early civilizations of Egypt and Mesopotamia. This section discusses the major world religions that came from the same areas.

Organizing Your Thoughts

Use the chart below to help you take notes. Write two beliefs or facts that show the differences among the three religions. Then write two ways that the religions are similar.

1. Different — Judaism Christianity Islam — Alike 3.
2. Different — Alike 4.

Copyright © by The McGraw-Hill Companies, Inc.

215

216

Close

Have students create a bulletin board display about the major religious holidays and observances of the different world religions. Ask them to use images and captions to explain the significance of these celebrations in selected contemporary societies. At a minimum, they should mention the major holidays of the three monotheistic religions discussed in this section.

TEACH

Ask: **How do you find an unknown phone number?** *(check the directory or call directory assistance)* **How do you find out what programs are showing on television on any given day?** *(check an on-screen or print television guide)* Point out that a library card catalog serves the same function—it indicates the location of resources in a library like a phone directory and summarizes those resources like a television guide. Tell students that in this feature they will learn about different library research tools. **L1**

Additional Skills Practice

1. **How is a dictionary organized?** *(alphabetically)* **How are encyclopedias, biographical dictionaries, and card catalogs organized?** *(alphabetically)*
2. **Where would you find the location of cities in Norway?** *(atlas)*
3. **Where would you find a listing of recent articles written about Iceland?** *(periodical guide)*

Additional Skills Resources

 Chapter Skills Review

 Building Geography Skills for Life

GLENCOE TECHNOLOGY

 **Skillbuilder Interactive Workbook CD-ROM, Level 1**

This interactive CD-ROM reinforces student mastery of essential social studies skills.

Study and Writing Skill

Using Library Resources

Your teacher has assigned a major research report, so you go to the library. As you wander the aisles surrounded by books, you wonder: Where do I start my research? Which reference tools should I use?

Learning the Skill

Libraries contain many resources. Here are brief descriptions of important ones:

- **Encyclopedia:** set of books containing short articles on many subjects arranged alphabetically
- **Biographical Dictionary:** brief biographies listed alphabetically by last names
- **Atlas:** collection of maps and charts
- **Almanac:** reference updated yearly that provides current statistics and historical information on a wide range of subjects
- **Card Catalog:** listing of every book in the library, either on cards or on a computer database; search for books by author, subject, or title
- **Periodical Guide:** set of books listing topics covered in magazines and newspaper articles
- **Computer Database:** collections of information organized for rapid search and retrieval
- **World Wide Web:** collection of information on the Internet accessed with a Web browser *(Caution: Some information may not be reliable.)*

Practicing the Skill

Suppose you are assigned a research report dealing with Islam. Read the questions below, and then decide which of the resources listed here you would use to answer each question and why.

1. During which years did Muhammad lead Muslims?
2. What is the current number of Muslims in the world today?
3. What was Muhammad's early life like? What happened to the Islamic religion after he died?

Applying the Skill

Using library resources, research the achievements of early Jews, Christians, and Muslims in the areas of architecture, math, science, and/or medicine. Present the information you find to the class.

◀ The Kaaba, Islam's most sacred shrine, is in the courtyard of Makkah's Grand Mosque.

Practicing the Skill Answers

1. encyclopedia, biographical dictionary
2. almanac, World Wide Web
3. encyclopedia, biographical dictionary

Applying the Skill

You might wish to inform the school librarian before assigning this activity so that he or she can research the available materials and thus be prepared for students' research.

Reading Review

Section 1 Mesopotamia and Ancient Egypt

Terms to Know

civilization
city-state
polytheism
theocracy
cuneiform
empire
delta
pharaoh
pyramid
hieroglyphics
papyrus

Main Idea

The peoples of Mesopotamia and Egypt were among the first to build civilizations.

✓ History The first civilizations developed in Mesopotamia, which was located in the Fertile Crescent.

✓ History Early advancements in Mesopotamia, Sumer, and Babylon were in farming, writing, and government.

✓ Geography The Egyptians depended on the Nile River for their livelihood.

✓ History Ancient Egypt is known for pharaohs, pyramids, hieroglyphics, and mummies.

Section 2 Three World Religions

Terms to Know

monotheism
covenant
prophet
messiah
disciple
five pillars of faith
hajj

Main Idea

Three of the world's monotheistic religions—Judaism, Christianity, and Islam—developed in Southwest Asia.

✓ History Judaism is the world's oldest monotheistic religion. The Jews' belief in one God was later shared by Christianity and Islam.

✓ Religion Christians believe Jesus is the Messiah and the Son of God.

✓ Religion Muslims are followers of Islam. Muslims believe Allah is the one God, and Muhammad is the messenger.

◀ Desert areas begin where the fertile Nile River Valley ends.

Reading Review

Use the Chapter 16 Reading Review to preview, review, condense, or reteach the chapter.

Preview/Review

Use the Terms to Know lists to help students review and study.

Activity Organize the class into teams and quiz them on the Terms to Know. Offer a definition and ask each team to identify the correct term. If they do so correctly, they win a point; if they do not, the other team has an opportunity to do so.

Vocabulary PuzzleMaker CD-ROM reinforces the vocabulary terms used in Chapter 16.

The Interactive Tutor Self-Assessment CD-ROM allows students to review Chapter 16 content.

Condense

Have students read the Chapter 16 summary statements.

Guided Reading Activities

Audio Program

Reteach

Reteaching Activity

Reading Essentials and Study Guide

Reading Strategy — Read to Write

Understanding the Past Have students create a display that shows achievements and advances that occurred in this region long ago that are still influencing us today. Explain that students can present their results in a poster or a written report. Whatever means they choose, students should describe both technical achievements, such as the use of irrigation, writing systems, and a calendar, and cultural achievements, such as the establishment of a system of laws and the founding of specific religious beliefs. L2

EE6 The Uses of Geography: Standards 17 and 18

Assessment and Activities

GLENCOE TECHNOLOGY

MindJogger Videoquiz
Use MindJogger Videoquiz to review the Chapter 16 content.

Available in DVD and VHS

Using Key Terms

1. c
2. g
3. h
4. d
5. e
6. j
7. f
8. a
9. b
10. i

Reviewing the Main Ideas

11. a large, steplike Sumerian tower with a temple on the top
12. Sumer
13. the *Epic of Gilgamesh*
14. the 60-minute hour, the 60-second minute, and the 360-degree circle
15. widespread trading and the alphabet
16. Hykos; bronze and iron weapons and horse-drawn chariots
17. to preserve the body for the afterlife
18. They are different names for God.
19. Some Jews believed the messiah would deliver them from the rule of the Romans. Christians believed the messiah would lead them to eternal life after death.
20. different holy books, different holy days, different prophets

Chapter 16 Assessment and Activities

Using Key Terms

Match the terms in Part A with their definitions in Part B.

A.

1. civilization
2. theocracy
3. cuneiform
4. pharaoh
5. polytheism
6. covenant
7. monotheism
8. hajj
9. disciple
10. city-state

B.

a. holy journey in Islam
b. follower
c. culture that has reached the level of development where people can specialize their skills
d. god-king of ancient Egypt
e. belief in many gods
f. belief in one God
g. ruled by religious leader who is also a king
h. ancient form of writing in Sumer
i. city and its surrounding countryside
j. agreement

Reviewing the Main Ideas

Section 1 Mesopotamia and Ancient Egypt

11. **History** What was a ziggurat?
12. **History** Where did the earliest city-states arise?
13. **History** What was the world's first known story?
14. **History** What concepts did we borrow from the Babylonians?
15. **Culture** For what two things are the Phoenicians known?
16. **History** Who were the Asians that invaded ancient Egypt? What technology did they share?
17. **History** Why did the Egyptians embalm their dead?

Section 2 Three World Religions

18. **Religion** What is the similarity between Yahweh and Allah?
19. **Religion** What is the role of the messiah in Jewish and Christian religious belief?
20. **Religion** Judaism, Christianity, and Islam are similar in their belief of one supreme god. List some of the differences among the three religions.

NATIONAL GEOGRAPHIC Egypt and Southwest Asia

Place Location Activity

On a separate sheet of paper, match the letters on the map with the numbered places listed below.

1. Persian Gulf
2. Lower Egypt
3. Euphrates River
4. Mediterranean Sea
5. Nile River
6. Israel
7. Upper Egypt
8. Saudi Arabia
9. Makkah (Mecca)
10. Jerusalem

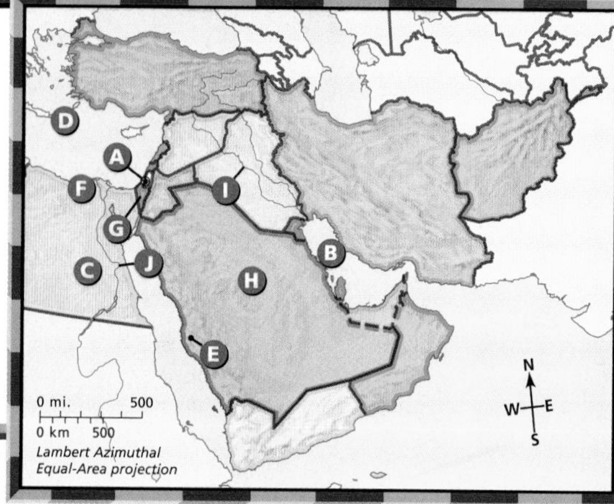

480

NATIONAL GEOGRAPHIC Place Location Activity

1. B
2. F
3. I
4. D
5. J
6. G
7. C
8. H
9. E
10. A

Critical Thinking

21. Laws define a society's rules of conduct and allow a king to enforce those rules.
22. Judaism: Torah
Christianity: Bible
Islam: Quran

Self-Check Quiz Visit ***The World and Its People*** Web site at twip.glencoe.com and click on **Chapter 16—Self-Check Quizzes** to prepare for the Chapter Test.

Critical Thinking

21. **Analyzing Information** Hammurabi wrote a code of laws to help him rule better. How would laws help a king rule?
22. **Categorizing Information** Create a chart like the one below. Complete the name of the holy book for each of the religions listed.

Religion	Holy Book
Judaism	
Christianity	
Islam	

Comparing Regions Activity

23. **Culture** As you have learned, ancient Egyptians followed a polytheistic religion. The early Greeks did as well. Use the Internet to find information on ancient Egyptian gods and goddesses and classical Greek gods and goddesses. Create a chart to compare the gods and goddesses of each.

Mental Mapping Activity

24. **Focusing on the Region** Create a simple outline map of Egypt and Southwest Asia. Draw in the Nile, Tigris, and Euphrates Rivers. Shade the areas where the early civilizations of ancient Egypt and Mesopotamia were located. Label the cities of Giza, Jerusalem, Babylon, and Makkah (Mecca) on your map.

Technology Skills Activity

25. **Using the Internet** Search the Internet and find several newspapers that publish online. Use at least three different sources to research recent discoveries about any ancient cultures in the region of North Africa or Southwest Asia. Use the computer to create a report on this topic. You may want to include visual materials for display.

Standardized Test Practice

Directions: Study the map below, and then answer the question that follows.

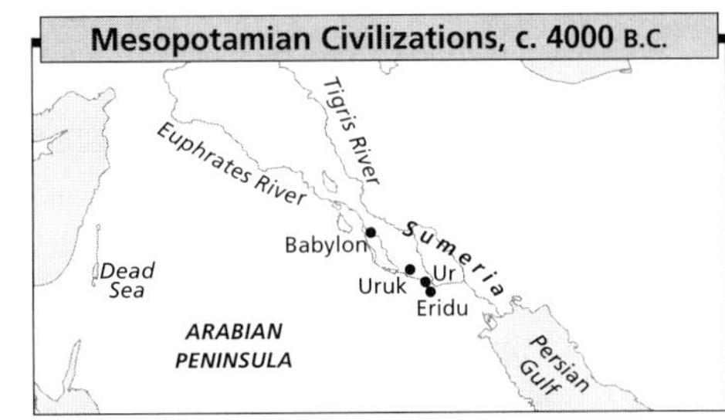

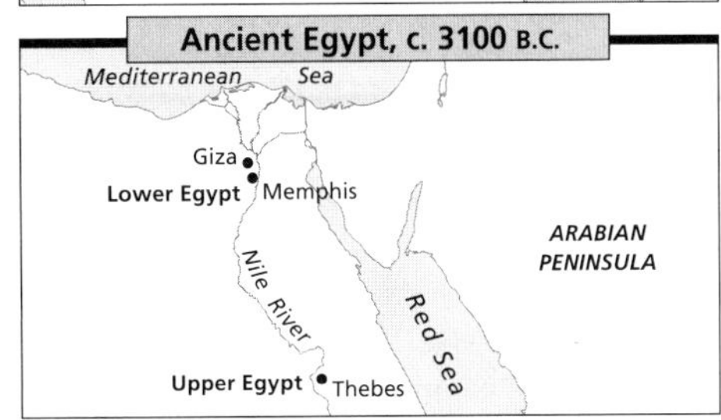

1. **What characteristic did the first Egyptian and Mesopotamian civilizations share?**
   - A They were established in the same year.
   - B Both civilizations began in North Africa.
   - C They both developed on the banks of rivers.
   - D People in both civilizations relied on hunting to obtain food.

Test-Taking Tip: When you answer a map question, do *not* rely on your memory of the map. Instead, check each answer choice against the information on the map and get rid of answer choices that are incorrect. Eliminating even one wrong choice will help you locate the correct answer.

481

Assessment and Activities

Standardized Test Practice

1. C

Tested Objectives: Analyzing a map, drawing conclusions

Chapter Test Bonus Question

This question may be used for extra credit on the chapter test.

What provided the key that unlocked the meaning of hieroglyphics? *(Rosetta Stone)*

Social Studies online

Have students visit the Web site at twip.glencoe.com to review Chapter 16 and take the Self-Check Quiz.

FOLDABLES™ Study Organizer Dinah Zike's Foldables

Culminating Activity Create a Venn diagram on the board using the information from students' foldables. Have students add or remove information from their foldables based upon the students' suggestions.

Comparing Regions Activity

23. Students' charts should identify and compare Egyptian and Greek gods and goddesses.

Mental Mapping Activity

24. This exercise helps students visualize the location of early Egyptian and Mesopotamian civilizations. All attempts at freehand mapping should be accepted.

Technology Skills Activity

25. Students should list the three sources from the Internet that they used for their reports. Their reports may include text, diagrams, time lines, and other illustrations to relate information on a recent discovery.

Chapter 17 Resources

Note: The following materials may be used when teaching Chapter 17.
Section level support materials are shown at point of use in the margins of the Teacher Wraparound Edition.

Timesaving Tools

TeacherWorks™ All-In-One Planner and Resource Center

- **Interactive Teacher Edition** See the **Interactive Teacher Edition** CD-ROM to electronically integrate your Teacher Wraparound Edition and blackline masters.
- **Interactive Lesson Planner** Organize your week, month, semester, or year with all the lesson helps you need. The **Interactive Lesson Planner** CD-ROM contains all Chapter 17 resources.

Use Glencoe's **Presentation Plus!** multimedia teacher tool to easily present dynamic lessons that visually excite your students. Using Microsoft PowerPoint® you can customize the presentations to create your own personalized lessons.

TEACHING TRANSPARENCIES

Graphic Organizer Transparency 10 L2

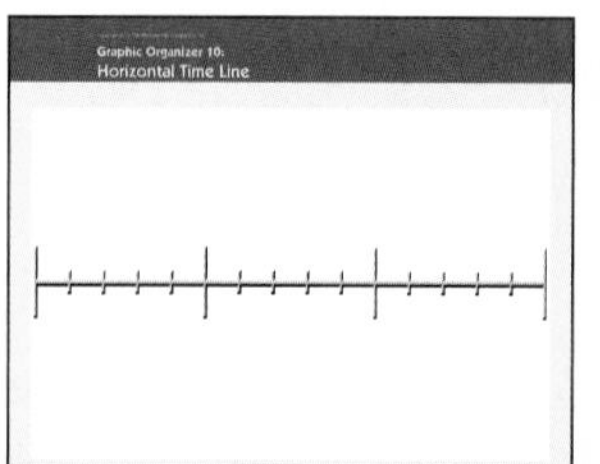

In-text Map Transparency L1

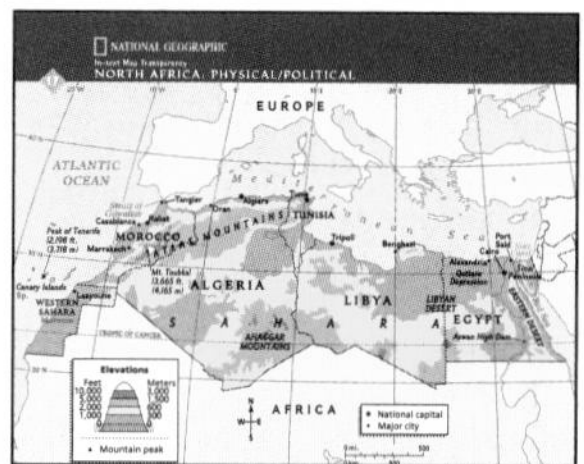

FOLDABLES™ Study Organizer

Dinah Zike's Foldables

Foldables are three-dimensional, interactive graphic organizers that help students practice basic writing skills, review key vocabulary terms, and identify main ideas. Additional chapter activities can be found in the ***Reading and Study Skills Foldables*** booklet.

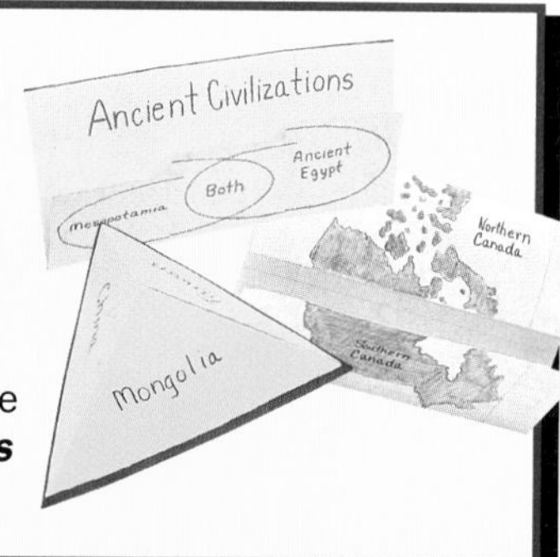

MAP AND GEOGRAPHY SKILLS

Chapter Map Activity L2

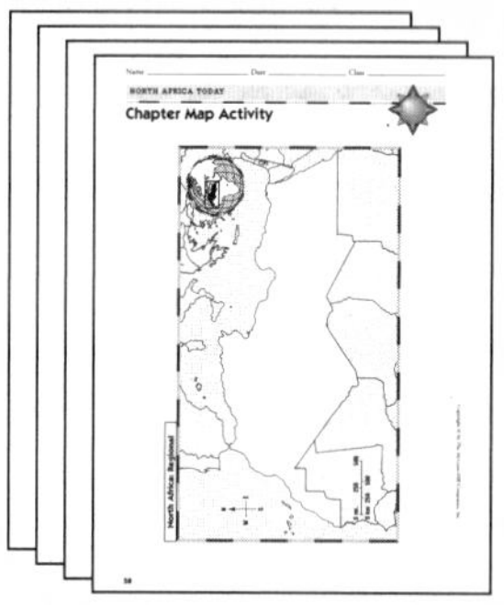

GeoLab Activity L2

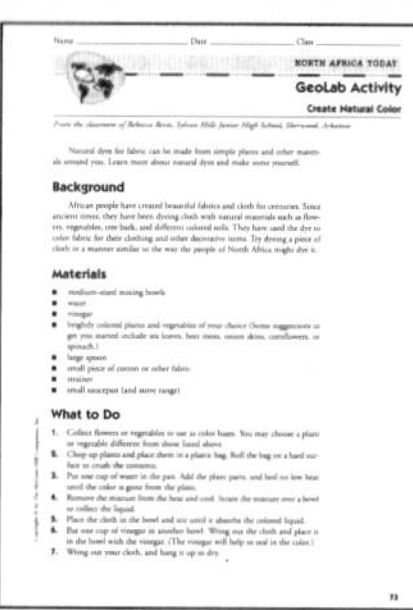

READING SUPPORT

Vocabulary Activity L1

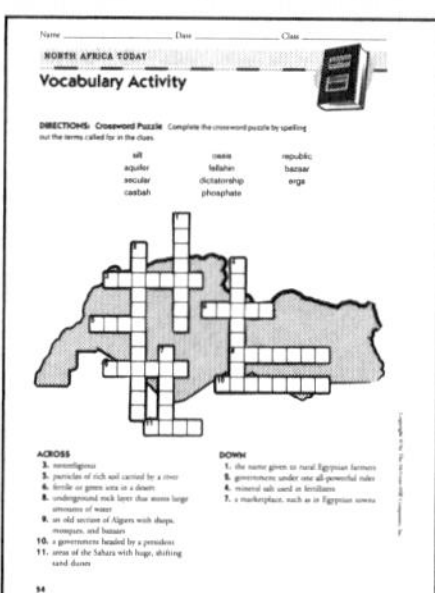

Workbook Activity L1

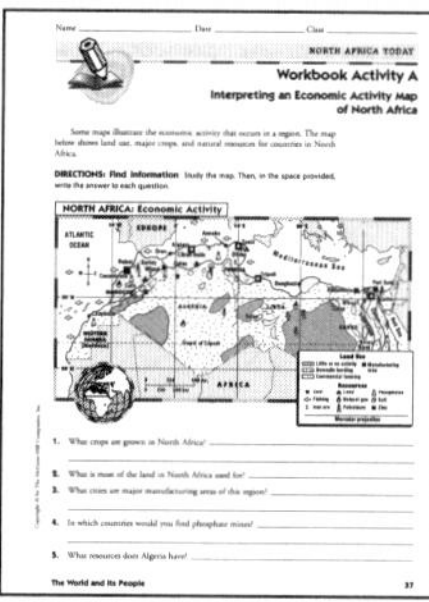

Reading and Writing Skills Activity L1/ELL

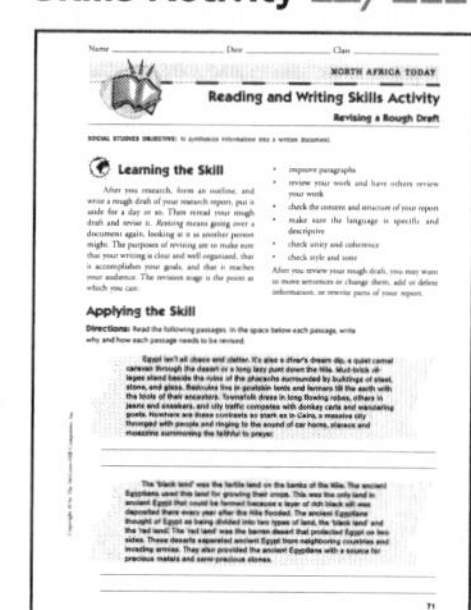

DIFFERENTIATED INSTRUCTION

Use these review and reinforcement materials to help less-proficient readers, English learners, and gifted and talented students.

Reteaching Activity L1

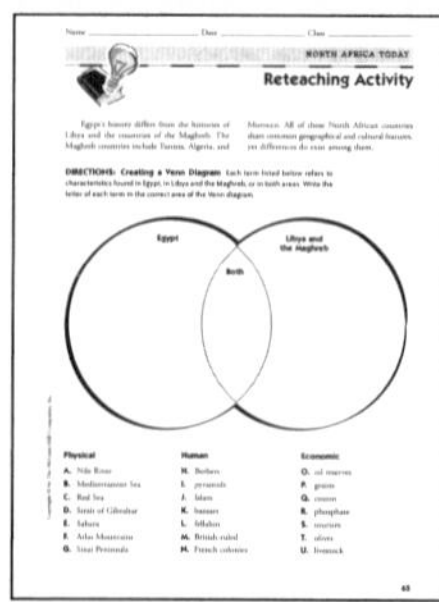

Chapter Skills Review L2

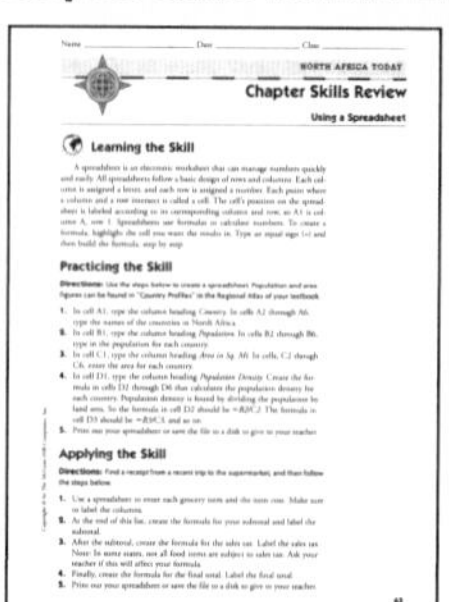

Cooperative Learning Activity L1/ELL

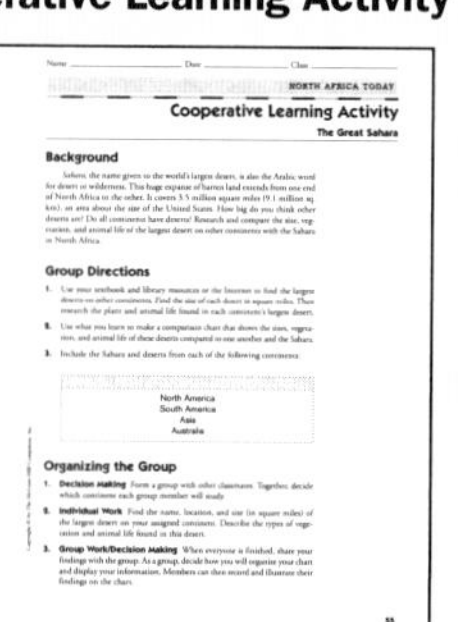

Enrichment Activity L3

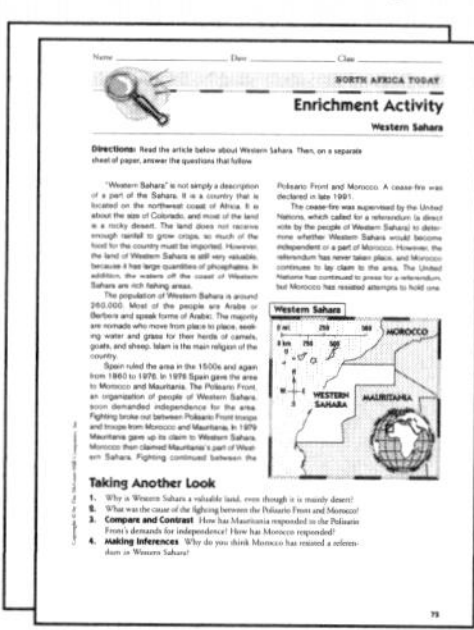

ASSESSMENT

Chapter Test, Form A L2

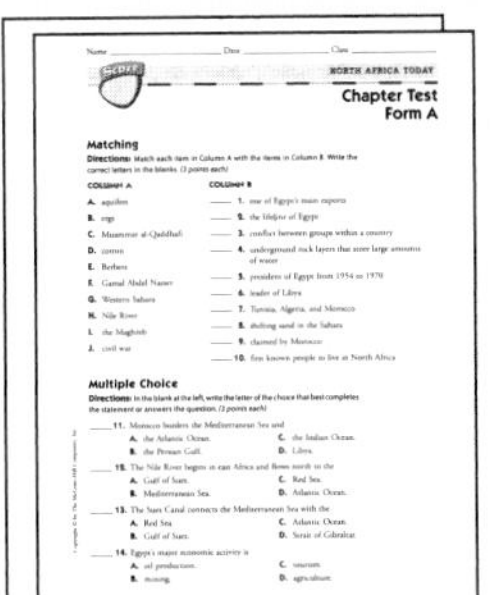

Chapter Test, Form B L2

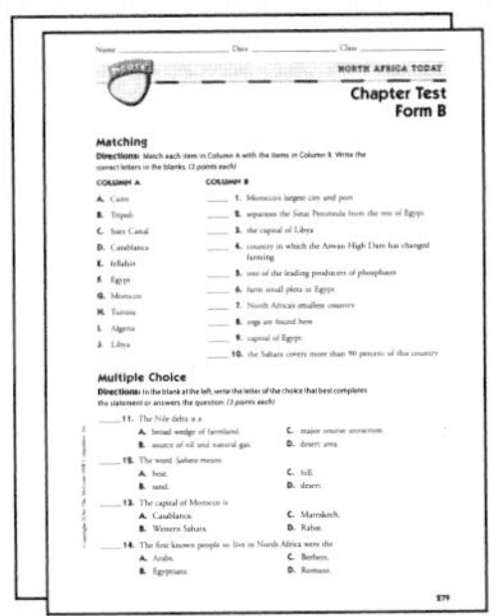

Performance Assessment Activity L1/ELL

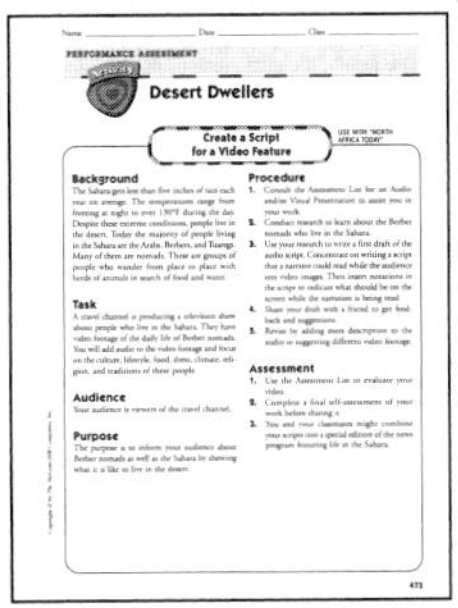

ExamView® Pro Testmaker CD-ROM

STANDARDIZED ASSESSMENT SKILLS

GLENCOE'S ASSESSMENT ADVANTAGE

Critical Thinking Skills Activity L2

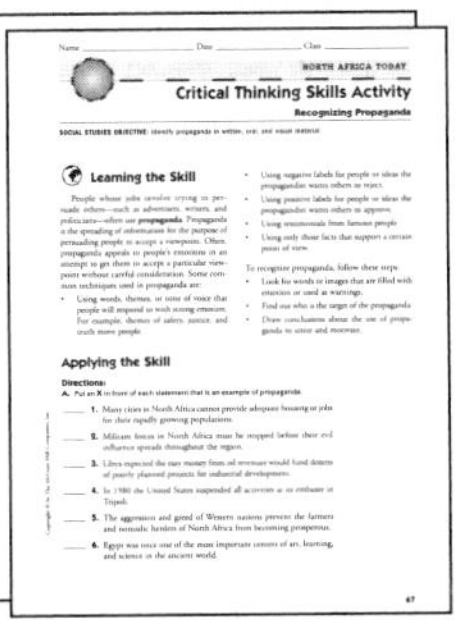

Map and Graph Skills Activity L2

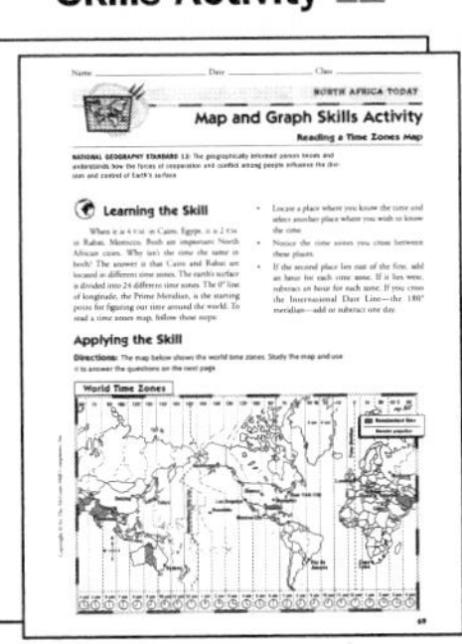

Standardized Test Skills Practice Workbook Activity L2

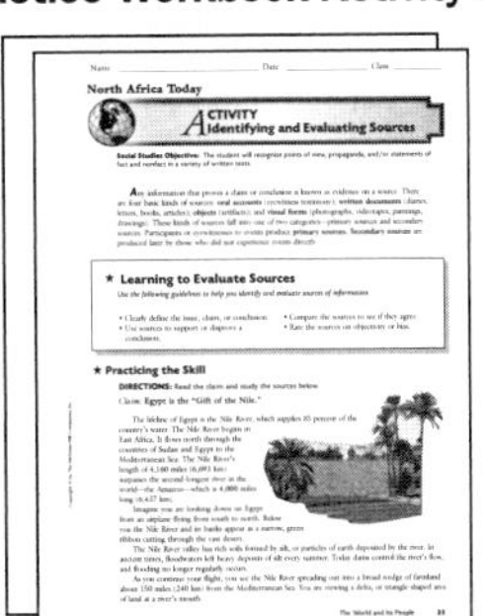

HOME INVOLVEMENT

Take-Home Review Activity L1

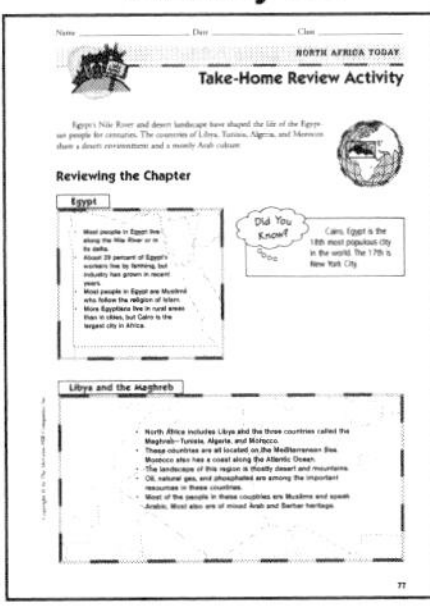

MULTIMEDIA

- National Geographic's The World and Its People
- MindJogger Videoquiz
- Vocabulary PuzzleMaker CD-ROM
- Interactive Tutor Self-Assessment CD-ROM
- ExamView® Pro Testmaker CD-ROM
- TeacherWorks CD-ROM
- StudentWorks CD-ROM
- Skillbuilder Interactive Workbook CD-ROM, Level 1
- Presentation Plus! CD-ROM
- Audio Program

SPANISH RESOURCES

The following Spanish language materials are available in the Spanish Resources binder:

- Spanish Summaries
- Spanish Vocabulary Activities
- Spanish Guided Reading Activities
- Spanish Quizzes and Tests
- Spanish Take-Home Review Activities
- Spanish Reteaching Activities

Meeting National Standards

Geography for Life

The following standards are covered in Chapter 17:

Section 1
- **EE2 Places and Regions: Standard 6**
- **EE3 Physical Systems: Standards 7, 8**
- **EE4 Human Systems: Standard 12**

Section 2
- **EE1 The World in Spatial Terms: Standard 3**
- **EE2 Places and Regions: Standards 4, 5**
- **EE4 Human Systems: Standards 10, 12**
- **EE5 Environment and Society: Standards 15, 16**

State and Local Objectives

____

____

____

____

____

Chapter 17 Planning Guide

SECTION RESOURCES

Daily Objectives	Reproducible Resources	Multimedia Resources
Section 1 **Egypt** **1.** Explain how the environment has shaped life in Egypt. **2.** Discuss how Egyptians earn a living. **3.** Describe how Egypt has changed throughout its history. **4.** Outline what kind of government Egypt has.	Reproducible Lesson Plan Daily Lecture and Discussion Notes Note-taking Guide Guided Reading Activity* Reading Essentials and Study Guide* Section Quiz*	Daily Focus Skills Transparency GeoQuiz Transparency In-text Map Transparency Vocabulary PuzzleMaker CD-ROM Interactive Tutor Self-Assessment CD-ROM ExamView® Pro Testmaker CD-ROM
Section 2 **Libya and the Maghreb** **1.** Describe how land and climate shape Libya and the Maghreb. **2.** Identify what resources Libya and the Maghreb have. **3.** Discuss the forms of government in Libya and the Maghreb.	Reproducible Lesson Plan Daily Lecture and Discussion Notes Note-taking Guide Guided Reading Activity* Reading Essentials and Study Guide* Section Quiz*	Daily Focus Skills Transparency Vocabulary PuzzleMaker CD-ROM Interactive Tutor Self-Assessment CD-ROM ExamView® Pro Testmaker CD-ROM Presentation Plus! CD-ROM MindJogger Videoquiz

00:00 **Out of Time?** Assign the **Reading Essentials and Study Guide*** for this chapter.

*Also available in Spanish

KEY TO ABILITY LEVELS

Teaching strategies have been coded for varying learning styles and abilities.

L1 **BASIC** activities for all students
L2 **AVERAGE** activities for average to above-average students
L3 **CHALLENGING** activities for above-average students
ELL **ENGLISH LANGUAGE LEARNER** activities

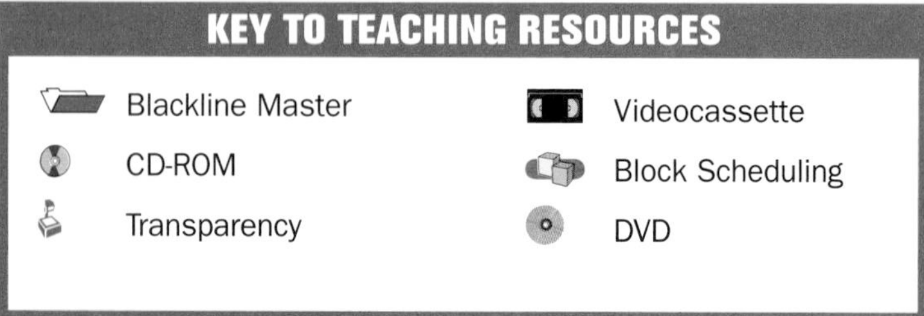

Flying World Flags

Brent Adcox
Cornersville High School
Cornersville, Tennessee

Students often remember more about a country after researching its flag. Have students peruse the Country Profiles for this unit, looking particularly at the country flags within each "stamp." Each student should select one flag to research. First, students should write a paragraph summarizing why their flag looks the way it does. What do the colors and emblems symbolize? Then each student should re-create the flag, either using markers on paper or paint on cloth. If possible, laminate the flags and decorate the classroom with them.

Meeting Special Needs

In addition to the Differentiated Instruction strategies found in each section, the following resources are also suitable for your special needs students:

- ***ExamView® Pro Testmaker CD-ROM*** allows teachers to tailor tests by reducing answer choices.
- The ***Audio Program*** includes the entire narrative of the student edition so that less-proficient readers can listen to the words as they read them.
- The ***Reading Essentials and Study Guide*** provides the same content as the student edition but is written two grade levels below the textbook.
- ***Guided Reading Activities*** give less-proficient readers point-by-point instructions to increase comprehension as they read each textbook section.
- ***Enrichment Activities*** include a stimulating collection of readings and activities for gifted and talented students.

NATIONAL GEOGRAPHIC TEACHER'S CORNER

Index to National Geographic Magazine:

The following articles may be used for research relating to this chapter:

- "Libya: An End to Isolation?" by Andrew Cockburn, November 2000.
- "Valley of the Mummies," by Donovan Webster, October 1999.
- "Abusir Tombs," by Zahi Hawass, November 1998.

National Geographic Society Products:

To order the following products for use with this chapter, call National Geographic Society at 1-800-368-2728:

- *Pharaoh's Voyage for Eternity* (Video)
- *Who Built the Pyramids?* (Video)
- *National Geographic Atlas of the World, Seventh Edition* (Book)

NGS ONLINE

Access National Geographic's Web site for current events, activities, links, interactive features, and archives. www.nationalgeographic.com

Find the latest coverage of geography in the news, atlas updates, cartographic activities with interactive maps, an online map store, and links at www.nationalgeographic.com/maps

SOCIAL STUDIES Online

Use our Web site for additional resources. All essential content is covered in the Student Edition.

You and your students can visit twip.glencoe.com, the Web site companion to *The World and Its People*. This innovative integration of electronic and print media offers your students a wealth of opportunities. The student text directs students to the Web site for the following options:

- Chapter Overviews
- Student Web Activities
- Self-Check Quizzes
- Textbook Updates

Answers are provided for you in the Web Activity Lesson Plan. Additional Web resources and Interactive Tutor puzzles are also available.

Introducing
Chapter 17

Social Studies Online

Introduce students to chapter content and key terms by having them access Chapter Overview 17 at twip.glencoe.com

Chapter Objectives

1. Explain the importance of the Nile River to Egypt's people.
2. Describe the cultural achievements of Egypt.
3. Compare the economies of Libya and the Maghreb.
4. Examine ways of life in North Africa.

GLENCOE TECHNOLOGY

NATIONAL GEOGRAPHIC

The World and Its People Video Program

Chapter 16 North Africa
The following segments enhance the study of this chapter:

- **Mummy of Abusir**
- **The Longest River**
- **Pyramids of Giza**

MindJogger Videoquiz

Use MindJogger Videoquiz to preview the Chapter 17 content.

Both programs available in DVD and VHS

Chapter 17 North Africa Today

The World and Its People NATIONAL GEOGRAPHIC

To learn more about the people and places of North Africa, view ***The World and Its People*** **Chapter 16** video.

Social Studies Online

Chapter Overview Visit ***The World and Its People*** Web site at twip.glencoe.com and click on **Chapter 17—Chapter Overviews** to preview information about North Africa.

482

Reading Strategy — Purpose for Reading

Use the **Read and Say Something** reading strategy to introduce the chapter. Have the students read the Making Connections feature on page 489. Assign partners and have them say something to each other about the reading. Tell them that they can say anything they want that is related to the selection. They should focus on their reactions to ideas, descriptions, images, and confusing information. Ask them to write down the main points of their discussion and then have partners share their discussions with the class. Tell the students that, in this chapter, they will be studying modern Egypt and North Africa. **L1**

Introducing Chapter 17

FOLDABLES Study Organizer

Identifying Main Ideas Make this foldable to help you identify key facts about the people and places of North Africa.

Step 1 Fold the paper from the top right corner down so the edges line up. Cut off the leftover piece.

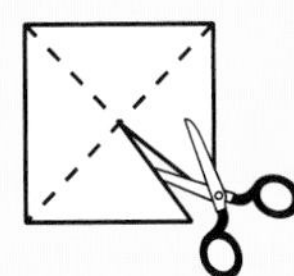
Fold a triangle. Cut off the extra edge.

Step 2 Fold the triangle in half. Unfold.

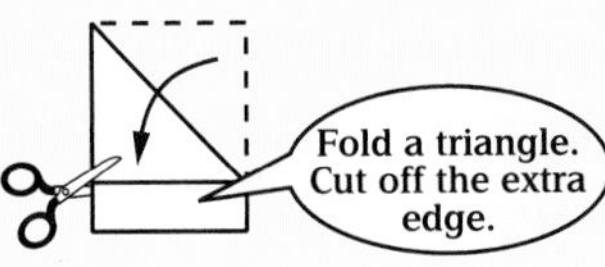
The folds will form an X that creates four equal sections.

Step 3 Cut up one fold line and stop at the middle. This forms two triangular flaps.

Step 4 Draw an X on one tab and label the other three the following: Egypt, Libya, and The Maghreb.

Libya
The Maghreb
Egypt

Step 5 Fold the X flap under the other flap and glue together.

The Maghreb
Egypt
This makes a three-sided pyramid.

Reading and Writing As you read, write main ideas inside the foldable under each appropriate pyramid wall.

Why It Matters

Transitions

North Africa is made up of five independent countries. In past centuries, however, a series of powerful empires ruled in this part of the world. Arabs brought the religion of Islam to North Africa. In the twentieth century, the discovery of oil brought great wealth to parts of the region. Today these countries are struggling to preserve their traditions while also adapting to the modern world.

▲ Berber market at an oasis in Morocco

About the Photo

Morocco faces similar challenges as other developing nations and is trying to achieve solid economic growth. Approximately 50 percent of its labor force population is involved in agriculture. As a result, when droughts occur as they did in 1999 and 2000, economic growth slows. Thus, to be less dependent on agriculture, Morocco is trying to modernize its industrial sector. Morocco is also trying to promote free trade with the European Union and the United States and to attract foreign investment.

FOLDABLES Study Organizer — Dinah Zike's Foldables

Purpose Students will make and use a foldable to summarize the main ideas of the chapter. This reading strategy requires students to read with the purpose of identifying and describing key facts about the countries of North Africa. As the students read, they are required to record what they have learned about the geography, economy, and culture of the countries of North Africa.

Have students complete the ***Reading and Study Skills Foldables*** activity for this chapter.

Why It Matters

One reason North African nations struggle is that they import more goods than they export. Egypt, for example, is one of the North African countries which produces oil. In a recent year, it produced almost 304 million barrels of oil. Petroleum and petroleum products make up more than one fifth of Egypt's exports. Other exports are cotton yarn, cloth, clothing, and metals. All totaled, the country ships more than $5 billion worth of goods to other countries. However, Egypt imports more than $15 billion worth of machinery, food, wood, paper, and other products. Have students research other countries of North Africa and identify the different types of challenges they face.

1 FOCUS

Section Objectives

1. Explain how the environment has shaped life in Egypt.
2. Discuss how Egyptians earn a living.
3. Describe how Egypt has changed throughout its history.
4. Outline what kind of government Egypt has.

BELLRINGER Skillbuilder Activity

Project transparency and have students answer the question.

Daily Focus Skills Transparency

Reading Preview

■ **Activating Prior Knowledge** Have students look at the physical map of North Africa in this section and point out the Suez Canal. **Ask:** **Why would this waterway be important?** *(It allows ships to move more quickly between the Mediterranean Sea and the Red Sea and, thus, to the Indian Ocean.)*

■ **Preteaching Vocabulary** Inform students that the word *delta* derives from the Greek alphabet letter delta, which is shaped like a triangle.

Guide to Reading

Main Idea

Egypt's Nile River and desert landscape have shaped the lives of the Egyptian people for hundreds of years.

Terms to Know

- silt
- oasis
- phosphate
- republic
- fellahin
- bazaar
- service industries
- mosque

Reading Strategy

Draw a chart like this one. Then list five physical features of Egypt and their effects on life in Egypt.

Physical Feature	Effect on Egyptians
→	
→	
→	
→	
→	

Section 1

Egypt

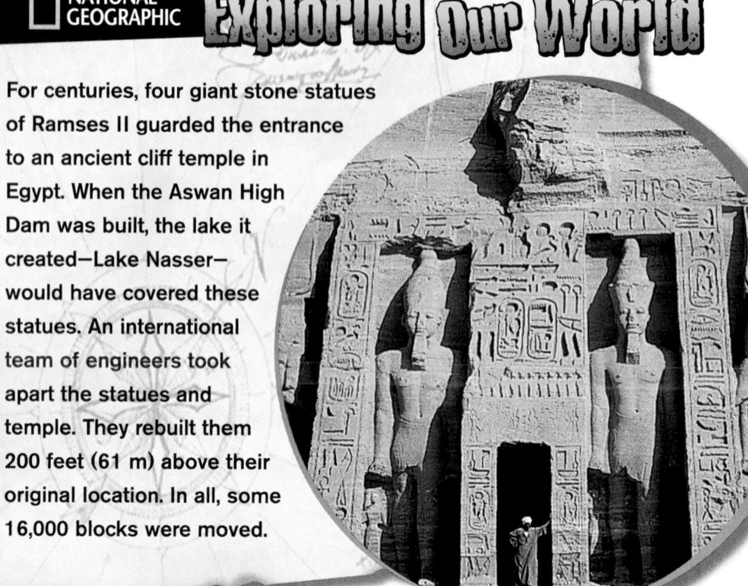

NATIONAL GEOGRAPHIC **Exploring Our World**

For centuries, four giant stone statues of Ramses II guarded the entrance to an ancient cliff temple in Egypt. When the Aswan High Dam was built, the lake it created—Lake Nasser—would have covered these statues. An international team of engineers took apart the statues and temple. They rebuilt them 200 feet (61 m) above their original location. In all, some 16,000 blocks were moved.

Egypt lies in Africa's northeast corner. Vast deserts sweep over most of the country. On the map on page 485, notice the **Nile River** running through Egypt. The Nile River, along with Egypt's location and deserts, has shaped life in Egypt for thousands of years.

Egypt's Land and Climate

Egypt is a large country that is about the same size as Texas and New Mexico together. Yet most of it is desert. Egypt's people crowd into less than 4 percent of the land, which is an area about twice the size of Maryland. The lifeline of Egypt is the Nile River, which supplies 85 percent of the country's water. Along the Nile's banks, you can see mud-brick villages, ancient ruins, and, once in a while, a city or town of modern buildings. The Nile River empties into the **Mediterranean Sea,** forming the Nile's delta. This fertile, low-lying land is built up from the soil carried downstream.

For centuries, the Nile's waters would rise in the spring. The swollen river carried **silt,** or small particles of rich soil. When it reached Egypt, the Nile flooded its banks. As the floodwaters withdrew, the

Section Resources

Reproducible Masters
- Reproducible Lesson Plan
- Daily Lecture and Discussion Notes
- Note-taking Guide
- Guided Reading Activity
- Reading Essentials and Study Guide
- Section Quiz

Transparencies
- Daily Focus Skills Transparency
- GeoQuiz Transparency
- In-text Map Transparency

Multimedia
- Vocabulary PuzzleMaker CD-ROM
- Interactive Tutor Self-Assessment CD-ROM
- Presentation Plus! CD-ROM
- ExamView® Pro Testmaker CD-ROM

silt was left behind, making the land better for farming. Today dams and channels control the river's flow for use in irrigation and in generating electric power.

Sinai Peninsula The triangle-shaped **Sinai** (SY•NY) **Peninsula** lies southeast of the Nile delta. This area is a major crossroads between Africa and Southwest Asia. A human-made waterway called the **Suez Canal** separates the Sinai Peninsula from the rest of Egypt. Egyptians and Europeans built the canal in the mid-1860s. The Suez Canal is still one of the world's most important waterways. Ships use the canal to pass from the Mediterranean Sea to the **Red Sea.** In making this journey, they avoid traveling all the way around Africa.

Desert Areas East of the Nile River spreads the **Eastern Desert,** also known as the Arabian Desert. West of the Nile is the much larger **Libyan** (LIH•bee•uhn) **Desert,** which covers about two-thirds of the country. Dotting both deserts are oases. An oasis is a fertile or green area in a desert. Plants grow here, giving these spots lush green growth in the midst of the hot sands.

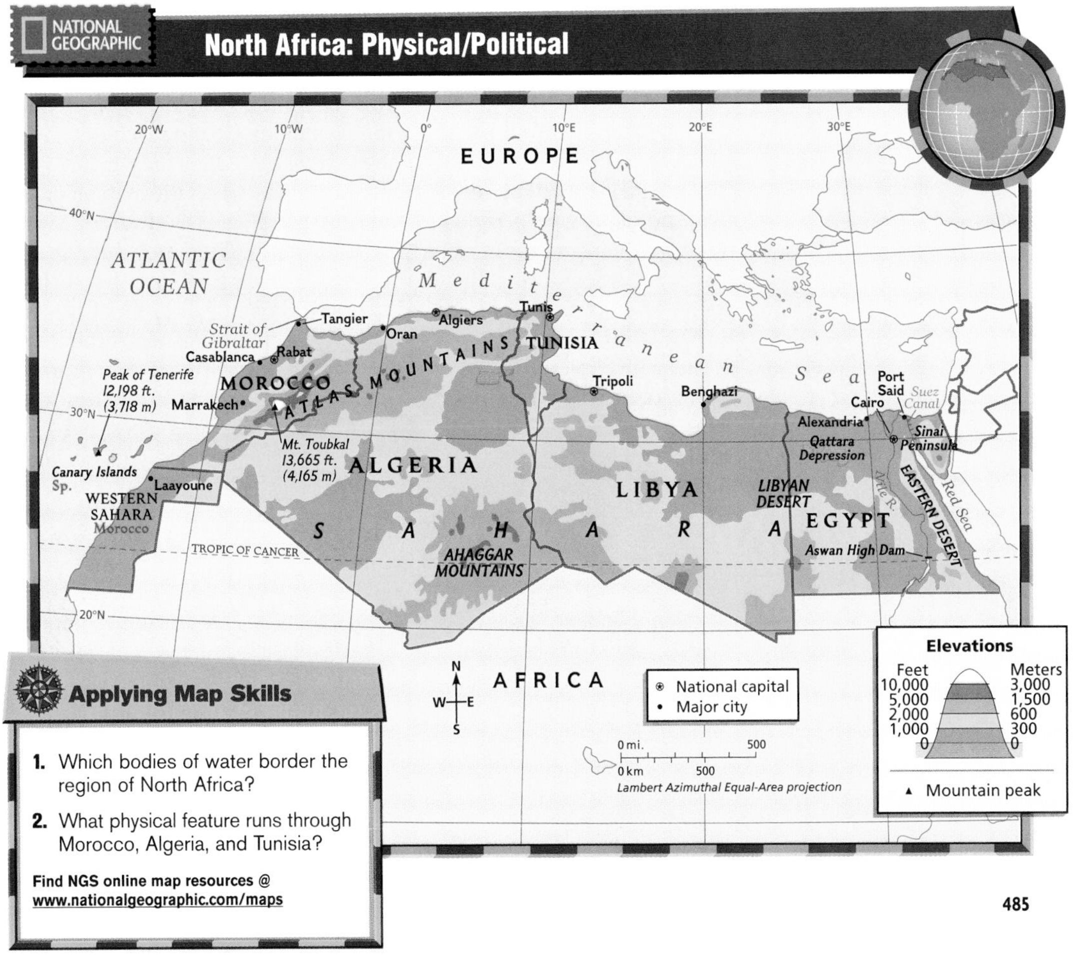

Applying Map Skills

1. Which bodies of water border the region of North Africa?
2. What physical feature runs through Morocco, Algeria, and Tunisia?

Find NGS online map resources @ www.nationalgeographic.com/maps

Reading Strategy: Reading the Text

Drawing Conclusions Have students make a chart comparing the positive and negative effects of the Aswan High Dam on life in Egypt. Then ask them to draw conclusions on whether the dam has done more harm or more good. Call on volunteers to state their conclusions and the reasons for them. After a few students have discussed their thoughts, have the class consider the question again to see if any students have changed their minds. Then have them write a paragraph explaining their positions. **L1**

*Use the **Reading Skills Handbook** for more reading strategies.*

2 TEACH

Reading Strategy

Writing a Paragraph Ask students to suggest words that might be used to describe a desert. Write their responses on the board. Then have students use the listed words to write a paragraph describing Egypt's desert lands. Call on volunteers to read their descriptions to the class. **L1**

Daily Lecture and Discussion Notes

NORTH AFRICA TODAY

Daily Lecture and Discussion Notes

Egypt

Did You Know? Egypt is much more than pyramids and monuments. People travel to the Red Sea for scuba diving adventures, they take romantic cruises down the Nile on festive riverboats, or they enjoy an evening at the grand opera. Egypt is a land bustling with life, sound, visual beauty, and excitement.

I. Egypt's Land and Climate

A. The Nile River is the world's longest river and supplies 85 percent of Egypt's water. The Nile flows north to the Mediterranean Sea where you find its delta—land formed from the soil deposited by a river at its mouth. For centuries, the Nile's waters would flood in the spring and drop **silt,** or small ... made land along the river good for farming.

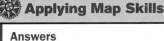

Applying Map Skills

Answers

1. Atlantic Ocean, Mediterranean Sea, Red Sea, and Strait of Gibraltar
2. Atlas Mountains

In-text Map Transparency Activity Point to the color in the key for elevations between 0 (sea level) and 1,000 feet (300 meters) and describe where this elevation is common in North Africa. Ask students to name the region in Egypt that is below sea level. *(Qattara Depression)*

Reading Check Answer

because ships using it can pass between the Mediterranean Sea and Red Sea without having to travel all the way around Africa

L1/ELL

Guided Reading Activity

Name ____________ Date ____________ Class ____________

NORTH AFRICA TODAY

Guided Reading Activity 1

Egypt

DIRECTIONS: Reading for Accuracy Reading the section and completing the activity below will help you learn more about the country of Egypt. Use your textbook to decide if a statement is true or false. Write **T** or **F**, and if a statement is false, rewrite it correctly.

____ 1. In Egypt today, the Nile floods in the spring, making fields fertile.

____ 2. The Sinai Peninsula is a major crossroads between Africa and Southwest Asia.

____ 3. The Suez Canal is helpful because it lets ships pass to the Red Sea without having to go around the continent of Africa.

____ 4. The deserts in Egypt are only to the east of the Nile.

____ 5. The Sahara is about the size of the United States.

____ 6. Egypt receives plenty of rainfall in the spring.

____ 7. Raw cotton, cotton yarn, and clothing are Egypt's only exports.

____ 8. Dams on the Nile River bring only harm to the farmers and their crops.

____ 9. Egypt was first ruled by a line of kings, or pharaohs, but now Egypt is a republic.

____ 10. More than half of the Egyptian people live in rural areas.

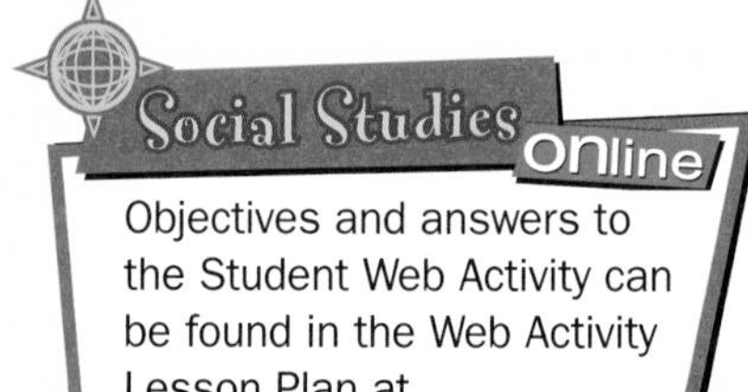

Objectives and answers to the Student Web Activity can be found in the Web Activity Lesson Plan at **twip.glencoe.com**

cotton

The Eastern and Libyan Deserts are part of the **Sahara,** which is the largest desert in the world. *Sahara* comes from the Arabic word meaning "desert." The Sahara is about the size of the United States. It stretches from Egypt westward across North Africa to the Atlantic Ocean.

A Desert Climate Wherever you go in Egypt, you find a dry desert climate with hot summers and mild winters. Egypt as a whole receives little rainfall. **Cairo,** the capital, averages only about 0.4 inch (1 cm) a year. In fact, some areas receive no rain for years at a time.

Springtime in Egypt brings hot winds instead of cooling rains. These winds move west across Egypt, reaching up to 87 miles (140 km) per hour. The powerful winds can harm crops and damage houses.

Reading Check Why is the Suez Canal one of the world's most important waterways?

Egypt's Economy

Egypt has a developing economy that has grown considerably in recent years. Although only about 2 percent of Egypt's land is used for farming, about 29 percent of Egypt's people work in agriculture. The best farmland lies in the fertile Nile River valley. Egypt's major crops include sugarcane, grains, vegetables, fruits, and cotton. Raw cotton, cotton yarn, and clothing are among the country's main exports.

Some farmers still work the land using the simple practices and tools of their ancestors. Many use modern methods and machinery. All, however, rely on dams to control the water needed for their fields. The largest dam is called the **Aswan High Dam.** Find it on the map on page 485. The dams give people control over the Nile's floodwaters. They can store the water for months behind the dams. Then they can release it several times during the year, rather than having just the spring floods. This control allows farmers to harvest two or three crops a year.

The dams bring challenges as well as benefits. Dams block the flow of silt, which means farmland is becoming less fertile. Farmers now rely more heavily on chemical fertilizers to grow crops. In addition, the dams prevent less freshwater from reaching the delta. So salt water from the Mediterranean Sea now flows deeper into the delta, making the land there less fertile.

Industry The Aswan High Dam provides hydroelectric power, which Egypt uses to run its growing industries. The largest industrial centers are the capital city of Cairo and the seaport of **Alexandria.** Egyptian factories make food products, textiles, and consumer goods. Tourism is another industry that is important to Egypt's economy. Visitors come to see the pyramids and majestic temples of ancient Egypt.

Egypt's main energy resource is oil, found in and around the Red Sea. Petroleum products make up almost half the value of Egypt's exports. Egypt is developing a gas export market as well. The country also has phosphates. A **phosphate** is a mineral salt used in fertilizer.

Social Studies online

Web Activity Visit ***The World and Its People*** Web site at twip.glencoe.com and click on **Chapter 17—Student Web Activities** to learn more about Egypt's history.

Reading Check On what crop are many of Egypt's exports based?

Differentiated Instruction

Meeting Special Needs: Visual/Spatial Organize students into three groups and provide each group with an outline map of Egypt. Have one group create a population density map, another a map showing major agricultural products and where they are grown, and the third a map showing major industrial centers. Display the completed maps. Then ask students to discuss how each map illustrates the importance of the Nile River to Egypt. **ELL**

Refer to *Inclusion for the Middle School Social Studies Classroom Strategies and Activities* in the TCR.

Food

Most Egyptian meals include fava beans that have been boiled for hours to make them soft. Egypt's national dish, *ful*, includes fava beans mixed with garlic, lemon juice, olive oil, onions, and parsley. Cubes of veal or lamb meat cooked on skewers are known as kabobs. Egyptians also eat tahini—a smooth paste made of sesame seeds that is eaten as a dip or sandwich spread. *Babaganoush* is another dipping paste, but it is made with eggplant and sesame. Instead of spoons, Egyptians usually use *aysh*, or bread, to scoop up food.

Looking Closer **How does Egyptian bread differ from the bread you eat?**

The Egyptians

In Chapter 16, you learned about the ancient Egyptians. Their advanced civilization included powerful pharaohs, the building of temples and pyramids, and advances in science and technology. From 300 B.C. to A.D. 300, however, Egypt fell under the influence of Greece and Rome. You may have heard of Cleopatra, an Egyptian queen who ruled during the time of the rise of the Roman Empire.

In A.D. 641, Arabs from Southwest Asia took control of Egypt. They practiced Islam, a religion based on the belief in one God known as Allah. Most of Egypt's people began to speak the Arabic language and became Muslims, as the followers of Islam are called. Today about 94 percent of Egypt's people are Muslims.

Egypt's Modern History By the end of the 1800s, all of Egypt, including the Suez Canal, had become part of the British Empire. Unhappy with British rule, the people of Egypt protested many times. Finally, in 1952 a group of army officers overthrew the British-supported king, and Egypt became independent. One of the army leaders, Gamal Abdel Nasser (guh•MAHL AHB•duhl NAH•suhr), was Egypt's president from 1954 to 1970. Nasser made Egypt one of the most powerful countries in the Muslim world.

Egypt is a **republic**, or a government headed by a president. A legislature makes the laws, but the president has broad powers in running the country. In the 1990s, some Islamic political and religious groups opposed the government. These groups used violence in an effort to reach their political goals. By the early 2000s, however, the government had stopped these attacks.

Rural and Urban Life Look at the population density map in the **Geography Handbook** on page 10. Most of Egypt's 72.1 million

Cooperative Learning Activity

Egyptian Feast Organize the class into several groups. Assign each group one of the following foods: *ful*, kabobs, tahini, *babaganoush, aysh, hummus*, and Turkish coffee. Ask the groups to find recipes for their food and to present the recipes in poster-size, step-by-step, illustrated diagrams. Then have them make or buy samples of the food to bring to class and share with one another. Tell the groups to work together to set up tables and put together place settings for the Egyptian feast. **L1/ELL**

Answer Answers will vary. Some students may note that Egyptian bread is round and flat, but it puffs up to make a pocket for meat and vegetables.

Egyptian Food Many women in rural Egypt bake bread in clay ovens like their ancestors did. Tell students that another famous Egyptian dish is *hummus,* which is tahini mixed with smashed chickpeas, lemon juice, and garlic.

Measure student knowledge of physical features.

GeoQuiz Transparency

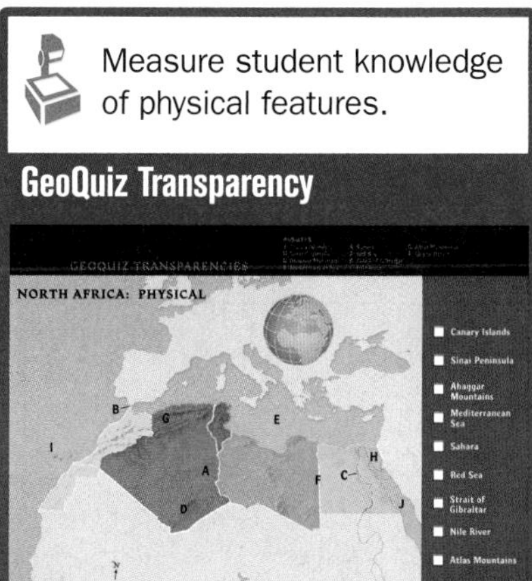

Assign Section 1 Assessment as homework or an in-class activity.

Have students use the Interactive Tutor Self-Assessment CD-ROM to review Section 1.

Chapter 17

Section 1, pages 484–488

L2

Section Quiz

Name ______________ Date ______________ Class ______________

Score — NORTH AFRICA TODAY

Section 1 Quiz

Egypt

DIRECTIONS: Matching Match each item in Column A with the items in Column B. Write the correct letters in the blanks. *(10 points each)*

COLUMN A	COLUMN B
A. bazaar	____ 1. land formed from soil deposited by a river at its mouth
B. mosque	____ 2. small particles of rich soil
C. delta	____ 3. place of worship for followers of Islam
D. fellahin	____ 4. marketplace
E. silt	____ 5. Egyptian peasant farmers

Reading Check Answer

1952

L1/ELL

Reading Essentials and Study Guide

Name ______________ Date ______________ Class ______________

NORTH AFRICA TODAY

Reading Essentials and Study Guide 1

Egypt

Key Terms

silt small particles of rich soil carried by running water
oasis fertile or green area in a desert
phosphate mineral salt used in fertilizers
republic government headed by a president
fellahin Egyptian peasant farmers
bazaar a marketplace
service industries businesses that provide services to people rather than producing goods

4 Close

Have students create a bulletin board display about Egypt with images and captions that highlight important features of the country and its people.

people live within 20 miles (32 km) of the Nile River. More than half of Egypt's people live in rural areas along this narrow valley. Most are peasant farmers called **fellahin** (FEHL•uh•HEEN). They live in villages and farm small plots of land that they rent from landowners. Many fellahin raise only enough food to feed their families. Any food left over is sold in towns at a **bazaar,** or marketplace.

Life is more modern in Egypt's cities. Many city dwellers live in high-rise apartments and have jobs in manufacturing, construction, or service industries. **Service industries** provide services to people rather than producing goods. In bustling ports like Alexandria and Port Said (sah•EED), people engage in trade.

Cairo is a huge and rapidly growing city. Almost 8 million people are crowded into its central area, with another 7 million living in its suburbs. It is the largest city in Africa. For centuries, Cairo has been a leading center of the Muslim world. Throughout the city you see schools, universities, and **mosques,** or places of worship for followers of Islam.

Cairo's population is increasing at a rapid rate. Why? First, Egypt is a country with a high birthrate. Second, many fellahin have moved to Cairo to find work. The crowded city cannot provide enough houses, schools, and hospitals for all of its people. Poverty, snarled traffic, and pollution have resulted.

Reading Check **When did Egypt become fully independent?**

Section 1 Assessment

Defining Terms

1. **Define** silt, oasis, phosphate, republic, fellahin, bazaar, service industries, mosque.

Recalling Facts

2. **Human/Environment Interaction** Why is the Nile River important to Egypt?
3. **History** Who was Gamal Abdel Nasser, and what did he do for Egypt?
4. **Culture** What are the major language and religion of Egypt?

Critical Thinking

5. **Understanding Cause and Effect** How has the Aswan High Dam helped and hurt Egypt?
6. **Problem Solving** What are some ways that the Egyptian government could help solve overcrowding in Cairo?

Graphic Organizer

7. **Organizing Information** In a chart like the one below, fill in three facts about Egypt for each category.

Agriculture	Industry
1.	1.
2.	2.
3.	3.

Applying Social Studies Skills

8. **Analyzing Maps** Study the physical/political map on page 485. In what direction would you go to get from Cairo to Alexandria?

Section 1 Assessment

1. The terms are defined in the Glossary.
2. It supplies 85 percent of Egypt's water.
3. Egypt's president from 1954 to 1970; made Egypt one of the most powerful countries in the Muslim world
4. Arabic; Islam
5. It provides hydroelectricity for manufacturing and enables farmers to raise two or three crops a year. However, the land is less fertile and farmers must use chemical fertilizers.
6. Students should use information in the section to formulate their solutions.
7. *Agriculture*—sugarcane, grains, vegetables, fruits, cotton; *Industry*—food products, textiles, consumer goods
8. northwest

Making Connections

ART | SCIENCE | CULTURE | TECHNOLOGY

An Egyptian Folktale

In many rural areas of modern Egypt, storytellers entertain the fellahin. Here is one Egyptian folktale in which a father tries to teach his son a valuable lesson.

What Will People Say?

Goha had a naughty son who would never do as he was told. When asked to do something, the boy had one ready answer. "But what will people say?" he would shake his head and say. Goha decided one day that it was time to teach his son a useful lesson, and prove to the boy that pleasing everyone was an impossible thing. This is what Goha did:

He mounted his donkey and started to the market, after ordering his son to follow him along behind on foot. In a little while they came across a group of women doing their washing at the bank of the river.

The women bawled over to Goha, "Do you have a rock instead of a heart, you merciless man? How do you have the shamelessness to ride while that poor boy of yours runs along behind?"

So, Goha got off the donkey and ordered the boy to mount, while he himself followed on foot. After some time they came across a group of old men sunning themselves at the corner of a field. One of the old men . . . yelled out in a loud and shaky voice, "I do declare! If that ain't the way to bring up an ingrate. Yes sir-ree, if you want no respect from your boy, that's the way to get it." . . .

Goha said to his son. "Have you heard? Let us both ride now."

So, father and son mounted the donkey and they continued on their way. Soon they met with some animal lovers, who called out in a scolding voice, . . . "How dare you ride that skinny donkey when the two of you together have flesh and bones weighing more than that poor beast?"

Goha said to his son, "I think now we had better let the donkey lead the way while we both follow on foot. . . ."

It was not long, however, before they became the prey to a crowd of jokers and jesters, who hooted and said, ". . . Either let this poor weary donkey ride on one of you, or both of you carry him. That way he shall be spared the misery of walking." . . .

From a nearby tree [Goha] cut a strong stout branch about three yards long. Next, taking some strong rope he had with him, he tied the donkey's front hoofs together, and then his hind hoofs together. He then slipped the branch between the donkey's legs so that the two ends of the branch stuck out at either end.

That done, Goha called his son, and said, "Now you put one end of this branch on your shoulder, and I will bear the other end." . . .

When finally they arrived at the market, a great crowd gathered . . . following the strange sight . . . until at last a policeman managed to break through the group. The policeman addressed Goha, saying, "You will accompany me to the police station, and from there, my fine cracked friends, you may expect to go straight to the madhouse."

Goha turned to this son, and said, "This, my son, is the result of troubling yourself over what other people will say."

An Egyptian boy leads his donkey. ▼

Making the Connection

1. What happens to Goha and his son at the end?
2. Who do you think should have ridden the donkey? Explain.
3. **Summarizing Information** Write the moral, or lesson, of this folktale in your own words.

Making the Connection

1. They are sent to the police station and, from there, to a madhouse (place for insane people) because of their bizarre behavior.
2. Answers will vary. Students should explain the reasons for their choices.
3. Students' responses should be similar to "Pleasing everyone is impossible," or "You should not base your actions on what other people will think or say."

TEACH

Ask students if they know any American folktales. Students may mention stories about Paul Bunyan, Daniel Boone, Betsy Ross, Davy Crockett, or Pecos Bill. There are also folktales about George Washington chopping down the cherry tree. **Ask:** **What do folktales seem to have in common?** *(Students may recognize that folktales often extol the virtues of heroes or teach a lesson.)* In many folktales, there are usually animals demonstrating human behaviors—whether foolish or noble. **L2**

More About Egyptian Writers

Naguib Mahfouz is one of Egypt's most famous novelists. Although he writes about local subjects, the universal significance of his work is widely recognized. In 1988 he became the first Arabic writer to win the Nobel Prize for Literature. His most famous work is *The Cairo Trilogy*. In these three novels, Mahfouz explores the modern transformation of Egypt by focusing on several generations of a Cairo family.

Interdisciplinary Connections

Literature Ask students to write their own folktales having the same moral as the Egyptian folktale: It is impossible to please everyone.

Chapter 17

Section 2, pages 490–493

1 Focus

Section Objectives

1. Describe how land and climate shape life in Libya and the Maghreb.
2. Identify what resources Libya and the Maghreb have.
3. Discuss the forms of government in Libya and the Maghreb.

BELLRINGER Skillbuilder Activity

Project transparency and have students answer the question.

Daily Focus Skills Transparency

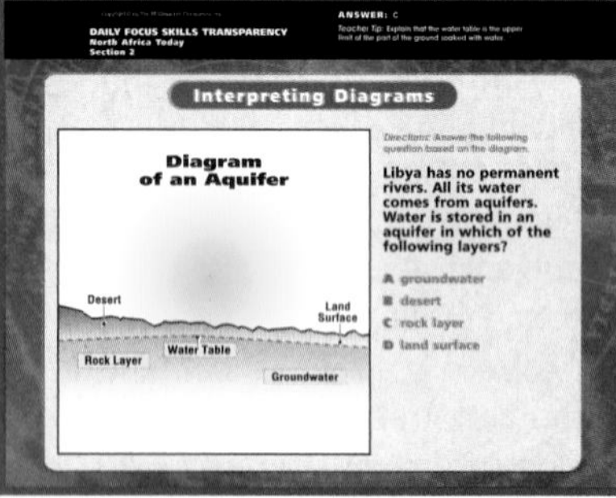

Reading Preview

- **Activating Prior Knowledge**

Ask: Why might the people in North Africa's countries live mainly on the coast? *(because the Sahara covers much of the land)*

- **Preteaching Vocabulary**

Point out to students that several Terms to Know have Latin roots: *aqua* ("water"); *dictare* ("to say"); *civilis* ("citizen"); *saecularis* ("age"); *constituere* ("to set up"). Ask students to identify the correct term from each root. *(aquifer, dictatorship, civil war, secular, constitutional monarchy)*

Guide to Reading

Main Idea

The countries of Libya, Tunisia, Algeria, and Morocco share a desert environment and a mostly Arab culture.

Terms to Know

- aquifer
- dictatorship
- erg
- civil war
- secular
- casbah
- constitutional monarchy

Reading Strategy

Draw a diagram like this one. In the four outer ovals, list facts about each country. In the center oval, write two facts that all four countries have in common.

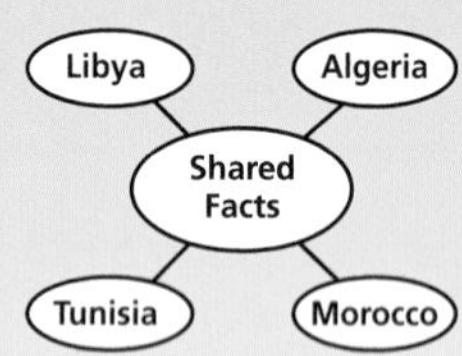

Section 2

Libya and the Maghreb

NATIONAL GEOGRAPHIC Exploring Our World

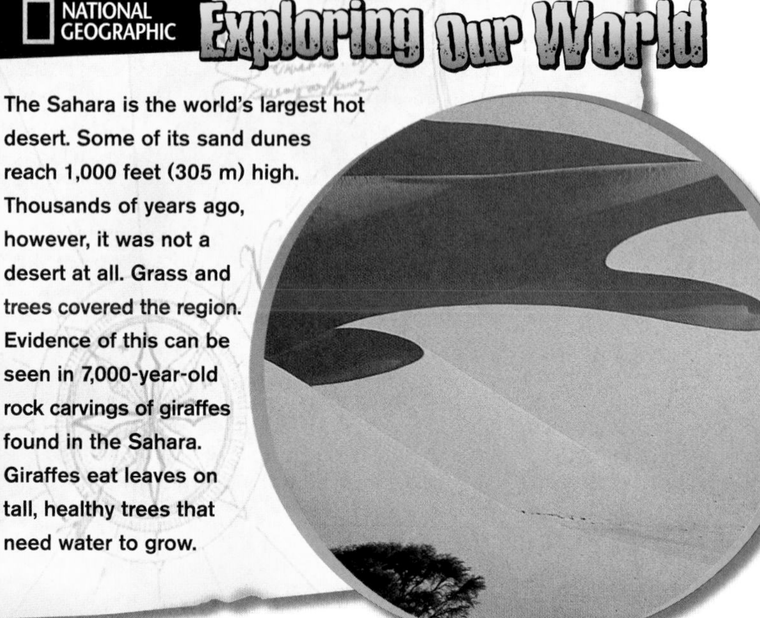

The Sahara is the world's largest hot desert. Some of its sand dunes reach 1,000 feet (305 m) high. Thousands of years ago, however, it was not a desert at all. Grass and trees covered the region. Evidence of this can be seen in 7,000-year-old rock carvings of giraffes found in the Sahara. Giraffes eat leaves on tall, healthy trees that need water to grow.

Libya, Tunisia, Algeria, and Morocco make up the rest of North Africa. Like Egypt, these countries have economies based on oil and other resources in the Sahara. Unlike Egypt, however, none of these nations enjoys the benefits of a life-giving river such as the Nile.

Libya

Libya is slightly larger than Alaska. Except for coastal lowlands, Libya is a desert area with only a few oases. In fact, the Sahara covers more than 90 percent of Libya. During the spring and fall, dust-heavy winds blow from the desert. When these fierce winds strike, temperatures in coastal areas can reach 110°F (43°C).

Libya has no permanent rivers, but aquifers lie beneath the vast desert. **Aquifers** are underground rock layers that store large amounts of water. In the 1990s, the government built pipelines to carry underground water from the desert to coastal areas.

Section Resources

Reproducible Masters
- Reproducible Lesson Plan
- Daily Lecture and Discussion Notes
- Note-taking Guide
- Guided Reading Activity
- Reading Essentials and Study Guide
- Section Quiz

Transparencies
- Daily Focus Skills Transparency

Multimedia
- Vocabulary PuzzleMaker CD-ROM
- Interactive Tutor Self-Assessment CD-ROM
- Presentation Plus! CD-ROM
- ExamView® Pro Testmaker CD-ROM
- MindJogger Videoquiz

The discovery of oil in Libya in 1959 brought the country great wealth. Libya's government uses oil money to import food, build schools and hospitals, and maintain a strong military.

Libya's People and History Almost all of Libya's 5.5 million people have mixed Arab and Berber heritage. The Berbers were the first people known to live in North Africa. During the A.D. 600s, Arabs brought Islam and the Arabic language to North Africa. Since then, Libya has been a Muslim country, and most of its people speak Arabic.

About 86 percent of Libyans live along the Mediterranean coast. Most live in two modern cities—**Tripoli,** the capital, and Benghazi (behn•GAH•zee). Libya became independent in 1951 under a king. In 1969 a military officer named Muammar al-Qaddhafi (kuh•DAH•fee) gained power and overthrew the king. Qaddhafi set up a **dictatorship,** or a government under the control of one all-powerful leader.

Reading Check How has Libya been governed since 1969?

Tunisia

Tunisia, Algeria, and **Morocco** form a region known as the **Maghreb.** *Maghreb* means "the land farthest west" in Arabic. These three countries were given this name because they are the westernmost part of the Arabic-speaking Muslim world.

About the size of the state of Georgia, Tunisia is North Africa's smallest country. Find it on the map on page 485. Northern and central Tunisia have Mediterranean or steppe climates, which provide some rainfall. Along the fertile eastern coast, farmers grow wheat, olives, citrus fruits, and vegetables.

Tunisian factories produce food products, textiles, and oil products. In addition, tourism is a growing industry. Many visitors enjoy Tunisia's sunny shores and explore its Roman ruins and outdoor markets.

Past and Present Tunisia's coastal location has drawn people, ideas, and trade throughout the centuries. In ancient times, Phoenician sailors founded the city of Carthage in northern Tunisia. This city was the center of a powerful trading empire and challenged Rome for control of the Mediterranean. Rome defeated and destroyed Carthage.

During the following centuries, Tunisia was part of several Muslim empires. It was a colony of France until becoming an independent republic in 1956. You can still see French influence in the cities.

Almost all of Tunisia's 9.9 million people are of mixed Arab and Berber ancestry. They speak Arabic and practice Islam. **Tunis,** with more than 1,000,000 people, is the capital and largest urban area.

Reading Check Why can farming take place in Tunisia?

Algeria

About one and a half times the size of Alaska, Algeria is the largest country in North Africa. Along the Mediterranean coast, you find hills, plains, and Algeria's best farmland. Inland, the land slopes up to the

Bazaar!

Taha Hammam makes pottery to sell at the bazaar. "Going to the bazaar is a lot like going to an American mall," he says. "It's a big party where everyone talks and eats and buys and sells things." Taha lives in Algiers. Although Taha wears jeans and sneakers, his parents dress in traditional clothes. His mother wears a black outer dress over a bright housedress and covers her hair with a long veil that reaches the ground. Taha's father dresses in a long robe. In school, Taha studies Arabic, religion, social studies, arithmetic, science, and art.

2 TEACH

Reading Strategy

Organizing Information
Have students create a five-column chart with the names of the four countries in this section across columns 2 through 5. In the first column, have them write the word "Category." Under that heading, have them list these row labels: "Landforms," "Climate," "Economy," "Government," and "People." Then have them fill in the correct information about each country as they read the section. L1

Daily Lecture and Discussion Notes

NORTH AFRICA TODAY

Daily Lecture and Discussion Notes
Libya and the Maghreb

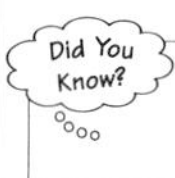

A common misconception about the Sahara, the world's largest desert, is that a majority of its $3\frac{1}{2}$ million square miles is covered by sand. Most of this land, which is roughly equal to the size of the United States, is covered by rocky plateaus and gravelly plains, not sand.

I. Libya

A. The Sahara covers 90 percent of Libya. Libya has no permanent rivers, but **aquifers**—underground rock layers that store large amounts of water—lie beneath the vast desert. Pipelines carry water from the desert to the coast.

B. The discovery of oil in 1959 brought Libya great wealth, which the government ... and hospitals, and maintain a strong army.

Reading Check Answer
by a dictator

Reading Check Answer
because this country is largely covered by Mediterranean or steppe climates

Reading Strategy **Reading the Text**

Paraphrasing Remind students that paraphrasing is retelling something in one's own words. Model how to paraphrase. Read "Libya" from Section 2 aloud. Then close your book and explain the information in your own words. Next, have students read the other subsections and call on students to paraphrase for the rest of the class what has been read. Tell students that if they are having trouble paraphrasing, then it is probably a sign that they should reread the material. L1

*Use the **Reading Skills Handbook** for more reading strategies.*

✓ Reading Check Answer

civil war between the secular government and Muslims who want laws based on Muslim beliefs

More About the Photo

Berbers Once very isolated, Berbers have mingled with other groups—mostly Arabs. Currently, *Berber* is used to identify people who speak the different dialects of the Berber language.

Caption Answer Because they live in the mountains, many follow a herding way of life.

L1/ELL

Guided Reading Activity

Name ______ Date ______ Class ______

NORTH AFRICA TODAY

Guided Reading Activity 2

Libya and the Maghreb

DIRECTIONS: Outlining Reading and completing the outline below will help you learn more about Libya and the Maghreb. Use your textbook to fill in the blanks.

I. Libya
  A. The ______ covers more than 90 percent of Libya.
    1. Water from ______ in the desert is piped to coastal areas.
    2. The discovery of ______ brought the country great wealth.
  B. The people are of mixed Arab and ______ heritage.
    1. Most live along the ______ ______.
    2. Libya's capital is ______, and the government is a ______.
II. Tunisia is part of a region known as the ______.

______ country.

Assess

Assign Section 2 Assessment as homework or an in-class activity.

Have students use the Interactive Tutor Self-Assessment CD-ROM to review Section 2.

NATIONAL GEOGRAPHIC **On Location**

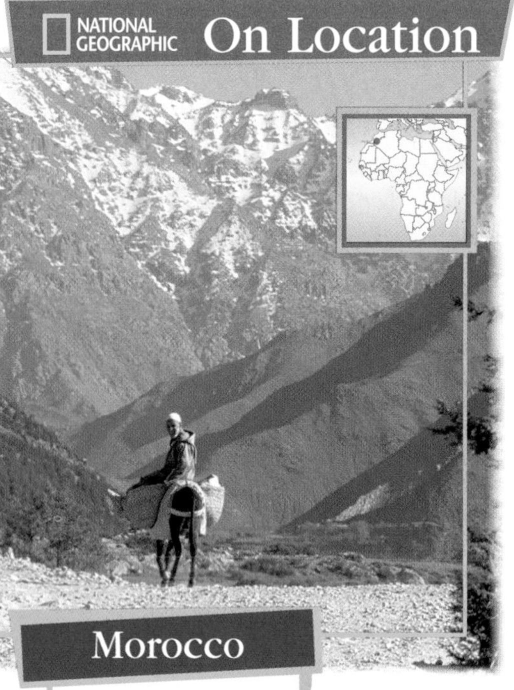

Morocco

Even though North Africa is mostly hot, snow can fall high in the Atlas Mountains where this Berber lives.

Human/Environment Interaction **How does the environment influence the lives of the Berbers?**

Atlas Mountains. Another range—the Ahaggar (uh•HAH•guhr)—lies in southern Algeria. Between these mountain ranges are areas of the Sahara known as **ergs,** or huge, shifting sand dunes.

Like neighboring Libya, Algeria must import about one-third of its food. It pays for this food by selling oil and natural gas pumped from the Sahara. These deposits have helped Algeria's industrial growth, but widespread poverty remains. Many Algerians have moved to European countries to find work.

The Algerians About 31.7 million people live in Algeria. They have mixed Arab and Berber heritage. Most of them are Muslim and speak Arabic. If you visited Algeria, you would discover centuries-old Muslim traditions blending with those of France. Why? From 1834 to 1962, Algeria was a French colony. In 1954, Algerian Arabs wanting freedom rose up against the French. A bloody **civil war,** or conflict between different groups inside a country, erupted. When the fighting ended in 1962, Algeria won independence. Many of the French fled to France.

Today Algeria is a republic, with a strong president and a legislature. In the early 1990s, Muslim political parties opposed many of the government's **secular,** or nonreligious, policies. The Muslims gained enough support to win a national election. The government, however, rejected the election results and imprisoned many Muslim opponents. An ongoing civil war has taken many lives.

Algiers, the country's capital and largest city, has nearly 2.2 million people. Many of them live in the newer sections of the city, with modern buildings and broad streets. They enjoy visiting the older sections of the city, though, which are called **casbahs.** There they walk down narrow streets, stopping to bargain with merchants in bazaars.

✓ **Reading Check** **What conflict has affected Algeria since the early 1990s?**

Morocco

Slightly larger than California, Morocco borders two bodies of water—the Mediterranean Sea on the north and the Atlantic Ocean on the west. The map on page 485 shows that Morocco's northern tip almost touches Europe. Here you will find the **Strait of Gibraltar.** It separates Africa and Europe by only 8 miles (13 km).

Farmers on Morocco's fertile coastal plains grow sugar beets, grains, fruits, and vegetables for sale to Europe. Many raise livestock, especially sheep. Morocco is a leading producer of phosphates, and tourism has grown as well. Visitors flock to cities like **Marrakech** and **Casablanca.** In marketplaces called souks (SOOKS), sellers in traditional hooded robes offer wares made of leather, copper, and brass.

Differentiated Instruction

Meeting Special Needs: English Learners Explain that in English, certain words and phrases signal time changes, sequences, and other relationships among ideas or events. On the board, write the following: *of these, in ancient times, today, over the centuries, however, finally, during this period, nevertheless.* Then read the material aloud from Section 2. Stop after each paragraph to ask if there were words or phrases from the list on the board. **Ask: What relationships among events or ideas do the words point out? ELL**

Refer to *Inclusion for the Middle School Social Studies Classroom Strategies and Activities* in the TCR.

Morocco's History and People Morocco was first settled by the Berbers thousands of years ago. Their descendants still herd and farm in the foothills of the Atlas Mountains. During the A.D. 600s, Arab invaders swept into Morocco. A century later, Arabs and Berbers together crossed the Strait of Gibraltar and conquered Spain. Their descendants, called Moors, ruled parts of Spain and developed an advanced civilization. Christian Spanish rulers drove them out in the late 1400s. Many descendants of the Moors live in Morocco today.

In the early 1900s, the Moroccan kingdom weakened, and France and Spain gained control. In 1956 Morocco became independent once again. Today the country is a constitutional monarchy, where a king or queen is head of state, but elected officials run the government. In Morocco, the monarch still holds many powers, however.

Beginning in the 1970s, Morocco claimed the desert region of **Western Sahara.** The discovery of minerals there sparked a costly war between Morocco and a rebel group that wanted Western Sahara to be independent. The United Nations had tried to sponsor a vote to allow the people of Western Sahara to decide their own future, but nothing has been resolved.

Morocco has about 30.7 million people. Casablanca, the largest city, is home to about 3.4 million people. **Rabat,** with 2.3 million, is the capital. Moroccan culture is based on Arab, Berber, and African traditions. Their music blends rhythms of these groups. Artists here are known for their carpets, pottery, jewelry, brassware, and woodwork.

✓Reading Check **Who were the Moors?**

Assessment

Defining Terms

1. Define aquifer, dictatorship, erg, civil war, secular, casbah, constitutional monarchy.

Recalling Facts

2. History Who were the Berbers?
3. Culture Why do many Algerians speak French?
4. History Why is there a dispute over control of Western Sahara?

Critical Thinking

5. Making Generalizations How have the physical features of North Africa affected where people live?
6. Identifying Alternatives How might the countries studied in this section improve their economies?

Graphic Organizer

7. Organizing Information Draw a diagram like the one below. Choose one country from this section and fill in each outer part of the diagram with a fact about that country.

Country

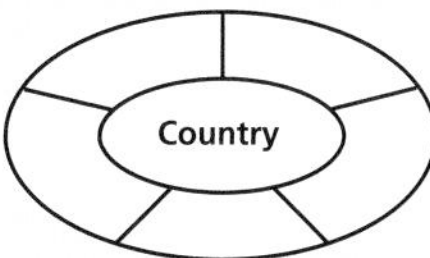

Applying Social Studies Skills

8. Analyzing Maps Study the map on page 485. Rabat is located on the coast of which country? Along what body of water is it located?

Section 2 Assessment

1. The terms are defined in the Glossary.
2. the first people known to have lived in North Africa
3. because Algeria was once a French colony
4. The discovery of minerals started a war between Morocco and a rebel group that wanted Western Sahara to be independent.
5. Most people live along the coast or near rivers or oases because much of the land is desert.
6. Answers will vary but might include taking advantage of the region's mineral resources.
7. Answers will vary depending on the country chosen.
8. Morocco; Atlantic Ocean

Chapter 17

Section 2, pages 490–493

L2

Section Quiz

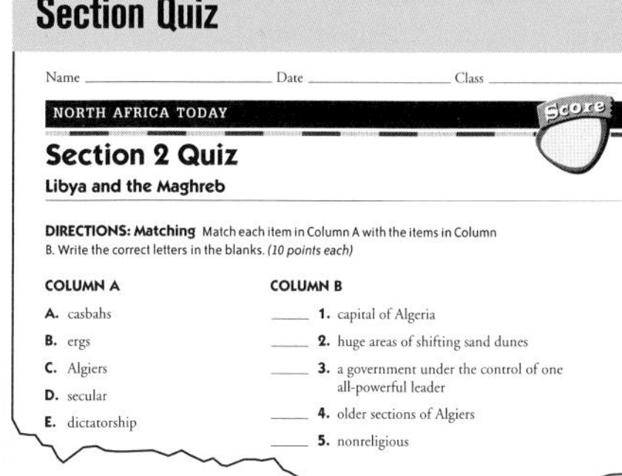

Name ______ Date ______ Class ______

NORTH AFRICA TODAY

Score

Section 2 Quiz

Libya and the Maghreb

DIRECTIONS: Matching Match each item in Column A with the items in Column B. Write the correct letters in the blanks. *(10 points each)*

COLUMN A	COLUMN B
A. casbahs	___ 1. capital of Algeria
B. ergs	___ 2. huge areas of shifting sand dunes
C. Algiers	___ 3. a government under the control of one all-powerful leader
D. secular	___ 4. older sections of Algiers
E. dictatorship	___ 5. nonreligious

✓ Reading Check Answer

descendants of Arabs and Berbers in Morocco who conquered much of Spain in the A.D. 600s

L1/ELL

Reading Essentials and Study Guide

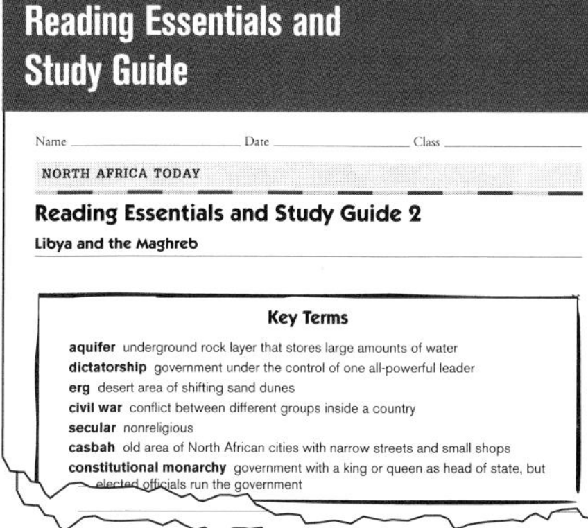

Name ______ Date ______ Class ______

NORTH AFRICA TODAY

Reading Essentials and Study Guide 2

Libya and the Maghreb

Key Terms

aquifer underground rock layer that stores large amounts of water
dictatorship government under the control of one all-powerful leader
erg desert area of shifting sand dunes
civil war conflict between different groups inside a country
secular nonreligious
casbah old area of North African cities with narrow streets and small shops
constitutional monarchy government with a king or queen as head of state, but elected officials run the government

4 CLOSE

Have students write a 10-question quiz that reflects what they think are the most important characteristics of the countries in this section.

TEACH

This skill teaches students to work with a spreadsheet program on the computer. Review the activity with students, and then allow them computer time to complete the activity. Students will create a spreadsheet that shows the total amount of oil produced in 1980, 1990, and 2000 by North African countries, as well as the total amount produced per year by each country. Ask volunteers for suggestions of types of information that could be placed on spreadsheets. *(budgets, grades, and schedules)* **L1**

Additional Skills Practice

1. **What is the name of the cell that shows oil production in Egypt in 2000?** *(D3)*
2. **How would you write the formula to show the total oil production in 1990 for all the countries?** *(=C2+C3+C4+C5+C6)*
3. **What formula would you use to calculate the percentage of total oil production in 2000 represented by Libya?** *(=D4/D7)*

Additional Skills Resources

 Chapter Skills Review

 Building Geography Skills for Life

Technology Skill

Using a Spreadsheet

A **spreadsheet** is an electronic worksheet that can manage numbers quickly and easily. Spreadsheets are powerful tools because you can change or update information, and the spreadsheet automatically performs the calculations.

Learning the Skill

All spreadsheets follow a basic design of rows and columns. Each column is assigned a letter, and each row is assigned a number. Each point where a column and a row intersect is called a *cell.* The cell's position on the spreadsheet is labeled according to its corresponding column and row—*A1* is column A, row 1; *B2* is column B, row 2; and so on.

Spreadsheets use *formulas* to calculate numbers. To create a formula, highlight the cell you want the results in. Type an equal sign (=) and then build the formula, step-by-step. If you type the formula *=B4+B5+B6* in cell B7, the numbers in these cells are added together, and the sum shows up in cell B7.

To use division, the formula would look like this: *=A5/C2.* This divides A5 by C2. An asterisk (*) signifies multiplication: *=(B2*C3)+D1* means that you want to multiply B2 times C3, and then add D1.

Practicing the Skill

Use these steps to create a spreadsheet.

1. In cells B1, C1, and D1, type the years 1980, 1990, and 2000. In cell E1, type the word *Total.*
2. In cells A2 through A6, type the names of North Africa's countries. In cell A7, type the word *Total.*
3. In row 2, enter the number of tons of oil produced by Algeria in 1980, 1990, and 2000.
4. Repeat step 3 in rows 3 through 6 for each country. You can find the information you need for each country in a world almanac or an encyclopedia.
5. Create a formula that tells which cells to add together so the computer can calculate the number of tons of oil for each country. For example, in cell E2, you should type *=B2+C2+D2* to find the total amount of oil that Algeria produced in those years.

B2 =

	A	B	C	D	E
1		1980	1990	2000	Total
2	Algeria				
3	Egypt				
4	Libya				
5	Morocco				
6	Tunisia				
7	Total				
8					

▲ **The computer highlights the cell in which you are working.**

Applying the Skill

Use the spreadsheet you have created to answer these questions: Which country is the largest producer of oil? Has it always been number one? Are countries in North Africa together producing more oil or less oil today than they did 20 years ago?

Practicing the Skill Answers

1.–5. Students should follow the directions to create a spreadsheet.

Applying the Skill
Encourage students to use world almanacs, the Internet, and other resources to find the statistics for their spreadsheets so they can answer the questions.

Chapter 17 Reading Review

Section 1 Egypt

Terms to Know
silt
oasis
phosphate
republic
fellahin
bazaar
service industries
mosque

Main Idea
Egypt's Nile River and desert landscape have shaped the lives of the Egyptian people for hundreds of years.

✓Location Most people in Egypt live along the Nile River or in its delta.

✓Economics About 29 percent of Egypt's people work in agriculture, but industry has grown in recent years.

✓Culture Most people in Egypt are Muslims who follow the religion of Islam.

✓Culture More Egyptians live in rural areas than in cities, but Cairo is the largest city in Africa.

Section 2 Libya and the Maghreb

Terms to Know
aquifer
dictatorship
erg
civil war
secular
casbah
constitutional monarchy

Main Idea
The countries of Libya, Tunisia, Algeria, and Morocco share a desert environment and a mostly Arab culture.

✓Region North Africa includes Libya and the three countries called the Maghreb—Tunisia, Algeria, and Morocco.

✓Location These countries are all located on the Mediterranean Sea. Morocco also has a coast along the Atlantic Ocean.

✓Region The landscape of this region is mostly desert and mountains.

✓Economics Oil, natural gas, and phosphates are among the important resources in these countries.

✓Culture Most of the people in these countries are Muslims and speak Arabic. Most also are of mixed Arab and Berber heritage.

◀ The pyramids at Giza, Egypt

Reading Review

Use the Chapter 17 Reading Review to preview, review, condense, or reteach the chapter.

Preview/Review
Use the Terms to Know lists to help students review and study.

Activity Have students group the terms according to one of the following categories: physical geography, economics, or human geography. Read the terms aloud, one at a time, and ask for volunteers to categorize each.

Vocabulary PuzzleMaker CD-ROM reinforces the vocabulary terms used in Chapter 17.

The Interactive Tutor Self-Assessment CD-ROM allows students to review Chapter 17 content.

Condense
Have students read the Chapter 17 summary statements.

Guided Reading Activities

Audio Program

Reteach

Reteaching Activity

Reading Essentials and Study Guide

Reading Strategy — Read to Write

Environment and Society Have students complete the sentence, "The countries of North Africa are influenced by physical geography in these ways: . . . ." Explain that students should present their answers in a written report. Students' answers should reveal how each of these countries is influenced by the Sahara, scarce water supplies, the Atlas Mountains, proximity to the Mediterranean Sea, and so on. L2

Assessment and Activities

GLENCOE TECHNOLOGY

MindJogger Videoquiz
Use MindJogger Videoquiz to review the Chapter 17 content.

 Available in DVD and VHS

Using Key Terms

1.	f	6.	a
2.	g	7.	i
3.	e	8.	h
4.	c	9.	b
5.	d	10.	j

Reviewing the Main Ideas

11. Cairo
12. Mediterranean Sea and Red Sea
13. dry desert with 0.4 inch (1 cm) of rainfall a year
14. *Any four:* sugarcane, grains, vegetables, fruits, cotton
15. republic
16. It has no permanent rivers.
17. the land farthest west
18. Phoenicians
19. France
20. oil or petroleum

Critical Thinking

21. because the rest of the region is covered by the Sahara
22. *Possible answers:* 300 B.C. to A.D. 300—Greece and Rome rule Egypt; 641—Arabs control Egypt; 1800s—Egypt becomes part of British Empire; 1952—Egypt becomes independent; 1954—Gamal Abdel Nasser becomes president

Chapter 17 Assessment and Activities

Using Key Terms

Match the terms in Part A with their definitions in Part B.

A.

1. oasis	6. dictatorship
2. secular	7. silt
3. mosque	8. erg
4. casbah	9. aquifer
5. bazaar	10. republic

B.

a. government under an all-powerful leader
b. underground rock layer that stores water
c. old area of cities with narrow streets and small shops
d. marketplace
e. place of worship for Muslims
f. fertile or green area in a desert
g. nonreligious
h. desert region of shifting sand dunes
i. particles of soil deposited by water
j. government headed by a president

Reviewing the Main Ideas

Section 1 Egypt

11. **Place** What is the capital of Egypt?
12. **Movement** Which two bodies of water does the Suez Canal connect?
13. **Place** Describe the climate and rainfall in Egypt.
14. **Economics** Name four of Egypt's agricultural products.
15. **Government** What type of government does Egypt have today?

Section 2 Libya and the Maghreb

16. **Human/Environment Interaction** Why must Libya depend on aquifers for water?
17. **Region** What does *maghreb* mean?
18. **History** Who founded the city of Carthage in Tunisia?
19. **History** What foreign country controlled Algeria from 1834 to 1962?
20. **Economics** What energy resource is important to almost all of North Africa's countries?

NATIONAL GEOGRAPHIC North Africa

Place Location Activity

On a separate sheet of paper, match the letters on the map with the numbered places listed below.

1. Red Sea	6. Nile River
2. Morocco	7. Cairo
3. Libya	8. Tunisia
4. Algeria	9. Tripoli
5. Atlas Mountains	10. Sinai Peninsula

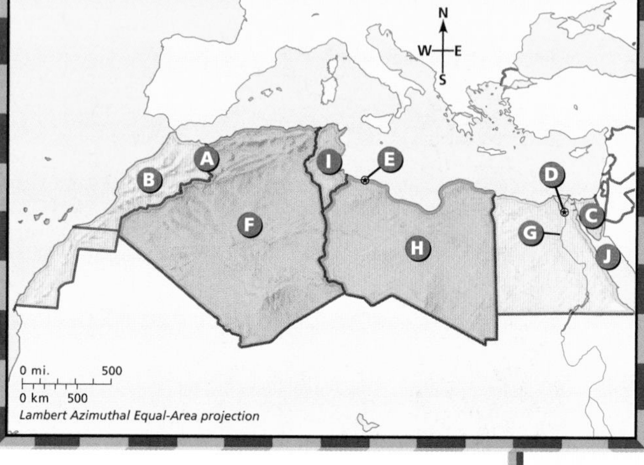

NATIONAL GEOGRAPHIC Place Location Activity

1. J	6. G
2. B	7. D
3. H	8. I
4. F	9. E
5. A	10. C

Comparing Regions Activity

23. Students' paragraphs should describe how their lives would be affected as a result of water shortages.

Self-Check Quiz Visit ***The World and Its People*** Web site at twip.glencoe.com and click on **Chapter 17—Self-Check Quizzes** to prepare for the Chapter Test.

Critical Thinking

21. **Understanding Cause and Effect** Why are the most densely populated areas of North Africa along the Mediterranean Sea and the Nile River?
22. **Sequencing Information** On a time line like the one below, label five events or eras in Egyptian history. Include their dates.

Comparing Regions Activity

23. **Geography** Turn the page to read about the severe shortages of water in the regions of North Africa and Southwest Asia. It is likely that your region does not currently face this challenge. For an entire day, notice all the different ways you use water. Write a paragraph about how your day would change if you lived in a region where water shortages were common. What might you have to do differently?

Mental Mapping Activity

24. **Focusing on the Region** Draw a simple outline map of North Africa, then label the following:
    - Mediterranean Sea
    - Red Sea
    - Atlantic Ocean
    - Nile River
    - Atlas Mountains
    - Egypt
    - Libya
    - Morocco
    - Tunisia
    - Algeria

Technology Skills Activity

25. **Using the Internet** Use the Internet to research life in the desert. Besides the Sahara, what other large deserts are there in the world? What kinds of life do deserts support? How do humans adapt to life in the desert? Are deserts changing in size and shape? Why? Use your research to create a bulletin board display on "Desert Life."

Standardized Test Practice

Directions: Study the graph, and then answer the question that follows.

Percentage of North Africa's People Living in Each Country

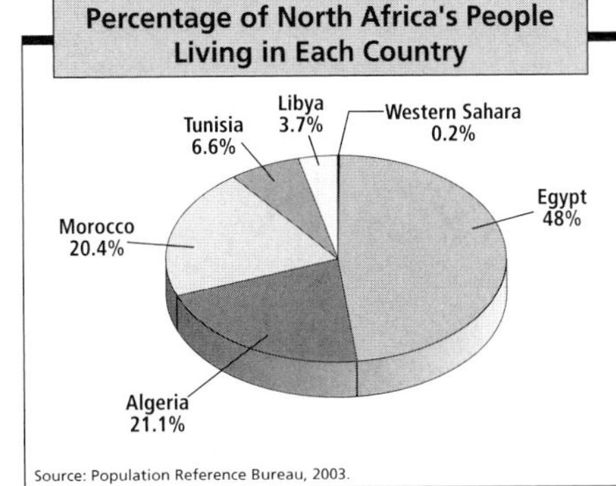

Source: Population Reference Bureau, 2003.

1. **According to the graph above, which one of the following statements is true?**
   - F Almost half of the people of North Africa live in Egypt.
   - G Almost half of the people of North Africa live in Algeria.
   - H Egypt's land area is much larger than Algeria's land area.
   - J Algeria's land area is much larger than Libya's land area.

Test-Taking Tip: When analyzing circle or pie graphs, first look at the title to see what the graph shows. Next read each section of the "pie" and compare the sections to one another. Notice that no actual population figures are given on the pie graph, only percentages. All the pie sections are different sizes, but together they add up to 100 percent.

Assessment and Activities

Standardized Test Practice

1. F

Tested Objectives: Reading a graph, analyzing information

Chapter Test Bonus Question

This question may be used for extra credit on the chapter test.

Which country is famous for its souks, or markets, where dealers sell leather, copper, and brass goods? *(Morocco)*

Social Studies Online

Have students visit the Web site at twip.glencoe.com to review Chapter 17 and take the Self-Check Quiz.

Dinah Zike's Foldables

Culminating Activity Have students quiz partners using the information written on their foldables.

Mental Mapping Activity

24. This exercise helps students visualize the countries and geographic features they have been studying and understand the relationship among various points.

Technology Skills Activity

25. Students might investigate other major deserts such as the Gobi and the Taklimakan in Asia, the Kalahari and Namib in Africa, the Atacama in South America, and Death Valley in North America. Their bulletin boards should reveal similarities and differences among these deserts.

Write the following heading on the board: "Water, water everywhere." Ask students to identify various sources of water. Guide them by offering such examples as oceans, lakes, rivers, glaciers, and so on. List their responses under the heading. Then point out that water covers about 70 percent of the earth's surface. L1

Analyzing Information Ask students to speculate how the earth could have a shortage of water when the amount of water never changes. Explain that less than 1 percent of the world's water is fresh and readily accessible. Then point out that this water is distributed very unevenly across the earth, and remind students that North Africa and Southwest Asia are among the world's driest regions. L1

Meeting National Standards

Geography for Life

The following standards are met in the Student Edition feature:

EE5 Environment and Society: Standards 14, 15, 16

EE6 The Uses of Geography: Standard 18

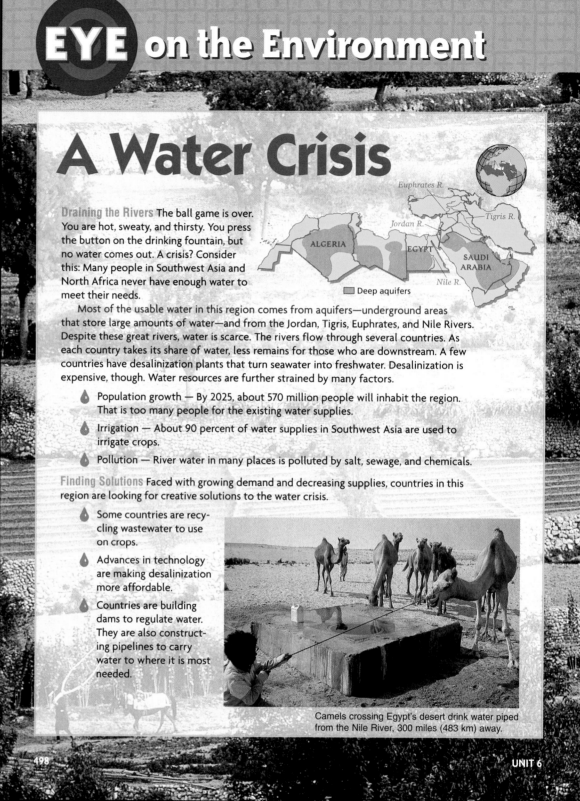

EYE on the Environment

A Water Crisis

Draining the Rivers The ball game is over. You are hot, sweaty, and thirsty. You press the button on the drinking fountain, but no water comes out. A crisis? Consider this: Many people in Southwest Asia and North Africa never have enough water to meet their needs.

Most of the usable water in this region comes from aquifers—underground areas that store large amounts of water—and from the Jordan, Tigris, Euphrates, and Nile Rivers. Despite these great rivers, water is scarce. The rivers flow through several countries. As each country takes its share of water, less remains for those who are downstream. A few countries have desalinization plants that turn seawater into freshwater. Desalinization is expensive, though. Water resources are further strained by many factors.

- Population growth — By 2025, about 570 million people will inhabit the region. That is too many people for the existing water supplies.
- Irrigation — About 90 percent of water supplies in Southwest Asia are used to irrigate crops.
- Pollution — River water in many places is polluted by salt, sewage, and chemicals.

Finding Solutions Faced with growing demand and decreasing supplies, countries in this region are looking for creative solutions to the water crisis.

- Some countries are recycling wastewater to use on crops.
- Advances in technology are making desalinization more affordable.
- Countries are building dams to regulate water. They are also constructing pipelines to carry water to where it is most needed.

Camels crossing Egypt's desert drink water piped from the Nile River, 300 miles (483 km) away.

More About the Issues

Irrigation The earliest recorded use of irrigation occurred in Mesopotamia in Southwest Asia. Today irrigation remains a major use of freshwater in the region. Problems related to traditional methods of irrigation continue to plague the region's farmers, however. Because the climate is so hot and dry, surface irrigation systems lose a high percentage of water to evaporation. High rates of evaporation lead to the accumulation of certain minerals in the soil—and these minerals can make the soil unproductive for farming. Many governments in the region are using new technology to address such problems.

NATIONAL GEOGRAPHIC

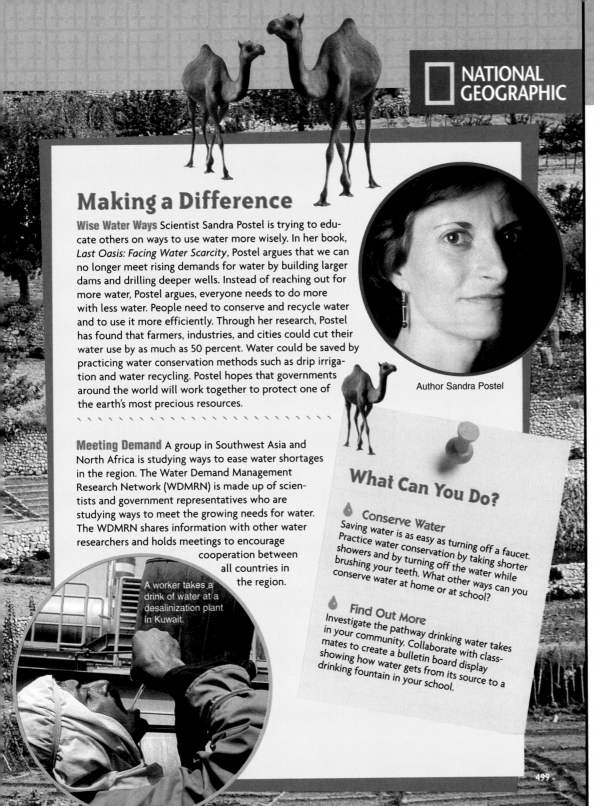

Making a Difference

Wise Water Ways Scientist Sandra Postel is trying to educate others on ways to use water more wisely. In her book, *Last Oasis: Facing Water Scarcity*, Postel argues that we can no longer meet rising demands for water by building larger dams and drilling deeper wells. Instead of reaching out for more water, Postel argues, everyone needs to do more with less water. People need to conserve and recycle water and to use it more efficiently. Through her research, Postel has found that farmers, industries, and cities could cut their water use by as much as 50 percent. Water could be saved by practicing water conservation methods such as drip irrigation and water recycling. Postel hopes that governments around the world will work together to protect one of the earth's most precious resources.

Author Sandra Postel

Meeting Demand A group in Southwest Asia and North Africa is studying ways to ease water shortages in the region. The Water Demand Management Research Network (WDMRN) is made up of scientists and government representatives who are studying ways to meet the growing needs for water. The WDMRN shares information with other water researchers and holds meetings to encourage cooperation between all countries in the region.

A worker takes a drink of water at a desalinization plant in Kuwait.

What Can You Do?

Conserve Water
Saving water is as easy as turning off a faucet. Practice water conservation by taking shorter showers and by turning off the water while brushing your teeth. What other ways can you conserve water at home or at school?

Find Out More
Investigate the pathway drinking water takes in your community. Collaborate with classmates to create a bulletin board display showing how water gets from its source to a drinking fountain in your school.

499

What Can You Do? Teacher Tips

Conserve Water Many publications list simple ways that people can reduce their use of water. Encourage students to find and report these steps to the class.

Find Out More Suggest that students look for answers to such questions as: What is the source of the community's drinking water? How is this water treated and transported to homes? What problems confront the community's water supply?

GLOBAL ISSUES

Interdependence Establishing a fair system of access to freshwater is a worldwide problem. Even within the United States, some western states are engaged in legal battles with each other over water rights.

Have students work individually or in groups to complete the What Can You Do? activities.

Discuss with students the What Can You Do? activities. Consider inviting a representative of the local water utility to the class to give a presentation on water-related issues and to answer students' questions.

For an additional regional case study, use the following:

Environmental Case Study

Chapter 18 Resources

Note: The following materials may be used when teaching Chapter 18.
Section level support materials are shown at point of use in the margins of the Teacher Wraparound Edition.

Timesaving Tools

TeacherWorks™ All-In-One Planner and Resource Center

- **Interactive Teacher Edition** See the **Interactive Teacher Edition** CD-ROM to electronically integrate your Teacher Wraparound Edition and blackline masters.
- **Interactive Lesson Planner** Organize your week, month, semester, or year with all the lesson helps you need. The **Interactive Lesson Planner** CD-ROM contains all Chapter 18 resources.

Use Glencoe's **Presentation Plus!** multimedia teacher tool to easily present dynamic lessons that visually excite your students. Using Microsoft PowerPoint® you can customize the presentations to create your own personalized lessons.

TEACHING TRANSPARENCIES

Graphic Organizer Transparency 3 L2

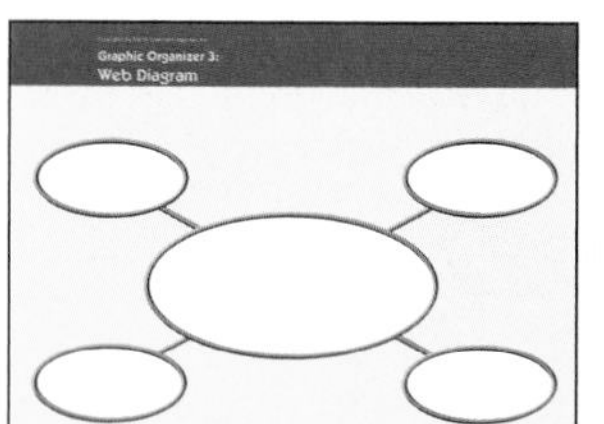

In-text Map Transparency L1

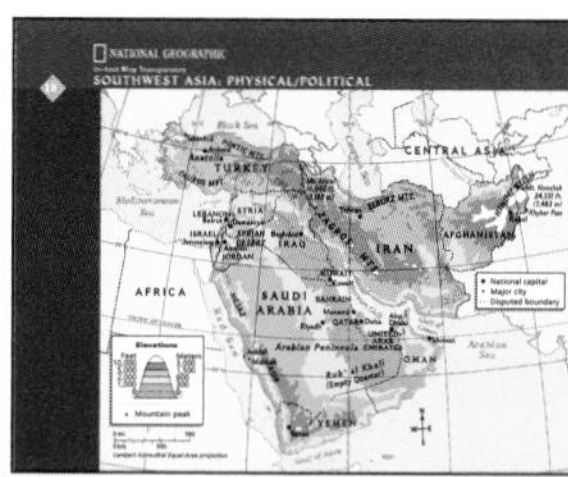

FOLDABLES™ Study Organizer

Dinah Zike's Foldables

Foldables are three-dimensional, interactive graphic organizers that help students practice basic writing skills, review key vocabulary terms, and identify main ideas. Additional chapter activities can be found in the ***Reading and Study Skills Foldables*** booklet.

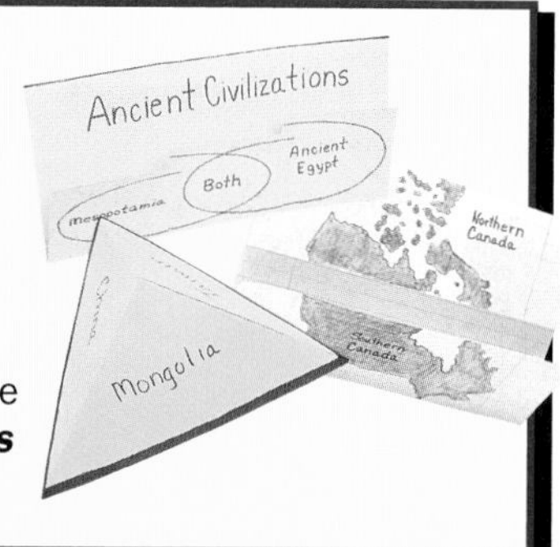

MAP AND GEOGRAPHY SKILLS

Chapter Map Activity L2

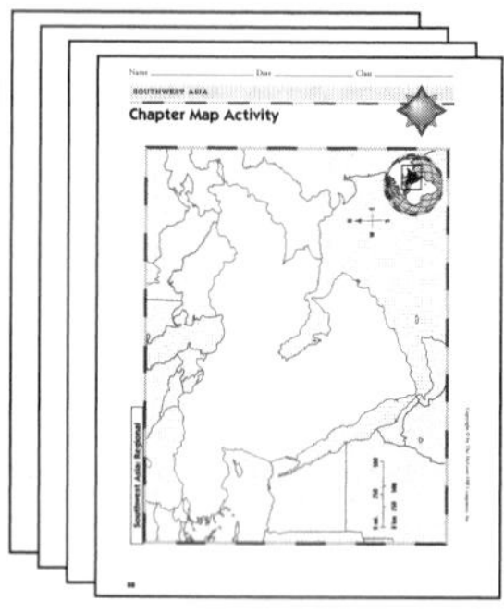

GeoLab Activity L2

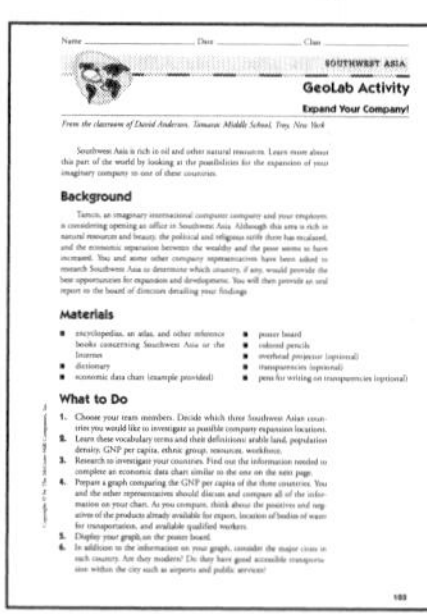

READING SUPPORT

Vocabulary Activity L1

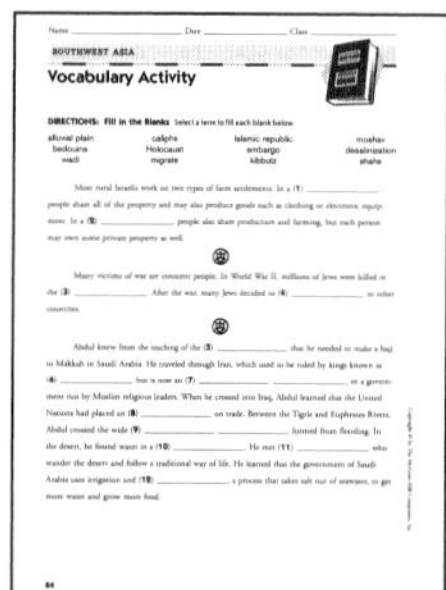

Workbook Activity L1

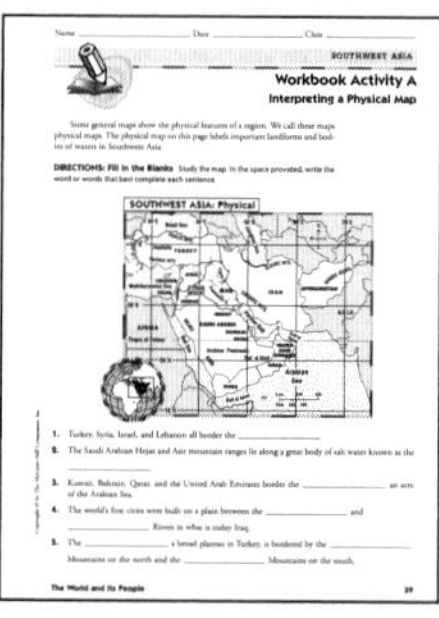

Reading and Writing Skills Activity L1/ELL

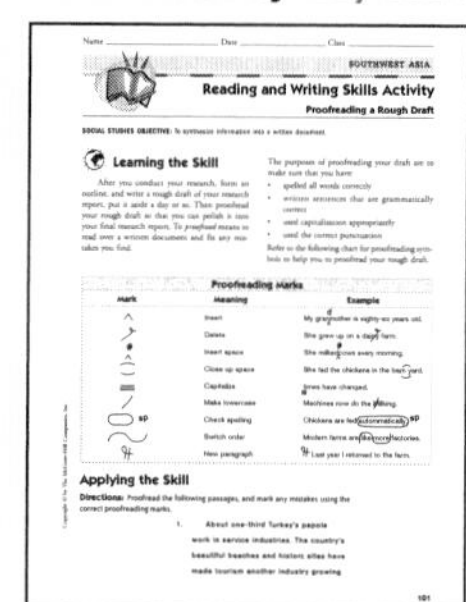

DIFFERENTIATED INSTRUCTION

Use these review and reinforcement materials to help less-proficient readers, English learners, and gifted and talented students.

Reteaching Activity L1

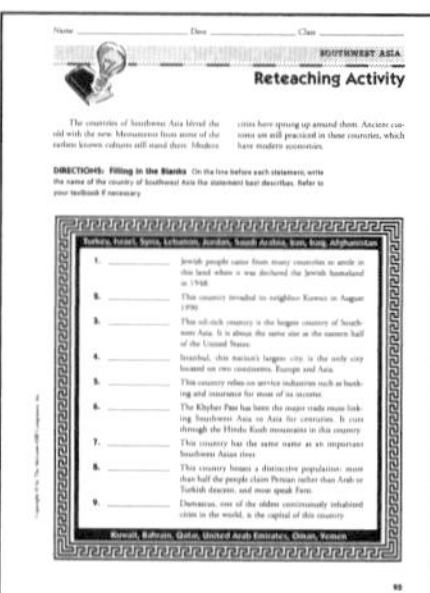

Chapter Skills Review L2

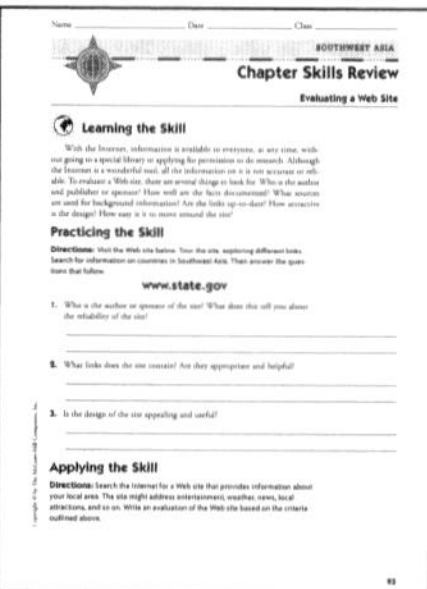

Cooperative Learning Activity L1/ELL

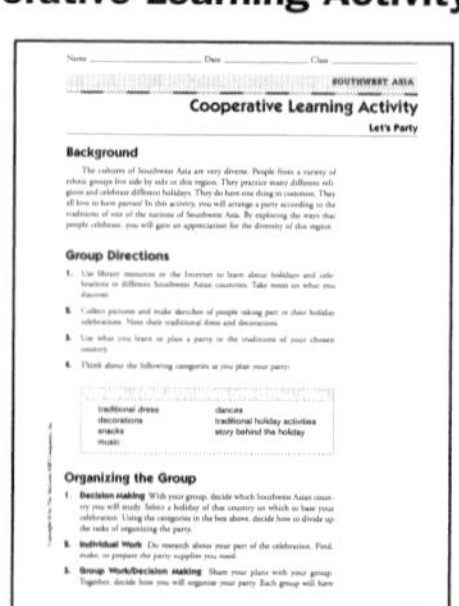

Enrichment Activity L3

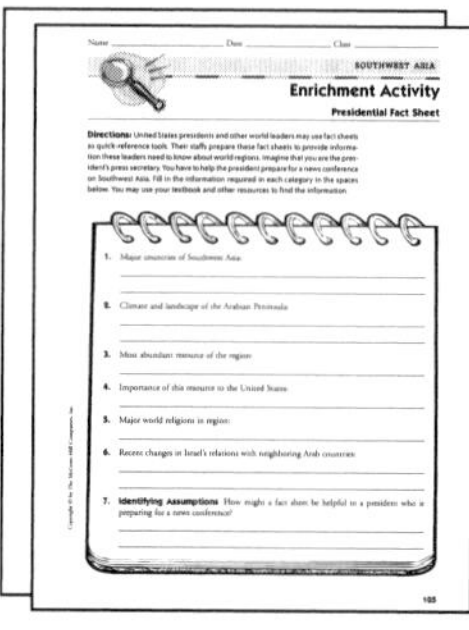

ASSESSMENT

Chapter Test, Form A L2

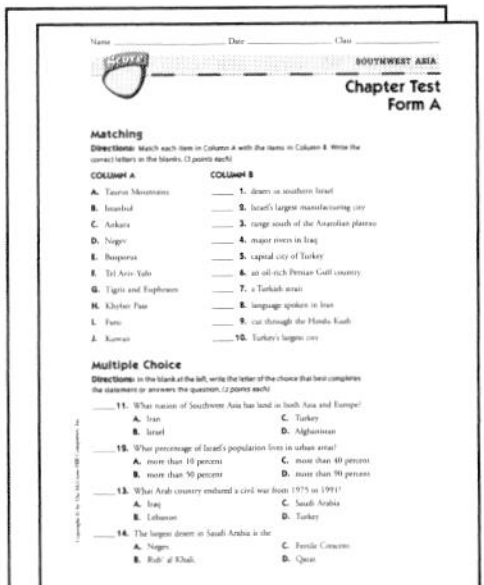

Chapter Test, Form B L2

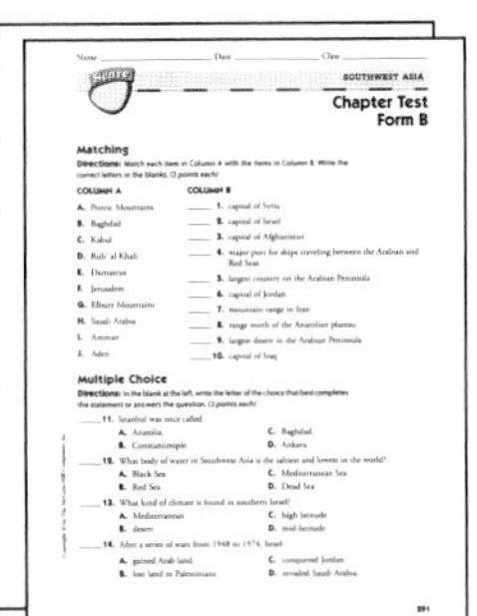

Performance Assessment Activity L1/ELL

ExamView® Pro Testmaker CD-ROM

STANDARDIZED ASSESSMENT SKILLS

Critical Thinking Skills Activity L2

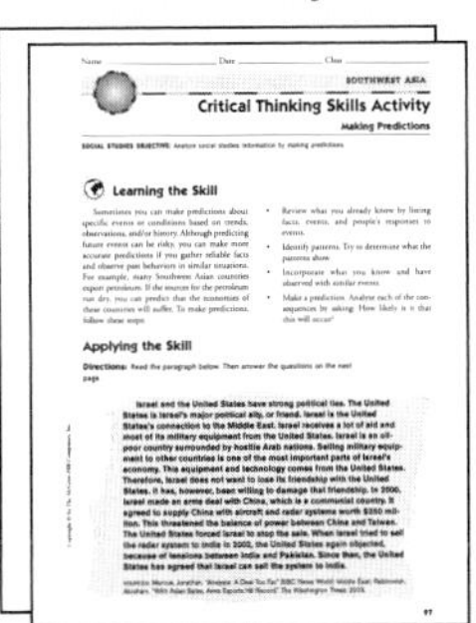

Map and Graph Skills Activity L2

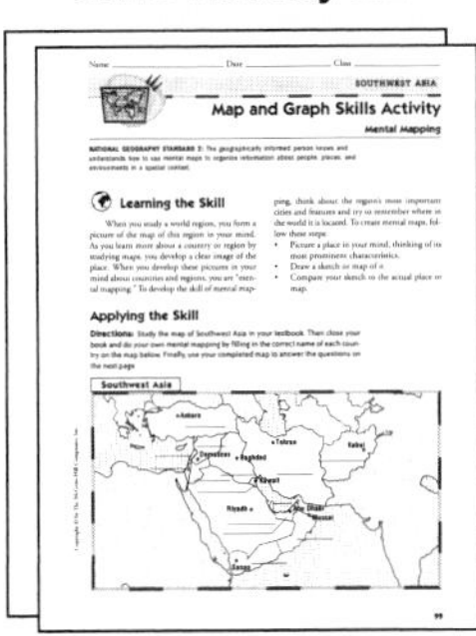

Standardized Test Skills Practice Workbook Activity L2

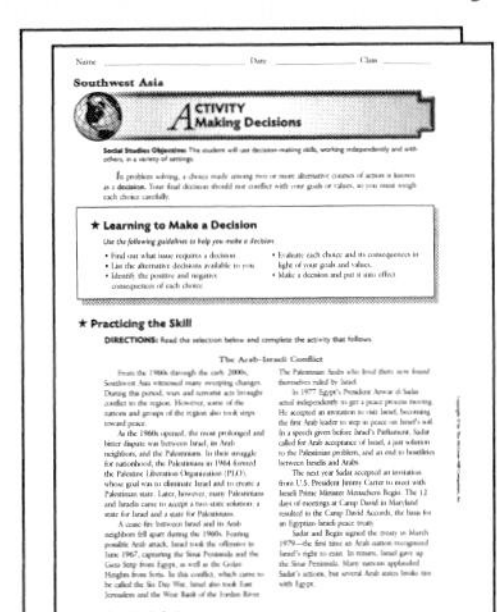

HOME INVOLVEMENT

Take-Home Review Activity L1

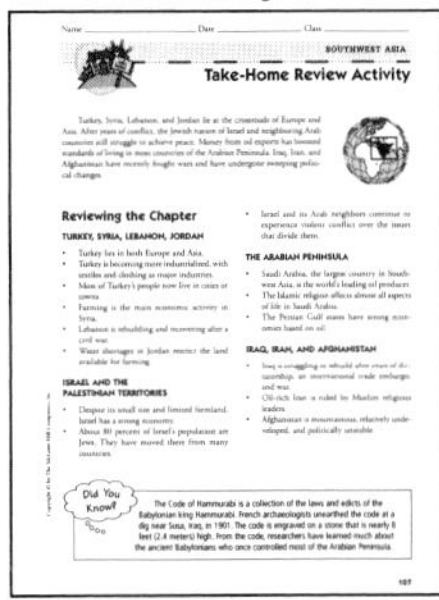

MULTIMEDIA

- **National Geographic's The World and Its People**
- **MindJogger Videoquiz**
- **Vocabulary PuzzleMaker CD-ROM**
- **Interactive Tutor Self-Assessment CD-ROM**
- **ExamView® Pro Testmaker CD-ROM**
- **TeacherWorks CD-ROM**
- **StudentWorks CD-ROM**
- **Skillbuilder Interactive Workbook CD-ROM, Level 1**
- **Presentation Plus! CD-ROM**
- **Audio Program**

SPANISH RESOURCES

The following Spanish language materials are available in the Spanish Resources binder:

- **Spanish Summaries**
- **Spanish Vocabulary Activities**
- **Spanish Guided Reading Activities**
- **Spanish Quizzes and Tests**
- **Spanish Take-Home Review Activities**
- **Spanish Reteaching Activities**

Meeting National Standards

Geography for Life

The following standards are covered in Chapter 18:

Section 1 **EE4 Human Systems: Standards 9, 10, 11, 12, 13**
EE6 The Uses of Geography: Standard 17

Section 2 **EE4 Human Systems: Standards 9, 10, 11, 12**
EE5 Environment and Society: Standards 14, 15

Section 3 **EE2 Places and Regions: Standards 4, 5, 6**
EE3 Physical Systems: Standards 7, 8

Section 4 **EE1 The World in Spatial Terms: Standards 1, 2, 3**

State and Local Objectives

Chapter 18 Planning Guide

SECTION RESOURCES

Daily Objectives	Reproducible Resources	Multimedia Resources
Section 1 **Turkey, Syria, Lebanon, and Jordan** **1.** Identify where most of Turkey's people live. **2.** Describe how Syria's people support themselves. **3.** Explain why Lebanon's economy was almost destroyed. **4.** Discuss why Jordan is said to be a land of contrasts.	Reproducible Lesson Plan Daily Lecture and Discussion Notes Note-taking Guide Guided Reading Activity* Reading Essentials and Study Guide* Section Quiz*	Daily Focus Skills Transparency GeoQuiz Transparency In-text Map Transparency Vocabulary PuzzleMaker CD-ROM Interactive Tutor Self-Assessment CD-ROM ExamView® Pro Testmaker CD-ROM Presentation Plus! CD-ROM
Section 2 **Israel and the Palestinian Territories** **1.** Describe the land and climate of Israel and the Palestinian territories. **2.** Explain how Israel has developed a strong economy. **3.** Discuss how the past has affected the people of Israel and the Palestinian territories.	Reproducible Lesson Plan Daily Lecture and Discussion Notes Note-taking Guide Guided Reading Activity* Reading Essentials and Study Guide* Section Quiz*	Daily Focus Skills Transparency GeoQuiz Transparency Vocabulary PuzzleMaker CD-ROM Interactive Tutor Self-Assessment CD-ROM ExamView® Pro Testmaker CD-ROM Presentation Plus! CD-ROM
Section 3 **The Arabian Peninsula** **1.** Outline what Saudi Arabia has achieved with its oil revenues. **2.** Explain why Saudi Arabia is important to the world's Muslims. **3.** Describe how oil affects the lives of people in the Persian Gulf states.	Reproducible Lesson Plan Daily Lecture and Discussion Notes Note-taking Guide Guided Reading Activity* Reading Essentials and Study Guide* Section Quiz*	Daily Focus Skills Transparency Vocabulary PuzzleMaker CD-ROM Interactive Tutor Self-Assessment CD-ROM ExamView® Pro Testmaker CD-ROM Presentation Plus! CD-ROM
Section 4 **Iraq, Iran, and Afghanistan** **1.** Explain why the economy of Iraq has slowed. **2.** Discuss how a religious government came to power in Iran. **3.** Describe Afghanistan's land and culture.	Reproducible Lesson Plan Daily Lecture and Discussion Notes Note-taking Guide Guided Reading Activity* Reading Essentials and Study Guide* Section Quiz*	Daily Focus Skills Transparency Vocabulary PuzzleMaker CD-ROM Interactive Tutor Self-Assessment CD-ROM ExamView® Pro Testmaker CD-ROM Presentation Plus! CD-ROM MindJogger Videoquiz

00:00 **Out of Time?** Assign the **Reading Essentials and Study Guide*** for this chapter.

*Also available in Spanish

KEY TO ABILITY LEVELS

Teaching strategies have been coded for varying learning styles and abilities.

- **L1 BASIC** activities for all students
- **L2 AVERAGE** activities for average to above-average students
- **L3 CHALLENGING** activities for above-average students
- **ELL ENGLISH LANGUAGE LEARNER** activities

KEY TO TEACHING RESOURCES

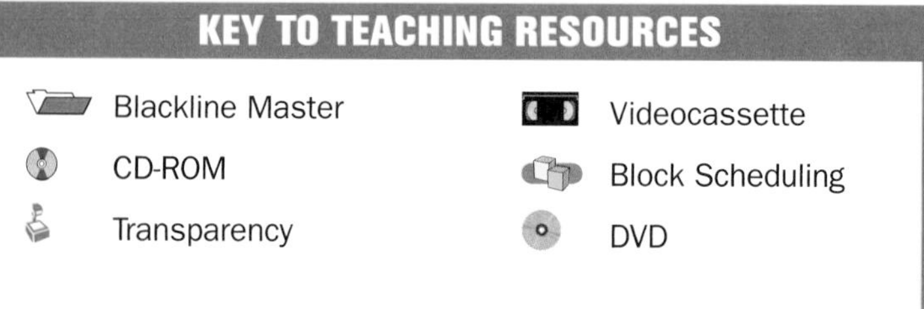

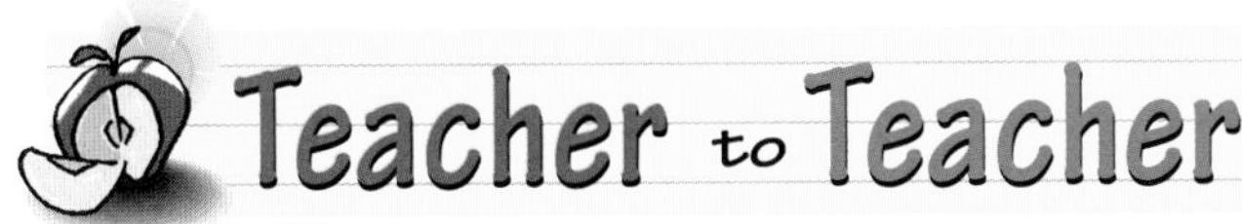

Culture Reinforcement

Have students use papier-mâché and Popsicle™ sticks to create the homes and towns of other cultures. For example, they could construct a model of Petra or build a mosque. After building the structure, students should use various mediums to add color and texture. Finally, have students explain the relationship that exists between the society or culture they have chosen and their architecture.

Rick Lyndsey
Roosevelt Full Service
West Palm Beach, Florida

Meeting Special Needs

In addition to the Differentiated Instruction strategies found in each section, the following resources are also suitable for your special needs students:

- ***ExamView® Pro Testmaker CD-ROM*** allows teachers to tailor tests by reducing answer choices.
- The ***Audio Program*** includes the entire narrative of the student edition so that less-proficient readers can listen to the words as they read them.
- The ***Reading Essentials and Study Guide*** provides the same content as the student edition but is written two grade levels below the textbook.
- ***Guided Reading Activities*** give less-proficient readers point-by-point instructions to increase comprehension as they read each textbook section.
- ***Enrichment Activities*** include a stimulating collection of readings and activities for gifted and talented students.

NATIONAL GEOGRAPHIC TEACHER'S CORNER

Index to National Geographic Magazine:

The following articles may be used for research relating to this chapter:

- "Wrath of the Gods" and "Earthquake in Turkey," by Rick Gore, July 2000.
- "In Focus: Golan Heights," June 2000.
- "Yemen United," by Andrew Cockburn, April 2000.

National Geographic Society Products:

To order the following products for use with this chapter, call National Geographic Society at 1-800-368-2728:

- *Healing the Earth* (Video)
- *Israel* (Video)
- *National Geographic Desk Reference* (Book)

NGS ONLINE

Access National Geographic's Web site for current events, activities, links, interactive features, and archives.
www.nationalgeographic.com

Find the latest coverage of geography in the news, atlas updates, cartographic activities with interactive maps, an online map store, and links at www.nationalgeographic.com/maps

SOCIAL STUDIES Online

Use our Web site for additional resources. All essential content is covered in the Student Edition.

You and your students can visit twip.glencoe.com, the Web site companion to *The World and Its People*. This innovative integration of electronic and print media offers your students a wealth of opportunities. The student text directs students to the Web site for the following options:

- Chapter Overviews
- Student Web Activities
- Self-Check Quizzes
- Textbook Updates

Answers are provided for you in the Web Activity Lesson Plan. Additional Web resources and Interactive Tutor puzzles are also available.

Introducing
Chapter 18

Introduce students to chapter content and key terms by having them access Chapter Overview 18 at twip.glencoe.com

Chapter Objectives

1. Identify the most heavily populated regions of Southwest Asia.
2. Describe how religion has affected the development of Southwest Asia.
3. Evaluate the influence of oil on the lives of people on the Arabian Peninsula.
4. Compare the economies and cultures of the countries in this region.

GLENCOE TECHNOLOGY

NATIONAL GEOGRAPHIC

The World and Its People Video Program

Chapter 17 Southwest Asia
The following segments enhance the study of this chapter:

- **Holy City**
- **The Empty Quarter**
- **Hidden Treasure**

MindJogger Videoquiz

Use MindJogger Videoquiz to preview the Chapter 18 content.

Both programs available in DVD and VHS

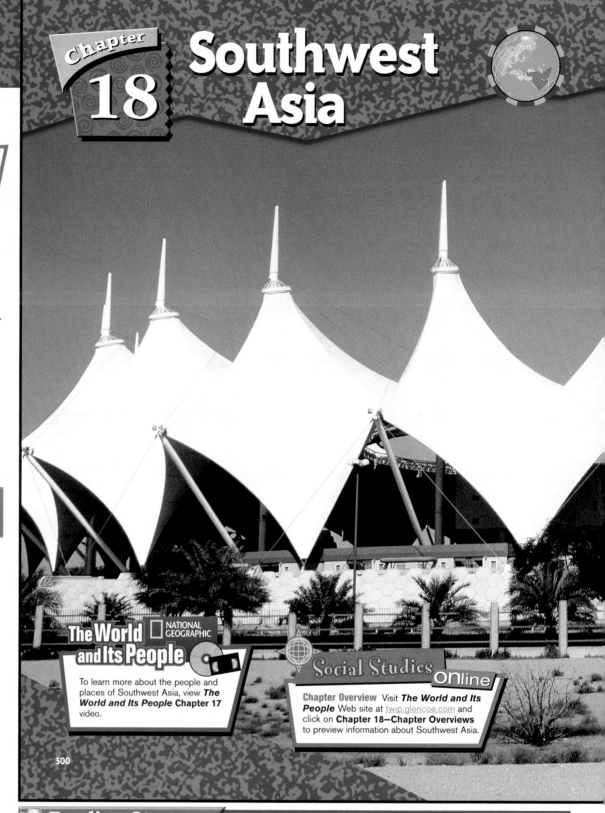

Chapter 18 Southwest Asia

The World and Its People NATIONAL GEOGRAPHIC

To learn more about the people and places of Southwest Asia, view ***The World and Its People*** **Chapter 17** video.

Social Studies online

Chapter Overview Visit ***The World and Its People*** Web site at twip.glencoe.com and click on **Chapter 18—Chapter Overviews** to preview information about Southwest Asia.

500

Reading Strategy — Purpose for Reading

Capsule Vocabulary is a reading strategy that includes four steps: talking, listening, writing, and reading. These steps help students learn vocabulary. Write the words *migrate, Dead Sea, Holocaust, kibbutz, embargo, Iraq,* and *Jerusalem* on the board or on an overhead transparency. Organize students into pairs and have them start a "conversation" using as many of the words as possible. Ask students to write these conversations in their notebooks. Conclude the activity by explaining that they will learn the correct definitions of these terms as they study the chapter. They should then correct or enhance their responses from the conversations as they study the chapter. L1

Introducing Chapter 18

Categorizing Information If you ask yourself questions while reading your textbook, it will help you focus on what you are reading. Make this foldable to help you ask and answer questions about the people and places in Southwest Asia.

Step 1 Fold a sheet of paper in half from side to side, leaving a ½ inch tab along the side.

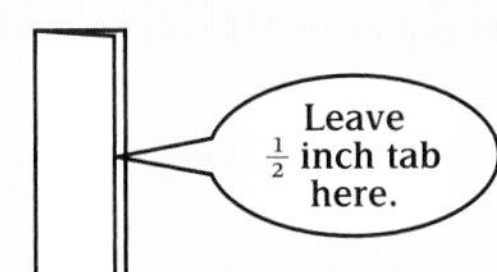
Leave ½ inch tab here.

Step 2 Turn the paper and fold it into fourths.

Fold in half, then fold in half again.

Step 3 Unfold and cut up along the three fold lines.

This will make four tabs.

Step 4 Label as shown.

Turkey, Syria, Lebanon, Jordan | Israel and the Palestinian Territories | The Arabian Peninsula | Iraq, Iran, Afghanistan

Reading and Writing As you read the chapter, ask yourself questions about these countries. Write your questions and answers under each appropriate tab.

▲ King Fahd Stadium in Riyadh, Saudi Arabia

Why It Matters

Crossroads

Because of its location near Europe and Asia, Southwest Asia remains at the "crossroads of the world" even today. The world depends upon the oil and gas resources found here. These resources make the events that unfold in these oil-rich countries of interest to many nations. Achieving peace in this region is of global importance.

About the Photo

The discovery of oil in the 1930s has allowed rapid development of the Arabian Peninsula. Governments have tried to preserve their cultural heritage while promoting improvements. One outcome of development has been the rapid growth of urban centers and the resulting need for increased public facilities. The photo illustrates how tradition has been preserved in modern structures. It shows the King Fahd Stadium, which can hold up to 70,000 spectators and has been the site of international competitions. The design of the structure is intended to represent the tents of Bedouin travelers. **Ask: How does this photo show the relationship between the Arab culture and modern architecture?**

FOLDABLES™ Study Organizer — Dinah Zike's Foldables

Purpose When making this foldable, students are required to ask themselves questions about the countries and regions of Southwest Asia. This reading strategy requires students to ask questions of the chapter material as they read it, thereby helping them focus on main ideas and to better understand the material.

Have students complete the ***Reading and Study Skills Foldables*** activity for this chapter.

Why It Matters

Organize students into groups of five. Inform the groups that their task is to create an illustrated wall chart showing an important feature of the region and its significance to the people living there and to the world. Examples might be the oil, the Suez Canal, and the Turkish Straits. Have the groups display and discuss their completed charts.

Focus

Section Objectives

1. Identify where most of Turkey's people live.
2. Describe how Syria's people support themselves.
3. Explain why Lebanon's economy was almost destroyed.
4. Discuss why Jordan is said to be a land of contrasts.

BELLRINGER
Skillbuilder Activity

Project transparency and have students answer the question.

Daily Focus Skills Transparency

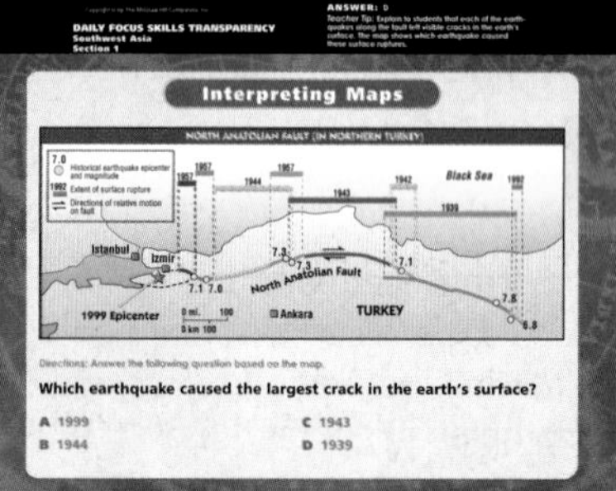

Reading Preview

■ **Activating Prior Knowledge**
Ask: In what kinds of locations do cities often rise and thrive? *(along transportation routes such as waterways; amid areas rich in farmland or resources)*

■ **Preteaching Vocabulary**
Have students check the definitions of the words in Terms to Know. Direct them to use each term correctly in a sentence.

Section 1 Turkey, Syria, Lebanon, Jordan

Guide to Reading

Main Idea

Turkey, Syria, Lebanon, and Jordan lie at the crossroads of Europe and Asia.

Terms to Know

- migrate
- bedouins

Reading Strategy

Create a chart like this one, and fill in at least two key facts about each country.

Country	Fact #1	Fact #2
Turkey		
Syria		
Lebanon		
Jordan		

NATIONAL GEOGRAPHIC Exploring Our World

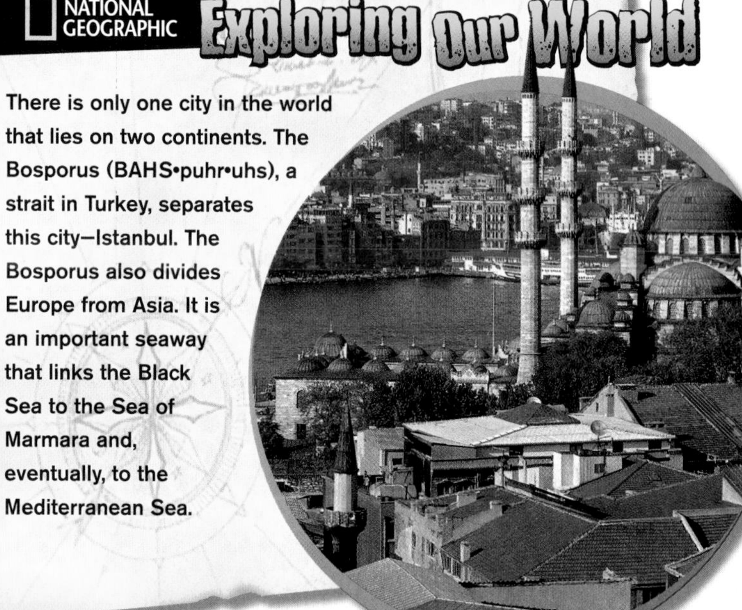

There is only one city in the world that lies on two continents. The Bosporus (BAHS•puhr•uhs), a strait in Turkey, separates this city—Istanbul. The Bosporus also divides Europe from Asia. It is an important seaway that links the Black Sea to the Sea of Marmara and, eventually, to the Mediterranean Sea.

A little larger than Texas, **Turkey** has a unique location—it bridges the continents of Asia and Europe. The large Asian part of Turkey occupies the peninsula known as Asia Minor. The much smaller European part lies on Europe's Balkan Peninsula. Three important waterways—the **Bosporus**, the **Sea of Marmara** (MAHR•muh•ruh), and the **Dardanelles** (DAHRD•uhn•EHLZ) separate the Asian and European parts of Turkey. Together, these waterways are called the Turkish Straits. Find these bodies of water on page RA19 of the **Reference Atlas.**

Turkey

In the center of Turkey is **Anatolia** (A•nuh•TOH•lee•uh), a plateau region rimmed by mountains. The **Pontic Mountains** border the plateau on the north. The **Taurus Mountains** tower over it on the south. Severe earthquakes often occur in northern Turkey, causing much damage and death. Lowland plains curve along Turkey's three coasts.

Section Resources

Reproducible Masters
- Reproducible Lesson Plan
- Daily Lecture and Discussion Notes
- Note-taking Guide
- Guided Reading Activity
- Reading Essentials and Study Guide
- Section Quiz

Transparencies
- Daily Focus Skills Transparency
- GeoQuiz Transparency
- In-text Map Transparency

Multimedia
- Vocabulary PuzzleMaker CD-ROM
- Interactive Tutor Self-Assessment CD-ROM
- Presentation Plus! CD-ROM
- ExamView® Pro Testmaker CD-ROM

Turkey's climate varies throughout the country. The Anatolian plateau experiences the hot, dry summers and cold, snowy winters of the steppe climate. People living in the coastal areas enjoy a Mediterranean climate—hot, dry summers and mild, rainy winters.

Many of Turkey's people are farmers who live in the mild coastal areas. There they raise livestock and plant crops such as cotton, tobacco, fruits, and nuts for export. On the drier inland plateau, farmers grow mostly wheat and barley for use at home.

Turkey is seeking to join the European Union. The country has rich mineral resources of coal, copper, and iron. The most important industrial activities are oil refining and the making of textiles and clothing. Turkish factory workers also process foods and make cars, steel, and building materials. The country's beautiful beaches and historic sites have made tourism another growing industry.

Turkey's People Most of Turkey's 71.2 million people live in the northern part of Anatolia, on coastal plains, or in valleys. Almost 100 percent are Muslims, or followers of Islam. Turkish is the official language,

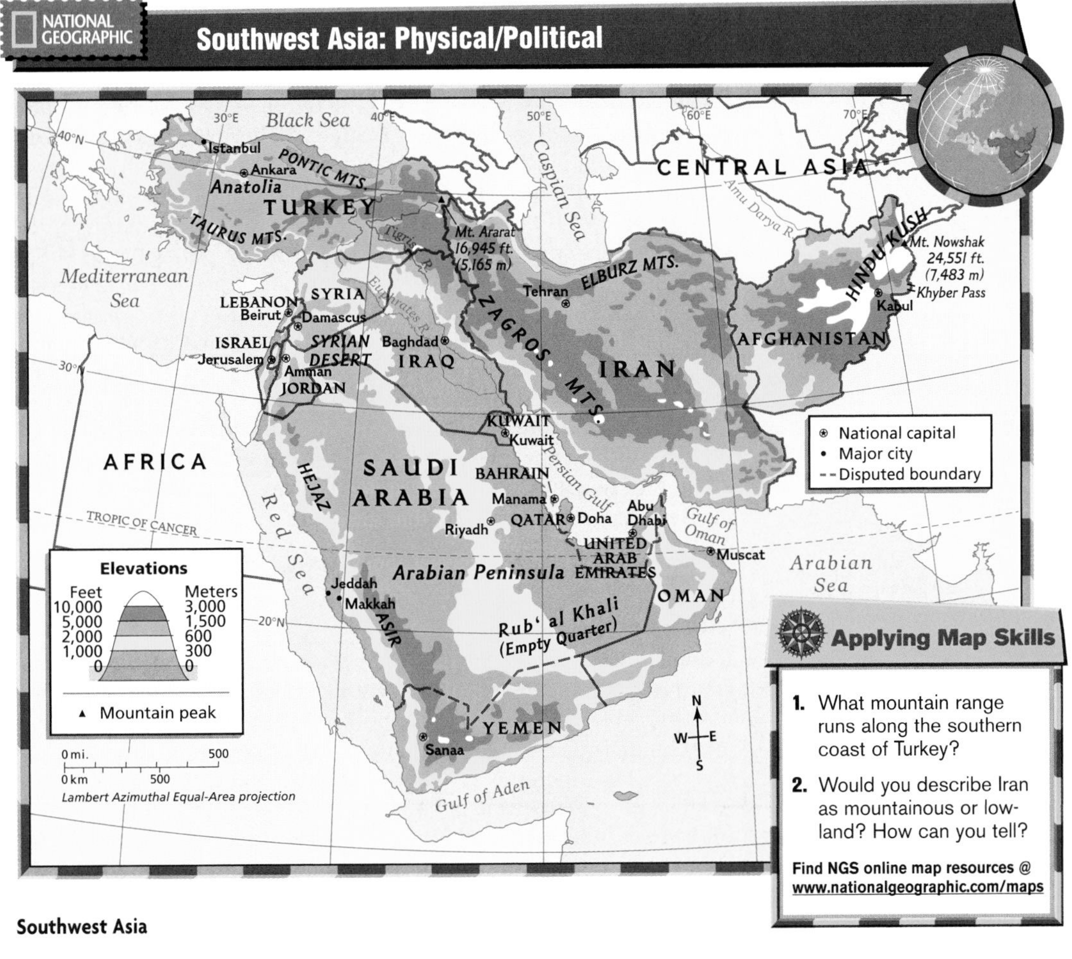

Southwest Asia

Reading Strategy Reading the Text

Identifying the Main Idea Remind students that the main idea of a reading selection can often be found in the first or last sentence. Some selections, however, do not have the main idea stated directly, and the reader has to use the details in the selection to figure it out. Have students read Section 1 and identify the main ideas. Ask students to explain how they identified the main ideas. L1

*Use the **Reading Skills Handbook** for more reading strategies.*

2 TEACH

Synthesizing Information

Help students create a web diagram illustrating the characteristics of Turkey's population. In the center circle, write "71.2 million people." Draw spokes with circles representing characteristics such as languages, religions, and occupations. Have students fill in the circles. L1

Daily Lecture and Discussion Notes

SOUTHWEST ASIA

Daily Lecture and Discussion Notes

Turkey, Syria, Lebanon, Jordan

Did You Know? Turkey is home to some of the oldest permanent human settlements. In Çatal Hüyük, Turkey, archaeologists have unearthed some of the oldest known examples of pottery, textiles, and plastered walls. Some of these artifacts date back to 7,000 B.C.

I. Turkey

A. Turkey is located on two continents. Three important waterways—the Bosporus, the Sea of Marmara, and the Dardanelles—separate the Asian and European parts of Turkey. Together, these waterways are called the Turkish Straits.

Applying Map Skills

Answers

1. Taurus Mountains
2. mountainous; because most of the country is at higher elevations

In-text Map Transparency Activity Ask students to identify the color and elevation for the plateau region in Turkey called the Anatolia. *(orange, between 5,000 feet, or 1,500 meters, and 2,000 feet, or 600 meters)*

Chapter 18

Section 1, pages 502–506

L1/ELL

Guided Reading Activity

SOUTHWEST ASIA

Guided Reading Activity 1

Turkey, Syria, Lebanon, Jordan

Reading Check Answer

It is the only city in the world that is located on two continents.

Measure student knowledge of physical features.

GeoQuiz Transparency

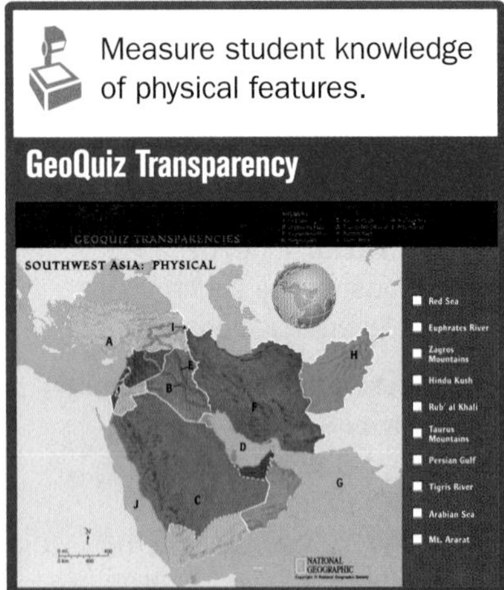

Festival Time

Kudret Özal lives in Söğüt, Turkey. Every year, she and her family attend a festival that honors a warrior ancestor. She says, "At night everyone gathers to sing, dance, and tell jokes and stories." According to custom, Kudret wears clothing that covers her head, arms, shoulders, and legs.

but Kurdish and Arabic are also spoken. Kurdish is the language of the Kurds, an ethnic group who make up about 20 percent of Turkey's people. They are seeking to unite with other Kurds from Iraq, Iran, and Syria to form an independent homeland. The Turkish government has tried to turn the Kurds away from Kurdish culture and language. Tensions between the two groups have resulted in violent clashes.

Almost 70 percent of Turkey's people live in cities or towns. **Istanbul** is Turkey's largest city with nearly 9 million people. It is the only city in the world located on two continents. Istanbul is known for its beautiful palaces, museums, and mosques. Because of its location at the entrance to the **Black Sea,** Istanbul is a major trading center. Turkey's capital and second-largest city is **Ankara.**

History and Culture Istanbul began as a Greek port called Byzantium more than 2,500 years ago. Later it was renamed Constantinople after the Roman emperor Constantine the Great. For almost 1,000 years, the city was the glittering capital of the Byzantine Empire.

Many of Turkey's people today are descendants of an Asian people called Turks. These people migrated to Anatolia during the A.D. 900s. To migrate means to move from one place to another. One group of Turks—the Ottomans—conquered Constantinople in the 1400s. They, too, renamed the city, calling it Istanbul. The city served as the capital of a powerful Muslim empire called the Ottoman Empire. This empire once ruled much of southeastern Europe, North Africa, and Southwest Asia. The map on page 518 shows the extent of this empire.

World War I led to the breakup of the Ottoman Empire. During most of the 1920s and 1930s, Kemal Atatürk, a military hero, served as Turkey's first president. He introduced many political and social changes to modernize the country. Turkey soon began to consider itself European as well as Asian. Many Turkish people, however, continued to value the Islamic faith. During the 1990s, Muslim and secular, or nonreligious, political groups struggled for control of Turkey's government.

Throughout the country, you can see traditional Turkish arts: colored tiles, finely woven carpets, and beautifully decorated books. Turkish culture, however, has its modern side as well. Folk music blends traditional and modern styles. Turkey also has recently produced many outstanding films that deal with social and political issues.

Reading Check **What is unusual about Turkey's largest city?**

Syria

South of Turkey, **Syria** has been a center of trade for centuries. Syria was a part of many empires, but in 1946 it became an independent country. Since the 1960s, one political party has controlled Syria's government. It does not allow many political freedoms.

Syria's land includes fertile coastal plains and valleys along the Mediterranean Sea. Inland mountains running north and south keep moist sea winds from reaching the eastern part of Syria. The vast **Syrian Desert** covers this eastern region.

Differentiated Instruction

Meeting Special Needs: Interpersonal Many ancient sites in Southwest Asia contain artifacts from simple pottery and carved stone to elaborate and beautiful works of wrought gold or silver. The governments of Southwest Asia work to preserve these remains of their heritage. Encourage students to help preserve the heritage of their own community. By volunteering at a local museum, library, or historical society, they can work to keep the past alive. Their work could range from preparing informational materials to cataloging materials or acting as a tour guide. **L1**

Refer to *Inclusion for the Middle School Social Studies Classroom Strategies and Activities* in the TCR.

Agriculture is Syria's main economic activity. Farmers grow mostly cotton, wheat, and fruit. The Syrian government has built dams on the **Euphrates River,** which flows through the country. These dams provide water for irrigation as well as hydroelectric power for cities and industries. Turkey, Syria's upstream neighbor, is building a huge dam that will reduce the flow of water to Syria and Iraq. Future conflict over water from this river is a possibility.

Like many other countries of Southwest Asia, Syria has reserves of oil—the country's main export. Other industries are food processing and textiles. Syrian fabrics have been highly valued since ancient times.

The Syrians Almost half of Syria's 17.5 million people live in rural areas. A few are bedouins—nomadic desert peoples who follow a traditional way of life. Most other Syrians live in cities. **Damascus,** the capital, is one of the oldest continuously inhabited cities in the world. It was founded as a trading center more than 4,000 years ago.

The people of Syria are mostly Arab Muslims. In many Syrian cities, you can see spectacular mosques and palaces. As in other Arab countries, hospitality is a major part of life. Group meals are a popular way of strengthening Syrian family ties and friendships. Common foods are lamb, flat bread, and bean dishes flavored with garlic and lemon.

✓Reading Check **On what river has Syria built dams?**

Lebanon

Lebanon is about half the size of New Jersey. Because the country is so small, you can swim in the warm Mediterranean Sea in the west, then throw snowballs in the mountains in the east—all in the same day.

Cedar trees once covered Lebanon. Now only a few lonely groves survive in a protected area. Still, Lebanon is the most densely wooded of all the Southwest Asian countries. Pine trees thrive on the mountains.

More than 60 percent of Lebanon's people work in service industries such as banking and insurance. Manufactured products include food, cement, textiles, chemicals, and metal products. Lebanese farmers grow citrus fruits, vegetables, grains, olives, and grapes on coastal land. Shrimp are harvested from the Mediterranean Sea.

The Lebanese People More than 88 percent of Lebanon's nearly 4.2 million people live in coastal urban areas. **Beirut** (bay•ROOT), the capital and largest city, was once a major banking and business center. European tourists called Beirut "the Paris of the East" because of its elegant shops and sidewalk cafés. Today, however, Beirut is still rebuilding after a civil war that lasted from 1975 to 1991.

Lebanon's civil war arose between Muslims and Christians. About 70 percent of the Lebanese are Arab Muslims. Most of the rest are Arab Christians. Many lives were lost in the war and many people fled as refugees. Lebanon's economy was almost destroyed. Israel invaded Lebanon during the war, finally withdrawing all its troops in 2000.

Arabic is the most widely spoken language in Lebanon. French is also an official language. Why? France ruled Lebanon before the country

Believe It or Not!

Petra

One of Jordan's major tourist attractions, Petra was built during the 300s B.C. The city's temples and monuments were carved out of cliffs in the Valley of Moses in Jordan. It was a major center of the spice trade that reached as far as China, Egypt, Greece, and India. Archaeologists have found dams, rock-carved channels, and ceramic pipes that brought water to the 30,000 people who once lived here.

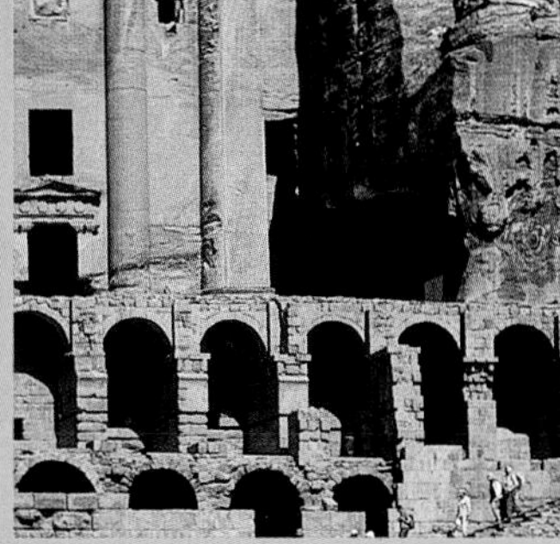

Chapter 18

Section 1, pages 502–506

✓ Reading Check Answer

Euphrates River

Assign Section 1 Assessment as homework or an in-class activity.

Have students use the Interactive Tutor Self-Assessment CD-ROM to review Section 1.

L2

Section Quiz

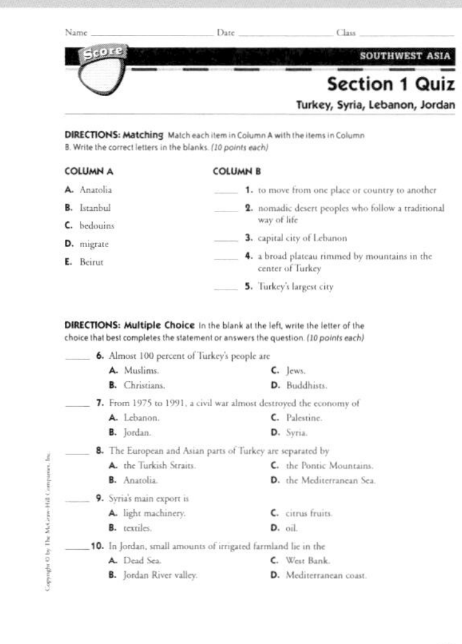

Name ______ Date ______ Class ______

Score

SOUTHWEST ASIA

Section 1 Quiz

Turkey, Syria, Lebanon, Jordan

DIRECTIONS: Matching Match each item in Column A with the items in Column B. Write the correct letters in the blanks. *(10 points each)*

COLUMN A	COLUMN B
A. Anatolia	____ 1. to move from one place or country to another
B. Istanbul	____ 2. nomadic desert peoples who follow a traditional way of life
C. bedouins	____ 3. capital city of Lebanon
D. migrate	____ 4. a broad plateau rimmed by mountains in the center of Turkey
E. Beirut	____ 5. Turkey's largest city

DIRECTIONS: Multiple Choice In the blank at the left, write the letter of the choice that best completes the statement or answers the question. *(10 points each)*

____ 6. Almost 100 percent of Turkey's people are
A. Muslims. C. Jews.
B. Christians. D. Buddhists.

____ 7. From 1975 to 1991, a civil war almost destroyed the economy of
A. Lebanon. C. Palestine.
B. Jordan. D. Syria.

____ 8. The European and Asian parts of Turkey are separated by
A. the Turkish Straits. C. the Pontic Mountains.
B. Anatolia. D. the Mediterranean Sea.

____ 9. Syria's main export is
A. light machinery. C. citrus fruits.
B. textiles. D. oil.

____10. In Jordan, small amounts of irrigated farmland lie in the
A. Dead Sea. C. West Bank.
B. Jordan River valley. D. Mediterranean coast.

283

Team-Teaching Activity

Science Point out that people have been living in cities in Southwest Asia for thousands of years. Records dating to the 1400s B.C. refer to Damascus. Invite a science teacher to class to describe how archaeologists piece together clues to ancient civilizations. If possible, have him or her supplement the presentation with photographs showing the partial evidence from which archaeologists work. Then organize students into groups and give them photographs of two ancient objects that you have cut into pieces of random sizes. Have the groups try to reassemble their "artifacts," and then try to interpret what they were used for. Have the groups share their findings with the class. **L1 ELL** 

EE6 The Uses of Geography: Standard 17

Chapter 18

Section 1, pages 502–506

Reading Check Answer

It was badly damaged in a civil war that lasted from 1975 to 1991.

Reading Check Answer

phosphate, potash, pottery, chemicals, and processed foods

L1/ELL

Reading Essentials and Study Guide

Name ______ Date ______ Class ______

SOUTHWEST ASIA

Reading Essentials and Study Guide 1

Turkey, Syria, Lebanon, Jordan

Key Terms

migrate to move from one place to another

bedouins nomadic desert people who follow a traditional way of life

Drawing From Experience

What is a shish kebab? Hint: You may have eaten one at a cookout. It is grilled meat and vegetables on a small metal rod. In Turkey, where the idea began, the rod would likely hold pieces of lamb and eggplant.

In this section, you will learn about Turkey, a land that lies on two continents. You will also learn about three other countries in this region—Syria, Lebanon, and Jordan.

Organizing Your Thoughts

Use the chart below to help you take notes. For each country, give one fact about its land and one fact about its cities.

Country	Fact About Land	Fact About Cities
Turkey	1.	2.
Syria	3.	4.
Lebanon	5.	6.
Jordan	7.	8.

228 229

CLOSE

Reading Strategy

Organizing Information
Have students create a concept web for each country in the section that includes facts about its geography, economy, history, and culture.

became independent in the 1940s. Local foods reflect a blend of Arab, Turkish, and French influences.

Reading Check Why is Beirut in the process of rebuilding?

Jordan

A land of contrasts, **Jordan** stretches from the fertile Jordan River valley in the west to dry, rugged country in the east. Jordan lacks water resources. Irrigated farmland lies in the Jordan River valley, however. Here farmers grow wheat, fruits, and vegetables. Jordan's desert is home to tent-dwelling bedouins who raise livestock.

Jordan also lacks energy resources. Many people work in service and manufacturing industries. The leading manufactured goods are phosphate, potash, pottery, chemicals, and processed foods.

People and Government Most of Jordan's 5.5 million people are Arab Muslims. They include more than 1 million Palestinian refugees. **Amman** is the capital and largest city. On a site occupied since prehistoric times, Amman has Roman and other ancient ruins.

During the early 1900s, the Ottoman Empire ruled this area. After the Ottoman defeat in World War I, the British set up a territory that became known as Jordan. It gained independence in 1946. The country has a constitutional monarchy. Elected leaders govern, but a king is the official head of state. From 1952 to 1999, King Hussein I ruled Jordan. He worked to blend the country's traditions with modern ways. The present leader of Jordan is Hussein's son, King Abdullah II.

Reading Check What are Jordan's leading manufactured goods?

Assessment

Defining Terms

1. **Define** migrate, bedouins.

Recalling Facts

2. **Economics** Name five of Turkey's agricultural products.
3. **Place** What landform covers eastern Syria?
4. **Place** What is the capital of Lebanon?

Critical Thinking

5. **Understanding Cause and Effect** How could a dam on the Euphrates River cause a conflict among Turkey, Syria, and Iraq?
6. **Analyzing Information** How has Istanbul's location made it a trading center?

Graphic Organizer

7. **Organizing Information** Draw a diagram like this one. Inside the large oval, list characteristics that Syria, Lebanon, and Jordan share.

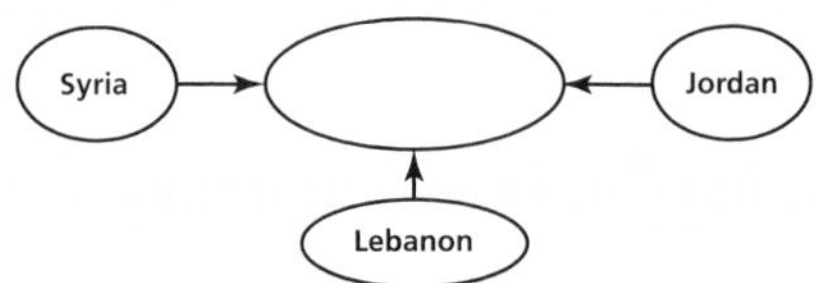

Applying Social Studies Skills

8. **Analyzing Maps** Study the map on page 503. What borders Turkey on the north? On the south?

506

Section 1 Assessment

1. The terms are defined in the Glossary.
2. *Possible answers:* cotton, tobacco, fruits, nuts, wheat, and barley
3. Syrian Desert
4. Beirut
5. because dams built by one country upstream reduce the flow of water to other countries downstream
6. It is located at the entrance to the Black Sea.
7. Students' diagrams should use facts from the section.
8. The Black Sea borders Turkey on the north and the Mediterranean Sea borders it on the south.

Making Connections

ART | SCIENCE | CULTURE | TECHNOLOGY

Carpet Weaving

For thousands of years, people have been making the hand-knotted floor coverings sometimes called Persian or Turkish rugs. Valued for their rich color and intricate design, these handmade rugs are unique works of art.

History

Most experts think that the nomadic peoples of Asia were among the first to make hand-knotted carpets. They used their carpets as wall coverings, curtains, saddlebags, and coverings for the bare ground in their tents. The soft, thick rugs blocked out the cold and could also be used as a bed or blanket.

As the nomads moved from place to place, they spread the art of carpet making to new lands and peoples. Throughout the years, the greatest carpet-producing areas have included Turkey, the republics of the Caucasus, Persia (Iran), and Turkmenistan. People in other countries, including Afghanistan, Pakistan, Nepal, India, and China, also became skilled carpet weavers.

Weaving and Knotting

Early nomads wove their carpets from sheep's wool on simple wooden looms that could be rolled up for traveling. Each carpet was woven with two sets of threads. The *warp* threads run from top to bottom, and the *weft* threads are woven from side to side. Hand-tied knots form the carpet's colorful pattern. A skillful weaver can tie about 15 knots a minute. The best carpets can have more than 500 knots per square inch!

Color and Design

The beauty of woven carpets comes from the endless combination of colors and designs. Over the years, various regions developed their own carpet patterns. These were passed down from generation to generation. Often the images hold special meanings. For instance, the palm and coconut often symbolize happiness and blessings.

▲ Turkish carpet weavers

The very first rugs were colored gray, white, brown, or black—the natural color of the wool. Then people learned to make dyes from plants and animals. The root of the madder plant, as well as certain insects, provided red and pink dye. Turmeric root and saffron supplied shades of yellow, and the indigo plant provided blue.

Making the Connection

1. How did the art of carpet weaving spread from one place to another?
2. What creates the pattern in a Turkish carpet?
3. **Drawing Conclusions** In what way do hand-knotted carpets combine art with usefulness?

Making Connections

Teach

Explain to students that rugs are made by tying knots of yarn or thread onto a stiff backing. **Ask:** **What is the most efficient and quickest way to do this?** *(by machine)* Explain that although most rugs are made by machines today, for most of human history—and still today in some places of the world—another process is used. Then have them read the feature. **L1**

More About Carpets

The oldest known woven carpet—dating from the 200s B.C.—was used by the Huns, a Turkish people, and includes the figures of cavalry riders, deer, flowers, and an abstract checkerboard pattern.

Interdisciplinary Connections

Art Carpet designs vary around the world, although natural patterns like flowers and abstract designs with geometric shapes are common. One typical characteristic of woven carpets is to use a repeated pattern. Give students a piece of graph paper and have them design their own pattern for a woven carpet.

Making the Connection

1. As nomads moved from place to place, they brought the craft with them.
2. the color and arrangement of knots
3. *Possible answer:* Each is handmade and a unique work of beauty, but each also serves a useful purpose, such as covering the floor or acting as curtains.

Chapter 18

Section 2, pages 508–512

Focus

Section Objectives

1. Describe the land and climate of Israel and the Palestinian territories.
2. Explain how Israel has developed a strong economy.
3. Discuss how the past has affected the people of Israel and the Palestinian territories.

BELLRINGER
Skillbuilder Activity

Project transparency and have students answer the question.

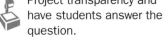

Daily Focus Skills Transparency

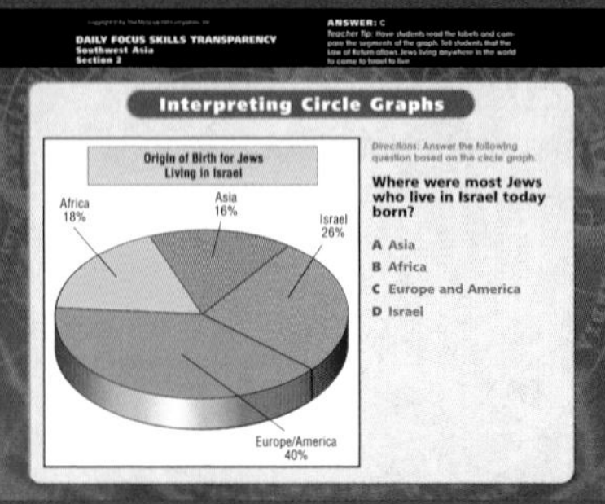

Reading Preview

■ **Activating Prior Knowledge**
Ask students what they know about Israel and the Palestinian territories from current events.

■ **Preteaching Vocabulary**
Have students study the Terms to Know list and think of ways to remember spellings. This may include dividing words into syllables or finding smaller words within each word.

Guide to Reading

Main Idea

After years of conflict, the Jewish nation of Israel and neighboring Arab countries still struggle to achieve peace.

Terms to Know

- kibbutz
- moshav
- Holocaust

Reading Strategy

Create a time line like this one. Write four key events on the time line that have occurred in Israel since 1948.

Section 2

Israel and the Palestinian Territories

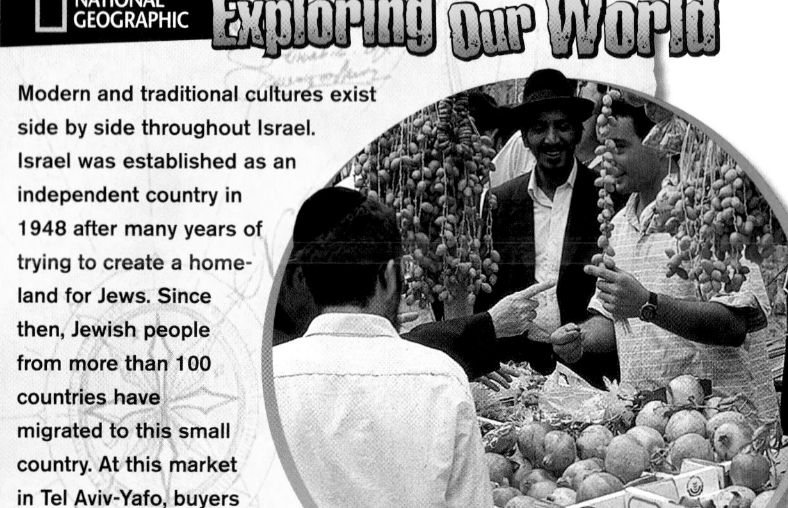

Modern and traditional cultures exist side by side throughout Israel. Israel was established as an independent country in 1948 after many years of trying to create a homeland for Jews. Since then, Jewish people from more than 100 countries have migrated to this small country. At this market in Tel Aviv-Yafo, buyers and sellers talk about current events and sports.

Israel lies at the eastern end of the Mediterranean Sea. Slightly larger than New Jersey, it is 256 miles (412 km) long from north to south and only 68 miles (109 km) wide from east to west.

Israel's Land and Climate

The mountains of Galilee lie in Israel's far north. East of these mountains is a plateau called the **Golan Heights.** South of the Golan Heights, between Israel and Jordan, is the **Dead Sea.** At 1,349 feet (411 m) below sea level, the shores of the Dead Sea are the lowest place on the earth's surface. The Dead Sea is also the earth's saltiest body of water—about nine times saltier than ocean water. The map on page 511 shows you where the Golan Heights and the Dead Sea are located.

In southern Israel, a desert called the **Negev** (NEH•GEHV) covers almost half the country. A fertile plain no more than 20 miles (32 km) wide lies along the country's Mediterranean coast. To the east, the

Section Resources

Reproducible Masters
- Reproducible Lesson Plan
- Daily Lecture and Discussion Notes
- Note-taking Guide
- Guided Reading Activity
- Reading Essentials and Study Guide
- Section Quiz

Transparencies
- Daily Focus Skills Transparency
- GeoQuiz Transparency

Multimedia
- Vocabulary PuzzleMaker CD-ROM
- Interactive Tutor Self-Assessment CD-ROM
- Presentation Plus! CD-ROM
- ExamView® Pro Testmaker CD-ROM

Jordan River cuts through the floor of a long, narrow valley before flowing into the Dead Sea.

Northern Israel has a Mediterranean climate with hot, dry summers and mild winters. About 40 inches (102 cm) of rain fall in the north each year. Southern Israel has a desert climate. Summer temperatures soar higher than 120°F (49°C), and annual rainfall is less than 1 inch (2.5 cm).

✓ Reading Check What plateau is found in northeastern Israel?

Israel's Economy

Israel's best farmland stretches along the Mediterranean coastal plain. For centuries, farmers here have grown citrus fruits, such as oranges, grapefruits, and lemons. Citrus fruits are still Israel's major agricultural export. Farther inland, you find that the desert actually blooms. This is possible because farmers add fertilizers to the soil and carefully use scarce water resources. In very dry areas, crops are grown with drip irrigation. This method uses computers to release specific amounts of water from underground tubes to the roots of plants. Israeli farmers also plant certain fruits and vegetables that do not absorb salts, such as the Negev tomatoes. As a result of technology, Israel's farmers feed not only the country's people—they even export some food to other countries.

Southwest Asia: Climate

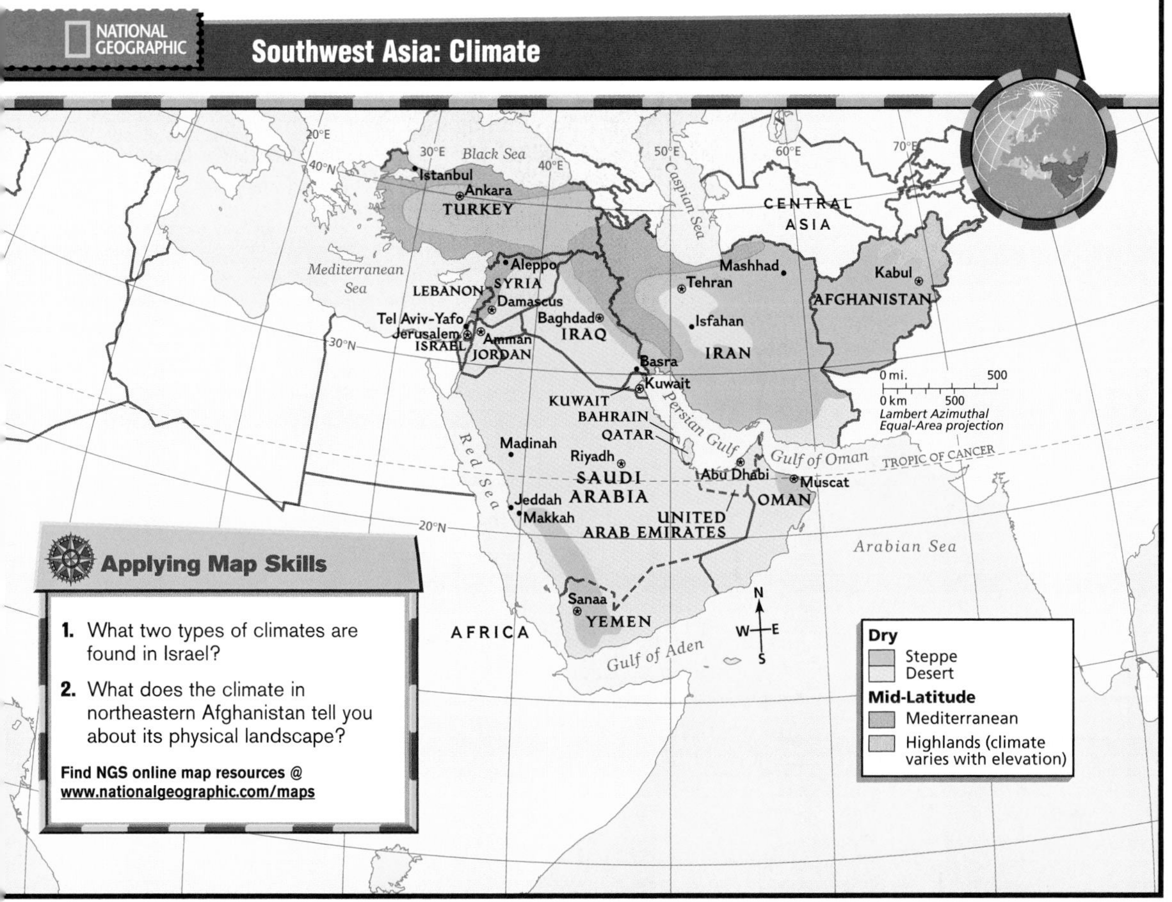

Applying Map Skills

1. What two types of climates are found in Israel?
2. What does the climate in northeastern Afghanistan tell you about its physical landscape?

Find NGS online map resources @ www.nationalgeographic.com/maps

Reading Strategy: Reading the Text

Clarifying Ideas Tell students that when they clarify what they have read, they are looking at different sections of the text in order to clear up what is confusing. Remind students that authors often build ideas on each another. If students do not clarify a confusing passage, then they may not understand main ideas or information that comes later. After students have read the section, have them go back and reread a confusing section more slowly. They should look up words they do not know and ask questions about what they do not understand. L1

*Use the **Reading Skills Handbook** for more reading strategies.*

TEACH

Making Comparisons Write "Modern Israel" and "Ancient Palestine" on the board. Have students examine the text and photographs in this section to find items that might be classified under each heading. Discuss ways that modern Israel reflects its ancient heritage. L1

Daily Lecture and Discussion Notes

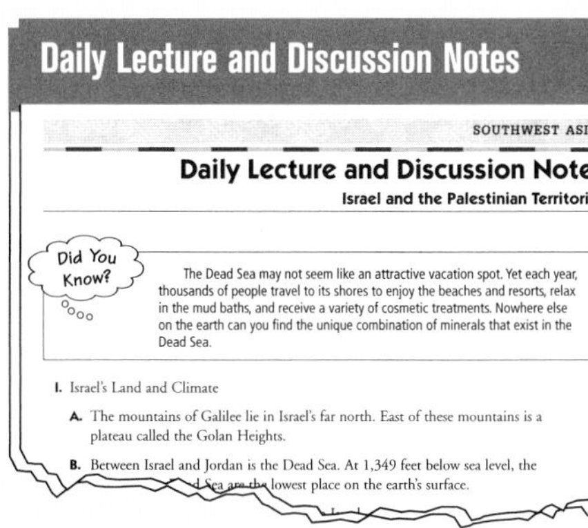

SOUTHWEST ASIA

Daily Lecture and Discussion Notes

Israel and the Palestinian Territories

Did You Know?

The Dead Sea may not seem like an attractive vacation spot. Yet each year, thousands of people travel to its shores to enjoy the beaches and resorts, relax in the mud baths, and receive a variety of cosmetic treatments. Nowhere else on the earth can you find the unique combination of minerals that exist in the Dead Sea.

I. Israel's Land and Climate

A. The mountains of Galilee lie in Israel's far north. East of these mountains is a plateau called the Golan Heights.

B. Between Israel and Jordan is the Dead Sea. At 1,349 feet below sea level, the Dead Sea are the lowest place on the earth's surface.

✓ Reading Check Answer

Golan Heights

Applying Map Skills

Answers

1. desert, Mediterranean
2. A highland climate reflects high elevations.

Skills Practice

How would you describe the relative location of a Mediterranean climate? *(tends to be near large bodies of water like the Mediterranean, Black, and Caspian Seas)*

More About the Photo

Israel A moshav differs from a kibbutz in that under the moshav system, each farm family owns its own land but sells its produce through the moshav. Members of a kibbutz, on the other hand, own and work the land in common. Sometimes a kibbutz also produces manufactured goods.

Caption Answer by using fertilizer and carefully using scarce water resources

Reading Check Answer

Tel Aviv-Yafo

L1/ELL

Guided Reading Activity

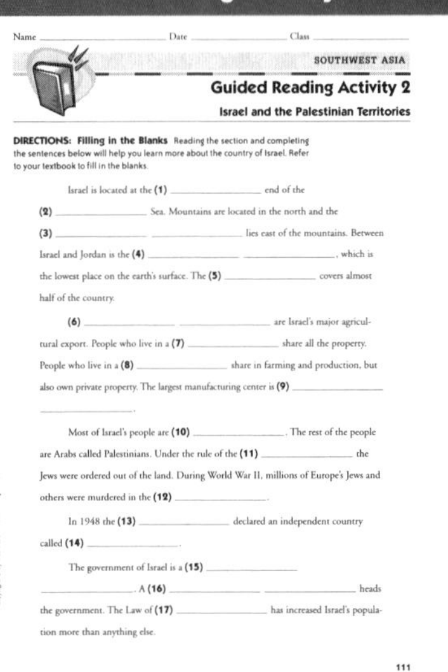

Name ______ Date ______ Class ______

SOUTHWEST ASIA

Guided Reading Activity 2

Israel and the Palestinian Territories

DIRECTIONS: Filling in the Blanks Reading the section and completing the sentences below will help you learn more about the country of Israel. Refer to your textbook to fill in the blanks.

Israel is located at the **(1)** ______ end of the **(2)** ______ Sea. Mountains are located in the north and the **(3)** ______ ______ lies east of the mountains. Between Israel and Jordan is the **(4)** ______ ______, which is the lowest place on the earth's surface. The **(5)** ______ covers almost half of the country.

(6) ______ ______ are Israel's major agricultural export. People who live in a **(7)** ______ share all the property. People who live in a **(8)** ______ share in farming and production, but also own private property. The largest manufacturing center is **(9)** ______ ______.

Most of Israel's people are **(10)** ______. The rest of the people are Arabs called Palestinians. Under the rule of the **(11)** ______ the Jews were ordered out of the land. During World War II, millions of Europe's Jews and others were murdered in the **(12)** ______.

In 1948 the **(13)** ______ declared an independent country called **(14)** ______.

The government of Israel is a **(15)** ______ ______. A **(16)** ______ ______ heads the government. The Law of **(17)** ______ has increased Israel's population more than anything else.

111

NATIONAL GEOGRAPHIC On Location

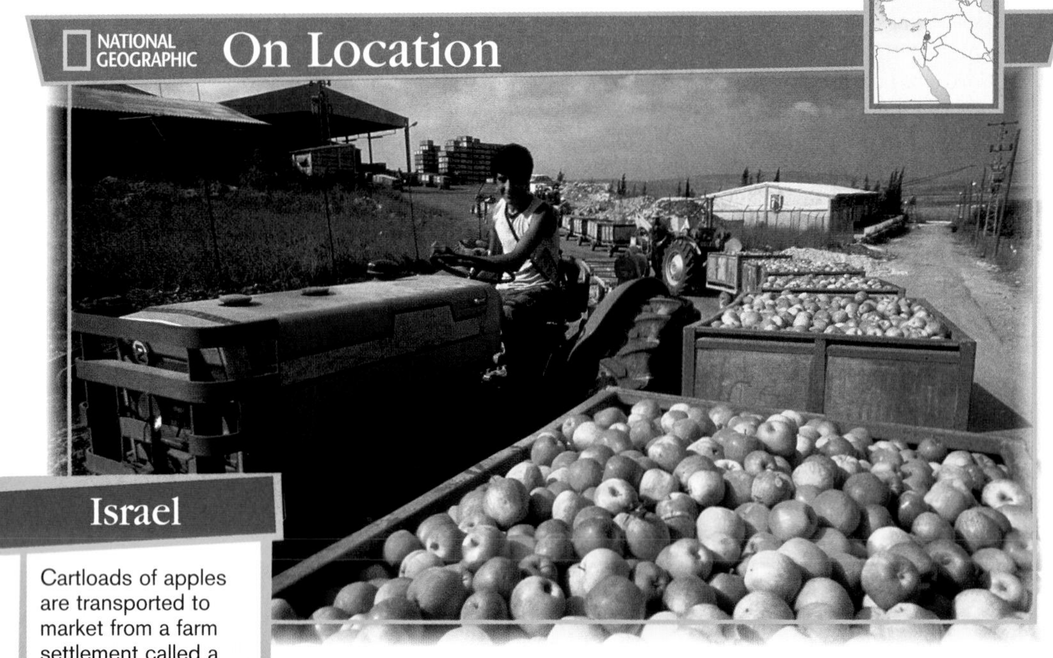

Israel

Cartloads of apples are transported to market from a farm settlement called a kibbutz in Metulla, Israel.

Place How do Israeli farmers make the desert bloom?

About 9 percent of Israelis live and work on farm settlements. Many join together to grow and sell crops. People in one type of settlement called a **kibbutz** (kih•BUTS) share all of the property. They may also produce goods such as clothing and electronic equipment. Another kind of settlement is called a **moshav** (moh•SHAHV). People in a moshav share in farming, production, and selling, but each person is allowed to own some private property as well.

Israel is the most industrialized country in Southwest Asia. Its economic development has been supported by large amounts of aid from European nations and the United States. Israel's skilled workforce produces electronic products, clothing, chemicals, food products, and machinery. Diamond cutting and polishing is also a major industry. The largest manufacturing center is the urban area of **Tel Aviv-Yafo.**

Mining is also important to Israel's economy. The Dead Sea area is rich in deposits of potash. The Negev is also a source of copper and phosphate, a mineral used in making fertilizer.

Reading Check **What city is the largest manufacturing center in Israel?**

The Israeli People

The area that is today Israel has been home to different groups of people over the centuries. The ancient traditions of these groups have led to current conflicts among their descendants. About 80 percent of Israel's 6.7 million people are Jews. The other 20 percent belong to an Arab people called Palestinians. Most Palestinians are Muslims, but some are Christians.

Differentiated Instruction

Meeting Special Needs: Interpersonal Point out that the problems between Israel and the Palestinian Arabs have existed for many years. Mention that several presidents and other top-ranking officials of the United States have tried to mediate between the two sides to reach a solution. Some schools have peer mediation programs. If that is the case in your school, invite a peer counselor to class to describe what mediation is and how it works. If not, describe the process yourself. After the presentation, have students write a paragraph summarizing how mediation might be applied to the Israeli-Palestinian conflict. **L2**

Refer to *Inclusion for the Middle School Social Studies Classroom Strategies and Activities* in the TCR.

As you learned in Chapter 16, the ancient Jews under King David created a kingdom in about 1000 B.C. Over time, the region was ruled by Greeks, Romans, Byzantines, Arabs, and Ottoman Turks. Under the Romans, the area was called Palestine. The Jews twice revolted against Roman rule but failed to win their freedom. In response, the Romans ordered all Jews out of the land.

Prejudice against the Jews caused them much hardship. In the late 1800s, some European Jews began to move back to Palestine. These settlers, known as Zionists, had planned to set up a safe homeland for Jews in their ancestral land.

The Birth of Israel During World War I, the British won control of Palestine. They supported a Jewish homeland there. Most of the people living in Palestine, however, were Arabs who also claimed the area as their homeland. To keep peace with the local Arab population, the British began to limit the number of Jews entering Palestine.

During World War II, Germans killed millions of Europe's Jews and others. The mass imprisonment and slaughter of European Jews is known as the **Holocaust.** It brought worldwide attention to Jews. After World War II, many remaining Jews were left homeless. The number who wanted to migrate to Palestine increased.

In 1947 the United Nations voted to divide Palestine into a Jewish and an Arab state. The Arabs in Palestine and in neighboring countries disagreed with this division. In May 1948, the British left the area, and the Jews set up the independent country of Israel in their part of Palestine. David Ben-Gurion (BEHN•gur•YAWN) became Israel's first leader.

War soon broke out between Israel and its Arab neighbors. The war ended in 1949 with Israel's victory. Many Palestinian Arabs fled to neighboring countries and became refugees. At the same time, many Jews from Europe and other nations began moving to the new state of Israel.

Israel later fought other wars with its Arab neighbors. In one conflict, Israel won control of neighboring Arab areas, such as the **West Bank** and the **Gaza Strip.** Palestinian Arabs, now left homeless, demanded their own country. During the 1970s and 1980s, many Palestinians and Israelis died fighting one another. Steps toward peace began when Israel and Egypt signed a treaty in 1979. Agreements made between Israel and Palestinian Arab leaders in 1993 and between Israel and Jordan in 1994 also moved the region toward peace.

Applying Map Skills

1. Where is the Gaza Strip located?
2. What city is located within the West Bank?

Find NGS online map resources @ www.nationalgeographic.com/maps

Chapter 18

Section 2, pages 508–512

Applying Map Skills

Answers

1. along the Mediterranean Sea
2. Jerusalem

Skills Practice

What country borders Israel on the southwest? *(Egypt)*

ASSESS

Assign Section 2 Assessment as homework or an in-class activity.

Have students use the Interactive Tutor Self-Assessment CD-ROM to review Section 2.

L2

Section Quiz

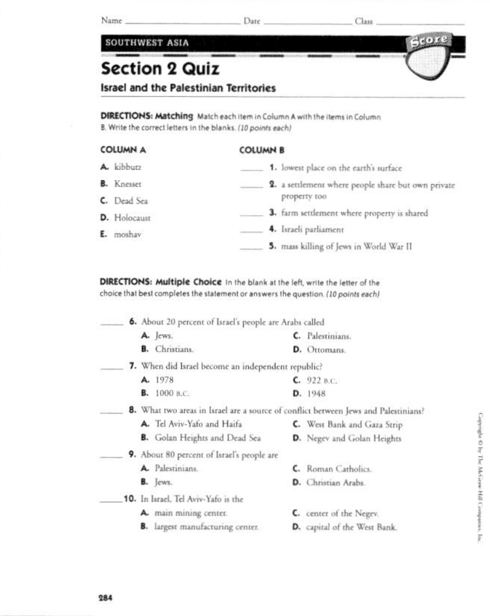

Name ______ Date ______ Class ______

SOUTHWEST ASIA

Score

Section 2 Quiz

Israel and the Palestinian Territories

DIRECTIONS: Matching Match each item in Column A with the items in Column B. Write the correct letters in the blanks. *(10 points each)*

COLUMN A	COLUMN B
A. kibbutz	____ 1. lowest place on the earth's surface
B. Knesset	____ 2. a settlement where people share but own private property too
C. Dead Sea	____ 3. farm settlement where property is shared
D. Holocaust	____ 4. Israeli parliament
E. moshav	____ 5. mass killing of Jews in World War II

DIRECTIONS: Multiple Choice In the blank at the left, write the letter of the choice that best completes the statement or answers the question. *(10 points each)*

____ 6. About 20 percent of Israel's people are Arabs called
A. Jews. C. Palestinians.
B. Christians. D. Ottomans.

____ 7. When did Israel become an independent republic?
A. 1978 C. 922 B.C.
B. 1000 B.C. D. 1948

____ 8. What two areas in Israel are a source of conflict between Jews and Palestinians?
A. Tel Aviv-Yafo and Haifa C. West Bank and Gaza Strip
B. Golan Heights and Dead Sea D. Negev and Golan Heights

____ 9. About 80 percent of Israel's people are
A. Palestinians. C. Roman Catholics.
B. Jews. D. Christian Arabs.

____ 10. In Israel, Tel Aviv-Yafo is the
A. main mining center. C. center of the Negev.
B. largest manufacturing center. D. capital of the West Bank.

284

Team-Teaching Activity

Government Israel's government is often in the news because the political strength or weakness of the current prime minister has an effect on peace negotiations with its neighbors. Invite a government teacher to class to explain the parliamentary system used in Israel, including such issues as the role of the prime minister and the cabinet, the large number of political parties, coalition governments, votes of no confidence, and the part played by Arab Israeli members of the Knesset. L1

EE4 Human Systems: Standard 9

Chapter 18

Section 2, pages 508–512

Measure student knowledge of political entities.

GeoQuiz Transparency

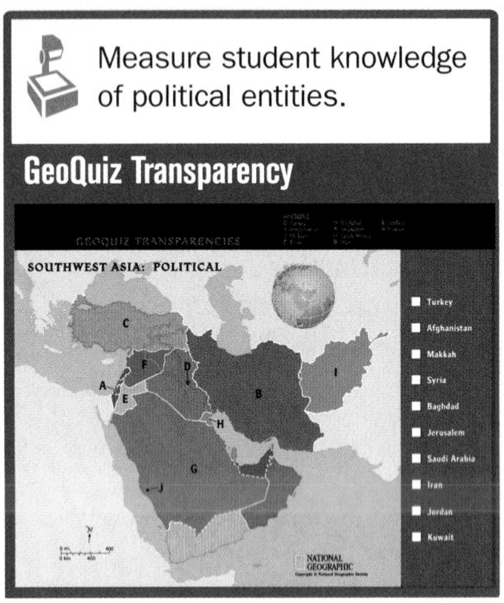

✓ Reading Check Answer

West Bank and Gaza Strip

L1/ELL

Reading Essentials and Study Guide

Name ______ Date ______ Class ______

SOUTHWEST ASIA

Reading Essentials and Study Guide 2

Israel and the Palestinian Territories

Key Terms

kibbutz Israeli farm settlement in which the people share farming, production, selling, and all property

moshav Israeli farm settlement in which the people share farming, production, and selling, but may own some private property

Holocaust mass imprisonment and killing of European Jews by German Nazis during World War II

CLOSE

Ask students to imagine that they are visiting the Palestinian territories. Have them write a postcard to a friend describing what they see.

In the 1993 agreement, Israel agreed to turn over two areas to the Palestinians. The West Bank lies on the western bank of the Jordan River and surrounds **Jerusalem.** The Gaza Strip is located on the Mediterranean coast and shares a border with Egypt. Find these areas on the map on page 511. Palestinians now have limited control of some of these areas. Yet some Jews still live in these two regions, and tensions between the two groups remain. Many issues—particularly control of Jerusalem—need to be settled before Palestinians achieve independence. In addition, Palestinian Arabs have fewer freedoms and economic opportunities than their Jewish neighbors. In late 2000, violence erupted again because of the inability to resolve these issues.

Israel Today More than 90 percent of Israel's people live in urban areas. The largest cities are Jerusalem, Tel Aviv-Yafo, and Haifa (HY•fuh). Israel proclaimed Jerusalem as its capital in 1950.

A single law—the Law of Return—increased Israel's population more than any other factor. Passed in 1950, the law states that Jews anywhere in the world can come to Israel to live. As a result, Jewish people have moved to Israel from many countries.

Israel is a democratic republic, which is a government headed by elected officials. A president represents the country at national events. A prime minister heads the government. The Israeli parliament, or Knesset, meets in a modern building in Jerusalem.

✓ Reading Check **Over what two areas do Palestinians have limited control?**

Section 2 Assessment

Defining Terms

1. Define kibbutz, moshav, Holocaust.

Recalling Facts

2. Location What is the lowest place on the earth's surface? What is its elevation?

3. History What is a Zionist?

4. Place What percentage of Israel's people live in urban areas? What percentage farm?

Critical Thinking

5. Analyzing Information What is the major disagreement between Israel and the Palestinians?

6. Drawing Conclusions Why do you think Israel has worked so hard to develop its agricultural and manufacturing industries?

Graphic Organizer

7. Organizing Information On a diagram like this one, list three things that helped Israel's agricultural success.

Applying Social Studies Skills

8. Analyzing Maps Study the map on page 511. What country borders Israel to the north? To the northeast? To the east?

Section 2 Assessment

1. The terms are defined in the Glossary.
2. shores of the Dead Sea; 1,349 feet (411 m) below sea level
3. European Jew who settled in Palestine in the late 1800s to make a safe homeland for Jews
4. more than 90 percent; 9 percent
5. Palestinian Arabs have demanded their own country and the return of their ancestral lands.
6. *Possible answer:* to help ensure its survival through a prosperous economy amid an unstable region
7. using fertilizer on soil, carefully using scarce water resources, using computers and technology to irrigate
8. Lebanon; Syria; Jordan

Section 3

The Arabian Peninsula

Guide to Reading

Main Idea
Money from oil exports has boosted standards of living in most countries of the Arabian Peninsula.

Terms to Know
- wadi
- desalinization
- caliph

Reading Strategy
Create a diagram like this one and give four examples of how oil has benefited the Arabian Peninsula.

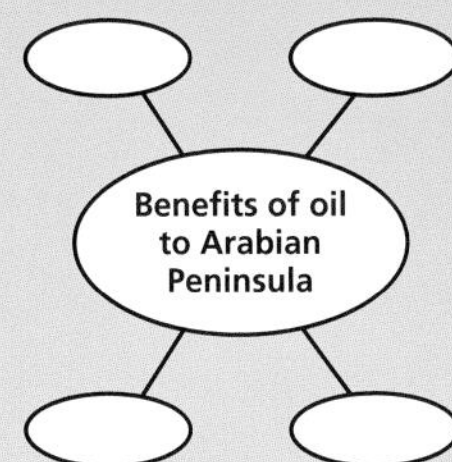

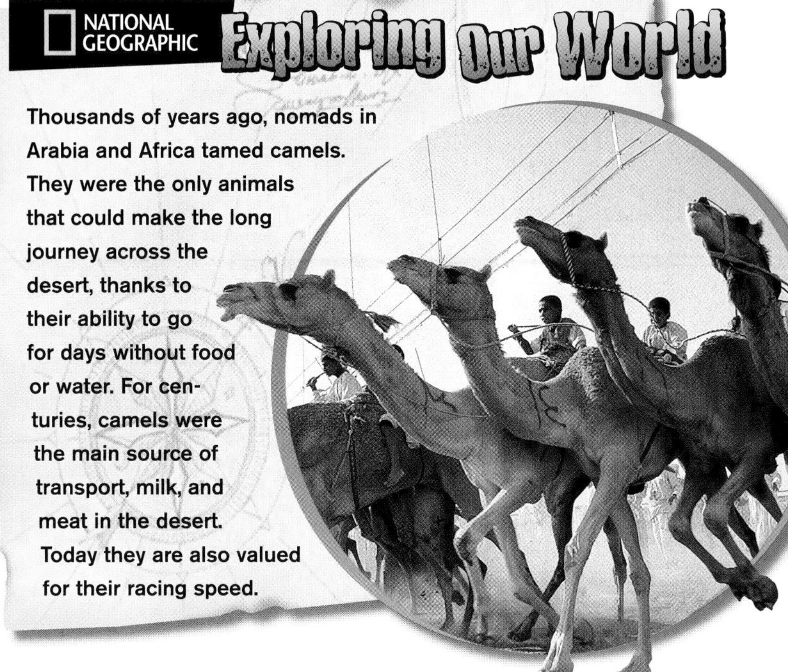

Thousands of years ago, nomads in Arabia and Africa tamed camels. They were the only animals that could make the long journey across the desert, thanks to their ability to go for days without food or water. For centuries, camels were the main source of transport, milk, and meat in the desert. Today they are also valued for their racing speed.

Find the Arabian Peninsula on the map on page 503. Notice that its highest elevations are in the south. The mostly desert land in the north borders Iraq, then it slopes toward the **Persian Gulf.**

Saudi Arabia

Saudi Arabia, the largest country in Southwest Asia, is about the size of the eastern half of the United States. Vast deserts cover this region. The largest and harshest desert is the **Rub' al Khali,** or Empty Quarter, in the southeast. The Empty Quarter has mountains of sand that reach heights of more than 1,000 feet (305 m).

Because of the generally dry, desert climate, Saudi Arabia has no rivers or permanent bodies of water. Highlands dominate the southwest, however, and rainfall there irrigates fertile croplands in the valleys. Water sometimes comes from seasonal **wadis,** or dry riverbeds filled by rainwater from rare downpours. The desert also holds oases.

1 Focus

Section Objectives
1. Outline what Saudi Arabia has achieved with its oil revenues.
2. Explain why Saudi Arabia is important to the world's Muslims.
3. Describe how oil affects the lives of people in the Persian Gulf states.

Reading Preview

■ **Activating Prior Knowledge** Have students describe how a country might be affected if it relied on another country for oil.

■ **Preteaching Vocabulary** Remind students to break down words by their prefixes, suffixes, and roots to understand their meanings.

Section Resources

Reproducible Masters
- Reproducible Lesson Plan
- Daily Lecture and Discussion Notes
- Note-taking Guide
- Guided Reading Activity
- Reading Essentials and Study Guide
- Section Quiz

Transparencies
- Daily Focus Skills Transparency

Multimedia
- Vocabulary PuzzleMaker CD-ROM
- Interactive Tutor Self-Assessment CD-ROM
- Presentation Plus! CD-ROM
- ExamView® Pro Testmaker CD-ROM

TEACH

Synthesizing Information Encourage students to make up a riddle for the location of each country in the Arabian Peninsula. Have volunteers read their riddles aloud. Then call on the class to identify the countries. L1

Daily Lecture and Discussion Notes

SOUTHWEST ASIA

Daily Lecture and Discussion Notes
The Arabian Peninsula

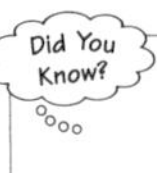

In Saudi Arabia, socializing with friends and family is the most popular form of entertainment. Public movie theaters are not allowed, but radio, television, and home videos are popular. Many Saudi men enjoy traditional sports, such as camel racing and horse racing. They also play basketball, soccer, and volleyball.

I. Saudi Arabia

A. Vast deserts cover Saudi Arabia, the largest country in Southwest Asia. The largest and harshest desert is the Rub' al Khali, or Empty Quarter. It has ... that reach heights of more than 1,000 feet.

Analyzing the Graph

Answer
64.1 percent

Skills Practice
What region has the least amount of oil reserves? *(U.S. and Canada)*

NATIONAL GEOGRAPHIC

World Oil Reserves

Analyzing the Graph

Southwest Asia has more known oil than all other regions of the world combined.

Region What percentage of the world's known oil reserves does Southwest Asia hold?

Visit twip.glencoe.com and click on **Chapter 18—Textbook Updates.**

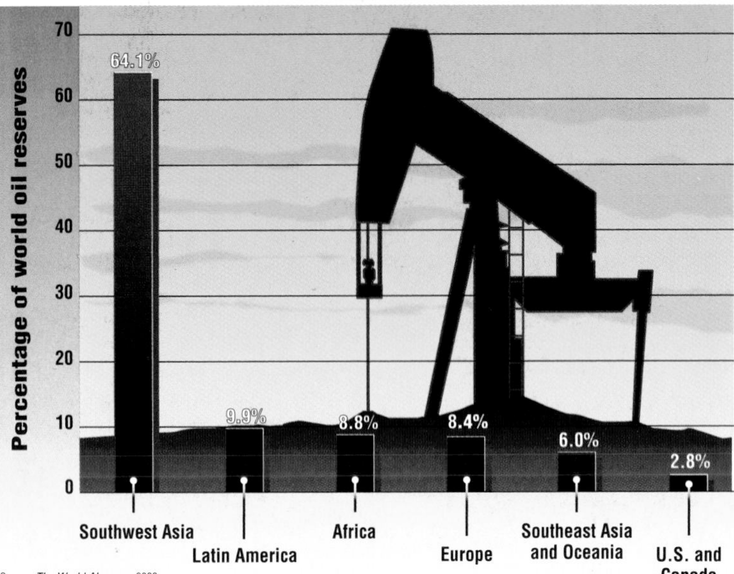

Source: *The World Almanac*, 2002.

An Oil-Based Economy Saudi Arabia holds a major share of the world's oil. This entire region is by far the world's leading producer of oil. The graph above compares the amount of oil reserves in Southwest Asia with those of other regions.

Since 1960 Saudi Arabia and some other oil producers have formed the Organization of Petroleum Exporting Countries (OPEC). Together they work to increase income from the sale of oil. Today OPEC countries supply more than 40 percent of the world's oil. By increasing or reducing supply, they are able to influence world oil prices.

Oil has helped Saudi Arabia boost its standard of living. Money earned by selling oil has built schools, hospitals, roads, and airports. Aware that someday its oil will run out, Saudi Arabia's government has been trying to broaden the economy. In recent years, it has given more emphasis to industry and agriculture. To get more water and grow more food, the government has spent much money on irrigation and **desalinization.** This is a process that takes salt out of seawater.

Spread of Islam In Chapter 16, you learned about Muhammad and the holy Islamic city of Makkah, which is located in western Saudi Arabia. After Muhammad died in A.D. 632, his closest followers chose a new leader known as a **caliph,** or "successor." Caliphs were both political and religious leaders.

Under the early caliphs, Arab Muslims conquered neighboring lands and created a vast empire. By A.D. 750, Islamic expansion—shown on the map on page 518—included North Africa and what is

Reading Strategy — Reading the Text

Reviewing Tell students that when they review their notes, they are more likely to remember what they have read. Students should think about the main ideas and organize them using graphic organizers and outlines to remember the information more easily. Remind students to take a few minutes each day to review their notes. This strategy helps students as they prepare for quizzes and tests. L1

Use the ***Reading Skills Handbook*** *for more reading strategies.*

now Spain extending almost to India. As time passed, many of the conquered peoples accepted Islam and the Arabic language.

By the end of the A.D. 900s, the Arab Empire had broken up into smaller kingdoms. During the next few centuries, waves of invaders known as Mongols swept into the Muslim world from central Asia. The Ottoman Turks, as you learned in Section 1, later moved into the region. They created a Muslim empire that lasted until the early 1900s.

Between the 700s and 1300s, scholars in the Arab Empire made many contributions to mathematics, astronomy, chemistry, medicine, and the arts. They also preserved much of the learning of the ancient Greeks and Romans. When Arabic texts were translated into Latin, European scholars could study the ancient works they thought had been lost after the fall of Rome.

The People Today In 1932 a monarchy led by the Saud family unified the country's many clans. The Saud family still rules today. Most of the 24.1 million Saudis live in towns and villages either along the oil-rich Persian Gulf coast or around oases. The capital and largest city, **Riyadh** (ree•YAHD), sits amid a large oasis in central Saudi Arabia. Once a small town, Riyadh now has skyscrapers and busy highways.

As in other Muslim countries, Islam strongly influences life in Saudi Arabia. Government, business, school, and home schedules are timed to Islam's five daily prayers and two major yearly celebrations. Much government attention has been given to preparing Makkah and Madinah for the several million Muslims who visit each year. Saudi customs concerning the roles of women in public life are stricter than in most other Muslim countries. Saudi women may work outside the home but only in jobs that avoid close contact with men.

Reading Check What influences almost every part of Saudi Arabian culture?

The Persian Gulf States

Kuwait (ku•WAYT), **Bahrain** (bah•RAYN), **Qatar** (KAH•tuhr), and the **United Arab Emirates** are located along the Persian Gulf. Beneath their flat deserts and offshore areas lie vast deposits of oil. The Persian Gulf states have used profits from oil exports to build prosperous economies. Political and business leaders, however, are aware that oil revenues depend on constantly changing world oil prices. As a result, they have encouraged the growth of other industries. Their goal is to build a more varied economy.

The people of the Persian Gulf states once made a living from activities such as pearl diving, fishing, and camel herding. Now they have modern jobs in the oil and natural gas industries. They also enjoy a high standard of living. Using income from oil, their governments provide free education, health care, and other services. Many workers from other countries have settled in these countries. They work in the modern cities and oil fields to benefit from the economic boom.

Reading Check How have the economies of the Persian Gulf states changed since the discovery of oil?

Social Studies Online
Web Activity Visit The World and Its People Web site at twip.glencoe.com and click on Chapter 18—Student Web Activities to learn more about the Islamic religion.

Chapter 18

Section 3, pages 513–516

Reading Check Answer

Islamic religion

L1/ELL

Guided Reading Activity

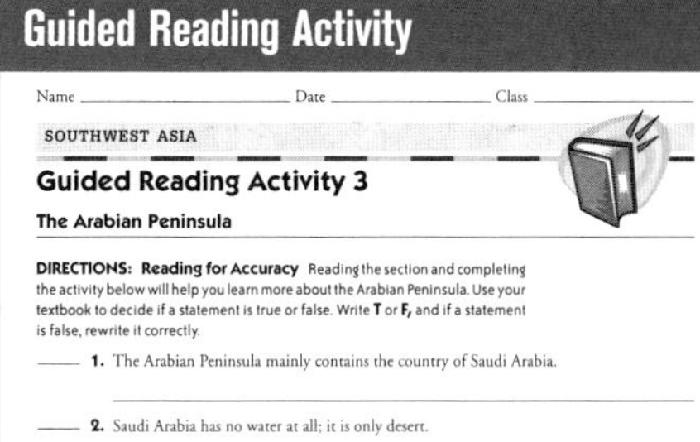
Name ______ Date ______ Class ______

SOUTHWEST ASIA

Guided Reading Activity 3

The Arabian Peninsula

DIRECTIONS: Reading for Accuracy Reading the section and completing the activity below will help you learn more about the Arabian Peninsula. Use your textbook to decide if a statement is true or false. Write **T** or **F**, and if a statement is false, rewrite it correctly.

____ 1. The Arabian Peninsula mainly contains the country of Saudi Arabia.

____ 2. Saudi Arabia has no water at all; it is only desert.

____ 3. Saudi Arabia's economy is based on oil.

Reading Check Answer

They have become prosperous.

Objectives and answers to the Student Web Activity can be found in the Web Activity Lesson Plan at twip.glencoe.com

Assign Section 3 Assessment as homework or an in-class activity.

Have students use the Interactive Tutor Self-Assessment CD-ROM to review Section 3.

Differentiated Instruction

Meeting Special Needs: Visual/Spatial Organize students into groups of five. Inform the groups that their task is to create an illustrated wall chart showing the major geographic features of the Arabian Peninsula. Ensure that each group member is assigned a task, including research, art and design, writing, constructing the chart, and so on. Have groups display and discuss their completed charts. L1

L2

Section Quiz

Name ____________ Date ____________ Class ____________

Score

SOUTHWEST ASIA

Section 3 Quiz

The Arabian Peninsula

DIRECTIONS: Matching Match each item in Column A with the items in Column B. Write the correct letters in the blanks. *(10 points each)*

COLUMN A	COLUMN B
A. desalinization	____ 1. dry riverbeds filled by rainwater from rare downpours
B. Yemen	____ 2. religious leader of Islam
C. wadis	____ 3. process of removing salt from seawater
D. caliph	____ 4. a country at the southern end of the Arabian Peninsula
E. Muscat	____ 5. the capital city of Oman

Reading Check Answer

It is the only country of the Arabian Peninsula without large deposits of oil.

L1/ELL

Reading Essentials and Study Guide

Name ____________ Date ____________ Class ____________

SOUTHWEST ASIA

Reading Essentials and Study Guide 3

The Arabian Peninsula

Key Terms

wadi dry riverbed occasionally filled by rainwater
desalinization process of taking salt out of seawater
caliph political and religious leader of Muslims

Drawing From Experience

CLOSE

Reading Strategy

Writing a Paragraph Have students write a paragraph describing how oil and Islam affect life in the countries of the Arabian Peninsula.

▲ A village in Oman

Oman and Yemen

At the southeastern and southern ends of the Arabian Peninsula are the countries of **Oman** and **Yemen.** Oman is largely desert, but its bare land yields oil—the basis of the country's economy. Until recently, most of the people of Oman lived in rural villages. The oil industry has drawn many of these people—and foreigners—to **Muscat,** the country's capital. Other natural resources include natural gas, copper, marble, and limestone. Agricultural products include dates, bananas, camels, and cattle.

Oman's location also has made the country important to world oil markets. The northern part of Oman guards the strategic Strait of Hormuz. Oil-bearing tankers have to go through this narrow waterway to pass from the Persian Gulf into the **Arabian Sea.**

Southwest of Oman lies Yemen, which is made up of a narrow coastal plain and inland mountains. In ancient times, Yemen was famous for its rich trade in fragrant tree resins such as myrrh (MUHR) and frankincense. Yemen's capital, the walled city of **Sanaa** (sahn•AH), was once a crossroads for camel caravans that carried goods from as far away as China.

Today Yemen is the only country of the Arabian Peninsula that does not have large deposits of oil. Most of the people are farmers or herd sheep and cattle. They live in the high fertile interior where Sanaa is located. Farther south lies Aden (AH•duhn), a major port for ships traveling between the Arabian Sea and the Red Sea.

Reading Check What makes Yemen different from other countries in the Arabian Peninsula?

Assessment

Defining Terms

1. **Define** wadi, desalinization, caliph.

Recalling Facts

2. **Place** What is the Empty Quarter?
3. **Government** Who rules Saudi Arabia, and what is its form of government?
4. **Culture** What is the significance of the city of Makkah?

Critical Thinking

5. **Analyzing Information** Why is the Strait of Hormuz considered to be of such strategic importance?
6. **Drawing Conclusions** How do the nations of OPEC affect your life?

Graphic Organizer

7. **Organizing Information** On a diagram like this one, list three ways that Islam influences life in Saudi Arabia.

Applying Social Studies Skills

8. **Analyzing Graphs** Study the graph on page 514. Which region of the world has the second-largest reserves of oil?

Section 3 Assessment

1. The terms are defined in the Glossary.
2. largest and harshest desert in Saudi Arabia
3. It is a monarchy ruled by members of the Saud family.
4. It is Islam's holiest city, and all Muslims are expected to make a journey to it in their lives.
5. Oil tankers must pass through this narrow strait on the way from the Persian Gulf to the Arabian Sea.
6. They control the production and price of oil, which affects the availability and prices of gasoline and other petroleum-based products.
7. Answers will vary.
8. Latin America

Guide to Reading

Main Idea

Iraq, Iran, and Afghanistan have recently fought wars and have undergone sweeping political changes.

Terms to Know

- alluvial plain
- embargo
- shah
- Islamic republic

Reading Strategy

Create a chart like this one and list one fact about the people in each country.

Country	People
Iraq	
Iran	
Afghanistan	

Section 4 Iraq, Iran, and Afghanistan

NATIONAL GEOGRAPHIC Exploring Our World

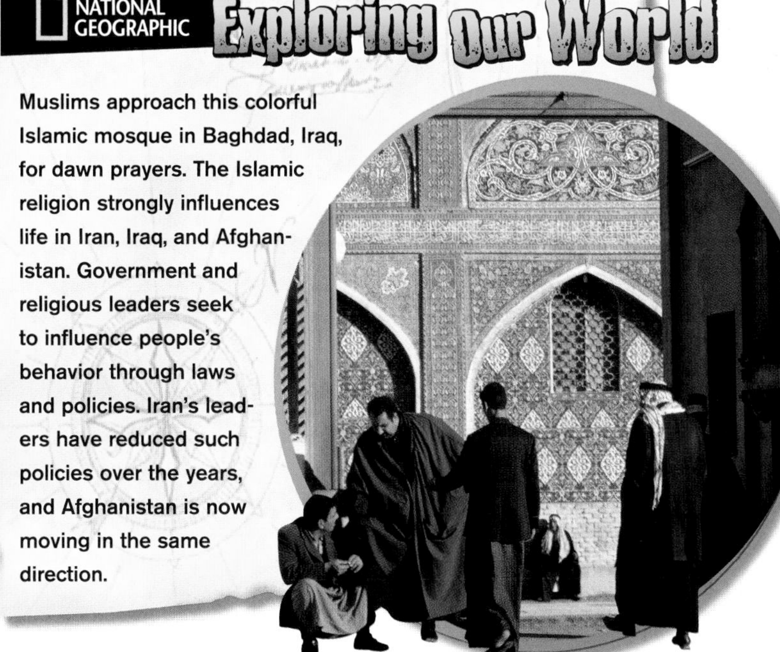

Muslims approach this colorful Islamic mosque in Baghdad, Iraq, for dawn prayers. The Islamic religion strongly influences life in Iran, Iraq, and Afghanistan. Government and religious leaders seek to influence people's behavior through laws and policies. Iran's leaders have reduced such policies over the years, and Afghanistan is now moving in the same direction.

Iraq, Iran, and Afghanistan are located in a region where some of the world's oldest civilizations developed. This region has experienced turmoil throughout history and even today.

Iraq

As you read in Chapter 16, the world's first known cities arose between the Tigris and Euphrates Rivers. These rivers are the major geographic features of **Iraq.** Between the two rivers is an **alluvial plain,** or an area built up by rich fertile soil left by river floods. Most farming takes place here. Farmers grow wheat, barley, dates, cotton, and rice.

Oil is the country's major export. Iraq's factories process foods and make textiles, chemicals, and construction materials.

People and Government About 70 percent of Iraq's 24.2 million people live in urban areas. **Baghdad,** the capital, is the largest city.

517

1 Focus

Section Objectives

1. Explain why the economy of Iraq has slowed.
2. Discuss how a religious government came to power in Iran.
3. Describe Afghanistan's land and culture.

BELLRINGER Skillbuilder Activity

Project transparency and have students answer the question.

Daily Focus Skills Transparency

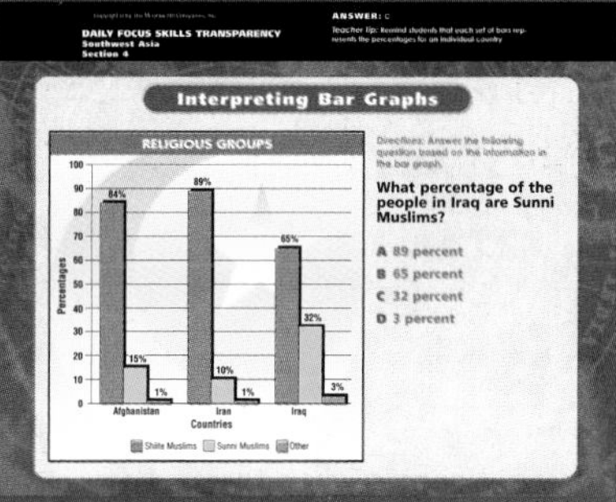

Reading Preview

■ **Activating Prior Knowledge** **Where did the earliest civilization arise in Egypt?** *(along the Nile River)*

■ **Preteaching Vocabulary** Have students guess at the meaning of the term *Islamic republic* based on what they know about the two words.

Section Resources

Reproducible Masters
- Reproducible Lesson Plan
- Daily Lecture and Discussion Notes
- Note-taking Guide
- Guided Reading Activity
- Reading Essentials and Study Guide
- Section Quiz

Transparencies
- Daily Focus Skills Transparency

Multimedia
- Vocabulary PuzzleMaker CD-ROM
- Interactive Tutor Self-Assessment CD-ROM
- Presentation Plus! CD-ROM
- ExamView® Pro Testmaker CD-ROM
- MindJogger Videoquiz

Chapter 18

Section 4, pages 517–520

TEACH

Determining Cause and Effect Challenge students to determine the impact that climate and landscape have on economic activities, housing, clothing, and recreation in Iraq, Iran, and Afghanistan. Note their responses on the board. Ask students to use these examples to write a paragraph explaining the cause-and-effect relationship between physical geography and life in these countries. L3

Daily Lecture and Discussion Notes

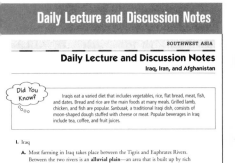

SOUTHWEST ASIA

Daily Lecture and Discussion Notes

Iraq, Iran, and Afghanistan

Did You Know?

Iraqis eat a varied diet that includes vegetables, rice, flat bread, meat, fish, and dates. Bread and rice are the main foods at many meals. Grilled lamb, chicken, and fish are popular. Sanbusak, a traditional Iraqi dish, consists of moon-shaped dough stuffed with cheese or meat. Popular beverages in Iraq include tea, coffee, and fruit juices.

I. Iraq

A. Most farming in Iraq takes place between the Tigris and Euphrates Rivers. Between the two rivers is an **alluvial plain**—an area that is built up by rich fertile soil left by river floods.

...port. Baghdad is the capital and largest city. Muslim Arabs

Applying Map Skills

Answers

1. 632–661

2. no

Skills Practice

Where did Islam begin?

(in Arabia)

Reading Check Answer

Tigris and Euphrates Rivers

NATIONAL GEOGRAPHIC

Spread of Islam

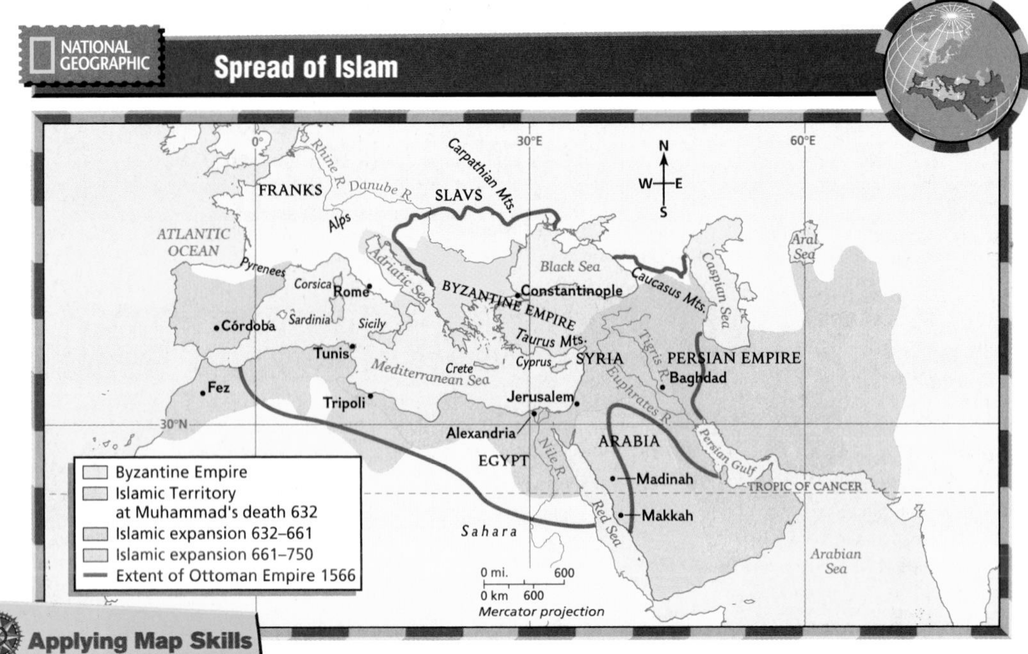

Applying Map Skills

1. Which period of Islamic expansion included Egypt?

2. Did Islamic territory completely encircle the Mediterranean Sea?

Find NGS online resources @ www.nationalgeographic.com/maps

From the A.D. 700s to 1200s, Baghdad was the center of a large Muslim empire that made many advances in the arts and sciences. Muslim Arabs make up the largest group in Iraq's population. The second-largest group consists of another Muslim people, the Kurds, who want to form their own country.

Modern Iraq gained its independence as a kingdom in 1932. In 1958 the last king was overthrown in a revolt. Since then, military leaders have governed Iraq as a dictatorship. Dictator Saddam Hussein ruled with an iron hand from 1979 to 2003. In the 1980s, Iraq fought a bloody war with its neighbor Iran. Then in 1990, partly because of a dispute over oil, Iraq invaded neighboring Kuwait. This action led to the Persian Gulf War in 1991. A United Nations force led by the United States pushed Iraqi troops out of Kuwait.

Saddam stayed in power despite losing the war. He refused to agree to demands from the United Nations that he give up his vast store of destructive weapons. As a result, the United Nations continued an embargo on trade with Iraq that it had introduced before the war. An **embargo** is an order that restricts trade with another country. This severely damaged Iraq's economy.

In the early 2000s, the United Nations sent experts into Iraq to search for weapons of mass destruction. The United States did not believe Saddam was fully cooperating. In March 2003, American and British forces invaded Iraq. Less than a month later, Saddam was overthrown, and plans were made to create a democratic government in Iraq. Then Saddam was captured by a U.S.-led coalition in December 2003.

Reading Check **What two rivers have influenced the history of Iraq?**

Differentiated Instruction

Meeting Special Needs: Verbal/Linguistic Suggest that students who learn better verbally re-create the information in the maps in the chapter in verbal form. Have them review each map—political, physical, climate, economic activity, and population density—to identify what information they can learn about the three countries in the section. Guide students' observations by asking questions such as: **What physical features influence the climate of these countries? Where do most people live in each country? What resources influence economic activities in these countries?** Then have them write their findings in sentences and use these as study aids. L1

Refer to *Inclusion for the Middle School Social Studies Classroom Strategies and Activities* in the TCR.

Iran

Once known as Persia, **Iran** is slightly larger than Alaska. Two vast ranges—the **Elburz Mountains** and the **Zagros Mountains**—surround a central desert plateau. Iran is an oil-rich nation. The first oil wells in Southwest Asia were drilled here in 1908. Like Saudi Arabia, Iran is trying to promote other industries in order to become less dependent on oil earnings. Major Iranian industries produce textiles, metal goods, construction materials, and beautiful carpets valued worldwide. Farmers grow wheat, rice, sugar beets, and cotton. Some use ancient underground channels to bring water to their fields. Iran is also the world's largest producer of pistachio nuts.

The Iranian People Iran's 66.6 million people differ from those of other Southwest Asian countries. More than one-half are Persians, not Arabs or Turks. The Persians' ancestors migrated from Central Asia centuries ago. They speak Farsi, or Persian, the official language of Iran. Other languages include Kurdish, Arabic, and Turkish. About 65 percent of Iranians live in urban areas. **Tehran,** located in northern Iran, is the largest city and the capital. Iran is also home to about 2 million people from Iraq and Afghanistan who have fled recent wars. Nearly 98 percent of Iran's people practice some form of Islam.

Iran's Government About 2,000 years ago, Iran was the center of the powerful Persian Empire ruled by kings known as **shahs.** In 1979 religious leaders overthrew the last monarchy. Iran is now an **Islamic republic,** a government run by Muslim religious leaders. The government has introduced laws based on its understanding of the Quran. Many Western customs seen as a threat to Islam are forbidden here.

✓ Reading Check How do Iranians differ in ethnic background from most other Southwest Asians?

Iran and Afghanistan

An Iranian family picnics in the hills above Tehran (below left). Under the Taliban, women in Afghanistan were rarely allowed in public (below right).

Government What form of government does Iran have? What group led Afghanistan in the 1990s?

NATIONAL GEOGRAPHIC **On Location**

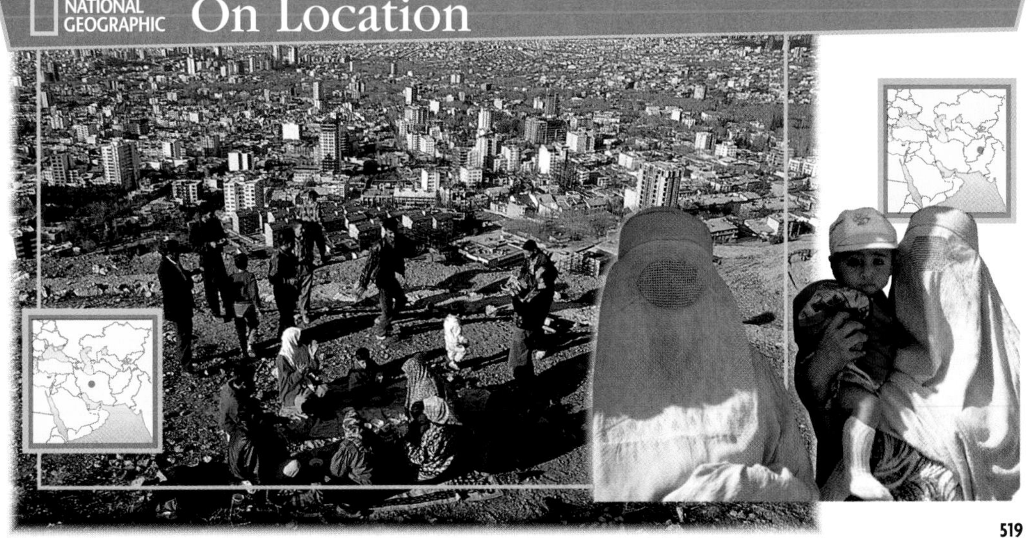

Chapter 18

Section 4, pages 517–520

More About the Photos

Women in Afghanistan
When women appear in public in Afghanistan, they wear a long gown called a *burka* that covers them from head to foot.

Caption Answer an Islamic republic; a group called the Taliban

L1/ELL

Guided Reading Activity

Name ______ Date ______ Class ______

SOUTHWEST ASIA

Guided Reading Activity 4

Iraq, Iran, and Afghanistan

DIRECTIONS: Outlining Reading the section and completing the outline below will help you learn more about the countries of Iraq, Iran, and Afghanistan. Refer to your textbook to fill in the blanks.

I. Iraq

A. The ______ and ______ Rivers are the major geographic features of this country.

1. Farming takes place on an ______ ______.

2. ______ is the country's major export.

B. About 70 percent of the people live in ______ areas.

______ make up the largest population group.

✓ Reading Check Answer

More than half are Persians, not Arabs or Turks, as found in other Southwest Asian countries, and they speak Farsi.

3 Assess

Assign Section 4 Assessment as homework or an in-class activity.

Have students use the Interactive Tutor Self-Assessment CD-ROM to review Section 4.

Critical Thinking Activity

Recognizing Bias Tell students that in 2003 Shirin Ebadi, a lawyer and human rights activist, became Iran's first Nobel Peace Prize winner. Add that she advocated greater rights for women and children and tried to change Iranian laws related to divorce and inheritance. Then read the following quote from a BBC news report: "Shirin Ebadi has written books calling for greater legal protection for Iranian children and disclosing alleged human rights violations by the Iranian authorities. . . official reactions [to her prize] have been low-key." **Ask: Why do you think Iranian officials had little to say about Iran's first Nobel Peace Prize winner?** *(because she was critical of their policies)* **L2**

Chapter 18

Section 4, pages 517–520

L2

Section Quiz

Name ____________ Date ____________ Class ____________

SOUTHWEST ASIA

Score

Section 4 Quiz

Iraq, Iran, and Afghanistan

DIRECTIONS: Matching Match each item in Column A with the items in Column B. Write the correct letters in the blanks. *(10 points each)*

COLUMN A	COLUMN B
A. alluvial plain	____ **1.** capital city of Iran
B. embargo	____ **2.** area that is built up by rich fertile soil left by river floods
C. shahs	____ **3.** Persian kings
D. Islamic republic	____ **4.** an order that restricts or prohibits trade with another country
E. Tehran	____ **5.** government run by Muslim religious leaders

L1/ELL

Reading Essentials and Study Guide

Name ____________ Date ____________ Class ____________

SOUTHWEST ASIA

Reading Essentials and Study Guide 4

Iraq, Iran, and Afghanistan

Key Terms

alluvial plain area built up by rich soil left by river floods
embargo limit or ban on trade with a country
shah former king of Iran
Islamic republic government run by Muslim religious leaders

Drawing From Experience

... that you are a girl living in Afghanistan. Until several years ... freedoms that you currently have. You would ...

The Tigris and Euphrates ... Persian Gulf. Between the Tigris and Euphrates ... of rich soil built up by river floods.

Reading Check Answer

the Khyber Pass

Close

Reading Strategy

Comparing Have students write three paragraphs comparing the countries in this section, with one paragraph each on their economies, government, and people.

Afghanistan

Landlocked **Afghanistan** (af•GA•nuh•STAN) is mostly covered with the rugged peaks of the **Hindu Kush** mountain range. The Khyber (KY•buhr) Pass cuts through the mountains and for centuries has been a major trade route linking Southwest Asia with other parts of Asia. The capital, **Kabul** (KAH•buhl), lies in a valley.

Afghanistan's 28.7 million people are divided into about 20 different ethnic groups. The two largest groups are the Pashtuns and the Tajiks. Almost 70 percent of the people farm, growing wheat, fruits, and nuts and herding sheep and goats.

A Country at War During the 1980s, the Afghan people fought against Soviet troops who had invaded their country. When the Soviets left Afghanistan in 1989, the Afghan people faced poverty, food shortages, and rising crime. The country collapsed into civil war. For leadership, many people turned to the Taliban, a group of fighters educated at Islamic schools in Pakistan. They set up very strict laws based on their view of Islam. For example, men had to grow beards, and women had to completely cover themselves in public and could not hold jobs or go to school. In October 2001, after the attacks on the World Trade Center and Pentagon, the United States accused the Taliban of supporting terrorists and began bombing Taliban forces. By mid-November, the Taliban government had collapsed. The United Nations then began working with local leaders to create a new government for Afghanistan.

Reading Check What trade route cuts through the Hindu Kush?

Assessment

Defining Terms

1. **Define** alluvial plain, embargo, shah, Islamic republic.

Recalling Facts

2. **Economics** What is Iraq's major export?
3. **Culture** What are the two largest ethnic groups in Iraq?
4. **Government** What type of government does Iran have?

Critical Thinking

5. **Understanding Cause and Effect** Why did American and British forces invade Iraq?
6. **Drawing Conclusions** Why do you think the Afghan people turned to the Taliban for leadership after the Soviets left?

Graphic Organizer

7. **Organizing Information** Create a chart like this one for each of the following countries: Iraq, Iran, and Afghanistan. Then write one fact about the country under each heading.

Country		
Capital	Landforms	Agriculture
People	Religion	Government

Applying Social Studies Skills

8. **Analyzing Maps** Study the map on page 503. Between what bodies of water is Iran located?

Section 4 Assessment

1. The terms are defined in the Glossary.
2. oil
3. Muslim Arabs and Kurds
4. an Islamic republic
5. The United States government did not believe that Saddam Hussein was cooperating with United Nations weapons inspectors.
6. They believed the Taliban could help them solve their problems of poverty, food shortages, and rising crime.
7. Students should complete the table with information from the section.
8. the Persian Gulf and the Caspian Sea

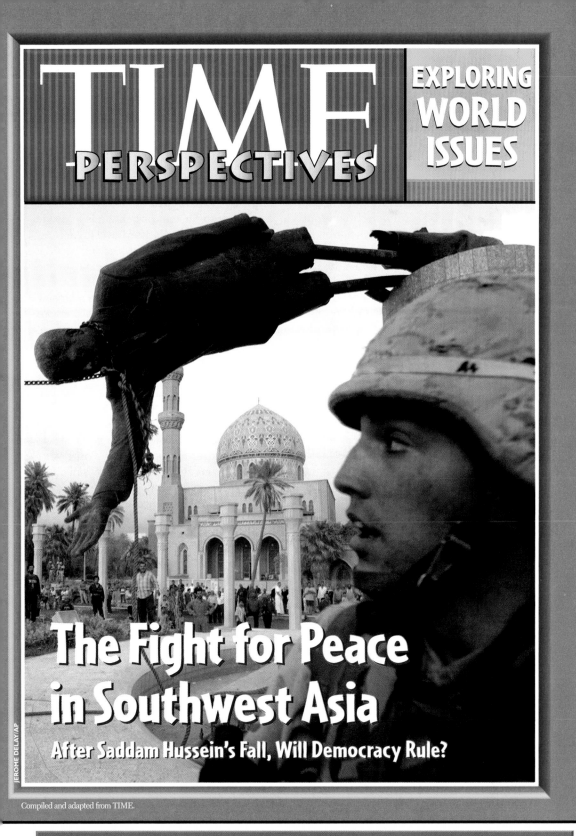

TIME PERSPECTIVES

EXPLORING WORLD ISSUES

The Fight for Peace in Southwest Asia

After Saddam Hussein's Fall, Will Democracy Rule?

JEROME DELAY/AP

Compiled and adapted from TIME.

TIME PERSPECTIVES

Exploring World Issues

Teacher Background

In 1990 Iraqi troops occupied neighboring Kuwait. United States President George H. W. Bush brought together an international coalition that freed Kuwait and destroyed Iraq's forces. Iraqi dictator Saddam Hussein, however, continued to rule Iraq. More than a decade later, President George W. Bush issued Saddam Hussein an ultimatum: relinquish power and allow Iraqis to form a new government. Hussein refused to step down.

Preparing the Student

In March 2003 United States warships in the Red Sea and Persian Gulf launched 40 satellite-guided missiles into Baghdad. Hussein condemned the attack as "criminal" while President Bush promised the operation would disarm Iraq, free its people, and "defend the world from grave danger."

Making Connections

Southwest Asia Copy a map that includes Iraq, Kuwait, Red Sea, Persian Gulf, Afghanistan, the Gaza Strip, Israel, Jordan, Baghdad, Iran, Turkey, Saudi Arabia, the United Arab Emirates, Syria, Bahrain, Oman, and Qatar. Cut apart the copy along the countries' boundaries, scramble the pieces, tape to a sheet of paper, and make copies of the scrambled map. Organize the students into groups and give each group a copy. Tell students to cut out the pieces and use their knowledge of the area and the shapes of the boundaries to reassemble the map. Have them compare their completed puzzle to the original map of the region. L2

1 Focus

Recognizing Bias Read the following comments by Senator Robert Byrd (D-WV) on the invasion of Iraq: "[T]oday I weep for my country. . . . No more is the image of America one of strong, yet benevolent peacekeeper. The image of America has changed. Around the globe, our friends mistrust us, our word is disputed, our intentions are questioned." **Ask: Did Senator Byrd approve of the U.S. invasion of Iraq? Do you agree with his statements? Why or why not? L1**

Where Iraq's Muslims Live

ANSWER
The region contains Sunnis, who do not support help from the United States or the United Kingdom in the rebuilding of Iraq; Mosul

EXPLORING WORLD ISSUES

A Shi'ite confronts U.S. troops in An Najaf.

Oil is Iraq's biggest industry.

War Without End?

In early April 2003, a platoon of U.S. soldiers stood outside a mosque in the city of An Najaf, Iraq. They had been in Iraq since March 19, when troops from several nations, led by U.S. forces, invaded the country. By the end of April, the invaders accomplished their goal, ending the rule of Saddam Hussein, Iraq's cruel dictator.

But in early April, the fighting was still going on, especially in cities like An Najaf. An Najaf is one of Iraq's holiest cities. It is the burial place of Ali, the cousin and son-in-law of Muhammad, the last and greatest prophet of Islam. Every year tens of thousands of **Shi'ite** (SHEE•EYET) **Muslims** travel to An Najaf to visit the **mosque,** or place of worship. Shi'ites (also called Shia) belong to one of the two main branches of Islam.

The American soldiers were searching for gunmen who had shot at U.S. troops from inside the mosque. Hundreds of Shi'ites blocked their way. The Shi'ites were ready to fight to protect their sacred house of worship. "In the city, okay," one man shouted in broken English. "In the mosque, no!"

Acting quickly, the platoon leader calmed them down. "Drop to one knee!" he ordered his troops. "Point your weapons at the ground. Now smile!"

The Iraqis smiled back. Some even laughed. A moment of danger had passed.

Where Iraq's Muslims Live

Making Inferences Why did most attacks against Americans by Sunnis take place between Baghdad and Tikrit? Where would you expect to hear Kurdish spoken?

A Terrorist Act

Almost five months later, a bomb exploded outside the same mosque. It killed Ayatollah Mohammed Baqir al-Hakim, a key Shi'ite leader. Some Shi'ites hated al-Hakim. They thought he was too friendly with Americans. Small groups of **Sunni** (SOO•NEE) **Muslims** felt the same way. Sunnis are members of the second branch of Islam.

After Saddam Hussein was toppled, small bands of Sunnis continued to attack U.S. troops. These groups demanded that the U.S. and its allies leave Iraq. Fighting raged on for months. ▪

Reading Strategy **Reading the Text**

Using Maps Remind students of the following map reading tips: Read the title of the map to understand what information will be presented. Look at the inset map for a general idea of where the region is located in relation to other regions. Examine the map key to know what the colors and symbols represent on the map. Look at the map as a whole. Ask yourself: What patterns can be seen? How is this information related to the text? Answer any questions about the map that are presented. Have students use these tips as they look at the map in this section that shows where Iraq's Muslims live. **L1**

Use the ***Reading Skills Handbook*** *for more reading strategies.*

Members of Iraq's temporary government had the job of writing a new constitution.

A man votes to elect city officials in Bahrain.

Bahraini women voted for the first time in 2002.

Putting Iraq on Its Feet

The fighting that drove Saddam Hussein from power left wreckage that had to be cleaned up. U.S. forces began tackling these problems in late April 2003, just six weeks after the war had begun. Rebuilding Iraq meant two things. First, it meant fixing just about everything. Electric power plants, water pumping stations, roads, schools, and hospitals had all been in terrible shape for years. The oil industry, once Iraq's major moneymaker, had collapsed.

The second part of rebuilding Iraq was more difficult. It required Iraqis to create a **democracy,** or government in which citizens vote for their leaders, from scratch. They had to agree on the shape of the new government. They had to draw up a **constitution,** or body of laws, that described how each part of the government worked. They had to hold free elections, appoint judges, and hire people to make the government function.

At the time, Afghanistan was struggling with similar problems. Freed from a cruel dictatorship in 2002, Afghanis were inventing their own democracy. Their constitution is a reminder of how important religion is in Southwest Asia. "No law," it says, "will be made that will oppose Islamic principles."

Fresh Air

The events in Iraq helped support moves toward more open government in the following countries.

- In 2002 voters in Bahrain elected their **parliament,** or lawmaking body, for the first time in 30 years.
- In 2003 men and women in Oman were given the right to vote in parliamentary elections.
- Qatar's new constitution, adopted in 2003, guarantees freedom of the press and women's voting rights.
- Kuwait's parliament approved a 2003 plan to let women vote and run for city offices.

These changes, small as they may seem, had a powerful impact on other nations in the area. Along with the Iraq war, they even convinced the princes who run Saudi Arabia to open the door to democracy slightly. Saudis will be able to elect some city officials in 2004.

In the fall of 2003, Jordan's King Abdullah II commented on the changes occurring in his country. "We are at the beginning of a new stage in terms of democracy and freedom," he said.

EXPLORING THE ISSUE

1. **Summarizing** What does the title of this entire feature mean?
2. **Making Generalizations** What do you think the subtitle "Fresh Air" says about this specific article?

523

2 Teach

Reading Strategy

Identifying Main Ideas
As students read each subsection, have them summarize the main idea in a three- or four-word headline. Ask volunteers to share their headlines with the class, and tell the class to match each headline with the correct subsection. L1

More About the Photos

A 2003 Gallup poll of 1,178 Baghdadis revealed that respondents thought the main reason the U.S. invaded Iraq was to control its oil. Only 1% thought Americans invaded "to establish democracy."

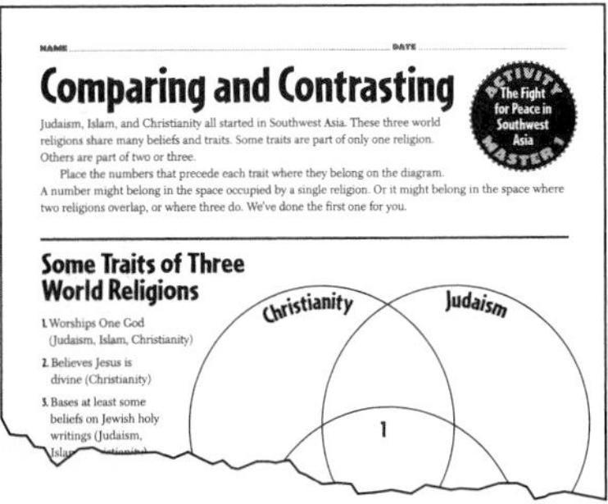
Comparing and Contrasting

Activity Masters: The Fight for Peace in Southwest Asia

Some Traits of Three World Religions

1. Worships One God (Judaism, Islam, Christianity)
2. Believes Jesus is divine (Christianity)

EXPLORING THE ISSUE

ANSWERS

1. The title means helping Iraqis to rebuild their country and to establish democracy.
2. A possible answer is that "Fresh Air" refers to a new kind of government in Southwest Asia—a democracy.

Team-Teaching Activity

History Have a teacher who is knowledgeable about the role of religion in Southwest Asian governments update the class on what has been happening in this region since this report was written. Request that the teacher discuss how Islamic religious beliefs influence the establishment of democratic governments. Have students describe their views concerning the incorporation of religious beliefs into government. L2

Recommended Internet Sites

www.state.gov/p/nea/

The Web site of the Bureau of Near Eastern Affairs offers highlights on U.S. involvement in Southwest Asian countries.

www.apjme.org

The Alliance for Peace and Justice in the Middle East established this Web site to raise awareness of injustices committed during Middle East conflicts.

Making Comparisons Tell students that Dubai, one of seven states in the United Arab Emirates, is ruled by a royal family and has no constitution or elections. Its legal system, however, is flexible enough to allow the sale of liquor in hotels and to offer reduced prison sentences to inmates who read the Quran. Also, Dubai's women have the same educational and legal rights as males and may hold government jobs. **Ask: How does life in Dubai compare to life in Iran? L2**

EXPLORING THE ISSUE

ANSWERS

1. Ebadi challenged the Iranian government by defending people it mistreated.
2. a poor economy, curfews, and limits enforced by morality police

TIME PERSPECTIVES

Demand for Freedom in Iran

In 1979 Iranians had had enough of their **shah,** or king. In their eyes, he acted more like a European than an Iranian. Shi'ite Muslim **clerics,** or religious leaders, took control of the government. They turned the nation upside down. Women who held jobs and wore what they wanted, for example, could now do neither.

One of the women who lost her right to work was Shirin Ebadi, a devout Muslim and a judge. The clerics allowed only men to be judges. So Ebadi quit and began practicing law. She spent the next 20 years defending the rights of people who had been mistreated by the government.

The government and its supporters weren't happy to be challenged. Ebadi was thrown into jail for a short time and threatened with death. But she never looked back. "The beauty of life," she said, "is to fight in a difficult situation, like it is in Iran."

Pressure for Change

During the late 1990s, millions of Iranians couldn't find jobs. Political freedoms were nonexistent. Curfews and "morality police" limited even basic activities such as when people could go shopping, where they could meet, and what clothing they could choose to wear in public. Iranians demanded a stronger economy and more freedom. Ebadi became one of their leaders.

HASAN SARBAKHSHIAN/AP

▲ Students gathered in Tehran, Iran's capital, to demand democracy.

When the government failed to respond to the demands, some Iranians looked abroad for assistance. "Tell the Americans to help us, to liberate us like they did the Iraqis and Afghanis," a government employee begged an American reporter.

Shirin Ebadi wants peaceful change, a position that won her praise from around the world. In 2003 she was awarded the Nobel Prize for Peace. "The prize does not just belong to me," she told a crowd of thousands who had come to cheer her. "It belongs to all the freedom-loving people who are working for democracy, freedom, and human rights in Iran."

EXPLORING THE ISSUE

1. **Explaining** What did Shirin Ebadi do that made the government angry with her?
2. **Cause and Effect** What led to the demands for freedom?

524

Differentiated Instruction

Meeting Special Needs: Gifted and Talented Organize students into two groups for a class debate. Have students research and construct arguments for and against the intervention of the United States in countries to establish democracies. Students should use the Internet and library sources to find arguments and facts that support or refute this intervention. Students might also address and evaluate the effectiveness of different types of intervention, including military involvement, diplomatic pressure, or economic sanctions. After students have debated the issue, discuss it as a class. L3

Road Map to Nowhere?

The **Palestinians** are the grandchildren and great-grandchildren of the 600,000 Palestinians who fled their homes during an Arab-Israeli war in 1948. They believe that Israel took their land, and they want it back. A violent cycle of revenge-attack-revenge began between the two peoples.

The Israelis argue that they didn't chase the Palestinians off their land. They point out that tens of thousands of Palestinians remained, and that their offspring are now Israeli citizens. The Israelis say they are willing to help Palestinians set up their own country on land next door to Israel. But first they want the Palestinians to agree that they have no right to Israel's land.

Keeping Hope Alive

The United States has proposed a "road map for peace" between the Israelis and Palestinians. The goal was an independent Palestinian state by 2005. In early June 2003, both sides accepted the plan. But two months later the violence began again, and the road map reached a dead end.

People on both sides refused to give up hope. In October 2003, a group of Palestinians and Israelis announced that they had worked out their own road map. Members of the group didn't represent their governments. They just wanted to prove that it was possible to find a way to peace through **negotiations,** or compromise.

"We were told over and over that there was no [Palestinian] to talk to," said an Israeli who helped work out the plan. "It now turns out that there is someone to talk to and something to talk about."

RINA CASTELNUOVO/AP

▲ Palestinian and Israeli signers of a 2003 peace pact with President Bush and Jordan's king (right)

A Palestinian agreed. "In all previous negotiations with Israel," he said, "nobody could have hoped to have achieved this dream." Millions of Israelis and Arabs are hoping that such a dream will soon come true.

Despite hopes on both sides, the road to peace remains long and difficult. The region's cycle of violence continues and it is not easy to stop. Political disagreements in Israel, unrest in the Palestinian areas, and instability in neighboring Lebanon complicate the issue. Whether any of the proposed "roadmaps" eventually leads to peace remains to be seen. ▪

EXPLORING THE ISSUE

1. **Making Predictions** How do you think the Arab-Israeli conflict will end?
2. **Problem Solving** Identify problems that keep the conflict alive. What changes would you make to solve them?

525

Teach

Ask students: What have you heard about the Arab-Israeli conflict? What do you know about the differences between the two groups? How are their religions and customs different? What do you think each side wants? Encourage the students to be nonjudgmental in their views of those customs and religions that may differ from their own. Write the major points made by students on the board. Ask the other students whether they agree or disagree with each statement. L1

Did You Know?

A British group—Oxford Research International—polled 3,244 Iraqis in October and November of 2003. Ninety percent of those surveyed wanted a democratic government, and only 12 percent wanted "a government made up mainly of religious leaders."

EXPLORING THE ISSUE

ANSWERS

1. *Possible answer:* The conflict will end with Palestinian and Israeli states existing together.
2. The problems are the Palestinians' claim to Israeli land and cycles of violence; answers will vary.

Interdisciplinary Activity

Literature Phyllis Bennis works for the Institute for Policy Studies in Washington and is the author of *Before and After: U.S. Foreign Policy and the September 11th Crisis* and *Beyond the Storm: A Gulf Crisis Reader*. Find a copy of her 2003 book, *Understanding the Palestinian-Israeli Conflict: A Primer*. It provides easy-to-understand answers to questions such as "Why is there so much violence in the Middle East?" "What's the difference between Jews and Israelis?" "Where did the Israelis come from?" and "Why are Palestinians in Israel at all?" Assign each student a question from the book and tell him or her to read the answer. Then have the student summarize the reading for the class. L1

EE4 Human Systems: Standard 12

Current Events Journal

As students review the report, have them list groups of people in Southwest Asia who need help, such as refugees. Then ask them to search the Internet for organizations that reach out to these groups. Tell them to write the name of an organization and a brief description of its mission next to each group on their list.

EXPLORING THE ISSUE

ANSWERS

1. All the efforts involve young people.
2. A possible answer is that both girls want to promote understanding among people of the world.

NAME ______ DATE ______

Interpreting Tables

Activity Master 2 — The Fight for Peace in Southwest Asia

What can you learn when you compare facts about Afghanistan, Iraq, and Israel? A lot, as you will see when you examine the table below. The table shows whether the nations are dictatorships, democracies, or "in transition"—in between. It compares the strength of their economies, the effectiveness of their healthcare systems, and the emphasis they place on education. Study the table and decide whether the statements about it are true (T) or false (F).

How Healthy Are Three Southwest Asian Nations?

	Afghanistan	Iraq	Israel
Government	In transition (former dictatorship)	In transition (former dictatorship)	Democracy
Population	28,717,213	24,683,313	6,116,533
Median age[1]	19 years	19 years	29 years
GDP[2]	$19 billion	$58 billion	$122 billion
Hospital beds	0.4 per 1,000 persons	1.5 per 1,000 persons (1998)	6 per 1,000 persons (1994)
Infant mortality[3]	142 out of 1,000	55 out of 1,000	7 out of 1,000
Life expectancy	male, 48 years female, 46 years	male, 67 years female, 69 years	male, 77 years female, 81 years
		ale, 10.3	male, 14.3 female, 15.2

TIME PERSPECTIVES

Rebuilding Iraq: What Can One Person Do?

Putting Iraq back together is a job for experts. Right? Wrong! Volunteers from all over the United States are doing what they can to help Iraqis get back on their feet. Here are some examples:

Children in Platteville, Iowa, sent school supplies to the city of Tikrit, Iraq, where there's a shortage of pencils and paper. "We hear parents teach their children to hate Americans," said Dayna Andersen, 15. "If we do something good for them, maybe they will think differently." Dayna's brother, a U.S. soldier in Iraq, distributed the supplies.

Students in middle schools throughout the United States wrote essays in support of Operation Tribute to Freedom. OTF is a U.S. Defense Department program that encourages Americans to show appreciation for U.S. soldiers in Iraq and Afghanistan. For information, contact **www.defenselink.mil/specials/tribute**

In Salem, Oregon, Allison Pollard and 14 other teenagers raised $5,000 to bring a 10-month-old Iraqi child to the United States for a life-saving heart operation.

Esra Naama, a graduate of Irvine High School in Irvine, California, is helping to raise money to set up an Internet café in Baghdad. An **Internet café** is a place where people can gather to rent computers and surf the Internet. "It'll help the Iraqi people learn about the world and how the world learns," said Esra, who came to the United States from Iraq when she was 11 years old.

▲ **Californian Esra Naama raised money to start an Internet café in Baghdad, Iraq.**

The United Nations has a big idea. It set up five-day soccer camps for teenagers from Iraq and three other Arab nations. Each team is made up of players from all four nations. The UN hopes that the camps will help build lasting bonds between people from each country. This sort of project is too elaborate for volunteers. But there's nothing to stop students from raising money for soccer balls and shipping them to children in Iraq. ☐

EXPLORING THE ISSUE

1. **Categorizing** What do these volunteer efforts have in common?
2. **Making Inferences** What do you think motivates volunteers like Dayna Andersen and Esra Naama?

526

Your Government and You

The United States government has long been involved in the quest for peace in the Middle East. The United States embassy in Israel maintains a Web site (www.usembassy-israel.org.il/) that contains a discussion of U.S. peace-keeping efforts, along with related documents and photographs. Have students pick a specific topic or event (such as the 1978 Camp David Accords) and use this Web site to research it and write a report. L2

REVIEW AND ASSESS

UNDERSTANDING THE ISSUE

1. **Defining Key Terms** Write definitions for the following terms: *Shi'ite Muslim, mosque, Sunni Muslim, democracy, constitution, parliament, shah, cleric, Palestinian, negotiation, Internet café.*

2. **Writing to Inform** In a 300-word article about Iraq, describe an emotional scene that you read about or saw on TV. Describe your reaction.

3. **Writing to Persuade** What is the most important thing that Americans should know about Iraq? Put your answer in a brief letter to the editor of your local newspaper. Support your letter with facts. Use at least four of the key terms above.

INTERNET RESEARCH ACTIVITY

4. Navigate to Columbia University's Middle East and Jewish Studies site at **www.columbia.edu/cu/lweb/indiv/mideast/cuvlm**. Scroll down to Middle East Resources by Subject. Click on the links until you find a site that interests you. Write two paragraphs explaining what the site taught you.

5. Navigate to **www.cpa-iraq.org**, the home page of the Coalition Provisional Authority. What is the Coalition doing to combat terrorism in Iraq? Make a list of the coalition's activities and title it, "The CPA's Job in Iraq." Share your list with your classmates. Go to **www.baghdadbulletin.com** for an Iraqi view of the rebuilding of Iraq.

BEYOND THE CLASSROOM

6. **Visit your school or local library.** Find out more about Islam, the world's second-largest religion. What event led to the split between the Shi'ites (or Shia) and the Sunnis?

REUTERS

▲ **These Muslim boys study Islam at religious schools.**

7. **Research a country** such as Iraq, Northern Ireland, or Bosnia where people have suffered from terrorist attacks. Find out how groups or individuals outside the government have tried to end the violence. Present your findings to the class.

Believers Who Share a Common Ground

Religion plays a big role in Southwest Asia and North Africa. This graph suggests why. It shows what religions are practiced in the region's 10 largest nations.

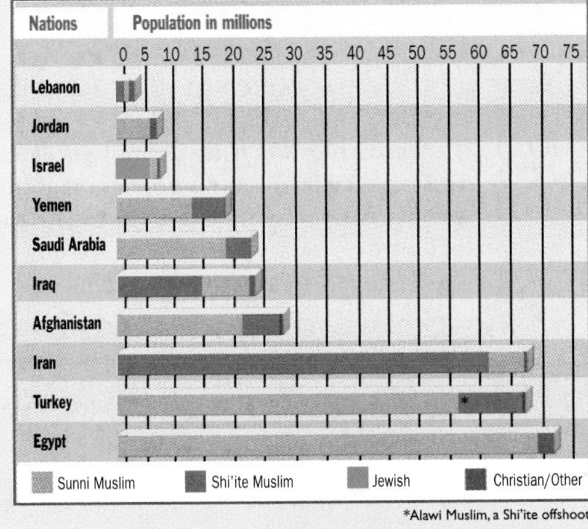

*Alawi Muslim, a Shi'ite offshoot

BUILDING GRAPH READING SKILLS

1. **Analyzing the Data** In how many of these nations are Sunnis the largest Muslim group?
2. **Making Inferences** Under Saddam Hussein, Sunnis held most of the power in the Iraqi government. Why might Iraqi Shi'ites feel they have more of a right than Sunnis to hold top government jobs today?
3. **Drawing Conclusions** Where might competition between Sunnis and Shi'ites be strongest? Where might it be weakest?

FOR UPDATES ON WORLD ISSUES GO TO www.timeclassroom.com/glencoe

527

3 ASSESS

Have students take the TIME Reports Quiz or do the Alternative Assessment project for this unit provided in the Teacher's Classroom Resources.

Keeping a Log

Stories About Southwest Asia

BUILDING GRAPH READING SKILLS

ANSWERS

1. six
2. Shi'ites outnumber Sunnis in Iraq. Also, Sunnis are associated with the rule of Saddam Hussein, who lost power; thus, Sunnis have no right to hold top government jobs.
3. Lebanon or Iraq; Jordan or Egypt

4 CLOSE

Reading Strategy

Writing a Paragraph Ask students to write a paragraph starting with this sentence: *Peace in Southwest Asia is important because....*

Culminating Activity

To close this lesson, have students complete the Review and Assess section questions and activities above. Students should use classroom discussion, contextual clues, and their student dictionaries to write definitions for terms. Before assigning the Internet activities, it is recommended that you review your school district policy on student Internet use.

Focus on Debate

Have students debate the pro and con positions of the following statement: **Peace is possible in Southwest Asia if countries embrace democracy. L2**

 **EE4 Human Systems: Standard 13**

TEACH

Ask students how researching on the Internet is different from using books or other print materials. *(Students should note that it is easier to find information using the Internet, but it can be more difficult to know and trust the source of the information.)*

Have students find Web sites about other volunteer organizations. Ask students if the sites are reliable sources of information. Encourage volunteers to explain why. The rest of the students may want to go to the sites as they are discussed so that they can understand the explanations. Conclude the activity by having students summarize the steps they feel are most important when evaluating a Web site. **L1**

Additional Skills Resources

Chapter Skills Review

Technology Skill

Evaluating a Web Site

The Internet has become a valuable research tool. It is convenient to use, and the information contained on the Internet is plentiful. However, some Web site information is not necessarily accurate or reliable. When using the Internet as a research tool, you must distinguish between quality information and inaccurate or incomplete information. You also must consider the source of the information and whether facts or opinions are presented.

▲ The Peace Corps Web site is government sponsored.

Learning the Skill

There are a number of things to consider when you are evaluating a Web site. Most important is to check the accuracy of the source and content. The author and publisher or sponsor of the site should be clearly indicated. You must also determine the usefulness of the site. The information on the site should be current, and the design and organization of the site should be appealing and easy to navigate.

To evaluate a Web site, ask yourself the following questions:

- Are the facts on the site documented?
- Does the site contain a bibliography?
- Is the author clearly identified?
- Does the site explore the topic in-depth or only provide generalizations?
- Does the site contain links to other useful and up-to-date resources?
- Is the information easy to access? Is it properly labeled?

Practicing the Skill

Visit the Peace Corps Web site listed below and answer the following questions.

1. Who is the author or sponsor of the Web site?
2. What links does the site contain? Are they appropriate to the topic?
3. What sources were used for the information contained on the site?
4. Does the site explore the topic in-depth? Why or why not?
5. Is the design of the site appealing? Why or why not?

Applying the Skill

Locate two Web sites about Iran. Evaluate them for accuracy and usefulness, and then compare them to the Peace Corps site listed below.

www.peacecorps.gov/kids/index.html

Practicing the Skill Answers

1. the Peace Corps Department of Communications
2. links to the Peace Corps Web site; yes
3. the U.S. government and the Peace Corps
4. yes; it provides information about the history and goals of the Peace Corps, along with information about living in different countries.
5. yes; it is tailored to children and is colorful, clear, and easy to use.

Applying the Skill

Suggest that students try a search engine like Google to find Web sites about Iran.

Reading Review

Section 1 Turkey, Syria, Lebanon, Jordan

Terms to Know
migrate
bedouins

Main Idea
Turkey, Syria, Lebanon, and Jordan lie at the crossroads of Europe and Asia.

✓Location Turkey lies in both Europe and Asia.
✓Economics Turkey is becoming more industrialized, with textiles and clothing as major industries. Tourism is also a growing industry.
✓Culture Most of Turkey's people now live in cities or towns.
✓Economics Farming is the main economic activity in Syria.
✓History Lebanon is rebuilding and recovering after a civil war.
✓Place Water shortages in Jordan restrict the land available for farming.

Section 2 Israel and the Palestinian Territories

Terms to Know
kibbutz
moshav
Holocaust

Main Idea
After years of conflict, the Jewish nation of Israel and neighboring Arab countries still struggle to achieve peace.

✓Culture About 80 percent of Israel's population are Jews. They have moved to Israel from many countries.
✓History Israel and its Arab neighbors continue to experience violent conflict over the issues that divide them.

Section 3 The Arabian Peninsula

Terms to Know
wadi
desalinization
caliph

Main Idea
Money from oil exports has boosted standards of living in most countries of the Arabian Peninsula.

✓Economics Saudi Arabia is the world's leading oil producer.
✓Culture The Islamic religion affects almost all aspects of life in Saudi Arabia.
✓Economics The Persian Gulf states have strong economies based on oil.

Section 4 Iraq, Iran, and Afghanistan

Terms to Know
alluvial plain
embargo
shah
Islamic republic

Main Idea
Iraq, Iran, and Afghanistan have recently fought wars and have undergone sweeping political changes.

✓Economics Iraq is recovering from an international trade embargo and war.
✓Culture Oil-rich Iran is ruled by Muslim religious leaders.
✓Place Afghanistan is mountainous and relatively undeveloped.

Reading Review

Use the Chapter 18 Reading Review to preview, review, condense, or reteach the chapter.

Preview/Review

Use the Terms to Know lists to help students review and study.

Activity Have students identify the country for which each term is relevant. Read the terms aloud, one at a time, and ask for volunteers to categorize each. Note that some terms may apply to more than one country.

Vocabulary PuzzleMaker CD-ROM reinforces the vocabulary terms used in Chapter 18.

The Interactive Tutor Self-Assessment CD-ROM allows students to review Chapter 18 content.

Condense

Have students read the Chapter 18 summary statements.

Guided Reading Activities

Audio Program

Reteach

Reteaching Activity

Reading Essentials and Study Guide

Reading Strategy Read to Write

Creating Maps Have students create illustrated maps of Southwest Asia. Their maps could highlight the region's geographical features, with illustrations showing the different types of climates, vegetation, or landscapes. Students might show the region's resources and economic activities. The maps could also display the important historical and cultural sites found throughout the region. Encourage students to illustrate their maps with photographs and other images that demonstrate the variety of this region. Maps should contain written descriptions of the different features using correct grammar, punctuation, and sentence structure. L1

EE1 The World in Spatial Terms: Standards 1, 3

Assessment and Activities

GLENCOE TECHNOLOGY

MindJogger Videoquiz
Use MindJogger Videoquiz to review the Chapter 18 content.

 Available in DVD and VHS

Using Key Terms

1. e
2. a
3. f
4. i
5. j
6. d
7. c
8. g
9. h
10. b

Reviewing the Main Ideas

11. Istanbul
12. the Bosporus, Sea of Marmara, and Dardanelles
13. It is an ancient trading center and one of the world's oldest continuously inhabited cities.
14. It had elegant shops and sidewalk cafés.
15. 1948
16. Israeli law that says Jews from anywhere in the world can go to Israel to live.
17. Organization of Petroleum Exporting Countries
18. Riyadh
19. between the Tigris and Euphrates Rivers
20. More than half are Persians, not Arabs or Turks as in other Southwest Asian countries, and they speak Farsi.
21. the Hindu Kush mountain range

Critical Thinking

22. Answers will vary. They should, however, match the goods that might be traded with the appropriate method of transportation and the routes available.

Chapter 18 Assessment and Activities

 Using Key Terms

Match the terms in Part A with their definitions in Part B.

A.

1. migrate
2. desalinization
3. alluvial plain
4. wadi
5. caliph
6. bedouins
7. Holocaust
8. kibbutz
9. embargo
10. shah

B.

a. taking salt out of seawater
b. Iran's former monarch
c. mass slaughter of European Jews
d. nomadic, desert people
e. to move from one place to another
f. area built up from soil deposited by river floods
g. Israeli farm or settlement where people share property
h. restriction on trade
i. dry riverbed filled by rainwater from rare downpours
j. successor to Muhammad

 Reviewing the Main Ideas

Section 1 Turkey, Syria, Lebanon, Jordan

11. **Place** What is Turkey's largest city?
12. **Place** What bodies of water form the Turkish Straits?
13. **Place** What makes Damascus an important city?
14. **History** Why was Beirut called "the Paris of the East"?

Section 2 Israel and the Palestinian Territories

15. **History** When was the modern nation of Israel created?
16. **Government** What is the Law of Return?

Section 3 The Arabian Peninsula

17. **Economics** What is OPEC?
18. **Place** What is the capital of Saudi Arabia?

Section 4 Iraq, Iran, and Afghanistan

19. **Economics** Where does most of the farming in Iraq take place?
20. **Culture** How do the people of Iran differ from other Southwest Asian peoples?
21. **Place** What landform makes up much of Afghanistan?

NATIONAL GEOGRAPHIC Southwest Asia

Place Location Activity

On a separate sheet of paper, match the letters on the map with the numbered places listed below.

1. Persian Gulf
2. Zagros Mountains
3. Euphrates River
4. Turkey
5. Iran
6. Israel
7. Iraq
8. Saudi Arabia
9. Makkah
10. Jerusalem

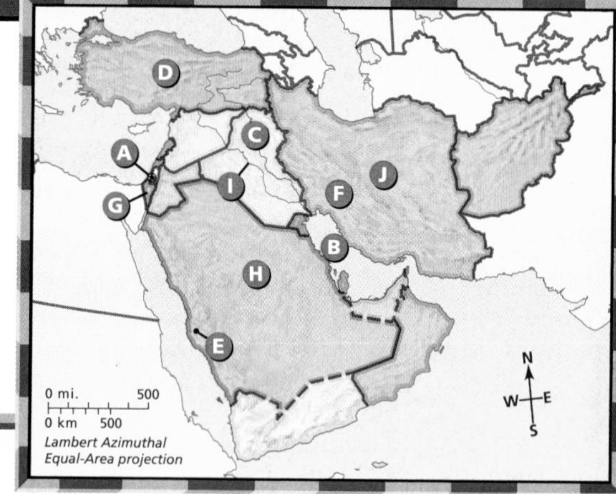

530

NATIONAL GEOGRAPHIC Place Location Activity

1. B
2. F
3. I
4. D
5. J
6. G
7. C
8. H
9. E
10. A

23. Oil is important because of its value throughout the world for fuels and petroleum-based products. Its abundance in any particular country gives that country power. Water is obviously vital to life as well as to farming, the economy, and trade. Its scarcity in any particular country makes that country vulnerable to neighbors who have a larger supply of water.

Social Studies Online

Self-Check Quiz Visit ***The World and Its People*** Web site at twip.glencoe.com and click on **Chapter 18—Self-Check Quizzes** to prepare for the Chapter Test.

Critical Thinking

22. **Evaluating Information** Goods were moved from Southwest Asia to other parts of the world through several routes. How are goods brought to your community? Make a list of all the routes a product would take to get from Southwest Asia to your town.
23. **Analyzing Information** On a chart like this, list a reason for the importance of oil and water to Southwest Asia and one result of their abundance or scarcity.

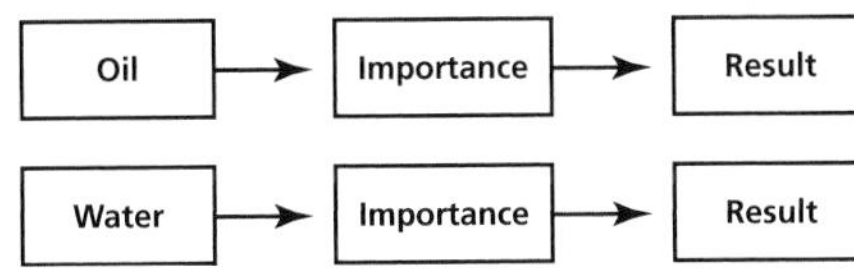

Comparing Regions Activity

24. **Culture** For one week, count the number of stories in your local newspaper about countries in Southwest Asia. Then count the number of stories about European countries. Which number is greater? Why do you think this is so?

Mental Mapping Activity

25. **Focusing on the Region** Draw a simple outline map of Southwest Asia, and then label the following:

- Turkey
- Persian Gulf
- Red Sea
- Israel
- Mediterranean Sea
- Iran
- Saudi Arabia
- Yemen
- Iraq
- Afghanistan

Technology Skills Activity

26. **Using the Internet** Search the Internet and find several newspapers that publish current events online. Research an event that took place in one of the countries of Southwest Asia. Create a poster about the event.

Standardized Test Practice

Directions: Study the graph below, and then answer the question that follows.

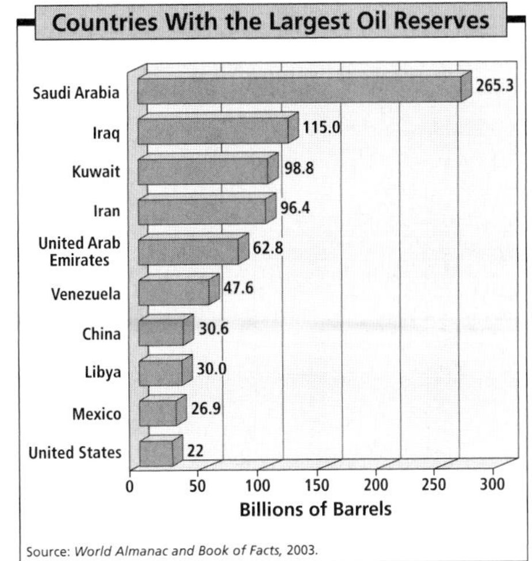

1. How many of the ten countries with the largest oil reserves are located in Southwest Asia?

A one
B three
C five
D seven

Test-Taking Tip: You need to rely on your memory as well as analyze the graph to answer this question. Look at each country, then think back to the countries you studied in Chapter 18. Which of those listed on the graph did you just learn about?

Assessment and Activities

Standardized Test Practice

1. C

Tested Objectives:
Analyzing a graph, synthesizing information

Chapter Test Bonus Question

This question may be used for extra credit on the chapter test.

What group of people have partial control of the West Bank and Gaza Strip? *(Palestinian Arabs)*

Have students visit the Web site at twip.glencoe.com to review Chapter 18 and take the Self-Check Quiz.

FOLDABLES Study Organizer — Dinah Zike's Foldables

Culminating Activity
Have students quiz a partner using the questions and answers that they wrote on their foldables.

Comparing Regions Activity

24. Students may predict that the number of stories about countries in Southwest Asia might be greater than those about European countries as a result of the political unrest in this region.

Mental Mapping Activity

25. This exercise helps students visualize the countries and geographic features they have been studying. All attempts at freehand mapping should be accepted.

Technology Skills Activity

26. Students should search the Internet for an online newspaper containing articles about an event that occurred in Southwest Asia. Their posters might include maps, text, and illustrations.

Unit 7 Planning Guide

- If you teach BOTH Eastern and Western world regions in one year, use the columns in red to help you pace your lessons.
- **If you teach ONLY Eastern or Western world regions in one year, use the columns in blue to help you pace your lessons.**

ALTERNATIVE PACING CHARTS

	Unit 7		Chapter 19		Chapter 20		Chapter 21	
	Both East and West	Either East or West	Both East and West	Either East or West	Both East and West	Either East or West	Both East and West	Either East or West
Day 1	Unit Opener, Regional Atlas	Unit Opener, Regional Atlas	Chapter Opener, Section 1	Chapter Opener, Section 1	Chapter Opener, Section 1	Chapter Opener, Section 1	Chapter Opener, Section 1	Chapter Opener, Section 1
Day 2	Regional Atlas	Regional Atlas	Section 1, Critical Thinking Skill	Section 1	Section 1, Making Connections	Section 1	Making Connections, Section 2	Section 1
Day 3	Regional Atlas	Regional Atlas	Section 2	Section 1, Critical Thinking Skill	Section 2	Making Connections, Section 2	Social Studies Skill, Section 3	Making Connections, Section 2
Day 4		Regional Atlas	Section 2, Making Connections, Review	Section 2	Section 3	Section 3	Section 3, Review	Section 2
Day 5			Chapter Assessment	Section 2	Section 4	Section 4	Chapter Assessment	Social Studies Skill, Section 3
Day 6			NGS Geography and History	Section 2, Making Connections	TIME Reports	TIME Reports		Section 3
Day 7				Review	TIME Reports, Critical Thinking Skill, Review	TIME Reports		Review
Day 8				Chapter Assessment	Chapter Assessment	Critical Thinking Skill, Review		Chapter Assessment
Day 9				Chapter Assessment		Chapter Assessment		
Day 10				NGS Geography and History				

Note: The following materials may be used when teaching Unit 7.
Chapter level support materials can be found on the chapter resource pages.

TEACHING TRANSPARENCIES

Political Map Transparency L2

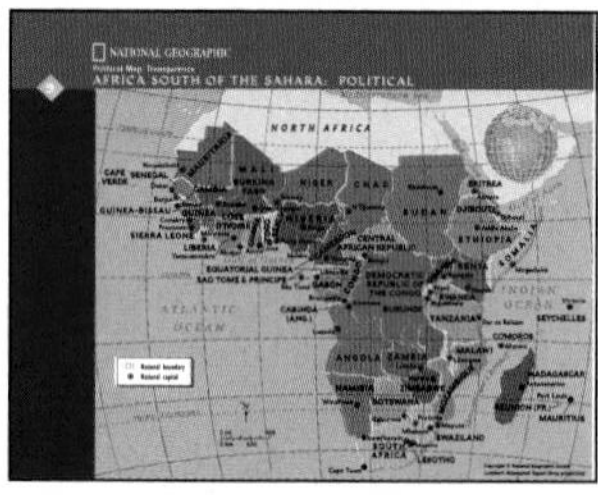

Map Overlay Transparencies L2

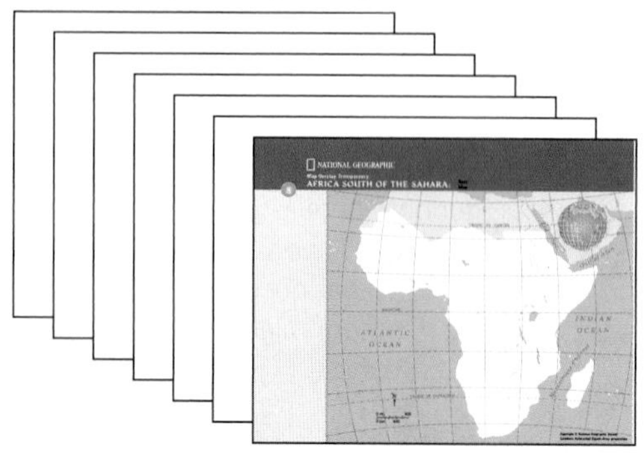

World Cultures Transparencies L2

Unit 7 Resources

INTERDISCIPLINARY CONNECTIONS

World Literature Reading L2

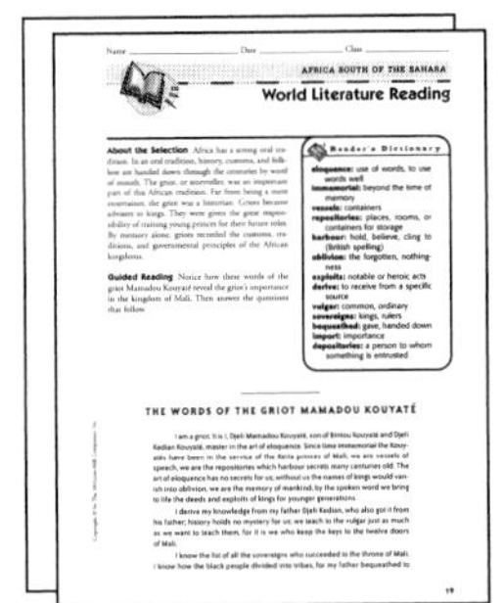

Economics and Geography Activity L2

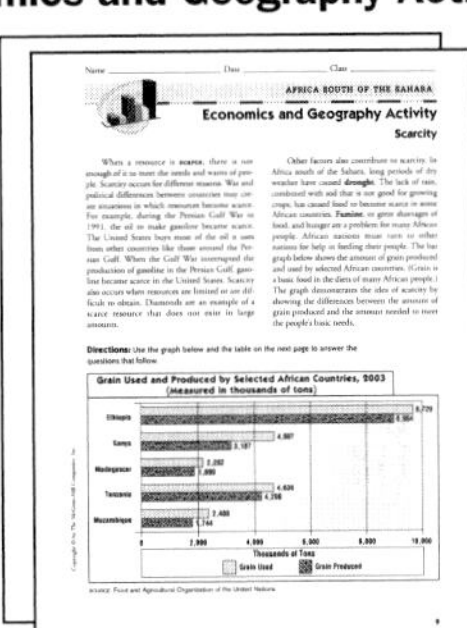

History and Geography Activity L2

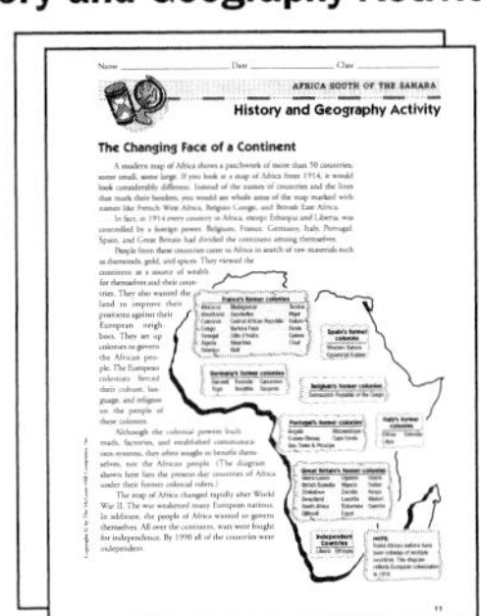

INTERDISCIPLINARY CONNECTIONS

Foods Around the World L1/ELL

World Music: A Cultural Legacy

CIVIC INVOLVEMENT

Citizenship Activity L1

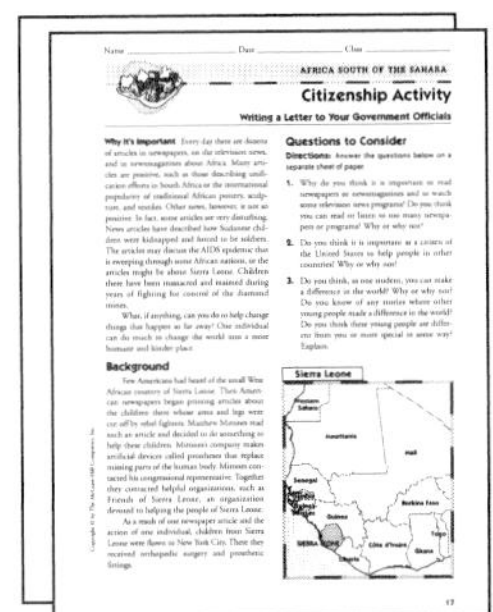

Environmental Case Study L2

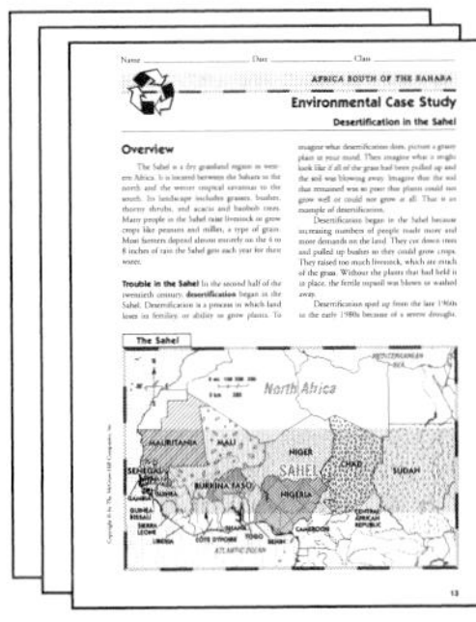

MAP AND GEOGRAPHY SKILLS

Building Geography Skills for Life

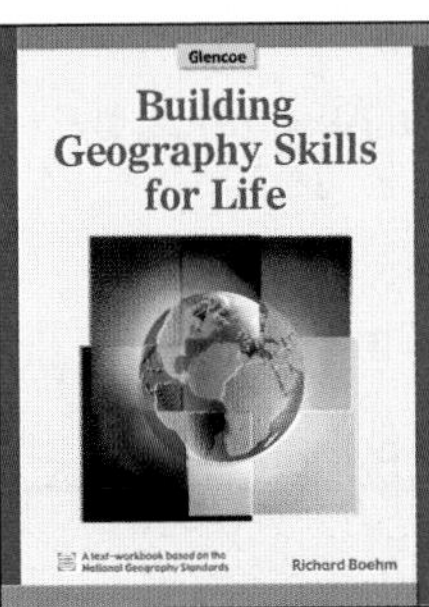

NGS Focus on Geography Literacy L2

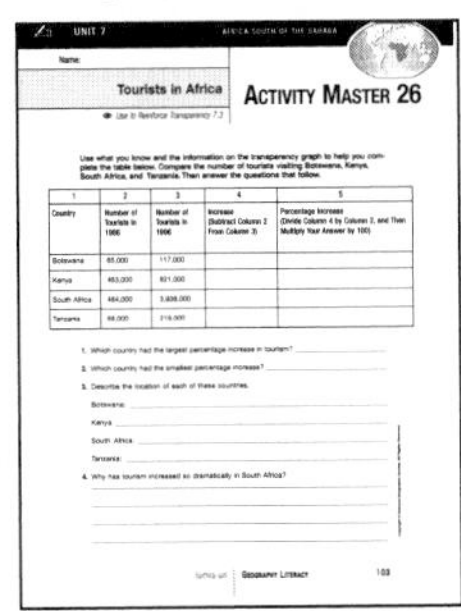

Regional Atlas Activity L2

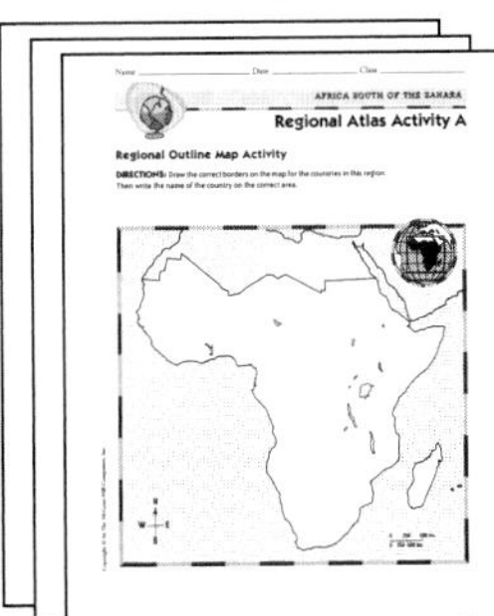

KEY TO ABILITY LEVELS

Teaching strategies have been coded for varying learning styles and abilities.

L1 **BASIC** activities for all students

L2 **AVERAGE** activities for average to above-average students

L3 **CHALLENGING** activities for above-average students

ELL **ENGLISH LANGUAGE LEARNER** activities

ASSESSMENT

Unit Pretests L2

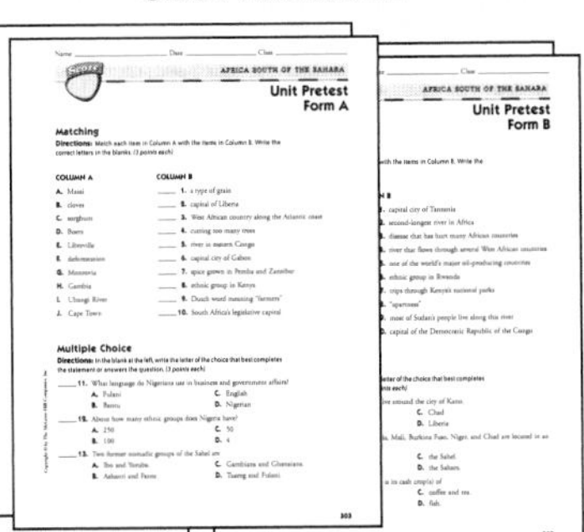

Unit Posttests L2

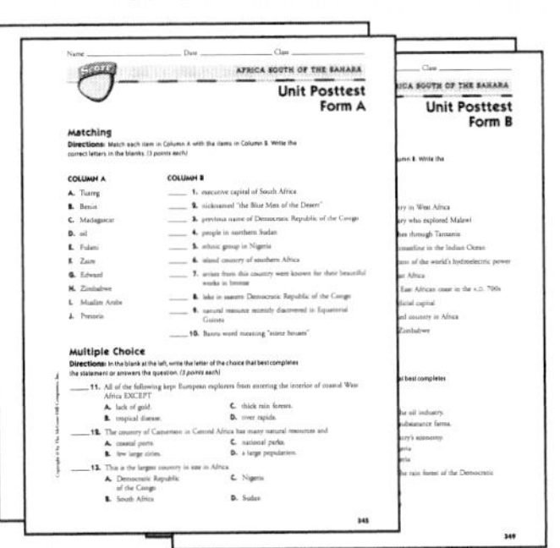

Glencoe Professional Development and Teacher Support Materials

- **Reading in the Content Area for the Middle School Classroom**
- **Inclusion Strategies for the Middle School Social Studies Classroom**
- **Character Education for the Middle School Classroom**
- **Teaching Strategies for the Social Studies Classroom**
- **Reproducible Lesson Plans**
- **Outline Map Resource Book**
- **Writing Process Transparencies for Middle School**
- **Social Studies: Reading Strategies**

Additional Unit 7 Resources

- **Timed Readings Plus in Social Studies** help students increase their reading rate and fluency while maintaining comprehension. The 400-word passages are similar to those found on state and national assessments.
- **Reading in the Content Area: Social Studies** concentrates on six essential reading skills that help students better comprehend what they read. The book includes 75 high-interest nonfiction passages written at increasing levels of difficulty.
- **Reading Fluency** helps students read smoothly, accurately, and expressively.
- **Jamestown's Reading Improvement,** by renowned reading expert Edward Fry, focuses on helping build your students' comprehension, vocabulary, and skimming and scanning skills.
- **Critical Reading Series** provides high-interest books, each written at three reading levels.

For more information about these products, see the Jamestown Education materials in the Classroom Solutions in the front of this Teacher Wraparound Edition. To order these products, call Glencoe at 1-800-334-7344.

The following videotape program is available from Glencoe:

- **Nelson Mandela: Journey to Freedom** 0-7670-0113-3

To order, call Glencoe at 1-800-334-7344. To find classroom resources to accompany many of these, check:

A&E Television: www.aetv.com

The History Channel: www.historychannel.com

Reading List Generator CD-ROM

GLENCOE BOOKLINK

The Glencoe BookLink CD-ROM is a database that allows you to search more than 15,000 titles to create a customized reading list for your students.

- Reading lists can be organized by students' reading level, author, genre, theme, or area of interest.
- The database provides Degrees of Reading Power™ (DRP) and Lexile™ readability scores for all selections.
- A brief summary of each selection is included.

Leveled reading suggestions for this unit:

For students at a Grade 5 reading level:
- ***Nzingha: Warrior Queen of Matamba,*** by Patricia McKissack.

For students at a Grade 6 reading level:
- ***A Family in Nigeria,*** by Carol Barker.

For students at a Grade 7 reading level:
- ***Light Shining Through the Mist,*** by Tom L. Matthews.

To order this CD-ROM, call Glencoe at 1-800-334-7344.

Extending the Content

Readings for the Teacher
- ***Africa 2000,*** by Charles H. Cutter. The World Today Series. Harper's Ferry, WV: Stryker-Post, 2000.
- ***Into the House of the Ancestors: Inside the New Africa,*** by Karl Maier, New York, NY: John Wiley & Sons, 1999.

Multimedia Resources
- **Glencoe Social Studies Primary Source Document Library CD-ROM**
- ***East Africa: Tanzania and Zanzibar.*** Lonely Planet. 1997. VHS.

Service Learning Project

Connecting Classroom With Community

Many people in Africa suffer from poor nutrition. Many people in industrialized societies have problems of poor nutrition as well. Obesity rates are high in the United States. Encourage students to organize a campaign to promote good nutrition. Have them look up the recommendations of the Food Guide Pyramid and the cautions that nutritionists offer regarding eating such substances as fats, sodium, and sugar. Then have them stage a Nutrition Fair in which they teach others how to create balanced diets.

Content Background Notes

Use this additional information as lecture notes or discussion prompts throughout the study of Unit 7.

Chapter 19 West Africa (pp. 548–565)

The British Liberia It is well known that freed slaves from the United States settled in Liberia, creating a home for African Americans who wished to resettle in Africa. Less well known is Sierra Leone, where British antislavery crusaders created settlements for freed slaves from Jamaica and North America—nearly 40 years before the first American freed slaves settled in Liberia. About 1,200 of these settlers had been enslaved in the American colonies. Promised their freedom—and land—by the British, they escaped from bondage and fought alongside British troops during the American Revolution. When the war ended, they were resettled in Nova Scotia, but the British never fulfilled the promise to give them land. In 1792 these 1,200 people traveled to Sierra Leone, where they founded Freetown—now the country's capital.

After 1808, when the British banned the slave trade, Sierra Leone became an important base for British naval ships that patrolled African waters and seized slave ships. From 1807 to 1864, the British brought more than 50,000 Africans who were liberated from these ships to settle in Sierra Leone.

The Palaces of Abomey The town of Abomey, in modern Benin, was once the flourishing capital of the kingdom of Abomey (formerly called Dahomey). The kingdom was a powerful state in West Africa from the late 1600s to the mid-1800s. Today archaeologists are working at the site of the Royal Palaces. Among the finds are a series of bas-reliefs that were used to decorate an area called the Hall of Jewels. These reliefs celebrated the achievements of the Fon people, who founded Abomey. Rain and insects have damaged the reliefs. As a result, the archaeological work must begin with restoring the bas-reliefs. Then archaeologists will develop plans for their long-term preservation.

Chapter 20 Central and East Africa (pp. 568–601)

Human Origins The Great Rift Valley, an ancient rock formation, has proven beneficial to archaeologists seeking evidence of the earliest humans. Many important fossils have been uncovered in East Africa, from Ethiopia to Kenya and Tanzania. Early in the 1900s, scientists believed that humans had originated in Asia. In 1959 Mary Leakey—who worked along with her husband Louis—discovered teeth and a human skull that were about 1.75 million years old. This was twice as old as scientists had thought the human race to be, and the find turned their attention to Africa.

Many digs have taken place along the Great Rift Valley since then, and scientists have made many spectacular finds. Evidence found by the Leakeys, their son Richard, and other archaeologists suggests that several kinds of early humans and near-humans lived side by side in the area a few million years ago. Sometime between 4 million and 2 million years ago, the near-human strains died out. The true humans eventually evolved into *Homo sapiens*. *National Geographic* magazine has published a series of articles titled "The Dawn of Humans" over the years. These articles summarize the various finds made in Africa and in other parts of the world.

The Megatransect In late 1999, J. Michael Fay began an ambitious walk through the rain forests of Central Africa. Beginning at Bomassa, Congo, a town on the Sangha River (a tributary of the mighty Congo), Fay planned to march about 1,200 miles (1,931 km) through 13 forests that adjoin. His goal was to make an accurate survey of the plant and animal life in these forests—before continued human intervention destroys them. Like Meriwether Lewis, Fay recorded in notebooks everything he saw. His records also included sound recordings and videotapes. Fay also used high-technology methods—a GPS device—to help track his route. Low-tech solutions were useful, too. Each day one of Fay's companions played out a cord from a handheld device that measured the distance walked that day. Since the adventurers were sure that the line would be eaten by insects, they brought plenty of spare cords.

Chapter 21 Southern Africa—A Varied Region (pp. 602–621)

Telling the Truth During the apartheid era, many black South Africans suffered at the hands of white officials and police officers. In the mid-1990s, when the majority black government was first formed in South Africa, there was concern that revenge could poison race relations and hamper the new government's efforts to build for the future. One of the key steps in avoiding this problem was the creation of South Africa's Truth and Reconciliation Commission. The Commission was chaired by Desmond Tutu, the black archbishop of the Anglican Church in South Africa, who had won a Nobel Peace Prize for his stand against apartheid.

Tutu led the Commission through hearings that included statements from more than 20,000 people. The purpose was to help South Africans be reconciled to the past by telling the truth about it—and then forgiving those who committed atrocities. As one Commission member said: "If we cannot understand what made people think and do what they did, these conflicts will arise again within our society." As part of its mission to tell the full story of apartheid, the Commission's final report revealed crimes committed not only by government forces but also by those who struggled against apartheid.

00:00 Out of Time?

If time does not permit teaching each chapter in this unit, you may use the **Reading Essentials and Study Guide** for each chapter.

Unit Overview

The three chapters of this unit introduce students to a cultural region that covers most of the continent of Africa. The countries in this region share the following features:

- a location almost entirely in the Tropics
- the world's fastest-growing and youngest population
- challenges to the environment, especially natural resources and wildlife
- a struggle to improve the quality of life
- political and economic difficulties caused in part by a colonial past

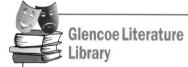

Glencoe Literature Library

As students study the unit, have them read *Journey to Jo'burg: A South African Story* by Beverley Naidoo from the **Glencoe Literature Library.** The Glencoe Literature Library consists of novels and other readings for middle school students, along with study guides that offer instructional support and student activities.

Unit 7

Waterfront of Cape Town, South Africa

Woman making butter in Chad

532

Using the Illustration

Visual Instruction Many African countries have set aside land as nature preserves to save the endangered animals of Africa—and to generate income by attracting ecotourists. Among the most famous parks are Kruger National Park in South Africa, Tsavo in Kenya, and Serengeti in Tanzania. Recently South Africa, Mozambique, and Zimbabwe agreed to combine Kruger with parks in the two other countries, forming a larger entity that can better protect species by giving them ample space to migrate. Have students investigate and report on one of Africa's parks, creating a poster that shows the location of the park, what visitors can see, and what programs are being used to study or protect the animals, and the economic benefits they give to African countries. ELL L2

 **EE3 Physical Systems: Standard 8**

Introducing Unit 7

NATIONAL GEOGRAPHIC

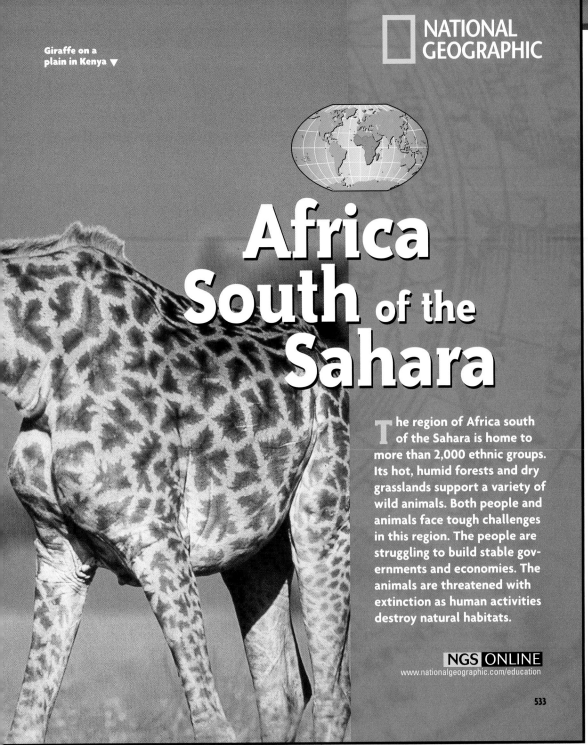

Giraffe on a plain in Kenya ▼

Africa South of the Sahara

The region of Africa south of the Sahara is home to more than 2,000 ethnic groups. Its hot, humid forests and dry grasslands support a variety of wild animals. Both people and animals face tough challenges in this region. The people are struggling to build stable governments and economies. The animals are threatened with extinction as human activities destroy natural habitats.

NGS ONLINE
www.nationalgeographic.com/education

533

Current Events Journal

In their notebooks, have students write words or phrases that they associate with Africa. Tell them to refer back to their lists as they read the unit. They may need to cross off some words or phrases as they add new ones.

NGS ONLINE
www.nationalgeographic.com/education

This online resource provides lesson plans, atlas updates, cartographic activities with interactive maps, an online map store, and geography links.

Unit Launch Activity

Why Study Africa? Africa faces difficult challenges. Ethnic divisions have disrupted many countries in recent years. AIDS has reached epidemic proportions in some countries. Developing nations struggle to establish order and economic growth as they compete against more industrialized countries. Traditional values and practices are challenged by the modern world. Some countries are threatened by desertification, habitat loss, poaching, and the effects of resource extraction. Inform students of these challenges and have them list ideas for possible solutions. Have them refer back to their lists when they have completed the unit and explain why their ideas would or would not work. L2

EE4 Human Systems: Standards 10, 13

LESSON PLAN

Using the Regional Atlas
These features and activities may be used as an introduction to the unit or as teaching tools throughout the course of the unit.

FOCUS

Objectives

1. Identify the major landforms in the region.
2. Explain how climate affects life in this region.
3. Describe the chief resources and economic activities of the region.
4. Discuss the different peoples who live in the region.

5-Minute Precheck

Have students look at the physical map of Africa in this unit's Regional Atlas. Have them focus on the countries that are part of Africa south of the Sahara. **Ask: Where is Africa south of the Sahara in relation to the Tropics?** *(Almost the entire region lies within the Tropics.)* **What effect will this location have on the region?** *(Climates will tend to be hot.)*

Focus on: Africa South of the Sahara

STRADDLING THE EQUATOR, Africa south of the Sahara lies almost entirely within the Tropics. Famous for its remarkable wildlife, this region also has the world's fastest-growing human population. Settling ethnic rivalries and improving low standards of living are just two of the challenges facing the people in this region.

The Land

Africa south of the Sahara has the highest overall elevation of any world region. A narrow band of low plains hugs the Atlantic and Indian Ocean coastlines. Inland, the land rises from west to east in a series of steplike plateaus. Separating the plateaus are steep cliffs. The region has no long mountain ranges and few towering peaks, although Mt. Kenya and Kilimanjaro are exceptions. At 19,340 feet (5,895 m), Kilimanjaro's summit is the highest point on the African continent.

Thundering Waterways Great rivers arise in this region's interior highlands. As rivers spill from one plateau to the next, they create thundering waterfalls, such as the spectacular Victoria Falls (facing page). It is known locally as *Mosi oa Tunya*—"smoke that thunders." Although the Nile River is Africa's longest river, the Congo River is a giant in its own right, winding 2,715 miles (4,370 km) through Africa's heart, near the Equator. Many of Africa's rivers provide hydroelectric power as well as transportation to areas that are too remote for overland travel.

Continental Rift The Great Rift Valley slices through eastern Africa like a steep-walled gash in the continent. The valley, formed by movements of the earth's crust, extends from Southwest Asia southward to the Zambezi River in Mozambique. It cradles a chain of deep lakes, some of which hold more species of fish than any other inland body of water in the world.

The Climate

Imagine that you are standing at the Equator in Africa. If you traveled north or south from there, you would pass through four major climate regions, one after the other.

Rain Forests and Savannas Tropical rain forests lie along the Equator and fill the great basin of the Congo River in central and western Africa. Heavy storms bring 80 inches (203 cm)

Content Background

The Bantu Much of Africa south of the Sahara is inhabited by descendants of the Bantu people who once lived in West Africa. About 500 B.C., this group lived by farming, hunting, and fishing. Over hundreds of years, they developed the ability to mine and to work metals. As a result, they had iron tools for farming and iron tips for hunting weapons. With more food, the population grew. About 2,000 years ago, the population had increased so much that some Bantu moved to new areas searching for new land. Over hundreds of years, Bantu-speaking groups spread throughout central, eastern, and southern Africa. Today about 60 to 80 million of their descendants live in Africa, speaking the many Bantu-related languages.

UNIT 7

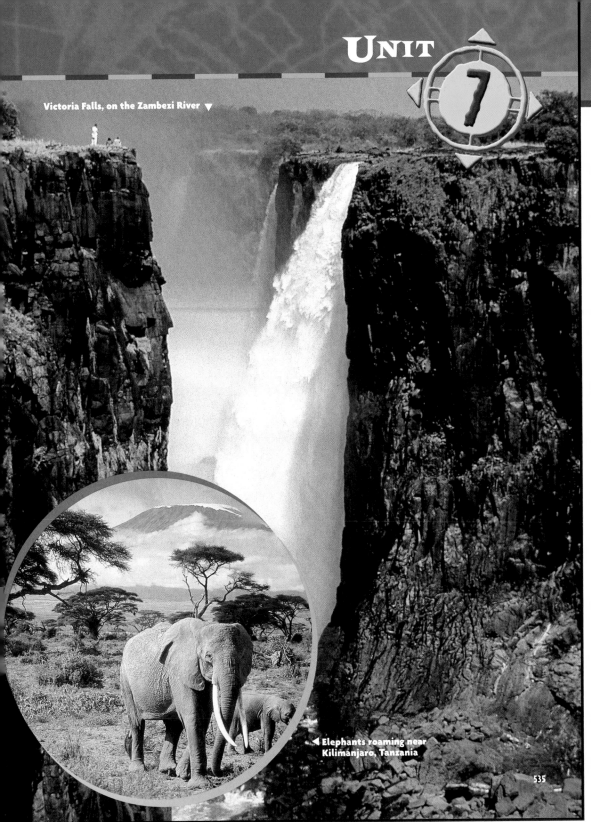

Victoria Falls, on the Zambezi River ▼

◀ Elephants roaming near Kilimanjaro, Tanzania

535

Unit 7

2 TEACH

Making a Graph Have students use an atlas to find the lengths of the major rivers of Africa: the Nile, Congo, Niger, Zambezi, and Orange. Have them make a graph comparing the lengths of these rivers *(4,241, 2,715, 2,590, 1,700, and 1,300 miles, respectively)*. Then have them write a sentence summarizing the comparison of the rivers' lengths. **L1**

More About the Photos

Victoria Falls Victoria Falls—at about 5,500 feet (1,676 m) wide—is about two times wider than Niagara Falls. The Zambezi River drops 355 feet (108 m), about twice as deep as the drop at Niagara Falls. After the river drops, it cuts through a narrow gorge and then rolls violently in a pool called the Boiling Point before continuing on to the sea.

Kilimanjaro In 1999 GPS was used to find the accurate elevation of Kilimanjaro. The new figure, 19,340 feet (5,895 m), is nearly 10 feet (3 m) shorter than previously calculated.

Eyewitness to Geography

Africa's Rain Forest Writer Douglas H. Chadwick, writing in *National Geographic,* described the dense rain forest and climate of Central Africa: "There was no sunset on the forest floor. There never is. Deep shadows welled up from the swamps and root tangles, and evening wove them together until it was night. The air stayed hot. This was the end of the dry season for the northern Republic of Congo. Thunderstorms were beginning to sweep the region with torrents of rain. But they never brought enough to really cool things down. They only added to the steam. Just eating dinner—lifting a fork, chewing—made me sweat."

NATIONAL GEOGRAPHIC

Regional Atlas

Building Skills

Sequencing Suggest that students create a time line of African history based on the information under the subsection The People.

Did You Know

South Africa produces about one-third of the world's gold.

Cultural Kaleidoscope

Benin Animism is a traditional religion practiced in Benin and other areas of West Africa. The religion is based on a belief that all things in nature have spirits.

More About the Photo

Farming Agriculture in Africa is a difficult way of life—only about 6 percent of the continent is arable land. In addition, sporadic rainfall in many areas makes it difficult to have highly productive farms. Despite these challenges, about two-thirds of the people farm or herd animals.

or more of rain each year. The canopy is the primary layer of rain forests and is alive with flowers, fruits, monkeys, parrots, and snakes.

As you move away from the Equator, rain forests give way to tropical savannas. These vast grasslands are home to some of the continent's most famous large mammals, including elephants, lions, rhinoceroses, and giraffes.

Steppe and Desert Climates As you move farther from the Equator, rainfall becomes scarce, and tropical savannas give way to drier steppes. Finally you encounter very dry areas where deserts dominate the landscape. Deserts cover more of Africa than any other continent. The largest deserts south of the Sahara are the Namib and the Kalahari.

The Economy

Africa south of the Sahara is rich in mineral resources, but these resources are not evenly distributed. Nigeria has huge reserves of oil. South Africa has fabulous deposits of gold and diamonds, making it the wealthiest country in the region. Overall, however, Africa south of the Sahara has the lowest standard of living of any world region.

Struggling to Develop Manufacturing plays only a small role in the region's economy. In the past, colonial rulers used Africa as a source of raw materials and left the continent largely undeveloped. Today the nations south of the Sahara are struggling to industrialize.

Most people in Africa south of the Sahara still depend on small-scale farming or livestock herding for their livelihoods. They are usually able to raise only enough food to feed their families. Some farmers work on plantations that grow crops for export to other countries. Such crops include coffee, cacao, cotton, peanuts, tea, bananas, and sisal (a fiber). Drought is a constant problem for the region's farmers.

The People

Thousands of years ago, great kingdoms and empires developed in Africa south of the Sahara. In the northeast, one kingdom extended its rule into Egyptian territory. In West Africa, wealthy empires emerged by trading salt for gold.

From Kingdoms to Nations In the 1400s and 1500s, Europeans began trading with African societies, carrying away gold, spices, ivory, and enslaved people. By the late 1800s, European nations had

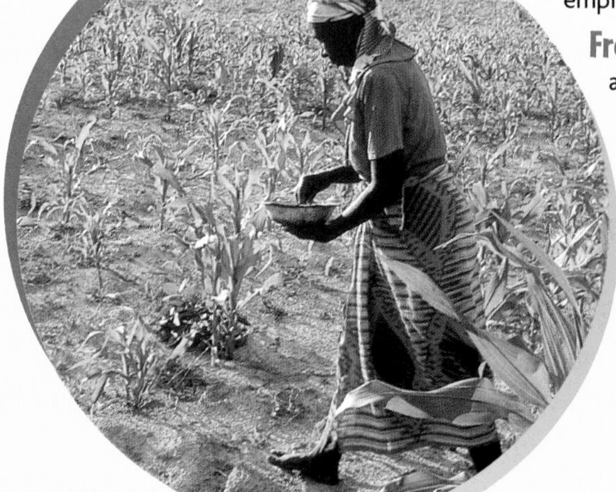

◀ Woman fertilizing crops in Zimbabwe

Fun Facts

- **Lesotho** This country has no forests and is subject to severe soil erosion. The government sponsors projects to help the environment. Tree Planting Day is an official holiday celebrated on March 21.
- **Namibia** The Namib Desert has some of the largest sand dunes in the world. In the southern part of the desert, dunes reach heights of 660 feet (201 m) and may spread up to 1 mile (1.6 km) wide. Tourists come here to sandboard.
- **Rwanda** Rwanda's oral literary tradition consists of myths, fables, folktales, poetry, and proverbs. Relatively few Rwandans can read and write, so stories are passed from one generation to another by storytellers.

claimed almost all of Africa. For profit and political advantage, they carved the continent into colonies. In the process, they ripped apart once-unified regions and threw together ethnic groups that did not get along.

Most African nations won their independence in the mid-1900s. Many countries that emerged from colonial rule were politically unstable and had crippled economies.

Varied Lifestyles Today more than 711 million people inhabit Africa south of the Sahara. They represent some 2,000 ethnic groups and speak 800 different languages. Nearly three-fourths of the population live in rural areas. Although Africa is the least urbanized continent, its cities are growing. Lured by the promise of better living conditions, people are flocking to African cities. These are among the fastest-growing urban areas in the world.

Crowded market in Lagos, Nigeria ▼

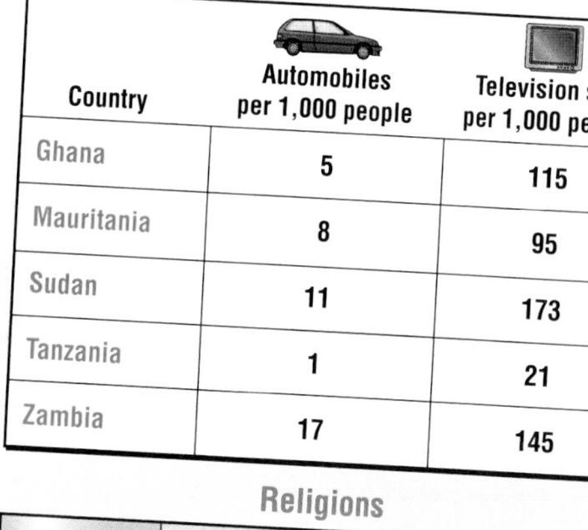

Data Bits

Country	Automobiles per 1,000 people	Television sets per 1,000 people
Ghana	5	115
Mauritania	8	95
Sudan	11	173
Tanzania	1	21
Zambia	17	145

Religions

Country	Islam	Christian	Traditional Beliefs
Ghana	16%	63%	21%
Mauritania	100%	—	—
Sudan	70%	5%	25%
Tanzania	35%	30%	35%
Zambia	24-49%	50-75%	1%

Sources: *World Development Indicators, 2002; World Almanac, 2004.*

Exploring the Region

1. What happens when Africa's rivers flow from one plateau to another?
2. Which climate zone is centered on the Equator?
3. What makes South Africa the region's most prosperous country?
4. How did colonial rule affect Africa south of the Sahara?

537

More About the Photo

Markets Traditional markets remain the chief vehicle for selling goods to consumers in much of Africa south of the Sahara. In Nigeria and other countries, women dominate these markets, where food and small goods are sold.

Assign the Exploring the Region questions as homework or as an in-class activity.

Reteach
Have students write a summary of the information under the four headings. Remind them to include the main idea and supporting details.

Enrich
Have students research and report on one of the geographic features of Africa south of the Sahara.

Reading Strategy

Writing a Paragraph Have students write a paragraph completing the sentence "Africa south of the Sahara is a region marked by . . . ."

Answers to Exploring the Region

1. They create substantial waterfalls.
2. tropical rain forest
3. fabulous deposits of gold and diamonds
4. European nations ripped apart once-unified regions and threw together ethnic groups that did not get along; they also did little to develop economies in Africa.

NATIONAL GEOGRAPHIC **REGIONAL ATLAS**

Africa South of the Sahara

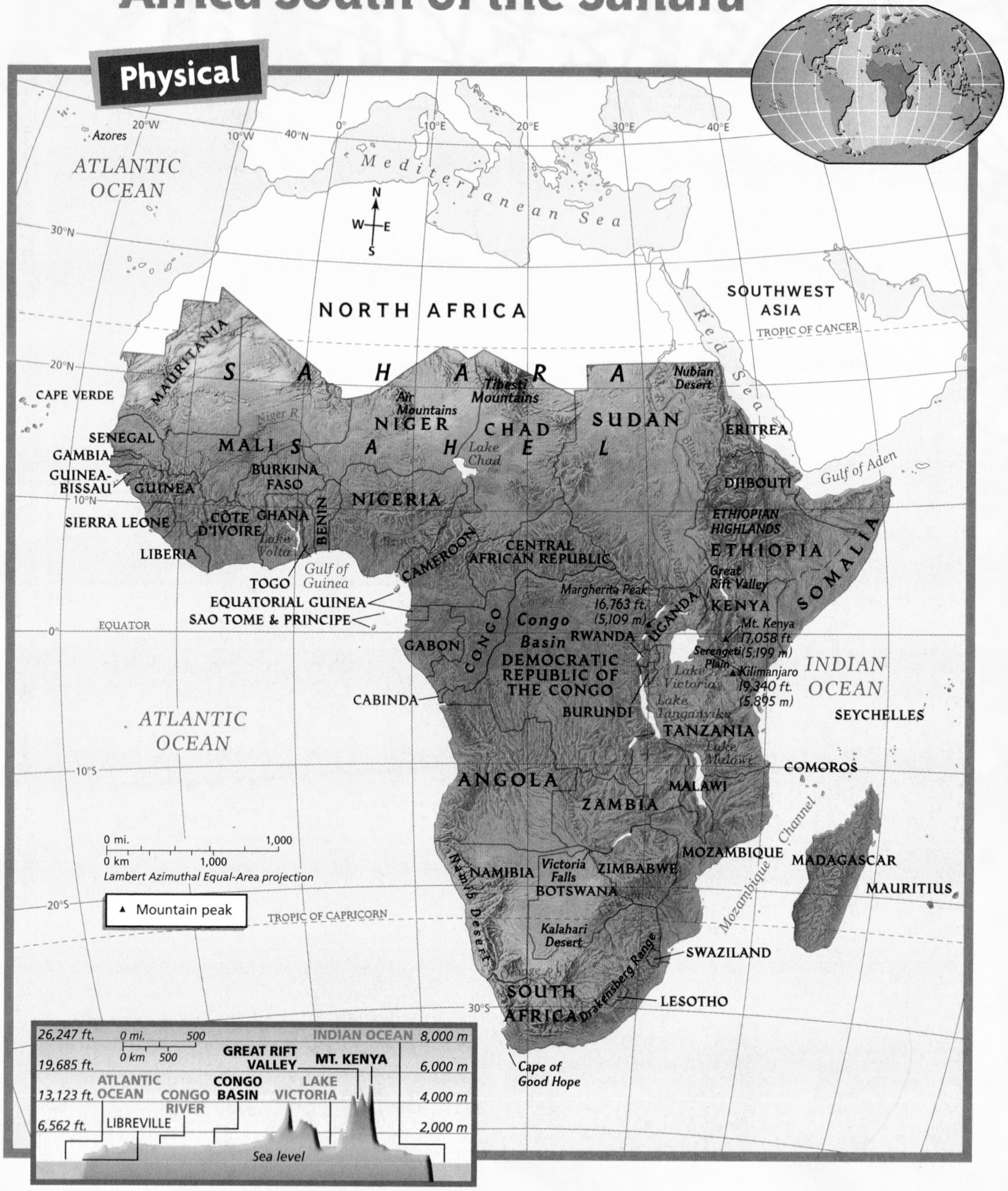

Physical

0 mi. 1,000
0 km 1,000
Lambert Azimuthal Equal-Area projection

▲ Mountain peak

538 UNIT 7

Lesson Plan

Using the Regional Atlas
These features and activities may be used as an introduction to the unit or as teaching tools throughout the course of the unit.

Focus

Objectives

1. Locate the region and describe its major landforms.
2. Identify the countries and capitals of the region.
3. Compare the populations of the countries in the region.
4. Discuss the chief economic products of the countries.

5-Minute Precheck

Have students look at the political map in the Regional Atlas. Have them write down the four countries they think are the largest in area. Then have them check the Country Profiles to see if they were correct. *(Sudan, Democratic Republic of the Congo, Chad, Niger)*

More About the Profile

In order to show a variety of physical features, this cross section along the Equator begins at Libreville in Gabon and ends in Somalia.

Content Background

Cameroon's Deadly Lake Lake Nyos, in Cameroon, sits on a pool of hot magma. This magma lets out carbon dioxide gas, which is dangerous. The gas builds up in the bottom of the lake. In August 1986, the pressure of this gas became too great, and it escaped into the air in a killing cloud that soon settled over nearby villages. Thousands of animals and 1,700 people died. After a decade passed, people began to return to the lakeshore. The gases are building up again, however. Scientists are installing a series of pipes from the gas layer to the surface. They hope to release the gas slowly over time so they can prevent another massive, deadly leak. **Ask:** **Why would people want to live by Lake Nyos and what effect would it have on their lives? L1**

UNIT 7

Political

ATLANTIC OCEAN
Azores Port.
Mediterranean Sea
NORTH AFRICA
SOUTHWEST ASIA
Boundary claimed by Sudan
Red Sea
TROPIC OF CANCER
CAPE VERDE Praia
MAURITANIA Nouakchott
SENEGAL Dakar
GAMBIA Banjul
GUINEA-BISSAU Bissau
GUINEA Conakry
SIERRA LEONE Freetown
LIBERIA Monrovia
CÔTE D'IVOIRE Yamoussoukro Abidjan
MALI Bamako
BURKINA FASO Ouagadougou
GHANA Accra
TOGO Lomé
BENIN Porto-Novo
NIGER Niamey
NIGERIA Abuja
CHAD N'Djamena
Lake Chad
SUDAN Khartoum
ERITREA Asmara
DJIBOUTI Djibouti
Gulf of Aden
ETHIOPIA Addis Ababa
SOMALIA Mogadishu
CAMEROON Yaoundé
CENTRAL AFRICAN REPUBLIC Bangui
EQUATORIAL GUINEA Malabo
SAO TOME & PRINCIPE São Tomé
GABON Libreville
CONGO Brazzaville
CABINDA Ang.
DEMOCRATIC REPUBLIC OF THE CONGO Kinshasa
UGANDA Kampala
KENYA Nairobi
Lake Victoria
RWANDA Kigali
BURUNDI Bujumbura
Lake Tanganyika
TANZANIA Dar es Salaam
INDIAN OCEAN
SEYCHELLES Victoria
COMOROS Moroni
Lake Malawi
MALAWI Lilongwe
ANGOLA Luanda
ZAMBIA Lusaka
ZIMBABWE Harare
MOZAMBIQUE Maputo
Mozambique Channel
MADAGASCAR Antananarivo
MAURITIUS Port Louis
RÉUNION Fr.
NAMIBIA Windhoek
BOTSWANA Gaborone
SOUTH AFRICA Pretoria Bloemfontein Cape Town
SWAZILAND Mbabane
LESOTHO Maseru
ATLANTIC OCEAN
EQUATOR
TROPIC OF CAPRICORN
Niger R. Benue R. Congo R. Blue Nile R. White Nile R. Nile R. Zambezi R. Limpopo R. Orange R.
N W E S
National capital
0 mi. 1,000
0 km 1,000
Lambert Azimuthal Equal-Area projection

MAP STUDY

1. What plain is shared by Kenya and Tanzania?
2. What is the capital of Nigeria?

539

Unit 7

2 TEACH

Synthesizing Information Have students study the physical features of this region. Then have them choose a place or geographic feature shown on the map. Have them write at least five adjectives to describe their place or feature. Call on students to share their adjectives. Then have other students try to identify the place or feature. **L1**

Using a Map Have students look at the political map on this page. **Ask:** **Which country has a coastline on two oceans?** *(South Africa)* **What 15 countries are landlocked?** *(Mali, Burkina Faso, Niger, Chad, Ethiopia, Central African Republic, Uganda, Rwanda, Burundi, Malawi, Zambia, Zimbabwe, Botswana, Swaziland, Lesotho)* **What six countries are only on islands?** *(Cape Verde Islands, São Tomé and Príncipe, Madagascar, Comoros, Seychelles, Mauritius)* **L1**

MAP STUDY

Answers

1. Serengeti Plain
2. Abuja

Skills Practice
What country is completely surrounded by South Africa? *(Lesotho)* **Which is longer, the Atlantic Ocean coast or the Indian Ocean coast?** *(Atlantic)*

Regional Atlas Activity

Mental Mapping Help students develop a mental map of Africa south of the Sahara by playing a location game. Assign one or more countries to each student. Instruct students to write clues about the location of the countries they were assigned. *(Example: This country is east of Gabon. It borders the Central African Republic. It is west and north of the Democratic Republic of the Congo. It has a coastline on the Atlantic Ocean. Answer—Congo.)* Have each student read these clues, one at a time, until a classmate can identify the country. You could also use the clues as part of a team competition. Award points based on the number of clues a team needs to correctly identify the country, with more points received the fewer the clues used. **L2**

 **EE1 The World in Spatial Terms: Standard 2**

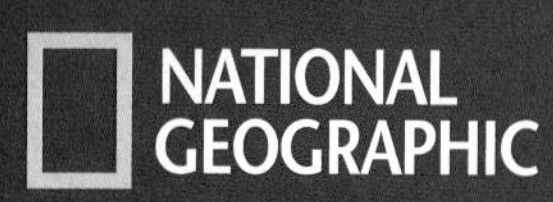

REGIONAL ATLAS

Africa South of the Sahara

Making Generalizations Have students study the map on this page and then make a generalization based on its information. *(Example: Most nations with diamond deposits are in southern Africa.)* Ask for volunteers to read their generalizations aloud. L1

Interdisciplinary Connections

Economics Minerals are not the only valuable resource in Africa. Markets for crocodile leather and leopard fur have resulted in severely reduced numbers of Nile crocodiles and leopards. Rhinoceroses have been hunted to near extinction for their horns. Elephant ivory is also popular, and the number of African elephants has plummeted.

MAP STUDY

Answers
1. diamonds, rubies, emeralds, and sapphires
2. Atlantic Ocean

Skills Practice
In what countries are emeralds mined? *(Tanzania, Mozambique, Zambia, Zimbabwe, Botswana, South Africa, and Madagascar)*

Gems and Minerals

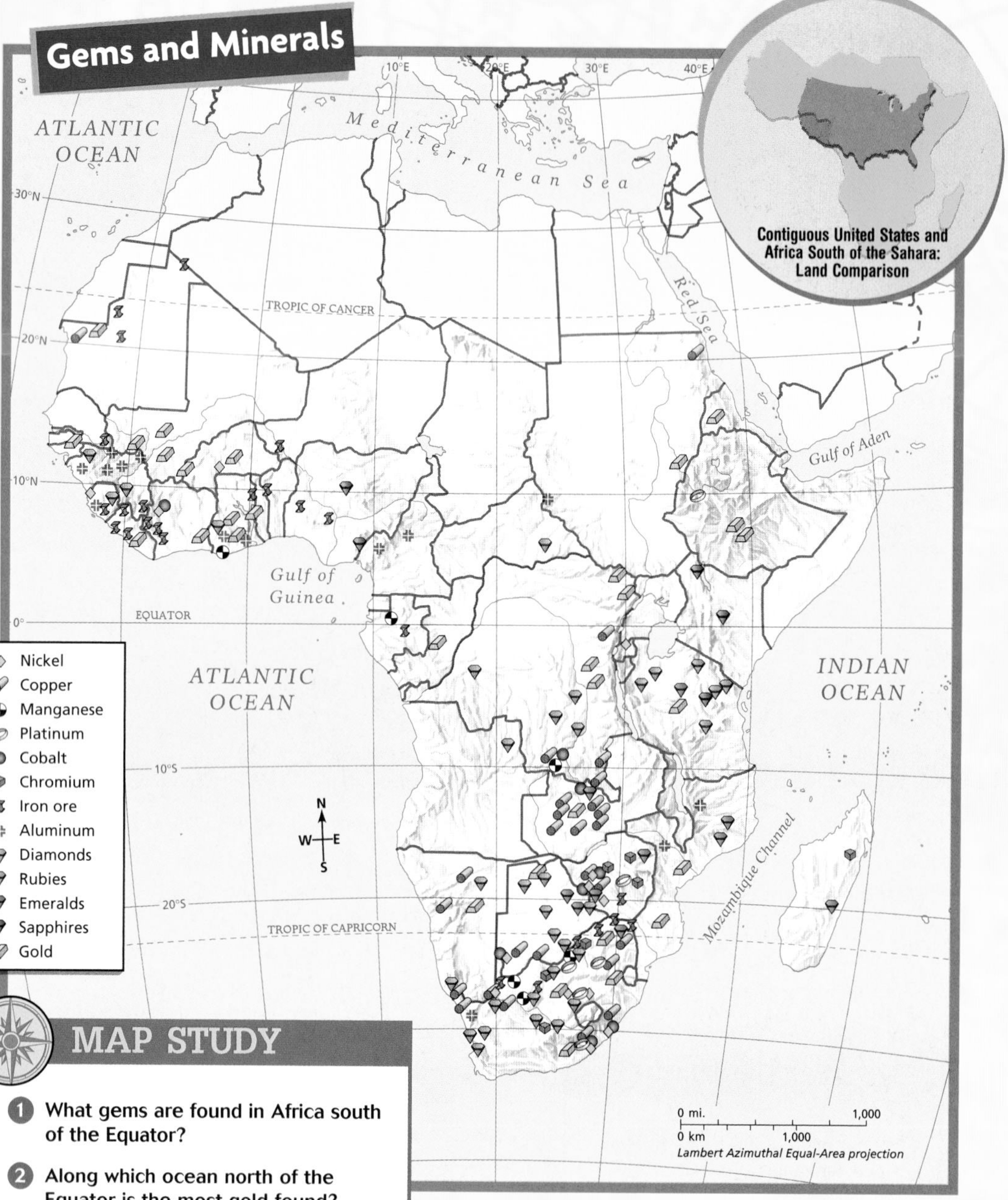

MAP STUDY

1. What gems are found in Africa south of the Equator?
2. Along which ocean north of the Equator is the most gold found?

UNIT 7

Regional Atlas Activity

Locating Places A United Nations report recently predicted that conflict over water is likely to become a significant problem in Africa in the next 25 years. The report says that 11 countries are currently in a situation of water scarcity or water stress, meaning that the country has less than 42 cubic feet (1.2 cu. m) of water per person per year. The report predicts that 14 more countries are likely to join this list in the coming years, accounting for nearly half of Africa's people. The report expects the most severe problems in areas where countries share rivers or lakes. Have students look at the physical map and identify areas where this situation applies. L1

 **EE6 The Uses of Geography: Standard 18**

Geo Extremes

① HIGHEST POINT
**Kilimanjaro (Tanzania)
19,340 ft. (5,895 m) high**

② LOWEST POINT
**Lake Assal (Djibouti)
512 ft. (156 m)
below sea level**

③ LONGEST RIVER
**Nile River
4,241 mi.
(6,825 km) long**

④ LARGEST LAKE
**Lake Victoria (Kenya, Uganda, and Tanzania)
26,834 sq. mi.
(69,500 sq. km)**

⑤ LARGEST ISLAND
**Madagascar
226,642 sq. mi.
(587,000 sq. km)**

⑥ HOTTEST PLACE
**Dalol, Denakil Depression (Ethiopia)
93°F (34°C) annual average temperature**

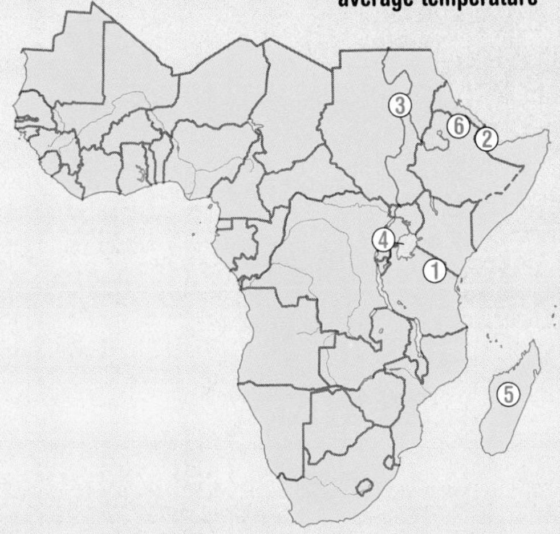

COMPARING POPULATION: United States and Selected Countries of Africa South of the Sahara

UNITED STATES

NIGERIA

DEMOCRATIC REPUBLIC OF THE CONGO

SOUTH AFRICA

KENYA

SENEGAL

(one figure) = 30,000,000

Source: *Population Reference Bureau*, 2003.

SELECTED RURAL AND URBAN POPULATIONS: Africa South of the Sahara

	Rural	Urban
WEST AFRICA		
Niger	79%	21%
Cape Verde	36%	64%
CENTRAL AFRICA		
Angola	65%	35%
Central African Republic	58%	42%
EAST AFRICA		
Rwanda	94%	6%
Djibouti	16%	84%
SOUTHERN AFRICA		
Lesotho	71%	29%
South Africa	42%	58%

Source: *The World Almanac*, 2004.

GRAPHIC STUDY

1. What is the longest river in Africa?
2. Of the African countries shown in the chart at lower right, which is least urbanized? Which is most urbanized?

Unit 7
Regional Atlas

Cultural Kaleidoscope

Lesotho As many as 250,000 men at a time may be gone from this country to work in the mines of South Africa. As a result, women do most of the farming and make many day-to-day family decisions.

TRAVEL GUIDE

When visiting Cape Verde, you may enjoy the *Funáná,* lively dance music with a strong beat. The music was forbidden in Cape Verde during colonial times. After the islands became independent, the music was revived.

Did You Know

Basket weaving is an important craft in Rwanda. Weavers use fibers from banana plants to make waterproof baskets. A family's social standing may be determined by the number and quality of baskets it owns.

GRAPHIC STUDY

Answers
1. the Nile
2. Rwanda; Djibouti

Skills Practice
How many people live in Kenya? *(about 40 million)* **How does Kenya's population compare to Nigeria's?** *(Nigeria's population is nearly four times larger.)*

FUN FACTS

- **Africa** About 90 percent of Africa lies within the Tropics—the largest tropical region of any continent.
- **Chad** The Tibesti Mountains cover an area of more than 50,000 square miles (129,500 sq. km) and reach heights of over 11,000 feet (3,353 m). One of the world's most rugged and inaccessible places, the Tibesti Mountains have long served as a refuge for desert bandits.
- **Namibia** About 100,000 people in Namibia and other parts of southwest Africa speak Khoisan languages. These languages are not related to any others spoken in Africa. Many words in Khoisan are expressed with unusual "click" sounds.

Current Events Journal

Have students write at least five questions about the physical geography of Africa south of the Sahara. Tell students to include direction, key, scale, or physical map questions such as: **In what direction would you travel from Ethiopia to Somalia?** *(east)*; **How does Senegal compare in elevation to Burundi?** *(Senegal is a lowland coastal plain from 0 to 1,000 feet above sea level; Burundi is a mountainous region from 5,000 to 10,000 feet high.)* Allow time for students to write questions and challenge one another. You may also want to repeat this activity at the end of the unit.

Did You Know

Burkina Faso means "land of the honest people." Burkina Faso's economy is heavily dependent on cattle, goats, and sheep. About 50 percent of the country's export income is derived from the sale of livestock.

Travel Guide

Telephones are rare in Cameroon and mail service is unreliable. People communicate by *radio trattoir,* or "pavement radio." This is a system of passing news by verbal relay.

NATIONAL GEOGRAPHIC

Regional Atlas

Country Profiles

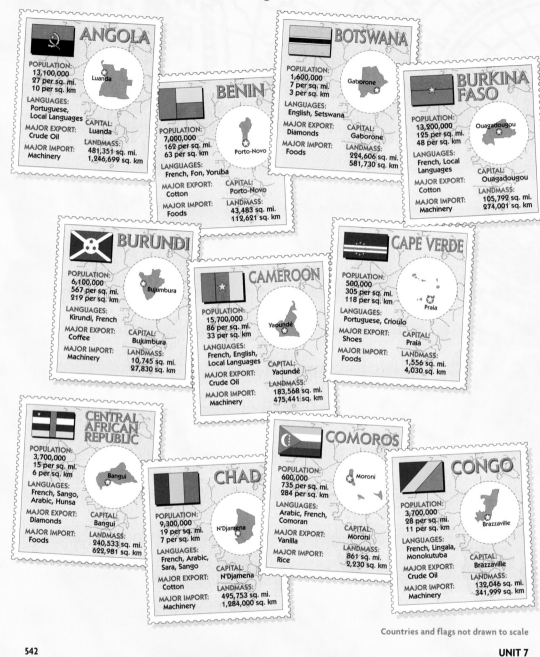

ANGOLA
POPULATION: 13,100,000; 27 per sq. mi.; 10 per sq. km
LANGUAGES: Portuguese, Local Languages
MAJOR EXPORT: Crude Oil
MAJOR IMPORT: Machinery
CAPITAL: Luanda
LANDMASS: 481,351 sq. mi.; 1,246,699 sq. km

BENIN
POPULATION: 7,000,000; 162 per sq. mi.; 63 per sq. km
LANGUAGES: French, Fon, Yoruba
MAJOR EXPORT: Cotton
MAJOR IMPORT: Foods
CAPITAL: Porto-Novo
LANDMASS: 43,483 sq. mi.; 112,621 sq. km

BOTSWANA
POPULATION: 1,600,000; 7 per sq. mi.; 3 per sq. km
LANGUAGES: English, Setswana
MAJOR EXPORT: Diamonds
MAJOR IMPORT: Foods
CAPITAL: Gaborone
LANDMASS: 224,606 sq. mi.; 581,730 sq. km

BURKINA FASO
POPULATION: 13,200,000; 125 per sq. mi.; 48 per sq. km
LANGUAGES: French, Local Languages
MAJOR EXPORT: Cotton
MAJOR IMPORT: Machinery
CAPITAL: Ouagadougou
LANDMASS: 105,792 sq. mi.; 274,001 sq. km

BURUNDI
POPULATION: 6,100,000; 567 per sq. mi.; 219 per sq. km
LANGUAGES: Kirundi, French
MAJOR EXPORT: Coffee
MAJOR IMPORT: Machinery
CAPITAL: Bujumbura
LANDMASS: 10,745 sq. mi.; 27,830 sq. km

CAMEROON
POPULATION: 15,700,000; 86 per sq. mi.; 33 per sq. km
LANGUAGES: French, English, Local Languages
MAJOR EXPORT: Crude Oil
MAJOR IMPORT: Machinery
CAPITAL: Yaoundé
LANDMASS: 183,568 sq. mi.; 475,441 sq. km

CAPE VERDE
POPULATION: 500,000; 305 per sq. mi.; 118 per sq. km
LANGUAGES: Portuguese, Crioulo
MAJOR EXPORT: Shoes
MAJOR IMPORT: Foods
CAPITAL: Praia
LANDMASS: 1,556 sq. mi.; 4,030 sq. km

CENTRAL AFRICAN REPUBLIC
POPULATION: 3,700,000; 15 per sq. mi.; 6 per sq. km
LANGUAGES: French, Sango, Arabic, Hunsa
MAJOR EXPORT: Diamonds
MAJOR IMPORT: Foods
CAPITAL: Bangui
LANDMASS: 240,533 sq. mi.; 622,981 sq. km

CHAD
POPULATION: 9,300,000; 19 per sq. mi.; 7 per sq. km
LANGUAGES: French, Arabic, Sara, Sango
MAJOR EXPORT: Cotton
MAJOR IMPORT: Machinery
CAPITAL: N'Djamena
LANDMASS: 495,753 sq. mi.; 1,284,000 sq. km

COMOROS
POPULATION: 600,000; 735 per sq. mi.; 284 per sq. km
LANGUAGES: Arabic, French, Comoran
MAJOR EXPORT: Vanilla
MAJOR IMPORT: Rice
CAPITAL: Moroni
LANDMASS: 861 sq. mi.; 2,230 sq. km

CONGO
POPULATION: 3,700,000; 28 per sq. mi.; 11 per sq. km
LANGUAGES: French, Lingala, Monokutuba
MAJOR EXPORT: Crude Oil
MAJOR IMPORT: Machinery
CAPITAL: Brazzaville
LANDMASS: 132,046 sq. mi.; 341,999 sq. km

Countries and flags not drawn to scale

Content Background

African Families Family is extremely important in many African countries. In Cameroon, a family may house and feed a distant relative who is in need, even when it causes hardship. In Zimbabwe, parents care for their children and expect the children to care for them in their old age. For centuries, families across Africa were typically extended families, with several generations living in the same household. In recent decades, urbanization and the development of a money economy have changed that, and the nuclear family became more common. The stresses caused by war and AIDS have ravaged the family further in some countries. **Ask: What are the similarities and differences in the way Africans and Americans feel about families? L1**

Unit 7

For more information on countries in this region, refer to the Nations of the World Data Bank in the Appendix.

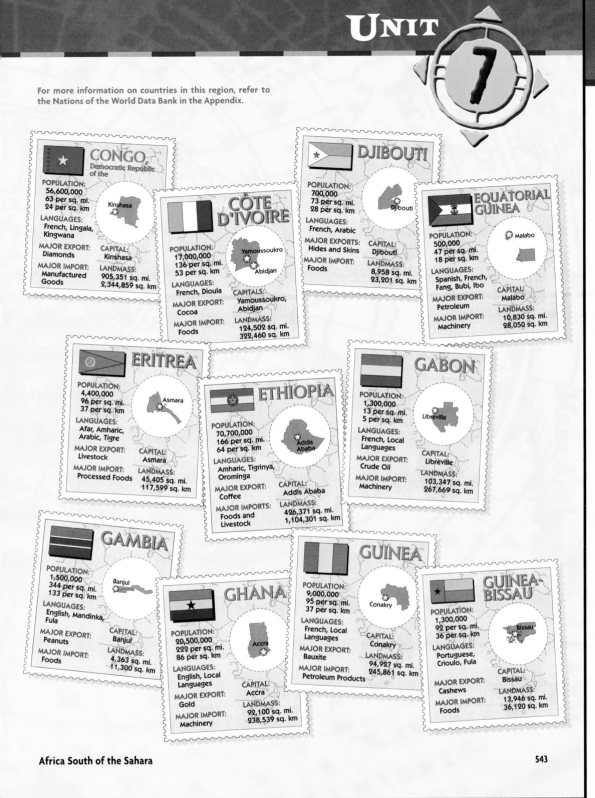

CONGO, Democratic Republic of the
POPULATION: 56,600,000; 63 per sq. mi.; 24 per sq. km
LANGUAGES: French, Lingala, Kingwana
MAJOR EXPORT: Diamonds
MAJOR IMPORT: Manufactured Goods
CAPITAL: Kinshasa
LANDMASS: 905,351 sq. mi.; 2,344,859 sq. km

CÔTE D'IVOIRE
POPULATION: 17,000,000; 136 per sq. mi.; 53 per sq. km
LANGUAGES: French, Dioula
MAJOR EXPORT: Cocoa
MAJOR IMPORT: Foods
CAPITALS: Yamoussoukro, Abidjan
LANDMASS: 124,502 sq. mi.; 322,460 sq. km

DJIBOUTI
POPULATION: 700,000; 73 per sq. mi.; 28 per sq. km
LANGUAGES: French, Arabic
MAJOR EXPORTS: Hides and Skins
MAJOR IMPORT: Foods
CAPITAL: Djibouti
LANDMASS: 8,958 sq. mi.; 23,201 sq. km

EQUATORIAL GUINEA
POPULATION: 500,000; 47 per sq. mi.; 18 per sq. km
LANGUAGES: Spanish, French, Fang, Bubi, Ibo
MAJOR EXPORT: Petroleum
MAJOR IMPORT: Machinery
CAPITAL: Malabo
LANDMASS: 10,830 sq. mi.; 28,050 sq. km

ERITREA
POPULATION: 4,400,000; 96 per sq. mi.; 37 per sq. km
LANGUAGES: Afar, Amharic, Arabic, Tigre
MAJOR EXPORT: Livestock
MAJOR IMPORT: Processed Foods
CAPITAL: Asmara
LANDMASS: 45,405 sq. mi.; 117,599 sq. km

ETHIOPIA
POPULATION: 70,700,000; 166 per sq. mi.; 64 per sq. km
LANGUAGES: Amharic, Tigrinya, Orominga
MAJOR EXPORT: Coffee
MAJOR IMPORTS: Foods and Livestock
CAPITAL: Addis Ababa
LANDMASS: 426,371 sq. mi.; 1,104,301 sq. km

GABON
POPULATION: 1,300,000; 13 per sq. mi.; 5 per sq. km
LANGUAGES: French, Local Languages
MAJOR EXPORT: Crude Oil
MAJOR IMPORT: Machinery
CAPITAL: Libreville
LANDMASS: 103,347 sq. mi.; 267,669 sq. km

GAMBIA
POPULATION: 1,500,000; 344 per sq. mi.; 133 per sq. km
LANGUAGES: English, Mandinka, Fula
MAJOR EXPORT: Peanuts
MAJOR IMPORT: Foods
CAPITAL: Banjul
LANDMASS: 4,363 sq. mi.; 11,300 sq. km

GHANA
POPULATION: 20,500,000; 222 per sq. mi.; 86 per sq. km
LANGUAGES: English, Local Languages
MAJOR EXPORT: Gold
MAJOR IMPORT: Machinery
CAPITAL: Accra
LANDMASS: 92,100 sq. mi.; 238,539 sq. km

GUINEA
POPULATION: 9,000,000; 95 per sq. mi.; 37 per sq. km
LANGUAGES: French, Local Languages
MAJOR EXPORT: Bauxite
MAJOR IMPORT: Petroleum Products
CAPITAL: Conakry
LANDMASS: 94,927 sq. mi.; 245,861 sq. km

GUINEA-BISSAU
POPULATION: 1,300,000; 92 per sq. mi.; 36 per sq. km
LANGUAGES: Portuguese, Crioulo, Fula
MAJOR EXPORT: Cashews
MAJOR IMPORT: Foods
CAPITAL: Bissau
LANDMASS: 13,946 sq. mi.; 36,120 sq. km

Country Profiles Activity

Have students prepare a chart that lists the countries profiled here by region—West Africa, Central Africa, East Africa, and southern Africa. Their chart might include the name of the country, the capital, the population, and the chief exports. Then have them compare the main economic activities in the different regions. L1

EE1 The World in Spatial Terms: Standard 1

Unit 7 Regional Atlas

According to tradition, Ethiopians are descendants of the Biblical rulers Solomon and the Queen of Sheba.

World Music: A Cultural Legacy

World Art and Architecture Transparencies

Cultural Kaleidoscope

Niger Students in Niger get their teacher's attention by snapping their fingers rather than raising their hands.

Cultural Kaleidoscope

Liberia Liberia was founded as a settlement for African Americans who were freed from slavery. It was founded in 1822, and the first settlement was named Monrovia after American President James Monroe. The American connection is also evident in the country's flag, which has a total of 11 red and white stripes and a single white star in a field of deep blue.

Because of its elevation, Lesotho does not have a tropical climate like that of the surrounding region. For the same reason, Lesotho is free of many of the diseases common in other parts of Africa.

Country Profiles

KENYA
POPULATION: 31,600,000; 141 per sq. mi.; 54 per sq. km
LANGUAGES: English, Swahili
MAJOR EXPORT: Tea
MAJOR IMPORT: Machinery
CAPITAL: Nairobi
LANDMASS: 224,081 sq. mi.; 580,370 sq. km

LESOTHO
POPULATION: 1,800,000; 153 per sq. mi.; 59 per sq. km
LANGUAGES: English, Sesotho, Zulu, Xhosa
MAJOR EXPORT: Clothing
MAJOR IMPORT: Corn
CAPITAL: Maseru
LANDMASS: 11,718 sq. mi.; 30,350 sq. km

LIBERIA
POPULATION: 3,300,000; 77 per sq. mi.; 30 per sq. km
LANGUAGES: English, Local Languages
MAJOR EXPORT: Diamonds
MAJOR IMPORT: Natural Gas
CAPITAL: Monrovia
LANDMASS: 43,000 sq. mi.; 111,370 sq. km

MADAGASCAR
POPULATION: 17,000,000; 75 per sq. mi.; 29 per sq. km
LANGUAGES: French, Malagasy
MAJOR EXPORT: Coffee
MAJOR IMPORT: Machinery
CAPITAL: Antananarivo
LANDMASS: 226,656 sq. mi.; 587,039 sq. km

MALAWI
POPULATION: 11,700,000; 255 per sq. mi.; 98 per sq. km
LANGUAGES: Chewa, English
MAJOR EXPORT: Tobacco
MAJOR IMPORT: Foods
CAPITAL: Lilongwe
LANDMASS: 45,745 sq. mi.; 118,480 sq. km

MALI
POPULATION: 11,600,000; 24 per sq. mi.; 9 per sq. km
LANGUAGES: French, Bambara
MAJOR EXPORT: Cotton
MAJOR IMPORT: Machinery
CAPITAL: Bamako
LANDMASS: 478,838 sq. mi.; 1,240,190 sq. km

MAURITANIA
POPULATION: 2,900,000; 7 per sq. mi.; 3 per sq. km
LANGUAGES: Hasaniya Arabic, Wolof
MAJOR EXPORT: Fish
MAJOR IMPORT: Foods
CAPITAL: Nouakchott
LANDMASS: 395,954 sq. mi.; 1,025,521 sq. km

MAURITIUS
POPULATION: 1,200,000; 1,550 per sq. mi.; 598 per sq. km
LANGUAGES: English, Creole, Bhojpuri, French
MAJOR EXPORT: Sugar
MAJOR IMPORT: Foods
CAPITAL: Port Louis
LANDMASS: 788 sq. mi.; 2,041 sq. km

MOZAMBIQUE
POPULATION: 17,500,000; 56 per sq. mi.; 22 per sq. km
LANGUAGES: Portuguese, Local Languages
MAJOR EXPORT: Cashews
MAJOR IMPORT: Foods
CAPITAL: Maputo
LANDMASS: 309,494 sq. mi.; 801,590 sq. km

NAMIBIA
POPULATION: 1,900,000; 6 per sq. mi.; 2 per sq. km
LANGUAGES: English, Afrikaans, Local Languages
MAJOR EXPORT: Diamonds
MAJOR IMPORT: Construction Materials
CAPITAL: Windhoek
LANDMASS: 318,259 sq. mi.; 824,291 sq. km

NIGER
POPULATION: 12,100,000; 25 per sq. mi.; 10 per sq. km
LANGUAGES: French, Hausa, Djerma
MAJOR EXPORT: Uranium Ore
MAJOR IMPORT: Manufactured Goods
CAPITAL: Niamey
LANDMASS: 489,189 sq. mi.; 1,267,000 sq. km

Countries and flags not drawn to scale

Content Background

Lake Malawi Fish Malawi sits on the shores of Lake Malawi, home to more different species of fish than any other freshwater lake in the world. Malawi uses this resource in an unusual way—divers collect the beautifully colored fish and sell them to companies that market them for aquarium collectors around the world. Some fish can bring hundreds of dollars to the diver who catches them.

UNIT 7

For more information on countries in this region, refer to the Nations of the World Data Bank in the Appendix.

NIGERIA

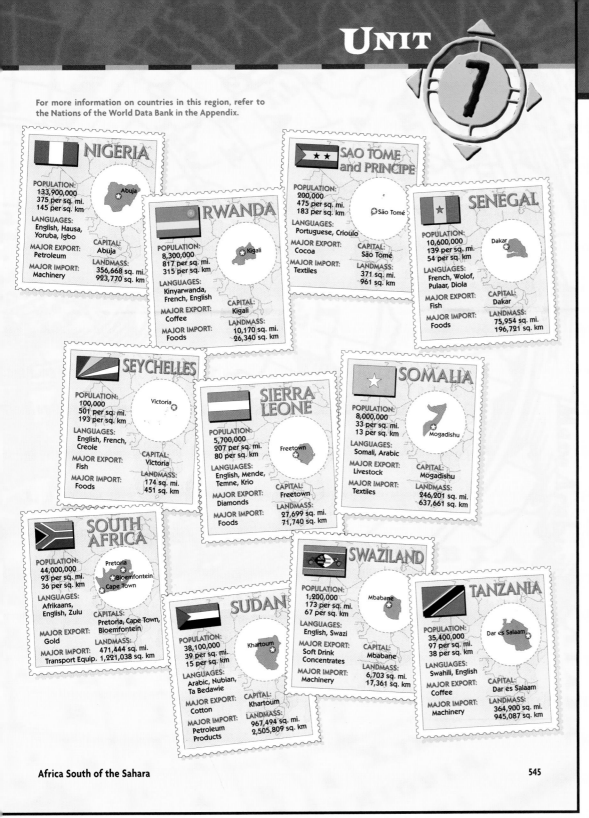

POPULATION: 133,900,000; 375 per sq. mi.; 145 per sq. km
LANGUAGES: English, Hausa, Yoruba, Igbo
MAJOR EXPORT: Petroleum
MAJOR IMPORT: Machinery
CAPITAL: Abuja
LANDMASS: 356,668 sq. mi.; 923,770 sq. km

RWANDA

POPULATION: 8,300,000; 817 per sq. mi.; 315 per sq. km
LANGUAGES: Kinyarwanda, French, English
MAJOR EXPORT: Coffee
MAJOR IMPORT: Foods
CAPITAL: Kigali
LANDMASS: 10,170 sq. mi.; 26,340 sq. km

SAO TOME and PRINCIPE

POPULATION: 200,000; 475 per sq. mi.; 183 per sq. km
LANGUAGES: Portuguese, Crioulo
MAJOR EXPORT: Cocoa
MAJOR IMPORT: Textiles
CAPITAL: São Tomé
LANDMASS: 371 sq. mi.; 961 sq. km

SENEGAL

POPULATION: 10,600,000; 139 per sq. mi.; 54 per sq. km
LANGUAGES: French, Wolof, Pulaar, Diola
MAJOR EXPORT: Fish
MAJOR IMPORT: Foods
CAPITAL: Dakar
LANDMASS: 75,954 sq. mi.; 196,721 sq. km

SEYCHELLES

POPULATION: 100,000; 501 per sq. mi.; 193 per sq. km
LANGUAGES: English, French, Creole
MAJOR EXPORT: Fish
MAJOR IMPORT: Foods
CAPITAL: Victoria
LANDMASS: 174 sq. mi.; 451 sq. km

SIERRA LEONE

POPULATION: 5,700,000; 207 per sq. mi.; 80 per sq. km
LANGUAGES: English, Mende, Temne, Krio
MAJOR EXPORT: Diamonds
MAJOR IMPORT: Foods
CAPITAL: Freetown
LANDMASS: 27,699 sq. mi.; 71,740 sq. km

SOMALIA

POPULATION: 8,000,000; 33 per sq. mi.; 13 per sq. km
LANGUAGES: Somali, Arabic
MAJOR EXPORT: Livestock
MAJOR IMPORT: Textiles
CAPITAL: Mogadishu
LANDMASS: 246,201 sq. mi.; 637,661 sq. km

SOUTH AFRICA

POPULATION: 44,000,000; 93 per sq. mi.; 36 per sq. km
LANGUAGES: Afrikaans, English, Zulu
MAJOR EXPORT: Gold
MAJOR IMPORT: Transport Equip.
CAPITALS: Pretoria, Cape Town, Bloemfontein
LANDMASS: 471,444 sq. mi.; 1,221,038 sq. km

SUDAN

POPULATION: 38,100,000; 39 per sq. mi.; 15 per sq. km
LANGUAGES: Arabic, Nubian, Ta Bedawie
MAJOR EXPORT: Cotton
MAJOR IMPORT: Petroleum Products
CAPITAL: Khartoum
LANDMASS: 967,494 sq. mi.; 2,505,809 sq. km

SWAZILAND

POPULATION: 1,200,000; 173 per sq. mi.; 67 per sq. km
LANGUAGES: English, Swazi
MAJOR EXPORT: Soft Drink Concentrates
MAJOR IMPORT: Machinery
CAPITAL: Mbabane
LANDMASS: 6,703 sq. mi.; 17,361 sq. km

TANZANIA

POPULATION: 35,400,000; 97 per sq. mi.; 38 per sq. km
LANGUAGES: Swahili, English
MAJOR EXPORT: Coffee
MAJOR IMPORT: Machinery
CAPITAL: Dar es Salaam
LANDMASS: 364,900 sq. mi.; 945,087 sq. km

Regional Atlas Activity

Explaining the Great Rift Valley Landforms Have small groups investigate how landforms in and around the Great Rift Valley were formed. Groups should research volcanoes, earthquakes, or glaciers and their effect on this part of the region. Direct groups to use library and reliable Internet resources to gather information. When they have completed their research, groups should pool their findings to create a bulletin board display about the forces that have shaped the landforms in East Africa. Encourage students to include illustrative visuals (diagrams, pictures, and so on) in the display. L2

EE3 Physical Systems: Standard 7

Unit 7
Regional Atlas

During the 1600s and 1700s, Madagascar was used as a base by pirates. Among them was the notorious Scottish pirate named Captain Kidd.

TRAVEL GUIDE

The people of Mali never use the left hand to accept food or money. When shaking hands, a Malian shows special respect by touching his or her right elbow with the fingers of the left hand.

Interdisciplinary Connections

Science The Welwitschia is a plant that grows in the Namib Desert. Its trunk spreads to a width of more than 5 feet (1.5 m). Two giant green leaves grow out from the trunk and split into ribbonlike shreds. The plants may live as long as 2,000 years.

Regional Atlas

Country Profiles

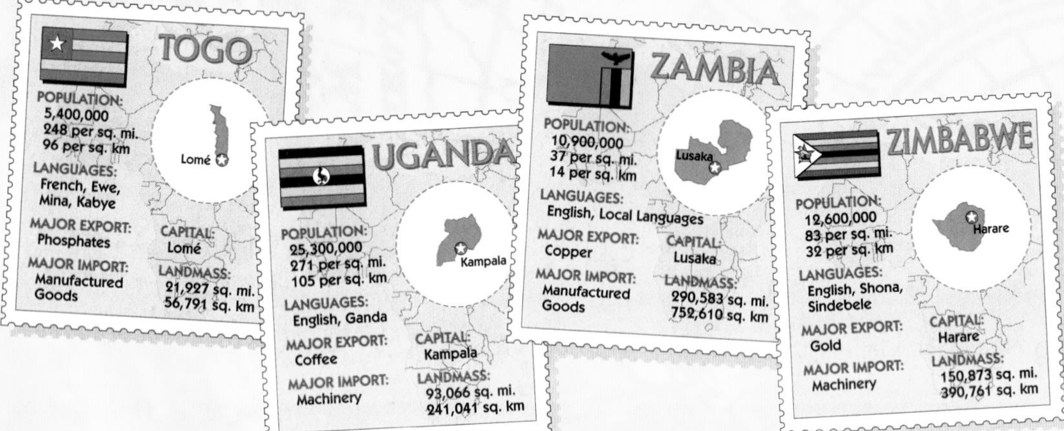

Countries and flags not drawn to scale

BUILDING CITIZENSHIP

Closing the Door on Racism By 1994, South Africa's racist policy of apartheid was officially over. Nelson Mandela became the first black person to be elected president of South Africa. Just three years earlier he had been released from jail after spending 27 years there for antiapartheid activities. When he became president, he created a panel to grant pardons to both blacks and whites who had admitted to committing political crimes in the past. Mandela believed that only by "closing the door" on the past could the country move on to its future.

Why do you think Nelson Mandela was willing to pardon people?

▼ **Women at an antiapartheid rally in South Africa**

The flags of African countries often represent the history or culture of the country. For example, the "Y" shape in the South African flag symbolizes a divided people going forward in unity. Research the flag of an African country and write a paragraph about the meaning of the flag.

Interdisciplinary Connections

History The triangular trade is the term used for the trade network that linked enslaved Africans, plantations in the Americas, and European manufacturing. The triangular trade benefited the British, French, and Dutch economies from the late 1600s through the 1700s, when it reached its peak.

BUILDING CITIZENSHIP

Answer Trying to find and punish all the people who had committed crimes would continue the hatred that had divided South Africa. By pardoning political crimes, Mandela focused the country on a unified future rather than a divided past.

Write About It! Students' answers will vary but should include a description or drawing of the flag. Although not always official, the colors on African flags frequently refer to the people, resources, environment, and other characteristics of the country.

Content Background

Culture and History Between A.D. 1000 and 1500, the Shona people built nearly 300 stone-walled fortresses throughout southern Africa. The largest was called Great Zimbabwe, meaning "house of stone." It was the religious and trading center of the Shona kingdom. Great Zimbabwe included fortress walls, temples, marketplaces, and homes spread out on a fertile, gold-rich plateau south of the Zambezi River. The most impressive part of the city was an area called the Great Enclosure, which had an outer wall 16.5 feet (5 m) thick and 32 feet (9.8 m) high. Inside the wall, a maze of interior walls and hidden passages protected the house of the king, the Great Temple, and other religious buildings.

UNIT 7

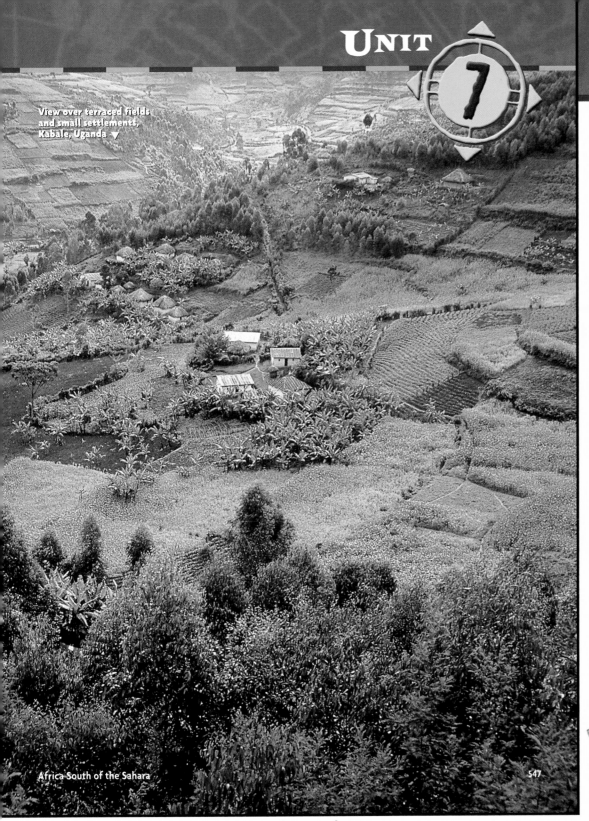

View over terraced fields and small settlements, Kabale, Uganda

Africa South of the Sahara 547

Fun Facts

- **Côte d'Ivoire** French sailors came to this region in the late 1400s in search of ivory. They are responsible for the name, which means "Ivory Coast."
- **Ghana** In Ghana, it is impolite and defiant for a child to look an adult in the eye.
- **Guinea** At family celebrations in Guinea, *griots,* or traditional singers, are hired to sing about individual guests.

Assign the Building Citizenship as homework or as an in-class activity.

Reteach

Give students an outline map of the region. Have them complete the map by writing in the names of major physical features, including

- Mountains (Tibesti Mountains, Mt. Kenya, Kilimanjaro, Drakensberg Range)
- Plateaus (Ethiopian Highlands)
- Deserts (Sahara, Sahel, Namib Desert, Kalahari Desert)
- Lakes (Lake Victoria, Lake Tanganyika, Lake Malawi)
- Rivers (Niger River, Congo River, Blue Nile River, White Nile River, Zambezi River)
- Other (Great Rift Valley, Serengeti Plain, Victoria Falls)

Enrich

Have students choose a country in Africa south of the Sahara. Have them research that country and prepare a bulletin board display that discusses the main ethnic, religious, and language groups in the country.

Reading Strategy

Summarizing Have students write a paragraph that summarizes what they think are the main physical, economic, and cultural characteristics shared by the countries of Africa south of the Sahara.

Chapter 19 Resources

Note: The following materials may be used when teaching Chapter 19.
Section level support materials are shown at point of use in the margins of the Teacher Wraparound Edition.

Timesaving Tools

TeacherWorks™ All-In-One Planner and Resource Center

- **Interactive Teacher Edition** See the **Interactive Teacher Edition** CD-ROM to electronically integrate your Teacher Wraparound Edition and blackline masters.
- **Interactive Lesson Planner** Organize your week, month, semester, or year with all the lesson helps you need. The **Interactive Lesson Planner** CD-ROM contains all Chapter 19 resources.

Use Glencoe's **Presentation Plus!** multimedia teacher tool to easily present dynamic lessons that visually excite your students. Using Microsoft PowerPoint® you can customize the presentations to create your own personalized lessons.

TEACHING TRANSPARENCIES

Graphic Organizer Transparency 15 L2

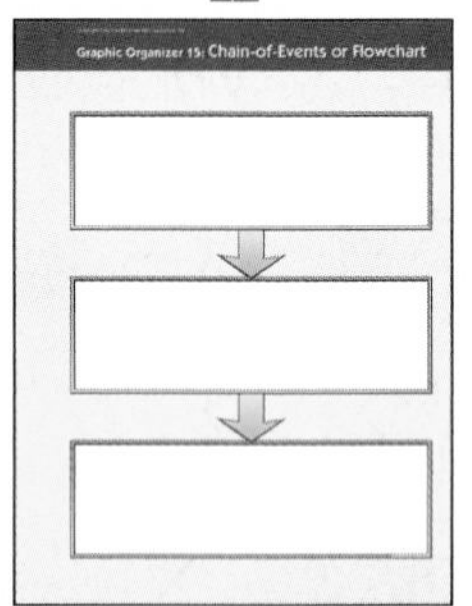

In-text Map Transparency L1

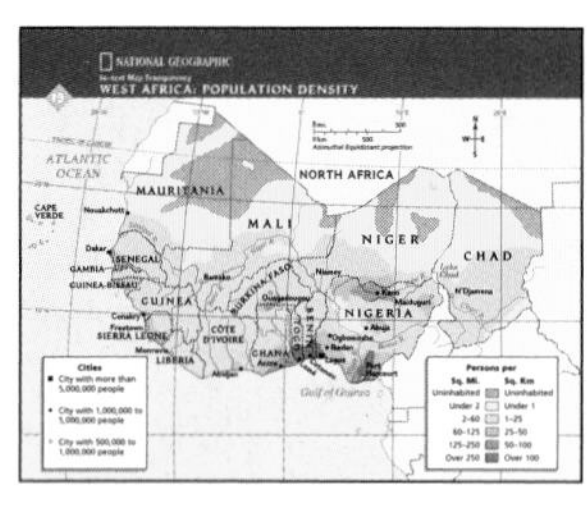

FOLDABLES™ Study Organizer Dinah Zike's Foldables

Foldables are three-dimensional, interactive graphic organizers that help students practice basic writing skills, review key vocabulary terms, and identify main ideas. Additional chapter activities can be found in the ***Reading and Study Skills Foldables*** booklet.

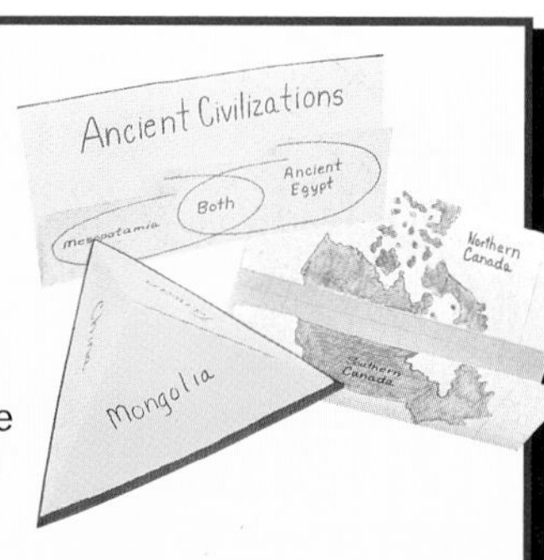

MAP AND GEOGRAPHY SKILLS

Chapter Map Activity L2

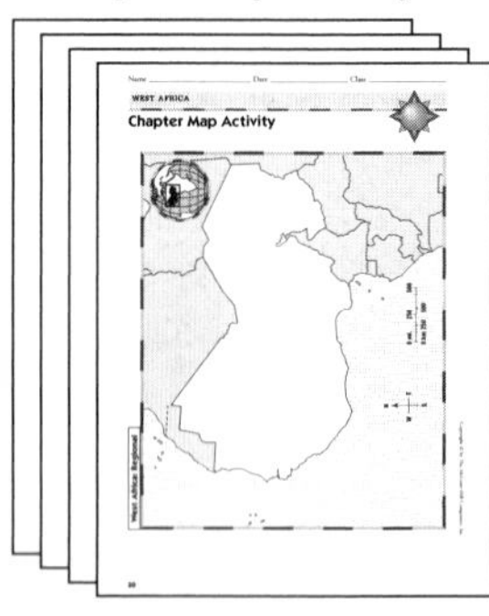

GeoLab Activity L2

READING SUPPORT

Vocabulary Activity L1

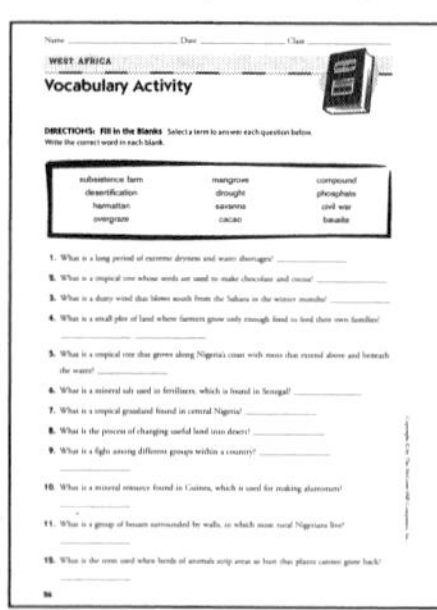

Workbook Activity L1

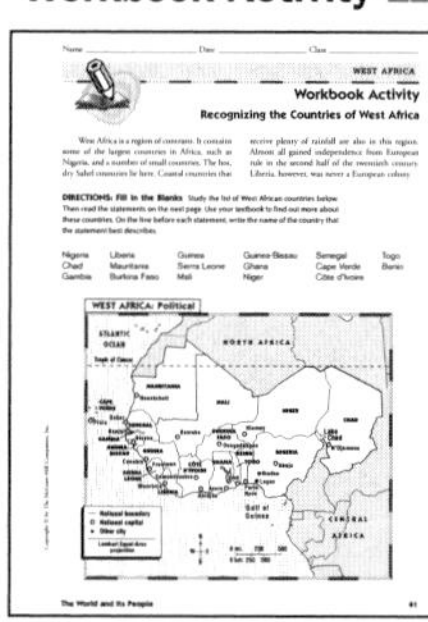

Reading and Writing Skills Activity L1/ELL

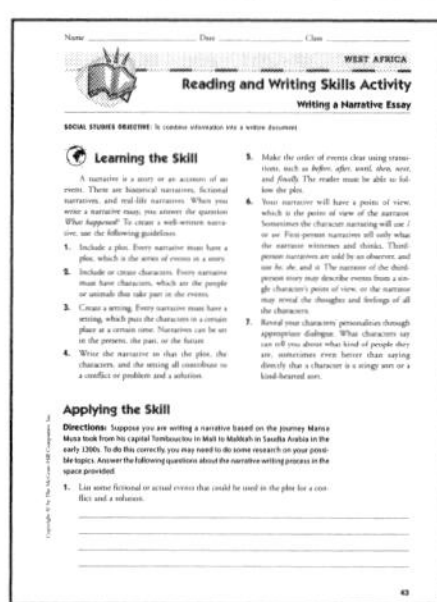

DIFFERENTIATED INSTRUCTION

Use these review and reinforcement materials to help less-proficient readers, English learners, and gifted and talented students.

Reteaching Activity L1

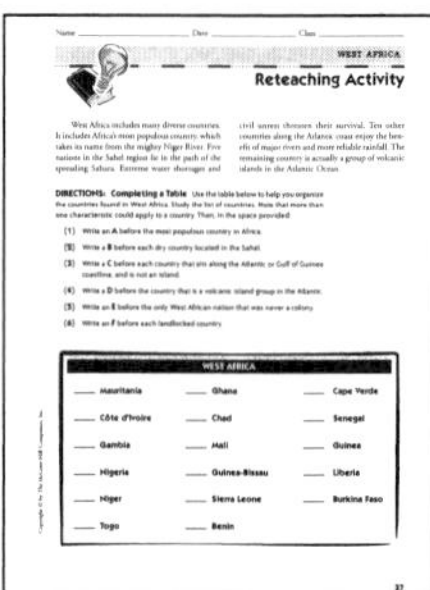

Chapter Skills Review L2

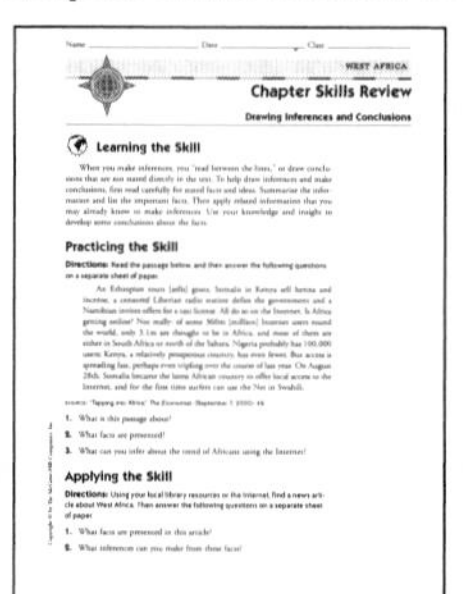

Cooperative Learning Activity L1/ELL

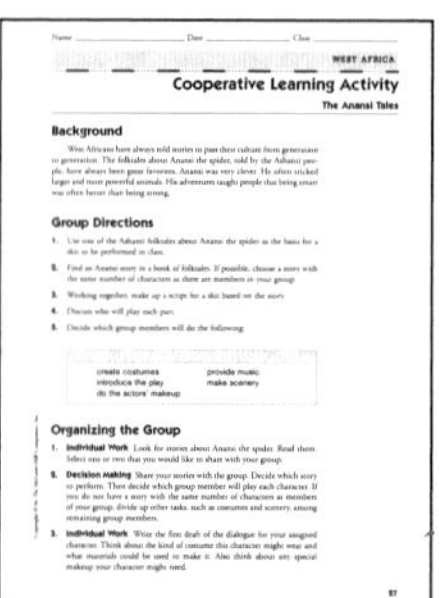

Enrichment Activity L3

ASSESSMENT

Chapter Test, Form A L2

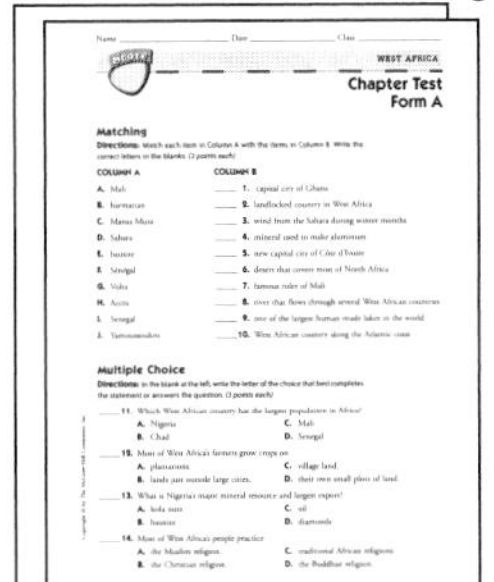

Chapter Test, Form B L2

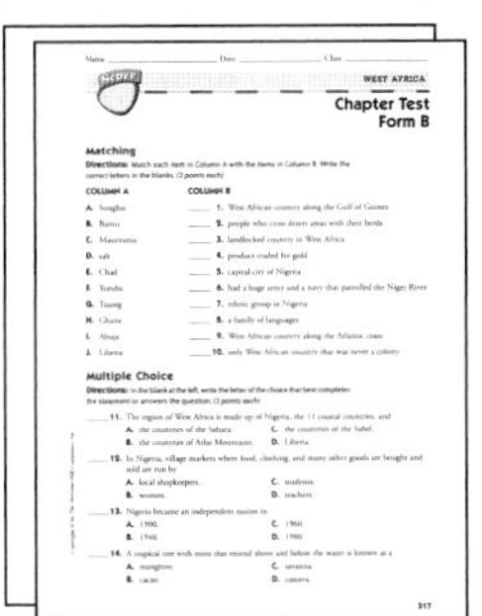

Performance Assessment Activity L1/ELL

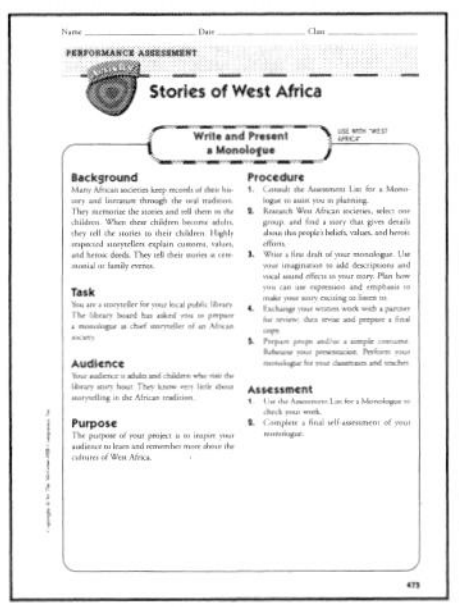

ExamView® Pro Testmaker CD-ROM

STANDARDIZED ASSESSMENT SKILLS

Critical Thinking Skills Activity L2

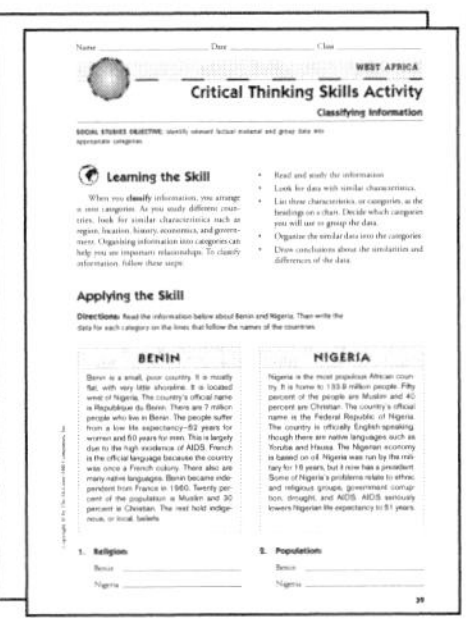

Map and Graph Skills Activity L2

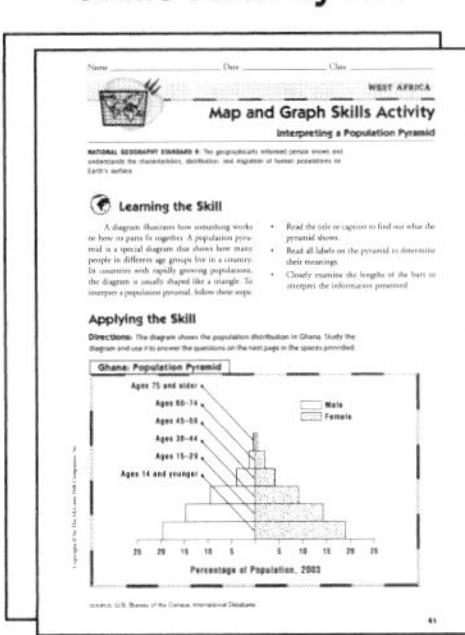

Standardized Test Skills Practice Workbook Activity L2

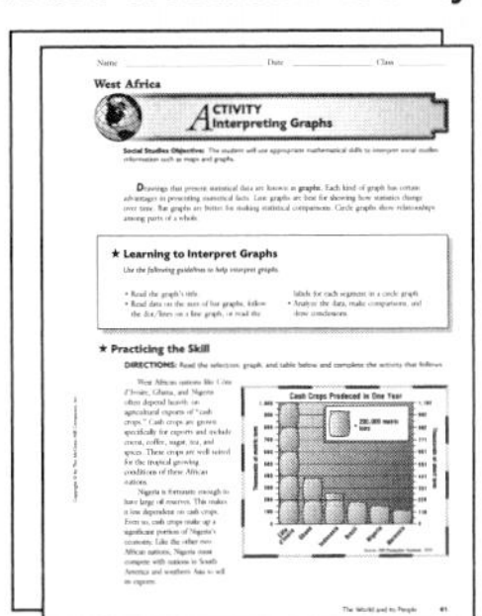

HOME INVOLVEMENT

Take-Home Review Activity L1

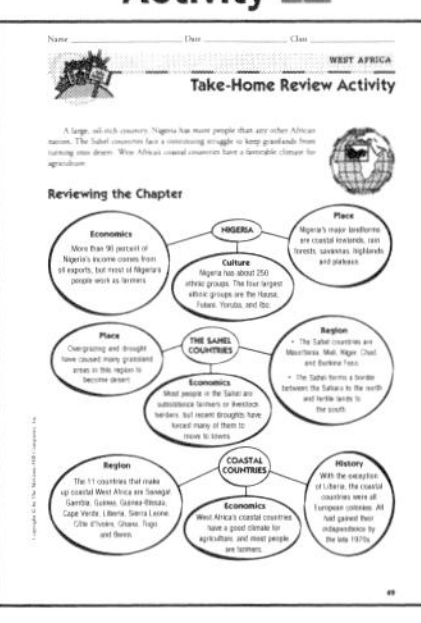

MULTIMEDIA

- National Geographic's The World and Its People
- MindJogger Videoquiz
- Vocabulary PuzzleMaker CD-ROM
- Interactive Tutor Self-Assessment CD-ROM
- ExamView® Pro Testmaker CD-ROM
- TeacherWorks CD-ROM
- StudentWorks CD-ROM
- Skillbuilder Interactive Workbook CD-ROM, Level 1
- Presentation Plus! CD-ROM
- Audio Program

SPANISH RESOURCES

The following Spanish language materials are available in the Spanish Resources binder:

- Spanish Summaries
- Spanish Vocabulary Activities
- Spanish Guided Reading Activities
- Spanish Quizzes and Tests
- Spanish Take-Home Review Activities
- Spanish Reteaching Activities

Meeting National Standards

Geography for Life

The following standards are covered in Chapter 19:

Section 1 **EE1 The World in Spatial Terms: Standards 1, 2, 3**
EE4 Human Systems: Standards 9, 10

Section 2 **EE2 Places and Regions: Standards 4, 5, 6**
EE3 Physical Systems: Standards 7, 8
EE4 Human Systems: Standards 9, 10, 11, 12, 13
EE5 Environment and Society: Standards 14, 15, 16

State and Local Objectives

Chapter 19 Planning Guide

SECTION RESOURCES

Daily Objectives	Reproducible Resources	Multimedia Resources
Section 1 **Nigeria—African Giant** **1.** Describe the land and climates found in Nigeria. **2.** Explain Nigeria's economy. **3.** Compare Nigeria's ethnic groups.	Reproducible Lesson Plan Daily Lecture and Discussion Notes Note-taking Guide Guided Reading Activity* Reading Essentials and Study Guide* Section Quiz*	Daily Focus Skills Transparency GeoQuiz Transparency Vocabulary PuzzleMaker CD-ROM Interactive Tutor Self-Assessment CD-ROM ExamView® Pro Testmaker CD-ROM Presentation Plus! CD-ROM
Section 2 **The Sahel and Coastal West Africa** **1.** Describe the Sahel's location and its history. **2.** Explain how people in the Sahel countries live. **3.** Compare the coastal countries, their history, and peoples.	Reproducible Lesson Plan Daily Lecture and Discussion Notes Note-taking Guide Guided Reading Activity* Reading Essentials and Study Guide* Section Quiz*	Daily Focus Skills Transparency In-text Map Transparency Vocabulary PuzzleMaker CD-ROM Interactive Tutor Self-Assessment CD-ROM ExamView® Pro Testmaker CD-ROM Presentation Plus! CD-ROM MindJogger Videoquiz

00:00 **Out of Time?** Assign the **Reading Essentials and Study Guide*** for this chapter.

*Also available in Spanish

KEY TO ABILITY LEVELS

Teaching strategies have been coded for varying learning styles and abilities.

L1 **BASIC** activities for all students
L2 **AVERAGE** activities for average to above-average students
L3 **CHALLENGING** activities for above-average students
ELL **ENGLISH LANGUAGE LEARNER** activities

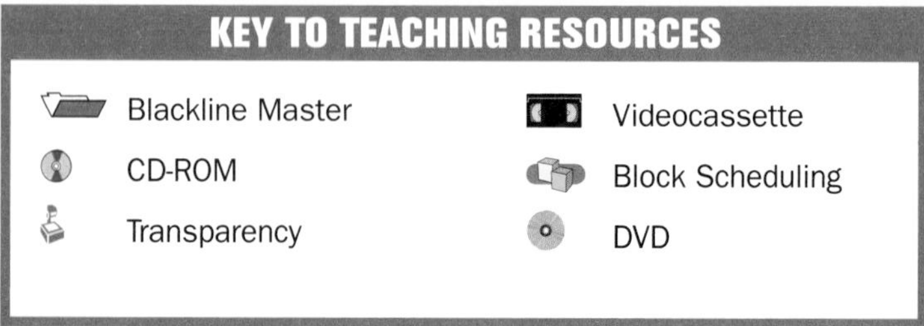

World Hunger

Peter John Arroyo
Space Coast Middle School
Port St. John, Florida

Remind students that hunger is often commonplace among people living in developing countries. Many of the people are subsistence farmers who grow only enough to feed their families. Plan a Hunger Awareness Day at school to show students the seriousness of world hunger. To prepare for this event, ask students to (1) find 20 Web sites regarding world hunger; (2) find two hunger events advertised on the Internet with an explanation of how students can get involved; and (3) design and produce a poster regarding world hunger. Display the posters around the school on the designated Hunger Awareness Day. Have each student turn in a one-page report listing the 20 Web sites they found as well as a paragraph summarizing what they learned about world hunger.

Meeting Special Needs

In addition to the Differentiated Instruction strategies found in each section, the following resources are also suitable for your special needs students:

- ***ExamView*® *Pro Testmaker CD-ROM*** allows teachers to tailor tests by reducing answer choices.
- The ***Audio Program*** includes the entire narrative of the student edition so that less-proficient readers can listen to the words as they read them.
- The ***Reading Essentials and Study Guide*** provides the same content as the student edition but is written two grade levels below the textbook.
- ***Guided Reading Activities*** give less-proficient readers point-by-point instructions to increase comprehension as they read each textbook section.
- ***Enrichment Activities*** include a stimulating collection of readings and activities for gifted and talented students.

NATIONAL GEOGRAPHIC TEACHER'S CORNER

Index to National Geographic Magazine:

The following articles may be used for research relating to this chapter:

- "People of Heaven," by Peter Godwin, August 2000.
- "African Marriage Rituals," by Carol Beckwith and Angela Fisher, November 1999.
- "African Gold," by Carol Beckwith and Angela Fisher, October 1996.

National Geographic Society Products:

To order the following products for use with this chapter, call National Geographic Society at 1-800-368-2728:

- *Africa* (Video)
- *Endangered Animals: Survivors on the Brink* (Video)
- *PictureShow: Ancient Civilizations: Africa* (CD-ROM)

NGS ONLINE

Access National Geographic's Web site for current events, activities, links, interactive features, and archives. www.nationalgeographic.com

Find the latest coverage of geography in the news, atlas updates, cartographic activities with interactive maps, an online map store, and links at www.nationalgeographic.com/maps

SOCIAL STUDIES Online

Use our Web site for additional resources. All essential content is covered in the Student Edition.

You and your students can visit twip.glencoe.com, the Web site companion to *The World and Its People.* This innovative integration of electronic and print media offers your students a wealth of opportunities. The student text directs students to the Web site for the following options:

- Chapter Overviews
- Student Web Activities
- Self-Check Quizzes
- Textbook Updates

Answers are provided for you in the Web Activity Lesson Plan. Additional Web resources and Interactive Tutor puzzles are also available.

Introducing Chapter 19

Social Studies Online

Introduce students to chapter content and key terms by having them access Chapter Overview 19 at twip.glencoe.com

Chapter Objectives

1. Identify the physical features and climates of the countries of West Africa.
2. Explain how West Africa's economies relate to the natural resources in the region.
3. Compare the different peoples that live in West Africa.
4. Explain the impact of historical influences on West Africa.

GLENCOE TECHNOLOGY

NATIONAL GEOGRAPHIC

The World and Its People Video Program

Chapter 19 West Africa
The following segments enhance the study of this chapter:

- **Dino Dig**
- **Rain Forest Walkway**

MindJogger Videoquiz

Use MindJogger Videoquiz to preview the Chapter 19 content.

Both programs available in DVD and VHS

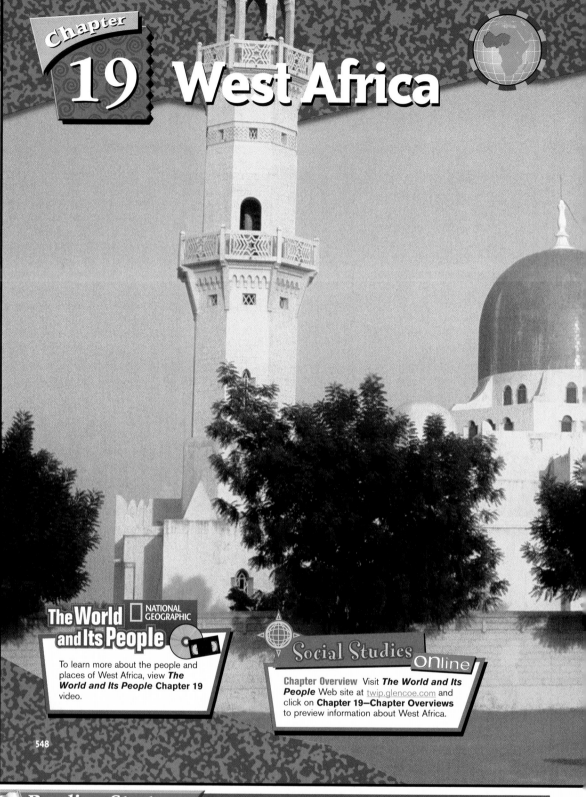

Chapter 19 West Africa

The World and Its People NATIONAL GEOGRAPHIC

To learn more about the people and places of West Africa, view ***The World and Its People*** **Chapter 19** video.

Social Studies Online

Chapter Overview Visit ***The World and Its People*** Web site at twip.glencoe.com and click on **Chapter 19—Chapter Overviews** to preview information about West Africa.

548

Reading Strategy — Purpose for Reading

Have students use the **Think/Pair/Share** reading strategy to activate prior knowledge. **Think**—Ask students to write everything they know about the time period when Africans were enslaved in the United States. **Pair**—Have students share their responses with a partner. **Share**—Ask students to share their responses with the entire class. Conclude the activity by explaining that many African Americans can trace their ancestry to West Africa. Tell them that they will be learning more about this region of the world in the chapter. L1

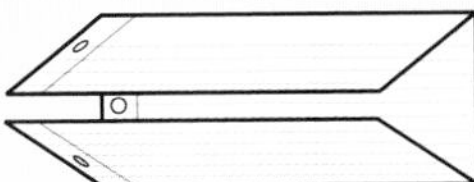

Summarizing Information Make this foldable to determine what you already know, identify what you want to know, and summarize what you learn about West Africa.

Step 1 Fold a sheet of paper into thirds from top to bottom.

Step 2 Turn the paper horizontally, unfold, and label the three columns as shown.

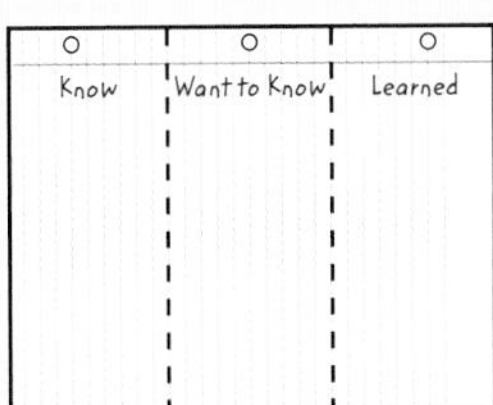

Reading and Writing Before you read the chapter, write what you already know about West Africa under the "Know" tab. Write what you want to know about West Africa under the "Want to Know" tab. Then, as you read the chapter, write what you learn under the "Learned" tab. Be sure to include information you wanted to know (from the second column).

Why It Matters

Cultural Roots

Many African Americans today can trace their roots to West Africa. Enslaved peoples were carried from the "slave coast" of West Africa to the Americas in the 1600s and 1700s. Liberia was founded as a haven for returning Africans. West Africa also includes Nigeria, the continent's most populous country.

◀ The Central Mosque of Kano, Nigeria

About the Photo

Kano is one of the largest cities in Nigeria. It is located in the northern part of the country, which is where much of Nigeria's Islamic population lives. Christianity was established in the southern part of the country by Protestant and Roman Catholic missionaries in the late nineteenth century. Today, both Christianity and Islam continue to be the major religions in Nigeria, though many people also follow the practices and beliefs of the indigenous African religions. Independent Nigerian churches, such as Cherubim and Seraphim, combine Christian worship with African religious practices like drumming and dancing.

Introducing

Chapter 19

Dinah Zike's Foldables

Purpose This activity will provide students with an opportunity to review what they know and think about what they would like to know about West Africa. The resulting foldable can be used as an assessment tool at the end of the chapter to determine what students have learned.

Have students complete the ***Reading and Study Skills Foldables*** activity for this chapter.

Why It Matters

European contact has had a profound influence on Nigeria and the rest of West Africa. Have students use resources to identify a list of ways that European contact has affected these nations. *(Possible responses: slave trade, religion, exploitation of resources, language, division of ethnic groups to form countries)* Organize students into groups and have each group research and present one topic on the list, discussing the history of the subject as well as the positive and negative effects on Africa.

Chapter 19

Section 1, pages 550–554

Focus

Section Objectives

1. Describe the land and climates found in Nigeria.
2. Explain Nigeria's economy.
3. Compare Nigeria's ethnic groups.

BELLRINGER Skillbuilder Activity

Project transparency and have students answer the question.

Daily Focus Skills Transparency

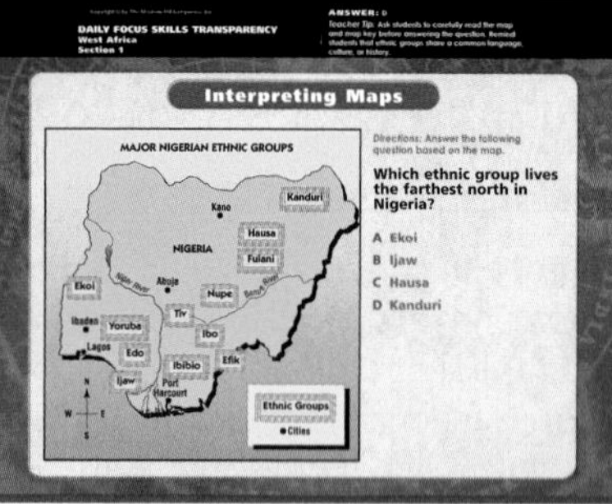

Reading Preview

■ **Activating Prior Knowledge**
Ask: What region of the world has the largest share of the world's oil reserves? *(Southwest Asia)* Point out that some countries in other regions have substantial quantities of oil as well.

■ **Preteaching Vocabulary**
Have students find the definition of *cacao*. What similar word refers to hot chocolate? *(cocoa)* Point out that a spelling mistake, perhaps made by European explorers, resulted in the different words.

Guide to Reading

Main Idea

Nigeria is a large, oil-rich country that has more people than any other African nation.

Terms to Know

- mangrove
- savanna
- harmattan
- subsistence farm
- cacao
- compound
- civil war

Reading Strategy

Create a chart like the one below. Then list two facts about Nigeria in each category.

Nigeria	Fact #1	Fact #2
Land		
Economy		
People		

Nigeria—African Giant

In 1991 Abuja replaced Lagos as Nigeria's capital. The new city was built in an undeveloped region in central Nigeria. Today Abuja has new buildings and a network of roads linking it with other parts of the country. It also has schools. These children prepare to pray at the Islamic Academy in Abuja.

The West African country of **Nigeria** gets its name from the **Niger River,** which flows through western and central Nigeria. One of the largest nations in Africa, Nigeria is more than twice the size of California.

From Tropics to Savannas

Nigeria has a long coastline on the **Gulf of Guinea,** an arm of the Atlantic Ocean. Along Nigeria's coast, the land is covered with mangrove swamps. A **mangrove** is a tropical tree with roots that extend both above and beneath the water. As you travel inland, the land becomes vast tropical rain forests. Small villages appear in only a few clearings. The forests gradually thin into savannas in central Nigeria. **Savannas** are tropical grasslands with only a few trees. Highlands and plateaus also make up this area. Most of the country has a tropical savanna climate with high average temperatures and seasonal rains. The grasslands of

Section Resources

Reproducible Masters
- Reproducible Lesson Plan
- Daily Lecture and Discussion Notes
- Note-taking Guide
- Guided Reading Activity
- Reading Essentials and Study Guide
- Section Quiz

Transparencies
- Daily Focus Skills Transparency
- GeoQuiz Transparency

Multimedia
- Vocabulary PuzzleMaker CD-ROM
- Interactive Tutor Self-Assessment CD-ROM
- Presentation Plus! CD-ROM
- ExamView® Pro Testmaker CD-ROM

the far north have a dry steppe climate. In the winter months, a dusty wind called the **harmattan** blows south from the Sahara.

✓Reading Check What kinds of vegetation are found in Nigeria?

Economic Challenges

Nigeria is one of the world's major oil-producing countries. More than 90 percent of the country's income comes from oil exports. The government has used oil profits to build highways, schools, skyscrapers, and factories. These factories make food products, textiles, chemicals, machinery, and vehicles. Still, more than one-third of Nigeria's people lack jobs and live in poverty.

Nigeria began to experience economic troubles during the 1980s. As a result of falling world oil prices, Nigeria's income dropped. At the same time, many people left their farms in search of better-paying jobs in the cities. In addition, a few years of low rainfall meant smaller harvests, so food production fell. Nigeria—which had once exported food—had to import food to feed its people.

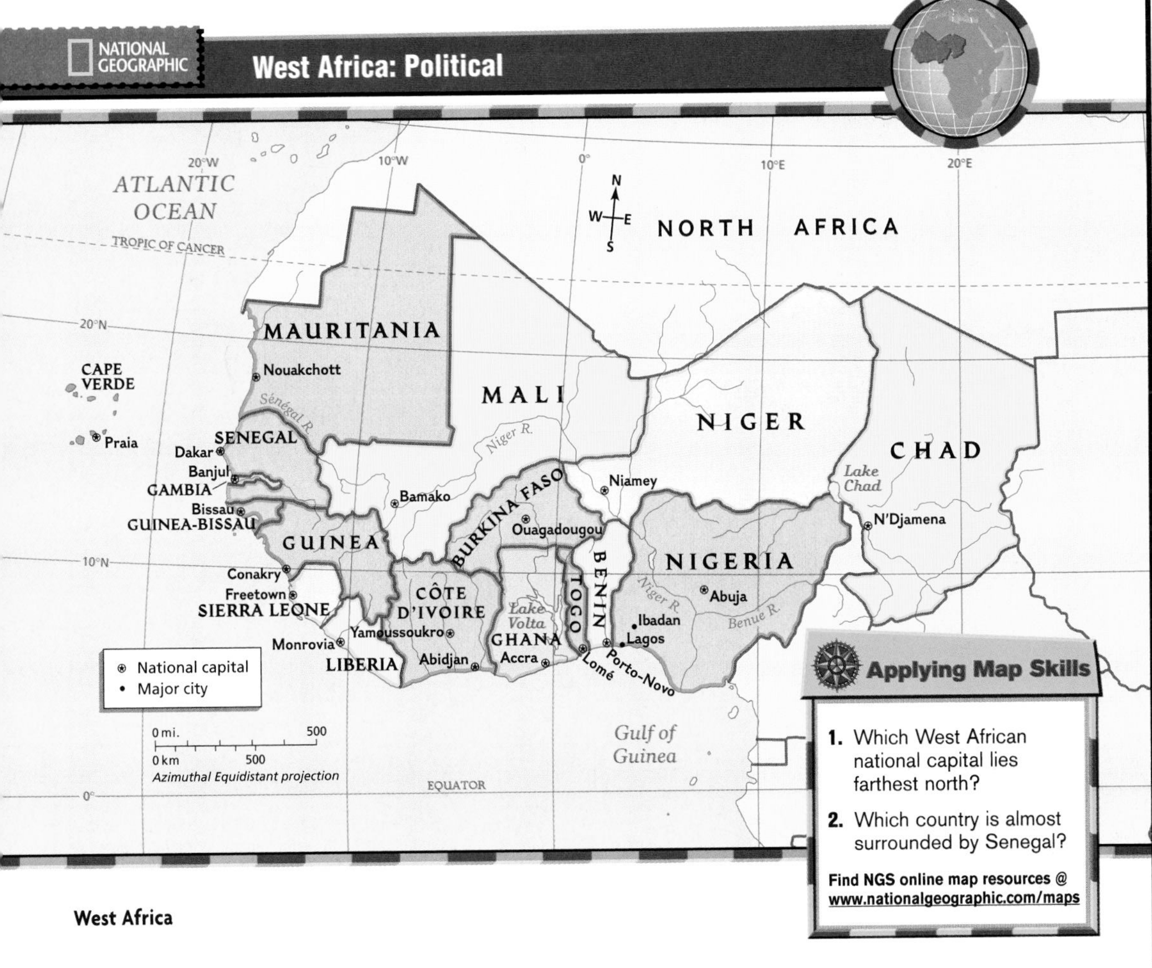

Applying Map Skills

1. Which West African national capital lies farthest north?
2. Which country is almost surrounded by Senegal?

Find NGS online map resources @ www.nationalgeographic.com/maps

West Africa

Reading Strategy **Reading the Text**

Sequencing Have students discuss how history has affected ways of life in Nigeria. Suggest that they begin with the arrival of Europeans in the late 1400s and end with the situation today. Ask students to pay close attention to how European influences affected ethnic groups, religions, and languages in Nigeria. You might invite a teacher with a background in world history to talk to the class about the end of colonialism in the 1960s. Then have students work in groups to construct a time line showing what they think are the key historical events in Nigeria. Students should use the information in their textbooks and the Internet to construct their time lines. L1

*Use the **Reading Skills Handbook** for more reading strategies.*

Teach

Reading Strategy

Making Inferences For some questions, the answers are "right there," whereas others require students to "think and search," or to interpret the information in the text. Give examples of these questions. **Ask:** **Where is Nigeria's coastline?** *(The answer, along the Gulf of Guinea, is found on the previous page.)* **Is the land drier in the north or south of the country?** *(The answer can be inferred from the fact that the south has swamps and rain forests whereas the north has a dry climate.)* Have students pose questions of these two types. L1

Daily Lecture and Discussion Notes

WEST AFRICA

Daily Lecture and Discussion Notes

Nigeria —African Giant

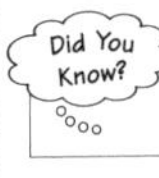

A majority of the people of Nigeria speak more than one language. They may use the language of their ethnic group on most occasions and use English or another language at other times.

I. From Tropics to Savanna

A. Along Nigeria's coast on the Gulf of Guinea, the land is covered with mangrove swamps. A **mangrove** is a tropical tree with roots that extend both above and beneath the water.

B. As you travel inland, Nigeria's land becomes a vast tropical rain forest. The ... highlands, plateaus, and savannas in central Nigeria. ... only a few trees.

✓Reading Check Answer

mangrove swamps, rain forests, and savannas

Applying Map Skills

Answers

1. Nouakchott
2. Gambia

Despite oil resources, Nigeria's people mainly work as farmers. Most have **subsistence farms,** or small plots where farmers grow just enough food to feed their families. Some work on larger farms that produce such cash crops as rubber, peanuts, palm oil, and cacao. The **cacao** is a tropical tree whose seeds are used to make chocolate and cocoa. Nigeria is a leading producer of cacao beans.

✓ Reading Check **How has Nigeria's government used profits from oil sales?**

Nigeria's People

About 133.9 million people live in Nigeria—more people than in any other country in Africa. The map on page 560 shows that most of the people live along the coast and around the city of **Kano** in the north.

One of the strongest bonds that Africans have is a sense of belonging to a group or a family. Nigeria has about 250 ethnic groups. The four largest are the Hausa (HOW•suh), Fulani (foo•LAH•nee), Yoruba (YAWR•uh•buh), and Ibo (EE•boh). Nigerians speak many different African languages. They use English in business and government

NATIONAL GEOGRAPHIC

West Africa: Physical

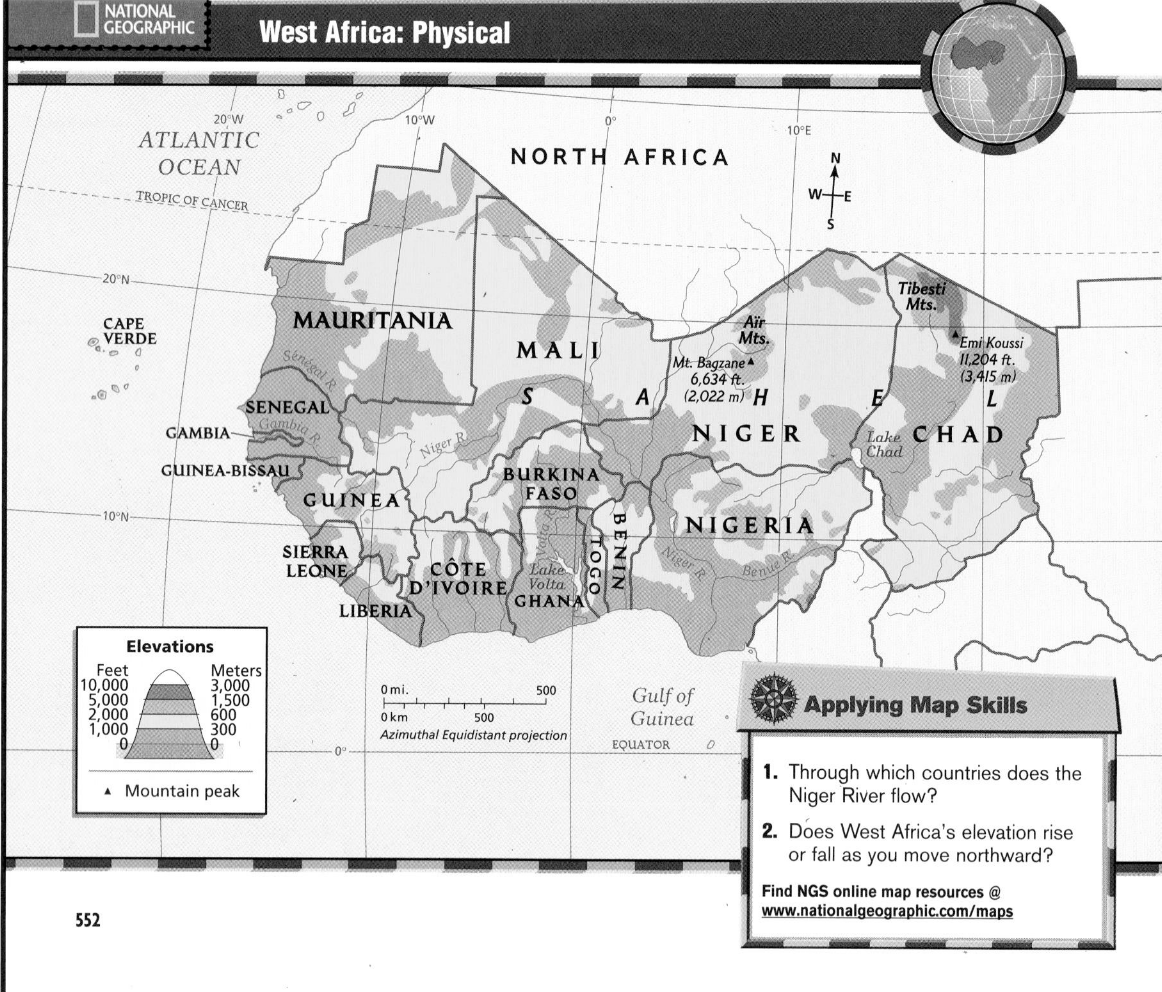

Applying Map Skills

1. Through which countries does the Niger River flow?
2. Does West Africa's elevation rise or fall as you move northward?

Find NGS online map resources @ www.nationalgeographic.com/maps

552

✓ **Reading Check Answer**

to build highways, schools, skyscrapers, and factories

Did You Know?

Lagos, the chief city in Nigeria, spreads across four islands in the Gulf of Guinea and spills over onto mainland Africa. Lagos is Nigeria's major industrial center and was, until 1991, the country's capital.

L1/ELL

Guided Reading Activity

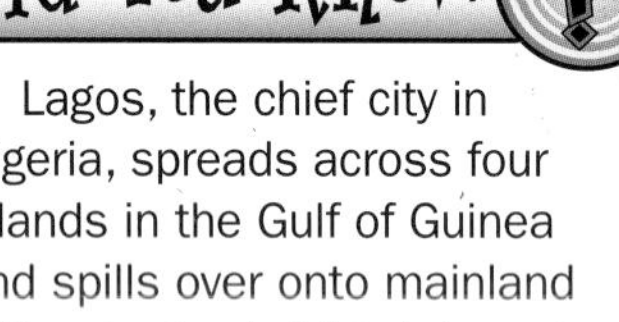
Name ____ Date ____ Class ____

WEST AFRICA

Guided Reading Activity 1

Nigeria—African Giant

DIRECTIONS: Filling in the Blanks Reading the section and completing the sentences below will help you learn more about the country of Nigeria. Use your textbook to fill in the blanks.

Nigeria's land is covered with (1) ____ swamps. The farther inland you travel, the land becomes (2) ____ . Finally, the land becomes (3) ____ in central Nigeria. During the winter, a dusty wind called the (4) ____ blows south from the Sahara.

... income comes from (5) ____ More than

Applying Map Skills

Answers

1. Guinea, Mali, Niger, Benin (border of), and Nigeria
2. The land rises as you move north.

Skills Practice

What river flows from the east to join the Niger River in Nigeria? *(Benue River)*

Differentiated Instruction

Meeting Special Needs: Visual/Spatial

Visual learners can better grasp the different features of Nigeria by locating information on maps as the information is read. Pair visual learners with other students. Have the other students read key passages in the text. As they do so, have the visual learners find the correct map for this information and see how the map shows what the text describes. **L1**

Refer to *Inclusion for the Middle School Social Studies Classroom Strategies and Activities* in the TCR.

NATIONAL GEOGRAPHIC On Location

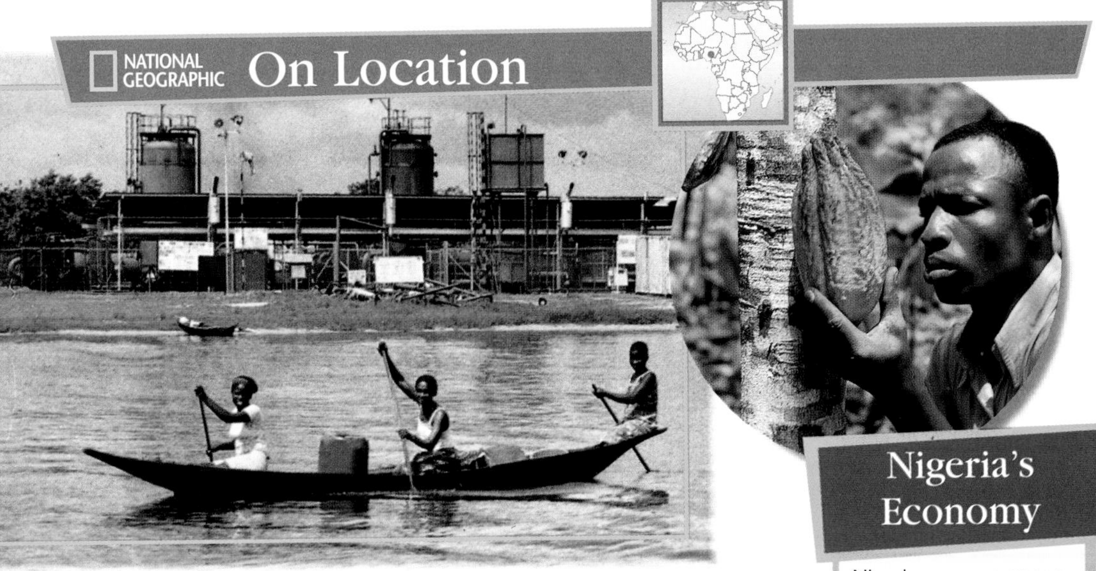

Nigeria's Economy

Nigerian women canoe past an oil refinery in the Niger River delta (above left). Cacao pods are harvested in Nigeria (above).

Human/Environment Interaction What are Nigeria's important cash crops?

affairs, though. About one-half of Nigeria's people are Muslim, and another 40 percent are Christian. The remaining 10 percent practice traditional African religions.

About 60 percent of Nigerians live in rural villages. The typical family lives in a **compound,** or a group of houses surrounded by walls. Usually the village has a weekly market run by women. The women sell locally grown products such as meat, cloth, yams, nuts, and palm oil. The market also provides a chance for friends to meet.

Long-standing rural ways are changing, however. Many young men now move to the cities to find work and often send money to their families. The women stay in the villages to raise children and to farm the land. The men return home to see their families when they are able.

Nigeria's largest city is the port of **Lagos,** the former capital. Major banks, department stores, and restaurants serve the 13.5 million people who live in Lagos and its surrounding areas. **Ibadan** (EE•bah•DAHN), Kano, and Abuja (ah•BOO•jah) lie inland. **Abuja,** the present capital, is a planned city that was begun during the 1980s.

Nigerians take pride in both old and new features of their culture. Artists make elaborate wooden masks, metal sculptures, and colorful cloth. Nigerians pass on stories, sayings, and riddles by word of mouth from one generation to the next. In 1986 Nigerian writer Wole Soyinka (WAW•lay shaw•YIHNG•ka) became the first African to win the Nobel Prize in literature.

History and Government The earliest known inhabitants of the area were the Nok people. They lived between the Niger and Benue Rivers between 500 B.C. and A.D. 200. The Nok were known as skilled metalworkers and traders. Farming peoples who spoke dialects of the Bantu family of languages began to move from the Niger River region

More About the Photos

Niger River The Niger River is Africa's third-longest river, after the Nile and the Congo. The Malinke people call it the *Joliba,* meaning "great river." Originating in Guinea, the river flows northeast before it turns south.

Caption Answer rubber, peanuts, palm oil, and cacao

3 ASSESS

Assign Section 1 Assessment as homework or an in-class activity.

Have students use the Interactive Tutor Self-Assessment CD-ROM to review Section 1.

L2

Section Quiz

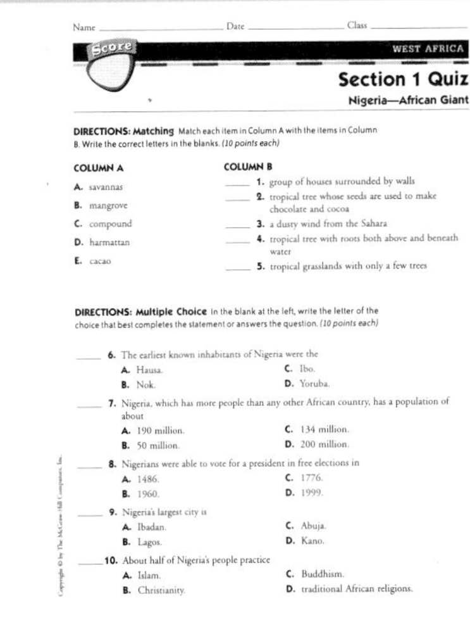

Name ______ Date ______ Class ______

WEST AFRICA

Section 1 Quiz

Nigeria—African Giant

DIRECTIONS: Matching Match each item in Column A with the items in Column B. Write the correct letters in the blanks. *(10 points each)*

COLUMN A	COLUMN B
A. savannas	____ 1. group of houses surrounded by walls
B. mangrove	____ 2. tropical tree whose seeds are used to make chocolate and cocoa
C. compound	____ 3. a dusty wind from the Sahara
D. harmattan	____ 4. tropical tree with roots both above and beneath water
E. cacao	____ 5. tropical grasslands with only a few trees

DIRECTIONS: Multiple Choice In the blank at the left, write the letter of the choice that best completes the statement or answers the question. *(10 points each)*

____ 6. The earliest known inhabitants of Nigeria were the
A. Hausa. C. Ibo.
B. Nok. D. Yoruba.

____ 7. Nigeria, which has more people than any other African country, has a population of about
A. 190 million. C. 134 million.
B. 50 million. D. 200 million.

____ 8. Nigerians were able to vote for a president in free elections in
A. 1486. C. 1776.
B. 1960. D. 1999.

____ 9. Nigeria's largest city is
A. Ibadan. C. Abuja.
B. Lagos. D. Kano.

____ 10. About half of Nigeria's people practice
A. Islam. C. Buddhism.
B. Christianity. D. traditional African religions.

311

Critical Thinking Activity

Analyzing Information As they read the section on Nigeria, have students identify serious challenges that Nigeria might face in the future. Have them list at least one challenge for each subheading. For example, for the section From Tropics to Savannas, the challenge might be "communicating with isolated villages in the rain forest." Tell students that they also need to explain why they chose that challenge. When they have finished, have volunteers read their suggestions aloud. Have the class discuss possible ways Nigeria could work to meet these challenges. L2

EE6 The Uses of Geography: Standard 18

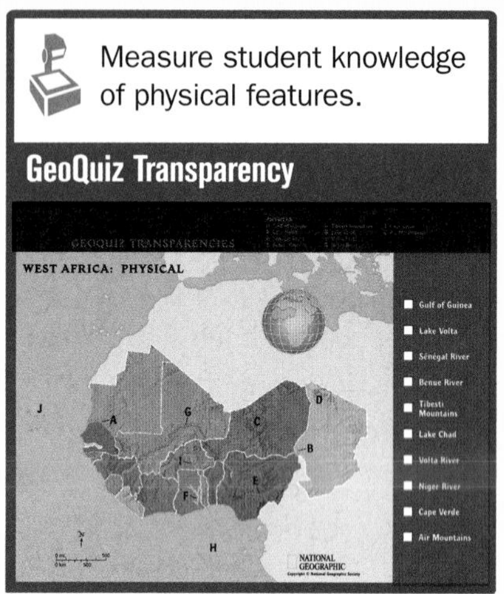

into Central and East Africa. Today Bantu-speaking peoples occupy most of Africa south of the Congo River.

Over the centuries, powerful city-states and kingdoms became centers of trade and the arts. People in what is today northern Nigeria came in contact with Muslim cultures and adopted Islam. People in the south developed cultures based on traditional African religions.

During the 1400s, Europeans arrived in Africa looking for gold and Africans to take overseas as enslaved laborers. In 1884 European leaders divided most of Africa into colonies. The borders of these colonies often sliced through ethnic lands. As a result, many ethnic groups found their members living in two or more separate territories. By the early 1900s, the British had taken control of Nigeria.

In 1960 Nigeria finally became an independent country. Ethnic, religious, and political disputes soon tore it apart, however. One ethnic group, the Ibo, tried to set up its own country. A **civil war**—a fight between different groups within a country—resulted. In this bloody war, starvation and conflict led to 2 million deaths. The Ibo were defeated, and their region remained part of Nigeria.

Nigeria has faced the challenge of building a stable government. Military leaders have often ruled the country. In 1999 Nigerians were able to vote for a president in free elections. Nigerians continue to work toward greater national unity, but they face enormous problems.

✓ Reading Check What are the four largest ethnic groups in Nigeria?

✓ Reading Check Answer

Hausa, Fulani, Yoruba, and Ibo

Section 1 Assessment

Defining Terms

1. **Define** mangrove, savanna, harmattan, subsistence farm, cacao, compound, civil war.

Recalling Facts

2. **Place** Describe the changes in Nigeria's physical geography as you move from the coast inland.
3. **Place** What is the capital of Nigeria?
4. **Culture** How many ethnic groups are represented by the people of Nigeria?

Critical Thinking

5. **Understanding Cause and Effect** Why did a drop in oil prices cause economic troubles in Nigeria in the 1980s?
6. **Drawing Conclusions** Why do you think an ethnic group, such as the Ibo, would want to set up their own country?

Graphic Organizer

7. **Organizing Information** On a time line like the one below, place the following events and their dates in order: Nigeria becomes independent; Nok people work in metal and trade for goods; Free elections are held; British take control of Nigeria.

Applying Social Studies Skills

8. **Analyzing Maps** Study the physical map on page 552. Into what larger body of water does the Niger River empty?

554 CHAPTER 19

L1/ELL

Reading Essentials and Study Guide

Name ______ Date ______ Class ______

WEST AFRICA

Reading Essentials and Study Guide 1

Nigeria–African Giant

Key Terms

mangrove tropical tree with roots both above and below the water
savanna tropical grassland with only a few trees
harmattan dusty wind that blows from the Sahara
subsistence farm small plot where farmers can grow only enough to feed their families
cacao tropical tree whose seeds are used to make chocolate and cocoa
compound group of houses surrounded by walls
civil war a fight among different groups within a country

Close

Have students write a pen-pal letter to a Nigerian teenager named Elizabeth Tofa. Their letters should reflect what they have learned about Nigeria.

Section 1 Assessment

1. The terms are defined in the Glossary.
2. coastline with swamps; vast tropical rain forest; highlands and plateaus with savannas; grasslands
3. Abuja
4. about 250
5. Nigeria's income dropped, which meant there was less money to build highways, schools, buildings, and factories.
6. to control their own lives and ensure their own interests
7. 300 B.C. to A.D. 200: Nok people work in metal and trade; early 1900s: British take control of Nigeria; 1960: Nigeria becomes independent; 1999: free elections are held
8. Gulf of Guinea (or Atlantic Ocean)

Critical Thinking Skill

Drawing Inferences and Conclusions

Suppose your teacher brought a colorful wooden mask to class, and a classmate said, "That's from Nigeria." You might infer that your classmate has an interest in African art and, therefore, recognizes the mask as coming from Nigeria.

Yoruba wood masks ▲

Learning the Skill

To *infer* means to evaluate information and arrive at a conclusion. When you make inferences, you "read between the lines," or draw conclusions that are not stated directly in the text. You must use the available facts *and* your own knowledge and experience to form a judgment or opinion about the material.

Use the following steps to help you draw inferences and make conclusions:

- Read carefully for stated facts and ideas.
- Summarize the information and list the important facts.
- Apply related information that you may already know to make inferences.
- Use your knowledge and insight to develop some conclusions about these facts.

Practicing the Skill

Read the passage below, and then answer the questions that follow.

> Nigerian art forms reflect the people's beliefs in spirits and nature. Yoruba masks are carved out of wood, reflecting the forces of nature and gods. The masks are used in ceremonies to help connect with the spirit of their ancestors. The masks also appear at funerals in order to please the spirits of the dead. Of all the Yoruba masks, the helmet masks of the Epa cult are the most spectacular.

1. What topic is the writer describing?
2. What facts are presented?
3. What can you infer about the role of masks in Nigerian life?
4. What do you already know about religious ceremonies?
5. What conclusion can you make about traditional religions in Nigeria?

Applying the Skill

Study the photos of Nigerians on page 553. What can you infer about life in Nigeria from the photographs? What evidence supports this inference, or conclusion?

GO TO Practice key skills with **Glencoe Skillbuilder Interactive Workbook, Level 1.**

TEACH

Give students the following situation: Suppose you walk into your family's living room late at night. The television is on, and a sibling is sleeping on the couch. The floor is covered with popcorn. **Ask:** **What do you think happened?** *(The sibling fell asleep with the television on and dropped the popcorn.)* Explain that in reaching this conclusion, students made inferences—that is, they reached a conclusion based on the available evidence. **L1**

Additional Skills Practice

1. **What conclusion could you draw about the weather from seeing the wet footprints of a cat on the kitchen floor?** *(that it is raining or snowing)*
2. **What could you infer about the environment from the fact that a group of people used camels to transport goods?** *(The people probably lived in a desert.)*

Additional Skills Resources

- Chapter Skills Review
- Building Geography Skills for Life

Skillbuilder Interactive Workbook CD-ROM, Level 1

This interactive CD-ROM reinforces student mastery of essential social studies skills.

Practicing the Skill Answers

1. the connection between Yoruba art forms and spirits and nature
2. Yoruba masks are made of wood; masks are used in ceremonies, including funerals.
3. They play a role in spiritual life.
4. Answers will vary.
5. They involve beliefs in spirits that interact with living people.

Applying the Skill

Answers will vary but might include such inferences as: Cacao is an important economic crop; Nigeria includes both traditional aspects (as shown by the women in canoes) and modern aspects (shown by the oil factory).

FOCUS

Section Objectives

1. Describe the Sahel's location and its history.
2. Explain how people in the Sahel countries live.
3. Compare the coastal countries, their history, and peoples.

BELLRINGER Skillbuilder Activity

Project transparency and have students answer the question.

Daily Focus Skills Transparency

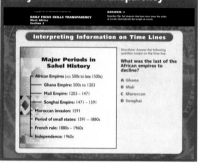

DAILY FOCUS SKILLS TRANSPARENCY
West Africa
Section 2

ANSWER: D
Teacher Tip: Tell students that time lines show the order of events and indicate the length of events.

Interpreting Information on Time Lines

Major Periods in Sahel History

- African Empires (A.D. 500s to late 1500s)
  - Ghana Empire: 500s to 1203
  - Mali Empire: 1203 – 1471
  - Songhai Empire: 1471 – 1591
- Moroccan invasion: 1591
- Period of small states: 1591 – 1880s
- French rule: 1880s – 1960s
- Independence: 1960s

Directions: Answer the following question based on the time line.

What was the last of the African empires to decline?

A Ghana
B Mali
C Moroccan
D Songhai

Reading Preview

■ **Activating Prior Knowledge**
Ask: Can a desert grow and shrink? Explain that in this section students will learn that a desert can grow and that its growth has important effects on people's lives.

■ **Preteaching Vocabulary**
Have students define the first three words in the Terms to Know and use them in a sentence that shows a cause-and-effect relationship.

Guide to Reading

Main Idea

The Sahel countries face a continuing struggle to keep grasslands from turning into desert, but the coastal countries receive plenty of rainfall.

Terms to Know

- overgraze
- drought
- desertification
- bauxite
- phosphate

Reading Strategy

Create five charts like this one, filling in at least one key fact about five West African countries for each category.

Country	
Land	
Economy	
Culture	

The Sahel and Coastal West Africa

Slowly but surely, the desert is creeping into grassy inland areas of West Africa north of Nigeria. Over the past 100 years, a stretch of the Sahara about 100 miles (161 km) wide has swallowed parts of countries in West Africa. This is due in part to population growth. The already limited resources are being used up faster than they can be replaced.

Five countries—**Mauritania** (MAWR•uh•TAY•nee•uh), **Mali** (MAH•lee), **Burkina Faso** (bur•KEE•nuh FAH•soh), **Niger** (NY•juhr), and **Chad**—are located in an area known as the **Sahel.** The word *Sahel* comes from an Arabic word that means "border." In addition to the Sahel countries, West Africa includes 11 coastal countries.

Land and History of the Sahel

The Sahel receives little rainfall, so only short grasses and small trees can support grazing animals. Most people have traditionally herded livestock. Their flocks, unfortunately, have overgrazed the land in some places. When animals **overgraze** land, they strip areas so bare that plants cannot grow back. Then bare soil is blown away by winds.

In the Sahel, dry and wet periods usually follow each other. When the seasonal rains do not fall, drought takes hold. A **drought** is a long period of extreme dryness and water shortage. The latest drought

Section Resources

Reproducible Masters
- Reproducible Lesson Plan
- Daily Lecture and Discussion Notes
- Note-taking Guide
- Guided Reading Activity
- Reading Essentials and Study Guide
- Section Quiz

Transparencies
- Daily Focus Skills Transparency
- In-text Map Transparency

Multimedia
- Vocabulary PuzzleMaker CD-ROM
- Interactive Tutor Self-Assessment CD-ROM
- Presentation Plus! CD-ROM
- ExamView® Pro Testmaker CD-ROM
- MindJogger Videoquiz

occurred in the 1980s. Rivers dried up, crops failed, and millions of animals died. Thousands of people died of starvation. Millions of others fled to more productive southern areas. Overgrazing and drought have led to **desertification** where grasslands have become deserts.

Empires From the A.D. 500s to 1500s, three great African empires—Ghana, Mali, and Songhai (SAWNG•hy)—arose in the Sahel. The empire of Ghana flourished between the A.D. 700s and 1100s. The empire was located at the upper parts of the Senegal and Niger Rivers. The people of Ghana knew how to make iron weapons, which they used to conquer neighboring groups of farmers and herders. Ghana could field an army of 200,000 warriors.

Ghana also had major deposits of gold. The wealth of the king's court was legendary. Crossing the empire were trade routes that connected gold mines in West Africa with copper and salt mines in the Sahara. Ghana prospered by taxing the goods that traders moved north and south along these routes.

The empire of Mali defeated Ghana in the A.D. 1200s. It, too, built its wealth and power on the gold and salt trade. Turn to page 566 to learn more about the rich salt trade. Mali's most famous ruler, Mansa Musa, made a journey in grand style to Makkah. This is the holy city of Islam located in the Arabian Peninsula. A faithful Muslim, Mansa Musa made his capital, Tombouctou (TOH•book•TOO), a leading center of Islamic learning. People came from all over the Muslim world to study there.

In the 1400s, Songhai replaced Mali as the most powerful West African empire. A huge army and a navy that patrolled the Niger River made Songhai the largest of the three trading empires. Songhai's rulers welcomed teachers, poets, and religious leaders from Asia and Europe.

Moroccan invaders with guns defeated Songhai in the late 1500s. During the 1800s, the Sahel region came under French rule. The French created five colonies in the area. In 1960 these five colonies

EXPLORING CULTURE

Clothing

To protect themselves from the hot Saharan sun, the Tuareg people wear layers of clothing under their long flowing robes. These loose cotton clothes help slow the evaporation of sweat and conserve body moisture. As a sign of respect for their superiors, Tuareg men cover their mouths and faces with veils. Women usually wear veils only for weddings. The veils are made of blue cloth dyed from crushed indigo. The blue dye easily rubs off onto the skin, earning the men the nickname "the Blue Men of the Desert."

Looking Closer How is the clothing of the Tuareg appropriate for the land in which they live?

Reading Strategy — Reading the Text

Writing a Story The peoples of West Africa have a long tradition of oral literature that has been preserved by special artists named *griots*. Griots are storytellers who relate the achievements of an ethnic group. In relating the achievements of warriors and heroes, they preserve the traditions and values of the group. Invite a language arts teacher to class to outline the typical elements of oral literature in general and of the griots in particular. Then invite students to write a story showing these elements and give an oral performance of it. **L1**

*Use the **Reading Skills Handbook** for more reading strategies.*

TEACH

Analyzing Information

Have students research and report on the music of Africa south of the Sahara. Suggest that they include information on how the music spread to the United States and influenced spirituals, jazz, blues, and rock and roll. **L2**

Daily Lecture and Discussion Notes

WEST AFRICA

Daily Lecture and Discussion Notes

The Sahel and Coastal West Africa

Did You Know? Only about 10 percent of Mauritania's children attend primary school, and an even smaller percentage attend high school. The country's first university, the University of Nouakchott, opened in 1983.

I. Land and History of the Sahel

A. Five countries—Mauritania, Mali, Burkina Faso, Niger, and Chad—are located in an area known as the Sahel, which means "border."

B. Most people in the Sahel have traditionally herded livestock. Their flocks have overgrazed the land in some places. When animals **overgraze** land, they strip plants cannot grow back. Then bare soil is blown away by

Answer It protects them from the heat and conserves body moisture.

Ask students: **How is the clothing that you and your classmates wear suited to the climate in which you live?** Discuss their responses, and point out differing clothing needs with the change of seasons.

Chapter 19

Section 2, pages 556–561

✓ Reading Check Answer

Areas are stripped, and plants cannot grow back. Bare soil is then blown away by the winds.

L1/ELL

Guided Reading Activity

Name ______ Date ______ Class ______

WEST AFRICA

Guided Reading Activity 2

The Sahel and Coastal West Africa

DIRECTIONS: Outlining Reading the section and completing the outline below will help you learn more about the Sahel and coastal West Africa. Refer to your textbook to fill in the blanks.

I. The Sahel
- A. The Sahel receives little ______.
  1. Most people have traditionally herded ______.
  2. The Sahel experiences ______, or long periods of extreme dryness.
  3. ______ occurs when grassland areas become desert.
- B. From the 500s to 1500s, ______ great African empires—______, ______, and ______—arose in the Sahel.
- C. Most people live in the ______ areas of the Sahel.
  1. They are ______ farmers.
  2. For years, many people were ______.
- D. Mali, Burkina Faso, Niger, and Chad suffer from their ______ location.
- E. Most people of the Sahel follow the ______ religion.

II. The Coastal Countries
- A. The landscape of West Africa's coastal countries includes ______ swamps, rain forests, and highland areas.
- B. The powerful kingdoms of ______ and ______ ruled the coastal region in early times.
- C. Most people in Gambia, Senegal, and Guinea work in ______.
- D. Guinea is also rich in ______ and ______.
- E. ______ is the only West African nation that was never a colony.
- F. The largest ethnic groups in Ghana are the ______ and ______.
- G. ______ in Ghana is one of the world's largest artificial lakes.

53

✓ Reading Check Answer

Droughts forced many to move to towns.

became the independent nations of Mauritania, Mali, Upper Volta (now Burkina Faso), Niger, and Chad.

✓Reading Check How has overgrazing affected the Sahel?

The People of the Sahel

The Sahel countries are large in size but have small populations. The population density map on page 560 shows that most people live in the southern areas of the Sahel. Rivers flow here, and the land can be farmed or grazed. Yet even these areas do not have enough water and fertile land to support large numbers of people.

Today most people in the Sahel live in small towns. They are subsistence farmers who grow grains, such as millet and sorghum (SAWR•guhm). For years, many people were nomads. Groups such as the Tuareg (TWAH•rehg), for example, would cross the desert with herds of camels. The Fulani herded cattle, goats, and sheep. The recent droughts forced many of them to give up their traditional way of life and move to the towns. Here they often live in crowded camps of tents.

Mauritania borders the Atlantic Ocean. Rich fishing waters lie off the coast, but ships from other countries have overfished the area. Still, Mauritania's chief exports include fish and iron ore. The other four Sahel countries suffer from their landlocked location and lack of good transportation. Mali hopes to develop its gold mining industry. Niger has reserves of uranium, a mineral used for making nuclear fuels. Chad has petroleum deposits yet lacks the money needed to build pipelines.

The people of the Sahel practice a mix of African, Arab, and European traditions. Most are Muslims and follow the Islamic religion. They speak Arabic as well as a variety of African languages. In many of the larger cities, French is also spoken.

✓Reading Check Why have many people in the Sahel given up nomadic ways?

West Africa's Coastal Countries

Look at the map on page 552 to locate the **Cape Verde** Islands off the Atlantic Coast. Skipping to **Senegal,** follow the countries in order around the coast: **Gambia, Guinea-Bissau, Guinea, Sierra Leone, Liberia, Côte d'Ivoire, Ghana, Togo,** and **Benin.**

Tropical Landscape Sandy beaches, thick mangrove swamps, and rain forests cover the shores of West Africa's coastal countries. Highland areas with grasses and trees lie inland. Several major rivers flow from these highlands to the coast. They include the Sénégal, Gambia, Volta, and Niger Rivers. Rapids and shallow waters prevent large ships from traveling far inland.

Because they border the ocean, the coastal countries receive plenty of rainfall. Warm currents in the **Gulf of Guinea** create a moist, tropical rain forest climate in most coastal lowlands year-round. For many years, tropical disease, thick rain forests, and river rapids kept European explorers from entering the interior.

Monoculture

The economies of some West African countries, such as Côte d'Ivoire, depend upon the production of one or two major crops. This practice is called monoculture. Although this has the advantage of being able to produce enough product to export, it also has disadvantages. If worldwide demand for the product drops, the price also drops. A major drought or epidemic could destroy harvests and wipe out the nation's only major source of income.

Differentiated Instruction

Meeting Special Needs: Interpersonal Organize students into five groups and assign one of the Sahel countries to each group. Have group members research and prepare a mini-lesson about their assigned country. Each lesson should cover such topics as landscapes, resources, economic activities, and cultures. Then form new groups consisting of one member from each original group. Have each member in the new groups teach the other group members about the country he or she researched. **L1**

Refer to *Inclusion for the Middle School Social Studies Classroom Strategies and Activities* in the TCR.

Deforestation is a problem along the densely settled West African coast. Forests have been cleared to make space for palm, coffee, cacao, and rubber plantations, as well as for many small farms. As people migrate in search of work, they have formed concentrated settlements around port cities such as **Abidjan** (Côte d'Ivoire), **Accra** (Ghana), and Lagos and **Port Harcourt** (Nigeria). Oil discoveries in eastern Nigeria are now attracting even more people to the West African coast.

Despite rich agricultural resources, coastal West African countries import more in industrial goods than they export in natural products. Why? Agricultural products often rise and fall in price suddenly, and their value is not equal to finished goods. To meet their countries' needs, governments have to borrow money from international organizations.

NATIONAL GEOGRAPHIC On Location

Niger Highway

Rivers of West Africa provide not only water but transportation. Here, freight boats on the Niger River deliver goods to Benin's people.

Place **What prevents large ships from traveling far inland on West Africa's rivers?**

History In early times, the powerful and wealthy kingdoms of Ashanti and Abomey ruled West Africa's coastal region. These kingdoms were centers of trade, learning, and the arts. Benin artists sculpted beautiful works in bronze. Intricate woodcarvings and masks represented gods, spirits, or ancestors. African dance and music also served a religious purpose. The dances were a means of communicating with the spirits. Without a written language, African dances and songs became a way to pass legends and religious traditions from generation to generation.

The Slave Trade From the late 1400s to the early 1800s, Europeans set up trading posts along the West African coast. From these posts, they traded with Africans for gold, ivory, and enslaved people. Many African states had sold people as slaves long before Europeans reached Africa. Most of these slaves were prisoners of war captured in local battles. After the development of European sailing ships, however, the slave trade became a major source of income for the kings of West African states.

Europeans enslaved millions of Africans and forced them to work on plantations and in mines in the Americas. This trade in human beings was a disaster for West Africa. The removal of so many young and skilled people devastated West African families, villages, and economies.

The French, British, and Portuguese eventually divided up the coastal region and set up colonies to obtain the region's rich resources. In 1957 Ghana became the first country in Africa to become independent. By the late 1970s, no West African country was under European rule.

✓ **Reading Check** What enabled West African kings to prosper from the slave trade?

Chapter 19

Section 2, pages 556–561

More About the Photo

West Africa's Rivers The Gambia River is used for transportation, freight deliveries, and mail. The river is also navigated by oceangoing vessels.

Caption Answer rapids and shallow water

✓ Reading Check Answer

European sailing ships

3 ASSESS

Assign Section 2 Assessment as homework or an in-class activity.

Have students use the Interactive Tutor Self-Assessment CD-ROM to review Section 2.

L2

Section Quiz

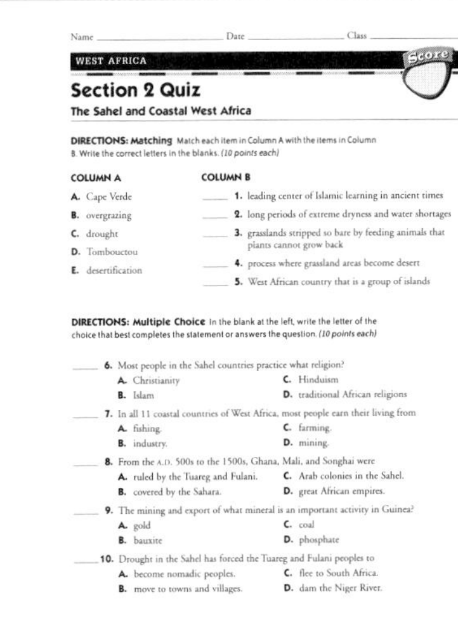

Name ______ Date ______ Class ______

WEST AFRICA Score

Section 2 Quiz

The Sahel and Coastal West Africa

DIRECTIONS: Matching Match each item in Column A with the items in Column B. Write the correct letters in the blanks. *(10 points each)*

COLUMN A	COLUMN B
A. Cape Verde	____ **1.** leading center of Islamic learning in ancient times
B. overgrazing	____ **2.** long periods of extreme dryness and water shortages
C. drought	____ **3.** grasslands stripped so bare by feeding animals that plants cannot grow back
D. Tombouctou	____ **4.** process where grassland areas become desert
E. desertification	____ **5.** West African country that is a group of islands

DIRECTIONS: Multiple Choice In the blank at the left, write the letter of the choice that best completes the statement or answers the question. *(10 points each)*

____ **6.** Most people in the Sahel countries practice what religion?
A. Christianity **C.** Hinduism
B. Islam **D.** traditional African religions

____ **7.** In all 11 coastal countries of West Africa, most people earn their living from
A. fishing. **C.** farming.
B. industry. **D.** mining.

____ **8.** From the A.D. 500s to the 1500s, Ghana, Mali, and Songhai were
A. ruled by the Tuareg and Fulani. **C.** Arab colonies in the Sahel.
B. covered by the Sahara. **D.** great African empires.

____ **9.** The mining and export of what mineral is an important activity in Guinea?
A. gold **C.** coal
B. bauxite **D.** phosphate

____ **10.** Drought in the Sahel has forced the Tuareg and Fulani peoples to
A. become nomadic peoples. **C.** flee to South Africa.
B. move to towns and villages. **D.** dam the Niger River.

312

Content Background

A Grand Caravan Mansa Musa's pilgrimage to Makkah included 12,000 slaves carrying gold-covered staffs. About 80 camels set out with 300 pounds of gold each, which the emperor generously distributed during the trip. This journey notified the world of the wealth of West Africa. In fact, so much gold was given away on Mansa Musa's journey that the world price of gold fell.

Cultural  Kaleidoscope

Côte d'Ivoire French missionaries brought Christianity to Côte d'Ivoire in the 1600s. The church of Our Lady of Peace in Yamoussoukro is the largest Christian place of worship in Africa.

 Applying Map Skills

Answers

1. Lagos, Ibadan, Ogbomosho, Abuja, and Kano
2. along the Gulf of Guinea

In-text Map Transparency Activity Remind students that they should try to identify patterns when looking at a population density map. They should quickly scan the map to locate where the populations are most and least dense. Ask students questions that make them think about why certain areas are more populated than others. **Ask: Why are northern Mali and central Mauritania largely uninhabited?** *(These areas are deserts.)*

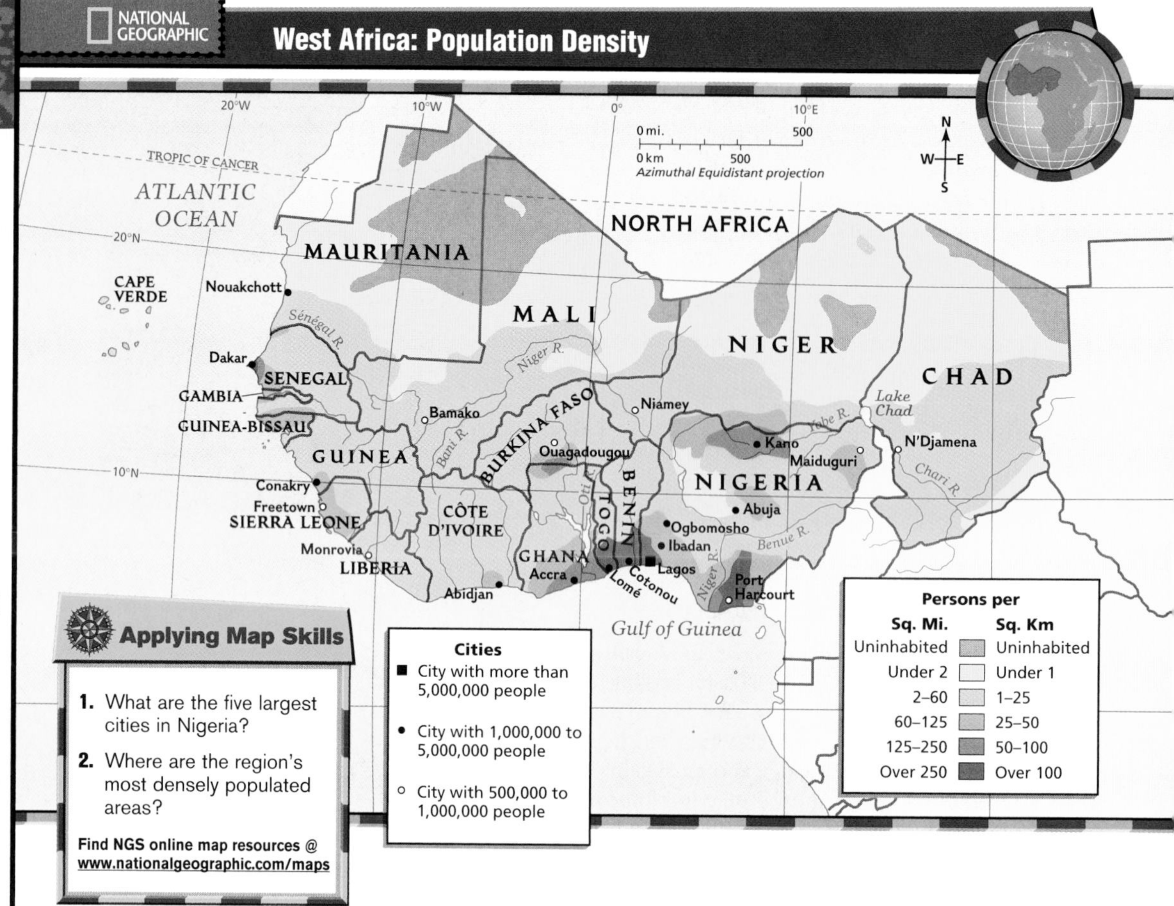

Applying Map Skills

1. What are the five largest cities in Nigeria?
2. Where are the region's most densely populated areas?

Find NGS online map resources @ www.nationalgeographic.com/maps

People of Coastal West Africa

People in coastal West Africa cherish family ties. Some practice traditional African religions, whereas others are Christian or Muslim. Local African languages are spoken in everyday conversation. Reflecting the region's colonial histories, languages such as French, English, and Portuguese are used in business and government. If you were to visit the modern coastal cities of West Africa, you would see some people dressed in Western-style business clothes and others in traditional African clothing. **Dakar** (dah•KAHR), Senegal's capital, is known for its European cafés, bustling outdoor markets, and tree-lined streets.

Most of the people in Gambia, Senegal, and Guinea work in agriculture. Guinea is also rich in bauxite and diamonds. **Bauxite** is a mineral used to make aluminum. Phosphate mining takes place in Senegal. **Phosphate** is a mineral salt used in fertilizers.

Liberia is the only West African nation that was never a colony. African Americans freed from slavery founded Liberia in 1822. **Monrovia,** the capital, was named for James Monroe—the president of

Differentiated Instruction

Meeting Special Needs: Naturalist Organize the class into two teams, and then split each team into smaller groups. Have the groups in one half create dioramas showing the environment of the rain forest in the coastal countries of West Africa. Have the groups in the other half create dioramas showing the environment of the steppe areas in the Sahel countries. Have the different groups write questions about the geographic features shown in the models of the other group. When each team presents its dioramas to the class, they should answer the questions and explain the features they highlighted. Afterwards, have students compare the features in the models. In what other world regions can these environments be found? L1

the United States when Liberia was founded. From 1989 to 2003, a civil war cost many lives and destroyed much of the country's economy.

Like Liberia, Sierra Leone was founded as a home for people freed from slavery. The British ruled Sierra Leone from 1787 to 1961. Most of the land is used for farming, but the country also has mineral resources, especially diamonds. Here, too, civil war has hurt the economy.

Côte d'Ivoire has a French name that means "ivory coast." From the late 1400s to the early 1900s, a trade in elephant ivory tusks in Côte d'Ivoire brought profits to European traders. Today the ivory trade is illegal, and the country protects its few remaining elephants. The port of Abidjan is the largest urban area and economic center. It has towering office buildings and wide avenues. Most countries' embassies are in Abidjan, but **Yamoussoukro** (YAH•moo•SOO•kroh), some 137 miles (220 km) inland, is the official capital.

Ghana's people belong to about 100 ethnic groups. The Ashanti and the Fante are the largest. Many groups still keep their local kings, but these rulers have no political power. The people respect these ceremonial rulers and look to them to keep traditions alive. About 35 percent of Ghana's people live in cities. **Accra,** on the coast, is the capital and largest city. A giant dam on the Volta River provides hydroelectric power to urban areas. The dam also has created **Lake Volta,** one of the world's largest artificial lakes.

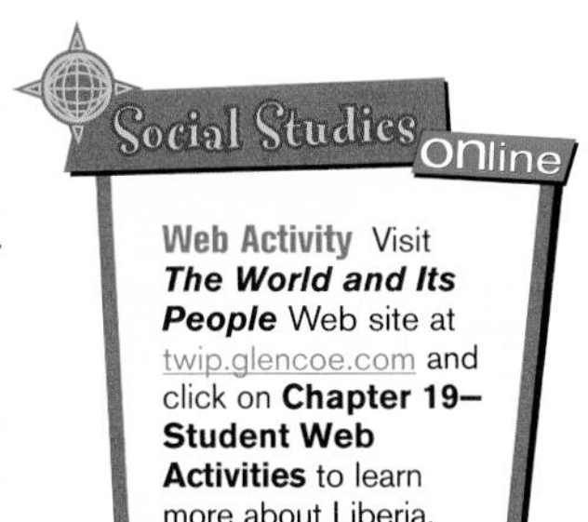

Social Studies online
Web Activity Visit *The World and Its People* Web site at twip.glencoe.com and click on Chapter 19—Student Web Activities to learn more about Liberia.

Reading Check What are the capitals of Ghana and Côte d'Ivoire?

Section 2 Assessment

Defining Terms

1. **Define** overgraze, drought, desertification, bauxite, phosphate.

Recalling Facts

2. **History** What three great empires ruled in the Sahel from the A.D. 500s to 1500s?
3. **History** Which West African country was never a colony?
4. **Government** How much political power do the local kings in Ghana have?

Critical Thinking

5. **Making Predictions** What challenges do you think will arise as people move from the Sahel to more productive areas?
6. **Drawing Conclusions** Why do governments of coastal West African countries have to borrow money?

Graphic Organizer

7. **Organizing Information** On a chart like this one, write at least three different facts about the three ancient African empires of Ghana, Mali, and Songhai.

Ghana	Mali	Songhai

Applying Social Studies Skills

8. **Analyzing Maps** Study the population density map on page 560. Why would you expect the heavy population centers to be located along the coast?

Section 2 Assessment

1. The terms are defined in the Glossary.
2. Ghana, Mali, and Songhai
3. Liberia
4. none; they are ceremonial.
5. Answers might include overcrowding and stresses on available resources.
6. Agricultural exports often do not earn enough to pay for industrial imports, so the countries cannot meet their people's needs.
7. All three empires controlled the trade in gold, salt, and other goods; Mali's ruler, Mansa Musa, made his capital, Tombouctou, a leading center of Islamic learning; invaders from North Africa defeated Songhai, the last of the great empires, in the late 1500s.
8. They are close to ports and oil discoveries.

Social Studies Online

Objectives and answers to the Student Web Activity can be found in the Web Activity Lesson Plan at twip.glencoe.com

Reteach

Have students list three key facts about each country discussed in this section.

Reading Check Answer

Accra; Yamoussoukro

L1/ELL

Reading Essentials and Study Guide

Name ____ Date ____ Class ____

WEST AFRICA

Reading Essentials and Study Guide 2

The Sahel and Coastal West Africa

Key Terms

overgraze animals strip the land so bare that plants cannot grow back
drought long period of extreme dryness and water shortages
desertification process of grasslands turning into deserts
bauxite mineral used to make aluminum
phosphate mineral salt used in fertilizers

 Close

Have students use the maps and text in this chapter to write a 10-question quiz that reflects what they think are the most important characteristics of the coastal countries of West Africa.

Making Connections

ART | SCIENCE | CULTURE | TECHNOLOGY

TEACH

Ask: What kinds of buildings are common to all societies? *(Examples are government buildings, recreational facilities, museums, stadiums or arenas, transportation facilities, and shopping areas.)* Help students understand that religious structures fall in this category. L1

More About Great Mosque

A visitor to Djenné described the spring repair of the Great Mosque in this way: "This is a festival at once awesome, messy, meticulous, and fun. For weeks beforehand mud is cured. . . . [When the signal comes,] a hundred voices roar, and the throng sets off on a massive mud-fetch. . . . Crowds of young women, heads erect under the burden of buckets brimming with water, approach. . . . Other teams, bringing mud, charge shouting through the main square and swarm across the mosque's terrace."

Interdisciplinary Connections

Architecture Have students research a famous building in their own community. Have them prepare a poster that shows how the structure reflects the physical environment.

Great Mosque of Djenné

In the West African city of Djenné (jeh•NAY), Mali, stands a huge structure built entirely of mud. It is the Great Mosque of Djenné, and it covers an area the size of a city block. Considered one of Africa's greatest architectural wonders, the existing Great Mosque is actually the third mosque to occupy the location.

Djenné

Located between the Sahara and the African savanna, the city of Djenné was an important crossroads on a trade route connecting northern and southern Africa. Caravans and boats carried gold, salt, and other goods through the city.

During the A.D. 1200s, the ruler of Djenné ordered the construction of the first Great Mosque. Having recently converted to Islam, he had his palace torn down to make room for the huge house of worship. The city became an important Islamic religious center. Over the years, political and religious conflicts led to a decline in the city. People abandoned the Great Mosque, and a second, much smaller one replaced it. Then in 1906, builders began to raise a new Great Mosque. Today the Great Mosque is once more an important part of the religious life of the Djenné people.

The Great Mosque

The Great Mosque of Djenné was built facing east toward Makkah, the holy city of Islam. It is constructed from the same sun-dried mud bricks as most of the rest of the city. The mud walls of the mosque vary in thickness between 16 and 24 inches (41 and 61 cm), providing insulation to keep the interior cool. Roof vents can be removed at night to allow cooler air inside.

With its five stories and three towers, or minarets, the mosque rises above the surrounding buildings. Inside the mosque, the main prayer hall is open to the sky. Although the mosque contains loudspeakers that are used to issue the call to prayer, there are few other modern improvements.

Maintaining the Mosque

Rain, wind, and heat can damage mud structures, and the Great Mosque would soon deteriorate without care. Each spring the people of Djenné plaster the mosque from top to bottom with fresh mud. It is a festival day, and nearly everyone volunteers. Workers climb up the sides of the mosque on wooden rods permanently mounted to the walls. They dump mud and water onto the walls, then smooth it with their bare hands. The townspeople know that, with such care, the Great Mosque will remain a place of worship for generations to come.

Making the Connection

1. When was the first Great Mosque built?
2. What elements of the Great Mosque help keep the inside cool?
3. **Making Comparisons** In what way is the Great Mosque like the other buildings in Djenné? In what way is it different?

◀ Great Mosque of Djenné

Making the Connection

1. A.D. 1200s
2. The mud walls provide insulation to keep the interior cool; roof vents can be removed at night to allow cooler air inside.
3. It is similar to other buildings in that it is made of sun-dried mud brick. It is different because it faces toward Makkah, because it is taller than other buildings in the city, and because people from all over the city help repair the walls each spring.

Chapter 19 Reading Review

Section 1 Nigeria—African Giant

Terms to Know
- mangrove
- savanna
- harmattan
- subsistence farm
- cacao
- compound
- civil war

Main Idea

Nigeria is a large, oil-rich country that has more people than any other African nation.

✓ **Place** Nigeria's major landforms are coastal lowlands, savannas, highlands, plateaus, and partly dry grasslands.

✓ **Economics** More than 90 percent of Nigeria's income comes from oil exports.

✓ **Culture** Nigeria has about 250 ethnic groups. The four largest ethnic groups are the Hausa, Fulani, Yoruba, and Ibo.

Section 2 The Sahel and Coastal West Africa

Terms to Know
- overgraze
- drought
- desertification
- bauxite
- phosphate

Main Idea

The Sahel countries face a continuing struggle to keep grasslands from turning into desert, but the coastal countries receive plenty of rainfall.

✓ **Region** The Sahel countries are Mauritania, Mali, Niger, Chad, and Burkina Faso.

✓ **Region** The Sahel receives little rainfall, so only short grasses and small trees can support grazing animals.

✓ **Human/Environment Interaction** Overgrazing and drought have caused many grassland areas in this region to become desert.

✓ **Region** The 11 countries that make up coastal West Africa are Senegal, Gambia, Guinea, Guinea-Bissau, Cape Verde, Liberia, Sierra Leone, Côte d'Ivoire, Ghana, Togo, and Benin.

✓ **Economics** West Africa's coastal countries import more in industrial goods than they export in natural products.

The port of Abidjan, Côte d'Ivoire ▶

Reading Review

Use the Chapter 19 Reading Review to preview, review, condense, or reteach the chapter.

Preview/Review

Use the Terms to Know lists to help students review and study.

Activity Have students draw up a matching quiz of 10 terms and their definitions from the chapter. Then have them exchange quizzes with another student and take the quiz their partners prepared.

Vocabulary PuzzleMaker CD-ROM reinforces the vocabulary terms used in Chapter 19.

The Interactive Tutor Self-Assessment CD-ROM allows students to review Chapter 19 content.

Condense

Have students read the Chapter 19 summary statements.

Guided Reading Activities

Audio Program

Reteach

Reteaching Activity

Reading Essentials and Study Guide

Reading Strategy Read to Write

Comparing and Contrasting Have students research to compare and contrast urban and rural ways of life in West Africa in a one-page essay. Topics might address the similarities and differences between economies, family life, and religious beliefs. Students should analyze why rural people are more likely to preserve traditional ways of life than urban people. Essays should be logically organized and use transitional words that denote similarities and differences. L1

Assessment and Activities

GLENCOE TECHNOLOGY

MindJogger Videoquiz
Use MindJogger Videoquiz to review the Chapter 19 content.

Available in DVD and VHS

Using Key Terms

1. i
2. c
3. h
4. j
5. b
6. d
7. a
8. e
9. g
10. f

Reviewing the Main Ideas

11. oil
12. because different ethnic groups have sought control over the country or tried to set up their own country
13. Wole Soyinka
14. Hausa, Fulani, Yoruba, Ibo
15. border
16. Ghana
17. Mali's most famous ruler and a Muslim who made Tombouctou a leading center of Islamic learning
18. Islam
19. overgrazing and drought
20. Rapids and shallow waters prevent it.
21. African states selling people as slaves to Europeans and Asians
22. Ashanti and Fante

Chapter 19 Assessment and Activities

Using Key Terms

Match the terms in Part A with their definitions in Part B.

A.

1. overgraze
2. harmattan
3. drought
4. mangrove
5. compound
6. phosphate
7. desertification
8. cacao
9. subsistence farm
10. savanna

B.

a. process in which deserts expand
b. a group of houses surrounded by a wall
c. a dusty wind that blows south from the Sahara
d. mineral salt used in fertilizers
e. tropical tree whose seeds are used to make cocoa and chocolate
f. tropical grassland with scattered trees
g. produces enough to support a family's needs
h. extended period of extreme dryness
i. when animals strip the land so bare that plants cannot grow
j. tropical tree with roots above and beneath the water

Reviewing the Main Ideas

Section 1 Nigeria—African Giant

11. **Economics** What is Nigeria's major export?
12. **Economics** Name one reason Nigeria had economic troubles in the 1980s.
13. **Culture** Who was the first African to win the Nobel Prize in literature?
14. **History** Why have there been so many conflicts in Nigeria since 1960?

Section 2 The Sahel and Coastal West Africa

15. **Region** What is the meaning of the word *Sahel?*
16. **History** What was the earliest trading empire in West Africa?
17. **History** Who was Mansa Musa?
18. **Culture** What religion do most people of the Sahel follow?
19. **History** What has led to desertification in the Sahel?
20. **Movement** Why are ships unable to sail very far inland in coastal West Africa?
21. **History** What was the slave trade?
22. **Culture** What are the largest ethnic groups in Ghana?

West Africa

Place Location Activity

On a separate sheet of paper, match the letters on the map with the numbered places listed below.

1. Gulf of Guinea
2. Nigeria
3. Niger River
4. Liberia
5. Cape Verde
6. Lagos
7. Mali
8. Ghana
9. Chad
10. Monrovia

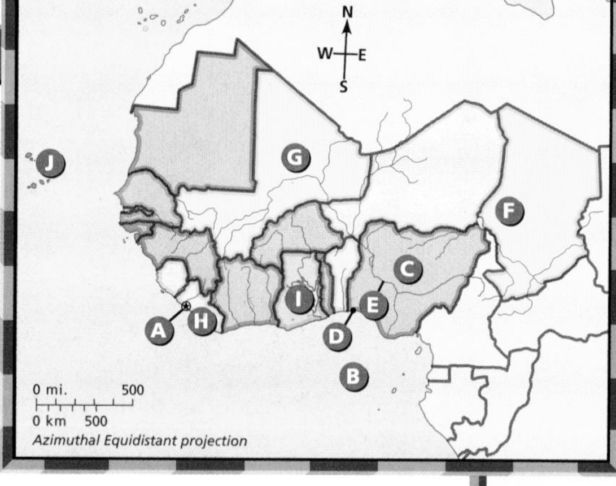

NATIONAL GEOGRAPHIC Place Location Activity

1. B
2. C
3. E
4. H
5. J
6. D
7. G
8. I
9. F
10. A

Critical Thinking

23. Answers will vary but might include such challenges as desertification, ethnic conflict, or economic development.
24. Time lines will vary. Have students justify why they chose the five events as the most important.

Self-Check Quiz Visit ***The World and Its People*** Web site at twip.glencoe.com and click on **Chapter 19—Self-Check Quizzes** to prepare for the Chapter Test.

Critical Thinking

23. **Evaluating Information** What do you feel is the major challenge facing the countries of West Africa today? Explain your answer.
24. **Sequencing Information** After reviewing this chapter, choose what you feel are five of the most important events in the history of West Africa. Place those events and their dates on a time line like this one.

Comparing Regions Activity

25. **Culture** West African arts have had a powerful impact on other cultures. Out of West Africa came detailed bronze work, musical rhythms, and wooden masks. The influence of African art is apparent in the work of Spanish artist Pablo Picasso. He painted geometric shapes and figures, as well as masklike faces. Research to find other ways African arts and music have influenced cultures.

Mental Mapping Activity

26. **Focusing on the Region** Create a simple outline map of West Africa, and then label the following:
    - Niger River
    - Senegal
    - Atlantic Ocean
    - Côte d'Ivoire
    - Gulf of Guinea
    - Chad
    - Tropic of Cancer
    - Mali
    - Nigeria
    - Mauritania
    - Niger
    - Liberia

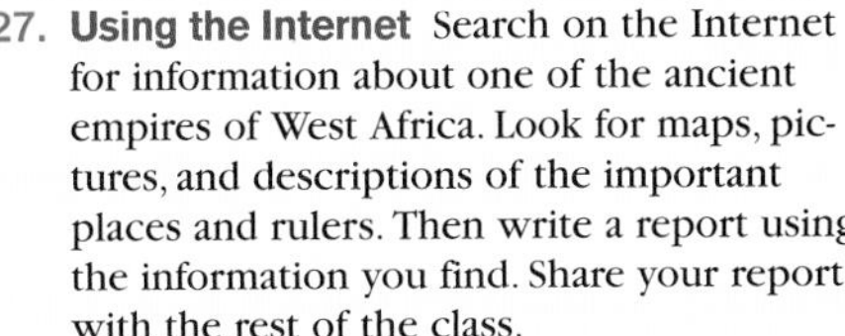

Technology Skills Activity

27. **Using the Internet** Search on the Internet for information about one of the ancient empires of West Africa. Look for maps, pictures, and descriptions of the important places and rulers. Then write a report using the information you find. Share your report with the rest of the class.

Standardized Test Practice

Directions: Study the graph, and then answer the question that follows.

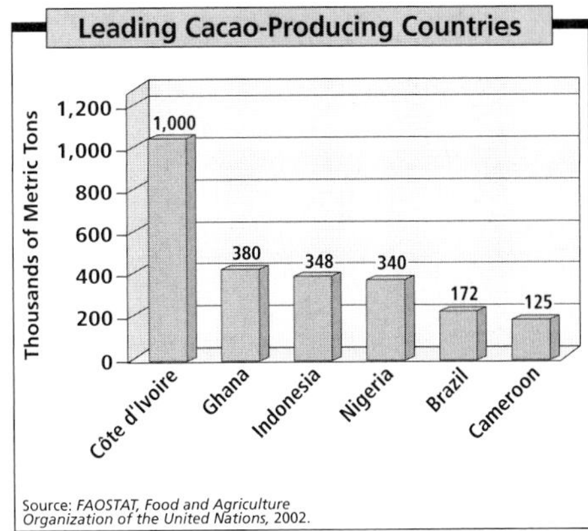

1. What countries on the graph are leading cacao-producing countries from West Africa?

A Ghana, Indonesia, and Nigeria
B Côte d'Ivoire, Ghana, and Indonesia
C Côte d'Ivoire, Nigeria, and Cameroon
D Côte d'Ivoire, Ghana, and Nigeria

Test-Taking Tip: The important words in this question are "from West Africa." You need to use information on the graph as well as information you learned in Chapter 19 to answer this question. As with any graph, read the title bar and information along the side and bottom of the graph first. Then analyze and compare the sizes of the bars to one another.

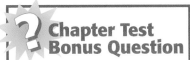

565

Assessment and Activities

Standardized Test Practice

1. D

Tested Objectives:
Reading a bar graph, synthesizing information

Chapter Test Bonus Question

This question may be used for extra credit on the chapter test.

This country in West Africa was founded by African Americans who had been freed from slavery in the United States. It was never a colony. What country is it? *(Liberia)*

Have students visit the Web site at twip.glencoe.com to review Chapter 19 and take the Self-Check Quiz.

FOLDABLES™ Study Organizer **Dinah Zike's Foldables**

Culminating Activity Have students use library sources to answer any questions that they still might have about West Africa. Students should add this information to their foldables.

Comparing Regions Activity

25. Students should provide examples that show how African art and music has influenced other cultures.

Mental Mapping Activity

26. This exercise helps students visualize the countries and geographic features they have been studying. Accept all attempts at freehand mapping that show places in the correct relationship to one another.

Technology Skills Activity

27. Students' projects should include not only the report but also the evaluation of Internet sources. You may wish to discuss what criteria to use in evaluating the Web sites before students conduct their assessment.

People trade salt and other goods at a market on the Niger River in ancient Africa.

1 Focus

Ask: **Have you ever traded items with a friend?** Have volunteers describe the situation and how the two people arrived at an understanding of the value of the two items traded. Then explain that trading has existed between groups of people for thousands of years. Point out that in Africa, people traded for a good that students might consider very common. **L1**

2 Teach

Tracing Trade Routes

Ask: **What is the most important resource in the world today?** *(Possible responses: oil, water, food)* **What makes these goods so valuable?** *(Oil is needed to power cars and industries; water and food are needed for survival.)* Have students choose one good that is exported and research where it is found or produced and what routes it follows when it is sold. **L1**

Meeting National Standards

Geography for Life

The following standards are met in the Student Edition feature:

EE1 The World in Spatial Terms: Standard 3

EE4 Human Systems: Standard 11

EE5 Environment and Society: Standard 16

PLEASE PASS THE SALT:

Africa's Salt Trade

Passing the salt at dinner may not be a big deal, but in parts of Africa, salt built empires. How did such a basic substance come to play such an important role in Africa?

Good as Gold

Salt is essential for life. Every person contains about 8 ounces (227 g) of salt—enough to fill several saltshakers. Salt helps muscles work, and it aids in digesting food. In hot climates, people need extra salt to replace the salt lost when they sweat. In tropical Africa, salt has always been precious.

Salt is plentiful in the Sahara and scarce in the forests south of the Sahara (in present-day countries such as Ghana and Côte d'Ivoire). These conditions gave rise to Africa's salt trade. Beginning in the A.D. 300s, Berbers drove camels carrying European glassware and weapons from Mediterranean ports into the Sahara. At the desert's great salt deposits, such as those near the ancient sites of Terhazza and Taoudenni, they traded European wares for salt.

The salt did not look like the tiny crystals in a saltshaker. It was in the form of large slabs, as hard as stone. The slabs were pried from hardened salt deposits that were left on the land long ago when landlocked seas evaporated. The salt slabs were loaded onto camels, and the animals were herded south. To people in the south, salt was literally worth its weight in gold. The slabs were cut into equal-sized blocks and exchanged for gold and other products such as ivory and kola nuts. Salt was also traded for enslaved people.

Rise and Decline

Camels arrived in Africa from Asia in A.D. 300. Before that time only a trickle of trade, mostly carried by human porters, made it across the blistering desert. In time, caravans of thousands of camels loaded with tons of salt arrived at southern markets.

Local kings along the trade routes put taxes—payable in gold—on all goods crossing their realms. The ancient empires of Mali, Ghana, and Songhai rose to great power from wealth brought by the salt trade.

Trade routes also provided avenues for spreading ideas and inventions. By the A.D. 800s, Arab traders brought to Africa a system of weights and measures, a written language, and the concept of money. They also brought a new religion—Islam.

Today trucks have replaced many of the camels. Salt no longer dominates trade in the region. However, salt is still important, and the salt trade continues in Mali and in the markets of other West African nations.

QUESTIONS

1. What goods were exchanged in the salt trade?
2. How did the salt trade affect regions south of the Sahara?

A present-day salt caravan in Niger ▶

566

Answers to the Questions

1. European wares, gold, ivory, kola nuts, enslaved people
2. Local kings rose to power by collecting tax on the salt and other trade goods; trade routes helped spread ideas and inventions.

NATIONAL GEOGRAPHIC

Salt Trade Routes

ATLANTIC OCEAN
Mediterranean Sea
SAHARA
ASIA
Terhazza
Taoudenni
NIGER
Nile R.
Red Sea
Lake Chad
CÔTE D'IVOIRE
GHANA
0 mi. 1,000
0 km 1,000
Songhai
Mali
Ghana
Salt deposit
Trade routes
Present boundaries

GEOGRAPHY & HISTORY

Time Line

- **300s:** Camels introduced to the Sahara
- **700–900:** Berbers develop caravan routes linking Mediterranean ports to West Africa
- **900s:** Islam enters West Africa
- **900–1100:** Kingdom of Ghana flourishes
- **1200–1450:** Kingdom of Mali controls West Africa
- **c. 1312–1327:** Reign of Mansa Musa over Mali
- **1450–1590:** Kingdom of Songhai thrives

Did You Know

In the ancient Roman Empire, soldiers were paid with a ration of salt. Money was later substituted for actual salt, but the Latin word referring to the ration—*salarium*—was kept. This word is the root of the word *salary.*

3 ASSESS

Have students answer the questions on page 566.

4 CLOSE

Reading Strategy

Writing a Paragraph Have students write a paragraph explaining why the salt trade arose in West Africa and what impact this trade had.

Geography and History Activity

Trade Routes Have students research the oceangoing trade routes that connected cities on the east coast of Africa to the Muslim and Indian worlds. Have them create an illustrated map or poster that shows the routes followed, the main trading ports, and the goods that were exchanged. Have them also report on how the exchanges affected society and culture in East Africa. L2

EE1 The World in Spatial Terms: Standard 1

Chapter 20 Resources

Note: The following materials may be used when teaching Chapter 20.
Section level support materials are shown at point of use in the margins of the Teacher Wraparound Edition.

Timesaving Tools

TeacherWorks™ All-In-One Planner and Resource Center

- **Interactive Teacher Edition** See the **Interactive Teacher Edition** CD-ROM to electronically integrate your Teacher Wraparound Edition and blackline masters.
- **Interactive Lesson Planner** Organize your week, month, semester, or year with all the lesson helps you need. The **Interactive Lesson Planner** CD-ROM contains all Chapter 20 resources.

Use Glencoe's **Presentation Plus!** multimedia teacher tool to easily present dynamic lessons that visually excite your students. Using Microsoft PowerPoint® you can customize the presentations to create your own personalized lessons.

TEACHING TRANSPARENCIES

Graphic Organizer Transparency 1 L2

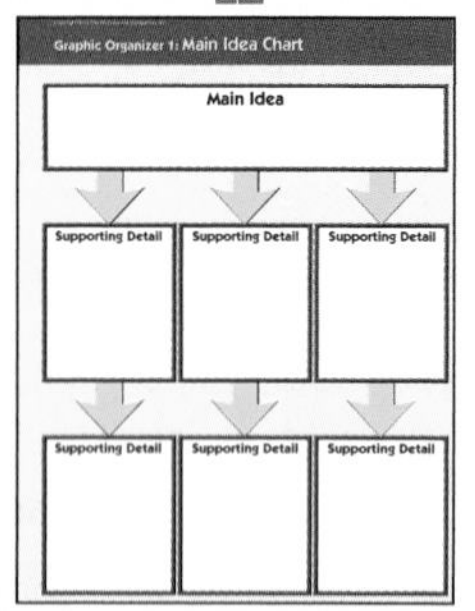

In-text Map Transparency L1

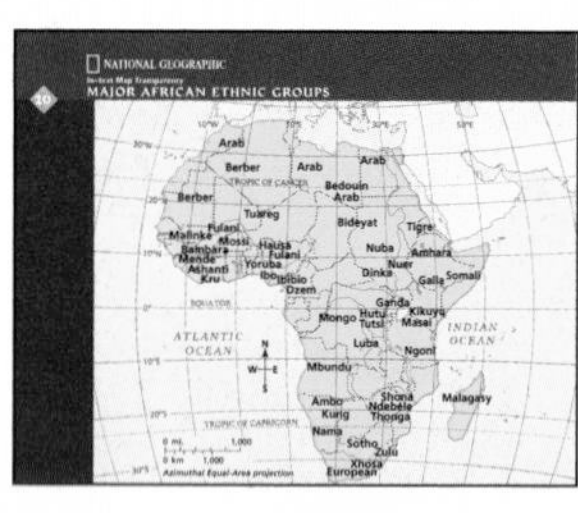

FOLDABLES™ Study Organizer

Dinah Zike's Foldables

Foldables are three-dimensional, interactive graphic organizers that help students practice basic writing skills, review key vocabulary terms, and identify main ideas. Additional chapter activities can be found in the *Reading and Study Skills Foldables* booklet.

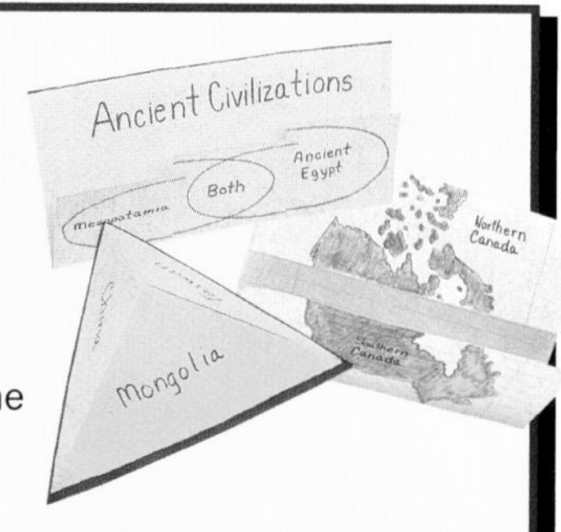

MAP AND GEOGRAPHY SKILLS

Chapter Map Activity L2

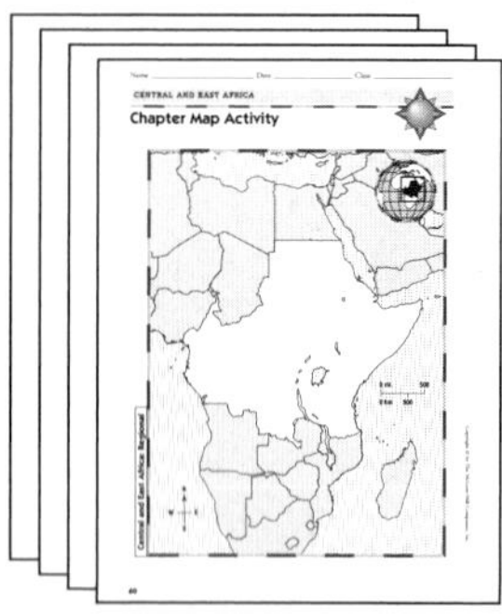

GeoLab Activity L2

READING SUPPORT

Vocabulary Activity L1

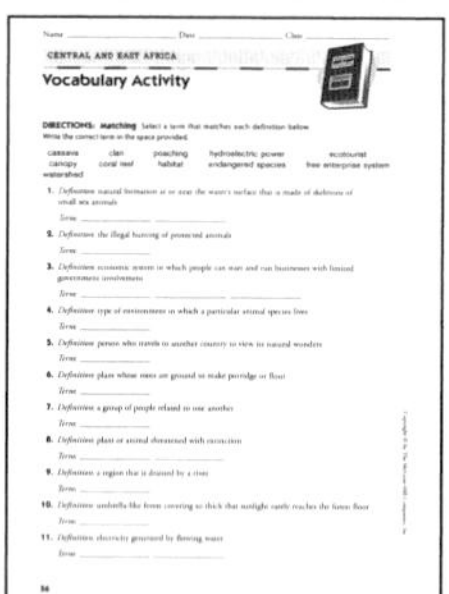

Workbook Activity L1

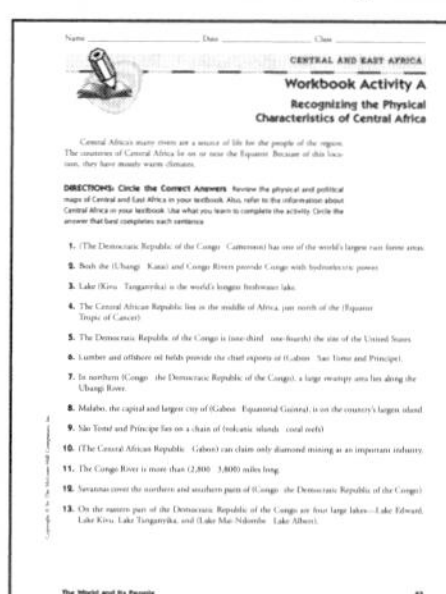

Reading and Writing Skills Activity L1/ELL

DIFFERENTIATED INSTRUCTION

Use these review and reinforcement materials to help less-proficient readers, English learners, and gifted and talented students.

Reteaching Activity L1

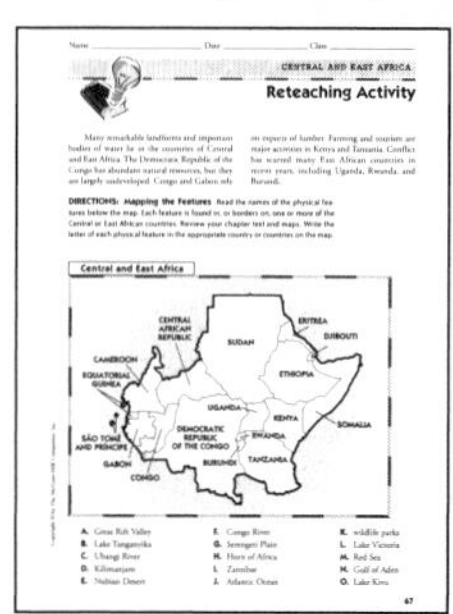

Chapter Skills Review L2

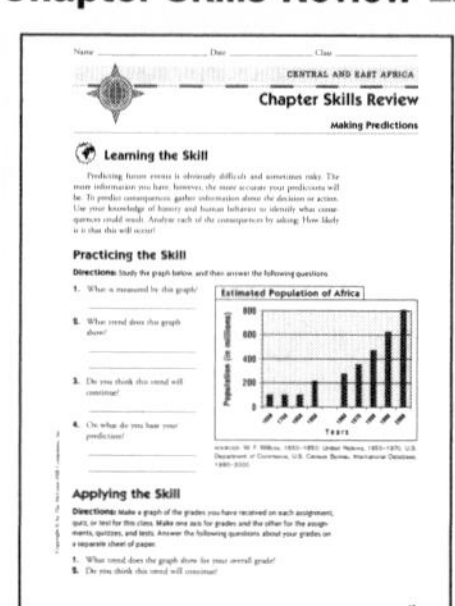

Cooperative Learning Activity L1/ELL

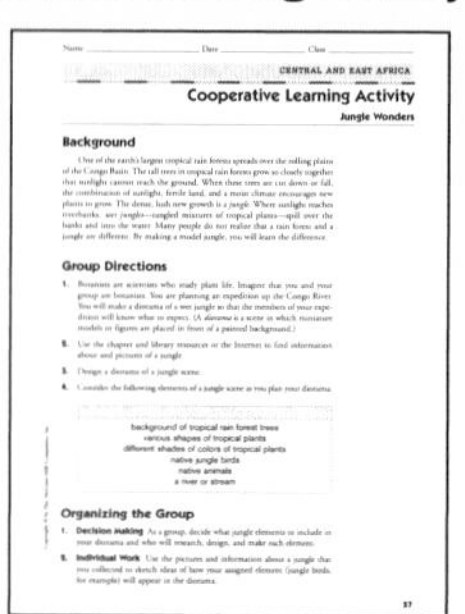

Enrichment Activity L3

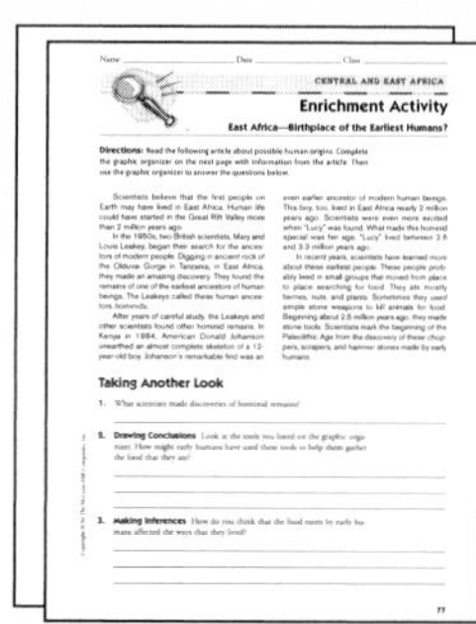

ASSESSMENT

Chapter Test, Form A L2

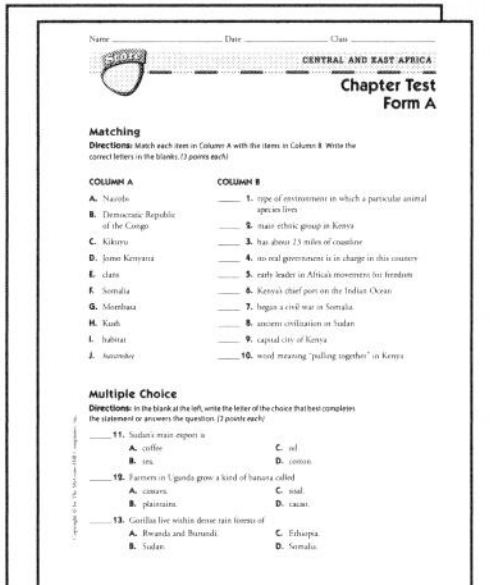

Chapter Test, Form B L2

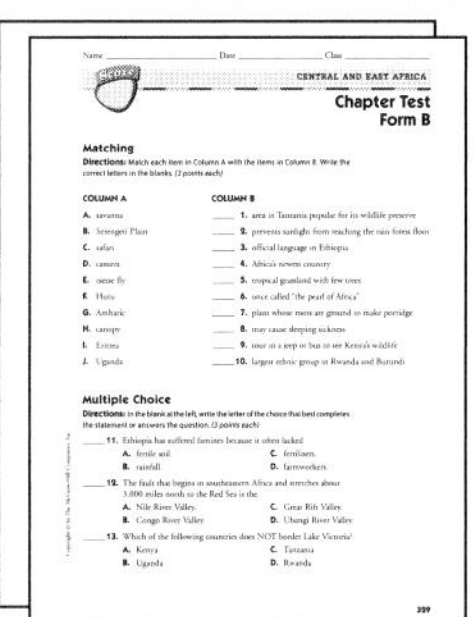

Performance Assessment Activity L1/ELL

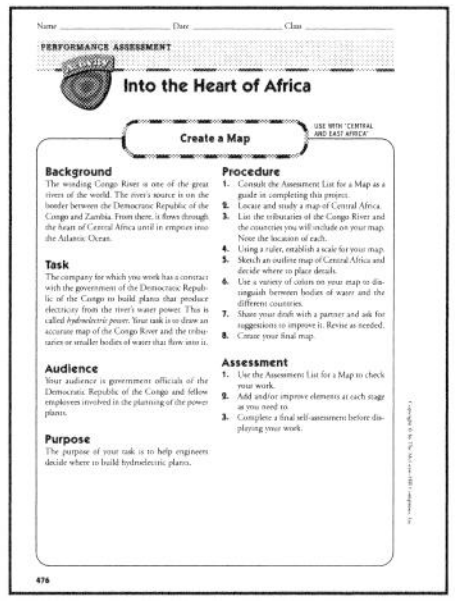

ExamView® Pro Testmaker CD-ROM

STANDARDIZED ASSESSMENT SKILLS

Critical Thinking Skills Activity L2

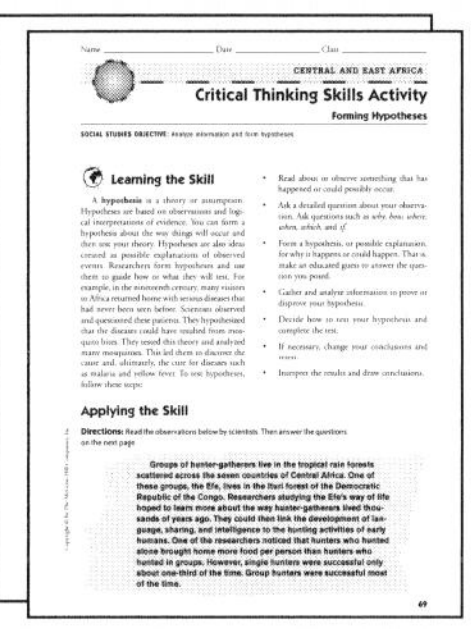

Map and Graph Skills Activity L2

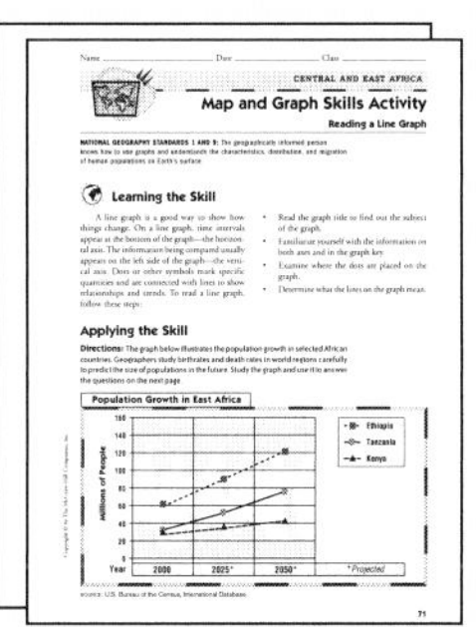

Standardized Test Skills Practice Workbook Activity L2

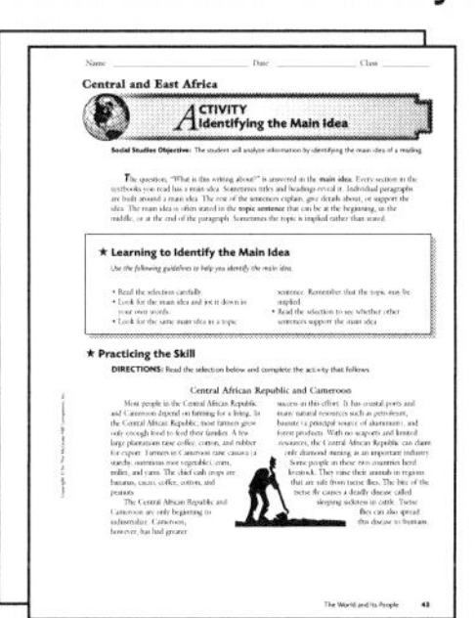

HOME INVOLVEMENT

Take-Home Review Activity L1

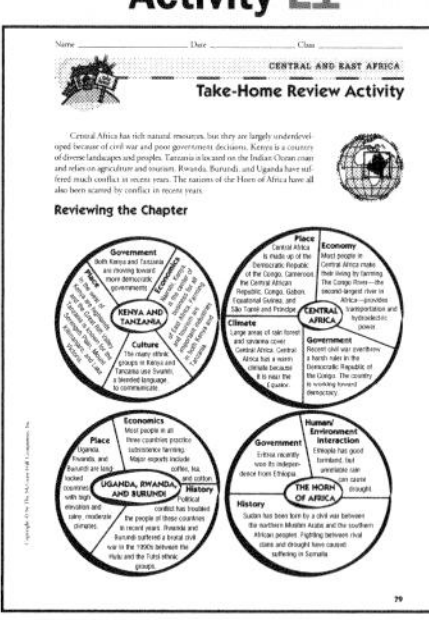

MULTIMEDIA

- National Geographic's The World and Its People
- MindJogger Videoquiz
- Vocabulary PuzzleMaker CD-ROM
- Interactive Tutor Self-Assessment CD-ROM
- ExamView® Pro Testmaker CD-ROM
- TeacherWorks CD-ROM
- StudentWorks CD-ROM
- Skillbuilder Interactive Workbook CD-ROM, Level 1
- Presentation Plus! CD-ROM
- Audio Program

SPANISH RESOURCES

The following Spanish language materials are available in the Spanish Resources binder:

- Spanish Summaries
- Spanish Vocabulary Activities
- Spanish Guided Reading Activities
- Spanish Quizzes and Tests
- Spanish Take-Home Review Activities
- Spanish Reteaching Activities

Meeting National Standards

Geography for Life

The following standards are covered in Chapter 20:

Section 1 — **EE4 Human Systems: Standards 9, 10, 12, 13**

Section 2 — **EE4 Human Systems: Standards 9, 10, 11, 13**
EE5 Environment and Society: Standards 14, 15, 16

Section 3 — **EE2 Places and Regions: Standards 4, 6**
EE4 Human Systems: Standards 9, 10, 12, 13
EE5 Environment and Society: Standard 14

Section 4 — **EE2 Places and Regions: Standards 4, 6**
EE5 Environment and Society: Standard 15

Chapter 20 Planning Guide

SECTION RESOURCES

Daily Objectives	Reproducible Resources	Multimedia Resources
Section 1 **Central Africa** 1. Describe the landforms found in the countries of Central Africa. 2. Explain the factors preventing countries from reaching their economic potential. 3. Compare the economies and people of the countries in this region.	Reproducible Lesson Plan Daily Lecture and Discussion Notes Note-taking Guide Guided Reading Activity* Reading Essentials and Study Guide* Section Quiz*	Daily Focus Skills Transparency GeoQuiz Transparency Vocabulary PuzzleMaker CD-ROM Interactive Tutor Self-Assessment CD-ROM ExamView® Pro Testmaker CD-ROM Presentation Plus! CD-ROM
Section 2 **People of Kenya and Tanzania** 1. Identify the landforms found in Kenya and Tanzania. 2. Describe the activities most important to these countries' economies. 3. Compare the histories and people of Kenya and Tanzania.	Reproducible Lesson Plan Daily Lecture and Discussion Notes Note-taking Guide Guided Reading Activity* Reading Essentials and Study Guide* Section Quiz*	Daily Focus Skills Transparency GeoQuiz Transparency Vocabulary PuzzleMaker CD-ROM Interactive Tutor Self-Assessment CD-ROM ExamView® Pro Testmaker CD-ROM Presentation Plus! CD-ROM
Section 3 **Uganda, Rwanda, and Burundi** 1. Explain how landforms affect the climates of Uganda, Rwanda, and Burundi. 2. Identify the farm products grown in these countries. 3. Describe how ethnic conflict has hurt these countries.	Reproducible Lesson Plan Daily Lecture and Discussion Notes Note-taking Guide Guided Reading Activity* Reading Essentials and Study Guide* Section Quiz*	Daily Focus Skills Transparency Vocabulary PuzzleMaker CD-ROM Interactive Tutor Self-Assessment CD-ROM ExamView® Pro Testmaker CD-ROM Presentation Plus! CD-ROM
Section 4 **The Horn of Africa** 1. Identify the landforms in the Horn of Africa. 2. Explain how the people of the region earn a living. 3. Describe the conflicts that have affected these countries.	Reproducible Lesson Plan Daily Lecture and Discussion Notes Note-taking Guide Guided Reading Activity* Reading Essentials and Study Guide* Section Quiz*	Daily Focus Skills Transparency In-text Map Transparency Vocabulary PuzzleMaker CD-ROM Interactive Tutor Self-Assessment CD-ROM ExamView® Pro Testmaker CD-ROM Presentation Plus! CD-ROM MindJogger Videoquiz

00:00 **Out of Time?** Assign the **Reading Essentials and Study Guide*** for this chapter.

*Also available in Spanish

KEY TO ABILITY LEVELS

Teaching strategies have been coded for varying learning styles and abilities.

- L1 **BASIC** activities for all students
- L2 **AVERAGE** activities for average to above-average students
- L3 **CHALLENGING** activities for above-average students
- ELL **ENGLISH LANGUAGE LEARNER** activities

KEY TO TEACHING RESOURCES

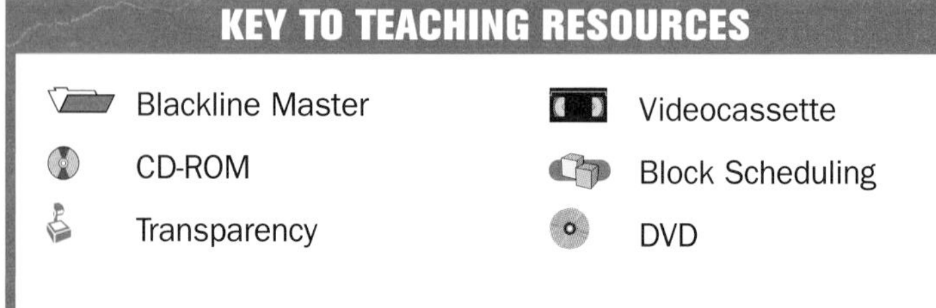

Solutions to Poaching

Dawn Forman
Hawthorne Junior/ Senior High
Gainesville, Florida

This is a cooperative learning activity in which students develop solutions to the problem of poaching in African countries such as Kenya, Uganda, and Rwanda. Organize students into groups and have groups use the Internet to research the causes of poaching. Students should find at least five Web sites to use as sources of information. Have students list as many options as they can think of. They should then consider each of their options, weighing the advantages and disadvantages, before arriving at solutions. Have each group prepare a poster highlighting the causes of poaching and at least two solutions to prevent poaching. This activity helps students feel like they can make a difference.

Meeting Special Needs

In addition to the Differentiated Instruction strategies found in each section, the following resources are also suitable for your special needs students:

- ***ExamView® Pro Testmaker CD-ROM*** allows teachers to tailor tests by reducing answer choices.
- The ***Audio Program*** includes the entire narrative of the student edition so that less-proficient readers can listen to the words as they read them.
- The ***Reading Essentials and Study Guide*** provides the same content as the student edition but is written two grade levels below the textbook.
- ***Guided Reading Activities*** give less-proficient readers point-by-point instructions to increase comprehension as they read each textbook section.
- ***Enrichment Activities*** include a stimulating collection of readings and activities for gifted and talented students.

NATIONAL GEOGRAPHIC TEACHER'S CORNER

Index to National Geographic Magazine:

The following articles may be used for research relating to this chapter:

- "Masai Passage to Manhood," by Carol Beckwith, September 1999.
- "Zanzibar's Endangered Red Colobus Monkey," by Tom Struhsaker, November 1998.
- "In Focus: Central Africa's Cycle of Violence," by Mike Edwards, June 1997.

National Geographic Society Products:

To order the following products for use with this chapter, call National Geographic Society at 1-800-368-2728:

- *Africa* (Video)
- *PicturePack: Ancient Civilizations: Ancient Africa* (Transparencies)
- *PictureShow: Ancient Civilizations: Africa* (CD-ROM)

NGS ONLINE

Access National Geographic's Web site for current events, activities, links, interactive features, and archives.
www.nationalgeographic.com

Find the latest coverage of geography in the news, atlas updates, cartographic activities with interactive maps, an online map store, and links at www.nationalgeographic.com/maps

SOCIAL STUDIES Online

Use our Web site for additional resources. All essential content is covered in the Student Edition.

You and your students can visit twip.glencoe.com, the Web site companion to *The World and Its People.* This innovative integration of electronic and print media offers your students a wealth of opportunities. The student text directs students to the Web site for the following options:

- Chapter Overviews
- Student Web Activities
- Self-Check Quizzes
- Textbook Updates

Answers are provided for you in the Web Activity Lesson Plan. Additional Web resources and Interactive Tutor puzzles are also available.

Introduce students to chapter content and key terms by having them access Chapter Overview 20 at twip.glencoe.com

Chapter Objectives

1. Compare the geography and cultures of the countries of Central Africa.
2. Describe the geography and economy of Kenya and Tanzania.
3. Describe the geography, history, and people of Uganda, Rwanda, and Burundi.
4. Explain the similarities and differences among the countries of the Horn of Africa.

GLENCOE TECHNOLOGY

NATIONAL GEOGRAPHIC

The World and Its People Video Program

Chapters 20 and 21
East and Central Africa
The following segments enhance the study of this chapter:

- **Korup National Forest**
- **Photographing Ndoki**
- **Great Rift Valley**
- **Gorillas**

MindJogger Videoquiz

Use MindJogger Videoquiz to preview the Chapter 20 content.

Both programs available in DVD and VHS

Chapter 20 Central and East Africa

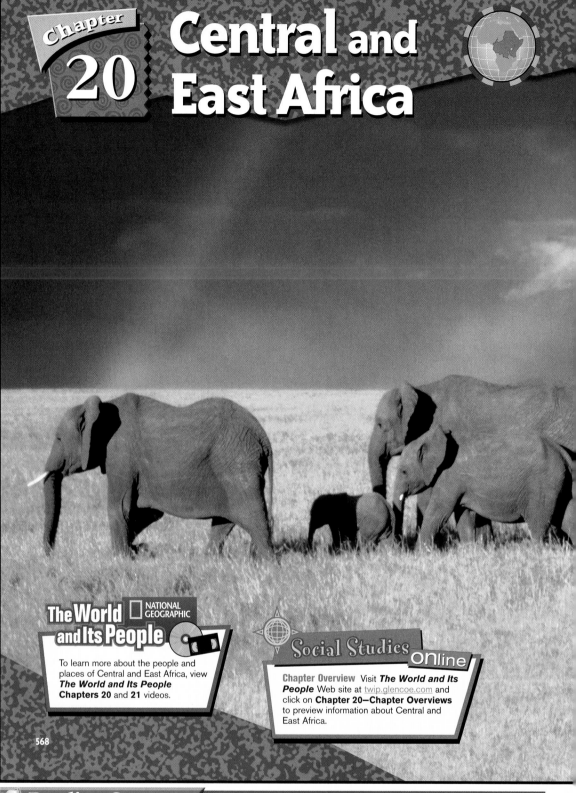

The World and Its People NATIONAL GEOGRAPHIC

To learn more about the people and places of Central and East Africa, view ***The World and Its People*** **Chapters 20** and **21** videos.

Social Studies Online

Chapter Overview Visit ***The World and Its People*** Web site at twip.glencoe.com and click on **Chapter 20—Chapter Overviews** to preview information about Central and East Africa.

568

Reading Strategy Purpose for Reading

Have students use **Free Writes** to think about Central and East Africa. Students should look at a physical map of Central and East Africa. Ask them to write about what the physical features of the area might reveal about how people live in the region. They may also comment on interesting geographical features. Emphasize that there are no wrong answers in this activity—it is important that all ideas are accepted. Students should then share their responses with the class. Conclude the activity by explaining that they will learn about this region and its people in this chapter. L1

FOLDABLES™ Study Organizer

Compare-Contrast Make this foldable to compare and contrast traditional and modern cultures in Central and East Africa.

Step 1 Fold one sheet of paper in half from side to side.

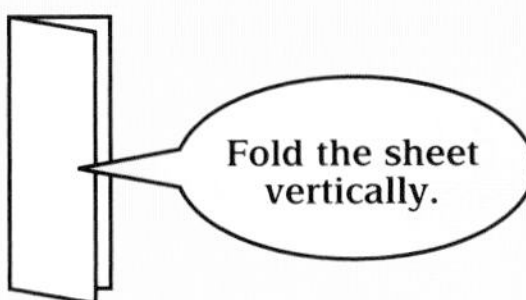

Step 2 Fold again, one inch from the top. (Tip: The middle knuckle of your index finger is about one inch long.)

Step 3 Open and label as shown.

Reading and Writing As you read this chapter, record information in the two columns of your foldable chart. Be sure to write the information you find in the appropriate column of your foldable.

▲ Elephants on the Serengeti Plain in Tanzania

Why It Matters

Rich in Heritage

Some of Africa's most important early civilizations flourished in the location that is now part of Central and East Africa. These societies grew to become large and complex as they developed the skills to master the region's difficult environment. They were successful farmers, herders, metalworkers, artisans, and merchants. Today the people of this region are facing difficult challenges just to survive.

About the Photo

Tanzania is home to five large national parks: Mikumi, Ngurdoto, Arusha, Manyara, and Serengeti. They cover 10,000 square miles. The parks' management is based on detailed studies of the ecology in each area. These studies are done by scientists funded by many international organizations. This ensures that the animals and plants are protected. Outside of these parks, employees of the Game Department of Tanzania not only have to fight poaching, but they must also protect crops. For example, elephants have often been known to damage banana and maize crops on the north edge of Manyara National Park. Sometimes game wardens have to shoot the same wild animals they are trying to protect.

Introducing
Chapter 20

FOLDABLES™ Study Organizer **Dinah Zike's Foldables**

Purpose Students will make and use a foldable to collect and organize information about traditional and modern cultures in East and Central Africa. Students will analyze similarities and differences of traditional cultures and modern cultures in East and Central Africa by using the foldable.

Have students complete the ***Reading and Study Skills Foldables*** activity for this chapter.

Why It Matters

Help students understand how the increase in life expectancy and population have caused a conflict between human interests and animal conservation. Ask them if they have ever had people stay at their house for a visit. Ask them how it felt to give up their beds and share living space. Then have them imagine that the guests decided to live with the family. How would they feel about the crowded living conditions? Imagine that these guests made it more difficult to get food. Now think of the "guests" as African people, and themselves as African wildlife. Tell students that with East African people living longer and more children surviving infancy, the population has increased dramatically in recent years. As people need more land, the animal habitat is shrinking.

Focus

Section Objectives

1. Describe the landforms found in the countries of Central Africa.
2. Explain the factors preventing countries from reaching their economic potential.
3. Compare the economies and people of the countries in this region.

BELLRINGER
Skillbuilder Activity

Project transparency and have students answer the question.

Daily Focus Skills Transparency

Interpreting Cause-and-Effect Relationships

Historic Flags of the Democratic Republic of the Congo

1885–1960

1963–1971

1960–1963

1971–Present

What do you think might cause a country to change its national flag?

Reading Preview

Activating Prior Knowledge Ask students what kind of natural resources are valuable to a country. Explain that they will read about Central Africa, which has all of these resources, but they are undeveloped.

Preteaching Vocabulary Consult a dictionary and read aloud definitions of *canopy*. Have students discuss why the treetops in rain forests are called a canopy. *(They form a covering for the forest.)*

Guide to Reading

Main Idea

Central Africa has rich natural resources that are largely undeveloped because of civil war and poor government decisions.

Terms to Know

- canopy
- hydroelectric power
- tsetse fly
- deforestation

Reading Strategy

Create a chart like this one. Choose two countries of Central Africa. Then list two facts about the people of each country.

Country	Fact #1	Fact #2

Section 1 Central Africa

NATIONAL GEOGRAPHIC Exploring Our World

In the 2000 Olympic Summer Games, the gold medal in men's soccer went to Cameroon's team, the Indomitable Lions. The streets of Cameroon's capital, Yaoundé, and other cities were jammed with wildly excited fans screaming with joy. Cameroon's president even declared the following Monday a national holiday to celebrate the victory.

Central Africa includes seven countries. They are the **Democratic Republic of the Congo, Cameroon,** the **Central African Republic, Congo, Gabon** (ga•BOHN), **Equatorial Guinea,** and **São Tomé** (sow too•MAY) **and Príncipe** (PRIHN•sih•pee). Africa's second-longest river—the **Congo River**—flows through the center of the Democratic Republic of the Congo in the very heart of Africa.

Democratic Republic of the Congo

One-fourth the size of the United States, the Democratic Republic of the Congo has only about 23 miles (37 km) of coastline. Most of its land borders other African countries—nine in all.

High, rugged mountains rise in the eastern part of the country. Here you will find four large lakes—Lake Albert, Lake Edward, Lake Kivu, and Lake Tanganyika. **Lake Tanganyika** is the longest freshwater lake in the world. It is also the second deepest, after Russia's Lake Baikal. Savannas, or tropical grasslands with few trees, cover the highlands in the far north and south of the country. In these areas, lions and leopards stalk antelopes and zebras for food.

Section Resources

Reproducible Masters

- Reproducible Lesson Plan
- Daily Lecture and Discussion Notes
- Note-taking Guide
- Guided Reading Activity
- Reading Essentials and Study Guide
- Section Quiz

Transparencies

- Daily Focus Skills Transparency
- GeoQuiz Transparency

Multimedia

- Vocabulary PuzzleMaker CD-ROM
- Interactive Tutor Self-Assessment CD-ROM
- Presentation Plus! CD-ROM
- ExamView® Pro Testmaker CD-ROM

One of the world's largest rain forests covers the center of the Democratic Republic of the Congo. The treetops form a **canopy**, or an umbrella-like forest covering. The canopy is so thick that sunlight rarely reaches the forest floor. More than 750 different kinds of trees grow here. The rain forests are being destroyed at a rapid rate, however, as they are cleared for timber and farmland.

The mighty Congo River—about 2,800 miles (4,506 km) long—weaves its way through the country on its journey to the Atlantic Ocean. The river current is so strong that it carries freshwater about 100 miles (161 km) into the ocean. The Congo River and its tributaries, such as the Kasai River, provide **hydroelectric power**, or electricity generated by flowing water. In fact, these rivers produce more than 10 percent of all the world's hydroelectric power. The Congo River is also the country's highway for trade and travel.

Resources and Industry The Democratic Republic of the Congo has the opportunity to be a wealthy nation. The country exports gold, petroleum, diamonds, and copper. It is a main source of diamonds, as shown on the graph below. Most of these diamonds are used in strong industrial tools that cut metal. The country's factories make steel, cement, tires, shoes, textiles, processed foods, and beverages.

The Democratic Republic of the Congo has not been able to take full advantage of its rich resources, however. Why? One reason is the difficulty of transportation. Many of the minerals are found deep in the country's interior. Lack of roads and the thick rain forests make it hard to reach these areas. Another reason is political unrest. For many years, power-hungry leaders kept the nation's wealth for themselves. Then a

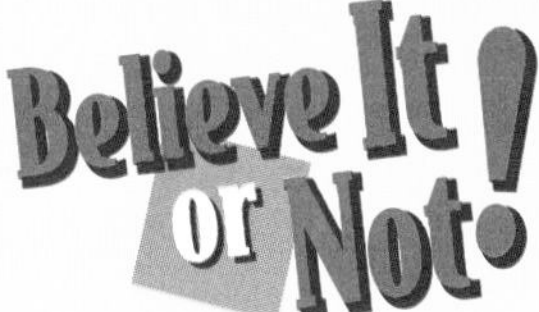

The Okapi

The Democratic Republic of the Congo is the only home for the okapi (oh•KAH•pee). With its long, tough tongue, the okapi pulls leaves off the branches of young trees. Its tongue is so long that the okapi can use it to clean its eyes.

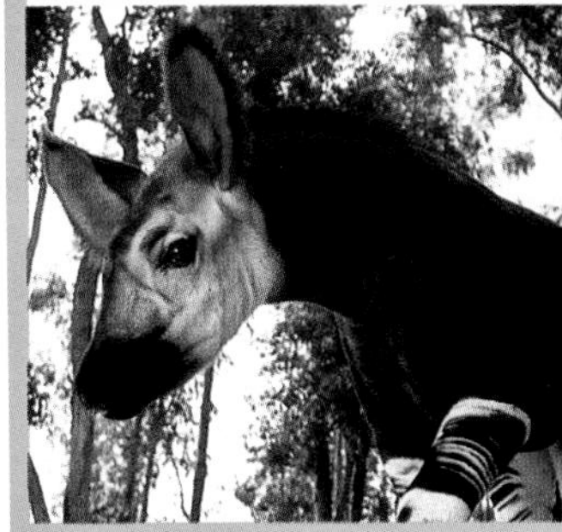

NATIONAL GEOGRAPHIC

Leading Diamond-Producing Countries

Analyzing the Graph

Three of the world's top diamond-producing countries are in Africa south of the Sahara.

Economics **Which two countries produce the most diamonds in Africa?**

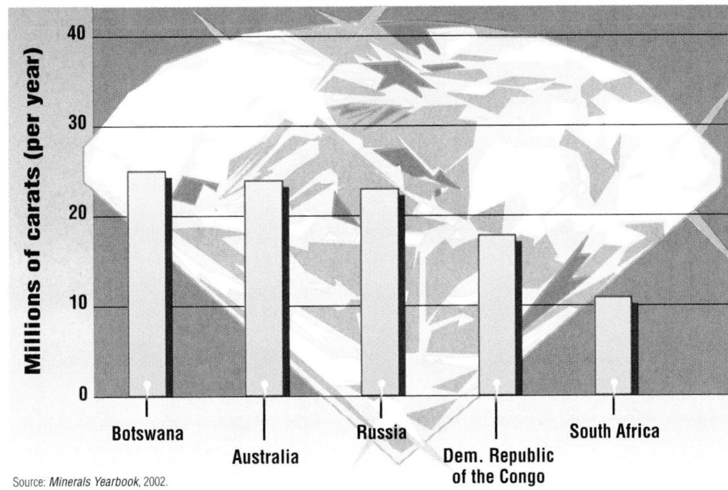

Textbook Update

Visit twip.glencoe.com and click on **Chapter 20—Textbook Updates.**

Chapter 20

Section 1, pages 570–575

2 Teach

Analyzing a Map Have students look at the physical map of Africa in the Reference Atlas. Have them locate the Democratic Republic of the Congo and note its location in relation to other countries. Have them speculate on how its size, location, and short coastline might affect its history and economic development. Tell them to write their ideas and check them as they study the section. **L1**

Daily Lecture and Discussion Notes

CENTRAL AND EAST AFRICA

Daily Lecture and Discussion Notes

Central Africa

Did You Know? Music is a major art in the Democratic Republic of the Congo. The rhythm of drums dominates Congolese music. Urban Congolese have developed their own form of jazz, which blends elements of modern jazz and traditional Congolese music.

I. Democratic Republic of the Congo

A. Mountains rise in the eastern part of the Democratic Republic of the Congo. Four lakes are found here—Lake Albert, Lake Edward, Lake Kivu, and Lake Tanganyika. Savannas cover the highlands in the far north and south of the country. In these areas, lions and leopards stalk antelopes and zebras for food.

...ests covers the center of the Democratic

Analyzing the Graph

Answer

Botswana and the Democratic Republic of the Congo

Skills Practice

About how many diamonds are produced each year in the Democratic Republic of the Congo? *(about 18,000,000 carats)*

Reading Strategy — Reading the Text

Drawing Conclusions Have students list obstacles to the economic development of the Democratic Republic of the Congo. Next, have them identify and list the country's major resources. Then encourage students to use this information to draw conclusions about the most serious economic challenges facing the people of this country. Finally, have them suggest steps that people could take to try to overcome those challenges, including future technological innovations. **L1**

*Use the **Reading Skills Handbook** for more reading strategies.*

Applying Map Skills

Answers

1. Kenya, Tanzania, Uganda
2. Ethiopia

Skills Practice

How does Central Africa's elevation change as you move from west to east? *(The elevation increases.)*

Cultural Kaleidoscope

Democratic Republic of the Congo Among the ethnic groups living in this vast land are the Mbuti—people who grow no higher than about 59 inches (150 cm) of adult height. The Mbuti live a nomadic, hunter-gatherer life.

Measure student knowledge of physical features.

GeoQuiz Transparency

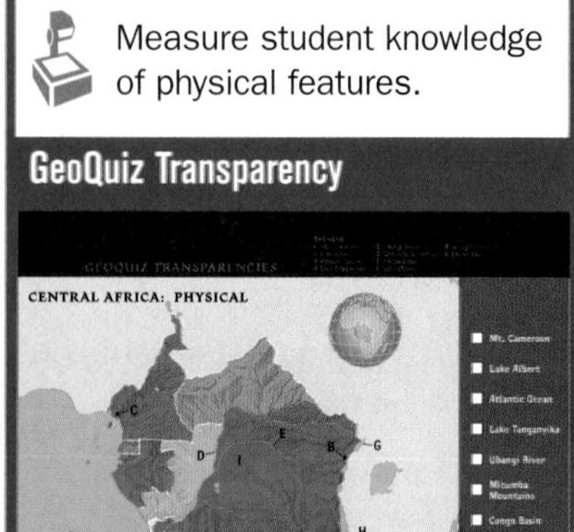

civil war broke out in the late 1990s. This war hurt efforts to develop the country's economy. In 2002 an agreement was signed by all remaining warring parties to end the fighting.

The Congolese People The Democratic Republic of the Congo's 56.6 million people consist of more than 200 different ethnic groups. One of these groups is the Kongo people, after whom the country is named. The country's official language is French, but many people speak local languages, such as Lingala or Kingwana. More than 75 percent of Congolese are Christians, mostly Roman Catholic.

Most Congolese people live in rural, or country, areas. Less than one-third are city dwellers. Still, **Kinshasa,** the capital, has about 6 million people. Because of civil war, life in this country is unsettled. Many people in the cities are without work.

In rural areas, people follow traditional ways of life. They plant seeds, tend fields, and harvest crops. Most of the harvest goes to feeding the

NATIONAL GEOGRAPHIC

Central and East Africa: Physical

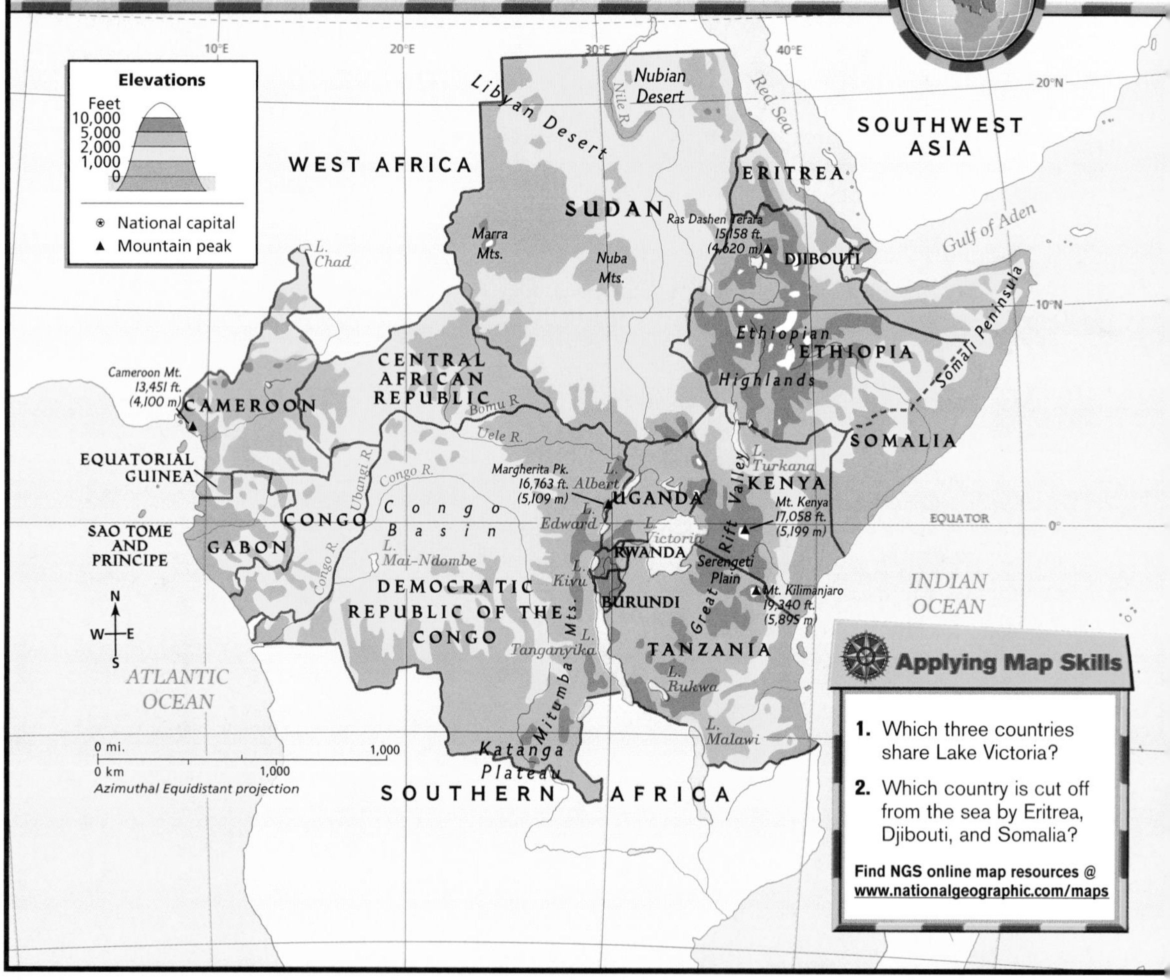

Applying Map Skills

1. Which three countries share Lake Victoria?
2. Which country is cut off from the sea by Eritrea, Djibouti, and Somalia?

Find NGS online map resources @ www.nationalgeographic.com/maps

Differentiated Instruction

Meeting Special Needs: Verbal/Linguistic Suggest that students who learn better verbally re-create the information in the maps and charts in the chapter in verbal form. Have them review each map to identify what information they can learn. Guide students' observations by asking questions such as: **What physical features influence the climate of these countries? Which ethnic groups live in each country? What resources influence economic activities in these countries?** Then have them write their findings in sentences and use these as study aids. **L1**

Refer to *Inclusion for the Middle School Social Studies Classroom Strategies and Activities* in the TCR.

family. Any extra goes to the local market—or to the boats moving along the rivers—to sell or trade for goods the people need.

History and Government The Congo region was first settled about 10,000 years ago. The Bantu people—ancestors of most of the Congolese people today—moved here from Nigeria around the A.D. 600s and 700s. Several powerful kingdoms arose in the savannas south of the rain forests. The largest of these was the Kongo.

In the late 1400s, European traders arrived in Central Africa. During the next 300 years, European and African agents enslaved many people from the Congo region. Most of these Africans were transported to the Americas.

NATIONAL GEOGRAPHIC **On Location**

Market Day

This marketplace in Kinshasa, Democratic Republic of the Congo, is bustling with activity.

Culture How is this market different from where your family shops? How is it similar?

The current Democratic Republic of the Congo was once a European colony. It became independent in 1960 and was named Zaire. A harsh dictator named Mobutu Sese Seko ruled Zaire until civil wars in neighboring Rwanda and Burundi sparked a civil war in Zaire. In 1997 Mobutu's government was finally overthrown, and again the country was given a new name. Zaire became the Democratic Republic of the Congo and another dictator took power. In 2002 the country began to set up a representative government and is still working on the transition.

✓ Reading Check **What was the Democratic Republic of the Congo formerly called?**

Cameroon and the Central African Republic

Find Cameroon and the Central African Republic on the map on page 572. These countries lie just north of the Equator. Most people in the Central African Republic and Cameroon farm for a living. A few large plantations raise cacao, cotton, tobacco, and rubber for export. Some people herd livestock in areas that are safe from tsetse flies. A parasite that is often transmitted by the bite of the **tsetse (SEET•see) fly** causes a deadly disease called sleeping sickness. Turn to page 576 to find out more about sleeping sickness.

These two countries are only beginning to industrialize, or base their economies more on manufacturing and less on farming. Cameroon has had greater success in this effort. It has coastal ports and forest products, petroleum, and bauxite. The Central African Republic can claim only diamond mining as an important industry.

Chapter 20

Section 1, pages 570–575

More About the Photo

Market Day Farmers grow cassava, plantains, corn, rice, beans, and peanuts. Surplus harvest goes to market. At this market in Kinshasa, the Democratic Republic of the Congo's capital, located along the Congo River, there is a wide variety of goods traded. The Congo links shoppers and merchants to this nation's only ocean port at Matadi.

Caption Answer enclosed supermarkets vs. open air, crowding, packaging, bartering vs. money use; comparable to farmers' markets, people get the goods they need

✓ Reading Check Answer

Zaire

L1/ELL

Guided Reading Activity

Name ______ Date ______ Class ______

CENTRAL AND EAST AFRICA

Guided Reading Activity 1

Central Africa

DIRECTIONS: Reading for Accuracy Reading the section and completing the activity below will help you learn more about Central Africa. Refer to your textbook to decide if a statement is true or false. Write **T** or **F**, and if a statement is false, rewrite it correctly.

____ 1. The Democratic Republic of the Congo is half the size of the United States.

____ 2. Four lakes—Lake Albert, Lake Edward, Lake Kivu, and Lake Tanganyika—are all found in the eastern part of the country.

____ 3. The Democratic Republic of the Congo has taken advantage of all of its resources and is, therefore, a wealthy nation.

____ 4. One of the four major ethnic groups is the Kongo people after whom the country was named.

____ 5. The countries of Cameroon and the Central African Republic are located south of the Equator.

____ 6. The people of both countries farm for a living.

____ 7. The Central African Republic has several important industries.

____ 8. Both Congo and Gabon were once ruled by France.

____ 9. The Ubangi River supports much of Congo's farmlands and industries.

____ 10. The main economic activities of Equatorial Guinea are farming, fishing, and forestry.

____ 11. The biggest crop export of São Tomé and Príncipe is timber.

82

Team-Teaching Activity

History Invite a teacher with a background in world history to class to explain how the legacy of colonialism has caused problems for the countries of Africa. The discussion could include such points as the failure of European countries to train people who could administer government functions, the generally inadequate educational systems, national borders made problematic by ethnic differences, and damaging economic policies. Specifics from the history of the Democratic Republic of the Congo could be used to exemplify these problems. Have students discuss what role the United States might play today to help African nations overcome their challenges. L1 

EE2 Places and Regions: Standard 6

More About the Photos

Rural Living In equatorial countries, the weather is hot and rainy. People want houses that will shelter them from the rain but that will allow air to circulate. In Gabon, lumber is abundant, so wooden roofs are common. The eastern Democratic Republic of the Congo is a grassland, so thatched roofs are used.

Caption Answer Climate and available materials influence house styles.

Reading Check Answer

It has a greater variety of resources and coastal ports that can be used to ship goods.

Reading Check Answer

lumber and oil

ASSESS

Assign Section 1 Assessment as homework or an in-class activity.

Have students use the Interactive Tutor Self-Assessment CD-ROM to review Section 1.

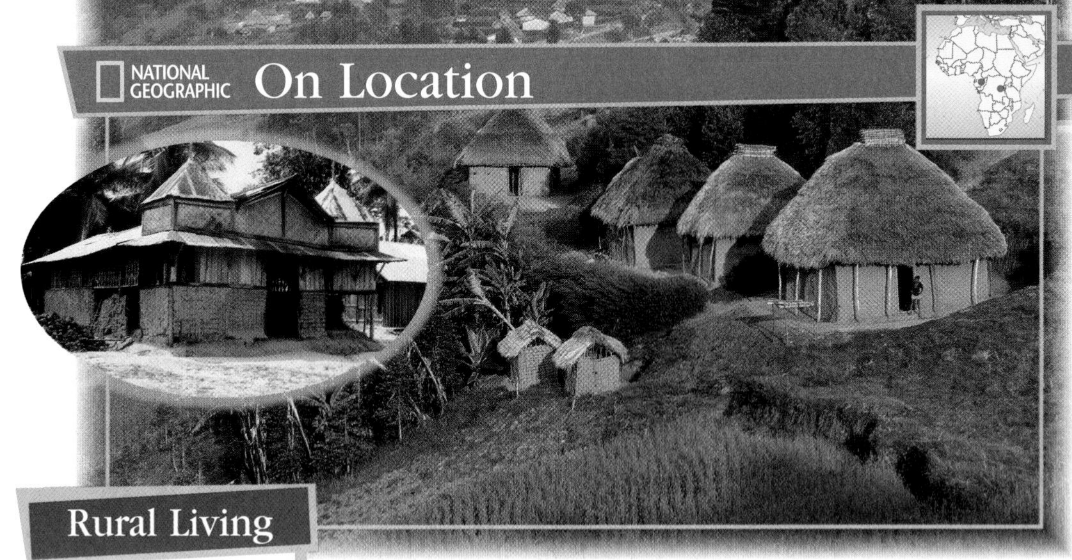

NATIONAL GEOGRAPHIC On Location

Rural Living

A row of thatch houses stands in a village in rural Democratic Republic of the Congo (right). This village in Gabon (above) boasts a very different type of house.

Culture **Why might house styles differ from country to country?**

A colony of France from 1910 until 1960, the Central African Republic recognizes French as its official language. Yet most of its people speak Sango, the national language of the Central African Republic. This helps ease communication among the many ethnic groups. Cameroon was divided between the British and the French until 1960. As a result, it uses both English and French as its official languages.

Reading Check **Why has Cameroon had greater success than the Central African Republic in industrializing?**

Congo and Gabon

Congo and Gabon both won their independence from France in 1960. A plain stretches along the Atlantic coast of Congo and rises to low mountain ranges and plateaus. Here the Congo River supports most of the country's farmlands and industries. To the north, a large swampy area along the Ubangi River supports dense vine thickets and tropical trees. Both the Ubangi and Congo Rivers provide Congo with hydroelectric power. They also provide access to the Atlantic Ocean for trade and transport.

More than half of Congo's and Gabon's people farm small plots of land. Both countries' economies rely on exports of lumber. They are beginning to depend more on rich offshore oil fields, however, for their main export. Congo also exports diamonds. Gabon suffers from deforestation, or the widespread cutting of too many trees. Gabon also has valuable deposits of manganese and uranium.

Only about 1.3 million people live in Gabon—mainly along rivers or in the coastal capital, **Libreville.** Congo's 3.7 million people generally live along the Atlantic coast or near the capital, **Brazzaville.**

Reading Check **What two exports are most important to Congo and Gabon?**

Cooperative Learning Activity

Travel Brochure Put students into groups to create a four-page travel brochure that highlights the attractions of one of the countries in this chapter. Explain that the travel brochure should include both physical and cultural features that visitors would want to see. Remind students that one part of the brochure should have practical information such as clothing appropriate for climate, language(s) used in the country, and currency. Advise students that an effective brochure includes appealing visuals as well as brief, engaging text. **L2**

EE2 Places and Regions: Standard 4

Island Countries

Once a Spanish colony, Equatorial Guinea won its independence in 1968. Equatorial Guinea includes land on the mainland of Africa and five islands. Today the country is home to about 500,000 people. Most live on the mainland, although the capital and largest city—**Malabo** (mah•LAH•boh)—is on the country's largest island.

Farming, fishing, and forestry are the country's main economic activities. For many years, timber and cacao grown in the islands' rich volcanic soil were the main exports. Oil was recently discovered and now leads all other exports.

The island country of São Tomé and Príncipe gained its independence from Portugal in 1975. The Portuguese had first settled here about 300 years earlier. At that time, no people lived on the islands. Today about 200,000 people live here, with almost all of them living on the main island of São Tomé.

São Tomé and Príncipe are volcanic islands. As a result, the soil is rich and productive. Farmers on the islands grow various crops, including coconuts and bananas for export. The biggest export crop is cacao, which is used to make cocoa and chocolate.

✓ Reading Check Which of these island countries is also located on the African mainland?

Section 1 Assessment

Defining Terms

1. **Define** canopy, hydroelectric power, tsetse fly, deforestation.

Recalling Facts

2. **Economics** Why has the Democratic Republic of the Congo not been able to take full advantage of its resources?
3. **Place** How has Cameroon's location helped it prosper?
4. **Economics** What natural resource was recently discovered in Equatorial Guinea?

Critical Thinking

5. **Evaluating Information** Why do you think Europeans wanted to colonize parts of Africa such as the Congo?
6. **Understanding Cause and Effect** How could furniture buyers in the United States affect lumber exports in Central Africa?

Graphic Organizer

7. **Organizing Information** Complete a chart like this with one fact about each country.

Country	Fact
Democratic Republic of the Congo	
Cameroon	
Central African Republic	
Congo	
Gabon	
Equatorial Guinea	
São Tomé & Príncipe	

Applying Social Studies Skills

8. **Analyzing Maps** Study the physical map on page 572. The Ubangi River forms part of the boundaries of which countries?

Section 1 Assessment

1. The terms are defined in the Glossary.
2. because transportation is difficult and there is political unrest
3. Cameroon has coastal ports that stimulate trade and bring both money and goods into the country.
4. oil
5. *Possible answer:* Europeans desired natural resources in the region.
6. Answers should focus on the desire of American buyers for the valuable woods in the region. If deforestation decreases the supply of wood for international trade, the economies of Central Africa will slump.
7. Answers will vary.
8. Central African Republic, Congo, and Democratic Republic of the Congo

Chapter 20

Section 1, pages 570–575

L2

Section Quiz

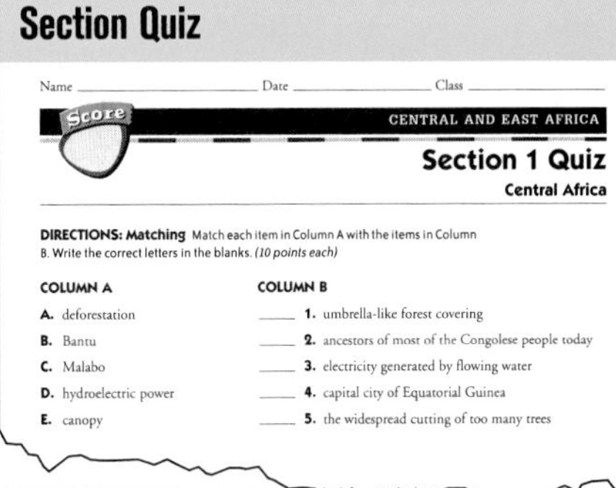

Name ______ Date ______ Class ______

Score

CENTRAL AND EAST AFRICA

Section 1 Quiz

Central Africa

DIRECTIONS: Matching Match each item in Column A with the items in Column B. Write the correct letters in the blanks. *(10 points each)*

COLUMN A	COLUMN B
A. deforestation	____ 1. umbrella-like forest covering
B. Bantu	____ 2. ancestors of most of the Congolese people today
C. Malabo	____ 3. electricity generated by flowing water
D. hydroelectric power	____ 4. capital city of Equatorial Guinea
E. canopy	____ 5. the widespread cutting of too many trees

✓ Reading Check Answer

Equatorial Guinea

L1/ELL

Reading Essentials and Study Guide

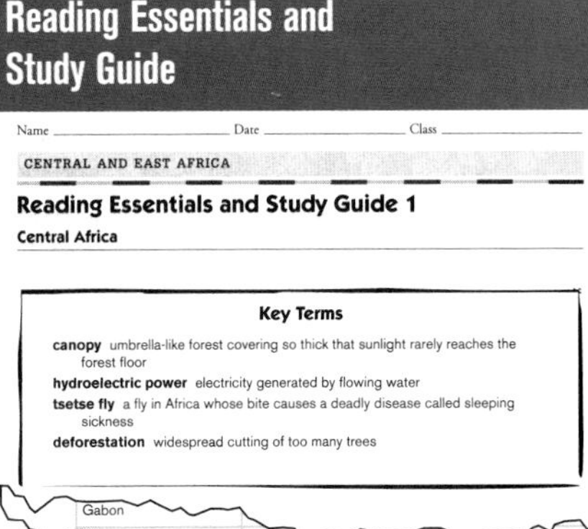

Name ______ Date ______ Class ______

CENTRAL AND EAST AFRICA

Reading Essentials and Study Guide 1

Central Africa

Key Terms

canopy umbrella-like forest covering so thick that sunlight rarely reaches the forest floor
hydroelectric power electricity generated by flowing water
tsetse fly a fly in Africa whose bite causes a deadly disease called sleeping sickness
deforestation widespread cutting of too many trees

4 CLOSE

Reading Strategy

Writing a Paragraph Have students take an imaginary trip along the Congo River and describe in a paragraph the landscapes they would see.

Teach

Point out that there are two kinds of diseases. Noncommunicable diseases are based on inheritance or lifestyle, whereas communicable diseases are spread by contact. Ask students if they have ever had a cold or flu. Point out that these are common diseases spread from one person to another. Explain that some diseases are transmitted by contact with animals. L1

More About Tsetse Flies

The threat of sleeping sickness has had a significant impact on settlement patterns in Africa. People avoid areas with large numbers of these flies, cutting down on the land that can be used for farming and other purposes.

Interdisciplinary Connections

Science Malaria is another dangerous disease that afflicts people in Africa, as well as in other areas of the world. Have students research the disease to find out where it is found, what causes the disease, what health problems it causes, how it is treated, and what steps are being taken to prevent it. Have them present their findings to the class in an illustrated report or oral presentation.

Making Connections

ART | SCIENCE | CULTURE | TECHNOLOGY

Battling Sleeping Sickness

Since the 1300s, people in Africa south of the Sahara have battled a disease now commonly called sleeping sickness. Yet it was not until the early 1900s that scientists began to understand the disease and that it was transmitted through the bite of an infected tsetse fly.

The Tsetse Fly

Found only in parts of Africa, the tsetse fly is the common name for any of about 21 species of flies that can transmit sleeping sickness. The flies are larger than the houseflies common to the United States. Tsetse flies thrive in forests and in areas of thick shrubbery and trees near lakes, ponds, and rivers.

Although the bite of a tsetse fly is painful, the bite itself is not necessarily harmful. What gives the tsetse fly its dreadful reputation is the disease-causing parasite it may carry.

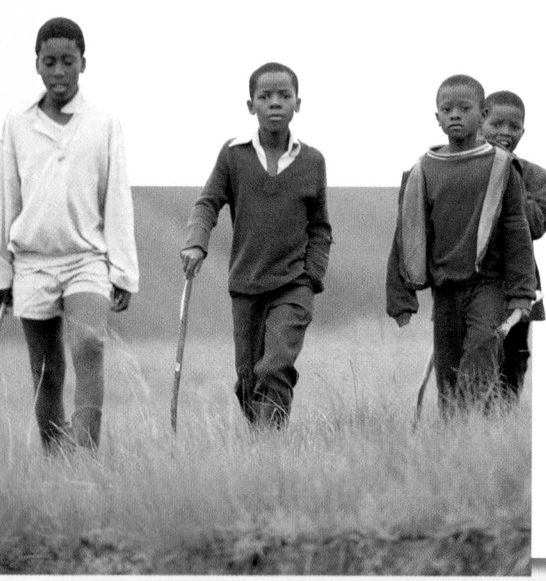

Sleeping Sickness

The World Health Organization (WHO) estimates that more than 60 million people in Africa are at risk of being infected with sleeping sickness. As many as 500,000 people carry the disease. If left untreated, the disease leads to a slow breakdown of bodily functions and, eventually, death. Sleeping sickness is not always fatal. When the disease is treated in its early stages, most people recover. Treatment is expensive, however, and many of those infected lack medical care. Even if they are cured, they may become infected again.

Governments Work Together

Preventing the spread of sleeping sickness requires a united action on the part of the governments of the many African nations affected by the disease. Thirty-seven African countries lie within the African tsetse belt. This belt covers a total of more than 6 million square miles (10 million sq. km) in an area stretching from Senegal to South Africa. African leaders have met in conferences and passed a resolution to get rid of tsetse flies from the continent. Perhaps working together to fight a common enemy will encourage the governments to consult on other regional issues as well.

Making the Connection

1. Where do tsetse flies live?
2. What causes sleeping sickness?
3. **Drawing Conclusions** Why is treatment of infected humans only part of the solution to eliminating sleeping sickness?

◀ **Children in Central Africa have learned to report bites of the tsetse fly.**

Making the Connection

1. in forests and thick shrubbery near lakes, ponds, and rivers in some areas of Africa south of the Sahara
2. a parasite that some tsetse flies carry
3. Natural areas where the flies live must be cleared to reduce the number of flies, which will limit the danger to people. In addition, animals that have the parasite need to be removed so that the parasite is not spread.

Section 2

People of Kenya and Tanzania

Guide to Reading

Main Idea

Kenya and Tanzania are countries in East Africa with diverse landscapes and peoples.

Terms to Know

- coral reef
- poaching
- free enterprise system
- cassava
- sisal
- habitat
- ecotourist

Reading Strategy

Create a chart like this one. Then list facts about the land, economy, and people of Kenya and Tanzania.

Fact	Kenya	Tanzania
Land		
Economy		
People		

NATIONAL GEOGRAPHIC **Exploring Our World**

The Masai (mah•SY) are one of Kenya's many ethnic groups. Rituals have shaped their lives for hundreds of years. Young men take part in an important four-day ceremony. When it ends, they become elders and help make group decisions. In the ceremony, elders tell them, "Drop your weapons and use your head and wisdom instead."

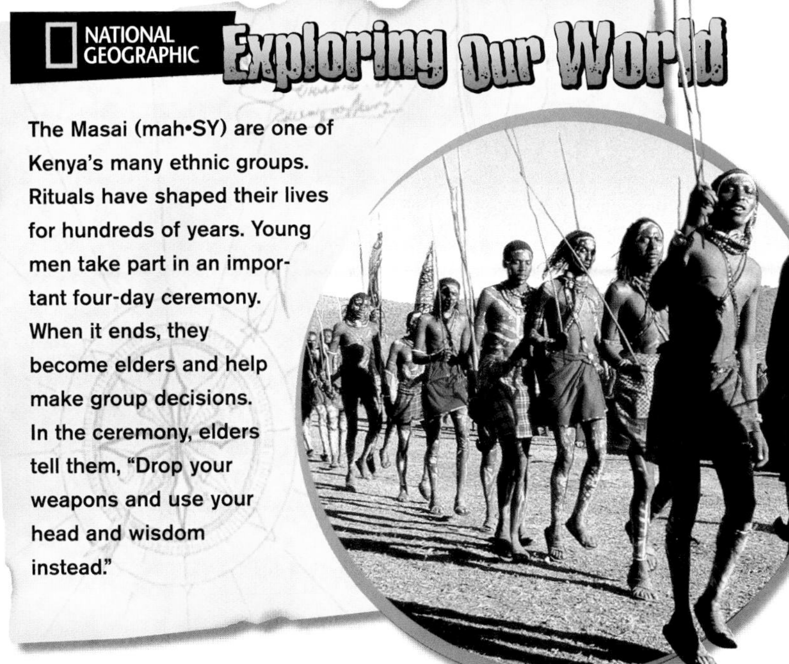

Both traditional and modern cultures meet in the East African country of **Kenya.** The Masai follow ways of life similar to their ancestors, whereas city dwellers live in apartments and work in offices.

Kenya

Kenya is about two times the size of Nevada. The country's Indian Ocean coastline has stretches of white beaches lined with palm trees. Offshore lies a **coral reef,** a natural formation at or near the water's surface that is made of the skeletons of small sea animals. In the central part of the country, lions, elephants, rhinoceroses, and other wildlife roam an upland plain. Millions of acres are set aside by the government to protect plants and wildlife. Still, in recent years there has been heavy **poaching,** or the illegal hunting of protected animals.

In the western part of the country are highlands and the **Great Rift Valley.** This valley is really a fault—a crack in the earth's crust.

577

1 Focus

Section Objectives

1. Identify the landforms found in Kenya and Tanzania.
2. Describe the activities most important to these countries' economies.
3. Compare the histories and people of Kenya and Tanzania.

BELLRINGER Skillbuilder Activity

Project transparency and have students answer the question.

Daily Focus Skills Transparency

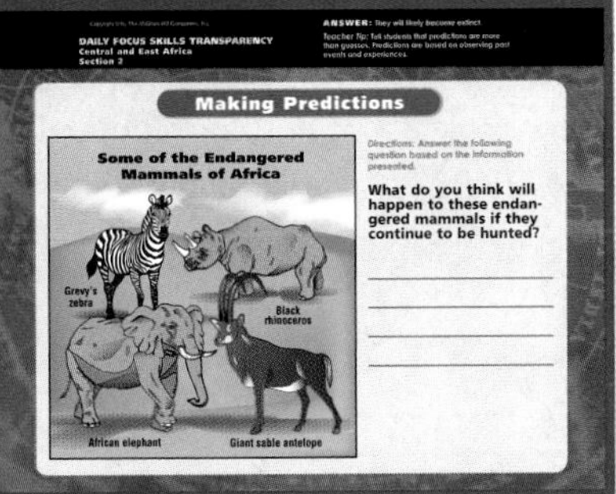

Reading Preview

■ **Activating Prior Knowledge** **Ask:** What do you think of when you hear the word *Africa?* Most students think of wildlife, the hot climate, and different cultures. Tell students that Kenya has a mix of both traditional and modern cultures.

■ **Preteaching Vocabulary** Have students sound out any unfamiliar word syllable by syllable.

Section Resources

Reproducible Masters

- Reproducible Lesson Plan
- Daily Lecture and Discussion Notes
- Note-taking Guide
- Guided Reading Activity
- Reading Essentials and Study Guide
- Section Quiz

Transparencies

- Daily Focus Skills Transparency
- GeoQuiz Transparency

Multimedia

- Vocabulary PuzzleMaker CD-ROM
- Interactive Tutor Self-Assessment CD-ROM
- Presentation Plus! CD-ROM
- ExamView® Pro Testmaker CD-ROM

2 TEACH

Reading Strategy

Determining Cause and Effect Kenya's chief exports are coffee and tea, which earn about half the country's income from foreign trade. **Ask:** What might happen to Kenya's foreign trade in a year with bad weather? *(Trade income would drop because the coffee and tea harvests decrease.)* What happens if other countries begin producing more coffee or tea? *(Kenya will either sell less or the price will decline, meaning that the value of Kenya's products will go down.)* What would you suggest that the government of Kenya do to improve the economy in light of these issues? *(Possible responses: concentrate on developing manufacturing; encourage more tourism)* **L1**

Literature

Micere Githae Mugo taught at Nairobi University in Kenya, where she was a fierce critic of the government. After a 1982 coup failed, the government cracked down on university students and teachers. Mugo left the country before she could be arrested. Since then, she has lived and taught in Zimbabwe and the United States.

Answer The phrase means "Make your own life."

(See the photo on page 40.) The Great Rift Valley begins in southeastern Africa and stretches about 3,000 miles (4,825 km) north to the Red Sea. Lakes have formed in many places, and volcanoes also dot the area. One of them—**Mt. Kenya**—rises 17,058 feet (5,199 m) high. It is in the Great Rift Valley that fossils of early human ancestors have been found. These fossils date back about 4 million years.

Kenya's Economy Kenya has a developing economy based on a free enterprise system. This means that people can start and run businesses with limited government involvement. Kenya's capital, **Nairobi** (ny•ROH•bee), has become a center of business for all of East Africa. The city's good transportation and communications systems have encouraged foreign companies to set up regional headquarters here.

Many Kenyans remain poor, however. Farmers raise corn, bananas, cassava, and sweet potatoes. Cassava is a plant whose roots are ground to make porridge. Some larger farms raise coffee and tea for export. In recent years, corrupt practices of government officials have hurt the economy.

One of the fastest-growing industries in Kenya is tourism. Thousands of tourists visit each year. Visitors often take tours called safaris in

Literature

A CHANGING KENYA

As developing countries modernize, traditional ways of life often change. In the following poem, Kenyan poet and playwright Micere Githae Mugo expresses the challenge of living in a changing world.

WHERE ARE THOSE SONGS?
by Micere Githae Mugo

Where are those songs
my mother and yours
always sang
fitting rhythms
to the whole
vast span of life?
. . . .
I have forgotten
my mother's song
my children
will never know.

This I remember:
Mother always said
sing child sing
make a song
and sing
beat out your own rhythms
the rhythms of your life
but make the song soulful
and make life
sing
. . . .

From "Where are those Songs" by Micere G. Mugo. Reprinted by permission of the author.

Analyzing Literature

What do you think the poet's mother meant when she said to "beat out your own rhythms"?

Reading Strategy Reading the Text

Classifying Information Have students identify the major economic activities in Kenya and Tanzania. *(agriculture, international businesses, tourism)* Then have them create a graphic organizer that identifies these main activities and shows the subdivisions that make up each. **L1**

*Use the **Reading Skills Handbook** for more reading strategies.*

jeeps and buses to see the country's wildlife in its natural surroundings.

History and Government In the A.D. 700s, Arab traders from Southwest Asia settled along the East African coast. As Arab culture blended with African, the Swahili language eventually emerged. The name *Swahili* comes from an Arabic word meaning "of the coast." The language has features of several African languages, as well as Arabic. Today Kenya's two official languages are Swahili and English.

The British made Kenya a colony in 1920 after World War I. They took land from the Africans and set up farms to grow coffee and tea for export. By the 1940s, Kenya's African groups, such as the Mau Mau, fought in violent civil wars to end British rule. Kenya finally won its independence in 1963 and became a republic. The country's first president, Jomo Kenyatta (JOH•moh kehn•YAHT•uh), won respect as an early leader in Africa's movement for freedom. Under Kenyatta, Kenya enjoyed economic prosperity and had a stable government. In recent years, the economy has weakened. In response, many Kenyans have demanded democratic changes.

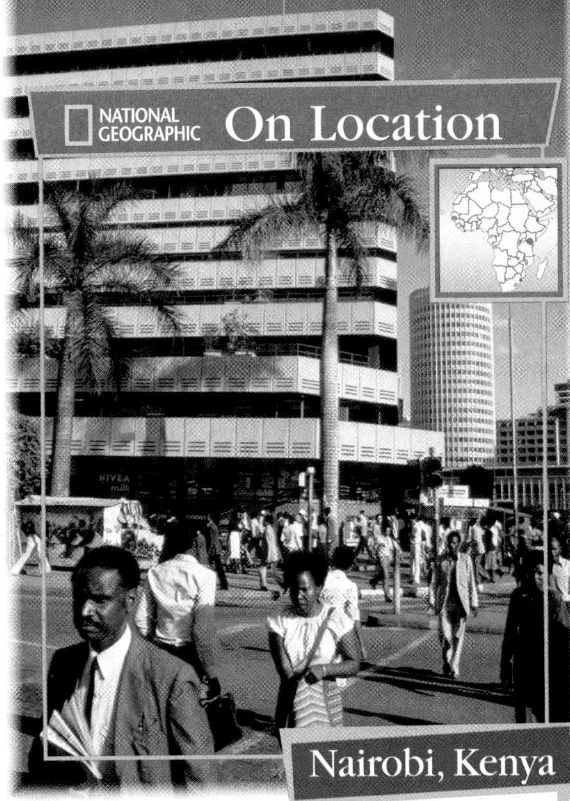

Nairobi, Kenya

Like most cities, Kenya's capital has crowded markets, high-rise office buildings, and elegant mansions. Many city workers maintain close ties to relatives in the countryside.

Place **About how many people live in Nairobi?**

Kenya Today Kenya's roughly 31 million people are divided among 40 different ethnic groups. The Kikuyu (kee•KOO•yoo) people are Kenya's main group, making up almost one-fourth of the population. Most Kenyans live in rural areas where they struggle to grow crops. Many people have moved to cities in search of a better life.

The people of Kenya believe in *harambee,* which means "pulling together." The spirit of *harambee* has led the different ethnic groups to build schools and clinics in their communities. They have raised money to send good students to universities.

About one-third of Kenya's people live in cities. Nairobi is the largest city, with about 2.3 million people. **Mombasa** (mohm•BAH•sah) is Kenya's chief port on the Indian Ocean. This city has the best harbor in East Africa, making it an ideal site for oceangoing trade.

Reading Check **What city is Kenya's chief port?**

Tanzania

Tourists flock to Tanzania's **Serengeti** (SEHR•uhn•GEH•tee) **Plain.** It is famous for its wildlife preserve, huge grasslands, and patches of trees and shrubs. To the north, near the Kenyan border, a snowcapped

More About the Photo

Nairobi Kenya's capital was founded in the 1890s as a rail center when the British built a railroad in East Africa. It became the capital of British East Africa in 1905 and remained Kenya's capital after gaining independence.

Caption Answer about 2.3 million people

L1/ELL

Guided Reading Activity

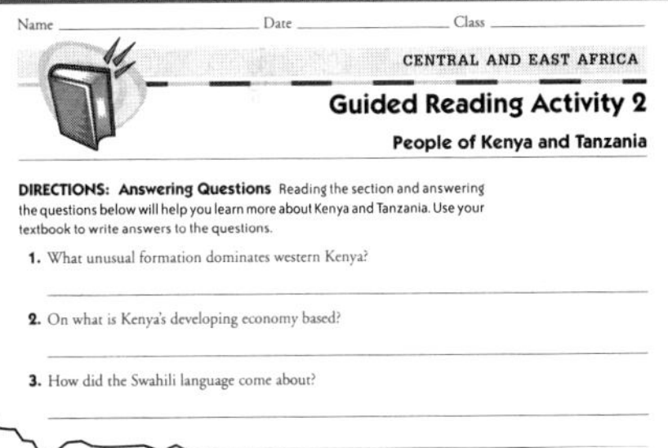
Name Date Class
CENTRAL AND EAST AFRICA
Guided Reading Activity 2
People of Kenya and Tanzania
DIRECTIONS: Answering Questions Reading the section and answering the questions below will help you learn more about Kenya and Tanzania. Use your textbook to write answers to the questions.
1. What unusual formation dominates western Kenya?
2. On what is Kenya's developing economy based?
3. How did the Swahili language come about?
...changes recently?

Mombasa

3 ASSESS

Assign Section 2 Assessment as homework or an in-class activity.

Have students use the Interactive Tutor Self-Assessment CD-ROM to review Section 2.

Differentiated Instruction

Meeting Special Needs: Logical/Mathematical How valuable is tourism in Kenya? Each lion produces $27,000 in income, and a herd of elephants generates $610,000 from tourists. The money is used to maintain the country's parks and to support tribes living in the area. Give students the following information: The average acre of land in Kenya has a value of $0.36 in terms of the crops it produces. That same acre, if used as a game preserve, generates $18 in income from tourists. Have students calculate the increased value of land from tourism over agriculture. *(The increase is $17.64 per acre, or 5,000%.)* Then have students discuss the potential drawbacks of relying on tourism. L1

Chapter 20

Section 2, pages 577–581

L2

Section Quiz

Name ______ Date ______ Class ______

CENTRAL AND EAST AFRICA

Score

Section 2 Quiz

People of Kenya and Tanzania

DIRECTIONS: Matching Match each item in Column A with the items in Column B. Write the correct letters in the blanks. *(10 points each)*

COLUMN A	COLUMN B
A. poaching	____ 1. a natural formation near the water's surface made of skeletons of sea animals
B. sisal	____ 2. illegal hunting of protected animals
C. coral reef	____ 3. plant fiber used to make rope and twine
D. Kilimanjaro	____ 4. mountain peak in northern Tanzania
E. Zanzibar	____ 5. island off the eastern coast of Tanzania

Measure student knowledge of physical features.

GeoQuiz Transparency

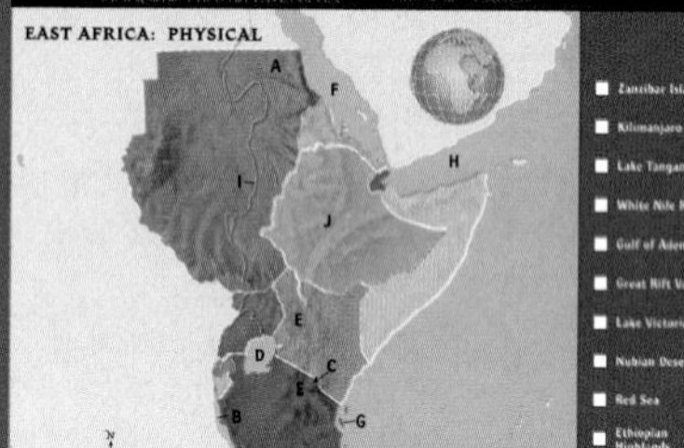

Applying Map Skills

Answers

1. Dar es Salaam
2. Tanzania, Equatorial Guinea, São Tomé and Príncipe, Eritrea

Skills Practice

What capital sits on the shores of Lake Victoria? *(Kampala, Uganda)*

NATIONAL GEOGRAPHIC

Central and East Africa: Political

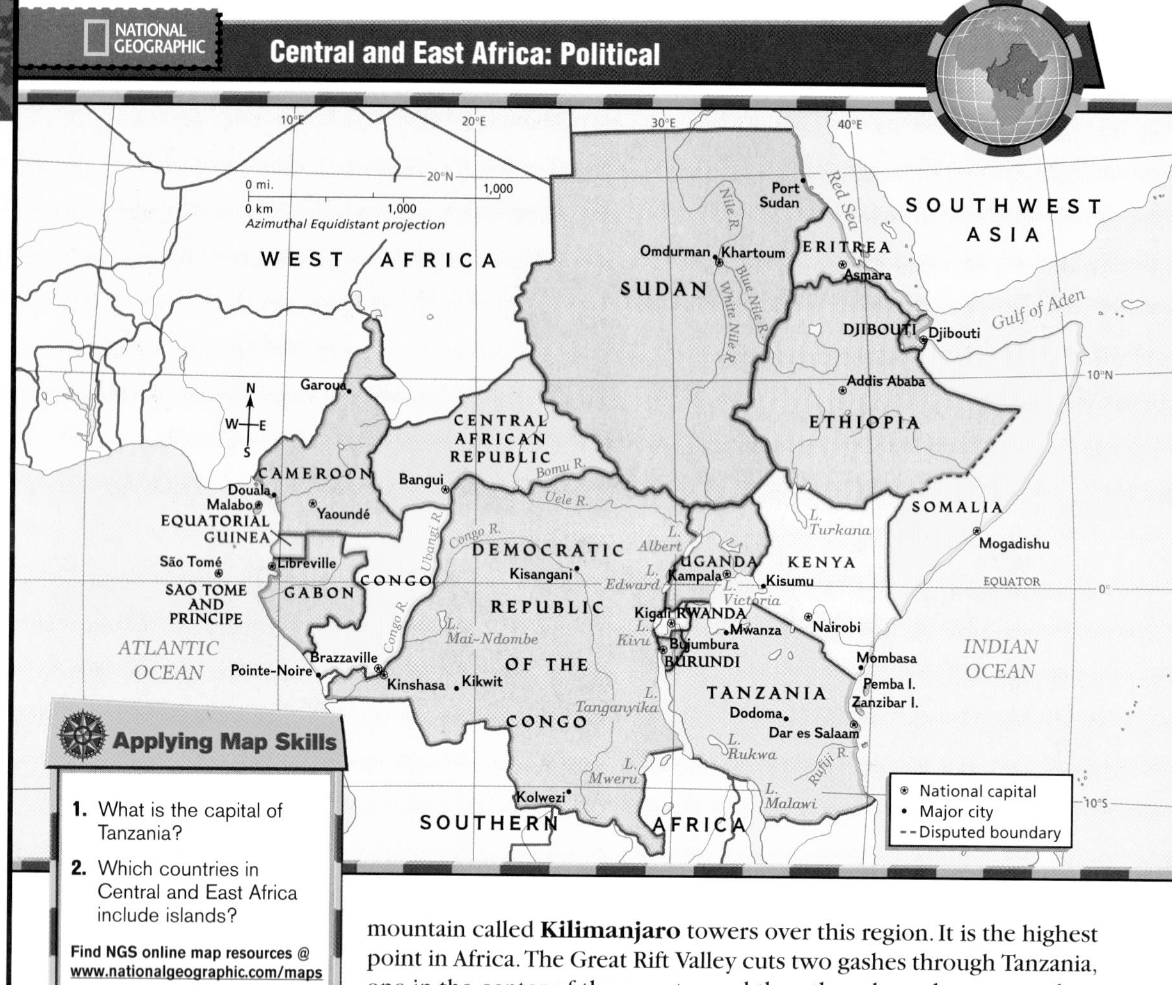

Applying Map Skills

1. What is the capital of Tanzania?
2. Which countries in Central and East Africa include islands?

Find NGS online map resources @ www.nationalgeographic.com/maps

mountain called **Kilimanjaro** towers over this region. It is the highest point in Africa. The Great Rift Valley cuts two gashes through Tanzania, one in the center of the country and the other along the western border. Unusual fish swim in the deep, dark waters of Lake Tanganyika (TAN•guhn•YEE•kuh). Lake Victoria, also in Tanzania, is Africa's largest lake and one of the sources of the Nile River.

Tanzania's Economy More than 80 percent of all Tanzanians work in farming or herding. Important export crops are coffee and sisal, a plant fiber used to make rope and twine. Do you enjoy eating baked ham? If so, you might have tasted the spice called cloves, often used to flavor ham. The islands of Zanzibar and Pemba, off the coast of Tanzania, produce more cloves than any other place in the world.

Tourism is a fast-growing industry in Tanzania. The government has set aside several national parks to protect the habitats of the country's wildlife. A habitat is the type of environment in which a particular animal species lives. Serengeti National Park covers about 5,600 square miles (14,504 sq. km). Lions and wild dogs hunt among thousands of

Team-Teaching Activity

Language Arts Invite a language arts teacher to class to discuss the formation of languages in relation to Swahili, one of the languages spoken in Tanzania as well as in Kenya. Have the teacher explain how Swahili combines Arabic with local African languages from the coast and how the language was spread by coastal traders and caravans that entered the interior of East Africa. Ask students to suggest other examples of languages created by combining elements of two distinct languages and how these languages might have been created. They might mention Haitian Creole, formed of French and African languages, and the "Spanglish" that combines Spanish and English in the United States. **ELL**

EE4 Human Systems: Standards 10, 12

zebras, wildebeests, and antelopes. The park attracts many **ecotourists,** or people who travel to another country to view its natural wonders.

Tanzania's leaders are also taking steps to preserve farmland. In recent years, many trees have been cut down. Without trees, the land cannot hold soil or rainwater in place. As a result, the land dries out, and soil blows away. To prevent the land from becoming desert, the government of Tanzania has announced a new policy. For every tree that is cut down, five new trees should be planted.

History and Government In 1964 the island country of Zanzibar united with the former German colony of Tanganyika to form Tanzania. Since then, Tanzania has been one of Africa's more politically stable republics. During the 1960s, Tanzania's socialist government controlled the economy. By the 1990s, however, it had moved toward a free enterprise system. In taking this step, Tanzania's leaders hoped to improve the economy and reduce poverty. Meanwhile, the government also moved toward more democratic elections with more than one political party.

Culture Tanzania's 35.4 million people include more than 120 different ethnic groups. Each group has its own language, but most people also speak Swahili. The two main religions are Christianity and Islam. Tanzanian music and dance dominate much of East Africa's culture. In **Dar es Salaam,** Tanzania's capital, you can hear strong rhythms and Swahili lyrics performed by local dance bands.

✓Reading Check What is Tanzania doing to preserve farmland?

I Am a Samburu

Nimfa Lekuuk is a member of the Samburu of northern Kenya. The word *Samburu* means "the people with the white goats." Nimfa wears the traditional clothes of Samburu women. She is in standard 7 now. "Standard" is the Kenyans' term for *grade.* She studies language, math, history, geography, science, arts and crafts, and religions.

Section 2 Assessment

Defining Terms

1. **Define** coral reef, poaching, free enterprise system, cassava, sisal, habitat, ecotourist.

Recalling Facts

2. **Place** Describe the Great Rift Valley.
3. **Culture** What are Kenya's official languages?
4. **Culture** What are the two major religions of Tanzania?

Critical Thinking

5. **Making Inferences** Why might two countries such as Tanganyika and Zanzibar unite?
6. **Drawing Conclusions** Why would the government of Tanzania put so much effort into preserving its national parks?

Graphic Organizer

7. **Organizing Information** Review the information about the history and government of Kenya. Then, on a time line like the one below, label four important events and their dates in Kenya's history.

Applying Social Studies Skills

8. **Analyzing Maps** Study the political map on page 580. Name the four bodies of water that border Tanzania. On which body of water is Dar es Salaam located?

Chapter 20

Section 2, pages 577–581

Reading Strategy

Reteach
Have students write newspaper headlines that summarize the main idea of each subsection.

✓ Reading Check Answer

For every tree that is cut down, five new trees are to be planted.

L1/ELL

Reading Essentials and Study Guide

Name Date Class

CENTRAL AND EAST AFRICA

Reading Essentials and Study Guide 2

People of Kenya and Tanzania

Key Terms

coral reef natural formation near the water's surface that is made of skeletons of small sea animals
poaching illegal hunting of protected animals
free enterprise system economic system in which people can start and run businesses with little government involvement
cassava plant whose roots are ground to make porridge
sisal plant fiber used to make rope and twine
habitat environment in which a certain kind of animal lives
... who travels to another country to view its natural wonders

Enrich
Have students prepare oral reports about the Serengeti or other national parks or preserves of Tanzania.

Close

Have students explain why Tanzania would be of interest to the following scientists: a geologist, an archaeologist, an anthropologist, and a zoologist.

Section 2 Assessment

1. The terms are defined in the Glossary.
2. a highlands area in southeastern Africa, 3,500 miles long, formed by a fault, with many lakes and volcanoes
3. Swahili and English
4. Christianity and Islam
5. *Possible answer:* to combine economic and political strengths
6. to attract tourists for economic profit
7. Possible answers: 700s—Arabs settle in coastal areas; 1920—becomes colony of England; 1940s—civil wars against British rule; 1963—Kenya becomes an independent republic
8. Indian Ocean, Lake Malawi, Lake Tanganyika, Lake Victoria; Indian Ocean

FOCUS

Section Objectives

1. Explain how landforms affect the climates of Uganda, Rwanda, and Burundi.
2. Identify the farm products grown in these countries.
3. Describe how ethnic conflict has hurt these countries.

BELLRINGER Skillbuilder Activity

Project transparency and have students answer the question.

Daily Focus Skills Transparency

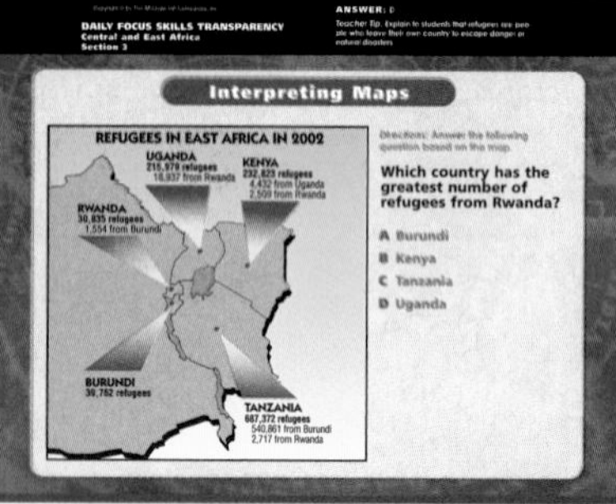

Reading Preview

■ **Activating Prior Knowledge** Ask students if they think Africa has low or high population density. *(They are likely to answer "low.")* Tell them that in this section they will read about countries that have very high population densities.

■ **Preteaching Vocabulary** Ask students what the word *refuge* means. *(safe place)* Ask them to guess at the meaning of *refugee.* Then have them look up the word in the Glossary to verify their guesses.

Guide to Reading

Main Idea

Uganda, Rwanda, and Burundi have suffered much conflict in recent years.

Terms to Know

- plantains
- autonomy
- watershed
- endangered species
- genocide
- refugee

Reading Strategy

Make a chart like this one. On the left, write the cause of conflict in each country under that country's name. Then write the effects of that conflict.

Cause of conflict in:	Effects of conflict
Uganda	
Rwanda	
Burundi	

Section 3

Uganda, Rwanda, and Burundi

NATIONAL GEOGRAPHIC Exploring Our World

If you walk through the mountain rain forests of Rwanda, you might feel you are being watched. Who's watching you? It could be one of the world's 600 remaining gorillas—the rarest and largest of the great apes. Every day these gorillas face the threat of death from poachers, loss of their habitat, disease, and civil war.

West of Kenya and Tanzania lie **Uganda, Rwanda,** and **Burundi.** All three are landlocked—they have no land touching a sea or an ocean. Instead, they use three large lakes for transportation and trade.

Uganda

Once called "the pearl of Africa," Uganda is a fertile, green land of mountains, lakes, and wild animals. About the size of Oregon, the country consists mainly of a central plateau. South of the plateau is **Lake Victoria.** Although Uganda lies on the Equator, temperatures are mild because of the country's high elevation.

Uganda's rich soil and plentiful rain make the land good for farming. About 80 percent of Uganda's workers are employed in agriculture. The map on page 583 shows that most farmers work on subsistence farms. They grow **plantains**—a kind of banana—cassava, potatoes, corn, and grains. Some plantations grow coffee, cotton, and tea for

Section Resources

Reproducible Masters
- Reproducible Lesson Plan
- Daily Lecture and Discussion Notes
- Note-taking Guide
- Guided Reading Activity
- Reading Essentials and Study Guide
- Section Quiz

Transparencies
- Daily Focus Skills Transparency

Multimedia
- Vocabulary PuzzleMaker CD-ROM
- Interactive Tutor Self-Assessment CD-ROM
- Presentation Plus! CD-ROM
- ExamView® Pro Testmaker CD-ROM

export. Coffee makes up nearly three-fourths of Uganda's exports. Uganda's few factories make cement, soap, sugar, metal, and shoes.

The Ugandans Uganda's 25.3 million people live mainly in rural villages in the southern part of the country. **Kampala,** the capital, lies on the shores of Lake Victoria, making it a port city for local trade.

About two-thirds of Ugandans are Christians. The remaining one-third practice Islam or traditional African religions. At one time there were large numbers of Hindus and Sikhs from South Asia living in the country. A dictator, Idi Amin, drove them out in 1972. Recently, the Ugandan government has invited them back, and many have returned.

Ugandans belong to more than 40 different ethnic groups. They have a rich cultural heritage of songs, folktales, and poems. In the past, these were passed only by word of mouth from one generation to the next. Today this heritage is also preserved in books. Traditions are also reflected in the Ugandans' diet. Meals often include beans, beef, goat, mutton, cornmeal, and a variety of tropical fruits.

History and Government For much of the 1900s, the British ruled Uganda. After Uganda won its freedom in 1962, fighting broke out among ethnic groups. Under their kings, these ethnic groups had enjoyed autonomy, or self-government, in their local territories. These kings lost power in 1967, and the ethnic regions were tightly bound to the central government. The dictator Idi Amin's cruel rule

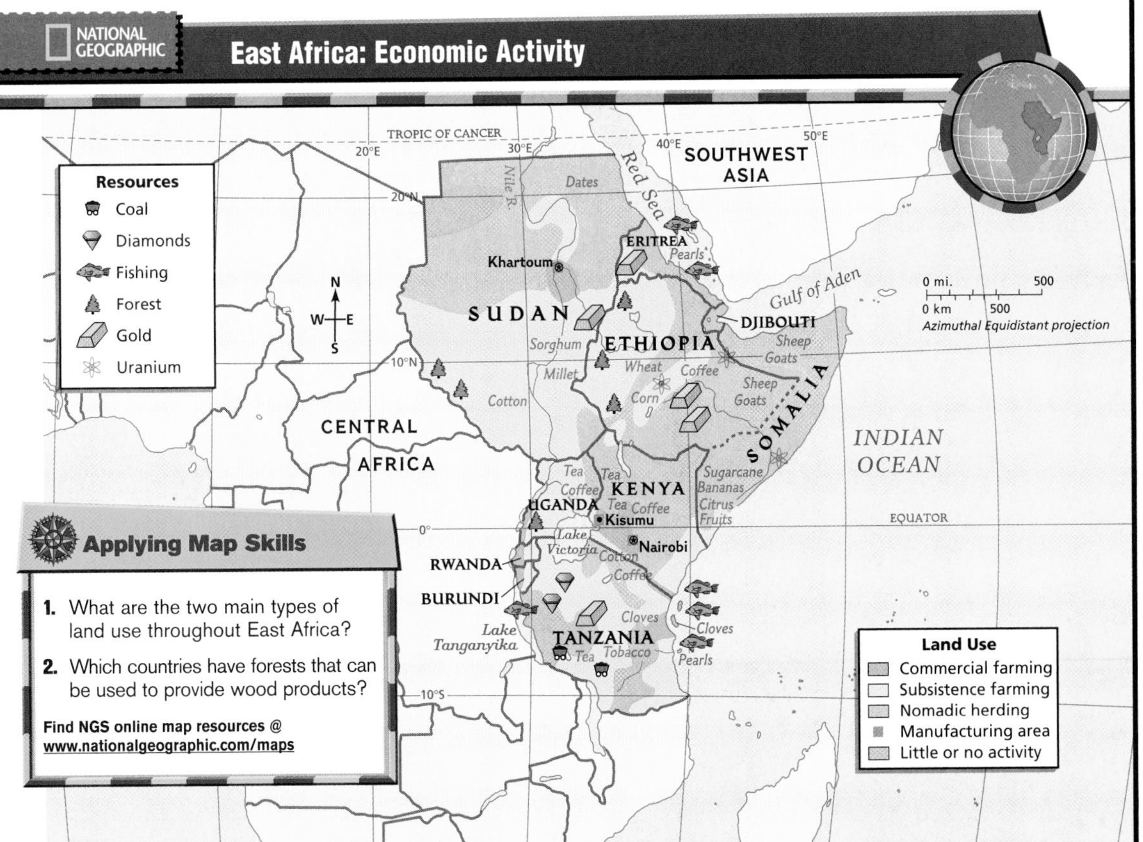

Applying Map Skills

1. What are the two main types of land use throughout East Africa?
2. Which countries have forests that can be used to provide wood products?

Find NGS online map resources @ www.nationalgeographic.com/maps

Reading Strategy — Reading the Text

Providing Reading Support Use flexible classroom organization to provide support and guidance to struggling readers. Students might: read aloud to partners who can help with difficult words; read silently with partners, having them "on-call" to help with difficult sections in the text; or follow along in their books as they listen to a taped reading or as student volunteers read aloud. **L1**

*Use the **Reading Skills Handbook** for more reading strategies.*

Chapter 20

Section 3, pages 582–585

TEACH

Reading Strategy

Making Generalizations
Have students look at Uganda, Rwanda, and Burundi on the maps in this chapter. **Ask:** **Based on what you see on these maps, why are these three countries studied together?** *(Possible answers: similar geography, all landlocked, similar economic activities)* **L1**

Daily Lecture and Discussion Notes

CENTRAL AND EAST AFRICA

Daily Lecture and Discussion Notes
Uganda, Rwanda, and Burundi

The Okebu people are one of seven ethnic groups in northwest Uganda. They have a long, rich tradition in the art of ironworking. During colonial rule of Uganda, the Okebu were not allowed to practice their skills. Today only a few Okebu remain skilled workers of iron.

I. Uganda
A. Uganda is a fertile, green land with mountains, lakes, and wild animals. It has a large central plateau.
B. Although Uganda lies on the Equator, temperatures are mild because of the

Applying Map Skills

Answers

1. nomadic herding and subsistence farming
2. Sudan, Ethiopia, Uganda

Skills Practice
What economic activity do the people of Burundi carry out in Lake Tanganyika? *(fishing)*

Chapter 20

Section 3, pages 582–585

More About the Photo

Lake Victoria Lake Victoria is the largest lake in Africa and the third-largest in the world. The Caspian Sea is first, and Lake Superior is second.

Caption Answer Uganda, Kenya, and Tanzania

Reading Check Answer

a republic with an elected president and legislature

L1/ELL

Guided Reading Activity

Name ______ Date ______ Class ______

CENTRAL AND EAST AFRICA

Guided Reading Activity 3

Uganda, Rwanda, and Burundi

DIRECTIONS: Outlining Reading the section and completing the outline below will help you learn more about the countries of inland East Africa. Use your textbook to fill in the blanks.

I. ______ was once called the "Pearl of Africa."
  A. It is a ______ land with mountains, lakes, and wild animals.
    1. The country consists mainly of a central ______.
    2. ______ ______ cause mild temperatures.
  B. Most people are employed in ______.
    1. Most farmers work on ______ ______.
    2. ______ makes up nearly three-fourths of Uganda's exports.
  ... to more than ______ different ethnic groups.

Assess

Assign Section 3 Assessment as homework or an in-class activity.

Have students use the Interactive Tutor Self-Assessment CD-ROM to review Section 3.

L2

Section Quiz

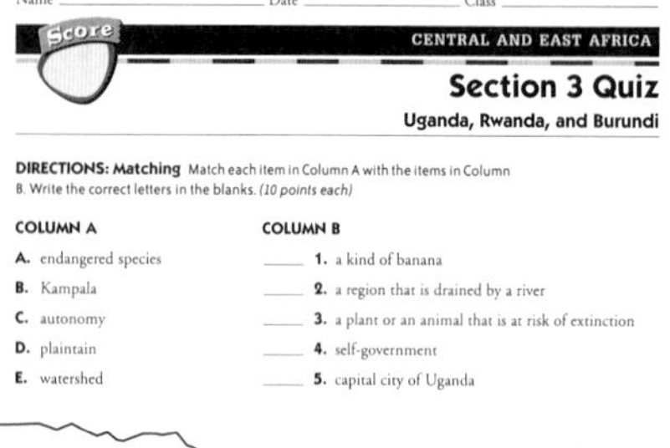

Name ______ Date ______ Class ______

Score

CENTRAL AND EAST AFRICA

Section 3 Quiz

Uganda, Rwanda, and Burundi

DIRECTIONS: Matching Match each item in Column A with the items in Column B. Write the correct letters in the blanks. *(10 points each)*

COLUMN A	COLUMN B
A. endangered species	____ 1. a kind of banana
B. Kampala	____ 2. a region that is drained by a river
C. autonomy	____ 3. a plant or an animal that is at risk of extinction
D. plaintain	____ 4. self-government
E. watershed	____ 5. capital city of Uganda

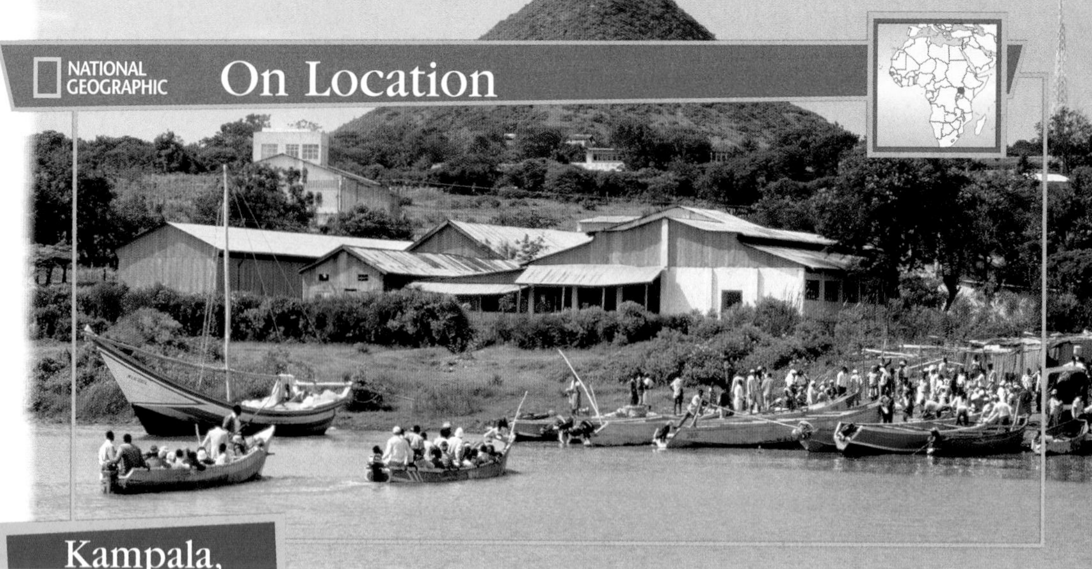

Kampala, Uganda

Public transportation in Kampala includes passenger boats on Lake Victoria.

Region Which countries border Lake Victoria?

hurt Uganda throughout much of the 1970s. Since the mid-1990s, the national government has allowed ethnic groups to once again have kings, but only as local ceremonial leaders.

Uganda's economy has recently seen solid growth. Uganda also has a stable government. It is a republic with an elected president and legislature. Still, the future is clouded. Uganda, along with other African countries, faces the threat of the disease called AIDS. Hundreds of thousands of Ugandans have died from it, and many more are infected with HIV, the virus that causes AIDS.

Reading Check What kind of government does Uganda have today?

Rwanda and Burundi

Rwanda and Burundi are located deep in inland East Africa. Each of the two countries is about the same size as Maryland. They both have mountains, hills, and high plateaus. They sit on the ridge that separates the Nile and Congo watersheds. A **watershed** is a region that is drained by a river. To the west of the ridge, water runs into the Congo River and flows to the Atlantic Ocean. To the east, water eventually becomes part of the Nile River and flows north to the Mediterranean Sea.

As in Uganda, high elevation gives Rwanda and Burundi a moderate climate even though they lie near the Equator. Heavy rains allow dense forests to grow. Within these forests live gorillas. Scientists have classified gorillas as an **endangered species**—a plant or an animal threatened with extinction. Learn more about protecting gorillas on page 76.

Farmers in Burundi and Rwanda work small plots that dot the hillsides. Coffee is the main export crop. The people who live along Lake Kivu and Lake Tanganyika also fish. Because Burundi and Rwanda are

Differentiated Instruction

Meeting Special Needs: Logical/Mathematical Give students the following figures, which represent the population (in millions) of the countries of East Africa: Burundi—6.1; Djibouti—0.7; Eritrea—4.4; Ethiopia—70.7; Kenya—31.6; Rwanda—8.3; Somalia—8.0; Tanzania—35.4; Uganda—25.3. Have students create a bar graph that displays this information. Students may want to use graph paper to construct their bar graphs. Be sure students use consistent increments to reflect the population information. L2

Refer to *Inclusion for the Middle School Social Studies Classroom Strategies and Activities* in the TCR.

landlocked, they have trouble getting their goods to foreign buyers. Few paved roads and no railroads exist. Most goods must be transported by road to Lake Tanganyika, where boats take them to Tanzania or the Democratic Republic of the Congo. Another route is by dirt road to Tanzania and then by rail to Dar es Salaam.

Ethnic Conflict Rwanda and Burundi have large populations and small areas. As a result, they are among the most densely populated countries in Africa. Rwanda, for example, has an average of 817 people per square mile (315 per sq. km). Yet only 5 percent of the people live in cities.

Two ethnic groups—the Hutu and the Tutsi—form most of the population of Rwanda and Burundi. The Hutu make up 80 percent or more of the population in both countries, but the Tutsi traditionally controlled the governments and economies. A constant power struggle between these two groups erupted into a full-scale civil war and genocide in the 1990s. **Genocide** is the deliberate murder of a group of people because of their race or culture. A Hutu-led government in Rwanda killed hundreds of thousands of Tutsi people. Two million more became **refugees,** or people who flee to another country to escape persecution or disaster. The fighting between the Hutu and Tutsi has lessened, but both countries face many challenges as they try to rebuild with the help and cooperation of the international community.

Reading Check Which ethnic group makes up the majority of the population in Rwanda and Burundi?

Social Studies Online

Web Activity Visit ***The World and Its People*** Web site at twip.glencoe.com and click on **Chapter 20—Student Web Activities** to learn more about Rwanda's mountain gorillas.

Section 3 Assessment

Defining Terms

1. **Define** plantains, autonomy, watershed, endangered species, genocide, refugee.

Recalling Facts

2. **Location** Explain the factors that affect Uganda's climate.
3. **Place** What is the capital of Uganda?
4. **Region** What endangered species lives in the forests of Rwanda and Burundi?

Critical Thinking

5. **Understanding Cause and Effect** How could a deadly epidemic, such as AIDS, affect a country's economy?
6. **Analyzing Information** How have ethnic differences created problems for Uganda, Rwanda, and Burundi?

Graphic Organizer

7. **Organizing Information** Draw a diagram like the one below. Then write two facts about Uganda under each of the category headings in the outer ovals.

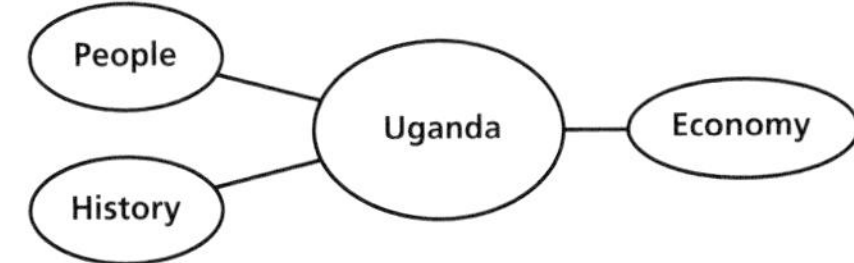

Applying Social Studies Skills

8. **Analyzing Maps** Study the economic activity map on page 583. Which countries in East Africa have gold resources?

Chapter 20

Section 3, pages 582–585

Social Studies Online

Objectives and answers to the Student Web Activity can be found in the Web Activity Lesson Plan at twip.glencoe.com

Reading Check Answer

Hutu

L1/ELL

Reading Essentials and Study Guide

Name ____ Date ____ Class ____

CENTRAL AND EAST AFRICA

Reading Essentials and Study Guide 3

Uganda, Rwanda, and Burundi

Key Terms

plantains a kind of banana
autonomy self-government
watershed region drained by a river
endangered species plant or animal under the threat of completely dying out
genocide deliberate murder of a group of people because of their race or culture
refugee person who flees to another country to escape danger or disaster

4 Close

Reading Strategy

Organizing Information

Have students create a concept web for Uganda, Rwanda, and Burundi that includes facts about the geography, history, and culture of each country.

Section 3 Assessment

1. The terms are defined in the Glossary.
2. its location on the Equator and its high altitude
3. Kampala
4. gorillas
5. Answers should include such issues as the cost of health care, loss of workers, and loss of skilled people who could help build the country's future.
6. Ethnic differences have led to conflict, civil war, and massive killings.
7. Students' diagrams will vary.
8. Tanzania, Sudan, Eritrea, and Ethiopia

Chapter 20

Section 4, pages 586–590

Focus

Section Objectives

1. Identify the landforms in the Horn of Africa.
2. Explain how the people of this region earn a living.
3. Describe the conflicts that have affected these countries.

BELLRINGER
Skillbuilder Activity

Project transparency and have students answer the question.

Daily Focus Skills Transparency

Interpreting Information on Tables

Which city do you think has a desert climate? Why?

Reading Preview

■ **Activating Prior Knowledge** Have students look at a political map of northern East Africa. **Ask:** **Why do you think the region from Eritrea to Somalia is called "the Horn of Africa"?**

■ **Preteaching Vocabulary** Have students find the Terms to Know and describe their definitions in their own words.

Guide to Reading

Main Idea

The countries of the Horn of Africa have all been scarred by conflict in recent years.

Terms to Know

- plate
- clan

Reading Strategy

Make a chart like this one. Then fill in two facts that are true of each country.

Country	Fact #1	Fact #2
Sudan		
Ethiopia		
Eritrea		
Djibouti		
Somalia		

The Horn of Africa

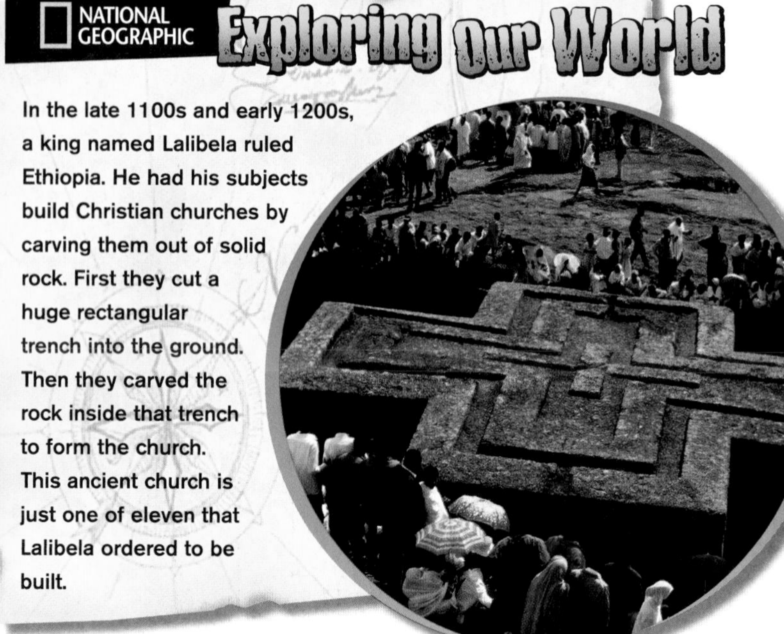

NATIONAL GEOGRAPHIC Exploring Our World

In the late 1100s and early 1200s, a king named Lalibela ruled Ethiopia. He had his subjects build Christian churches by carving them out of solid rock. First they cut a huge rectangular trench into the ground. Then they carved the rock inside that trench to form the church. This ancient church is just one of eleven that Lalibela ordered to be built.

The northern part of East Africa is a region called the Horn of Africa. This region got its name because it is shaped like a horn that juts out into the Indian Ocean. The countries here are **Sudan, Ethiopia, Eritrea** (EHR•uh•TREE•uh), **Djibouti** (jih•BOO•tee), and **Somalia.**

Sudan

Sudan is the largest country in Africa—about one-third the size of the continental United States. The northern part is covered by the sand dunes of the Sahara and Nubian Desert. Nomads raise camels and goats here. The most fertile part of the country is the central region. In this area of grassy plains, the two main tributaries of the Nile River—the **Blue Nile River** and the **White Nile River**—join together at **Khartoum** (kahr•TOOM), Sudan's capital. The southern part of Sudan receives plenty of rain and has some fertile soil. It also holds one of the world's largest swamps, which drains into the White Nile.

Most of Sudan's people live along the Nile River or one of its tributaries. They use water from the Nile to irrigate their fields. Farmers grow sugarcane, grains, nuts, dates, and cotton—the country's leading

Section Resources

Reproducible Masters

- Reproducible Lesson Plan
- Daily Lecture and Discussion Notes
- Note-taking Guide
- Guided Reading Activity
- Reading Essentials and Study Guide
- Section Quiz

Transparencies

- Daily Focus Skills Transparency
- In-text Map Transparency

Multimedia

- Vocabulary PuzzleMaker CD-ROM
- Interactive Tutor Self-Assessment CD-ROM
- Presentation Plus! CD-ROM
- ExamView® Pro Testmaker CD-ROM
- MindJogger Videoquiz

export. Sheep and gold are other important exports. Recently discovered oil fields in the south offer another possibility of income.

Sudan's Past and Present In ancient times, Sudan was the center of a powerful civilization called Kush. The people of Kush had close cultural and trade ties with the Egyptians to the north. Kushites traded metal tools for cotton and other goods from India, Arabia, and China. They built a great capital at Meroë (MAR•oh•EE). It had huge temples, stone palaces, and small pyramids. Kush began to lose power around A.D. 350.

During the A.D. 500s, missionaries from Egypt brought Christianity to the region. About 900 years later, Muslim Arabs entered northern Sudan and converted its people to Islam. From the late 1800s to the 1950s, the British and the Egyptians together ruled the country. Sudan became an independent nation in 1956. Since then, military leaders have generally taken over.

In the 1980s, the government began a "reign of terror" against the southern Christian peoples. The fighting has disrupted the economy and caused widespread hunger, especially in the south. A recent drought—a long period of extreme dryness and water shortages—made the situation

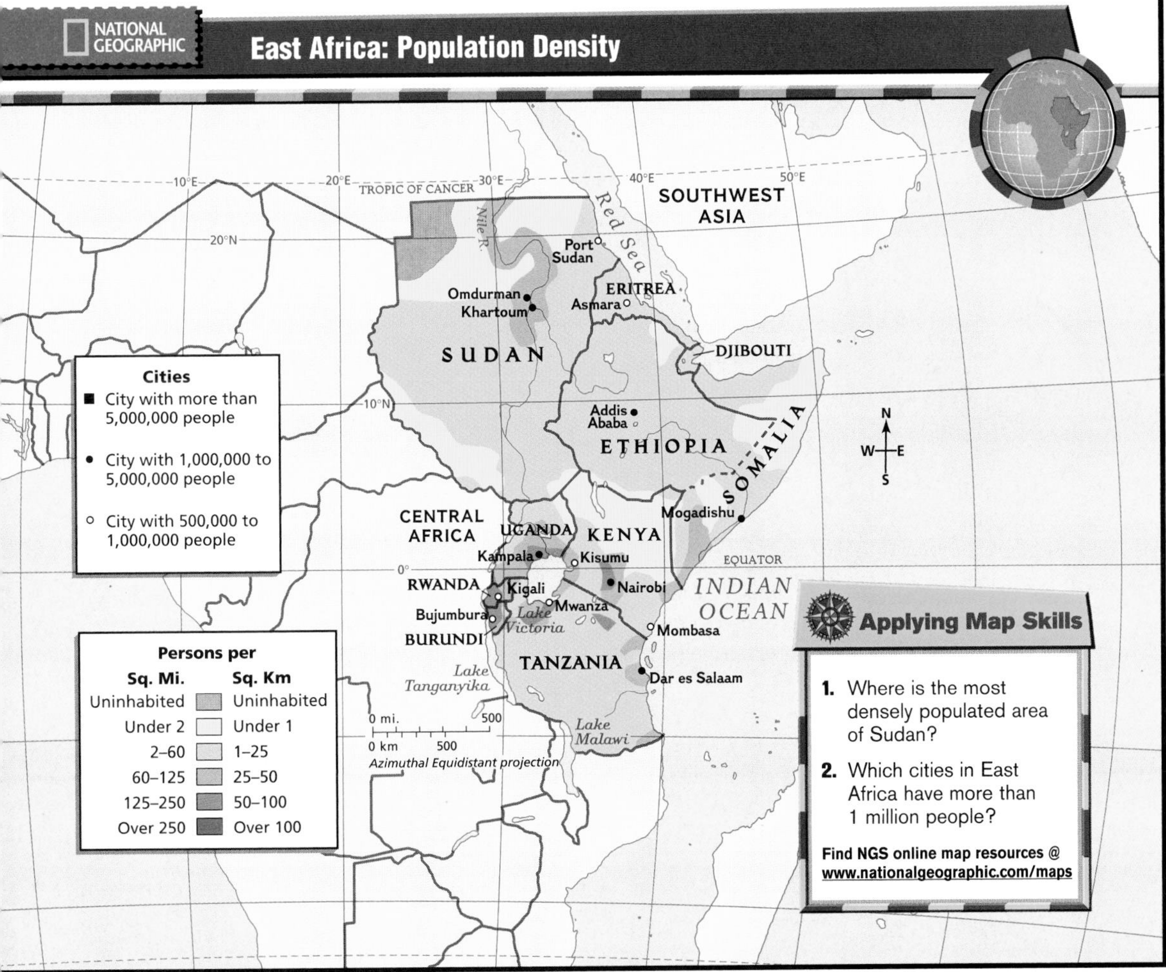

Applying Map Skills

1. Where is the most densely populated area of Sudan?
2. Which cities in East Africa have more than 1 million people?

Find NGS online map resources @ www.nationalgeographic.com/maps

Reading Strategy — Reading the Text

Summarizing Invite the history teacher to class to discuss the factors that allowed Ethiopia to remain free of European colonial control. The teacher might wish to refer to the map of the independence dates of African nations on page 615 to show how extensive this colonial control was. After the presentation, have students write a paragraph summarizing what they have learned. L1

*Use the **Reading Skills Handbook** for more reading strategies.*

2 TEACH

Reading a Map Quiz students on the countries of the Horn of Africa by having them look at the map on this page and asking the following questions: **Which country is the largest?** *(Sudan)* **Which is the smallest?** *(Djibouti)* **Which has the longest coastline?** *(Somalia)* **Which border the Red Sea?** *(Sudan, Eritrea)* **Which is landlocked?** *(Ethiopia)* **L1**

Daily Lecture and Discussion Notes

CENTRAL AND EAST AFRICA

Daily Lecture and Discussion Notes

The Horn of Africa

Did You Know? The main dish in the Sudanese diet is *ful* (also spelled *fool*). This dish consists of broad beans cooked in oil. Goat, lamb, beef, and chicken are served occasionally, but the majority of the Sudanese people do not eat much meat.

I. Sudan

A. The Horn of Africa contains Sudan, Ethiopia, Eritrea, Djibouti, and Somalia.

B. Sudan is the largest country in Africa—about one-third the size of the continental United States.

C. Northern Sudan is covered by the Sahara and Nubian Desert. The central ... because of the Blue Nile and White Nile Rivers, which join at ... Sudan is swampy, with some fertile soil.

Applying Map Skills

Answers

1. the area along the Nile River in the northern part of the country
2. Omdurman, Khartoum, Addis Ababa, Mogadishu, Kampala, Nairobi, Dar es Salaam

Skills Practice

What is the population density of Djibouti? *(2–60 persons per square mile or 1–25 persons per square Kilometer)*

✓ Reading Check Answer

cotton

Cultural Kaleidoscope

Ethiopia About 40 percent of the people of Ethiopia belong to the Ethiopian Orthodox Christian Church. This faith is different from both Roman Catholicism and Eastern Orthodox religions because it includes many customs adapted from Judaism. For example, the Ethiopian Church observes the Sabbath on Saturday, not Sunday; cantors chant the liturgy; and there is an emphasis on clean and unclean foods.

L1/ELL

Guided Reading Activity

Name ________ Date ________ Class ________

CENTRAL AND EAST AFRICA

Guided Reading Activity 4

The Horn of Africa

DIRECTIONS: Filling in the Blanks Reading the section and completing the sentences below will help you learn more about the Horn of Africa. Use your textbook to fill in the blanks.

The Horn of Africa is located at the **(1)** ________ part of East Africa. The largest country in Africa, **(2)** ________, is one-third the size of the United States. Most people live along the **(3)** ________. In ancient times, a civilization called **(4)** ________ dominated this area. **(5)** ________ ________ entered northern Sudan in the 1400s. Sudan became independent in **(6)** ________ ...

✓ Reading Check Answer

a famine in the 1980s

worse. Millions have starved to death, and major outbreaks of diseases have swept through the country. The war continues despite occasional peace talks aimed at granting the south greater independence. The **TIME Perspectives** feature on pages 591–597 looks at Sudanese refugees.

✓Reading Check What is the main export of Sudan?

Ethiopia

Landlocked Ethiopia is almost twice the size of Texas. Ethiopia's landscape varies from hot lowlands to rugged mountains. The central part of Ethiopia is a highland plateau sliced through by the Great Rift Valley. The valley forms deep river gorges and sparkling waterfalls. Mild temperatures and good soil make the highlands Ethiopia's best farming region. Farmers raise grains, sugarcane, potatoes, and coffee. Coffee is a major export crop. The southern highlands are believed to be the world's original home of coffee.

Rain is not consistent in many parts of Ethiopia. Low rainfall can lead to drought, and then Ethiopia's people suffer. In the 1980s, a drought caused famine, which attracted the world's attention. At that time, a drought turned fields once rich in crops into seas of dust. Despite food aid, more than 1 million Ethiopians died from starvation and disease.

Ethiopia's History and People Scientists have found what they believe to be the remains of the oldest known human ancestors in Ethiopia. Recorded history reveals that, thousands of years ago, Ethiopian officials traveled to Egypt to meet with the pharaohs of that land. Later, Ethiopia developed important trade links to the Roman Empire. In the A.D. 300s, many Ethiopians accepted Christianity.

▲ In May 2000, this woman voted in Ethiopia's second-ever democratic election.

For centuries, kings and emperors ruled Ethiopia. During the late 1800s, Ethiopia successfully withstood European attempts to control it. The last emperor was overthrown in 1974, and the country suffered under a military dictator. Now it is trying to build a democratic government. This goal was hindered by warfare with neighboring Eritrea, a small country that broke away from Ethiopia in 1993.

With 70.7 million people, Ethiopia has more people than any other country in East Africa. The capital, **Addis Ababa** (AH•dihs AH•bah•BAH), is the largest city in the region. About 85 percent of Ethiopians live in rural areas.

Muslims form about 45 percent of Ethiopia's population. About 40 percent are Ethiopian Orthodox. Others practice traditional African religions. Almost 80 languages are spoken in Ethiopia. Amharic, similar to Hebrew and Arabic, is Ethiopia's official language.

✓Reading Check What crisis brought Ethiopia to the world's attention?

Eritrea

Ethiopia may be one of Africa's oldest countries, but Eritrea is certainly the newest. In 1993, after 30 years of war, Eritrea won its independence from Ethiopia. Eritrea sits on the shores of the Red Sea. It has

Differentiated Instruction

Meeting Special Needs: Kinesthetic Have students research and create a model of the landscape of one of the countries in this section. They might also create a model of the Nile River from its beginnings through the Sudan. They can use clay, dough made from flour and water, or other materials. Have them paint their models to show different elevation levels and prepare a key explaining the colors used. Have them also create an accompanying sheet that shows the vegetation and economic activities found at different elevations. **ELL L2**

Refer to *Inclusion for the Middle School Social Studies Classroom Strategies and Activities* in the TCR.

NATIONAL GEOGRAPHIC

Major African Ethnic Groups

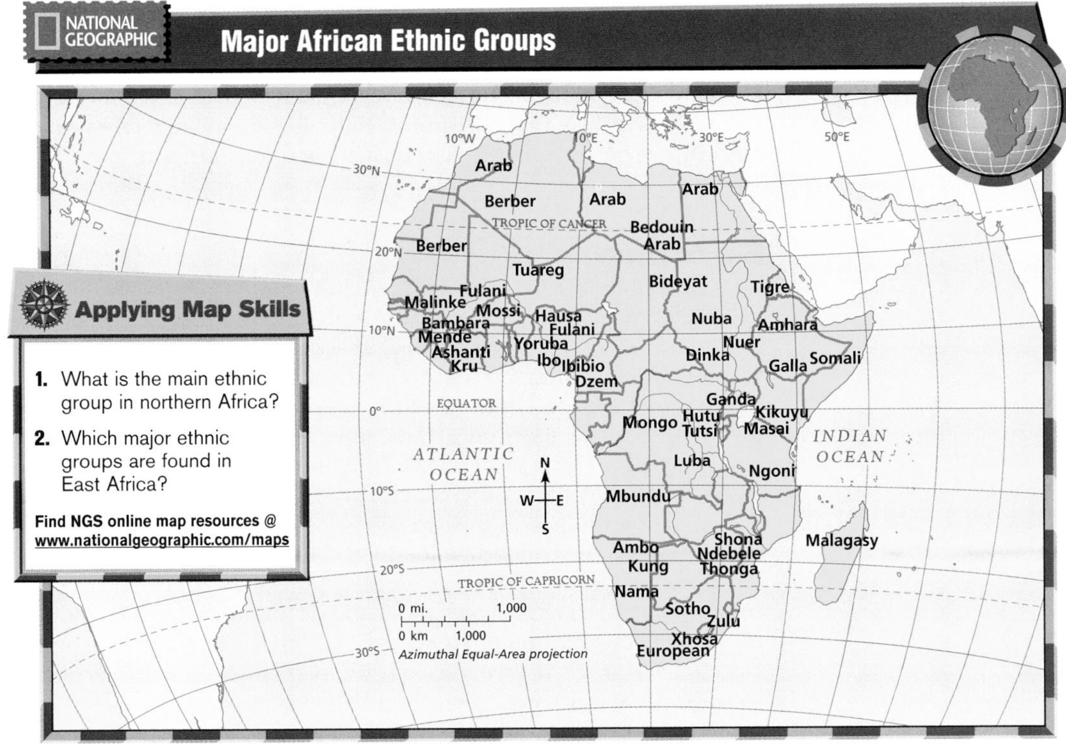

Applying Map Skills

1. What is the main ethnic group in northern Africa?
2. Which major ethnic groups are found in East Africa?

Find NGS online map resources @ www.nationalgeographic.com/maps

a narrow plain that stretches about 600 miles (966 km) along the coast. When Eritrea became a country, Ethiopia became landlocked.

Most of Eritrea's 4.4 million people farm. Farming here is uncertain work because the climate is dry. The long war with Ethiopia also hurt farming. The war did have a positive effect on some of Eritrea's people, however. Women formed about one-third of the army that won the war. After the war ended, the new government passed laws that gave women more rights than they ever had before.

Reading Check When and from what country did Eritrea win independence?

Djibouti

Evidence that the earth is undergoing change can be seen in Djibouti. This country lies at the northern tip of the Great Rift Valley, where three of the earth's plates join. **Plates** are huge slabs of rock that make up the earth's crust. In Djibouti, two of these plates are pulling away from each other. As they separate, fiery hot rock rises to the earth's surface, causing volcanic activity.

Djibouti wraps around a natural harbor at the point where the Red Sea meets the Gulf of Aden. This tiny country is one of the hottest, driest places on the earth. Its landscape is covered by rocky desert. Here and there, you will find the desert interrupted by salt lakes and rare patches of grassland.

Applying Map Skills

Answers

1. Arab
2. Tigre, Amhara, Galla, Somali, Nuba, Nuer, Dinka, Ganda, Hutu, Tutsi, Masai, Kikuyu, and Ngoni

In-text Map Transparency Activity After students have answered the questions, remind them that the map shows only the major African ethnic groups. Ask students to describe whether they think this ethnic diversity encourages or prevents cooperation among African nations.

in 1993 from Ethiopia

3 ASSESS

Assign Section 4 Assessment as homework or an in-class activity.

Have students use the Interactive Tutor Self-Assessment CD-ROM to review Section 4.

Critical Thinking Activity

Synthesizing Information Organize students into ten groups. Inform groups that their task is to create a wall poster on one of the five countries in this region; assign two groups to each country. Then assign each of the two country groups two of the following areas of study—land and climate; economy; history and government; or culture. Groups should develop or locate a number of images that illustrate their areas. They then should create their section of the poster. Some group members might do artwork or design, while others might write captions. Have groups combine their finished sections to create the wall poster. **L1**

EE2 Places and Regions: Standard 4

Chapter 20

Section 4, pages 586–590

L2

Section Quiz

Name ______ Date ______ Class ______

CENTRAL AND EAST AFRICA — Score

Section 4 Quiz

The Horn of Africa

DIRECTIONS: Matching Match each item in Column A with the items in Column B. Write the correct letters in the blanks. *(10 points each)*

COLUMN A	COLUMN B
A. Addis Ababa	____ 1. groups of people related to one another
B. Amharic	____ 2. capital city of Ethiopia
C. plates	____ 3. capital city of Sudan
D. Khartoum	____ 4. Ethiopian language similar to Arabic and Hebrew
E. clans	____ 5. huge slabs of rock that make up the earth's crust

Reading Check Answer

because it sits where three of the earth's plates join

Reading Check Answer

disputes between different clans

L1/ELL

Reading Essentials and Study Guide

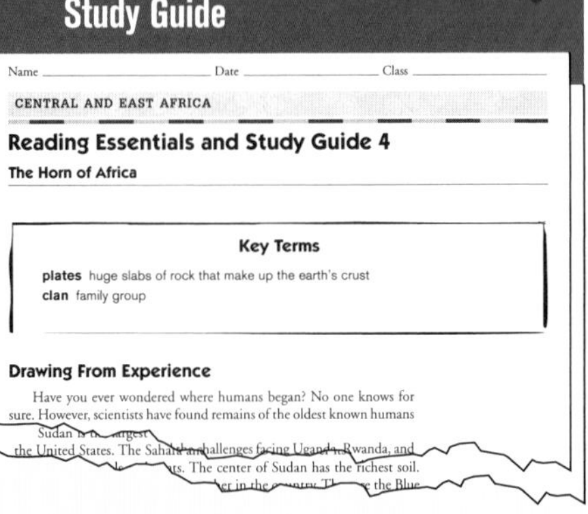
Name ______ Date ______ Class ______

CENTRAL AND EAST AFRICA

Reading Essentials and Study Guide 4

The Horn of Africa

Key Terms

plates huge slabs of rock that make up the earth's crust
clan family group

Drawing From Experience

Have you ever wondered where humans began? No one knows for sure. However, scientists have found remains of the oldest known humans

CLOSE

Have students create a bulletin board display about one of the countries in the Horn of Africa with images and captions that highlight important features of the country and its people.

Djibouti's 700,000 people are mostly Muslims. In the past, they lived a nomadic life of herding. Because of Djibouti's dry climate, farming and herding are difficult. In recent years, many people have moved to the capital city, also called **Djibouti.** Here they have found jobs in the city's docks, because the city is a busy international seaport.

Reading Check Why does Djibouti experience volcanic activity?

Somalia

Somalia borders the Gulf of Aden and the Indian Ocean. Shaped like the number seven, the country is almost as large as Texas. Like Eritrea and Djibouti, much of Somalia is hot and dry, which makes farming difficult. Most of Somalia's people are nomadic herders on the country's plateaus. In the south, rivers provide water for irrigation. Farmers here grow fruits, sugarcane, and bananas.

Nearly all the people of Somalia are Muslims, but they are deeply divided. They belong to different **clans,** or groups of people who are related to one another. In the late 1980s, disputes between these clans led to civil war. When a drought struck a few years later, hundreds of thousands of people starved to death. The United States and other countries tried to restore some order and distribute food. The fighting continued, however, and often kept the aid from reaching the people who needed it. Even today, armed groups control various parts of Somalia. There is no real government that is in charge.

Reading Check What kind of conflict led to civil war in Somalia?

Section 4 Assessment

Defining Terms

1. **Define** plate, clan.

Recalling Facts

2. **Place** What is the capital of Ethiopia?
3. **History** What is the only country of East Africa that was never colonized by Europeans?
4. **Government** Describe the current political situation in Somalia.

Critical Thinking

5. **Making Inferences** What factors do you think might have led to the settlement of Khartoum, Sudan's capital?
6. **Understanding Cause and Effect** How did a war bring increased rights to women in Eritrea?

Graphic Organizer

7. **Organizing Information** On a diagram like the one below, list the major religions practiced in countries of the Horn of Africa. Write the religions under each country's name.

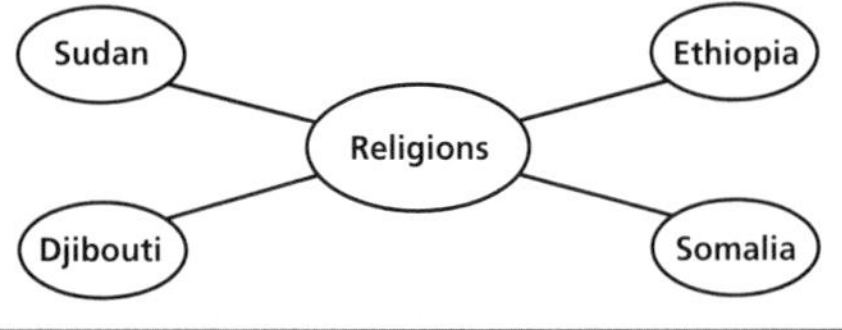

Applying Social Studies Skills

8. **Analyzing Maps** Study the ethnic groups map on page 589. What major ethnic groups are found in the Horn of Africa?

590 CHAPTER 20

Section 4 Assessment

1. The terms are defined in the Glossary.
2. Addis Ababa
3. Ethiopia
4. There is no real government in charge, but armed groups control various parts of the country.
5. *Possible answer:* Because it sits where the White and Blue Niles meet, it was probably an important site for trading and transportation both down the Nile and up the two branches.
6. Because women fought in the army that won the war for independence, the government passed laws that gave women more rights.
7. *Sudan*—Islam; *Ethiopia*—Islam, Christianity; *Djibouti*—Islam; *Somalia*—Islam
8. Tigre, Nuba, Nuer, Dinka, Galla, Somali, Ganda, Kikuyu, Masai, Hutu, Tutsi, Ngoni, Amhara

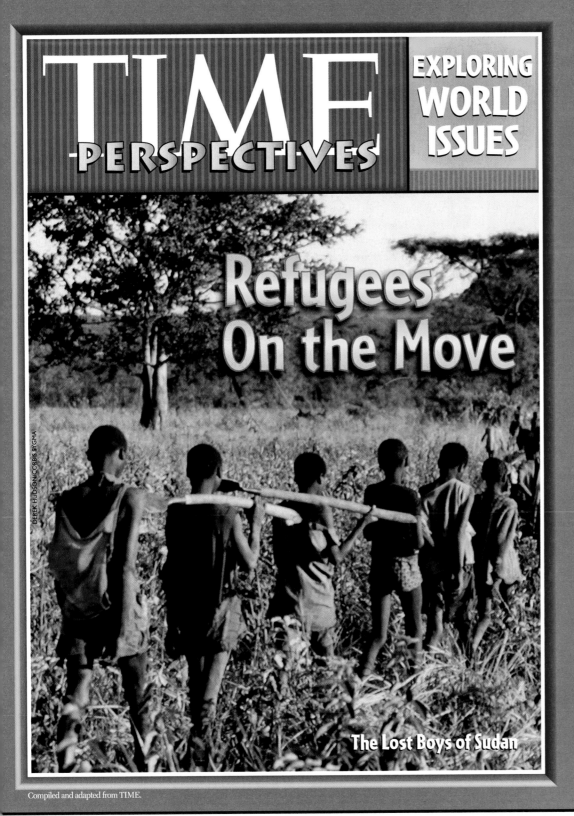

TIME PERSPECTIVES

EXPLORING WORLD ISSUES

Refugees On the Move

The Lost Boys of Sudan

DEREK HUDSON/CORBIS SYGMA

Compiled and adapted from TIME.

Exploring World Issues

Teacher Background

The Office of the United Nations High Commissioner on Refugees (UNHCR) was first set up in 1951 and assigned the task of resettling European refugees left homeless after World War II. At that time there were approximately 1.2 million refugees, most of whom were resettled in Europe.

Today, the number of refugees is much greater. This has put an enormous strain on the UNHCR and other organizations and countries wanting to help displaced persons.

TIME REPORTS

AFRICA SOUTH OF THE SAHARA

Refugees on the Move

THEME: CONFLICT AND MOVEMENT

Guide To Teaching With This Unit

Inside this Unit Three activity masters are designed to help your students understand the plight of millions of people who have lost their homes because of war or fear of persecution.

international action for the protection of refugees and for the resolution of refugee problems. Another UN agency, the Relief and Works Agency for Palestine Refugees in the Near East, provides services to 3.8 million Palestinian refugees.

The United States resettles more refugees than any other nation. But some ... such as Armenia and ... more refugees in

In regions of little stability, permanence is relative. Point out the statistic in the table dealing with returnees that shows hundreds of thousands of Afghanis returning home in 2000. Not noted is the fact that hundreds of thousands of Afghanis fled to Pakistan the next year to avoid the fighting prompted by the hunt for the terrorist Osama bin Laden. Have students bring the Afghanis' story up to date by digging up the latest figures on

Preparing the Student

In many parts of Africa, religious and cultural conflicts have led to refugee problems. Many of these conflicts have their roots in colonialism. When Europeans created countries in Africa, they determined boundaries without regard to cultural allegiances. The artificial states that were formed often threw together people of different ethnic groups with different languages and age-old rivalries. Colonial government also worsened political inequalities that had already existed among the different groups.

Making Connections

Diversity **Ask students:** **What do you think the words *diverse* and *inclusive* mean when Americans use them to discuss their society? Do you think America is an inclusive society? Why or why not?** Discuss the fact that many nations are composed of different groups that do not get along. These groups may have very different customs, religions, and views of the world. They do not subscribe to America's concept of "strength through diversity." When one group gains control of the government, it may attempt to destroy other groups, even to the point of killing them or forcing them to flee for their lives. These people become refugees. Many come to the United States. Compare the way these citizens might be treated in their country to their life in the United States.

TIME PERSPECTIVES

EXPLORING WORLD ISSUES

At a refugee camp, boys collected sticks and reeds to make huts, then cooked a rare meal of beans.

1 Focus

Ask students to write a paragraph summarizing what they understand about refugees in the world, not just in Africa. Remind them that this is not to place fault or blame but to explain the circumstances surrounding the problem, including as many causes as they can surmise.

Then put students in small groups to share their paragraphs and to create a list of nonjudgmental statements about what they believe are the main causes of the refugee crisis and the main issues needing to be resolved. Finally, bring the groups back together and create a master list. Let the students debate the merits of all the points included on the list. L3

Africans on the Move

ANSWER

None of these countries have refugees leaving their borders, but they are countries with internal displacements.

Evaluating Information

Pass out a copy of the Universal Declaration of Human Rights that was adopted by the UN in 1948. You can obtain it at www.un.org/rights. It has 30 articles. Have students read it and then in groups or individually ask them to choose the five rights that they think are most important. Afterwards have the class share their ratings and explain why they think some rights are more important than others. L2

The Lost Boys of Sudan

In November 1987, William Deng was tending cattle several miles from his village in southern Sudan. Two brothers and some cousins were with him. One afternoon they heard distant gunfire but ignored it. "The next morning," William said, "we saw the smoke. I climbed a tree and saw that my whole village was burned."

They raced to the village. There they learned that government troops had swept through. "Nobody was left standing," William said. "Some were wounded; some were killed. My father was dead. So we just ran away. I was 5."

The boys headed toward Ethiopia. Crossing marshlands and desert, they joined thousands of other Sudanese, mostly boys. They walked for two months. They ate berries, dried leaves, birds, and mice—anything they could find. Thousands died. "You think that maybe later that will be you," said one boy.

Into Ethiopia

The survivors finally reached a refugee camp in Ethiopia. **Refugees** are people forced by fear to find refuge, or shelter, outside their countries.

In 1991 Ethiopia closed its camps. Soldiers forced all of the "Lost Boys of Sudan," as they came to be called, back to their homeland.

After a year in Sudan, 10,000 of the boys fled to a refugee camp in Kenya. And there they stayed—some for as long as 10 years.

All Too Common

Sadly, William's experience is not unique. Throughout Africa south of the Sahara, millions of people have had to flee their homes. Most live in crowded camps set up by groups such as the United Nations. There they wait—until it is safe to go home, or until another country lets them stay.

Africans on the Move

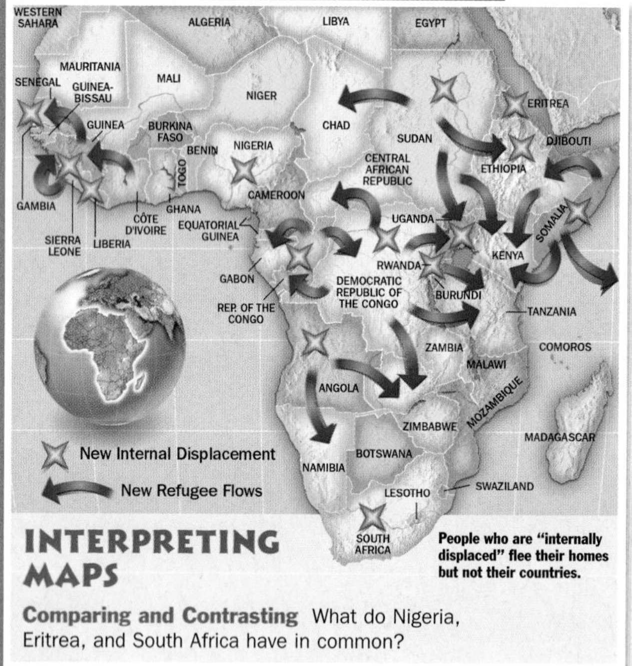

INTERPRETING MAPS

Comparing and Contrasting What do Nigeria, Eritrea, and South Africa have in common?

592

Team-Teaching Activity

Psychology Have a teacher who is knowledgeable about psychology discuss the adjustment problems these children faced when their families were killed and they were forced to leave their homes. The teacher may want to introduce Maslow's Hierarchy of Needs. At first the children struggled to meet their most fundamental physical needs, such as food, shelter, and safety. Those who survived and were sent to other countries to start a new life could try to meet higher-level needs, such as love and esteem. These needs can be met when people are accepted and cared for by those around them and learn skills to support themselves. After students have finished reading this report, have them discuss how the "Lost Boys of Sudan" fit this psychological pattern. L2

 **EE4 Human Systems: Standard 9**

Older boys "adopted" younger ones.

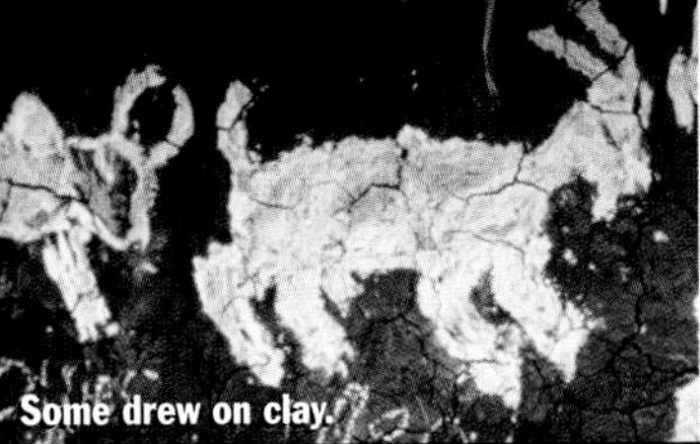
Some drew on clay.

The youngest wore the faces of suffering.

TOP PHOTOS: DEREK HUDSON/CORBIS SYGMA

The Lost Boys are victims of a Sudanese civil war that began in 1983. U.S. president George W. Bush explained in 2001, "Some 2 million Sudanese have lost their lives; 4 million more have lost their homes." The Sudan, he concluded, is a "disaster area for human rights."

Human rights include the right to safety, to food, and to shelter, among other things. In democracies, they also include the rights of citizens to choose their own leaders and to express opinions that are different from the government's.

Defining Refugees' Rights

In 1951, members of the United Nations agreed to guarantee basic human rights to refugees. They signed a **convention,** or special document, that gives refugees a unique legal status, or position. That status gives them the right to **asylum,** or safety, in foreign countries. It also gives them the right to be treated like any other foreign resident of their host country.

The convention defines refugees as people who leave their countries to flee **persecution.** Persecution is unfair treatment based on such characteristics as race, religion, or ethnic background. Recently the United Nations expanded this definition. Today people whose governments can't protect them from the dangers of war are also entitled to refugee status, the UN says.

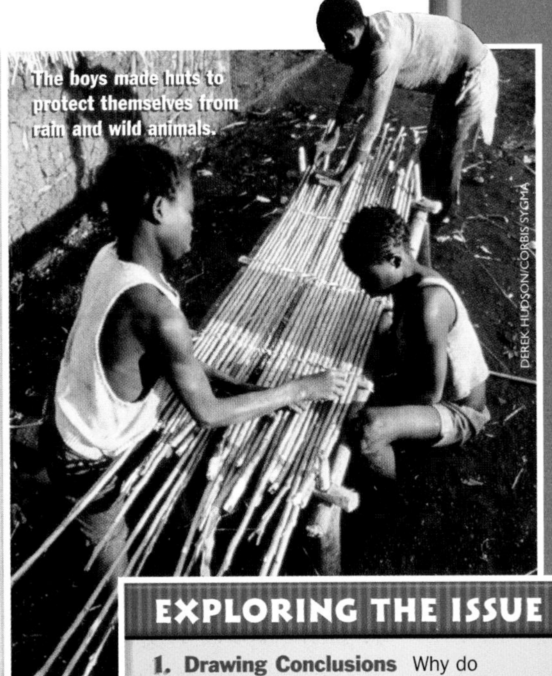
The boys made huts to protect themselves from rain and wild animals.

DEREK HUDSON/CORBIS SYGMA

EXPLORING THE ISSUE

1. **Drawing Conclusions** Why do you think thousands of the Lost Boys traveled together instead of alone?
2. **Making Predictions** How might your life change if you no longer had the basic human rights listed here?

Environmental Refugees

People who flee natural disasters, such as floods and famines, aren't refugees. They are "displaced persons" or "environmental refugees." Immigrants aren't refugees, either. Immigrants may leave their countries to get an education or find a better job. Refugees like the Lost Boys of Sudan have little choice. They flee their countries to find safety. ☐

593

2 TEACH

Reading Strategy

Identifying Main Ideas As students read each subsection, have them write one sentence that expresses the main idea. Have volunteers offer their sentences and discuss to what extent they do or do not capture the main idea. L1

More About the Photos

Lost Boys Ask: Where do you think these young people learned the skills they needed to build their own shelters?

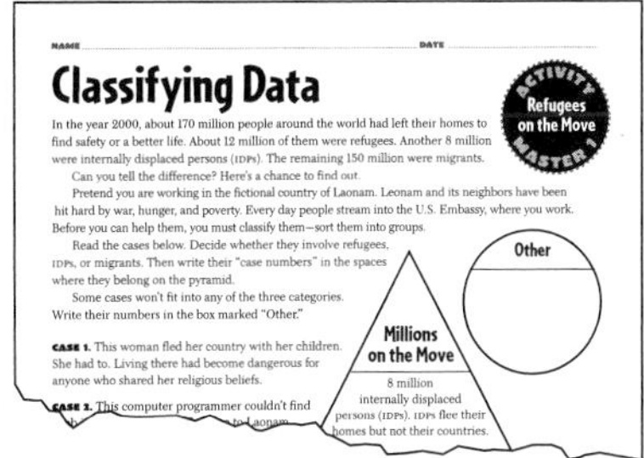
NAME .... DATE ....

Classifying Data

ACTIVITY MASTER 1 — Refugees on the Move

In the year 2000, about 170 million people around the world had left their homes to find safety or a better life. About 12 million of them were refugees. Another 8 million were internally displaced persons (IDPs). The remaining 150 million were migrants.

Can you tell the difference? Here's a chance to find out.

Pretend you are working in the fictional country of Laonam. Leonam and its neighbors have been hit hard by war, hunger, and poverty. Every day people stream into the U.S. Embassy, where you work. Before you can help them, you must classify them—sort them into groups.

Read the cases below. Decide whether they involve refugees, IDPs, or migrants. Then write their "case numbers" in the spaces where they belong on the pyramid.

Some cases won't fit into any of the three categories. Write their numbers in the box marked "Other."

CASE 1. This woman fled her country with her children. She had to. Living there had become dangerous for anyone who shared her religious beliefs.

CASE 2. This computer programmer couldn't find

Millions on the Move

8 million internally displaced persons (IDPs). IDPs flee their homes but not their countries.

Other

EXPLORING THE ISSUE

ANSWERS

1. *Possible answers:* a group provides more protection and emotional support; they could share their skills; older boys could care for younger ones
2. Answers will vary.

Differentiated Instruction

Meeting Special Needs: Intrapersonal Write the following questions: Do you think you would have the ability to survive on your own as these young people did? What qualities do you have that you think would help you survive? How do you think this experience would change the way you felt about others and how you lived your life in the future? Organize students into small groups and have them discuss their responses to these questions. Then have them write a short essay that summarizes their responses. L2

Refer to *Inclusion for the Middle School Social Studies Classroom Strategies and Activities* in the TCR.

Recommended Internet Sites

www.unhcr.ch
This is the official Web site of the United Nations High Commissioner for Refugees, which contains up-to-date information on refugees, along with statistics. Clicking on Research/Evaluation will take you to Teaching Tools.

www.refugeeinternational.org
This Web site provides reports on current refugee problems.

Synthesizing Information
Have groups pick a country with refugee camps. Each group should research ways that the UN, its member nations, and relief organizations are helping the refugees. Groups should make a presentation that answers the following: **What are conditions like in the camps? Are there schools for the children? How can the organizations find permanent homes and jobs for the refugees? L2**

EXPLORING THE ISSUE

ANSWERS

1. Displaced people disrupt the countries into which they flee and require possibly scarce food, shelter, and medical care. They may spread diseases, such as AIDS.
2. Governments may not have the resources to provide these services. They may not want to encourage refugees to stay or more to enter their country.

TIME PERSPECTIVES

Africa's Troubled Past

Refugees have existed in many places, not only countries in Africa. Yet rarely has the flow of refugees been as widespread as it is today. Worldwide, about 35 million people were on the move in 2002. Nearly 22 million of them were **internally displaced persons (IDPs)**—people who flee to safety inside their own countries. About 13 million more were refugees seeking freedom from war and persecution outside their countries. During 2002, Africa alone held more than 3 million refugees and at least 11 million IDPs.

The Impact of Violence

The presence of these uprooted people is reshaping Africa. Away from their villages, refugees no longer grow crops, worsening food shortages. The crush of refugees drains the resources of the already poor countries that host them. And refugees sometimes spread AIDS, a disease that by 2001 had killed the parents of 12 million African children.

Many experts trace Africa's refugee problem back to the late 1800s. That's when European nations began to carve the continent into colonies. Africa's 2,000 ethnic groups speak around one thousand languages. But European colonizers failed to respect those differences. They set up boundaries that split individual ethnic groups into many pieces. Other borders forced traditional enemies such as Rwanda's Hutu and Tutsi to share the same space.

ELIZABETH L. GILBERT/CORBIS SYGMA

▲ **War chased thousands of terrified Burundians into the Congo in 1995.**

How America Is Different

Colonists living in Britain's 13 colonies didn't face such problems in 1776. When the U.S. was born, most Americans spoke English and shared similar values. They were ready to rule themselves as a democracy.

Africa's colonies became independent nearly two centuries later. But they contained groups that had little interest in working together. That made it hard for democracy to take root. In many nations, armed groups muscled their way to power. Such struggles for control turned millions of Africans into refugees. ■

EXPLORING THE ISSUE

1. **Making Inferences** In what ways might Africa's refugee problem hurt all Africans?
2. **Analyzing Information** How might the refugee problem keep governments from building roads and providing services such as education and health care?

Critical Thinking Activity

Making Comparisons Have students think about what they have read and learned about concerning the Israeli-Palestinian conflict Have the class respond to the following questions: **How is the plight of today's Palestinian refugees similar to that of the Sudanese? How is it different? L2**

 **EE4 Human Systems: Standard 9**

TIME REPORTS

Struggling to Survive

When refugees enter another country, they may face dangers. In 1997, for example, soldiers rounded up refugees who had lived many years in Tanzania. They forced the refugees into camps. "I never thought the Tanzanian government would do this to us," said a woman who fled Burundi in 1971. "I am now held in a refugee camp, but my children are still outside. They have no money to come here."

Even refugees allowed to stay in private homes face risks. "We are frequently arrested by the police," said an Ethiopian who fled to Kenya. "They require bribes before they will release us."

Refugee Children

For children, refugee life brings special problems. Those separated from their parents must fend for themselves. Some girls and boys are forced to become soldiers. Others must work for little or no pay. Abby, 14, fled the war in Sierra Leone. Now she lives in a refugee camp in Guinea. "In the morning," she said, "I fetch water, sweep, and pray. Then I go find a job for the day. I usually pound rice. I get no food, only [a tiny amount of money]. I will be in the sun until evening. I feel pain all over my body. I don't go to school. I live with my grandmother, and she is very old. I need to take care of her."

Many of the overcrowded camps are dirty and unhealthy. But until their countries become safe again, the refugees have few choices. Either they stay in the camps, or they return home to the horrors they fled.

AFP PHOTO/NEWSCOM

▲ A Hutu woman and child walk to a refugee camp near the Rwanda-Tanzania border.

EXPLORING THE ISSUE

1. **Drawing Conclusions** What do you think makes many refugee camps so difficult to live in?
2. **Problem Solving** Gather information from the text to identify problems faced by refugees in camps. Consider changes that might be made to the camps to improve life there.

Understanding Cause and Effect Afghanistan has a long history of people fleeing the country as refugees. After the September 11, 2001, terrorist attacks on the United States, even more Afghans fled the country, knowing U.S. retaliation was coming. Have students research and write a report about the history of Afghan refugees, the problems they have faced, and to what countries they have fled. L2

Did You Know?

In October 2003, the Kakuma refugee camp in Kenya housed 86,000 people. The refugees outnumber the local people.

EXPLORING THE ISSUE

ANSWERS

1. People are separated from their homes and families, so they lack a traditional support system. Camps are often crowded and lack sanitary facilities, causing disease.
2. *Problems include:* separation of families, overcrowding, unsanitary conditions, harassment by soldiers or governments, and child exploitation. The UN, its member countries, and relief agencies can combine resources of money, manpower, and political pressure to improve conditions in camps and help return refugees to their homes.

Interdisciplinary Activity

Literature Considerable literature has been written by and about refugees. Following World War II, many books were written by European Jews who were displaced during the war and by people from eastern Europe who fled Soviet persecution. Have students read a biographical work or a work of fiction about a refugee from an area in which they are interested. When they are done reading, they should write a book report. Instruct them to focus on the feelings of the primary character(s). **Why did the characters become refugees? What difficulties did they have in adjusting to their new homeland? L3**

EE4 Human Systems: Standard 10

Current Events Journal

Instruct students to go to the Web site of the United Nations High Commissioner for Refugees (www.unhcr.ch) to find the current listing of the 10 countries with the most refugees fleeing their borders. They should use this information to create a pie chart showing the percentage of refugees coming from each of the 10 countries.

EXPLORING THE ISSUE

ANSWERS

1. *Possible answers:* using everyday appliances, understanding laws and what is expected of you in school; understanding American slang and customs
2. *Possible answers:* helping them with grocery shopping, cooking dinner, doing the laundry, and going to the bank

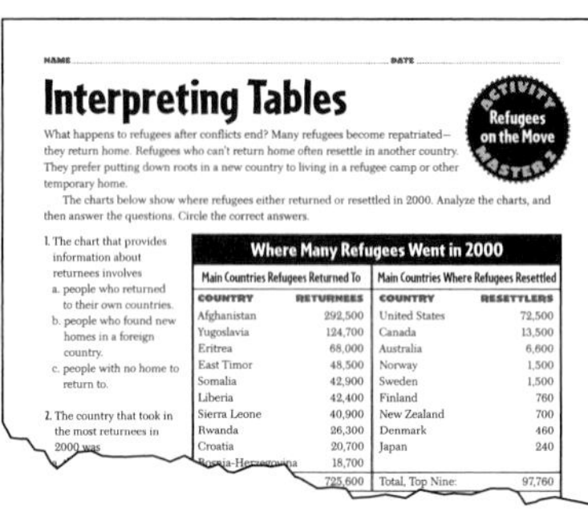

NAME .... DATE ....

Interpreting Tables

ACTIVITY MASTER 2 — Refugees on the Move

What happens to refugees after conflicts end? Many refugees become repatriated—they return home. Refugees who can't return home often resettle in another country. They prefer putting down roots in a new country to living in a refugee camp or other temporary home.

The charts below show where refugees either returned or resettled in 2000. Analyze the charts, and then answer the questions. Circle the correct answers.

1. The chart that provides information about returnees involves
   a. people who returned to their own countries.
   b. people who found new homes in a foreign country.
   c. people with no home to return to.
2. The country that took in the most returnees in 2000 was

Where Many Refugees Went in 2000

Main Countries Refugees Returned To		Main Countries Where Refugees Resettled	
COUNTRY	RETURNEES	COUNTRY	RESETTLERS
Afghanistan	292,500	United States	72,500
Yugoslavia	124,700	Canada	13,500
Eritrea	68,000	Australia	6,600
East Timor	48,500	Norway	1,500
Somalia	42,900	Sweden	1,500
Liberia	42,400	Finland	760
Sierra Leone	40,900	New Zealand	700
Rwanda	26,300	Denmark	460
Croatia	20,700	Japan	240
Bosnia-Herzegovina	18,700		
	725,600	Total, Top Nine:	97,760

TIME PERSPECTIVES

Helping Refugees: What Can One Person Do?

Countries that offer asylum to refugees are known as **host countries.** Starting life over in a host country can be hard for refugees and their families. William Deng and Joseph Maker are among more than 3,000 Lost Boys of Sudan who have found refuge in the United States. William lives in Grand Rapids, Michigan. Joseph lives in Houston, Texas, as do 170 other Lost Boys. In both places, local people taught them how to take buses, shop, and even use faucets and refrigerators. Many of those helpers were volunteers.

Eventually, many refugees who get such help grow to love their adopted country. They come to love it as much as or even more than people born there.

STEVE LISS

◀ These Michigan second graders are learning English at school.

Strangers in a New Land

HOUSTON CHRONICLE

▲ Joseph Maker found a warm welcome in Houston, Texas.

Joseph Maker and fellow Lost Boys felt they had landed on another planet when they reached Houston, their new home. They had to be taught to use electricity, running water, air conditioners, flush toilets, stoves, and telephones.

Packaged foods baffled them. At the refugee camp in Kenya, they had eaten the same meal—beans and lentils—every day for nine years. In Houston they discovered junk food—and the fear of getting fat. "I've heard in America, people can become big," said Joseph's friend James Thon Aleer.

The newcomers also had to learn new ways to act. In Sudan, it's disrespectful to look into the eyes of the person you're speaking to. In America, it's impolite to look away. Joseph and his friends adopted the American way, something they think helped all of them get jobs.

One thing they picked up quickly was American humor. The tag on James Thon Aleer's key chain says "Don't Mess with Texas."

EXPLORING THE ISSUE

1. **Categorizing** If you were an African refugee in your community, what things might confuse you the most?
2. **Problem Solving** How might volunteers help refugees adapt to life in your community?

Your Government and You

Many countries around the world, including the United States, grant asylum to refugees. Each year, the United States sets quotas for the number of refugees it will accept from different continents. This number has been shrinking, from 142,000 in 1992 to 70,000 in 2003. Organize students into groups. **Ask:** **How can we encourage our government to become more active in helping refugees? What can we do on an individual basis to help refugees around the world and in our communities?** Have the groups share their responses and decide which options are best. If possible, implement one of the solutions. **L3**

REVIEW AND ASSESS

UNDERSTANDING THE ISSUE

1. **Defining Key Terms** Write definitions for the following terms: *refugee, human rights, convention, asylum, persecution, internally displaced person,* and *host country.*

2. **Writing to Inform** Write a 250-word article about the refugee issue. Use the key terms listed above.

3. **Writing to Persuade** "There is no greater sorrow on Earth than the loss of one's native land." A Greek thinker wrote those words about 2,500 years ago. Is his statement as true today? Write a short essay to explain.

INTERNET RESEARCH ACTIVITIES

4. With your teacher's help, use Internet resources to find information on issues involving refugees in the world, particularly in Africa today. Write a brief report on current "refugee hot spots" in Africa south of the Sahara. Be prepared to report on these problems in class.

5. With your teacher's help, choose two nations in Africa south of the Sahara. Then use Internet resources to learn more about these countries. Concentrate your research on refugee problems in your chosen nations and report your findings to the class.

BEYOND THE CLASSROOM

6. **Visit your school or local library** to find books in which young refugees share their experiences. (Enter the key words "refugee children" on the **Amazon.com** Web site, and you can find some titles to start with.) Bring those books to class to share with your classmates.

STEVE LISS

▲ This Hmong boy from Laos now lives in Wisconsin.

7. **Research a refugee problem outside Africa.** List ways that it is like—and different from—refugee problems in Africa. Report your findings to your classmates.

8. **Work in groups** to come up with ways young people could make it easier for newcomers to your community. Put your suggestions on a poster. Include phone numbers of groups that provide services for refugees. Display the poster for all students to see.

Where the World's Refugees Come From

(Top Sources of Refugees as of January 1, 2003)

Afghanistan	3,500,000
Palestinians	3,000,000
Burma	510,000
Sudan	475,000
Angola	410,000
Congo-Kinshasa	410,000
Burundi	400,000
Vietnam	302,000
Somalia	300,000
Iraq	294,000
Eritrea	290,000
Liberia	280,000
Croatia	251,000
El Salvador	203,000
China	178,000
Total	**10,803,000**

Around the world in 2002, some 13 million people lived as refugees. This table lists the 15 nations that most of them fled. Besides refugees, nearly 22 million others are internally displaced persons (IDPs). IDPs seek safety inside their nations' borders but far from their homes.

Source: U.S. Committee for Refugees

BUILDING SKILLS FOR READING TABLES

1. **Categorizing** Use your text to categorize the 15 nations listed here under one of five regions: Africa, Central America, Eastern Europe, Southeast Asia, and Southwest Asia.
2. **Analyzing Data** Which of the above regions have the greatest and smallest number of refugees?
3. **Transferring Data** Create a bar graph based on the country data in this table.

FOR UPDATES ON WORLD ISSUES GO TO www.timeclassroom.com/glencoe

3 ASSESS

Have students take the TIME Reports Quiz or do the Alternative Assessment project for this unit provided in the Teacher's Classroom Resources.

NAME .... DATE ....

Recording Oral History

ACTIVITY MASTER 3 — Refugees on the Move

You don't live where you do by chance. Someone—a parent, a grandparent, or even a great-grandparent—decided to move there.

Who made that decision? Where did that person's ancestors live? This activity will give you an opportunity to find out. It shows you how to piece together a brief oral history of your family. Simply ask a family member to help you trace the path your family took to where you live now.

There are only two rules. First, trace the ancestors of only one adult member of your family. Second, don't go back any farther than four generations. That would take you back to the great-grandparents of the adult providing the information.

Try to get as many answers as you can to the questions on this page. You may want to ask other questions, too. Write those questions and their answers on the back of this sheet of paper. Finally, share your oral history with your classmates.

1. What year did your family move to your town or city?
2. Who made the decision to move there?
3. What was the reason for moving to your town or city? (to be close to work, to live near relatives, etc.)

BUILDING SKILLS FOR READING TABLES

ANSWERS

1. *Africa:* Sudan, Burundi, Angola, Liberia, Somalia, Congo-Kinshasa, Eritrea; *Central America:* El Salvador; *Eastern Europe:* Croatia; *Southeast Asia:* Burma, Vietnam, China; *Southwest Asia:* Palestinians, Afghanistan, Iraq
2. *greatest:* Southwest Asia; *smallest:* Central America
3. The bar graph can illustrate the number of refugees in each country or region.

4 CLOSE

Reading Strategy

Writing a Paragraph Ask students to write a paragraph starting with this sentence: *The plight of refugees is a global issue because . . . .*

Culminating Activity

To close this lesson, have students complete the Review and Assess section questions and activities above. Students should use classroom discussion, contextual clues, and their student dictionaries to write definitions for terms. Before assigning the Internet activities, it is recommended that you review your school district policy on student Internet use.

Focus on Debate

Have students debate the pro and con position of the following: **The United States should take in as many refugees as possible, provide them with what they need to live, and help them develop skills they need to get jobs and become productive citizens.** **L2**

TEACH

Ask: What is the weather going to be like tomorrow? How do you know? *(Possible responses: heard or read a weather report; guessing based on what the weather is like today)* Point out that in this situation, either the weather reporter or the students themselves were making a prediction. Explain that in this feature, students will learn how to use data to make their predictions more reliable than by just guessing. L1

Additional Skills Practice

1. **Why should you analyze trends before making predictions?** *(to make the predictions more accurate)*
2. **How can you generate lists of possible consequences of an action?** *(Possible answers: brainstorming; talking to other people)*

Additional Skills Resources

 Chapter Skills Review

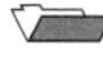 Building Geography Skills for Life

GLENCOE TECHNOLOGY

 **Skillbuilder Interactive Workbook CD-ROM, Level 1**

This interactive CD-ROM reinforces student mastery of essential social studies skills.

Critical Thinking Skill

Making Predictions

Predicting consequences is sometimes difficult and risky. The more information you have, however, the more accurate your predictions will be.

Learning the Skill

Follow these steps to learn how to better predict consequences:

- Gather information about the decision or action that you are considering.
- Use your knowledge of history and human behavior to identify what consequences could result.
- Analyze each of the consequences by asking yourself: How likely is it that this will occur?

Practicing the Skill

Study the graph below, and then answer these questions:

1. What is measured on this graph? Over what time period?
2. In what year did the fewest tourists visit Kenya?
3. What trend does the graph show?
4. Do you think that this trend is likely to continue?
5. On what do you base this prediction?
6. List three possible consequences of this trend.

Applying the Skill

Analyze three articles in your local newspaper. Predict three consequences of the actions in each of the articles. On what do you base your predictions?

GO TO Practice key skills with **Glencoe Skillbuilder Interactive Workbook, Level 1.**

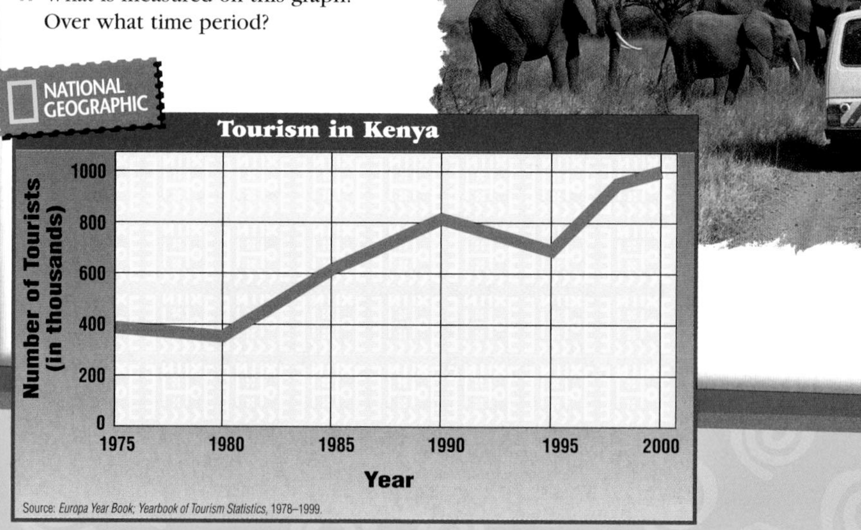

598

Practicing the Skill Answers

1. tourism in Kenya; 1975–2000
2. 1980
3. that the number of tourists visiting Kenya has steadily increased
4. yes, but at a slower rate
5. The rise in tourists evened out a little bit from 1997 to 2000, but it continued to increase.
6. *Possible answers:* Kenya's economy will continue benefiting from tourism, but at a slower rate. The wildlife in Kenya will continue to be protected for tourism purposes. Perhaps more land will be set aside for nature preserves to draw more tourists to the country.

Applying the Skill

Ask students to hand in copies of the articles along with their predictions.

Reading Review

Section 1 Central Africa

Terms to Know
canopy
hydroelectric power
tsetse fly
deforestation

Main Idea
Central Africa has rich natural resources that are largely undeveloped because of civil war and poor government decisions.

✓Movement The Congo River—the second-largest river in Africa—provides transportation and hydroelectric power.
✓Economics The Democratic Republic of the Congo has many resources but has not been able to take full advantage of them.
✓Culture Sango is the national language of the Central African Republic. It eases communication among the many ethnic groups.
✓Economics The economies of Congo and Gabon rely on exports of lumber.

Section 2 People of Kenya and Tanzania

Terms to Know
coral reef
poaching
free enterprise system
cassava
sisal
habitat
ecotourist

Main Idea
Kenya and Tanzania are countries in East Africa with diverse landscapes and peoples.

✓Place Western Kenya is marked by highlands and the Great Rift Valley.
✓Economics Many people in Kenya are farmers. Coffee and tea are grown for export. Tourism is also a major industry in Kenya.
✓Culture Kenya's people speak Swahili and English.
✓Economics Farming and tourism are Tanzania's main economic activities.
✓Government Tanzania's government has been stable and democratic.

Section 3 Uganda, Rwanda, and Burundi

Terms to Know
plantains
autonomy
watershed
endangered species
genocide
refugee

Main Idea
Uganda, Rwanda, and Burundi have suffered much conflict in recent years.

✓Place Uganda, Rwanda, and Burundi are landlocked countries with high elevation and rainy, moderate climates.
✓Economics Most people in all three countries practice subsistence farming.
✓History Rwanda and Burundi suffered a brutal civil war in the 1990s between the Hutu and the Tutsi ethnic groups.

Section 4 The Horn of Africa

Terms to Know
plate
clan

Main Idea
The countries of the Horn of Africa have all been scarred by conflict in recent years.

✓History Sudan has been torn by a civil war between the northern Muslim Arabs and the southern African peoples.
✓Place Ethiopia has good farmland, but scarce rainfall can cause drought.
✓Government Eritrea recently won its independence from Ethiopia.
✓History Civil war and drought have caused suffering in Somalia.

Reading Review

Use the Chapter 20 Reading Review to preview, review, condense, or reteach the chapter.

Preview/Review

Use the Terms to Know lists to help students review and study.

Activity Have students create crossword puzzles for 10 of the terms from the chapter, exchange papers with another student, and try to complete their partner's puzzle.

Vocabulary PuzzleMaker CD-ROM reinforces the vocabulary terms used in Chapter 20.

The Interactive Tutor Self-Assessment CD-ROM allows students to review Chapter 20 content.

Condense

Have students read the Chapter 20 summary statements.

Guided Reading Activities

Audio Program

Reteach

Reteaching Activity

Reading Essentials and Study Guide

Reading Strategy Read to Write

Creating Illustrated Encyclopedias
Have students work in small groups to create an illustrated encyclopedia for East and Central Africa. Offer the following as a sample entry: "T is for Tanganyika . . . a lake in southeastern Central Africa on the border between the Democratic Republic of the Congo and Tanzania. Lake Tanganyika is the world's longest freshwater lake and the second-deepest, after Lake Baikal in Russia." Students may consult almanacs and encyclopedias for items beginning with certain letters. Display the finished encyclopedias. L1

EE2 Places and Regions: Standard 4

Assessment and Activities

GLENCOE TECHNOLOGY

MindJogger Videoquiz
Use MindJogger Videoquiz to review the Chapter 20 content.

Available in DVD and VHS

Using Key Terms

1.	f	6.	c
2.	i	7.	a
3.	e	8.	b
4.	j	9.	d
5.	h	10.	g

Reviewing the Main Ideas

11. Lack of roads and thick rain forests make it hard to transport mineral resources for trade.
12. French; it was a colony of France prior to gaining independence.
13. the Portuguese
14. "pulling together"
15. on the islands of Zanzibar and Pemba
16. lions, wild dogs, wildebeests, zebras, antelope
17. coffee
18. Goods are taken by road to Lake Tanganyika, then sent by boat to Tanzania or the Democratic Republic of the Congo.
19. Hutu and Tutsi
20. Sudan
21. Eritrea

Chapter 20 Assessment and Activities

Using Key Terms

Match the terms in Part A with their definitions in Part B.

A.

1. canopy
2. tsetse fly
3. poaching
4. endangered species
5. habitat
6. genocide
7. hydroelectric power
8. clan
9. refugee
10. ecotourist

B.

a. electricity created by flowing water
b. family, or group of related people
c. deliberate murder of a group of people because of race or culture
d. person who flees to another country for safety
e. hunting and killing animals illegally
f. topmost layer of a rain forest
g. person who travels to view natural wonders
h. environment where an animal species lives
i. insect whose bite can cause sleeping sickness
j. plant or animal in danger of dying out

Reviewing the Main Ideas

Section 1 Central Africa

11. **Economy** How has transportation affected the economy of the Democratic Republic of the Congo?
12. **Culture** What is the official language of the Central African Republic? Why?
13. **History** Who originally settled São Tomé and Príncipe?

Section 2 People of Kenya and Tanzania

14. **Culture** What does the term *harambee* mean to Kenyans?
15. **Economics** In which part of Tanzania are cloves produced?
16. **Region** Name some of the animals that live on the Serengeti Plain.

Section 3 Uganda, Rwanda, and Burundi

17. **Economics** What is Uganda's main export?
18. **Movement** How do Burundi and Rwanda get their goods to foreign buyers?
19. **Culture** What two ethnic groups fought in Rwanda and Burundi?

Section 4 The Horn of Africa

20. **Place** What is the largest country in Africa?
21. **Place** What is Africa's newest country?

Central and East Africa

Place Location Activity

On a separate sheet of paper, match the letters on the map with the numbered places listed below.

1. Congo River
2. Cameroon
3. Kenya
4. Central African Republic
5. Sudan
6. Tanzania
7. Democratic Republic of the Congo
8. Somalia
9. Rwanda
10. Gabon

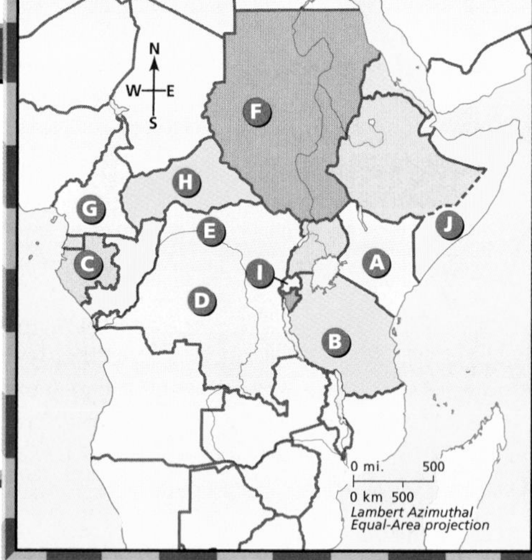

NATIONAL GEOGRAPHIC

Place Location Activity

1.	E	6.	B
2.	G	7.	D
3.	A	8.	J
4.	H	9.	I
5.	F	10.	C

Critical Thinking

22. Good transportation is needed to move goods to markets.
23. Trees are cut; land cannot hold soil or rain water in place; land dries; soil blows away; desert

Comparing Regions Activity

24. Students should identify 10 coffee-producing countries and compare their geographies to the geography of Central and East Africa.

Self-Check Quiz Visit ***The World and Its People*** Web site at twip.glencoe.com and click on **Chapter 20—Self-Check Quizzes** to prepare for the Chapter Test.

Critical Thinking

22. **Drawing Conclusions** Central and East Africa depend on agriculture as a main economic activity. Why is a good transportation system important to an agricultural society?
23. **Sequencing Information** In a diagram like the one below, describe and put in order the steps that can lead to the creation of a desert.

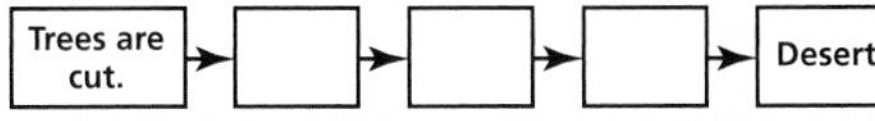

Comparing Regions Activity

24. **Geography** Did you know that a plant originally from the plateaus of central Ethiopia is used to make one of the most sought after products in the world? Your teachers or other adults may drink this product every day. It is coffee! Ethiopia is the country that produces the most coffee in Africa. What other countries in the world produce coffee? List ten coffee-producing countries. Compare the countries' geographies to the geography of central and east Africa. How are they similar and different?

Mental Mapping Activity

25. **Focusing on the Region** Create a simple outline map of Africa, and then label the following:
    - Sudan
    - Cameroon
    - Kenya
    - Tanzania
    - Democratic Republic of the Congo
    - Lake Victoria
    - Uganda
    - Congo River
    - Nile River

Technology Skills Activity

26. **Developing a Multimedia Presentation** Choose one of Africa's endangered animals and create a multimedia presentation about it. Include pictures or video clips of the animal, maps of its habitat area, and the steps being taken to protect this animal.

Standardized Test Practice

Directions: Study the map below, and then answer the question that follows.

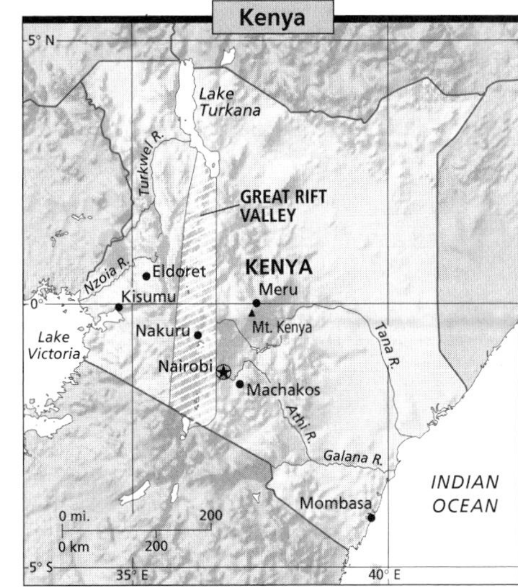

1. **About how many miles is it from Nairobi to Mombasa?**
   F 100 miles
   G 200 miles
   H 300 miles
   J 400 miles

Test-Taking Tip: Look carefully at the map key to understand its *scale,* or distance from one point to another. If you find it difficult to judge distances visually, use a small piece of scrap paper to measure the units described in the key.

Assessment and Activities

Standardized Test Practice

1. H

Tested Objectives:
Analyzing a map, drawing conclusions

Chapter Test Bonus Question

This question may be used for extra credit on the chapter test.

What type of ecosystem covers a large portion of Central Africa north and south of the Equator? *(tropical rain forest)*

Have students visit the Web site at twip.glencoe.com to review Chapter 20 and take the Self-Check Quiz.

FOLDABLES™ Study Organizer **Dinah Zike's Foldables**

Culminating Activity Have students create a poster board mural that shows images of traditional and modern cultures in Central and East Africa.

Mental Mapping Activity

25. This exercise helps students visualize the countries and geographic features they have been studying. Accept all attempts at freehand mapping that show places in the correct relationship to one another.

Technology Skills Activity

26. Students might apply what they have learned about endangered animals in other parts of the world and include that information in their presentations.

Chapter 21 Resources

Note: The following materials may be used when teaching Chapter 21.
Section level support materials are shown at point of use in the margins of the Teacher Wraparound Edition.

Timesaving Tools

TeacherWorks™ All-In-One Planner and Resource Center

- **Interactive Teacher Edition** See the **Interactive Teacher Edition** CD-ROM to electronically integrate your Teacher Wraparound Edition and blackline masters.
- **Interactive Lesson Planner** Organize your week, month, semester, or year with all the lesson helps you need. The **Interactive Lesson Planner** CD-ROM contains all Chapter 21 resources.

Use Glencoe's **Presentation Plus!** multimedia teacher tool to easily present dynamic lessons that visually excite your students. Using Microsoft PowerPoint® you can customize the presentations to create your own personalized lessons.

TEACHING TRANSPARENCIES

Graphic Organizer Transparency 4 L2

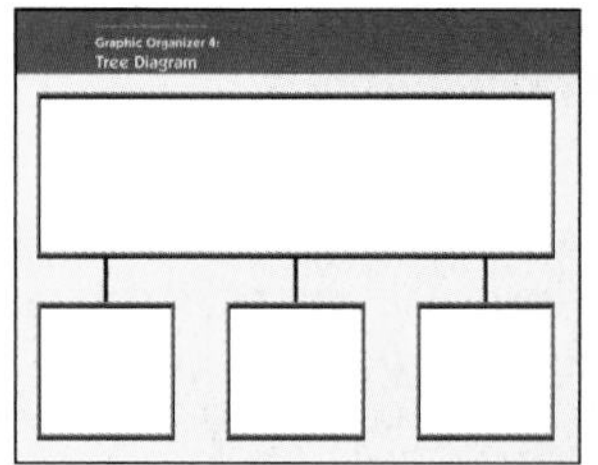

In-text Map Transparency L1

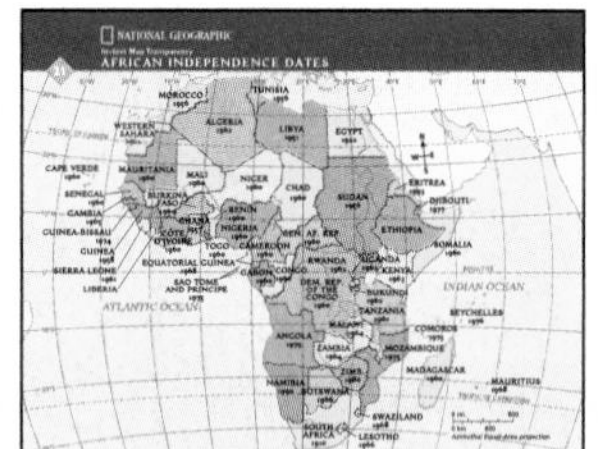

FOLDABLES™ Study Organizer

Dinah Zike's Foldables

Foldables are three-dimensional, interactive graphic organizers that help students practice basic writing skills, review key vocabulary terms, and identify main ideas. Additional chapter activities can be found in the ***Reading and Study Skills Foldables*** booklet.

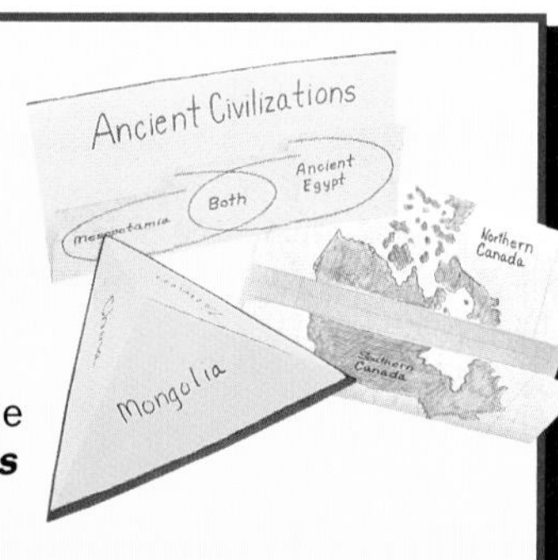

MAP AND GEOGRAPHY SKILLS

Chapter Map Activity L2

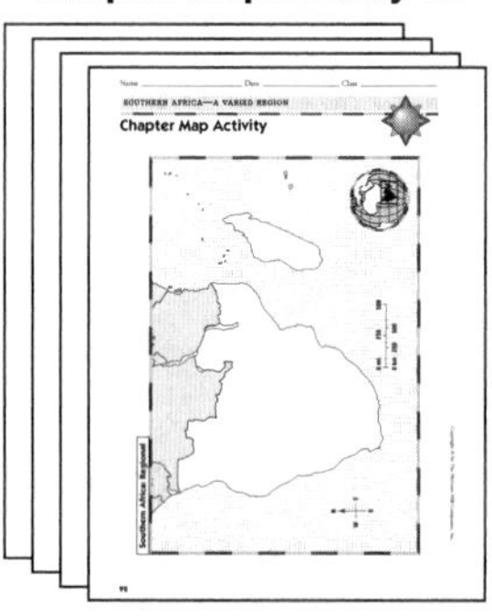

GeoLab Activity L2

READING SUPPORT

Vocabulary Activity L1

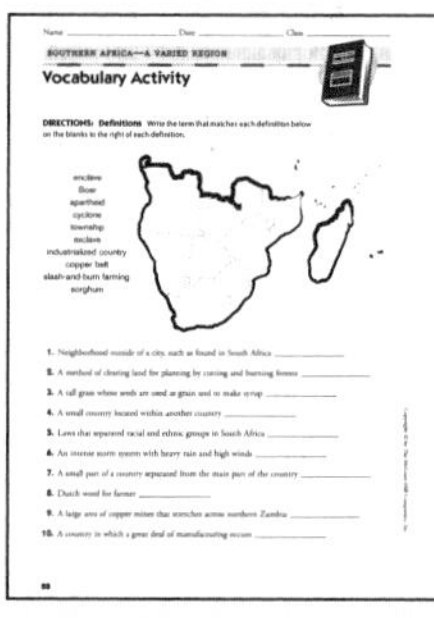

Workbook Activity L1

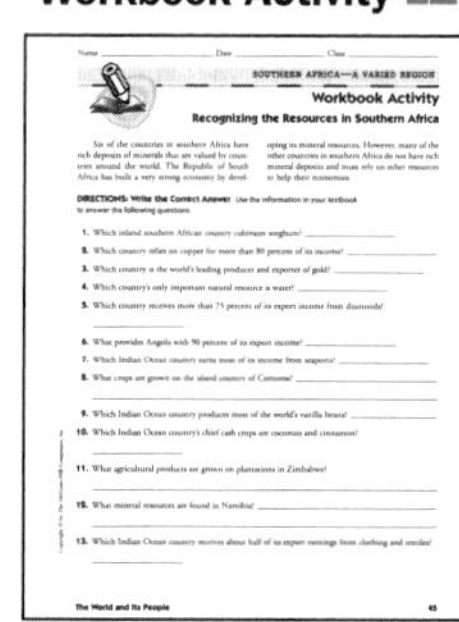

Reading and Writing Skills Activity L1/ELL

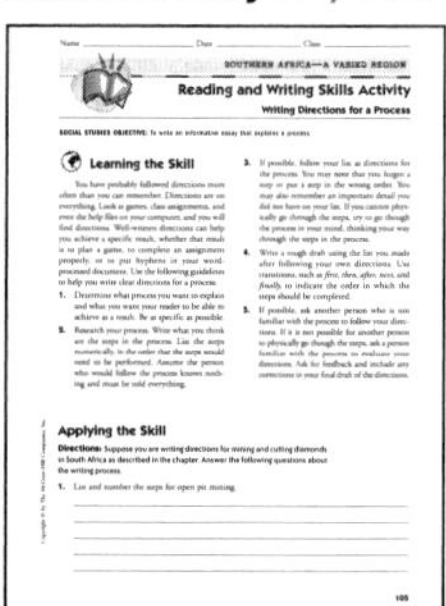

DIFFERENTIATED INSTRUCTION

Use these review and reinforcement materials to help less-proficient readers, English learners, and gifted and talented students.

Reteaching Activity L1

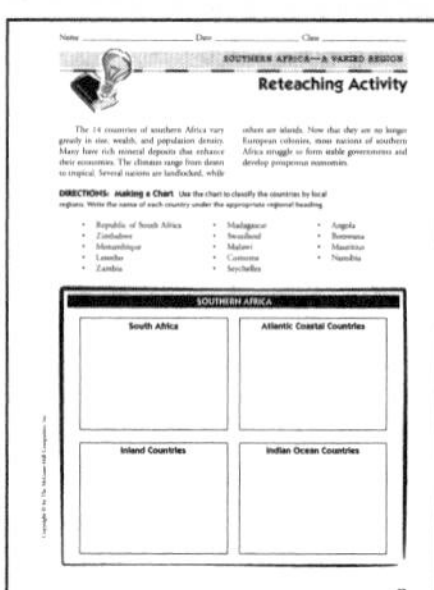

Chapter Skills Review L2

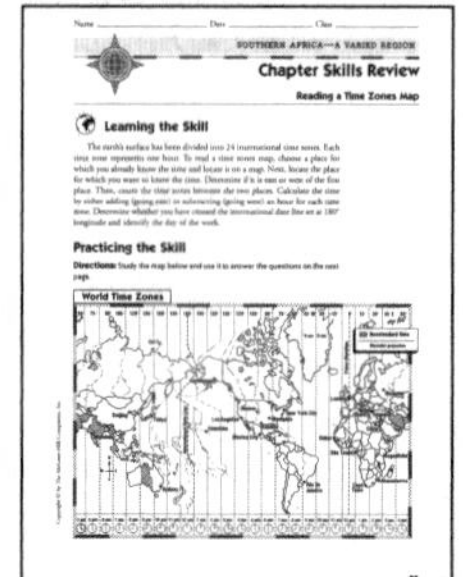

Cooperative Learning Activity L1/ELL

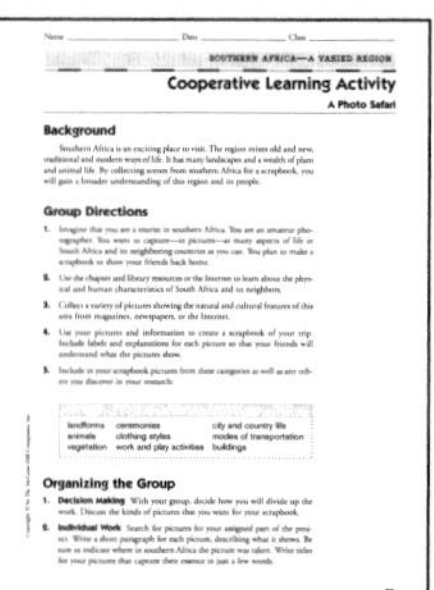

Enrichment Activity L3

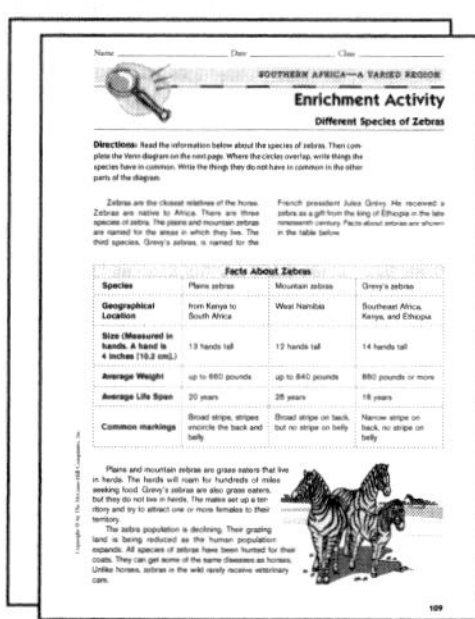

ASSESSMENT

Chapter Test, Form A L2

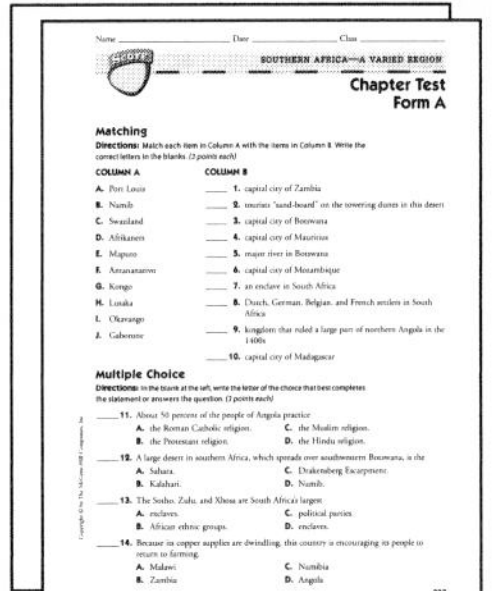

Chapter Test, Form B L2

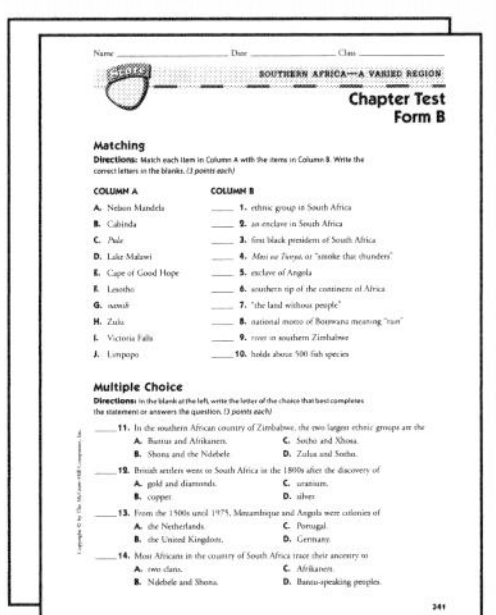

Performance Assessment Activity L1/ELL

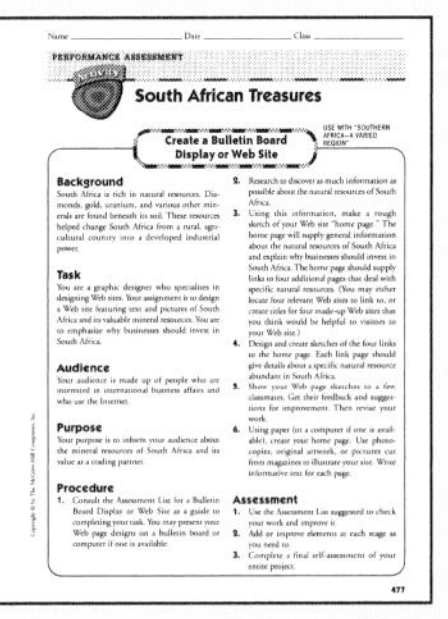

ExamView® Pro Testmaker CD-ROM

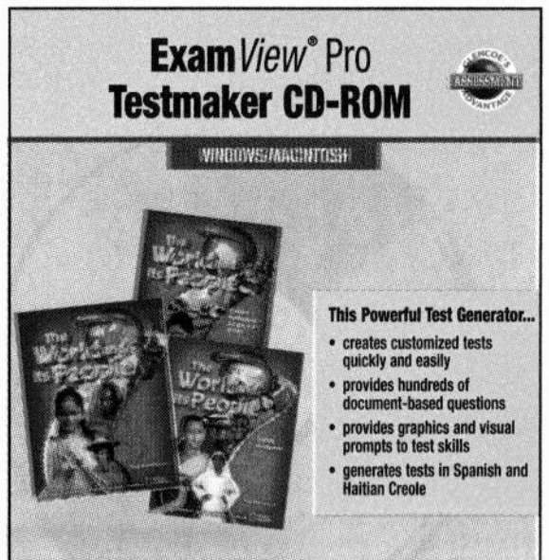

STANDARDIZED ASSESSMENT SKILLS

Critical Thinking Skills Activity L2

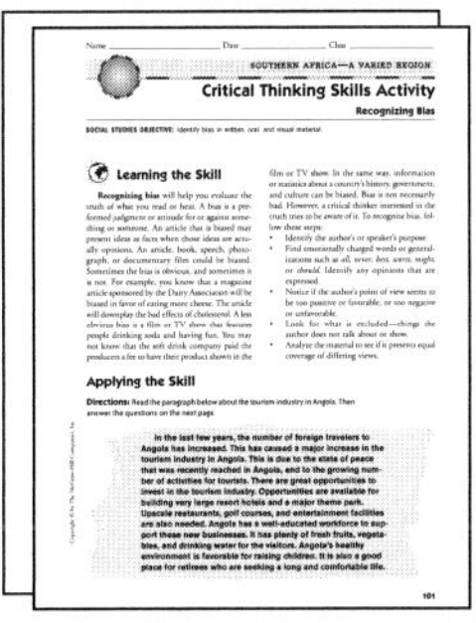

Map and Graph Skills Activity L2

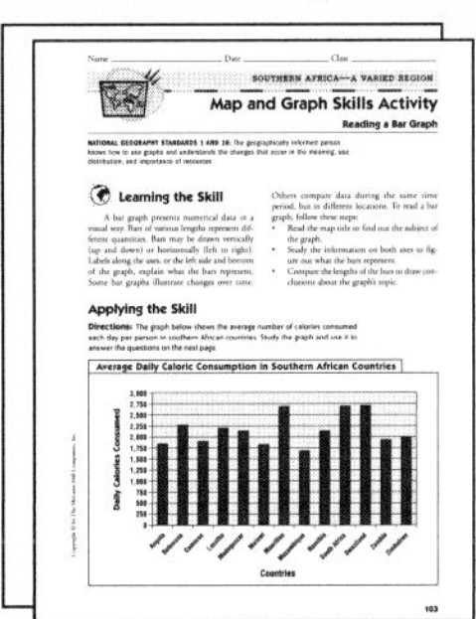

Standardized Test Skills Practice Workbook Activity L2

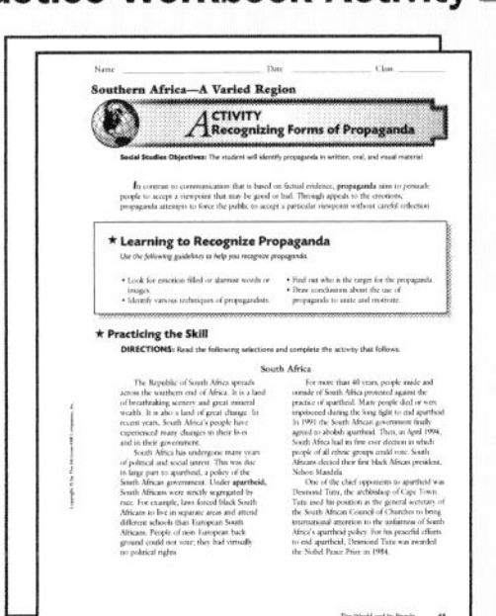

HOME INVOLVEMENT

Take-Home Review Activity L1

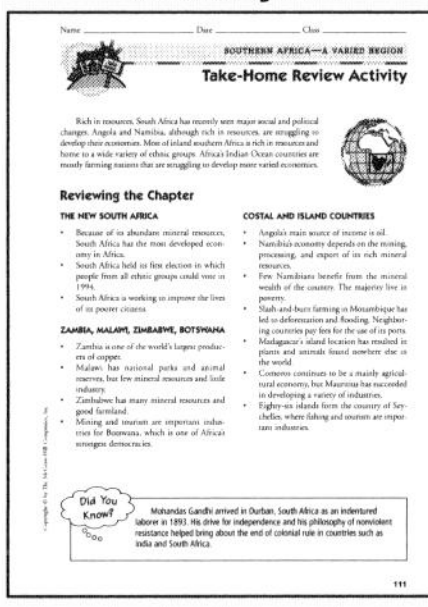

MULTIMEDIA

- National Geographic's The World and Its People
- MindJogger Videoquiz
- Vocabulary PuzzleMaker CD-ROM
- Interactive Tutor Self-Assessment CD-ROM
- ExamView® Pro Testmaker CD-ROM
- TeacherWorks CD-ROM
- StudentWorks CD-ROM
- Skillbuilder Interactive Workbook CD-ROM, Level 1
- Presentation Plus! CD-ROM
- Audio Program

SPANISH RESOURCES

The following Spanish language materials are available in the Spanish Resources binder:

- **Spanish Summaries**
- **Spanish Vocabulary Activities**
- **Spanish Guided Reading Activities**
- **Spanish Quizzes and Tests**
- **Spanish Take-Home Review Activities**
- **Spanish Reteaching Activities**

Meeting National Standards

Geography for Life

The following standards are covered in Chapter 21:

Section 1 **EE4 Human Systems: Standards 9, 10, 12**
EE5 Environment and Society: Standard 16

Section 2 **EE2 Places and Regions: Standard 4**
EE3 Physical Systems: Standards 7, 8
EE5 Environment and Society: Standards 14, 15, 16

Section 3 **EE2 Places and Regions: Standard 4**
EE5 Environment and Society: Standards 14, 15, 16

State and Local Objectives

Chapter 21 Planning Guide

SECTION RESOURCES

Daily Objectives	Reproducible Resources	Multimedia Resources
Section 1 **The New South Africa** **1.** Describe the landforms and resources of the Republic of South Africa. **2.** Discuss the people and recent changes in the Republic of South Africa.	Reproducible Lesson Plan Daily Lecture and Discussion Notes Note-taking Guide Guided Reading Activity* Reading Essentials and Study Guide* Section Quiz*	Daily Focus Skills Transparency Vocabulary PuzzleMaker CD-ROM Interactive Tutor Self-Assessment CD-ROM ExamView® Pro Testmaker CD-ROM Presentation Plus! CD-ROM
Section 2 **Zambia, Malawi, Zimbabwe, Botswana** **1.** Identify Zambia's most important resource. **2.** Describe the economy and history of Malawi. **3.** Explain the challenges to Zimbabwe's economy. **4.** Discuss how climate affects Botswana's people.	Reproducible Lesson Plan Daily Lecture and Discussion Notes Note-taking Guide Guided Reading Activity* Reading Essentials and Study Guide* Section Quiz*	Daily Focus Skills Transparency Vocabulary PuzzleMaker CD-ROM Interactive Tutor Self-Assessment CD-ROM ExamView® Pro Testmaker CD-ROM Presentation Plus! CD-ROM
Section 3 **Coastal and Island Countries** **1.** Compare the landforms and economies of Angola and Namibia. **2.** Explain what has caused deforestation in Mozambique and Madagascar. **3.** Discuss why Madagascar has such unusual plants and animals.	Reproducible Lesson Plan Daily Lecture and Discussion Notes Note-taking Guide Guided Reading Activity* Reading Essentials and Study Guide* Section Quiz*	Daily Focus Skills Transparency In-text Map Transparency Vocabulary PuzzleMaker CD-ROM Interactive Tutor Self-Assessment CD-ROM ExamView® Pro Testmaker CD-ROM Presentation Plus! CD-ROM MindJogger Videoquiz

00:00 **Out of Time?** Assign the **Reading Essentials and Study Guide*** for this chapter.

*Also available in Spanish

KEY TO ABILITY LEVELS

Teaching strategies have been coded for varying learning styles and abilities.

L1 **BASIC** activities for all students
L2 **AVERAGE** activities for average to above-average students
L3 **CHALLENGING** activities for above-average students
ELL **ENGLISH LANGUAGE LEARNER** activities

KEY TO TEACHING RESOURCES

Blackline Master
CD-ROM
Transparency
Videocassette
Block Scheduling
DVD

Teacher to Teacher

African Masks

Ida Haskew Smith
South Pittsburg Elementary
South Pittsburg, Tennessee

Explain to students that masks are an important art form in Africa. When Africans put on a mask, they stop being themselves and become the force or spirit they are trying to please. Usually masks were worn by dancers at important ceremonies, such as ceremonies for the dead, initiations into secret societies, preparations for war, or rituals to ward off evil spirits or to appeal to good spirits. Masks also had to affect human onlookers. Their power was increased as the masks swayed and bobbed with the motions of the dancers wearing them. Have students make their own masks out of paper, feathers, and other items, much like the various ethnic groups in Africa. Students' masks, however, must reflect their own communities' resources and/or historical interests.

Meeting Special Needs

In addition to the Differentiated Instruction strategies found in each section, the following resources are also suitable for your special needs students:

- ***ExamView® Pro Testmaker CD-ROM*** allows teachers to tailor tests by reducing answer choices.
- The ***Audio Program*** includes the entire narrative of the student edition so that less-proficient readers can listen to the words as they read them.
- The ***Reading Essentials and Study Guide*** provides the same content as the student edition but is written two grade levels below the textbook.
- ***Guided Reading Activities*** give less-proficient readers point-by-point instructions to increase comprehension as they read each textbook section.
- ***Enrichment Activities*** include a stimulating collection of readings and activities for gifted and talented students.

NATIONAL GEOGRAPHIC TEACHER'S CORNER

Index to National Geographic Magazine:

The following articles may be used for research relating to this chapter:

- "Zulu: People of Heaven, Heirs to Violence," by Peter Godwin, August 2000.
- "Cheetahs: Ghosts of the Grasslands," by Richard Conniff, December 1999.
- "Restoring Madagascar," by Virginia Morell, February 1999.

National Geographic Society Products:

To order the following products for use with this chapter, call National Geographic Society at 1-800-368-2728:

- *Africa* (Video)
- *South Africa: After Apartheid* (Video)
- *National Geographic Desk Reference* (Book)

NGS ONLINE

Access National Geographic's Web site for current events, activities, links, interactive features, and archives.
www.nationalgeographic.com

Find the latest coverage of geography in the news, atlas updates, cartographic activities with interactive maps, an online map store, and links at www.nationalgeographic.com/maps

SOCIAL STUDIES Online

Use our Web site for additional resources. All essential content is covered in the Student Edition.

You and your students can visit twip.glencoe.com, the Web site companion to *The World and Its People.* This innovative integration of electronic and print media offers your students a wealth of opportunities. The student text directs students to the Web site for the following options:

- Chapter Overviews
- Student Web Activities
- Self-Check Quizzes
- Textbook Updates

Answers are provided for you in the Web Activity Lesson Plan. Additional Web resources and Interactive Tutor puzzles are also available.

Introducing
Chapter 21

Social Studies Online

Introduce students to chapter content and key terms by having them access Chapter Overview 21 at twip.glencoe.com

Chapter Objectives

1. Describe the geography, history, economy, and people of the Republic of South Africa.
2. Summarize the physical features, people, and histories of the inland countries of southern Africa.
3. Compare the geography, economies, and cultures of the coastal and island countries of southern Africa.

GLENCOE TECHNOLOGY

NATIONAL GEOGRAPHIC

The World and Its People Video Program

Chapter 22 South Africa and Its Neighbors

The following segments enhance the study of this chapter:

- **Soweto**
- **Leaping Lemurs**
- **Sand and Sea**

MindJogger Videoquiz

Use MindJogger Videoquiz to preview the Chapter 21 content.

Both programs available in DVD and VHS

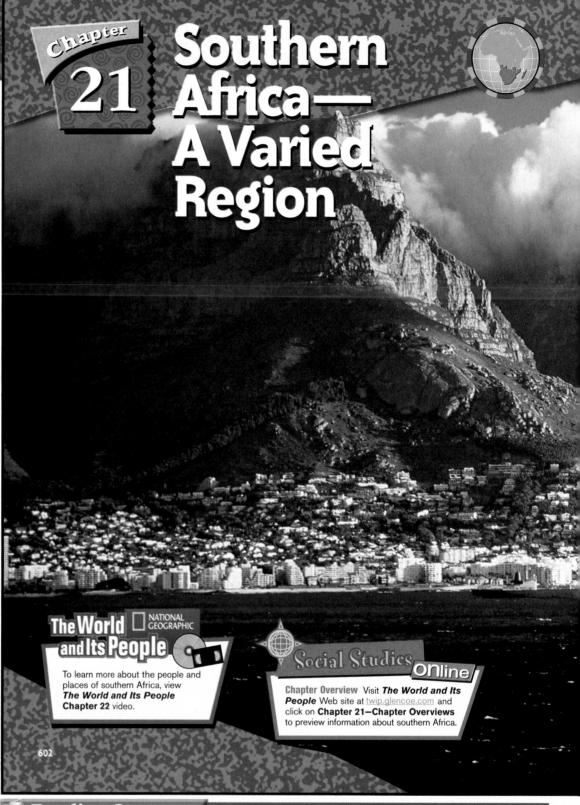

Chapter 21 Southern Africa—A Varied Region

The World and Its People — NATIONAL GEOGRAPHIC

To learn more about the people and places of southern Africa, view ***The World and Its People*** **Chapter 22** video.

Social Studies Online

Chapter Overview Visit ***The World and Its People*** Web site at twip.glencoe.com and click on **Chapter 21—Chapter Overviews** to preview information about southern Africa.

602

Reading Strategy — Purpose for Reading

Brainstorming and **One-Sentence Summaries** are effective ways to help students think about and summarize a discussion topic. Organize the class into groups of three or four students. Ask them to talk about gold and diamonds. They should begin the discussion by answering the question "Why are gold and diamonds important?" After about two minutes, have them summarize what they have discussed. Students should begin each summary by saying, "Gold is important because.... Diamonds are important because...." Conclude the discussion by explaining that the students will learn why these and other minerals are important to southern Africa in the chapter. **L1**

Why It Matters

Challenges

Even though many countries in southern Africa are rich in resources, challenges still exist. They are working to develop their economies or deal with other social and political changes. For example, South Africa was virtually isolated from the world community because of its racist policies. Today, after decades of struggling for justice and equality, South Africa faces new challenges. Poverty and the spread of AIDS plague the lives of many people.

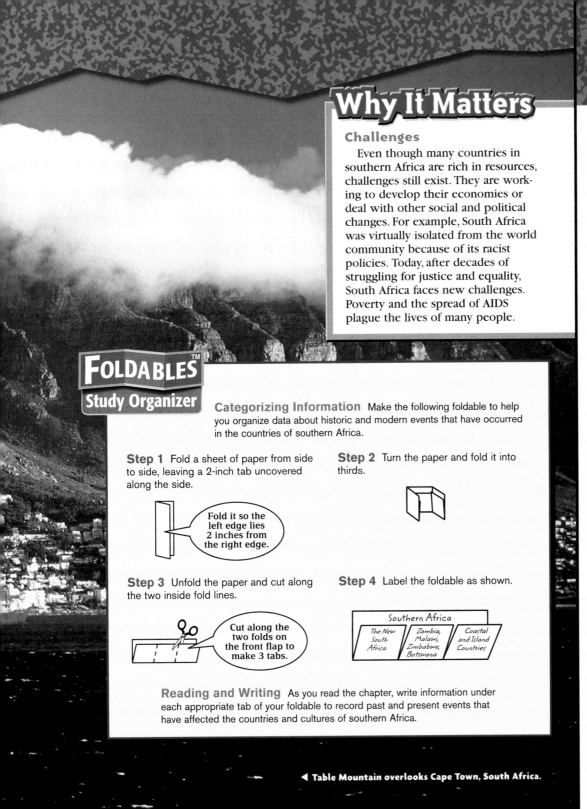

FOLDABLES™ Study Organizer

Categorizing Information Make the following foldable to help you organize data about historic and modern events that have occurred in the countries of southern Africa.

Step 1 Fold a sheet of paper from side to side, leaving a 2-inch tab uncovered along the side.

Fold it so the left edge lies 2 inches from the right edge.

Step 2 Turn the paper and fold it into thirds.

Step 3 Unfold the paper and cut along the two inside fold lines.

Cut along the two folds on the front flap to make 3 tabs.

Step 4 Label the foldable as shown.

Southern Africa
The New South Africa
Zambia, Malawi, Zimbabwe, Botswana
Coastal and Island Countries

Reading and Writing As you read the chapter, write information under each appropriate tab of your foldable to record past and present events that have affected the countries and cultures of southern Africa.

◀ Table Mountain overlooks Cape Town, South Africa.

About the Photo

On the coasts of nations around the world, towns have grown to provide safe harbors and a place to exchange and distribute goods brought there by ship. Fresh water and food are needed by the crew, and shore leave is prized. When a merchant sells some of his cargo, new cargo can then be purchased and brought back to the home port for sale. Shipping is very important to the economies of many countries. While Cape Town is the most populous port city in South Africa, it follows Durban in shipping volume. Port Elizabeth and East London are also major ports.

Introducing

Chapter 21

Dinah Zike's Foldables

Purpose This activity requires students to create a foldable and organize information from the chapter on it. Students are required to record historic and modern events that occurred in the Republic of South Africa, inland southern Africa, and the coastal and island countries of southern Africa on the appropriate tabs of the foldable.

Have students complete the ***Reading and Study Skills Foldables*** activity for this chapter.

Why It Matters

Help students understand the idea of creating a new, improved government system. Ask them to think of a time when they saw or experienced bullying on the playground. Game rules are designed to make sure all children are treated fairly and to keep them safe. The citizens of South Africa are emerging from a struggle for justice and equality. Have students imagine they are writing laws for such a new government. Brainstorm the most important rights and freedoms they would guarantee their citizens. Then, have small groups choose five ideas and write them as laws.

Chapter 21

Section 1, pages 604–607

Focus

Section Objectives

1. Describe the landforms and resources of the Republic of South Africa.
2. Discuss the people and recent changes in the Republic of South Africa.

BELLRINGER
Skillbuilder Activity

Project transparency and have students answer the question.

Daily Focus Skills Transparency

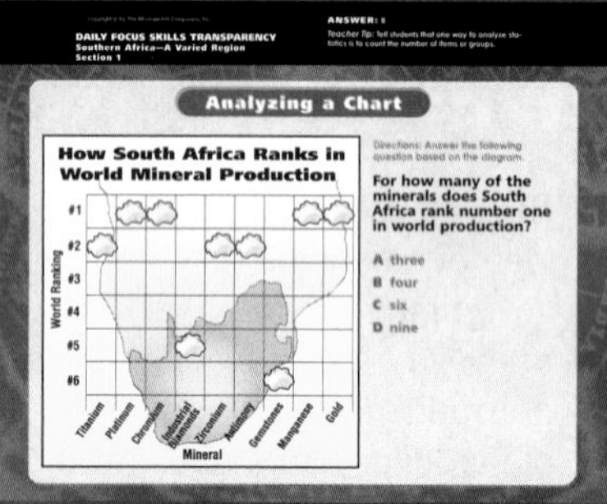

Reading Preview

■ **Activating Prior Knowledge** Tell students that South Africa's location south of the Equator is about the same as Texas's location north of the Equator. Explain that they will see how South Africa is similar to Texas.

■ **Preteaching Vocabulary** Have students use their knowledge of prefixes to guess at the meaning of *enclave* in the Terms to Know.

Guide to Reading

Main Idea

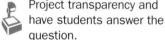

South Africa has great mineral wealth and has recently seen major social and political changes.

Terms to Know

- industrialized country
- Boer
- apartheid
- township
- enclave

Reading Strategy

Create a time line like this one. Then list five key events and their dates in South Africa's history.

The New South Africa

Cape Town's Table Mountain is famous for its flat top. A cable car takes people to the top. If you are physically fit and have four hours to spare, you can also climb the mountain. From the top, you can see Cape Town—South Africa's legislative capital. The country's executive capital is Pretoria, and the judicial capital is Bloemfontein.

South Africa (officially called the Republic of South Africa) is a land of beautiful scenery and great mineral wealth. Here you will find Africa's biggest mammal—the African elephant. You will also find the smallest mammal—the miniature shrew. To protect these creatures, the government has set aside land as national parks.

A Land Rich in Resources

South Africa, located at the southern tip of Africa, touches the Atlantic and Indian Oceans. The **Namib Desert** is in the northwest. The **Cape of Good Hope** is the southernmost point of Africa.

South Africa is the most industrialized country in Africa. An **industrialized country** is one in which a great deal of manufacturing occurs. Not all South Africans benefit from this prosperous economy, however. In rural areas, many people live in poverty and continue to depend on subsistence farming.

Section Resources

Reproducible Masters
- Reproducible Lesson Plan
- Daily Lecture and Discussion Notes
- Note-taking Guide
- Guided Reading Activity
- Reading Essentials and Study Guide
- Section Quiz

Transparencies
- Daily Focus Skills Transparency

Multimedia
- Vocabulary PuzzleMaker CD-ROM
- Interactive Tutor Self-Assessment CD-ROM
- Presentation Plus! CD-ROM
- ExamView® Pro Testmaker CD-ROM

In terms of mineral resources, South Africa is one of the richest countries in the world. It is the world's largest producer and exporter of gold. It has large deposits of diamonds, chromite, platinum, and coal as well. The country also exports machinery, chemicals, clothing, and processed foods. Crops cultivated on irrigated, high-technology farms include corn, wheat, fruits, cotton, sugarcane, and potatoes. Ranchers on the central plains raise sheep, cattle for beef, and dairy cows.

✓Reading Check **How have South Africa's resources helped its economy?**

South Africa's History and People

About 44 million people live in South Africa. Black African ethnic groups make up about 78 percent of the population. Most trace their ancestry to Bantu-speaking peoples who settled throughout Africa between A.D. 100 and 1000. The largest ethnic groups in South Africa today are the Sotho (SOO•too), Zulu, and Xhosa (KOH•suh).

In the 1600s, the Dutch settled in South Africa. They were known as the **Boers,** a Dutch word for farmers. German, Belgian, and French settlers joined them. Together these groups were known as Afrikaners

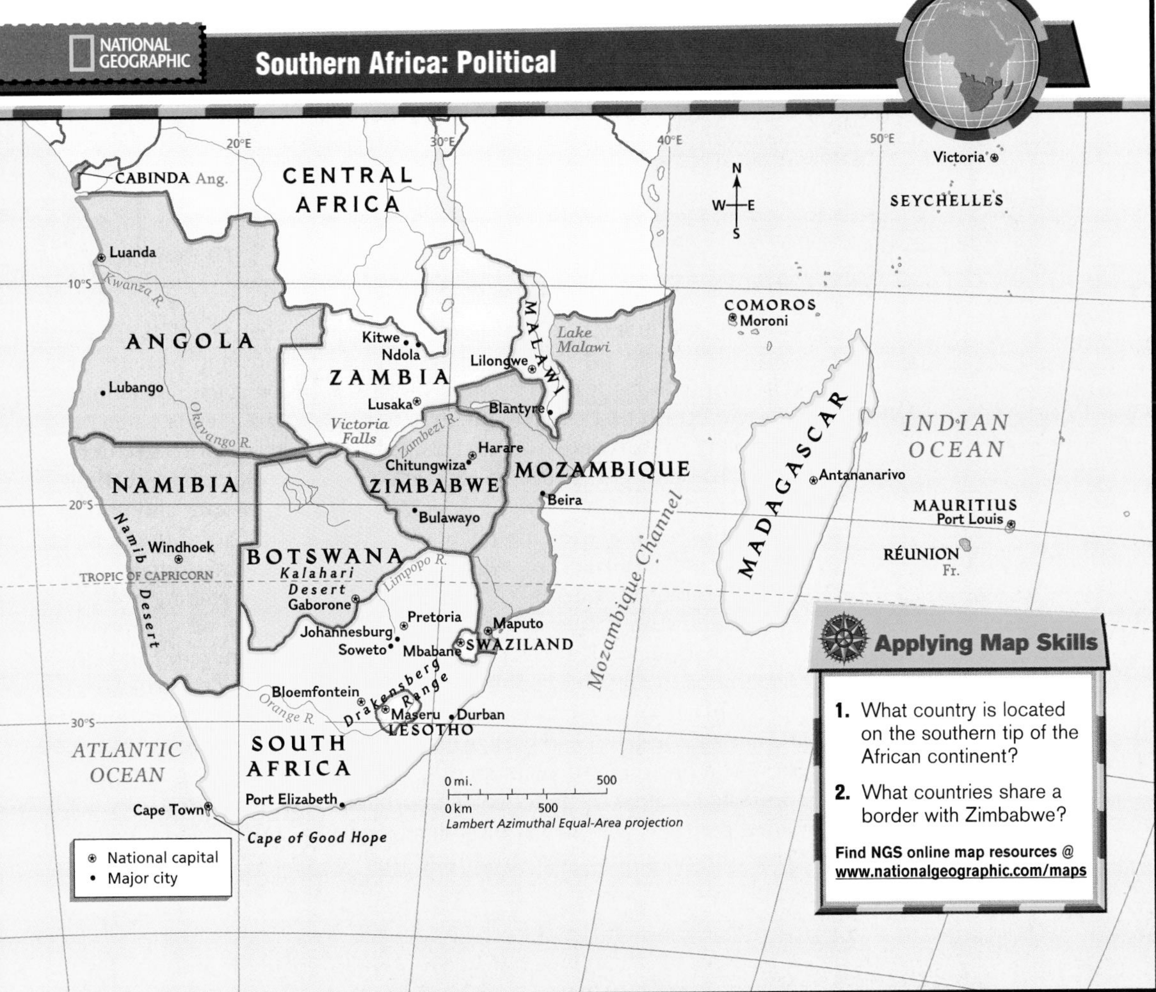

Applying Map Skills

1. What country is located on the southern tip of the African continent?
2. What countries share a border with Zimbabwe?

Find NGS online map resources @ www.nationalgeographic.com/maps

Reading Strategy — Reading the Text

Sequencing Invite a teacher to class with a background in world history to talk about the history of South Africa, explaining how the policy of apartheid first developed and how it came to be abandoned. Have the teacher cover such key events as the arrival of the British, the Boers' Great Trek, the Boer War and conflict with the Zulus, independence, and the formation of the white minority government. Then have him or her discuss the extent of apartheid laws, the homelands policy, life in the townships, and the struggle against apartheid—both at home and in the international community. Have students select a topic to research and prepare an annotated time line that uses text and images to explain what happened and why. L1

Use the ***Reading Skills Handbook*** *for more reading strategies.*

Chapter 21

Section 1, pages 604–607

TEACH

Reading Strategy

Categorizing Information
Create a four-column chart, using the following as column headings: "The Land," "The Economy," "The History," and "The People." Then relate a set of facts about the Republic of South Africa. Have students write each fact under the appropriate heading. L1

Daily Lecture and Discussion Notes

SOUTHERN AFRICA—A VARIED REGION

Daily Lecture and Discussion Notes

The New South Africa

Did You Know? The Republic of South Africa has three capitals. Parliament meets in Cape Town, the legislative capital. All government departments have their headquarters in Pretoria, the administrative capital. The highest court meets in Bloemfontein, the country's judicial capital.

I. A Land Rich in Resources

A. In South Africa you will find the continent's biggest mammal, the African elephant, and smallest mammal, the miniature shrew. To protect these creatures, the government has set aside land as national parks.

✓ Reading Check Answer

The economy is supported by several types of resources—minerals, industrial and consumer goods, agriculture, and ranching.

Applying Map Skills

Answers
1. South Africa
2. South Africa, Botswana, Zambia, and Mozambique

Skills Practice
What country is completely surrounded by South Africa? *(Lesotho)*

L1/ELL

Guided Reading Activity

Name ________ Date ________ Class ________

SOUTHERN AFRICA—A VARIED REGION

Guided Reading Activity 1

The New South Africa

DIRECTIONS: Answering Questions Reading the section and answering the questions below will help you learn more about the Republic of South Africa. Use your textbook to write answers to the questions.

1. How does South Africa protect its native animals?

2. What bodies of water border South Africa?

...of minerals are found in South Africa?

Primary Source

Answer Nelson Mandela spent 27 years in prison because of his fight against apartheid. He is comparing his walk out of prison to the long road that blacks in South Africa must "walk" to political freedom. The walk is a symbol of the small steps that must be taken in order to reach the final goal of freedom and respect.

ASSESS

Assign Section 1 Assessment as homework or an in-class activity.

Have students use the Interactive Tutor Self-Assessment CD-ROM to review Section 1.

Primary Source

NELSON MANDELA

(1918–)

As a young man, Nelson Mandela spoke out against apartheid and was arrested. He spent a total of 27 years in jail before being released in 1990.

"It was during those long and lonely years [in prison] that my hunger for the freedom of my own people became a hunger for the freedom of all people, white and black. I knew as well as I knew anything that the oppressor must be liberated just as surely as the oppressed. A man who takes away another man's freedom is a prisoner of hatred, he is locked behind the bars of prejudice and narrow-mindedness. When I walked out of prison, that was my mission, to liberate the oppressed and the oppressor both. . . . We have not taken the final step of our journey, but the first step on a longer and even more difficult road. For to be free is not merely to cast off one's chains, but to live in a way that respects and enhances the freedom of others."

From *The Long Walk to Freedom: The Autobiography of Nelson Mandela* by Nelson Mandela.

Analyzing Primary Sources

What do you think Mandela is referring to in the title of his autobiography, ***The Long Walk to Freedom***? What is the walk a symbol for?

and spoke their own language—Afrikaans (A•frih•KAHNS). They pushed Africans off the best land and set up farms and plantations. They brought many laborers from India to work on sugar plantations.

The British first came to South Africa in the early 1800s. Later, the discovery of diamonds and gold attracted many more British settlers. Tensions between the British and the Afrikaners resulted in the 1902 defeat of the Afrikaners in the Boer War. In 1910 Afrikaner and British territories became the Union of South Africa. It was part of the British Empire and was ruled by whites. Black South Africans founded the African National Congress (ANC) in 1912 in hopes of gaining power.

In 1948 the whites set up a system of apartheid, or "apartness." **Apartheid** (uh•PAHR•TAYT) made it illegal for different races and ethnic groups to mix, thus limiting the rights of blacks. For example, laws forced black South Africans to live in separate areas, called "homelands." People of non-European background were not even allowed to vote.

For more than 40 years, people inside and outside South Africa protested against the practice of apartheid. Many black Africans were jailed for their actions in the long struggle for justice and equality. The United Nations declared that apartheid was "a crime against

Differentiated Instruction

Meeting Special Needs: Kinesthetic Demonstrate why seasons in southern Africa are opposite those in the Northern Hemisphere. Clear a circular space in the room and have a student stand in the center with a flashlight (representing the sun). Have another student hold a globe and stand at the outer edge of the circle. Stick a piece of tape on a place in the Northern Hemisphere and another on a city in southern Africa. Remind the student to tilt the globe slightly. Have the "sun" shine the light on the globe and have students identify which hemisphere gets the most light. Move the globe to three other positions, representing the change of seasons, and ask the class to note how the amount of light reaching the two hemispheres changes. If possible, dim the lights so that the illumination from the flashlight stands out more. **L1**

humanity." Many countries cut off trade with South Africa. Finally, in 1991 apartheid ended. South Africa held its first democratic election in April 1994. Voters elected Nelson Mandela as the country's first black president.

The People South Africa has 11 official languages, including Afrikaans, English, Zulu, and Xhosa. About two-thirds of South Africans are Christians, whereas the rest practice traditional African religions.

One of the challenges facing South Africa today is to develop a better standard of living for its poorer people. Most European South Africans live in modern homes and enjoy a high standard of living. Most black, Asian, and mixed-group South Africans live in rural areas and crowded **townships,** or neighborhoods outside cities. The government has introduced measures to improve education and basic services.

Another challenge facing South Africa is the AIDS epidemic. Millions of people throughout Africa have been infected with HIV, the virus that causes AIDS. South Africa is one of the countries hit hardest.

Lesotho and Swaziland Within South Africa lie two other African nations—**Lesotho** (luh•SOO•too) and **Swaziland.** These tiny kingdoms are **enclaves**—small countries located inside a larger country. Both are poor countries that depend heavily on South Africa. Lesotho's only natural resource is water, some of which it sells to South Africa. Many of Lesotho's and Swaziland's people are engaged in subsistence farming. Others work in mines in South Africa.

▲ Although altitude and poor soil make farming difficult in Lesotho, most people are subsistence farmers.

✓ Reading Check **How do Lesotho and Swaziland earn money from South Africa?**

Section 1 Assessment

Defining Terms

1. **Define** industrialized country, Boer, apartheid, township, enclave.

Recalling Facts

2. **Place** Name the largest mammal and the smallest mammal in Africa.
3. **Government** Who is Nelson Mandela?
4. **Culture** What challenges face South Africa?

Critical Thinking

5. **Drawing Conclusions** How did the rest of the world view apartheid?
6. **Analyzing Information** Why do you think workers in Lesotho and Swaziland travel to South Africa to work in mines?

Graphic Organizer

7. **Organizing Information** In a chart like the one below, write the resources and products of South Africa in the two boxes.

South Africa	
Resources	Products

Applying Social Studies Skills

8. **Analyzing Maps** Study the political map on page 605. What are the three national capitals of the Republic of South Africa?

L2

Section Quiz

Name ______ Date ______ Class ______

SOUTHERN AFRICA—A VARIED REGION

Score

Section 1 Quiz

The New South Africa

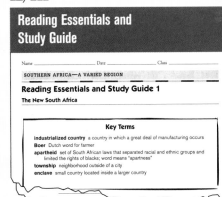

DIRECTIONS: Matching Match each item in Column A with the items in Column B. Write the correct letters in the blanks. (10 points each)

COLUMN A	COLUMN B
A. townships	___ 1. the southernmost point of Africa
B. Boers	___ 2. Dutch who settled in South Africa in the 1600s
C. apartheid	___ 3. small countries located in a larger country
D. Cape of Good Hope	___ 4. neighborhoods outside South Africa's cities
E. enclaves	___ 5. laws that separated racial and ethnic groups and limited the rights of blacks

✓ Reading Check Answer

by selling water to South Africa and some of their people work in South Africa's mines

L1/ELL

Reading Essentials and Study Guide

Name ______ Date ______ Class ______

SOUTHERN AFRICA—A VARIED REGION

Reading Essentials and Study Guide 1

The New South Africa

Key Terms

industrialized country a country in which a great deal of manufacturing occurs
Boer Dutch word for farmer
apartheid set of South African laws that separated racial and ethnic groups and limited the rights of blacks; word means "apartness"
township neighborhood outside of a city
enclave small country located inside a larger country

Close

Have students answer the question: **How did apartheid violate human rights?** *(Blacks did not have the same rights as whites, including the right to vote.)*

Section 1 Assessment

1. The terms are defined in the Glossary.
2. African elephant; miniature shrew
3. the first black African president of South Africa
4. developing a better standard of living for its poor people; fighting AIDS
5. The United Nations declared that apartheid was "a crime against humanity."
6. because their own countries do not have enough jobs
7. *Resources:* gold, diamonds, chromite, platinum, coal, fertile soil, land for herding; *Products:* machinery, chemicals, clothing, processed foods, corn, wheat, fruits, cotton, sugarcane, potatoes, sheep, cattle for beef, dairy cows
8. Pretoria, Bloemfontein, and Cape Town

Teach

Ask students if they have heard the expression "a diamond in the rough." **Ask:** **What does the phrase mean?** *(something precious that has not yet been polished to show its brilliance)* Explain that in this feature, they will learn how diamonds are formed, mined, shaped, and polished. **L1**

More About Diamonds

About 80 percent of diamonds are used for industrial cutting and polishing. Diamonds were once used in phonograph needles, which were used to play vinyl records on turntables.

Interdisciplinary Connections

Science Diamonds, the hardest substance found in nature, are also the most desired because of their brilliance and sparkle. When diamonds are cut well, they reflect more light than other gems. The largest diamond was dug from a mine near Pretoria, in South Africa. It was about the size of a person's fist and weighed 3,106 carats (about 1.4 pounds [.64 kg]). When cut, it made nine large jewels and more than 100 smaller ones. The largest jewel was called the Star of Africa.

Making Connections

ART | SCIENCE | CULTURE | TECHNOLOGY

Mining and Cutting Diamonds

A diamond is a mineral made entirely of carbon. It is the hardest known substance on the earth and the most popular gemstone. Most diamonds formed billions of years ago deep inside the earth's mantle. There, intense pressure and heat transformed carbon into diamond crystal.

Mining

There are two major techniques used for mining diamonds: open pit and underground mining. In open pit mining, the earth is dug out in layers, creating a series of roads that circle down into a pit. After drills and explosives loosen the rock containing diamonds, workers use shovels and trucks to remove it. When the pit becomes too deep to reach easily, underground mining may begin.

Underground mining requires sinking a shaft into the ground and tunneling to the rock. Explosives blast the rock loose, and the resulting rubble is crushed and carried to the surface for further processing.

To remove the diamonds, the crushed rock is mixed with water and placed in a washing pan. Heavier minerals, such as diamonds, settle to the bottom, while lighter material rises to the top and overflows. Next, the heavier mixture travels to a grease table. Diamonds cling to the grease while other wetted minerals flow past. Workers continue the sorting and separating by hand.

Cutting

The newly mined diamond resembles a piece of glass, not a sparkling jewel. To enhance their brilliance and sparkle, gem-quality diamonds are precisely cut and polished. The cutter uses high-speed diamond-tipped tools to cut facets, or small flat surfaces, into the stone. One of the most popular diamond cuts is the brilliant cut, which has 58 facets. The job of the cutter requires extreme skill, because the diamond's beauty depends on how the angles of the facets are cut.

Making the Connection

1. What are diamonds made of?
2. Why are gemstone diamonds cut and polished?
3. **Making Comparisons** How are open pit and underground diamond mining techniques alike? How are they different?

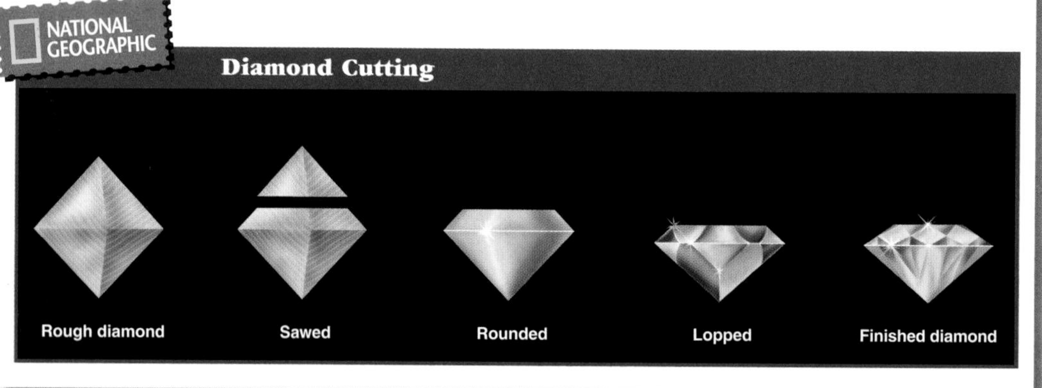

Making the Connection

1. carbon
2. to eliminate imperfections and to enhance brilliance and sparkle
3. Both methods involve separating diamonds from the surrounding rock. Open pit mining involves digging out the rock that contains diamonds in layers creating a pit. Underground mining involves tunneling to the rock that contains diamonds.

Guide to Reading

Main Idea

Most of inland southern Africa is rich in resources and home to a wide variety of ethnic groups.

Terms to Know

- copper belt
- sorghum

Reading Strategy

Create a chart like this one. Then list the main economic activities of each country.

Country	Economic Activities
Zambia	
Malawi	
Zimbabwe	
Botswana	

Section 2

Zambia, Malawi, Zimbabwe, Botswana

NATIONAL GEOGRAPHIC **Exploring Our World**

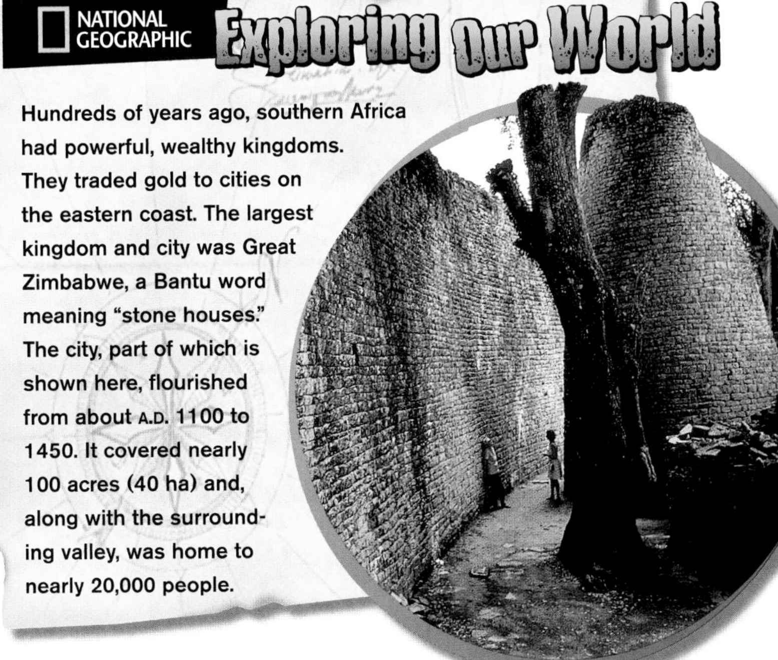

Hundreds of years ago, southern Africa had powerful, wealthy kingdoms. They traded gold to cities on the eastern coast. The largest kingdom and city was Great Zimbabwe, a Bantu word meaning "stone houses." The city, part of which is shown here, flourished from about A.D. 1100 to 1450. It covered nearly 100 acres (40 ha) and, along with the surrounding valley, was home to nearly 20,000 people.

The four countries of inland southern Africa include **Zambia, Malawi** (mah•LAH•wee), **Zimbabwe,** and **Botswana** (baht•SWAH•nah). Find these four countries on the map on page 605. They have several things in common. First, they all are landlocked. A high plateau dominates much of their landscape and gives them a mild climate. Second, about 70 percent of the people practice subsistence farming in rural villages. Thousands move to cities each year to look for work.

Zambia

Zambia is slightly larger than Texas. The **Zambezi** (zam•BEE•zee) **River**—one of southern Africa's longest rivers—crosses the country. The Kariba Dam spans the river and creates a large amount of hydroelectricity. Also along the Zambezi River are the spectacular Victoria Falls, named in honor of British Queen Victoria, who ruled in the 1800s. The falls are known locally as *Mosi oa Tunya,* or "smoke that thunders."

Focus

Section Objectives

1. Identify Zambia's most important resource.
2. Describe the economy and history of Malawi.
3. Explain the challenges to Zimbabwe's economy.
4. Discuss how climate affects Botswana's people.

BELLRINGER
Skillbuilder Activity

Project transparency and have students answer the question.

Daily Focus Skills Transparency

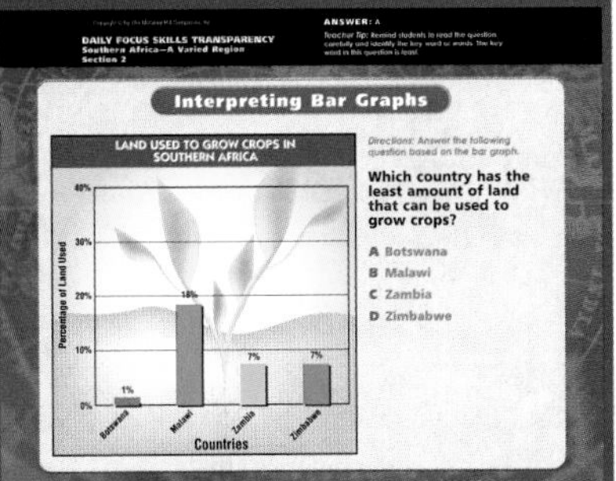

Reading Preview

- **Activating Prior Knowledge** Have students find Zambia, Malawi, Zimbabwe, and Botswana on a map. **Ask:** How does location make economic development difficult for these countries? *(Transportation of goods is difficult since these countries are landlocked.)*
- **Preteaching Vocabulary** Have students speculate about the meaning of *copper belt* and then find it in the text to check their answers.

Section Resources

Reproducible Masters
- Reproducible Lesson Plan
- Daily Lecture and Discussion Notes
- Note-taking Guide
- Guided Reading Activity
- Reading Essentials and Study Guide
- Section Quiz

Transparencies
- Daily Focus Skills Transparency

Multimedia
- Vocabulary PuzzleMaker CD-ROM
- Interactive Tutor Self-Assessment CD-ROM
- Presentation Plus! CD-ROM
- ExamView® Pro Testmaker CD-ROM

2 TEACH

Reading Strategy

Organizing Information Have students scan the section for names of crops and resources found in these four countries. Then have them copy the information into a chart with the headings "Country," "Crops," and "Resources." Remind them to use their charts as study aids. L1

Daily Lecture and Discussion Notes

SOUTHERN AFRICA—A VARIED REGION

Daily Lecture and Discussion Notes

Zambia, Malawi, Zimbabwe, Botswana

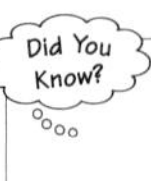

As the spread of the HIV virus continues in Africa, Zambia is wrestling with the idea of requiring its presidential candidates to be tested for the virus before they are allowed to run for office. The country's Permanent Human Rights Commission hopes that debate on the issue can result in a national consensus.

I. Zambia

A. The Zambezi River crosses Zambia. The Kariba Dam spans the river, and it is also the source of the spectacular Victoria Falls.

B. A large area of copper mines, known as a **copper belt,** stretches across northern ... world's major producers of copper, Zambia relies on it for

Reading Check Answer

Zambia's economy suffers because its income goes down.

Reading Check Answer

green plains and grasslands

What's for Dinner?

Kabemba Mwape hurries home from the market in Chavuma, Zambia. He carries a live pig on the back of his bike. Although Kabemba's family will enjoy the pig for dinner, they usually eat porridge. Kabemba's family is relatively wealthy. They can afford to pay for meat, bicycles, and the high price of school uniforms and books for Kabemba's education. He knows English, but he speaks his native language of Lozi while he is at the market.

A large area of copper mines, known as a copper belt, stretches across northern Zambia. One of the world's major producers of copper, Zambia relies on it for more than 80 percent of its income. As a result, when world copper prices go down, Zambia's income goes down too. As copper reserves dwindle, the government has encouraged city dwellers to return to farming. Zambia must import much of its food.

Once a British colony, Zambia gained its independence in 1964. The country's 10.9 million people belong to more than 70 ethnic groups and speak many languages. English is the official language. Those who live in urban areas such as **Lusaka,** the capital, work in mining and service industries. Villagers grow corn, rice, and other crops to support their families. Most people eat porridge made from corn.

Reading Check What happens to Zambia when copper prices go down?

Malawi

Green plains and grasslands cover western areas of narrow Malawi. Vast herds of elephants, zebras, and antelope roam animal reserves here. The Great Rift Valley runs through eastern Malawi. In the middle of it lies beautiful **Lake Malawi.** This lake holds about 500 fish species, more than any other inland body of water in the world. Malawi is also famous for its more than 400 orchid species.

Malawi is one of the world's least developed countries. The economy relies on agriculture. Malawi exports tobacco, tea, and sugar. Farmers also grow sorghum, a tall grass whose seeds are used as grain and to make syrup. Malawi depends on economic assistance.

Bantu-speaking people arrived in the area about 2,000 years ago, bringing with them knowledge of iron-working. During the mid-1800s, Scottish missionary David Livingstone came to Malawi. He was the most famous European explorer to reach Malawi. Today most people here are Protestant Christians as a result of the teachings of missionaries.

In 1964 the British colony became independent. Malawi has recently returned to democratic government after a long period of rule by a dictator. As a result of years of harsh government, modern Malawi writers emphasize themes such as human rights and abuse of power.

Malawi is one of the most densely populated countries in Africa. It has about 255 people per square mile (98 people per sq. km). Jobs are scarce, so thousands seek work in South Africa and Zambia.

Reading Check What types of landforms cover western Malawi?

Zimbabwe

Crossing Zimbabwe, you might think you were in the western United States. The vast plateau is studded with large outcrops of rock. The **Limpopo River** winds through southern lowlands. The Zambezi River crosses the north.

Mining gold, copper, iron ore, and asbestos provides most of the country's income. Some large plantations grow coffee, cotton, and tobacco. Europeans own many of the large plantations, whereas most

Reading Strategy Reading the Text

Taking Notes Students who do not read efficiently benefit from having a specific purpose for reading. Point out the Reading Strategy at the beginning of the section. Have students read the instructions and copy the chart into their notebooks. Then have them look for information to fill in the chart as they read. L1

*Use the **Reading Skills Handbook** for more reading strategies.*

Sculpture

Since the 1950s, Shona artists in Zimbabwe have carved attractive stone figures that are highly valued throughout the world. Mostly self-taught, Shona sculptors use sand and beeswax to polish the stone and heat it with fire to bring out the stone's color. They rarely begin carving with a specific subject in mind. Instead, the artists allow the qualities of the stone to determine the figure they will create. Many artists believe that the spirit in the stone speaks to them.

Looking Closer **An example of Shona work is this sculpture of an African bird (below right). What other figures from their environment do you think Shona artists sculpt?**

Africans own only small plots. Since the 1980s, the government has tried to redistribute land to Africans, but recently this has caused chaos and violence. This has, in turn, hurt the economy and caused widespread shortages of basic goods. Recently, President Robert Mugabe has been criticized, and in 2003 groups of people launched strikes to pressure him to retire early.

Nearly 34 percent of Zimbabwe's adult population has AIDS. This negatively affects the economy. People who have the disease often cannot work to support their families. The government lacks the means to deal with the AIDS crisis effectively.

Zimbabwe takes its name from an ancient African city and trading center—Great Zimbabwe. This remarkable stone fortress was built by an ethnic group called the Shona in the A.D. 1100s to 1400s. The Shona and the Ndebele (ehn•duh•BEH•leh) ruled large stretches of south-central Africa until the late 1800s. In the 1890s, the British controlled the area and called it Rhodesia. They named it after Cecil Rhodes, a British businessman who expanded British rule in Africa.

Africans eventually organized into political groups and fought European rule. In 1980 free elections brought an independent African government to power. The country was renamed Zimbabwe. Today Zimbabwe has about 12.6 million people. About one-fourth of the population is Christian. Others practice traditional African religions. The largest city is **Harare** (hah•RAH•ray), the capital.

Art and music in Zimbabwe come in many forms. Some artists, as shown above, work with stone. Others carve beautiful wood sculptures and make pottery. Musicians play instruments such as a talking drum, which when played sounds like it is "talking."

Reading Check How has AIDS affected Zimbabwe's economy?

Web Activity Visit ***The World and Its People*** Web site at twip.glencoe.com and click on **Chapter 21—Student Web Activities** to learn more about Zimbabwe.

Much of the stone used in Shona sculpture—serpentine, steatite, and others—is mined in the mountainous regions of Zimbabwe. Many artists in Zimbabwe make a living through sales of their works in foreign galleries.

Answer Answers may include animals found in the savanna such as elephants, giraffes, antelopes, cheetahs, and lions.

Social Studies Online

Objectives and answers to the Student Web Activity can be found in the Web Activity Lesson Plan at twip.glencoe.com

Reading Check Answer

Many workers have been lost; many children have become orphans, which means they need additional help to survive; and health care costs have risen.

3 ASSESS

Assign Section 2 Assessment as homework or an in-class activity.

Have students use the Interactive Tutor Self-Assessment CD-ROM to review Section 2.

Differentiated Instruction

English Learners Pair English learners with students fluent in English and have students use the SQ3R (survey, question, read, recite, review) strategy together. Direct partners to read the section independently and collaborate for the recite step, with English learners orally sharing with fluent speakers answers they found to the questions raised before reading. For review, partners should return to the text and work together to refine or expand on the answers to the questions. **ELL**

Chapter 21

Section 2, pages 609–612

L2

Section Quiz

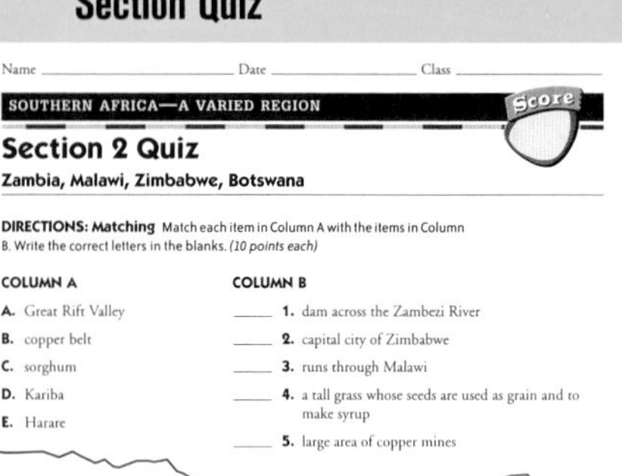
Name ______ Date ______ Class ______

SOUTHERN AFRICA—A VARIED REGION

Section 2 Quiz

Zambia, Malawi, Zimbabwe, Botswana

DIRECTIONS: Matching Match each item in Column A with the items in Column B. Write the correct letters in the blanks. (10 points each)

COLUMN A	COLUMN B
A. Great Rift Valley	____ 1. dam across the Zambezi River
B. copper belt	____ 2. capital city of Zimbabwe
C. sorghum	____ 3. runs through Malawi
D. Kariba	____ 4. a tall grass whose seeds are used as grain and to make syrup
E. Harare	____ 5. large area of copper mines

Reading Check Answer

diamonds

L1/ELL

Reading Essentials and Study Guide

Name ______ Date ______ Class ______

SOUTHERN AFRICA—A VARIED REGION

Reading Essentials and Study Guide 2

Zambia, Malawi, Zimbabwe, Botswana

Key Terms

copper belt large area of copper mines

sorghum tall grass whose seeds are used as grain and to make syrup

Drawing From Experience

Have you ever seen a waterfall? Imagine one that is a mile wide and ... This is the roaring Victoria Falls in Zambia. Earth scien... modern wonders of the world.

Zambia

... than Texas. The long Zambezi River crosses it. ... from the river's flow. The Zambezi's

4 CLOSE

Give students an outline map of southern Africa. Have them create an annotated map that describes the geography, resources, and products of the inland countries.

Stable Democracy

AIDS is a serious problem in many African countries. The governments of some countries, such as Zimbabwe, do not have the resources to deal with the disease. Other countries, such as Botswana, are working with the international community to combat the spread of AIDS. Because of Botswana's stable, democratic government, clinics have been established, roads are well maintained, and medical supplies can be quickly distributed.

Botswana

Botswana lies in the center of southern Africa. The vast **Kalahari Desert** spreads over southwestern Botswana. This hot, dry area has rolling, red sands and low, thorny shrubs. The **Okavango River** in the northwest forms one of the largest swamp areas in the world. This area of shifting streams is home to an abundance of wildlife.

Botswana's national emblem (as well as its basic monetary unit) is a one-word motto—*Pula*—meaning "rain." In Botswana, there is never much of it. From May to October, the sun bakes the land. Droughts occur often, and many years can pass before the rains fall again.

Botswana is rich in mineral resources. Diamonds account for more than 75 percent of the country's export income. Thousands of tourists visit Botswana's game preserves every year. Farming is difficult, and the country grows only about 50 percent of the food it needs. It must import the rest. To earn a living, many people work in South Africa for several months a year.

After nearly 80 years of British colonial rule, Botswana became independent in 1966. Today it has one of Africa's strongest democracies. Many of Botswana's people are Christians, although a large number practice traditional African religions. The official language is English, but 90 percent of the population speak an African language called Setswana. **Gaborone** is the capital and largest city. Here, and in other large cities in Africa, Western lifestyles and clothing are common.

Reading Check What is Botswana's biggest source of export income?

Section 2 Assessment

Defining Terms

1. **Define** copper belt, sorghum.

Recalling Facts

2. **Economics** What is Zambia's most important export?
3. **Place** What makes Lake Malawi unique?
4. **Culture** Where did Zimbabwe get its name?

Graphic Organizer

5. **Organizing Information** Choose two of the countries in this section. Write the name and three facts about each country in the outer ovals. Where the ovals overlap, write facts that are true of both countries.

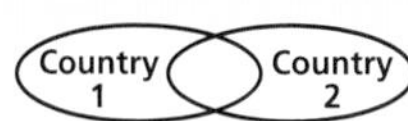

Critical Thinking

6. **Synthesizing Information** Imagine that someone from Great Zimbabwe traveled to Zimbabwe today. What do you think he or she would describe as the greatest difference between then and now?
7. **Analyzing Information** Why do you think the people of Botswana chose *Pula*, or "rain," as their motto?

Applying Social Studies Skills

8. **Analyzing Maps** Study the political map on page 605. What five African nations does the Tropic of Capricorn cross?

612 CHAPTER 21

Section 2 Assessment

1. The terms are defined in the Glossary.
2. copper
3. It holds more fish species than any other lake in the world.
4. from Great Zimbabwe, an ancient African city and trading center
5. Answers will vary depending on the countries chosen.
6. Answers might suggest the technology in use today.
7. Answers should include the importance of rain to the people of Botswana.
8. Namibia, Botswana, South Africa, Mozambique, and Madagascar

Social Studies Skill

Reading a Time Zones Map

The earth rotates 360° in 24 hours. The earth's surface has been divided into 24 time zones. Each time zone represents 15° longitude, or the distance that the earth rotates in 1 hour.

Learning the Skill

The Prime Meridian, or 0° longitude, is the starting point for figuring out time around the world. Traveling west from 0° longitude, it becomes 1 hour earlier for each time zone crossed. Traveling east, it becomes 1 hour later for each time zone crossed. The international date line is set at the 180° line of longitude. Traveling west across this imaginary line, you add a day. Traveling east, you subtract a day. To read a time zones map:

- Choose a place for which you already know the time and locate it on the map.
- Locate another place and determine if it is east or west of the first place.
- Count the time zones between the two.
- Calculate the time by either adding (going east) or subtracting (going west) an hour for each time zone.
- Determine whether you have crossed the date line, and identify the day of the week.

Practicing the Skill

1. On the map below, if it is 4 P.M. in Miami, what time is it in Cape Town?
2. If it is 10:00 A.M. in Tokyo on Tuesday, what day and time is it in Moscow?

Applying the Skill

Imagine you have a friend living in Rome, Italy. What time (your time) would you call if you wanted to talk to your friend after 7:00 P.M.?

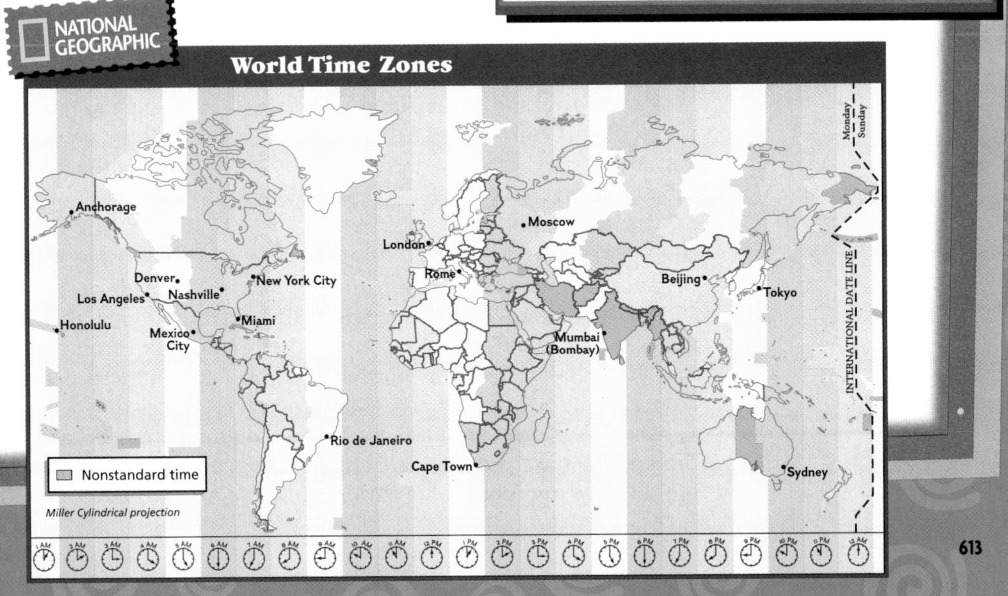

613

Social Studies Skill

TEACH

Ask: Why do countries not set their clocks to the same time? Provide this explanation: The earth rotates 360° in 24 hours; therefore, when it is day on one side of the earth, it is night on the other. To clarify time relationships among places, the world has been divided into time zones based on the earth's rotation. Then have students read the skill feature. L1

Additional Skills Practice

1. Suppose you leave Nashville at 8:00 P.M. on an eight-hour flight to Rome. What time will you arrive in Rome? *(11:00 A.M. the next day)*
2. Suppose you leave Los Angeles on Monday and travel westward to Sydney, Australia. On what day will you arrive in Sydney? Why? *(Tuesday; since you crossed the International Date Line going westward, you add a day.)*

Additional Skills Resources

- Chapter Skills Review
- Building Geography Skills for Life

GLENCOE TECHNOLOGY

Skillbuilder Interactive Workbook CD-ROM, Level 1

This interactive CD-ROM reinforces student mastery of essential social studies skills.

Practicing the Skill Answers

1. 11:00 P.M.
2. 4:00 A.M. on Tuesday

Applying the Skill

After 1:00 P.M. in the Eastern time zone of North America, 12:00 P.M. in the Central time zone; 11:00 A.M. in the Mountain time zone; 10:00 A.M. in the Pacific time zone; and 9:00 A.M. in Alaska

Focus

Section Objectives

1. Compare the landforms and economies of Angola and Namibia.
2. Explain what has caused deforestation in Mozambique and Madagascar.
3. Discuss why Madagascar has such unusual plants and animals.

BELLRINGER
Skillbuilder Activity

Project transparency and have students answer the question.

Daily Focus Skills Transparency

Reading Preview

■ **Activating Prior Knowledge** Several African countries are islands. Have students identify what challenges island countries might face.

■ **Preteaching Vocabulary** Have students find the meaning of the word *exclave* in the text. Have students use their knowledge of prefixes to compare the definitions of *exclave* and *enclave*.

Guide to Reading

Main Idea

Africa's coastal and island countries are struggling to develop their economies.

Terms to Know

- exclave
- slash-and-burn farming
- cyclone

Reading Strategy

Create a chart like the one below. Then fill in two key facts about each of southern Africa's coastal and island countries.

Country	Fact #1	Fact #2
Angola		
Namibia		
Mozambique		
Madagascar		
Comoros		
Seychelles		
Mauritius		

Section 3

Coastal and Island Countries

NATIONAL GEOGRAPHIC **Exploring Our World**

Ostriches, lions, and elephants have found a way of surviving in the Namib Desert located along Namibia's Atlantic Ocean coast. Most nights a damp fog forms over the ocean. This fog floats inland, carrying moisture as far as 60 miles (97 km). Some of the hardy animals here survive by eating moistened tree leaves or finding small water holes.

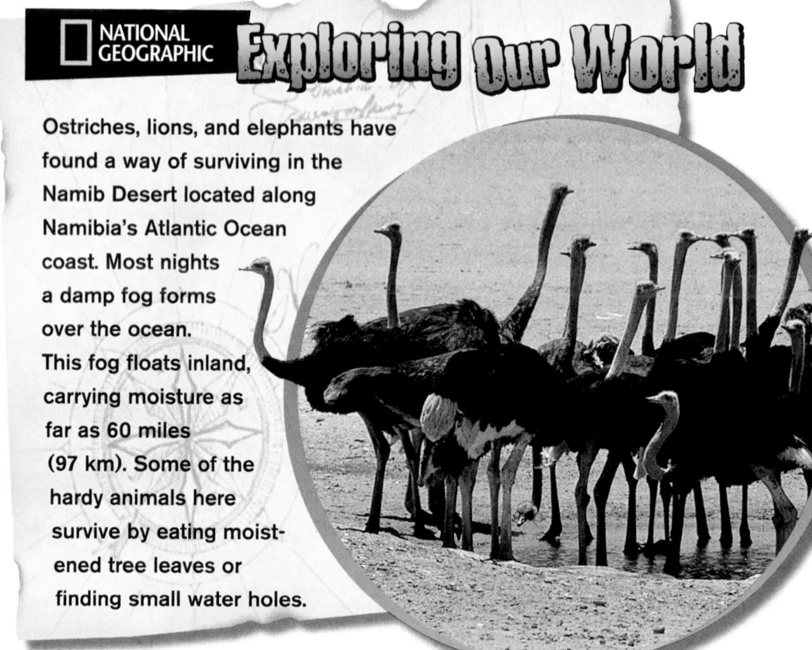

Angola and **Namibia** have long coastlines on the Atlantic Ocean. **Mozambique** and four island countries—**Madagascar** (MA•duh•GAS•kuhr), **Comoros** (KAH•muh•ROHZ), **Seychelles** (say•SHEHL), and **Mauritius** (maw•RIH•shuhs)—are located in southern Africa's Indian Ocean region.

Angola

Angola is almost twice the size of Texas. The map on page 605 shows you that Angola also includes a tiny exclave called **Cabinda.** An **exclave** is a small part of a country that is separated from the main part. Hilly grasslands cover northern Angola. The southern part of the country is a rocky desert. In Cabinda, rain forests thrive.

Angola's main economic activity is agriculture. About 85 percent of the people make their living from subsistence farming. Some farmers grow coffee and cotton for export. Angola's main source of income,

Section Resources

Reproducible Masters
- Reproducible Lesson Plan
- Daily Lecture and Discussion Notes
- Note-taking Guide
- Guided Reading Activity
- Reading Essentials and Study Guide
- Section Quiz

Transparencies
- Daily Focus Skills Transparency
- In-text Map Transparency

Multimedia
- Vocabulary PuzzleMaker CD-ROM
- Interactive Tutor Self-Assessment CD-ROM
- Presentation Plus! CD-ROM
- ExamView® Pro Testmaker CD-ROM
- MindJogger Videoquiz

however, is oil. Oil deposits off the coast of Cabinda account for 90 percent of Angola's export earnings. Other important industries include diamond mining, fish processing, and textiles. Still, Angola is not a wealthy country. Different groups have struggled for control of the country, which has hurt the economy.

Most of Angola's people trace their ancestry to the Bantu-speaking peoples who spread across much of Africa many centuries ago. In the 1400s, the Kongo kingdom ruled a large part of northern Angola.

From the 1500s until its independence in 1975, Angola was a colony of Portugal. Portugal is still an important trading partner, and Portuguese is the official language. Bantu and other African languages are also widely spoken. Almost 50 percent of Angolans practice the Roman Catholic faith brought to Angola by the Portuguese.

After Angola gained its independence, civil war broke out among different political and ethnic groups. The fighting has lasted more than 25 years and continues to bring great suffering to the people.

Reading Check With so many resources, why is Angola's economy weak?

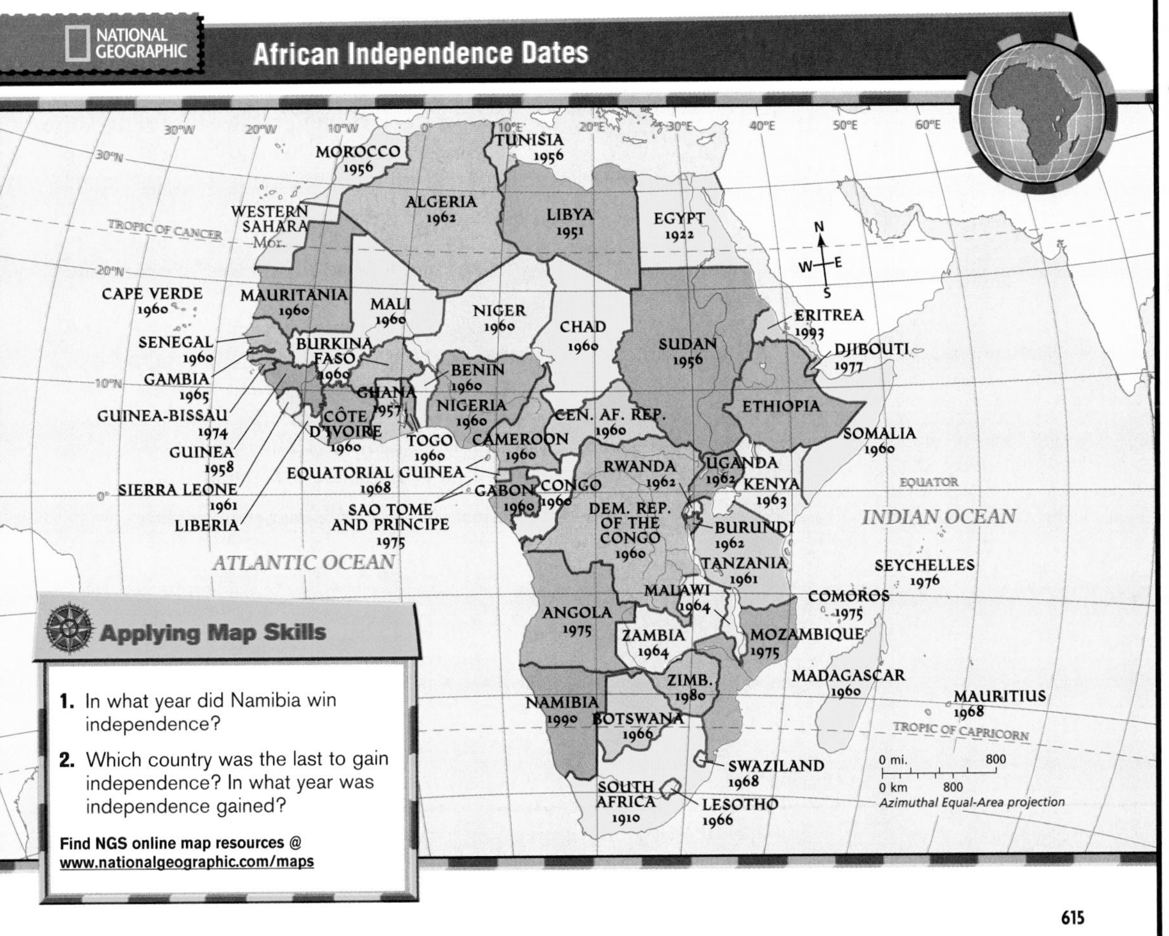

Applying Map Skills

1. In what year did Namibia win independence?
2. Which country was the last to gain independence? In what year was independence gained?

Find NGS online map resources @ www.nationalgeographic.com/maps

TEACH

Reading Strategy

Making Comparisons Have students make a chart comparing Angola and Namibia. Bases of comparison may include landscapes, economic activities, history, and people. Have volunteers share their comparisons with the class. L1

Reading Check Answer

Groups struggling for control of the country have hurt the economy.

Applying Map Skills

Answers
1. 1990
2. Eritrea; 1993

In-text Map Transparency Activity After students have answered the questions about the map, discuss it as a class. **Ask: When did most of the African countries gain their independence?** *(during the 1960s and 1970s)* **What world events might have contributed to the independence of African countries?** *(World War I and World War II)* **How do you think these events influenced the struggle for independence?** *(Students may speculate that European nations were weakened economically and militarily and could no longer maintain them as colonies.)*

Reading Strategy — Reading the Text

Taking Notes As students read the section, have them take notes on note cards. Notes should be recorded in the student's own words and labeled with the page number where the entire text is found. Students should try to answer *who, what, where, when, why,* and *how* to help them create their notes. L1

*Use the **Reading Skills Handbook** for more reading strategies.*

Daily Lecture and Discussion Notes

SOUTHERN AFRICA—A VARIED REGION

Daily Lecture and Discussion Notes
Coastal and Island Countries

Did You Know? The Chokwe people live in Angola and Zambia. They do not recognize a single leader, but instead are loyal to local chiefs. The chiefs consult with a group of elders and ritual experts before making decisions.

I. Angola

A. Angola has a long coastline on the Atlantic Ocean. It is about twice the size of Texas.

B. Angola includes a tiny exclave called Cabinda. An **exclave** is a small part of a country that is separated from the main part.

Reading Check Answer

1990

More About the Photo

Maputo Maputo and two other Mozambique ports—Beira and Nacala—have among the finest harbors in all of Africa.

Caption Answer a fierce civil war

L1/ELL

Guided Reading Activity

Name ______ Date ______ Class ______

SOUTHERN AFRICA—A VARIED REGION

Guided Reading Activity 3
Coastal and Island Countries

DIRECTIONS: Reading for Accuracy Reading the section and completing the activity below will help you learn more about southern Africa's coastal and island countries. Refer to your textbook to decide if a statement is true or false. Write **T** or **F**, and if a statement is false, rewrite it correctly.

____ 1. Angola is a tiny country that also contains an enclave.

____ 2. Angola earns most of its export revenue from agriculture.

____ 3. Civil war still goes on in Angola today among political and ethnic groups.

NATIONAL GEOGRAPHIC On Location

Maputo, Mozambique

A high-rise building is being constructed in Maputo. Hotels and industrial projects are helping the city's economy grow.

Economics What slowed industrial growth in Maputo in the 1980s and 1990s?

Namibia

Namibia is one of Africa's newest countries. Namibia became independent in 1990 after 75 years of rule by the Republic of South Africa. Before that, it was a colony of Germany.

A large plateau runs through the center of the country. This area of patchy grassland is the most populous section of Namibia. The rest is made up of deserts. The **Namib Desert,** located along Namibia's Atlantic coast, is a narrow ribbon of towering dunes and rocks. Tourists come from all over the world to "sand-board" down these dunes. The Kalahari Desert stretches across the southeastern part of the country. As you might guess, most of Namibia has a hot, dry climate.

Namibia has rich deposits of diamonds, copper, gold, zinc, silver, and lead. It is a leading producer of uranium, a substance used to make nuclear fuels. The economy depends on the mining, processing, and exporting of these minerals.

Despite this mineral wealth, most of Namibia's people live in poverty. The income from mineral exports goes to a small group of Namibia's people and to the foreign companies that have invested in Namibia's mineral resources. As a result, half of the country's people depend on subsistence farming, herding, and working in food industries.

Only 1.9 million people live in Namibia. It is one of the most sparsely populated countries in Africa. In fact, in the language of Namibia's Nama ethnic group, *namib* means "the land without people." Most Namibians belong to African ethnic groups. A small number are of European ancestry. Namibians speak African languages, whereas most of the white population speaks Afrikaans and English.

Reading Check **When did Namibia become an independent country?**

Mozambique

Sand dunes, swamps, and fine natural harbors line Mozambique's long Indian Ocean coastline. In the center of this Y-shaped country stretches a flat plain covered with grasses and tropical forests.

Most people in Mozambique are farmers. Some practice **slash-and-burn farming**—a method of clearing land for planting by cutting and burning forests. Slash-and-burn farming, along with commercial logging, has caused deforestation. Deforestation can, in turn, lead to flooding during the rainy season. Such floods drove more than one million people from their homes in early 2000. Mozambique also

Differentiated Instruction

Meeting Special Needs: Visual/Spatial Organize students into five groups and assign one of the five countries covered in this section to each. Instruct students to develop an illustrated poster with three or more images that convey the variety of life in their assigned country. For example, they might choose a coffee plantation, a landscape showing deforestation, or a street market in Antananarivo to portray Madagascar. Suggest that they obtain their images by drawing them or by researching on the Internet. Call on each group to display their images and explain the significance of each. **L1**

Refer to *Inclusion for the Middle School Social Studies Classroom Strategies and Activities* in the TCR.

experiences deadly cyclones. A cyclone is an intense storm system with heavy rain and high circular winds.

Mozambique's major crops are cashews, cotton, sugarcane, tea, coconuts, and tropical fruits. The main source of income, however, comes from its seaports. South Africa, Zimbabwe, Swaziland, and Malawi all pay to use the docks at **Maputo,** the capital, and other ports.

During the 1980s and early 1990s, a fierce civil war slowed industrial growth. In recent years, however, foreign companies have begun to invest in metal production, natural gas, fishing, and transportation services.

Most of Mozambique's 17.5 million people belong to one of 16 major African ethnic groups. A former colony of Portugal, Mozambique's official language is Portuguese, but most people speak African languages. About half of the people practice traditional African religions. Most of the rest are Muslim or Christian.

Reading Check What is a negative result of slash-and-burn farming?

Madagascar

The island of Madagascar broke away from the African mainland about 160 million years ago. As a result, it has many plants and animals that are not found elsewhere. Its economy relies on agriculture, including fishing and forestry. It produces most of the world's vanilla beans. The main cash crop is coffee, and rice is also grown. About 80 percent of the island has been slashed and burned. The government has taken steps to save the remaining forests and to reduce poverty.

Only about 22 percent of Madagascar's people are city dwellers. **Antananarivo** (AHN•tah•NAH•nah•REE•voh), the capital, lies in the central plateau. Called "Tana" for short, this city is known for its colorful street markets, where craftspeople sell a variety of products.

Music revolves around dance rhythms that reflect Madagascar's Southeast Asian and African heritage. The people are known for their rhythmic style of singing accompanied only by hand clapping.

Reading Check Why does Madagascar have wildlife that appears nowhere else on the earth?

▲ This ring-tailed lemur lives on the island of Madagascar.

Small Island Countries

Far from Africa in the Indian Ocean are three other island republics—Comoros, Seychelles, and Mauritius. The people of these countries have many different backgrounds.

Comoros The three islands of Comoros were formed by volcanoes thousands of years ago. Dense tropical forests cover the islands today. Most of the approximately 600,000 people are farmers. The main crops are rice, vanilla, cloves, coconuts, and bananas. Even though agriculture employs 80 percent of the workforce, Comoros cannot grow enough food for its growing population. The government is trying to encourage industry, including tourism.

The people of Comoros are a mixture of Arabs, Africans, and people from Madagascar. They speak Arabic, French, and Comoran. Most

Chapter 21

Section 3, pages 614–618

Reading Check Answer

deforestation

Reading Check Answer

because it separated from the mainland 160 million years ago

ASSESS

Assign Section 3 Assessment as homework or an in-class activity.

Have students use the Interactive Tutor Self-Assessment CD-ROM to review Section 3.

L2

Section Quiz

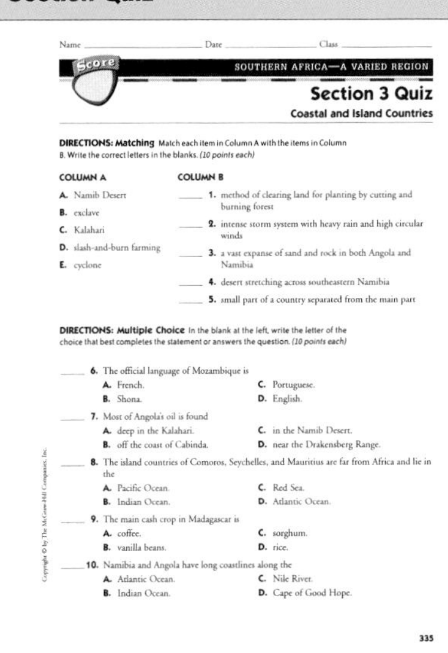

Name ______ Date ______ Class ______

SOUTHERN AFRICA—A VARIED REGION

Section 3 Quiz

Coastal and Island Countries

DIRECTIONS: Matching Match each item in Column A with the items in Column B. Write the correct letters in the blanks. *(10 points each)*

COLUMN A	COLUMN B
A. Namib Desert	____ 1. method of clearing land for planting by cutting and burning forest
B. exclave	____ 2. intense storm system with heavy rain and high circular winds
C. Kalahari	____ 3. a vast expanse of sand and rock in both Angola and Namibia
D. slash-and-burn farming	____ 4. desert stretching across southeastern Namibia
E. cyclone	____ 5. small part of a country separated from the main part

DIRECTIONS: Multiple Choice In the blank at the left, write the letter of the choice that best completes the statement or answers the question. *(10 points each)*

____ 6. The official language of Mozambique is
A. French. C. Portuguese.
B. Shona. D. English.

____ 7. Most of Angola's oil is found
A. deep in the Kalahari. C. in the Namib Desert.
B. off the coast of Cabinda. D. near the Drakensberg Range.

____ 8. The island countries of Comoros, Seychelles, and Mauritius are far from Africa and lie in the
A. Pacific Ocean. C. Red Sea.
B. Indian Ocean. D. Atlantic Ocean.

____ 9. The main cash crop in Madagascar is
A. coffee. C. sorghum.
B. vanilla beans. D. rice.

____ 10. Namibia and Angola have long coastlines along the
A. Atlantic Ocean. C. Nile River.
B. Indian Ocean. D. Cape of Good Hope.

335

Team-Teaching Activity

Science Invite the science teacher to class to explain the short-term benefits but long-term costs of slash-and-burn agriculture. Ask the teacher to discuss the large expanse of land needed to support slash-and-burn farming over a period of many years and the amount of time required to allow the land to rebound. Have him or her also discuss the pros and cons of the techniques used in settled farming, such as using fertilizers, leaving fields fallow, cycling through crops, planting windbreaks, and so on. After the presentation is complete, have students create charts comparing the two sets of agricultural techniques. L2

EE5 Environment and Society: Standard 14

Chapter 21

Section 3, pages 614–618

Reading Strategy

Reteach

Have students organize the content of the section into outline form.

volcanoes

L1/ELL

Reading Essentials and Study Guide

Name ______ Date ______ Class ______

SOUTHERN AFRICA—A VARIED REGION

Reading Essentials and Study Guide 3

Coastal and Island Countries

Key Terms

exclave small part of a country that is separated from the main part
slash-and-burn farming method of clearing land for planting by cutting and burning forest
cyclone intense storm system with heavy rain and high winds

Drawing From Experience

Enrich

Have students research one of the animals unique to Madagascar and report on its characteristics.

Ask students to prepare a travelogue for one of the countries in this section that tells visitors about the most important and interesting features of the country.

practice Islam. Once ruled by France, the people of Comoros declared their independence in 1975. Since then, they have suffered from fighting among political groups for control of the government.

Seychelles The country of Seychelles is a group of 86 islands. About half of the islands are granite with high green peaks. The rest are small, flat coral islands with few people. Nearly 90 percent of the country's roughly 100,000 people live on Mahé, the largest island.

Seychelles was not inhabited until the 1700s. It has been under French and then British rule, but it finally became independent in 1976. Most of the country's people are of mixed African, European, and Asian descent. Coconuts and cinnamon are the chief cash crops. Fishing and tourism are important industries as well.

Mauritius Like Comoros, the islands of Mauritius were formed by volcanoes. Palm-dotted white beaches line the coasts. Sugar is the main agricultural export. Major industries are located in **Port Louis,** the capital. Clothing and textiles account for about half of the country's export earnings. Tourism is an important industry too.

Mauritians come from many different backgrounds. About 70 percent are descendants of settlers from India. The rest are of African, European, or Chinese ancestry. Because of this varied ethnic heritage, the foods of Mauritius have quite a mix of ingredients. You can sample Indian chicken curry, Chinese pork, African-made roast beef, and French-style vegetables.

Reading Check What created the islands of Comoros and Mauritius?

Assessment

Defining Terms

1. **Define** exclave, slash-and-burn farming, cyclone.

Recalling Facts

2. **Economics** What is Angola's main source of income?
3. **Place** Which two deserts are in Namibia?
4. **Location** Where are most of the world's vanilla beans grown?

Critical Thinking

5. **Understanding Cause and Effect** Why is Namibia one of the most sparsely populated countries in Africa?
6. **Evaluating Information** How do the foods of Mauritius show its heritage?

Graphic Organizer

7. **Organizing Information** Create a diagram like the one below. Then write facts about Madagascar that fit the category heading in each of the outer ovals.

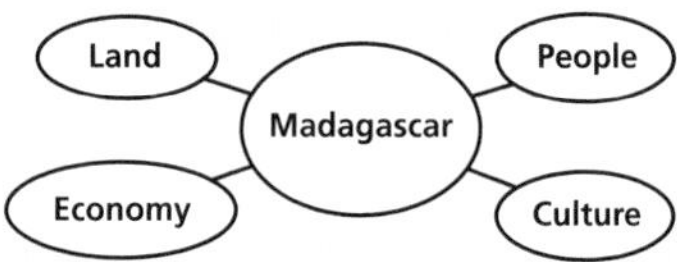

Applying Social Studies Skills

8. **Analyzing Maps** Study the map of African independence dates on page 615. Which southern African country first achieved independence?

618

Section 3 Assessment

1. The terms are defined in the Glossary.
2. oil
3. the Namib and the Kalahari
4. Madagascar
5. Most of Namibia is uninhabitable desert.
6. People of widely varied ethnicities have brought their homeland's foods with them.
7. Students should cite facts from the section.
8. South Africa

Reading Review

Section 1 The New South Africa

Terms to Know
- industrialized country
- Boer
- apartheid
- township
- enclave

Main Idea

South Africa has great mineral wealth and has recently seen major social and political changes.

✓Economics Because of its abundant mineral resources, South Africa has the most industrialized economy in Africa.

✓Government In 1994 South Africa held its first democratic election in which people from all ethnic groups could vote.

✓Government South Africa is working to improve the lives of its poorer citizens.

Section 2 Zambia, Malawi, Zimbabwe, Botswana

Terms to Know
- copper belt
- sorghum

Main Idea

Most of inland southern Africa is rich in resources and home to a wide variety of ethnic groups.

✓Economics Zambia is one of the world's largest producers of copper.

✓Economics Zimbabwe has many mineral resources and good farmland.

✓Economics Mining and tourism earn money for Botswana, but many of its people work in South Africa for several months each year.

Section 3 Coastal and Island Countries

Terms to Know
- exclave
- slash-and-burn farming
- cyclone

Main Idea

Africa's coastal and island countries are struggling to develop their economies.

✓Economics Angola's main source of income is oil.

✓Culture Few Namibians benefit from the country's rich mineral wealth. Most live in poverty.

✓Human/Environment Interaction Slash-and-burn farming in Mozambique has led to deforestation and flooding. Neighboring countries pay fees for the use of Mozambique's ports.

✓Location Madagascar's island location has resulted in many plants and animals found nowhere else in the world.

✓Economics Comoros continues to be a mainly agricultural economy, but Mauritius has succeeded in developing a variety of industries.

✓Economics Eighty-six islands form the country of Seychelles.

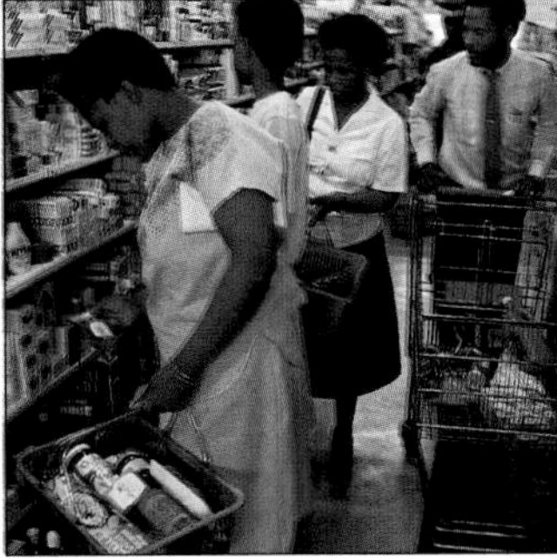

▲ A supermarket in Gabarone, Botswana, provides shoppers with a variety of food products.

Reading Review

Use the Chapter 21 Reading Review to preview, review, condense, or reteach the chapter.

Preview/Review

Use the Terms to Know lists to help students review and study.

Activity Assign students a selection of related terms from each section and have them write a paragraph using the assigned words. Have volunteers read their sentences aloud.

Vocabulary PuzzleMaker CD-ROM reinforces the vocabulary terms used in Chapter 21.

The Interactive Tutor Self-Assessment CD-ROM allows students to review Chapter 21 content.

Condense

Have students read the Chapter 21 summary statements.

Guided Reading Activities

Audio Program

Reteach

Reteaching Activity

Reading Essentials and Study Guide

Reading Strategy Read to Write

Creating an Illustrated Report Have students prepare an illustrated report that demonstrates how physical geography and climate affect the people of one of the countries in southern Africa. Remind them that in discussing physical geography, they should address not only the location of the country and the landforms found in it but also the natural resources, which can have an impact on the economy. Suggest that they include different kinds of maps in their report, and remind them to include keys and captions that explain the information on each map. L1

EE1 The World in Spatial Terms: Standards 1, 3

Assessment and Activities

GLENCOE TECHNOLOGY

MindJogger Videoquiz
Use MindJogger Videoquiz to review the Chapter 21 content.

Available in DVD and VHS

Using Key Terms

1.	e	6.	a
2.	b	7.	j
3.	f	8.	c
4.	g	9.	h
5.	i	10.	d

Reviewing the Main Ideas

11. Cape of Good Hope
12. 1994
13. water
14. Zambezi River
15. northern Zambia
16. donations, loans, and foreign aid
17. an ancient African city
18. Great Britain
19. Portugal
20. "the land without people"
21. Portuguese
22. coffee

Chapter 21 Assessment and Activities

Using Key Terms

Match the terms in Part A with their definitions in Part B.

A.

1. copper belt
2. cyclone
3. exclave
4. slash-and-burn farming
5. township
6. apartheid
7. Boer
8. industrialized country
9. sorghum
10. enclave

B.

a. separating racial and ethnic groups
b. storm with high circular winds
c. country that relies on manufacturing
d. small nation located inside a larger country
e. large area of copper mines
f. small part of a nation separated from the main part of the country
g. areas of forest are cleared by burning
h. tall grass used as grain and to make syrup
i. settlement outside cities in South Africa
j. Dutch farmer in South Africa

Reviewing the Main Ideas

Section 1 The New South Africa

11. **Location** What is the southernmost point of Africa?
12. **History** When was South Africa's first election allowing all people to vote?
13. **Economics** What is Lesotho's only important natural resource?

Section 2 Zambia, Malawi, Zimbabwe, Botswana

14. **Place** What river crosses Zambia?
15. **Economics** Where is the copper belt?
16. **Economics** How are the people of Malawi supported?
17. **History** What was Great Zimbabwe?
18. **History** Who ruled Botswana for nearly 80 years?

Section 3 Coastal and Island Countries

19. **History** What European country colonized Angola?
20. **Culture** What does *namib* mean?
21. **Culture** What is the official language of Mozambique?
22. **Economics** What is Madagascar's main cash crop?

NATIONAL GEOGRAPHIC Southern Africa

Place Location Activity

On a separate sheet of paper, match the letters on the map with the numbered places listed below.

1. Madagascar
2. Lake Malawi
3. Zambezi River
4. Kalahari Desert
5. Angola
6. Zimbabwe
7. Pretoria
8. Mozambique
9. South Africa
10. Namibia

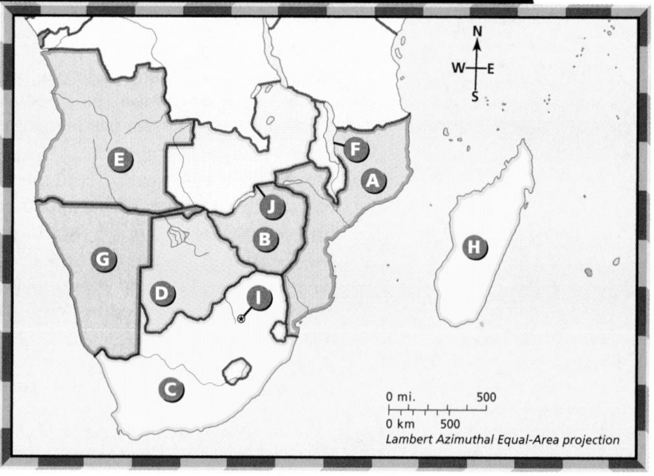

NATIONAL GEOGRAPHIC Place Location Activity

1.	H	6.	B
2.	F	7.	I
3.	J	8.	A
4.	D	9.	C
5.	E	10.	G

Critical Thinking

23. *Possible answer:* South Africa has abundant mineral resources; a variety of industries, including manufacturing; productive farms and ranches; and uses high-technology approaches to production.
24. Answers will vary, but positive factors might include an end to reliance on uncertain single-commodity exports and increased income; negatives might include pollution and loss of traditional cultures.

Self-Check Quiz Visit ***The World and Its People*** Web site at twip.glencoe.com and click on **Chapter 21—Self-Check Quizzes** to prepare for the Chapter Test.

Critical Thinking

23. **Supporting Generalizations** What facts support the statement "South Africa has the most industrialized economy in Africa"?

24. **Evaluating Information** Many countries of southern Africa are hoping to build and improve their industries. On a chart like the one below, list the positive and negative aspects of industrialization under the correct headings.

Industrialization	
Positives	Negatives

Comparing Regions Activity

25. **History** Use the map on page 615 to create a time line that shows when each African country gained independence. In a different color, add dates that are important to the history of the United States civil rights movement. Do you see any overlap of the two sets of dates? Think about possible links between these two regions and their activities.

Mental Mapping Activity

26. **Focusing on the Region** Create a simple outline map of southern Africa, and then label the following:

- Atlantic Ocean
- Lesotho
- Madagascar
- Angola
- South Africa
- Cape Town
- Namib Desert
- Mozambique
- Indian Ocean
- Botswana

Technology Skills Activity

27. **Using the Internet** The Zulu are a well-known ethnic group in Africa. Research this group on the Internet. Write a speech answering these questions: Who are the Zulu? How have they affected the history of southern Africa? Where do they live today?

Standardized Test Practice

Directions: Study the map below, and then answer the question that follows.

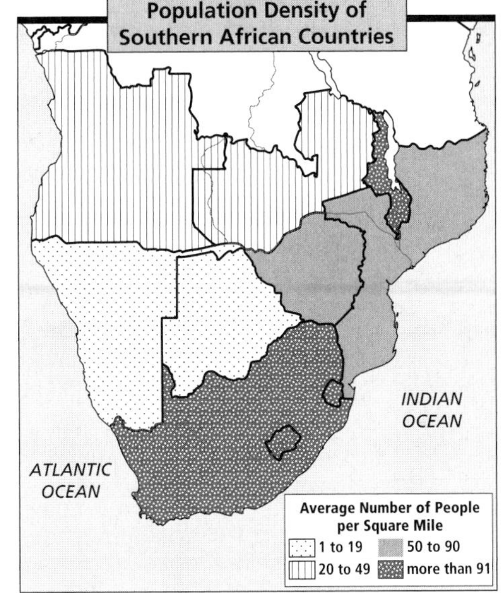

1. Of the following, which country has the fewest people per square mile?

A Lesotho
B Malawi
C South Africa
D Namibia

Test-Taking Tip: This question involves recalling where countries are located as well as using the legend. Start with the answer choices. Think about what you learned about each country. You may be able to get rid of wrong answer choices simply by recalling these facts.

Assessment and Activities

Standardized Test Practice

1. D

Tested Objectives:
Reading a map, analyzing information

Chapter Test Bonus Question

This question may be used for extra credit on the chapter test.

Where does the ring-tailed lemur live? *(Madagascar)*

Social Studies Online

Have students visit the Web site at twip.glencoe.com to review Chapter 21 and take the Self-Check Quiz.

Dinah Zike's Foldables

Culminating Activity Have students create an illustrated time line that shows events listed on their foldables.

Comparing Regions Activity

25. Many important dates during the United States civil rights movement and the independence of African countries occurred during the 1960s. Students may note that public outcry against racism might have contributed to the changes in these two regions.

Mental Mapping Activity

26. This exercise helps students visualize the countries and geographic features they have been studying. Accept all attempts at freehand mapping that show places in the correct relationship to one another.

Technology Skills Activity

27. For variety, you might assign some students to research other peoples who live in southern Africa.

Unit 8 Planning Guide

- If you teach BOTH Eastern and Western world regions in one year, use the columns in red to help you pace your lessons.
- **If you teach ONLY Eastern or Western world regions in one year, use the columns in blue to help you pace your lessons.**

ALTERNATIVE PACING CHARTS

Unit 8		Chapter 22		Chapter 23		Chapter 24		Chapter 25	
Both East and West	**Either East or West**	Both East and West	**Either East or West**	Both East and West	**Either East or West**	Both East and West	**Either East or West**	Both East and West	**Either East or West**
Day 1 Unit Opener, Regional Atlas Day 2 Regional Atlas	**Day 1** Unit Opener, Regional Atlas **Day 2** Regional Atlas **Day 3** Regional Atlas **Day 4** Regional Atlas	Day 1 Chapter Opener, Section 1 Day 2 Section 1, Making Connections Day 3 Section 2, Social Studies Skill Day 4 Section 3 Day 5 Section 3, Review Day 6 Chapter Assessment	**Day 1** Chapter Opener, Section 1 **Day 2** Section 1 **Day 3** Making Connections, Section 2 **Day 4** Section 2, Social Studies Skill **Day 5** Section 3 **Day 6** Review **Day 7** Chapter Assessment	Day 1 Chapter Opener, Section 1 Day 2 Making Connections, Section 2 Day 3 TIME Reports Day 4 TIME Reports, Section 3 Day 5 Section 3, Critical Thinking Skill, Review Day 6 Chapter Assessment Day 7 NGS Geography and History	**Day 1** Chapter Opener, Section 1 **Day 2** Section 1 **Day 3** Making Connections, Section 2 **Day 4** TIME Reports **Day 5** Section 3 **Day 6** Critical Thinking Skill, Review **Day 7** Chapter Assessment **Day 8** NGS Geography and History	Day 1 Chapter Opener, Section 1 Day 2 Section 1, Making Connections Day 3 Section 2 Day 4 Critical Thinking Skill, Review Day 5 Chapter Assessment	**Day 1** Chapter Opener, Section 1 **Day 2** Section 1 **Day 3** Section 1 **Day 4** Section 2, Making Connections **Day 5** Section 2 **Day 6** Section 2, Critical Thinking Skill **Day 7** Review **Day 8** Chapter Assessment	Day 1 Chapter Opener, Section 1 Day 2 Section 1, Social Studies Skill Day 3 Section 2 Day 4 Making Connections, Review Day 5 Chapter Assessment	**Day 1** Chapter Opener, Section 1 **Day 2** Section 1 **Day 3** Section 1, Social Studies Skill **Day 4** Section 2 **Day 5** Section 2, Making Connections **Day 6** Review **Day 7** Chapter Assessment **Day 8** Chapter Assessment

Note: The following materials may be used when teaching Unit 8.
Chapter level support materials can be found on the chapter resource pages.

TEACHING TRANSPARENCIES

Political Map Transparency L2

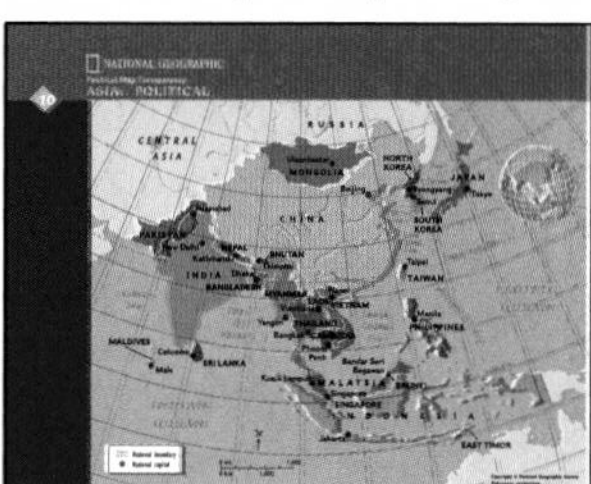

Map Overlay Transparencies L2

World Cultures Transparencies L2

Unit 8 Resources

INTERDISCIPLINARY CONNECTIONS

World Literature Reading L2

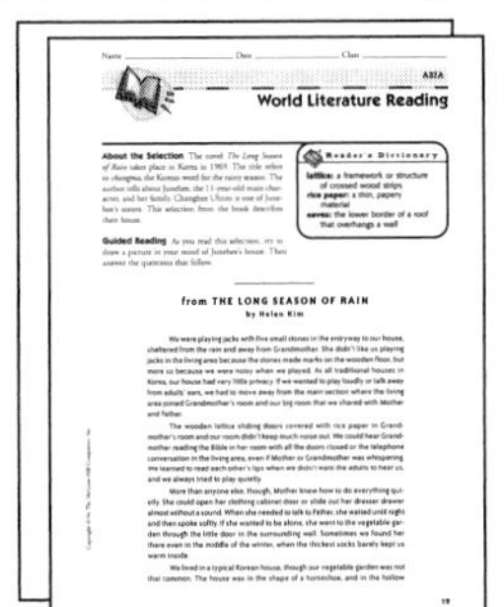

Economics and Geography Activity L2

History and Geography Activity L2

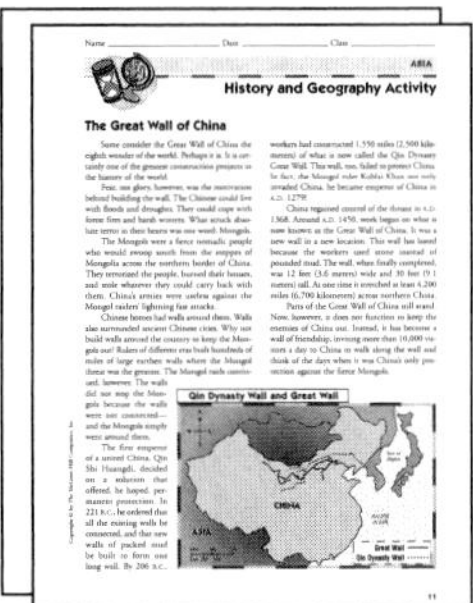

INTERDISCIPLINARY CONNECTIONS

Foods Around the World L1/ELL

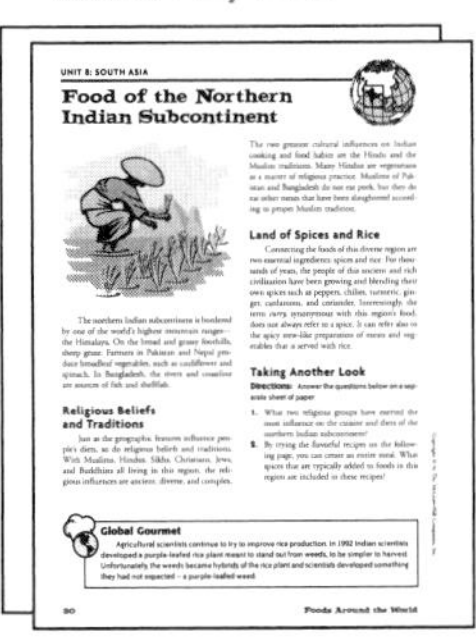

World Music: A Cultural Legacy

CIVIC INVOLVEMENT

Citizenship Activity L1

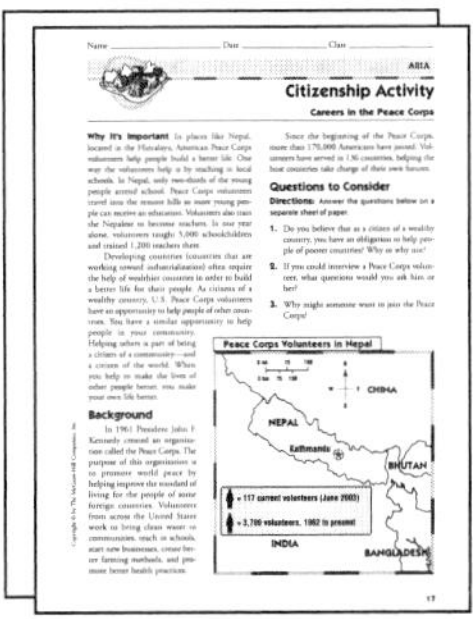

Environmental Case Study L2

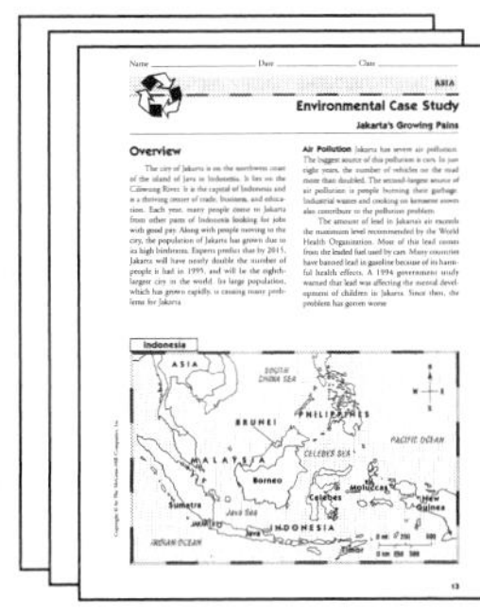

MAP AND GEOGRAPHY SKILLS

Building Geography Skills for Life

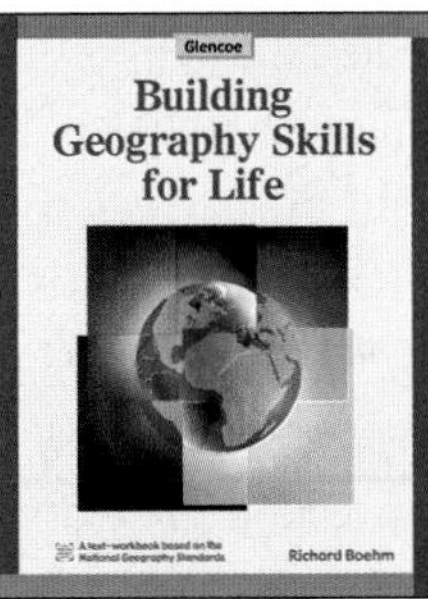

NGS Focus on Geography Literacy L2

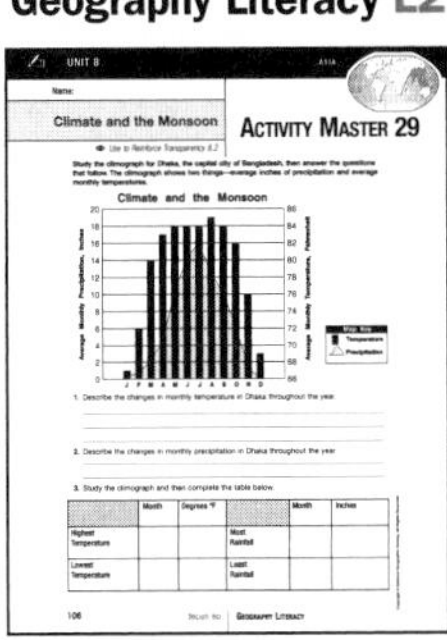

Regional Atlas Activity L2

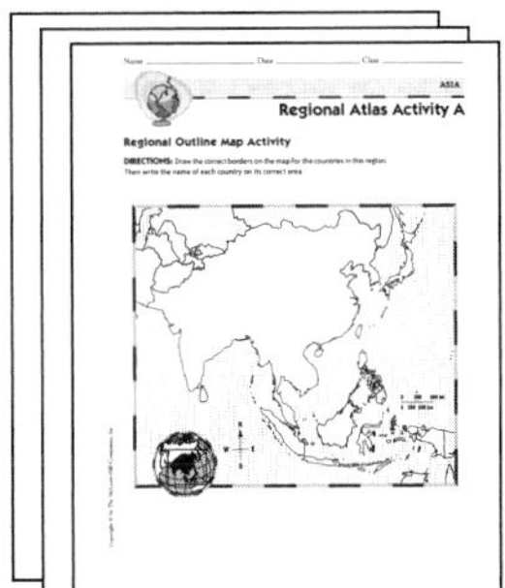

KEY TO ABILITY LEVELS

Teaching strategies have been coded for varying learning styles and abilities.

L1 **BASIC** activities for all students

L2 **AVERAGE** activities for average to above-average students

L3 **CHALLENGING** activities for above-average students

ELL **ENGLISH LANGUAGE LEARNER** activities

ASSESSMENT

Unit Pretests L2

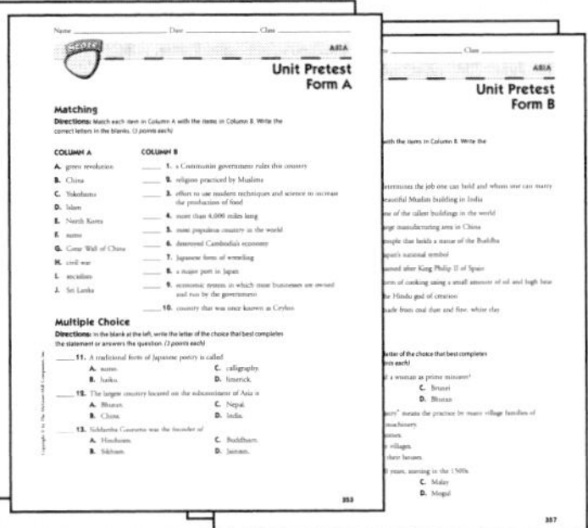

Unit Posttests L2

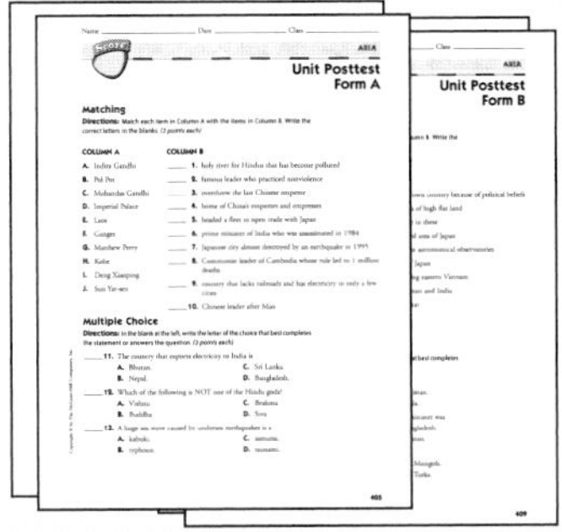

Glencoe Professional Development and Teacher Support Materials

- **Reading in the Content Area for the Middle School Classroom**
- **Inclusion Strategies for the Middle School Social Studies Classroom**
- **Character Education for the Middle School Classroom**
- **Teaching Strategies for the Social Studies Classroom**
- **Reproducible Lesson Plans**
- **Outline Map Resource Book**
- **Writing Process Transparencies for Middle School**
- **Social Studies: Reading Strategies**

Additional Unit 8 Resources

- **Timed Readings Plus in Social Studies** help students increase their reading rate and fluency while maintaining comprehension. The 400-word passages are similar to those found on state and national assessments.
- **Reading in the Content Area: Social Studies** concentrates on six essential reading skills that help students better comprehend what they read. The book includes 75 high-interest nonfiction passages written at increasing levels of difficulty.
- **Reading Fluency** helps students read smoothly, accurately, and expressively.
- **Jamestown's Reading Improvement,** by renowned reading expert Edward Fry, focuses on helping build your students' comprehension, vocabulary, and skimming and scanning skills.
- **Critical Reading Series** provides high-interest books, each written at three reading levels.

For more information about these products, see the Jamestown Education materials in the Classroom Solutions in the front of this Teacher Wraparound Edition. To order these products, call Glencoe at 1-800-334-7344.

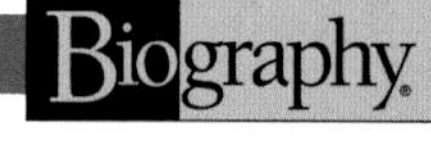

The following videotape programs are available from Glencoe:

- **The Great Wall of China** 0-7670-0361-6
- **Hirohito** 1-56501-461-8
- **Korea: The Forgotten War** 1-56501-540-1
- **Mahatma Gandhi: Pilgrim of Peace** 0-7670-0668-2
- **Democracy Crushed: Tiananmen Square** 0-7670-1459-6
- **Vietnam: A Soldier's Diary** 0-7670-0772-7
- **China's Boxer Rebellion** 0-7670-0617-8
- **China's Forbidden City** 0-7670-0649-6
- **Confucius: Words of Wisdom** 0-7670-0407-8

To order, call Glencoe at 1-800-334-7344. To find classroom resources to accompany many of these, check:

A&E Television: www.aetv.com

The History Channel: www.historychannel.com

Reading List Generator CD-ROM

GLENCOE BOOKLINK

The Glencoe BookLink CD-ROM is a database that allows you to search more than 15,000 titles to create a customized reading list for your students.

- Reading lists can be organized by students' reading level, author, genre, theme, or area of interest.
- The database provides Degrees of Reading Power™ (DRP) and Lexile™ readability scores for all selections.
- A brief summary of each selection is included.

Leveled reading suggestions for this unit:

For students at a Grade 5 reading level:

- ***I Remember India,*** by Anita Ganeri.

For students at a Grade 6 reading level:

- ***Eighth Moon,*** by Bette Lord.

For students at a Grade 7 reading level:

- ***The Great Wall: The Story of Thousands of Miles of Earth and Stone,*** by Elizabeth Mann.

To order this CD-ROM, call Glencoe at 1-800-334-7344.

Extending the Content

Readings for the Teacher

- ***India: A History,*** by John Keay. New York, NY: Atlantic Monthly Press, 2000.
- ***A History of Japan: From Stone Age to Superpower,*** by Kenneth G. Henshall. New York, NY: Palgrave, 1999.

Multimedia Resources

- **Glencoe World History Primary Source Document Library CD-ROM**
- **History and Culture of China.** Fairfield, Conn.: Queue. CD-ROM, Win/Mac.

Service Learning Project

Connecting Classroom With Community

China has a long tradition of honoring parents and ancestors. As a result, the elderly in this culture are accorded great respect. Suggest that students show similar respect in their own community by visiting a community center that serves senior citizens. They might assist clients with meals, record their memories to create a community memory bank, or simply provide company. Have students complete a project summary report that includes such information as: How did this project help my community? What did I learn while completing this project?

Content Background Notes

Use this additional information as lecture notes or discussion prompts throughout the study of Unit 8.

Chapter 22 South Asia (pp. 636–657)

Devastating Earthquake In January 2001, a powerful earthquake struck the northern Indian state of Gujarat. Tragically, the quake came on Republic Day, a national holiday that celebrates the country's independence. Early estimates suggested the death toll would reach 30,000, making the quake the worst in India's history and the worst in the world since a 1990 quake shook Iran. Other estimates put the damage caused by the quake at more than $5 billion. Some of the damage came to historical and cultural sites that attract millions of visitors. India had no nationwide disaster relief system. In the aftermath of the earthquake, the country's leaders began planning to create one.

The Sundarbans One of the treasures of Bangladesh is the Sundarbans, the swampy region formed by the deltas of the Ganges, Brahmaputra, and Meghna Rivers. This biologically rich area is home to one of the largest mangrove forests in the world. Bangladesh has created three wildlife sanctuaries in the region that total some 2,228 square miles (5,771 sq. km). The region is home to a large population of Bengal tigers and to more than 300 different kinds of birds. Other notable animals include the estuarine crocodile, Indian python, and king cobra. The region is still largely wild and virtually uninhabited, although some people live on its outskirts and enter the Sundarbans in the late spring to harvest honey.

Chapter 23 China and Its Neighbors (pp. 658–685)

Falun Gong One-time Chinese government employee Li Hongzhi hoped to help other Chinese build greater spiritual peace. In 1992 he founded a movement called Falun Gong, which means "Law of the Wheel-Breathing Exercise." Followers use meditation and exercise to achieve calm and good health.

The Chinese government is hardly calm about Falun Gong, however. In April 1999, the movement shocked China's rulers by sending 10,000 members to demonstrate outside Communist Party headquarters in Beijing. The crowd stood silently in place, with the goal of winning the government's recognition of their movement. They got just the reverse—in July 1999, the government declared Falun Gong illegal. Since then, it has charged the movement with threatening the government, disrupting social stability, and endangering the health of followers. Estimates of Falun Gong members range as high as 70 million. According to some, this number is greater than the number of people who belong to the country's Communist Party. Other countries, including the United States, have urged the Chinese government to refrain from persecuting members of the movement.

Chapter 24 Japan and the Koreas (pp. 688–705)

Oldest Monarchy Japan has the world's oldest monarchy—a continuous line of emperors and empresses that reaches back about 2,000 years. Current Emperor Akihito is the 125th emperor in that line. Nestled in the middle of bustling, modern Tokyo sits nearly 300 acres of parkland and private buildings that make up the Imperial Palace complex, home to Japan's emperors since 1869. The Palace complex is surrounded by moats and, in some areas, by walls and towers. Inside, Japan's imperial family and the workers who support them follow a life of tradition and privacy. Imperial guards and court officials protect the emperor and his family from the public, erecting what has been called the "chrysanthemum curtain," named for the flower that serves as the emperor's symbol.

Reconciliation in Korea In 2000 North Korea and South Korea moved closer than ever before toward improved relations. In June South Korean president Kim Dae-Jung met with North Korean leader Kim Jong Il, launching a series of steps toward decreasing tensions in the peninsula. These included agreements to set up permanent liaison offices; to hold regular, high-level talks; and to allow family members separated by the border for nearly 50 years to visit with one another. Later in 2000, the American secretary of state met with North Korea's leader as well, another indication of an improved situation in Korea. For his efforts to promote peace, South Korea's leader won the 2000 Nobel Peace Prize.

Chapter 25 Southeast Asia (pp. 706–721)

Muslim Pop One of the world's top singing groups is a quintet from Malaysia called Raihan. The group—whose name means "a sense of paradise"—sings traditional Islamic songs called *nasyids*. They perform the songs with the sound of contemporary pop music, however, giving the Islamic faith a modern feel. Audiences have responded to the group's music. Their first album not only became Malaysia's top seller but also broke previous records for sales of one album. Record companies in Malaysia quickly tried to sign up other religious singers to capture a share of the market. Even a group of female singers has appeared. These women—all married and mothers—had to ask their husbands' permission to perform.

00:00 Out of Time?

If time does not permit teaching each chapter in this unit, you may use the **Reading Essentials and Study Guide** for each chapter.

Unit Overview

The four chapters of this unit introduce students to a culture region in which a large percentage of the world's people live. The countries in this region share the following features:

- high population densities
- deadly natural hazards—typhoons, floods, volcanoes, earthquakes
- expanding economies
- rich natural resources
- ancient religions and cultures

Glencoe Literature Library

As students study the unit, have them read *The Clay Marble* by Minfong Ho from the **Glencoe Literature Library.** The Glencoe Literature Library consists of novels and other readings for middle school students, along with study guides that offer instructional support and student activities.

Unit 8

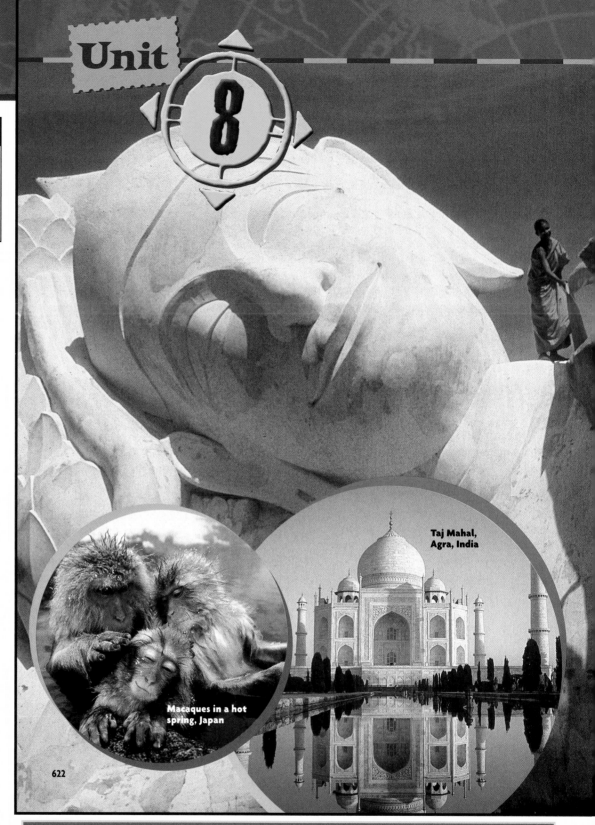

Taj Mahal, Agra, India

Macaques in a hot spring, Japan

622

Using the Illustration

Visual Instruction Buddha is typically shown in only a few poses. The reclining Buddha shown above represents the moment when he enters final nirvana. Thai artists tried to achieve the essence of an ancient sculpture believed to have been made in the Buddha's lifetime. Images of the Buddha are common throughout the region because kings hoped to gain credit for placing as many as possible in their realms. **Ask:** **What Asian countries besides Thailand are likely to display images of the Buddha?** Students can read the text to find which countries have large Buddhist populations. *(Bhutan, Cambodia, China, Japan, the Koreas, Laos, Mongolia, Myanmar, Nepal, Singapore, Sri Lanka, Vietnam)*

Introducing Unit 8

NATIONAL GEOGRAPHIC

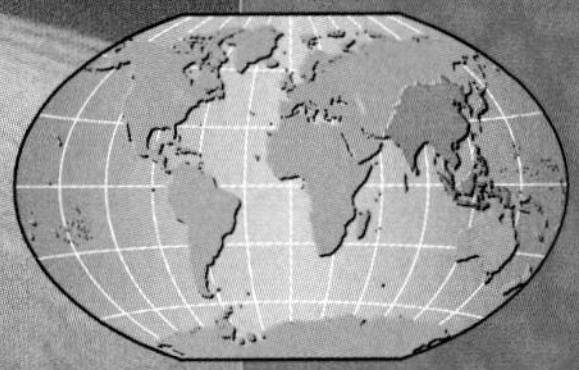

Asia

For many people in the Western Hemisphere, the region of Asia—in the Eastern Hemisphere—brings to mind exotic images. Ancient temples stand in dense rain forests. Farmers work in flooded rice fields. Pandas nibble bamboo shoots. Yet bustling cities, gleaming skyscrapers, and high-technology industries can also be found here. Turn the page to learn more about this region and its more than 3 billion people.

▲ Monks wrapping statue of Buddha in yellow cloth, Thailand

NGS ONLINE
www.nationalgeographic.com/education

623

Current Events Journal

Point out that India's rate of population growth—about 2 percent a year—is half of what it was 50 years ago. Inform students that the country has about 1 billion people. **Ask: With a growth rate of 2 percent, how many people are added to the country each year?** *(about 20 million)* Have students predict how this population growth might affect a country. Students should write their predictions in their journals. *(Predictions might include overcrowding, a lack of food and water, and strains on the economy and government.)* L1

NGS ONLINE
www.nationalgeographic.com/education

This online resource provides lesson plans, atlas updates, cartographic activities with interactive maps, an online map store, and geography links.

Unit Launch Activity

The Influence of China and India Asia has two of the oldest civilizations on the earth. China and India began to develop their civilizations thousands of years ago. Through trade, conquest, and religious conversion, these two civilizations strongly influenced many of their neighbors. Although other countries in Asia have their own distinctive cultures, China and India clearly have left their stamp on the ways of thinking and living in other countries. Before students begin studying the unit, inform them of the importance of these two cultures to the other countries of Asia. As they read, have them keep track of examples of this influence. When they have completed studying the unit, ask for volunteers to share their examples with the class. L1

EE4 Human Systems: Standard 9

Lesson Plan

Using the Regional Atlas

These features and activities may be used as an introduction to the unit or as teaching tools throughout the course of the unit.

Focus

Objectives

1. Identify the major landforms of Asia.
2. Explain how climate affects life in Asia.
3. Describe the chief resources and economic activities of Asia.
4. Discuss the different peoples who live in Asia.

5-Minute Precheck

Write "6 billion" on the board. Inform students that this number represents the population of the world. Then write "3.3 billion." **Ask:** **What does this number represent?** *(the population of Asia)* In view of this fact, have them consider Asia's importance to the world. Ask for volunteers to express their thoughts.

NATIONAL GEOGRAPHIC **Regional Atlas**

Focus on: Asia

The region of Asia is made up of surprisingly diverse landscapes. It includes a large chunk of the Asian continent, together with island groups that fringe its southern and eastern shores. Some of the world's oldest civilizations and religions had their beginnings in Asia. Now more than 3 billion people call this region home.

The Land

Covering roughly 7.8 million square miles (20.2 sq. km), the Asian region stretches from the mountains of western Pakistan to the eastern shores of Japan. It reaches from the highlands of northeastern China to the tropical islands of Indonesia. The region's long, winding coastlines are washed by two major oceans—the Indian and the Pacific—as well as many seas.

Lofty Landscape Several mountain ranges slice through central Asia. Most famous are the towering Himalaya. The earth's tallest peak—Mount Everest—is located here. North of the Himalaya lies the vast Plateau of Tibet, so high it has been called the Roof of the World. Beyond the plateau are two immense deserts: the Taklimakan and the Gobi.

Ring of Fire Other mountain ranges cut across northeastern China, run down the Korean Peninsula, and sweep through the peninsulas of Southeast Asia. Japan, Indonesia, and other mountainous islands lie offshore along the Ring of Fire. This is an area where adjoining plates of the earth's crust slip and buckle, setting off earthquakes and volcanic eruptions.

Mighty Rivers Great rivers begin in Asia's lofty center. On their journey to the sea, they flow through fertile plains in several countries. The most important rivers include the Indus in Pakistan, the Ganges and Brahmaputra in India and Bangladesh, the Yangtze and Yellow in China, and the Mekong in Southeast Asia.

The Climate

A person traveling across Asia would need clothes to suit almost every possible climate. The snowcapped mountains and high, windswept plateaus of northern and central Asia can be bitterly cold. The deserts can shimmer with heat by day, yet be frosty at night. Lowlands and coastal plains enjoy milder climates. The peninsulas of Southeast Asia and the islands straddling

Content Background

Population Asia has the two most populous countries in the world—China and India. It also includes several other countries with more than 100 million people (Indonesia, Pakistan, Japan, and Bangladesh). Population growth rates in China have declined in recent years, and the growth rates in Taiwan and South Korea are slowing to the same level as Japan, which is comparable to the low levels found in the industrialized West. Growth rates are also slowing in India, Indonesia, and Vietnam. Across the region, however, there is a large population of young people. This suggests that there will be another generation or two of high growth rates in many countries.

Unit 8

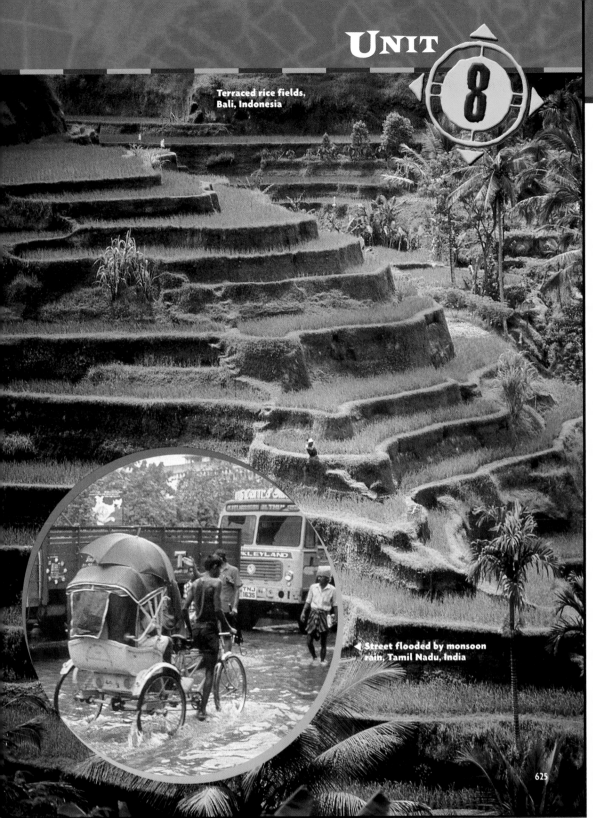

Terraced rice fields, Bali, Indonesia

◀ Street flooded by monsoon rain, Tamil Nadu, India

625

Unit 8

Regional Atlas

2 Teach

Using a Map Organize the class into pairs and have each pair map a route between two places in Asia. They can use the political and physical maps in the Reference Atlas. Ask the pairs to describe their route to the class, indicating the starting point and using directions to suggest the route traveled. Have them point out physical features they would encounter on the route and suggest ways that travelers could best overcome or circumvent these obstacles. L1

More About the Photos

Rice Rice is a grass, so it differs from wheat, corn, and other grains in needing wet conditions to grow. The terraces shown here allow farmers in mountainous Bali to retain water rather than lose it in runoff. In the Philippines, some terraces have been in use for 2,000 years.

Monsoon Rains Warm air in the summer brings heavy rain to many parts of Asia, including this city in India. Indian locales might average as much as 450 inches (1143 cm) of rain a year. Yet the Thar Desert, also in India, averages only 4 inches (10 cm).

Eyewitness to Geography

Nepal Writer T.D. Allman, writing in *National Geographic,* returned to Nepal nearly 40 years after he had first seen it as a Peace Corps worker. He and a Nepalese friend found many changes: "In Kathmandu we see sights that, whether grotesque or gratifying, were simply unimaginable not long ago. We see plastic garbage. (We can both remember when plastic was such a rare substance in Nepal it never would have been thrown away.) We see farm-raised fish for sale, also spinach, apples. Kathmandu has pollution that makes your lungs retch and—this amazes me—traffic jams. I'm also amazed, and pleased, by what you no longer see: harelip (now repaired by surgery) and goiter (iodine is now put in the salt)."

NATIONAL GEOGRAPHIC

REGIONAL ATLAS

Did You Know?

By the year 2010, the city of Calcutta, India, is expected to have more people than the entire country of Canada.

Interdisciplinary Connections

Technology Hong Kong has millions of people crammed onto a bit of mainland China and many islands. To enlarge the area, workers are blasting into the mountains on Kowloon Peninsula. They dump the rock and dirt that is dislodged onto the shore of the South China Sea. As a result, they are "growing" new land.

More About the Photo

Manufacturing in Asia
Japan's industrial output rose spectacularly from the 1950s to the 1990s, at which point the country began to suffer from a sharp recession. In the 1980s and early 1990s, four other Asian countries became economic powers. These "little tigers" were Hong Kong, Singapore, South Korea, and Taiwan. In the late 1990s, the major source of growth was China—aided, in part, by its absorption of Hong Kong.

the Equator have mostly tropical climates. They are cloaked in dense rain forests. Seasonal winds called monsoons blow across much of Asia, bringing dry weather in winter and drenching rains in summer.

The Economy

Agriculture is the major economic activity across most of Asia. The region's rugged mountains and vast deserts mean that only a small amount of the land is suitable for growing crops, however. For example, only about 10 percent of China's land can be used for agriculture. To feed the region's huge population, Asian farmers must make the most of every possible bit of farmland. Terraces allow farmers to grow rice on steep hillsides. Rice, which grows well in places with warm temperatures and plenty of water, is the most important food crop in Asia. China, India, Indonesia, and Bangladesh are the leading rice producers in the world.

Most of Asia's manufacturing takes place in Japan, South Korea, Taiwan, China, and India. China and India are rich in coal, iron ore, and other natural resources. Japan, however, has few mineral resources and must import fuel and nearly all the raw materials it uses. Still, Japan has become one of the world's leading manufacturers of cars, electronic products, and other goods. In some of the region's other countries, such as Laos, Vietnam, and Bhutan, industry is less developed.

The People

Nestled in fertile river valleys, some of the world's oldest civilizations arose in Asia thousands of years ago. Until the 1500s, Asia was more advanced than Europe in culture and technology. East Asians founded cities, set up states, and carved out trade routes.

Religious Traditions Ancient religions also took root in Asia. Both Hinduism and Buddhism, for example, originated in India. Hindus remain concentrated in India, but over time Buddhism spread throughout the region. The region's most widespread faith—Islam—began in Southwest Asia.

Europeans arrived in the region around 1500, bringing Christianity to some of the people. By the early 1800s, many Asian countries had fallen under European control. Many became European colonies and Western ideas spread throughout the region.

Modern Times In the early 1900s, Japan became Asia's leading power. World War II resulted in Japan's defeat, but it also ended Europe's hold on Asia. Nearly all of the Asian lands ruled by foreigners became independent by the mid-1900s.

◀ Robot welding car bodies in a factory, Japan

FUN FACTS

- **Indonesia** About 1 out of every 15 cups of coffee consumed around the world and about 1 in every 20 cups of tea come from crops grown on plantations in Indonesia.
- **China/Nepal** Mount Everest—the tallest mountain in the world—is named for Sir George Everest, a British colonial official who surveyed the Himalaya in the 1860s. Tibetans call the mountain *Chomolungma*, which means "Goddess Mother of the World."
- **Pakistan** K2 is another lofty mountain near Everest. It was so named because it was the second mountain measured in a survey of the Karakoram Range carried out in the 1850s.

Unit 8

In many cases, however, independence in Asia was followed by political turmoil and conflict. Much of the region was caught up in the global struggle between communist and noncommunist countries. Many countries were torn apart by civil wars between communists and other groups.

Today China, Vietnam, and North Korea have Communist governments. Nepal and Bhutan are ruled by traditional monarchs. Military leaders control Myanmar. Japan, India, and the Philippines are democracies.

About 3.6 billion people live in Asia. China, Indonesia, Bangladesh, and Japan are among the world's most heavily populated countries. Asia's population, however, is very unevenly distributed. Most Asians make their homes in river or mountain valleys or near seacoasts. As a result, some parts of Asia are among the most crowded places in the world. They include Bangladesh, eastern China, northern India, southern Japan, and the island of Java in Indonesia.

Jodhpur, India ▼

China

Data Bits

Data Bits	
Automobiles per 1,000 people	3
Television sets per 1,000 people	291
Democratic elections	No

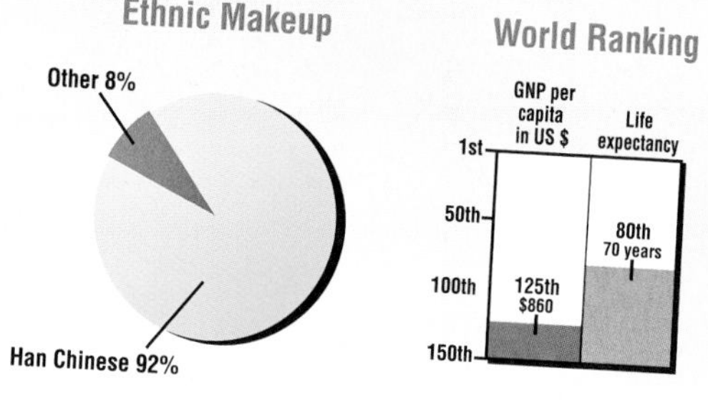

Population: Urban vs. Rural

Urban 37% | Rural 63%

Sources: *World Desk Reference*, 2000; *World Development Indicators*; *The World Factbook*, 2003; *The World Almanac*, 2004.

Exploring the Region

1. **Why is the Plateau of Tibet called the Roof of the World?**
2. **How do monsoons affect the region?**
3. **What is the most important food crop in Asia?**
4. **Name two religions that originated in the region.**

627

3 ASSESS

Assign the Exploring the Region questions as homework or as an in-class activity.

Reteach
Have students create an outline of the Regional Atlas introduction that highlights the characteristics making Asia a region.

Enrich
Have students research one of the major cities of South Asia, such as New Delhi or Hong Kong. Have students prepare a travel brochure that highlights fun and unique places to visit in the city. Ask for volunteers to share their brochures with the class.

4 CLOSE

Writing Questions Have students write one question that the information in the first four pages of the Regional Atlas would answer.

Answers to Exploring the Region

1. because of its high elevation
2. They bring dry weather in winter and drenching rains in summer.
3. rice
4. Hinduism and Buddhism

NATIONAL GEOGRAPHIC **REGIONAL ATLAS**

LESSON PLAN

Using the Regional Atlas
These features and activities may be used as an introduction to the unit or as teaching tools throughout the course of the unit.

Focus

Objectives

1. Locate Asia and describe its major landforms.
2. Identify the countries and capitals of Asia.
3. Analyze the monsoon patterns in Asia.
4. Compare the populations of the countries in Asia.

5-Minute Precheck

Have students look at the physical map on this page. **Ask:** **Would you say that most of the land in Asia was lowland or highland?** *(highland)* **What effect is that fact likely to have on agriculture?** *(The region has limited amounts of arable land as a result.)*

More About the Profile

In order to show a variety of physical features, this cross section begins at the India-Pakistan border and ends at Mount Fuji, Japan.

Asia

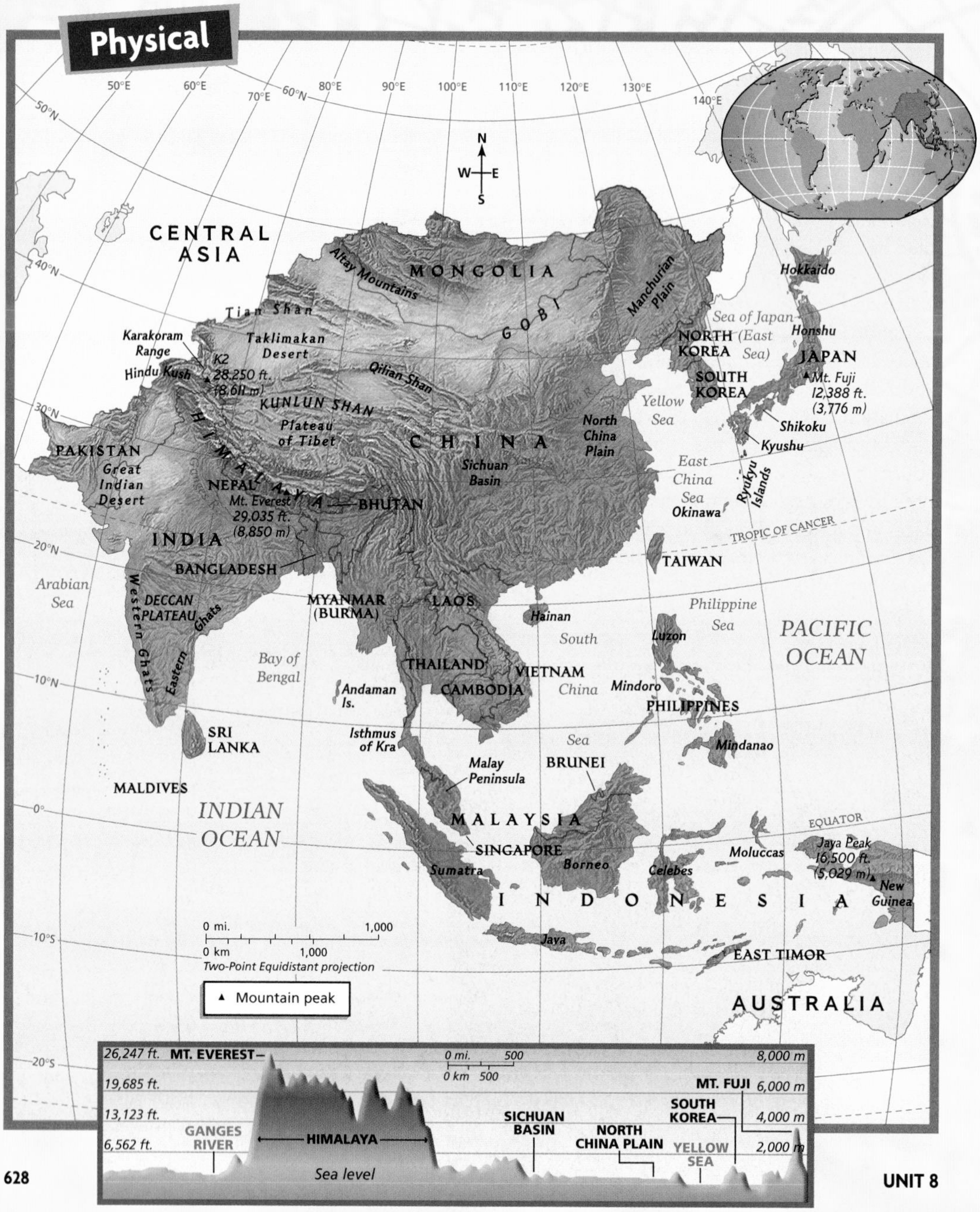

Physical

CENTRAL ASIA
MONGOLIA
Altay Mountains
GOBI
Manchurian Plain
Hokkaido
Tian Shan
Taklimakan Desert
Karakoram Range
Hindu Kush
K2 28,250 ft. (8,611 m)
Qilian Shan
KUNLUN SHAN
Plateau of Tibet
HIMALAYA
CHINA
Sichuan Basin
North China Plain
Sea of Japan (East Sea)
NORTH KOREA
SOUTH KOREA
Honshu
JAPAN
Mt. Fuji 12,388 ft. (3,776 m)
Shikoku
Kyushu
Yellow Sea
East China Sea
Okinawa
Ryukyu Islands
PAKISTAN
Great Indian Desert
NEPAL
Mt. Everest 29,035 ft. (8,850 m)
BHUTAN
INDIA
BANGLADESH
TROPIC OF CANCER
TAIWAN
Arabian Sea
Western Ghats
DECCAN PLATEAU
Eastern Ghats
MYANMAR (BURMA)
LAOS
Hainan
Philippine Sea
PACIFIC OCEAN
Bay of Bengal
South China Sea
Luzon
Andaman Is.
THAILAND
VIETNAM
CAMBODIA
Mindoro
PHILIPPINES
SRI LANKA
Isthmus of Kra
Mindanao
Malay Peninsula
BRUNEI
MALDIVES
INDIAN OCEAN
MALAYSIA
SINGAPORE
Sumatra
Borneo
Celebes
Moluccas
EQUATOR
Jaya Peak 16,500 ft. (5,029 m)
New Guinea
INDONESIA
Java
EAST TIMOR
AUSTRALIA
0 mi. 1,000
0 km 1,000
Two-Point Equidistant projection
▲ Mountain peak

26,247 ft. MT. EVEREST
19,685 ft.
13,123 ft.
6,562 ft.
GANGES RIVER
HIMALAYA
Sea level
SICHUAN BASIN
NORTH CHINA PLAIN
YELLOW SEA
SOUTH KOREA
MT. FUJI
8,000 m
6,000 m
4,000 m
2,000 m
0 mi. 500
0 km 500

628 UNIT 8

Regional Atlas Activity

Making Comparisons Assign each student a city in Asia on the map in the Reference Atlas. Then have the students find a city in the Western Hemisphere along the same line of latitude as the Asian city they have been assigned. Tell students to use the maps in this Regional Atlas and the text to compare one aspect of the two cities, such as the landforms or population density. Instruct them to present their comparisons in the form of a chart. L2

EE1 The World in Spatial Terms: Standard 1

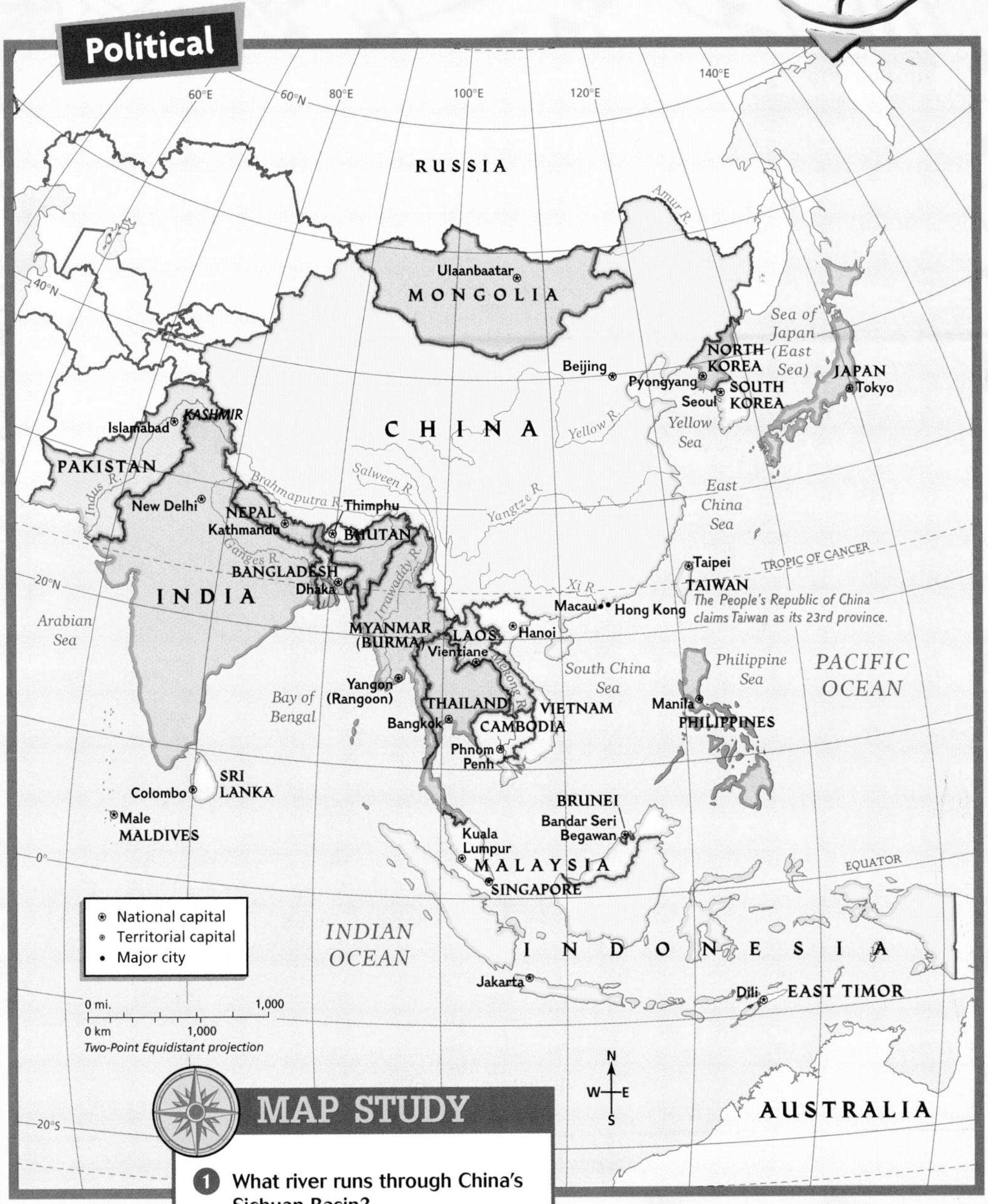

UNIT 8

Political

- ⊛ National capital
- ⊙ Territorial capital
- • Major city

0 mi. 1,000
0 km 1,000
Two-Point Equidistant projection

MAP STUDY

1. What river runs through China's Sichuan Basin?
2. What is the capital of Thailand?

Asia 629

Unit 8

2 TEACH

Reading Strategy

Making Comparisons Give students a pair of countries in Asia. Have them use the maps on these two pages to compare the two countries in terms of size, location, and physical features. Then have them write a paragraph about their comparisons. Ask for volunteers to read their paragraphs to the class. L1

MAP STUDY

Answers

1. Yangtze River
2. Bangkok

Skills Practice

What is the largest country in Asia? *(China)* **What seven rivers have their sources in the Plateau of Tibet?** *(Indus, Ganges, Brahmaputra, Irrawaddy, Mekong, Yangtze, Salween)*

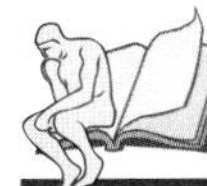

THE HUMANITIES CONNECTION

World Music: A Cultural Legacy

World Art and Architecture Transparencies

Regional Atlas Activity

Hindu Festivals Organize students into groups, and then assign each group one of the following Hindu festivals: Diwali, Durga Puja or Dassehra, Holi, Janannath, Makara-Sankranti, Pongal, Ramlila, and Vaisakhi. Ask groups to find out what their festival commemorates and how Hindus celebrate it. Have groups share their findings with the class in an oral report, a visual display, or a skit. L1

EE4 Human Systems: Standard 10

NATIONAL GEOGRAPHIC

REGIONAL ATLAS

Building Skills

Making Generalizations
Have students study the map on this page and then develop a generalization based on its information. *(Example: Monsoon winds affect regions near the coast more than those in the interior.)* Ask for volunteers to read their generalizations to the class.

Interdisciplinary Connections

Science The wet monsoons bring about 60 inches (152 cm) of rain to most of Southeast Asia each year, although some areas can receive several times that amount.

MAP STUDY

Answers

1. more than 60 inches
2. northeast

Skills Practice
How many inches of rain do northwest China and Mongolia receive each year? *(less than 20 inches)*

Asia

Monsoons

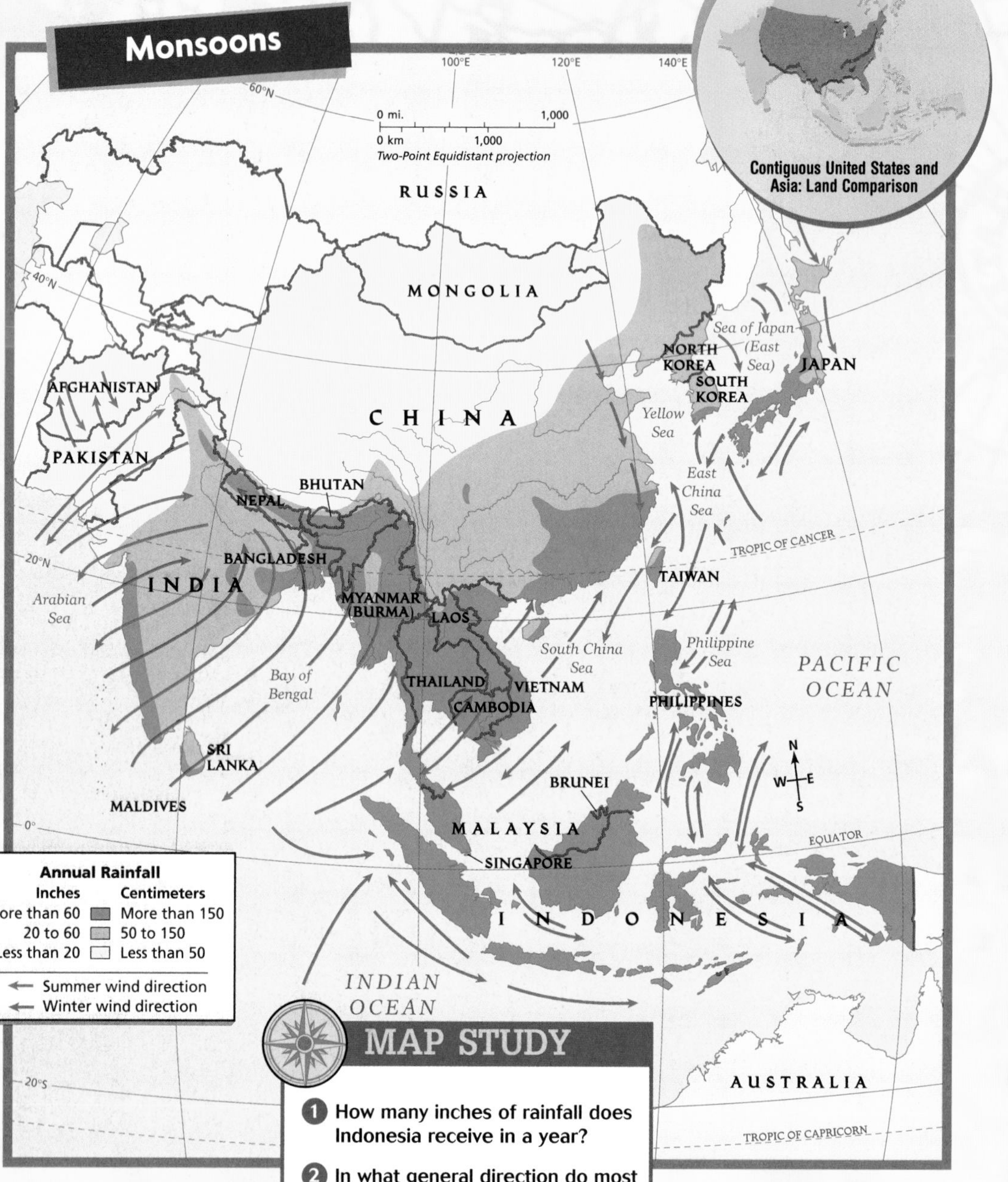

0 mi. 1,000
0 km 1,000
Two-Point Equidistant projection

Contiguous United States and Asia: Land Comparison

Annual Rainfall

Inches		Centimeters
More than 60		More than 150
20 to 60		50 to 150
Less than 20		Less than 50

← Summer wind direction
← Winter wind direction

MAP STUDY

1. How many inches of rainfall does Indonesia receive in a year?
2. In what general direction do most of the summer monsoons blow?

630 UNIT 8

Content Background

The Spratly Islands China, Taiwan, Vietnam, Malaysia, and the Philippines all claim the Spratly Islands in the South China Sea. These countries are not interested in what is on these mostly uninhabited islands but in what might be *beneath* them—deposits of oil and other valuable resources. How are such disputes settled? One criterion for assigning possession is based on claims dating back to ancient times, but none of the countries has had lasting possession. Maintaining control for 50 consecutive years makes a strong claim, but, again, none of the five qualifies. The United Nations Law of the Sea allows countries to claim islands within 200 miles of their shores, but this does not apply to any of the five countries either.

Unit 8

Unit 8 Regional Atlas

Geo Extremes

① HIGHEST POINT
Mt. Everest (Nepal and Tibet) 29,035 ft. (8,850 m) high

② LOWEST POINT
Turpan Depression (China) 505 ft. (154 m) below sea level

③ LONGEST RIVER
Yangtze (China) 3,964 mi. (6,380 km) long

④ LARGEST DESERT
Gobi (Mongolia and China) 500,000 sq. mi. (1,295,000 sq. km)

⑤ HIGHEST WATERFALL
Mawsmai (India) 1,148 ft. (350 m) high

⑥ LARGEST ISLAND
New Guinea (Indonesia and Papua New Guinea) 306,000 sq. mi. (792,536 sq. km)

⑦ WETTEST PLACE
Mawsynram (India) 467 in. (1,186 cm) average annual rainfall

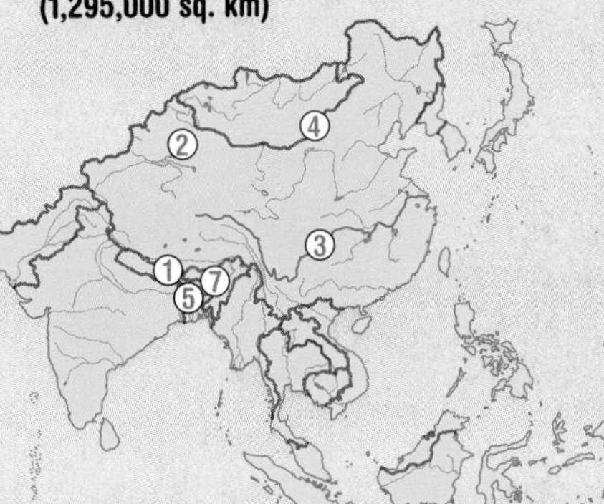

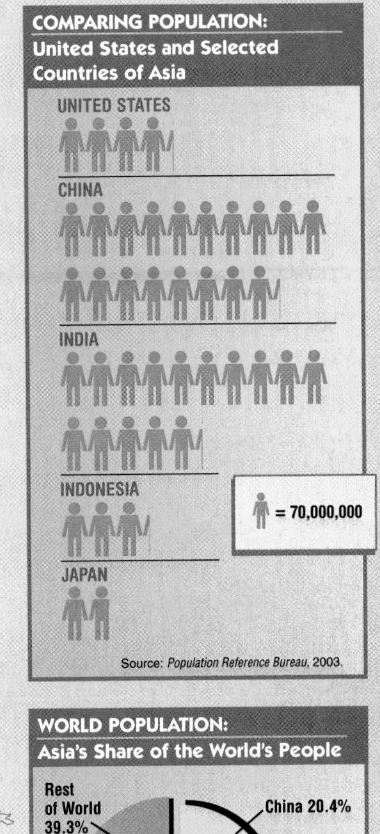

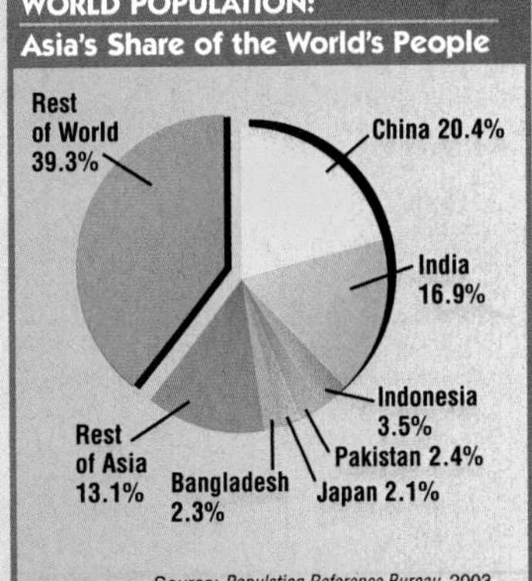

GRAPHIC STUDY

1. The highest point in Asia is also the highest point in the world. What is it?
2. What percentage of the world's population lives in Asia?

Did You Know

Asia covers more square miles than Australia, Europe, and North America combined.

Mongolia has a much smaller population than the countries shown in this graph. In fact, livestock outnumbers people 12 to 1 in Mongolia. The horse is the principal means of transportation.

GRAPHIC STUDY

Answers

1. Mount Everest
2. 60.7 percent

Skills Practice

How does China compare in population to the United States? *(It is about 4 1/2 times larger.)* **How does India's population compare to the United States'?** *(It is about 3 1/2 times larger.)* **How does Indonesia compare?** *(It is about three-fourths the size of the U.S.)*

FUN FACTS

- **Bhutan** This Himalayan country is called Land of the Thunder Dragon because of its violent storms.
- **China/Mongolia** *Gobi* is Mongolian for "place without water."
- **India** In the ancient Indian language of Sanskrit, *Himalaya* means "abode of snow."
- **Indonesia** More Muslims live in Indonesia than in any other country in the world.
- **Singapore** The name *Singapore* is derived from the Sanskrit *Singa Pur,* which means "city of the lion." This name was probably given to the area by Sumatrans who settled there in the 1200s.

REGIONAL ATLAS

Current Events Journal

Have students use the Country Profiles to write down which Asian countries speak European languages. *(French: Cambodia, Laos; English: Brunei, India, Malaysia, Maldives, Pakistan, Philippines, Singapore, Sri Lanka; Portuguese: East Timor)* **Ask: Why do you think English, French, and Portuguese are spoken in these countries?** *(They once were colonies of these countries; the Philippines was controlled by Spain and then the United States until it gained its independence after World War II.)*

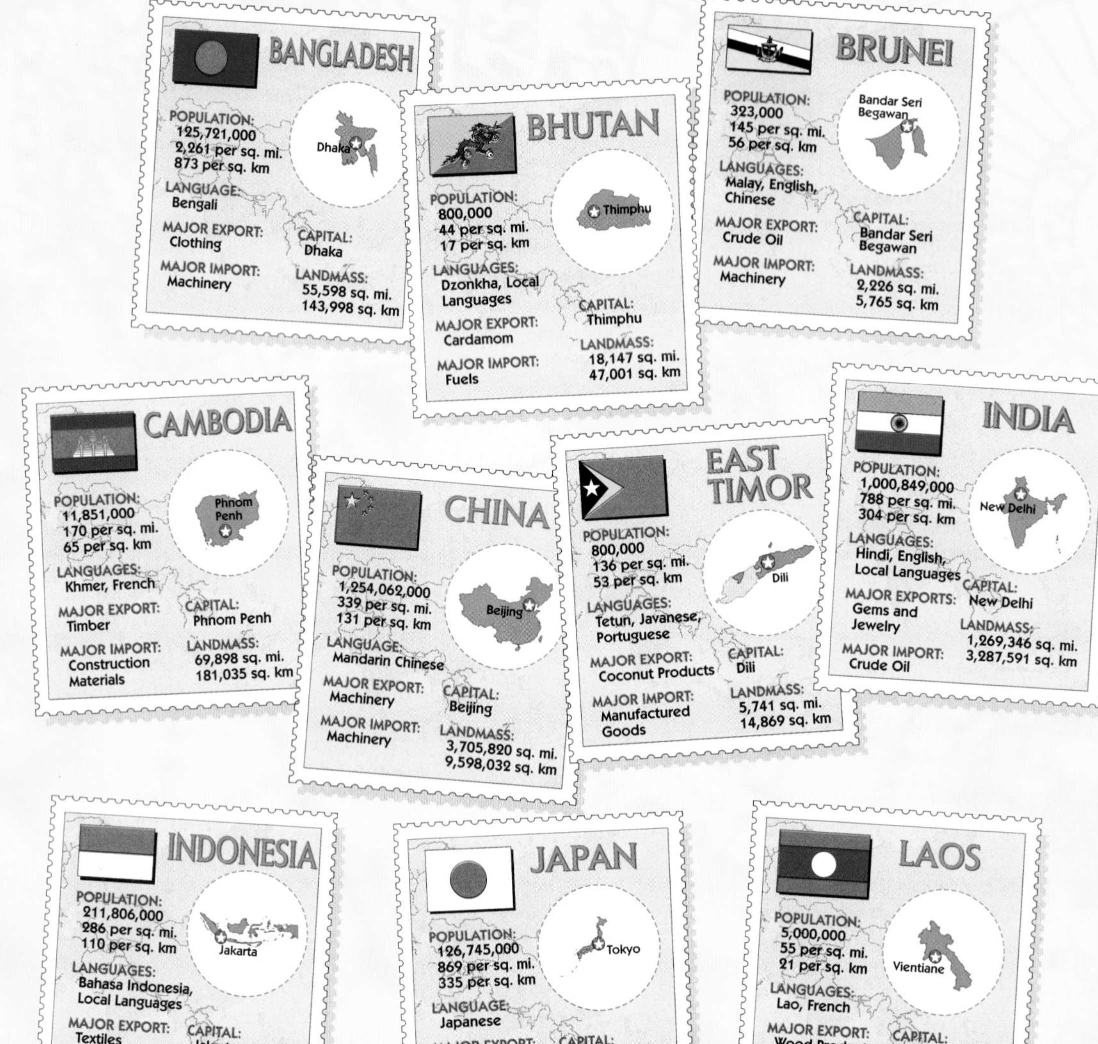

Countries and flags not drawn to scale

632 UNIT 8

Regional Atlas Activity

Acrostic Poems Assign each student a country or physical feature in Asia. Give students time to research their subject and then have them develop an acrostic poem describing the place. An acrostic poem is one in which the first word in each line begins with a letter of the subject's name. *(For example, the words for* China *could be Communist government; Home to Hong Kong; Industrializing; Near North Korea; Ancient culture.)* **L2**

EE2 Places and Regions: Standard 4

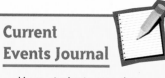

For more information on countries in this region, refer to the Nations of the World Data Bank in the Appendix.

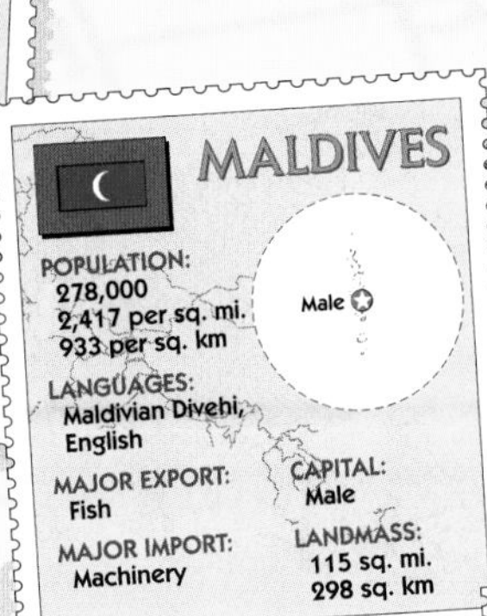

MALDIVES
POPULATION:
278,000
2,417 per sq. mi.
933 per sq. km
LANGUAGES:
Maldivian Divehi, English
MAJOR EXPORT:
Fish
MAJOR IMPORT:
Machinery
CAPITAL:
Male
LANDMASS:
115 sq. mi.
298 sq. km
Male

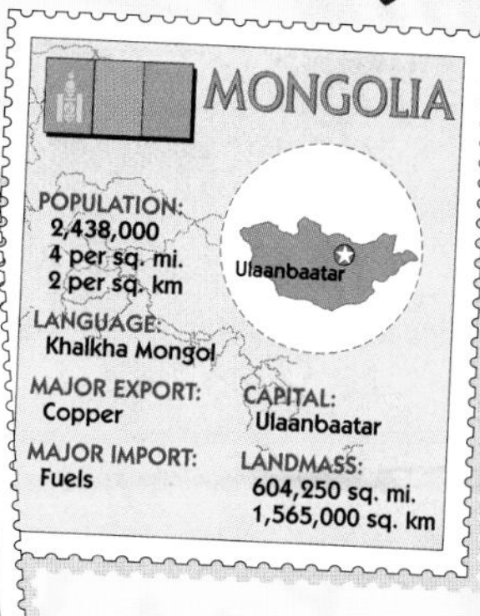

MYANMAR

POPULATION:
48,081,000
184 per sq. mi.
71 per sq. km

LANGUAGES:
Burmese, Local Languages

MAJOR EXPORT:
Beans

MAJOR IMPORT:
Machinery

CAPITAL:
Yangon (Rangoon)

LANDMASS:
261,218 sq. mi.
676,552 sq. km

Yangon (Rangoon)

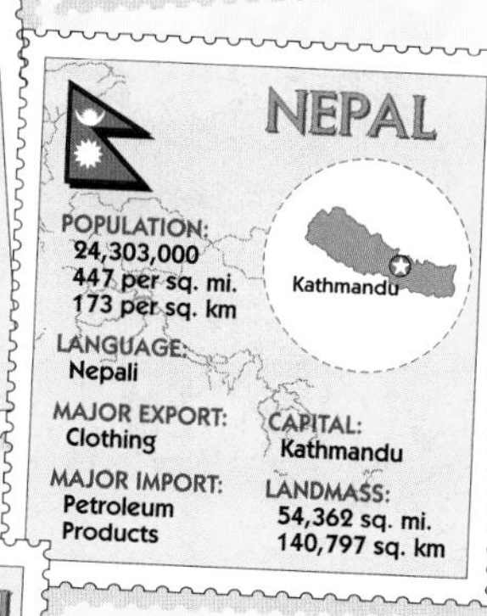

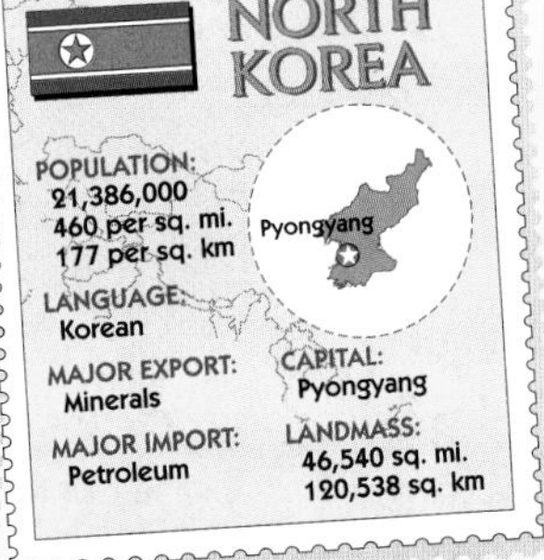

NORTH KOREA
POPULATION:
21,386,000
460 per sq. mi.
177 per sq. km
LANGUAGE:
Korean
MAJOR EXPORT:
Minerals
MAJOR IMPORT:
Petroleum
CAPITAL:
Pyongyang
LANDMASS:
46,540 sq. mi.
120,538 sq. km
Pyongyang

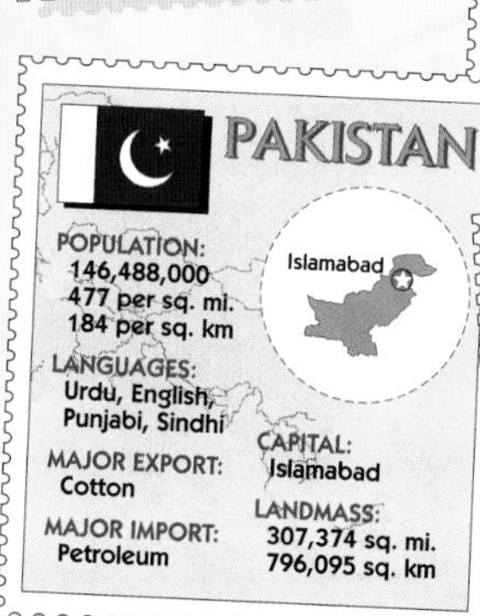

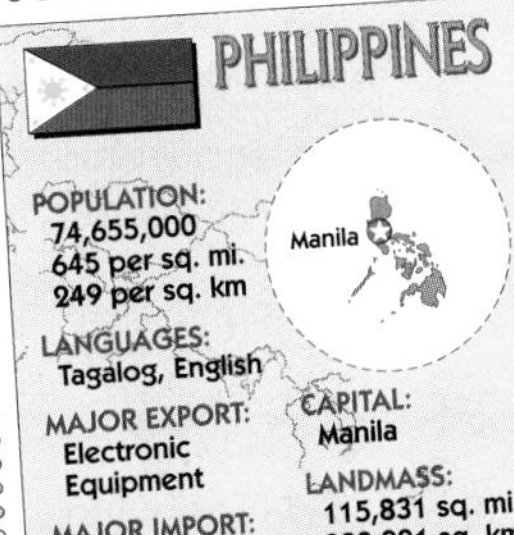

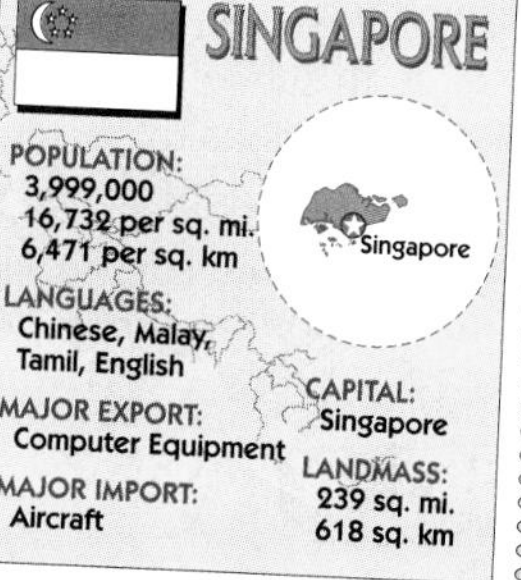

Interdisciplinary Connections

Art People in Japan have made an art—called *origami*—out of folding paper. They create decorative objects such as animals, fish, or flowers. There are about 100 traditional origami patterns, but each year new designs are developed.

History Sikhism, which combines elements of Hinduism and Islam, was founded by Guru Nanak, who lived between 1469 and 1539. Sikhs differ from Hindus in that they reject the caste system, the priesthood, pilgrimages, begging, and bathing in sacred streams. Sikhs accept the equality of men and women and believe in one God. Their holiest place is the Golden Temple at Amritsar in the state of Punjab.

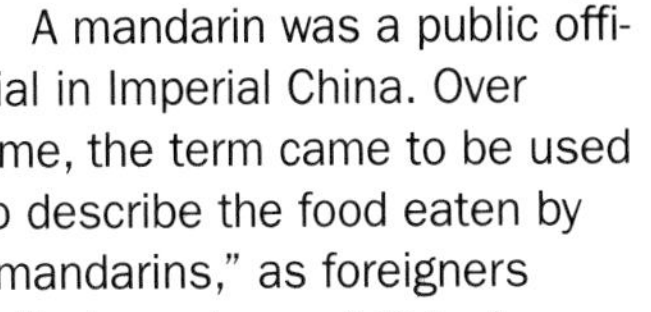

A mandarin was a public official in Imperial China. Over time, the term came to be used to describe the food eaten by "mandarins," as foreigners called members of China's upper class.

Country Profiles Activity

Using Maps Play a geographical riddle game with students in which you give them a set of directions and they have to identify both the starting point and the endpoint. For example, you could say, "From this city, you move by ship south into the Indian Ocean, turn to the east, and then head northeast to reach a city in Myanmar." *(starting point: Colombo, Sri Lanka; ending point: Yangon)* Organize students into teams and allow each team a few seconds to provide the answer. If they cannot, give another team a chance to do so. Award points for correct answers and create a fictional award such as "Champion Puzzle Solvers" for the team with the most points. L2

EE1 The World in Spatial Terms: Standard 1

Regional Atlas

Country Profiles

SOUTH KOREA
POPULATION:
46,873,000
1,226 per sq. mi.
473 per sq. km
LANGUAGE:
Korean
MAJOR EXPORT:
Electronic Equipment
MAJOR IMPORT:
Machinery
CAPITAL:
Seoul
LANDMASS:
38,230 sq. mi.
99,016 sq. km
Seoul

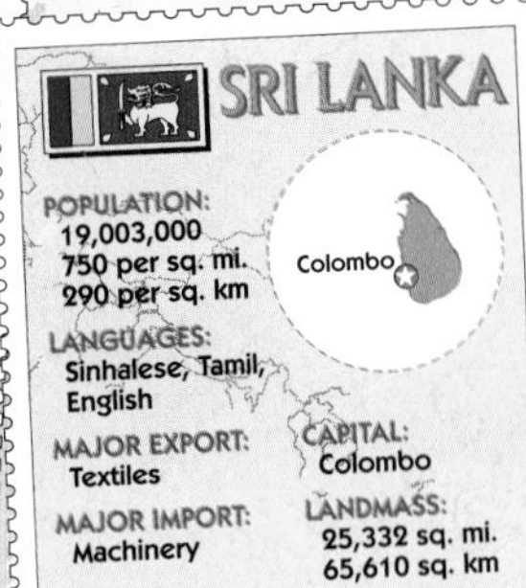

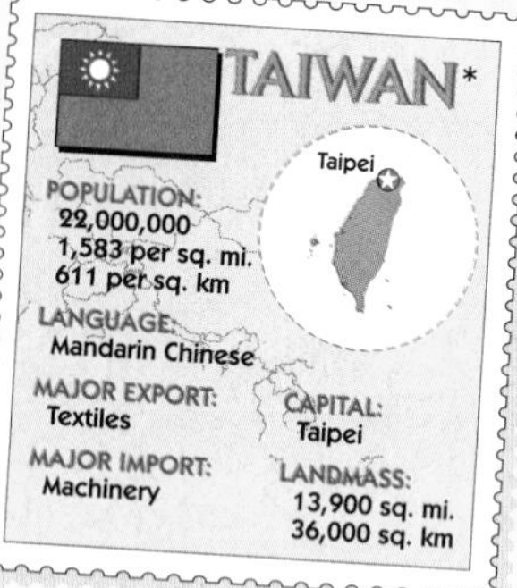

TAIWAN*
POPULATION:
22,000,000
1,583 per sq. mi.
611 per sq. km
LANGUAGE:
Mandarin Chinese
MAJOR EXPORT:
Textiles
MAJOR IMPORT:
Machinery
CAPITAL:
Taipei
LANDMASS:
13,900 sq. mi.
36,000 sq. km
Taipei

* The People's Republic of China claims Taiwan as its 23rd province.

THAILAND
POPULATION:
61,818,000
311 per sq. mi.
120 per sq. km
LANGUAGES:
Thai, Local Languages
MAJOR EXPORT:
Manufactured Goods
MAJOR IMPORT:
Machinery
CAPITAL:
Bangkok
LANDMASS:
198,457 sq. mi.
514,001 sq. km
Bangkok

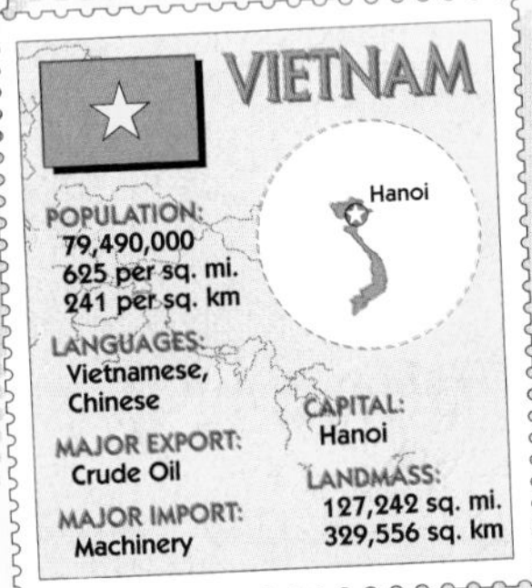

Countries and flags not drawn to scale

Cultural Kaleidoscope

Malaysia Malaysians think that the durian is the best of all fruits. It has a green, spiny rind and a flavored, soft pulp. However, it gives off a rather strong odor that some people think is unpleasant.

Building Citizenship

Answer
The United States is founded on the concepts of equality and equal rights. Women contribute to all aspects of U.S. society. Women in American society have choices unheard of in many societies. American women may choose to stay home and run a household, or they may choose to work outside the home.

Write About It! Responses should include boys and girls together in school, girls and women involved in sports, more women in politics and business, and freedom to do anything that boys and men can do. Students should also realize that with these freedoms come risks and responsibilities. In sports, for example, girls risk being injured, which many cultures consider unacceptable.

BUILDING CITIZENSHIP

Women's Rights Not all countries have the same laws for men and women. In some countries, women are not allowed to own property, vote, go to school, or work. Part of the reason for this is that women's contributions to society in the area of raising children and running a household are not as valued as men's contributions.

Why is it important in the United States that men and women have equal rights and that those rights are protected by the law?

Imagine that you are a sixth grade exchange student from an Asian country. Write a letter to your sister at home describing some activities that girls in your American school take part in on an equal basis with boys.

Vietnamese mother and baby ▶

Fun Facts

- **Taiwan** Leaving rice in one's bowl is considered impolite in Taiwan. The Taiwanese teach their children to finish all of their food out of respect for their parents and for the farmers who grew it.
- **India** In India, wealthy people honor special guests by decorating rice dishes with thin sheets of silver or gold leaf.
- **Thailand** Thais always honor their king and his image. When the king's picture is on a stamp, Thais wet the stamp with a damp sponge rather than licking it, which would show disrespect.
- **The Koreas** Cooks in the Koreas try to serve meals that include all the traditional colors: red, green, yellow, white, and black.

UNIT 8

▲ Three generations of a Chinese family

Asia

635

More About the Photo

Family Since Kongfuzi (Confucius) began teaching in the 500s B.C., family has been a central feature of life in China. The philosopher urged that children should show deep respect to their parents, who gave the gift of life. Such an attitude, he said, was the most fundamental way of acting morally.

3 ASSESS

Organize students into groups. Have the groups use this unit's Regional Atlas to quiz one another on the physical and cultural characteristics of the countries of Asia.

Enrich
Have students choose one country from Asia and create an annotated map that uses images and captions to show the natural, cultural, and historical sites that a tourist might visit.

4 CLOSE

Reading Strategy

Summarizing Have students write one sentence that summarizes information about the physical features of Asia.

FUN FACTS

- **Bangladesh** When someone does a favor for someone else in Bangladesh, the custom is not to say thanks but to return the favor.
- **Brunei** The sultan of Brunei, with a net worth of more than $30 billion, is one of the richest people in the world.

Chapter 22 Resources

Note: The following materials may be used when teaching Chapter 22.
Section level support materials are shown at point of use in the margins of the Teacher Wraparound Edition.

Timesaving Tools

TeacherWorks™ All-In-One Planner and Resource Center

- **Interactive Teacher Edition** See the **Interactive Teacher Edition** CD-ROM to electronically integrate your Teacher Wraparound Edition and blackline masters.
- **Interactive Lesson Planner** Organize your week, month, semester, or year with all the lesson helps you need. The **Interactive Lesson Planner** CD-ROM contains all Chapter 22 resources.

Use Glencoe's **Presentation Plus!** multimedia teacher tool to easily present dynamic lessons that visually excite your students. Using Microsoft PowerPoint® you can customize the presentations to create your own personalized lessons.

TEACHING TRANSPARENCIES

Graphic Organizer Transparency 12 L2

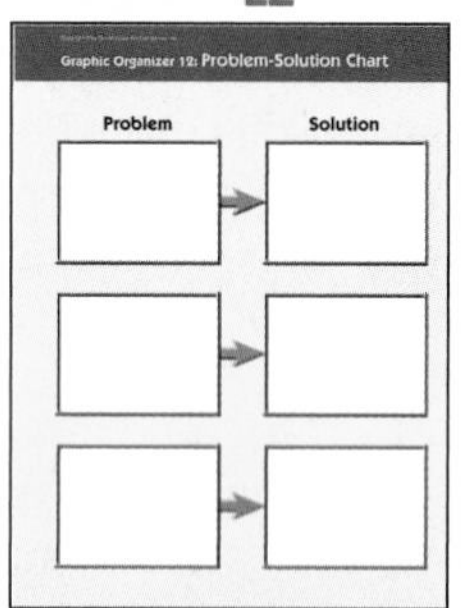

In-text Map Transparency L1

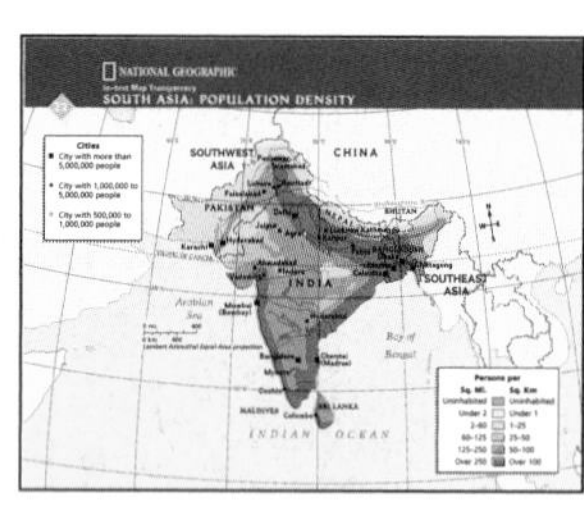

FOLDABLES™ Study Organizer

Dinah Zike's Foldables

Foldables are three-dimensional, interactive graphic organizers that help students practice basic writing skills, review key vocabulary terms, and identify main ideas. Additional chapter activities can be found in the ***Reading and Study Skills Foldables*** booklet.

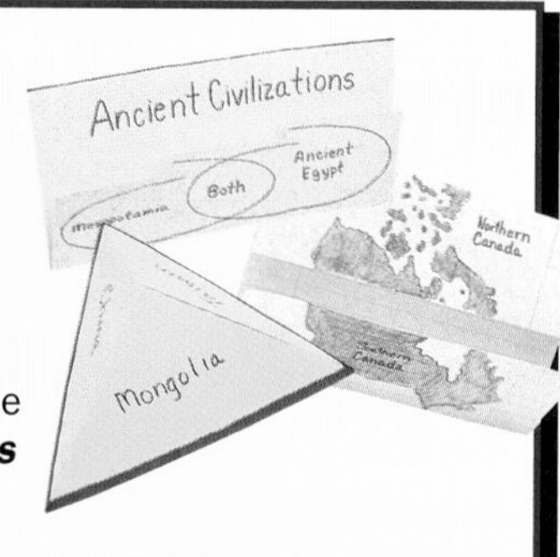

MAP AND GEOGRAPHY SKILLS

Chapter Map Activity L2

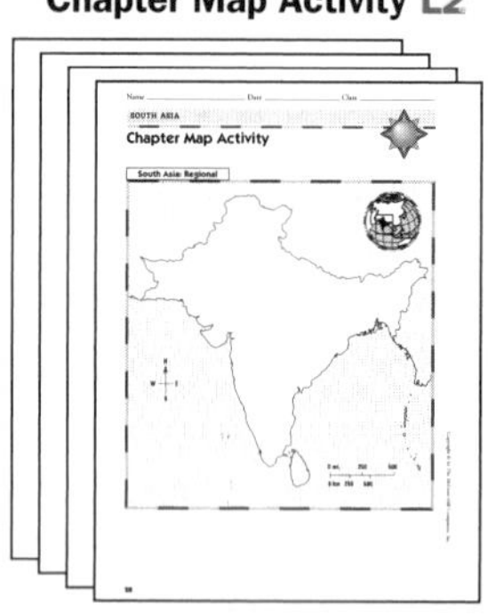

GeoLab Activity L2

READING SUPPORT

Vocabulary Activity L1

Workbook Activity L1

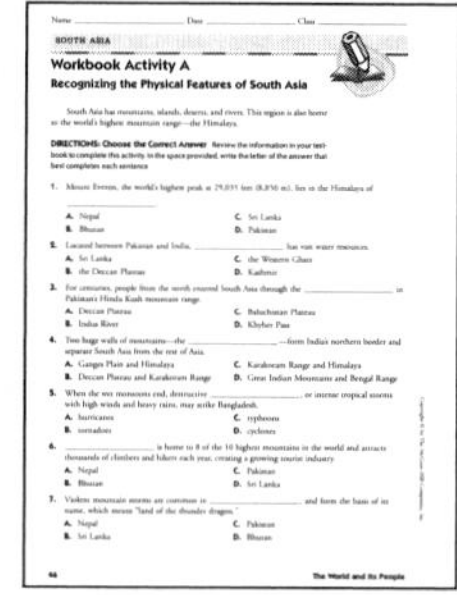

Reading and Writing Skills Activity L1/ELL

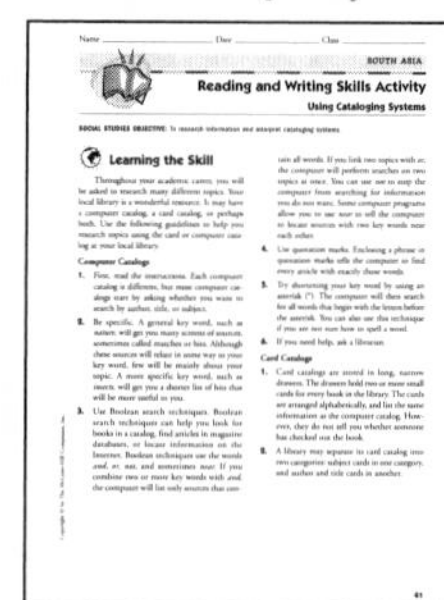

DIFFERENTIATED INSTRUCTION

Use these review and reinforcement materials to help less-proficient readers, English learners, and gifted and talented students.

Reteaching Activity L1

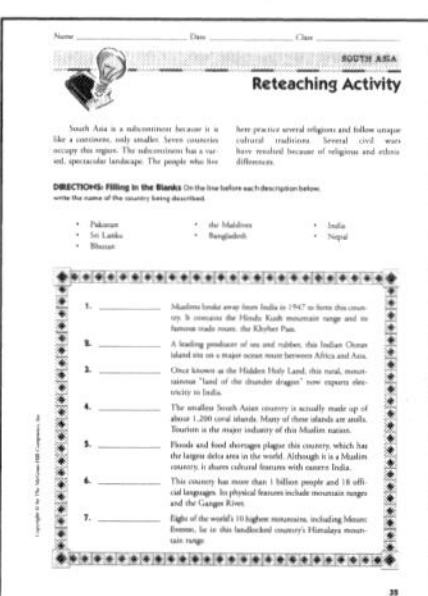

Chapter Skills Review L2

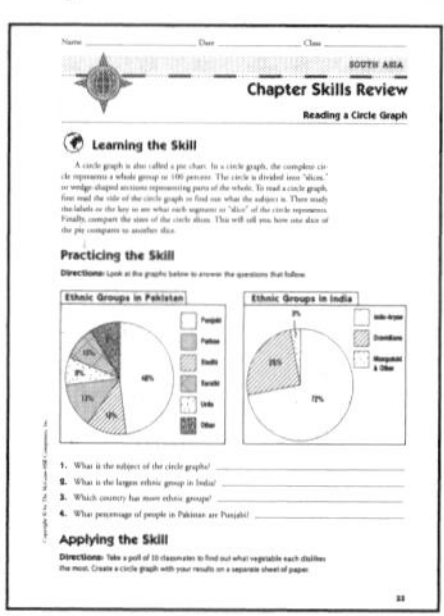

Cooperative Learning Activity L1/ELL

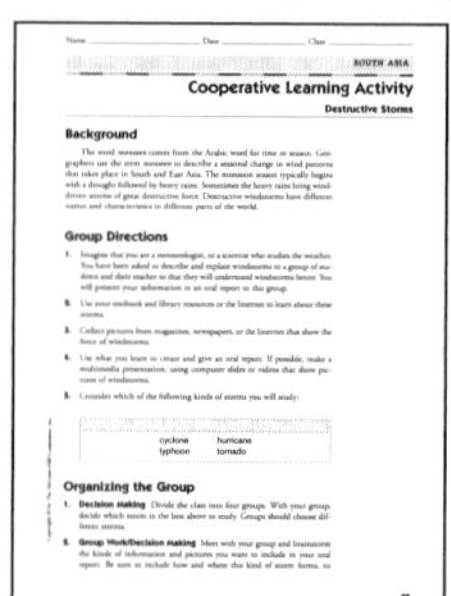

Enrichment Activity L3

ASSESSMENT

Chapter Test, Form A L2

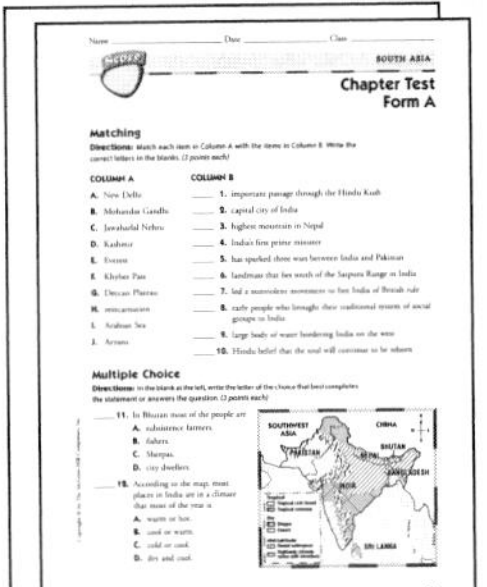

Chapter Test, Form B L2

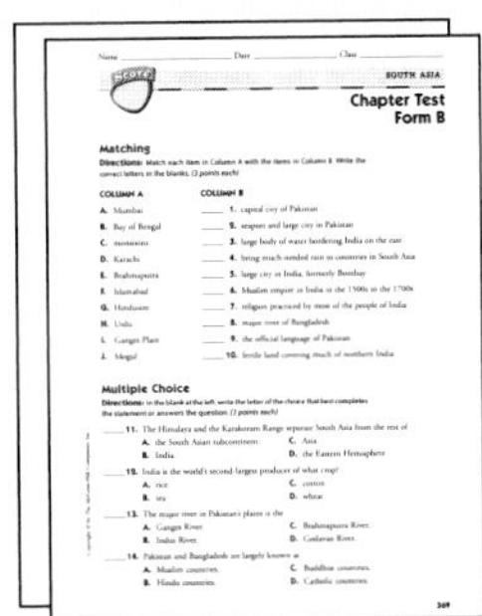

Performance Assessment Activity L1/ELL

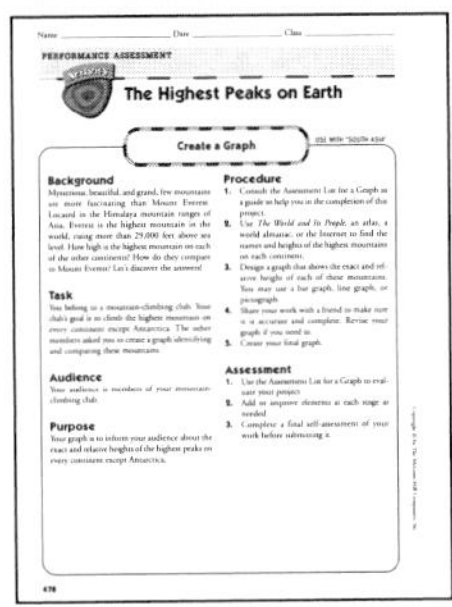

ExamView® Pro Testmaker CD-ROM

STANDARDIZED ASSESSMENT SKILLS

Critical Thinking Skills Activity L2

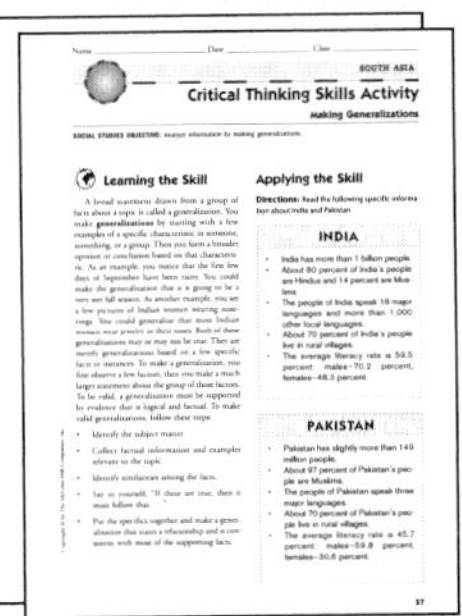

Map and Graph Skills Activity L2

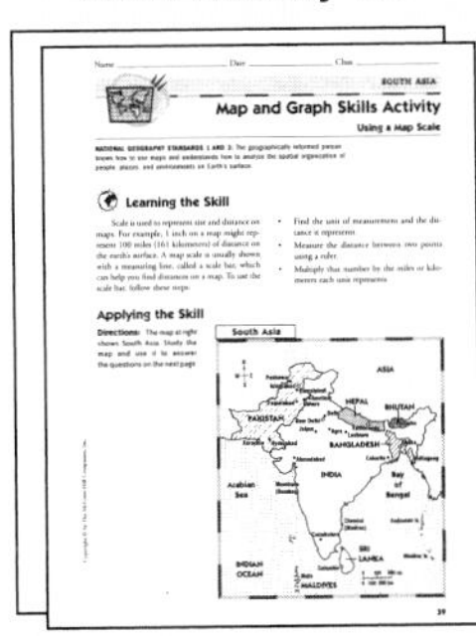

Standardized Test Skills Practice Workbook Activity L2

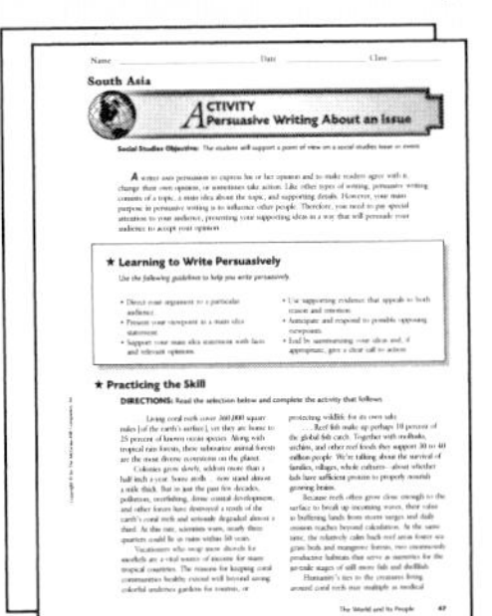

HOME INVOLVEMENT

Take-Home Review Activity L1

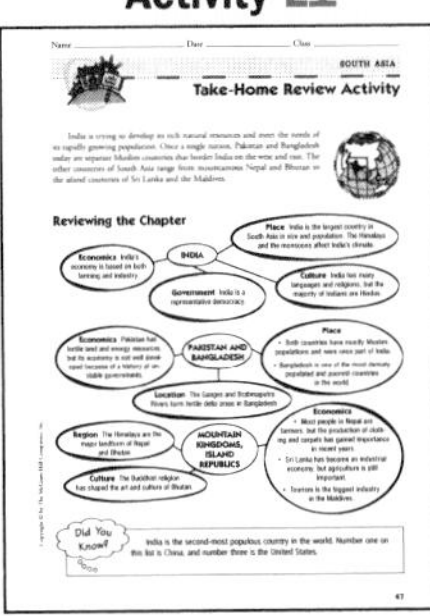

MULTIMEDIA

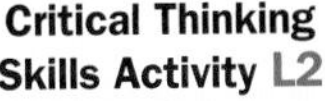

- National Geographic's The World and Its People
- MindJogger Videoquiz
- Vocabulary PuzzleMaker CD-ROM
- Interactive Tutor Self-Assessment CD-ROM
- ExamView® Pro Testmaker CD-ROM
- TeacherWorks CD-ROM
- StudentWorks CD-ROM
- Skillbuilder Interactive Workbook CD-ROM, Level 1
- Presentation Plus! CD-ROM
- Audio Program

SPANISH RESOURCES

The following Spanish language materials are available in the Spanish Resources binder:

- **Spanish Summaries**
- **Spanish Vocabulary Activities**
- **Spanish Guided Reading Activities**
- **Spanish Quizzes and Tests**
- **Spanish Take-Home Review Activities**
- **Spanish Reteaching Activities**

Meeting National Standards

Geography for Life

The following standards are covered in Chapter 22:

Section 1 **EE3 Physical Systems:** Standards 7, 8
EE4 Human Systems: Standards 9, 10, 11, 12, 13
EE5 Environment and Society: Standards 14, 15, 16

Section 2 **EE2 Places and Regions:** Standards 4, 6
EE5 Environment and Society: Standard 15

Section 3 **EE4 Human Systems:** Standards 9, 13
EE5 Environment and Society: Standards 14, 15

State and Local Objectives

____

____

Chapter 22 Planning Guide

SECTION RESOURCES

Daily Objectives	Reproducible Resources	Multimedia Resources
Section 1 **India—Past and Present** **1.** Explain how India's agriculture and industry have evolved. **2.** Discuss India's history and culture.	Reproducible Lesson Plan Daily Lecture and Discussion Notes Note-taking Guide Guided Reading Activity* Reading Essentials and Study Guide* Section Quiz*	Daily Focus Skills Transparency GeoQuiz Transparency Vocabulary PuzzleMaker CD-ROM Interactive Tutor Self-Assessment CD-ROM ExamView® Pro Testmaker CD-ROM Presentation Plus! CD-ROM
Section 2 **Pakistan and Bangladesh** **1.** Identify the main physical features in Pakistan and Bangladesh. **2.** Discuss how the people of these countries earn a living. **3.** Explain why the economies of these countries have made slow progress.	Reproducible Lesson Plan Daily Lecture and Discussion Notes Note-taking Guide Guided Reading Activity* Reading Essentials and Study Guide* Section Quiz*	Daily Focus Skills Transparency GeoQuiz Transparency Vocabulary PuzzleMaker CD-ROM Interactive Tutor Self-Assessment CD-ROM ExamView® Pro Testmaker CD-ROM Presentation Plus! CD-ROM
Section 3 **Mountain Kingdoms, Island Republics** **1.** Explain how geography has isolated Nepal and Bhutan. **2.** Describe what the people of Nepal and Bhutan do for a living. **3.** Discuss how the economy of Sri Lanka has changed. **4.** Understand the importance of the Maldives's location on the country's economy.	Reproducible Lesson Plan Daily Lecture and Discussion Notes Note-taking Guide Guided Reading Activity* Reading Essentials and Study Guide* Section Quiz*	Daily Focus Skills Transparency In-Text Map Transparency Vocabulary PuzzleMaker CD-ROM Interactive Tutor Self-Assessment CD-ROM ExamView® Pro Testmaker CD-ROM Presentation Plus! CD-ROM MindJogger Videoquiz

00:00 **Out of Time?** Assign the **Reading Essentials and Study Guide*** for this chapter.

*Also available in Spanish

KEY TO ABILITY LEVELS

Teaching strategies have been coded for varying learning styles and abilities.

L1 **BASIC** activities for all students
L2 **AVERAGE** activities for average to above-average students
L3 **CHALLENGING** activities for above-average students
ELL **ENGLISH LANGUAGE LEARNER** activities

KEY TO TEACHING RESOURCES

Blackline Master
CD-ROM
Transparency
Videocassette
Block Scheduling
DVD

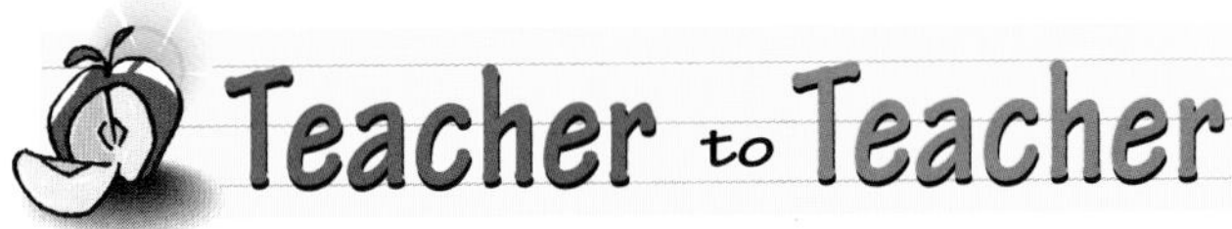

Religions of the World

Destin L. Haas
Benton Central
Junior/Senior High
Oxford, Indiana

Have students work in pairs and choose one of the following religions to research: Buddhism, Confucianism, Islam, Judaism, Hinduism, or Christianity. For the religion that pairs choose, they should find out the following information: (1) Where and when was it founded? (2) Who was the founder? (3) What is the holy book used? (4) What are some of the beliefs and practices of that religion? (5) What are some of the main holy days and what is their significance? (6) Where is the religion practiced in the world?

Pairs should present this information in three ways: (1) as a poster or another visual; (2) as an oral presentation; and (3) as a written report. They should include a bibliography.

Meeting Special Needs

In addition to the Differentiated Instruction strategies found in each section, the following resources are also suitable for your special needs students:

- ***ExamView® Pro Testmaker CD-ROM*** allows teachers to tailor tests by reducing answer choices.
- The ***Audio Program*** includes the entire narrative of the student edition so that less-proficient readers can listen to the words as they read them.
- The ***Reading Essentials and Study Guide*** provides the same content as the student edition but is written two grade levels below the textbook.
- ***Guided Reading Activities*** give less-proficient readers point-by-point instructions to increase comprehension as they read each textbook section.
- ***Enrichment Activities*** include a stimulating collection of readings and activities for gifted and talented students.

NATIONAL GEOGRAPHIC TEACHER'S CORNER

Index to National Geographic Magazine:

The following articles may be used for research relating to this chapter:

- "Nepal," by T.D. Allman, November 2000.
- "Rana Tharu Women," by Debra Kellner, September 2000.
- "In Search of the Clouded Leopard," by Jesse Oak Taylor-Ide, September 2000.

National Geographic Society Products:

To order the following products for use with this chapter, call National Geographic Society at 1-800-368-2728:

- *National Geographic Desk Reference* (Book)
- *National Geographic Atlas of the World, Seventh Edition* (Book)
- *Asia* (Video)

NGS ONLINE

Access National Geographic's Web site for current events, activities, links, interactive features, and archives.
www.nationalgeographic.com

Find the latest coverage of geography in the news, atlas updates, cartographic activities with interactive maps, an online map store, and links at www.nationalgeographic.com/maps

SOCIAL STUDIES Online

Use our Web site for additional resources. All essential content is covered in the Student Edition.

You and your students can visit twip.glencoe.com, the Web site companion to *The World and Its People.* This innovative integration of electronic and print media offers your students a wealth of opportunities. The student text directs students to the Web site for the following options:

- Chapter Overviews
- Student Web Activities
- Self-Check Quizzes
- Textbook Updates

Answers are provided for you in the Web Activity Lesson Plan. Additional Web resources and Interactive Tutor puzzles are also available.

Introducing
Chapter 22

Social Studies online

Introduce students to chapter content and key terms by having them access Chapter Overview 22 at twip.glencoe.com

Chapter Objectives

1. Describe the land, economy, and people of India.
2. Compare the land, economies and cultures of India's neighboring countries.

GLENCOE TECHNOLOGY

NATIONAL GEOGRAPHIC

The World and Its People Video Program

Chapter 23 South Asia

The following segments enhance the study of this chapter:

- **Indian Railways**
- **Mount Everest**

MindJogger Videoquiz

Use MindJogger Videoquiz to preview the Chapter 22 content.

Both programs available in DVD and VHS

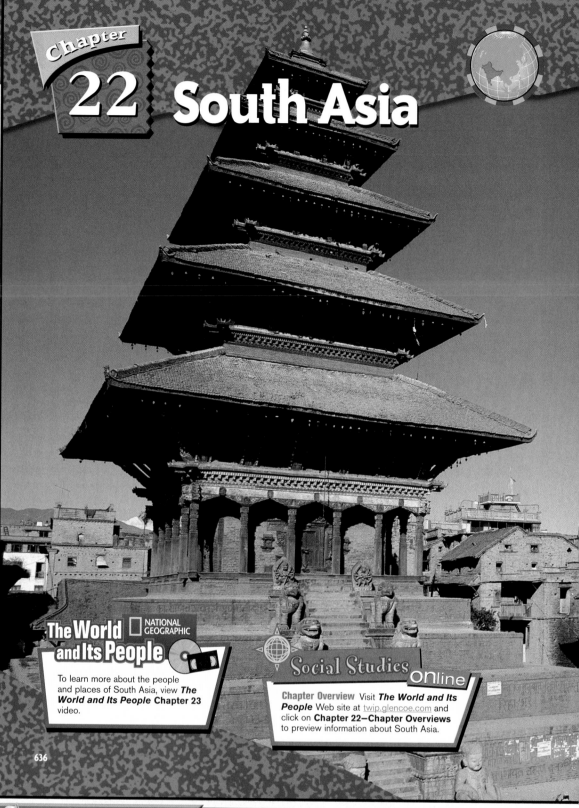

Chapter 22 South Asia

The World and Its People — NATIONAL GEOGRAPHIC

To learn more about the people and places of South Asia, view ***The World and Its People* Chapter 23** video.

Social Studies online

Chapter Overview Visit ***The World and Its People*** Web site at twip.glencoe.com and click on **Chapter 22—Chapter Overviews** to preview information about South Asia.

636

Reading Strategy — Purpose for Reading

Mindstreaming is a useful strategy to bring out students' background knowledge before beginning a chapter. This strategy can be used for activating knowledge about different countries in South Asia. Use the following directions for mindstreaming before students read about India. Organize students into pairs. Have Student A talk for one minute about India, telling everything he or she knows about the country. Student B listens without saying anything. Reverse the roles for one more minute. Finally, have pairs share their discussions with the class. Conclude the activity by identifying general themes that the students mentioned and ask them to watch for these themes as they read the chapter. L1

Categorizing Information Make this foldable to organize information from the chapter to help you learn more about the land, economy, government, history, and religions of seven South Asian countries.

Step 1 Collect four sheets of paper and place them about 1/2 inch apart.

Keep the edges straight.

Step 2 Fold up the bottom edges of the paper to form eight tabs.

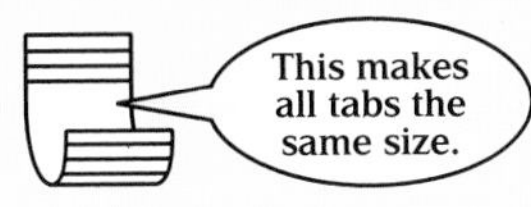

This makes all tabs the same size.

Step 3 When all the tabs are the same size, crease the paper to hold the tabs in place and staple the sheets together. Turn the paper and label each tab as shown.

SOUTH ASIA
Maldives
Bangladesh
Sri Lanka
Bhutan
Nepal
Pakistan
India

Staple together along the fold.

Reading and Writing As you read, use your foldable to write down the main ideas about each South Asian country. Record the main ideas under each appropriate tab of your foldable.

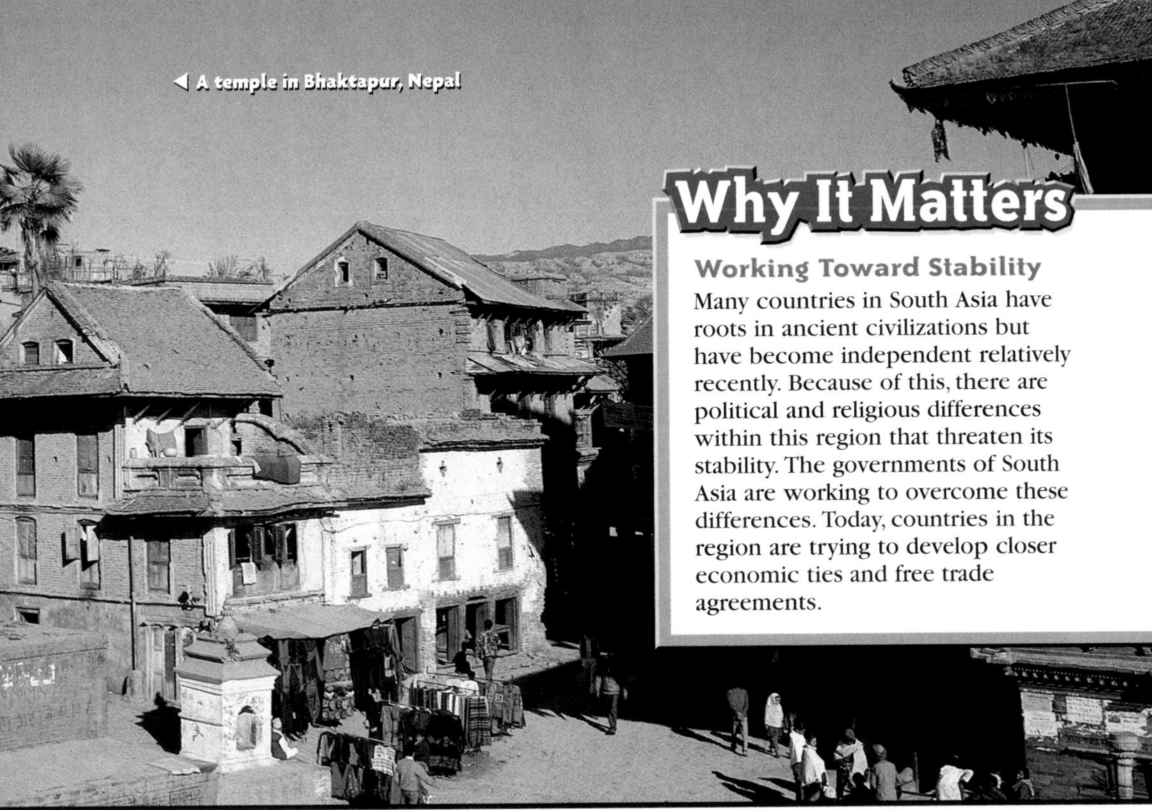

◄ A temple in Bhaktapur, Nepal

Why It Matters

Working Toward Stability

Many countries in South Asia have roots in ancient civilizations but have become independent relatively recently. Because of this, there are political and religious differences within this region that threaten its stability. The governments of South Asia are working to overcome these differences. Today, countries in the region are trying to develop closer economic ties and free trade agreements.

About the Photo

Bhaktapur is one of three major towns of the Kathmandu Valley in Nepal. This small valley is crowded with more than 2,500 large temples and monuments. It is known as the city of temples and shrines. Temples here are dedicated to a plethora of gods and goddesses from both Hinduism and Buddhism. The pagoda-style building, as seen in this temple's multiroofed structure and numerous spires, is one of several styles of architecture in the Kathmandu Valley. These buildings and monuments are still used by the many local people who worship as part of their everyday lives.

Introducing

Chapter 22

FOLDABLES™ Study Organizer **Dinah Zike's Foldables**

Purpose This activity requires students to create a table and organize information from the chapter on it. Students group information about each country in the chapter—as well as general information about South Asia—under the appropriate heading, in effect comparing the land, economy, government, history, and religions of the countries of South Asia.

Have students complete the ***Reading and Study Skills Foldables*** activity for this chapter.

Why It Matters

To give students some idea of the difficulty India faces in achieving democratic government, organize students into groups of five. To simulate the many languages spoken in India, tell the students that they can communicate only with the person sitting directly next to them (right or left). If they want to communicate across the circle, they must use an interpreter. They cannot correct the interpreter's translation of their thoughts since they (supposedly) cannot understand. Ask them to discuss an issue of highly emotional content, such as how much authority school officials should have in students' personal or private lives. They should soon become frustrated with the inability to communicate freely.

Chapter 22

Section 1, pages 638–642

Focus

Section Objectives

1. Explain how India's agriculture and industry have evolved.
2. Discuss India's history and culture.

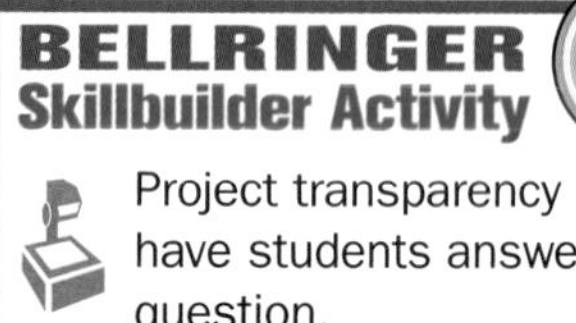

BELLRINGER Skillbuilder Activity

Project transparency and have students answer the question.

Daily Focus Skills Transparency

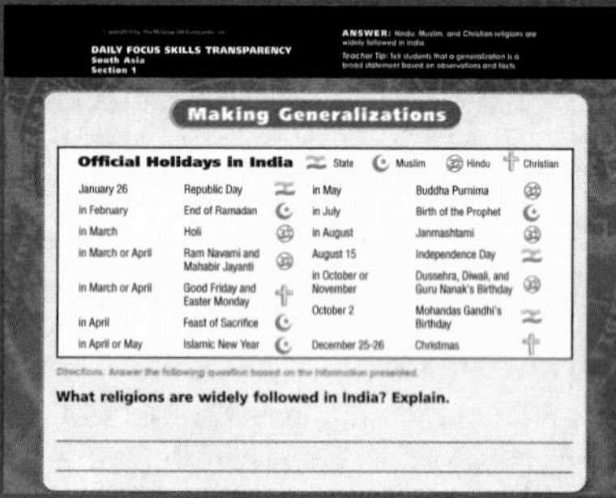

ANSWER: Hindu, Muslim, and Christian religions are widely followed in India.

Teacher Tip: Tell students that a generalization is a broad statement based on observations and facts.

DAILY FOCUS SKILLS TRANSPARENCY
South Asia
Section 1

Making Generalizations

Official Holidays in India — State, Muslim, Hindu, Christian

Date	Holiday	Date	Holiday
January 26	Republic Day	in May	Buddha Purnima
in February	End of Ramadan	in July	Birth of the Prophet
in March	Holi	in August	Janmashtami
in March or April	Ram Navami and Mahabir Jayanti	August 15	Independence Day
in March or April	Good Friday and Easter Monday	in October or November	Dussehra, Diwali, and Guru Nanak's Birthday
in April	Feast of Sacrifice	October 2	Mohandas Gandhi's Birthday
in April or May	Islamic New Year	December 25-26	Christmas

Directions: Answer the following question based on the information presented.

What religions are widely followed in India? Explain.

Reading Preview

■ **Activating Prior Knowledge** **Ask:** What country is the world's largest democracy? *(India)* As students read this section, have them discuss the similarities and differences between the democratic governments of India and the United States.

■ **Preteaching Vocabulary** Have students use context clues to understand a word's meaning. Articles such as *a, an,* and *the* often precede nouns. Verbs often end with *-ing* or *-ed.*

Guide to Reading

Main Idea

India is trying to develop its resources to meet the needs of its rapidly growing population.

Terms to Know

- subcontinent
- monsoon
- green revolution
- jute
- cottage industry
- pesticide
- caste
- reincarnation

Reading Strategy

Create a chart like this one. Then fill in at least two key facts about India under each category.

India	
Land	Economy
History	Religion

Section 1

India—Past and Present

NATIONAL GEOGRAPHIC Exploring Our World

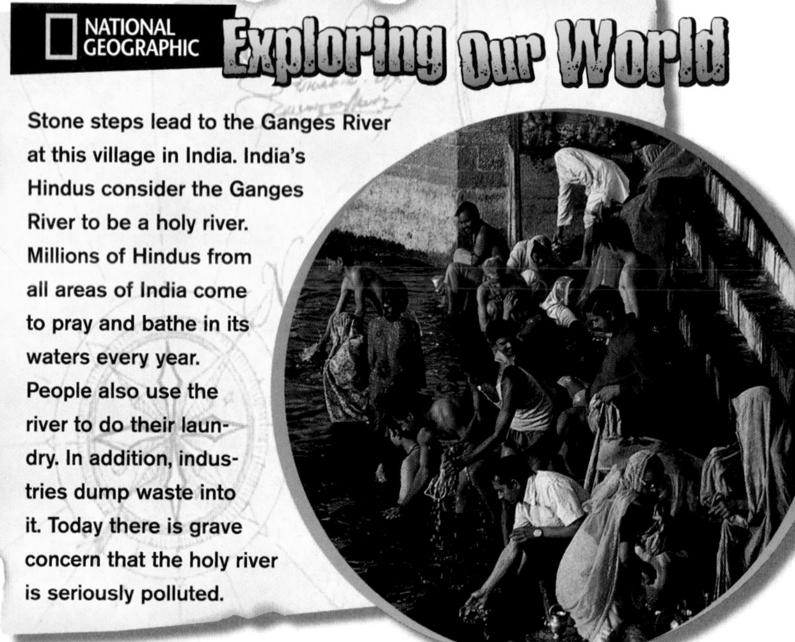

Stone steps lead to the Ganges River at this village in India. India's Hindus consider the Ganges River to be a holy river. Millions of Hindus from all areas of India come to pray and bathe in its waters every year. People also use the river to do their laundry. In addition, industries dump waste into it. Today there is grave concern that the holy river is seriously polluted.

India and several other countries—Pakistan, Bangladesh (BAHNG•gluh•DEHSH), Nepal, Bhutan, Sri Lanka, and the Maldives—make up the South Asian subcontinent. A **subcontinent** is a large landmass that is part of another continent but distinct from it.

India's Land and Economy

Two huge walls of mountains—the **Karakoram** (KAH•rah•KOHR•ahm) **Range** and the **Himalaya** (HIH•muh•LAY•uh)—form India's northern border and separate South Asia from the rest of Asia. (See the map on page 645.) The tallest mountains in the world, the Himalaya's snowcapped peaks average more than 5 miles (8 km) in height. Edging India's southern coasts are the **Eastern Ghats** and the **Western Ghats.** In central India, the **Satpura Range** divides the country.

North of the Satpura lies the vast **Ganges Plain.** It boasts some of the most fertile soil in the country and holds about 40 percent of India's

Section Resources

Reproducible Masters

- Reproducible Lesson Plan
- Daily Lecture and Discussion Notes
- Note-taking Guide
- Guided Reading Activity
- Reading Essentials and Study Guide
- Section Quiz

Transparencies

- Daily Focus Skills Transparency
- GeoQuiz Transparency

Multimedia

- Vocabulary PuzzleMaker CD-ROM
- Interactive Tutor Self-Assessment CD-ROM
- Presentation Plus! CD-ROM
- ExamView® Pro Testmaker CD-ROM

people. The **Ganges River** flows through the Ganges Plain to the **Bay of Bengal.** South of the Satpura Range lies the **Deccan Plateau.** Forests, farmland, and rich deposits of minerals make it a valuable region.

Most of India is warm or hot all year. The Himalaya block cold northern air from sweeping south into the country. **Monsoons,** or seasonal winds that blow steadily from the same direction for months, also influence the climate. During the rainy season (June through September), southern monsoon winds bring moist air from the Indian Ocean. The map on page 630 shows monsoon patterns for summer and winter.

The Green Revolution Today India produces most of the food it needs. In the past, it was very different. The world's worst recorded food disaster, known as the Bengal Famine, occurred in 1943 when the United Kingdom ruled India. An estimated 4 million people died of starvation that year alone. When India won its independence in 1947, government officials turned their attention to improving India's farm output. The **green revolution** was an effort to use modern techniques and science to increase production of food.

The government built dams to collect monsoon rains. The dams stored the water and spread it out through irrigation ditches during the dry season. Farmers could then plant more than one crop each year. New, stronger strains of wheat, rice, and corn were also developed that could withstand diseases and droughts and produce more grains.

India's farmers today raise a variety of crops, including rice, wheat, cotton, tea, sugarcane, and jute. **Jute** is a plant fiber used for making rope, burlap bags, and carpet backing. India is the world's second-largest rice producer, after China.

NATIONAL GEOGRAPHIC On Location

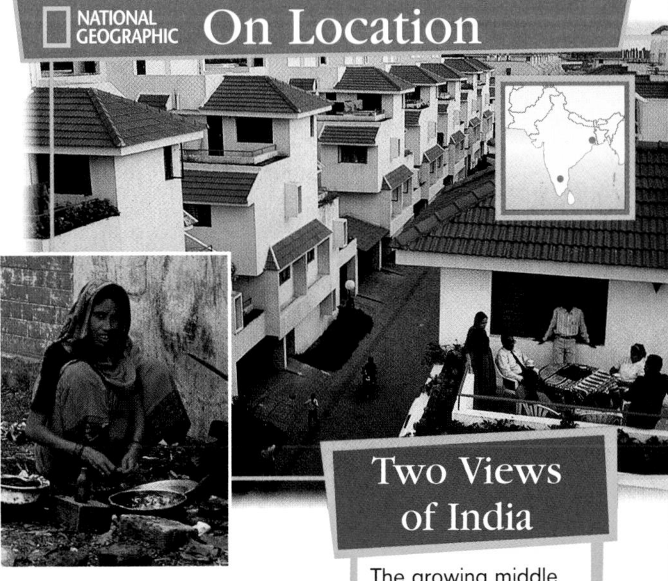

Two Views of India

The growing middle class lives comfortably in India's suburbs (above), but the poor in India's cities must struggle to survive (above left).

Human/Environment Interaction
How would the green revolution benefit India's people?

Industry Huge factories in India's cities turn out cotton textiles and produce iron and steel. Oil and sugar refineries loom over many urban skylines. Recently, many American computer companies have opened offices in India. Mining is another major industry. India has rich deposits of coal, iron ore, manganese, and bauxite. Its major exports are gems and jewelry.

Many Indian products are manufactured in cottage industries. A **cottage industry** is a home- or village-based industry in which family members, including children, supply their own equipment to make goods. Items produced in cottage industries include cotton cloth, silk cloth, rugs, leather products, and metalware.

TEACH

Making Comparisons Point out to students that India's monsoon winds cause distinct wet and dry seasons in that country. **Ask:** **What seasonal patterns affect climate in your community? What factors cause these patterns to occur? L1**

Daily Lecture and Discussion Notes

SOUTH ASIA

Daily Lecture and Discussion Notes
India—Past and Present

Did You Know? In 2000, India's population rose above 1 billion people for the first time. Only China has more people.

I. India's Land and Economy

A. India and several other countries—Pakistan, Bangladesh, Nepal, Bhutan, Sri Lanka, and the Maldives—make up the South Asian subcontinent. A **subcontinent** is a large landmass that is part of another continent but distinct from it.

B. Two huge walls of mountains—the Karakoram Range and the Himalaya—form ... parate South Asia from the rest of Asia. The ... malaya's ... average ...

More About the Photos

Bangalore These middle-class homes sit in a suburb of Bangalore, once the capital of a princely state and now the center of India's computer industry, earning it the name "India's Silicon Valley." Despite the country's increasing prosperity, more than one-third of the people live in poverty.

Caption Answer More food would be available and would be more affordable.

Reading Strategy — Reading the Text

Understanding Vocabulary Have students create a vocabulary worksheet that they can use as they begin to read the section. The columns should be labeled: *Unknown Word, Guessed Meaning, Context Meaning,* and *Dictionary Meaning.* Before they read the section, have students complete the first two columns. Then students should read the section to complete the next two columns. L1

*Use the **Reading Skills Handbook** for more reading strategies.*

✓ Reading Check Answer

Acres of forests and animal habitats have been destroyed; land and water have been polluted with industrial wastes and pesticides.

L1/ELL

Guided Reading Activity

Name ______ Date ______ Class ______

SOUTH ASIA

Guided Reading Activity 1

India—Past and Present

DIRECTIONS: Answering Questions Reading the section and answering the questions below will help you learn more about the country of India. Use your textbook to fill in the blanks.

1. What is a subcontinent?
2. What forms India's northern border?
3. Describe the climate of India.
4. What crops do India's farmers raise?
5. What is a cottage industry?
6. What are environmental challenges that India faces?
7. Where were the first Indian civilizations located?
8. Who led the Indian independence movement? How did he do this?
9. What is the main religion, and how does it affect life?
10. Where do most of the people live?
11. What is India's capital?

50

Answer Bangladesh, Nepal, Pakistan, Sri Lanka, Taiwan

Indigo Ancient Indian artisans elevated spinning, dyeing, and weaving to art forms. In fact, the word *indigo*—the blue dye that comes from the indigo plant—is derived from the name "India."

▲ This statue represents Siva, one of Hinduism's many deities.

Environmental Challenges India's economic growth has created challenges to its environment. Thousands of acres of forests have been cleared for farming. Both water and land have been polluted from industrial wastes and **pesticides,** or chemicals used to kill insects that destroy crops. Burning coal is also harmful. The Ganges River is considered by many experts to be one of the world's most polluted rivers.

All of these developments have played a part in destroying animal habitats. India's elephants, lions, tigers, leopards, monkeys, and panthers have been greatly reduced in number. The government has set up more than 350 national parks and preserves to save these animals.

✓ Reading Check **How has economic growth hurt India's environment?**

India's History and People

About 4,000 years ago, the first Indian civilization built well-planned cities along the **Indus River** valley in present-day Pakistan. In the 1500s B.C., warriors known as Aryans (AR•ee•uhns) entered the subcontinent from Central Asia. They set up kingdoms in northern India. Aryan beliefs gradually blended with the practices of the local people to form the religion of Hinduism.

Over time, Hinduism organized India's society into groups called castes. A **caste** is a social class based on a person's ancestry. Under such a system, people are born into a particular caste, which determines the jobs they can hold and whom they can marry. The caste system still influences Indian life, although laws now forbid unfair treatment of "lower" castes.

About 80 percent of India's people today are Hindus. Hindus honor many gods and goddesses, including Brahma the Creator, Vishnu the Preserver, and Siva the Destroyer. Hinduism teaches that after the body dies, the soul is reborn, often in an animal or human form. This process, called **reincarnation,** is repeated until the soul

EXPLORING CULTURE

Clothing

What is more comfortable than a pair of well-worn blue jeans? Denim—the strong blue cotton fabric—is part of modern life. Blue-dyed textiles (fabrics) are nothing new, however. They were being produced in India as long ago as 2700 B.C. Ancient Indians were among the first in the world to master techniques for dyeing cotton and other types of fabric. Using more than 300 different plants, Indian textile makers created brilliant fabric dyes. They also discovered how to make dyes permanent, so they would not wash out.

Looking Closer **Look at the Country Profiles on pages 632–634. Which countries' main export is cotton, textiles, or clothing?**

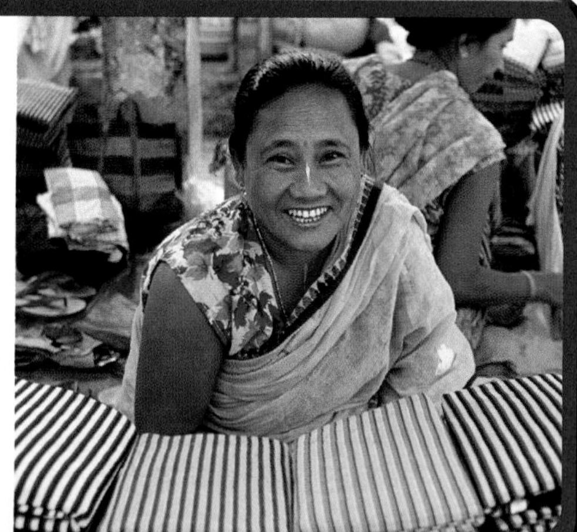

Differentiated Instruction

Meeting Special Needs: Kinesthetic Bring a small fan to class. Have several students stand shoulder to shoulder at the front of the class. Take the fan and position yourself behind the standing students. Point the fan toward the students and turn it on. Ask students seated in the main part of the classroom whether they feel the breeze from the fan. *(The standing students should effectively block the air; if they do not, aim the fan lower.)* Point out that the Himalaya act in the same way to block the cold winds from the north. **L1**

Refer to *Inclusion for the Middle School Social Studies Classroom Strategies and Activities* in the TCR.

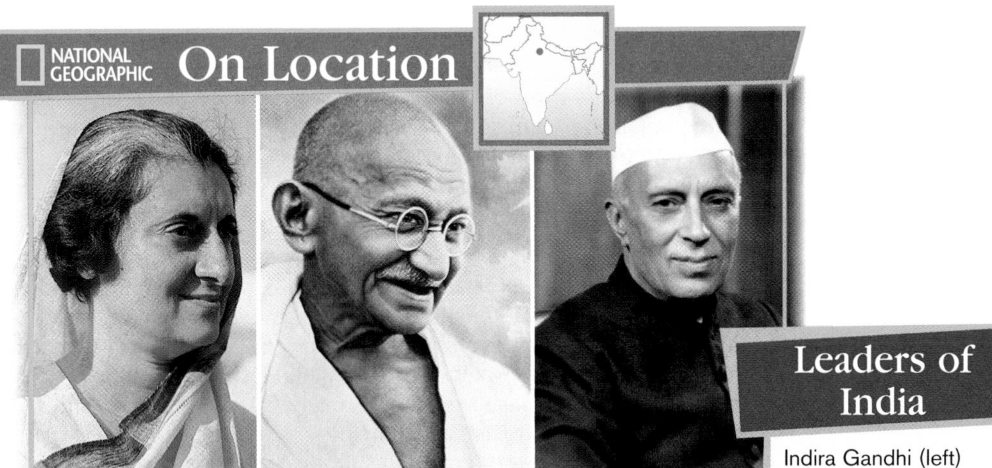

Leaders of India

Indira Gandhi (left) Mohandas Gandhi (center), and Jawaharlal Nehru (right) were instrumental in bringing democracy to India.

History **Which country ruled India before it won its independence?**

reaches perfection. For this reason, many Hindus believe it is wrong to kill any living creature. Cows are viewed as sacred and roam freely.

Buddhism started in India about 500 B.C. but largely declined there by 300 B.C. The religion of Islam has had much more influence on India's history. In the A.D. 700s, Muslims from Southwest Asia brought Islam to India. In the 1500s, they founded the Mogul Empire and ruled India for 200 years.

Today India's 140 million followers of Islam form one of the world's largest Muslim populations. Other religions include Christianity, Sikhism (SEE•KIH•zuhm), Buddhism, and Jainism (JY•NIH•zuhm). Conflict sometimes occurs among members of India's different religious groups. The Sikhs, who practice Sikhism, believe in one God as Christians and Muslims do, yet Sikhs also have other beliefs similar to Hindus. Many Sikhs would like to form their own country.

Religion has influenced the arts of India. Ancient Hindu builders constructed temples with hundreds of statues. Hindu writers composed stories about deities. Among Muslim achievements are large mosques, palaces, and forts. One of the finest Muslim buildings in India is the Taj Mahal. Turn to page 643 to learn more about this building.

Independence The British were the last of India's conquerors, ruling from the 1700s to the mid-1900s. They built roads, railroads, and seaports. They also made large profits from the plantations, mines, and factories they set up. An Indian leader named Mohandas Gandhi led a nonviolent movement to free India from Britain's rule. His efforts brought India independence from the United Kingdom in 1947.

Before independence, the British government had decided to divide India into two countries—one Hindu (India) and one Muslim (East and West Pakistan). After independence, millions of Hindus fled toward India. Muslims migrated toward Pakistan. Violence resulted from these mass migrations, and more than a million people were killed.

More About the Photos

Leaders of India A beloved leader in the Indian National Congress, Mohandas K. Gandhi, was called Mahatma, the "Great Soul," by millions of followers. Jawaharlal Nehru, also a nationalist, was the first prime minister of independent India. Indira Gandhi, the daughter of Jawaharlal Nehru, was prime minister of India from 1966 to 1977 and 1980 to 1984.

Caption Answer the United Kingdom

Measure student knowledge of physical features.

GeoQuiz Transparency

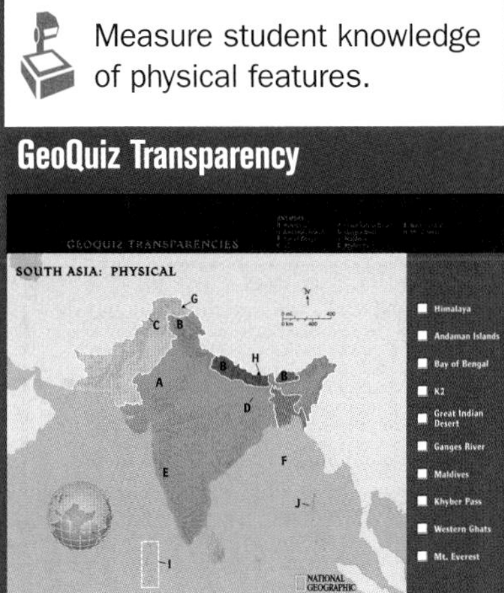

Assign Section 1 Assessment as homework or an in-class activity.

Have students use the Interactive Tutor Self-Assessment CD-ROM to review Section 1.

Content Background

Caste System India's caste system dates from about 1000 B.C., when the Aryans invaded the area. The Aryans had recognized four main groups, which gradually evolved into the four *varna: Brahman,* the priests; *Kshatriya,* warriors and officials; *Vaishya,* or merchants, craftspeople, and landed farmers; and *Shudra,* the peasants and workers. Giving this last group—the most numerous by far—the lowest status allowed the Aryans to maintain control over the majority population. A fifth group, the outcastes, included those who did not fit in the first four. Over time, these groups developed into nearly 3,000 smaller groups called *jati.* The lowest caste and the outcastes suffered discrimination. Mohandas Gandhi urged his country to abandon the system, and great strides have been made. In 1997 a member of the lowest caste was named India's president.

L2

Section Quiz

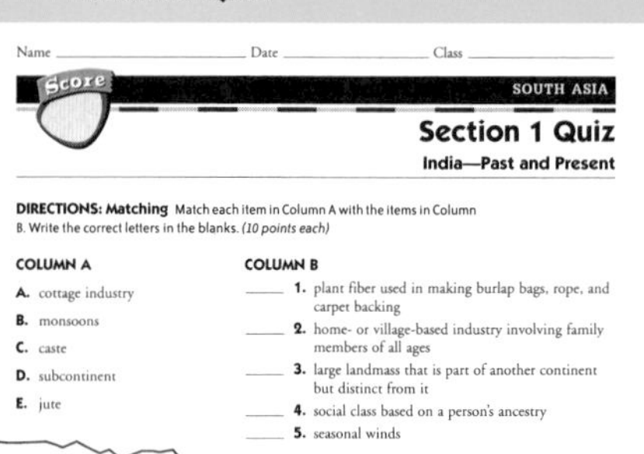
Name ______ Date ______ Class ______

Score — SOUTH ASIA

Section 1 Quiz

India—Past and Present

DIRECTIONS: Matching Match each item in Column A with the items in Column B. Write the correct letters in the blanks. *(10 points each)*

COLUMN A	COLUMN B
A. cottage industry	____ 1. plant fiber used in making burlap bags, rope, and carpet backing
B. monsoons	____ 2. home- or village-based industry involving family members of all ages
C. caste	____ 3. large landmass that is part of another continent but distinct from it
D. subcontinent	____ 4. social class based on a person's ancestry
E. jute	____ 5. seasonal winds

Reading Check Answer

about 70 percent

L1/ELL

Reading Essentials and Study Guide

Name ______ Date ______ Class ______

SOUTH ASIA

Reading Essentials and Study Guide 1

India—Past and Present

Key Terms

subcontinent large land area that is part of another continent but distinct from it
monsoon seasonal wind that blows steadily from the same direction for months
green revolution an effort to use modern methods to produce more food
jute plant fiber used to make rope, burlap bags, and carpet backing
cottage industry home- or village-based industry in which family members supply their own equipment to make goods
pesticide chemicals used to kill insects
caste social class based on a person's ancestry
...belief that when a body dies, the soul is reborn, often in an

Read to Learn

4 Close

Reading Strategy

Writing a Paragraph Ask students to write a paragraph stating how their lives might be different if they lived in India.

Government India has 25 states and 7 territories. **New Delhi** was built specifically to be the country's capital. India is a representative democracy. The head of state is a president, whose duties are mainly ceremonial. The real power lies with the prime minister. The first prime minister of India was Jawaharlal Nehru, who was elected in 1947. His daughter, Indira Gandhi, was also prime minister. She led India almost continually from 1966 until her assassination in 1984.

Daily Life More than 1 billion people call India their home. The country has 18 official languages, of which Hindi is the most widely used. English is often spoken in business and government, however. About 70 percent of the people live in rural villages. The government has been working to provide villagers with electricity, drinking water, better schools, and paved roads. Still, many villagers move to cities to find jobs and a better standard of living.

India's cities are very crowded. Bicycles, carts, animals, and people fill the streets. **Mumbai** (formerly Bombay), **Delhi, Calcutta,** and **Chennai** each have more than 5 million people and are growing rapidly. Modern high-rise buildings tower over slum areas where many live in deep poverty. In 1979 the well-known missionary Mother Teresa won the Nobel Peace Prize for her efforts to help the poor in Calcutta.

One of the most popular holidays is Diwali (dee•VAH•lee), the Festival of Lights. It is a Hindu celebration marking the coming of winter and the victory of good over evil. Indians also like watching movies. India's movie industry turns out more films than Hollywood.

Reading Check What percentage of India's people live in rural villages?

Section 1 Assessment

Defining Terms

1. **Define** subcontinent, monsoon, green revolution, jute, cottage industry, pesticide, caste, reincarnation.

Recalling Facts

2. **Location** What two mountain ranges form India's northern border?
3. **Culture** What is the most widely followed religion in India?
4. **History** Which Indian leader led a movement that brought India its independence in 1947?

Critical Thinking

5. **Understanding Cause and Effect** How do monsoon winds affect India's climate?
6. **Drawing Conclusions** What challenges do you think the caste system caused?

Graphic Organizer

7. **Organizing Information** India is becoming a more modern country but still has many traditional ways. Create a chart like this one. Then list both modern and traditional aspects of India.

Modern Aspects	Traditional Aspects

Applying Social Studies Skills

8. **Analyzing Maps** Look at the population density map on page 653. Where are the most densely populated areas of India?

Section 1 Assessment

1. The terms are defined in the Glossary.
2. Karakoram and Himalaya
3. Hinduism
4. Mohandas Gandhi
5. In the cool season, monsoon winds from the north bring dry air. In the wet seasons, monsoon winds from the Indian Ocean bring moist air and rain.
6. difficulty in building trust between groups and in providing equal healthcare, education, and opportunities to all citizens
7. *Modern:* high-rise buildings, movie industry, high-technology industries; *Traditional:* high percentage of rural villages, caste system, cottage industries
8. the north, in the Ganges River Plain, and on the southwest and southeast coastal plains

Making Connections

ART | SCIENCE | CULTURE | TECHNOLOGY

The Taj Mahal

Considered one of the world's most beautiful buildings, the Taj Mahal was built by the Muslim emperor Shah Jahan of India. He had it built to house the grave of his beloved wife, Mumtaz Mahal. She died in 1631 shortly after giving birth to their fourteenth child.

▲ The Taj Mahal, Agra, India

Background

While they were married, Mumtaz Mahal and Shah Jahan were constant companions. The empress went everywhere with her husband, even on military expeditions. She encouraged her husband to perform great acts of charity toward the poor. This earned her the love and admiration of the Indian people.

After his wife's death, Shah Jahan ordered the construction of the finest monument ever built. A team of architects, sculptors, calligraphers, and master builders participated in the design. More than 20,000 laborers and skilled craft workers from India, Persia, the Ottoman Empire, and Europe worked together to build the monument. For 22 years they worked to complete the Taj Mahal, which holds a tomb, mosque, rest house, elaborate garden, and arched gateway.

The Mausoleum

The central part of the Taj Mahal is the domed marble mausoleum, or tomb, built on a square marble platform. The central dome is 213 feet (65 m) tall, and four smaller domed chambers surround it. A high minaret, or tower, marks each corner of the platform.

Inside the central chamber, delicately carved marble screens enclose the caskets of Mumtaz Mahal and Shah Jahan. He was buried next to his wife after his death in 1666. Following Islamic tradition, the caskets face east toward Makkah, the holy city of Islam.

The white marble from which the mausoleum is built seems to change color throughout the day as it reflects light from the sun and moon. Detailed flower patterns are carved into the marble walls and inlaid with colorful gemstones. Verses from Islamic religious writings are etched in calligraphy into the stone archways.

Making the Connection

1. Who is buried in the Taj Mahal?
2. Who built the Taj Mahal and how long did it take?
3. **Understanding Cause and Effect** How did Shah Jahan's feelings for his wife affect the grave site he built for her?

Teach

Write the names of the following buildings: Washington Monument, Jefferson Memorial, Lincoln Memorial. **Ask:** **What do these structures have in common?** *(They are memorials to people who have died.)* Tell students that they are going to read about another famous memorial. L1

More About the Taj Mahal

The Taj Mahal embodies the principles of symmetry and balance. The four smaller domes balance the large central dome. Their pattern is repeated in the four graceful minarets. The four sides of the building each have a large central arch flanked by smaller arches on angled walls that create the Taj Mahal's octagonal shape. The desire for symmetry is very clear in two side buildings. On one side is a mosque, which faces east. On the opposite side is an identical structure called a *jawab,* or "answer," the purpose of which is to mirror the mosque and complete the sense of balance.

Interdisciplinary Connections

Art Have students create a work—through art, the written word, or song—that pays tribute to someone they respect or admire.

Making the Connection

1. Mumtaz Mahal and Shah Jahan
2. Shah Jahan ordered it built, requiring the work of more than 20,000 laborers and skilled craft workers. It took them 22 years to complete it.
3. *Possible answer:* His love for his wife led him to build for her tomb one of the finest monuments in the world.

FOCUS

Section Objectives

1. Identify the main physical features in Pakistan and Bangladesh.
2. Discuss how the people of these countries earn a living.
3. Explain why the economies of these countries have made slow progress.

BELLRINGER Skillbuilder Activity

Project transparency and have students answer the question.

Daily Focus Skills Transparency

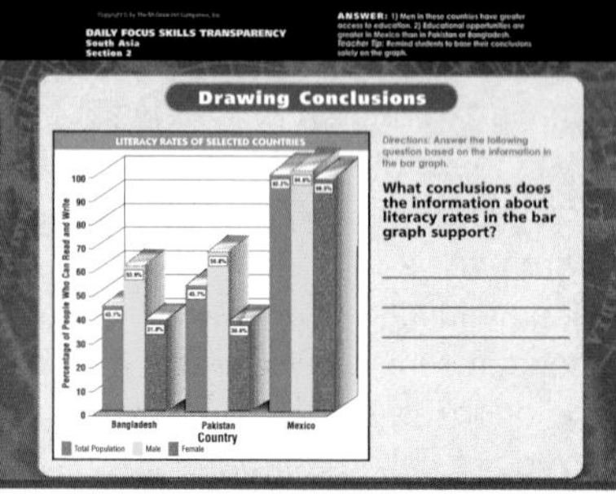

Reading Preview

■ **Activating Prior Knowledge** **Ask:** Which is a bigger problem for a farmer, too much rain or too little? Inform students that countries in South Asia suffer from these two opposite problems.

■ **Preteaching Vocabulary** Have students read the definition of the word *cyclone*. Then explain that the word comes from a Greek word meaning "circle." Ask volunteers to explain why the word has that origin.

Guide to Reading

Main Idea

Once a single nation, Pakistan and Bangladesh today are separate countries that border India on the west and east.

Terms to Know

- tributary
- delta
- cyclone

Reading Strategy

Draw a diagram like this one. In the outer ovals, write statements that are true of each country under the headings. Where the ovals overlap, write statements that are true of both countries.

Pakistan | Bangladesh

Section 2

Pakistan and Bangladesh

NATIONAL GEOGRAPHIC **Exploring Our World**

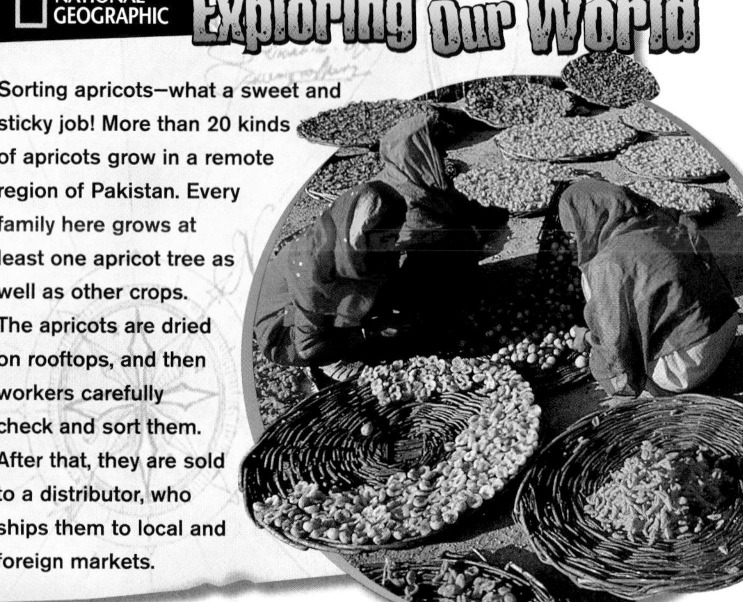

Sorting apricots—what a sweet and sticky job! More than 20 kinds of apricots grow in a remote region of Pakistan. Every family here grows at least one apricot tree as well as other crops. The apricots are dried on rooftops, and then workers carefully check and sort them. After that, they are sold to a distributor, who ships them to local and foreign markets.

Two countries in South Asia—**Pakistan** and **Bangladesh**—are largely Muslim. Although they share the same religion, the two countries have very different cultures and languages.

For many centuries, Pakistan and Bangladesh were part of India. In 1947 they separated from largely Hindu India and together formed one Muslim country called Pakistan. The western area was called West Pakistan, and the eastern area, East Pakistan. Cultural and political differences between the two led to a violent conflict in 1971. When the war ended, West Pakistan kept the name of Pakistan. East Pakistan became a separate new country called Bangladesh.

Pakistan

Pakistan is about twice the size of California. The country also claims **Kashmir,** a mostly Muslim territory on the northern border of India and Pakistan. Kashmir is currently divided between Pakistan and

Section Resources

Reproducible Masters

- Reproducible Lesson Plan
- Daily Lecture and Discussion Notes
- Note-taking Guide
- Guided Reading Activity
- Reading Essentials and Study Guide
- Section Quiz

Transparencies

- Daily Focus Skills Transparency
- GeoQuiz Transparency

Multimedia

- Vocabulary PuzzleMaker CD-ROM
- Interactive Tutor Self-Assessment CD-ROM
- Presentation Plus! CD-ROM
- ExamView® Pro Testmaker CD-ROM

India. Both countries want to control the entire region, mainly for its vast water resources. This dispute over Kashmir has sparked three wars between Pakistan and India. In fact, the conflict threatens the rest of the world because both Pakistan and India have nuclear weapons.

Towering mountains occupy most of northern and western Pakistan. The world's second-highest peak, **K2,** rises 28,250 feet (8,611 m) in the Karakoram Range. Another range, the **Hindu Kush,** lies in the far north. Several passes cut through its rugged peaks. The best known is the **Khyber Pass.** For centuries, it has been used by people traveling through South Asia from the north.

Plains in eastern Pakistan are rich in fertile soil deposited by rivers. The major river system running through these plains is the **Indus River** and its tributaries. A **tributary** is a small river that flows into a larger one. West of the Indus River valley, the land rises to form a mostly dry plateau. Another vast barren area—the **Great Indian Desert**—lies east of the Indus River valley and reaches into India.

Pakistan's Economy Pakistan has fertile land and enough energy resources to meet its needs. About half of the people are farmers. A

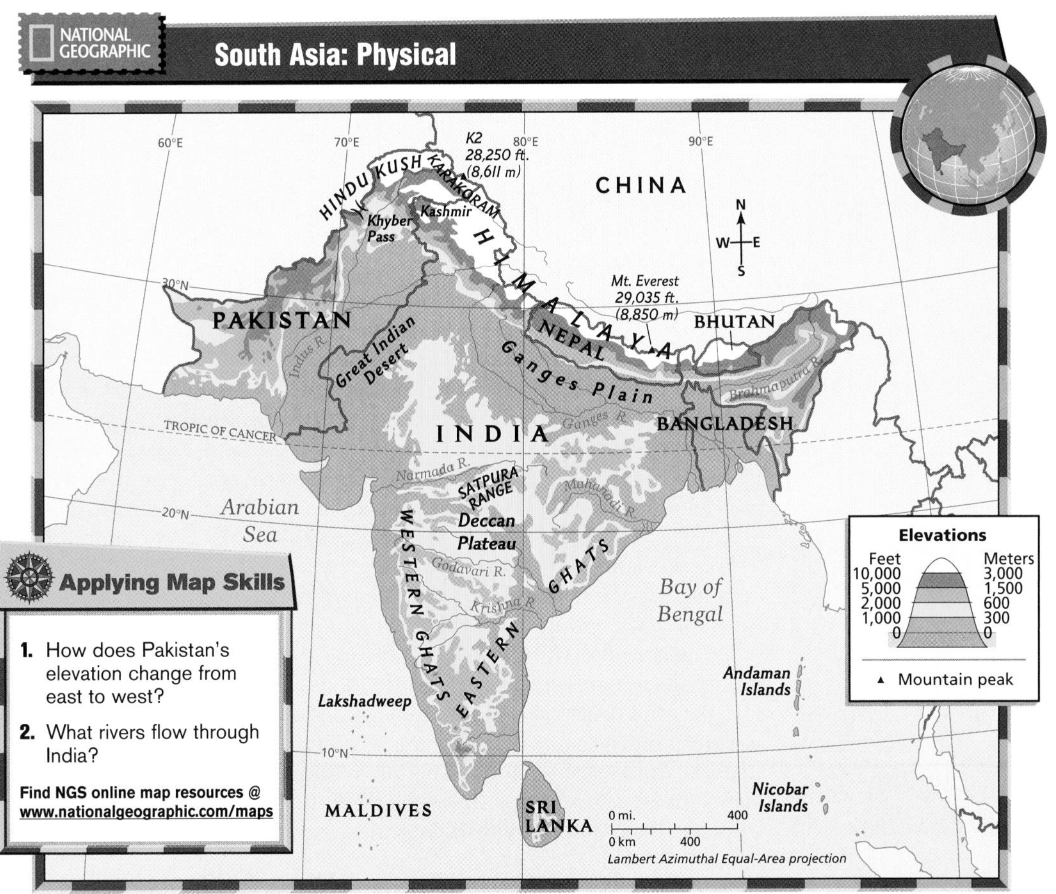

Applying Map Skills

1. How does Pakistan's elevation change from east to west?
2. What rivers flow through India?

Find NGS online map resources @ www.nationalgeographic.com/maps

Reading Strategy Reading the Text

Monitoring Comprehension Generally, there are five reasons students do not comprehend the material they read. They include 1) failure to understand a word; 2) failure to understand a sentence; 3) failure to understand how sentences relate to one another; 4) failure to understand how the information is organized; 5) lack of interest or concentration. Have students summarize the information in the section in their own words. Have them check their summaries against the Reading Review at the end of the chapter to see if they addressed all of the main ideas. **L1**

Use the ***Reading Skills Handbook*** *for more reading strategies.*

TEACH

Reading Maps Have students look at the physical map on this page. **Ask:** **How would you describe Bangladesh?** *(a lowland with many rivers)* Then have them look at the monsoons map in the Regional Atlas and ask: **What can you conclude about the amount of rainfall Bangladesh receives?** *(It receives much rain.)* **What might Bangladesh experience as a result of these facts?** *(flooding)* **L1**

Daily Lecture and Discussion Notes

SOUTH ASIA

Daily Lecture and Discussion Notes

Pakistan and Bangladesh

Did You Know? The events surrounding a Pakistani wedding last for three or four days. Trees, lampposts, and bushes near the bride's house are decorated with small, white lights, similar to the lights some Americans put up at Christmas. Pakistani brides wear red dresses at the wedding ceremony.

I. Pakistan

A. Pakistan is largely Muslim. It was once part of India, until 1947. In 1971 East and West Pakistan fought because of cultural and political differences. West Pakistan kept the name of Pakistan. East Pakistan changed its name to Bangladesh.

Applying Map Skills

Answers

1. Elevation gradually increases and then decreases
2. Brahmaputra, Ganges, Indus, Narmada, Mahanadi, Godavari, and Krishna Rivers

Skills Practice

Where do the Indus, Ganges, and Brahmaputra Rivers originate? *(in the Himalaya)*

Chapter 22

Section 2, pages 644–647

✓ Reading Check Answer

cotton, textiles

3 ASSESS

Assign Section 2 Assessment as homework or an in-class activity.

Have students use the Interactive Tutor Self-Assessment CD-ROM to review Section 2.

L2

Section Quiz

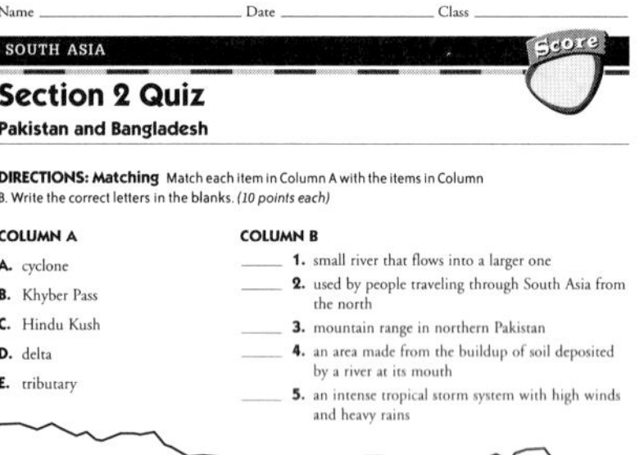

Name ______ Date ______ Class ______

SOUTH ASIA

Score

Section 2 Quiz

Pakistan and Bangladesh

DIRECTIONS: Matching Match each item in Column A with the items in Column B. Write the correct letters in the blanks. *(10 points each)*

COLUMN A	COLUMN B
A. cyclone	____ **1.** small river that flows into a larger one
B. Khyber Pass	____ **2.** used by people traveling through South Asia from the north
C. Hindu Kush	____ **3.** mountain range in northern Pakistan
D. delta	____ **4.** an area made from the buildup of soil deposited by a river at its mouth
E. tributary	____ **5.** an intense tropical storm system with high winds and heavy rains

Measure student knowledge of political entities.

GeoQuiz Transparency

large irrigation system helps them grow crops such as sugarcane, wheat, rice, and cotton. Cotton and textiles are the country's main exports. Other important industries include cement, fertilizer, food processing, and chemicals. Many people make metalware, pottery, and carpets in cottage industries. Pakistan's economy is struggling, however, because of frequent changes of government.

The Pakistanis Since independence, Pakistan has had many changes of government. Some of these governments and officials were elected, including a female prime minister, Benazir Bhutto. In other cases, the army seized power from an elected government. The most recent army takeover occurred in 1999, and military leaders still control the country.

About 97 percent of Pakistanis are Muslims. The influence of Islam is seen in large, domed mosques and people bowed in prayer at certain times of the day. Among the major languages are Punjabi and Sindhi. The official language, Urdu, is the first language of only 9 percent of the people. English is widely spoken in government.

Almost 70 percent of Pakistan's people live in rural villages. Most follow traditional customs and live in small homes of clay or sun-dried mud. Pakistanis live in large cities as well. **Karachi,** a seaport on the Arabian Sea, is a sprawling urban area. It has traditional outdoor markets, modern shops, and hotels. In the far north lies **Islamabad,** the capital. The government built this well-planned, modern city to draw people inland from crowded coastal areas. Most people in Pakistan's cities are factory workers, shopkeepers, and craft workers who live in crowded neighborhoods. Wealthier city dwellers live in modern homes.

✓ Reading Check **What are Pakistan's main exports?**

School's Out!

Adil Husain is on his way home from middle school. In Pakistan, public schooling ends after grade 10. After grade 10, Adil must decide whether to go to intermediate college (grades 11 and 12) and then the university. Like most Pakistanis, Adil is Muslim. He prays when he hears the call from the mosque. Afterward, he wants to start a game of cricket with his friends. "It's a lot like American baseball where teams of 11 players bat in innings and try to score runs. Our rules and equipment are different, though. You should try it!"

Bangladesh

Bangladesh, about the size of Wisconsin, is nearly surrounded by India. Although Bangladesh is a Muslim country like Pakistan, it shares many cultural features with eastern India.

If you saw Bangladesh for the first time, one word might come to mind—water. Two major rivers—the **Brahmaputra** (BRAHM•uh•POO•truh) and the **Ganges**—flow through the lush, low plains that cover most of Bangladesh. These two rivers unite with a third, smaller river before entering the Bay of Bengal. The combined rivers form the world's largest delta. A **delta** is a soil deposit located at the mouth of a river. In Bangladesh's delta area, the rivers constantly shift course, creating many thin fingers of land. The people depend on the rivers for transportation and for farming.

Bangladesh has tropical and subtropical climates. As in India, the monsoons affect Bangladesh. Raging floods often drown Bangladesh's low, flat land. Water also runs down from deforested slopes upriver in northern India. Together, these violent flows of water cause thousands of deaths and leave millions of people without homes. When the monsoons end, cyclones may strike Bangladesh. A **cyclone** is an intense tropical storm system with high winds and heavy rains. Cyclones, in

Differentiated Instruction

Meeting Special Needs: Naturalist To clarify why deforested slopes cause problems in heavy rains, ask students to compare what happens when rain falls on paved streets versus when it falls on planted areas. Students should recognize that in planted areas, the rain is more likely to soak into the earth. In paved areas, however, the water pools on the surface. Explain that mountains without trees act similarly to pavement—the water simply runs down the mountainsides. When the slopes are covered by trees, however, the roots of the plants can hold the water before it runs off. **L1 ELL**

Refer to *Inclusion for the Middle School Social Studies Classroom Strategies and Activities* in the TCR.

turn, can be followed by deadly tidal waves that surge from the Bay of Bengal. As deadly as the monsoons and cyclones can be, problems also occur if the rains come too late. When this happens, crops often fail and there is widespread hunger.

A Farming Economy Most people of Bangladesh earn their living by farming. Rice is the most important crop. The fertile soil and plentiful water make it possible for rice to be grown and harvested three times a year. Other crops include sugarcane, jute, and wheat. Cash crops of tea grow in hilly regions in the east. Despite good growing conditions, Bangladesh cannot grow enough food for its people. Its farmers have few modern tools and use outdated farming methods. In addition, the disastrous floods can drown crops and cause food shortages.

Bangladesh has an important clothing industry. It exports large amounts of manufactured clothing to other countries. You may even be wearing clothes that were made in Bangladesh.

The People With about 146.7 million people, Bangladesh is one of the most densely populated countries in the world. It is also one of the poorest countries. About 75 percent of the people live in rural areas. Because of floods, people in rural Bangladesh have to build their houses on platforms. Many people have moved to crowded urban areas to find work in factories. Their most common choice is **Dhaka** (DA•kuh), Bangladesh's capital and major port.

Most of Bangladesh's people speak Bengali. About 83 percent of the people are Muslim, and most of the rest are Hindus. Muslim influences are strong in the country's art, literature, and music.

✓ Reading Check What is an important industry in Bangladesh?

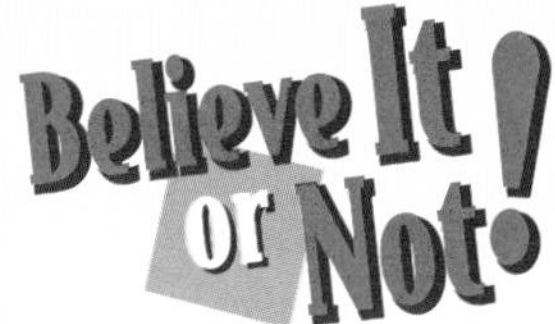

Ship Breakers

On a beach near Karachi, Pakistan, ship breakers haul an old cargo vessel to shore. Their next task? The men will use hammers, crowbars, and wrenches to pull the ship apart. They will then sell the pipes, chains, portholes, steel plates, and other reusable parts. The work is exhausting, but in this poor country, it is a way to make a living.

Section 2 Assessment

Defining Terms

1. **Define** tributary, delta, cyclone.

Recalling Facts

2. **Region** What region has been the source of conflict between Pakistan and India?
3. **History** Why has the Khyber Pass been important?
4. **Movement** Why was Islamabad built inland?

Critical Thinking

5. **Analyzing Information** Why can rice be grown three times a year in Bangladesh?
6. **Drawing Conclusions** Why are Pakistan's and Bangladesh's economies struggling?

Graphic Organizer

7. **Organizing Information** Draw a diagram like this one. At the ends of the arrows, list three effects on Bangladesh caused by summer monsoon rains.

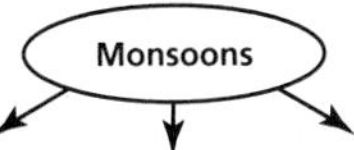

Applying Social Studies Skills

8. **Analyzing Maps** Look at the physical map on page 645. Which rivers have deltas in Bangladesh?

Section 2 Assessment

1. The terms are defined in the Glossary.
2. Kashmir
3. This pass through rugged mountains has been used for centuries by groups passing into South Asia.
4. to attract people there from crowded coastal areas
5. because the country has fertile soil and plentiful water
6. *Pakistan*—because of frequent changes of government; *Bangladesh*—because of problems caused by too much rain or rain coming too late in the year
7. *Possible answers*—create possibility for plentiful harvests; may cause flooding; may bring cyclones that cause widespread destruction
8. Ganges and Brahmaputra Rivers

Reading Strategy

Reteach

Have students write two paragraphs summarizing the main ideas about Pakistan in the first paragraph and Bangladesh in the second.

✓ Reading Check Answer

clothing

L1/ELL

Reading Essentials and Study Guide

Name ______ Date ______ Class ______

SOUTH ASIA

Reading Essentials and Study Guide 2
Pakistan and Bangladesh

Key Terms

tributary small river that flows into a larger one
delta buildup of soil dropped by a river at its mouth
cyclone strong tropical storm with high winds and heavy rains

Drawing From Experience

Do you like baseball? A favorite game in Pakistan is cricket. It is like ... but very different in others. For example, if you ... you don't have to run.

Enrich

Have students research and report on the role of women in either Pakistan or Bangladesh.

Close

Have students write a 10-question quiz that reflects what they think are the most important characteristics of Pakistan and Bangladesh.

TEACH

Conduct a survey in the class. Ask students how many arrive at school (1) on foot, (2) by bicycle, (3) on a school bus, (4) by public transportation, or (5) by car. Tally the results and then ask students to convert the responses to percentages. Create a circle and explain that it represents the whole class. Make a slice corresponding to the percentage of the first group of students. Then prompt students to make the remaining slices. L1

Additional Skills Practice

1. Suppose you had figures showing different areas where the government spent its money in a single year. **Ask:** **Could you use a circle graph to present these figures? Why or why not?** *(yes; because each spending area represents a part of all spending)*
2. Suppose you had figures showing how much the government spent for two different years. **Ask:** **Could you use a single circle graph to show these figures? Why or why not?** *(no; because a circle graph shows parts of a whole, not a comparison of two different totals)*

Additional Skills Resources

 Chapter Skills Review

 Building Geography Skills for Life

Social Studies Skill

Reading a Circle Graph

Have you ever watched someone serve pieces of pie? When the pie is cut evenly, everybody gets the same size slice. If one slice is cut a little larger, however, someone else gets a smaller piece.

Learning the Skill

A **circle graph** is like a sliced pie. Often it is even called a pie chart. In a circle graph, the complete circle represents a whole group—or 100 percent. The circle is divided into "slices," or wedge-shaped sections representing parts of the whole.

To read a circle graph, follow these steps:

- Read the title of the circle graph to find out what the subject is.
- Study the labels or the key to see what each "slice" represents.
- Compare the sizes of the circle slices.

Practicing the Skill

Look at the graph below to answer the following questions.

1. What is the subject of the circle graph?
2. Which religion in South Asia has the most followers?
3. What percentage practice Islam?
4. What is the combined percentage of Buddhist and Christian followers?

Applying the Skill

Quiz at least 10 friends about the capitals of India, Pakistan, and Bangladesh. Create a circle graph showing what percentage knew (a) all three capitals, (b) two capitals, (c) one capital, or (d) no capitals.

GO TO Practice key skills with **Glencoe Skillbuilder Interactive Workbook, Level 1.**

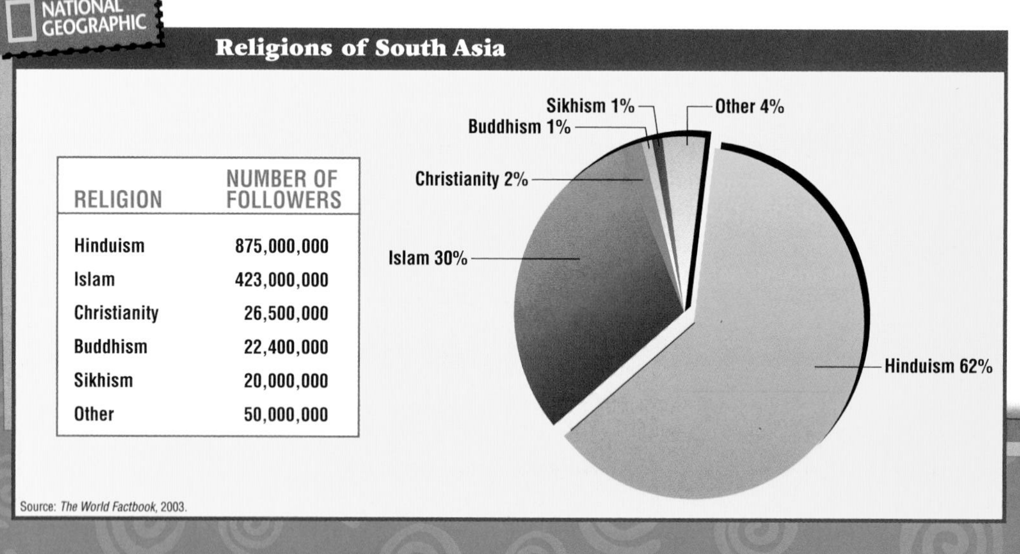

RELIGION	NUMBER OF FOLLOWERS
Hinduism	875,000,000
Islam	423,000,000
Christianity	26,500,000
Buddhism	22,400,000
Sikhism	20,000,000
Other	50,000,000

Practicing the Skill Answers

1. religions practiced in South Asia
2. Hinduism
3. 30 percent
4. 3 percent

Applying the Skill

Students' circle graphs will vary according to the results they obtained for their question, but each circle graph should contain up to four "slices"—knew all three capitals; knew two; knew one; and knew none (unless one of those categories had no respondents). Be sure that students include a key or labels to identify the slices.

Guide to Reading

Main Idea

The other countries of South Asia include mountainous Nepal and Bhutan and the island countries of Sri Lanka and the Maldives.

Terms to Know

- *dzong*
- atoll
- lagoon

Reading Strategy

Create a chart like this one. Then write the main economic activities of these countries in South Asia.

Country	Economic Activities
Nepal	
Bhutan	
Sri Lanka	
Maldives	

Section 3

Mountain Kingdoms, Island Republics

NATIONAL GEOGRAPHIC Exploring Our World

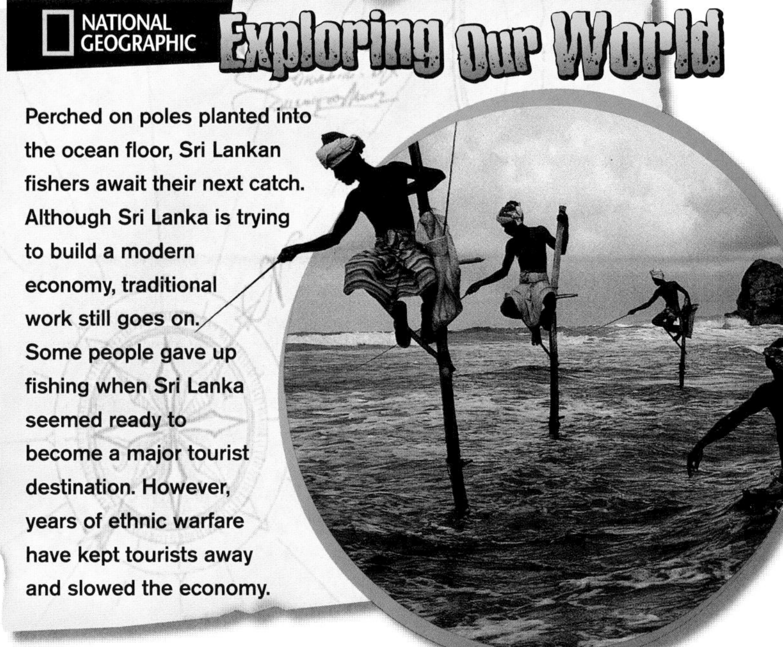

Perched on poles planted into the ocean floor, Sri Lankan fishers await their next catch. Although Sri Lanka is trying to build a modern economy, traditional work still goes on. Some people gave up fishing when Sri Lanka seemed ready to become a major tourist destination. However, years of ethnic warfare have kept tourists away and slowed the economy.

Of the four other countries of South Asia, two are landlocked kingdoms and two are island republics. **Nepal** and **Bhutan** both lie among the towering peaks of the Himalaya. The island countries of **Sri Lanka** and the **Maldives** lie south of India in the Indian Ocean.

Mountainous Nepal

Nepal—about the size of Arkansas—forms a steep stairway to the world's highest mountain range. The Himalaya, dominating about 80 percent of Nepal's land area, are actually three mountain ranges running side by side. Nepal is home to 8 of the 10 highest mountains in the world. **Mount Everest,** the highest, soars 29,035 feet (8,850 m).

Swift rivers cut through the lower ranges in the south, shaping fertile valleys. A flat, fertile river plain runs along Nepal's southern border with India. The plain includes farmland, swamps, and rain forests. Tigers, elephants, and other wild animals roam these forests.

Section Resources

Reproducible Masters

- Reproducible Lesson Plan
- Daily Lecture and Discussion Notes
- Note-taking Guide
- Guided Reading Activity
- Reading Essentials and Study Guide
- Section Quiz

Transparencies

- Daily Focus Skills Transparency
- In-text Map Transparency

Multimedia

- Vocabulary PuzzleMaker CD-ROM
- Interactive Tutor Self-Assessment CD-ROM
- Presentation Plus! CD-ROM
- ExamView® Pro Testmaker CD-ROM
- MindJogger Videoquiz

1 Focus

Section Objectives

1. Explain how geography has isolated Nepal and Bhutan.
2. Describe what the people of Nepal and Bhutan do for a living.
3. Discuss how the economy of Sri Lanka has changed.
4. Understand the importance of the Maldives's location on the country's economy.

BELLRINGER Skillbuilder Activity

Project transparency and have students answer the question.

Daily Focus Skills Transparency

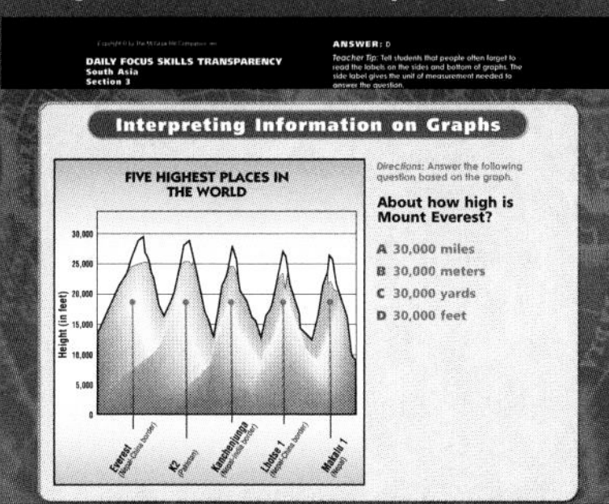

Reading Preview

■ **Activating Prior Knowledge** Countries in this section are either mountainous or located on islands. **Ask:** **What similar effect can result from these different types of geographies?** *(isolation from other lands)*

■ **Preteaching Vocabulary** Have students study the Terms to Know and think of ways to remember correct spellings. Ask for volunteers to suggest their strategies.

2 TEACH

Applying Information
Explain that the temperature drops 4°F for every 1,000 feet of increased elevation. Then ask students to calculate the temperature at the top of Mount Everest if the temperature at sea level is 80°F. *(-36 °F)* **L3**

Daily Lecture and Discussion Notes

SOUTH ASIA

Daily Lecture and Discussion Notes

Mountain Kingdoms, Island Republics

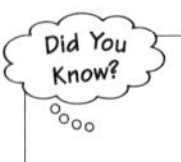

Did You Know? Some Hindus in Nepal practice polygyny, a form of marriage in which a husband has more than one wife. Polyandry, the practice of a wife having more than one husband, occurs among some of the Tibetan groups in northern Nepal.

I. Mountainous Nepal

A. Nepal's land forms a stairway to the world's highest mountain range—the Himalaya. Nepal is home to Mount Everest.

B. Nepal has fertile valleys and a humid subtropical climate in the south. The north has a highland climate.

...ends on farming. Nepal carries on limited trade with the

Objectives and answers to the Student Web Activity can be found in the Web Activity Lesson Plan at twip.glencoe.com

Applying Map Skills

Answers
1. subsistence farming
2. India and Sri Lanka

Social Studies Online

Web Activity Visit ***The World and Its People*** Web site at twip.glencoe.com and click on **Chapter 22—Student Web Activities** to learn more about Nepal.

Nepal has a humid subtropical climate in the south and a highland climate in the north. Monsoon rains often flood the southern plains area.

Nepal's economy depends almost entirely on farming. Farmers grow rice, sugarcane, wheat, corn, and potatoes to feed their families. Most fields are located on the southern plains or on terraced plots among the lower mountain slopes.

As the population increases, farmers move higher up the slopes. There they clear forests for new fields and use the cut trees for fuel. Stripped of trees, however, the slopes erode very easily. Valleys are often flooded, fields destroyed, and rivers filled with mud.

Nepal was not linked to other countries for centuries. Today, there are roads and air service to India and Pakistan, so trade is not as limited. Herbs, jute, rice, and wheat are exported to India. In return, Nepal imports gasoline, fertilizer, and machinery. Clothing and carpets now make up the country's most valuable exports. Nepal's rugged mountains attract thousands of climbers and hikers each year, creating a growing tourist industry.

Nepal's People Nepal has 25.2 million people. Most are related to peoples in northern India and Tibet. One group—the Sherpa—is known for its skill in guiding mountain climbers. About 85 percent of Nepal's people live in rural villages. A growing number live in **Kathmandu,** Nepal's capital and largest city. Nepal is a parliamentary democracy ruled by a prime minister, who is appointed by Nepal's king.

NATIONAL GEOGRAPHIC **South Asia: Economic Activity**

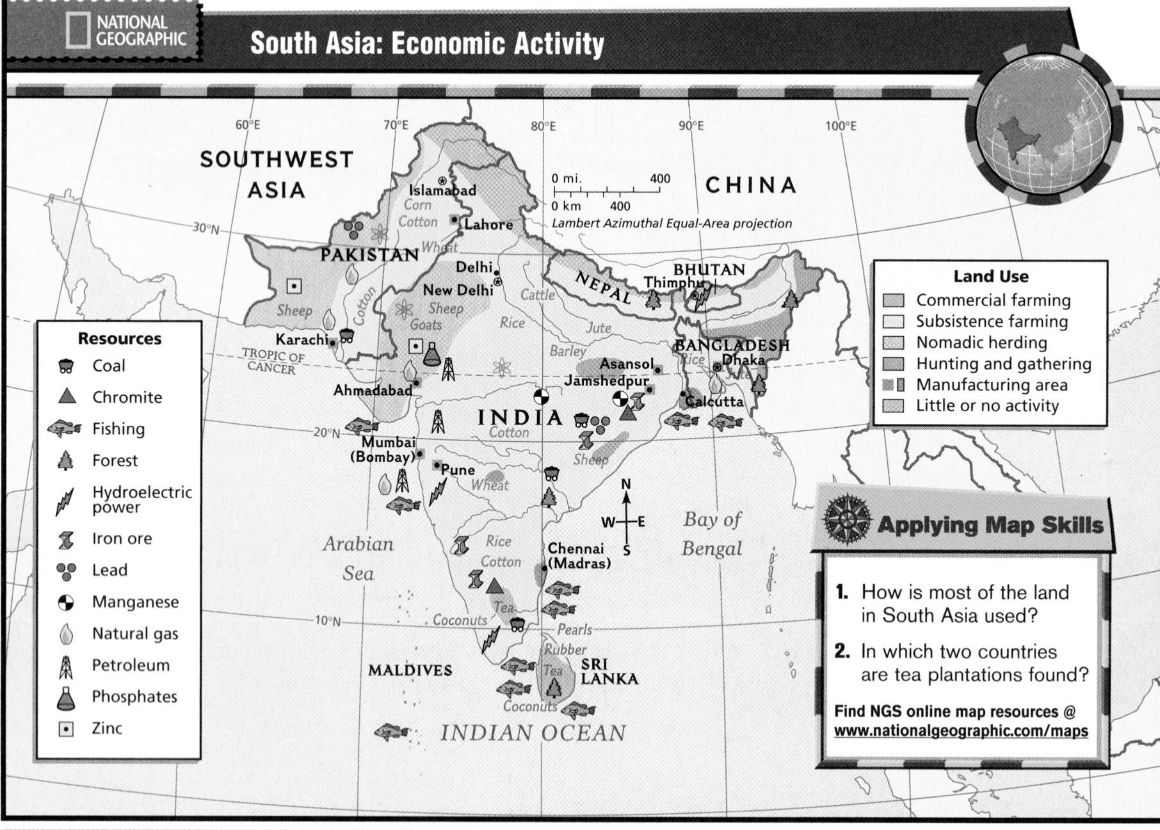

Applying Map Skills

1. How is most of the land in South Asia used?
2. In which two countries are tea plantations found?

Find NGS online map resources @ www.nationalgeographic.com/maps

Reading Strategy **Reading the Text**

Visualizing Mt. Everest—the highest peak in the world—attracts thousands of mountain climbers annually. Invite the science teacher to class to discuss the history of attempts to climb the mountain—from George Mallory's ill-fated 1924 foray to the first success by Sir Edmund Hillary and Tenzing Norgay in 1953 to the multiple ascents today. Have the teacher explain the dangers posed by the high altitudes and freezing temperatures and the benefits offered by modern equipment such as bottled oxygen, stronger synthetic rope, and better clothing. Then have students take the role of an Everest climber and write a diary entry explaining their fascination with this mighty mountain. **L1**

The founder of Buddhism, Siddartha Gautama (sihd•DAHR•tuh GAU•tuh•muh), was born in the Kathmandu region about 563 B.C. Raised as a prince, Gautama gave up his wealth and became a holy man in India. Known as the Buddha, or "Enlightened One," he taught that people could find peace from life's troubles by living simply, doing good deeds, and meditating. Buddhism later spread to other parts of Asia.

Today Hinduism is Nepal's official religion, but Buddhism is practiced as well. If you visit Nepal, you will find temples and monuments of both religions scattered throughout the country.

Reading Check What has helped Nepal trade with other countries?

NATIONAL GEOGRAPHIC On Location

Bhutan

This woman makes her living by herding yaks in one of Bhutan's mountain valleys.

Economics What is slowing Bhutan's economic progress?

Bhutan—Land of the Thunder Dragon

East of Nepal lies an even smaller kingdom—Bhutan. Bhutan is about half the size of Indiana. The map on page 650 shows you that a small part of India separates Bhutan from Nepal.

As in Nepal, the Himalaya are the major landform of Bhutan. Violent mountain storms are common and are the basis of Bhutan's name, which means "land of the thunder dragon." In the foothills of the Himalaya, the climate is mild. Thick forests cover much of this area. To the south—along Bhutan's border with India—lies an area of subtropical plains and river valleys.

More than 90 percent of Bhutan's people are subsistence farmers. They live in the fertile mountain valleys and grow the spice cardamom, oranges, rice, corn, and potatoes. People also herd cattle and yaks, which are a type of oxen. Bhutan is trying to develop its economy, but the very high mountains slow progress. Building roads is difficult, and there are no railroads. However, Bhutan has built hydroelectric plants to create electricity from rushing mountain waters. It now exports electricity to India. Tourism is a new industry, but the government limits the number of tourists to protect Bhutan's cultural traditions.

Bhutan's People Bhutan has about 900,000 people. Most speak the Dzonkha dialect and live in rural villages that dot southern valleys and plains. **Thimphu,** the capital, is located in the southern area.

Bhutan was once called the Hidden Holy Land because of its isolation and its Buddhist religion. In the 1960s, new roads and other connections opened Bhutan to the outside world. Most people remain deeply loyal to Buddhism. In Bhutan, Buddhist centers of prayer and study are called *dzongs.* They have shaped the country's art and culture.

Reading Check Answer

roads and air service to India and Pakistan

More About the Photo

Bhutan Yak herding is still the main occupation in the high mountain valleys of Bhutan. Restricted tourism by the Bhutanese government has preserved traditional ways, and this kingdom reflects a peaceful way of life long gone in other parts of the Himalaya.

Caption Answer The mountains make transportation difficult.

Current Events Journal

Have students write a script for tour guides who take tourists across Nepal and Bhutan. Suggest that writers describe the landforms, climate, plants, animals, and people of the countries. Encourage the writers to find facts in the text and other sources to give their descriptions local color.

Differentiated Instruction

Meeting Special Needs: Visual/Spatial Organize students into groups and inform them that their task is to create an illustrated pamphlet titled "The Story of Tea in Sri Lanka." Point out that the purpose of the pamphlet is to teach students in lower grades about this important Sri Lankan product. Suggest that group members research how tea is grown and processed, different types of tea, and the role that tea plays in the country's economy. Members can share various tasks—writing, artwork, design, and so on—among themselves. Display finished pamphlets in the classroom or in the school library. L1 ELL

EE4 Human Systems: Standard 11

Analyzing the Graph

Answer
Mount McKinley

Skills Practice
How much higher than Mount McKinley is Mount Everest?
(about 9,000 feet, or 2,700 m)

Reading Check Answer

Buddhism

L1/ELL

Guided Reading Activity

Name ______ Date ______ Class ______

SOUTH ASIA

Guided Reading Activity 3
Mountain Kingdoms, Island Republics

DIRECTIONS: Outlining Reading the section and completing the outline below will help you learn more about the other countries of South Asia. Use your textbook to fill in the blanks.

I. Nepal
A. The country forms a stairway to the ______.
B. The climate is ______ ______ in the south and ______ in the north.
C. The economy depends on ______.
D. Nepal's people are related to those in ______ ______ and

Did You Know?

In the Middle Ages, Muslim traders who found the island of Sri Lanka called it "Serendib." The name is related to the English word *serendipity,* which means a "delightful and unexpected surprise."

NATIONAL GEOGRAPHIC

Highest Mountain on Each Continent

Analyzing the Graph

Mount Everest is the tallest mountain on the earth.

Place **What is the tallest mountain in North America?**

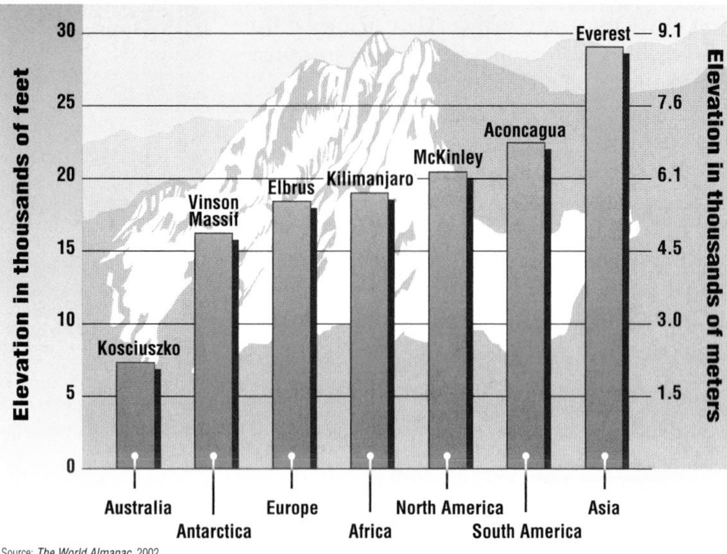

Source: *The World Almanac,* 2002.

For many years, Bhutan was ruled by strong kings. In 1998 the country began to move toward democracy. At that time, the ruling king agreed to share his power with an elected legislature.

Reading Check **What is the main religion in Bhutan?**

Sri Lanka—Brilliant Island

Pear-shaped Sri Lanka lies about 20 miles (32 km) off the southeastern coast of India. A little larger than West Virginia, Sri Lanka is a land of white beaches, dense forests, and abundant wildlife. Much of the country along the coast is rolling lowlands. Highlands cover the center. Rivers flow from the highlands, providing irrigation for crops.

The country has tropical climates with wet and dry seasons. Monsoon winds and heavy rains combine with the island's warm temperatures and fertile soil to make Sri Lanka a good place to farm.

Sri Lanka has long been known for its agricultural economy. Many farmers grow rice and other food crops in lowland areas. In the higher elevations, tea, rubber, and coconuts grow on large plantations. The country is one of the world's leading producers of tea and rubber.

The country is also famous for its sapphires, rubies, and other gemstones. Forests contain valuable woods, such as ebony and satinwood, as well as a variety of birds and animals. To protect the wildlife, the government has set aside land for national parks.

In the past 20 years, Sri Lanka's economy has become more industrialized. Factories produce textiles, fertilizers, cement, leather products, and wood products for export. New and growing industries

Content Background

Bhutan Buddhism gives Bhutan's people a deep sense of the sacredness of all life. As a result, no animals are killed. This deep belief, combined with the country's remoteness and lack of modernization, created some unusual situations. The capital of Thimphu has about 30,000 people. In recent years, more dogs than vehicles roamed the streets. There were no traffic lights and only a handful of gas stations in the town. One Westerner who visited Thimphu in the early 1990s noted that it was not unusual to find black bears or wild boars in people's yards.

include telecommunications, insurance, and banking. **Colombo,** the capital, is a bustling port on the country's western coast.

Sri Lanka's People For centuries, Sri Lanka prospered because of its location on an important ocean route between Africa and Asia. It was a natural stopping place for seagoing traders. Beginning in the 1500s, Sri Lanka—then known as Ceylon—came under the control of European countries. The British ruled the island from 1802 to 1948, when it became independent. In 1972 Ceylon took the name of Sri Lanka, an ancient term meaning "brilliant land." Today Sri Lanka is a republic with a president who carries out ceremonial duties. Real power is held by a prime minister, who is the head of government.

About 19.3 million people live here. They belong to two major ethnic groups: the Sinhalese (SIHN•huh•LEEZ) and the Tamils (TA•muhlz). Forming about 74 percent of the population, the Sinhalese live in the southern and western parts of the island. They speak Sinhalese and are mostly Buddhist. The Tamils make up about 18 percent of the population. They live in the north and east, speak Tamil, and are Hindus.

Since 1983 the Tamils and the Sinhalese have fought a violent civil war. The minority Tamils claim they have not been treated justly by the

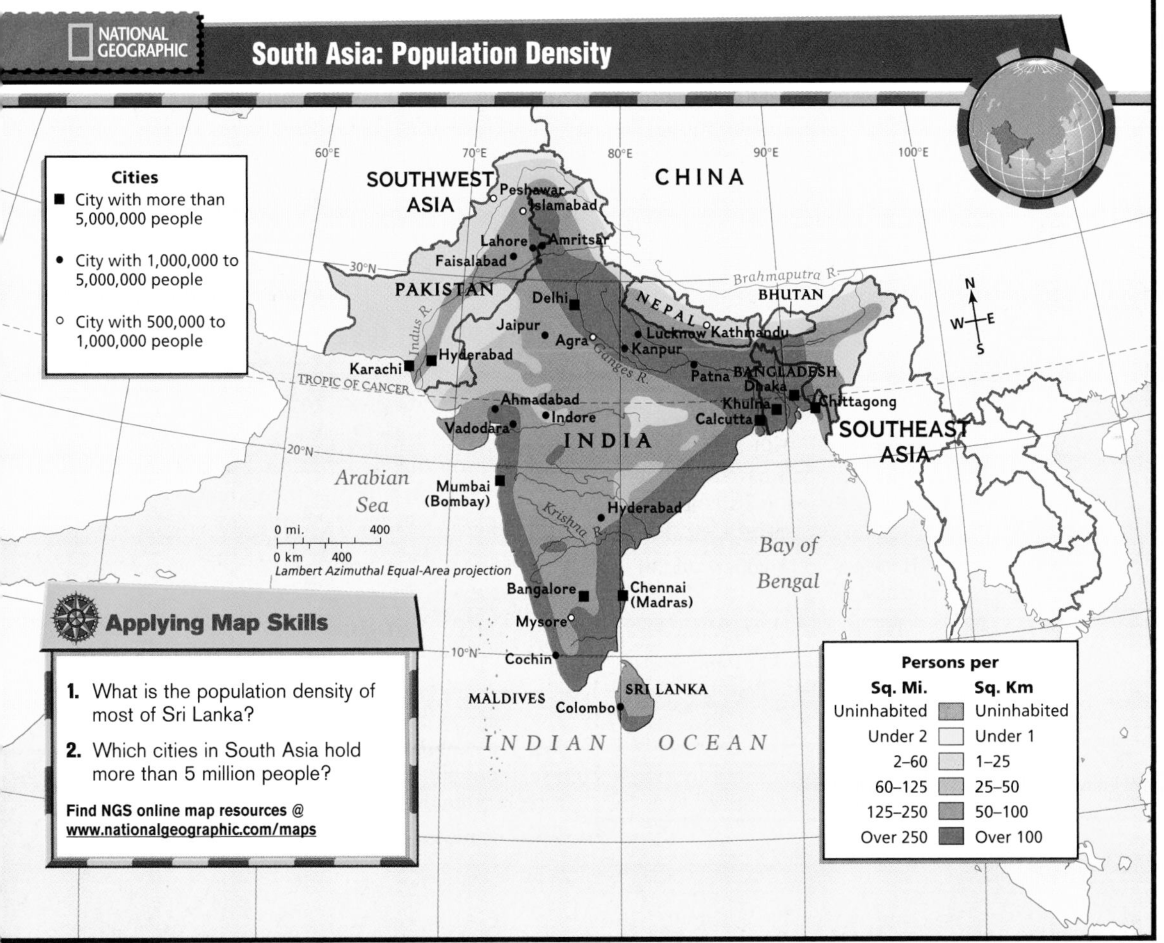

Applying Map Skills

1. What is the population density of most of Sri Lanka?
2. Which cities in South Asia hold more than 5 million people?

Find NGS online map resources @ www.nationalgeographic.com/maps

Content Background

Altitude Living in the high altitudes of the Himalaya requires physical adjustments to allow survival. The higher the altitude, the thinner the air. The drop in air pressure means that the alveoli, or air sacs, in the lungs cannot transmit as much oxygen to red blood cells. The Sherpas of Nepal have a swelling of blood vessels near the carotid arteries in the neck, some thickening of the walls of blood vessels in the lungs, and slightly increased blood pressure. Those who visit high altitudes for short periods may suffer altitude sickness, which can include shortness of breath, some nausea, and even chest pains. Even experienced climbers speak of the difficulties caused by the lack of oxygen. One climber who has scaled Everest four times describes the sensation as "like running on a treadmill and breathing through a straw."

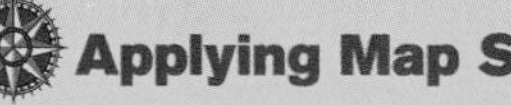

Applying Map Skills

Answers

1. 125–250 persons per square mile (50–100 per sq. km)
2. Bangalore, Karachi, Hyderabad, Mumbai, Delhi, Chennai, Calcutta, Khulna, Dhaka, and Chittagong

In-text Map Transparency Activity
Remind students to look for patterns as they study the map. **Ask:** **What geographic feature accounts for the high population density in central Pakistan?** *(the Indus River)*

3 Assess

Assign Section 3 Assessment as homework or an in-class activity.

Have students use the Interactive Tutor Self-Assessment CD-ROM to review Section 3.

L2

Section Quiz

Name ______ Date ______ Class ______

SOUTH ASIA

Section 3 Quiz

Mountain Kingdoms, Island Republics

DIRECTIONS: Matching Match each item in Column A with the items in Column B. Write the correct letters in the blanks. *(10 points each)*

COLUMN A	COLUMN B
A. dzong	____ 1. Buddhist center of prayer and study in Bhutan
B. Sinhalese	____ 2. ethnic group in northern and eastern Sri Lanka
C. Tamils	____ 3. ethnic group in southern and western Sri Lanka
D. atoll	____ 4. low-lying, ring-shaped island that surrounds a lagoon
E. Kathmandu	____ 5. capital city of Nepal

Chapter 22

Section 3, pages 649–654

Reading Check Answer

majority Sinhalese, minority Tamils

Reading Strategy

Reteach
Have students prepare an outline of the section content, listing the subheadings and writing three or four key facts under each.

Reading Check Answer

tourism

L1/ELL

Reading Essentials and Study Guide

Name ______ Date ______ Class ______

SOUTH ASIA

Reading Essentials and Study Guide 3
Mountain Kingdoms, Island Republics

Key Terms
dzong Buddhist center of prayer and study in Bhutan
atoll low-lying, ring-shaped island that surrounds a lagoon
lagoon shallow pool of water near a larger body of water

Drawing From Experience
Imagine that your town has no roads. Now imagine that high mountains ...

Close

Reading Strategy

Writing a Paragraph Have students write a paragraph that completes the sentence, "[*Name of country*] is unusual because . . . ." Tell them they can write about any of the countries in the section.

majority Sinhalese. They want to set up a separate Tamil nation in northern Sri Lanka. Thousands have lost their lives in the fighting. A cease-fire began in 2001 after nearly two decades of fighting.

Reading Check **What are the two main ethnic groups in Sri Lanka?**

The Maldives

About 370 miles (595 km) south of India lie the Maldives, made up of about 1,200 coral islands. Many of the islands are atolls. An **atoll** is a low-lying, ring-shaped island that surrounds a lagoon. A **lagoon** is a shallow pool of water near a larger body of water. Only 200 of the islands are inhabited. The climate of the Maldives is warm and humid throughout the year. Monsoons bring plenty of rain.

Most of the Maldives have poor, sandy soil. Only a limited number of crops can grow, including sweet potatoes, grains, and watermelon. In recent years, the Maldives's palm-lined sandy beaches and coral formations have attracted many tourists. As a result, tourism is now the largest industry. Fishing is the second-largest industry.

The first people to arrive in the Maldives came from southern India and Ceylon (Sri Lanka) several thousand years ago. Over the years, the islands' position near major sea routes brought traders from many other places. Today about 300,000 people live in the Maldives. Some 60,000 of them make their home in **Male** (MAH•lay), the capital. Most are Muslims. The islands, which came under British rule during the late 1890s, became independent in 1965. The local traditional ruler lost his throne three years later, and the Maldives became a republic.

Reading Check **What is the main industry in the Maldives?**

Assessment

Defining Terms

1. **Define** *dzong,* atoll, lagoon.

Recalling Facts

2. **Economics** What products have recently become Nepal's most valuable exports?
3. **Place** How do Bhutan's people earn a living?
4. **Economics** How has Sri Lanka's economy changed in the past 20 years?

Graphic Organizer

5. **Organizing Information** List four events from Sri Lanka's history and their dates on a time line like this one.

Critical Thinking

6. **Summarizing Information** What were the teachings of the Buddha?
7. **Formulating an Opinion** Do you agree with the decision of Bhutan's government to limit tourism? Why or why not?

Applying Social Studies Skills

8. **Analyzing Maps** Look at the population density map on page 653 and the physical map on page 645. What is the population density of the southern part of Nepal? The northern part? Explain the difference.

Section 3 Assessment

1. The terms are defined in the Glossary.
2. clothing and carpets
3. Most are subsistence farmers.
4. It has become more industrial.
5. *Possible answers:* 1500s—Came under control of European countries; 1802–1948—Ruled by Britain; 1972—Took the name Sri Lanka; 1983—Beginning of civil war between Sinhalese and Tamils
6. that people could find peace from life's troubles by living simply, doing good deeds, and praying
7. Answers will vary.
8. *South*—125–250 persons per square mile (50–100 per sq. km); *North*—Under 2 persons per square mile (1 per sq. km); the least populous part is covered by the Himalaya.

Chapter 22 Reading Review

Section 1 India—Past and Present

Terms to Know
subcontinent
monsoon
green revolution
jute
cottage industry
pesticide
caste
reincarnation

Main Idea
India is trying to develop its resources to meet the needs of its rapidly growing population.

✓ Place India is the largest country in South Asia in size and population.
✓ Place The Himalaya and the monsoons affect India's climate.
✓ Economics India's economy is based on farming and industry.
✓ Culture India has many languages and religions, but the majority of Indians are Hindus.
✓ Government India is a representative democracy.

Section 2 Pakistan and Bangladesh

Terms to Know
tributary
delta
cyclone

Main Idea
Once a single nation, Pakistan and Bangladesh today are separate countries that border India on the west and east.

✓ History Cultural and political differences between Pakistan and Bangladesh led to war and separation in 1971.
✓ Economics Pakistan has fertile land and energy resources, but its economy is not well developed because of a history of unstable governments.
✓ Location The Ganges and Brahmaputra Rivers form deltas in Bangladesh.
✓ Place Bangladesh is a densely populated and poor country.

Section 3 Mountain Kingdoms, Island Republics

Terms to Know
dzong
atoll
lagoon

Main Idea
The other countries of South Asia include mountainous Nepal and Bhutan and the island countries of Sri Lanka and the Maldives.

✓ Region The Himalaya are the major landform of Nepal and Bhutan.
✓ Economics Most people in Nepal are farmers, but the production of clothing and carpets has gained importance in recent years.
✓ Culture The Buddhist religion has shaped the art and culture of Bhutan.
✓ Economics Sri Lanka has industrialized, but agriculture is still important.
✓ Economics Tourism is the biggest industry in the Maldives.

◀ A teacher and his students have class outdoors on a pleasant day in Bhutan.

655

Reading Review

Use the Chapter 22 Reading Review to preview, review, condense, or reteach the chapter.

Preview/Review

Use the Terms to Know lists to help students review and study.

Activity Form the class into two teams and give the teams a quiz of the chapter's terms by reading a definition and having them identify the correct word.

Vocabulary PuzzleMaker CD-ROM reinforces the vocabulary terms used in Chapter 22.

The Interactive Tutor Self-Assessment CD-ROM allows students to review Chapter 22 content.

Condense

Have students read the Chapter 22 summary statements.

Guided Reading Activities

Audio Program

Reteach

Reteaching Activity

Reading Essentials and Study Guide

Reading Strategy Read to Write

Designing a Web Page South Asia is home to several important religions, including Hinduism, Buddhism, Islam, Jainism, and Sikhkism. Have students research one of these religions and prepare an outline for a Web site about that religion. Students' outlines should show what the topic and main idea will be on each Web page. The outlines might also suggest illustrations that could be included on each Web page. If students have time and interest, suggest that they design the opening page for the Web site or show how one of the detailed pages would look.

EE4 Human Systems: Standard 10

Assessment and Activities

GLENCOE TECHNOLOGY

MindJogger Videoquiz
Use MindJogger Videoquiz to review the Chapter 22 content.

 Available in DVD and VHS

Using Key Terms

1.	b	6.	i
2.	g	7.	f
3.	h	8.	a
4.	j	9.	e
5.	d	10.	c

Reviewing the Main Ideas

11. the Karakoram and Himalaya ranges
12. They block cold air from the north.
13. cotton cloth, silk cloth, rugs, leather products, metalware
14. groups called castes
15. Indus River
16. Crops fail and there is widespread hunger.
17. farm
18. Kathmandu
19. because of its isolation and Buddhist religion
20. The minority Tamils want an independent state.
21. It is on an important ocean route between Africa and Asia.

Chapter 22 Assessment and Activities

Using Key Terms

Match the terms in Part A with their definitions in Part B.

A.

1. monsoon
2. cyclone
3. green revolution
4. jute
5. subcontinent
6. reincarnation
7. pesticide
8. caste
9. *dzong*
10. cottage industry

B.

a. social class based on a person's ancestry
b. seasonal wind
c. family members supply their own equipment to make goods
d. large landmass that is part of another continent but distinct from it
e. Buddhist center for prayer and study
f. chemical used to kill insects
g. intense storm system with high winds
h. a government effort to use modern farming methods
i. the belief that after the body dies, the soul is reborn
j. plant fiber used for making rope, burlap bags, and carpet backing

Reviewing the Main Ideas

Section 1 India—Past and Present

11. **Place** What forms a barrier between South Asia and the rest of Asia?
12. **Place** How do the Himalaya affect India's climate?
13. **Economics** What kinds of goods are produced by India's cottage industries?
14. **History** What did Hinduism organize India's society into?

Section 2 Pakistan and Bangladesh

15. **Place** What river flows through Pakistan?
16. **Human/Environment Interaction** What often happens when the rains come too late in Bangladesh?
17. **Economics** What do most of the people of Bangladesh do for a living?

Section 3 Mountain Kingdoms, Island Republics

18. **Place** What is Nepal's capital?
19. **History** Why was Bhutan once called the Hidden Holy Land?
20. **History** What is the basis of the civil war in Sri Lanka?
21. **Location** How did Sri Lanka's location allow it to prosper for many centuries?

South Asia

Place Location Activity

On a separate sheet of paper, match the letters on the map with the numbered places listed below.

1. Ganges River
2. New Delhi
3. Brahmaputra River
4. Indus River
5. Sri Lanka
6. Himalaya
7. Bangladesh
8. Mumbai
9. Western Ghats
10. Deccan Plateau

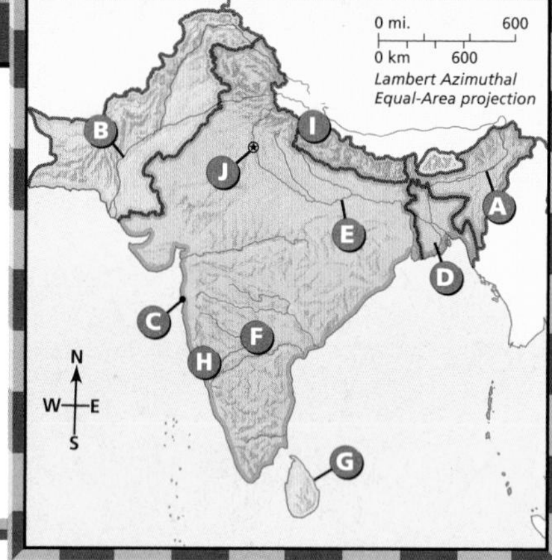

Place Location Activity

1.	E	6.	I
2.	J	7.	D
3.	A	8.	C
4.	B	9.	H
5.	G	10.	F

Critical Thinking

22. Answers will vary but might include such issues as undernourishment, poor health care, and educational problems. Solutions might include lowering the birthrate, producing more food, and developing industry.
23. Answers will vary depending on the physical feature selected.

Self-Check Quiz Visit ***The World and Its People*** Web site at twip.glencoe.com and click on **Chapter 22–Self-Check Quizzes** to prepare for the Chapter Test.

Critical Thinking

22. **Identifying Alternatives** In this chapter you read about South Asia, a region with much poverty. What problems do you think a country faces when it has so many poor people? What are some solutions to this poverty?

23. **Understanding Cause and Effect** Create a diagram like this one. List a physical feature of South Asia in the left-hand box. In the right-hand box, explain how that feature affects people's lives.

[ ] → [ ]

Comparing Regions Activity

24. **Culture** The Taj Mahal in India is one of the world's most impressive structures. Also impressive are the pyramids in Egypt. Use the information in your textbook to write a paragraph describing each. Include why each was built and compare the reasons.

Mental Mapping Activity

25. **Focusing on the Region** Create a simple outline map of South Asia, and then label the following:

- Ganges River
- Sri Lanka
- Kashmir
- Pakistan
- Nepal
- Indian Ocean
- Bhutan
- Bangladesh
- Ganges Plain
- New Delhi

Technology Skills Activity

26. **Using the Internet** Use the Internet to research tourism in one of the following countries: Nepal, India, or Sri Lanka. Create a travel brochure about a trip to the country, featuring information on the equipment and clothing that is needed, the availability of guides, costs, and so on.

Standardized Test Practice

Directions: Study the graph below, and then answer the questions that follow.

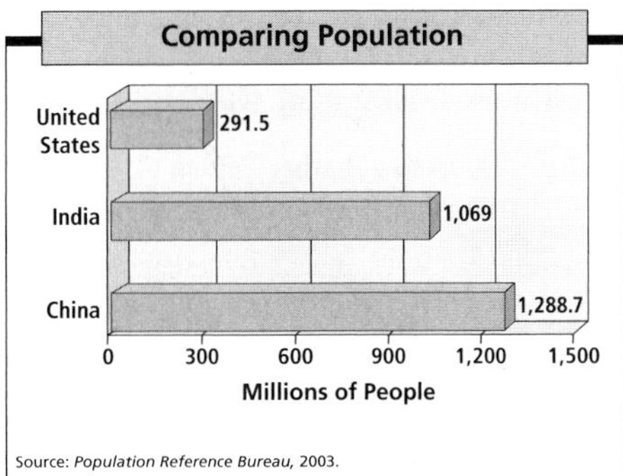

1. How many people live in India?

A 1,069
B 1,000,069
C 1,069,000,000
D 1,069,000,000,000

2. About how many more people live in India than in the United States?

F 2.5 times as many
G 3.6 times as many
H 4.5 times as many
J 5.6 times as many

Test-Taking Tip: You often need to use math skills in order to understand graphs. Look at the information along the sides and bottom of the graph to find out what the bars on the graph mean. Notice that on the graph above, the numbers represent millions of people. Therefore, you need to multiply the number on each bar by 1,000,000 to get the correct answer.

Assessment and Activities

Standardized Test Practice

1. C
2. G

Tested Objectives: Reading a graph, analyzing information

Chapter Test Bonus Question

This question may be used for extra credit on the chapter test.

What religion is practiced by most people in Pakistan? *(Islam)*

Social Studies Online

Have students visit the Web site at twip.glencoe.com to review Chapter 22 and take the Self-Check Quiz.

FOLDABLES™ Study Organizer Dinah Zike's Foldables

Culminating Activity Have students change their main ideas into questions and ask a partner to answer them.

Comparing Regions Activity

24. Students' paragraphs should describe and compare the Taj Mahal and the pyramids.

Mental Mapping Activity

25. This exercise helps students visualize the countries and geographic features of South Asia. Accept all attempts at freehand mapping that show places in the correct relationship to one another.

Technology Skills Activity

26. Students' brochures could be enhanced with photographs from the chosen country.

Chapter 23 Resources

Note: The following materials may be used when teaching Chapter 23.
Section level support materials are shown at point of use in the margins of the Teacher Wraparound Edition.

Timesaving Tools

TeacherWorks™ All-In-One Planner and Resource Center

- **Interactive Teacher Edition** See the **Interactive Teacher Edition** CD-ROM to electronically integrate your Teacher Wraparound Edition and blackline masters.
- **Interactive Lesson Planner** Organize your week, month, semester, or year with all the lesson helps you need. The **Interactive Lesson Planner** CD-ROM contains all Chapter 23 resources.

Use Glencoe's **Presentation Plus!** multimedia teacher tool to easily present dynamic lessons that visually excite your students. Using Microsoft PowerPoint® you can customize the presentations to create your own personalized lessons.

TEACHING TRANSPARENCIES

Graphic Organizer Transparency 7 L2

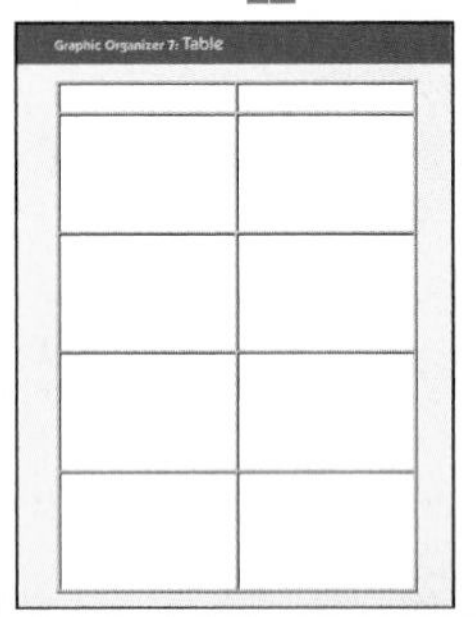

In-text Map Transparency L1

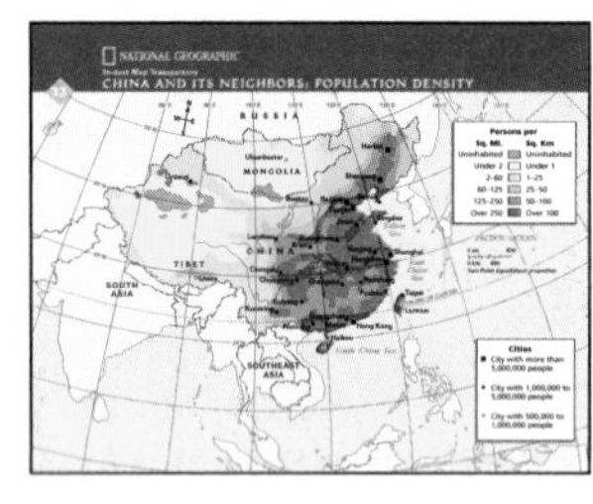

FOLDABLES™ Study Organizer

Dinah Zike's Foldables

Foldables are three-dimensional, interactive graphic organizers that help students practice basic writing skills, review key vocabulary terms, and identify main ideas. Additional chapter activities can be found in the ***Reading and Study Skills Foldables*** booklet.

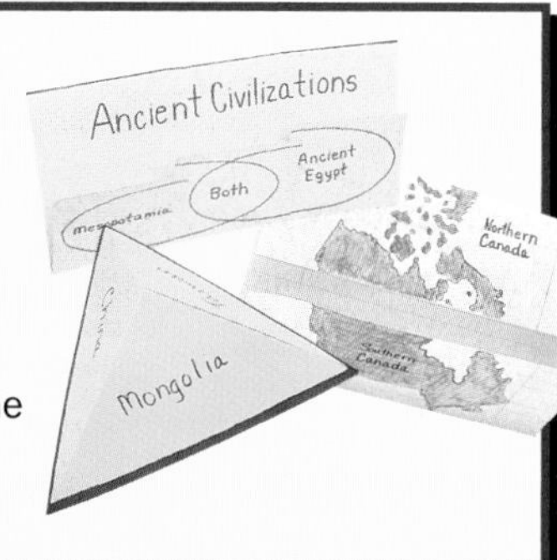

MAP AND GEOGRAPHY SKILLS

Chapter Map Activity L2

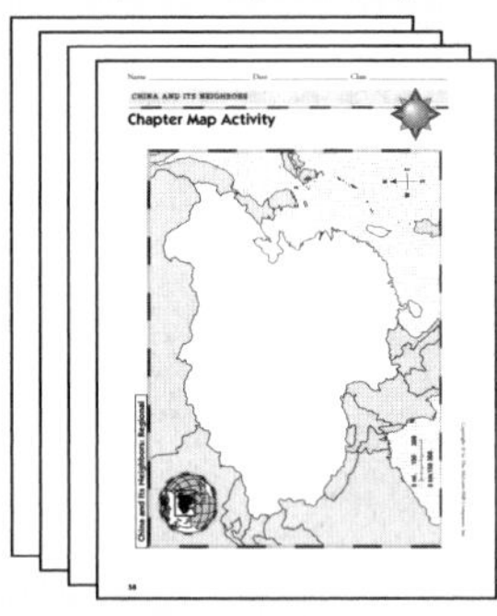

GeoLab Activity L2

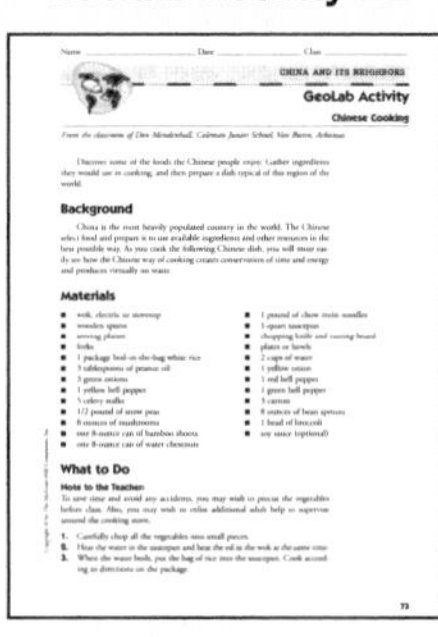

READING SUPPORT

Vocabulary Activity L1

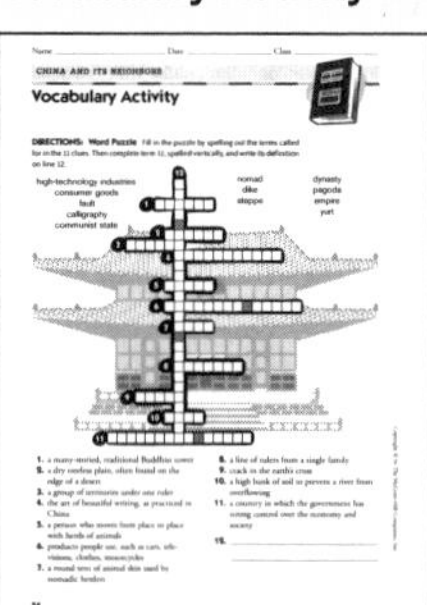

Workbook Activity L1

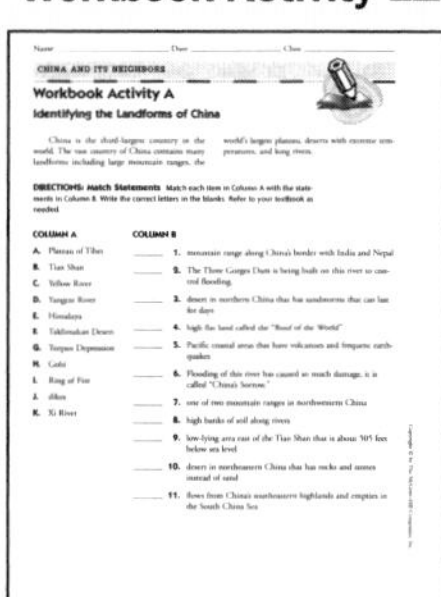

Reading and Writing Skills Activity L1/ELL

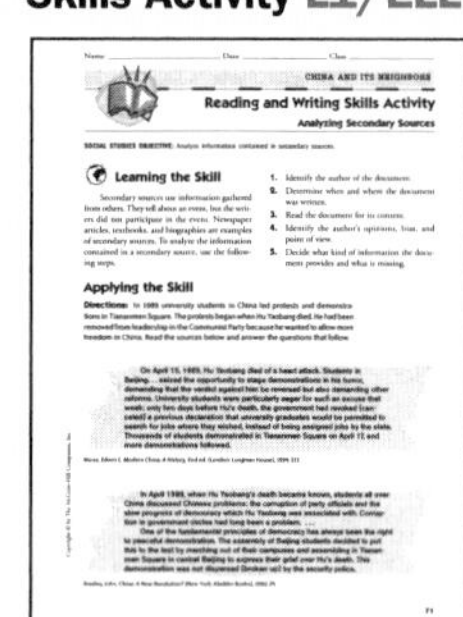

DIFFERENTIATED INSTRUCTION

Use these review and reinforcement materials to help less-proficient readers, English learners, and gifted and talented students.

Reteaching Activity L1

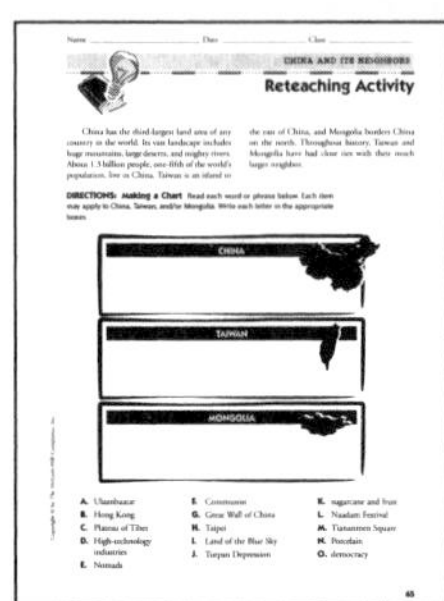

Chapter Skills Review L2

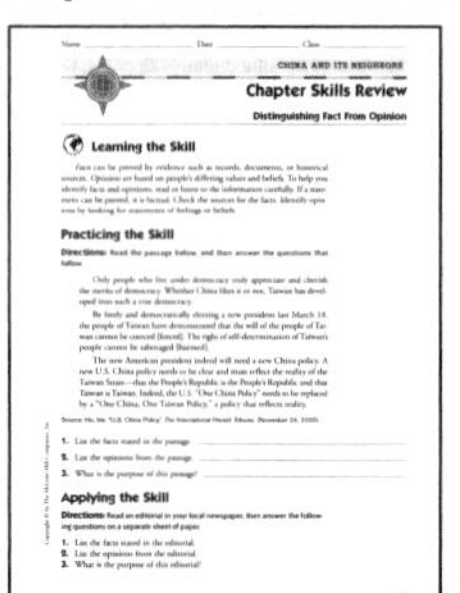

Cooperative Learning Activity L1/ELL

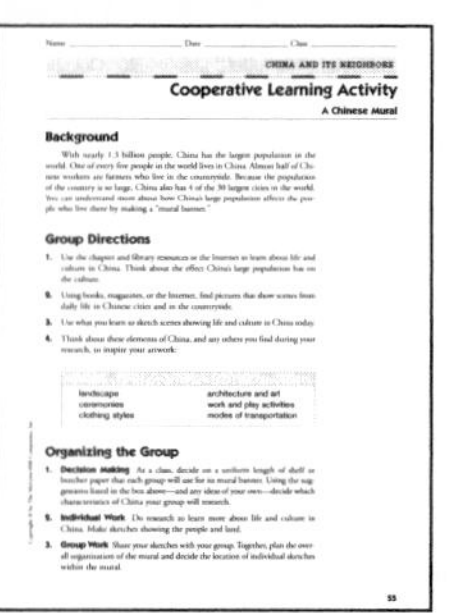

Enrichment Activity L3

ASSESSMENT

Chapter Test, Form A L2

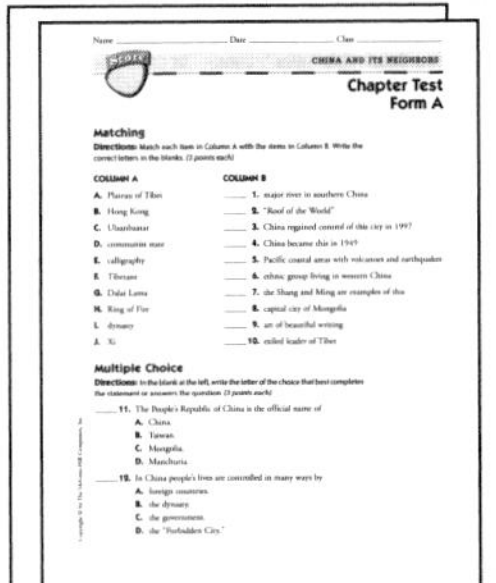

Chapter Test, Form B L2

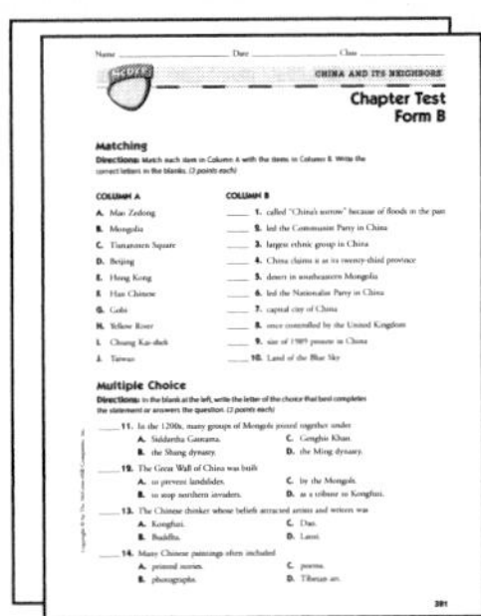

Performance Assessment Activity L1/ELL

ExamView® Pro Testmaker CD-ROM

STANDARDIZED ASSESSMENT SKILLS

Critical Thinking Skills Activity L2

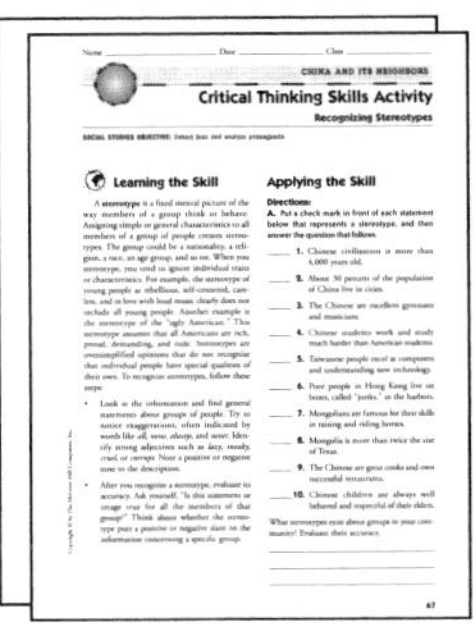

Map and Graph Skills Activity L2

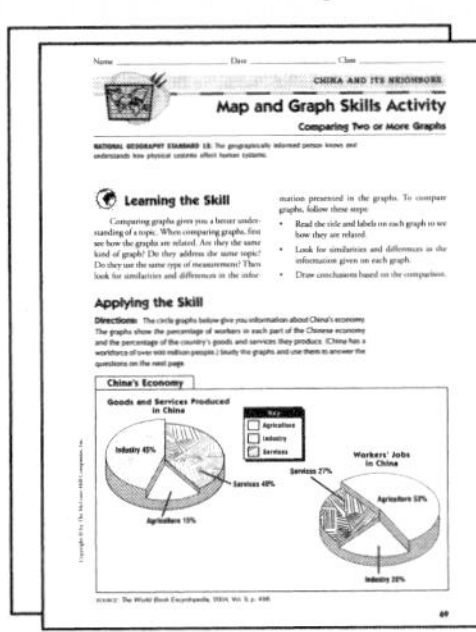

Standardized Test Skills Practice Workbook Activity L2

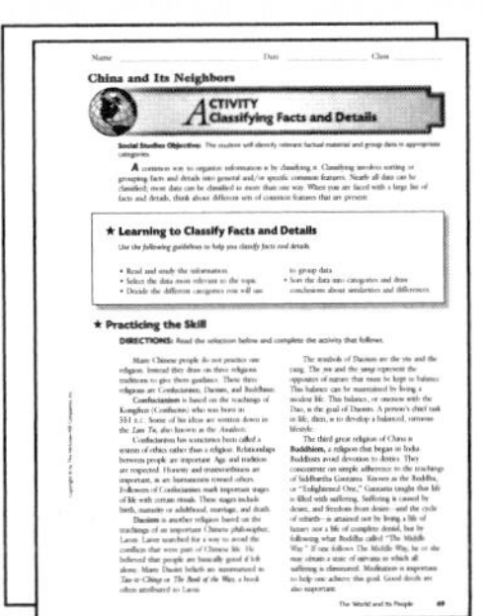

HOME INVOLVEMENT

Take-Home Review Activity L1

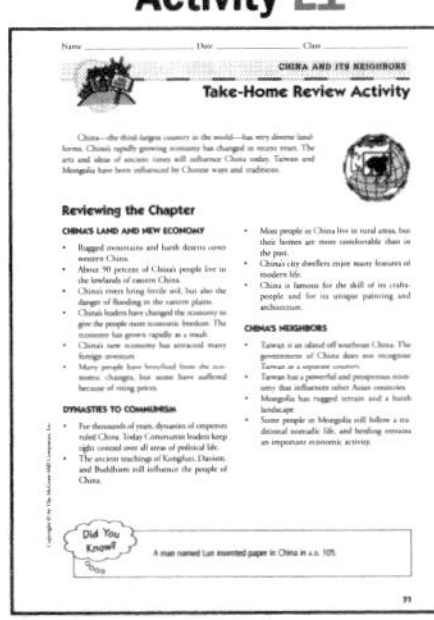

MULTIMEDIA

- National Geographic's The World and Its People
- MindJogger Videoquiz
- Vocabulary PuzzleMaker CD-ROM
- Interactive Tutor Self-Assessment CD-ROM
- ExamView® Pro Testmaker CD-ROM
- TeacherWorks CD-ROM
- StudentWorks CD-ROM
- Skillbuilder Interactive Workbook CD-ROM, Level 1
- Presentation Plus! CD-ROM
- Audio Program

SPANISH RESOURCES

The following Spanish language materials are available in the Spanish Resources binder:

- Spanish Summaries
- Spanish Vocabulary Activities
- Spanish Guided Reading Activities
- Spanish Quizzes and Tests
- Spanish Take-Home Review Activities
- Spanish Reteaching Activities

Meeting National Standards

Geography for Life

The following standards are covered in Chapter 23:

Section 1 **EE2 Places and Regions: Standards 4, 5, 6**
EE5 Environment and Society: Standards 14, 15, 16

Section 2 **EE4 Human Systems: Standards 9, 10, 11, 12, 13**
EE6 The Uses of Geography: Standards 17, 18

Section 3 **EE2 Places and Regions: Standards 4, 5, 6**
EE4 Human Systems: Standards 9, 10, 11, 12, 13

State and Local Objectives

Chapter 23 Planning Guide

SECTION RESOURCES

Daily Objectives	Reproducible Resources	Multimedia Resources
Section 1 **China's Land and New Economy** **1.** Discuss the varied landforms found in China. **2.** Describe how China's economy is changing.	Reproducible Lesson Plan Daily Lecture and Discussion Notes Note-taking Guide Guided Reading Activity* Reading Essentials and Study Guide* Section Quiz*	Daily Focus Skills Transparency GeoQuiz Transparency Vocabulary PuzzleMaker CD-ROM Interactive Tutor Self-Assessment CD-ROM ExamView® Pro Testmaker CD-ROM Presentation Plus! CD-ROM
Section 2 **Dynasties to Communism** **1.** Explain how China's history influences life there today. **2.** Contrast urban and rural China. **3.** Summarize what arts China is known for.	Reproducible Lesson Plan Daily Lecture and Discussion Notes Note-taking Guide Guided Reading Activity* Reading Essentials and Study Guide* Section Quiz*	Daily Focus Skills Transparency In-text Map Transparency Vocabulary PuzzleMaker CD-ROM Interactive Tutor Self-Assessment CD-ROM ExamView® Pro Testmaker CD-ROM Presentation Plus! CD-ROM
Section 3 **China's Neighbors** **1.** Explain why many people moved to Taiwan. **2.** Describe the people of Mongolia.	Reproducible Lesson Plan Daily Lecture and Discussion Notes Note-taking Guide Guided Reading Activity* Reading Essentials and Study Guide* Section Quiz*	Daily Focus Skills Transparency Vocabulary PuzzleMaker CD-ROM Interactive Tutor Self-Assessment CD-ROM ExamView® Pro Testmaker CD-ROM Presentation Plus! CD-ROM MindJogger Videoquiz

00:00 **Out of Time?** Assign the **Reading Essentials and Study Guide*** for this chapter.

*Also available in Spanish

KEY TO ABILITY LEVELS

Teaching strategies have been coded for varying learning styles and abilities.

L1 **BASIC** activities for all students
L2 **AVERAGE** activities for average to above-average students
L3 **CHALLENGING** activities for above-average students
ELL **ENGLISH LANGUAGE LEARNER** activities

KEY TO TEACHING RESOURCES

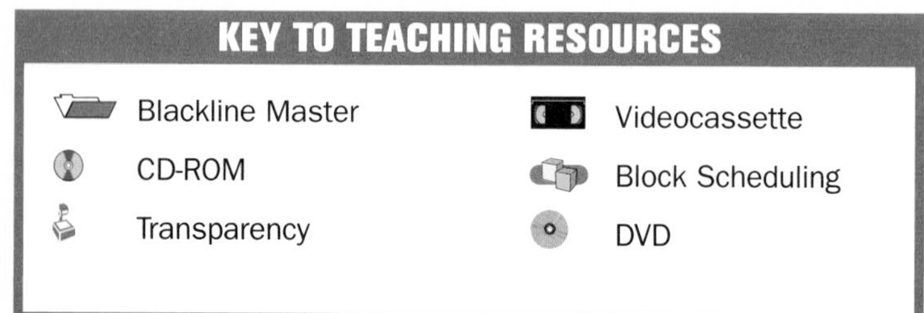

Charting Population Growth

Janet S. D'Meo-Townley
Park Middle School
Scotch Plains, New Jersey

Have students use Skittles® to represent the population and simulate population growth. Between two paper plates, shake two Skittles. For every *S* that shows, add another Skittle to the plate. Record the number on a table. Repeat this process for 15 shakes (or "generations"), and graph the data in a table. A variation of this activity is to remove one Skittle for every two Skittles that touch, in addition to adding a Skittle for every *S* that shows. Graph the data and make predictions about future population growth, particularly for Asian countries.

Meeting Special Needs

In addition to the Differentiated Instruction strategies found in each section, the following resources are also suitable for your special needs students:

- ***ExamView® Pro Testmaker CD-ROM*** allows teachers to tailor tests by reducing answer choices.
- The ***Audio Program*** includes the entire narrative of the student edition so that less-proficient readers can listen to the words as they read them.
- The ***Reading Essentials and Study Guide*** provides the same content as the student edition but is written two grade levels below the textbook.
- ***Guided Reading Activities*** give less-proficient readers point-by-point instructions to increase comprehension as they read each textbook section.
- ***Enrichment Activities*** include a stimulating collection of readings and activities for gifted and talented students.

TEACHER'S CORNER

Index to National Geographic Magazine:

The following articles may be used for research relating to this chapter:

- "Beijing: New Face for the Ancient Capital," by Todd Carrel, March 2000.
- "Black Dragon River," by Simon Winchester, February 2000.
- "Tibet Embraces the New Year," by Ian Baker, January 2000.

National Geographic Society Products:

To order the following products for use with this chapter, call National Geographic Society at 1-800-368-2728:

- *Asia* (Video)
- *PicturePack: Ancient Civilizations: Ancient China* (Transparencies)
- *PictureShow: Ancient Civilizations: India and China* (CD-ROM)

NGS ONLINE

Access National Geographic's Web site for current events, activities, links, interactive features, and archives. www.nationalgeographic.com

MapMachine

Find the latest coverage of geography in the news, atlas updates, cartographic activities with interactive maps, an online map store, and links at www.nationalgeographic.com/maps

SOCIAL STUDIES *Online*

Use our Web site for additional resources. All essential content is covered in the Student Edition.

You and your students can visit twip.glencoe.com, the Web site companion to *The World and Its People.* This innovative integration of electronic and print media offers your students a wealth of opportunities. The student text directs students to the Web site for the following options:

- Chapter Overviews
- Student Web Activities
- Self-Check Quizzes
- Textbook Updates

Answers are provided for you in the Web Activity Lesson Plan. Additional Web resources and Interactive Tutor puzzles are also available.

Introducing Chapter 23

Social Studies Online

Introduce students to chapter content and key terms by having them access Chapter Overview 23 at twip.glencoe.com

Chapter Objectives

1. Discuss the landforms and climates of China.
2. Contrast the economy of China in the past to the economy today.
3. Explain the influence of China's past on the people today.
4. Describe the geography and people of Taiwan and Mongolia.

GLENCOE TECHNOLOGY

NATIONAL GEOGRAPHIC

The World and Its People Video Program

Chapter 24 China

The following segments enhance the study of this chapter:

- **The Giant Panda**
- **Minority Games**

MindJogger Videoquiz

Use MindJogger Videoquiz to preview the Chapter 23 content.

Both programs available in DVD and VHS

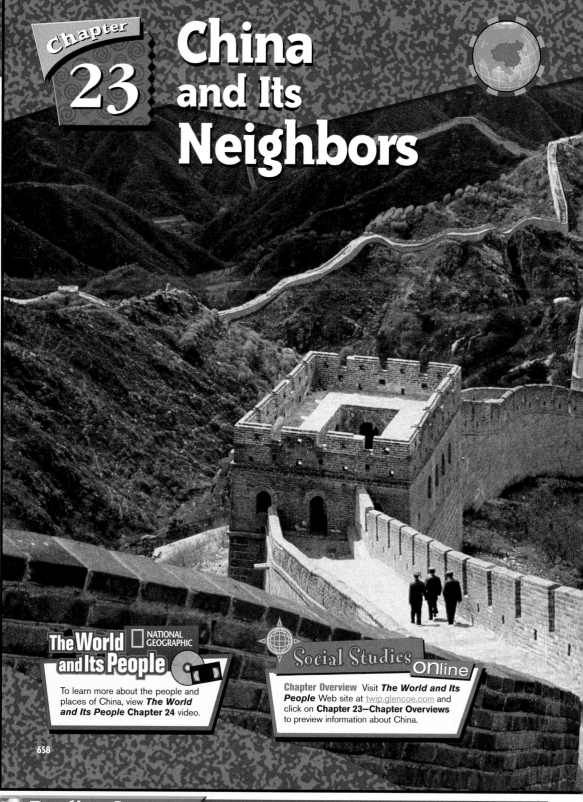

Chapter 23 China and Its Neighbors

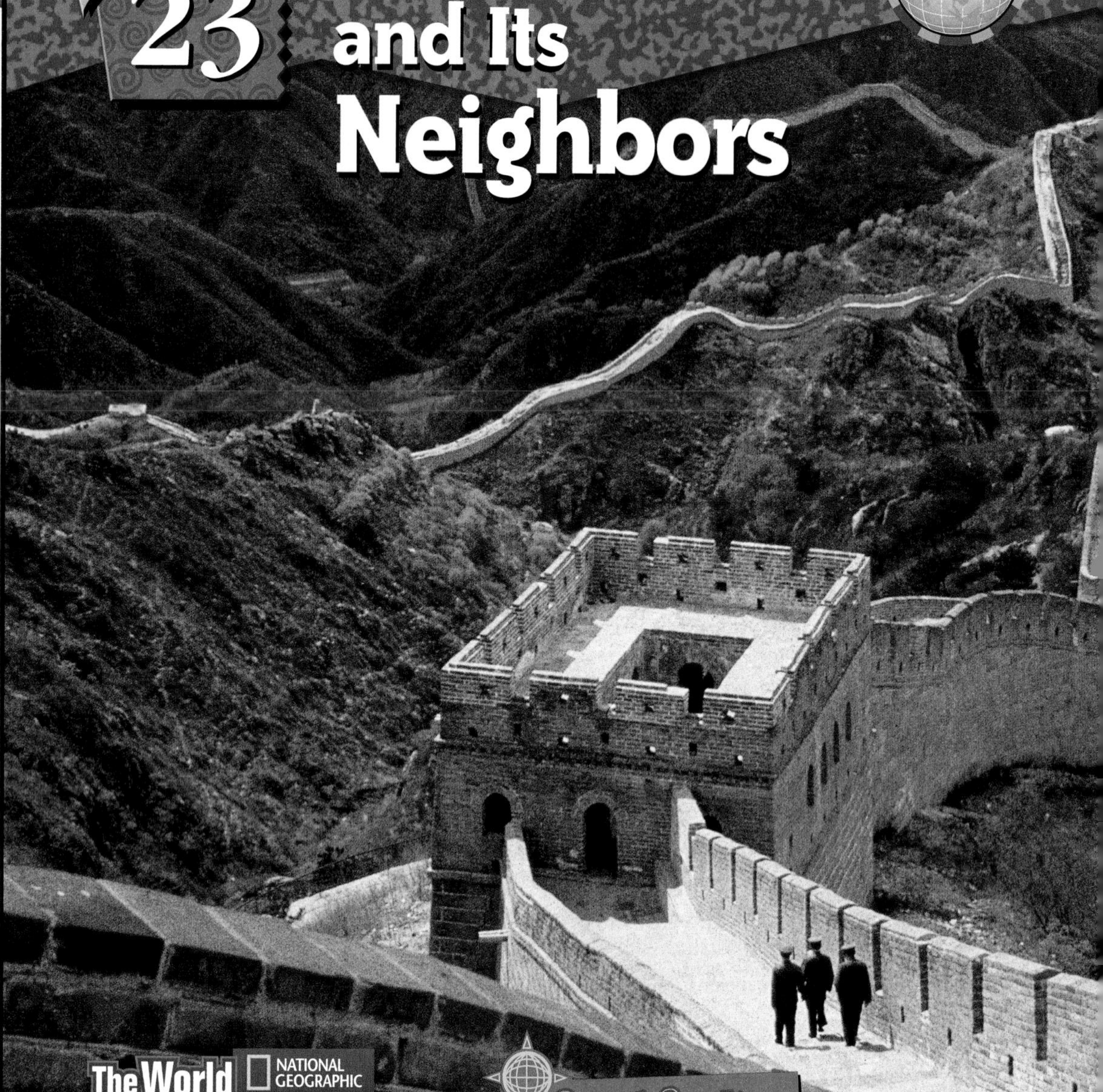

The World and Its People NATIONAL GEOGRAPHIC

To learn more about the people and places of China, view ***The World and Its People*** **Chapter 24** video.

Social Studies Online

Chapter Overview Visit ***The World and Its People*** Web site at twip.glencoe.com and click on **Chapter 23—Chapter Overviews** to preview information about China.

658

Reading Strategy — Purpose for Reading

Free Writes are used to explore student background knowledge and engage students. Have students examine the pictures, maps, and graphs throughout the chapter. **Ask:** **What do these images tell you about China and its neighboring countries?** Emphasize that there are no wrong answers to the question; it is important that all ideas are accepted. Have students discuss their answers as a class. Conclude the activity by explaining that students will be learning about China, Taiwan, and Mongolia in the chapter. **L1**

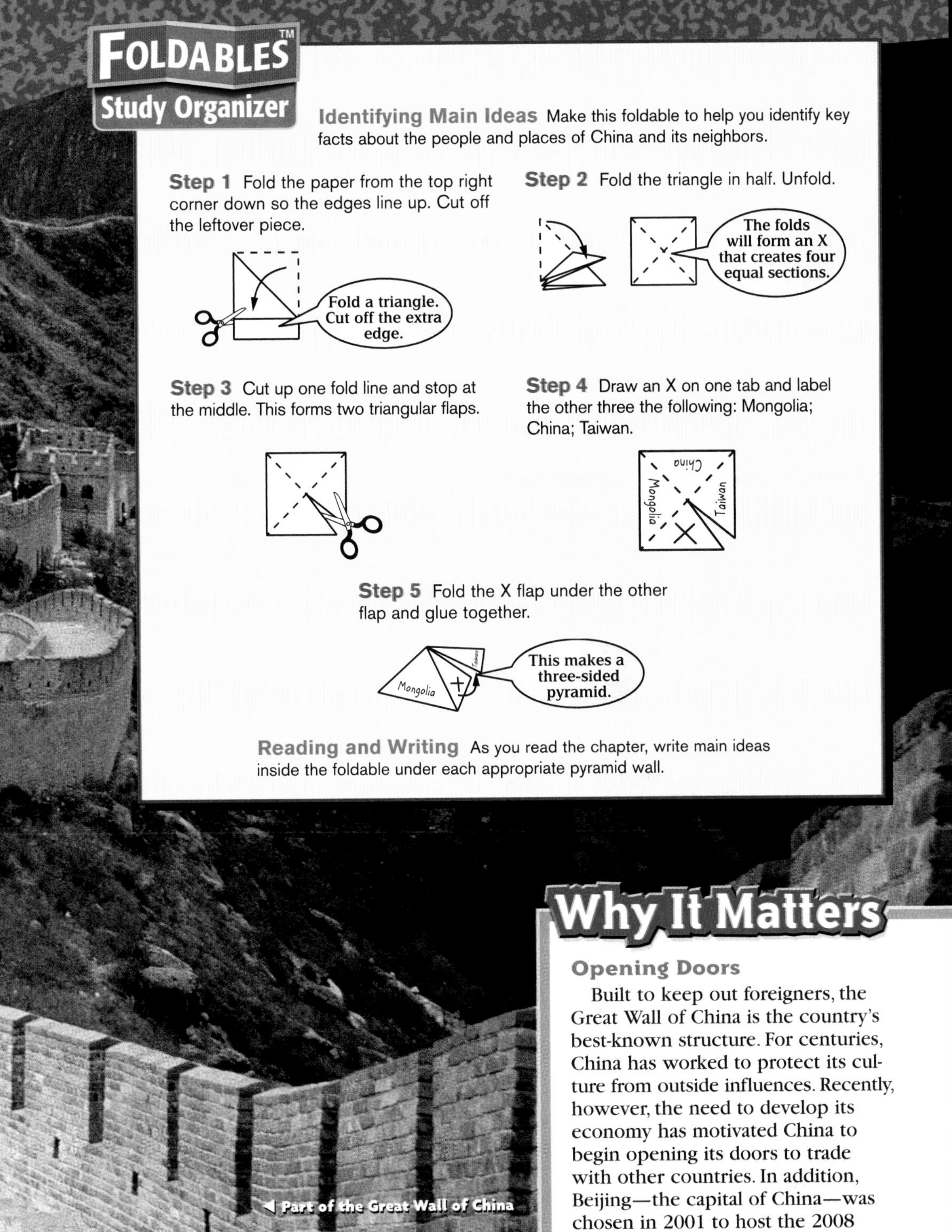
FOLDABLES™
Study Organizer
Fold a triangle. Cut off the extra edge.
The folds will form an X that creates four equal sections.
China
Mongolia
Taiwan
Mongolia
This makes a three-sided pyramid.

Identifying Main Ideas Make this foldable to help you identify key facts about the people and places of China and its neighbors.

Step 1 Fold the paper from the top right corner down so the edges line up. Cut off the leftover piece.

Step 2 Fold the triangle in half. Unfold.

Step 3 Cut up one fold line and stop at the middle. This forms two triangular flaps.

Step 4 Draw an X on one tab and label the other three the following: Mongolia; China; Taiwan.

Step 5 Fold the X flap under the other flap and glue together.

Reading and Writing As you read the chapter, write main ideas inside the foldable under each appropriate pyramid wall.

◀ Part of the Great Wall of China

Why It Matters

Opening Doors

Built to keep out foreigners, the Great Wall of China is the country's best-known structure. For centuries, China has worked to protect its culture from outside influences. Recently, however, the need to develop its economy has motivated China to begin opening its doors to trade with other countries. In addition, Beijing—the capital of China—was chosen in 2001 to host the 2008 Summer Olympics.

About the Photo

In the northern part of China are the cold, windswept plains of Inner Mongolia. These plains provide the only easy land route into the agricultural region of China from western Asia. Ch'in Shih Huang Ti originally started to build the Great Wall along this frontier during the Han period (202 B.C. to A.D. 220), one of the magnificent periods in China's long history. The purpose of the wall was to keep the nomads of Inner Mongolia and other "barbarians" from attacking settled areas in agricultural China.

FOLDABLES™ Study Organizer **Dinah Zike's Foldables**

Purpose This activity provides students with the opportunity to practice identifying the main ideas in the chapter. After students read a section, they should write the main ideas that are presented on the inside of the foldables. Students can use their foldables as an assessment tool.

Have students complete the ***Reading and Study Skills Foldables*** activity for this chapter.

Why It Matters

Ask students why the Great Wall is an obsolete concept for isolating a nation today. Students should respond that the Internet has made instant communication a virtual fact of life. Ask students to vote on this question: Which machine (technology) would you rather be without—a computer or a car? Many students will realize that their computer can take them places cars will never go.

Chapter 23

Section 1, pages 660–664

1 Focus

Section Objectives

1. Discuss the varied landforms found in China.
2. Describe how China's economy is changing.

BELLRINGER
Skillbuilder Activity

Project transparency and have students answer the question.

Daily Focus Skills Transparency

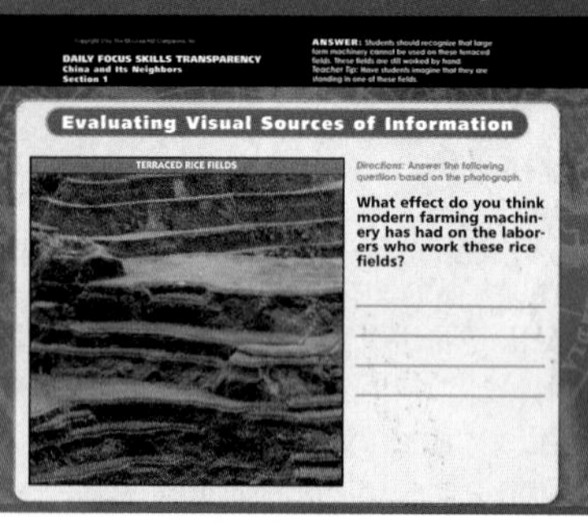

Reading Preview

- **Activating Prior Knowledge** **Ask:** How can the panda—which lives in sparsely populated wild areas—survive in China? *(China is a large and populated country, but it has some very isolated and untamed areas.)*

- **Preteaching Vocabulary** When students encounter a word within a section, have them try to pick another word or phrase to describe it.

Guide to Reading

Main Idea

China—the third-largest country in the world—has very diverse landforms. China's rapidly growing economy has changed in recent years.

Terms to Know

- dike
- fault
- communist state
- consumer goods

Reading Strategy

Create a diagram like this one. Then list two facts under each heading in the outer ovals.

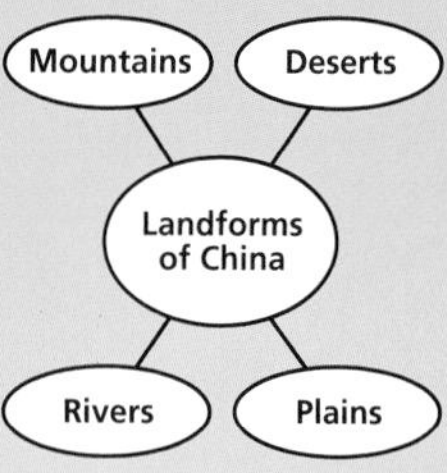

Section 1

China's Land and New Economy

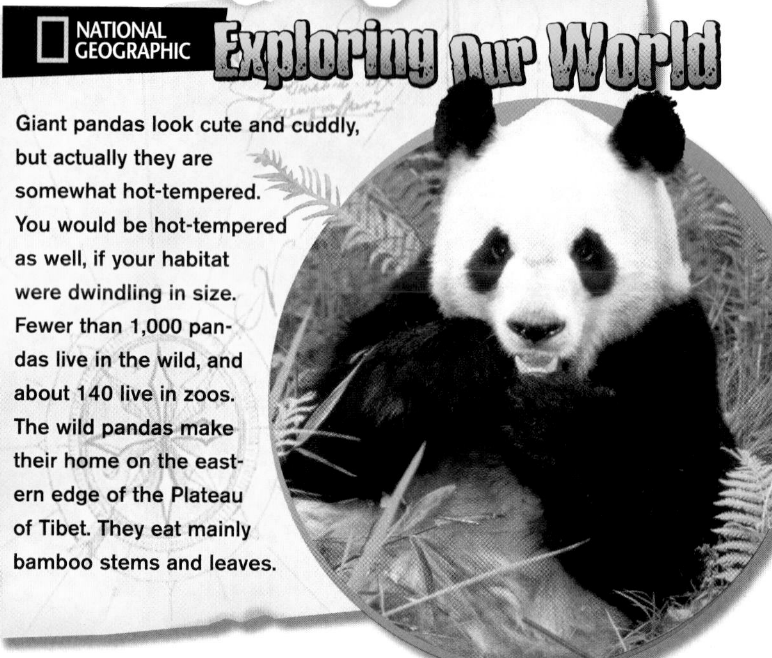

Giant pandas look cute and cuddly, but actually they are somewhat hot-tempered. You would be hot-tempered as well, if your habitat were dwindling in size. Fewer than 1,000 pandas live in the wild, and about 140 live in zoos. The wild pandas make their home on the eastern edge of the Plateau of Tibet. They eat mainly bamboo stems and leaves.

China (officially called the People's Republic of China) lies in the central part of eastern Asia. It is the third-largest country in area, after Russia and Canada. China is just slightly larger than the United States.

China's Landscape

The map on the next page shows the many landforms that are within China's vast area. Rugged mountains cover about one-third of the country. Find the **Himalaya, Kunlun Shan, Tian Shan,** and **Altay Mountains** on the map.

Also located in China is the world's largest plateau. This high, flat land, commonly called the "Roof of the World," is really the **Plateau of Tibet.** Its height averages about 14,800 feet (4,500 m) above sea level. Scattered shrubs and grasses cover the plateau's harsh landscape. Pandas, golden monkeys, and other rare animals roam the thick forests found at the eastern end of this plateau.

Section Resources

Reproducible Masters
- Reproducible Lesson Plan
- Daily Lecture and Discussion Notes
- Note-taking Guide
- Guided Reading Activity
- Reading Essentials and Study Guide
- Section Quiz

Transparencies
- Daily Focus Skills Transparency
- GeoQuiz Transparency

Multimedia
- Vocabulary PuzzleMaker CD-ROM
- Interactive Tutor Self-Assessment CD-ROM
- Presentation Plus! CD-ROM
- ExamView® Pro Testmaker CD-ROM

In addition to very high elevations, western China has some extremely low areas. The Turpan Depression, east of the Tian Shan, lies about 505 feet (154 m) *below* sea level. It is partly filled with salt lakes. It also is the hottest area of China. Daytime temperatures can reach as high as 122°F (50°C).

In northwestern China, mountain ranges circle desert areas. One of these areas is the **Taklimakan Desert**—an isolated region with very high temperatures. Sandstorms here can last for days and create huge, drifting sand dunes. Farther east lies another desert, the **Gobi.** About twice the size of Texas, the Gobi has rocks and stones instead of sand.

The map below shows that eastern China has plains along the Yellow, East China, and South China Seas. About 90 percent of China's people live on these fertile plains. Rich in minerals, eastern China is the site of the largest urban manufacturing areas, including **Beijing** and **Shanghai.** In hilly areas, farmers grow crops on terraced fields. Northern China holds many natural resources as well. China is a world leader in mining coal and iron ore. Tourists visit southeastern China to see its scenic waterfalls and steep gorges.

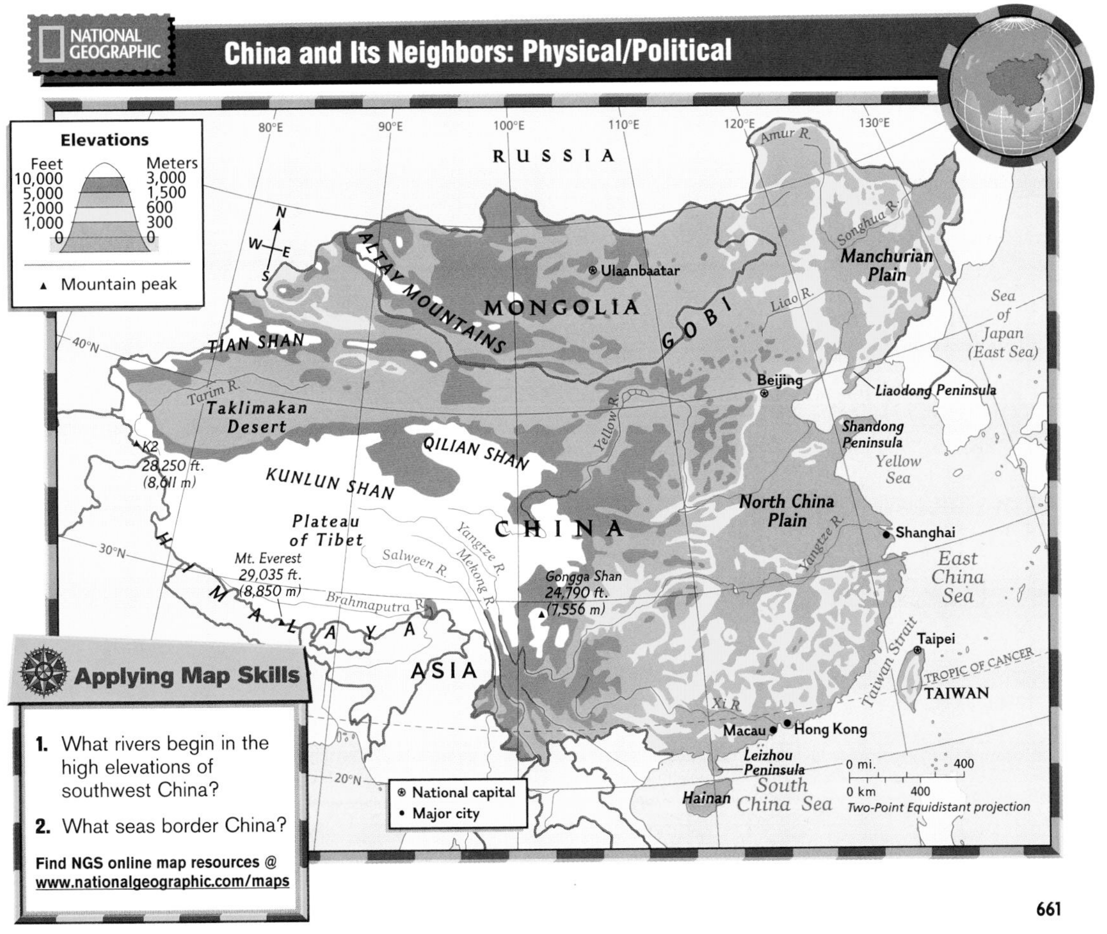

Applying Map Skills

1. What rivers begin in the high elevations of southwest China?
2. What seas border China?

Find NGS online map resources @ www.nationalgeographic.com/maps

661

TEACH

Reading Strategy

Analyzing Information Tell students to write the headings "Early People's Republic of China" and "China Today" in their notebooks. Tell them that as they read the section, they should record facts about China's economy under the appropriate heading. Then have them write a paragraph comparing and contrasting the economy of China in these two periods. Ask students to summarize how trade has influenced the facts they recorded under "China Today." L1

Daily Lecture and Discussion Notes

CHINA AND ITS NEIGHBORS

Daily Lecture and Discussion Notes

China's Land and New Economy

Did You Know? Using satellite data, scientists have discovered more than 600 miles of the Great Wall of China that had been buried beneath sand, dirt, and silt.

I. China's Landscape

A. Many landforms are found within China's vast area, which is slightly larger than the United States. One-third of China is covered by mountains—the Himalaya, Kunlun Shan, Tian Shan, and Altay Mountains.

B. The Plateau of Tibet, the world's largest plateau, is also located in China. This ... called the Roof of the World. Its height averages about 14,800 ... Depression, in contrast, lies about 505 feet

Applying Map Skills

Answers

1. Yellow, Yangtze, Mekong, Salween, Brahmaputra
2. Yellow Sea, East China Sea, South China Sea

Skills Practice

Describe the elevation of western China. *(highland plateaus and mountains)*

Reading Strategy — Reading the Text

Visualizing Invite a language arts teacher to class to discuss the main features of descriptive writing. The teacher should touch on such subjects as using vivid words, giving details, comparing, drawing on words that convey the five senses (sight, hearing, smell, taste, and touch), and having a vantage point from which the scene is described. After reviewing these principles, have students write a paragraph describing a walk through one region of China. Then ask volunteers to read their paragraphs aloud, and have the class discuss how the piece reveals elements of descriptive writing and helps form a mental map of the region. L1

*Use the **Reading Skills Handbook** for more reading strategies.*

Chapter 23

Section 1, pages 660–664

Objectives and answers to the Student Web Activity can be found in the Web Activity Lesson Plan at twip.glencoe.com

Reading Check Answer

Flooding causes damage and kills many people.

Analyzing the Graph

Answer
about 170 million tons

Skills Practice
What country ranks second in rice production? *(India)*

L1/ELL

Guided Reading Activity

Name ______ Date ______ Class ______

CHINA AND ITS NEIGHBORS

Guided Reading Activity 1

China's Land and New Economy

DIRECTIONS: Reading for Accuracy Reading the section and completing the activity below will help you learn more about China's land and economy. Refer to your textbook to decide if a statement is true or false. Write **T** or **F**, and if a statement is false, rewrite it correctly.

____ 1. Mountains cover about one-third of China.

____ 2. The rest of China is very fertile and full of grasslands.

____ 3. The Yellow River valley is a very important farming area.

...brought much devastation from flooding until d...

Social Studies Online

Web Activity Visit ***The World and Its People*** Web site at twip.glencoe.com and click on **Chapter 23—Student Web Activities** to learn more about China's rivers.

Rivers Three of China's major waterways—the **Yangtze** (YANG• SEE), **Yellow,** and **Xi** (SHEE) **Rivers**—flow through the plains and southern highlands. They serve as important transportation routes and also as a source of soil. How? For centuries, these rivers have flooded their banks in the spring. The floodwaters have deposited rich soil to form flat river basins that can be farmed. China's most productive farmland is found in valleys formed by these major rivers.

Despite their benefits, the rivers of China have also brought much suffering. The Chinese call the Yellow River "China's sorrow." In the past, its flooding cost hundreds of thousands of lives and caused much damage. Floods in July and August 1998 killed at least 3,000 and caused an estimated $20 billion in damage. To help control floods, the Chinese have built dams and **dikes,** or high banks of soil, along the rivers. Turn to page 665 to learn more about the Three Gorges Dam, a project that is underway on the Yangtze River.

An Unsteady Land In addition to floods, people in eastern China face another danger—earthquakes. Their part of the country stretches along the Ring of Fire, a name that describes Pacific coastal areas with volcanoes and frequent earthquakes. Eastern China lies along a **fault,** or crack in the earth's crust. As a result, earthquakes in this region are common—and can be very violent. Because so many people live in eastern China, these earthquakes can be disastrous.

Reading Check **What problem does China have with its large rivers?**

NATIONAL GEOGRAPHIC

Leading Rice-Producing Countries

Analyzing the Graph

The most important food crop in Asia is rice.

Economics **How many millions of tons of rice does China produce in a year?**

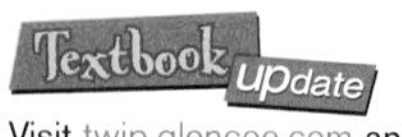

Visit twip.glencoe.com and click on **Chapter 23—Textbook Updates.**

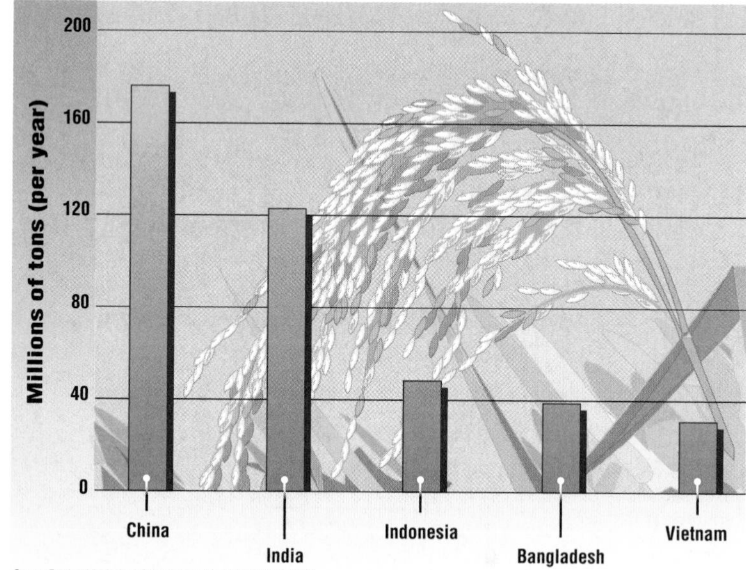

Differentiated Instruction

Meeting Special Needs: Naturalist Have students work in groups to create a diorama of the regions of China. Students should research to learn more about each region, such as average temperatures and rainfall and the kinds of plants and animals found there. The research will yield images that they can use as the basis for their display. Have the groups work together to assemble the display. When it is complete, have the class compare and contrast the different regions of China. They should also describe how the physical geography affects the lives of the people who live in the region. In their descriptions, students might include such aspects as patterns of population, location of economic activities, and foreign and domestic policies that have been influenced by the region's geography. **L1 ELL**

A New Economy

Since 1949, China has been a communist state in which the government has strong control over the economy and society as a whole. This means that government officials—not individuals or businesses—decide what crops to grow, what products to make, and what prices to charge. China discovered that the communist system created many problems. China fell behind other countries in technology, and manufactured goods were of poor quality.

In recent years, China's leaders have begun many changes to make the economy stronger. Without completely giving up communism, the government has allowed many features of a free enterprise system to take hold. Under this system, the government allows individuals to choose what jobs they want and where to start their own businesses. Workers can keep the profits they make. Farmers can grow and sell what they wish.

As a result of these and other changes, China's economy has boomed. Factories produce textiles, chemicals, electronic equipment, airplanes, ships, and machinery. Many of the items you own were probably made in China. Farm output has also risen rapidly. Because of mountains and deserts, only 10 percent of China's land is able to be farmed. Yet China is now a world leader in producing various agricultural products, including rice, tea, wheat, and potatoes.

Foreign Trade Eager to learn about new business methods, China has asked other countries to invest in, or put money into, Chinese businesses. Many companies in China are now jointly owned by Chinese and foreign businesspeople. Foreign companies expect two benefits from investing in China. First, they can pay Chinese workers less than they pay workers in their own countries. Second, companies in China have hundreds of millions of possible customers for their goods.

Results of Growth Because of economic growth, more of China's people are able to get jobs in manufacturing and service industries. Wages have increased, and more goods are available to buy. Some Chinese now enjoy a higher standard of living. They can afford consumer goods, or products people buy for themselves, such as

NATIONAL GEOGRAPHIC On Location

Ancient and Modern

In China's rural areas, ancient farming methods are still used (above left). However, in industrialized cities, high technology is being developed (above).

Government **How has the government affected the economy in China?**

Chapter 23

Section 1, pages 660–664

More About the Photos

Ancient and Modern Modernization efforts by China's communist government in both agriculture and industry have allowed China's economy to boom in recent years. The government's aim is to build a society with strict political control—tightly governing the media and all political activities—but relatively free economic opportunity.

Caption Answer It has moved from a command economy to more of a free enterprise system.

3 ASSESS

Assign Section 1 Assessment as homework or an in-class activity.

Have students use the Interactive Tutor Self-Assessment CD-ROM to review Section 1.

L2

Section Quiz

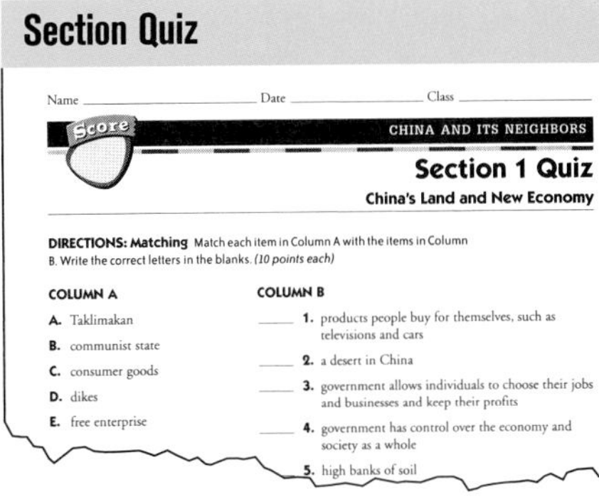

Name ______ Date ______ Class ______

CHINA AND ITS NEIGHBORS

Score

Section 1 Quiz

China's Land and New Economy

DIRECTIONS: Matching Match each item in Column A with the items in Column B. Write the correct letters in the blanks. *(10 points each)*

COLUMN A	COLUMN B
A. Taklimakan	____ 1. products people buy for themselves, such as televisions and cars
B. communist state	____ 2. a desert in China
C. consumer goods	____ 3. government allows individuals to choose their jobs and businesses and keep their profits
D. dikes	____ 4. government has control over the economy and society as a whole
E. free enterprise	____ 5. high banks of soil

Critical Thinking Activity

Formulating an Opinion Discuss the vote in the United States Congress in 2000 to have permanent normal trade relations with China. Critics of the plan cited China's poor record on human rights and the environment and the possibility that increased trade with China would lead to American manufacturing jobs being transferred to China, where labor costs are lower. Supporters argued that by increasing trade, the United States could contribute to slowly transforming China to behave more desirably in these areas. Have students research the current scope of American trade with China and how the situation is currently viewed. L2

EE4 Human Systems: Standard 11

Chapter 23

Section 1, pages 660–664

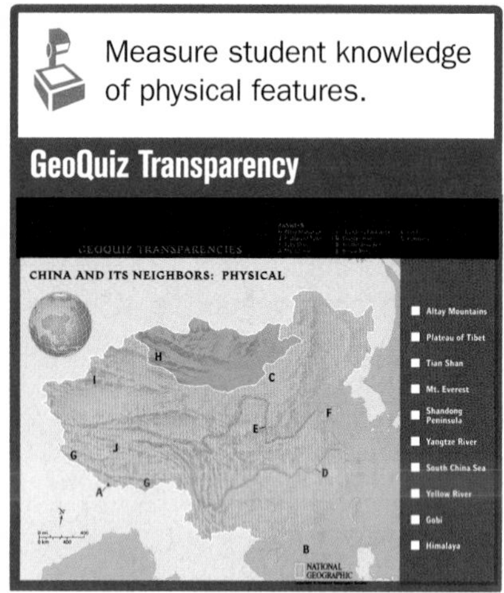

Reading Check Answer

China's promise to allow Western freedoms and capitalism to exist side-by-side with communism in Hong Kong and Macau

L1/ELL

Reading Essentials and Study Guide

Name ______ Date ______ Class ______

CHINA AND ITS NEIGHBORS

Reading Essentials and Study Guide 1

China's Land and New Economy

Key Terms

dike high bank of soil
fault crack in the earth's crust
communist state country in which the government has strong control over the economy and society as a whole
consumer goods goods people buy to use for themselves, such as televisions and cars

Close

Have students summarize a paragraph from the section in a sentence. Collect the sentences, omit key words, and have students supply the missing words.

Labor Costs

There's a good chance your clothes and shoes were manufactured in China. Some American companies can manufacture their products at much lower costs in China because the wages paid to workers there are low by U.S. standards. These companies pay more and offer better working conditions than Chinese employers. Still, some Americans are concerned about exploiting Chinese workers to make higher profits for U.S. companies.

televisions, cars, and motorcycles. Not everyone has adjusted well to the new economy, however. Many Chinese find that prices have risen faster than their incomes. Some Chinese have become very rich, while others remain poor.

China's economic growth has also harmed the environment. Many factories dump poisonous chemicals into rivers. Others burn coal, which gives off smoke that pollutes the air. This pollution leads to lung disease, which is the number one cause of death in China.

Hong Kong and Macau The cities of **Hong Kong** and **Macau** (muh•KOW) are an important part of the economic changes taking place in China. Both of these cities were once controlled by European countries—Hong Kong by the United Kingdom, and Macau by Portugal. China regained control of Hong Kong in 1997 and of Macau in 1999. Both are centers of manufacturing, trade, and finance. Chinese leaders hope that the successful businesses in these cities will help spur economic growth in the rest of the country.

At the same time, foreign companies that are considering investing in these cities must ask themselves whether China will stand by its "one country, two systems" pledge. The pledge refers to China's promise to allow Western freedoms and capitalism to exist side by side with Chinese communism. The **Time Perspectives: Exploring World Issues** on pages 671–677 takes a look at the economies and political freedoms of China and other countries in East Asia.

Reading Check To what does "one country, two systems" refer?

Section 1 Assessment

Defining Terms

1. **Define** dike, fault, communist state, consumer goods.

Recalling Facts

2. **Place** Name China's two large deserts.
3. **Region** What two very important functions do China's rivers perform?
4. **Economics** What has caused China's economy to boom?

Critical Thinking

5. **Summarizing Information** How are China's rivers both a blessing and a disaster?
6. **Making Comparisons** How is a communist economic system different from a free enterprise system?
7. **Analyzing Information** What benefits does China receive from foreign investments?

Graphic Organizer

8. **Organizing Information** Create a diagram like this one. In the proper places on the oval, fill in the physical features you would encounter if you traveled completely around China.

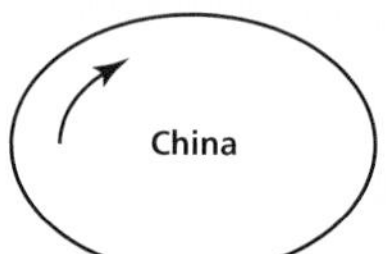

Applying Social Studies Skills

9. **Analyzing Maps** Look at the map on page 661. What is the capital of China?

664

Section 1 Assessment

1. The terms are defined in the Glossary.
2. Taklimakan, Gobi
3. They carry fertile soil to land and provide transportation.
4. more free enterprise
5. They improve soil and provide transportation, but flooding causes extreme damage.
6. communist: government controls economy; free enterprise: individuals run businesses.
7. Investment teaches new business methods and encourages economic growth.
8. Students should identify the Atlay Mountains, the Gobi Desert, the Manchurian Plain, the North China Plain, the Plateau of Tibet, and the Taklimakan Desert.
9. Beijing

Making Connections

ART | SCIENCE | CULTURE | TECHNOLOGY

The Three Gorges Dam

Since 1919, Chinese officials have dreamed of building a dam across the Yangtze, the third-longest river in the world. Curving through the heart of China, the river provides an important highway for moving people and products from town to town. Yet the Yangtze is unpredictable. For thousands of years, floods have harmed the millions of people who live along its banks. Now construction is under way to build the dam.

The Dam

In 1994 the Chinese government began a 17-year-long project to build the Three Gorges Dam. It will eventually be 1.5 miles (2.4 km) wide and more than 600 feet (183 m) high. The dam is being built about halfway between the cities of Chongqing and Wuhan. (See the map on page 668.) The dam will benefit China in several ways. First, it will control water flow and stop floods. Second, its system of locks will allow large ships to travel inland. This will reduce trade and transportation costs for the millions of people who live inland. Third, the dam will create electricity using turbines, or water-driven engines.

Controversy

Even with all the proposed benefits, many people within China and elsewhere have questioned the wisdom of building the dam. When completed, the dam will create a deep reservoir nearly 400 miles (644 km) long. This reservoir will flood more than 100 towns and force nearly 1.2 million people to move. Many of these people must leave the farms that their families have worked for centuries. Historians point out that the reservoir will also wash away more than 1,000 important historical sites, including the homeland of the first people to settle the region about 4,000 years ago.

Environmentalists caution that the dam may create pollution and health risks. Industrial sites, once they lie underwater, may leak hazardous chemicals. Sewage from communities surrounding the dam could flow directly into the reservoir and into the Yangtze River. In the past, this problem was less serious because the fast-moving waters of the Yangtze carried waste quickly out to sea.

Making the Connection

1. How have the unpredictable waters of the Yangtze River affected the Chinese?
2. Create a physical map of China showing the major rivers. Mark where the Three Gorges Dam is being built.
3. **Interpreting Points of View** List three reasons in support of constructing the Three Gorges Dam and three reasons against it.

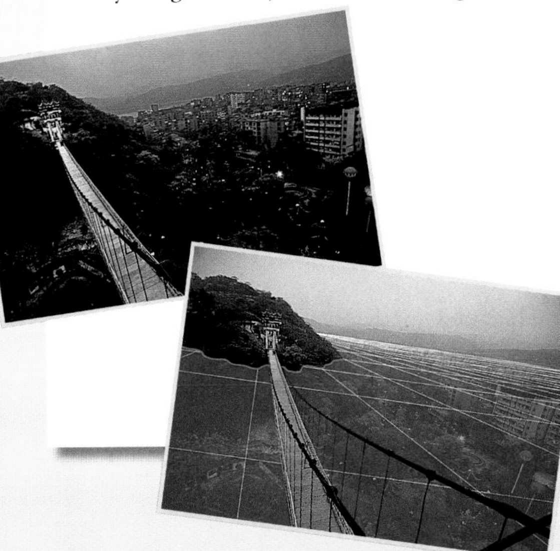

This is the city of Fengdu today (top) and as it will look when the dam and reservoir are completed (bottom).

Making the Connection

1. Flooding has caused massive death and destruction.
2. Students' maps should show the Yellow, Yangtze, and Xi Rivers, among others. Students should locate the Three Gorges Dam about halfway between the cities of Chongqing and Wuhan on the Yangtze River.
3. *For:* eliminate flooding, allow oceangoing vessels to gain access to the interior, and generate electricity; *Against:* displace nearly 1.2 million people, destroy historical sites, and cause pollution

Teach

Inform students that it takes about four hours to drive from New York City to Boston. Explain that the reservoir created by the Three Gorges Dam will be about the same length as the distance between those two cities.

More About Three Gorges Dam

Problems such as cost overruns are plaguing the dam-building project. Some experts believe that the dam will cost three times the original estimate.

Interdisciplinary Connections

Math Give students the following figures, which show the number of megawatts of electricity generated by the world's four largest dams:

Itaipu (Brazil and Paraguay)—12,600
Grand Coulee (U.S.)—6,494
Guri (Venezuela)—10,000
Tucuruii (Brazil)—4,245

Have students compare these figures to the 18,200 megawatts projected as the output of the Three Gorges Dam. They could express their comparisons as a bar graph.

Focus

Section Objectives

1. Explain how China's history influences life there today.
2. Contrast urban and rural China.
3. Summarize what arts China is known for.

BELLRINGER
Skillbuilder Activity

Project transparency and have students answer the question.

Daily Focus Skills Transparency

Identifying Points of View

Quotations from Kongfuzi, a Chinese Philosopher

"When you have faults, do not fear to abandon them."

"Have no friends not equal to yourself."

What do you think the philosopher meant by the second quotation?

Reading Preview

■ **Activating Prior Knowledge**
Ask: What do you think of when you hear the word *China*? List responses and have students identify which are examples of Chinese culture.

■ **Preteaching Vocabulary**
Ask students what they think *human rights* and *exile* mean. Then have them search the section to confirm their guesses.

Guide to Reading

Main Idea

The arts and ideas of ancient times still influence China today.

Terms to Know

- dynasty
- human rights
- exile
- calligraphy
- pagoda

Reading Strategy

Create a chart like this one. Then list two key facts in the right column for each item in the left column.

China	
History	
Government	
Urban and Rural Life	
Arts	

Dynasties to Communism

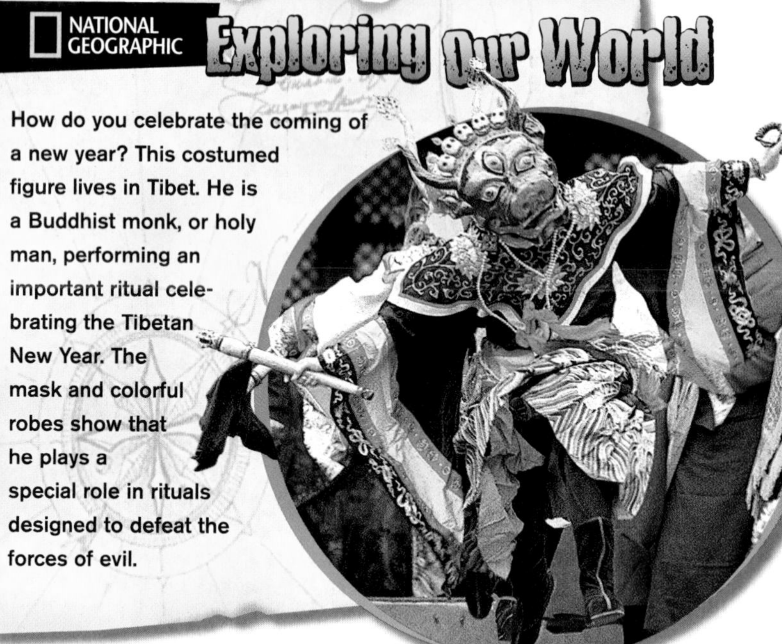

How do you celebrate the coming of a new year? This costumed figure lives in Tibet. He is a Buddhist monk, or holy man, performing an important ritual celebrating the Tibetan New Year. The mask and colorful robes show that he plays a special role in rituals designed to defeat the forces of evil.

China's population of 1.29 billion is about one-fifth of the world's people. About 92 percent of these people belong to the ethnic group called Han Chinese. They have a distinctive culture. The remaining 8 percent belong to 55 other ethnic groups. Most of these groups, such as the Tibetans, live in the western part of China. They have struggled to protect their traditions from Han Chinese influences.

China's History

China's civilization is more than 4,000 years old. For many centuries until the early 1900s, rulers known as emperors or empresses governed China. Many lived in the Imperial Palace, located in the heart of **Beijing,** China's capital. A **dynasty,** or line of rulers from a single family, would hold power until it was overthrown. Then a new leader would start a new dynasty. Under the dynasties, China built a highly developed culture and conquered neighboring lands.

Section Resources

Reproducible Masters
- Reproducible Lesson Plan
- Daily Lecture and Discussion Notes
- Note-taking Guide
- Guided Reading Activity
- Reading Essentials and Study Guide
- Section Quiz

Transparencies
- Daily Focus Skills Transparency
- In-text Map Transparency

Multimedia
- Vocabulary PuzzleMaker CD-ROM
- Interactive Tutor Self-Assessment CD-ROM
- Presentation Plus! CD-ROM
- ExamView® Pro Testmaker CD-ROM

As their civilization developed, the Chinese tried to keep out foreign invaders. In many ways, this was easy. On most of China's borders, natural barriers such as seas, mountains, and deserts already provided protection. Still, invaders threatened from the north. To defend this area, the Chinese began building the Great Wall of China about 2,200 years ago. Over the centuries, the wall was continually rebuilt and lengthened. In time, it snaked more than 4,000 miles (6,437 km) from the Yellow Sea in the east to the deserts of the west. It still stands today.

Beliefs and Inventions Chinese thinkers believed that learning was a key to good behavior. About 500 B.C., a thinker named Kongfuzi (KOONG•FOO•DZUH), or Confucius, taught that people should be polite, honest, brave, and wise. Children were to obey their parents, and every person was to respect the elderly and obey the country's rulers. Kongfuzi's teachings shaped China's government and society until the early 1900s.

During Kongfuzi's time, another thinker named Laozi (LOW•DZUH) arose. His teachings, called Daoism (DOW•IH•zuhm), stated that people should live simply and in harmony with nature. While Kongfuzi's ideas appealed to government leaders, Laozi's beliefs attracted artists and writers.

Buddhism came to China from Central Asia about A.D. 100. This religion taught that meditation, wisdom, and morality could help people find relief from life's problems. Over time, the Chinese mixed Buddhism, Daoism, and the ideas of Kongfuzi. This mixed spiritual heritage still influences many Chinese people today.

The early Chinese were inventors as well as thinkers. Did you know that they were using paper and ink before people in other parts of the world? Other Chinese inventions include silk, the magnetic compass, printed books, gunpowder, and fireworks. For hundreds of years, China was the most advanced civilization in the world.

Communist China Foreign influences increasingly entered China during the 1700s and 1800s. Europeans especially wanted to get fine Chinese goods such as silk, tea, and pottery. The United Kingdom and other countries used military power to force China to trade.

In 1911 a Chinese uprising under the Western-educated Dr. Sun Yat-sen overthrew the last emperor. China became a republic, or a country governed by elected leaders. Disorder followed until the Nationalist political party took over. The Communist Party gained power as well. After World War II, the Nationalists and the Communists fought for control of China. General Chiang Kai-shek (jee•AHNG KY•SHEHK) led the Nationalists. Mao Zedong (MOW DZUH•DOONG) led the Communists.

In 1949 the Communists won and set up the People's Republic of China under Mao Zedong and Zhou Enlai (JOH ehn•LY). The Nationalists fled to the offshore island of Taiwan. There they set up a rival government.

✓ Reading Check **Why was the Great Wall of China built?**

Believe It or Not!

Clay Warriors

One of the most fascinating archaeological finds in China was the clay army buried to guard the tomb of China's first emperor. The huge vault, covering 20 square miles (52 sq. km), was discovered in 1974. The clay warriors stand in four separate underground pits. In pit one are 6,000 life-size figures in military formation. Pit two contains 1,400 chariots and men. The third pit has an elite command force, and the fourth pit is empty, possibly abandoned before the work was completed. Each of the nearly 7,500 foot soldiers, horsemen, archers, and chariot riders were individually crafted more than 2,200 years ago.

Chapter 23

Section 2, pages 666–670

Teach

Reading Strategy

Organizing Information Suggest that students divide their notebooks into three columns labeled "Ancient History," "Recent Times," and "China Today." Then have them categorize their notes in the correct period. L1

Daily Lecture and Discussion Notes

CHINA AND ITS NEIGHBORS

Daily Lecture and Discussion Notes

Dynasties to Communism

The two main Chinese dialects are Mandarin and Cantonese. The sound of these languages is quite different, and most Chinese speak only one dialect. However, all Chinese writing uses the same set of characters. There is no connection between the written and spoken forms of the language.

I. China's History

A. China's civilization is about 4,000 years old. For centuries—until the early 1900s—rulers known as emperors or empresses governed China. A **dynasty,** or a line of rulers from a single family, would hold power until it was overthrown. Under the dynasties, China built a highly developed culture and conquered neighboring lands.

B. As their civilization developed, the Chinese tried to keep out foreign invaders. To defend against invaders from the north, the Chinese began building the Great Wall of China about 2,200 years ago. It still stands today.

C. Chinese thinkers believed that learning was a key to good behavior. About 500 B.C., a thinker named Kongfuzi, or Confucius, taught that people should be polite, honest, brave, and wise. During Kongfuzi's time, another thinker named Laozi arose. His teachings, called Daoism, stated that people should live simply and in harmony with nature.

D. Around A.D. 100, Buddhism arose in China. Buddhism taught that prayer, wisdom, and good deeds could help people find relief from life's problems.

E. In 1911 the Chinese overthrew the last emperor. China became a republic.

F. After World War II, the Nationalists and the Communists fought for control of China. In 1949 the Communists won and set up the People's Republic of China under Mao Zedong. The Nationalists, led by Chiang Kai-shek, fled to Taiwan.

DISCUSSION QUESTION

How long is the Great Wall of China? *(It is more than 4,000 miles long from the Yellow Sea in the east to the deserts of the west.)*

176

✓ Reading Check Answer

to defend China from invaders coming from the north

Reading Strategy — Reading the Text

Taking Notes Remind students to read long paragraphs or section chunks before recording notes. If a student waits until the end of the chapter before he or she takes notes, main ideas and supporting details may be forgotten. By reading small sections at a time, one has enough information to choose the most important ideas without losing track of the flow of those ideas. Concepts are reinforced before the reader moves on to the next section. L1

*Use the **Reading Skills Handbook** for more reading strategies.*

Current Events Journal

Show a photo of the Chinese students who protested in Tiananmen Square in 1989 and have students write what freedoms they would have asked for if they had lived in China at that time. Ask students to compare the role of citizens in China with the role of citizens in the United States.

Applying Map Skills

Answers

1. Harbin, Shenyang, Beijing, Tianjin, Shanghai, Hangzhou, Hong Kong
2. Over 250 persons per square mile (over 100 per sq. km)

In-text Map Transparency Activity

Ask: What is the population density of most of Mongolia? *(under 2 persons per square mile, or under 1 per square km)* Have students predict what Mongolia might be like based upon its low population density. *(Students may note that Mongolia might not have large commercial centers or cities.)*

China's Government and Society

After 1949 the Communists completely changed the mainland of China. All land and factories were taken over by the government. Farmers were organized onto large government farms, and women joined the industrial workforce. Dams and improved agricultural methods brought some economic benefits. Yet many government plans went wrong, and individual freedoms were lost. Many people were killed because they opposed communism.

After Mao Zedong died in 1976, a new Communist leader, Deng Xiaoping (DUHNG SYOW•PING), decided to take a new direction. He wanted to make China a more open country. One way to do this was to give people more economic freedom. The government kept tight control over all political activities, however. It continued to deny individual freedoms and acted harshly against any Chinese who criticized its actions. In 1989 about 100,000 students and workers gathered in Beijing's Tiananmen (TEE•EHN•AHN•MEHN) Square. The students and workers called for democracy and demanded political reforms in China. The government answered by sending tanks and troops. These government forces killed or injured thousands of protesters and arrested thousands more.

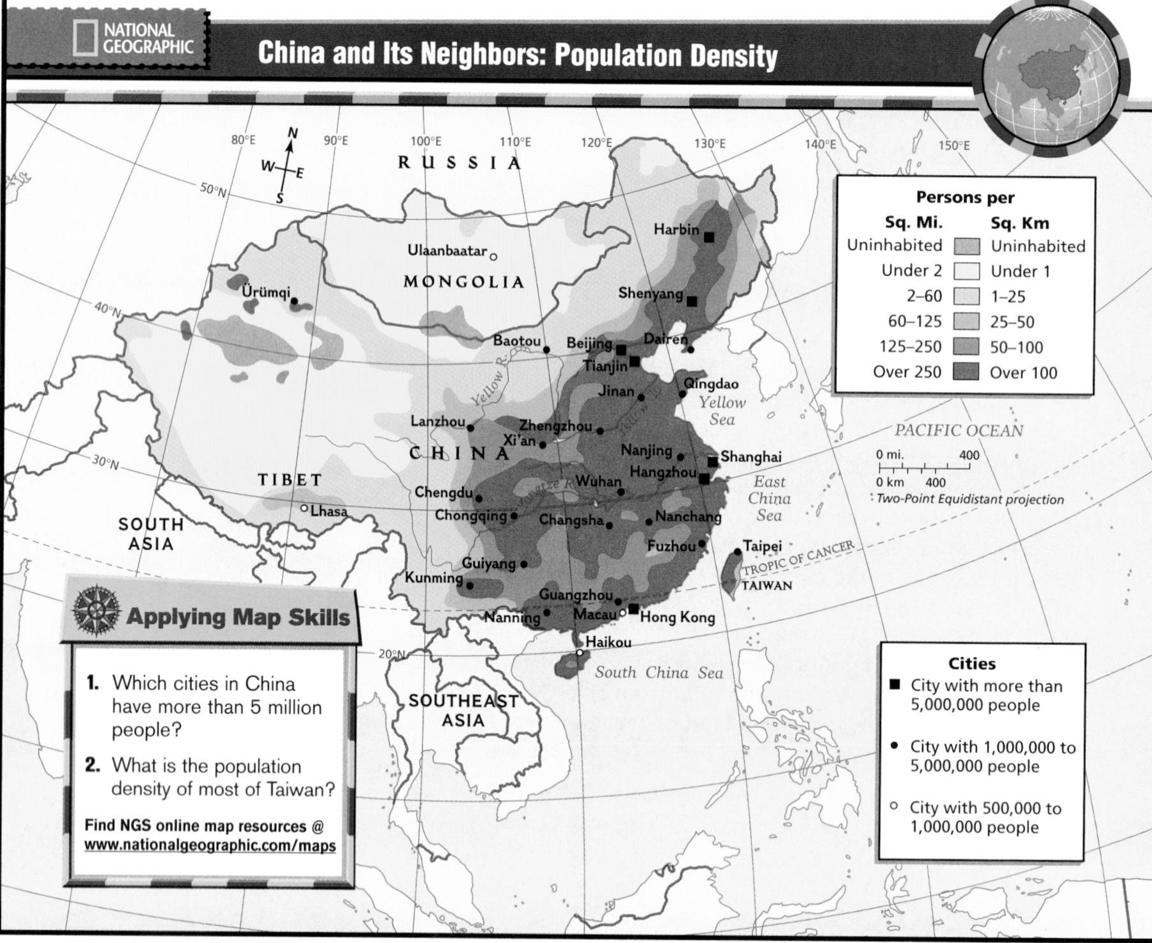

Differentiated Instruction

Meeting Special Needs: Visual/Spatial Have students prepare a bulletin board display that presents and explains the individual and group achievements of ancient China. Students can portray such activities as making silk; creating bronzes; inventing gunpowder, paper, ink, printing, and paper money; and so on. Their displays should include illustrations of each achievement and brief captions describing the significance of each. **L1 ELL**

Refer to *Inclusion for the Middle School Social Studies Classroom Strategies and Activities* in the TCR.

Countries around the world have protested the Chinese government's continued harsh treatment of people who criticize it. They say that Chinese leaders have no respect for **human rights.** These are the basic freedoms and rights, such as freedom of speech, that all people should enjoy. Because of China's actions, some people say that other countries should not trade with China.

China's leaders have also been criticized for their actions in Tibet. Tibet was once a separate Buddhist kingdom. China took control of the area in 1950 and crushed a rebellion there about nine years later. The Tibetan people have demanded independence since then. The Dalai Lama (DAH•ly LAH•muh), the Buddhist leader of Tibet, now lives in exile in India. Someone in **exile** is unable to live in his or her own country because of political beliefs. The Dalai Lama travels around the world trying to win support for his people.

NATIONAL GEOGRAPHIC On Location

Urban Life

Hundreds of thousands of people use bicycles—not cars—to get around Beijing and other cities.

Place About how many people live in China's cities?

Rural Life About 63 percent of China's people live in rural areas. The map on page 668 shows that most Chinese are crowded into the fertile river valleys of eastern China. Families work hard in their fields. They often use hand tools because mechanical equipment is too expensive.

Village life has improved in recent years. Most rural families now live in three- or four-room houses. They have enough food and some modern appliances. Many villages have community centers. People gather there to watch movies and play table tennis and basketball.

Urban Life More than 503 million Chinese people live in cities. China's cities are growing rapidly as people leave farms hoping to find better-paying jobs. Living conditions in the cities are crowded, but most homes and apartments have heat, electricity, and running water. Many people now earn enough money to buy extra clothes and televisions. They also have more leisure time to attend concerts or Chinese operas, walk in parks, or visit zoos.

Reading Check Why have people in other countries criticized China's government?

China's Culture

China is famous for its traditional arts. Chinese craft workers make bronze bowls, jade jewelry, decorated silk, glazed pottery, and fine porcelain. The Chinese are also known for their painting, sculpture, and architecture.

Chapter 23

Section 2, pages 666–670

More About the Photo

Beijing Beijing has not always been the capital of China, but it has served in that role almost continuously since the 1200s. The northern section contains the Imperial City, the ancient capital. At the heart of this area is the famous Forbidden City, where the imperial family lived.

Caption Answer more than 503 million people

L1/ELL

Guided Reading Activity

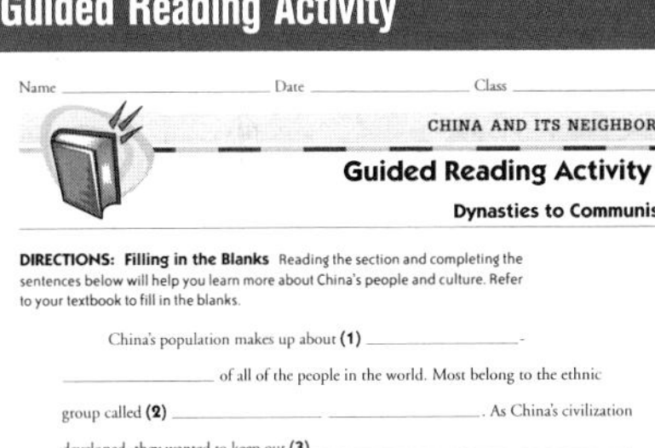
Name ______ Date ______ Class ______

CHINA AND ITS NEIGHBORS

Guided Reading Activity 2

Dynasties to Communism

DIRECTIONS: Filling in the Blanks Reading the section and completing the sentences below will help you learn more about China's people and culture. Refer to your textbook to fill in the blanks.

China's population makes up about **(1)** ______ of all of the people in the world. Most belong to the ethnic group called **(2)** ______. As China's civilization developed, they wanted to keep out **(3)** ______. To defend the northern area, they built the **(4)** ______.

Reading Check Answer

because of Chinese leaders' harsh treatment of people who criticize them and for their treatment of Tibet

3 Assess

Assign Section 2 Assessment as homework or an in-class activity.

Have students use the Interactive Tutor Self-Assessment CD-ROM to review Section 2.

Critical Thinking Activity

Synthesizing Information Give students the following sayings of Kongfuzi: (1) Have no friends not equal to yourself. (2) When you have faults, do not fear to abandon them. (3) Learning without thought is labor lost; thought without learning is perilous. (4) The cautious seldom err. Have students discuss the sayings and, after a specified time, reach a consensus about what the sayings mean. Ask students to present their interpretations of the sayings in poster form. L1

EE4 Human Systems: Standard 10

Chapter 23

Section 2, pages 666–670

L2

Section Quiz

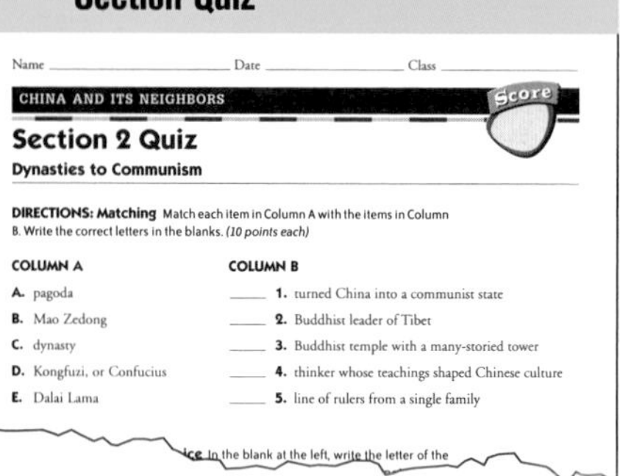
Name ______ Date ______ Class ______

CHINA AND ITS NEIGHBORS

Score

Section 2 Quiz

Dynasties to Communism

DIRECTIONS: Matching Match each item in Column A with the items in Column B. Write the correct letters in the blanks. *(10 points each)*

COLUMN A	COLUMN B
A. pagoda	____ 1. turned China into a communist state
B. Mao Zedong	____ 2. Buddhist leader of Tibet
C. dynasty	____ 3. Buddhist temple with a many-storied tower
D. Kongfuzi, or Confucius	____ 4. thinker whose teachings shaped Chinese culture
E. Dalai Lama	____ 5. line of rulers from a single family

...ice In the blank at the left, write the letter of the

Reteach

List the key people discussed in this section. Then have students identify each and explain their significance in history and their influence today.

Reading Check Answer

in pagodas

L1/ELL

Reading Essentials and Study Guide

Name ______ Date ______ Class ______

CHINA AND ITS NEIGHBORS

Reading Essentials and Study Guide 2

Dynasties to Communism

Key Terms

dynasty line of rulers from a single family
human rights basic freedoms and rights that all people should enjoy
exile unable to live in one's own country because of political beliefs
calligraphy the art of beautiful writing
pagoda temple with many-storied towers

...rom Experience

...Histor... ...6,000 years old. Until the early 1900s, emp...

Close

Have students create a travelogue that describes the sights and sounds they would experience in a trip through China.

▲ Bronze vessel from the Shang dynasty

▲ Porcelain bowl from the Ming dynasty

The Chinese love of nature has influenced painting and poetry. Chinese artists paint on long panels of paper or silk. Artwork often shows scenes of mountains, rivers, and forests. Artists attempt to portray the harmony between people and nature.

Many Chinese paintings include a poem written in **calligraphy,** which is the art of beautiful writing. Chinese writing is different from the print you are reading right now. It uses characters that represent words or ideas instead of letters that represent sounds. There are more than 50,000 Chinese characters, but the average person recognizes only about 4,000 to 5,000.

The Chinese developed bronze casting and the first porcelain centuries ago. Porcelain is made from coal dust and fine, white clay. Painted porcelain vases from early China are considered to be priceless today.

Most buildings in China's cities are modern. Yet traditional buildings still stand. Some have large, tiled roofs with edges that curve gracefully upward. Others are Buddhist temples with many-storied towers called **pagodas.** These buildings hold large statues of the Buddha.

Foods Cooking differs greatly from region to region in China. In coastal areas, people enjoy fish, crab, and shrimp dishes. Central China is famous for its spicy dishes made with hot peppers. A typical Chinese meal includes vegetables with bits of meat or seafood, soup, and rice or noodles. Often the meat and vegetables are cooked quickly in a small amount of oil over very high heat. This method—called stir-frying—allows the vegetables to stay crunchy.

✓Reading Check **Where would you find statues of Buddha in China?**

Assessment

Defining Terms

1. **Define** dynasty, human rights, exile, calligraphy, pagoda.

Recalling Facts

2. **History** Name two thinkers who influenced life in China.
3. **History** Who led the Nationalists after World War II? Who led the Communists after World War II? Who won control of China?
4. **Culture** What scenes are commonly found in Chinese paintings?

Critical Thinking

5. **Making Predictions** How might the teachings of Kongfuzi prevent rebellions in China?
6. **Summarizing Information** Why did Europeans want to force China to trade with them?

Graphic Organizer

7. **Organizing Information** Create a time line like this one. Then list at least five dates and their events in China's history.

Applying Social Studies Skills

8. **Analyzing Maps** Look at the population density map on page 668. How does the population density in western China differ from eastern China?

670

Section 2 Assessment

1. The terms are defined in the Glossary.
2. Kongfuzi and Laozi
3. Nationalists: Chiang Kai-shek; Communists: Mao Zedong; the Communists
4. scenes of nature, such as landscapes of mountains, rivers, and forests
5. He taught that people should obey the country's rulers.
6. They wanted fine Chinese goods such as silk, tea, and pottery.
7. Answers will vary. Students should use dates in the section for their time lines.
8. Population density in eastern China is far greater than in the west.

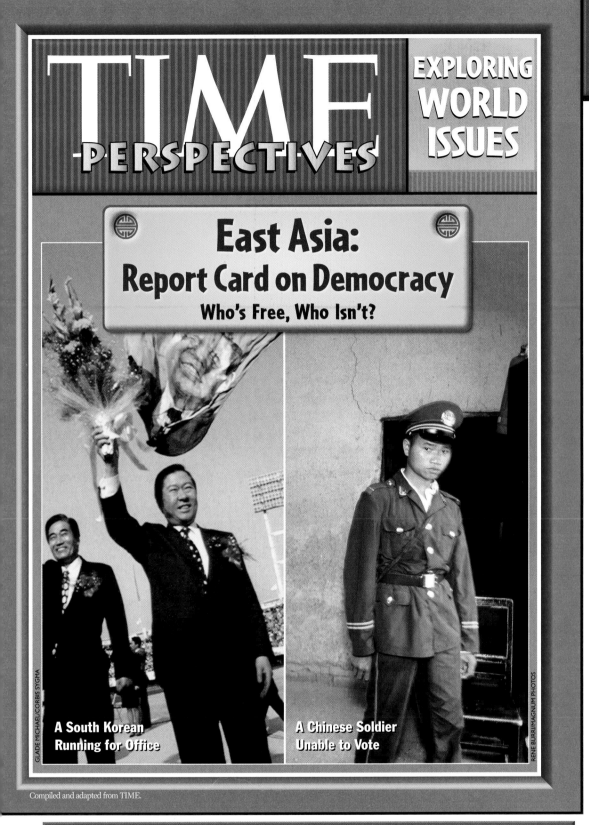

TIME PERSPECTIVES

EXPLORING WORLD ISSUES

East Asia: Report Card on Democracy

Who's Free, Who Isn't?

A South Korean Running for Office

GLADE MICHAEL/CORBIS SYGMA

A Chinese Soldier Unable to Vote

RENE BURRI/MAGNUM PHOTOS

Compiled and adapted from TIME.

EXPLORING WORLD ISSUES

Teacher Background

For many centuries, China was the dominant civilization of East Asia. It influenced many other East Asian countries in culture, education, government, and the arts.

China invaded Korea in 109 B.C. More than 300 years later, Koreans regained control of their country but adopted elements of Chinese culture such as Confucianism, Buddhism, and calligraphy.

In 552 a Korean king introduced the Japanese court to Buddhism. The religion sparked Japanese interest in all things Chinese. For centuries afterward, Japan and China carried on a cultural exchange.

TIME REPORTS ASIA

East Asia: Report Card on Democracy

THEME: CAPITALISM AND DEMOCRACY

Guide To Teaching With This Unit

Inside This Unit Two activity masters are designed to help your students understand the impact of capitalism and democracy—or their absence—in East Asia. A third looks ahead to the 2008 Olympic Games,

freedom—capitalism—often breeds political freedom, as it did in Taiwan and South Korea. How might capitalism lead to democracy in China? Have your students suggest answers.

Background Democracy took a long time to reach East Asia. Japan's first democratic constitution was written after World War

Using the Reproducibles

Using a Time Line traces the ups and downs of China's economy since 1949. How does a time line help readers "see" change over time? What changes triggered China's explosive growth? (Note the events of 1976, 1978, and 1979.) How is job growth a good measure of economic growth?

Comparing Statistics invites students to un-

Preparing the Student

From 1905 to 1945, Korea was part of the Japanese empire. After defeating Japan in World War II, the United States and the Soviet Union divided Korea at the 38th parallel, creating North Korea and South Korea.

In 1949 Mao Zedong established a Communist dictatorship in China. Chinese Nationalists fled to the island of Taiwan and established a government there.

Making Connections

Totalitarianism **Ask students:** **Have you ever felt restricted by the United States government's laws and regulations? Name some ways the government restricts your freedom.** Explain that in China and North Korea, people's rights are restricted. The Chinese and North Koreans have only one political party and criticizing it can be dangerous. Ask students to compare and contrast the limits and functions of communist and democratic governments. Ask them to identify reasons for limiting the power of government. L1

TIME PERSPECTIVES

North Koreans at Pyongyang, their nation's capital. North Korean generals dedicate a new statue.

1 Focus

Ask: How would you like your government to decide where you live and what you do for a living? What would be the advantages and disadvantages? Write "Advantages" and "Disadvantages" on the board and list each student's response below the correct heading. L1

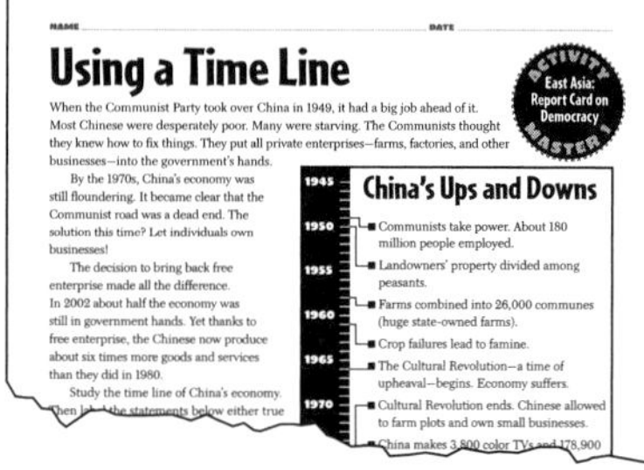

Who's Free, Who's Not in East Asia

ANSWER

five; two; North Korea; not free

Escape From Horror

Kang Kil-Ok made a terrifying journey in 1997. In the dead of night, she fled from North Korea to China over the frozen Tumen River. North Korean border guards shot at her and missed. "Somehow," Kang said later, "we made it to the other side."

In recent years more than 300,000 brave North Koreans have escaped to China. These people felt they had no choice. North Korea is one of the world's most brutal dictatorships. Its citizens have very few rights. The nation's Communist government assigns citizens jobs and places to live. It tells those who run farms and factories what and how much to produce. It jails and even executes people who refuse to follow orders. The result is a nation whose people must face many hardships. There are shortages of just about everything: fuel, fertilizer, electricity, food, and medicine.

During the 1990s, a severe food shortage left as many as two million North Koreans dead. The United States and other nations sent millions of dollars of food aid into the country. The government, however, distributed most of it to North Korea's 1.2 million soldiers and the families of top officials.

Kang left North Korea after her mother died. Kang's brother had already gone to China. When he disappeared, police beat their mother to get her to tell them where he went. "My mother's knees were so badly bruised, she couldn't even stand up," Kang said. "They kicked her with boots and whacked her with sticks. It made me realize I had to leave North Korea, too." Her mother died three months later.

Most of those who flee North Korea have a common goal. They hope to stay in China long enough to find a way to South Korea, one of Asia's most modern, democratic nations.

North Korea's Freedom House Score:
Not Free. *Political Rights:* 7. *Civil Liberties:* 7.

Who's Free, Who's Not in East Asia

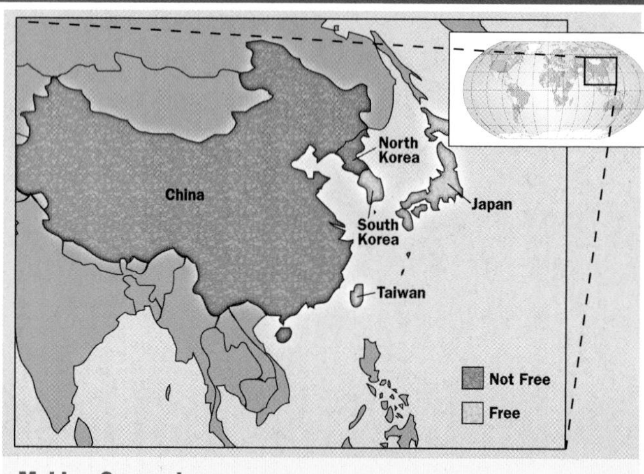

Making Comparisons
How many countries are there in East Asia? How many are not free? Which country borders China? Is it free or not free?

672

Team-Teaching Activity

Communications Explain to students that Kang's brother did not escape totalitarian government when he fled to China. According to Sharon Hom, executive director of Human Rights in China, "China leads the world in Internet and media censorship." Have a communications teacher speak to the class about why totalitarian governments attempt to control access to the Internet and outside broadcasts or communications. The teacher should explain that the Chinese government tightly regulates Internet cafes, chat rooms, Web sites, and e-mail use; blocks access to search engines; and imprisons students, writers, and activists for expressing their views on the Web. Have students name other countries besides China who might try to control Internet use and discuss why they would do so. L2

A busy street in Beijing, China's capital

Shanghai, China, is home to many new businesses.

Chinese shoppers in a Shanghai department store

China: A Nation on the Move

In China, Kang lived in constant fear. The Chinese send **escapees** they capture back to North Korea. Those sent home are tossed into jail, tortured, and sometimes executed.

Like North Korea, China is not a free country. Citizens can't vote to choose their leaders. They have few basic rights. Communist Party leaders make all the important decisions. Thousands of people are in jail today simply because they dared to criticize the government.

In one important way, China is freer than North Korea. It lets people run their own businesses. For 30 years, the government ran all the nation's enterprises, from farms to restaurants. But the farms barely produced enough to feed the nation of 1.3 billion people. China's factories at that time produced poorly-made goods.

During the late 1970s, the government let its citizens own businesses and farm their own plots of land. The chance to earn good pay in private business has given the Chinese a reason to work harder. Today only the United States produces more goods and services than China.

After four years in China, Kang found out that her brother was in South Korea. He sent her the money to pay people to smuggle her out of China. In June 2001, she landed at the airport outside Seoul, South Korea's capital.

China's Freedom House Score: Not Free. *Political Rights:* 7. *Civil Liberties:* 6.

What Is a Democracy?

A **democracy** is a government in which the final authority rests with the nation's people. Voters elect representatives who carry out the people's wishes.

Democracies are not all the same. All grant their people **political rights.** They hold free elections and allow political parties to compete for votes. Stronger democracies also protect the **civil liberties,** or freedoms, of every citizen.

The U.S. government is the second type. An organization called Freedom House gives it top grades for its defense of liberty and political rights. Freedom House is a private, not-for-profit organization based in Washington, D.C. It has promoted democratic values around the world since the 1940s.

Every year Freedom House decides how well the world's nations are defending the rights and freedoms of their citizens. Then it gives each nation two grades: one for political rights, one for civil liberties. The scores range from 1 (best) to 7 (worst). You will find the 2003 scores for East Asian nations at the end of each article in this report.

EXPLORING THE ISSUE

1. **Cause and Effect** Why did Kang leave North Korea?
2. **Making Inferences** China has 1.3 billion citizens. How might this have helped Kang stay there for four years?

673

2 TEACH

Reading Strategy

Identifying Main Ideas As students finish reading each subsection, ask them for one-sentence summaries of that subsection. Write the summaries on the board. **L1**

More About the Photos

More than 503 million Chinese people live in cities. This figure is more than one and one-half times the entire population of the United States but little more than one-third of the total population of China.

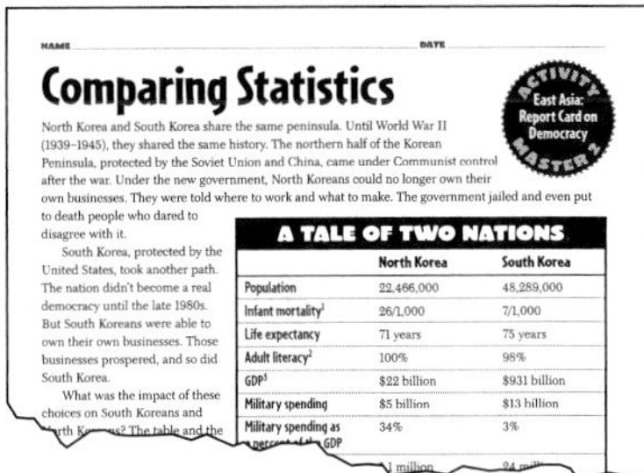

NAME ______ DATE ______

Comparing Statistics

Activity Master 2 — East Asia: Report Card on Democracy

North Korea and South Korea share the same peninsula. Until World War II (1939–1945), they shared the same history. The northern half of the Korean Peninsula, protected by the Soviet Union and China, came under Communist control after the war. Under the new government, North Koreans could no longer own their own businesses. They were told where to work and what to make. The government jailed and even put to death people who dared to disagree with it.

South Korea, protected by the United States, took another path. The nation didn't become a real democracy until the late 1980s. But South Koreans were able to own their own businesses. Those businesses prospered, and so did South Korea.

What was the impact of these choices on South Koreans and North Koreans? The table and the

A TALE OF TWO NATIONS

	North Korea	South Korea
Population	22,466,000	48,289,000
Infant mortality[1]	26/1,000	7/1,000
Life expectancy	71 years	75 years
Adult literacy[2]	100%	98%
GDP[3]	$22 billion	$931 billion
Military spending	$5 billion	$13 billion
Military spending as a percent of the GDP	34%	3%
[illegible]	[illegible] million	24 [illegible]

EXPLORING THE ISSUE

ANSWERS

1. because the North Korean government persecutes its people and grants them few rights
2. *Possible answer:* Kang went unnoticed in the crowded country.

Differentiated Instruction

Meeting Special Needs: Logical/Mathematical Have students fold a sheet of paper to create four columns. Tell them to head each column with one of the following categories of consumer goods: toys, electronics, clothing, and school supplies. **Say:** **Visit a store that offers a wide variety of items and look at 6 to 10 items in each category. Record the country where each item was made in the correct column. Then draw a bar graph that shows how many items in each category were made in China and how many were made in other countries.** Ask students to pool their results and use them to create a class bar graph on the board. **L2**

Refer to *Inclusion for the Middle School Social Studies Classroom Strategies and Activities* in the TCR.

Recommended Internet Sites

iso.hrichina.org

This Web site was founded by Chinese scholars and scientists to report abuses and to monitor the implementation of human rights in China.

www.askasia.org

This Web site contains a number of lesson plans and activities about Asia and North and South Korea.

www.asiasource.org

This Web site includes country profiles, articles about business and economics, and stories about policy and government for China, North Korea, South Korea, Taiwan, Japan, and other Asian countries.

EXPLORING THE ISSUE

ANSWERS

1. Citizens in South Korea can vote to choose their leaders.
2. In South Korea, Kang can say what she wants, which she could not do in North Korea or in China.

TIME PERSPECTIVES

South Korea: The Feel of Freedom

For Kang, South Korea seemed like another planet. Only eleven nations produce more goods and services than South Korea. One of those nations is China, whose population is 27 times larger than South Korea's.

PHOTODISC/PUNCHSTOCK

▲ Seoul, South Korea's capital, pulses with life. It is an exciting symbol of the nation's success.

On average, each South Korean produces 20 times more than each North Korean. South Korea boasts the largest automobile factory in the world. The same factory builds trains that cruise at 180 miles an hour (300 km/h). Seoul is a dazzling mix of skyscrapers and neon—signs of the nation's success.

Politically, South Korea is far different from North Korea and China. Its five major political parties and several smaller ones battle for votes in fair elections. About 70 percent of the nation's eligible voters take part. In the United States, that figure is closer to 50 percent.

Getting used to a society that allows so much competition is hard for North Koreans. "We are so used to living with what we are given," said Byung, who escaped from North Korea with his wife, mother, and two small sons. Byung won't reveal his last name. He is afraid that the North Korean government will punish those of his relatives who remain behind. "We don't understand that it is up to us to find and hold a job. The biggest surprise is that everyone is free here to say what they want."

Kang agrees. "I know what freedom feels like here," she said.

South Korea isn't a perfect democracy, though. Its officials sometimes accept money in exchange for making decisions that benefit individuals or businesses. The government often arrests people suspected of being Communists. But overall, South Korea is one of Asia's strongest democracies.

South Korea's Freedom House Score: Free. *Political Rights:* 1. *Civil Liberties:* 2.

EXPLORING THE ISSUE

1. **Explaining** How is South Korea different from North Korea and China politically?
2. **Analyzing** What does Kang mean when she says she knows what freedom feels like?

674

Critical Thinking Activity

Drawing Conclusions The Chinese people saw the collapse of the Soviet Union and other eastern European countries and the political upheaval and economic hardships that have befallen that entire region. In addition, they have seen extensive fighting in eastern Europe. All of these governments were previously communist. **Ask:** Do you think seeing the collapse of the Communist governments of eastern Europe made the Chinese people more or less likely to fight for democracy? Why? L2

EE4 Human Systems: Standard 13

Taiwan: Young Tiger

Taiwan is an island province of China. Its citizens like to view it as a separate country, however, because it has been on its own since 1949. Politically, Taiwan boasts four major parties and many smaller ones. Citizens vote for their leaders in open elections. Some politicians have been arrested for "buying" votes.

Like South Korea, Taiwan is called an "Asian Tiger" because of its powerful economy. Private businesses drive the economy. Money earned from exports and imports fuels it.

The mayor of Taipei, Taiwan's capital, celebrates his reelection.

SIMON KWANG/REUTERS/NEWSCOM

Independent courts protect the rights of the Taiwanese. However, women and minorities often face discrimination on the job. Journalists must be careful about what they say. Many observers are impressed that the Taiwanese enjoy so many freedoms. This is because Taiwan didn't hold its first free presidential election until 1996.

Taiwan's Freedom House Score: Free. *Political Rights:* 2. *Civil Liberties:* 2.

Japan: Shining Democracy

Japan is one of the world's greatest success stories. Its economy is the world's third strongest, after those of the United States and China.

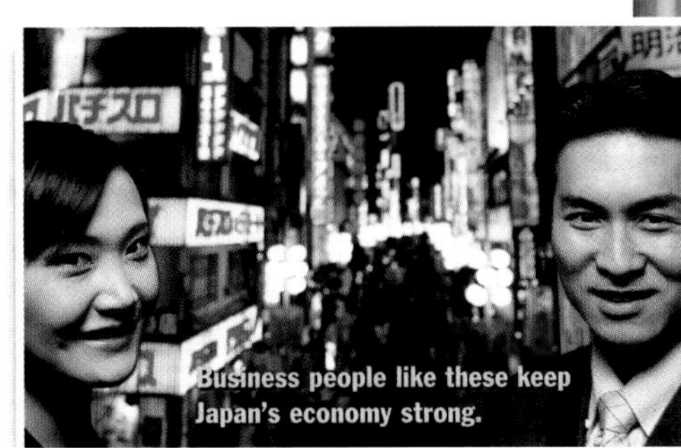

Business people like these keep Japan's economy strong.

PHOTODISC/PUNCHSTOCK

Japan's experiment with democracy began in 1947, soon after its defeat in World War II. At the time, Japan's emperor held most of the power. In 1947 a new **constitution** transferred that power to the people. The emperor became a **figurehead,** a ceremonial leader without much power.

As in Taiwan, women and minority group members often feel like second-class citizens. But Japan's courts do all they can to protect citizens' rights.

Japan's Freedom House Score: Free. *Political Rights:* 1. *Civil Liberties:* 2.

EXPLORING THE ISSUE

1. **Evaluating Information** How can you tell that Taiwan and Japan are ruled by law?
2. **Analyzing Information** What makes Taiwan's and Japan's democracies alike?

Expressing Problems Clearly Have volunteers research the traditional roles of Chinese and Japanese women and report their findings to the class. **Ask:** What problems have traditional expectations caused for women in Taiwan and Japan today? Will eliminating traditional roles for women solve their problems? What new problems might the absence of traditional roles cause for Taiwanese and Japanese women? L1

Did You Know

In 2001 demand for Taiwan's high-tech exports decreased. As a result, unemployment soared, and the Taiwanese experienced a recession for the first time since 1975.

EXPLORING THE ISSUE

ANSWERS

1. Both countries have courts that protect the rights of the people.
2. Both the Taiwanese and Japanese elect their leaders.

Interdisciplinary Activity

Art Survey the class to find out how many students already enjoy *anime* (Japanese cartoons) and *manga* (Japanese comics). Tell those who do not recognize the terms that they probably have seen examples of these art forms: their signature trait is the large, childlike eyes of the characters. Point out that *manga*—comic books or graphic novels—make up three-fifths of all the printed matter purchased in Japan and that many *anime* film features and TV shows are based on *manga*. Add that *anime* and *manga* are two of Japan's most successful exports to the United States. The first Japanese *anime* TV show, *Tetsuawan Atom* ("The Mighty Atom"), ran for 10 years and appeared in the United States as *Astro Boy*. Present an *anime* feature to students and then have them compare *anime* to American-made animated features. L1

EE4 Human Systems: Standard 10

Current Events Journal

Tell students to read two or more articles about human rights abuses in East Asia. Based on ideas discussed in the section titled "Promoting Democracy: What Can One Person Do?" have students write about the actions they personally can take in response to these abuses.

EXPLORING THE ISSUE

ANSWERS

1. Answers will vary.
2. Both ways involve writing to government officials. In the first instance, you write to your congressperson. In the second, you write to the leader of another nation.

NAME ________ DATE ________

Classifying Data

ACTIVITY MASTERS — East Asia: Report Card on Democracy

The Chinese are working hard to get their country ready to host the 2008 Summer Olympic Games. Here's a chance for you to learn about the history of some summer and winter Olympic sports.

Match each sports history fact with the picture of the sport that it describes. Write the letter of the picture beside the fact. You might want to try this Olympic challenge on your family. Go for the gold!

a. Archery b. Baseball c. Bobsled d. Canoe/Kayak

Synchronized Swimming h. Water Polo

Promoting Democracy: What Can One Person Do?

According to Freedom House, there are more democracies today than at any time in history. Still, more than 2 billion people don't live in democratic nations. They are denied the right to vote and to enjoy the sort of freedoms that Americans take for granted.

This is an issue that concerns people everywhere. In 2002 representatives of more than 100 democracies met in Seoul, South Korea. They discussed ways to spread democracy. One solution they came up with had to do with schools. They agreed to try to persuade developing nations to teach **civics,** or courses about democracy.

This approach has been successful before. After World War II, schools in Germany and Japan, the two defeated powers, began to teach civics courses. Today those two nations enjoy the many benefits of freedom.

What can you do to help promote civics courses abroad? You can write to your representative in Congress. Explain why you think the U.S. government should help other nations develop such courses. Send the letter to your local newspaper, too.

Another way you can help spread democracy is to work with groups such as Amnesty International. Dozens of such groups are trying to make democracy catch on throughout the world. When they discover a government abusing its citizens' rights, these groups say so. Amnesty International gets its thousands of supporters to write letters to the government's top leader. One letter won't change the world. But thousands of them remind leaders who act irresponsibly that the world is watching. To see how such campaigns work, go to Amnesty International's Web page, **www.amnestyusa.org**. Click on "Act Now!"

In prosperous East Asia, cell phones are everywhere.

LELAND BOBBÉ/CORBIS

"What you do may seem terribly insignificant," Mohandas Gandhi said, "but it is terribly important that you do it anyway." Gandhi knew what he was talking about. He led the campaign that won India its independence in 1947.

EXPLORING THE ISSUE

1. **Finding the Main Idea** Come up with a title that will tell readers what this article is about.
2. **Compare and Contrast** This article suggests two ways to spread democracy. How are they alike? How are they different?

Your Government and You

Secretary of State Colin Powell has said, "China and the United States have very, very important common interests." He has stated that these include economic and trade interests. However, our government is very concerned about the lack of human rights in China. The U.S. State Department has a site that discusses the relationship between China and the U.S. (www.usembassy-china.org.cn). This site contains useful information on many topics, including economic relationships and human rights issues. Have students choose a speech or report on the site and summarize it. L3

REVIEW AND ASSESS

UNDERSTANDING THE ISSUE

1. **Defining Key Terms** Write the definitions for the following terms: *democracy, political rights, civil liberties, escapee, constitution, figurehead, civics.*
2. **Writing to Inform** Imagine you are a North Korean and have just escaped to China. Write a letter to a friend and explain why you left North Korea.
3. **Writing to Persuade** In a brief essay, explain what the Chinese people would gain if their country were a democracy.

INTERNET RESEARCH ACTIVITY

4. The Internet is changing politics throughout Asia. In South Korea, online newspapers like *OhmyNews* can sway elections. *OhmyNews* posts hundreds of stories every day. Ordinary citizens write most of them. Go to **www.ohmynews.com.** Click around and study the pictures. What do the pictures suggest about the subjects South Koreans seem most interested in? Make a list and compare it with those of your classmates.
5. In China, millions of people have access to the Internet. China's courts have jailed people who use the Internet to criticize the government. Type in the key words "China" and "Internet" on an Internet search engine to find out why China's government both likes and fears the Internet. Write a short essay with your answers.

BEYOND THE CLASSROOM

6. **Visit your school or local library** to learn more about democracy in East Asia. Working in three groups, learn what it was like to live in Taiwan, South Korea, or Japan before these lands became democratic. Discuss your findings with your classmates.
7. **Research a former Communist nation** in Europe. What problems did that nation face while reinventing itself as a democracy? Write your findings in a short report.

CHRIS STEELE PERKINS/MAGNUM PHOTOS

▲ **In Tokyo, teens like to wear "street clothes."**

Taiwan: From Dictatorship to Democracy

How one "Asian Tiger" went from military rule to free elections

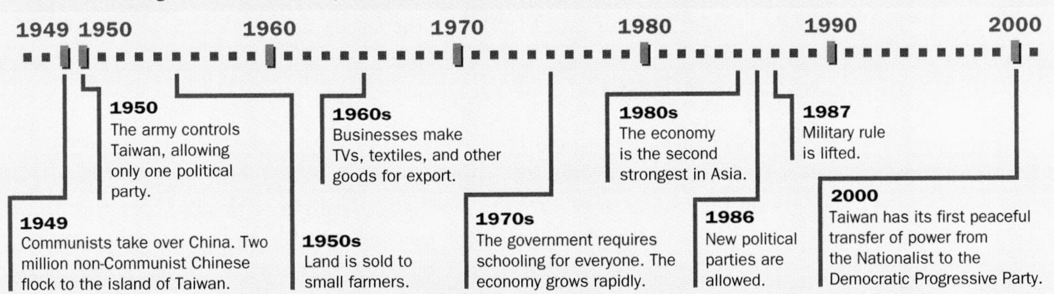

1949 1950 1960 1970 1980 1990 2000
1950 The army controls Taiwan, allowing only one political party.
1949 Communists take over China. Two million non-Communist Chinese flock to the island of Taiwan.
1960s Businesses make TVs, textiles, and other goods for export.
1950s Land is sold to small farmers.
1970s The government requires schooling for everyone. The economy grows rapidly.
1980s The economy is the second strongest in Asia.
1986 New political parties are allowed.
1987 Military rule is lifted.
2000 Taiwan has its first peaceful transfer of power from the Nationalist to the Democratic Progressive Party.

BUILDING TIME LINE SKILLS

1. **Analyzing Data** How many years does this time line cover? What major changes took place during that time?
2. **Making Inferences** Which came first in Taiwan, economic growth or democracy? Why wasn't it the other way around?

FOR UPDATES ON WORLD ISSUES GO TO www.timeclassroom.com/glencoe

3 ASSESS

Have students take the TIME Reports Quiz or do the Alternative Assessment project for this unit provided in the Teacher's Classroom Resources.

BUILDING TIME LINE SKILLS

ANSWERS

1. 47; two million non-Communist Chinese flock to Taiwan; businesses export goods; the government mandates education for everyone; democracy replaces military rule.
2. economic growth; educated citizens can make informed economic choices.

4 CLOSE

Reading Strategy

Writing a Paragraph Ask students to write a paragraph starting with this sentence: *People throughout the world should be concerned about spreading democracy because....*

Culminating Activity

To close this lesson, have students complete the Review and Assess section questions and activities above. Students should use classroom discussion, contextual clues, and their student dictionaries to write definitions for terms. Before assigning the Internet activities, it is recommended that you review your school district policy on student Internet use.

Focus on Debate

Have students debate the pro and con positions of the following statement: **As long as Chinese and North Korean leaders put people in jail for criticizing the government, democracy will never be established. L2**

 **EE4 Human Systems: Standard 13**

1 Focus

Section Objectives

1. Explain why many people moved to Taiwan.
2. Describe the people of Mongolia.

BELLRINGER Skillbuilder Activity

Project transparency and have students answer the question.

Daily Focus Skills Transparency

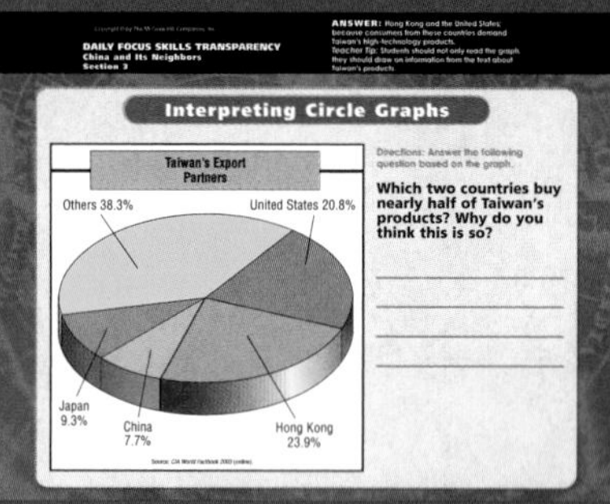

Reading Preview

■ **Activating Prior Knowledge** Remind students that the Communists took over China in 1949. **Ask: What do you think happened to those who had fought against the Communists?** Explain that in this section, students will find out.

■ **Preteaching Vocabulary** Explain what a *yurt* is. Then ask students what other word in the Terms to Know is related to yurt *(nomad)*. Why? *(A portable home would be useful to nomadic people.)*

Guide to Reading

Main Idea

Taiwan and Mongolia have been influenced by Chinese ways and traditions.

Terms to Know

- high-technology industry
- steppe
- nomad
- empire
- yurt

Reading Strategy

Create a diagram like this one. Then write statements that are true of each country under their headings in the outer ovals. Where the ovals overlap, write statements that are true of both countries.

Section 3

China's Neighbors

In the remote, harsh land of western Mongolia, a centuries-old tradition continues. Hunters train eagles to bring their kill back to the human hunter. The people say that female eagles make the best hunters. Because they weigh more than males, they can capture larger prey. Like all eagles, they have superb vision—eight times better than a human's.

Taiwan is an island close to China's mainland, and Mongolia borders China on the north. Throughout their histories, Taiwan and Mongolia have had close ties to their larger neighbor.

Taiwan

About 100 miles (161 km) off the southeastern coast of China lies the island country of **Taiwan.** It is slightly smaller than the states of Connecticut and Massachusetts put together. Through Taiwan's center runs a ridge of steep, forested mountains. On the east, the mountains descend to a rocky coastline. On the west, they fall away to a narrow, fertile plain. This flat area is home to the majority of the island's people. Like southeastern China, Taiwan has mild winters and hot, rainy summers.

Taiwan's Economy Taiwan has one of the world's most prosperous economies. Taiwan's wealth comes largely from high-technology industries, manufacturing, and trade with other countries. **High-technology industries** produce computers and other kinds of

Section Resources

Reproducible Masters
- Reproducible Lesson Plan
- Daily Lecture and Discussion Notes
- Note-taking Guide
- Guided Reading Activity
- Reading Essentials and Study Guide
- Section Quiz

Transparencies
- Daily Focus Skills Transparency

Multimedia
- Vocabulary PuzzleMaker CD-ROM
- Interactive Tutor Self-Assessment CD-ROM
- Presentation Plus! CD-ROM
- ExamView® Pro Testmaker CD-ROM
- MindJogger Videoquiz

electronic equipment. Workers in Taiwan's factories make many different products, including computers, calculators, radios, televisions, and telephones. You have probably seen goods from Taiwan sold in stores in your community.

Taiwan has a growing economic influence on its Asian neighbors. Many powerful companies based in Taiwan have recently built factories in the People's Republic of China and Thailand. Despite their political differences, Taiwan and mainland China have strengthened their economic ties since the 1990s.

Agriculture also contributes to Taiwan's economy. The island's mountainous landscape limits the amount of land that can be farmed. Still, some farmers have built terraces on mountainsides to grow rice. Other major crops include sugarcane, citrus fruits, sweet potatoes, pineapples, tea, and soybeans. In fact, Taiwan's farmers produce enough food to feed their own people and also enough to export.

Taiwan's History and People For centuries, Taiwan was part of China's empire. Then in 1895, Japan took the island after defeating China in war. The Japanese developed the economy of Taiwan but treated the people very harshly. After Japan's loss in World War II, Taiwan was returned to China.

In 1949 the Nationalists under Chiang Kai-shek arrived in Taiwan from the Chinese mainland. Along with them came more than 1.5 million refugees fleeing Communist rule. Fearing a Communist invasion, the Nationalists kept a large army in the hope of someday retaking the mainland. They also blocked other political groups from sharing in the government.

By the early 1990s, local Taiwanese were allowed more opportunities in government. The one-party system ended, and Taiwan became a democracy. Taiwan is still officially part of China, but many people would like to declare Taiwan independent. China claims Taiwan as its twenty-third province and believes that it should be under China's control. China has threatened to use force against Taiwan if the island declares its independence.

About 75 percent of Taiwan's 22.6 million people live in urban areas. The most populous city—with 2.6 million people—is the capital, **Taipei.** This bustling center of trade and commerce has tall skyscrapers and modern stores. If you stroll through the city, however, you will see Chinese traditions. Buddhist temples, for example, still reflect traditional Chinese architecture.

Reading Check Why is Taiwan's economy one of the world's strongest?

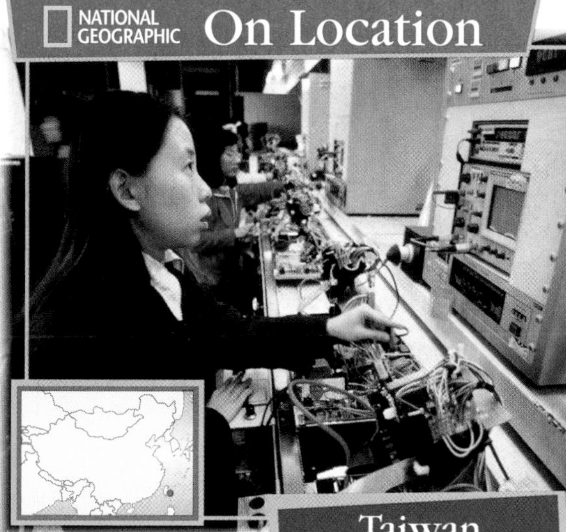

Taiwan

Many electronic industries have headquarters in Taiwan.

Place What kinds of products do high-technology factories in Taiwan produce?

Teach

Reading Strategy

Outlining Have students prepare an outline of the section by writing down the subheadings and listing four or five key points under each. L1

Daily Lecture and Discussion Notes

CHINA AND ITS NEIGHBORS

Daily Lecture and Discussion Notes

China's Neighbors

Did You Know? About 30 daily newspapers are published in Taiwan. Most families own a TV set and one or more radios.

I. Taiwan

A. Taiwan is a prosperous island about 100 miles off China's southeastern coast. Taiwan's wealth comes largely from high-technology industries, manufacturing, and trade with other countries. **High-technology industries** produce computers and other kinds of electronic equipment.

B. ... contributes to Taiwan's booming economy. Some farmers have ... to grow rice. Other major crops include

More About the Photo

Taiwan's Economy The prosperity of Taiwan is evident in this fact: About 80 percent of Taiwan's people own their own homes, the highest rate of home ownership in the world.

Caption Answer computers, calculators, radios, televisions, and telephones

Reading Check Answer

It relies on high-tech industries, manufacturing, and trade with other countries.

Reading Strategy: Reading the Text

Preparing to Read Remind students to use the following tips to stay alert while reading assignments independently. Select a place to read that is quiet and there are no distractions. Try to develop an interest in what is about to be read by relating it to something that you have heard or read about. Work for short time intervals, and take breaks during these intervals. Vary the type of subject being read to avoid boredom. Reward yourself for finishing a reading task, like taking a walk or making a phone call to a friend. L1

*Use the **Reading Skills Handbook** for more reading strategies.*

More About the Photo

Ulaanbaatar Mongolia's capital was originally called *Da Khure,* after the monastery founded there. In 1911 the city became *Niislel Khureheh* ("capital of Mongolia"). The current name, given in 1924, means "Red Hero" and reflects the Communist regime of the time.

Caption Answer because the country has more than 260 days of sunshine per year

L1/ELL

Guided Reading Activity

Name ______________ Date ______________ Class ______________

CHINA AND ITS NEIGHBORS

Guided Reading Activity 3

China's Neighbors

DIRECTIONS: Outlining Reading the section and completing the outline below will help you learn more about Taiwan and Mongolia. Refer to your textbook to fill in the blanks.

I. Taiwan
  A. Taiwan is an ______________ country.
    1. It has a ridge of steep ______________ through its center.
    2. The majority of the people live on the flat, fertile ______________.
    3. Taiwan has ______________ winters and hot, rainy summers.
  B. Taiwan has a very ______________ economy.
    1. Its wealth comes from ______________-______________ industries.
    2. ... has a growing economic influence on its ______________

3 Assess

Assign Section 3 Assessment as homework or an in-class activity.

Have students use the Interactive Tutor Self-Assessment CD-ROM to review Section 3.

NATIONAL GEOGRAPHIC **On Location**

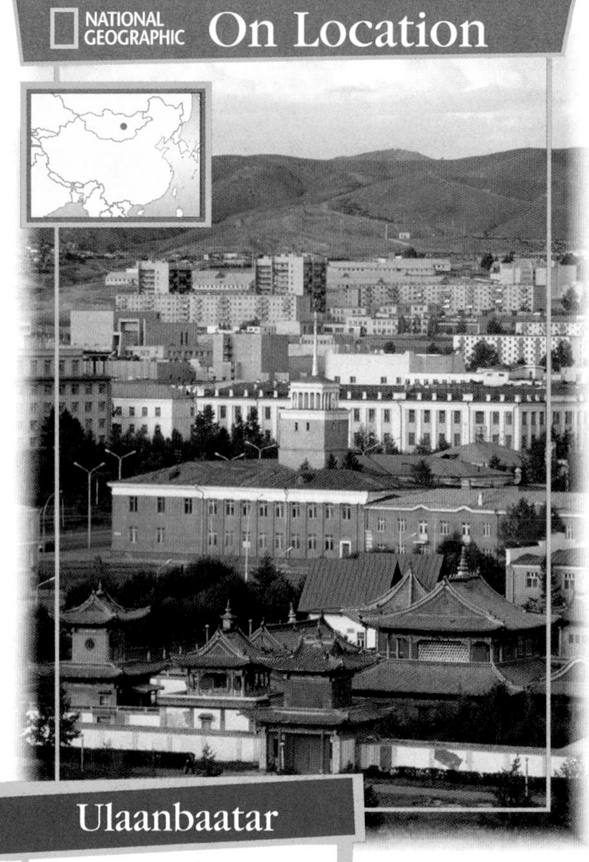

Ulaanbaatar

Ulaanbaatar in Mongolia began as a Buddhist community in the early 1600s. Today it is a modern cultural and industrial center.

Place **Why is Mongolia known as the Land of the Blue Sky?**

Mongolia

Landlocked **Mongolia** is a country about the size of Alaska. Rugged mountains and high plateaus rise in the west and central regions. The bleak landscape of the Gobi spreads over the southeast. The rest of the country is covered by **steppes,** which are dry treeless plains often found on the edges of a desert.

Known as the Land of the Blue Sky, Mongolia boasts more than 260 days of sunshine per year. Yet its climate has extremes. Rainfall is scarce, and fierce dust storms sometimes sweep across the landscape. It is very hot in the summer. In the winter, temperatures fall below freezing at night.

For centuries, most of Mongolia's people were **nomads.** Nomads are people who move from place to place with herds of animals. Even today, many Mongolians tend sheep, goats, cattle, or camels on the country's vast steppes. Important industries in Mongolia use products from these animals. Some factories use wool to make textiles and clothing. Others use the hides of cattle to make leather and shoes. Some farmers grow wheat and other grains. Mongolia also has deposits of copper and gold.

Mongolia's History and People Mongolia's people are famous for their skills in raising and riding horses. In the past, they also were known as fierce fighters. In the 1200s, many groups of Mongols joined together under one leader, Genghis Khan (JEHNG•guhs KAHN). He led Mongol armies on a series of conquests. The Mongols eventually carved out the largest land empire in history, ruling 80 percent of Eurasia by A.D. 1300. An **empire** is a collection of different territories under one ruler. The Mongol Empire stretched from China all the way to eastern Europe.

During the 1300s, the Mongol Empire weakened and fell apart. China ruled the area that is now Mongolia from the 1700s to the early 1900s. In 1924 Mongolia gained independence and created a strict Communist government under the guidance of the Soviet Union. The country finally became a democracy in 1990. Since then, the Mongolian economy has moved slowly from government control to a free enterprise system.

Differentiated Instruction

Meeting Special Needs: Visual/Spatial Have students create a map of East Asia using color-coding to show which countries have a communist system or a free enterprise system. Have students also add symbols to represent the type of government in each East Asian country. Make sure students include a map key. **L1**

Refer to *Inclusion for the Middle School Social Studies Classroom Strategies and Activities* in the TCR.

About 85 percent of Mongolia's 2.5 million people are Mongols. They speak the Mongol language. About 60 percent of the people live in urban areas. The largest city is the capital, **Ulaanbaatar** (OO•LAHN•BAH•TAWR). Mongolians in the countryside live on farms. A few still follow the nomadic life of their ancestors. These herder-nomads live in **yurts,** large circle-shaped structures made of animal skins that can be packed up and moved from place to place.

Mongolians still enjoy the sports and foods of their nomadic ancestors. The favorite meal is boiled sheep's meat with rice, washed down with tea. The biggest event of the year is the Naadam Festival, held all over the country in mid-summer. It consists of a number of sporting events, including wrestling, archery, and horse racing.

Since before the days of the Mongol Empire, most people in Mongolia have been Buddhists. Buddhism has long influenced Mongolian art, music, and literature. Traditional music has a wide range of instruments and singing styles. In one style of Mongolian singing, male performers produce harmonic sounds from deep in the throat, releasing several notes at once.

For centuries, Buddhist temples and other holy places dotted the country. Under communism, religious worship was discouraged. Many of these historic buildings were either destroyed or left to decay. Today people are once again able to practice their religion. They have restored or rebuilt many of their holy buildings.

✓ Reading Check What religion do most Mongolians practice?

The Race Is On!

Magnai races his older brother across the Mongolian steppes. Magnai learned to ride horses when he was three years old. "You should visit my country. It's a Mongol tradition to welcome all visitors with hot tea, cheese, fresh cream, and candies. Even in the cities, people offer their homes to visitors."

Section 3 Assessment

Defining Terms

1. **Define** high-technology industry, steppe, nomad, empire, yurt.

Recalling Facts

2. **Economics** What kinds of products are made in Taiwan?
3. **Government** Why has Taiwan not claimed independence from China?
4. **History** Which Mongol warrior conquered much of Eurasia by A.D. 1300?

Critical Thinking

5. **Understanding Cause and Effect** Why did many people flee to Taiwan from China in 1949?
6. **Drawing Conclusions** Why do you think Communist leaders discouraged religious worship in Mongolia?

Graphic Organizer

7. **Organizing Information** Create a diagram like this one. Then write either Taiwan or Mongolia in the center oval. Write at least one fact about the country under the headings in each of the outer ovals.

History — Government — Economy — Culture

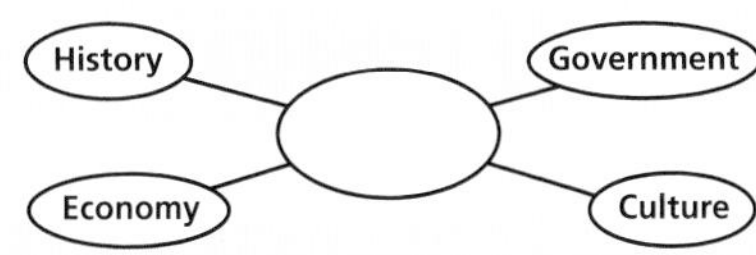

Applying Social Studies Skills

8. **Analyzing Maps** Look at the map on page 661. What mountains rise in western Mongolia? What desert is found in southern and southeastern Mongolia?

Section 3 Assessment

1. The terms are defined in the Glossary.
2. computers and other types of electronic goods
3. China has threatened to use force against the island if it does so.
4. Genghis Khan
5. They did not wish to live under Communist rule.
6. *Possible answer:* Communism discourages any religious worship as an attempt to gain the people's undivided allegiance to the state.
7. Diagrams will vary.
8. Altay Mountains; Gobi

Chapter 23

Section 3, pages 678–681

L2

Section Quiz

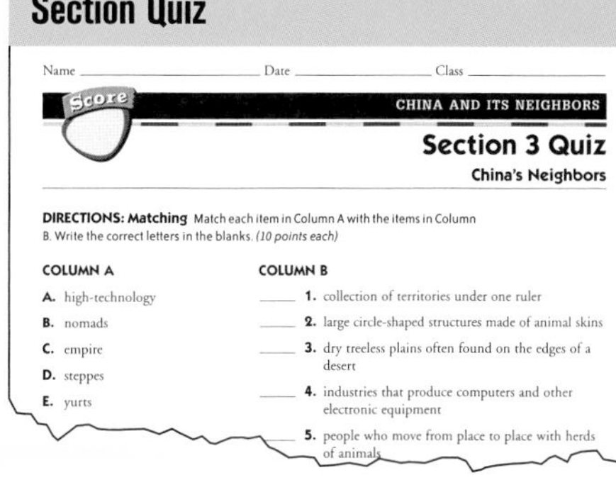

Name ______ Date ______ Class ______

Score — CHINA AND ITS NEIGHBORS

Section 3 Quiz

China's Neighbors

DIRECTIONS: Matching Match each item in Column A with the items in Column B. Write the correct letters in the blanks. *(10 points each)*

COLUMN A	COLUMN B
A. high-technology	____ 1. collection of territories under one ruler
B. nomads	____ 2. large circle-shaped structures made of animal skins
C. empire	____ 3. dry treeless plains often found on the edges of a desert
D. steppes	____ 4. industries that produce computers and other electronic equipment
E. yurts	____ 5. people who move from place to place with herds of animals

✓ Reading Check Answer

Buddhism

L1/ELL

Reading Essentials and Study Guide

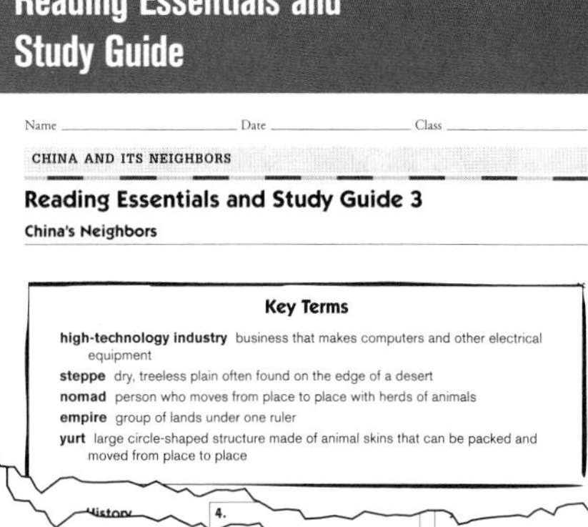

Name ______ Date ______ Class ______

CHINA AND ITS NEIGHBORS

Reading Essentials and Study Guide 3

China's Neighbors

Key Terms

high-technology industry business that makes computers and other electrical equipment
steppe dry, treeless plain often found on the edge of a desert
nomad person who moves from place to place with herds of animals
empire group of lands under one ruler
yurt large circle-shaped structure made of animal skins that can be packed and moved from place to place

4 CLOSE

Reading Strategy

Writing a Paragraph Have students write about Taiwan and Mongolia, explaining how both are influenced by China and different from China.

TEACH

Write the following phrases: "The movie grossed $35 million on its opening weekend of business." "The movie was exciting—you should see it!" **Ask:** **Which sentence states a fact and which states an opinion?** *(The first is a fact, the second an opinion.)* Ask students to explain the difference. **L1**

Additional Skills Practice

1. **Are all opinions of equal value? Does anything make one person's opinion more valid than another person's opinion?** *(Possible answer: Informed, or expert, opinions should carry more validity than uninformed opinions.)*
2. **Some people say, "Statistics never lie." Is that true or not?** *(Possible answer: Statistics can be misleading if they do not try to present a full picture of the situation being analyzed.)*

Additional Skills Resources

 Chapter Skills Review

 Building Geography Skills for Life

GLENCOE TECHNOLOGY

 **Skillbuilder Interactive Workbook CD-ROM, Level 1**

This interactive CD-ROM reinforces student mastery of essential social studies skills.

Critical Thinking Skill

Distinguishing Fact From Opinion

Distinguishing fact from opinion can help you make reasonable judgments about what others say and write. Facts can be proved by evidence such as records, documents, or historical sources. Opinions are based on people's differing values and beliefs.

Learning the Skill

The following steps will help you identify facts and opinions:

- Read or listen to the information carefully. Identify the facts. Ask: Can these statements be proved? Where would I find information to prove them?
- If a statement can be proved, it is factual. Check the sources for the facts. Often statistics sound impressive, but they may come from an unreliable source.
- Identify opinions by looking for statements of feelings or beliefs. The statements may contain words like *should, would, could, best, greatest, all, every,* or *always.*

Practicing the Skill

Read the paragraph below, and then answer the questions that follow.

Anyone who thinks the Internet is not used in China has been asleep at the mouse. China's government-owned factories and political system may seem old-fashioned. When it comes to cyberspace, however, China is moving at Net speed. Internet use is growing explosively. In 1997 only 640,000 Chinese were using the Internet. By 2000, the number had increased to 12.3 million. The Phillips Group estimates that by 2005, the online population should hit 85 million.

1. Identify facts. Can you prove that Chinese Internet use is increasing?
2. Note opinions. What phrases alert you that these are opinions?
3. What is the purpose of this paragraph?

Applying the Skill

Watch a television commercial. List one fact and one opinion that are stated. Does the fact seem reliable? How can you prove the fact?

GO TO Practice key skills with **Glencoe Skillbuilder Interactive Workbook, Level 1.**

◄ **Chinese students attend an Internet exhibit in Beijing.**

Practicing the Skill Answers

1. "In 1997 only 640,000 Chinese were using the Internet. By 2000, the number had increased to 12.3 million." These facts prove Internet use is increasing.
2. The rhetorical writing in the first few sentences, and the estimate of Internet usage in 2005, are opinions. Phrases such as "old-fashioned," "Net speed," and "should" signify opinion.
3. to show that China is becoming modernized and its Internet usage is growing rapidly

Applying the Skill

Ask volunteers to share their examples of facts and opinions from television commercials. Have the class discuss what key words in the sentences suggest that they are fact or opinion.

Reading Review

Section 1 China's Land and New Economy

Terms to Know
- dike
- fault
- communist state
- consumer goods

Main Idea

China—the third-largest country in the world—has very diverse landforms. China's rapidly growing economy has changed in recent years.

✓ Place Rugged mountains and harsh deserts cover western and northern China.

✓ Culture About 90 percent of China's people live in the lowlands of eastern China.

✓ Place China's rivers bring fertile soil along with the danger of flooding to the eastern plains.

✓ Economics China's leaders have changed the economy to give the people more economic freedom. The economy has grown rapidly as a result.

✓ Economics Many companies in China are now jointly owned by Chinese and foreign businesspeople. This is because foreign companies can pay workers less than they pay workers in their own countries, and they have millions of possible customers in the Chinese people.

Section 2 Dynasties to Communism

Terms to Know
- dynasty
- human rights
- exile
- calligraphy
- pagoda

Main Idea

The arts and ideas of ancient times still influence China today.

✓ History The ancient teachings of Kongfuzi, Daoism, and Buddhism still influence the people of China.

✓ History For thousands of years, dynasties of emperors ruled China. Today Communist leaders keep tight control over all areas of political life.

✓ Culture China is famous for the skill of its craft workers and for its distinctive painting and architecture.

Section 3 China's Neighbors

Terms to Know
- high-technology industry
- steppe
- nomad
- empire
- yurt

Main Idea

Taiwan and Mongolia have been influenced by Chinese ways and traditions.

✓ Government Taiwan is an island off southeast China. The government of China does not recognize Taiwan as a separate country.

✓ Economics Taiwan's prosperous economy has influenced other Asian economies.

✓ Place Mongolia has rugged terrain and a harsh landscape.

✓ Culture Some people in Mongolia still follow a traditional nomadic lifestyle, and herding remains an important economic activity.

Reading Review

Use the Chapter 23 Reading Review to preview, review, condense, or reteach the chapter.

Preview/Review

Use the Terms to Know lists to help students review and study.

Activity Have students group the terms according to category—physical geography or human geography. Read the terms aloud, one at a time, and ask for volunteers to categorize each term.

Vocabulary PuzzleMaker CD-ROM reinforces the vocabulary terms used in Chapter 23.

The Interactive Tutor Self-Assessment CD-ROM allows students to review Chapter 23 content.

Condense

Have students read the Chapter 23 summary statements.

Guided Reading Activities

Audio Program

Reteach

Reteaching Activity

Reading Essentials and Study Guide

Reading Strategy Read to Write

Summarizing Information Have students create the front page of a newspaper that addresses historical developments and current events in China. Students should use their textbooks and the Internet to organize and write articles that highlight China's history and current event issues, including topics about the economy, government, and culture. Students may photocopy pictures, maps, graphs, or charts that illustrate ideas found in their articles. Have students present their newspapers to the class. L1

Chapter 23 Assessment and Activities

Using Key Terms

Match the terms in Part A with their definitions in Part B.

A.

1. fault
2. dynasty
3. exile
4. high-technology industry
5. dike
6. communist state
7. pagoda
8. calligraphy
9. human rights
10. yurt

B.

a. a building with many-storied towers
b. country whose government has strong control over the economy and society
c. high bank of soil along a river to prevent flooding
d. basic freedoms and rights
e. crack in the earth's crust
f. the art of beautiful writing
g. nomadic tent made of animal skins
h. state of being unable to live in one's own country because of political beliefs
i. line of rulers from the same family
j. industry that produces electronic equipment

Reviewing the Main Ideas

Section 1 China's Land and New Economy

11. **Place** Where do most of China's people live?
12. **Place** What major rivers flow through the plains and southern highlands of China?
13. **Human/Environment Interaction** How has the new economy contributed to air pollution in China?
14. **Economics** Give three reasons why China's economy has boomed.

Section 2 Dynasties to Communism

15. **Culture** What are the ideas of Kongfuzi? Of Laozi?
16. **History** Name three Chinese inventions.
17. **Government** What kind of government did China have between 1911 and 1949?

Section 3 China's Neighbors

18. **Economics** Why is Taiwan's economy important in Asia?
19. **Place** How does Mongolia's landscape prevent much farming?
20. **Economics** How are Mongolia's main industries related to herding?

China & Neighbors

Place Location Activity

On a separate sheet of paper, match the letters on the map with the numbered places listed below.

1. Plateau of Tibet
2. Yellow River
3. Yangtze River
4. Hong Kong
5. Gobi
6. Beijing
7. Mongolia
8. Shanghai
9. Taklimakan Desert
10. Himalaya

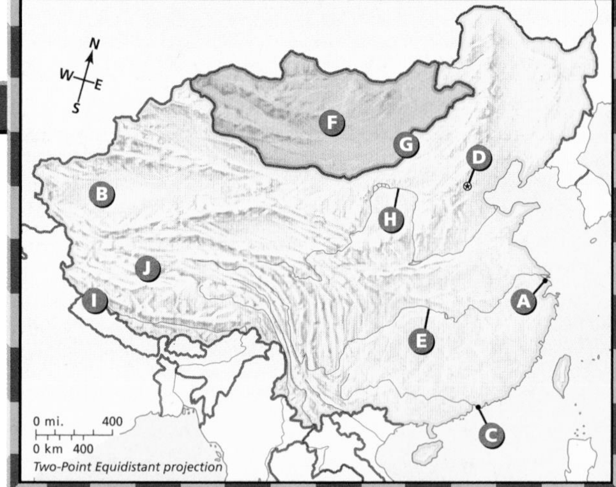

Assessment and Activities

GLENCOE TECHNOLOGY

MindJogger Videoquiz
Use MindJogger Videoquiz to review the Chapter 23 content.

Available in DVD and VHS

Using Key Terms

1.	e	6.	b
2.	i	7.	a
3.	h	8.	f
4.	j	9.	d
5.	c	10.	g

Reviewing the Main Ideas

11. in the eastern part of the country
12. Yangtze, Yellow, Xi
13. Increased industrialization has meant more burning of coal to produce energy, which pollutes the air.
14. *Possible answers:* individuals can choose their jobs, decide where to start businesses, keep profits; foreign company investments
15. Kongfuzi believed that people should be polite, honest, brave, and wise; that children should obey parents; and that subjects should obey rulers. Laozi believed that people should live simply and in harmony with nature.
16. *Possible answers:* paper, ink, silk, magnetic compass, printed books, gunpowder, fireworks
17. a republic
18. because it has one of the world's most prosperous economies and has a growing economic influence on its Asian neighbors
19. The land is very dry, and much of it is covered by mountains or desert.
20. The main industries use wool to make textiles and clothing or cattle hides to make leather and shoes.

NATIONAL GEOGRAPHIC Place Location Activity

1.	J	6.	D
2.	H	7.	F
3.	E	8.	A
4.	C	9.	B
5.	G	10.	I

Critical Thinking

21. *Possible answer:* Chinese rulers did not want Europeans to influence the Chinese people. They were mainly interested in internal development and protecting their borders from invaders.
22. Students' charts should contain facts about China.

Self-Check Quiz Visit ***The World and Its People*** Web site at twip.glencoe.com and click on **Chapter 23—Self-Check Quizzes** to prepare for the Chapter Test.

Critical Thinking

21. **Drawing Conclusions** Why do you think China wanted to be isolated from European countries in the 1700s and 1800s?
22. **Organizing Information** Create a chart like the one below. Under each heading, write at least two facts about China.

Land	Economy	History	Government	People

Comparing Regions Activity

23. **Culture** Research to find information on Chinese art and architecture. Then choose a country in eastern Europe, such as Ukraine, and research its art traditions. How are the art forms similar and different? Include illustrations and photos of what you find.

Mental Mapping Activity

24. **Focusing on the Region** Create a simple outline map of China and its neighbors, and then label the following:

- Himalaya
- Yellow River
- Taiwan
- Beijing
- Gobi
- Ulaanbaatar
- Yangtze River
- Hong Kong

Technology Skills Activity

25. **Developing a Multimedia Presentation** Using the Internet, research one of the arts of China. You might choose painting, architecture, literature, music, or a craft such as casting bronze or making silk. Create a museum exhibit that presents your findings. Include photographs that show examples of works from different periods in Chinese history.

Standardized Test Practice

Directions: Study the map below, and then answer the questions that follow.

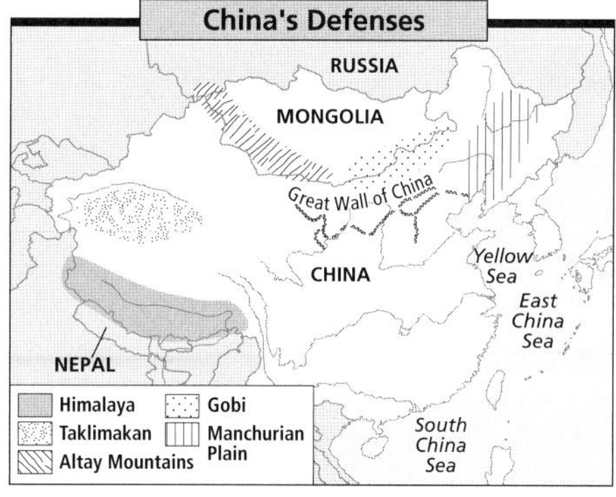

1. **Where is the Gobi?**
   - **A** Near China's Russian border
   - **B** In the southwestern part of China
   - **C** In the Himalaya
   - **D** Along China's border with Mongolia
2. **Which of the following is a human-made defense?**
   - **F** The Great Wall of China
   - **G** The Gobi
   - **H** The Taklimakan
   - **J** The Himalaya

Test-Taking Tip: Look for key words that will help you find the correct answer. An example is *human-made* in question 2. In this case, all of the answer choices are *natural* defenses of China except for the correct answer. Look at the map closely, using its title, the key, and the information shown on the map to find the correct answer choice.

685

Assessment and Activities

Standardized Test Practice

1. D
2. F

Tested Objectives: Reading a map, analyzing information

Chapter Test Bonus Question

This question may be used for extra credit on the chapter test.

What city was recently returned to China by the United Kingdom? *(Hong Kong)*

Have students visit the Web site at twip.glencoe.com to review Chapter 23 and take the Self-Check Quiz.

Dinah Zike's Foldables

Culminating Activity
Organize students into groups of four. Have students choose the main ideas from each of their foldables that best summarizes the section information. Write these ideas on the board and discuss whether they summarize the information correctly.

Comparing Regions Activity

23. Students should accurately describe the similarities and differences between the art forms.

Mental Mapping Activity

24. This exercise helps students visualize China. Accept all attempts at freehand mapping.

Technology Skills Activity

25. Remind students that museum exhibits identify the object and when and where it was made. They also list the materials used and briefly describe the features that show how the object expresses—and departs from—a particular artistic style or period.

1 Focus

Ask students to name highways or industrial complexes in their area that are named for a product or an industry. List their contributions. Then point out that one of the world's oldest and most famous trade routes was named for a product—the Silk Road. L1

2 Teach

Classifying Information
Have students suggest ways that people exchange ideas today. Have them classify their suggestions into the categories "direct contact" (such as travel to other countries) and "long-distance communication" (such as using radio, television, telephones, or the Internet). L2

Meeting National Standards

Geography for Life
The following standards are met in the Student Edition feature:

EE1 The World in Spatial Terms: Standards 1, 3
EE2 Places and Regions: Standards 4, 6
EE4 Human Systems: Standard 11
EE5 Environment and Society: Standards 15, 16

Soft and sleek, silk is a valuable textile.

The Silk Road

Was there really a road made of silk? Well, not exactly. Silk, however, was one of the main products carried along the Silk Road—a system of trade routes that linked ancient China and the empires of the West. When Chinese silk became fashionable in Rome, the precious cloth traveled the Silk Road.

A Risky Route

The road itself was anything but soft and smooth. Traveling from China, camels laden with silk and other cargo trudged through deserts, including the Taklimakan, a name meaning "go in and you won't come out." Sandstorms and intense heat made passage difficult. Farther along the route, the Pamir mountain range thrust an ice- and snow-covered barrier in the way. The road was dangerous as well. Bandits attacked often, stealing valuable goods.

Few traveled the entire 4,000-mile (6,437-km) series of routes. Instead, merchants bought goods in trading posts and oases along the way and sold them at other markets farther along, much as relay runners pass a baton.

Chinese Secret Agent

Zhang Qian, an agent on a secret mission for Chinese Emperor Wudi, may have started the silk trade. In 139 B.C. invaders swept into China, despite China's Great Wall. Zhang Qian was sent far into Central Asia to find allies to help fight the invaders. He found no allies. Instead, he brought back strong horses for the military, which he had bought with bolts of silk.

Soon the Chinese were trading silk with the Parthian Empire, which is present-day Iran. It is said that Rome wanted silk after its soldiers spotted silk banners fluttering above Parthian troops. By the A.D. 100s, China and Rome were trading a variety of goods. From the East came such exotic items as silk, spices, and fruits. Rome paid in glass, wool, and ivory, but mostly in gold.

Ideas also traveled the Silk Road. From India, the religion of Buddhism reached China. Christianity and Islam spread eastward as well. Chinese techniques for making paper and explosives traveled west. Western methods of cloth manufacturing and better gun design went to China. The process for making silk, however, traveled nowhere until much later. The Chinese successfully guarded their secret—that silk was made from the strands of a silkworm's cocoon.

For centuries, goods and ideas traveled between East and West. In the 1300s, however, the Silk Road began to decline as sea routes proved safer than land routes. Nevertheless, even today, parts of the Silk Road are busy with trade—and tourism. In addition to camels, tour buses now travel the caravan routes.

QUESTIONS

1. How is the Silk Road "made of silk"?
2. What were some obstacles along the Silk Road?

A man and his camel travel the Silk Road in China. ▶

686

Answers to the Questions

1. because silk was the chief good that was traded along the road
2. the harsh Taklimakan Desert; the high, cold Pamir Mountains; bandit attacks

NATIONAL GEOGRAPHIC

Silk Road Routes

Silk Road
Velikiy Novgorod
Moscow
Istanbul (Constantinople)
Caspian Sea
Aral Sea
Black Sea
Mediterranean Sea
RUSSIA
MONGOLIA
Pamirs
Taklimakan Desert
Anxi
Xi'an
CHINA
Antioch
IRAN
Samarqand
Baghdad
IRAQ
INDIA
AFRICA
Arabian Sea
Bay of Bengal
South China Sea
N S W E
0 mi. 1,000
0 km 1,000
Miller projection

Time Line

- **139 B.C.:** Zhang Qian travels west into Central Asia
- **130 B.C.–A.D. 900:** First period in which Silk Road flourishes
- **c. 100 B.C.:** Hybrid camels are bred to carry goods
- **c. 100 B.C.–A.D. 600:** Independent principalities arise in Central Asia along Silk Road
- **c. A.D. 100:** Kushan people of Afghanistan first use the stirrup, which spreads along the Silk Road
- **c. A.D. 100:** Buddhism begins to spread along Silk Road
- **c. A.D. 1300:** Silk Road begins to decline in importance for trade

3 Assess

Have students answer the questions on page 686.

4 Close

Have students make a list of the kinds of goods that are traded around the world today. Which do they think are as valuable and desirable as silk was in more ancient times?

Geography and History Activity

Using Maps Have students compare the map of the Silk Road to the map of Asia in the Reference Atlas. Have them make a list of the countries through which the Silk Road passed.

EE4 Human Systems: Standard 11

Chapter 24 Resources

Note: The following materials may be used when teaching Chapter 24.
Section level support materials are shown at point of use in the margins of the Teacher Wraparound Edition.

Timesaving Tools

TeacherWorks™ All-In-One Planner and Resource Center

- **Interactive Teacher Edition** See the **Interactive Teacher Edition** CD-ROM to electronically integrate your Teacher Wraparound Edition and blackline masters.
- **Interactive Lesson Planner** Organize your week, month, semester, or year with all the lesson helps you need. The **Interactive Lesson Planner** CD-ROM contains all Chapter 24 resources.

Use Glencoe's **Presentation Plus!** multimedia teacher tool to easily present dynamic lessons that visually excite your students. Using Microsoft PowerPoint® you can customize the presentations to create your own personalized lessons.

TEACHING TRANSPARENCIES

Graphic Organizer Transparency 11 L2

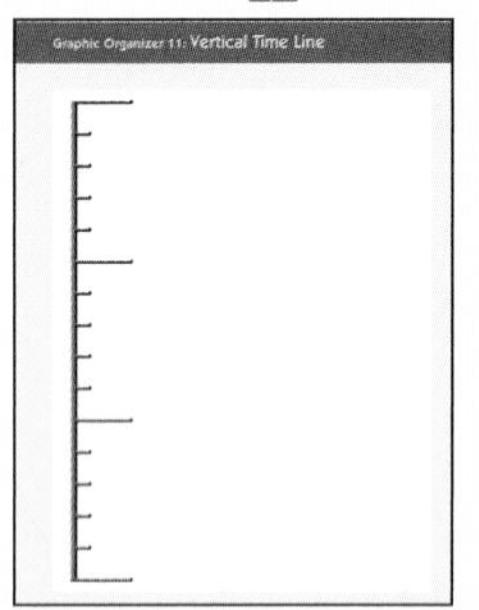

In-text Map Transparency L1

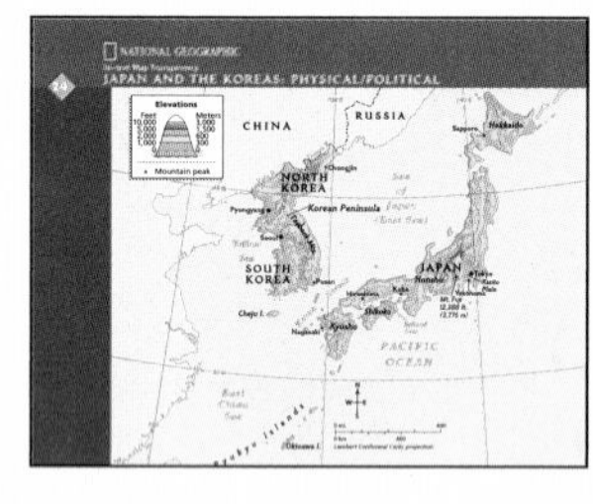

FOLDABLES™ Study Organizer

Dinah Zike's Foldables

Foldables are three-dimensional, interactive graphic organizers that help students practice basic writing skills, review key vocabulary terms, and identify main ideas. Additional chapter activities can be found in the ***Reading and Study Skills Foldables*** booklet.

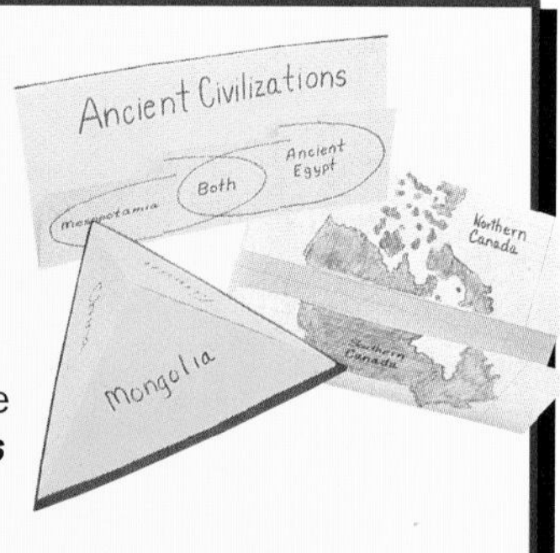

MAP AND GEOGRAPHY SKILLS

Chapter Map Activity L2

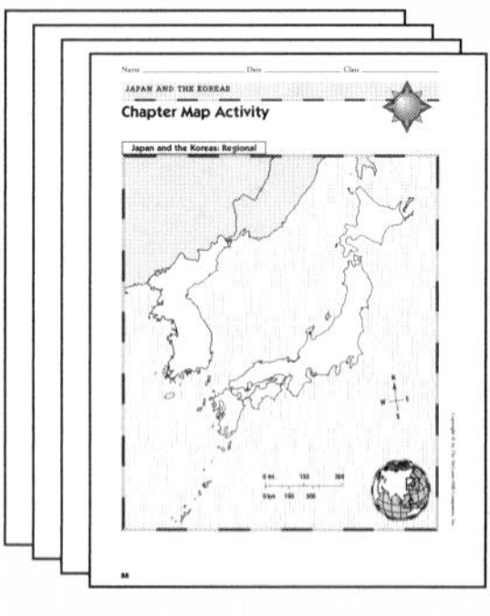

GeoLab Activity L2

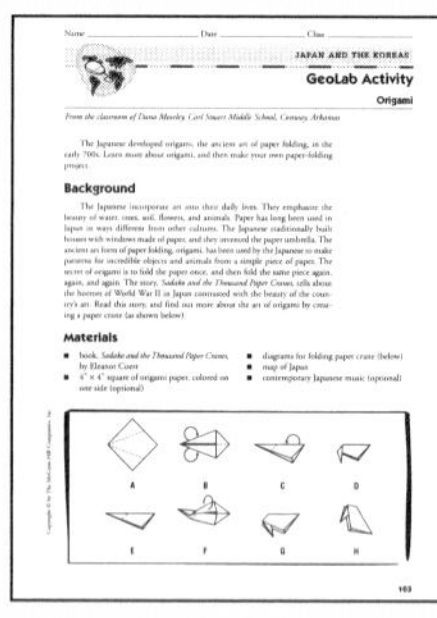

READING SUPPORT

Vocabulary Activity L1

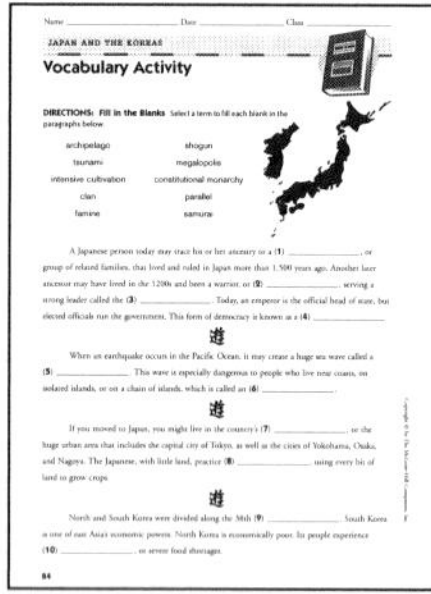

Workbook Activity L1

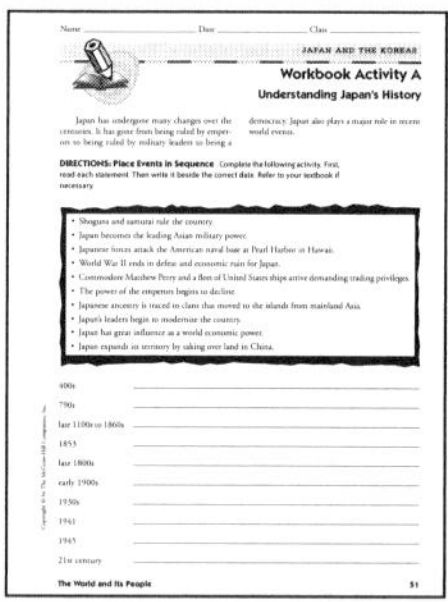

Reading and Writing Skills Activity L1/ELL

DIFFERENTIATED INSTRUCTION

Use these review and reinforcement materials to help less-proficient readers, English learners, and gifted and talented students.

Reteaching Activity L1

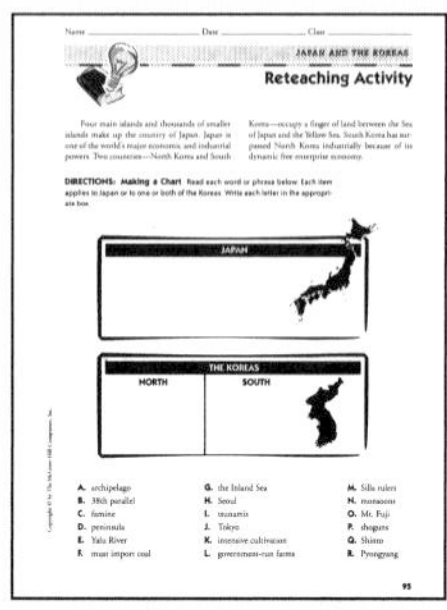

Chapter Skills Review L2

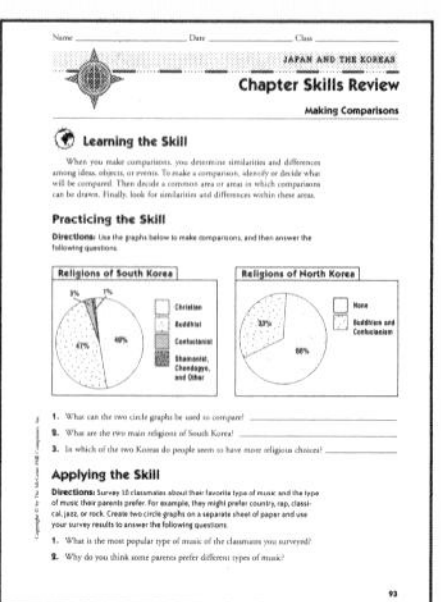

Cooperative Learning Activity L1/ELL

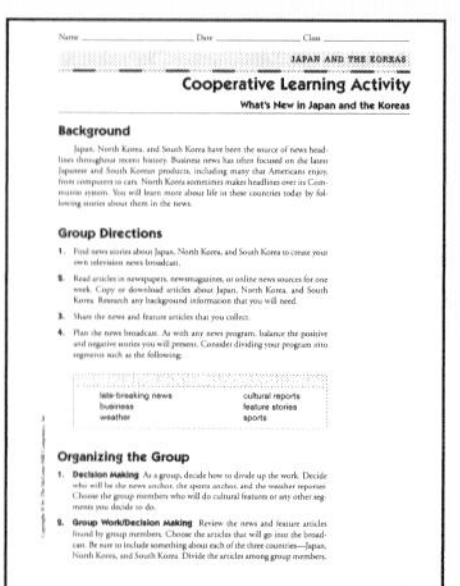

Enrichment Activity L3

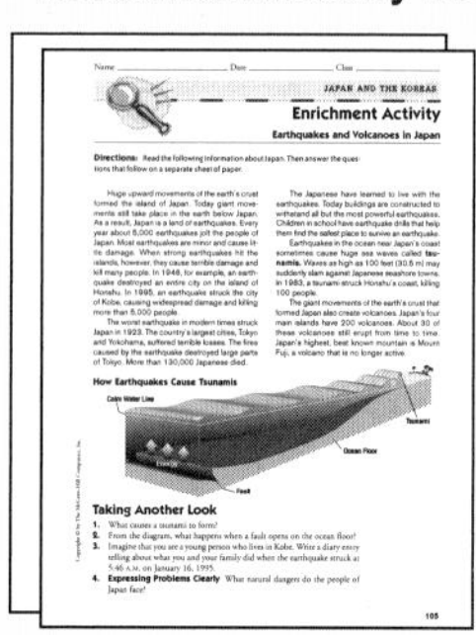

ASSESSMENT

Chapter Test, Form A L2

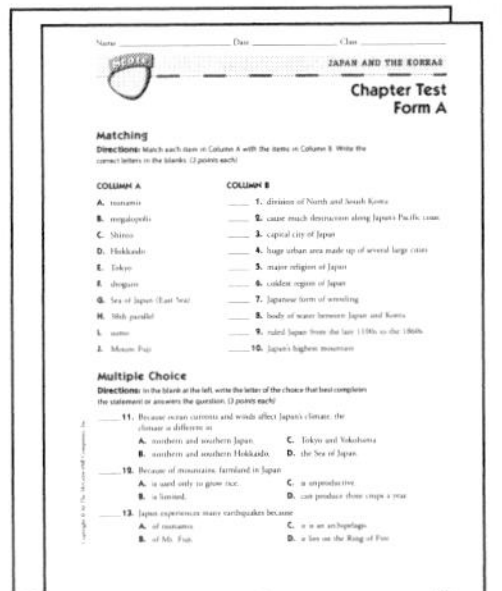

Chapter Test, Form B L2

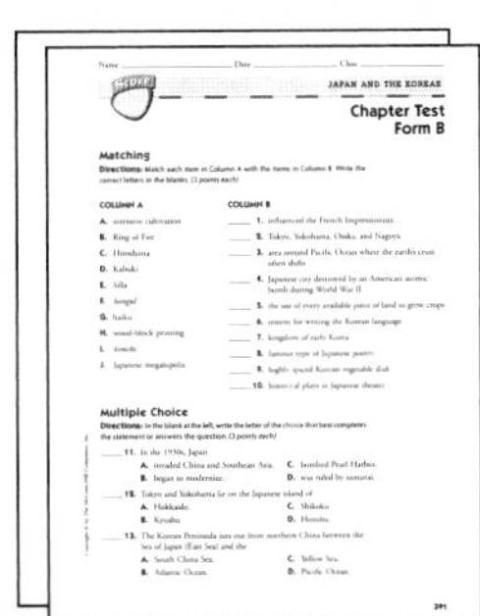

Performance Assessment Activity L1/ELL

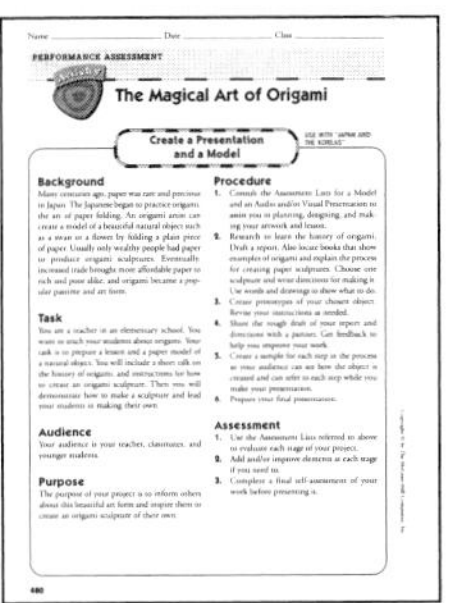

ExamView® Pro Testmaker CD-ROM

STANDARDIZED ASSESSMENT SKILLS

Critical Thinking Skills Activity L2

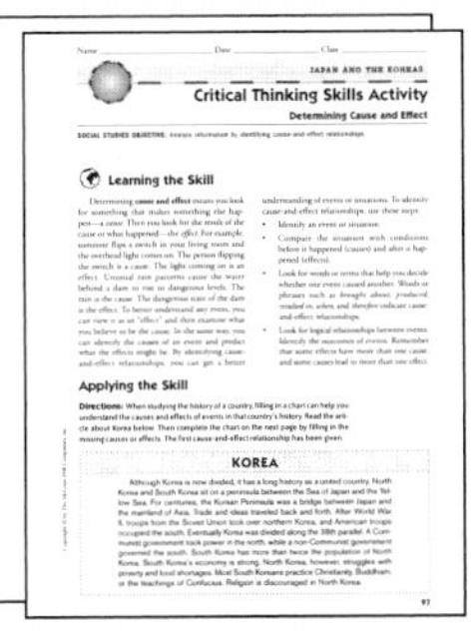

Map and Graph Skills Activity L2

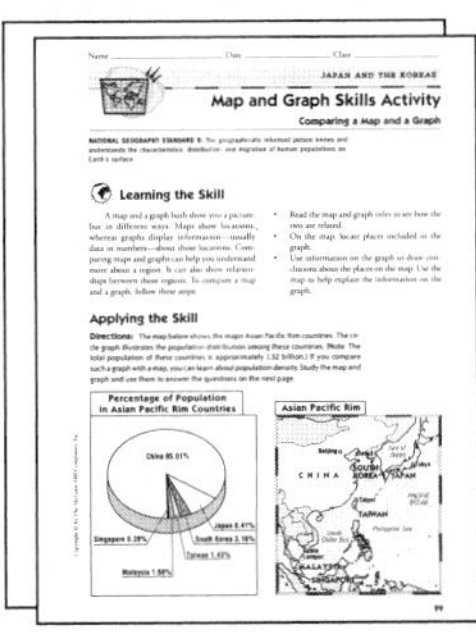

Standardized Test Skills Practice Workbook Activity L2

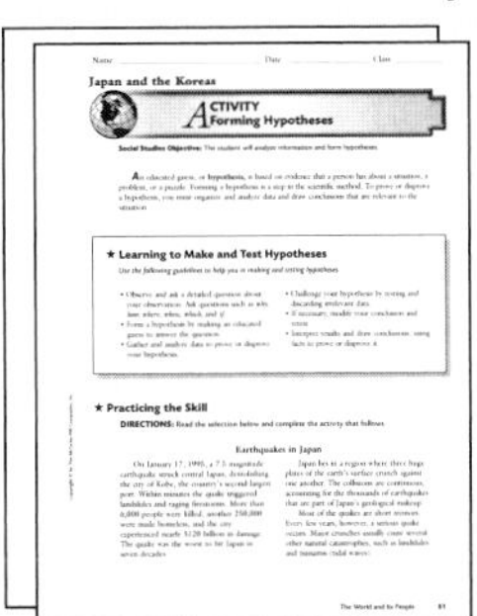

HOME INVOLVEMENT

Take-Home Review Activity L1

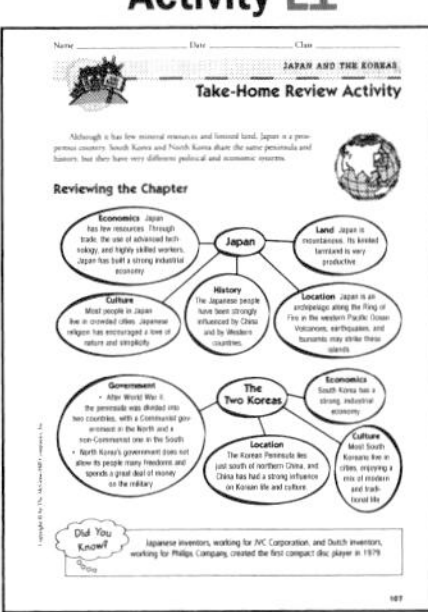

MULTIMEDIA

- National Geographic's The World and Its People
- MindJogger Videoquiz
- Vocabulary PuzzleMaker CD-ROM
- Interactive Tutor Self-Assessment CD-ROM
- ExamView® Pro Testmaker CD-ROM
- TeacherWorks CD-ROM
- StudentWorks CD-ROM
- Skillbuilder Interactive Workbook CD-ROM, Level 1
- Presentation Plus! CD-ROM
- Audio Program

SPANISH RESOURCES

The following Spanish language materials are available in the Spanish Resources binder:

- **Spanish Summaries**
- **Spanish Vocabulary Activities**
- **Spanish Guided Reading Activities**
- **Spanish Quizzes and Tests**
- **Spanish Take-Home Review Activities**
- **Spanish Reteaching Activities**

Meeting National Standards

Geography for Life

The following standards are covered in Chapter 24:

Section 1 **EE4 Human Systems:** Standards 9, 10, 11, 12, 13

EE5 Environment and Society: Standards 14, 15, 16

Section 2 **EE4 Human Systems:** Standards 9, 10, 11, 12, 13

EE5 Environment and Society: Standards 14, 15, 16

EE6 The Uses of Geography: Standard 17

State and Local Objectives

Chapter 24 Planning Guide

SECTION RESOURCES

Daily Objectives	Reproducible Resources	Multimedia Resources
Section 1 **Japan—Past and Present** **1.** Explain what economic activities are important in Japan. **2.** Describe how the past has influenced Japan. **3.** Summarize how religion has shaped culture in Japan.	Reproducible Lesson Plan Daily Lecture and Discussion Notes Note-taking Guide Guided Reading Activity* Reading Essentials and Study Guide* Section Quiz*	Daily Focus Skills Transparency In-text Map Transparency Vocabulary PuzzleMaker CD-ROM Interactive Tutor Self-Assessment CD-ROM ExamView® Pro Testmaker CD-ROM Presentation Plus! CD-ROM
Section 2 **The Two Koreas** **1.** Locate the Korean Peninsula. **2.** Explain why the two Koreas are divided. **3.** Compare life in North and South Korea.	Reproducible Lesson Plan Daily Lecture and Discussion Notes Note-taking Guide Guided Reading Activity* Reading Essentials and Study Guide* Section Quiz*	Daily Focus Skills Transparency Vocabulary PuzzleMaker CD-ROM Interactive Tutor Self-Assessment CD-ROM ExamView® Pro Testmaker CD-ROM Presentation Plus! CD-ROM MindJogger Videoquiz

00:00 **Out of Time?** Assign the **Reading Essentials and Study Guide*** for this chapter.

*Also available in Spanish

KEY TO ABILITY LEVELS

Teaching strategies have been coded for varying learning styles and abilities.

L1 **BASIC** activities for all students
L2 **AVERAGE** activities for average to above-average students
L3 **CHALLENGING** activities for above-average students
ELL **ENGLISH LANGUAGE LEARNER** activities

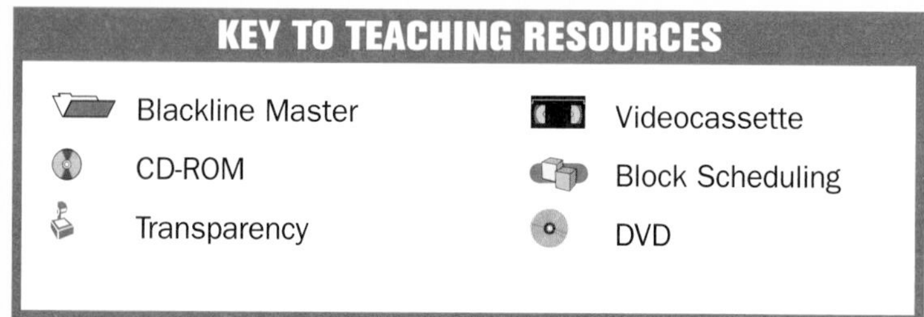

Making a Human Graph

Nancy Pund
Deltona Middle School
Deltona, Florida

Ask students to define the terms *culture* and *culture region.* Ask them to describe the traits that define culture *(language, religions, customs, food, clothing styles, and so on).* As students give ideas, write the topics on the board, across the top. Ask students to choose the one thing that they think most defines them culturally, and then have them stand in a straight row in front of that topic on the board. Record the number of students in each row. Then have the students transfer that information to a bar graph or pictograph.

Meeting Special Needs

In addition to the Differentiated Instruction strategies found in each section, the following resources are also suitable for your special needs students:

- ***ExamView® Pro Testmaker CD-ROM*** allows teachers to tailor tests by reducing answer choices.
- The ***Audio Program*** includes the entire narrative of the student edition so that less-proficient readers can listen to the words as they read them.
- The ***Reading Essentials and Study Guide*** provides the same content as the student edition but is written two grade levels below the textbook.
- ***Guided Reading Activities*** give less-proficient readers point-by-point instructions to increase comprehension as they read each textbook section.
- ***Enrichment Activities*** include a stimulating collection of readings and activities for gifted and talented students.

TEACHER'S CORNER

Index to National Geographic Magazine:

The following articles may be used for research relating to this chapter:

- "Japan's Imperial Palace," by Robert M. Poole, January 2001.
- "Sumo," by T.R. Reid, July 1997.
- "Okinawa: Claiming Its Birthright," by Arthur Zich, June 1997.

Additional National Geographic Society Products:

To order the following products for use with this chapter, call National Geographic Society at 1-800-368-2728:

- *National Geographic Desk Reference* (Book)
- *Asia* (Video)
- *Japan: Families of the World Series* (Video)

NGS ONLINE

Access National Geographic's Web site for current events, activities, links, interactive features, and archives.
www.nationalgeographic.com

MapMachine

Find the latest coverage of geography in the news, atlas updates, cartographic activities with interactive maps, an online map store, and links at www.nationalgeographic.com/maps

SOCIAL STUDIES Online

Use our Web site for additional resources. All essential content is covered in the Student Edition.

You and your students can visit twip.glencoe.com, the Web site companion to *The World and Its People.* This innovative integration of electronic and print media offers your students a wealth of opportunities. The student text directs students to the Web site for the following options:

- Chapter Overviews
- Student Web Activities
- Self-Check Quizzes
- Textbook Updates

Answers are provided for you in the Web Activity Lesson Plan. Additional Web resources and Interactive Tutor puzzles are also available.

Introducing Chapter 24

Social Studies Online

Introduce students to chapter content and key terms by having them access Chapter Overview 24 at twip.glencoe.com

Chapter Objectives

1. Explain the significance of the location of Japan and the two Koreas.
2. Describe the economy and culture of Japan.
3. Compare the economies and governments of North and South Korea.

GLENCOE TECHNOLOGY

NATIONAL GEOGRAPHIC

The World and Its People Video Program

Chapter 25 Japan and the Koreas

The following segments enhance the study of this chapter:

- **Tokyo Fish Market**
- **The Haenyo of Cheju**

MindJogger Videoquiz

Use MindJogger Videoquiz to preview the Chapter 24 content.

Both programs available in DVD and VHS

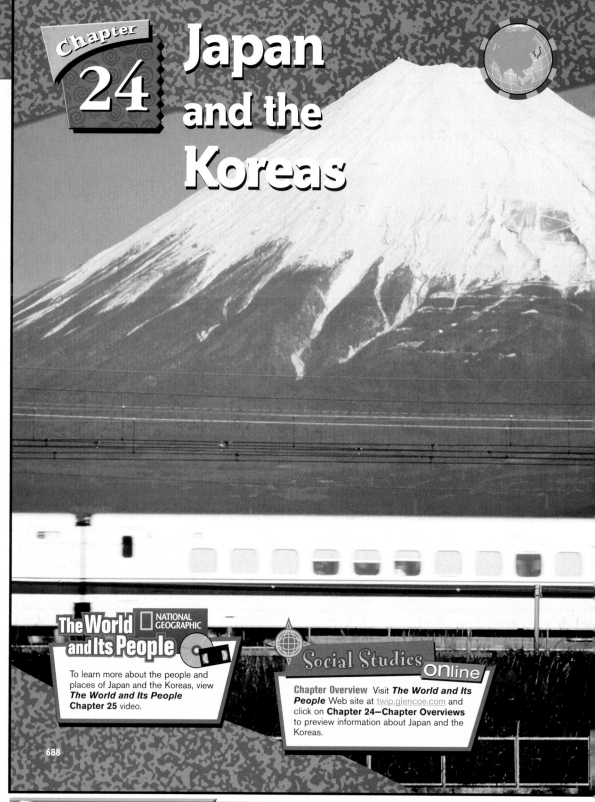

Chapter 24 Japan and the Koreas

The World and Its People NATIONAL GEOGRAPHIC

To learn more about the people and places of Japan and the Koreas, view ***The World and Its People*** **Chapter 25** video.

Social Studies Online

Chapter Overview Visit ***The World and Its People*** Web site at twip.glencoe.com and click on **Chapter 24—Chapter Overviews** to preview information about Japan and the Koreas.

688

Reading Strategy — Purpose for Reading

Use the **K–W–L** reading strategy to draw on student's prior knowledge of Japan and the Koreas. Have students divide notebook paper into three columns. In the first column, have them write "What Do I **K**now About Japan and North and South Korea?" In the middle column, have them write "What Do I **W**ant to Know?" In the last column, have them write "What Have I **L**earned?" Ask them to complete the first two columns. You may want them to discuss what they wrote with a partner and then have partners share their responses with the class. Finally, ask students to add information to the last column as they study the chapter. L1

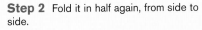

FOLDABLES™ Study Organizer

Compare-Contrast Make this foldable to help you compare and contrast the people and places of Japan and the Koreas.

Step 1 Fold one sheet of paper in half from top to bottom.

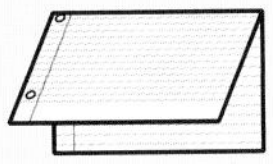

Step 2 Fold it in half again, from side to side.

Step 3 Unfold the paper once. Sketch an outline of the Koreas and Japan across both tabs and label them as shown.

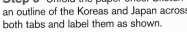

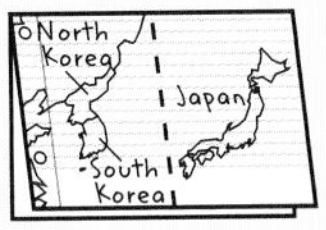

Step 4 Cut up the fold of the top flap only.

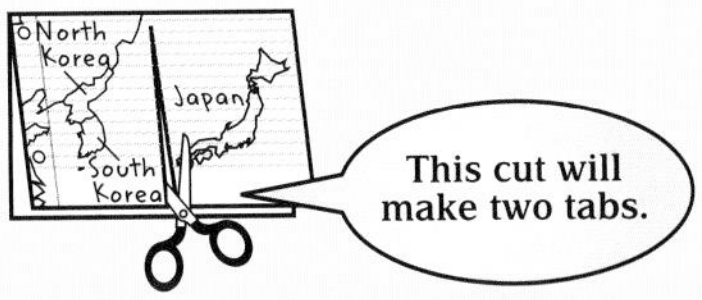

Reading and Writing As you read the chapter, write what you learn about these countries under the appropriate tab. Use your notes to determine how these countries are alike and different.

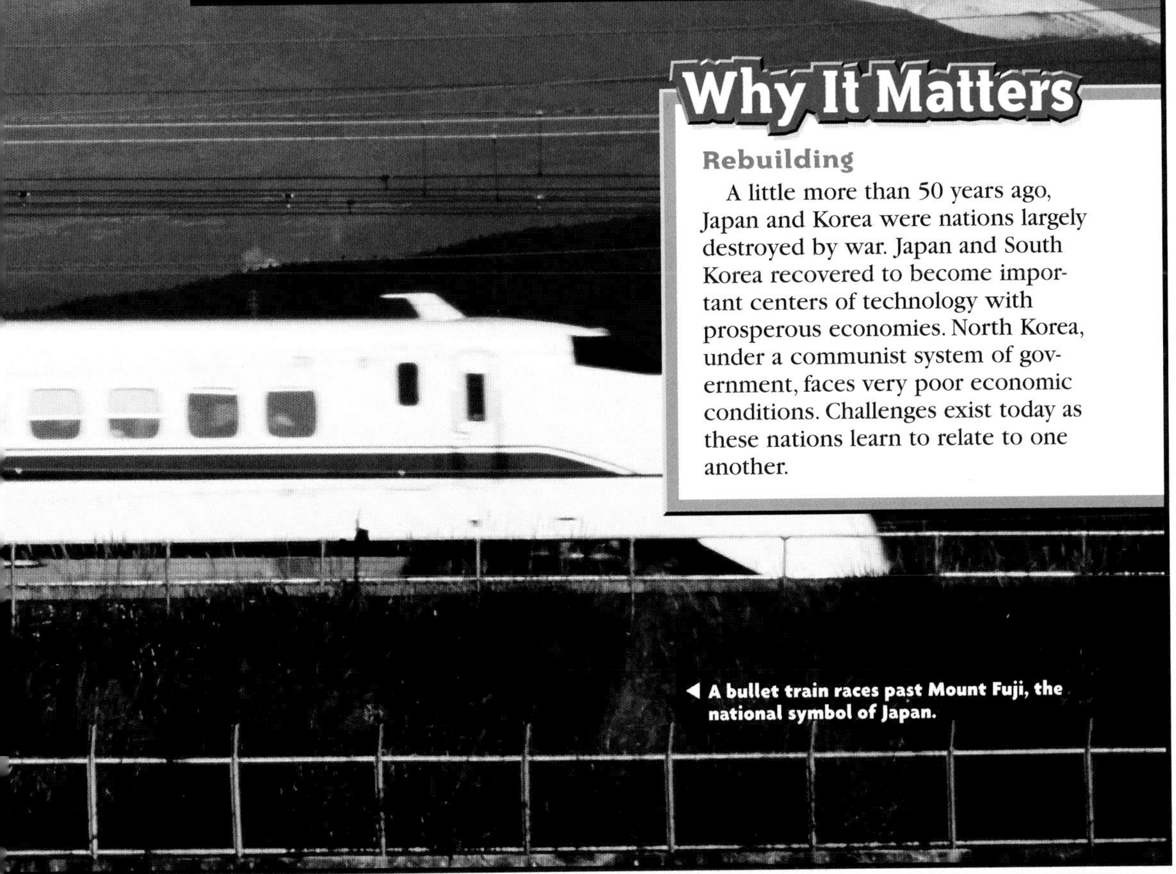

Why It Matters

Rebuilding

A little more than 50 years ago, Japan and Korea were nations largely destroyed by war. Japan and South Korea recovered to become important centers of technology with prosperous economies. North Korea, under a communist system of government, faces very poor economic conditions. Challenges exist today as these nations learn to relate to one another.

◀ **A bullet train races past Mount Fuji, the national symbol of Japan.**

FOLDABLES™ Study Organizer **Dinah Zike's Foldables**

Purpose Students make and use a foldable to help them organize the similarities and differences between Japan and the Koreas. As students read the chapter and fill in information on their foldables, they analyze the similarities and differences of the people and places of Japan and the Koreas.

Have students complete the ***Reading and Study Skills Foldables*** activity for this chapter.

Why It Matters

Tell students that Japan's industrial output rose spectacularly from the 1950s to the 1990s when a sharp recession settled in. Meanwhile, four of Japan's neighbors earned the nickname "little dragons." They were Hong Kong, Singapore, South Korea, and Taiwan. Ask students why that nickname might have been given to them. *(because of their fierce economic growth)* Ask students what country they think experienced the most economic growth during the late 1990s. *(China)*

About the Photo

Mount Fuji, a dormant volcano, is one of Japan's most famous tourist attractions and one of the country's great natural wonders. In this photo ancient meets modern with Mount Fuji overlooking one of Japan's modern marvels—the bullet train. Japan is where regular, high-speed railways were born. The country's Shinkansen ("bullet train") network has been developed over more than 35 years, and today carries more than 100 million passengers per year at speeds up to 170 miles per hour. The city of Tokyo takes a central position in the Shinkansen network with most lines starting there and carrying passengers to the west and north of the densely populated nation. The bullet trains have a reputation for being safe, fast, comfortable, and quiet.

Chapter 24

Section 1, pages 690–696

Focus

Section Objectives

1. Explain what economic activities are important in Japan.
2. Describe how the past has influenced Japan.
3. Summarize how religion has shaped culture in Japan.

BELLRINGER
Skillbuilder Activity

Project transparency and have students answer the question.

Daily Focus Skills Transparency

DAILY FOCUS SKILLS TRANSPARENCY
Japan and the Koreas
Section 1

Analyzing Statistics

Japanese Baseball 2003 Season Results

Pacific League Champs
Fukuoka Daiei Hawks
82 Wins
55 Losses, 3 Ties
Home: 40W, 29L, 1T
Road: 42W, 26L, 2T

Central League Champs
Hanshin Tigers
87 Wins
51 Losses, 2 Ties
Home: 50W, 20L
Road: 37W, 31L, 2T

Which team had the higher winning percentage at home? What was that team's home winning percentage?

Reading Preview

■ **Activating Prior Knowledge** **Ask:** What are symbols of the United States? *(bald eagle, flag, Statue of Liberty)* Then ask students to give ideas about items that symbolize Japan.

■ **Preteaching Vocabulary** Have students use the Reference Atlas and show them examples of archipelagoes, such as Japan, the Philippines, and Hawaii. Then have students formulate a definition of the word based on these examples.

Guide to Reading

Main Idea

Although Japan's people have few mineral resources, they have built a prosperous country.

Terms to Know

- tsunami
- archipelago
- intensive cultivation
- clan
- shogun
- samurai
- constitutional monarchy
- megalopolis

Reading Strategy

Create a chart like this one. In the right column, write a fact about Japan for each topic in the left column.

Japan	Fact
Land	
Economy	
History	
People	

Section 1

Japan—Past and Present

NATIONAL GEOGRAPHIC **Exploring Our World**

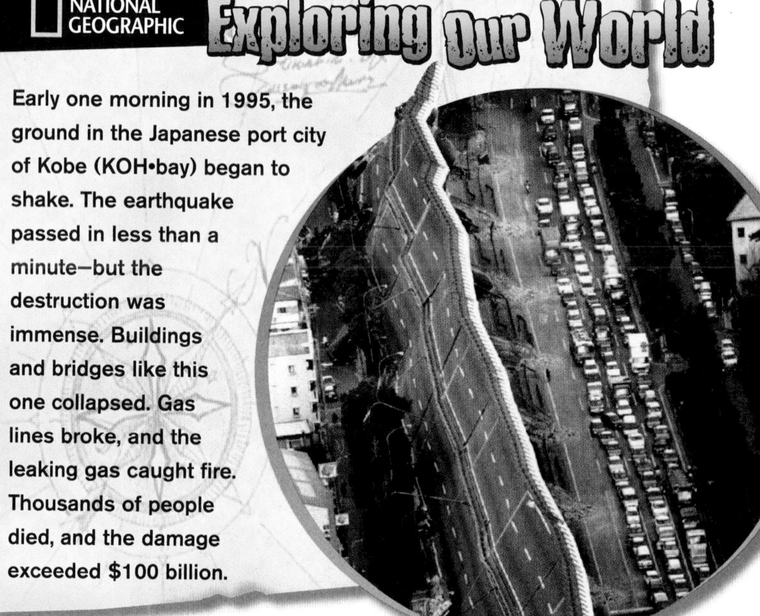

Early one morning in 1995, the ground in the Japanese port city of Kobe (KOH•bay) began to shake. The earthquake passed in less than a minute—but the destruction was immense. Buildings and bridges like this one collapsed. Gas lines broke, and the leaking gas caught fire. Thousands of people died, and the damage exceeded $100 billion.

The city of Kobe suffered an earthquake because Japan lies on the Ring of Fire. This name refers to an area surrounding the Pacific Ocean where the earth's crust often shifts. Japan experiences thousands of earthquakes each year. People in Japan also have to deal with **tsunamis** (tsu•NAH•mees). These huge sea waves caused by undersea earthquakes are very destructive along Japan's Pacific coast.

Japan's Mountainous Islands

Japan is an **archipelago** (AHR•kuh•PEH•luh•GOH), or a group of islands, off the coast of eastern Asia between the Sea of Japan and the Pacific Ocean. Four main islands and thousands of smaller ones make up Japan's land area. The largest islands are **Hokkaido** (hoh•KY•doh), **Honshu, Shikoku** (shee•KOH•koo), and **Kyushu** (KYOO•SHOO).

These islands are actually the peaks of mountains that rise from the floor of the Pacific Ocean. The mountains are volcanic, but many are

Section Resources

Reproducible Masters

- Reproducible Lesson Plan
- Daily Lecture and Discussion Notes
- Note-taking Guide
- Guided Reading Activity
- Reading Essentials and Study Guide
- Section Quiz

Transparencies

- Daily Focus Skills Transparency
- In-text Map Transparency

Multimedia

- Vocabulary PuzzleMaker CD-ROM
- Interactive Tutor Self-Assessment CD-ROM
- Presentation Plus! CD-ROM
- ExamView® Pro Testmaker CD-ROM

no longer active. The most famous peak is **Mount Fuji,** Japan's highest mountain and national symbol. Rugged mountains and steep, forested hills dominate most of Japan. Narrowly squeezed between the seacoast and the mountains are plains. The **Kanto Plain** in eastern Honshu is Japan's largest plain. **Tokyo,** the capital, and **Yokohama,** one of Asia's major port cities, are located here. You will find most of Japan's cities, farms, and industries on the coastal plains.

No part of Japan is more than 70 miles (113 km) from the sea. In bay areas along the jagged coasts lie many fine harbors and ports. The northern islands receive cold Arctic Ocean winds and currents. The Pacific Ocean, in contrast, sends warm ocean currents to the southern part of Japan.

✓Reading Check **What are the two major landforms in Japan?**

NATIONAL GEOGRAPHIC **Japan and the Koreas: Physical/Political**

Applying Map Skills

1. What bodies of water lie between Japan and the Koreas?
2. What is Japan's highest peak? How high is it?

Find NGS online map resources @ www.nationalgeographic.com/maps

2 TEACH

Understanding Cause and Effect Give students a fact about Japan, such as "lies on the Ring of Fire." Then have them predict effects that might result from this fact. *(danger of earthquakes; need to have organized civil defense measures; need to design buildings to withstand earthquakes)* L1

Daily Lecture and Discussion Notes

JAPAN AND THE KOREAS

Daily Lecture and Discussion Notes
Japan—Past and Present

Did You Know? The Japanese call their country *Nippon* or *Nihon,* which means "source of the sun." The name *Japan* may have come from *Zipangu,* the Italian name given to the country by Marco Polo, a Venetian traveler of the late 1200s. Polo had heard of the Japanese islands while traveling through China.

I. Japan's Mountainous Islands

A. Japan lies on the Ring of Fire and experiences thousands of earthquakes a year. People in Japan also have to deal with **tsunamis.** These huge sea waves, caused by undersea earthquakes, are very destructive along Japan's Pacific coast.

B. Japan is an **archipelago,** or a group of islands, off the coast of eastern Asia ... of Japan and the Pacific Ocean. Four main islands and ... up Japan's land area. The four largest islands

✓ Reading Check Answer

mountains and hills

Applying Map Skills

Answers

1. Sea of Japan, Korea Strait
2. Mt. Fuji; 12,388 ft. (3,776 m)

In-text Map Transparency Activity Have students look at the map. **Ask:** Why is the "Inland Sea" so named? *(because the island of Shikoku protects it from the open ocean)*

Reading Strategy **Reading the Text**

Analyzing Information Write the following Japanese proverb: "Failure is the source of success." Then ask students to analyze the information under Japan's Economy and Japan's History and Government for examples that confirm the proverb. For each example, direct students to find passages that describe a failure and the success that came from that failure. Encourage students to share and compare their examples and passages. L1

*Use the **Reading Skills Handbook** for more reading strategies.*

Creating a Display Ask students to create collages titled "Life in the Ring of Fire," showing earthquakes and volcanoes in Japan. Students might include maps that show where these events occurred, time lines highlighting the worst incidences, photographs showing the extent of the damage, and first-person accounts of what it was like to live through these disasters. L1

Literature

Answer Sadako was suffering from an illness caused by a military action. In some sense she was a soldier in the war. She was a symbol of what had happened to the nation as a whole. People wanted her to recover just as Japan was to recover.

Current Events Journal

Suggest that students use graphic organizers to link related information about Japan. For example, they can divide their notes about physical geography under the headings "Landforms" and "Bodies of Water." They could split information on the economy under "Industry" and "Agriculture."

Japan's Economy

Japan's industries have benefited from having highly skilled workers. The people of Japan value hard work, cooperation, and education. After high school graduation, many Japanese students go on to a local university.

Industry Japan has few mineral resources, so it must import raw materials, such as iron ore, coal, and oil. However, Japan is an industrial giant known around the world for the variety and quality of its manufactured goods. Japan's modern factories use new technology and robots to make their products quickly and carefully. These products include automobiles and other vehicles. The graph on page 12 in the **Geography Handbook** shows you that Japan leads the world in automobile production. Japan's factories also produce consumer goods such as electronic equipment, watches, small appliances, and calculators. Other factories produce industrial goods such as steel, cement, fertilizer, plastics, and fabrics.

Literature

SADAKO AND THE THOUSAND PAPER CRANES
by Eleanor Coerr

This book tells the true story of a young Japanese girl living in the aftermath of World War II. Radiation from the atomic bomb dropped on Hiroshima caused Sadako to get leukemia. Sadako turned to the ancient art of origami (folding paper to make objects) for strength and courage.

While Sadako closed her eyes, Chizuko put some pieces of paper and scissors on the bed . . . "I've figured out a way for you to get well," she said proudly. "Watch!" She cut a piece of gold paper into a large square. In a short time she had folded it over and over into a beautiful crane. Sadako was puzzled. "But how can that paper bird make me well?" "Don't you remember that old story about the crane?" Chizuko asked. "It's supposed to live for a thousand years. If a sick person folds one thousand paper cranes, the gods will grant her wish and make her healthy again." . . . With the golden crane nearby she felt safe and lucky. Why, in a few weeks she would be able to finish the thousand. Then she would be strong enough to go home.

Source: *Sadako and the Thousand Paper Cranes* by Eleanor Coerr. Copyright 1977. The Putnam Publishing Group.

Analyzing Literature

Sadako died before she finished making the one thousand paper cranes, but she became a national heroine in Japan. What was it about Sadako that made other Japanese people feel connected to her and proud of her?

Differentiated Instruction

Meeting Special Needs: Auditory/Musical For students whose learning style reflects a sensitivity to pitch, melody, rhythm, and tone, help them locate recorded examples of East Asian music. Have students listen to the various examples, identifying how they are similar or different in terms of instruments, rhythms, tone, and so on. Allow students to prepare a presentation that summarizes facts about East Asian music. They may discuss different styles, instruments, or performers that are found in each country of the region. L2

Agriculture Farmland in Japan is very limited. Yet farmers use fertilizers and modern machinery to produce high crop yields. They also practice **intensive cultivation,** which means they grow crops on every available piece of land. Crops grow on terraces cut in hillsides and even between buildings and highways. In warmer areas, farmers harvest two or three crops a year. The chief crop is rice, a basic part of the Japanese diet. Other important crops include sugar beets, potatoes, fruits, and tea. Seafood is an important part of the people's diet as well. Japan's fishing fleet is one of the world's largest and provides nearly 15 percent of the world's fish.

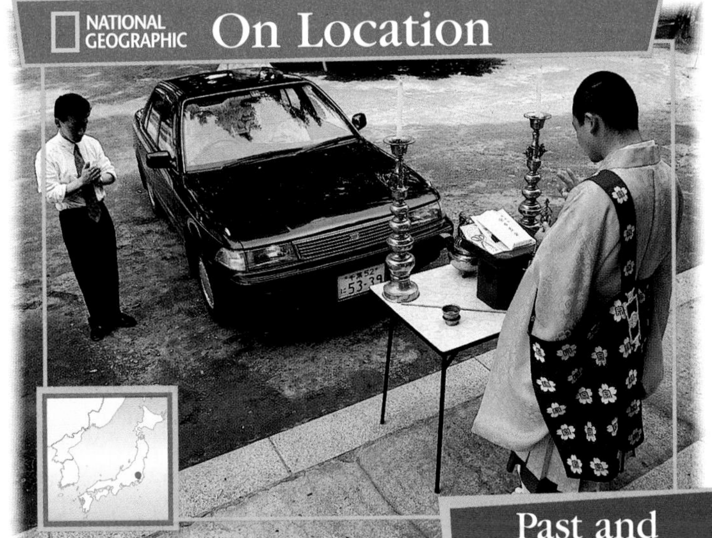

Past and Present

Past and present come together in Japan. Here, a priest of the ancient Shinto religion blesses a family's shiny new car.

Place Where was this car probably made? Why?

Economic Challenges Japan is one of the world's leading exporters. Because of trade restrictions, the country imports few finished goods from other countries, however. This has led to disagreements with trading partners who want to export more goods to Japan.

Another challenge facing Japan is preserving the environment. Air pollution from power plants has produced acid rain. Because of overfishing, supplies of seafood have dropped. The government has passed laws to limit the amount of fish that can be caught each year.

✓Reading Check What are some products made by Japanese manufacturers?

Japan's History and Government

Japan's history reaches back many centuries. The Japanese trace their ancestry to various **clans,** or groups of related families. These clans originally came from the mainland of Asia and lived on the islands as early as the late A.D. 400s.

The Japanese developed close ties with China on the Asian mainland. Ruled by emperors, Japan modeled its society on the Chinese way of life. The Japanese also borrowed the Chinese system of writing and accepted the Buddhist religion brought by Chinese missionaries. Today most Japanese practice Buddhism along with Shinto, Japan's own traditional religion.

In the 790s, the power of emperors began to decline. From the late 1100s to the 1860s, Japan was ruled by **shoguns,** or military leaders, and powerful land-owning warriors known as the **samurai.**

More About the Photo

Shinto Although the religion had been followed for centuries, Shinto did not have a name in Japan until the A.D. 500s. Then, as Buddhism made gains, traditional beliefs were given the name Shinto, which means "the way of *kami*" (the spiritual or divine).

Caption Answer Japan; it is the world's leading car manufacturer.

Did You Know

Japan produces more garbage than any other country in the world—except the United States.

✓ Reading Check Answer

automobiles and other motor vehicles, consumer goods (electronic equipment, watches, small appliances, and calculators), steel, cement, fertilizer, plastics, fabrics

Travel Guide

Some Japanese dishes are made with raw fish. Raw fish that is served alone is called *sashimi.* Raw fish that is served with rice and vinegar is *sushi.* If the cook adds vegetables to the dish—or substitutes vegetables for the fish—the dish is called *norimaki.*

Team-Teaching Activity

Science Invite a science teacher to class to discuss the different engineering methods that can be used to prevent extensive earthquake damage. For example, earthquakes make soft soil dangerous, causing buildings erected on such soil to collapse—unless they have pilings that are sunk very deep into the earth. Japanese cities may suffer extensive damage because—since wood is scarce and expensive—house walls tend not to have much wood, making the walls more likely to move and, as a result, roofs to collapse. After the presentation, have students work in groups to prepare posters listing "Do's and Don'ts of Engineering in Earthquake Zones." L1

EE5 Environment and Society: Standard 15

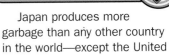

✓ Reading Check Answer

constitutional monarchy

Cultural Kaleidoscope

Japan Tea came to Japan from China around A.D. 800. It quickly became a beverage of the rich, although the poor occasionally used it as a medicine. In the 1400s, the practice of drinking tea became very popular throughout Japan. This was due, in part, to the Japanese court's adoption of the Buddhist tea ceremony.

L1/ELL

Guided Reading Activity

Name ______ Date ______ Class ______

JAPAN AND THE KOREAS

Guided Reading Activity 1

Japan—Past and Present

DIRECTIONS: Answering Questions Reading the section and answering the questions below will help you learn more about the country of Japan. Use your textbook to write answers to the questions.

1. Why does Japan experience so many earthquakes and tsunamis?
2. What makes up Japan's land area?
3. What is Japan known for in industry?
4. What do Japanese farmers practice?
5. What are Japan's economic challenges?
6. Where do the Japanese trace their ancestry?
7. Who ruled Japan after the emperors' power declined?
8. Where do most of Japan's people live?
9. What do the two major religions of Japan teach?
10. What Japanese sports have origins in the past?

110

[illegible] and Sataka Aya walk along ash-covered sidewalks to Kurokami Junior High School. Why are they wearing hard hats? Their city is near Japan's Mount Oyama Volcano, which has just erupted. Yukiko and Aya have grown up facing the dangers of volcanic eruptions, earthquakes, and tsunamis. At school their first class starts at 8:30 A.M., and their last class ends at 3:40 P.M. Yukiko and Aya must go to school every second Saturday of the month too.

Like China, Japan did not want to trade with foreign countries. In 1853 the United States government sent a fleet headed by Commodore Matthew Perry to Japan to demand trading privileges. In response to this action and other outside pressures, the Japanese started trading with other countries.

In the late 1800s, Japanese leaders began to use Western ideas to modernize the country, improve education, and set up industries. By the early 1900s, Japan was the leading military power in Asia.

In the 1930s, Japan needed more resources for its growing population. It took land in China and spread its influence to Southeast Asia. In 1941 Japanese forces attacked the American naval base at Pearl Harbor in Hawaii. This attack caused the United States to enter World War II. After four years of fighting, Japan surrendered when the United States dropped atomic bombs on the cities of **Hiroshima** and **Nagasaki.** By that time, many of Japan's cities lay in ruins and the economy had collapsed. With help from the United States, Japan became a democracy and quickly rebuilt its ruined economy.

Government Japan's democracy is in the form of a **constitutional monarchy.** The emperor is the official head of state, but elected officials run the government. Voters elect representatives to the national legislature. The political party with the most members chooses a prime minister to lead the government.

Japan has great influence as a world economic power. In addition, it gives large amounts of money to poorer countries. Japan is not a military power, though. Because of the suffering that World War II caused, the Japanese have chosen to keep Japan's military small.

The government of Japan has improved health care and education for its people. Japan has the lowest infant death rate in the world, and its literacy rate is 100 percent. The crime rate in Japan is very low.

✓ Reading Check **What kind of government does Japan have?**

Japan's People and Culture

About the size of California, Japan has 127.5 million people—nearly one-half the population of the United States. Most of Japan's people belong to the same Japanese ethnic background. Look at the map on page 700 to see where most of Japan's people live. About 80 percent are crowded into urban areas on the coastal plains. The four large cities of Tokyo, Yokohama, Nagoya, and Osaka form a **megalopolis,** or a huge urban area made up of several large cities and communities near them.

Japan's cities have tall office buildings and busy streets. Homes and apartments are small and close to one another. Many city workers crowd into subway trains to get to work. Men work long hours and arrive home very late. Women often quit their jobs to raise children and return to work outside the home when the children are grown.

You still see signs of traditional life, even in the cities. Parks and gardens give people a chance to take a break from the busy day. It is

Team-Teaching Activity

Government Invite a teacher with a background in government to discuss the parliamentary system of government in Japan. The discussion should address such issues as elections, the selection of the prime minister and the cabinet, coalition governments, and votes of no confidence. Then have students make a chart comparing government in Japan to that in the United States, placing the similarities in one column and the differences in another. L1 

EE4 Human Systems: Standard 12

common to see a person dressed in a traditional garment called a kimono walking with another person wearing a T-shirt and jeans.

Only 21 percent of Japan's people live in rural areas. In both rural and urban Japan, the family traditionally has been the center of one's life. Each family member had to obey certain rules. Grandparents, parents, and children all lived in one house. Many family groups today consist only of parents and children.

▲ *Evening Snow, Mt. Fuji,* by Toyokuni II is a wood-block print from the 1830s.

Religion Many Japanese practice two religions—Shinto and Buddhism. Shinto began in Japan many centuries ago. It teaches respect for nature, love of simple things, and concern for cleanliness and good manners. Shinto is different from other religions. First, there is no person who founded or started the religion. Shinto did not spread to many other areas of the world, but stayed mostly in Japan. Second, there is no collection of writings that make up scripture, such as the Bible or the Quran. In addition to Shinto, Buddhism teaches respect for nature and the need to achieve inner peace.

Traditional Arts Japan's religions have influenced the country's arts. Many paintings portray the beauty of nature, often with a few simple brush strokes. Some even include verses of poetry. Haiku (HY•koo) is a well-known type of Japanese poetry that is written according to a specific formula. Turn to page 697 to learn more about haiku.

Japanese artists became famous for a style of painting (borrowed from the Chinese) known as wood-block printing. It involved carving a picture into a block of wood, applying ink to the raised surface of the carved block, and printing the picture on paper or some other surface. Japanese

Customs

Japanese people greet each other by bowing. The person who has a lower social status usually bows first, the lowest, and the longest. The lower you bow, the more you honor and respect the other person. The most common bow lasts for one or two seconds. A very low bow is used for a superior or for a formal occasion, such as a first meeting, and may be held for about three seconds. Bows are also a nonverbal way to say thank you, good-bye, and to apologize. Many times, especially when saying good-bye, both people bow several times.

Looking Closer **Which man in this photo is of lower status? How can you tell?**

Content Background

Shinto All Japanese belong to the State Shinto—Japan's official religion. Shinto has no founder or sacred book. Its followers worship numerous gods, emperors, heroes, and ancestors. State Shinto demands loyalty to the emperor, who is believed to be descended from the Sun Goddess. Another division of Shinto, Shrine Shinto, centers its rites around state-supported shrines. At these locales, priests pray for peace, good harvests, and prosperity for all. Festivals held at these shrines incorporate many Buddhist practices.

EXPLORING CULTURE

Answer The man on the right is of lower social status; he is bowing lower than the man on the left.

Techniques Bowing techniques range from a small nod of the head to a long, 90 degree bow. Bowing properly is of such importance that there are classes in many companies and schools in Japan on how to bow properly.

3 Assess

Assign Section 1 Assessment as homework or an in-class activity.

Have students use the Interactive Tutor Self-Assessment CD-ROM to review Section 1.

L2

Section Quiz

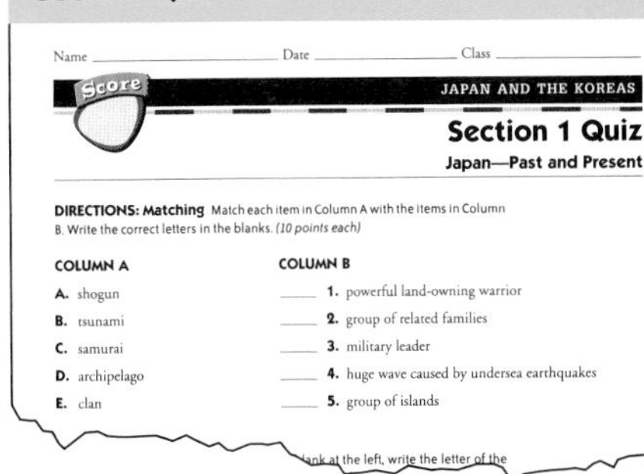

Name ______ Date ______ Class ______

Score

JAPAN AND THE KOREAS

Section 1 Quiz

Japan—Past and Present

DIRECTIONS: Matching Match each item in Column A with the items in Column B. Write the correct letters in the blanks. *(10 points each)*

COLUMN A	COLUMN B
A. shogun	____ 1. powerful land-owning warrior
B. tsunami	____ 2. group of related families
C. samurai	____ 3. military leader
D. archipelago	____ 4. huge wave caused by undersea earthquakes
E. clan	____ 5. group of islands

Reading Strategy

Reteach
Have students write a paragraph explaining how a lack of land resources in Japan has affected the use of technology there.

Reading Check Answer

Shinto, Buddhism

L1/ELL

Reading Essentials and Study Guide

Name ________ Date ________ Class ________
JAPAN AND THE KOREAS
Reading Essentials and Study Guide 1
Japan—Past and Present

Key Terms
tsunami huge sea wave caused by an undersea earthquake
archipelago group of islands
intensive cultivation growing crops on every available piece of land
clan group of related families
shogun military leader in Japan
samurai powerful land-owning warrior in Japan
constitutional monarchy government headed by a king or queen, but run by elected officials
...rban area made up of several large cities and communities

Enrich
Have students use primary and secondary sources to research the culture of the samurai and prepare a display summarizing their findings.

Close

Reading Strategy

Writing a Paragraph Have students write a paragraph analyzing what is unique about Japan and how Japan is like other countries.

wood-block prints enjoyed a golden age in the 1800s. They eventually made their way to Europe, influencing the French Impressionists.

The Japanese also have a rich heritage of literature and drama. Many scholars believe that the world's first novel came from Japan. The novel is called *The Tale of Genji* and was written by a noblewoman about A.D. 1000. Since the 1600s, Japanese theatergoers have attended the historical plays of the Kabuki theater. In Kabuki plays, actors wearing brilliantly colored costumes perform on colorful stages.

Many of Japan's sports have their origins in the past. A popular sport is sumo, an ancient Japanese form of wrestling. In sumo, two players each try to force the other to touch the ground with any part of their body other than their feet. Participants in sumo typically weigh at least 300 pounds (136 kg). Two ancient martial arts—judo and karate—also developed in this area. Today martial arts are practiced both for self-defense and for exercise.

Modern Pastimes Along with traditional arts, the people of Japan enjoy modern pastimes. Many Japanese are enthusiastic about baseball, a sport borrowed from American culture. There are professional baseball leagues in Japan, and several Japanese players have become stars in the major leagues of the United States. Despite Japan's strong emphasis on education, life is not all work for Japanese young people. They enjoy rock music, modern fashions, television, and movies. Japanese cartoons and video games are popular around the world.

Reading Check What two main religions are practiced in Japan?

Section 1 Assessment

Defining Terms

1. **Define** tsunami, archipelago, intensive cultivation, clan, shogun, samurai, constitutional monarchy, megalopolis.

Recalling Facts

2. **Location** Why does Japan experience earthquakes?
3. **History** Who were the samurai?
4. **Culture** How have Japan's religions influenced the country's arts?

Critical Thinking

5. **Summarizing Information** Why do the Japanese not want a large military?
6. **Synthesizing Information** Name three values of the Japanese people that enable them to be such skilled workers.

Graphic Organizer

7. **Organizing Information** Create a diagram like this one. List Japan's economic successes in the large oval and its economic challenges in each of the smaller ovals.

Applying Social Studies Skills

8. **Analyzing Maps** Look at the physical/political map on page 691. What physical features are located near Tokyo, Japan?

Section 1 Assessment

1. The terms are defined in the Glossary.
2. It sits on the Ring of Fire, an area where the earth's crust often shifts.
3. powerful land-owning warriors who ruled Japan from the late 1100s to the 1860s
4. Shinto and Buddhism teach respect for nature, and many paintings and poems express the beauty of nature.
5. because of the suffering caused by World War II
6. education, hard work, cooperation
7. *Successes:* industrial giant; intensive cultivation of land; productive fishing fleet; *Challenges:* disagreements with trading partners; pollution; overfishing
8. Kanto Plain, Mt. Fuji, Tone River

Making Connections

ART | SCIENCE | CULTURE | TECHNOLOGY

Haiku

Haiku is a type of poetry that first became popular in Japan during the 1600s. A haiku is a three-line poem, usually about nature and human emotions. The traditional haiku requires 17 syllables—5 in the first line, 7 in the second line, and 5 in the third line. All of the haiku below, written by famous Japanese poets, concern the subject of New Year's Day.*

For this New Year's Day,
The sight we gaze upon shall be
Mount Fuji.
Sôkan

That is good, this too is good,—
New Year's Day
In my old age.
Rôyto

New Year's Day;
Whosoever's face we see,
It is care-free.
Shigyoku

New Year's Day:
My hovel,
The same as ever.
Issa

New Year's Day:
What luck! What luck!
A pale blue sky!
Issa

The dawn of New Year's Day;
Yesterday,
How far off!
Ichiku

▲ This Japanese wood-block print shows two girls playing a New Year's game.

The first dream of the year;
I kept it a secret,
And smiled to myself.
Shô-u

*Translation may have affected the number of syllables.

Making the Connection

1. How does the poet Shigyoku think most people react to New Year's Day?
2. From his poem, how can you tell that Ichiku sees the New Year as a new beginning?
3. **Making Comparisons** Compare the two poems by Issa. How does his mood change from one to the other?

Making the Connection

1. It makes them feel lighthearted and carefree.
2. He conveys the idea that yesterday is gone and forgotten.
3. In the first poem, Issa indicates that his life will continue being miserable. In the second, he feels blessed by the beauty of the world around him.

TEACH

Ask students to name some poems they have read and to describe their reactions to these poems. Then remind students that reading poetry is different from reading prose. Poetry demands more of the reader than prose does. In a short story or novel, the reader can often understand the plot without necessarily understanding every word. A poem, however, should be read slowly and carefully several times. Each word is important for understanding a poem's meaning. L1

More About Haiku

Perhaps the foremost master of haiku was Matsuo Basho, who lived in the 1600s. At first a samurai, Basho became a noted poet and critic. The haiku form had existed before him, but it had become trivial and silly. Basho's gemlike verses elevated the haiku to a new art form that used compressed language to suggest eternal truths.

Interdisciplinary Connections

Literature Originally, haiku were meant to describe something in nature while evoking an emotional response. Have students attempt writing a haiku about nature. Remind them that the best haiku use very concrete details.

Chapter 24

Section 2, pages 698–701

1 Focus

Section Objectives

1. Locate the Korean Peninsula.
2. Explain why the two Koreas are divided.
3. Compare life in North and South Korea.

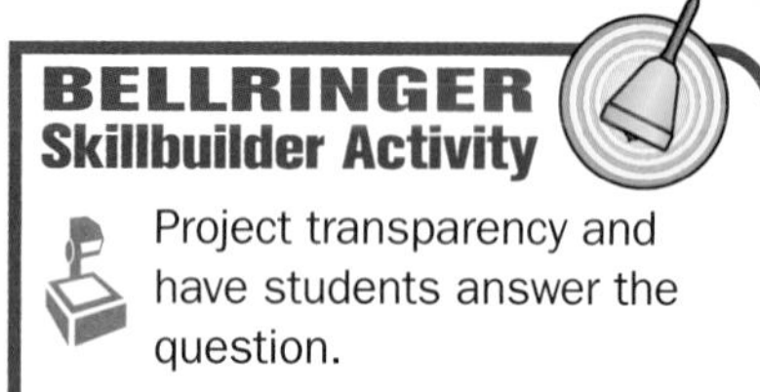

BELLRINGER Skillbuilder Activity

Project transparency and have students answer the question.

Daily Focus Skills Transparency

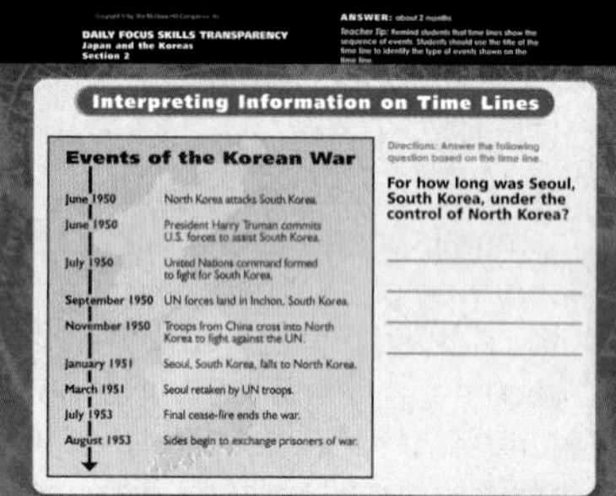

ANSWER: about 2 months

Teacher Tip: Remind students that time lines show the sequence of events. Students should use the title of the time line to identify the type of events shown on the time line.

DAILY FOCUS SKILLS TRANSPARENCY
Japan and the Koreas
Section 2

Interpreting Information on Time Lines

Events of the Korean War

June 1950	North Korea attacks South Korea.
June 1950	President Harry Truman commits U.S. forces to assist South Korea.
July 1950	United Nations command formed to fight for South Korea.
September 1950	UN forces land in Inchon, South Korea.
November 1950	Troops from China cross into North Korea to fight against the UN.
January 1951	Seoul, South Korea, falls to North Korea.
March 1951	Seoul retaken by UN troops.
July 1953	Final cease-fire ends the war.
August 1953	Sides begin to exchange prisoners of war.

Directions: Answer the following question based on the time line.

For how long was Seoul, South Korea, under the control of North Korea?

Reading Preview

■ **Activating Prior Knowledge** Ask students why they think these two countries share the same name but are separated. After students have suggested reasons, have them read the section.

■ **Preteaching Vocabulary** Tell students to pronounce unfamiliar words aloud when they encounter them. This strategy often triggers one's memory of the word's meaning.

Guide to Reading

Main Idea

South Korea and North Korea share the same peninsula and history, but they have very different political and economic systems.

Terms to Know

- parallel
- famine

Reading Strategy

Create a time line like this one to record four important dates and their events in Korean history.

Section 2 The Two Koreas

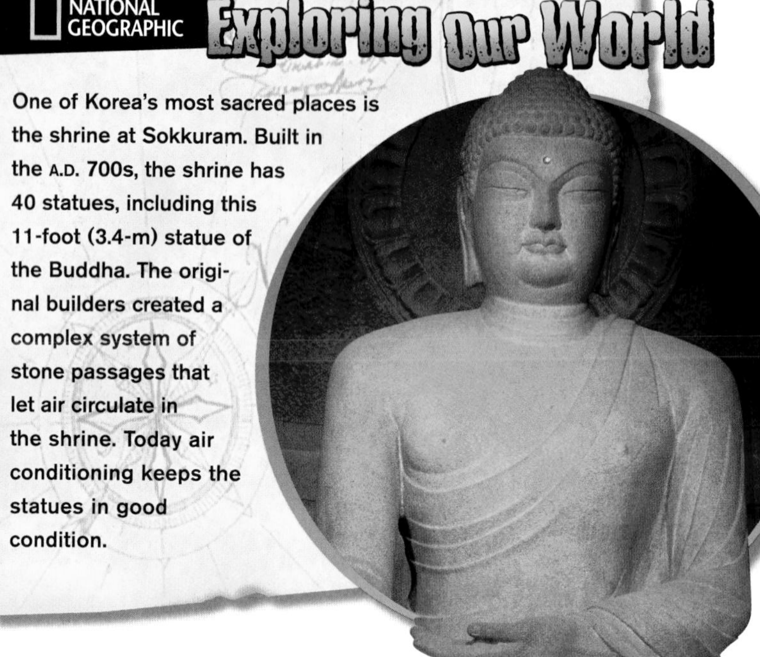

One of Korea's most sacred places is the shrine at Sokkuram. Built in the A.D. 700s, the shrine has 40 statues, including this 11-foot (3.4-m) statue of the Buddha. The original builders created a complex system of stone passages that let air circulate in the shrine. Today air conditioning keeps the statues in good condition.

The **Korean Peninsula** juts out from northern China, between the Sea of Japan (East Sea) and the Yellow Sea. For centuries, this peninsula held a unified country. Today the peninsula is divided into two nations—Communist **North Korea** and non-Communist **South Korea.**

A Divided Country

The history of human activity on the Korean Peninsula can be traced back thousands of years. From the 100s B.C. until the early A.D. 300s, neighboring China ruled Korea. When Chinese control ended, separate Korean kingdoms arose throughout the peninsula.

From A.D. 668 to 935, a single kingdom called Silla (SHIH•luh) united much of the peninsula. During this time, Korea made many cultural and scientific advances. For example, Silla rulers built one of the world's earliest astronomical observatories in the A.D. 600s. Other dynasties, or ruling families, followed the Silla.

In the 1400s, scholars invented a new way to write the Korean language. This new system—called *hangul* (HAHN•GOOL)—used fewer

Section Resources

Reproducible Masters

- Reproducible Lesson Plan
- Daily Lecture and Discussion Notes
- Note-taking Guide
- Guided Reading Activity
- Reading Essentials and Study Guide
- Section Quiz

Transparencies

- Daily Focus Skills Transparency

Multimedia

- Vocabulary PuzzleMaker CD-ROM
- Interactive Tutor Self-Assessment CD-ROM
- Presentation Plus! CD-ROM
- ExamView® Pro Testmaker CD-ROM
- MindJogger Videoquiz

than 30 symbols. This is far fewer than the thousands of characters needed to write Chinese. This means the Korean system is much easier to learn. One of the great achievements of early Koreans was pottery. Korean potters still make bowls and dishes that are admired worldwide.

The Korean Peninsula was a stepping stone between Japan and mainland Asia. Trade and ideas went back and forth. In 1910 the Japanese conquered Korea and made it part of their empire. They governed the peninsula until the end of World War II in 1945.

Division and War Troops from the Communist Soviet Union soon took over the northern half of Korea. American troops occupied the southern half. Korea eventually divided along the 38th **parallel,** or line of latitude. A Communist state arose in what came to be called North Korea. A non-Communist government controlled South Korea.

In 1950 the armies of North Korea attacked South Korea. They hoped to unite all of Korea under Communist rule. United Nations countries, led by the United States, rushed to support South Korea. China's Communist leaders eventually sent troops across the **Yalu River** to help North Korea. The Korean War finally ended in 1953—without a peace treaty or a victory for either side. By the 1960s, two separate countries had developed on the Korean Peninsula.

After years of bitterness, the two Koreas developed closer relations in the 1990s. In the year 2000, the leaders of North Korea and South Korea held a meeting for the first time since the division.

✓ **Reading Check** **Why is the Korean Peninsula divided?**

South Korea

Much of South Korea is covered by mountains. Most South Koreans live in coastal areas where they are affected by monsoons. During the summer, a monsoon from the south brings hot, humid weather. In the

Korean Border

More than 50 years after the fighting stopped in Korea, troops still patrol the border between North and South Korea (below left). Seoul, South Korea's modern capital (below right), is less than 25 miles (40 km) from the border.

Location **Where was the line of division drawn between the two countries?**

Reading Strategy — Reading the Text

Previewing Write the section objectives on the board before students begin reading the section. Go over each objective with the students to show them what they will be learning as they read. These objectives should remain on the board until the section is completed. After students have finished the section, review the objectives to be sure students have comprehended the material. L1

Use the ***Reading Skills Handbook*** *for more reading strategies.*

Chapter 24

Section 2, pages 698–701

TEACH

Categorizing Information

Organize students into two teams. Read them a series of statements, and require teams to say whether the statement applies to North Korea, South Korea, or both. L1

Daily Lecture and Discussion Notes

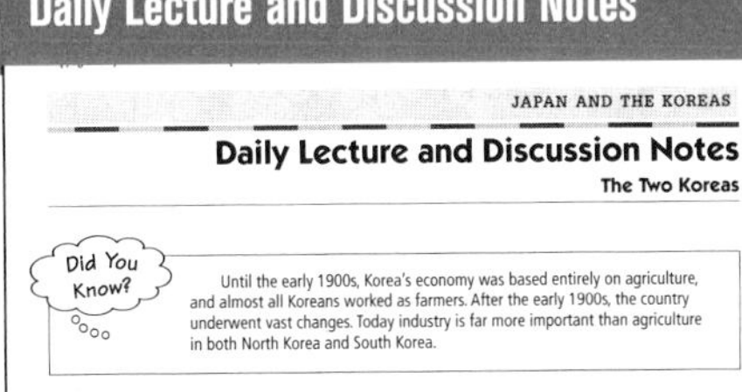

JAPAN AND THE KOREAS

Daily Lecture and Discussion Notes

The Two Koreas

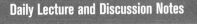

Did You Know? Until the early 1900s, Korea's economy was based entirely on agriculture, and almost all Koreans worked as farmers. After the early 1900s, the country underwent vast changes. Today industry is far more important than agriculture in both North Korea and South Korea.

I. A Divided Country

A. The Korean Peninsula juts out from northern China, between the Sea of Japan (East Sea) and the Yellow Sea. Today the peninsula is divided into two nations—Communist North Korea and non-Communist South Korea.

B. China ruled Korea until the A.D. 300s. From A.D. 668 to 935, a single kingdom ... peninsula. Other dynasties, or ruling families,

✓ Reading Check Answer

because troops from the Communist Soviet Union took control of the northern half of Korea, establishing a Communist state and American troops occupied the southern half of Korea, where a non-Communist government was established

More About the Photos

The Border The border between North and South Korea is a demilitarized zone (DMZ), where only small weapons are allowed.

Caption Answer along the 38th parallel

Chapter 24

Section 2, pages 698–701

L1/ELL

Guided Reading Activity

Name ______ Date ______ Class ______

JAPAN AND THE KOREAS

Guided Reading Activity 2

The Two Koreas

DIRECTIONS: Reading for Accuracy Reading the section and completing the activity below will help you learn more about North Korea and South Korea. Use your textbook to decide if a statement is true or false. Write **T** or **F**, and if a statement is false, rewrite it correctly.

____ 1. Korea was originally ruled by China.

____ 2. Korea has been independent since A.D. 668.

____ 3. Korea has been separated since the end of World War II.

____ 4. After the Korean War, Korea reunited.

____ 5. Monsoons affect the climate of South Korea.

____ 6. South Korea's economy is dominated by agriculture.

____ 7. Farming in North Korea provides food for the whole country.

____ 8. People of both Koreas belong to the same ethnic group.

____ 9. Mountains run through the majority of North Korea.

____ 10. North Korea's capital, Seoul, is little more than a farming village.

111

Applying Map Skills

Answers

1. over 250 people per square mile (over 100 per sq. km)
2. along the west coast of the Korean Peninsula

Skills Practice

What Japanese cities have more than 5 million people? *(Tokyo and Yokohama)*

Reading Check Answer

Christianity, Buddhism, and Confucianism

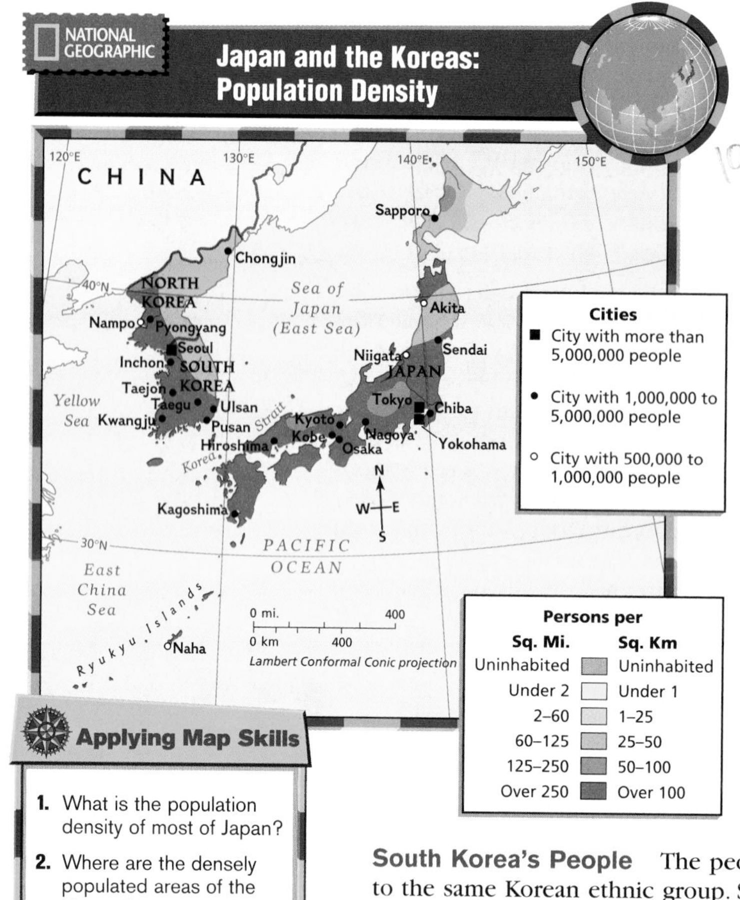

Applying Map Skills

1. What is the population density of most of Japan?
2. Where are the densely populated areas of the Koreas?

Find NGS online map resources @ www.nationalgeographic.com/maps

winter, a monsoon blows in from the north, bringing cold, dry weather.

South Korea is one of east Asia's economic powers, despite an economic crisis in the 1990s. Manufacturing and trade dominate South Korea's economy. The country is a leading exporter of ships, cars, textiles, computers, and electronic appliances.

South Korean farmers own their land, although most of their farms are very small. The major crops are rice, barley, onions, potatoes, cabbage, apples, and tangerines. Rice is the country's basic food item. One of the most popular Korean dishes is ***kimchi,*** a highly spiced blend of vegetables mixed with chili, garlic, and ginger. Many farmers also raise livestock, especially chickens. Some add to their income by fishing.

South Korea's People The people of the two Koreas belong to the same Korean ethnic group. South Korea has nearly 48 million people. About 80 percent live in cities and towns in the coastal plains. South Korea's capital, **Seoul,** is the largest city.

Most city dwellers live in tall apartment buildings. Many own cars, but they also use buses, subways, and trains to travel to and from work. In rural areas, people live in small, one-story homes made of brick or concrete blocks. A large number of South Koreans have emigrated to the United States since the end of the Korean War.

Buddhism, Confucianism, and Christianity are South Korea's major religions. The Koreans have developed their own culture, but Chinese religion and culture influenced the traditional arts of Korea. In Seoul, ancient palaces are modeled after the Imperial Palace in Beijing, China. Historic Buddhist temples dot the hills and valleys of the countryside.

Like Japan, Korea has a tradition of martial arts. Have you heard of tae kwon do? This martial art originated in Korea. Those who study it learn mental discipline as well as self-defense.

Reading Check **What are the major religions in South Korea?**

Differentiated Instruction

Meeting Special Needs: Naturalist Korean cooks balance their meals by following the rule of Five Flavors—including tastes that are salt, sweet, sour, bitter, and hot. Soy sauce and bean paste supply the salty flavor; honey, sugar, and sweet potatoes add sweetness; vinegar provides sourness; ginger contributes bitterness; and mustard and chili peppers add heat. Garlic, green onions, sesame seeds, cinnamon, and eggs are some of the other ingredients found in many Korean dishes. Have interested students bring some of these seasonings to class or prepare a Korean dish and bring it to class. **L1**

Refer to *Inclusion for the Middle School Social Studies Classroom Strategies and Activities* in the TCR.

North Korea

Separated from China by the Yalu River, North Korea is slightly larger than South Korea. Like South Korea, monsoons affect the climate here, but the central mountains block some of the winter monsoon.

The North Korean government owns and runs factories and farms. It spends much money on the military. Unlike prosperous South Korea, North Korea is economically poor. Coal and iron ore are plentiful, but industries suffer from old equipment and power outages.

Most of North Korea is hills and mountains separated by deep, narrow valleys. Although there is little land to farm, more than 30 percent of North Koreans are farmers. They work on large, government-run farms. These farms do not grow enough food to feed the country. A lack of fertilizer recently produced **famines,** or severe food shortages. North Korea relies heavily on international food aid.

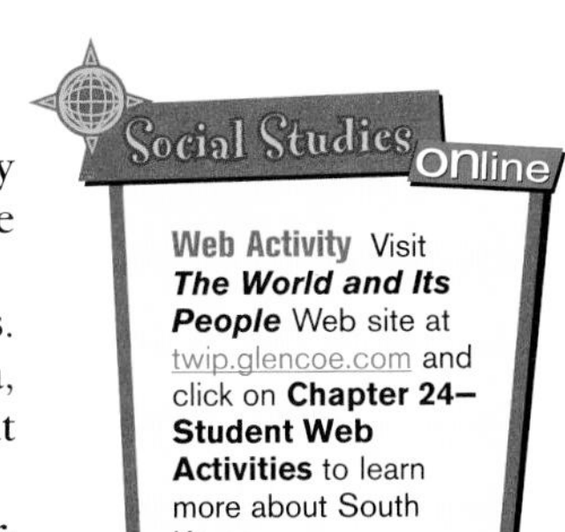

Web Activity Visit ***The World and Its People*** Web site at twip.glencoe.com and click on **Chapter 24—Student Web Activities** to learn more about South Korea.

North Korea's People North Korea has about 22.7 million people. About 60 percent live in urban areas along the coasts and river valleys. **Pyongyang** is the capital and largest city. Largely rebuilt since the Korean War, Pyongyang has many modern buildings and monuments to Communist leaders. Most of these monuments honor Kim Il Sung, who became North Korea's first ruler in the late 1940s. After Kim's death in 1994, his son Kim Jong Il became the ruler.

The government places the needs of the communist system over the needs of citizens. In 2002 North Korea stated it would make nuclear weapons. This has increased tensions with the United States and other countries who want North Korea to end their nuclear weapons program. Talks in 2003 failed to resolve the issue.

Reading Check Who controls the economy of North Korea?

Section 2 Assessment

Defining Terms

1. **Define** parallel, famine.

Recalling Facts

2. **Location** Where is the Korean Peninsula?
3. **History** Who were the Silla?
4. **Economics** What products are made in South Korea?

Critical Thinking

5. **Making Comparisons** How does the standard of living in South Korea differ from that in North Korea?
6. **Summarizing Information** What country has had the greatest influence on the culture and arts of South Korea? Explain.

Graphic Organizer

7. **Organizing Information** Create a diagram like this one. Write facts about each country's economy, government, and natural resources in the outer ovals. Where the ovals overlap, write facts that are common to both countries.

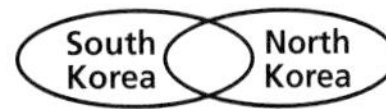

Applying Social Studies Skills

8. **Analyzing Maps** Turn to the population density map on page 700. What is the most populous city on the Korean Peninsula? In which country is it located?

Chapter 24

Section 2, pages 698–701

Assign Section 2 Assessment as homework or an in-class activity.

Have students use the Interactive Tutor Self-Assessment CD-ROM to review Section 2.

L2

Section Quiz

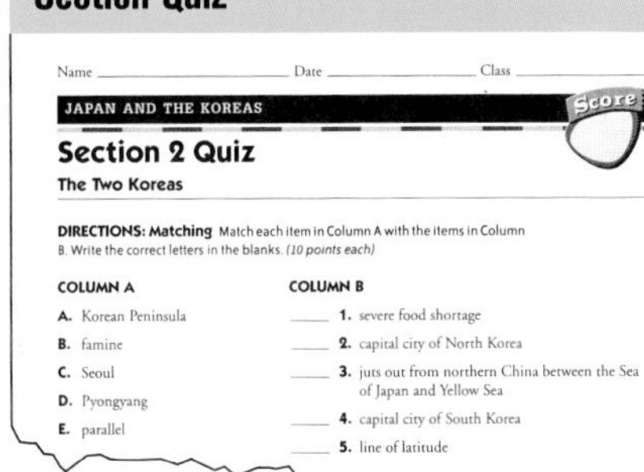

Name ______ Date ______ Class ______

JAPAN AND THE KOREAS

Score

Section 2 Quiz

The Two Koreas

DIRECTIONS: Matching Match each item in Column A with the items in Column B. Write the correct letters in the blanks. *(10 points each)*

COLUMN A	COLUMN B
A. Korean Peninsula	___ 1. severe food shortage
B. famine	___ 2. capital city of North Korea
C. Seoul	___ 3. juts out from northern China between the Sea of Japan and Yellow Sea
D. Pyongyang	___ 4. capital city of South Korea
E. parallel	___ 5. line of latitude

Objectives and answers to the Student Web Activity can be found in the Web Activity Lesson Plan at twip.glencoe.com

Reading Check Answer

the government

Have students prepare a bulletin board display comparing and contrasting the Koreas.

Section 2 Assessment

1. The terms are defined in the Glossary.
2. It juts out from northern China between the Sea of Japan and the Yellow Sea.
3. Korean rulers who united the peninsula and made cultural and scientific advances
4. ships, cars, textiles, computers, and electronic appliances
5. The standard of living in South Korea is quite high, but most people living in North Korea are very poor.
6. China; South Korea modeled its capital after the Chinese capital, and Buddhism influenced the country as well.
7. Diagrams should contain information from the section.
8. Seoul; South Korea

Critical Thinking Skill

TEACH

Give students the following situation: Suppose you want to buy a portable CD player, and you must choose among three models. Ask students what criteria they would use to make the purchase. *(Students may respond that they would compare such characteristics of the three models as price, sound quality, and size.)* **L1**

Additional Skills Practice

1. **In comparing two countries' economic performance, what factors might you compare?** *(products made, gross national product, or relative wealth of people)*
2. **In terms of physical geography, what factors can you use to compare two countries?** *(landforms, climate, location in relation to Equator, location in relation to other countries, size)*

Additional Skills Resources

 Chapter Skills Review

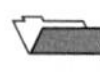 Building Geography Skills for Life

GLENCOE TECHNOLOGY

 **Skillbuilder Interactive Workbook CD-ROM, Level 1**

This interactive CD-ROM reinforces student mastery of essential social studies skills.

Critical Thinking Skill

Making Comparisons

When you make comparisons, you determine similarities and differences among ideas, objects, or events. By comparing maps and graphs, you can learn more about a region.

Learning the Skill

Follow these steps to make comparisons:

- Identify or decide what will be compared.
- Determine a common area or areas in which comparisons can be drawn.
- Look for similarities and differences within these areas.

Practicing the Skill

Use the map and graph below to make comparisons and answer these questions:

1. What is the title of the map? The graph?
2. How are the map and graph related?
3. Which country has the most exports and imports?
4. Does a country's size have any effect on the amount it exports? Explain.
5. What generalizations can you make about this map and graph?

Applying the Skill

Survey your classmates about an issue in the news. Summarize the opinions and write a paragraph comparing the different opinions.

GO TO Practice key skills with **Glencoe Skillbuilder Interactive Workbook, Level 1.**

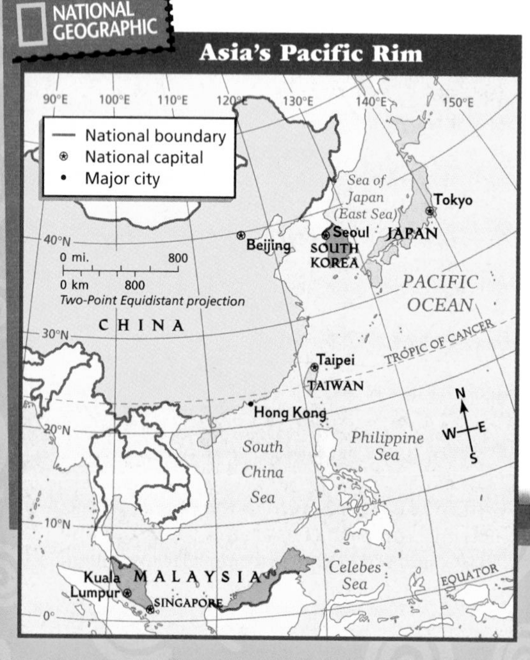

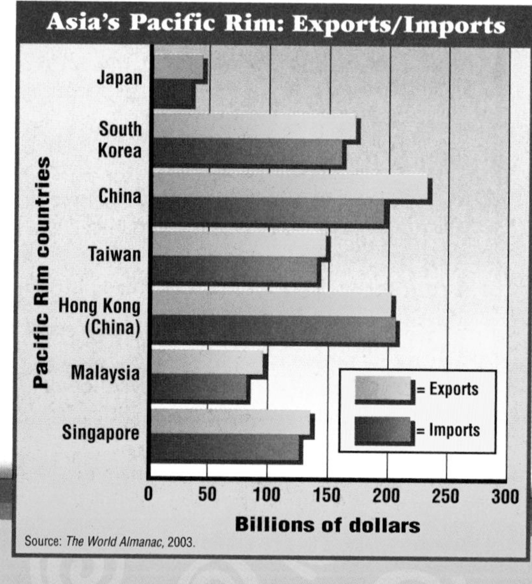

Practicing the Skill Answers

1. Asia's Pacific Rim; Asia's Pacific Rim: Exports/Imports
2. The graph includes places labeled on the map.
3. China
4. No; South Korea is much smaller in size than China, yet it exports almost as much as China.
5. Many countries and places along Asia's Pacific Rim are highly industrialized, and they spend billions of dollars in exports and earn billions of dollars in imports.

Applying the Skill

Students' answers will vary depending on the issue chosen and the opinions heard. Have them present their results in a graph.

Chapter 24 Reading Review

Section 1 Japan—Past and Present

Terms to Know
- tsunami
- archipelago
- intensive cultivation
- clan
- shogun
- samurai
- constitutional monarchy
- megalopolis

Main Idea

Although Japan's people have few mineral resources, they have built a prosperous country.

✓ Location Japan is an archipelago along the Ring of Fire in the western Pacific Ocean. Volcanoes, earthquakes, and tsunamis may strike these islands.

✓ Economics Japan is mountainous, but with intensive cultivation its limited farmland is very productive.

✓ Economics Japan has few resources. Through trade, the use of advanced technology, and highly skilled workers, Japan has built a strong industrial economy.

✓ History The Japanese people have been strongly influenced by China and also by Western countries.

✓ Culture Most people in Japan live in crowded cities.

✓ Culture Japanese religion has encouraged a love of nature and simplicity.

Section 2 The Two Koreas

Terms to Know
- parallel
- famine

Main Idea

South Korea and North Korea share the same peninsula and history, but they have very different political and economic systems.

✓ Culture The Korean Peninsula lies just south of northern China, and China has had a strong influence on Korean life and culture.

✓ Government After World War II, the peninsula became divided into two countries—Communist North Korea and non-Communist South Korea.

✓ Economics South Korea has a strong industrial economy.

✓ Culture Most South Koreans live in cities, enjoying a mix of modern and traditional life.

✓ Government North Korea's Communist government does not allow its people many freedoms and spends a great deal of money on the military. North Korea is economically poor.

Because of its beautiful forest-covered mountains, Korea was once known as the "Land of the Morning Calm." ▶

Reading Review

Use the Chapter 24 Reading Review to preview, review, condense, or reteach the chapter.

Preview/Review

Use the Terms to Know lists to help students review and study.

Activity Have students choose eight of the words, including some from each section, and create an illustrated glossary.

Vocabulary PuzzleMaker CD-ROM reinforces the vocabulary terms used in Chapter 24.

The Interactive Tutor Self-Assessment CD-ROM allows students to review Chapter 24 content.

Condense

Have students read the Chapter 24 summary statements.

Guided Reading Activities

Audio Program

Reteach

Reteaching Activity

Reading Essentials and Study Guide

Reading Strategy Read to Write

Writing Questions Open-ended questions provide evidence of comprehension. They also provide the opportunity for students to interpret the information based on their own understanding rather than that of the author's or the teacher's. Open-ended questions provide for synthesizing, reformulating, linking, and generalizing ideas. Have students write an open-ended question that addresses an idea or concept that students have learned about in the chapter. Students should then write the answer to this question on a separate piece of paper. Have students share their question with a partner and then check the answer. Students should then read their question and answer to the class. Have the class evaluate the question for clarity and content. L3

GLENCOE TECHNOLOGY

MindJogger Videoquiz
Use MindJogger Videoquiz to review the Chapter 24 content.

Available in DVD and VHS

Using Key Terms

1.	e	6.	i
2.	f	7.	d
3.	j	8.	a
4.	b	9.	g
5.	c	10.	h

Reviewing the Main Ideas

11. through intensive cultivation, or growing crops on every available piece of land
12. *Consumer goods:* electronic equipment, watches, small appliances, calculators, automobiles, and other vehicles; *Industrial goods:* steel, cement, fertilizer, plastics, and fabrics
13. It modernized, with improved education and newly started industries.
14. Tokyo, Yokohama, Nagoya, and Osaka
15. *Any three:* painting, poetry, literature, and drama (Kabuki)
16. China
17. After Soviet and American troops occupied the two halves of the country, two different governments—one Communist and one not—took power in the two halves.
18. The summer monsoon from the south brings hot, humid weather. The winter monsoon from the north brings cold, dry weather.
19. manufacturing and trade
20. Limited farmland produced even less food because there was not enough fertilizer.

Chapter 24 Assessment and Activities

Using Key Terms

Match the terms in Part A with their definitions in Part B.

A.

1. samurai
2. tsunami
3. intensive cultivation
4. shogun
5. archipelago
6. parallel
7. constitutional monarchy
8. clan
9. famine
10. megalopolis

B.

a. group of related families
b. military leader in early Japan
c. chain of islands
d. emperor is the official head of state, but elected officials run the government
e. powerful land-owning warriors in Japan
f. huge wave caused by an undersea earthquake
g. severe food shortage
h. huge urban area made up of several large cities
i. line of latitude
j. growing crops on every available piece of land

Reviewing the Main Ideas

Section 1 Japan—Past and Present

11. **Human/Environment Interaction** How do Japan's farmers achieve high crop yields?
12. **Economics** What consumer goods and industrial goods are made in Japan?
13. **History** How did Japan change in the late 1800s?
14. **Location** What four cities make up Japan's megalopolis?
15. **Culture** Name three of Japan's traditional arts.

Section 2 The Two Koreas

16. **Location** What large Asian nation lies north of the Korean Peninsula?
17. **History** Why did Korea become divided in 1945?
18. **Movement** How do summer and winter monsoons differ in Korea?
19. **Economics** What are the main economic activities in South Korea?
20. **Human/Environment Interaction** Why has North Korea suffered from famine in recent years?

Japan and the Koreas

Place Location Activity

On a separate sheet of paper, match the letters on the map with the numbered places listed below.

1. Mount Fuji
2. Sea of Japan (East Sea)
3. North Korea
4. South Korea
5. Tokyo
6. Honshu
7. Yalu River
8. Seoul
9. Pyongyang
10. Hokkaido

NATIONAL GEOGRAPHIC Place Location Activity

1.	B	6.	A
2.	F	7.	H
3.	I	8.	G
4.	E	9.	C
5.	J	10.	D

Critical Thinking

21. Answers will vary but might include the fact that all communist countries experience some difficulties in changing to a free market economy and that China, which has a communist system, is on the border and may pressure North Korea to act in certain ways.
22. Charts should contain information from the chapter.

Self-Check Quiz Visit ***The World and Its People*** Web site at twip.glencoe.com and click on **Chapter 24—Self-Check Quizzes** to prepare for the Chapter Test.

Critical Thinking

21. **Drawing Conclusions** Why might North Korea find it difficult to change from a communist system to a noncommunist system? Keep in mind the country's location.
22. **Organizing Information** Create a chart like this one. In each column, write two main ideas about Japan, South Korea, and North Korea as they relate to the topics in the first column.

Topic	Japan	South Korea	North Korea
Land			
Economy			
History			
People			

Comparing Regions Activity

23. **Geography** Compare the geography of the Korean Peninsula with the geography of Baja California. What are the similarities and/or differences? Write a paragraph describing them.

Mental Mapping Activity

24. **Focusing on the Region** Create a map of Japan and the Koreas, and add these labels:
- Honshu
- North Korea
- Korean Peninsula
- Yalu River
- Pacific Ocean
- Tokyo
- Seoul
- Hiroshima

Technology Skills Activity

25. **Using the Internet** Use the Internet to research traditional Japanese culture. You might look at Japanese gardens, Buddhism, literature, or painting. Create a bulletin board display with pictures and write captions that explain what the images show.

Standardized Test Practice

Directions: Read the paragraph below, and then answer the questions that follow.

In A.D. 1185 Japan's emperor gave political and military power to a shogun, or general. The shogun system proved to be quite strong. Even though the Mongol warrior Kublai Khan tried twice to invade Japan, he did not succeed. On the first invasion in 1274, Japanese warriors and the threat of a storm forced the Mongols to leave. On the second invasion in 1281, about 150,000 Mongol warriors came by ship, but a typhoon arose and destroyed the fleet. The Japanese thought of the storm as the kamikaze, or "divine wind." They believed that their islands were indeed sacred.

1. In what century did shoguns gain political power in Japan?

A tenth century
B eleventh century
C twelfth century
D thirteenth century

2. In what century did the Mongol warrior Kublai Khan try to invade Japan?

F tenth century
G eleventh century
H twelfth century
J thirteenth century

Test-Taking Tip: Century names are a common source of error. Remember, in Western societies, a baby's first year begins at birth and ends at age one. Therefore, if you are now 14 years old, you are in your fifteenth year. Using the same type of thinking, what century began in 1201?

705

Assessment and Activities

Standardized Test Practice

1. C
2. J

Tested Objective:
Analyzing information

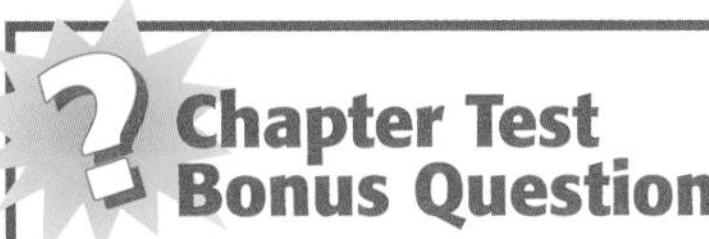

Chapter Test Bonus Question

This question may be used for extra credit on the chapter test.

How do ocean currents affect Japan's economy? *(The Pacific Ocean sends warm ocean currents to southern Japan. Warm water is better for fishing.)*

Have students visit the Web site at **twip.glencoe.com** to review Chapter 24 and take the Self-Check Quiz.

Dinah Zike's Foldables

Culminating Activity Have students write a one-page essay that describes the similarities and differences between Japan and the Koreas.

Comparing Regions Activity

23. Students' paragraphs should describe the similarities and/or differences between the Korean Peninsula and Baja California.

Mental Mapping Activity

24. This exercise helps students visualize the countries and geographic features they have been studying. Accept all attempts at freehand mapping that show places in the correct relationship to one another.

Technology Skills Activity

25. Have students discuss the different images that are found in their displays.

Chapter 25 Resources

Note: The following materials may be used when teaching Chapter 25.
Section level support materials are shown at point of use in the margins of the Teacher Wraparound Edition.

Timesaving Tools

TeacherWorks™ All-In-One Planner and Resource Center

- **Interactive Teacher Edition** See the **Interactive Teacher Edition** CD-ROM to electronically integrate your Teacher Wraparound Edition and blackline masters.
- **Interactive Lesson Planner** Organize your week, month, semester, or year with all the lesson helps you need. The **Interactive Lesson Planner** CD-ROM contains all Chapter 25 resources.

Use Glencoe's **Presentation Plus!** multimedia teacher tool to easily present dynamic lessons that visually excite your students. Using Microsoft PowerPoint® you can customize the presentations to create your own personalized lessons.

TEACHING TRANSPARENCIES

Graphic Organizer Transparency 13 L2

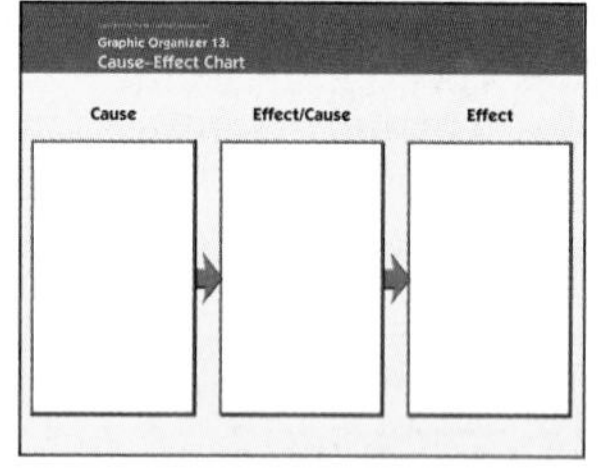

In-text Map Transparency L1

FOLDABLES™ Study Organizer

Dinah Zike's Foldables

Foldables are three-dimensional, interactive graphic organizers that help students practice basic writing skills, review key vocabulary terms, and identify main ideas. Additional chapter activities can be found in the ***Reading and Study Skills Foldables*** booklet.

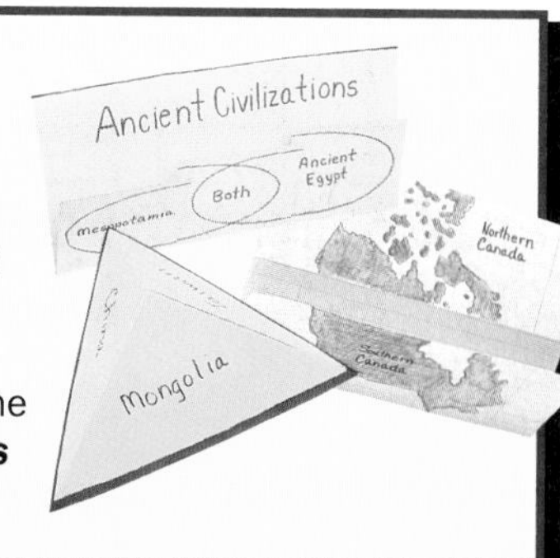

MAP AND GEOGRAPHY SKILLS

Chapter Map Activity L2

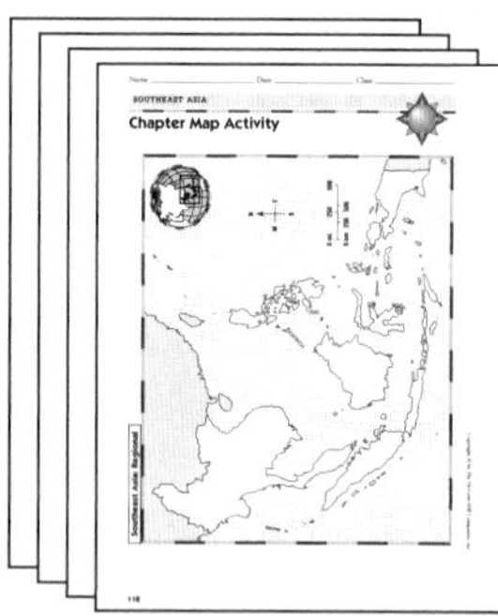

GeoLab Activity L2

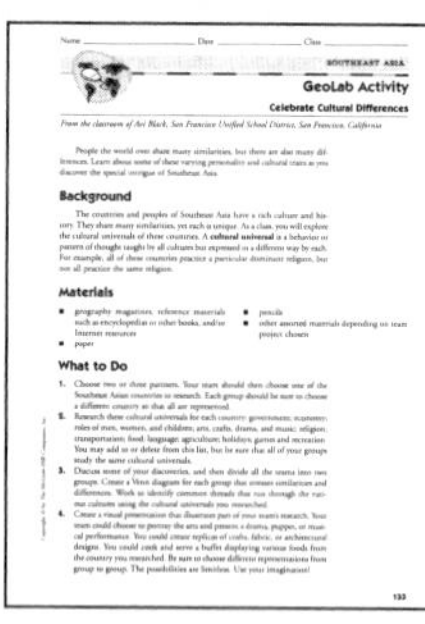

READING SUPPORT

Vocabulary Activity L1

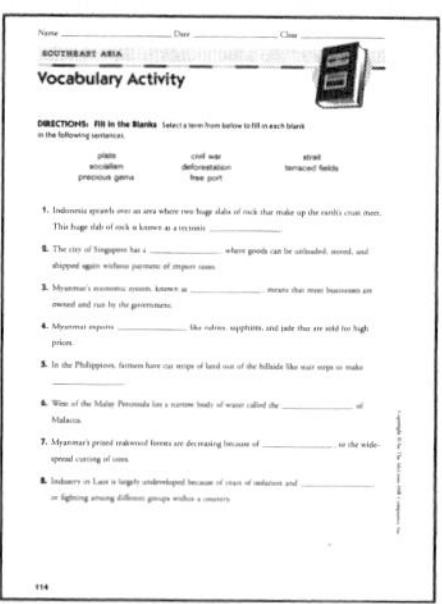

Workbook Activity L1

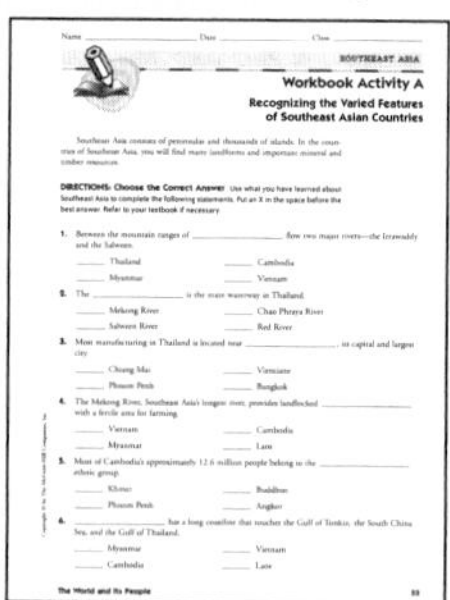

Reading and Writing Skills Activity L1/ELL

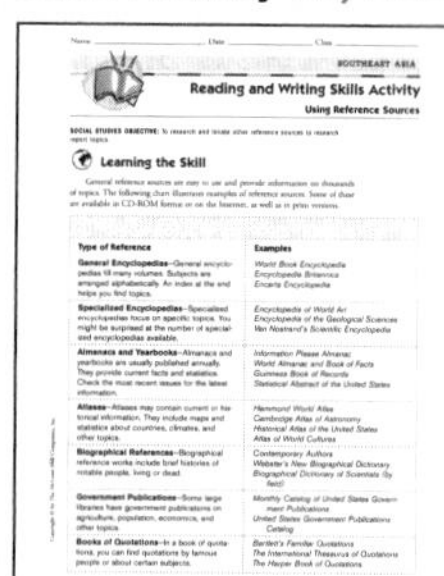

DIFFERENTIATED INSTRUCTION

Use these review and reinforcement materials to help less-proficient readers, English learners, and gifted and talented students.

Reteaching Activity L1

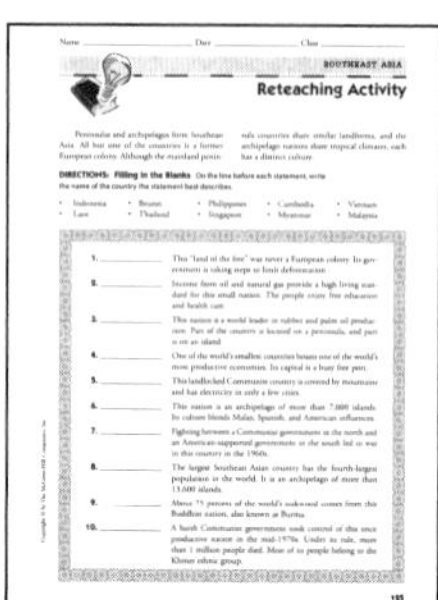

Chapter Skills Review L2

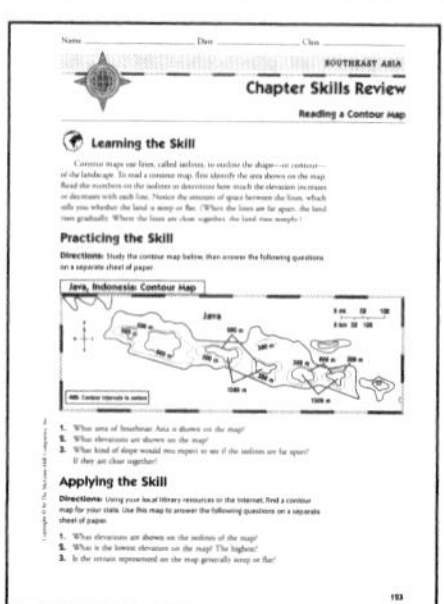

Cooperative Learning Activity L1/ELL

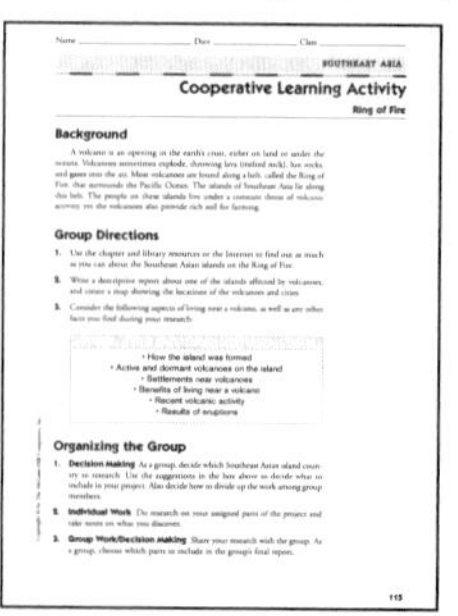

Enrichment Activity L3

ASSESSMENT

Chapter Test, Form A L2

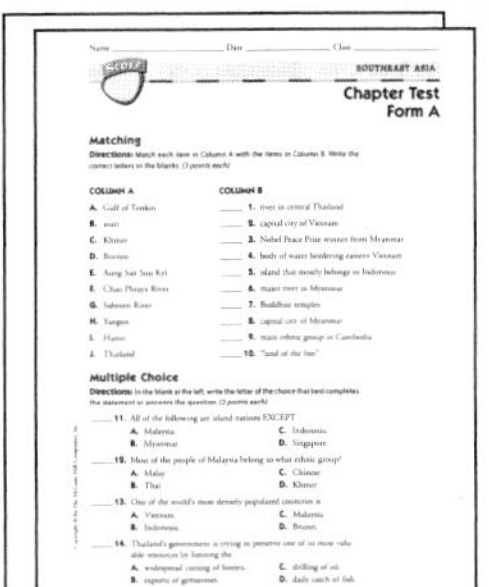

Chapter Test, Form B L2

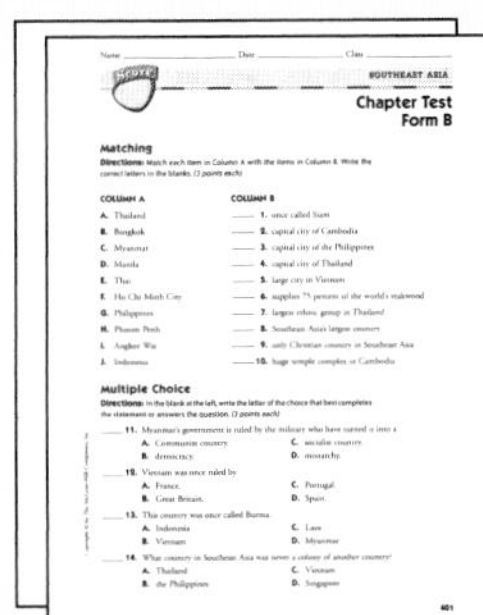

Performance Assessment Activity L1/ELL

ExamView® Pro Testmaker CD-ROM

STANDARDIZED ASSESSMENT SKILLS

Critical Thinking Skills Activity L2

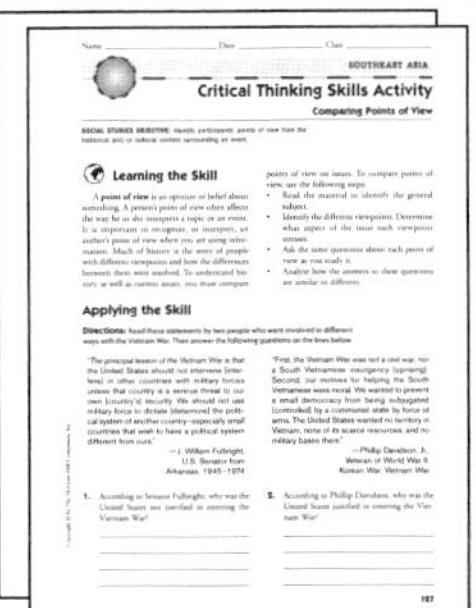

Map and Graph Skills Activity L2

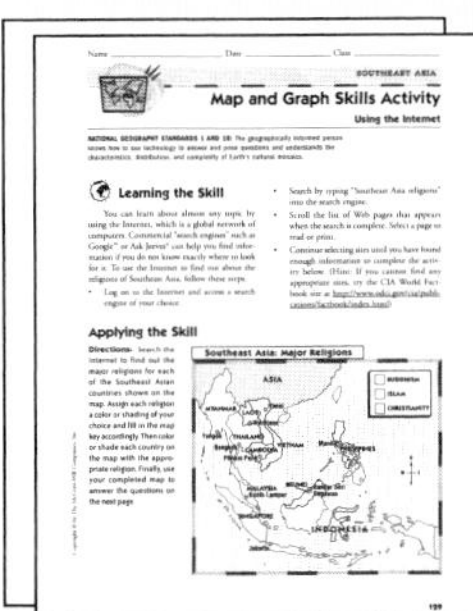

Standardized Test Skills Practice Workbook Activity L2

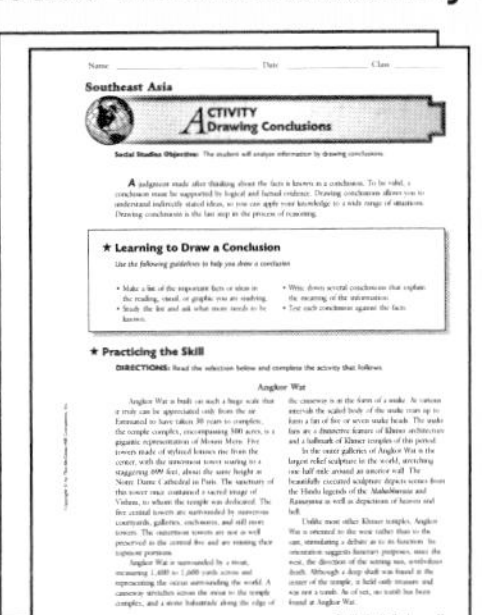

HOME INVOLVEMENT

Take-Home Review Activity L1

MULTIMEDIA

- National Geographic's The World and Its People
- MindJogger Videoquiz
- Vocabulary PuzzleMaker CD-ROM
- Interactive Tutor Self-Assessment CD-ROM
- ExamView® Pro Testmaker CD-ROM
- TeacherWorks CD-ROM
- StudentWorks CD-ROM
- Skillbuilder Interactive Workbook CD-ROM, Level 1
- Presentation Plus! CD-ROM
- Audio Program

SPANISH RESOURCES

The following Spanish language materials are available in the Spanish Resources binder:

- Spanish Summaries
- Spanish Vocabulary Activities
- Spanish Guided Reading Activities
- Spanish Quizzes and Tests
- Spanish Take-Home Review Activities
- Spanish Reteaching Activities

Meeting National Standards

Geography for Life

The following standards are covered in Chapter 25:

Section 1
EE1 The World in Spatial Terms: Standards 1, 2, 3
EE2 Places and Regions: Standards 4, 5, 6

Section 2
EE2 Places and Regions: Standards 4, 5, 6
EE3 Physical Systems: Standards 7, 8
EE4 Human Systems: Standards 9, 10, 11, 12, 13

State and Local Objectives

Chapter 25 Planning Guide

SECTION RESOURCES

Daily Objectives	Reproducible Resources	Multimedia Resources
Section 1 **Life on the Mainland** **1.** Describe the people and geography of Myanmar and Thailand. **2.** Explain how war has affected Laos and Cambodia. **3.** Discuss Vietnam and its history.	Reproducible Lesson Plan Daily Lecture and Discussion Notes Note-taking Guide Guided Reading Activity* Reading Essentials and Study Guide* Section Quiz*	Daily Focus Skills Transparency In-text Map Transparency GeoQuiz Transparency Vocabulary PuzzleMaker CD-ROM Interactive Tutor Self-Assessment CD-ROM ExamView® Pro Testmaker CD-ROM Presentation Plus! CD-ROM
Section 2 **Diverse Island Cultures** **1.** Compare the people and economic activities of the island countries of Southeast Asia. **2.** Name the groups that have influenced these countries.	Reproducible Lesson Plan Daily Lecture and Discussion Notes Note-taking Guide Guided Reading Activity* Reading Essentials and Study Guide* Section Quiz*	Daily Focus Skills Transparency Vocabulary PuzzleMaker CD-ROM Interactive Tutor Self-Assessment CD-ROM ExamView® Pro Testmaker CD-ROM Presentation Plus! CD-ROM MindJogger Videoquiz

00:00 **Out of Time?** Assign the **Reading Essentials and Study Guide*** for this chapter.

*Also available in Spanish

KEY TO ABILITY LEVELS

Teaching strategies have been coded for varying learning styles and abilities.

L1 **BASIC** activities for all students
L2 **AVERAGE** activities for average to above-average students
L3 **CHALLENGING** activities for above-average students
ELL **ENGLISH LANGUAGE LEARNER** activities

KEY TO TEACHING RESOURCES

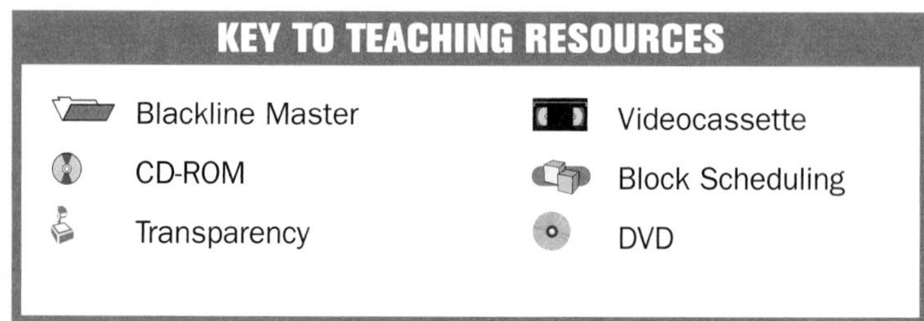

"Made in ???"

Daniel Hanczar
West Allegheny Middle School
Imperial, Pennsylvania

With parental permission, have students detach and bring to class clothing labels; tags from purses, book bags, tennis shoes, and towels; labels from canned goods or other food products; and so on. Then have students draw small pictures of the products, color them, and attach the "Made in . . ." or "Product of . . ." labels to the appropriate item. Post all pictures and labels on a large map of the world in their countries of origin. Have students pose and answer questions about the origins of their products, paying particular attention to any patterns they see among countries and world regions. Students enjoy seeing and learning where common items they buy originated.

Meeting Special Needs

In addition to the Differentiated Instruction strategies found in each section, the following resources are also suitable for your special needs students:

- ***ExamView® Pro Testmaker CD-ROM*** allows teachers to tailor tests by reducing answer choices.
- The ***Audio Program*** includes the entire narrative of the student edition so that less-proficient readers can listen to the words as they read them.
- The ***Reading Essentials and Study Guide*** provides the same content as the student edition but is written two grade levels below the textbook.
- ***Guided Reading Activities*** give less-proficient readers point-by-point instructions to increase comprehension as they read each textbook section.
- ***Enrichment Activities*** include a stimulating collection of readings and activities for gifted and talented students.

NATIONAL GEOGRAPHIC TEACHER'S CORNER

Index to National Geographic Magazine:

The following articles may be used for research relating to this chapter:

- "Wild Gliders: The Creatures of Borneo's Rain Forest Go Airborne," by Tim Laman, October 2000.
- "The Temples of Angkor," by Douglas Preston, August 2000.
- "Tam Dao: Vietnam's Sanctuary Under Siege," by Michael J. McRae, June 1999.

National Geographic Society Products:

To order the following products for use with this chapter, call National Geographic Society at 1-800-368-2728:

- *Asia* (Video)
- *PictureShow: Earth's Climate* (CD-ROM)
- *PicturePack: Geography of Asia* (Transparencies)

NGS ONLINE

Access National Geographic's Web site for current events, activities, links, interactive features, and archives.
www.nationalgeographic.com

Find the latest coverage of geography in the news, atlas updates, cartographic activities with interactive maps, an online map store, and links at www.nationalgeographic.com/maps

SOCIAL STUDIES Online

Use our Web site for additional resources. All essential content is covered in the Student Edition.

You and your students can visit twip.glencoe.com, the Web site companion to *The World and Its People.* This innovative integration of electronic and print media offers your students a wealth of opportunities. The student text directs students to the Web site for the following options:

- Chapter Overviews
- Student Web Activities
- Self-Check Quizzes
- Textbook Updates

Answers are provided for you in the Web Activity Lesson Plan. Additional Web resources and Interactive Tutor puzzles are also available.

Introduce students to chapter content and key terms by having them access Chapter Overview 25 at twip.glencoe.com

Chapter Objectives

1. Describe the land, resources, economies, and cultures of the mainland countries of Southeast Asia.
2. Compare the landforms, people, and economies of the island countries of Southeast Asia.

GLENCOE TECHNOLOGY

NATIONAL GEOGRAPHIC

The World and Its People Video Program

Chapter 26 Southeast Asia

The following segments enhance the study of this chapter:

- **Vietnamese New Year**
- **Philippine Hot Spot**
- **Bali**

MindJogger Videoquiz

Use MindJogger Videoquiz to preview the Chapter 25 content.

Both programs available in DVD and VHS

Chapter 25 Southeast Asia

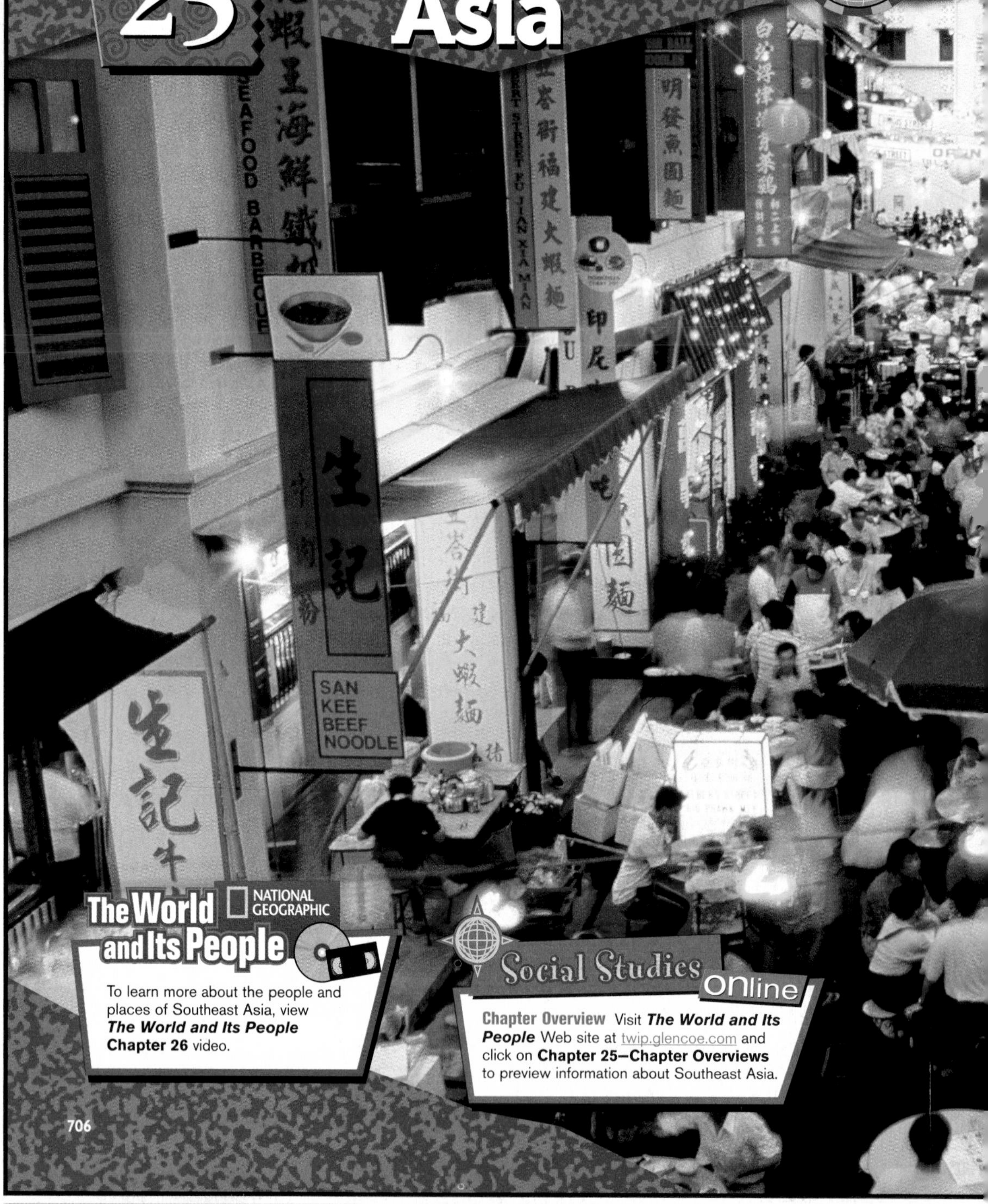

The World and Its People NATIONAL GEOGRAPHIC

To learn more about the people and places of Southeast Asia, view ***The World and Its People* Chapter 26** video.

Social Studies Online

Chapter Overview Visit ***The World and Its People*** Web site at twip.glencoe.com and click on **Chapter 25—Chapter Overviews** to preview information about Southeast Asia.

706

Reading Strategy — Purpose for Reading

Write the names of the countries in Southeast Asia on the board. Have students write everything they know or think they know about these nations in their notebooks. Have students work with a partner and compare their lists. They may add or delete information. Have each pair share one fact with the class. Make a master list on an overhead projector of all shared information. *(Students are likely to have heard of Vietnam due to the long war there; they may also know of other countries as a result of recent news stories.)* After students have read the chapter, review this list with the class to see which facts were confirmed, which were contradicted, and which were not covered. Those not covered can be topics for further research. L1

Identifying Main Ideas Make this foldable to help you identify key facts about the people and places of Southeast Asia.

Step 1 Fold the paper from the top right corner down so the edges line up. Cut off the leftover piece.

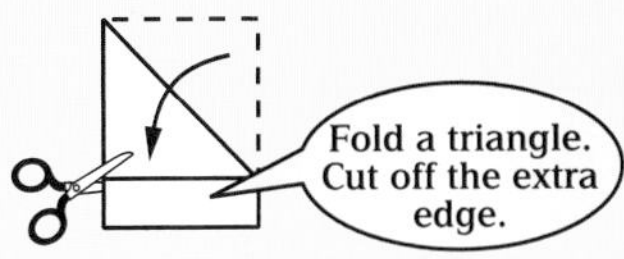
Fold a triangle.
Cut off the extra edge.

Step 2 Fold the triangle in half. Unfold.

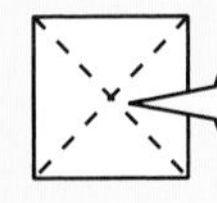
The folds will form an X that creates four equal sections.

Step 3 Cut up one fold line and stop at the middle. This forms two triangular flaps.

Step 4 Draw an X on one tab and label the other three the following: Mainland Countries, Indonesia, and Other Island Countries.

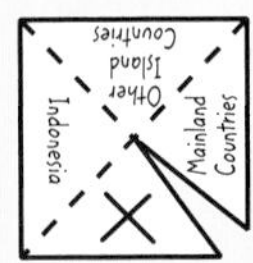
Other Island Countries
Indonesia
Mainland Countries

Step 5 Fold the X flap under the other flap and glue together.

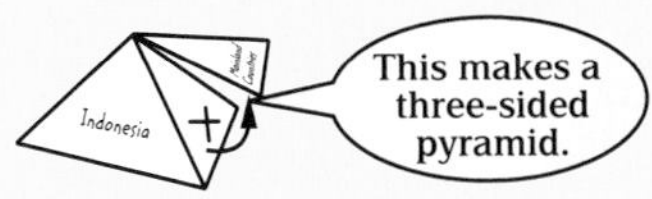
Indonesia
This makes a three-sided pyramid.

Reading and Writing As you read, write main ideas inside the foldable under each appropriate pyramid wall.

Why It Matters

A High Price for Prosperity

Some Southeast Asian countries—such as Indonesia, Malaysia, and Singapore—have become major economic centers. They manufacture goods and export natural resources. One possible negative impact of this economic prosperity might be the destruction of the region's beautiful landscapes.

▲ Outdoor restaurants are popular in Singapore.

About the Photo

Singapore, or "The Lion City" as the name *Singa Pur* translates, became a central seaport and exporter of rare and exotic foods in the nineteenth century. Among the precious cargo sailing from Singapore were sago, tea, sugar, cloves, coriander, cassia, nutmeg, and black pepper. Today the spirit of Singapore is captured best in its colorful open-air restaurants and street stands. Some of Singapore's most famous dishes—satays, laksa lemak, char kway teow (stir-fried rice noodles), chili crab, and otak-otak (spicy char-grilled fish cakes)—exemplify the island nation's love of chili and spices.

Introducing
Chapter 25

FOLDABLES Study Organizer Dinah Zike's Foldables

Purpose Students will make and use a foldable to summarize the main ideas after reading the chapter. This reading strategy requires students to read with the purpose of identifying and describing key facts about the countries of Southeast Asia. As the students read, they are required to record the main ideas about the geography, economy, and culture of the countries of Southeast Asia.

Have students complete the ***Reading and Study Skills Foldables*** activity for this chapter.

Why It Matters

Statistics are used to measure the economic growth of areas. Tell students that in order to be accurate you should compare categories that are similar. For example, the countries with the most computers are the United States, Japan, and Germany. But the countries with the highest *rate of computers per population* are Singapore, the United States, and Switzerland. Looking at rate "evens the playing field" for countries like those in Southeast Asia with smaller populations.

1 Focus

Section Objectives

1. Describe the people and geography of Myanmar and Thailand.
2. Explain how war has affected Laos and Cambodia.
3. Discuss Vietnam and its history.

BELLRINGER
Skillbuilder Activity

Project transparency and have students answer the question.

Daily Focus Skills Transparency

Reading Preview

■ **Activating Prior Knowledge** Point to Southeast Asia on a map of the world and show the region's proximity to China, India, and Australia. Ask students to collect evidence of these countries' influences on Southeast Asia as they read the section.

■ **Preteaching Vocabulary** Remind students that the prefix *de-* means "to remove or take away from." Ask students to use that clue to explain the meaning of the word *deforestation.*

Guide to Reading

Main Idea

The countries of mainland Southeast Asia rely on agriculture as a major source of wealth.

Terms to Know

- precious gems
- deforestation
- socialism
- civil war

Reading Strategy

Create a chart like this one for each of these countries: Myanmar, Thailand, Laos, Cambodia, and Vietnam. Fill in the right column on each chart with facts about the countries.

Country	
Topic	Key Fact
Land	
Economy	
People	

Section 1 Life on the Mainland

NATIONAL GEOGRAPHIC Exploring Our World

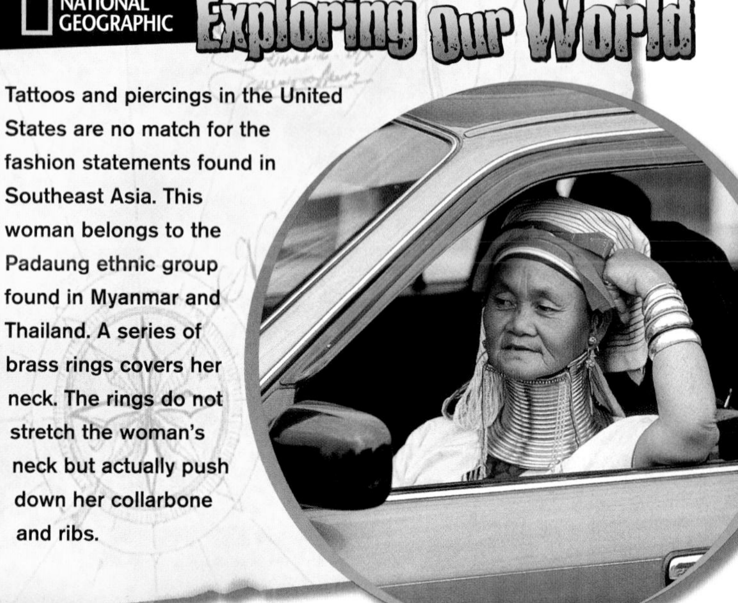

Tattoos and piercings in the United States are no match for the fashion statements found in Southeast Asia. This woman belongs to the Padaung ethnic group found in Myanmar and Thailand. A series of brass rings covers her neck. The rings do not stretch the woman's neck but actually push down her collarbone and ribs.

South of China and east of India lies Southeast Asia. This region includes thousands of islands and a long arm of land called the **Malay Peninsula.** Several countries lie entirely on the mainland of Southeast Asia. They are Myanmar, Thailand, Laos, Cambodia, and Vietnam.

Myanmar

Myanmar, also called Burma, is about the size of Texas. Rugged, steep mountains sweep through its western and eastern borders. Two wide rivers—the **Irrawaddy** (IHR•ah•WAH•dee) and the **Salween**—flow through vast lowland plains between these mountain ranges. Monsoons, or seasonal winds that blow over a continent for months at a time, cause wet summers and dry winters in Myanmar.

About two-thirds of the country's people farm. The main crops are rice, sugarcane, beans, and peanuts. Some farmers work their fields with tractors, but most rely on plows pulled by water buffalo.

Section Resources

Reproducible Masters
- Reproducible Lesson Plan
- Daily Lecture and Discussion Notes
- Note-taking Guide
- Guided Reading Activity
- Reading Essentials and Study Guide
- Section Quiz

Transparencies
- Daily Focus Skills Transparency
- GeoQuiz Transparency
- In-text Map Transparency

Multimedia
- Vocabulary PuzzleMaker CD-ROM
- Interactive Tutor Self-Assessment CD-ROM
- Presentation Plus! CD-ROM
- ExamView® Pro Testmaker CD-ROM

Myanmar exports wood products, gas, and foods such as beans and rice. The country provides about 75 percent of the world's teakwood. Myanmar's prized forests are decreasing, however, because of **deforestation.** This is the widespread cutting of trees. Fortunately, the country also exports precious gems. **Precious gems** are valuable stones such as rubies, sapphires, and jade.

Almost 75 percent of Myanmar's 49.5 million people live in rural areas. The most densely populated part of the country is the fertile Irrawaddy River valley. Many rural dwellers build their homes on poles above the ground for protection from floods and wild animals.

The capital and largest city, **Yangon** (formerly called Rangoon), is famous for its modern university and its gold-covered Buddhist temples. Buddhism is the main religion in Myanmar. Most people are of Burman heritage, and Burmese is the main language.

Myanmar was part of British India for many years. It became an independent republic in 1948. Since then, military leaders have turned Myanmar into a socialist country. **Socialism** is an economic system in which most businesses are owned and run by the government. Some

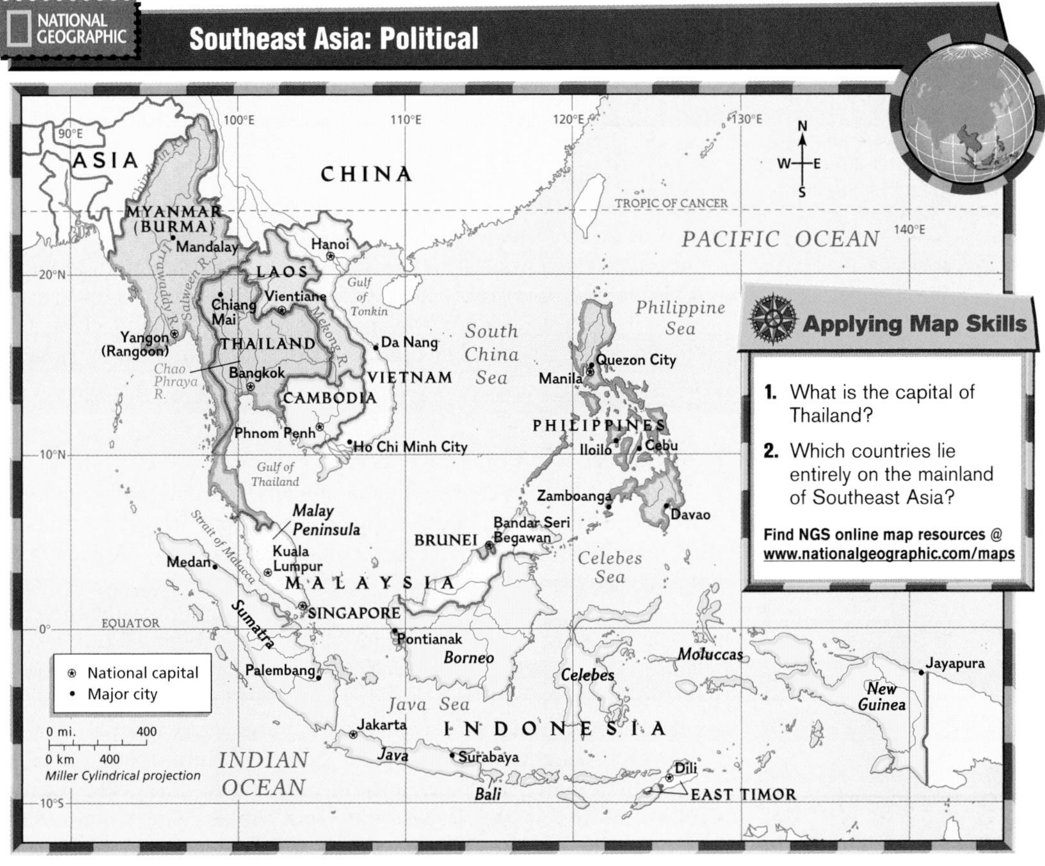

Applying Map Skills

1. What is the capital of Thailand?
2. Which countries lie entirely on the mainland of Southeast Asia?

Find NGS online map resources @ www.nationalgeographic.com/maps

Reading Strategy — Reading the Text

Taking Notes Remind students to follow these simple rules for taking good notes: 1) take notes on small sections of the chapter rather than after the entire chapter is read so that details are more easily remembered; 2) be selective about what ideas are recorded; 3) paraphrase readings; 4) take notes quickly and efficiently; 5) use organizational strategies such as creating graphic organizers or power notes to understand concepts and supporting details. L1

*Use the **Reading Skills Handbook** for more reading strategies.*

TEACH

Reading Strategy

Paraphrasing Information
Have students read the first paragraph on this page. Demonstrate paraphrasing by rewording the paragraph: Myanmar produces much of the world's teakwood. As a result, deforestation has occurred. Fortunately, though, Myanmar also exports precious gems. Have students practice the skill with other paragraphs in the section. L1

Daily Lecture and Discussion Notes

SOUTHEAST ASIA

Daily Lecture and Discussion Notes
Life on the Mainland

Did You Know? Popular spectator sports in Southeast Asia include soccer and a form of boxing that allows hitting with any part of the body. The favorite participant sport is *chinlon*, in which a ball of woven cane is passed from player to player by hitting it with the feet, knees, or head.

I. Myanmar

A. Myanmar, once called Burma, has mountain ranges and two wide rivers—the Irrawaddy and the Salween.

B. Myanmar has wet summers and dry winters influenced by monsoons, or seasonal winds that blow over a continent for months at a time.

Applying Map Skills

Answers

1. Bangkok
2. Myanmar, Thailand, Laos, Cambodia, and Vietnam

In-text Map Transparency Activity
Have students look at the map of Southeast Asia. Ask students to predict how they think the physical geography of the region affects people's lives.

L1/ELL

Guided Reading Activity

Name ____________ Date ____________ Class ____________

SOUTHEAST ASIA

Guided Reading Activity 1

Life on the Mainland

DIRECTIONS: Filling in the Blanks Reading the section and completing the sentences below will help you learn more about mainland Southeast Asia. Use your textbook to fill in the blanks.

Myanmar once was called **(1)** ____________. Mountains are located on its **(2)** ____________ and **(3)** ____________ borders. About two-thirds of the people **(4)** ____________.

Myanmar provides about 75 percent of the world's **(5)** ____________. These forests are decreasing because of **(6)** ____________. Myanmar is a **(7)** ____________ country.

...called **(8)** ____________. It is the only Southeast...

Reading Check Answer

the Irrawaddy River valley

Cultural Kaleidoscope

Thailand If you are in Thailand in April, you might get wet. Thais celebrate the New Year in April. They mark this holiday by pouring buckets of water on people. The tradition began as a gesture symbolizing hope for rain for crops.

Reading Check Answer

tin, tungsten

Measure student knowledge of physical features.

GeoQuiz Transparency

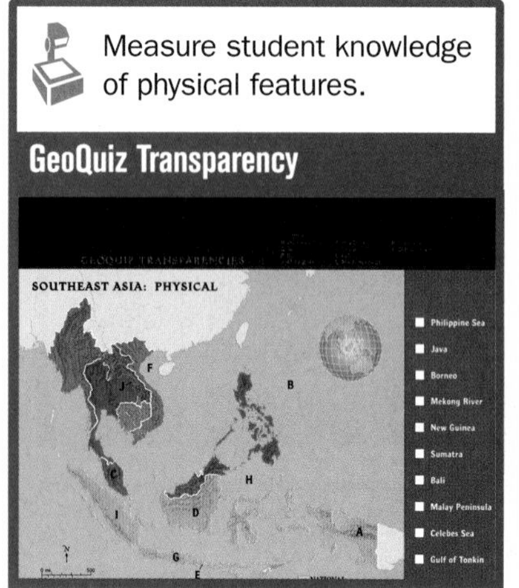

people have tried to build a democracy in Myanmar. A woman named Aung San Suu Kyi (AWNG SAN SOO CHEE) has become a leader in this struggle. In 1991 she was awarded the Nobel Peace Prize for her efforts but still faces opposition from the government today.

Reading Check Where is Myanmar's most densely populated area?

Thailand

The map on page 709 shows you that **Thailand** looks like a flower on a stem. The "flower" is the northern part, located on the mainland. The "stem" is a narrow strip on the Malay Peninsula. The country's main waterway—the **Chao Phraya** (chow PRY•uh) **River**—flows through a central plain. Like Myanmar, Thailand has wet summer monsoons and dry winter monsoons.

Once called Siam, *Thailand* means "land of the free." It is the only Southeast Asian country that has never been a European colony. The Thai people trace their independence as a kingdom back to the A.D. 1200s. Thailand is a constitutional monarchy with a king.

One of Thailand's agricultural products is rubber. The government has taken steps to limit deforestation to protect this industry. Thailand is also one of the world's leading producers of tin and tungsten. Most manufacturing is located near **Bangkok,** the capital. Workers make cement, textiles, computers, and electrical appliances. Tourism is an important industry as well.

Most of Thailand's 63.1 million people belong to the Thai ethnic group and practice Buddhism. Hundreds of Buddhist temples called *wats* dot the cities and countryside. Buddhist monks, or holy men, walk among the people to receive food offerings.

About 80 percent of Thais live in rural villages, although thousands look for jobs in Bangkok. This city has beautiful temples and royal palaces that are surrounded by modern skyscrapers and crowded streets. Bangkok has so many cars that daily traffic jams last for hours.

Reading Check Thailand is a leading producer of what two elements?

Teen Scene

Life as a Monk

After his grandfather died, Nattawud Daoruang became a novice Buddhist monk. "You see," he says, "Thai Buddhists believe they can get to paradise by holding on to a monk's robe. So I became a monk for a month to help my grandfather get to paradise. The novice monks had to get up at 5:00 A.M. and meditate. After that, we had free time so we read comics and played games on the monks' Play Station™. In the afternoons, we walked around the village with the monks to get food and drink."

Laos and Cambodia

Landlocked **Laos** is covered by mountains. Southern Laos includes a fertile area along the **Mekong** (MAY•KAWNG) **River,** Southeast Asia's longest river. Once a French colony, Laos became independent more than fifty years ago.

Laos is an economically poor country. Its Communist government has only recently allowed tourism. About 80 percent of Laos's 5.6 million people live in rural areas. Farmers grow rice, sweet potatoes, sugarcane, and corn along the Mekong's fertile banks. Industry is largely undeveloped because of isolation and years of civil war. A civil war is a fight among different groups within a country. Laos lacks railroads and has electricity in only a few cities. **Vientiane** (vyehn•TYAHN) is the largest city and capital. The Communist government discourages religion, but most Laotians remain Buddhists.

Differentiated Instruction

Meeting Special Needs: Less-proficient Readers Students who have difficulty with retaining what they read might remember the lesson better if they participate in partner reading. Pair students and have partners take turns reading paragraphs or sections of the text aloud. The partner not reading should follow the text as it is being read. At the end of each paragraph or section, students should quiz each other on the content. **L1 ELL**

Refer to *Inclusion for the Middle School Social Studies Classroom Strategies and Activities* in the TCR.

Architecture

The temple of Angkor Wat in northwestern Cambodia was built during the 1100s. Dedicated to the Hindu god Vishnu, much of the temple is covered with elaborately carved characters from Hindu legends. The Khmer people designed Angkor Wat to represent the Hindu view of the universe. The moat surrounding the temple stood for the oceans. The tall central tower symbolized Mount Meru, center of the universe and home of the various forms of the Hindu supreme being.

Looking Closer **How does the design of Angkor Wat reflect the beliefs of the builders?**

Cambodia For many years, **Cambodia** was a rich farming country that exported rice and rubber. By the 1980s, its economy was in ruins because of years of civil war and harsh Communist rule. Cambodia's few factories produce items such as wood products, textiles, and rubber.

Most of Cambodia's 12.6 million people belong to the Khmer (kuh•MEHR) ethnic group. About 82 percent live in rural villages. The rest live in cities such as the capital, **Phnom Penh** (puh•NAWM PEHN). Buddhism is Cambodia's main religion. About 1,000 years ago, Cambodia was the center of the vast Khmer Empire. During Khmer rule, huge temple complexes like Angkor Wat were built.

In modern times, Cambodia was under French rule, becoming independent in 1953. Since the 1960s, there has been almost constant warfare among rival political groups. A Communist government led by the dictator Pol Pot took control in the mid-1970s. Pol Pot forced many city dwellers to move to rural areas and work as farmers. More than 1 million Cambodians died. Some fled to other countries. In 1993 Cambodia brought back its king, but rivalry among political groups continues.

Reading Check **Why is Cambodia's economy in ruins?**

Vietnam

Vietnam's long eastern coastline borders the **Gulf of Tonkin,** the **South China Sea,** and the **Gulf of Thailand.** In the north lies the fertile delta of the Red River. A delta is an area of land formed by soil deposits at the mouth of a river. In the south you find the wide, swampy delta of the Mekong River. Monsoons bring wet and dry seasons.

Farmers grow large amounts of rice, sugarcane, cassava, sweet potatoes, corn, bananas, and coffee in river deltas. Vietnam's mountain forests provide wood, and the South China Sea yields large catches of fish.

Answer The carvings are characters from Hindu legends, and the overall design represents the Hindu view of the universe.

Khmer Temples Angkor Wat is the largest of more than 100 temples in the Angkor area. There are about 1,000 Khmer temples across Southeast Asia.

Reading Check Answer

The country has suffered almost constant warfare since the 1960s.

3 ASSESS

Assign Section 1 Assessment as homework or an in-class activity.

Have students use the Interactive Tutor Self-Assessment CD-ROM to review Section 1.

L2

Section Quiz

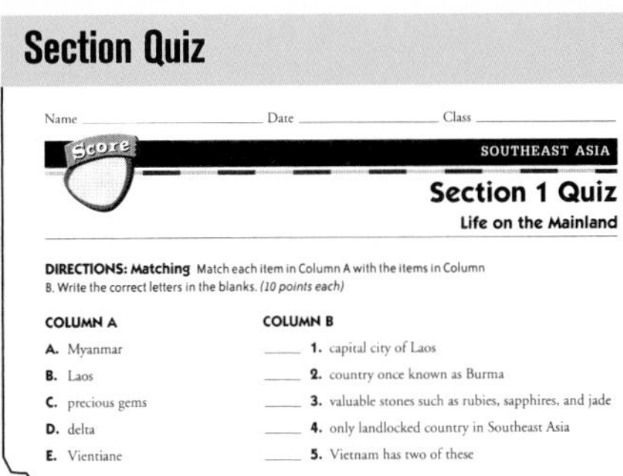

Name ______ Date ______ Class ______

Score

SOUTHEAST ASIA

Section 1 Quiz

Life on the Mainland

DIRECTIONS: Matching Match each item in Column A with the items in Column B. Write the correct letters in the blanks. *(10 points each)*

COLUMN A	COLUMN B
A. Myanmar	____ **1.** capital city of Laos
B. Laos	____ **2.** country once known as Burma
C. precious gems	____ **3.** valuable stones such as rubies, sapphires, and jade
D. delta	____ **4.** only landlocked country in Southeast Asia
E. Vientiane	____ **5.** Vietnam has two of these

Content Background

Angkor Explain how impressive the Angkor area is in terms not only of its art but also its technology. The entire complex was designed as a method of controlling the floodwaters of the river flowing through the area. By creating canals, artificial lakes, and irrigation channels, the Khmer rulers were able to keep the area as a vast, functioning rice paddy. The achievement helped support their rule—the kings, by controlling the water that ensured people's survival, demonstrated their power.

Reading Check Answer

Ho Chi Minh City

L1/ELL

Reading Essentials and Study Guide

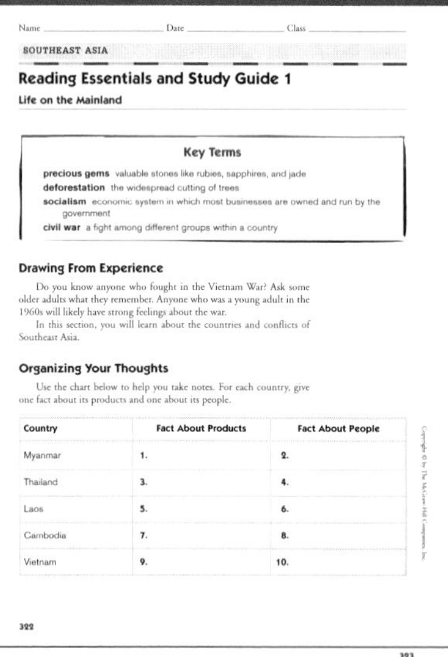

Name ______ Date ______ Class ______

SOUTHEAST ASIA

Reading Essentials and Study Guide 1

Life on the Mainland

Key Terms

precious gems valuable stones like rubies, sapphires, and jade
deforestation the widespread cutting of trees
socialism economic system in which most businesses are owned and run by the government
civil war a fight among different groups within a country

Drawing From Experience

Do you know anyone who fought in the Vietnam War? Ask some older adults what they remember. Anyone who was a young adult in the 1960s will likely have strong feelings about the war.

In this section, you will learn about the countries and conflicts of Southeast Asia.

Organizing Your Thoughts

Use the chart below to help you take notes. For each country, give one fact about its products and one about its people.

Country	Fact About Products	Fact About People
Myanmar	1.	2.
Thailand	3.	4.
Laos	5.	6.
Cambodia	7.	8.
Vietnam	9.	10.

Copyright © by The McGraw-Hill Companies, Inc.

322

323

4 CLOSE

Have students prepare a bulletin board display that uses images and captions to describe life in mainland Southeast Asia.

With almost 80.8 million people, Vietnam has the largest population in mainland Southeast Asia. About 75 percent live in rural villages. The largest urban area is **Ho Chi Minh** (HOH CHEE MIHN) **City,** named for the country's first Communist leader. Located in the south, it used to be called Saigon (sy•GAHN). Vietnam's capital, **Hanoi,** is located in the north. Most people are Buddhists and belong to the Vietnamese ethnic group. The rest are Chinese, Cambodians, and other Asian ethnic groups. Vietnamese is the major language, but Chinese, English, and French are also spoken.

The ancestors of Vietnam's people came from China more than 2,000 years ago. From the late 1800s to the mid-1950s, Vietnam was under French rule. Vietnamese Communists drove out the French in 1954. The Communist government controlled northern Vietnam, while an American-supported government ruled the south. In the 1960s, fighting between these two groups led to the Vietnam War. During this extended conflict, more than 2.5 million Americans helped fight against the Communists. The United States eventually withdrew its forces in 1973. Within two years, the Communists had captured the south. Many thousands of people fled Vietnam, settling in the United States and other countries.

In recent years, Vietnam's Communist leaders have opened the country to Western ideas, businesses, and tourists. They have also loosened government controls on the economy. In these two ways, the Communist leaders hope to raise Vietnam's standard of living.

Reading Check What is the largest urban area in Vietnam?

Section 1 Assessment

Defining Terms

1. **Define** precious gems, deforestation, socialism, civil war.

Recalling Facts

2. **Economics** What does Myanmar export?
3. **History** What led to the Vietnam War?
4. **Economics** What has slowed the economies of Laos and Cambodia?

Graphic Organizer

5. **Organizing Information** Create a time line like this one. Then list four events and their dates in Vietnam's history.

Critical Thinking

6. **Summarizing Information** What makes Thailand unique among the countries of Southeast Asia?
7. **Making Predictions** In recent years, the Communist leaders in Vietnam have tried to improve the country's standard of living. How do they hope to do this? Do you think these actions will help? Why or why not?

Applying Social Studies Skills

8. **Analyzing Maps** Look at the political map on page 709. What city is located at 21°N, 106°E?

712 CHAPTER 25

Section 1 Assessment

1. The terms are defined in the Glossary.
2. wood products, gas, and foods such as beans and rice
3. fighting between the Communists in the north and the American-supported government in the south
4. civil wars
5. c. A.D. 1: Ancestors of today's people come from China; late 1800s–1950s: France rules area; 1954: Vietnamese Communists drive French out; 1960s: Vietnam War; 1975: south captured by Communists
6. It is the only Southeast Asian country never to have been a colony.
7. by welcoming Western ideas, businesses, and tourists and by loosening government controls on the economy; answers will vary.
8. Hanoi, Vietnam

Social Studies Skill

Reading a Contour Map

A trail map would show the paths you could follow if you went hiking in the mountains. How would you know if the trail follows an easy, flat route, though, or if it cuts steeply up a mountain? To find out, you need a **contour map.**

Learning the Skill

Contour maps use lines to outline the shape—or contour—of the landscape. Each contour line connects all points that are at the same elevation. This means that if you walked along one contour line, you would always be at the same height above sea level.

Where the contour lines are far apart, the land rises gradually. Where the lines are close together, the land rises steeply. For example, one contour line may be labeled 1,000 meters (3,281 ft.). Another contour line very close to the first one may be labeled 2,000 meters (6,562 ft.). This means that the land rises 1,000 meters (3,281 ft.) in just a short distance.

To read a contour map, follow these steps:

- Identify the area shown on the map.
- Read the numbers on the contour lines to determine how much the elevation increases or decreases with each line.
- Locate the highest and lowest numbers, which indicate the highest and lowest elevations.
- Notice the amount of space between the lines, which tells you whether the land is steep or flat.

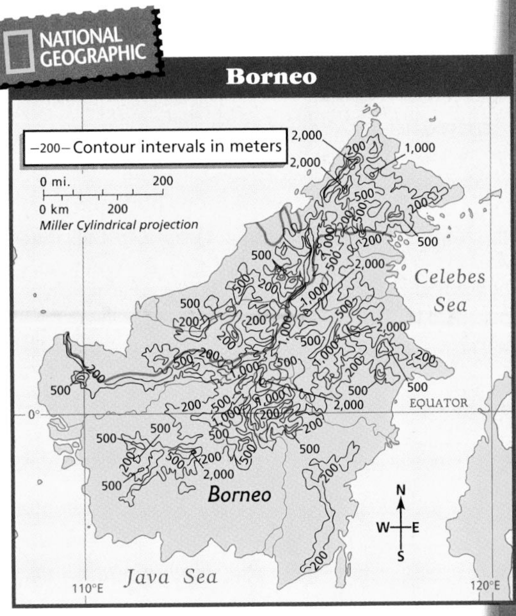

Practicing the Skill

Study the contour map above, and then answer the following questions.

1. What area is shown on the map?
2. What is the lowest elevation on the map?
3. What is the highest elevation on the map?
4. Where is the landscape flattest? How can you tell?
5. How would you describe the physical geography of this island?

Applying the Skill

Turn to page 10 in the **Geography Handbook.** Use the contour map of Sri Lanka to answer the five questions above.

Social Studies Skill

TEACH

Create a simple trail map with two routes leading from a town to a lake. One route should be short and direct, and the other should be long and circuitous. **Ask: Which route would you walk?** Most will select the shorter route. Then make contour lines to show that the shorter route goes over a mountain while the longer one covers flat land. Ask students again which route they would choose. L1

Additional Skills Practice

1. **What do contour lines show?** *(They show the points that have the same elevation.)*
2. **What kind of slope would you expect to see if contour lines are far apart?** *(gradual)*
3. **What kind of slope would you expect to see if contour lines are close together?** *(steep)*

Additional Skills Resources

 Chapter Skills Review

 Building Geography Skills for Life

GLENCOE TECHNOLOGY

 **Skillbuilder Interactive Workbook CD-ROM, Level 1**

This interactive CD-ROM reinforces student mastery of essential social studies skills.

Practicing the Skill Answers

1. the island of Borneo
2. 200 meters and lower
3. 2,000 meters
4. along the coast and the southern part of the island; there is a wide area before the first contour line occurs.
5. The island is rugged, with high elevations in the center.

Applying the Skill
Students should use the contour map of Sri Lanka to answer the questions.

1 Focus

Section Objectives

1. Compare the people and economic activities of the island countries of Southeast Asia.
2. Name the groups that have influenced these countries.

BELLRINGER Skillbuilder Activity

Project transparency and have students answer the question.

Daily Focus Skills Transparency

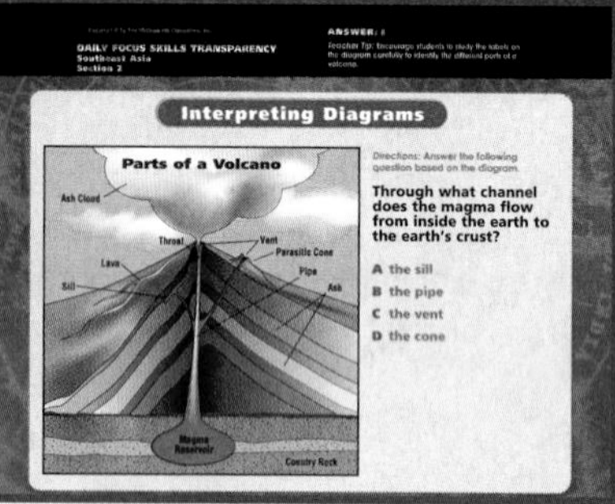

Reading Preview

- **Activating Prior Knowledge** **Ask:** What problems would you expect to find in governing a country of many islands? How would those problems change if the people were from many ethnic groups? Explain that in this section, students will read about a country that faces these problems.
- **Preteaching Vocabulary** Have students look up the meaning of *strait.* Then have volunteers explain how a country would benefit from having control of a strait.

Guide to Reading

Main Idea

The island countries of Southeast Asia have a variety of cultures and economic activities.

Terms to Know

- plate
- strait
- free port
- terraced field

Reading Strategy

Create a chart like this one. As you read, list two facts in the right column about each country in the left column.

Country	Facts
Indonesia	
East Timor	
Malaysia	
Singapore	
Brunei	
Philippines	

Section 2

Diverse Island Cultures

NATIONAL GEOGRAPHIC Exploring Our World

Villagers in Bali, Indonesia, carry food and gifts to a local Hindu temple. In Bali, it seems as though there is an unending chain of religious festivals. More than 60 festivals a year are dedicated to such events and items as percussion instruments, the birth of a Hindu goddess, woodcarving, and learning.

The island countries of Southeast Asia are Indonesia, East Timor, Malaysia, Singapore, Brunei (bru•NY), and the Philippines. **Indonesia** is Southeast Asia's largest country. It is an archipelago of more than 13,600 islands.

Indonesia and East Timor

The map on page 709 shows you the major islands of Indonesia—**Sumatra, Java,** and **Celebes** (SEH•luh•BEEZ). Indonesia also shares two large islands with other countries. Most of the island of **Borneo** belongs to Indonesia. In addition, Indonesia controls the western half of the island of Timor. Another country—**East Timor**—lies on the eastern half.

Indonesia lies where two of the earth's tectonic plates meet. Tectonic **plates** are huge slabs of rock that make up the earth's crust. Indonesia's location on top of these plates causes it to experience earthquakes.

Section Resources

Reproducible Masters

- Reproducible Lesson Plan
- Daily Lecture and Discussion Notes
- Note-taking Guide
- Guided Reading Activity
- Reading Essentials and Study Guide
- Section Quiz

Transparencies

- Daily Focus Skills Transparency

Multimedia

- Vocabulary PuzzleMaker CD-ROM
- Interactive Tutor Self-Assessment CD-ROM
- Presentation Plus! CD-ROM
- ExamView® Pro Testmaker CD-ROM
- MindJogger Videoquiz

The volcanoes that formed Indonesia have left a rich covering of ash that makes the soil good for farming. Because Indonesia lies on the Equator, its climate is tropical. Monsoons bring a wet season and a dry season. The tropical climate, combined with fertile soil, has allowed dense rain forests to spread.

Economic Activities Foreign companies build factories on the island of Java because labor is inexpensive. Agriculture provides work for nearly half of the people of Indonesia. Farmers grow rice, coffee, cassava, tea, and peanuts. The country of East Timor also has agricultural products such as coffee, mangoes, and vanilla.

Indonesia has large reserves of oil and natural gas. Its mines yield tin, silver, nickel, copper, bauxite, and gold. Dense rain forests provide teak and other valuable woods. Some companies that own large tracts of land are cutting down the trees very quickly. The environment suffers from this deforestation. When the trees are cut down, rich soil runs off into the sea during heavy rains.

People of Indonesia and East Timor Indonesia has about 220.5 million people—the fourth-largest population in the world. It is also one of the world's most densely populated countries. On Java you will find **Jakarta** (juh•KAHR•tuh), Indonesia's capital and largest city. It has modern buildings and streets crowded with cars and bicycles.

Forty-five percent of Indonesians belong to the Javanese ethnic group. The official language, Bahasa Indonesia, is taught in schools. Indonesia has more followers of Islam than any other country. Other religions, such as Christianity and Buddhism, are also practiced. On the beautiful island of **Bali,** Hindu beliefs are held by most of the people.

Thousands of years ago, Hindus and Buddhists from India settled the islands that are today Indonesia. Their descendants set up kingdoms. These kingdoms grew wealthy by controlling the trade that passed through the waterways between the Indian and Pacific Oceans. In the A.D. 1100s, traders from Southwest Asia brought Islam to the region. Four hundred years later, Europeans arrived to acquire the valuable spices grown here. They brought Christianity to the islands. The Dutch eventually controlled most of the islands as a colony. Independence finally came to Indonesia in 1949.

In the late 1990s, severe economic problems led to unrest. Indonesia's people forced their dictator to resign. Today the country has a democratic government. With so many different ethnic groups, many small political parties arise. As a result, Indonesia's leaders find it difficult to form a government that is strong enough to deal with challenges.

Most recently, the people of East Timor, who are largely Roman Catholic and were once ruled by Portugal, voted for independence from Indonesia. In 2002 East Timor was internationally recognized as independent and the world's newest democracy. About 800,000 people live here.

✓ Reading Check When did East Timor win its independence?

Exchange of Knowledge

Malacca, in Malaysia, was the richest seaport in the world in the 1500s. Merchants from India, China, and Japan met Portuguese, British, and Dutch traders. These merchants and traders were responsible for the exchange of knowledge as well as goods. Today, thanks to its geographic location, Singapore has replaced Malacca as the chief center of trade.

East Timor's Challenges

East Timor's road to freedom—finally won on May 20, 2002—was long and difficult. Independence has also brought challenges. One of Asia's poorest countries, East Timor suffers from the effects of war and drought. The possibility of wealth from untapped offshore oil and gas fields, however, may brighten East Timor's future.

Categorizing Information

Develop a database of Indonesia's characteristics, such as reserves of oil, location along shipping lanes, and a large population. Read these items one at a time and have students identify whether it describes Indonesia's physical geography, economy, or culture. Some features can be placed in more than one category. L1

Daily Lecture and Discussion Notes

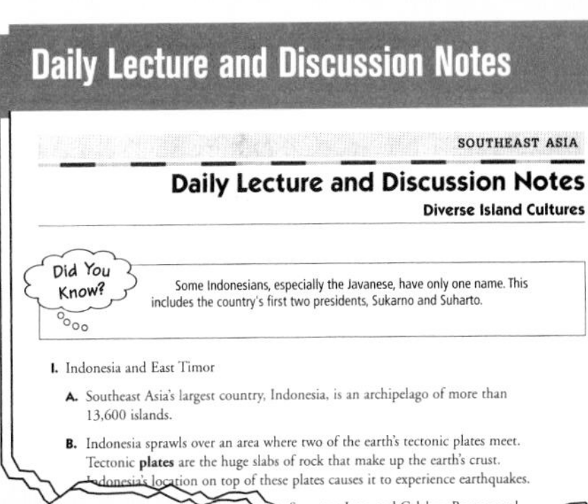

SOUTHEAST ASIA

Daily Lecture and Discussion Notes

Diverse Island Cultures

Did You Know? Some Indonesians, especially the Javanese, have only one name. This includes the country's first two presidents, Sukarno and Suharto.

I. Indonesia and East Timor

A. Southeast Asia's largest country, Indonesia, is an archipelago of more than 13,600 islands.

B. Indonesia sprawls over an area where two of the earth's tectonic plates meet. Tectonic **plates** are the huge slabs of rock that make up the earth's crust. Indonesia's location on top of these plates causes it to experience earthquakes.

✓ Reading Check Answer

2002

L1/ELL

Guided Reading Activity

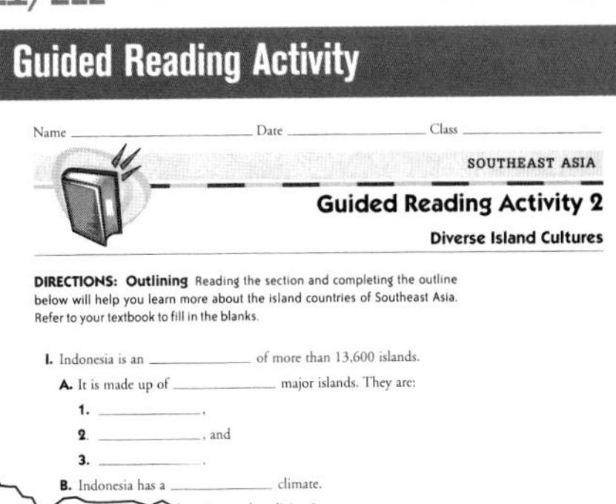

Name ______ Date ______ Class ______

SOUTHEAST ASIA

Guided Reading Activity 2

Diverse Island Cultures

DIRECTIONS: Outlining Reading the section and completing the outline below will help you learn more about the island countries of Southeast Asia. Refer to your textbook to fill in the blanks.

I. Indonesia is an ______ of more than 13,600 islands.

A. It is made up of ______ major islands. They are:

1. ______,

2. ______, and

3. ______.

B. Indonesia has a ______ climate.

Reading Strategy — Reading the Text

Monitoring Comprehension As students read the section, they might encounter text or information that they do not understand, and they should adjust their reading strategies to clarify the ideas. Model how this is done by reading "Indonesia and East Timor" aloud. As you read, say things such as "What do I think this subtopic might be about based on the heading?" *(predicting);* "Where is Indonesia in relation to East Timor?" *(visualizing);* "What have I heard about these countries, and is it correct based the information described here?" *(activating prior knowledge)* Modeling how you read helps students think about strategies they can use as they read independently. L1

*Use the **Reading Skills Handbook** for more reading strategies.*

More About the Photo

Rubber British scientist Joseph Priestly gave rubber its name when he learned it could be used to rub out pencil marks.

Caption Answer palm oil, petroleum, natural gas

Reading Check Answer

in Kuala Lumpur, Malaysia

3 Assess

Assign Section 2 Assessment as homework or an in-class activity.

Have students use the Interactive Tutor Self-Assessment CD-ROM to review Section 2.

L2

Section Quiz

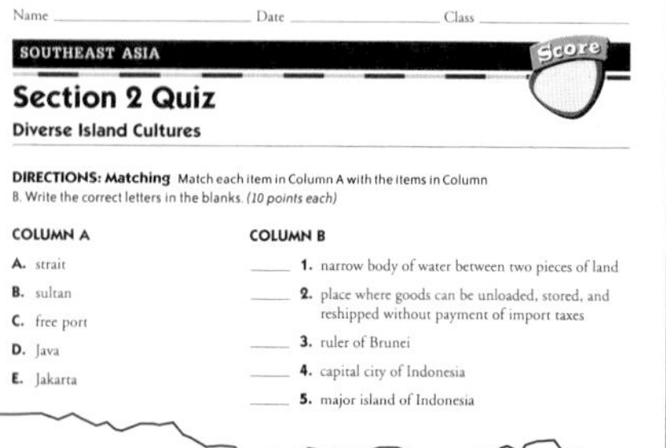

Name ______ Date ______ Class ______

SOUTHEAST ASIA Score

Section 2 Quiz
Diverse Island Cultures

DIRECTIONS: Matching Match each item in Column A with the items in Column B. Write the correct letters in the blanks. *(10 points each)*

COLUMN A	COLUMN B
A. strait	____ 1. narrow body of water between two pieces of land
B. sultan	____ 2. place where goods can be unloaded, stored, and reshipped without payment of import taxes
C. free port	____ 3. ruler of Brunei
D. Java	____ 4. capital city of Indonesia
E. Jakarta	____ 5. major island of Indonesia

Did You Know

More farmers die from snake bites in Malaysia than anywhere else in the world.

NATIONAL GEOGRAPHIC **On Location**

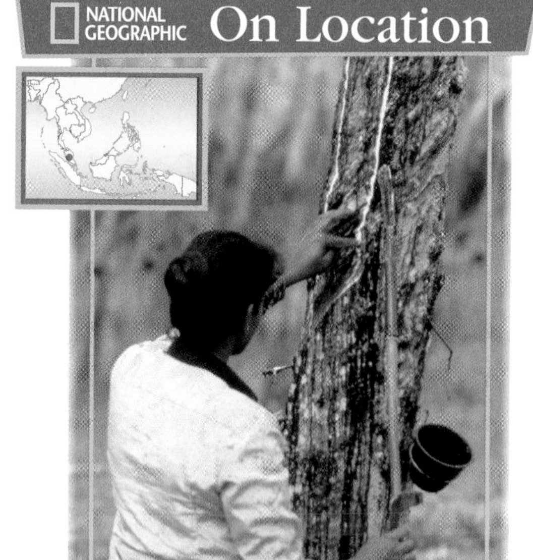

Malaysia

A Malaysian worker taps a rubber tree to get the milky liquid called latex.

Economics What other products does Malaysia export?

Malaysia

Malaysia is located on the southern end of the Malay Peninsula and also on the island of Borneo. Dense rain forests and rugged mountains make up the landscape. The **Strait of Malacca** lies to the west of the Malay Peninsula. A **strait** is a narrow body of water between two pieces of land. The Strait of Malacca is an important waterway for trade between the Indian Ocean and the Java Sea.

Malaysia is a world leader in exporting rubber and palm oil. The country also exports petroleum and natural gas. Malaysia is rich in tin, iron ore, copper, and bauxite. Consumer and high-technology goods, including microchips, are produced here. Malaysia's ports are important centers of trade as well. **Kuala Lumpur** (KWAH•luh LUM•PUR) is the capital and largest city. The Petronas Towers—among the world's tallest buildings—soar above this city. In contrast, many rural villagers live in thatched-roof homes built on posts a few feet off the ground.

Most of Malaysia's 25.1 million people belong to the Malay ethnic group. Their ancestors came from southern China thousands of years ago. In the 1800s, the British—who then ruled Malaysia—brought in Chinese and South Asian workers to mine tin and to work on rubber plantations. As a result, in marketplaces today you can hear Malay, Chinese, Tamil, and English spoken. Most Malaysians are Muslims, but there are also large numbers of Buddhists, Christians, and Hindus.

Reading Check Where are the Petronas Towers located?

Singapore, Brunei, and the Philippines

Singapore lies off the southern tip of the Malay Peninsula. It is made up of Singapore Island and 58 smaller islands. Singapore is one of the world's smallest countries, yet it has one of the world's most productive economies. The city of **Singapore** is the capital and takes up much of Singapore Island. Once covered by rain forests, Singapore Island now holds highways, factories, office buildings, and docks.

The city of Singapore has one of the world's busiest harbors. It is a **free port**. This is a place where goods can be unloaded, stored, and shipped again without payment of import taxes. Huge amounts of goods pass through this port. Singapore's many factories make high-tech goods, machinery, chemicals, and paper products. Because of their productive trade economy, the people of Singapore enjoy a high standard of living.

Differentiated Instruction

Meeting Special Needs: Visual/Spatial Malaysia and Indonesia are known for an art form called *batik*, a Javanese word meaning "drop." To create a *batik* pattern, wax is first dripped onto a fabric. When the fabric is dyed, the dye enters only the areas that are not covered by wax. After the dye has dried, the fabric is boiled to remove the wax. A beautiful pattern remains on the fabric. Show students some examples of Malaysian art and ask them to explain the relationship between Malaysia and the art they see. Then give them a blank sheet of paper and have them create a *batik* design that evokes the spirit of that art. **L1**

Refer to *Inclusion for the Middle School Social Studies Classroom Strategies and Activities* in the TCR.

Founded by the British in the early 1800s, Singapore became an independent republic in 1965. Most of the country's 4.2 million people are Chinese, but Malaysians and Indians make up about 25 percent of the population.

Brunei On the northern coast of Borneo lies another small nation—**Brunei.** Oil and natural gas exports provide about half of the country's income. Brunei's citizens receive free education and medical care, as well as low-cost housing, fuel, and food. Today the government is investing in new industries to avoid reliance on income from fuels. All political and economic decisions are made by Brunei's sultan, or ruler.

The Philippines The **Philippines** includes about 7,000 islands in the South China Sea. Volcanic mountains and forests dominate the landscape. About 40 percent of the people farm. They have built terraces on the steep mountain slopes. Terraced fields are strips of land cut out of a hillside like stair steps.

Cities in the Philippines are busy and modern. **Manila,** the country's capital, is a great commercial center. Factory workers here produce high-tech goods, food products, chemicals, clothing, and shoes.

Named after King Philip II of Spain, the Philippines spent more than 300 years as a Spanish colony. As a result of the Spanish-American War, the United States controlled the islands from 1898 until World War II. In 1946 the Philippines became an independent democratic republic.

The Philippines is the only Christian country in Southeast Asia. About 90 percent of Filipinos follow the Roman Catholic religion, brought to the islands by Spanish missionaries. The culture today blends Malay, Spanish, and American influences.

✓ Reading Check For whom was the Philippines named and why?

Web Activity Visit ***The World and Its People*** Web site at twip.glencoe.com and click on **Chapter 25—Student Web Activities** to learn more about the Philippines.

Section 2 Assessment

Defining Terms

1. Define plate, strait, free port, terraced field.

Recalling Facts

2. Location Which five islands are Indonesia's largest?
3. Economics Why do the people of Singapore enjoy a high standard of living?
4. Culture What religion do most Filipinos practice?

Critical Thinking

5. Making Inferences How does Brunei's government use its fuel income?
6. Drawing Conclusions Why is it difficult for government officials to rule Indonesia?

Graphic Organizer

7. Organizing Information Create a diagram like this one. In the center, list similarities of the countries listed. In the outer ovals, write two ways that the country differs from the others.

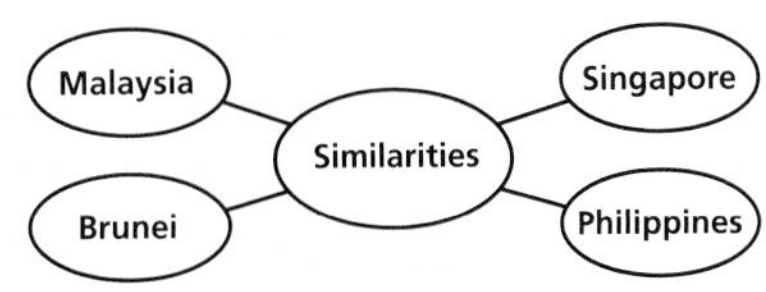

Applying Social Studies Skills

8. Analyzing Maps Look at the map on page 709. What countries share the island of Borneo?

Section 2 Assessment

1. The terms are defined in the Glossary.
2. Sumatra, Java, Celebes, Borneo, and New Guinea
3. because Singapore has a very productive trade economy
4. Roman Catholicism
5. Fuel income pays for free education and medical care and low-cost housing, food, and fuel for all the country's people.
6. There are many different ethnic groups and many small political parties.
7. Students' diagrams will vary.
8. Indonesia, Malaysia, and Brunei

Chapter 25

Section 2, pages 714–717

Objectives and answers to the Student Web Activity can be found in the Web Activity Lesson Plan at twip.glencoe.com

✓ Reading Check Answer

King Philip II of Spain; the Philippines were a Spanish colony.

L1/ELL

Reading Essentials and Study Guide

Name ____ Date ____ Class ____

SOUTHEAST ASIA

Reading Essentials and Study Guide 2

Diverse Island Cultures

Key Terms

plate huge slab of rock that makes up the earth's crust
strait narrow body of water between two pieces of land
free port place where goods can be unloaded, stored, and shipped again without payment of import taxes
terraced field strips of land cut out of a hillside like stair steps

Enrich

Have students research and report on the history of Spanish or American involvement in the Philippines.

CLOSE

Have students write a pen pal letter to a teenager in one of the island countries of Southeast Asia. Have them compare that country with the United States.

TEACH

Ask: Have you ever seen a puppet show? *(Students might mention puppet shows they saw as children on TV or in movies.)* Explain that in Indonesia, puppet shows are a very special part of the culture of all people, including adults. L1

More About Shadow Puppets

Despite the heavy demands placed on the *dalang* in shadow puppetry, there are many thousands of these performers entertaining people across Indonesia. Shadow puppets are found throughout Southeast Asia and in China. Only in Indonesia, however, are the shows performed by a single puppeteer.

Interdisciplinary Connections

Drama Have students work in groups to write a script for a short play. They might base it on a folktale. Then have them perform their play. If time allows, have students design puppets.

Making Connections

ART | SCIENCE | CULTURE | TECHNOLOGY

Shadow Puppets

Late at night, long after dark has fallen on a small stage in Java, a shadow puppet show is about to begin. The glow of a lamp shines behind a wide linen screen. Puppets stand hidden from direct view. The "good" characters are on the right. The "bad" ones are placed on the left. The audience waits anxiously on the other side of the screen. Once the story begins, the performance will continue until dawn.

▲ The *dalang* and his orchestra

The Performance

Wayang kulit, the ancient Indonesian shadow puppet theater, dates back at least 1,000 years. Today there are several thousand puppeteers. This makes shadow puppets the strongest theater tradition in Southeast Asia.

Shadow puppets are flat leather puppets. Many have movable limbs and mouths that are operated by sticks. During the show, the puppets cast their shadows onto the screen. The *dalang,* or puppeteer, sits behind the screen and manipulates the figures. He brings each to life in one of the more than 200 traditional puppet stories.

The Stories

Although Islam is now the major religion of Indonesia, much of the traditional shadow puppet theater is based on stories from two ancient Hindu epics from India. At one time, the principal purpose of shadow puppetry was to provide moral and religious instruction in Hinduism. Now the stories combine Hindu themes with elements of Buddhism and Islam, as well as Indonesian history and folklore. Often the performance is given in celebration of public or religious holidays or to honor a wedding or birth.

The Puppeteer

The skill of the *dalang* is critical to the show's success. The *dalang* operates all the puppets, narrates the story, provides sound effects, and directs the gong, drum, and flute orchestra that accompanies the puppet show. The puppeteer changes his voice to create an individual sound for each character. The *dalang* performs without a script or notes, adding jokes and making small changes to suit the crowd and the occasion. Because a shadow puppet show can last as long as nine hours, the *dalang* must have both a tremendous memory and great endurance.

Many *dalangs* carve their own puppets, having learned this art from earlier generations. Each figure must appear in a specific size, body build, and costume. Even the shape of the eyes tells about the figure's character and mood.

Making the Connection

1. How do shadow puppets move?
2. What kinds of stories do shadow puppet shows present?
3. **Drawing Conclusions** In what way is the *dalang* a master of many different art forms?

Making the Connection

1. They are operated by sticks.
2. traditional stories with religious themes and Indonesian history and folklore
3. The *dalang* must operate all the puppets, tell the story, use different voices for the puppets, and direct the music that accompanies the performance.

Reading Review

Section 1 Life on the Mainland

Terms to Know
- precious gems
- deforestation
- socialism
- civil war

Main Idea

The countries of mainland Southeast Asia rely on agriculture as a major source of wealth.

✓ Region Mainland Southeast Asia includes the countries of Myanmar, Thailand, Laos, Cambodia, and Vietnam.

✓ Place These countries have highland areas and lowland river valleys with fertile soil. Monsoons bring heavy rains in the summer.

✓ History Thailand is the only country in Southeast Asia that is free of the influence of colonial rule.

✓ Economics Conflict has hurt the economies of Laos, Cambodia, and Vietnam.

Section 2 Diverse Island Cultures

Terms to Know
- plate
- strait
- free port
- terraced field

Main Idea

The island countries of Southeast Asia have a variety of cultures and economic activities.

✓ Region The island countries of Southeast Asia include Indonesia, East Timor, Malaysia, Singapore, Brunei, and the Philippines.

✓ Place Indonesia—with the world's fourth-largest population—is an archipelago formed by volcanoes.

✓ Economics Indonesia has rich supplies of oil, natural gas, and minerals.

✓ Government Indonesia's leaders face the challenge of creating a nation out of a land with many different groups and political parties.

✓ Economics Malaysia produces palm oil and rubber, among other goods. Its capital, Kuala Lumpur, is a commercial center.

✓ Economics The port of Singapore is one of the world's busiest trading centers.

✓ Culture The Philippines shows the influence of Malaysian, Spanish, and American culture.

People in Bangkok, Thailand, face traffic snarls and pollution that are among the worst in the world. ▶

Reading Review

Use the Chapter 25 Reading Review to preview, review, condense, or reteach the chapter.

Preview/Review

Use the Terms to Know lists to help students review and study.

Activity Have students draw up a matching quiz of the 10 terms from the chapter and their definitions. Then have them exchange quizzes with another student and take the quiz their partners prepared.

Vocabulary PuzzleMaker CD-ROM reinforces the vocabulary terms used in Chapter 25.

The Interactive Tutor Self-Assessment CD-ROM allows students to review Chapter 25 content.

Condense

Have students read the Chapter 25 summary statements.

Guided Reading Activities

Audio Program

Reteach

Reteaching Activity

Reading Essentials and Study Guide

Reading Strategy — Read to Write

Creating a Country Photo Album Have students choose one of the countries studied in this chapter and imagine that they have visited there. Ask them to create a photo album that shows what they saw in the country. They should look for photographs that show the landscape, cities, places of interest, and people of their chosen country. With each photograph, have them write a brief caption that identifies the subject of the photo and gives additional information about it. L1

EE2 Places and Regions: Standard 4

GLENCOE TECHNOLOGY

MindJogger Videoquiz
Use MindJogger Videoquiz to review the Chapter 25 content.

Available in DVD and VHS

Using Key Terms

1. f
2. a
3. g
4. h
5. c
6. b
7. d
8. e

Reviewing the Main Ideas

9. cement, textiles, computers, electrical appliances
10. Buddhist temples in Thailand
11. Laos, Cambodia, and Vietnam
12. by opening the country to Western ideas, businesses, and tourists and by loosening government control of the economy
13. farming
14. Because Indonesia sits in the midst of several seas and near the Pacific and Indian Oceans, it is a convenient point from which to ship goods.
15. because of all the ethnic groups on the islands
16. It is a transportation corridor between the Indian Ocean and the Java Sea.
17. manufacturing
18. oil and natural gas
19. Most of the people are Roman Catholic, as in Spain.

Assessment and Activities

 Using Key Terms

Match the terms in Part A with their definitions in Part B.

A.

1. free port
2. deforestation
3. plate
4. strait
5. terraced field
6. civil war
7. socialism
8. precious gems

B.

a. the widespread cutting of trees
b. war fought between groups within a country
c. strip of land cut out of a hillside
d. economic system in which the government owns many businesses
e. stones such as rubies, sapphires, and jade
f. place where shipped goods are not taxed
g. slab of rock that makes up the earth's crust
h. narrow body of water that runs between two land areas

 Reviewing the Main Ideas

Section 1 Life on the Mainland

9. **Economics** What products do workers in Thailand make?
10. **Culture** What are *wats*?
11. **Economics** What countries have poor economies because of recent conflict?
12. **Economics** How is Vietnam trying to improve its economy?

Section 2 Diverse Island Cultures

13. **Economics** How do nearly half of the people of Indonesia make a living?
14. **Location** How does location make Indonesia a center of trade?
15. **Government** Why does Indonesia have many political parties?
16. **Location** Why is the Strait of Malacca important?
17. **Economics** What economic activities are important in Singapore in addition to its harbor industry?
18. **Economics** What resources have made Brunei wealthy?
19. **Culture** How does religion show Spanish influence in the Philippines?

Southeast Asia

Place Location Activity

On a separate sheet of paper, match the letters on the map with the numbered places listed below.

1. Mekong River
2. South China Sea
3. Gulf of Tonkin
4. Hanoi
5. Indonesia
6. Singapore
7. Thailand
8. Vietnam
9. Indian Ocean
10. Philippines

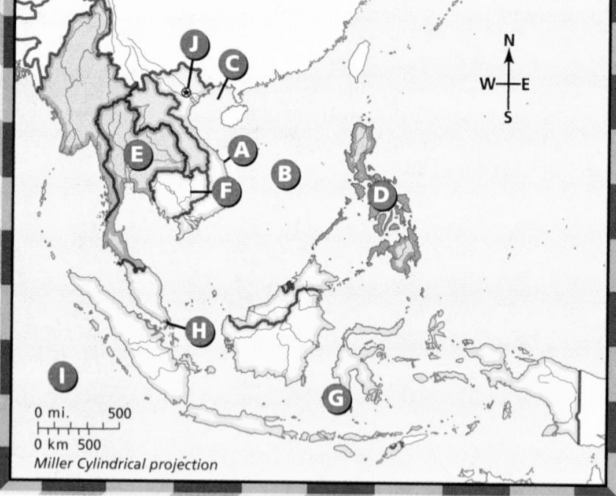

720

NATIONAL GEOGRAPHIC Place Location Activity

1. F
2. B
3. C
4. J
5. G
6. H
7. E
8. A
9. I
10. D

Critical Thinking

20. *Possible answer:* Unless they diversify, the country's economy will suffer and the standard of living will drop significantly due to the loss of oil revenues.
21. Students' charts will vary.

Comparing Regions Activity

22. Students' paragraphs should describe the similarities and differences of the island countries of Southeast Asia and the island countries in the Caribbean.

Self-Check Quiz Visit ***The World and Its People*** Web site at twip.glencoe.com and click on **Chapter 25—Self-Check Quizzes** to prepare for the Chapter Test.

Critical Thinking

20. **Predicting Outcomes** Experts believe that Brunei has enough oil reserves to last until 2018. What might happen to the country's economy and standard of living at that time?
21. **Organizing Information** Create a chart like this one. List three countries—Indonesia, a country from mainland Southeast Asia, and another from island Southeast Asia. Under the other columns, write two facts about each country you listed.

Country	Land	Economy	People

Comparing Regions Activity

22. **Geography** Compare the island countries of Southeast Asia to the island countries in the Caribbean. What landforms are similar and different? How does geography affect the economies of these island countries? Write a paragraph using the information you find.

Mental Mapping Activity

23. **Focusing on the Region** Draw a map of Southeast Asia, and then label the following:

- Borneo
- Irrawaddy River
- Java
- Malay Peninsula
- Philippines
- South China Sea
- Strait of Malacca
- Thailand

Technology Skills Activity

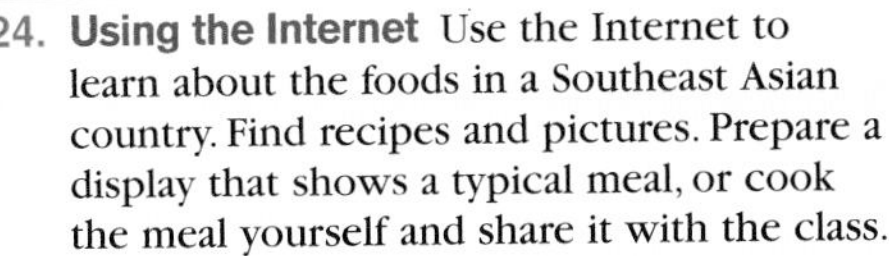

24. **Using the Internet** Use the Internet to learn about the foods in a Southeast Asian country. Find recipes and pictures. Prepare a display that shows a typical meal, or cook the meal yourself and share it with the class.

Standardized Test Practice

Directions: Study the graph below, and then answer the questions that follow.

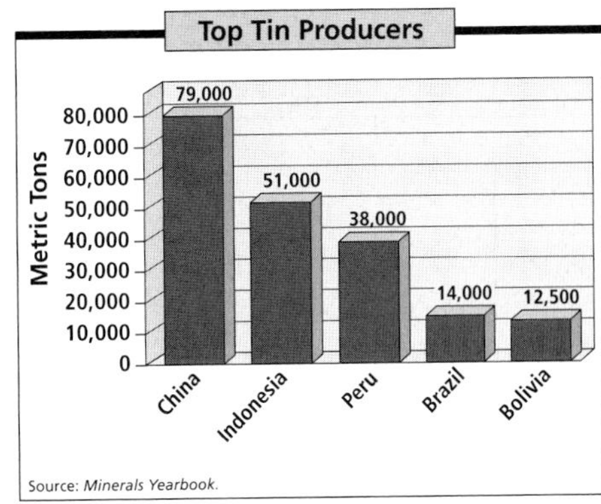

1. **About how much tin does Indonesia produce each year?**
   - **A** 51,000,000 metric tons
   - **B** 51,000 metric tons
   - **C** 51.00 million metric tons
   - **D** 51.00 billion metric tons
2. **About how much tin does Bolivia produce each year?**
   - **F** 12,500 metric tons
   - **G** 12,500,000 metric tons
   - **H** 12.5 million metric tons
   - **J** 12.5 billion metric tons

Test-Taking Tip: In order to understand any type of graph, look carefully around the graph for keys that show how it is organized. On this bar graph, the numbers along the left side represent the exact number shown. You do not have to multiply by millions or billions to find the number of metric tons.

Assessment and Activities

Standardized Test Practice

1. B
2. F

Tested Objectives: Reading a graph, analyzing information

Chapter Test Bonus Question

This question may be used for extra credit on the chapter test.

Which country in this region is named for a king of Spain? *(the Philippines)*

Our World Today Online

Have students visit the Web site at twip.glencoe.com to review Chapter 25 and take the Self-Check Quiz.

FOLDABLES™ Study Organizer — Dinah Zike's Foldables

Culminating Activity Pair students with partners to check that they included all of the chapter's main ideas on their foldables. Students should edit their foldables if necessary.

Mental Mapping Activity

23. This exercise helps students visualize the countries and geographic features they have been studying. Accept all attempts at freehand mapping that show places in the correct relationship to one another.

Technology Skills Activity

24. Several Internet sources offer international recipes. Large food stores often carry ingredients for international foods. As an alternative, students could contact an ethnic restaurant in the area that serves food from the region and obtain a menu of foods in that way.

Unit 9 Planning Guide

- If you teach BOTH Eastern and Western world regions in one year, use the columns in red to help you pace your lessons.
- If you teach ONLY Eastern or Western world regions in one year, use the columns in blue to help you pace your lessons.

ALTERNATIVE PACING CHARTS

Unit 9		Chapter 26		Chapter 27	
Both East and West	Either East or West	Both East and West	Either East or West	Both East and West	Either East or West
Day 1 Unit Opener, Regional Atlas **Day 2** Regional Atlas	**Day 1** Unit Opener, Regional Atlas **Day 2** Regional Atlas **Day 3** Regional Atlas	**Day 1** Chapter Opener, Section 1 **Day 2** Making Connections, Section 2 **Day 3** TIME Reports **Day 4** TIME Reports, Study and Writing Skill, Review **Day 5** Chapter Assessment	**Day 1** Chapter Opener, Section 1 **Day 2** Section 1, Making Connections **Day 3** Section 2 **Day 4** Section 2 **Day 5** TIME Reports **Day 6** TIME Reports, Study and Writing Skill **Day 7** Review **Day 8** Chapter Assessment **Day 9** Chapter Assessment	**Day 1** Chapter Opener, Section 1 **Day 2** Section 1, Study and Writing Skill **Day 3** Section 2 **Day 4** Making Connections, Review **Day 5** Chapter Assessment **Day 6** NGS Eye on the Environment	**Day 1** Chapter Opener, Section 1 **Day 2** Section 1 **Day 3** Section 1, Study and Writing Skill **Day 4** Section 2 **Day 5** Section 2, Making Connections **Day 6** Review **Day 7** Chapter Assessment **Day 8** NGS Eye on the Environment

Note: The following materials may be used when teaching Unit 9.
Chapter level support materials can be found on the chapter resource pages.

TEACHING TRANSPARENCIES

Political Map Transparency L2

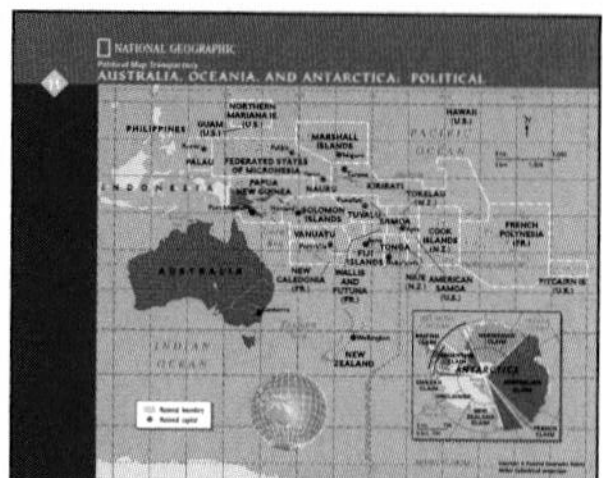

Map Overlay Transparencies L2

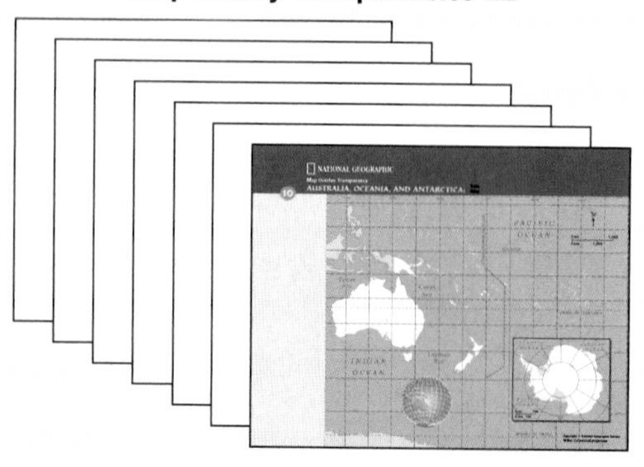

World Cultures Transparencies L2

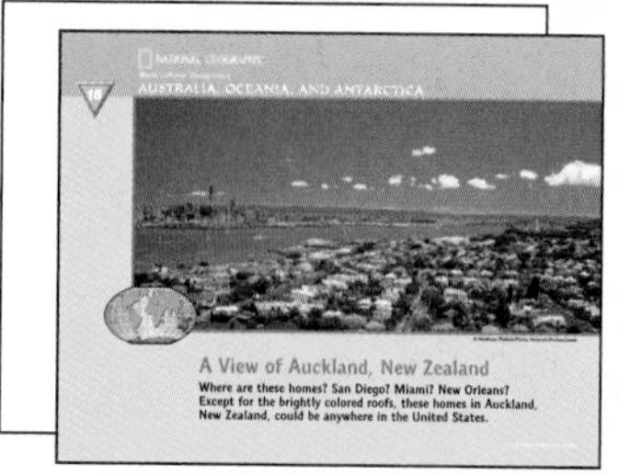

AUSTRALIA, OCEANIA, AND ANTARCTICA
A View of Auckland, New Zealand
Where are these homes? San Diego? Miami? New Orleans? Except for the brightly colored roofs, these homes in Auckland, New Zealand, could be anywhere in the United States.

Unit 9 Resources

INTERDISCIPLINARY CONNECTIONS

World Literature Reading L2

Economics and Geography Activity L2

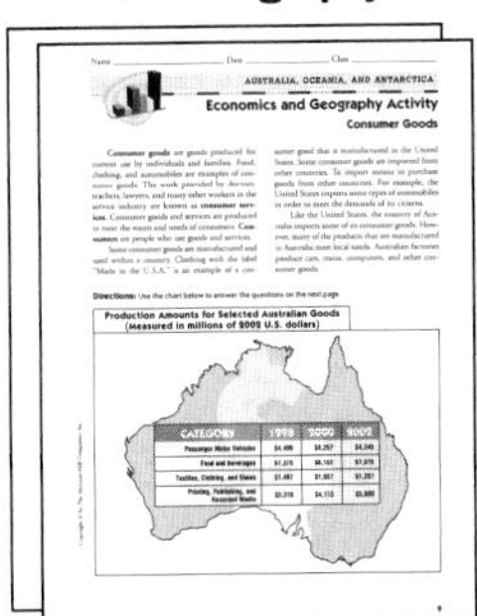

History and Geography Activity L2

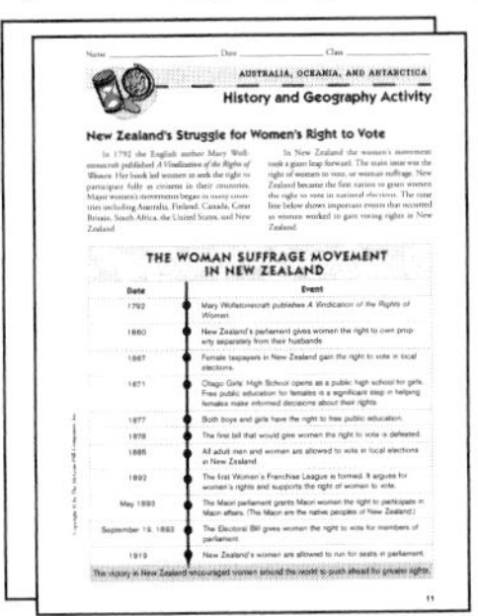

INTERDISCIPLINARY CONNECTIONS

Foods Around the World L1/ELL

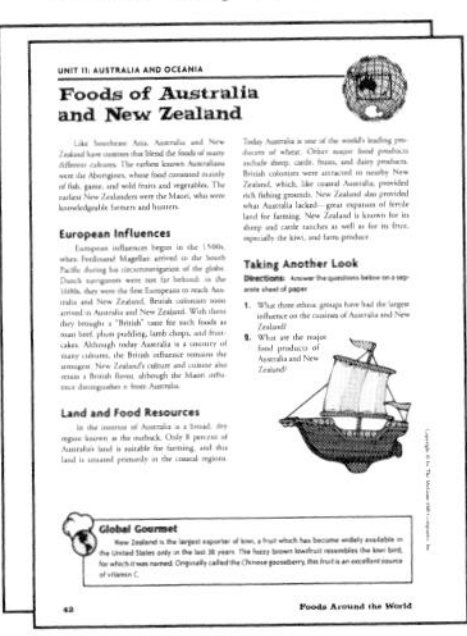

World Music: A Cultural Legacy

CIVIC INVOLVEMENT

Citizenship Activity L1

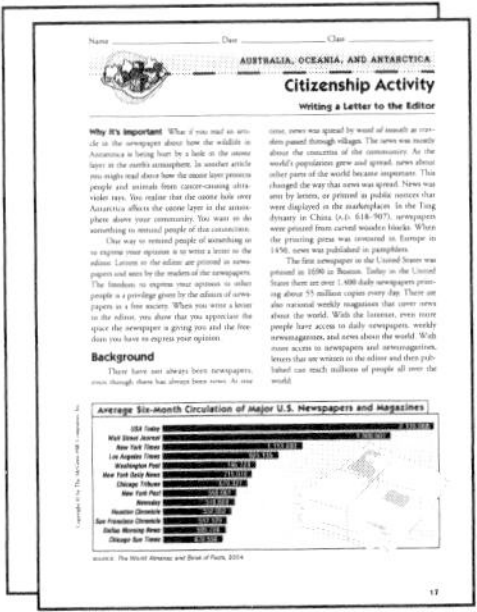

Environmental Case Study L2

MAP AND GEOGRAPHY SKILLS

Building Geography Skills for Life

NGS Focus on Geography Literacy L2

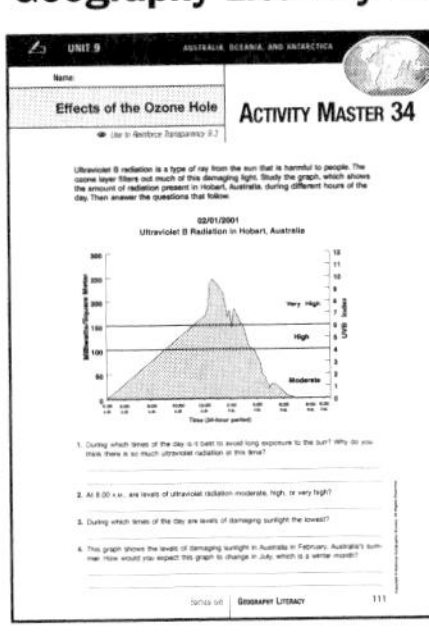

Regional Atlas Activity L2

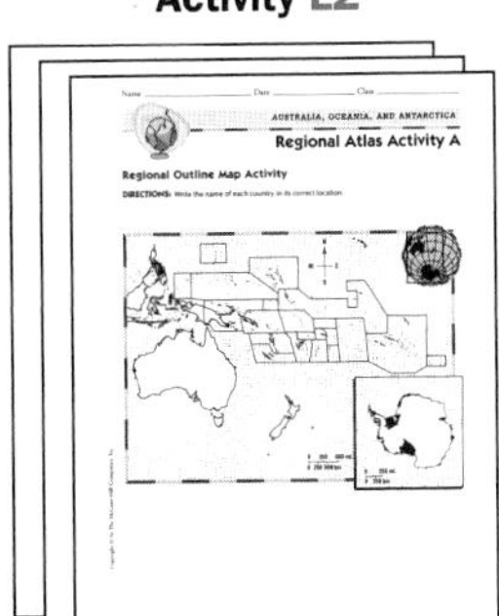

KEY TO ABILITY LEVELS

Teaching strategies have been coded for varying learning styles and abilities.

L1 **BASIC** activities for all students

L2 **AVERAGE** activities for average to above-average students

L3 **CHALLENGING** activities for above-average students

ELL **ENGLISH LANGUAGE LEARNER** activities

ASSESSMENT

Unit Pretests L2

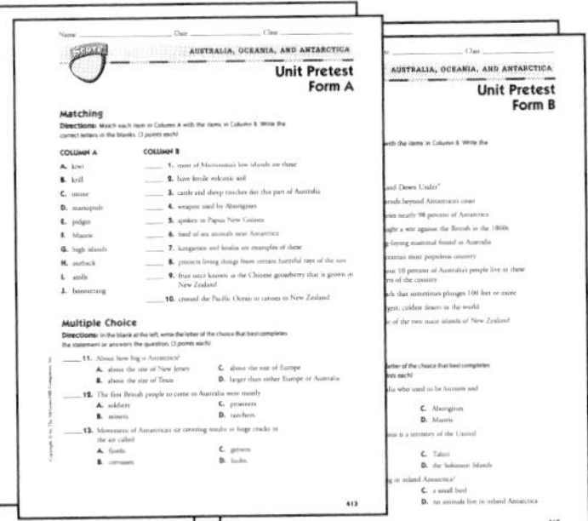

Unit Posttests L2

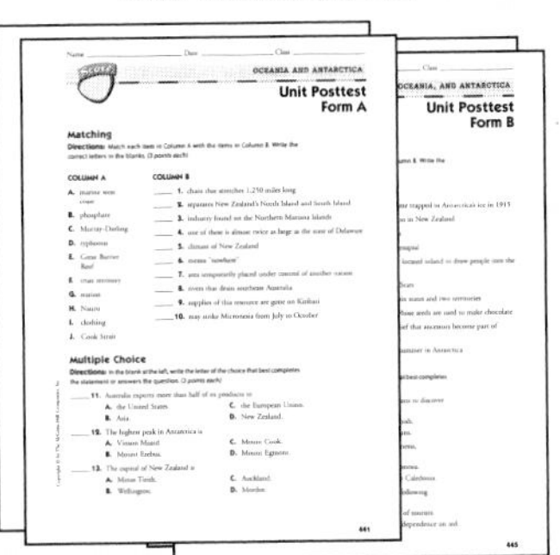

Glencoe Professional Development and Teacher Support Materials

- **Reading in the Content Area for the Middle School Classroom**
- **Inclusion Strategies for the Middle School Social Studies Classroom**
- **Character Education for the Middle School Classroom**
- **Teaching Strategies for the Social Studies Classroom**
- **Reproducible Lesson Plans**
- **Outline Map Resource Book**
- **Writing Process Transparencies for Middle School**
- **Social Studies: Reading Strategies**

Additional Unit 9 Resources

- **Timed Readings Plus in Social Studies** help students increase their reading rate and fluency while maintaining comprehension. The 400-word passages are similar to those found on state and national assessments.
- **Reading in the Content Area: Social Studies** concentrates on six essential reading skills that help students better comprehend what they read. The book includes 75 high-interest nonfiction passages written at increasing levels of difficulty.
- **Reading Fluency** helps students read smoothly, accurately, and expressively.
- **Jamestown's Reading Improvement,** by renowned reading expert Edward Fry, focuses on helping build your students' comprehension, vocabulary, and skimming and scanning skills.
- **Critical Reading Series** provides high-interest books, each written at three reading levels.

For more information about these products, see the Jamestown Education materials in the Classroom Solutions in the front of this Teacher Wraparound Edition. To order these products, call Glencoe at 1-800-334-7344.

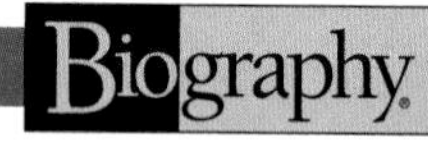

The following videotape program is available from Glencoe:

- **Admiral Richard Byrd** 1-56501-888-5

To order, call Glencoe at 1-800-334-7344. To find classroom resources to accompany many of these, check:

A&E Television: www.aetv.com

The History Channel: www.historychannel.com

Reading List Generator CD-ROM

GLENCOE **BOOKLINK**

The Glencoe BookLink CD-ROM is a database that allows you to search more than 15,000 titles to create a customized reading list for your students.

- Reading lists can be organized by students' reading level, author, genre, theme, or area of interest.
- The database provides Degrees of Reading Power™ (DRP) and Lexile™ readability scores for all selections.
- A brief summary of each selection is included.

Leveled reading suggestions for this unit:

For students at a Grade 5 reading level:

- ***To Find the Way,*** by Susan Nunes.

For students at a Grade 6 reading level:

- ***Down Under: Vanishing Cultures,*** by Jan Reynolds.

For students at a Grade 7 reading level:

- ***Australian Aborigines,*** by Richard Nile.

To order this CD-ROM, call Glencoe at 1-800-334-7344.

Extending the Content

Readings for the Teacher

- ***The Fatal Shore,*** by Robert Hughes. New York, NY: Alfred A. Knopf, 1994.
- ***A Natural History of Australia,*** by Tim M. Berra. San Diego, CA: Academic Press, 1998.

Multimedia Resources

- ***The Pacific World.*** New York: Educational Design, VHS.
- ***Touring New Zealand.*** Chicago: Questar, VHS.

Service Learning Project

Connecting Classroom With Community

Many islands in Oceania promote tourism as a vital part of their economies. Have students help an agency that promotes tourism in their community. They could participate in clean-up campaigns, work in promotional activities, or work in many different capacities at a local tourist attraction. After they have completed their work, have students complete a project summary report that includes such information as: How did this project help my community? What did I learn while completing this project?

Content Background Notes

Use this additional information as lecture notes or discussion prompts throughout the study of Unit 9.

Chapter 26 Australia and New Zealand (pp. 734–755)

Preserving the Land Australia's fragile landscape has suffered at the hands of humans. Only in recent years has the extent of the damage become known. In fact, that damage may not yet be fully clear. A report on the issue recently stated that Australia has far less information on "the condition and productive capacity of its land" than other industrialized nations.

Some signs of damage are evident. Australia's wheat belt, in western Australia, is suffering from salinity. The cause was deforestation, which was carried out to clear the fields for planting. The loss of trees caused the water table to rise, bringing underground salt water to the surface. One study says that 10 percent of the wheat-producing area is now affected by this problem but that the proportion may rise to 40 percent. The highly saline water also threatens the water supplies used by cities. The effects of deforestation have been harsh. About 40 percent of the country's forests have been cut down. That includes nearly three-fourths of the country's rain forests. In addition, an Australian government agency calls the country's record on animal extinctions "the worst for any country."

Splitting Families One reason for Australia's long history of poor relations between whites and Aborigines was the deliberate taking of children. From 1910 to the 1970s, nearly 100,000 Aborigine children were taken from their parents. Children who had light skins were adopted. Those who were darker were put in orphanages. The actions were part of the government's attempt to assimilate Aborigines into white culture. Recently, Australia's prime minister expressed his regret over the policy, calling it "a blemished chapter in our national history."

Saving the Whales All across the world, scientists are trying to understand why marine mammals occasionally beach themselves. Whatever the cause, the result is death—unless the creatures can be returned to the sea. A group in New Zealand has dedicated themselves to trying to do just that. Workers for Project Jonah roll the animals onto a mat that has inflatable pontoons attached. As the tide rises, the pontoons can be used to float the animal out to sea. In the 15 years it has used this system, the project has saved about 2,000 marine mammals.

The Kiwi The kiwi bird is the national symbol of New Zealand. Soon, however, it may be just a memory. The kiwi is a small flightless bird that has nostrils on its beak to sniff out worms—a unique feature among birds. The bird's numbers are falling sharply. There were an estimated 5 million kiwis in 1923, but now scientists think there are only about 70,000. A recent report said that an area rich in kiwis saw a population drop of 18 percent in one year alone. Stoats and possums eat the eggs, stoats and cats kill young birds, and dogs and ferrets attack adults. The result is an alarming decline in population—and a prediction that the bird will become extinct in the next 5 to 10 years unless the trend is reversed.

Chapter 27 Oceania and Antarctica (pp. 756–771)

Dangerous Place The city of Rabaul in Papua New Guinea has a dangerous distinction—it is the only community in the world built completely within the rim of a volcano. The crater formed by the volcano was created 6,000 years ago. Part of the volcano lies underwater. The crater filled with seawater—and formed a perfect harbor. That harbor attracted settlers and explains why Rabaul is located in such a dangerous place.

Open volcanic vents around the city prove that the volcano is still active. In 1994 one of those vents erupted, spreading a thick coat of volcanic ash over much of the city and forcing the evacuation of thousands of people. The warm, rainy climate of the South Pacific made the situation worse. Rain water mixed with the ash and then was baked into a hard, concretelike substance by the hot sun.

The government wants to abandon the city. It has tried to persuade businesses and people to live elsewhere by refusing to repair or rebuild Rabaul. Some in Rabaul still hold out hope that their city can revive. Geologists say that the volcano will erupt again. It has erupted every 50 or 60 years in the past. In fact, natives to the area have a saying that reveals their own understanding of the volcano's regularity. "Once in your lifetime," the saying goes, "you will hear Rabalanakaia, the Fire God, speak."

Introducing Unit 9

00:00 Out of Time?

If time does not permit teaching each chapter in this unit, you may use the **Reading Essentials and Study Guide** for each chapter.

Unit Overview

The two chapters that make up this unit introduce students to the geography and peoples of Australia, New Zealand, Oceania, and Antarctica. The chapters describe the physical and human features of these unique areas, including cultural and social issues. Before beginning to study the unit, point out to students the following features of these regions:

- location in or near the Pacific Ocean, mostly south of the Equator
- unique animals and plants
- specialized economies
- indigenous peoples

Fur seal on the beach, Antarctica

Boy selling fish, Samoa

722

Using the Illustration

Visual Instruction The people who live in Australia's outback live isolated lives in remote areas. Getting supplies to them is difficult. Trucks called "road trains" solve the problem. These trucks carry supplies like food, gasoline, and even animals to towns across the outback. These vehicles are so named because of their size—the cabs haul three long trailers' worth of supplies, making the vehicles so long that they need 62 wheels and so heavy that they weigh as much as 140 tons (127 t). **Ask:** **Can you think of places that are this remote in the United States? How do you think people get supplies in these places? What are some other ways that people in remote locations can stay in communication and receive information? L1**

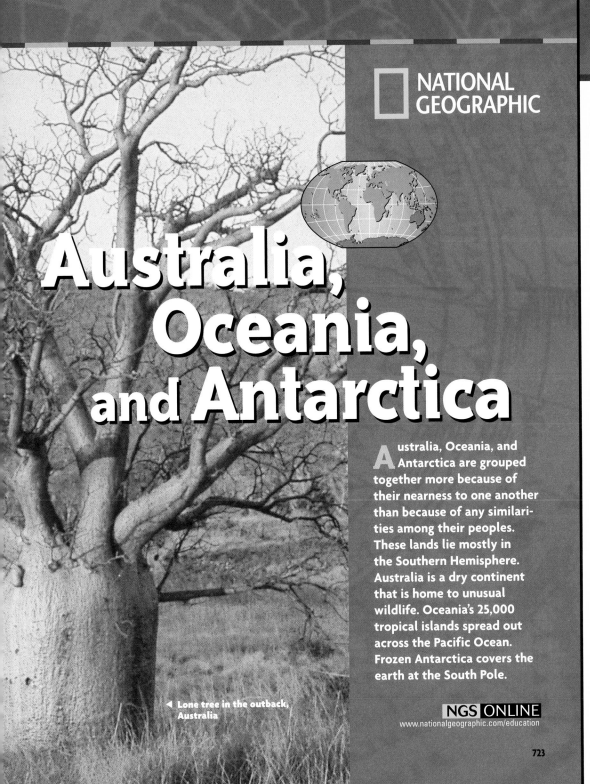

NATIONAL GEOGRAPHIC

Australia, Oceania, and Antarctica

Australia, Oceania, and Antarctica are grouped together more because of their nearness to one another than because of any similarities among their peoples. These lands lie mostly in the Southern Hemisphere. Australia is a dry continent that is home to unusual wildlife. Oceania's 25,000 tropical islands spread out across the Pacific Ocean. Frozen Antarctica covers the earth at the South Pole.

◀ Lone tree in the outback, Australia

NGS ONLINE
www.nationalgeographic.com/education

Current Events Journal

Many unique and interesting animals live in Australia, Oceania, and Antarctica. As students read the unit, have them choose one of these animals as the subject of a children's book. Have them write the story in their journals, possibly illustrating them with drawings of the subject's adventures.

NGS ONLINE

www.nationalgeographic.com/education

This online resource provides lesson plans, atlas updates, cartographic activities with interactive maps, an online map store, and geography links.

Unit Launch Activity

Finding Similarities Australia, New Zealand, Oceania, and Antarctica are all very different places. The hot desert of Australia is unlike the frigid land of Antarctica. The cool highland meadows of New Zealand contrast with the warm tropical beaches of Oceania. Yet these very different lands have many things in common as well. One unfortunate similarity is that the indigenous cultures of this region are in danger of being absorbed into a global culture. As students study the unit, have them take notes on the people who inhabit this area, focusing on the aspects that link them. Then have them create a presentation that uses text and pictures to explain what they found. L2

EE4 Human Systems: Standard 10

Lesson Plan

Using the Regional Atlas
These features and activities may be used as an introduction to the unit or as teaching tools throughout the course of the unit.

Focus

Objectives

1. Locate these regions and describe their landforms.
2. Discuss the impact that climate has on life in these regions.
3. Describe the economies of the countries in these regions.
4. Identify the chief characteristics of the people who live in these regions.

5-Minute Precheck

Have students look at the physical map of this region in the Reference Atlas. **Ask: In what hemisphere do Australia, New Zealand, Oceania, and Antarctica lie?** *(Southern)* **Why do the other areas have warmer climates than Antarctica?** *(They are closer to the Equator.)*

NATIONAL GEOGRAPHIC REGIONAL ATLAS

Focus on:

Australia, Oceania, and Antarctica

LYING ALMOST ENTIRELY in the Southern Hemisphere, this region includes two continents and thousands of islands scattered across the Pacific Ocean. Covering a huge portion of the globe from the Equator to the South Pole, the region includes landscapes ranging from polar to tropical.

The Land

Both a continent and a single country, Australia is a vast expanse of mostly flat land. A chain of hills and mountains known as the Great Dividing Range runs down the continent's eastern edge. Between this range of mountains and the Pacific Ocean lies a narrow strip of coastal land. West of the Great Dividing Range lies Australia's large—and very dry—interior. Here in the Australian "outback" are seemingly endless miles of scrubland, as well as three huge deserts.

Along Australia's northeastern coast lies the Great Barrier Reef. This famous natural wonder is the world's largest coral reef, home to brilliantly colored tropical fish and underwater creatures.

Across the Tasman Sea from Australia lies New Zealand, made up of two main islands—North Island and South Island—and many smaller ones. Both North Island and South Island have sandy beaches, emerald hillsides, and snow-tipped mountains. Plateaus and hills dominate the rest of New Zealand's landscape.

Oceania North and east of New Zealand is Oceania. Its roughly 25,000 islands lie scattered across the Pacific Ocean on both sides of the Equator. Some of these islands are volcanic. Others are huge formations of rock that have risen from the ocean floor. Still others are low-lying coral islands surrounded by reefs.

Antarctica The frozen continent, Antarctica covers and surrounds the South Pole. It is almost completely buried under an enormous sheet of ice. The ice is as much as 2 miles (3.2 km) thick in places and holds 70 percent of the world's freshwater.

The Climate

Australia is one of the driest continents in the world. Its eastern coast does receive rainfall from the Pacific Ocean. Mountains block this moisture from reaching inland areas, however. Much of Australia's outback has a desert climate.

No place in New Zealand is more than 80 miles (129 km) from the sea. This country has only one climate region: marine west coast.

Content Background

Australia's Wildlife Australia's kangaroos, koalas, and platypuses are loved around the world, but the continent also has its share of dangerous animals. The saltwater crocodile—which can reach sizes of 30 feet (9 m)—has been known to eat humans. There are several poisonous snakes, including three large members of the cobra family, the brown snake, the tiger snake, and the taipan, which can grow as long as 11 feet (3.4 m). More dangerous, perhaps, is a much smaller snake, the death adder, which reaches only 3 feet (1 m). The continent also has two venomous spiders, the funnel-web spider and the red back spider. If untreated, people bitten by either of these spiders can die.

Unit 9

Regional Atlas

▼ Sheep grazing near Mount Egmont, New Zealand

◀ Emperor penguins, Antarctica

725

2 TEACH

Making Generalizations
Have students look at the photographs in this Regional Atlas. **Ask:** **How would you describe these areas?** *(beautiful scenery, modern cities, unusual creatures, harsh landscapes)* **L1**

More About the Photos

New Zealand New Zealand's South Island is the more mountainous of its two land areas. The high, rugged mountains called the Southern Alps run along the western edge of the island. This chain includes New Zealand's highest peak, Mt. Cook, and 15 other mountains that are higher than 10,000 feet (3,048 m). The mountains also have more than 360 glaciers, including Tasman Glacier, which is 18 miles (29 km) long.

Penguins Penguins live in the colder ocean waters of the Southern Hemisphere. They spend most of their time in the water hunting for fish and other food. On land, they gather in large colonies called *rookeries* to raise their young. Some rookeries have one million or more birds.

Eyewitness to Geography

Antarctica Rock climber and writer Jon Krakauer described what he saw when climbing a peak in Antarctica: "Six hundred feet up the cleanly hewn face of a mountain called the Razor, the wind gusting off the polar plateau coated my beard with frost. I paused in mid-ascent, dangling from a bight of half-inch-thick rope, and attempted to shake the cramps from my aching forearms. The Antarctic ice cap lapped like a ghostly white sea against the base of the rock face, far below. On the horizon huge, jagged peaks bristled like granite quills from the vast sprawl of ice. Nowhere in all those frozen miles could I detect a sign of life. Never had I laid eyes on such a stark, barren—or beautiful—piece of Earth. It seemed like a waking dream. Hypnotized by the immensity and austerity of the landscape, I found it hard to stop goggling at the view and resume climbing."

NATIONAL GEOGRAPHIC **REGIONAL ATLAS**

Note-taking tip

Have students create a four-column chart with the headings "Australia," "New Zealand," "Oceania," and "Antarctica." Down the left side of their paper, have them write the topics "Land," "Climate," "Economy," and "People." Then suggest that they take notes as they read the unit by putting information about each topic under the appropriate column heading.

Building Skills

Outlining Have students prepare an outline of the Regional Atlas by writing the headings in their notebooks and listing key facts under each heading.

More About the Photo

French Polynesia French Polynesia is one of the world's largest producers of a fruit that is not eaten as a fruit but as a flavoring. Vanilla is technically the fruit of a type of orchid.

This means that New Zealand has mild temperatures and plentiful rainfall throughout the year.

The islands of Oceania have mostly tropical climates, with warm temperatures and distinct wet and dry seasons. Rain forests cover many of the islands.

Antarctica is one of the coldest and windiest places on the earth, as well as one of the driest. It receives so little precipitation that it is considered a desert—the world's largest cold desert.

The Economy

Mines dot the Australian landscape. Its ancient rocks and soils are rich in minerals such as uranium, bauxite, iron ore, copper, nickel, and gold. Little of Australia's land is good for growing crops. Instead, vast cattle and sheep ranches—or stations, as the Australians call them—spread across much of the country. The worst drought in almost 100 years occurred in 2002–2003, which had a negative impact on the economy.

Sheep far outnumber people in New Zealand, where pastures are lush and green almost year-round. New Zealand is one of the world's leading producers of lamb and wool. New Zealand's main crops include wheat, barley, potatoes, fruits, and vegetables.

The people of Oceania depend primarily on fishing and farming. Across much of Oceania, the soil and climate are not favorable for widespread agriculture. Islanders generally raise only enough food for themselves. Yet some larger islands have rich volcanic soil. In such places, cash crops of fruits, sugar, coffee, and coconut products are grown for export.

Antarctica is believed to be rich in mineral resources. To preserve Antarctica for research and exploration, however, many nations have agreed not to mine this mineral wealth. In fact, 43 nations signed the Antarctic Treaty in 1959 to commit to peace and science. They even agreed to share their scientific observations and results.

The People

The first settlers in this region probably came from Asia thousands of years ago. Australia's first inhabitants, the ancestors of today's Aborigines, may have arrived more than 40,000 years ago. Not until about A.D. 1000, however, did seafaring peoples reach the farthest islands of Oceania.

The British colonized Australia and New Zealand in the 1700s and 1800s. These two countries gained their independence in the early 1900s. Many South Pacific islands were not freed from colonial rule until after World War II. Today Australia and Oceania are a blend of European, traditional Pacific, and Asian cultures.

◀ Girl selling fruit, French Polynesia

FUN FACTS

- **Australia** Kangaroo predators include humans and wild dogs, called *dingoes*. Hunting is allowed in some parts of the country only if kangaroo populations become too large. Australians call male kangaroos *boomers*. Females are *blue fliers*. Young kangaroos are *joeys*.
- **Polynesia** Rapanui—also called Easter Island—is the most remote of the Polynesian islands. This tiny island lies some 1,200 miles (1,931 km) from its nearest Polynesian neighbor. It is famous for a number of stone statues of heads. Some of these imposing sculptures are as tall as 40 feet (12 m) and weigh as much as 50 tons (45 t).

Unit 9

Despite its vast size, this is the least populous of all the world's regions. It is home to only about 32 million people. More than half of these live in Australia, where they are found mostly in coastal cities such as Sydney and Melbourne. Roughly 4 million people live in New Zealand, which also has large urban populations along its coasts. Oceania is less urbanized. Antarctica has no permanent human inhabitants at all. Groups of scientists live and work on the frozen continent for brief periods to carry out their research.

▼ **The city of Melbourne, along the southeastern coast of Australia**

Australia

Data Bits

Automobiles per 1,000 people	485
Television sets per 1,000 people	716
Democratic elections	Yes

Ethnic Makeup

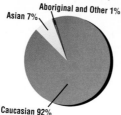

Caucasian 92%, Asian 7%, Aboriginal and Other 1%

World Ranking

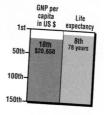

GNP per capita in US $: 18th, $20,650
Life expectancy: 8th, 78 years

Population: Urban vs. Rural

Urban 91%, Rural 9%

Sources: *World Desk Reference*, 2000; *World Development Indicators; The World Almanac*, 2004.

Exploring the Region

1. **Which two continents lie in this region?**
2. **Why is Antarctica considered a desert?**
3. **Why is so little of Australia's land good for farming?**
4. **Where do most of the region's people live?**

727

Answers to Exploring the Region

1. Australia, Antarctica
2. because it receives so little precipitation
3. because mountains along the east coast block rainfall from reaching the interior
4. More than half live in Australia, and about 4 million live in New Zealand.

Unit 9 Regional Atlas

More About the Photo

Melbourne The city of Melbourne itself is not large, but the metropolitan area includes more than 2 million people. The first impetus for the city's growth was the discovery of gold nearby in the 1850s. The city was Australia's capital until Canberra was founded.

3 Assess

Assign the Exploring the Region questions as homework or as an in-class activity.

Reteach
Have students work in small groups to write 10 questions on the Regional Atlas content. Then have groups use their questions to quiz other groups.

Enrich
Have students research and report on one of the islands or major physical landforms of the region.

4 Close

Reading Strategy

Writing a Paragraph Have students write a paragraph explaining why the countries in this unit are considered a cultural region.

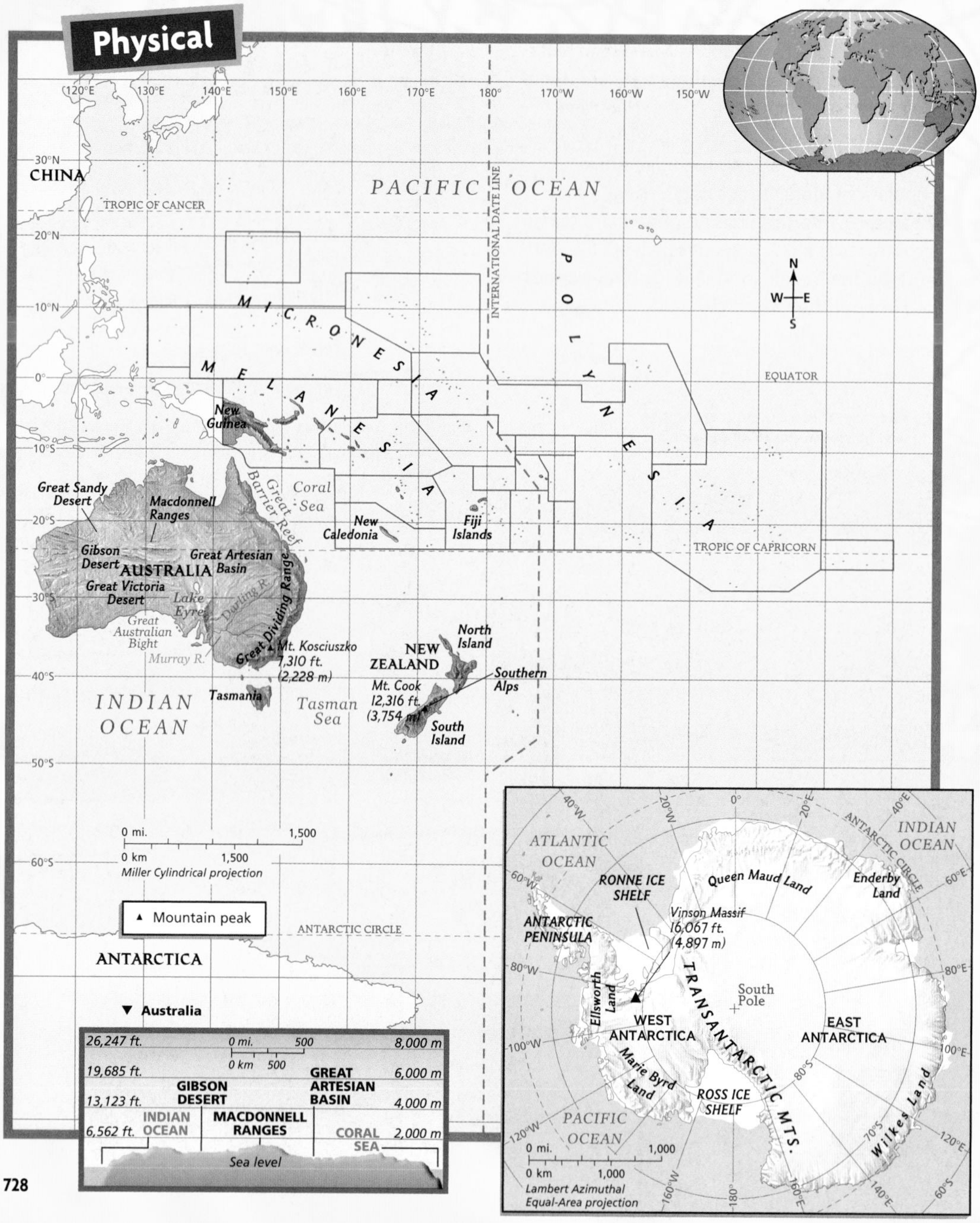

Lesson Plan

Using the Regional Atlas
These features and activities may be used as an introduction to the unit or as teaching tools throughout the course of the unit.

Focus

Objectives

1. Locate the countries in this region and describe their landforms and endangered environments.
2. Describe the populations of the countries in this region.
3. Identify key facts about these countries.

5-Minute Precheck

Ask: **How does Antarctica's climate affect life forms there?** *(Species that live on Antarctica have to be able to cope with blizzards, darkness for months, and brutal cold. Because of the climate's severity, Antarctica has no permanent human inhabitants, although scientists conduct research there.)*

More About the Profile

This cross section of Australia was taken along the Tropic of Capricorn at 23½°S latitude.

NATIONAL GEOGRAPHIC

Regional Atlas

Australia, Oceania, and Antarctica

Physical

728

Regional Atlas Activity

Analyzing Maps Explain that Western Australia covers one-third of the country and has the largest area of Australia's six states. It also has the lowest population density. Have students look at the map above. **Ask:** **Why is Western Australia so sparsely populated?** *(The deserts there discourage settlement.)* Explain that most Australians live in a crescent-shaped stretch of coast from the middle of the east coast to the southeast coast. **What factors explain why people settled there?** *(The low coastal plain and rivers made the area better for farming.)* **L1**

 **EE5 Environment and Society: Standard 15**

UNIT 9

Political

MAP STUDY

1. What body of water separates Australia from Melanesia?
2. What is the capital of the Fiji Islands?

Regional Atlas Activity

Practicing Map Skills Write the names of islands in Oceania on the board, and assign each island to a different student. Have each student use a globe or map to determine the absolute location of his or her island by finding its latitude and longitude. Then ask each student to express the island's relative location by figuring out its distance and direction from three or four other places. Direct students to list the absolute and relative locations on the board below the names of their islands. L2

EE1 The World in Spatial Terms: Standards 1, 3

2 TEACH

Drawing Conclusions Ask: Which country would you expect to have a cooler climate, Australia or New Zealand? Why? *(New Zealand, because Australia is nearer to the Equator)* What would you expect to be an important part of the economy of Oceania? *(fishing, sea products, and tourism)* L1

Interdisciplinary Connections

History The first European settlers in New Zealand were sealers and whalers. They set up stations on both islands to take advantage of the seals and whales in the nearby ocean.

History Ancestors of the Aborigines arrived in Australia during the Ice Age, before rising seas cut off the land passage between this continent and the rest of Asia.

MAP STUDY

Answers

1. Coral Sea
2. Suva

Skills Practice

What is the capital of Australia? *(Canberra)*

REGIONAL ATLAS

Interdisciplinary Connections

Science Some coral reefs were formed almost 600 million years ago and make up the earth's oldest ecosystems. Worldwide, there are more than 60,000 miles (96,560 km) of coral reefs lining the coastlines of some 109 nations.

If you like scuba diving, you would love visiting the Great Barrier Reef of Australia. This reef—the largest structure built by living creatures anywhere in the world—is home to more than 1,500 species of fish, 400 types of coral, 4,000 species of mollusks, and 22 types of whales.

MAP STUDY

Answers

1. low to medium risk
2. an area protected by the Antarctic Treaty

Skills Practice

What is the status of the coral reefs surrounding the Philippines? *(high risk)*

Australia, Oceania, and Antarctica

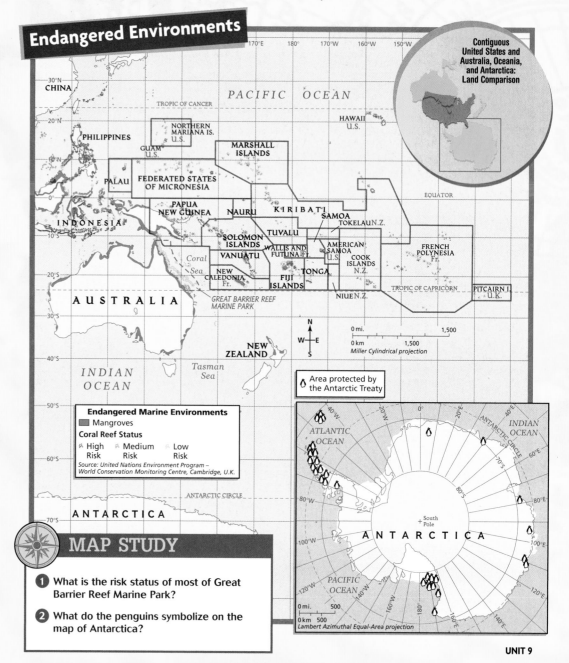

Endangered Environments

Contiguous United States and Australia, Oceania, and Antarctica: Land Comparison

Endangered Marine Environments

Mangroves

Coral Reef Status

High Risk | Medium Risk | Low Risk

Source: United Nations Environment Program – World Conservation Monitoring Centre, Cambridge, U.K.

Area protected by the Antarctic Treaty

Miller Cylindrical projection

Lambert Azimuthal Equal-Area projection

MAP STUDY

1. What is the risk status of most of Great Barrier Reef Marine Park?
2. What do the penguins symbolize on the map of Antarctica?

Content Background

The Great Barrier Reef The Great Barrier Reef has been under construction for perhaps as long as 30 million years. Pollution, commercial fishing, and tourism have caused damage to the reef in just decades, however. The Australian government has taken a number of steps to stop this damage. In 1975, for example, the government declared the reef a national park. Laws restrict where tourists can dive, snorkel, or carry out other activities. Other laws require ships that carry hazardous cargo to have specially trained pilots guide them through the area. The park authority has developed a plan setting aside certain parts of the reef for specific uses, which has become a model for other countries trying to preserve their own coral reefs.

UNIT 9

Geo Extremes

① HIGHEST POINT
Vinson Massif (Antarctica)
16,067 ft. (4,897 m) high

② LOWEST POINT
Bently Subglacial Trench (Antarctica)
8,366 ft. (2,550 m) below sea level

③ LONGEST RIVER
Murray-Darling (Australia)
2,310 mi. (3,718 km) long

④ LARGEST LAKE
Lake Eyre (Australia)
3,600 sq. mi. (9,324 sq. km)

⑤ LARGEST HOT DESERT
Great Victoria (Australia)
134,650 sq. mi. (348,742 sq. km)

⑥ LARGEST COLD DESERT
Antarctica
5,100,000 sq. mi. (13,209,000 sq. km)

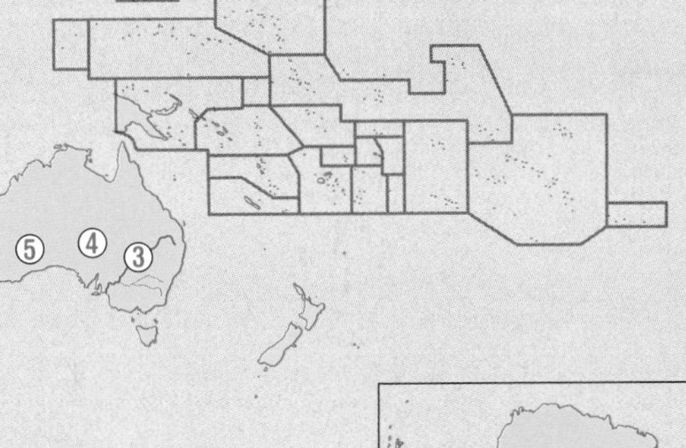

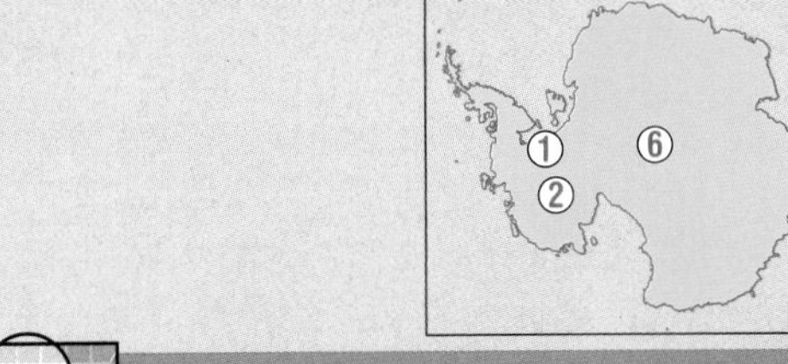

COMPARING POPULATION: United States and Selected Countries of Australia, Oceania, and Antarctica

UNITED STATES

AUSTRALIA

PAPUA NEW GUINEA

NEW ZEALAND

= 15,000,000

Source: *Population Reference Bureau*, 2003.

POPULATION GROWTH: Australia, 1958–2008

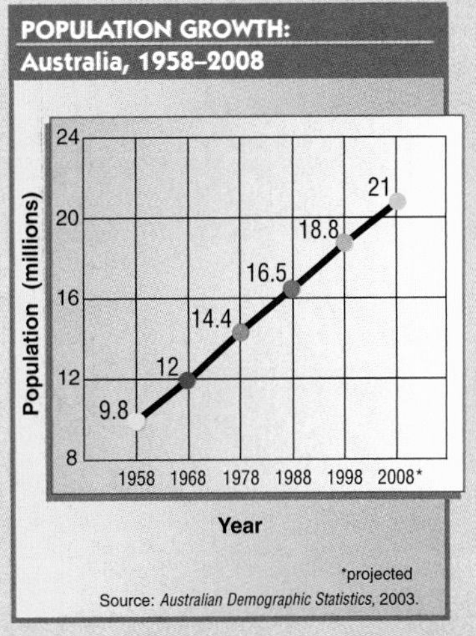

*projected

Source: *Australian Demographic Statistics*, 2003.

GRAPHIC STUDY

1. The largest cold desert in this region is also the largest desert in the *world*. What is it?
2. By how much is Australia's population expected to have grown between 1958 and 2008?

Unit 9 Regional Atlas

Did You Know

In the Canterbury Plains region of New Zealand's South Island, sheep outnumber people by about 20 to 1.

Cultural Kaleidoscope

New Zealand Most New Zealanders refer to themselves as *Kiwis*, after the symbol of their country. Maoris call white New Zealanders *Pakeha*—a Maori word meaning "fair skinned."

Did You Know

Antarctica is the world's highest continent, averaging 8,000 feet (2,438 m) in elevation.

GRAPHIC STUDY

Answers

1. Antarctica
2. by 11.2 million

Skills Practice

How does Australia compare to the United States in population? *(Australia has about 20 million people; the United States has about 290 million.)*

Regional Atlas Activity

Relative Location Have students write a description of the location of each feature listed under Geo Extremes. Instruct them that their descriptions should be based on relative location—where the features are in terms of other notable physical or cultural places. For example, they might write: "Vinson Massif, the highest point in the region, is at the southern end of the Antarctic Peninsula." Have students take turns locating the features on a map based on a classmate's description. **L1**

EE1 The World in Spatial Terms: Standard 3

NATIONAL GEOGRAPHIC

REGIONAL ATLAS

Country Profiles

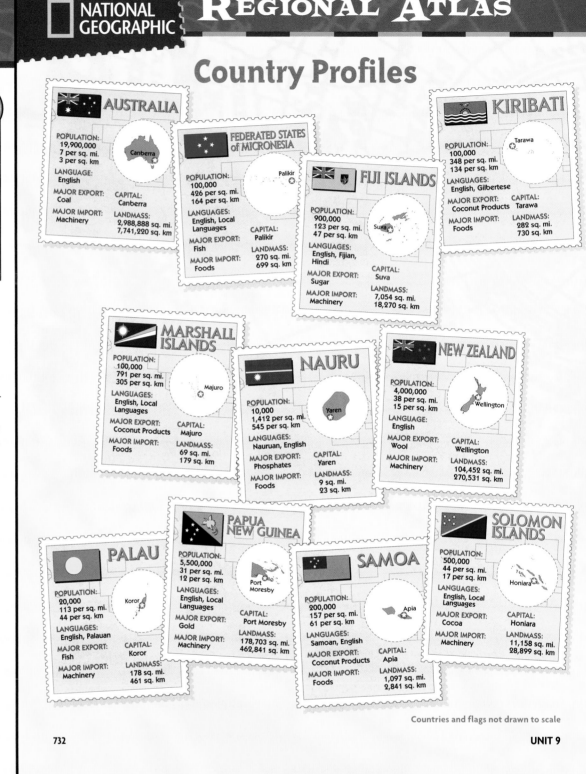

AUSTRALIA
POPULATION: 19,900,000; 7 per sq. mi.; 3 per sq. km
LANGUAGE: English
MAJOR EXPORT: Coal
MAJOR IMPORT: Machinery
CAPITAL: Canberra
LANDMASS: 2,988,888 sq. mi.; 7,741,220 sq. km

FEDERATED STATES of MICRONESIA
POPULATION: 100,000; 426 per sq. mi.; 164 per sq. km
LANGUAGES: English, Local Languages
MAJOR EXPORT: Fish
MAJOR IMPORT: Foods
CAPITAL: Palikir
LANDMASS: 270 sq. mi.; 699 sq. km

FIJI ISLANDS
POPULATION: 900,000; 123 per sq. mi.; 47 per sq. km
LANGUAGES: English, Fijian, Hindi
MAJOR EXPORT: Sugar
MAJOR IMPORT: Machinery
CAPITAL: Suva
LANDMASS: 7,054 sq. mi.; 18,270 sq. km

KIRIBATI
POPULATION: 100,000; 348 per sq. mi.; 134 per sq. km
LANGUAGES: English, Gilbertese
MAJOR EXPORT: Coconut Products
MAJOR IMPORT: Foods
CAPITAL: Tarawa
LANDMASS: 282 sq. mi.; 730 sq. km

MARSHALL ISLANDS
POPULATION: 100,000; 791 per sq. mi.; 305 per sq. km
LANGUAGES: English, Local Languages
MAJOR EXPORT: Coconut Products
MAJOR IMPORT: Foods
CAPITAL: Majuro
LANDMASS: 69 sq. mi.; 179 sq. km

NAURU
POPULATION: 10,000; 1,412 per sq. mi.; 545 per sq. km
LANGUAGES: Nauruan, English
MAJOR EXPORT: Phosphates
MAJOR IMPORT: Foods
CAPITAL: Yaren
LANDMASS: 9 sq. mi.; 23 sq. km

NEW ZEALAND
POPULATION: 4,000,000; 38 per sq. mi.; 15 per sq. km
LANGUAGE: English
MAJOR EXPORT: Wool
MAJOR IMPORT: Machinery
CAPITAL: Wellington
LANDMASS: 104,452 sq. mi.; 270,531 sq. km

PALAU
POPULATION: 20,000; 113 per sq. mi.; 44 per sq. km
LANGUAGES: English, Palauan
MAJOR EXPORT: Fish
MAJOR IMPORT: Machinery
CAPITAL: Koror
LANDMASS: 178 sq. mi.; 461 sq. km

PAPUA NEW GUINEA
POPULATION: 5,500,000; 31 per sq. mi.; 12 per sq. km
LANGUAGES: English, Local Languages
MAJOR EXPORT: Gold
MAJOR IMPORT: Machinery
CAPITAL: Port Moresby
LANDMASS: 178,703 sq. mi.; 462,841 sq. km

SAMOA
POPULATION: 200,000; 157 per sq. mi.; 61 per sq. km
LANGUAGES: Samoan, English
MAJOR EXPORT: Coconut Products
MAJOR IMPORT: Foods
CAPITAL: Apia
LANDMASS: 1,097 sq. mi.; 2,841 sq. km

SOLOMON ISLANDS
POPULATION: 500,000; 44 per sq. mi.; 17 per sq. km
LANGUAGES: English, Local Languages
MAJOR EXPORT: Cocoa
MAJOR IMPORT: Machinery
CAPITAL: Honiara
LANDMASS: 11,158 sq. mi.; 28,899 sq. km

Countries and flags not drawn to scale

Did You Know?

The *woomera* was one of the many useful tools employed by Australia's Aborigines. This wooden rod with a hooked end was used to launch spears a great distance. The Australian government named its rocket and missile testing range *Woomera* after this device.

Making Comparisons Have students use the Country Profiles stamps in this unit's Regional Atlas to create a chart showing the languages spoken in each country in the region. Then have students create another languages chart using the Country Profiles stamps from a different Regional Atlas in this text. Ask students to use the data in their two charts to write a brief summary comparing the number and types of languages spoken in these two world regions. L2

Organize students into groups. Have groups use the maps and graphs from this unit's Regional Atlas to quiz one another on the physical and human geography of Australia, New Zealand, Oceania, and Antarctica.

Country Profiles Activity

Ethnic Groups The countries in this region have people from many different groups. In Australia and New Zealand, some groups of people (the Aborigines and Maoris) are minorities, and the descendants of European settlers are in the majority. The islands of Oceania are mostly populated with islanders, but there are many other groups as well. Assign each student one of these countries. Have students research relations among the different groups in that country and report on their findings. L2

For more information on countries in this region, refer to the Nations of the World Data Bank in the Appendix.

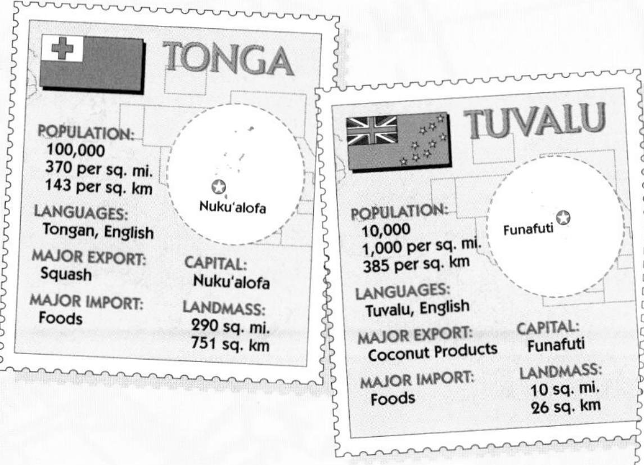

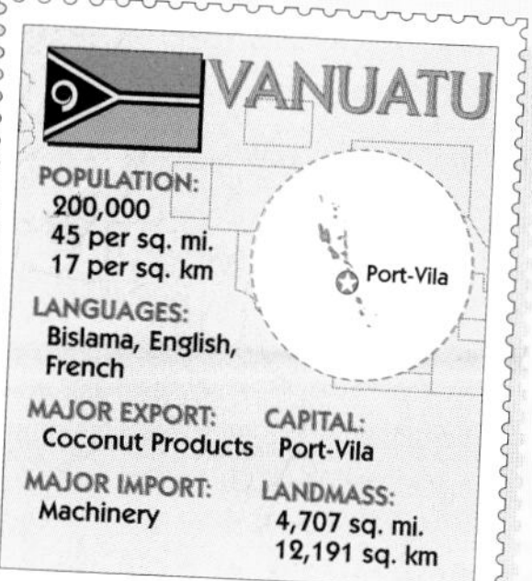

BUILDING CITIZENSHIP

Voting Nearly all eligible voters participate in elections in Australia. All citizens over 18 years old are required to vote in all local, state, and national elections. If they don't vote, they can be fined up to 50 Australian dollars. To make it easier, elections are held on Saturdays and voting is done at schools, churches, and other convenient locations. In the United States, only about half of eligible people vote in the presidential elections.

Why do so many people in the United States not exercise their right to vote?

This woman is exercising her right to vote.

WRITE ABOUT IT

Voting and participating in political activities are important parts of belonging to a democratic society. Yet in the United States, most people do not vote. Imagine you are the head of elections for your city and it is your responsibility to encourage people to vote in upcoming elections for mayor and the city council. Design a flyer that will be mailed to all households to encourage people to vote.

FUN FACTS

- **Tonga** The people of Tonga have always considered obesity as a sign of good health, especially among their leaders. The *Guinness Book of World Records* listed their 462-pound (210-kg) King Tapou as the world's heaviest monarch. In recent years, however, the government launched a weight awareness campaign, and the king lost 182 pounds (83 kg).
- **Papua New Guinea** Traditional musicians play the *kundu*—an hourglass-shaped drum covered with lizard skin.
- **New Zealand** The people of this country eat a food called Vegemite, made from yeast extract. They spread it on their bread as Americans spread peanut butter.

Reteach

Give students an outline map of the region. Have them complete the map by writing in the names of the islands and major physical features.

BUILDING CITIZENSHIP

Answer Students might respond that it is too much trouble to vote or that people do not feel that their vote is important. Point out that not all people have always been allowed to vote. Women and African Americans won the right to vote through protests and political battles.

Write About It! Flyers should be imaginative and interesting to attract people's attention and have basic information on date, time, and place for voting. They should also include motivation for people to participate, pointing out the importance of the election and the civic responsibility to vote.

4 CLOSE

Reading Strategy

Organizing Information
Have students prepare a chart that compares the populations of the different countries and territories in Oceania.

Chapter 26 Resources

Note: The following materials may be used when teaching Chapter 26.
Section level support materials are shown at point of use in the margins of the Teacher Wraparound Edition.

Timesaving Tools

TeacherWorks™ All-In-One Planner and Resource Center

- **Interactive Teacher Edition** See the **Interactive Teacher Edition** CD-ROM to electronically integrate your Teacher Wraparound Edition and blackline masters.
- **Interactive Lesson Planner** Organize your week, month, semester, or year with all the lesson helps you need. The **Interactive Lesson Planner** CD-ROM contains all Chapter 26 resources.

Use Glencoe's **Presentation Plus!** multimedia teacher tool to easily present dynamic lessons that visually excite your students. Using Microsoft PowerPoint® you can customize the presentations to create your own personalized lessons.

TEACHING TRANSPARENCIES

Graphic Organizer Transparency 5 L2

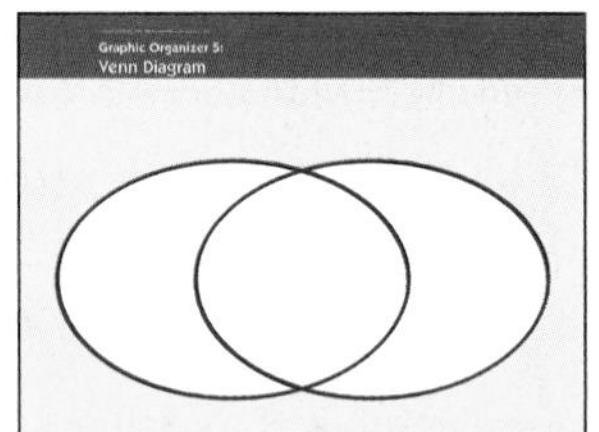

In-text Map Transparency L1

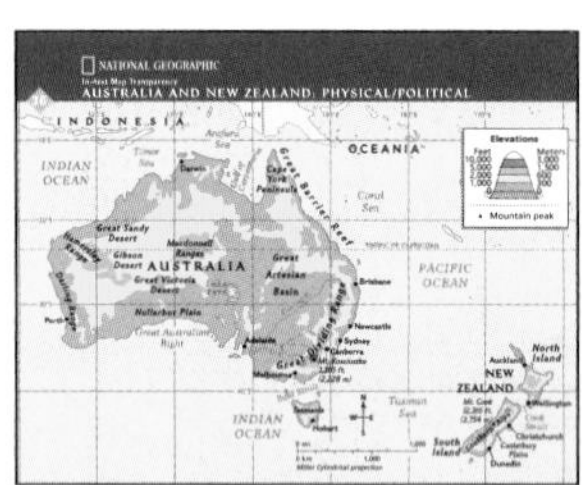

FOLDABLES™ Study Organizer

Dinah Zike's Foldables

Foldables are three-dimensional, interactive graphic organizers that help students practice basic writing skills, review key vocabulary terms, and identify main ideas. Additional chapter activities can be found in the ***Reading and Study Skills Foldables*** booklet.

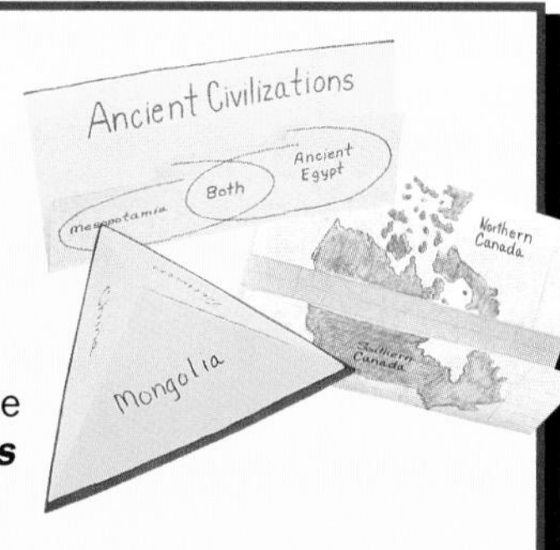

MAP AND GEOGRAPHY SKILLS

Chapter Map Activity L2

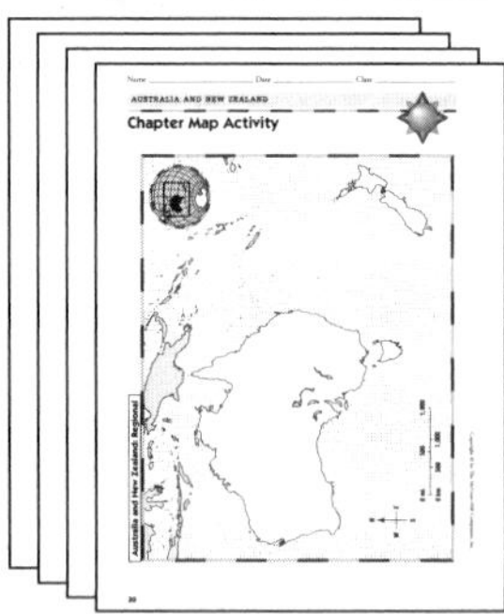

GeoLab Activity L2

READING SUPPORT

Vocabulary Activity L1

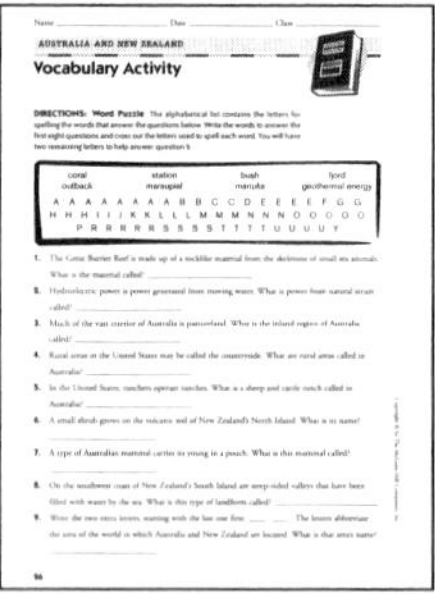

Workbook Activity L1

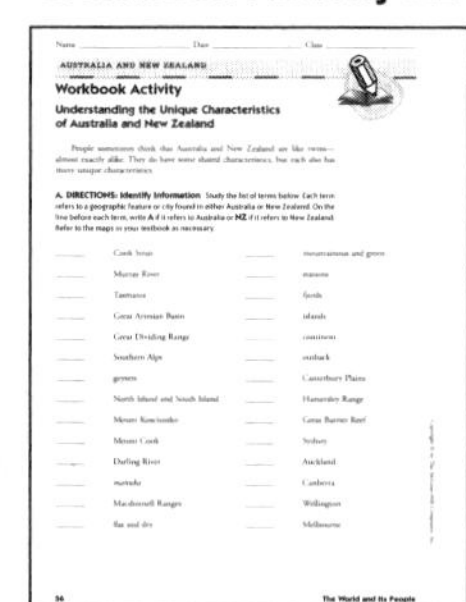

Reading and Writing Skills Activity L1/ELL

DIFFERENTIATED INSTRUCTION

Use these review and reinforcement materials to help less-proficient readers, English learners, and gifted and talented students.

Reteaching Activity L1

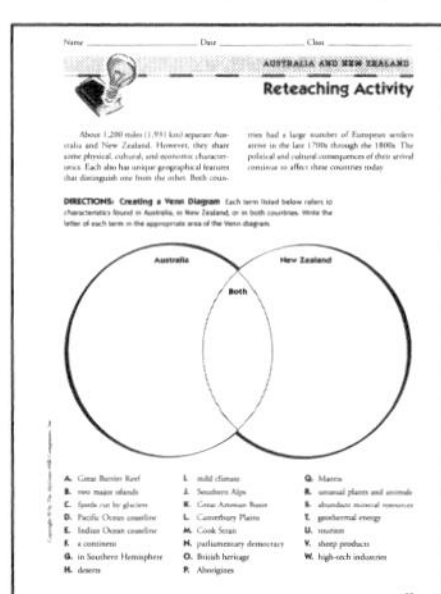

Chapter Skills Review L2

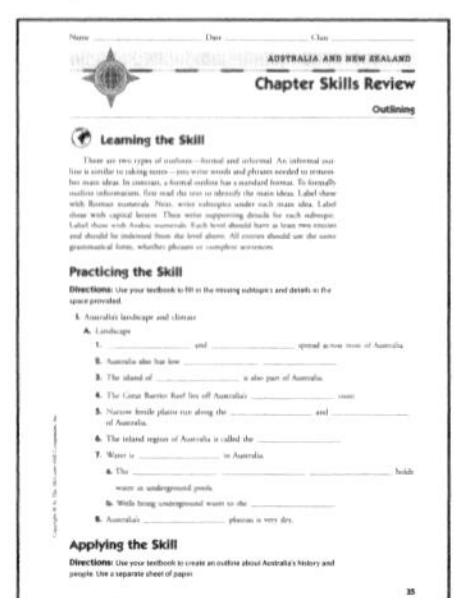

Cooperative Learning Activity L1/ELL

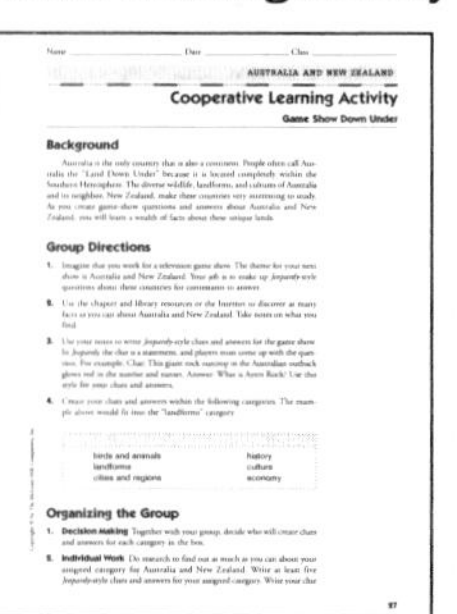

Enrichment Activity L3

ASSESSMENT

Chapter Test, Form A L2

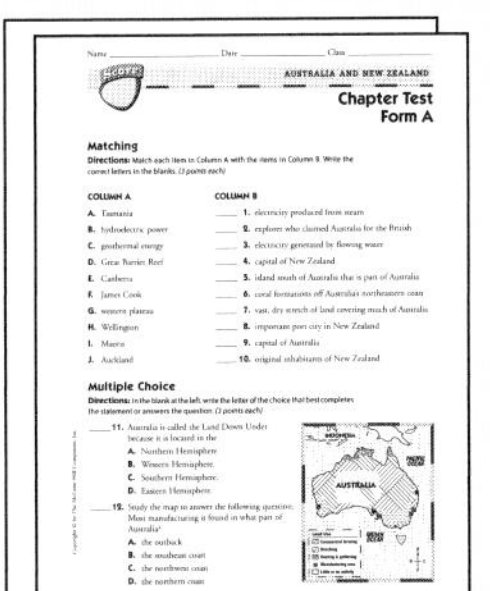

Chapter Test, Form B L2

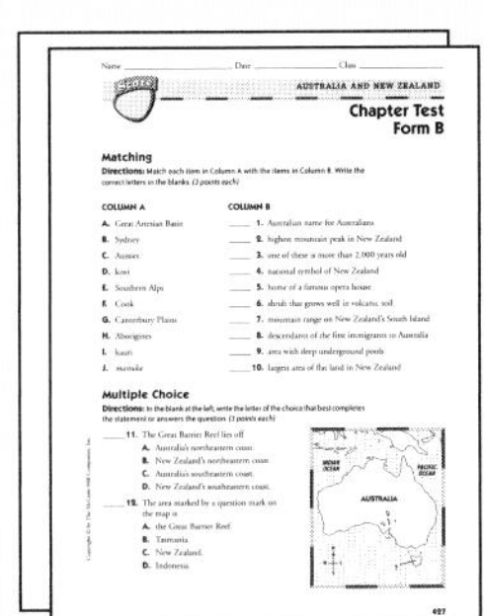

Performance Assessment Activity L1/ELL

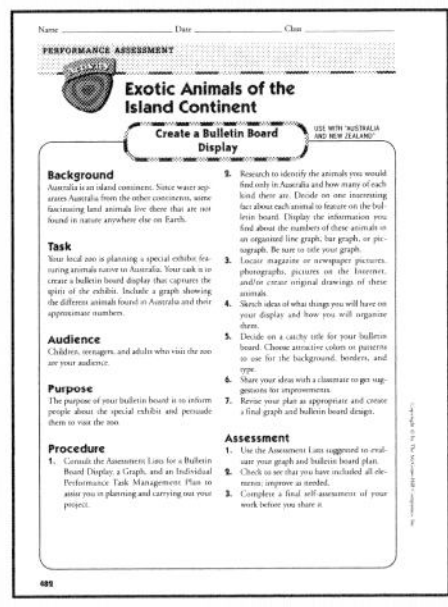

ExamView® Pro Testmaker CD-ROM

STANDARDIZED ASSESSMENT SKILLS

Critical Thinking Skills Activity L2

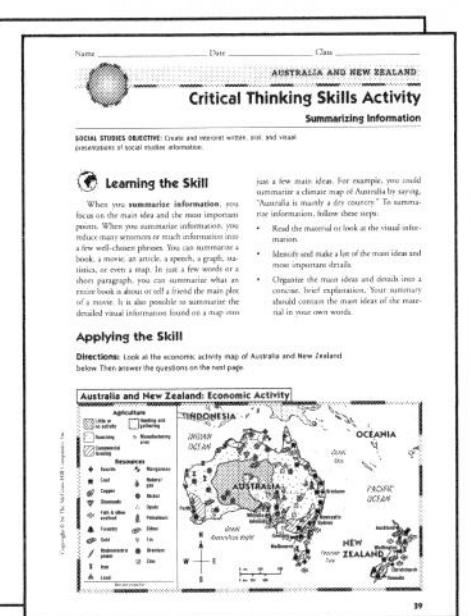

Map and Graph Skills Activity L2

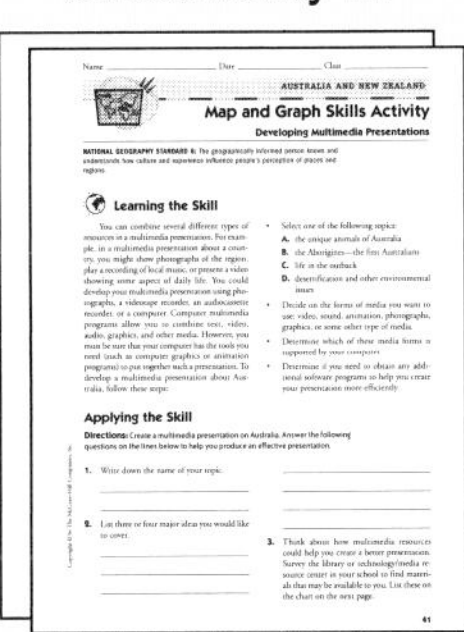

Standardized Test Skills Practice Workbook Activity L2

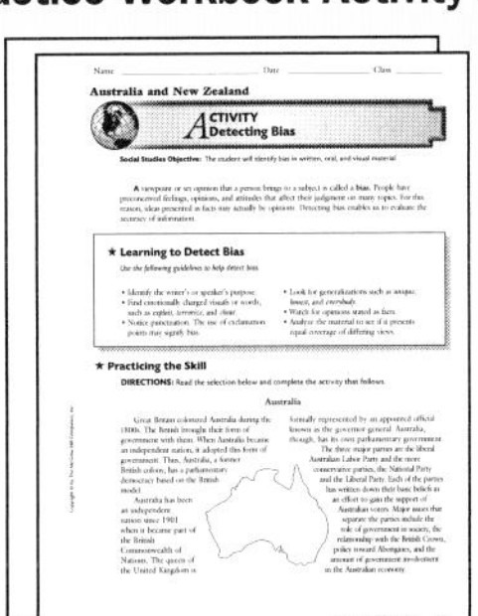

HOME INVOLVEMENT

Take-Home Review Activity L1

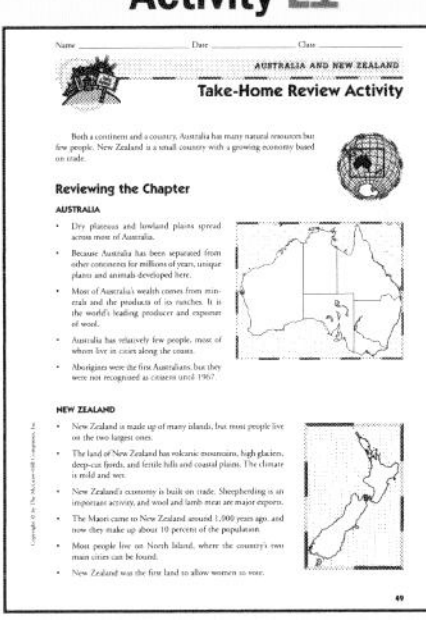

MULTIMEDIA

- National Geographic's The World and Its People
- MindJogger Videoquiz
- Vocabulary PuzzleMaker CD-ROM
- Interactive Tutor Self-Assessment CD-ROM
- ExamView® Pro Testmaker CD-ROM
- TeacherWorks CD-ROM
- StudentWorks CD-ROM
- Skillbuilder Interactive Workbook CD-ROM, Level 1
- Presentation Plus! CD-ROM
- Audio Program

SPANISH RESOURCES

The following Spanish language materials are available in the Spanish Resources binder:

- Spanish Summaries
- Spanish Vocabulary Activities
- Spanish Guided Reading Activities
- Spanish Quizzes and Tests
- Spanish Take-Home Review Activities
- Spanish Reteaching Activities

Meeting National Standards

Geography for Life

The following standards are covered in Chapter 26:

Section 1
EE2 Places and Regions: Standards 4, 5, 6
EE3 Physical Systems: Standards 7, 8
EE4 Human Systems: Standards 9, 10, 13

Section 2
EE4 Human Systems: Standards 9, 10, 11, 13

State and Local Objectives

Chapter 26 Planning Guide

SECTION RESOURCES

Daily Objectives	Reproducible Resources	Multimedia Resources
Section 1 **Australia—Land Down Under** **1.** Discuss how the people of Australia earn a living. **2.** Explain how history has influenced the people of Australia.	Reproducible Lesson Plan Daily Lecture and Discussion Notes Note-taking Guide Guided Reading Activity* Reading Essentials and Study Guide* Section Quiz*	Daily Focus Skills Transparency Vocabulary PuzzleMaker CD-ROM Interactive Tutor Self-Assessment CD-ROM ExamView® Pro Testmaker CD-ROM Presentation Plus! CD-ROM
Section 2 **New Zealand** **1.** Summarize what goods New Zealand's economy produces. **2.** Describe the ethnic groups in New Zealand.	Reproducible Lesson Plan Daily Lecture and Discussion Notes Note-taking Guide Guided Reading Activity* Reading Essentials and Study Guide* Section Quiz*	Daily Focus Skills Transparency In-text Map Transparency Vocabulary PuzzleMaker CD-ROM Interactive Tutor Self-Assessment CD-ROM ExamView® Pro Testmaker CD-ROM Presentation Plus! CD-ROM MindJogger Videoquiz

00:00 **Out of Time?** Assign the **Reading Essentials and Study Guide*** for this chapter.

*Also available in Spanish

KEY TO ABILITY LEVELS

Teaching strategies have been coded for varying learning styles and abilities.

- L1 **BASIC** activities for all students
- L2 **AVERAGE** activities for average to above-average students
- L3 **CHALLENGING** activities for above-average students
- ELL **ENGLISH LANGUAGE LEARNER** activities

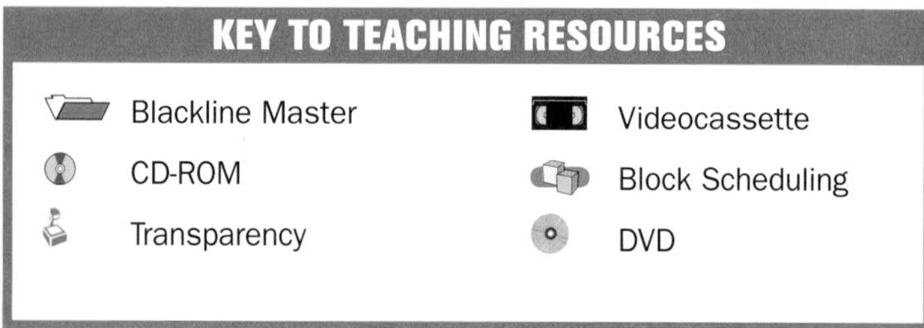

Teacher to Teacher

Sara Monschein
Oakridge Middle School
Naples, Florida

Lake Comparison

Have students gather information from the Internet regarding Lake Eyre in Australia, the Great Salt Lake in Utah, and the Dead Sea between Israel and Jordan. Ask them to make a chart or Venn diagram comparing the following information: (1) elevation at which the lakes lie; (2) the average annual temperature in the location; (3) the source of the salt content and the saline percentage in the lakes; (4) how the lake waters are used; (5) animal life near the lakes; and (6) other interesting information. When their research and charts are completed, have students write a paragraph summarizing the comparison.

Meeting Special Needs

In addition to the Differentiated Instruction strategies found in each section, the following resources are also suitable for your special needs students:

- ***ExamView® Pro Testmaker CD-ROM*** allows teachers to tailor tests by reducing answer choices.
- The ***Audio Program*** includes the entire narrative of the student edition so that less-proficient readers can listen to the words as they read them.
- The ***Reading Essentials and Study Guide*** provides the same content as the student edition but is written two grade levels below the textbook.
- ***Guided Reading Activities*** give less-proficient readers point-by-point instructions to increase comprehension as they read each textbook section.
- ***Enrichment Activities*** include a stimulating collection of readings and activities for gifted and talented students.

NATIONAL GEOGRAPHIC TEACHER'S CORNER

Index to National Geographic Magazine:

The following articles may be used for research relating to this chapter:

- "Kingdom of Coral: Australia's Great Barrier Reef," by Douglas H. Chadwick, January 2001.
- "Fiordland: New Zealand's Southern Sanctuary," by Kennedy Warne, December 2000.
- "Sydney: On Top of the World Down Under," by Bill Bryson, August 2000.

National Geographic Society Products:

To order the following products for use with this chapter, call National Geographic Society at 1-800-368-2728:

- *National Geographic Desk Reference* (Book)
- *Australia: Families of the World Series* (Video)
- *PicturePack: Coral Reefs* (Transparencies)

NGS ONLINE

Access National Geographic's Web site for current events, activities, links, interactive features, and archives. www.nationalgeographic.com

Find the latest coverage of geography in the news, atlas updates, cartographic activities with interactive maps, an online map store, and links at www.nationalgeographic.com/maps

SOCIAL STUDIES Online

Use our Web site for additional resources. All essential content is covered in the Student Edition.

You and your students can visit twip.glencoe.com, the Web site companion to *The World and Its People*. This innovative integration of electronic and print media offers your students a wealth of opportunities. The student text directs students to the Web site for the following options:

- Chapter Overviews
- Student Web Activities
- Self-Check Quizzes
- Textbook Updates

Answers are provided for you in the Web Activity Lesson Plan. Additional Web resources and Interactive Tutor puzzles are also available.

Introducing Chapter 26

Social Studies online

Introduce students to chapter content and key terms by having them access Chapter Overview 26 at twip.glencoe.com

Chapter Objectives

1. Discuss the geography and economy of Australia.
2. Describe the people and culture of Australia.
3. Explain how the geography of New Zealand affects its people and its relations with other countries.

GLENCOE TECHNOLOGY

NATIONAL GEOGRAPHIC

The World and Its People Video Program

Chapter 27 Australia and New Zealand

The following segments enhance the study of this chapter:

- **Amazing Animals**
- **Hot and Steamy**
- **Snakes**

MindJogger Videoquiz

Use MindJogger Videoquiz to preview the Chapter 26 content.

Both programs available in DVD and VHS

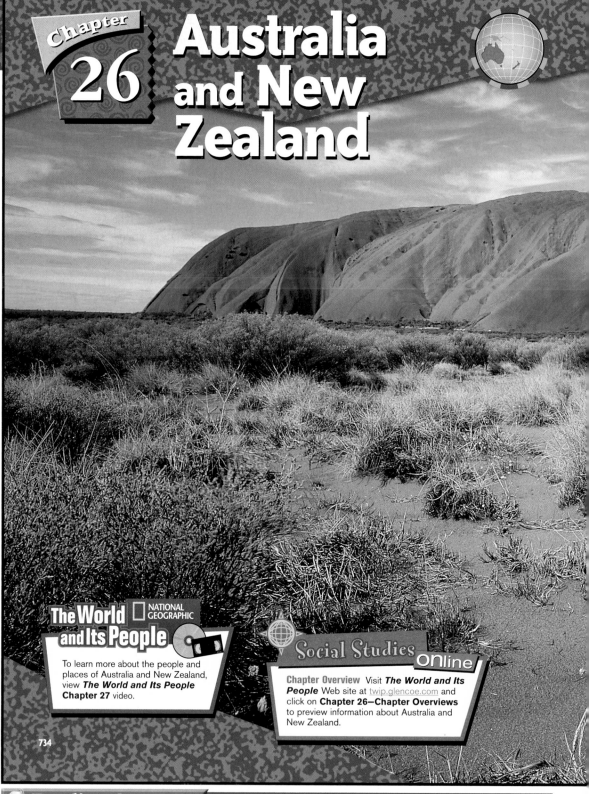

Chapter 26 Australia and New Zealand

The World and Its People NATIONAL GEOGRAPHIC

To learn more about the people and places of Australia and New Zealand, view ***The World and Its People*** **Chapter 27** video.

Social Studies online

Chapter Overview Visit ***The World and Its People*** Web site at twip.glencoe.com and click on **Chapter 26—Chapter Overviews** to preview information about Australia and New Zealand.

734

Reading Strategy — Purpose for Reading

Anticipation Guides test student background knowledge and focus their investigations in a lesson. Write "The Land Down Under" on the board or overhead. Have students brainstorm a list of what it means to live south of the Equator. Write their ideas on the board or overhead and have them copy three or four of these ideas in their notebooks. Ask them to either verify or correct this information as they study the chapter. L1

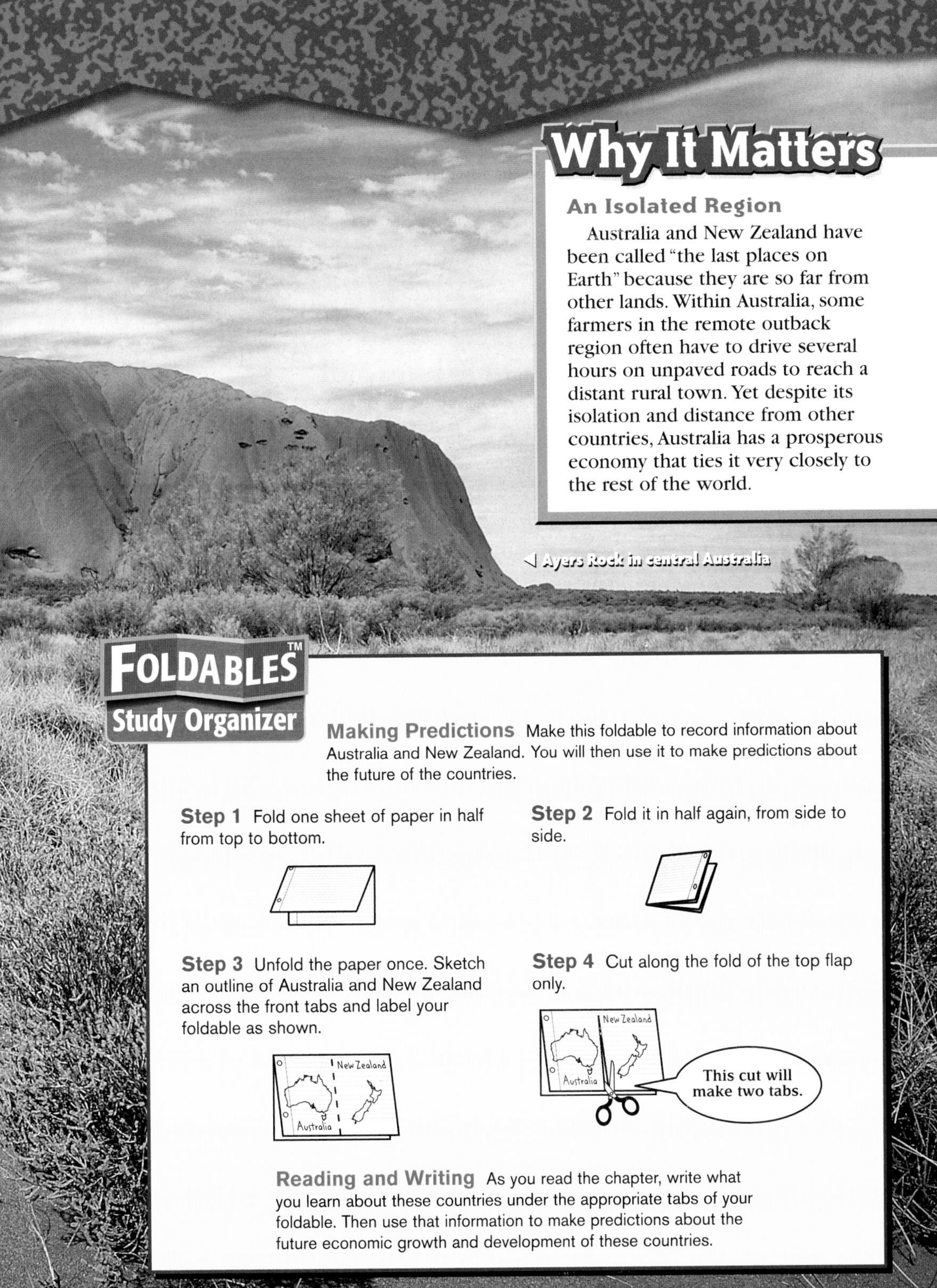

Why It Matters

An Isolated Region

Australia and New Zealand have been called "the last places on Earth" because they are so far from other lands. Within Australia, some farmers in the remote outback region often have to drive several hours on unpaved roads to reach a distant rural town. Yet despite its isolation and distance from other countries, Australia has a prosperous economy that ties it very closely to the rest of the world.

◁ Ayers Rock in central Australia

FOLDABLES™ Study Organizer

Making Predictions Make this foldable to record information about Australia and New Zealand. You will then use it to make predictions about the future of the countries.

Step 1 Fold one sheet of paper in half from top to bottom.

Step 2 Fold it in half again, from side to side.

Step 3 Unfold the paper once. Sketch an outline of Australia and New Zealand across the front tabs and label your foldable as shown.

Step 4 Cut along the fold of the top flap only.

Reading and Writing As you read the chapter, write what you learn about these countries under the appropriate tabs of your foldable. Then use that information to make predictions about the future economic growth and development of these countries.

About the Photo

Ayers Rock is the world's largest monolith, or stand-alone rock formation, in the world. It rises 1,143 feet (348 m) and is almost 6 miles (9 km) around the base. Considered one of the great wonders of the modern world, Ayers Rock is located in the Kata Tjuta National Park, which is owned and run by the local Aborigines. The Aboriginal name for the rock is Mount Uluru, and the whole area is an important center of the Aborigines' spiritual beliefs. Depending on the time of day and the atmospheric conditions, the rock can dramatically change color—anywhere from blue to glowing red.

Introducing Chapter 26

FOLDABLES™ Study Organizer — Dinah Zike's Foldables

Purpose Students will make and use a foldable to record information about Australia and New Zealand. As students read the chapter, they are required to write what they learn about these countries under the appropriate tabs on their foldables. They will then use this information to make predictions about the future economic growth and development of Australia and New Zealand.

Have students complete the ***Reading and Study Skills Foldables*** activity for this chapter.

Why It Matters

As students study the chapter, have them create a graphic organizer on poster board that shows how Australia and New Zealand are able to prosper economically, despite their isolation and distance from other countries. Students might use cause-effect or web diagrams that show how the geography contributes to the countries' economic growth. Have students explain their posters to the class after studying the chapter to prepare for assessment.

FOCUS

Section Objectives

1. Discuss how the people of Australia earn a living.
2. Explain how history has influenced the people of Australia.

BELLRINGER
Skillbuilder Activity

Project transparency and have students answer the question.

Daily Focus Skills Transparency

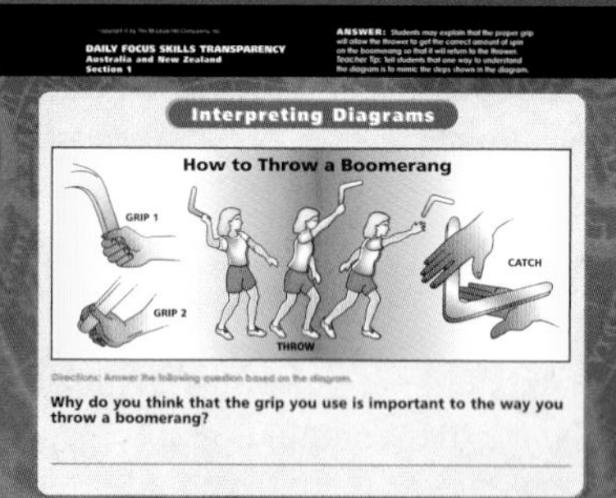

Reading Preview

■ **Activating Prior Knowledge** Write the words *kangaroo, koala,* and *platypus*. Ask students what they know about these animals. Explain that these three species—and several others—are unique to Australia. **Ask:** **What geographical feature explains why Australia has animals not found elsewhere in the world?** *(It is separated from other areas by water.)*

■ **Preteaching Vocabulary** Ask students to identify the words in the Terms to Know that were coined in Australia. *(outback, station, boomerang)*

Guide to Reading

Main Idea

Both a continent and a country, Australia has many natural resources but relatively few people.

Terms to Know

- coral reef
- outback
- station
- marsupial
- boomerang
- bush

Reading Strategy

Create a chart like this one. Then fill in two facts about Australia for each category.

Land	History
Climate	Government
Economy	People

Section 1

Australia—Land Down Under

NATIONAL GEOGRAPHIC **Exploring Our World**

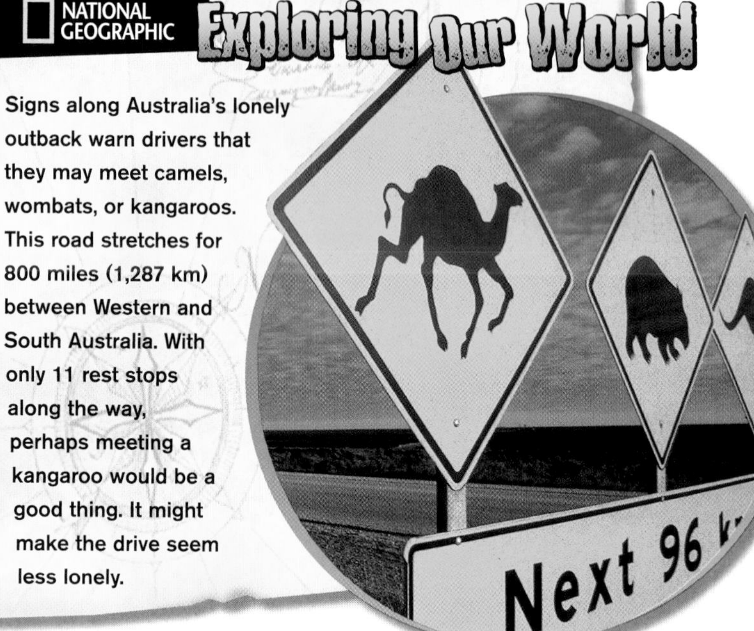

Signs along Australia's lonely outback warn drivers that they may meet camels, wombats, or kangaroos. This road stretches for 800 miles (1,287 km) between Western and South Australia. With only 11 rest stops along the way, perhaps meeting a kangaroo would be a good thing. It might make the drive seem less lonely.

Australia, the sixth-largest country in the world, is also a continent. It is sometimes referred to as the "Land Down Under" because it is located in the Southern Hemisphere.

Australia's Landscape

Plateaus and plains spread across most of Australia. The map on page 742 shows you that the country has low mountain ranges as well, including the **Great Dividing Range.** The island of **Tasmania** is also part of Australia. The **Great Barrier Reef** lies off the country's northeastern coast. Here, coral formations have piled up for millions of years to create a colorful chain that stretches 1,250 miles (2,012 km). A **coral reef** is a structure formed by the skeletons of small sea animals.

Narrow plains run along the south and southeast of Australia. These fertile flatlands hold the best farmland and most of the country's people. Two major rivers, the **Murray** and the **Darling,** drain this region.

Section Resources

Reproducible Masters

- Reproducible Lesson Plan
- Daily Lecture and Discussion Notes
- Note-taking Guide
- Guided Reading Activity
- Reading Essentials and Study Guide
- Section Quiz

Transparencies

- Daily Focus Skills Transparency

Multimedia

- Vocabulary PuzzleMaker CD-ROM
- Interactive Tutor Self-Assessment CD-ROM
- Presentation Plus! CD-ROM
- ExamView® Pro Testmaker CD-ROM

Australians use the name **outback** for the inland regions of their country. Mining camps and cattle and sheep ranches called **stations** dot this region. One cattle station is almost twice as large as Delaware.

Water is scarce in Australia. In the **Great Artesian Basin,** however, water lies in deep, underground pools. Ranchers drill wells and bring the underground water to the surface for their cattle. Australia's western plateau is even drier. Most people who cross the deserts and ranges on this vast plateau do so by airplane.

Web Activity Visit ***The World and Its People*** Web site at twip.glencoe.com and click on **Chapter 26—Student Web Activities** to learn more about the Great Barrier Reef.

Unusual Animals About 200 million years ago, the tectonic plate upon which Australia sits separated from the other continents. As a result, Australia's native plants and animals are not found elsewhere in the world. Two well-known Australian animals are kangaroos and koalas. Both are **marsupials,** or mammals that carry their young in a pouch. Turn to page 740 to read more about some of Australia's animals.

✓Reading Check Where do most of Australia's people live?

Australia's Economy

Australia has a strong, prosperous economy. The country is a treasure chest overflowing with mineral resources. These riches include iron ore, zinc, bauxite, gold, silver, opals, diamonds, and pearls. Australia

Literature

GREAT MOTHER SNAKE

Aboriginal Legend

Most cultures developed stories to help explain their beginnings. In this Aboriginal legend, the Great Mother Snake is credited with creating Australia as well as all of its human and animal inhabitants.

Aboriginal bark painting ▶

"... Then finally She awoke and brought from the womb on the Earth itself, man and woman. And they learned from the Mother Snake how to live in peace and harmony with all these creatures who were their spiritual cousins. ... And man and woman were now the caretakers of this land. And the Great Snake then entered a large water hole where she guards the fish and other water creatures, so that when the Aboriginal people fish they know to take only as much as they can eat, because if someone should take more than they need through greed or kills for pleasure, they know that one dark night, the Great Mother Snake will come ... and punish the one who broke this tribal law."

Source: *Great Mother Snake,* an Aboriginal legend.

Analyzing Literature

Why would it be important for people in this culture to take from the earth only as much as they needed?

Chapter 26

Section 1, pages 736–739

2 TEACH

Reading Strategy

Identifying Cause and Effect Give students a fact about Australia. *(The interior of the country is very dry.)* Have them state an effect that results from the fact. *(The land is not good for farming.)* **L1**

Objectives and answers to the Student Web Activity can be found in the Web Activity Lesson Plan at twip.glencoe.com

✓ Reading Check Answer

in the narrow plains along the south and southeast

Literature

Answer
for balance with nature and equality for everyone

Activity Ask students to think of another creation story that has a snake in it. The story of Adam and Eve will probably be mentioned. How is this story, or any others, the same or different from the Aboriginal legend?

Reading Strategy — Reading the Text

Monitoring Comprehension If there are sentences that are too long within the section for students to comprehend, help them create smaller ones by breaking them down. Commas are usually good places for separating ideas. **L1**

*Use the **Reading Skills Handbook** for more reading strategies.*

Chapter 26

Section 1, pages 736–739

Answer Students' descriptions might include references to "the full sails of a clipper ship," "the wings of a gull," "waves," and "praying hands."

Construction Problems
The Sydney Opera House was designed by Danish architect Jorn Utzon, and many problems arose during its construction. Much of the necessary technology needed to solve the problems had to be developed as the building was being constructed.

Reading Check Answer
raising livestock, especially cattle and sheep

L1/ELL

Guided Reading Activity

Name ______ Date ______ Class ______

AUSTRALIA AND NEW ZEALAND

Guided Reading Activity 1

Australia—Land Down Under

DIRECTIONS: Answering Questions Reading the section and answering the questions below will help you learn more about the country of Australia. Use your textbook to answer the questions.

1. Why is Australia called the "Land Down Under"?
2. What is the Great Barrier Reef?
3. Where do most people in Australia live?

Assess

Assign Section 1 Assessment as homework or an in-class activity.

Have students use the Interactive Tutor Self-Assessment CD-ROM to review Section 1.

Architecture

The Sydney Opera House—one of the most famous buildings in the world—stands on a peninsula jutting out into the harbor of Sydney, Australia. The soaring, shell-like roof and walls are made of reinforced concrete covered with gleaming white ceramic tiles. Inside are an opera house, concert hall, theater, and other entertainment facilities. Completed in 1973, the Sydney Opera House is regarded as a masterpiece of modern architecture.

Looking Closer What do you think this building resembles?

also has energy resources, including coal, oil, and natural gas. Mineral and energy resources make up more than one-third of Australia's exports.

Australia's dry climate limits farming. With irrigation, however, farmers grow grains, sugarcane, cotton, fruits, and vegetables. The main agricultural activity is raising livestock, especially cattle and sheep. Australia is the world's top producer and exporter of wool. Ranchers also ship beef and cattle hides.

Manufacturing includes processed foods, transportation equipment, metals, cloth, and chemicals. High-technology industries, service industries, and tourism also play a large role in the economy. Ocean shipping enables Australia to export goods to distant markets. More than half go to Asia. The United States is also an important market for exports.

Despite its huge area, Australia has only 19.9 million people. The country has long needed more skilled workers to develop its resources and build its economy. Thus, the government has encouraged immigration. More than 5 million immigrants have arrived in recent decades.

Reading Check **What is Australia's main agricultural activity?**

Australia's History and People

Australia's Aborigines (A•buh•RIHJ•neez) are the descendants of the first immigrants who came from Asia at least 40,000 years ago. For centuries, the nomadic Aborigines hunted, gathered plants, and searched for water. They developed a weapon called a **boomerang.** It is a flat, bent, wooden tool that hunters throw to stun prey. If the boomerang misses, it curves and sails back to the hunter.

The Dutch were the first Europeans to travel to Australia in the late 1600s. In 1770 Captain James Cook reached Australia and claimed it for Great Britain. At first the British government used Australia as a place

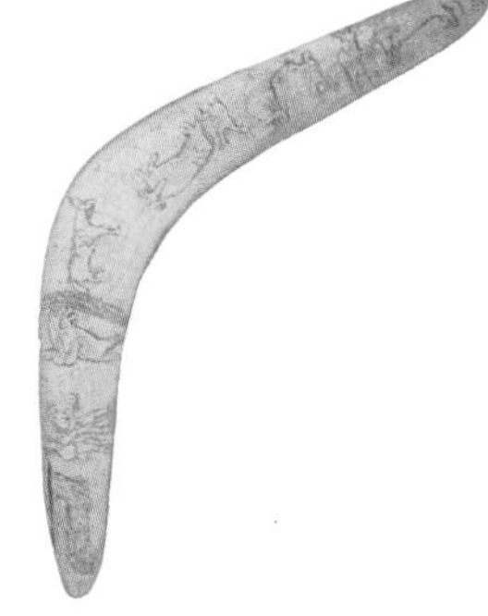

▲ Aboriginal boomerang

Differentiated Instruction

Meeting Special Needs: Visual/Spatial Give visual learners an outline map of Australia. As they study the section, they can take notes on the map. Suggest that they use different colors to indicate different kinds of information—green for physical and climate features, red for natural resources and economic activities, and blue for cities and cultural features, for example. This visual presentation will make it easier for visual learners to study the material. **L1 ELL**

Refer to *Inclusion for the Middle School Social Studies Classroom Strategies and Activities* in the TCR.

to send prisoners. Then the British set up colonies, especially after gold was discovered in the outback in 1851. Land was taken from the Aborigines, and many died of European diseases. Today nearly 300,000 Aborigines live in Australia. Many are moving to cities to find jobs. In 1967 the Australian government recognized the Aborigines as citizens.

The Government In 1901 the colonies united to form the Commonwealth of Australia. Today Australia has a British-style parliamentary democracy. A prime minister is the head of government. Australians still accept the British monarch as a ceremonial leader. Many Australians, however, would like their country to become a republic with an Australian president.

Like the United States, Australia has a federal system of government. This means that political power is divided between a national government and state governments. The country has six states and two territories, the **Northern Territory** and the **Australian Capital Territory.**

City and Rural Life About 90 percent of Australians live in cities. **Sydney** and **Melbourne** are the largest cities. **Canberra,** the capital, was a planned city located inland to draw people into the outback. About 10 percent of Australians live in rural areas known as the **bush.** Many rural people also live and work on the stations that dot the outback.

Australians speak English, but "Aussies," as they call themselves, have some different words. For example, Australians say "G'Day" as a form of hello and cook beef on a "barbie," or barbeque grill.

✓ **Reading Check** What kind of government does Australia have?

Dreamtime

Danny Ahmatt and John Meninga are Aborigines who live in Australia's Northern Territory. They live modern lives, but they also have traditional Aborigine beliefs. "We believe in *Dreamtime*," says Danny. "This means that our ancestors do not die but instead become part of nature. This is why we learn to respect our environment."

Section 1 Assessment

Defining Terms

1. **Define** coral reef, outback, station, marsupial, boomerang, bush.

Recalling Facts

2. **History** Why does Australia have animals that are not found on other continents?
3. **Economics** What are four mineral resources found in Australia?
4. **History** Who are the Aborigines?

Critical Thinking

5. **Understanding Cause and Effect** How does climate affect agriculture in Australia?
6. **Drawing Conclusions** How does life in Australia show that the country was once a colony of the United Kingdom?

Graphic Organizer

7. **Organizing Information** Create a time line like this one with at least four dates in Australia's history. Write the dates on one side of the line and the corresponding event on the opposite side.

Applying Social Studies Skills

8. **Analyzing Maps** Look at the physical/political map on page 742. What mountain peak represents the highest elevation in Australia? What mountain range is it part of?

Section 1 Assessment

1. The terms are defined in the Glossary.
2. because it is separated from other lands by oceans and seas
3. *Any four:* iron ore, zinc, bauxite, gold, silver, opals, diamonds, pearls
4. descendants of the first people to come to Australia—from Asia—at least 40,000 years ago
5. The dry climate limits farming.
6. use of the English language and a British-style parliamentary democracy
7. 1770—James Cook claimed Australia for Great Britain; 1851—gold discovered in outback and land taken from Aborigines; 1901—Commonwealth of Australia formed; 1967—Aborigines recognized as citizens
8. Mt. Kosciuszko; Great Dividing Range

L2

Section Quiz

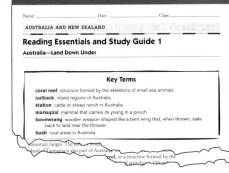

Name ______ Date ______ Class ______

Score — AUSTRALIA AND NEW ZEALAND

Section 1 Quiz
Australia—Land Down Under

DIRECTIONS: Matching Match each item in Column A with the items in Column B. Write the correct letters in the blanks. *(10 points each)*

COLUMN A	COLUMN B
A. outback	____ 1. mammals that carry their young in a pouch
B. stations	____ 2. structure formed by the skeletons of small sea animals
C. marsupials	____ 3. cattle and sheep ranches
D. the bush	____ 4. the inland regions of Australia
E. coral reef	____ 5. rural areas of Australia

✓ **Reading Check Answer**

Australia is a parliamentary democracy with a federal system of government.

L1/ELL

Reading Essentials and Study Guide

Name ______ Date ______ Class ______

AUSTRALIA AND NEW ZEALAND

Reading Essentials and Study Guide 1
Australia—Land Down Under

Key Terms

coral reef structure formed by the skeletons of small sea animals
outback inland regions of Australia
station cattle or sheep ranch in Australia
marsupial mammal that carries its young in a pouch
boomerang wooden weapon shaped like a bent wing that, when thrown, sails back to land near the thrower
bush rural areas in Australia

Reading Strategy

Writing a Paragraph Have students write a paragraph comparing life in North America to life in Australia.

Making Connections

Teach

Ask students to identify the major characteristics of the kangaroo and the koala. Note their suggestions on the board. Circle the word *pouch,* or add it if students do not identify this feature. Point out that the presence of the pouch puts both animals in the category of marsupials. Explain that the opossums of North America and the shrew opossums of South America are the only marsupials native to lands other than Australia. L1

More About Kangaroos

When they move slowly, kangaroos balance on their small front legs and their tails, shifting the larger hind legs forward. When they run, they hop. Kangaroos must move both hind legs together when on land—but in water, they can use them separately.

Interdisciplinary Connections

Science Koalas are almost the only animals to survive on eucalyptus leaves, which are very tough and have very few nutrients. They have developed adaptations that allow them to digest these leaves. One is a slow metabolism that permits a long period of time for digestion but requires little expenditure of energy. As a result, koalas may sleep 16 hours a day.

Making Connections

ART | SCIENCE | CULTURE | TECHNOLOGY

Australia's Amazing Animals

Australia is home to some fascinating and unusual animals. In fact, many of Australia's animal species are found nowhere else in the world.

Kangaroos

Ask people what comes to mind when they think of Australian animals, and they will probably say the kangaroo. Kangaroos are marsupials—mammals whose young mature inside a pouch on the mother's belly. The young kangaroo, called a joey, stays there for months, eating and growing. Australia is home to more than 50 species of kangaroo, ranging in size from the 6-foot (2-m) red kangaroo to the 9-inch (23-cm) musky rat-kangaroo. No matter what their size, all kangaroos have one thing in common—big hind feet. Kangaroos bound along at about 20 miles (32 km) per hour. In a single jump, a kangaroo can hop 10 feet (3 m) high and cover a distance of 45 feet (14 m).

Koalas

Because of their round face, big black nose, large fluffy ears, and soft fur, people sometimes call these animals koala bears. Yet they are not bears at all. The koala is a marsupial. The female's pouch opens at the bottom. Strong muscles keep the pouch shut and the young koalas, also called joeys, safe inside. The koala is a fussy eater who feeds only on leaves of eucalyptus trees. Although there are over 600 species of eucalyptus that grow in Australia, koalas eat only a few types. The leaves also provide the animals with all the moisture they need. Quiet, calm, and sleepy, koalas spend most of their time in the trees.

▲ Koala and joey

Platypus and Emu

The odd-looking platypus is one of the world's few egg-laying mammals. Sometimes called a duck-billed platypus, the animal has a soft, sensitive, skin-covered snout. The platypus is a good swimmer who lives in burrows along the streams and riverbanks of southern and eastern Australia. It uses its bill to stir the river bottom in search of food.

After the ostrich, the Australian emu is the world's second-largest bird. Although the emu cannot fly, its long legs enable it to run at speeds of up to 30 miles (48 km) per hour. Another interesting characteristic of the emu is its nesting behavior. Although the female lays the eggs, the male emu sits on them until they are ready to hatch.

◀ Kangaroo and joey

Emu ▼

Making the Connection

1. What are marsupials?
2. How far can a kangaroo hop in a single jump?
3. **Making Comparisons** Compare two different animals that live in Australia. How are they alike? How are they different?

Making the Connection

1. mammals whose young mature inside a pouch on the mother's belly
2. 10 feet (3 m) high and 45 feet (14 m) long
3. Comparisons will vary.

New Zealand

Guide to Reading

Main Idea

New Zealand is a small country with a growing economy based on trade.

Terms to Know

- geyser
- *manuka*
- fjord
- geothermal energy
- hydroelectric power

Reading Strategy

Create a time line like this one with at least four dates in New Zealand's history. Write the dates on one side of the line and the corresponding event on the opposite side.

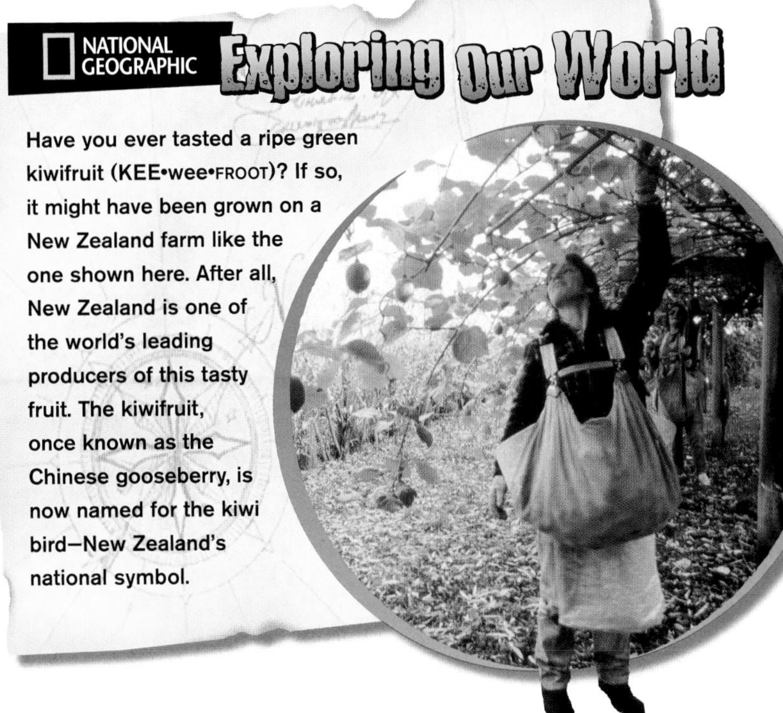

NATIONAL GEOGRAPHIC Exploring Our World

Have you ever tasted a ripe green kiwifruit (KEE•wee•FROOT)? If so, it might have been grown on a New Zealand farm like the one shown here. After all, New Zealand is one of the world's leading producers of this tasty fruit. The kiwifruit, once known as the Chinese gooseberry, is now named for the kiwi bird—New Zealand's national symbol.

New Zealand lies in the Pacific Ocean about 1,200 miles (1,931 km) southeast of its nearest neighbor, Australia. In contrast to Australia's flat, dry land, New Zealand is mountainous and very green. Its climate is mild and wet. Both New Zealand and Australia are located in the Southern Hemisphere, so their summer starts in December and their winter starts in June.

New Zealand's Land

New Zealand is about the size of Colorado. It includes two main islands—**North Island** and **South Island**—as well as many smaller islands. The **Cook Strait** separates the two main islands.

North Island A large plateau forms the center of North Island. Three active volcanoes and the inactive Mount Egmont are located here. You also find **geysers**, or hot springs that spout steam and water through a crack in the earth.

Small shrubs called ***manuka*** grow well in the plateau's fertile volcanic soil. Fertile lowlands, forested hills, and sandy beaches surround

741

Chapter 26

Section 2, pages 741–744

1 FOCUS

Section Objectives

1. Discuss New Zealand's land and how it affects its economy.
2. Describe the ethnic groups in New Zealand.

BELLRINGER Skillbuilder Activity

Project transparency and have students answer the question.

Daily Focus Skills Transparency

Interpreting Information on Tables

Which of the following statements is accurate?

A The number of people visiting New Zealand from other countries has increased each year.
B Few New Zealand residents visit other countries.
C Most people who visit New Zealand move there permanently.
D Total departures are greater than total arrivals in all three years.

Reading Preview

- **Activating Prior Knowledge** Ask students if they can identify "Old Faithful." After they name Yellowstone's landmark geyser, inform them that New Zealand has many geysers as well.
- **Preteaching Vocabulary** Explain that *geo-* comes from a Greek word meaning "earth" and that *thermal* comes from a Greek word for "heat." Then ask students what they think *geothermal energy* means.

Section Resources

Reproducible Masters
- Reproducible Lesson Plan
- Daily Lecture and Discussion Notes
- Note-taking Guide
- Guided Reading Activity
- Reading Essentials and Study Guide
- Section Quiz

Transparencies
- Daily Focus Skills Transparency
- In-text Map Transparency

Multimedia
- Vocabulary PuzzleMaker CD-ROM
- Interactive Tutor Self-Assessment CD-ROM
- Presentation Plus! CD-ROM
- ExamView® Pro Testmaker CD-ROM
- MindJogger Videoquiz

2 TEACH

Reading Strategy

Taking Notes Create a chart with the headings "Physical Features," "Economy," and "People." Have students copy the chart into their notebooks and then fill in details as they read the section. L1

Daily Lecture and Discussion Notes

AUSTRALIA AND NEW ZEALAND

Daily Lecture and Discussion Notes

New Zealand

Did You Know? New Zealand offers students free elementary and secondary education up to age 19. The law requires children from 6 through 15 years of age to attend school, but most youngsters enter school at 5. Many children under 5 attend free kindergartens or play centers.

I. New Zealand's Land

A. In contrast to Australia's flat, dry land, New Zealand is mountainous and very green. Its marine west coast climate is mild and wet.

B. New Zealand consists of two main islands—North Island and South Island—and many smaller islands. Cook Strait separates the two main islands.

... find **geysers,** or hot springs that spout steam and water

Reading Check Answer

South Island

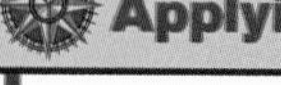

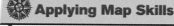

Applying Map Skills

Answers

1. Great Dividing Range
2. Wellington

In-text Map Transparency Activity Provide practice using cardinal and intermediate directions. **Ask:** **What body of water is west of South Island?** *(Tasman Sea)* **What mountain range is southwest of the Hamersley Range?** *(the Darling Range)* **Where is the Great Barrier Reef?** *(off Australia's northeast coast)*

North Island's central plateau. On the plateau's slopes, sheep and cattle graze. Fruits and vegetables are grown on the coastal lowlands.

South Island The **Southern Alps** run along South Island's western coast. Snowcapped **Mount Cook,** the highest peak in New Zealand, soars 12,316 feet (3,754 m). Glaciers lie on mountain slopes above green forests and sparkling blue lakes. Long ago, these glaciers cut deep **fjords** (fee•AWRDS), or steep-sided valleys, into the mountains. The sea has filled these fjords with crystal-blue waters.

To the east of the Southern Alps stretch the Canterbury Plains. They form New Zealand's largest area of flat or nearly flat land. Farmers grow grains and ranchers raise sheep here.

Plants and Animals New Zealanders take pride in their unique wildlife. Their national symbol is a flightless bird called the kiwi. Giant kauri (KOWR•ee) trees once dominated all of North Island. About 100 years ago, European settlers cut down many of these trees, using the wood to build homes and ships. Today the government protects kauri trees. One of them is more than 2,000 years old.

Reading Check **Which island of New Zealand has glaciers and fjords?**

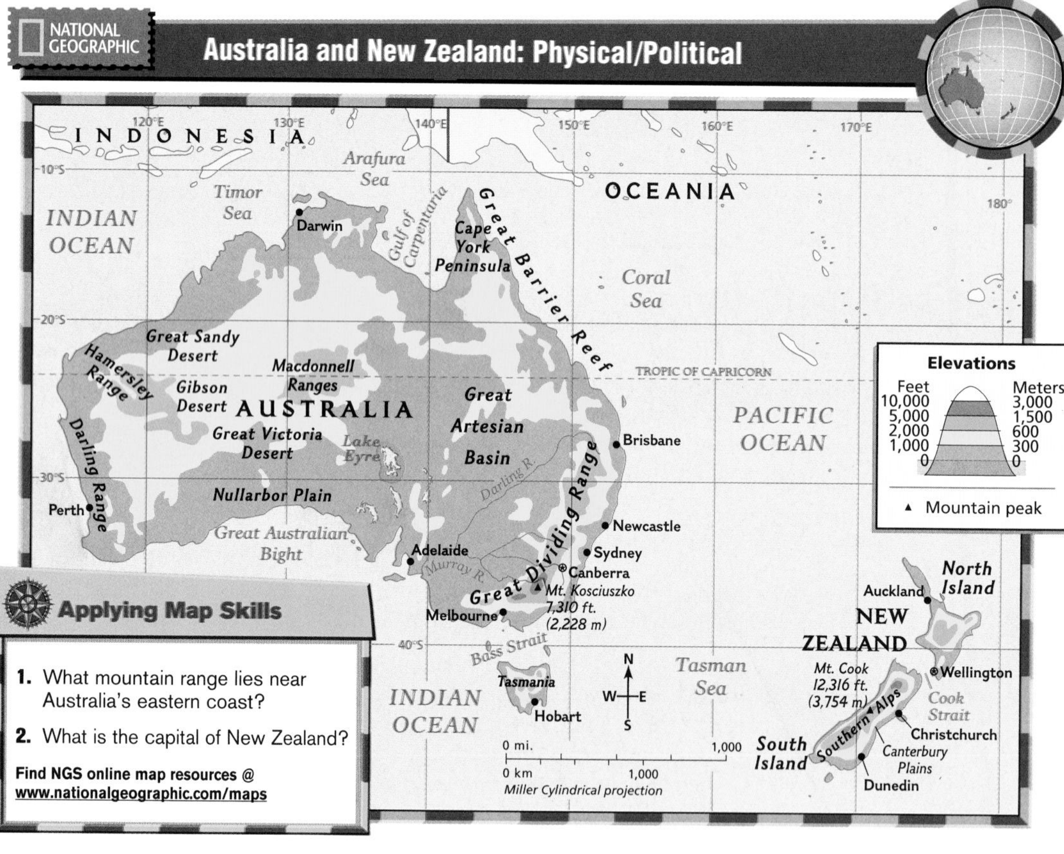

Applying Map Skills

1. What mountain range lies near Australia's eastern coast?
2. What is the capital of New Zealand?

Find NGS online map resources @ www.nationalgeographic.com/maps

Reading Strategy — Reading the Text

Reading a Map Remind students that before they answer the Applying Map Skills questions, they should try to identify certain elements on the map to understand what the map is showing. Students should read the title and study the overall land area. They then should find the map key that will tell them what symbols or colors stand for on the map. Students may also want to look for a compass rose so that they understand direction and the scale bar, which shows the relationship between map measurements and actual distances. Be sure students identify these elements on maps before they answer any questions. L1

*Use the **Reading Skills Handbook** for more reading strategies.*

New Zealand's Economy

New Zealand has a thriving agricultural economy. Sheep are an important agricultural resource. New Zealand is the second-leading wool producer in the world. Lamb meat is another important export. Apples, barley, wheat, and corn are the main crops.

Trade with other countries is an important part of New Zealand's economy. Its main trading partners are Australia, Japan, the United States, and the United Kingdom. There are benefits and dangers due to New Zealand's dependence on trade. If the economies of other countries are growing quickly, demand for goods from New Zealand will rise. If their economies slow, however, these countries will buy fewer products. This can cause hardship in New Zealand. In recent years, trade has increased, and New Zealanders enjoy a high standard of living.

Mining and Manufacturing New Zealand sits on top of the molten rock that forms volcanoes. As a result, it is rich in **geothermal energy**, or electricity produced from steam. The major source of energy, however, is **hydroelectric power**—electricity generated by flowing water. New Zealand also has coal, oil, iron ore, silver, and gold.

The country is rapidly industrializing. The main manufactured items are wood products, fertilizer, wool products, and shoes. Service industries and tourism also play large roles in the economy.

✓ Reading Check **How does its dependence on trade with other countries present both benefits and dangers to New Zealand?**

NATIONAL GEOGRAPHIC On Location

Maori

In recent years, the Maori culture has experienced a revival in New Zealand. Some Maoris dress in traditional costumes for special celebrations.

History **How did the Maoris arrive in New Zealand?**

New Zealand's History and People

People called the Maoris (MOWR•eez) are believed to have arrived in New Zealand between A.D. 950 and 1150. They probably crossed the Pacific Ocean in canoes from islands far to the northeast. Undisturbed for hundreds of years, the Maoris developed skills in farming, weaving, fishing, bird hunting, and woodcarving.

The first European explorers came to the islands in the mid-1600s. Almost 200 years passed before settlers—most of them

More About the Photo

Maoris The Maori name for New Zealand before the arrival of the Europeans was *Aotearoa*. The Maori people call their language *te reo*.

Caption Answer The Maoris came to New Zealand by canoe from islands far to the northeast.

✓ Reading Check Answer

High demand from those countries can lead to prosperity, but if demand slips, New Zealand's economy will suffer.

L1/ELL

Guided Reading Activity

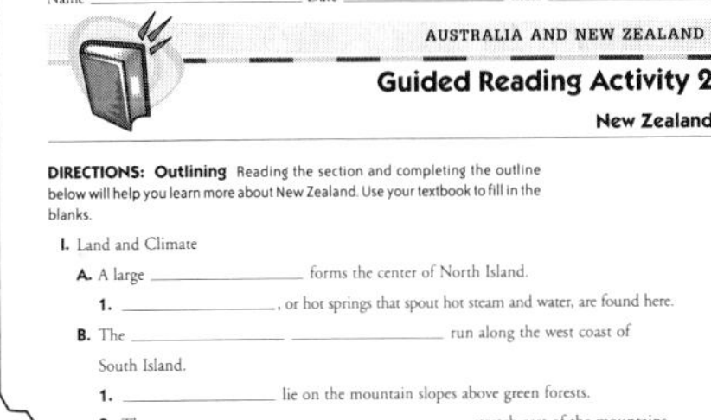

Name ______ Date ______ Class ______

AUSTRALIA AND NEW ZEALAND

Guided Reading Activity 2

New Zealand

DIRECTIONS: Outlining Reading the section and completing the outline below will help you learn more about New Zealand. Use your textbook to fill in the blanks.

I. Land and Climate

A. A large ______ forms the center of North Island.

1. ______, or hot springs that spout hot steam and water, are found here.

B. The ______ ______ run along the west coast of South Island.

1. ______ lie on the mountain slopes above green forests.

2. The ______ ______ stretch east of the mountains.

ASSESS

Assign Section 2 Assessment as homework or an in-class activity.

Have students use the Interactive Tutor Self-Assessment CD-ROM to review Section 2.

Differentiated Instruction

Meeting Special Needs: Naturalist Explain to students the mechanics of geysers so they understand why these phenomena erupt. In a geyser, water is at rest in a column of space within rock. That column of water must be sitting near hot magma within the earth. The heated rock causes the water at the bottom to boil, pushing out some of the water above it. The remaining water becomes even hotter, turning to steam and shooting out into the air. Most geysers are found in only two countries besides New Zealand—Iceland and the United States. **Ask:** **Where are geysers found in New Zealand? What other landforms are found there? L1**

Refer to *Inclusion for the Middle School Social Studies Classroom Strategies and Activities* in the TCR.

Chapter 26

Section 2, pages 741–744

L2

Section Quiz

Name ______ Date ______ Class ______

AUSTRALIA AND NEW ZEALAND

Score

Section 2 Quiz

New Zealand

DIRECTIONS: Matching Match each item in Column A with the items in Column B. Write the correct letters in the blanks. *(10 points each)*

COLUMN A	COLUMN B
A. kauri	____ 1. small shrubs
B. fjords	____ 2. flightless bird
C. geysers	____ 3. steep-sided valleys filled with sea water
D. kiwi	____ 4. hot springs that spout hot steam and water through a crack in the earth
E. *manuka*	____ 5. type of tree that once covered all of North Island

...the blank at the left, write the letter of the...

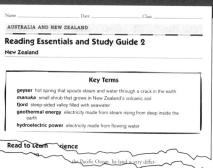

Reading Check Answer

the Maoris

L1/ELL

Reading Essentials and Study Guide

Name ______ Date ______ Class ______

AUSTRALIA AND NEW ZEALAND

Reading Essentials and Study Guide 2

New Zealand

Key Terms

geyser hot spring that spouts steam and water through a crack in the earth

manuka small shrub that grows in New Zealand's volcanic soil

fjord steep-sided valley filled with seawater

geothermal energy electricity made from steam rising from deep inside the earth

hydroelectric power electricity made from flowing water

Read to Learn ... ience

...the Pacific Ocean. Its land is very differ-...

Enrich

Have students research and report on traditional Maori crafts, either showing a variety of crafts or presenting in-depth information on one.

4 CLOSE

Reading Strategy

Organizing Information

Have students create a concept web for New Zealand that includes information about the geography, economy, history, and culture of the country.

British—arrived. In 1840 British officials signed a treaty with Maori leaders. In this treaty, the Maoris agreed to accept British rule in return for the right to keep their land. More British settlers eventually moved onto Maori land. War broke out in the 1860s—a war that the Maoris lost.

In 1893 the colony became the first land to give women the right to vote. New Zealand was also among the first places in which the government gave help to people who were elderly, sick, or out of work.

New Zealand became independent in 1907. The country is a parliamentary democracy in which elected representatives choose a prime minister to head the government. Five seats in the parliament can be held only by Maoris. Today about 10 percent of New Zealand's 4 million people are Maoris. The rest are mostly descendants of British settlers. Asians and Pacific Islanders, attracted by the growing economy, have increased the diversity of New Zealand's society.

About 86 percent of the people live in urban areas. The largest cities are **Auckland,** an important port, and **Wellington,** the capital. Both are on North Island, where about 75 percent of the people live.

New Zealanders take advantage of the country's mild climate and beautiful landscapes. They enjoy camping, hiking, hunting, boating, and mountain climbing in any season. They also play cricket and rugby, sports that originated in Great Britain.

Reading Check What group settled New Zealand about 1,000 years ago?

Section 2 Assessment

Defining Terms

1. **Define** geyser, *manuka,* fjord, geothermal energy, hydroelectric power.

Recalling Facts

2. **Region** How do New Zealand's land and climate compare to Australia's?
3. **Economics** What two animal products are important exports for New Zealand?
4. **History** Most of New Zealand's people are descendants of settlers from what European country?

Critical Thinking

5. **Analyzing Information** Why do you think New Zealand's government guarantees the Maoris a certain number of seats in the parliament?
6. **Making Predictions** With so many different peoples settling in New Zealand, how do you think the country's culture might change?

Graphic Organizer

7. **Organizing Information** Imagine that you are moving to New Zealand. Write a question you would ask for each topic in the chart below.

Physical features	Economy	Recreation
Climate	Government	Culture

Applying Social Studies Skills

8. **Analyzing Maps** Look at the map on page 742. Which New Zealand island has higher mountains? How can you tell?

Section 2 Assessment

1. The terms are defined in the Glossary.
2. New Zealand is smaller, more mountainous, and wetter than Australia.
3. wool, lamb meat
4. United Kingdom
5. *Possible answer:* to protect their rights
6. *Possible answer:* The country will probably develop a more diverse culture.
7. Students' questions will vary.
8. South Island; the map elevation key color of orange is present, showing elevations of 5,000–10,000 ft (1,500–3,000 m).

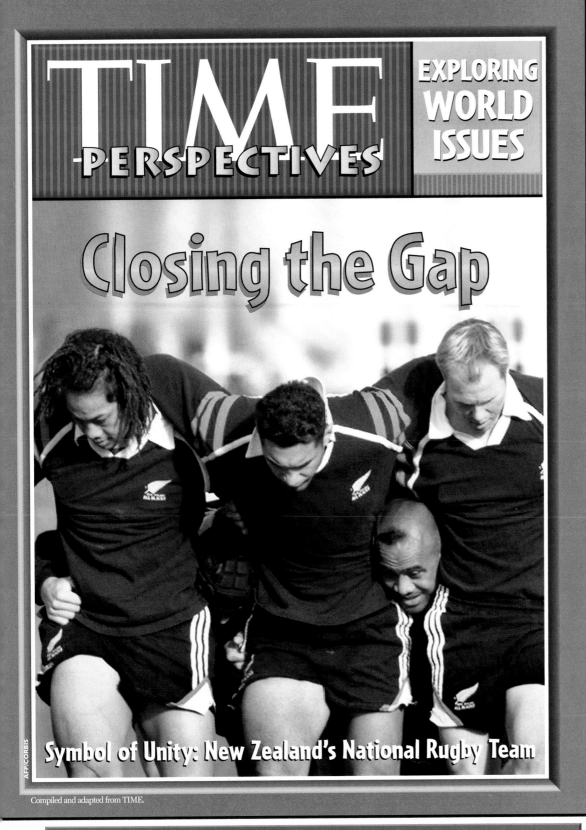

TIME PERSPECTIVES

EXPLORING WORLD ISSUES

Closing the Gap

Symbol of Unity: New Zealand's National Rugby Team

AFP/CORBIS

Compiled and adapted from TIME.

Making Connections

Tradition **Ask students:** **What kind of traditions does your family follow? What are some of the holidays your family celebrates?** Ask students to imagine that they could no longer celebrate these occasions. **Ask:** **How would that make you feel? Why do you think cultural traditions are important to people?** Then discuss the fact that when Europeans settled in various parts of the world, including New Zealand, Australia, and North America, they typically saw the cultures of those already living there as being inferior. They often discouraged these people from practicing their religions, celebrating festivals, or speaking their language. While attitudes have changed in recent times, the actions of the Europeans greatly affected these cultures.

Exploring World Issues

Teacher Background

Indigenous people around the world have suffered when others have settled on their lands. The Maoris of New Zealand are one example. After the immigration of Europeans, they were discouraged from following their traditions, and many succumbed to illnesses. Amidst a feeling of hopelessness, some began abusing alcohol. By the late nineteenth century, there were only approximately 40,000 remaining Maoris.

Today the Maoris number about 400,000. New Zealanders are now trying to right many of the wrongs committed against the Maoris.

TIME REPORTS

AUSTRALIA, OCEANIA, AND ANTARCTICA

Closing the Gap

THEME: CULTURAL DIVERSITY AND DIFFUSION

Guide To Teaching With This Unit

Inside This Unit Three activity masters are designed to build an understanding of New Zealand and Australia and of the status of indigenous people living there.

- Activity Master 1: A time line traces the Maori culture's origins and decline, and some of the milestones in the recent efforts to revive the culture.
- Activity Master 2: A statistical com-

that of the Pahekas (non-Maoris). Recent attempts to increase educational achievement, health, and economic opportunities for Maoris have met with some success. Many poor Paheka and Polynesian New Zealanders criticize these efforts. They believe the government's focus on Maoris ignores their plight. So it's likely that New Zealand, like all modern nations, will continue to work toward a balance.

Using the Reproducibles

data show that the two nations are alike? Which show they are different?

Building a Specialized Vocabulary employs an unfinished fictional conversation to encourage students to select the appropriate Maori words from context clues. Of course, learning words is only the first step in acquiring a language. Ask students: What besides words must students know to make themselves understood in English? (grammar, correct pronunciation, idiomatic expressions, etc.) Why might many New Zealanders want all students to be required to take Maori lan-

Preparing the Student

Students should be aware that the Maori people of New Zealand actually consist of a complex group of tribes and subtribes with a variety of customs and dialects.

Groups such as the Maoris, Aborigines, and Native Americans are commonly referred to as "indigenous peoples."

TIME PERSPECTIVES

EXPLORING WORLD ISSUES

DAVE E. HOUSER/ CORBIS

In their ancestors' clothes, Maoris do a fierce dance. Land is sacred to Australia's Aborigines (right).

1 Focus

If there are any Native American students in your classroom, you may wish to ask them to share whether they feel they are sometimes treated differently from others because of their culture. Otherwise you may want to ask the class if they feel Native Americans are treated differently from various groups. Ask students to explain their responses. As students know, Native Americans are the indigenous people of North America. This article discusses the indigenous people of New Zealand and Australia. L1

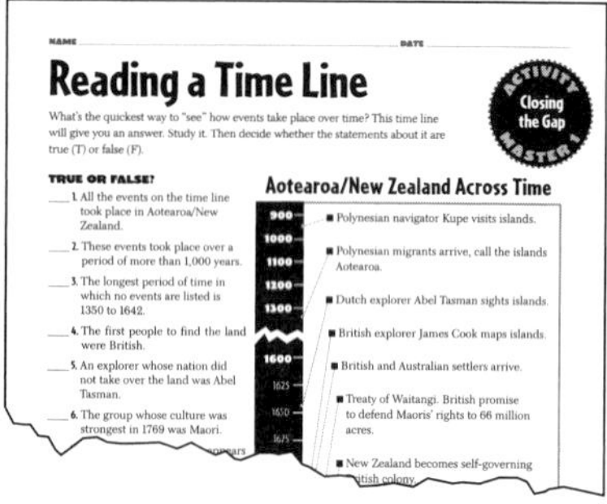

NAME ______ DATE ______

Reading a Time Line

ACTIVITY MASTER 1 — Closing the Gap

What's the quickest way to "see" how events take place over time? This time line will give you an answer. Study it. Then decide whether the statements about it are true (T) or false (F).

TRUE OR FALSE?

____ 1. All the events on the time line took place in Aotearoa/New Zealand.

____ 2. These events took place over a period of more than 1,000 years.

____ 3. The longest period of time in which no events are listed is 1350 to 1642.

____ 4. The first people to find the land were British.

____ 5. An explorer whose nation did not take over the land was Abel Tasman.

____ 6. The group whose culture was strongest in 1769 was Maori.

Aotearoa/New Zealand Across Time

900, 1000, 1100, 1200, 1300, 1600, 1625, 1650, 1675

- Polynesian navigator Kupe visits islands.
- Polynesian migrants arrive, call the islands Aotearoa.
- Dutch explorer Abel Tasman sights islands.
- British explorer James Cook maps islands.
- British and Australian settlers arrive.
- Treaty of Waitangi. British promise to defend Maoris' rights to 66 million acres.
- New Zealand becomes self-governing [British colony.]

Maori Iwi Lands

ANSWER

It is approximately 500 miles. At least part of the journey would have to be over water, which could be treacherous; in addition, much of the land is mountainous, and you would have to pass through other tribes' lands.

The New World Down Under

When Ngataua Omahuru was five years old, he made a big mistake. Ngataua (en•gah•TOW•ah) was a **Maori,** a native New Zealander. He and his family lived in the forest beneath Mount Taranaki, a volcano on New Zealand's North Island.

One day in 1869, Ngataua made the mistake of wandering away from his parents. A band of British soldiers kidnapped him.

New Zealand was a British colony then. Europeans had been settling there in great numbers for more than 40 years. They had moved onto Maori land, paying nothing or very little for it. Maoris who tried to protect their land were often forced off it at gunpoint.

Ngataua ended up in the home of William Fox, the head of the colony's government. Fox and his wife changed Ngataua's name to William Fox. They sent him to English schools. They cut all his links to the Maori world.

A Rich Culture

Through their religion, the Maoris felt close to their ancestors and to nature. They expressed themselves through song, poetry, weaving, woodcarving, and even tattooing. They were brave and clever warriors.

The British, called **Pakehas** (pa•KAY•haws) by the Maoris, did not value the Maori culture. The Pakehas were **ethnocentric,** or convinced that no way

Maori Iwi Lands

About 200 years ago, New Zealand was home to dozens of iwi, or tribes. This map shows where 10 of them were located.

INTERPRETING MAPS

Making Inferences Suppose you were a Ngapuhi living 200 years ago. About how far would you have had to travel to reach the Ngai Tahu? What might have made this trip difficult and dangerous?

746

Team-Teaching Activity

Sociology Have a teacher who's knowledgeable about sociology talk to the class about the importance of preserving different cultures throughout the world. Ask the teacher specifically to discuss the importance of traditions such as celebrating harvests and religious events, as well as birth, death, and marriage rituals. The teacher should emphasize the differences and similarities among cultural observances. For example, many cultures have "coming-of-age" ceremonies for young people. Emphasis should be placed on the fact that celebrating these kinds of events creates common bonds within the community. Have students write a paragraph describing a ritual they have participated in and how it made them feel. L1

 **EE4 Human Systems: Standard 10**

JOHN VAN HASSELT—CORBIS SYGMA

Maori and Pakeha children play together. The gap between the two groups is closing.

PAUL A. SOUDERS/CORBIS

Women in traditional dress perform Maori dances.

BETTINA A. STAMMEN

Aborigine Cathy Freeman lights the Olympic flame in 2000.

AL BELLO—ALLSPORT

of life was better than their own. They believed the Maoris would be better off leaving their ways behind.

That decision guided Pakeha thinking for a century. The Maoris were taught they had nothing in their culture to be proud of. Cut loose from their traditions but not fully accepted by whites, the Maoris fell on hard times.

They are still trying to recover. Compared with Pakehas, Maoris today learn less and earn less. They die more readily from cancer, diabetes, and heart disease.

New Zealanders are trying to close the gaps between the two groups. They are doing it both to be fair and to keep their nation strong. In 50 years, the Maoris will make up almost one-fourth of the country's population.

Australia's Ghosts

A similar issue haunts Australia, 1,200 miles (1,931 km) west of New Zealand. Australia's native people, the **Aborigines,** make up about 1 percent of the population. For tens of thousands of years, all of Australia was theirs.

In 1788 British settlers arrived. They began almost immediately to separate the Aborigines from their culture. They drove the Aborigines off land that they greatly respected, or considered **sacred.** The British killed many who resisted.

The Australian settlers repeated the New Zealand settlers' mistakes. They tried to make the first Australians more like them.

Some of their methods were especially harsh. The government decided that Aborigine children would be better off in the hands of white families. So from 1910 to 1971, as many as 100,000 Aborigine children were removed from their parents. White families adopted most of them. Few of the children ever saw their birth mothers again.

Fighting for Maori Rights

Ngataua Omahuru got to see his mother again. As a young lawyer, he returned to his homeland on business. His real family recognized him, and he saw how badly they had been treated. He devoted the rest of his life to helping the Maoris fight for their **rights,** or benefits guaranteed by law.

It would take the Maoris almost a century to get a fair hearing. By then, Maori foods, words, art, and songs had become part of New Zealand's culture. New Zealanders today realize just how much they would lose if the Maori way of life ever disappeared. ■

EXPLORING THE ISSUES

1. **Making Inferences** Why do you think British settlers believed their way of life was best?
2. **Problem Solving** If you could, what two things would you change to improve the Maoris' lives?

TEACH

Reading Strategy

Identifying Main Ideas

Ask students to identify the main idea of the section titled "The New World Down Under." Write several suggestions and have students discuss them. Students should understand the concept of *ethnocentricity.* **Ask:** **How did ethnocentricity play an important role in the Pakehas's treatment of the Maori?** **L1**

More About the Photos

Olympics **Ask:** **Why do you think Cathy Freeman was chosen to light the flame at the 2000 Olympics?**

NAME ________ DATE ________

Using Comparative Data

ACTIVITY Closing the Gap MASTER 2

How are Australia and New Zealand alike? In what ways are they different? The information on this page will help you find out. Put a check mark next to those items that might make it fun to visit each country.

Quick Facts About Two Nations Down Under

	AUSTRALIA	NEW ZEALAND
Land area	Slightly smaller than mainland U.S.	About the size of Colorado
Lowest point	Lake Eyre (52 ft. below sea level)	Pacific Ocean (0 ft.)
Highest Point	Mt. Kosciuszko (7,310 ft.)	Mt. Cook (12,316 ft.)
Population (2000 approx.)	19 million	4 million
Pop. Under 15 years old	4 million	864,000
Nickname for Citizens	Aussie	Kiwi
Ethnic [illegible]	European 92%, Asian 7%,	European 79%, Maori 10%, Pacific Islander 4%, Asian, others 7%

EXPLORING THE ISSUES

ANSWERS

1. *Possible answers:* the Maori culture was less advanced in their use of technology; their dress, customs, and manners might have seemed "improper" by British standards of the time.
2. Answers might include better health care, education, and job training.

Critical Thinking Activity

Understanding Cause and Effect Tell students that for about a hundred years after their arrival, the Pakehas continually told young Maoris that the Maori way of life, including its language, religion, and traditions, was inferior to European culture. **Ask:** **How do you think this affected the way these young people felt about themselves? How do you think it might affect their success in society?** Have students research an indigenous group other than Maoris or Aborigines. They should then write a report about how these groups were treated by outsiders who came to their lands, how it affected their culture and people, and what steps have been taken to improve their situation. **L2**

EE4 Human Systems: Standards 10, 13

Recommended Internet Sites

www.maori.org.nz
This Web site contains Maori history, examples of art and music, and a wide range of other information, along with links to related sites.

www.un.org/cyberschoolbus/
Click on "Indigenous People" to find teaching units on indigenous people, including cultural information, a discussion of their rights, and even a presentation on Maori schools.

www.aboriginalaustralia.com/
This Web site contains examples of Aboriginal art, discussions of culture, spirituality, sports, and other interesting information.

More About the Photos

Maoris Ask: Do you think these children would prefer wearing traditional clothing or Western-style clothing? Why?

EXPLORING THE ISSUES

ANSWERS

1. If the government chooses not to enforce a law (typically because the majority of people do not want it enforced), the law might as well not exist.
2. Many settlers did not agree with the treaty and routinely violated it. In order to enforce it, the government would have to go against British settlers.

TIME PERSPECTIVES

Broken Promises

Around noon on February 6, 1840, about 75 people stood under a tent in the coastal hamlet of Waitangi, New Zealand. The gathering included Maori chiefs, British settlers, missionaries, and military men.

They were there to sign a treaty. The treaty gave Great Britain the right to rule New Zealand. It gave the Maoris Great Britain's promise to protect them and their land.

The deal made sense to the Maoris. Shady businessmen had begun grabbing Maori land. The chiefs felt that Britain's military muscle was the only thing that could stop the thefts.

BETTMANN/CORBIS

▲ Maori children in traditional dress

Founding Charter

The **Treaty of Waitangi** became New Zealand's founding document. It is as important to New Zealanders as the U.S. Constitution is to Americans. It granted British citizenship to the Maoris. It also described how Maoris and European settlers would share responsibility for New Zealand.

But an agreement is only as strong as the will to enforce it. Greedy settlers took control of New Zealand's government. They used small conflicts as excuses to take over huge pieces of Maori land.

The Maoris tried to embarrass the Pakehas into living up to the treaty. They plowed up the lawns of rich settlers who lived on stolen land. They met Pakeha troops with singing children who offered the soldiers bread.

But in the end nothing, not even the support of many white settlers, could keep the Maoris from losing more land. **Waitangi Day** is a national holiday in New Zealand. Many Maoris refuse to celebrate it, and few people wonder why. ■

EXPLORING THE ISSUES

1. **Explaining** What does the sentence "An agreement is only as strong as the will to enforce it" mean?
2. **Making Inferences** Why might it have been hard for Great Britain's government to live up to its side of the agreement?

748

Differentiated Instruction

Meeting Special Needs: Visual/Spatial
The Maoris make extensive use of skin art, especially tattoos, which they call *kiri tuhi.* In many instances, both the application of the tattoo and its design have sacred meanings. Have students use reference books and the Internet to determine the types of symbols used and what they represent. Then have students draw examples of Maori tattoos on paper. They may want to combine several different symbols in their artwork. L1

Refer to *Inclusion for the Middle School Social Studies Classroom Strategies and Activities* in the TCR.

TIME REPORTS

Closing the Gap

How do you fix a problem that began some 200 years ago? New Zealanders have three answers. They hope to keep the Maori culture alive. They want Maoris to have the skills they need to succeed. And they want to pay the **iwi,** or tribes, for land their ancestors lost to the British colonists.

Maoritanga, the Maori way of life, is in trouble. Few people speak the Maori language. To help more people learn it, schools have begun to teach it. They also teach Maori traditions, along with Maori arts and crafts, music, and dance. Maoris now have an "all-Maori" TV channel too.

Prescription for Success

Equipping Maoris to succeed is another challenge. The government calls its solution "closing the gap"—in skills, wages, housing, and health care. Maoris are being encouraged to stay in school longer, so that they can find and keep good jobs.

The land issue is difficult. The government can't return land to the Maoris that it doesn't own without hurting the people who live on it now. The Maoris will be paid for lost land and other lost "treasures," such as fishing rights.

By 2001, the Waitangi Tribunal had awarded several iwi a total of $300 million. The tribunal, or claims court, won't finish its work until around 2012.

"The process [of sorting through Maori claims] is about more than money," one panel member said. "It is about renewing a relationship that was intended to be based on trust."

That was the spirit of the Treaty of Waitangi. This time, New Zealanders are determined to make it work.

▲ This is New Zealand's Prime Minister Helen Clark in 2001. New Zealand was the first land to let all women vote.

EXPLORING THE ISSUE

1. **Explaining** What does the title of this article mean? Where is the gap, and why do you think it exists?
2. **Drawing Conclusions** Why might some Maoris be unhappy with the Waitangi Tribunal's decisions?

Evaluating Information
Ask students to list the solutions New Zealanders have for rectifying past mistreatment of the Maoris. Then have students discuss and evaluate the methods New Zealanders are using to achieve these solutions. L2

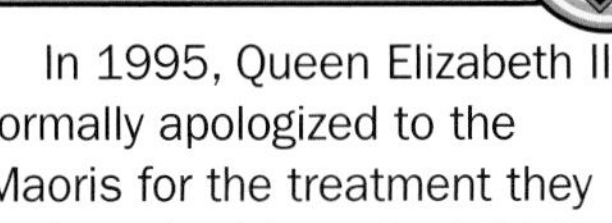

Did You Know?

In 1995, Queen Elizabeth II formally apologized to the Maoris for the treatment they had received from the British.

EXPLORING THE ISSUE

ANSWERS

1. The title means that the government of New Zealand is trying to provide equal wages, equal education, and equal treatment under the law for Maoris and Pakehas. In the past, Pakehas treated Maoris as inferiors, took their land, and discouraged their culture from flourishing.
2. The tribunal is compensating iwi with cash awards instead of returning the land that was taken from them.

Interdisciplinary Activity

Art Have students find a work of art by Maoris or Aborigines that transcends the boundaries of those cultures or societies and conveys a universal theme. Samples of artwork can be found in reference books and on the Internet. They should then write a brief report discussing the background of the work and what it means to them. The report should include illustrations and discuss what the artwork reveals about the Maori or Aborigine culture or religious beliefs. Students may work individually or in small groups. You may want to have the student examine music, literature, or poetry rather than works of visual art. L2

EE4 Human Systems: Standard 10

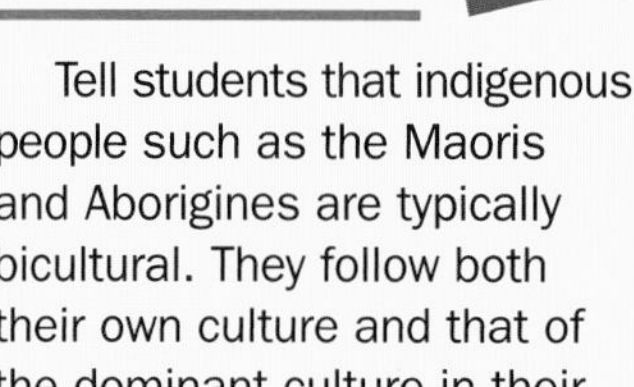

Current Events Journal

Tell students that indigenous people such as the Maoris and Aborigines are typically bicultural. They follow both their own culture and that of the dominant culture in their society.

Many people in America are multicultural, participating in traditions from various backgrounds. Have students write about two or three events or holidays from different cultures that they or people they know celebrate.

EXPLORING THE ISSUE

ANSWERS

1. *Possible answers:* Many people see the United States as a country where they can have freedoms and be successful if they work hard and have the needed skills, no matter what their ethnic background is.
2. Titles will vary.

Did You Know

The Waitangi Tribunal is governed by the expression *Kia puta ki te whai ao ki te ao marama,* meaning "From the world of darkness, moving into the world of light."

Bridging the Gaps at Home: What Can One Person Do?

Ngataua Omahuru, the Maori who was raised in the Pakeha world, did a lot to help his people. He was successful in part because he knew both worlds well.

Americans are fortunate to live in a country that has many cultures. But how many of us take the time to really understand another culture? If we did, we could help bridge the gaps that often keep Americans apart.

▲ **Auckland, with 400,000 people, is New Zealand's largest city.**

Here's one way to start. First, choose an immigrant group that you would like to learn more about. You'll have a lot of choices, because all Americans have immigrant roots. And that includes Native Americans, whose ancestors came from Asia thousands of years ago.

Detective Work

Second, get together with a couple of your classmates who share your interest in this group. As a team, find out all you can about it. One person could research when members of the group came to the United States in large numbers. Another team member could look into whether a particular event prompted them to leave their homeland at that time. Here are more questions for your team to consider: How did Americans view the newcomers? How have those views changed? How do members of this group see themselves today—as members of an ethnic group, as Americans, or as both? How has this group changed the way Americans define themselves?

Share your findings with the rest of the class. Write an article that summarizes your findings for a school newspaper or a Web page. Create a poster that depicts what you learned about this immigrant group. Display the poster at your school or local library. By doing so, you will help others appreciate the glittering mosaic of American life. ■

EXPLORING THE ISSUE

1. **Making Generalizations** In 2001, one of every 10 Americans had been born in another country. Why do you think the United States looks attractive to people from other countries?
2. **Cause and Effect** Write a new title for this *TIME Reports* feature. Share it with your classmates. Explain why you think your title fits the story.

Your Government and You

Explain the following situation: For more than 100 years, the U.S. government has held millions of acres of Native American land in trust accounts. As the trustee, the government owed the money that it received for timber sales and for leasing mineral and grazing rights to Native Americans. However, officials in the Departments of the Treasury and Interior have testified that the government has lost, misplaced, or mismanaged billions of dollars in revenue from Native American lands. In 1996 Eloise Cobell, a Native American representative, sued the Department of the Interior. However, as of 2003, the Department of the Interior still had not accounted for the lost funds or made any offers to compensate Native Americans. **Ask:** **How might the U.S. treatment of Native Americans compare to New Zealand's treatment of Maoris? L2**

EE4 Human Systems: Standard 13

REVIEW AND ASSESS

UNDERSTANDING THE ISSUE

1. **Defining Key Terms** Write definitions for the following terms: *Maori, Pakeha, ethnocentric, Aborigine, sacred, rights, Treaty of Waitangi, Waitangi Day, iwi, Maoritanga.*
2. **Writing to Inform** Write a short article describing the history of the Treaty of Waitangi. Use at least five of the terms listed above.
3. **Writing to Persuade** Why is it important to respect other cultures? Write a short article to support your view, using the experiences of New Zealand and Australia as examples.

INTERNET RESEARCH ACTIVITY

4. With your teacher's help, use Internet resources to learn more about New Zealand. Read about the history of the Maori language. Read about the Maori Language Commission, and what it does. How important is language to a culture's survival? Write a short essay answering that question, using facts you find in your search.
5. With your teacher's help, use Internet resources to find information on Maori food. Try to find specific sites that list Maori recipes in particular. Browse through the traditional recipes. Then write a 250-word article explaining how those recipes provide clues to where the Maoris live, how they cook, and what foods their great-grandparents ate.

BEYOND THE CLASSROOM

6. **Compare the map** on page 746 with the physical/political map of New Zealand on page 742. What does the physical/political map tell you about the land the iwi occupied? In a short essay, describe in general terms what one iwi's traditional land may have looked like.
7. **Visit your school or local library** to find books on the Maoris or Aborigines. (A good but long one is Peter Walker's *The Fox Boy*, which tells Ngataua Omahuru's story.) Prepare an oral book report to deliver in class. Make sure to note the author's point of view.

BETTINA A. STAMMEN

▲ **A banana leaf serves as a plate for traditional Maori food.**

The Making of a Multicultural Society

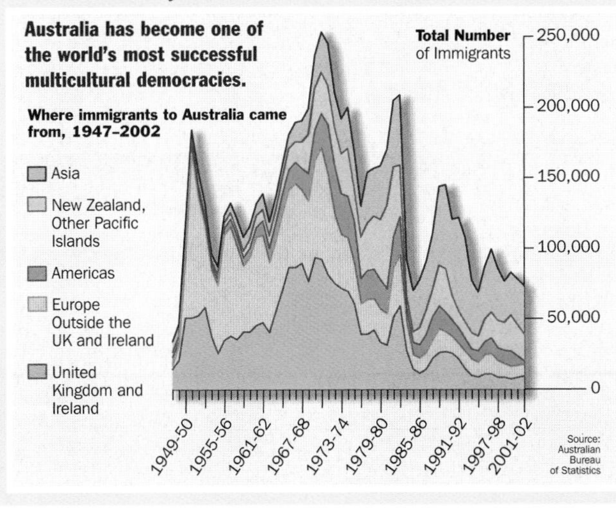

BUILDING GRAPH READING SKILLS

1. **Analyzing the Data** In 2002 there were about 89,000 immigrants. Which two places did most immigrants come from?
2. **Making Inferences** What might make people want to leave their homelands and settle in Australia?

FOR UPDATES ON WORLD ISSUES GO TO www.timeclassroom.com/glencoe

751

TIME REPORTS

3 ASSESS

Have students take the TIME Reports Quiz or do the Alternative Assessment project for this unit provided in the Teacher's Classroom Resources.

NAME ______ DATE ______

Building a Specialized Vocabulary (ACTIVITY Closing the Gap MASTERS)

For most of its history, the Maori language—*te reo Maori*—was only spoken. In the early 1800s, Christian missionaries changed that. They turned the language's sounds into letters.

That written language is taught today. About 120,000 Maoris and 25,000 Pahekas (non-Maoris) can speak Maori really well. That's less than 4 percent of New Zealand's population.

Can you speak *te reo Maori*? To find out, finish the conversation between Paul and Mere (Maori for Mary). Paul has come from England for a visit. Fill in the blanks by selecting Maori words and phrases from the glossary. You might want to share this activity with your family.

Welcome to My Country

Mere: ______, Paul. Welcome to ______. While you are visiting, maybe you can see a ______, an exciting ceremony, or hear an elder chant an ______. Ancestors are very important to Maoris. In the past, Maoris felt their ancestors' spirits when they visited their ______. But today, many Maoris are uncertain which ______ they ... to. We hope that learning

BUILDING GRAPH READING SKILLS

ANSWERS

1. Asia and New Zealand and other Pacific islands
2. *Possible answers:* the desire to start a new life, to pursue Australia's many job opportunities, or to settle on Australian land

4 CLOSE

Reading Strategy

Writing a Paragraph Ask students to write a paragraph starting with this topic sentence: *Preserving the culture of indigenous peoples, such as the Maoris and Aborigines, is important because . . . .*

Culminating Activity

To close this lesson, have students complete the Review and Assess section questions and activities above. Students should use classroom discussion, contextual clues, and their student dictionaries to write definitions for terms. Before assigning the Internet activities, it is recommended that you review your school district policy on student Internet use.

Focus on Debate

For further student understanding of the issue, have students debate the pro and con positions of the following topic: **The government owes compensation to indigenous people for property that it took from their ancestors. L2**

 **EE4 Human Systems: Standard 13**

TEACH

Give students the following situation: Suppose you had seen a new movie that you enjoyed and wanted to tell your friends about it. How would you relate what happened in the movie? Would you tell them everything that happened or only the main events? Most students realize that they would describe only the main events. Explain that an outline is similar to this condensed version of the movie's plot—it contains the main points of a piece of writing. **L1**

Additional Skills Practice

1. **Why are different symbols—Roman numerals, capital letters, and Arabic numbers—used to show different entries?** *(to organize points that belong together; to show things that are of the same level of importance)*
2. **What is the purpose of indenting entries?** *(to show how one level is subordinate to the previous one)*

Additional Skills Resources

 Chapter Skills Review

 Building Geography Skills for Life

GLENCOE TECHNOLOGY

 **Skillbuilder Interactive Workbook CD-ROM, Level 1**

This interactive CD-ROM reinforces student mastery of essential social studies skills.

Study and Writing Skill

Outlining

Outlining may be used as a starting point for writing. The writer begins with the rough shape of the material and gradually fills in the details in a logical manner. You may also use outlining as a method of note taking and organizing information as you read.

Learning the Skill

There are two types of outlines—formal and informal. An informal outline is similar to taking notes—you write words and phrases needed to remember main ideas. In contrast, a formal outline has a standard format. Follow these steps to formally outline information:

- Read the text to identify the main ideas. Label these with Roman numerals.
- Write subtopics under each main idea. Label these with capital letters.
- Write supporting details for each subtopic. Label these with Arabic numerals.
- Each level should have at least two entries that are indented from the level above.
- All entries should use the same grammatical form, whether they are phrases or complete sentences.

▼ A huge sheep herd pours down a ravine on New Zealand's North Island.

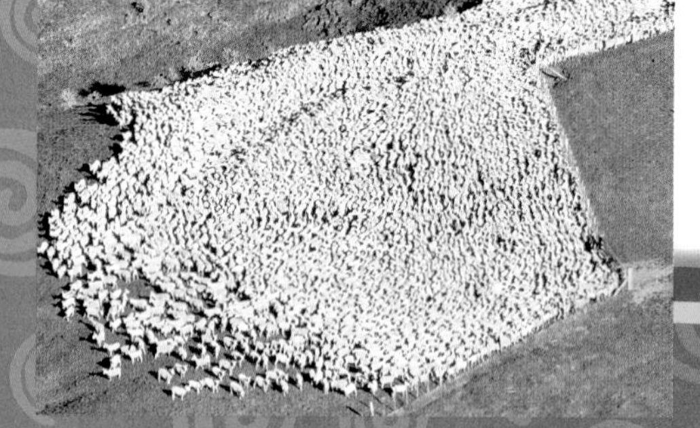

Practicing the Skill

On a separate sheet of paper, copy the following outline for Section 2 of this chapter. Then use your textbook to fill in the missing subtopics and details.

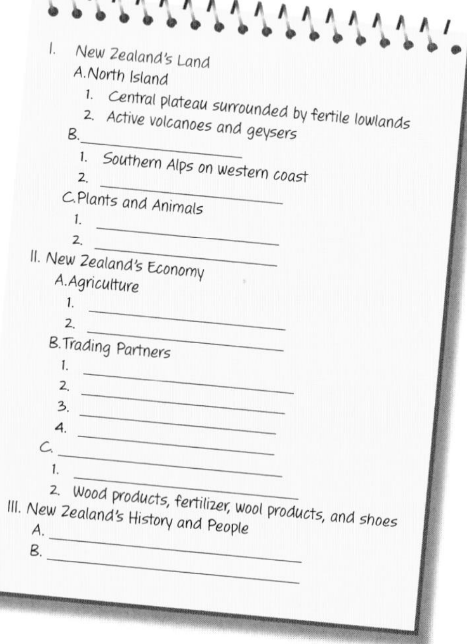

I. New Zealand's Land
  A. North Island
    1. Central plateau surrounded by fertile lowlands
    2. Active volcanoes and geysers
  B. ______
    1. Southern Alps on western coast
    2. ______
  C. Plants and Animals
    1. ______
    2. ______
II. New Zealand's Economy
  A. Agriculture
    1. ______
    2. ______
  B. Trading Partners
    1. ______
    2. ______
    3. ______
    4. ______
  C. ______
    1. ______
    2. Wood products, fertilizer, wool products, and shoes
III. New Zealand's History and People
  A. ______
  B. ______

Applying the Skill

Following the guidelines above, prepare an outline for Section 1 of this chapter.

GO TO Practice key skills with **Glencoe Skillbuilder Interactive Workbook, Level 1.**

Practicing the Skill Answers

I.B.—South Island
I.B.2.—Canterbury Plains in the east
I.C.1.—National symbol is kiwi
I.C.2.—Giant kauri trees
II.A.1.—Wool and lamb meat
II.A.2.—Apples, barley, wheat, and corn
II.B.1–4—Australia; Japan; United States; United Kingdom
II.C.—Mining and Manufacturing
II.C.1—Geothermal energy, hydroelectric power, coal, oil, iron ore, silver, gold
III.A.—Maori; came around 950 to 1150
III.B.—Europeans, mainly British, began arriving in the mid-1800s

Applying the Skill
Check outlines when completed.

Chapter 26 Reading Review

Section 1 Australia—Land Down Under

Terms to Know
coral reef
outback
station
marsupial
boomerang
bush

Main Idea
Both a continent and a country, Australia has many natural resources but relatively few people.

✓Place Dry plateaus and lowland plains spread across most of Australia.

✓History Because Australia has been separated from other continents for millions of years, unusual plants and animals developed here.

✓Economics Most of Australia's wealth comes from minerals and the products of its ranches. It is the world's leading producer and exporter of wool.

✓Culture Australia has relatively few people, most of whom live along the coasts.

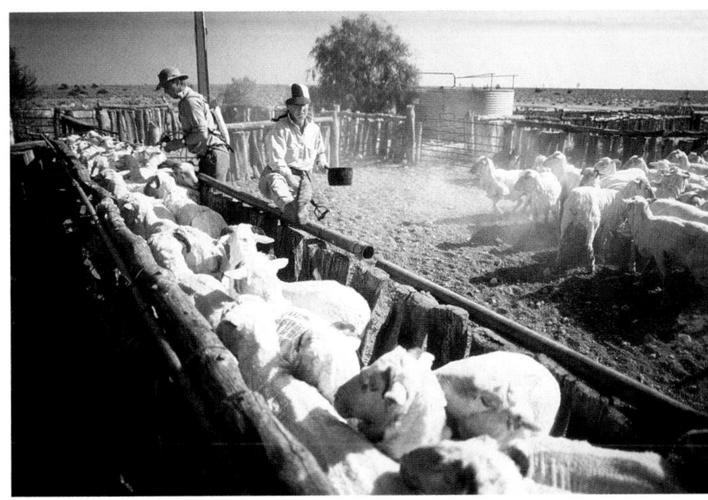

Australian ranchers in the outback ▶

Section 2 New Zealand

Terms to Know
geyser
manuka
fjord
geothermal energy
hydroelectric power

Main Idea
New Zealand is a small country with a growing economy based on trade.

✓Place New Zealand has volcanic mountains, high glaciers, deep-cut fjords, fertile hills, and coastal plains. The climate is mild and wet.

✓Economics New Zealand's economy is built on trade. Sheepherding is an important activity, and wool and lamb meat are major exports.

✓History The people called the Maoris first came to New Zealand about 1,000 years ago.

✓Culture Most people live on North Island, where the country's two main cities can be found.

✓History New Zealand was the first land to allow women to vote.

Reading Review

Use the Chapter 26 Reading Review to preview, review, condense, or reteach the chapter.

Preview/Review

Use the Terms to Know lists to help students review and study.

Activity Assign students a selection of terms from each section and have them write sentences using the assigned words. Have volunteers read their sentences aloud.

Vocabulary PuzzleMaker CD-ROM reinforces the vocabulary terms used in Chapter 26.

The Interactive Tutor Self-Assessment CD-ROM allows students to review Chapter 26 content.

Condense

Have students read the Chapter 26 summary statements.

Guided Reading Activities

Audio Program

Reteach

Reteaching Activity

Reading Essentials and Study Guide

Reading Strategy Read to Write

Writing an Editorial Have students use information in the chapter to write an editorial about how Australia and New Zealand might continue to grow economically. Editorials should include information about the current economic conditions in one of the countries and how these conditions can be improved in order to remain economically healthy. Students should use their textbooks and the Internet to find factual evidence to support their suggestions. Have students share their editorials with the class, and have the class discuss their opinions. L3

Assessment and Activities

GLENCOE TECHNOLOGY

MindJogger Videoquiz
Use MindJogger Videoquiz to review the Chapter 26 content.

Available in DVD and VHS

Using Key Terms

1.	b	6.	j
2.	e	7.	c
3.	h	8.	i
4.	a	9.	f
5.	g	10.	d

Reviewing the Main Ideas

11. because it is in the Southern Hemisphere
12. mining camps and cattle and sheep ranches
13. wool
14. Great Britain
15. about 90 percent
16. to draw people to settle in the outback
17. North Island
18. 1907
19. geothermal energy and hydroelectric power
20. about 10 percent
21. camping, hiking, hunting, boating, and mountain climbing

Chapter 26 Assessment and Activities

Using Key Terms

Match the terms in Part A with their definitions in Part B.

A.

1. boomerang
2. bush
3. station
4. geothermal energy
5. outback
6. *manuka*
7. marsupial
8. hydroelectric power
9. coral reef
10. geyser

B.

a. electricity produced from steam
b. flat, bent, wooden weapon that stuns prey or returns to the thrower
c. mammal that carries its young in a pouch
d. hot spring that shoots hot water into the air
e. rural area in Australia
f. structure formed by the skeletons of small sea animals
g. name for entire inland region of Australia
h. cattle or sheep ranch in Australia
i. electricity generated by flowing water
j. small shrub found in New Zealand

Reviewing the Main Ideas

Section 1 Australia—Land Down Under

11. **Location** Why is Australia called the "Land Down Under"?
12. **Place** For what is the outback used?
13. **Economics** What does Australia lead the world in producing and exporting?
14. **History** What country colonized Australia?
15. **Culture** What percentage of people live in Australia's cities?
16. **Location** Why was Canberra located inland?

Section 2 New Zealand

17. **Location** On which island do most New Zealanders live?
18. **History** When did New Zealand gain its independence from Britain?
19. **Economics** What are two sources of electric power in New Zealand?
20. **Culture** How many New Zealanders have Maori heritage?
21. **Human/Environment Interaction** What leisure activities do New Zealanders enjoy that are made possible by the country's climate?

Australia and New Zealand

Place Location Activity

On a separate sheet of paper, match the letters on the map with the numbered places listed below.

1. Auckland
2. Sydney
3. Tasmania
4. Great Barrier Reef
5. Great Dividing Range
6. Southern Alps
7. Great Artesian Basin
8. Wellington
9. Canberra
10. Melbourne

0 mi. 1,000
0 km 1,000
Miller Cylindrical projection

754

NATIONAL GEOGRAPHIC Place Location Activity

1.	C	6.	H
2.	E	7.	D
3.	I	8.	B
4.	G	9.	J
5.	F	10.	A

Critical Thinking

22. In Australia, the coastal areas are the most fertile. In New Zealand, the interior is mountainous.
23. Diagrams will vary.

Comparing Regions Activity

24. Suggest that students use the Internet or magazines to locate the maps and photographs that they will need. Discuss students' conclusions.

Self-Check Quiz Visit ***The World and Its People*** Web site at twip.glencoe.com and click on **Chapter 26—Self-Check Quizzes** to prepare for the Chapter Test.

Critical Thinking

22. **Understanding Cause and Effect** Why do most Australians and New Zealanders live in coastal areas?
23. **Organizing Information** Create two ovals like these. In the outer ovals, write four facts about each country under its heading. Where the ovals overlap, write three facts that are true of both countries.

Comparing Regions Activity

24. **Geography** Choose one of the physical features found in Australia or New Zealand. You might choose the Great Barrier Reef or the geysers or glaciers of New Zealand. Then choose a physical feature in the United States, such as Death Valley or the Grand Canyon. Create a poster that includes a map, photographs, and facts about each feature. What conclusions can you draw about similarities or differences between the two features?

Mental Mapping Activity

25. **Focusing on the Region** Create a simple outline map of Australia and New Zealand, and then label the following:
    - North Island
    - South Island
    - Auckland
    - Tasman Sea
    - Wellington
    - Darling River
    - Great Artesian Basin
    - Cook Strait

Technology Skills Activity

26. **Using the Internet** Use the Internet to find out more about one of Australia's or New Zealand's cities. Prepare a travel brochure for a tourist who might visit the city. Describe the city's main attractions.

Standardized Test Practice

Directions: Study the graph below, and then answer the question that follows.

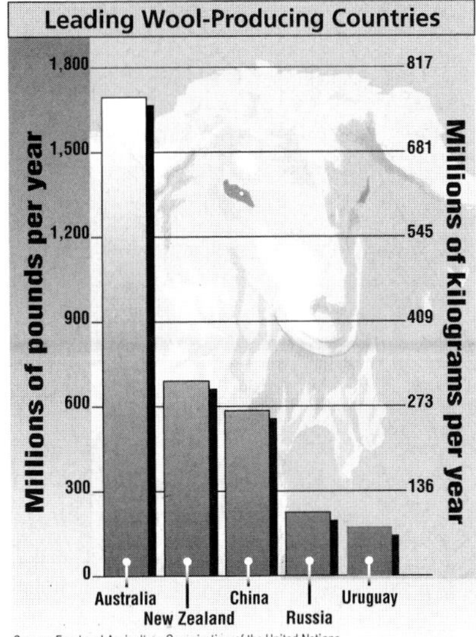

Source: Food and Agriculture Organization of the United Nations.

1. **How much wool does Australia produce per year?**
   - **A** 1,800 pounds
   - **B** 1,800,000 pounds
   - **C** about 1,700 pounds
   - **D** about 1,700,000,000 pounds

Test-Taking Tip: Remember to read the information along the sides of the graph to understand what the bars represent. In addition, eliminate answers that you know are wrong.

Assessment and Activities

Standardized Test Practice

1. D

Tested Objectives:
Reading a graph, analyzing information

Chapter Test Bonus Question

This question may be used for extra credit on the chapter test.

What area on New Zealand's South Island is good for farming? *(Canterbury Plains)*

Have students visit the Web site at twip.glencoe.com to review Chapter 26 and take the Self-Check Quiz.

FOLDABLES™ Study Organizer — Dinah Zike's Foldables

Culminating Activity Have students create a graphic organizer that shows how their predictions might lead to cause-and-effect relationships. Students should explain their graphic organizers to the class.

Mental Mapping Activity

25. This exercise helps students visualize the countries and geographic features they have been studying. Accept all attempts at free-hand mapping that show places in the correct relationship to one another.

Technology Skills Activity

26. Students' brochures could be enhanced with photographs of the city.

Chapter 27 Resources

Note: The following materials may be used when teaching Chapter 27.
Section level support materials are shown at point of use in the margins of the Teacher Wraparound Edition.

Timesaving Tools

TeacherWorks™ All-In-One Planner and Resource Center

- **Interactive Teacher Edition** See the **Interactive Teacher Edition** CD-ROM to electronically integrate your Teacher Wraparound Edition and blackline masters.
- **Interactive Lesson Planner** Organize your week, month, semester, or year with all the lesson helps you need. The **Interactive Lesson Planner** CD-ROM contains all Chapter 27 resources.

Use Glencoe's **Presentation Plus!** multimedia teacher tool to easily present dynamic lessons that visually excite your students. Using Microsoft PowerPoint® you can customize the presentations to create your own personalized lessons.

TEACHING TRANSPARENCIES

Graphic Organizer Transparency 3 L2

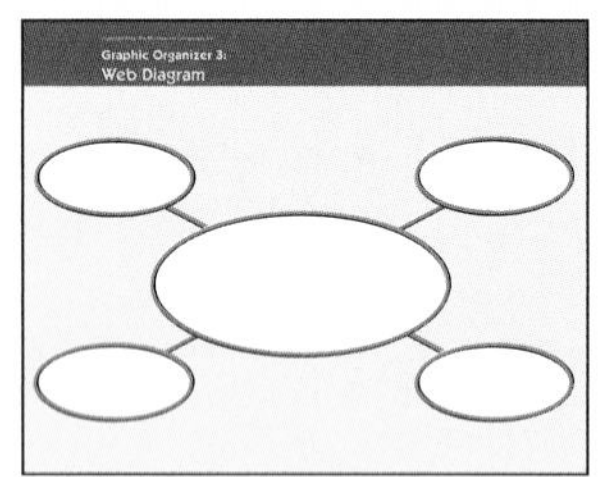

In-text Map Transparency L1

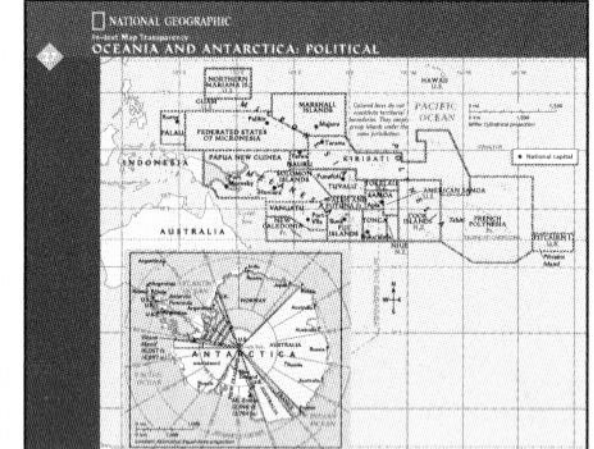

FOLDABLES™ Study Organizer

Dinah Zike's Foldables

Foldables are three-dimensional, interactive graphic organizers that help students practice basic writing skills, review key vocabulary terms, and identify main ideas. Additional chapter activities can be found in the ***Reading and Study Skills Foldables*** booklet.

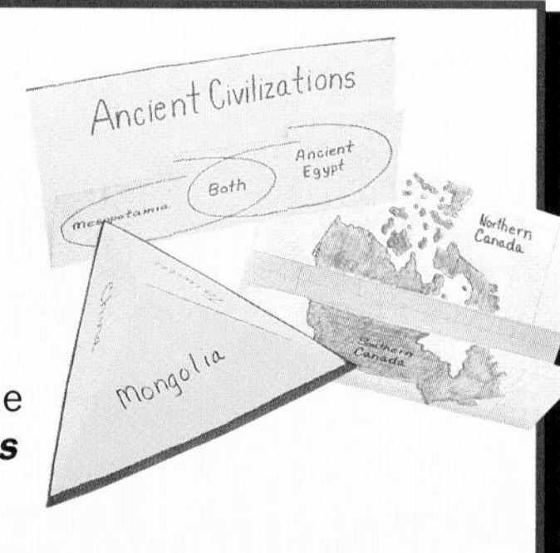

MAP AND GEOGRAPHY SKILLS

Chapter Map Activity L2

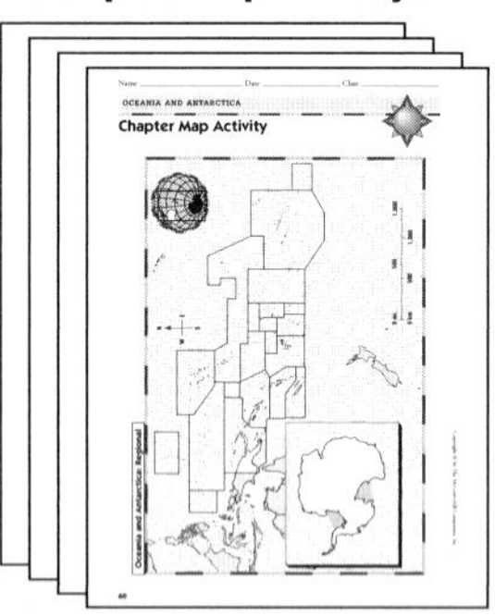

GeoLab Activity L2

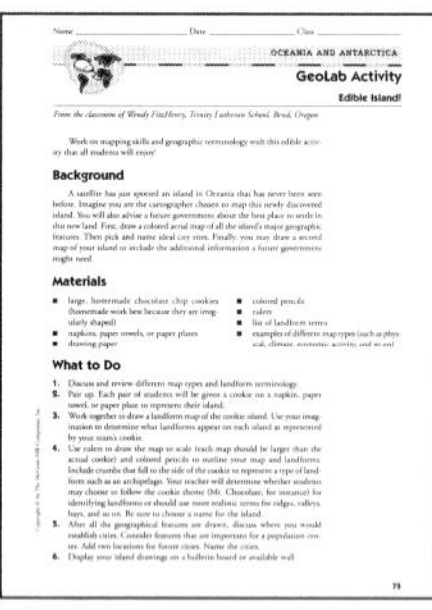

READING SUPPORT

Vocabulary Activity L1

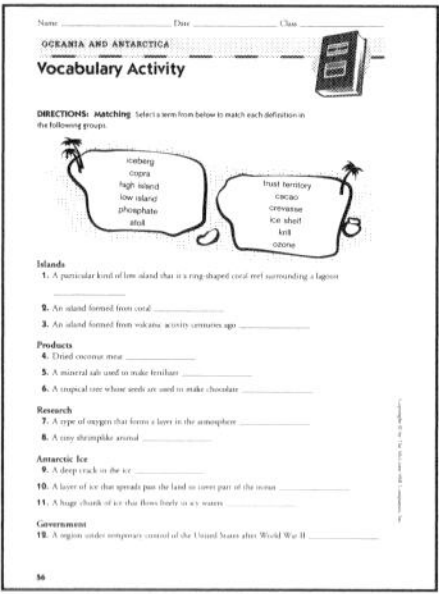

Workbook Activity L1

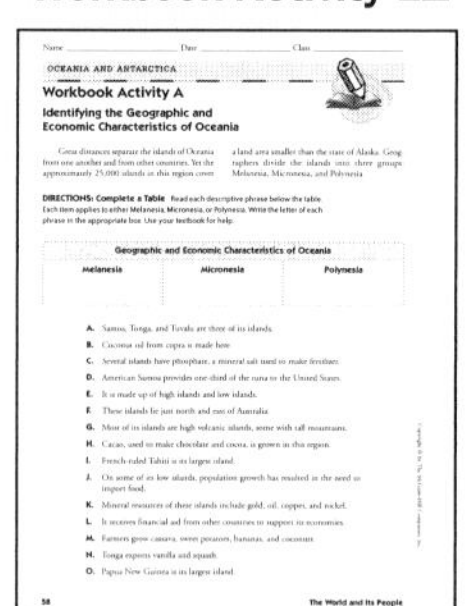

Reading and Writing Skills Activity L1/ELL

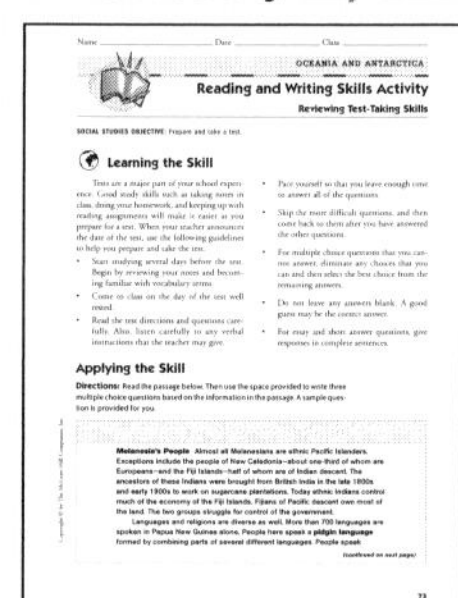

DIFFERENTIATED INSTRUCTION

Use these review and reinforcement materials to help less-proficient readers, English learners, and gifted and talented students.

Reteaching Activity L1

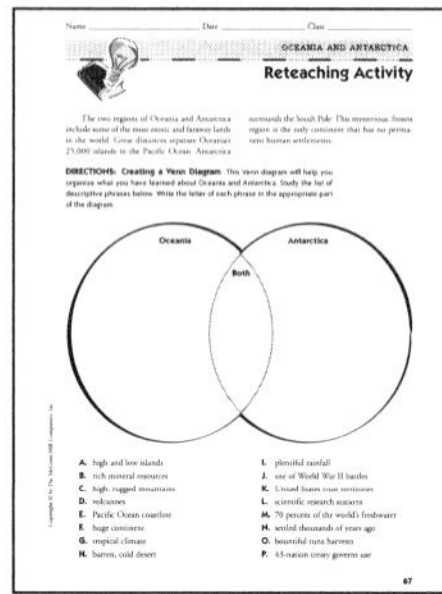

Chapter Skills Review L2

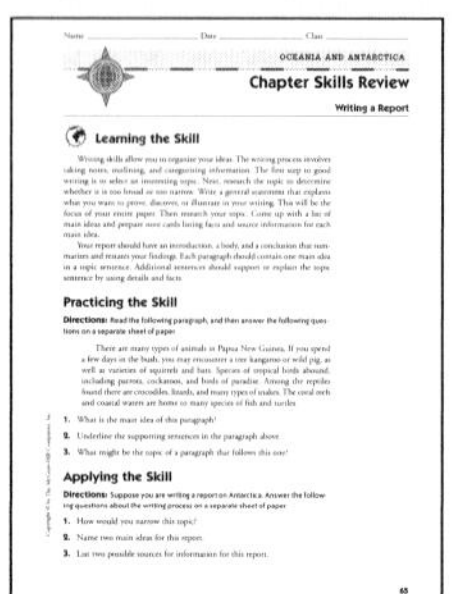

Cooperative Learning Activity L1/ELL

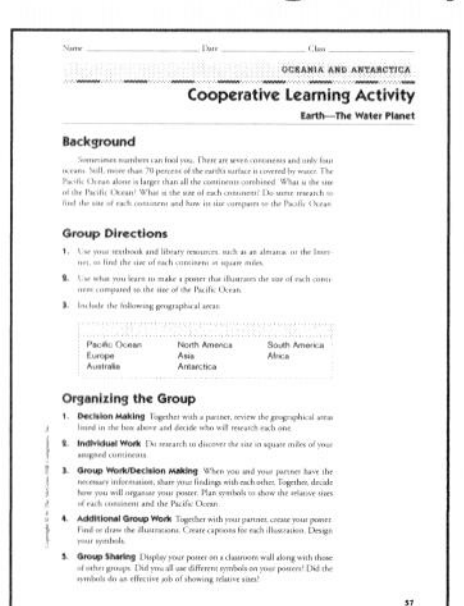

Enrichment Activity L3

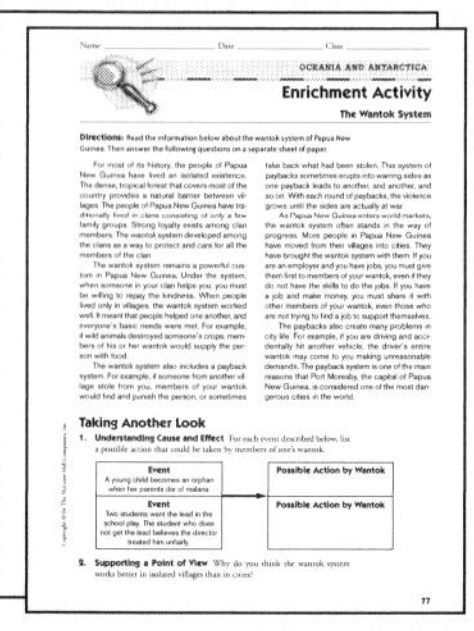

ASSESSMENT

Chapter Test, Form A L2

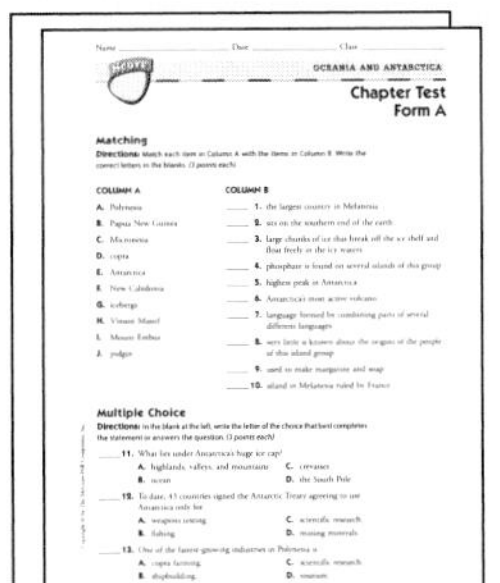

Chapter Test, Form B L2

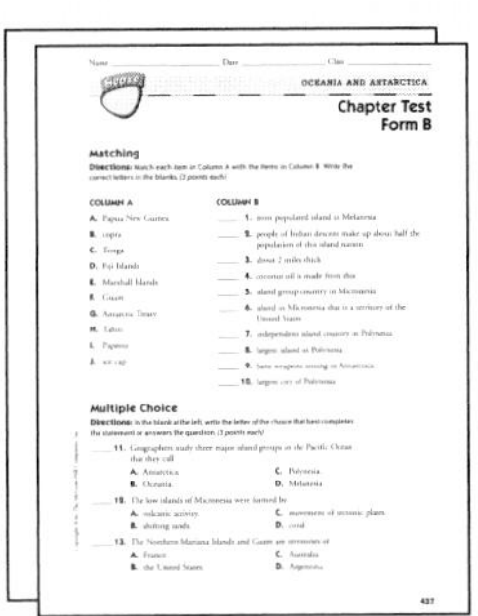

Performance Assessment Activity L1/ELL

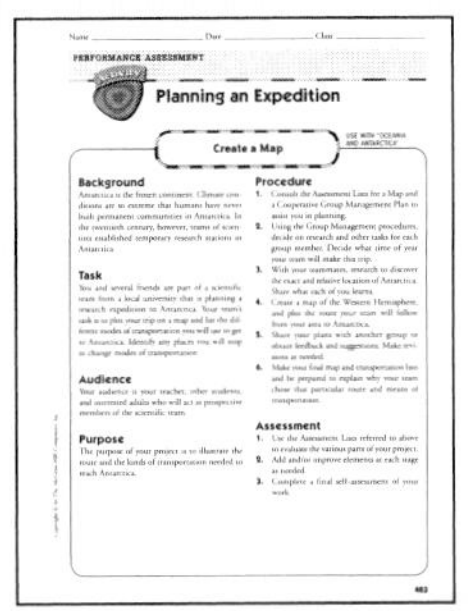

ExamView® Pro Testmaker CD-ROM

STANDARDIZED ASSESSMENT SKILLS

Critical Thinking Skills Activity L2

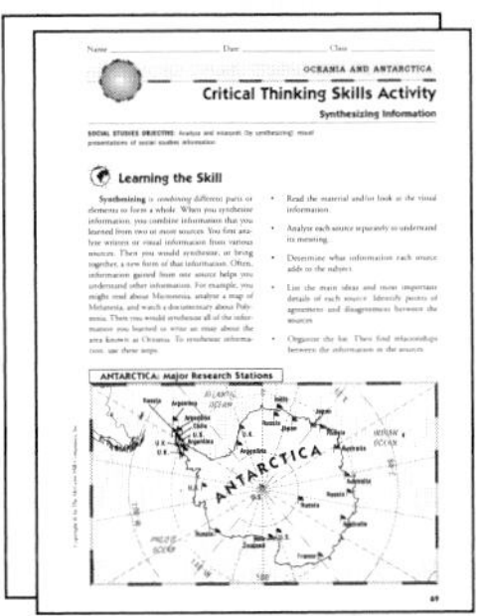

Map and Graph Skills Activity L2

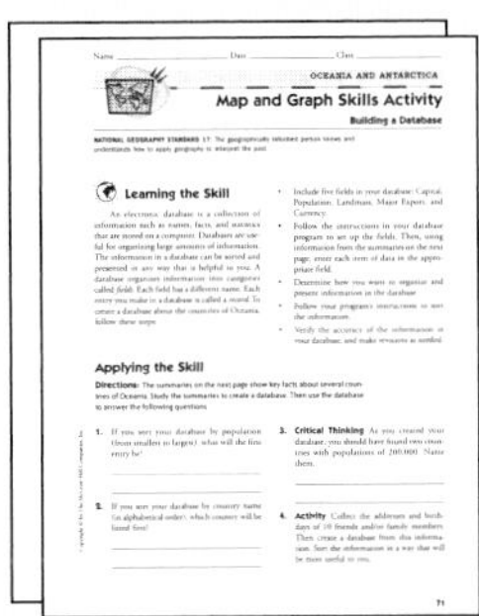

Standardized Test Skills Practice Workbook Activity L2

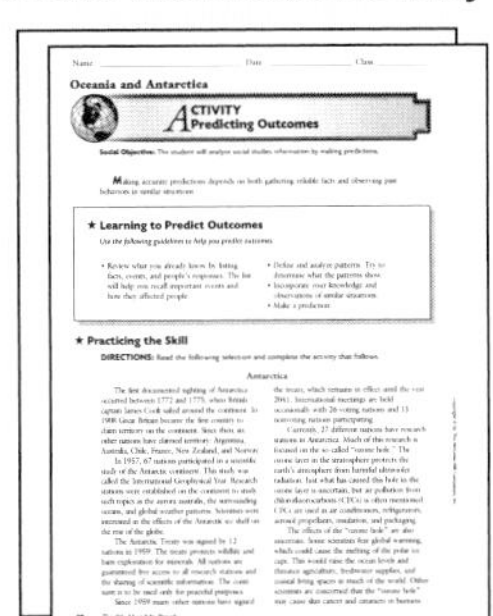

HOME INVOLVEMENT

Take-Home Review Activity L1

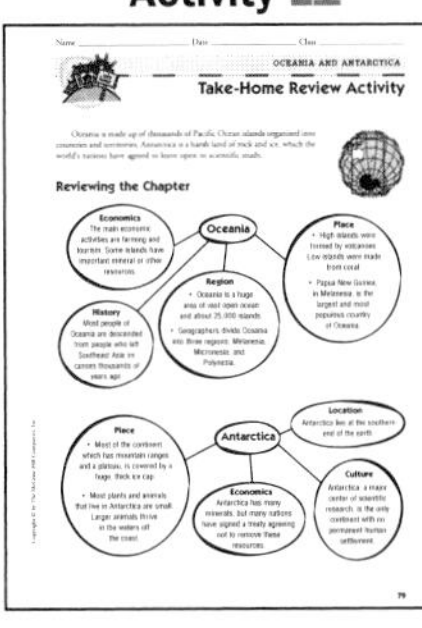

MULTIMEDIA

- National Geographic's The World and Its People
- MindJogger Videoquiz
- Vocabulary PuzzleMaker CD-ROM
- Interactive Tutor Self-Assessment CD-ROM
- ExamView® Pro Testmaker CD-ROM
- TeacherWorks CD-ROM
- StudentWorks CD-ROM
- Skillbuilder Interactive Workbook CD-ROM, Level 1
- Presentation Plus! CD-ROM
- Audio Program

SPANISH RESOURCES

The following Spanish language materials are available in the Spanish Resources binder:

- Spanish Summaries
- Spanish Vocabulary Activities
- Spanish Guided Reading Activities
- Spanish Quizzes and Tests
- Spanish Take-Home Review Activities
- Spanish Reteaching Activities

Meeting National Standards

Geography for Life

The following standards are covered in Chapter 27:

Section 1
- **EE1 The World in Spatial Terms: Standards 1, 3**
- **EE4 Human Systems: Standards 9, 10**
- **EE5 Environment and Society: Standard 14**

Section 2
- **EE3 Physical Systems: Standards 7, 8**
- **EE4 Human Systems: Standards 9, 10, 12, 13**
- **EE5 Environment and Society: Standard 15**
- **EE6 The Uses of Geography: Standard 17**

State and Local Objectives

___

___

Chapter 27 Planning Guide

SECTION RESOURCES

Daily Objectives	Reproducible Resources	Multimedia Resources
Section 1 **Pacific Island Cultures and Economies** **1.** Explain how the three regions of Oceania differ. **2.** Describe how the people of Oceania earn a living.	Reproducible Lesson Plan Daily Lecture and Discussion Notes Note-taking Guide Guided Reading Activity* Reading Essentials and Study Guide* Section Quiz*	Daily Focus Skills Transparency GeoQuiz Transparency In-text Map Transparency Vocabulary PuzzleMaker CD-ROM Interactive Tutor Self-Assessment CD-ROM ExamView® Pro Testmaker CD-ROM Presentation Plus! CD-ROM
Section 2 **The Frozen Continent** **1.** Describe what kinds of life are found in Antarctica. **2.** Explain why scientists study Antarctica.	Reproducible Lesson Plan Daily Lecture and Discussion Notes Note-taking Guide Guided Reading Activity* Reading Essentials and Study Guide* Section Quiz*	Daily Focus Skills Transparency Vocabulary PuzzleMaker CD-ROM Interactive Tutor Self-Assessment CD-ROM ExamView® Pro Testmaker CD-ROM Presentation Plus! CD-ROM MindJogger Videoquiz

00:00 **Out of Time?** Assign the **Reading Essentials and Study Guide*** for this chapter.

*Also available in Spanish

KEY TO ABILITY LEVELS

Teaching strategies have been coded for varying learning styles and abilities.

L1 **BASIC** activities for all students
L2 **AVERAGE** activities for average to above-average students
L3 **CHALLENGING** activities for above-average students
ELL **ENGLISH LANGUAGE LEARNER** activities

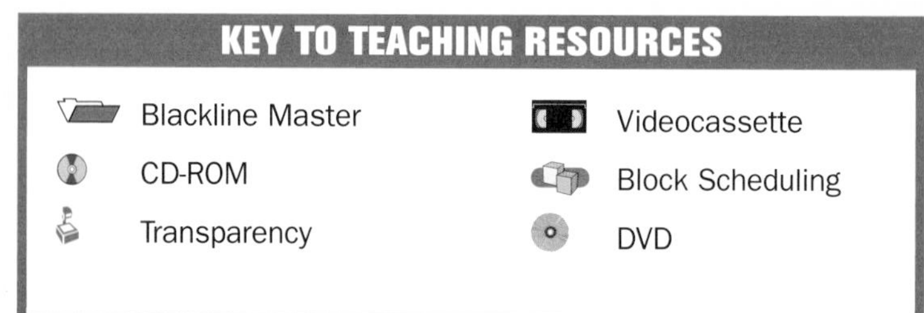

Teacher to Teacher

Joseph Turso
Wayne Hills High School
Wayne, New Jersey

Coloring Book

Have students make a coloring book about an island in Oceania. Have them research the island on the Internet or in encyclopedias to find such information as the island's landscape, climate, foods, clothing, economic activities, religions, festivals, types of money, and types of homes. Also have them research what teenagers on the island do for fun and learn in school. Then have students sketch simple drawings for each piece of information, with one sketch per page. At the bottom of the page, students should write a caption summarizing the sketch. Remind students to create a title page for the coloring book before binding the pages together. Donate the coloring books to an elementary school.

Meeting Special Needs

In addition to the Differentiated Instruction strategies found in each section, the following resources are also suitable for your special needs students:

- ***ExamView® Pro Testmaker CD-ROM*** allows teachers to tailor tests by reducing answer choices.
- The ***Audio Program*** includes the entire narrative of the student edition so that less-proficient readers can listen to the words as they read them.
- The ***Reading Essentials and Study Guide*** provides the same content as the student edition but is written two grade levels below the textbook.
- ***Guided Reading Activities*** give less-proficient readers point-by-point instructions to increase comprehension as they read each textbook section.
- ***Enrichment Activities*** include a stimulating collection of readings and activities for gifted and talented students.

NATIONAL GEOGRAPHIC TEACHER'S CORNER

Index to National Geographic Magazine:

The following articles may be used for research relating to this chapter:

- "Inside the Volcano," by Donovan Webster, November 2000.
- "Deep Sea Vents," by Richard A. Lutz, October 2000.
- "New Caledonia," by Thomas O'Neill, May 2000.

National Geographic Society Products:

To order the following products for use with this chapter, call National Geographic Society at 1-800-368-2728:

- *Antarctica* (Video)
- *Healing the Earth* (Video)
- *PicturePack: Geography of Oceania and Antarctica* (Transparencies)

NGS ONLINE

Access National Geographic's Web site for current events, activities, links, interactive features, and archives.
www.nationalgeographic.com

Find the latest coverage of geography in the news, atlas updates, cartographic activities with interactive maps, an online map store, and links at www.nationalgeographic.com/maps

SOCIAL STUDIES Online

Use our Web site for additional resources. All essential content is covered in the Student Edition.

You and your students can visit twip.glencoe.com, the Web site companion to *The World and Its People.* This innovative integration of electronic and print media offers your students a wealth of opportunities. The student text directs students to the Web site for the following options:

- Chapter Overviews
- Student Web Activities
- Self-Check Quizzes
- Textbook Updates

Answers are provided for you in the Web Activity Lesson Plan. Additional Web resources and Interactive Tutor puzzles are also available.

Introducing
Chapter 27

Social Studies Online

Introduce students to chapter content and key terms by having them access Chapter Overview 27 at twip.glencoe.com

Chapter Objectives

1. Identify the regions of Oceania.
2. Describe the economies and peoples of Oceania.
3. Discuss the scientific importance of Antarctica.

GLENCOE TECHNOLOGY

NATIONAL GEOGRAPHIC

The World and Its People Video Program

Chapter 28 Oceania and Antarctica

The following segments enhance the study of this chapter:

- **Antarctic Vacation**
- **Ice**
- **The Razor**

MindJogger Videoquiz

Use MindJogger Videoquiz to preview the Chapter 27 content.

Both programs available in DVD and VHS

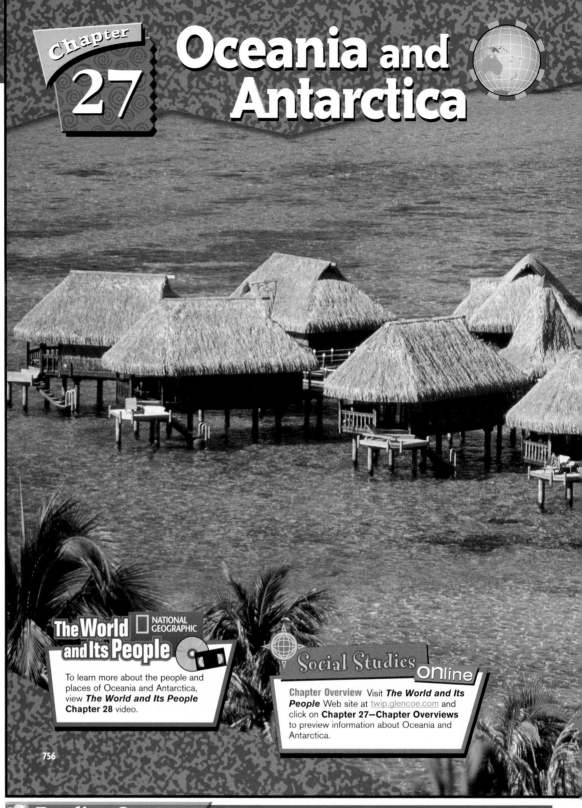

Chapter 27 Oceania and Antarctica

The World and Its People NATIONAL GEOGRAPHIC

To learn more about the people and places of Oceania and Antarctica, view ***The World and Its People* Chapter 28** video.

Social Studies Online

Chapter Overview Visit ***The World and Its People*** Web site at twip.glencoe.com and click on **Chapter 27—Chapter Overviews** to preview information about Oceania and Antarctica.

756

Reading Strategy — Purpose for Reading

The **Chapter Tour** is an important tool for generating student interest, previewing material to be covered, and identifying the author's craft. Have students skim the chapter and write about which section, pictures, and highlights are most interesting to them. Have them share the information with a partner and then with the entire class. Conclude the activity by telling students that they will be learning about Oceania and Antarctica. L1

FOLDABLES™ Study Organizer

Summarizing Information Make this foldable and use it to help you summarize what you learn about Oceania and Antarctica.

Step 1 Stack four sheets of paper, one on top of the other. On the top sheet of paper, trace a large circle.

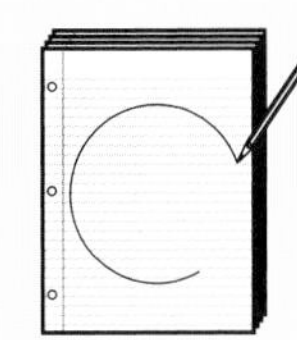

Step 2 With the papers still stacked, cut out all four circles at the same time.

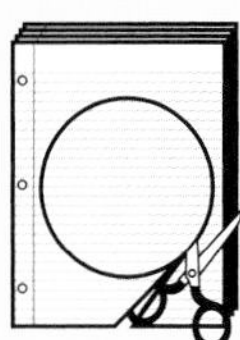

Step 3 Staple the paper circles together at one point around the edge.

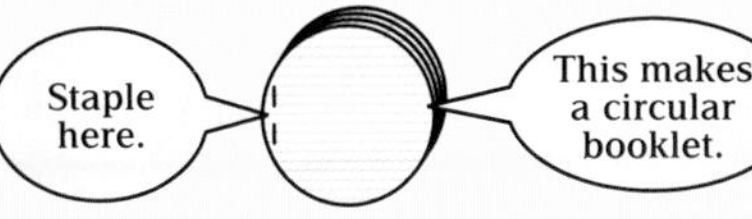
Staple here.
This makes a circular booklet.

Step 4 Label the front circle **Oceania** and take notes on the pages that open to the right. Flip the book over and label the back **Antarctica.** Take notes on the pages that open to the right.

Oceania

Reading and Writing As you read the chapter, write facts about the people and geography of Oceania and Antarctica in the appropriate places of your circular foldable booklet.

▲ Houses on stilts in Moorea Lagoon, Tahiti

Why It Matters

A World of Water

The water world of the Pacific Ocean covers one-third of the earth. It is larger than all the world's land areas combined. Tens of thousands of islands lie in this remote part of the globe. As technology shrinks the world, many societies of this region are struggling to maintain their cultural identities.

About the Photo

Ask students to study the photograph and use it to discuss how humans interact with and are affected by their environment. Why do the Tahitians build houses on stilts? Explain that the houses are built high off the ground because of the ocean tides. Some people from Oceania have become very adept at using stilts themselves. To avoid climbing ladders endlessly when visiting other houses, some islanders move among the houses on stilts of their own. In Tahiti, villages used to hold stilt races on festival days. Boys and girls of all ages would run like storks along the beaches.

Introducing Chapter 27

FOLDABLES™ Study Organizer **Dinah Zike's Foldables**

Purpose This activity requires students to create a booklet to organize information from the chapter. Students group information from the chapter into categories, in effect comparing the people and geography of Oceania and Antarctica.

Have students complete the ***Reading and Study Skills Foldables*** for this chapter.

Why It Matters

Global warming has a potentially devastating effect on Pacific Ocean island nations. Some islands may disappear entirely. Have students write and perform a skit about an island village that is threatened by rising sea levels. Assign different roles to be portrayed—some that want to stay and preserve the village, some that are forced to move, and some that want governments to solve the problem for them.

Focus

Section Objectives

1. Explain how the three regions of Oceania differ.
2. Describe how the people of Oceania earn a living.

BELLRINGER
Skillbuilder Activity

Project transparency and have students answer the question.

Daily Focus Skills Transparency

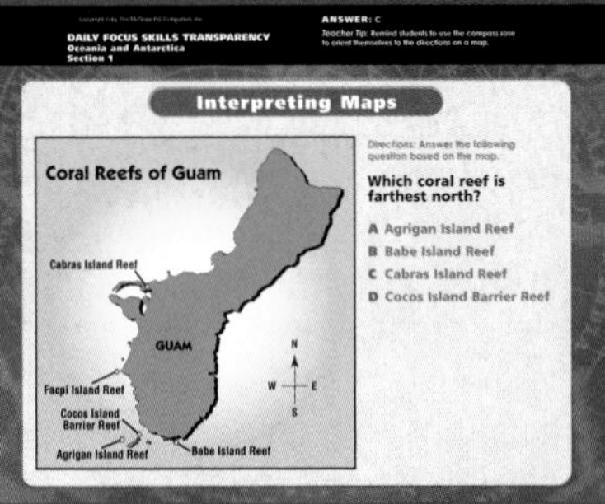

Reading Preview

Activating Prior Knowledge Ask students how many islands they think there are in Oceania. Then have them read the first paragraph of the section to find the answer.

Preteaching Vocabulary Ask students what they think *pidgin language* means. Then have them look up the words in the section to verify their guesses.

Guide to Reading

Main Idea

Oceania is made up of thousands of Pacific Ocean islands organized into countries and territories.

Terms to Know

- cacao
- copra
- pidgin language
- high island
- low island
- atoll
- phosphate
- trust territory

Reading Strategy

Create a chart like this one. In the right column, write two facts about each region.

Region	Facts
Melanesia	
Micronesia	
Polynesia	

Section 1

Pacific Island Cultures and Economies

NATIONAL GEOGRAPHIC **Exploring Our World**

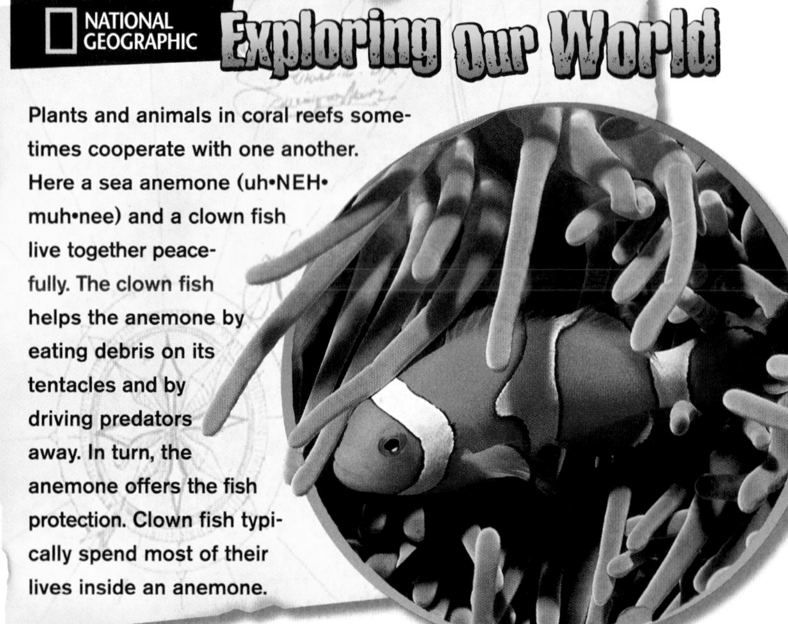

Plants and animals in coral reefs sometimes cooperate with one another. Here a sea anemone (uh•NEH•muh•nee) and a clown fish live together peacefully. The clown fish helps the anemone by eating debris on its tentacles and by driving predators away. In turn, the anemone offers the fish protection. Clown fish typically spend most of their lives inside an anemone.

Oceania is a culture region that includes about 25,000 islands in the Pacific Ocean. Geographers group Oceania into three main island regions—**Melanesia**, **Micronesia**, and **Polynesia.**

Melanesia

The islands of Melanesia lie across the **Coral Sea** from Australia. The largest country is **Papua New Guinea** (PA•pyu•wuh noo GIH•nee). Slightly larger than California, the country's 5.5 million people also make it Oceania's most populous island. Southeast of Papua New Guinea are three other independent island countries: the **Solomon Islands,** the **Fiji** (FEE•jee) **Islands,** and **Vanuatu** (VAN•WAH•TOO). Near these countries is **New Caledonia,** a group of islands ruled by France.

Rugged mountains and dense rain forests cover Melanesia's islands. Narrow, fertile plains hug the coastlines. Most of Melanesia has a tropical climate with temperatures between 70°F (21°C) and 80°F (27°C).

Section Resources

Reproducible Masters
- Reproducible Lesson Plan
- Daily Lecture and Discussion Notes
- Note-taking Guide
- Guided Reading Activity
- Reading Essentials and Study Guide
- Section Quiz

Transparencies
- Daily Focus Skills Transparency
- GeoQuiz Transparency
- In-text Map Transparency

Multimedia
- Vocabulary PuzzleMaker CD-ROM
- Interactive Tutor Self-Assessment CD-ROM
- Presentation Plus! CD-ROM
- ExamView® Pro Testmaker CD-ROM

Most Melanesians work on subsistence farms. Others work on farms that produce coffee, palm oil, and cacao for export. **Cacao** is a tropical tree whose seeds are used to make chocolate. Sugarcane is exported as sugar and molasses. Coconut oil from **copra,** or dried coconut meat, is used to make margarine, soap, and other products.

Some Melanesian islands hold rich mineral resources such as gold, oil, copper, and nickel. Several islands export timber and fish. Melanesia is also becoming a popular tourist destination.

Melanesia's People Almost all Melanesians are ethnic Pacific Islanders. Two island groups hold exceptions. About one-third of New Caledonia's people are Europeans. In the Fiji Islands, almost half of the people are of Indian descent. The ancestors of these Indians were brought from British India in the late 1800s and early 1900s to work on sugarcane plantations. Today ethnic Indians control much of the

NATIONAL GEOGRAPHIC

Oceania and Antarctica: Political

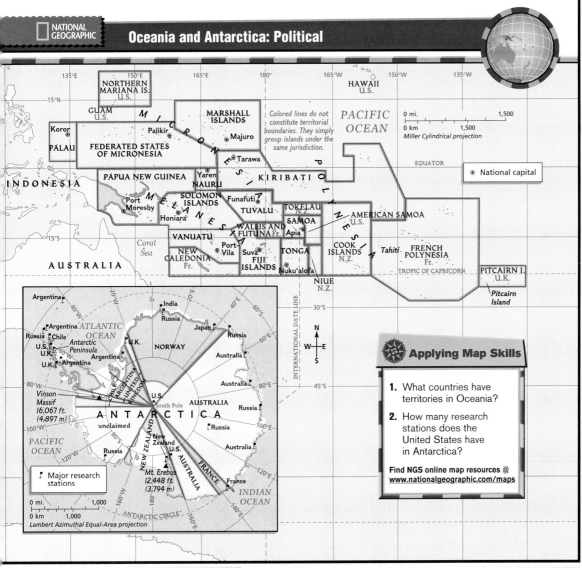

Colored lines do not constitute territorial boundaries. They simply group islands under the same jurisdiction.

⊛ National capital

Miller Cylindrical projection

Major research stations

Lambert Azimuthal Equal-Area projection

Applying Map Skills

1. What countries have territories in Oceania?
2. How many research stations does the United States have in Antarctica?

Find NGS online map resources @ www.nationalgeographic.com/maps

Reading Strategy — Reading the Text

Paraphrasing Remind students to paraphrase the information presented in the section. Comprehension and retention are greatly improved when one can explain the information in one's own words. Tell students to paraphrase chunks of information in the section rather than waiting until they have read the entire chapter so that they will remember the main ideas and supporting details more easily. Restating the main ideas in one's own words is one of the most important investments of time a reader can make. L1

*Use the **Reading Skills Handbook** for more reading strategies.*

Chapter 27

Section 1, pages 758–762

2 TEACH

Reading Strategy

Making Comparisons
Have students use the Nations of the World Databank in their textbooks to identify the countries that rank in the bottom 10 (180th to 190th) for Gross National Product (GNP). **Ask:** **What world region dominates this list?** *(Oceania)* Have students pose and answer five questions comparing other data about the countries on their lists. L1

Daily Lecture and Discussion Notes

OCEANIA AND ANTARCTICA

Daily Lecture and Discussion Notes

Pacific Island Cultures and Economies

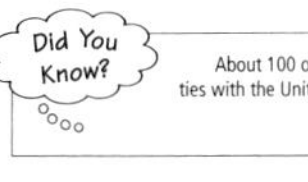

About 100 of Micronesia's 607 islands are inhabited. Because of its close ties with the United States, the U.S. dollar is the official currency of Micronesia.

I. Melanesia

A. Oceania includes about 25,000 islands. Geographers group Oceania into three main island regions—Melanesia, Micronesia, and Polynesia.

B. The largest country in Melanesia is Papua New Guinea. Other independent island countries are the Solomon Islands, the Fiji Islands, and Vanuatu.

Applying Map Skills

Answers

1. France, United Kingdom, United States, and New Zealand
2. three

In-text Map Transparency Activity As students look at the map, remind them to read the text that explains what the colored lines mean. **Then ask:** **What is the capital of Papua New Guinea?** *(Port Moresby)*

More About the Photos

Homes of Micronesia Some houses are built on stilts over water. When on land, the houses are much larger.

Caption Answer The house in this photo reflects the use of natural materials. The shape allows for the escape of heat. Rain flows down the roof without causing damage.

Reading Check Answer

Papua New Guinea

L1/ELL

Guided Reading Activity

Name ______ Date ______ Class ______

OCEANIA AND ANTARCTICA

Guided Reading Activity 1

Pacific Island Cultures and Economies

DIRECTIONS: Filling in the Blanks Reading the section and completing the sentences below will help you learn more about Oceania. Use your textbook to fill in the blanks.

Oceania is a region with about **(1)** ______ islands. These are grouped into **(2)** ______ main island regions. The first of these regions is **(3)** ______. These islands lie across the **(4)** ______ from Australia. The largest country in size and population is **(5)** ______ ______ ______. To the southeast are three other independent islands: the **(6)** ______ ______, the **(7)** ______ ______, and

Travel Guide

Across the Pacific islands, coconut is a staple. The Kiribati people, for example, eat coconut with fish, grate it into tea, and use its milk to sweeten breadfruit soup. For many islanders, coconut sap provides a rich source of vitamin C. Young boys on Kiribati cut *toddy,* meaning they gather coconut sap and boil it to make a thick, sweet molasses used to sweeten drinks or to make candy.

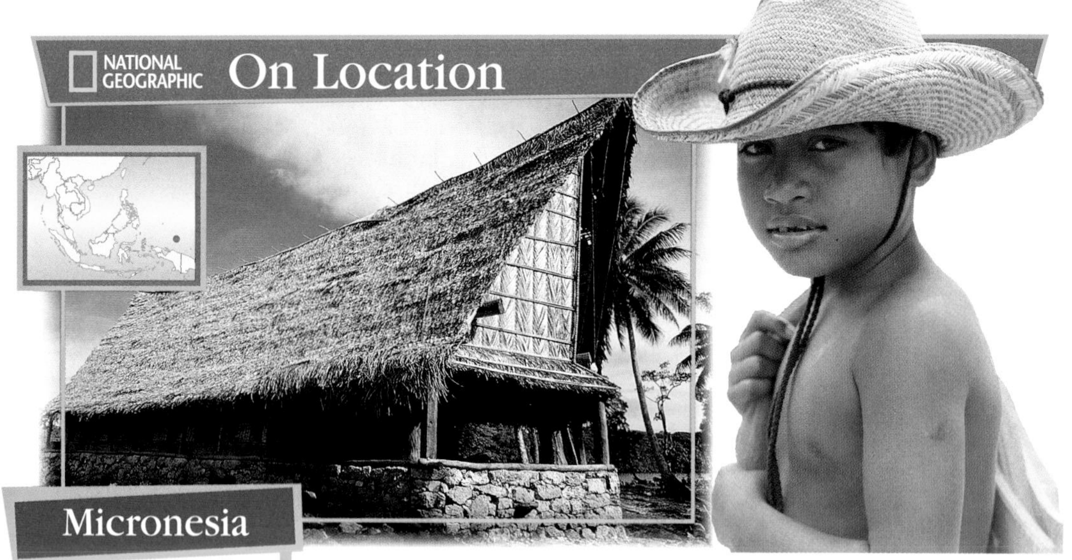

Micronesia

Many of the homes in Micronesia have thatched roofs and no walls (above left). This young boy is from the island of Yap in Micronesia (above right).

Culture **How does the house reflect an adaptation to the environment?**

economy of the Fiji Islands. Fijians of Pacific descent own most of the land. The two groups struggle for control of the government.

Melanesia's languages and religions are diverse. More than 700 languages are spoken in Papua New Guinea alone. People here speak a **pidgin language** formed by combining parts of several different languages. People speak English in the Fiji Islands. French is the main language of New Caledonia. Local traditional religions are practiced, but Christianity is widespread. The Indian population is mostly Hindu.

Many Melanesians live in small villages in houses made of grass or other natural materials. Recently, people have built concrete houses to protect themselves from tropical storms. Melanesians keep strong ties to their local group and often hold on to traditional ways. Only a small number live in cities, often working in businesses and government.

Reading Check **What is the largest country in Melanesia?**

Micronesia

The islands of Micronesia are scattered over a vast area of the Pacific Ocean. Independent countries include the **Federated States of Micronesia,** the **Marshall Islands, Palau** (puh•LOW), **Nauru** (nah•OO•roo), and **Kiribati** (KIHR•uh•BAH•tee). The **Northern Mariana Islands** and **Guam** are territories of the United States.

Micronesia is made up of two types of islands—high islands and low islands. Volcanic activity formed the mountainous **high islands** many centuries ago. Coral, or skeletons of millions of tiny sea animals, formed the **low islands.** Most of the low islands are **atolls,** or low-lying, ring-shaped islands that surround lagoons.

Like Melanesia, Micronesia has a tropical climate. From July to October, typhoons may strike. These tropical storms with heavy winds and rains cause deaths and much destruction in the islands.

Differentiated Instruction

Meeting Special Needs: Less-proficient Readers To help students remember the different Pacific island nations of Melanesia, Micronesia, and Polynesia, have them create a chart that organizes the section information. Students should list the countries in each category, along with details about their geography and their economies. Students can use these charts to prepare for the chapter test. L1

Refer to *Inclusion for the Middle School Social Studies Classroom Strategies and Activities* in the TCR.

On Micronesia's high islands, the volcanic soil is rich. Most people are subsistence farmers who grow cassava, sweet potatoes, bananas, and coconuts. Some high island farmers also raise livestock. People in the low islands rely on fishing.

Several Micronesian islands have **phosphate,** a mineral salt that is used to make fertilizer. Phosphate supplies are now gone on Kiribati, and they have almost run out on Nauru. The Federated States of Micronesia and the Marshall Islands have phosphate but lack the money to mine this resource.

Challenges in Micronesia include unemployment, overfishing, and overdependence on aid. Micronesia receives financial aid from the United States, the European Union, and Australia. With this money, the Micronesians have built roads, ports, airfields, and small factories. Clothing is made on the Northern Mariana Islands. Beautiful beaches draw tourists here.

Micronesia's People Southeast Asians first settled Micronesia about 4,000 years ago. Explorers, traders, and missionaries from European countries came in the 1700s and early 1800s. By the early 1900s, many European countries, the United States, and Japan held colonies here.

During World War II, the United States and Japan fought a number of bloody battles on Micronesian islands. After World War II, most of Micronesia was turned over to the United States as **trust territories.** Trust territories are areas temporarily placed under control of another nation. Some of these islands served as sites for hydrogen bomb testing. Since the 1970s, most have become independent.

Many of Micronesia's people are Pacific Islanders. They speak local languages, although English is spoken on Nauru, the Marshall Islands, and throughout the rest of Micronesia. Christianity, brought by Western missionaries, is the most widely practiced religion. Micronesians generally live in villages headed by local chiefs. In recent years, many young people have left the villages to find jobs in towns.

Reading Check In what two ways were Micronesia's islands formed?

Polynesia

Polynesia includes three independent countries—**Samoa, Tonga,** and **Tuvalu.** A vast group of islands is under French rule and is known as **French Polynesia. Tahiti,** Polynesia's largest island, is part of this French-ruled area. **American Samoa,** a United States territory, is also part of this region.

Most Polynesian islands are high volcanic islands, some with tall, rugged mountains. Other islands are low atolls. With little soil, the only vegetation is scattered coconut palms. Because Polynesia lies in the Tropics, the climate is hot and humid.

Polynesians fish or grow crops for their food. Some farmers export coconuts and tropical fruits. The main manufacturing activity is food processing. American Samoa supplies about one-third of the tuna brought into the United States. Tonga exports squash and vanilla.

The Fate of Nauru

Micronesia's most famous phosphate island is Nauru, an 8-square-mile coral atoll. The name *Nauru* means "nowhere." Over the last 90 years, Nauru's citizens have chosen to "consume" their island by mining the coral as phosphate and selling it as fertilizer. The government of Nauru is now working to develop other industries, such as fishing and tourism, in preparation for the day when the phosphate is gone.

Team-Teaching Activity

History Invite the history teacher to class to discuss the story of the mutiny on H.M.S. *Bounty* and the adventurous aftermath. Have the teacher describe the mission of the ship—to bring breadfruit trees to the West Indies in hope of providing a nutritious food for enslaved plantation workers there—the mutiny itself, and the fates of the mutineers and of Captain William Bligh and those who stayed with him. Have students use a globe to trace the route of the *Bounty* from England to Tahiti and to modern Tuvalu, where the mutiny occurred. Then have them follow Bligh's journey on an open boat to East Timor and the mutineers' voyage back to Tahiti and on to Pitcairn Island. L1 

EE1 The World in Spatial Terms: Standard 3

Chapter 27

Section 1, pages 758–762

Reading Check Answer

by volcanic activity or by the formation of coral atolls as a result of the buildup of skeletons of millions of tiny sea animals

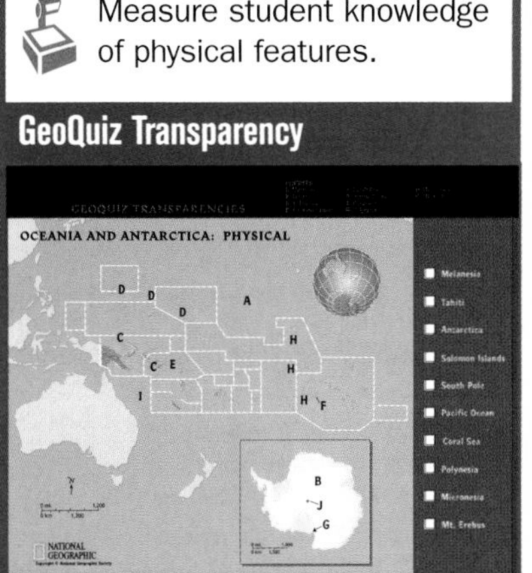

Measure student knowledge of physical features.
GeoQuiz Transparency
OCEANIA AND ANTARCTICA: PHYSICAL

Assign Section 1 Assessment as homework or an in-class activity.

Have students use the Interactive Tutor Self-Assessment CD-ROM to review Section 1.

L2

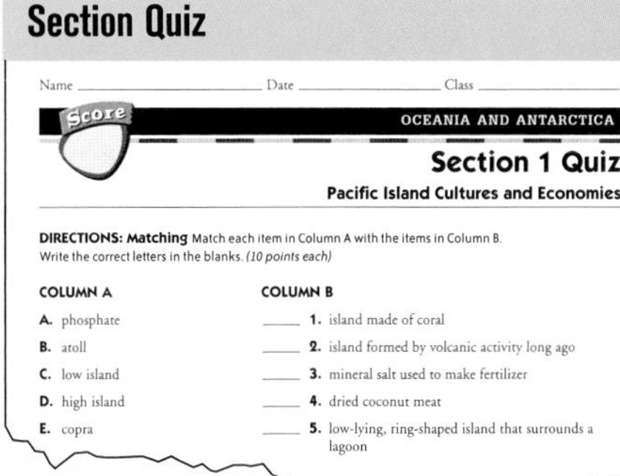
Section Quiz

Name ______ Date ______ Class ______

OCEANIA AND ANTARCTICA

Section 1 Quiz

Pacific Island Cultures and Economies

DIRECTIONS: Matching Match each item in Column A with the items in Column B. Write the correct letters in the blanks. (10 points each)

COLUMN A	COLUMN B
A. phosphate	____ 1. island made of coral
B. atoll	____ 2. island formed by volcanic activity long ago
C. low island	____ 3. mineral salt used to make fertilizer
D. high island	____ 4. dried coconut meat
E. copra	____ 5. low-lying, ring-shaped island that surrounds a lagoon

Reading Strategy

Reteach

Ask volunteers, using their own words, to express each paragraph's main idea and supporting details.

Reading Check Answer

Tahiti

L1/ELL

Reading Essentials and Study Guide

Name ______ Date ______ Class ______

OCEANIA AND ANTARCTICA

Reading Essentials and Study Guide 1

Pacific Island Cultures and Economies

Key Terms

cacao tropical tree whose seeds are used to make chocolate and cocoa
copra dried coconut meat
pidgin language language formed by combining parts of several different languages
high island island formed by volcanoes
low island island made of coral
atoll low-lying, ring-shaped island that surrounds a lagoon
phosphate mineral salt used to make fertilizer
trust territory land put under temporary control of another country

Drawing From Experience

Do you eat tuna sandwiches? If so, you may be eating a fish caught in Polynesian waters. American Samoans supply a third of the tuna eaten in the United States.

This section describes the tropical beauty of the islands that dot the Pacific Ocean.

Organizing Your Thoughts

Use the chart on the next page to help you take notes. Name the region of Oceania (Melanesia, Micronesia, or Polynesia) that best fits each topic. Also, write one fact about the topic.

Most of Melanesia has a tropical climate. Temperatures stay between 70 and 80 degrees all year.

4 Close

Have students imagine they have a chance to interview a teen who lives on one of these islands. Have them draft the questions they would ask.

Tourism is one of the fastest growing industries of Polynesia. Tourists come by air or sea to the emerald green mountains and white palm-lined beaches. New hotels, shops, and restaurants have been built to accommodate the needs of these tourists.

Polynesia's People Very little is known about the origins of the Polynesians. Historians believe that their ancestors used canoes to cross the Pacific Ocean from Asia hundreds of years before the birth of Christ. They also believe that the Polynesians must have been gifted navigators.

When the Polynesian people traveled from island to island, they carried everything they would need with them, including pigs, hens, and dogs. As soon as the Polynesians arrived at an island, they planted young banana and breadfruit trees. The influence of these early Polynesians can be seen today in the vegetation, languages, music, and dances of the southern Pacific islands.

During the late 1800s, several European nations divided Polynesia among themselves. They built military bases on the islands and later added airfields. The islands served as excellent refueling stops for long voyages across the Pacific. Beginning in the 1960s, several Polynesian territories chose independence, while others remained territories.

About 600,000 people live in Polynesia. Most Polynesians live in rural villages, but an increasing number of people are moving to towns and cities. **Papeete** (PAH•pay•AY•tay), located on Tahiti, is the capital of French Polynesia and the largest city in the region.

Reading Check What is the largest island in Polynesia?

Section 1 Assessment

Defining Terms

1. **Define** cacao, copra, pidgin language, high island, low island, atoll, phosphate, trust territory.

Recalling Facts

2. **Region** What three regions make up Oceania?
3. **Economics** What two kinds of economic activities are most important in these regions?
4. **History** What groups first settled the lands of Micronesia?

Critical Thinking

5. **Analyzing Information** How might overdependence on aid be a challenge for Micronesia?
6. **Drawing Conclusions** Why do many people in Melanesia speak a pidgin language?

Graphic Organizer

7. **Organizing Information** Create a chart like this one. List all the island groups of Oceania under their specific region. Then note whether they are independent countries or territories.

Melanesia	Micronesia	Polynesia	Country/Territory of ?

Applying Social Studies Skills

8. **Analyzing Maps** Look at the political map on page 759. Which territories are colonies of France?

Section 1 Assessment

1. The terms are defined in the Glossary.
2. Melanesia, Micronesia, and Polynesia
3. tourism and farming
4. Southeast Asians
5. As the amount of assistance fluctuates, so do the economies of Micronesia.
6. to communicate better because so many different languages are spoken
7. *Melanesia*: Papua New Guinea, Solomon Islands, Fiji Islands, Vanuatu; territory is France's New Caledonia. *Micronesia:* Federated States of Micronesia, Marshall Islands, Palau, Nauru, Kiribati; territories are the U.S.'s Northern Mariana Islands and Guam. *Polynesia:* Samoa, Tonga, Tuvalu; territories are French Polynesia (including Tahiti) and American Samoa.
8. New Caledonia, French Polynesia, and Wallis and Futuna

Study and Writing Skill

Writing a Report

Writing skills allow you to organize your ideas in a logical manner. The writing process involves using skills you have already learned, such as taking notes, outlining, and sequencing information.

Learning the Skill

Use the following guidelines to help you apply the writing process:

- Select an interesting topic. Do preliminary research to determine whether your topic is too broad or too narrow.
- Write one or two sentences that state what you want to prove, discover, or explain in your writing. This will be the focus of your entire paper.
- Research your topic and make a list of main ideas. List facts and source information for each main idea on note cards.
- Your report should have an introduction, a body, and a conclusion that summarizes and restates your findings.
- Each paragraph should express one main idea in a topic sentence. Additional sentences should support or explain the main idea by using details and facts.

An atoll in the Pacific Ocean ▼

Practicing the Skill

Read the following paragraph, and then answer the questions that follow.

> Most of Micronesia's low islands are atolls—low-lying, ring-shaped islands that surround lagoons. An atoll begins as a ring of coral that forms around the edge of a volcanic island. Over time, wind and water erode the volcano, wearing it down to sea level. Eventually, only the atoll remains above the surface. The calm, shallow seawater inside the atoll is called a lagoon.

1. What is the main idea of this paragraph?
2. What are the supporting sentences?
3. What might be the topic of an additional paragraph that follows this one?

Applying the Skill

Suppose you are writing a report on Oceania. Answer the following questions about the writing process.

1. How could you narrow this topic?
2. What are three main ideas?
3. Name three possible sources of information.

Practicing the Skill Answers

1. Most of Micronesia's low islands are atolls.
2. the remaining sentences that define atolls
3. *Possible answers:* type of vegetation and wildlife found on atolls, description of Micronesia's high islands

Applying the Skill

1. by choosing to focus on one island or group of islands or by focusing on one aspect of life
2. Papua New Guinea is the largest and geographically most diverse country of Oceania; mountains on Papua New Guinea divide different groups from one another; or Papua New Guinea exports coffee, palm oil, and cacao.
3. encyclopedia; almanac; Web site about the country

Teach

Give students the following situations: A student preparing a project about tourism in the South Pacific; a travel agent addressing colleagues at a convention about cost trends on cruises in Tahiti; an anthropologist describing traditional life on Samoa; a government leader on Nauru readying a speech about plans for the future of the country's economy. **Ask:** **What do all of these people have in common?** *(They are communicating information and ideas.)* **How can they most effectively carry out that task?** *(by writing down their ideas first)* **L1**

Additional Skills Practice

1. **What problem results when a topic is too broad?** *(There is too much material on which to report.)*
2. **How can outlining help you write a report?** *(It allows you to structure what you are going to say.)*

Additional Skills Resources

- Chapter Skills Review
- Building Geography Skills for Life

GLENCOE TECHNOLOGY

Skillbuilder Interactive Workbook CD-ROM, Level 1

This interactive CD-ROM reinforces student mastery of essential social studies skills.

1 Focus

Section Objectives

1. Describe what kinds of life are found in Antarctica.
2. Explain why scientists study Antarctica.

BELLRINGER Skillbuilder Activity

Project transparency and have students answer the question.

Daily Focus Skills Transparency

DAILY FOCUS SKILLS TRANSPARENCY
Oceania and Antarctica
Section 2

ANSWER: The chicks depart during the warmest months in Antarctica

Teacher Tip: Explain to students that a generalization is a basic idea that can be formed from a set of facts

Making Generalizations

Adelie and Emperor Penguins of Antarctica

	Adelie Penguins	Emperor Penguins
Size	29.5" (75 cm)	47" (120 cm)
Maximum weight	14 lbs. (6.5 kg)	99 lbs. (45 kg)
Egg laying	November	May
Hatching	December	July
Chicks depart	February	December/January
Main food	Krill	Squid and fish

Directions: Answer the following question based on the information about Adelie and Emperor penguins.

Why do you think both species of penguins have chicks departing the nest in December through February?

Reading Preview

■ **Activating Prior Knowledge** Ask students what value they think Antarctica has. After they have offered their ideas, tell them that they will learn of its value to scientists when they read this section.

■ **Preteaching Vocabulary** Have students scan the section to find the terms listed in the Terms to Know. Have them use each one in a sentence.

Guide to Reading

Main Idea

Antarctica is a harsh land of rock and ice. The world's nations have agreed to leave the frozen continent open to scientific study.

Terms to Know

- crevasse
- ice shelf
- iceberg
- krill
- ozone

Reading Strategy

Create a chart like the one below. Under each heading, fill in at least one fact about Antarctica.

Antarctica	
Land	Climate
Resources	People

Section 2 The Frozen Continent

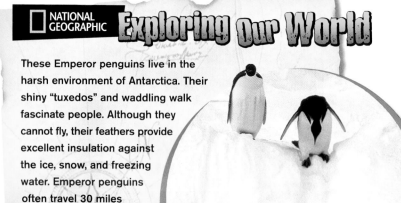

These Emperor penguins live in the harsh environment of Antarctica. Their shiny "tuxedos" and waddling walk fascinate people. Although they cannot fly, their feathers provide excellent insulation against the ice, snow, and freezing water. Emperor penguins often travel 30 miles (48 km) a day to bring food to their rookeries, or nests. Sometimes walking takes too long, so penguins simply slide on their bellies, which is called tobogganing.

Antarctica sits at the southern end of the earth. Icy ocean water surrounds it. Freezing ice covers it. Cold winds blow over it. The least explored of all the continents, this frigid mysterious land is larger than either Europe or Australia.

Unique Antarctica

Picture Antarctica as a rich, green land covered by forests and lush plants. Does this description match your mental image of the continent? Fossils discovered here reveal that millions of years ago, Antarctica was inhabited by dinosaurs and small mammals.

Today, however, a huge ice cap buries nearly 98 percent of Antarctica's land area. In some spots, this ice cap is 2 miles (3.2 km) thick—about the height of 10 tall skyscrapers stacked upon one another. This massive "sea" of ice holds about 70 percent of all the freshwater in the world.

The Antarctic ice cap is heavy and strong, and it also moves. In some areas, the ice cap forms **crevasses**, or cracks, that plunge more than 100 feet (30 m). At the Antarctic coast, the ice cap spreads past

Section Resources

Reproducible Masters

- Reproducible Lesson Plan
- Daily Lecture and Discussion Notes
- Note-taking Guide
- Guided Reading Activity
- Reading Essentials and Study Guide
- Section Quiz

Transparencies

- Daily Focus Skills Transparency

Multimedia

- Vocabulary PuzzleMaker CD-ROM
- Interactive Tutor Self-Assessment CD-ROM
- Presentation Plus! CD-ROM
- ExamView® Pro Testmaker CD-ROM
- MindJogger Videoquiz

the land into the ocean. This layer of ice above the water is called an ice shelf. Huge chunks of ice sometimes break off, forming icebergs, which float freely in the icy waters.

Highlands, Mountains, and Valleys Beneath most of the ice cap, however, Antarctica has highlands, mountains, and valleys—the same landforms you find on other continents. A long mountain range called the **Transantarctic Mountains** crosses the continent. The highest peak in Antarctica, the **Vinson Massif,** rises 16,067 feet (4,897 m). The Transantarctic Mountains sweep along the Antarctic Peninsula, which reaches within 600 miles (966 km) of South America's Cape Horn. East of the mountains is a high, flat plateau where you find the **South Pole,** the southernmost point of the earth. On an island called **Ross Island,** off Antarctica's coast, rises **Mount Erebus** (EHR•uh•buhs). It is Antarctica's most active volcano.

Climate Now that you have a mental picture of Antarctica's ice cap, think about this: Antarctica receives so little precipitation that it is the world's largest, coldest desert. Inland Antarctica receives no rain and hardly any new snow each year. Antarctica has a polar ice cap climate. Imagine summer in a place where temperatures may fall as low as −30°F (−35°C) and climb to only 32°F (0°C). Antarctic summers last from December through February. Winter temperatures along the coasts fall to −40°F (−40°C), and in inland areas to a low of −100°F (−73°C).

✓ Reading Check **What landforms are found under Antarctica's ice cap?**

NATIONAL GEOGRAPHIC **On Location**

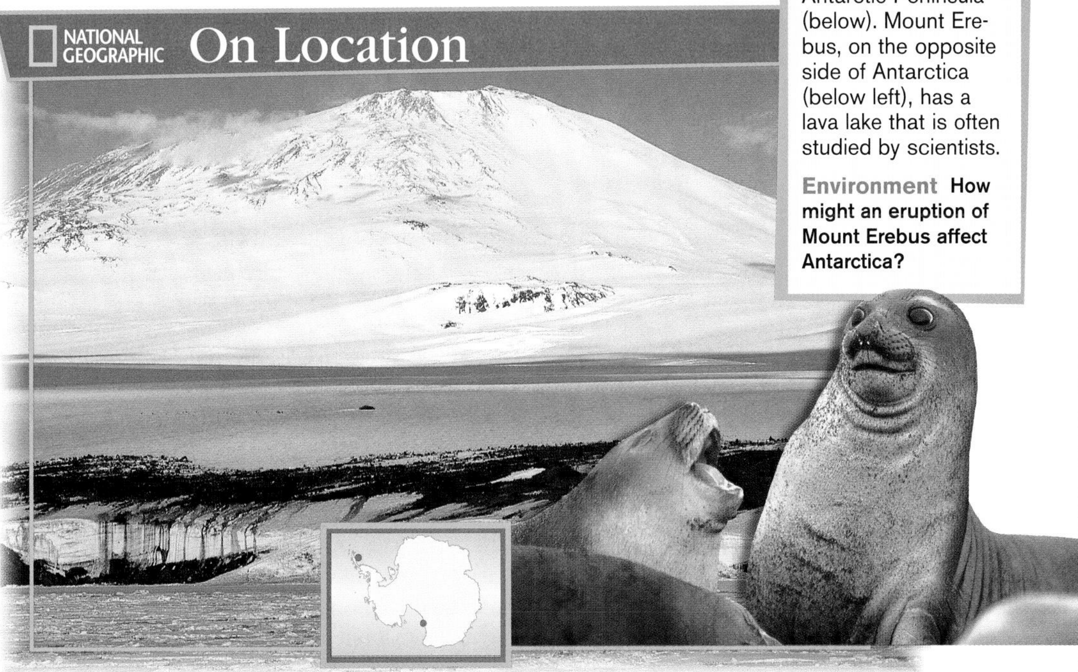

Antarctica

Elephant seals lounge on the coast of Elephant Island off the Antarctic Peninsula (below). Mount Erebus, on the opposite side of Antarctica (below left), has a lava lake that is often studied by scientists.

Environment How might an eruption of Mount Erebus affect Antarctica?

2 TEACH

Reading Strategy

Making Predictions Before students read the section, have them predict the kinds of animals, plants, and resources that might be found in Antarctica and list these in their notebooks. Have students check the accuracy of their predictions as they read. **L1**

Daily Lecture and Discussion Notes

OCEANIA AND ANTARCTICA

Daily Lecture and Discussion Notes
The Frozen Continent

Did You Know? The Antarctic Circle marks the edge of an area where the sun stays above the horizon one or more days each year. The sun never sets on the Antarctic Circle during the longest day of summer, about December 21. The sun never rises on the shortest day of winter, about June 21.

I. Unique Antarctica

A. Fossils discovered here reveal that millions of years ago, Antarctica's landscape was inhabited by dinosaurs and small mammals. Today, however, a huge ice cap buries nearly 98 percent of Antarctica's land area.

B. ...ice cap forms **crevasses,** or cracks, that plunge more than ... the ice cap spreads past the land to cover part...

✓ Reading Check Answer

highlands, valleys, and mountains

More About the Photos

Antarctica Since 1972, Mount Erebus has had continuous activity in the lava lake and occasional explosions that eject lava bombs onto the crater rim. Since the lava pools in the cone are open, it does not build up great pressure.

Caption Answer A small eruption can cause ice quakes in nearby glaciers, and a violent eruption might even cause parts of the land to break away.

Reading Strategy — Reading the Text

Understanding Vocabulary Have student use word maps when learning new vocabulary. Word maps are any kind of graphic that is designed to show relationships between words or concepts. A commonly used word map or concept web shows a central bubble containing a key word or idea. Bubbles that surround the center bubble may be used to show semantic relationships or to explain structure relationships. Have students create a word map for one of the words in the Terms to Know and have them explain it to the class. **L1**

*Use the **Reading Skills Handbook** for more reading strategies.*

L1/ELL

Guided Reading Activity

Name ______ Date ______ Class ______

OCEANIA AND ANTARCTICA

Guided Reading Activity 2

The Frozen Continent

DIRECTIONS: Reading for Accuracy Reading the section and completing the activity below will help you learn more about Antarctica. Use your textbook to decide if a statement is true or false. Write **T** or **F**, and if a statement is false, rewrite it correctly.

____ **1.** Antarctica is covered with freezing ice and is the least explored continent.

____ **2.** There are no landforms here. The continent is one huge sheet of ice.

____ **3.** Antarctica is the world's largest desert.

✓ Reading Check Answer

an international treaty to protect Antarctica's resources

✓ Reading Check Answer

to learn more about possible climate changes

Assign Section 2 Assessment as homework or an in-class activity.

Have students use the Interactive Tutor Self-Assessment CD-ROM to review Section 2.

L2

Section Quiz

Name ______ Date ______ Class ______

OCEANIA AND ANTARCTICA

Score

Section 2 Quiz

The Frozen Continent

DIRECTIONS: Matching Match each item in Column A with the items in Column B. Write the correct letters in the blanks. *(10 points each)*

COLUMN A	COLUMN B
A. crevasses	____ **1.** deep cracks in the ice cap
B. krill	____ **2.** layer of ice above the water in Antarctica
C. Transantarctic	____ **3.** tiny shrimplike creatures
D. ice shelf	____ **4.** mountain range that crosses Antarctica
E. Antarctic Treaty	____ **5.** prohibits any nation from taking resources from Antarctica

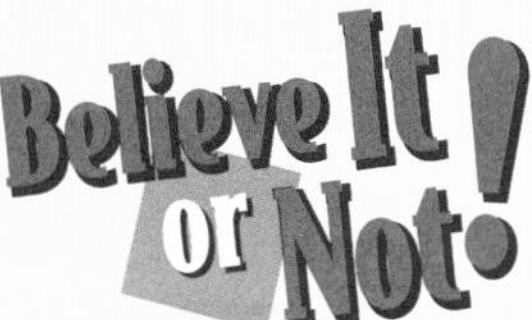

The *Endurance*

In January 1915, Ernest Shackleton and his crew in the *Endurance* became trapped in Antarctica's freezing seawater. In late October, ice crushed the wooden ship, forcing the explorers to abandon it (below). They spent five more months drifting on the ice until they reached open water and used lifeboats to get away.

Resources of Antarctica

Antarctica has a harsh environment, but it can still support life. Most of the plants and animals that live here are small, however. The largest inland animal is an insect that reaches only one-tenth of an inch in length. Penguins, fish, whales, and many kinds of flying birds live in or near the seas surrounding Antarctica. Many eat a tiny, shrimplike creature called **krill**.

Scientists believe that the ice of Antarctica hides a treasure chest of minerals. They have found major deposits of coal and smaller amounts of copper, gold, iron ore, manganese, and zinc. Petroleum might lie offshore.

These mineral resources have not yet been tapped. To do so would be very difficult and costly. Also, some people feel that removing these resources would damage Antarctica's fragile environment. Another reason is that different nations would disagree over who has the right to these resources. Forty-three nations have signed the Antarctic Treaty, which prohibits any nation from taking resources from the continent. It also bans weapons testing in Antarctica.

✓ Reading Check **What is the Antarctic Treaty?**

A Vast Scientific Laboratory

The Antarctic Treaty says that Antarctica should only be used for peaceful, scientific purposes. Many countries have scientific research stations here, but no single nation controls the vast continent. In January—summer in Antarctica—about 10,000 scientists come to study the land, plants, animals, and ice of this frozen land. Some 1,000 hardy scientists even stay during the harsh polar winter.

Much of the research focuses on ozone. **Ozone** is a type of oxygen that forms a layer in the atmosphere. The ozone layer protects all living things on the earth from certain harmful rays of the sun. In the 1980s, scientists discovered a weakening, or "hole," in this layer above Antarctica. If such weakening continues, the sun's harmful rays may cause skin cancer in humans and destroy plants. Turn to page 772 to learn more about the earth's ozone layer.

This frozen world attracts more than just scientists, though. Each year, a few thousand tourists come to Antarctica. Because it has such a harsh environment, however, Antarctica is the only continent in the world that has no permanent population.

✓ Reading Check **Why are scientists studying the ozone layer?**

Villa Las Estrellas

Humans can adapt to life under the most difficult of conditions. One example of this is the Villa Las Estrellas, or Village of the Stars. Located in Chile's Antarctic Territory, the "town" has a school, hospital, supermarket, post office, bank, telephone, television, and Internet service. There is even a gym and a sauna. Village residents include members of Chile's air force and their families, as well as scientists from

Differentiated Instruction

Meeting Special Needs: Less-proficient Readers Students who are less-proficient readers benefit from having a specific purpose for reading. Point out the Reading Strategy at the beginning of the section. Have students read the instructions and copy the grid into their notebooks. Then have them look for information to complete the chart as they read. **L1**

Refer to *Inclusion for the Middle School Social Studies Classroom Strategies and Activities* in the TCR.

various countries. In all, about 240 people can live in Villa Las Estrellas. Many stay for two years at a time.

Like Penguins Daily dress in Villa Las Estrellas consists of thermal underclothes, warm boots, and dark sunglasses to protect the eyes against the sun's strong ultraviolet rays. Villagers must survive extreme temperatures down to −13°F (−25°C) with an even more bone-chilling wind factor. They do not stay inside all day, however. Adults walk from house to house to visit their neighbors. The children seem to enjoy the experience more than anyone else. One resident described outdoor playtime: "The children go crazy over the snow and enjoy sledding or just tobogganing downhill on their stomachs. They look like penguins!"

Global Village The countries of Russia, China, Korea, Brazil, Poland, Argentina, and Uruguay have military or scientific bases close to the village. In Antarctica, normal tensions between countries do not seem to matter. Every Wednesday afternoon, the different bases send soccer teams to the Chilean gymnasium for a game of indoor soccer. Once a year, a "winter Olympics" is held in volleyball and basketball. Visitors to the different bases mix freely with the people who live in them. Villa Las Estrellas may be as close to a real global village as the earth has ever seen.

Social Studies Online

Web Activity Visit ***The World and Its People*** Web site at twip.glencoe.com and click on **Chapter 27—Student Web Activities** to learn more about Antarctica.

Reading Check What is one way that humans have adapted to the harsh Antarctic environment?

Section 2 Assessment

Defining Terms

1. **Define** crevasse, ice shelf, iceberg, krill, ozone.

Recalling Facts

2. **Place** What covers nearly 98 percent of Antarctica?
3. **Location** Where in Antarctica would you find the most living things?
4. **Human/Environment Interaction** Why do scientists come to Antarctica?

Critical Thinking

5. **Summarizing Information** Why have countries agreed not to use the resources of Antarctica?
6. **Writing Questions** Imagine that you are planning a trip to Antarctica. What questions would you ask scientists working there?

Graphic Organizer

7. **Organizing Information** Create a chart like the one below, and then look at the political map on page 759. In your chart, list the various national claims made in Antarctica by the world's countries. Then give the number of research stations for each country.

Countries With Claims in Antarctica	Number of Research Stations

Applying Social Studies Skills

8. **Analyzing Maps** Look at the physical map on page 728. What mountain range cuts across Antarctica?

Section 2 Assessment

1. The terms are defined in the Glossary.
2. an ice cap
3. along the coast
4. to study the ozone as well as plants, animals, ice, and resources of Antarctica
5. to protect its environment and avoid disputes over who owns them
6. Students' questions will vary.
7. Chile—1 station, Argentina—4 stations, U.K.—3 stations, Norway, Australia—3 stations, France—1 station, New Zealand—1 station, India has no claims but 1 station, Russia has no claims but 6 stations, U.S. has no claims but 3 stations, Japan has no claims but 1 station
8. the Transantarctic Mountains

Social Studies Online

Objectives and answers to the Student Web Activity can be found in the Web Activity Lesson Plan at twip.glencoe.com

Reading Check Answer

Possible answers: by wearing special warm clothing and dark sunglasses; by socializing with people from different countries

L1/ELL

Reading Essentials and Study Guide

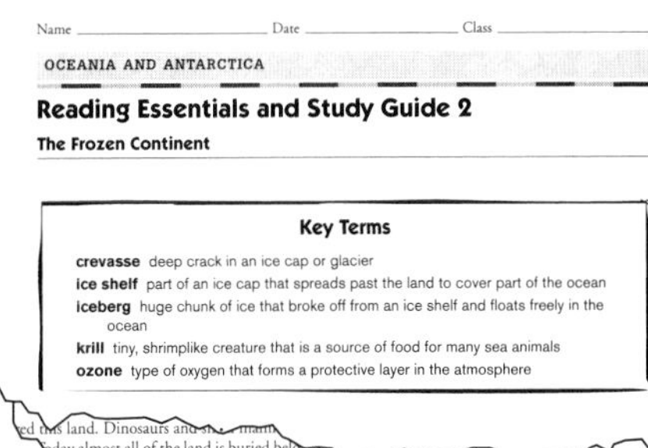
Name ______ Date ______ Class ______

OCEANIA AND ANTARCTICA

Reading Essentials and Study Guide 2

The Frozen Continent

Key Terms

crevasse deep crack in an ice cap or glacier
ice shelf part of an ice cap that spreads past the land to cover part of the ocean
iceberg huge chunk of ice that broke off from an ice shelf and floats freely in the ocean
krill tiny, shrimplike creature that is a source of food for many sea animals
ozone type of oxygen that forms a protective layer in the atmosphere

Enrich

Have students research and report on the current status of the ozone layer.

4 Close

Reading Strategy

Summarizing Have students write a summary explaining why Antarctica's environment is fragile and why its resources have not been tapped.

TEACH

Have students describe the environment of outer space. Possible answers include cold, dark, and lifeless. **Ask:** **Where is the best place on the earth to test ways of surviving in such an environment?** *(Antarctica)* Then have them read the feature. L1

More About Antarctica

In 2000, scientists from the United Kingdom published the first map of the landforms found beneath Antarctica's ice cap. The map was created by combining the results of research gathered by scientists from 15 different countries over a 50-year period.

Interdisciplinary Connections

Science Some scientists hope to take samples from Lake Vostok, a large lake in Antarctica. They wish to see if the lake contains any life-forms. The purpose is not only to learn about life in Antarctica itself but also to apply this knowledge to space. If there is life in harsh Antarctica, some scientists believe, similar forms may survive on the moons that circle other planets in the solar system.

Making Connections

ART | SCIENCE | CULTURE | TECHNOLOGY

Antarctica's Environmental Stations

For nearly 200 years, adventurers, explorers, geographers, and scientists have been drawn to the icy wilderness of Antarctica. Scientific research is the major human activity on this remarkable continent.

Polar Science

In the 1950s, countries began to talk of preserving Antarctica as an international laboratory for scientific research. Today a formal treaty guarantees free access and research rights for scientists of many countries. Antarctica now holds more than 40 research stations.

Types of Research

Geologists, biologists, climatologists, and astronomers are some of the many scientists who come to Antarctica to study. Understanding the earth's environment is a major focus. The Antarctic ice cap contains 90 percent of the world's ice and 70 percent of its freshwater. Changes here can affect the world's oceans and climates.

Scientists in Antarctica were the first to discover the holes in the ozone layer. Such holes can expose life on the earth to too much ultraviolet radiation.

Researchers in Antarctica also study the earth's history. Locked in the continent's ice crystals and air bubbles are clues to the earth's past. Fossils show how landmasses existed before the formation of today's continents.

The harsh living conditions of Antarctica provide another subject for study. The National Aeronautics and Space Administration (NASA) sends engineers and scientists to Antarctica to learn how to survive in extreme conditions, such as those humans might someday encounter on visits to other planets.

Research station at the South Pole ▶

Life at the Edge

Living and working in Antarctica's polar wilderness demands special equipment, well-trained people, and a sizable dose of caution. Freeze-dried food, layers of warm, quick-drying clothes, insulated boots, and specially designed pyramid tents keep researchers well-fed, warm, and dry. Researchers quickly learn the importance of staying inside during whiteout conditions, when snow and fog create a total lack of visibility.

The Antarctic environment is a fragile one, and researchers take care to protect it. All trash and wastes are removed from the continent. Mining of mineral resources is banned, and laws protect native plants and animals. Such care ensures that Antarctica will continue to hold exciting discoveries for years to come.

Making the Connection

1. What do researchers study in Antarctica?
2. What discovery did researchers make about the ozone layer?
3. **Summarizing Information** What items do researchers in Antarctica use to stay warm and dry?

Making the Connection

1. the earth's environment and atmosphere; the ice; fossils; living conditions in the cold
2. They found holes in the ozone layer, which can expose life on the earth to too much ultraviolet radiation.
3. warm, quick-drying clothes; insulated boots; and specially designed pyramid tents

Chapter 27 Reading Review

Section 1 Pacific Island Cultures and Economies

Terms to Know

- cacao
- copra
- pidgin language
- high island
- low island
- atoll
- phosphate
- trust territory

Main Idea

Oceania is made up of thousands of Pacific Ocean islands organized into countries and territories.

✓ Region Oceania is a huge area of vast open ocean and about 25,000 islands.

✓ Region Geographers divide Oceania into three regions: Melanesia, Micronesia, and Polynesia.

✓ Place High islands were formed by volcanoes. Low islands were made from coral.

✓ Place Papua New Guinea, in Melanesia, is the largest and most populous country of Oceania.

✓ Economics The main economic activities in Oceania are farming and tourism. Some islands have important minerals or other resources.

✓ History Most people of Oceania are descendants of people who left Southeast Asia on canoes thousands of years ago.

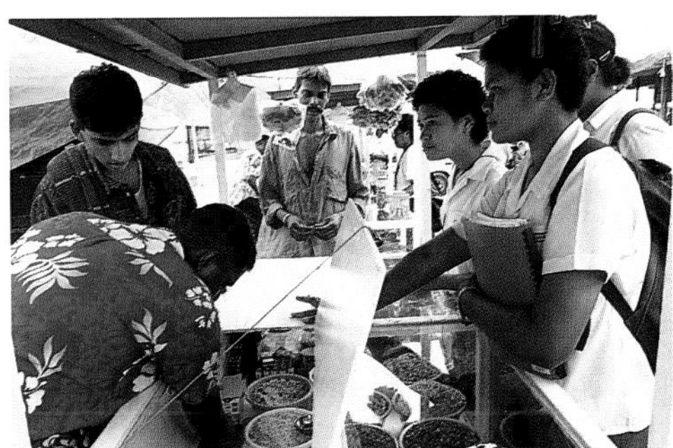

Fijian schoolgirls buy snacks from an Indian merchant in Suva. ▶

Section 2 The Frozen Continent

Terms to Know

- crevasse
- ice shelf
- iceberg
- krill
- ozone

Main Idea

Antarctica is a harsh land of rock and ice. The world's nations have agreed to leave the frozen continent open to scientific study.

✓ Location Antarctica lies at the southern end of the earth.

✓ Place Most of the continent, which has mountain ranges and a plateau, is covered by a huge, thick ice cap.

✓ Place Most plants and animals that live in Antarctica are small. Larger animals thrive in the waters off the coast.

✓ Economics Antarctica has many minerals, but many nations have signed a treaty agreeing not to remove these resources.

✓ Culture Antarctica is a major center of scientific research, but it is the only continent with no permanent human population.

Reading Review

Use the Chapter 27 Reading Review to preview, review, condense, or reteach the chapter.

Preview/Review

Use the Terms to Know lists to help students review and study.

Activity Organize the class into teams and quiz them on the Terms to Know. Offer a definition and ask each team to identify the correct term. If they do so correctly, they win a point; if they do not, the other team has an opportunity to do so.

Vocabulary PuzzleMaker CD-ROM reinforces the vocabulary terms used in Chapter 27.

The Interactive Tutor Self-Assessment CD-ROM allows students to review Chapter 27 content.

Condense

Have students read the Chapter 27 summary statements.

Guided Reading Activities

Audio Program

Reteach

Reteaching Activity

Reading Essentials and Study Guide

Reading Strategy: Read to Write

Creating a Travel Brochure Have students create a four-page travel brochure that highlights the attractions for one of the countries in Oceania. Explain that the travel brochure should include both physical and cultural features that visitors would want to see. Remind students that one part of the brochure should have practical information such as clothing appropriate for the climate, language used in the country, and currency employed. Advise students that an effective brochure includes appealing visuals as well as brief, engaging text. L1

 **EE2 Places and Regions: Standard 4**

GLENCOE TECHNOLOGY

MindJogger Videoquiz

Use MindJogger Videoquiz to review the Chapter 27 content.

Available in DVD and VHS

Using Key Terms

1. d
2. f
3. h
4. g
5. a
6. j
7. i
8. e
9. c
10. b

Reviewing the Main Ideas

11. They are descendants of workers brought by colonial powers.
12. high island; because it was formed by volcanic activity and has fertile soil
13. France
14. *Possible answers:* warm climate; beautiful beaches; attractive environment
15. Southeast Asia
16. It is Antarctica's most active volcano.
17. penguins
18. large amounts of coal and smaller quantities of copper, gold, iron ore, manganese, and zinc
19. Antarctic Treaty
20. to observe any possible changes in this layer, which protects all living things on the earth from dangerous rays of the sun

Chapter 27 Assessment and Activities

Using Key Terms

Match the terms in Part A with their definitions in Part B.

A.

1. pidgin language
2. copra
3. trust territory
4. ice shelf
5. phosphate
6. ozone
7. low island
8. iceberg
9. high island
10. krill

B.

- **a.** mineral salt used to make fertilizer
- **b.** tiny, shrimplike animal
- **c.** Pacific island formed by volcanic activity
- **d.** combines elements of several languages
- **e.** chunk of a glacier that floats free
- **f.** dried coconut meat
- **g.** layer of ice above water in Antarctica
- **h.** area temporarily placed under control of another nation
- **i.** Pacific island formed of coral
- **j.** layer in the atmosphere that blocks certain harmful rays of the sun

Reviewing the Main Ideas

Section 1 Pacific Island Cultures and Economies

11. **History** Why are there South Asians on the Fiji Islands?
12. **Human/Environment Interaction** Which is likely to have better farmland—a high island or a low island? Why?
13. **Government** New Caledonia is ruled by which European country?
14. **Economics** What attracts tourists to Oceania?
15. **History** From where did the people who first settled Oceania originally come?

Section 2 The Frozen Continent

16. **Place** What is significant about Mount Erebus?
17. **Location** What marine birds feed in the seas near Antarctica?
18. **Economics** What resources have been found in Antarctica?
19. **Government** What agreement bans the use of Antarctica's resources?
20. **Human/Environment Interaction** Why do scientists study the ozone layer in Antarctica?

Oceania and Antarctica

Place Location Activity

On a separate sheet of paper, match the letters on the map with the numbered places listed below.

1. Antarctic Peninsula
2. South Pole
3. Vinson Massif
4. Marshall Islands
5. Papua New Guinea
6. Fiji Islands
7. French Polynesia
8. Coral Sea
9. Solomon Islands

NATIONAL GEOGRAPHIC Place Location Activity

1. F
2. D
3. G
4. C
5. H
6. E
7. A
8. B
9. I

Critical Thinking

21. *Possible answer:* The warm, pleasant climate of Oceania makes life there easier in regards to clothing and shelter. Many crops grow in the fertile soil of the high islands, helped by the warm, tropical climate. The harsh climate of Antarctica has prevented permanent settlements, although technology allows a few scientists to stay there year-round.
22. Students' charts will vary.

Self-Check Quiz Visit ***The World and Its People*** Web site at twip.glencoe.com and click on **Chapter 27—Self-Check Quizzes** to prepare for the Chapter Test.

Critical Thinking

21. **Making Generalizations** You have read about two areas with very different climates. Write a generalization about how climate affects the way people live in each area.
22. **Organizing Information** Make a chart like this one. Under each heading, write a fact about each of the four regions you studied in this chapter: Melanesia, Micronesia, Polynesia, and Antarctica.

Landforms	Climate	Economy or Resources	People

Comparing Regions Activity

23. **Geography** The region of northern Siberia in Russia has one of the coldest climates in the world. Research to find what plants and animals live here. Compare this information to what lives on the continent of Antarctica. What similarities and differences do you see?

Mental Mapping Activity

24. **Focusing on the Region** Create an outline map of Antarctica. Refer to the map on page 728, and then label the following:
    - Antarctic Circle
    - Vinson Massif
    - Antarctic Peninsula
    - Pacific Ocean
    - Atlantic Ocean
    - South Pole

Technology Skills Activity

25. **Building a Database** Research three animals of Oceania. Create a database of the information you find. Include separate fields for the following items: name of species, location, type of habitat, diet, natural predators, and population status. Then use the database information to create a map showing the location of each species.

Standardized Test Practice

Directions: Read the paragraph below, and then answer the question that follows.

Because of the abundance of marine life in the clear Pacific waters, fresh fish is the primary traditional food of Oceania's people. This is especially true in the low coral islands, where there is little land suitable for farming. The rich volcanic soil of the high islands allows pineapples, coconuts, bananas, and sweet potatoes to grow. In Papua New Guinea, pork is a favorite food. Great feasts of pork, greens, and yams are social gatherings for whole villages. At these feasts, pigs are cooked for about eight hours over hot stones set in an "earth oven"—or large hole in the ground.

1. **Which of the following statements *best* summarizes the paragraph above?**

   F People in the high islands are able to grow and eat pineapples, bananas, and sweet potatoes.

   G In the low islands, the coral prevents much farming.

   H The Pacific Ocean is the source of the fish that most people eat.

   J Physical geography influences the traditional foods of Oceania's people.

Test-Taking Tip: When a question uses the word *best,* it means that more than one answer might be correct. Your job is to pick the *best* answer. This question also asks for a summary of the passage. Read through all of the answer choices before choosing the one that provides a more general restatement of the information.

771

Assessment and Activities

Standardized Test Practice

1. J

Tested Objectives: Summarizing information, making generalizations

This question may be used for extra credit on the chapter test.

What mineral is used to make fertilizers? *(phosphate)*

Have students visit the Web site at twip.glencoe.com to review Chapter 27 and take the Self-Check Quiz.

Dinah Zike's Foldables

Culminating Activity Have students present their foldables to the class to evaluate them to be sure that their summaries are accurate.

Comparing Regions Activity

23. Suggest that students create a graphic organizer to show the similarities and differences between Siberia and Antarctica.

Mental Mapping Activity

24. This exercise helps students visualize Antarctica. Accept all attempts at freehand mapping that show places in the correct relationship to one another.

Technology Skills Activity

25. Have students hand in both the database and the map. They might also include photographs of the animals they selected.

Ask: Why do people use umbrellas? *(to block the rain)* What would happen if an umbrella had holes in it? *(It would not block any—or as much—rain.)* Explain that a similar situation exists regarding the ozone layer. Then have students read the feature. L1

Understanding Cause and Effect On the board, write the words "Technological Advances," "Benefits," and "Drawbacks" at the top of three columns. Ask students for examples of different technologies that make life easier or more enjoyable. Examples include cars, televisions, computers, and telephones. Write their suggestions in the left column. Then ask students for their thoughts on how people have benefited from these inventions and write those in the second column. Have students find out what drawbacks might result from this development. Have them create posters that show the benefits and drawbacks of technology. L1

Meeting National Standards

Geography for Life

The following standards are met in the Student Edition feature:

EE3 Physical Systems: Standard 7

EE5 Environment and Society: Standard 15

OZONE

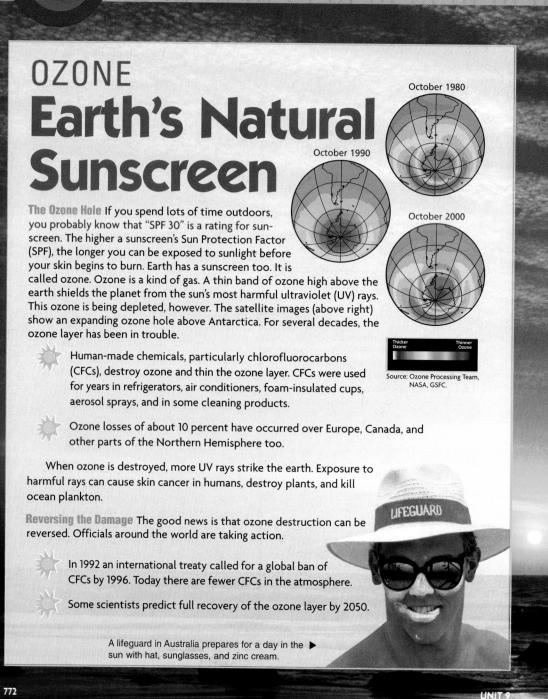

Earth's Natural Sunscreen

October 1980

October 1990

October 2000

Thicker Ozone — Thinner Ozone

Source: Ozone Processing Team, NASA, GSFC.

The Ozone Hole If you spend lots of time outdoors, you probably know that "SPF 30" is a rating for sunscreen. The higher a sunscreen's Sun Protection Factor (SPF), the longer you can be exposed to sunlight before your skin begins to burn. Earth has a sunscreen too. It is called ozone. Ozone is a kind of gas. A thin band of ozone high above the earth shields the planet from the sun's most harmful ultraviolet (UV) rays. This ozone is being depleted, however. The satellite images (above right) show an expanding ozone hole above Antarctica. For several decades, the ozone layer has been in trouble.

- Human-made chemicals, particularly chlorofluorocarbons (CFCs), destroy ozone and thin the ozone layer. CFCs were used for years in refrigerators, air conditioners, foam-insulated cups, aerosol sprays, and in some cleaning products.
- Ozone losses of about 10 percent have occurred over Europe, Canada, and other parts of the Northern Hemisphere too.

When ozone is destroyed, more UV rays strike the earth. Exposure to harmful rays can cause skin cancer in humans, destroy plants, and kill ocean plankton.

Reversing the Damage The good news is that ozone destruction can be reversed. Officials around the world are taking action.

- In 1992 an international treaty called for a global ban of CFCs by 1996. Today there are fewer CFCs in the atmosphere.
- Some scientists predict full recovery of the ozone layer by 2050.

LIFEGUARD

A lifeguard in Australia prepares for a day in the sun with hat, sunglasses, and zinc cream. ▶

More About the Issues

Ozone Layer The ozone layer over Australia and North America is also thinning, but the problem is at its worst in Antarctica because the cold air there breaks down CFCs, producing chlorine, which is very damaging to the ozone layer. When heightened UV rays damage plants, they threaten the entire food chain, including the animals that feed off the plants and people that eat those animals.

NATIONAL GEOGRAPHIC

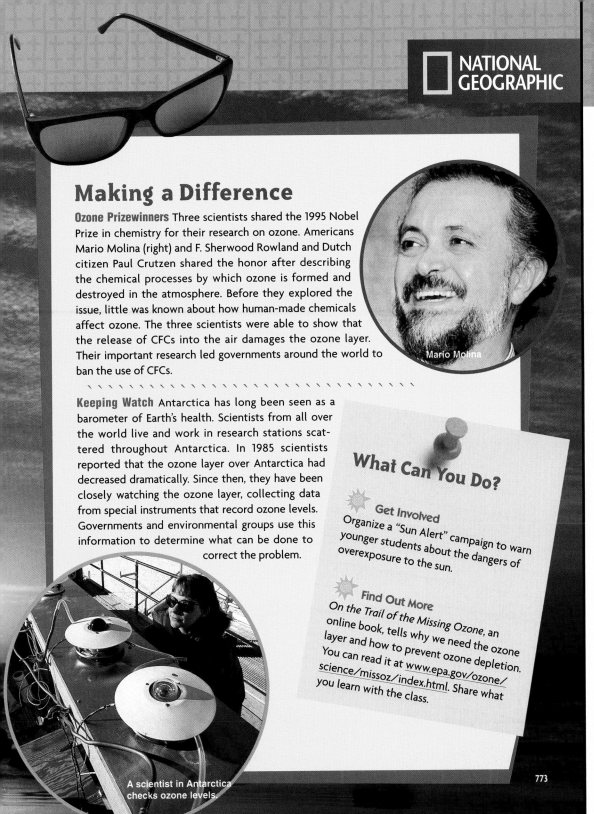

Making a Difference

Ozone Prizewinners Three scientists shared the 1995 Nobel Prize in chemistry for their research on ozone. Americans Mario Molina (right) and F. Sherwood Rowland and Dutch citizen Paul Crutzen shared the honor after describing the chemical processes by which ozone is formed and destroyed in the atmosphere. Before they explored the issue, little was known about how human-made chemicals affect ozone. The three scientists were able to show that the release of CFCs into the air damages the ozone layer. Their important research led governments around the world to ban the use of CFCs.

Mario Molina

Keeping Watch Antarctica has long been seen as a barometer of Earth's health. Scientists from all over the world live and work in research stations scattered throughout Antarctica. In 1985 scientists reported that the ozone layer over Antarctica had decreased dramatically. Since then, they have been closely watching the ozone layer, collecting data from special instruments that record ozone levels. Governments and environmental groups use this information to determine what can be done to correct the problem.

A scientist in Antarctica checks ozone levels.

What Can You Do?

Get Involved
Organize a "Sun Alert" campaign to warn younger students about the dangers of overexposure to the sun.

Find Out More
On the Trail of the Missing Ozone, an online book, tells why we need the ozone layer and how to prevent ozone depletion. You can read it at www.epa.gov/ozone/science/missoz/index.html. Share what you learn with the class.

773

What Can You Do? Teacher Tips

Get Involved Suggest that students create posters as part of the campaign. Remind them that, for younger students, their posters will be more effective if they rely on strong visuals rather than on verbal information.

Find Out More The book "On the Trail of the Missing Ozone" is available in comic strip form, as a text-only document, and in downloadable Adobe Acrobat format. To save time, you might wish to download and print out the document.

Skin Cancer Australia's sunny climate has its drawbacks. Sunburn and sunstroke are major health hazards, and Australians have one of the highest incidences of skin cancer in the world. The problem, of course, extends beyond Australia. Point out that there are nearly 40,000 new cases of melanoma—one type of skin cancer—in the United States each year, that the rate is growing faster than that of any other kind of cancer, and that the rate is expected to increase as the ozone layer continues to be depleted. Explain what steps students can take to limit those dangers, such as avoiding the sun in the middle of the day, wearing adequate clothing and hats, and using sunscreen.

Have students work individually or in groups to complete the What Can You Do? activities.

Discuss with students the What Can You Do? activities. Remind students that they also should follow the precautions for being in the sun.

For an additional regional case study, use the following:

Environmental Case Study

Appendix

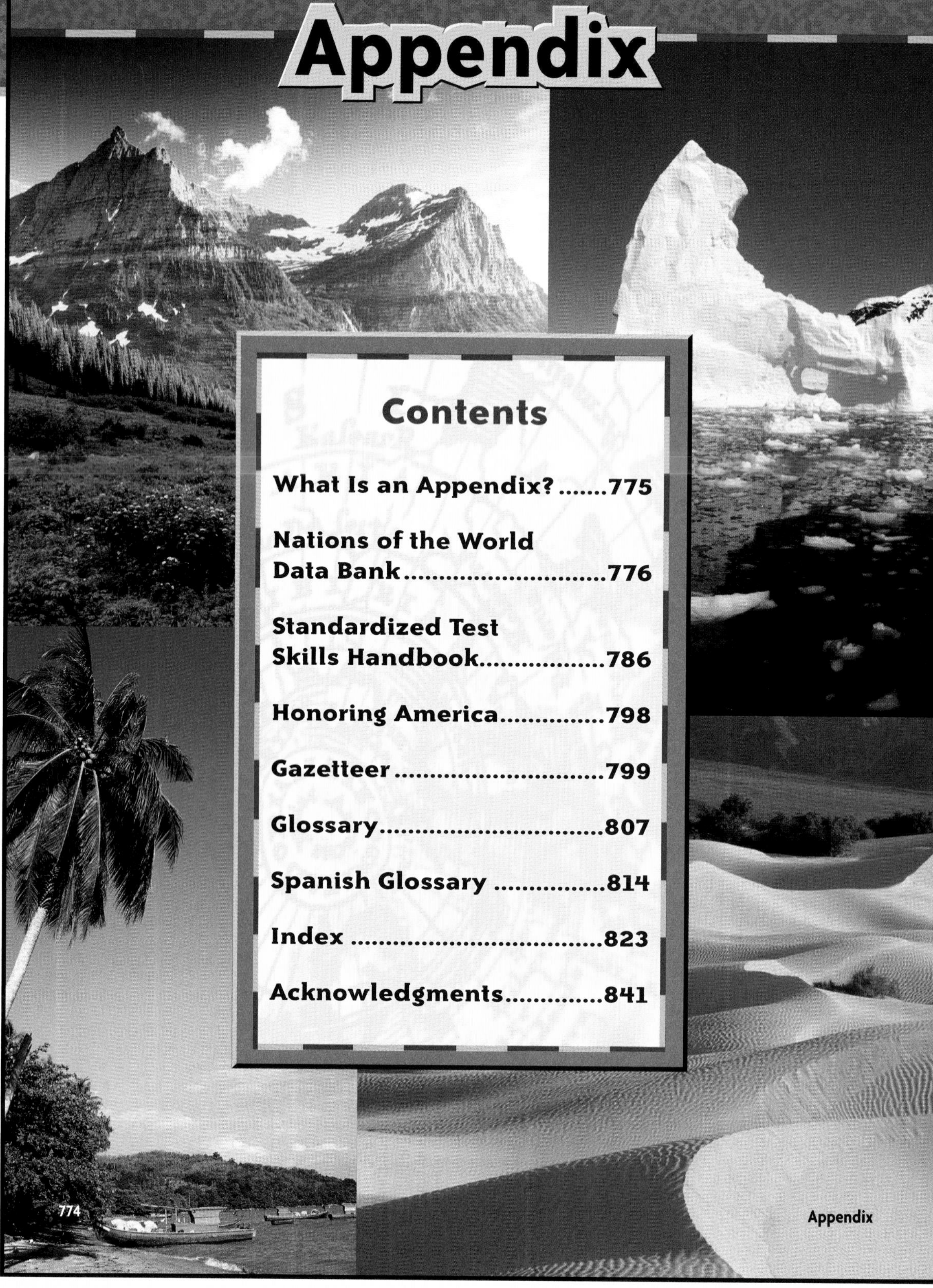

Contents

What Is an Appendix? 775

Nations of the World Data Bank 776

Standardized Test Skills Handbook 786

Honoring America 798

Gazetteer 799

Glossary 807

Spanish Glossary 814

Index 823

Acknowledgments 841

774

Appendix

What Is an Appendix?

An appendix is the additional material you often find at the end of books. The information below will help you learn how to use the Appendix in *The World and Its People.*

NATIONS OF THE WORLD DATA BANK

The **Nations of the World Data Bank** that begins on page 776 lists all of the world's countries and various categories of information for each. For example, each country's type of government, form of currency, and literacy rate—among other topics—are listed in the data bank.

SKILLS HANDBOOK

The **Standardized Test Skills Handbook** requires you to learn and apply many key skills that you will use throughout the study of geography as well as other subject areas.

GAZETTEER

A **gazetteer** is a geographical dictionary. It lists many important geographic features, most of the world's countries, and many cities of the world. Each entry also includes latitude and longitude and a page number where each entry can be found on a map in your textbook.

GLOSSARY AND SPANISH GLOSSARY

A **glossary** is a list of important or difficult terms found in a textbook. The glossary gives a definition of each term as it is used in the book. Since words sometimes have other meanings, you may wish to consult a dictionary to find other uses for the term. The glossary also includes page numbers telling you where in the textbook the term is used. The **Spanish glossary** is the English glossary translated into Spanish.

INDEX

An **index** is an alphabetical listing at the end of a book that includes the subjects of that book and the page numbers where those subjects can be found. The index in this book also lets you know that certain pages contain maps, graphs, photos, or paintings about the subject.

ACKNOWLEDGMENTS

This section lists photo credits and/or literary credits for the book. You can look at this section to find out where the publisher obtained the permission to use photographs or to use excerpts from other books.

Test Yourself!

Do you think you can use an appendix quickly and easily? Try it. Find the answers to these questions by using the Appendix on the following pages.

1. **What does *canopy* mean?**
2. **Where did you find what the word *canopy* means?**
3. **What is the Spanish word for *cassava?***
4. **What kind of currency does Spain use?**
5. **What are the latitude and longitude of Moscow?**
6. **On what pages can you find information about Cuba?**

Appendix User Tip

When using an appendix, be sure to notice and use the guide words at the top of the page. These guide words indicate the alphabetically first and last entries on that page.

Test Yourself! Answers

1. The definition of *canopy* is: the umbrella-like covering formed by the tops of trees in a rain forest.
2. Students can find this information in the Glossary.
3. Students can find the Spanish word for *cassava*, which is *yuca*, in the Spanish Glossary.
4. Students can find this answer by looking in the Nations of the World Data Bank. Spain's currency is the euro.
5. Students should look in the Gazetteer to find this information. It is 56°N 38°E.
6. Have students find Cuba in the Index.

By definition, an appendix is supplementary material attached to the end of a piece of writing. Students can use appendices to help them navigate through and understand the main material in their textbooks. Explain to them that they may use an appendix to find out what a word means, how to pronounce a word, or where else in the book they could find additional information about a particular word or topic.

Appendix User Tip

Be sure to review the beginning page of each section of an appendix. Often, the first page of a section contains a key that explains symbols or terms used in the entries of that section. For example, the abbreviation *ptg*, used in several index entries, refers to specific paintings that appear in the book.

Other Useful Information Found in Books:

Explain to students that useful material appears in the front of the book. Usually this information includes the following:

- The **title page** contains the book title, author's name, and the name of the publisher.
- The **copyright page** gives the publication date. Students should check this date to determine how current the book is.
- The **table of contents** lists the main topics covered in the book.

Nations of the World
DATA BANK

Today we are learning to understand the connected world in which we live. As technology makes communication easier, we interact globally more than ever. Each country has its own unique identity, however. Using this chart will help you compare and contrast information about government, economy, and culture.

COUNTRY Capital	GOVERNMENT: Type of Government	GOVERNMENT: Date Founded	ECONOMICS: *GNP Ranking	ECONOMICS: GNP Per Capita	ECONOMICS: Currency	SOCIAL & CULTURAL: Literacy	SOCIAL & CULTURAL: **Infant Mortality	SOCIAL & CULTURAL: Primary Religion(s)
Afghanistan Kabul	Republic	2001	101st	$270	Afghani	36%	143	Muslim
Albania Tirana	Republic	1991	131st	$760	Lek	87%	37	Muslim, Eastern Orthodox, Catholic
Algeria Algiers	Republic	1962	52nd	$1,500	Algerian Dinar	70%	38	Muslim
Andorra Andorra la Vella	Parliamentary Democracy	1993	155th	$15,600	Euro	100%	4	Catholic
Angola Luanda	Republic	1975	126th	$260	Kwanza	42%	194	Indigenous, Catholic, Protestant
Antigua and Barbuda St. John's	Parliamentary Democracy	1981	166th	$7,380	E. Car. Dollar	89%	21	Protestant, Catholic
Argentina Buenos Aires	Republic	1816	17th	$8,950	Argentine Peso	97%	16	Catholic
Armenia Yerevan	Republic	1991	137th	$560	Dram	99%	41	Eastern Orthodox
Australia Canberra	Parliamentary Democracy	1901	14th	$20,650	Australian Dollar	100%	5	Protestant, Catholic
Austria Vienna	Federal Republic	1918	22nd	$27,920	Euro	98%	4	Catholic
Azerbaijan Baku	Republic	1991	118th	$510	Manat	97%	82	Muslim
Bahamas Nassau	Parliamentary Democracy	1973	124th	$11,940	Bahamian Dollar	96%	26	Protestant, Catholic

*Gross National Product

**deaths/1,000 live births

COUNTRY Capital	Type of Government	Date Founded	*GNP Ranking	GNP Per Capita	Currency	Literacy	**Infant Mortality	Primary Religion(s)
Bahrain Manama	Monarchy	1971	104th	$7,800	Bahrain Dinar	89%	19	Muslim
Bangladesh Dhaka	Republic	1971	51st	$360	Taka	43%	66	Muslim, Hindu
Barbados Bridgetown	Parliamentary Democracy	1966	145th	$6,560	Barbados Dollar	97%	13	Protestant
Belarus Minsk	Republic	1991	61st	$2,150	Belarus Ruble	100%	14	Eastern Orthodox
Belgium Brussels	Constitutional Monarchy	1830	19th	$26,730	Euro	98%	5	Catholic, Protestant
Belize Belmopan	Parliamentary Democracy	1981	162nd	$2,670	Belizean Dollar	94%	27	Catholic, Protestant
Benin Porto-Novo	Republic	1960	133rd	$380	CFA Franc	41%	87	Indigenous, Christian, Muslim
Bhutan Thimphu	Constitutional Monarchy	1907	172nd	$430	Ngultrum	42%	105	Buddhist, Hindu
Bolivia La Paz, Sucre	Republic	1825	91st	$970	Boliviano	87%	56	Catholic
Bosnia and Herzegovina Sarajevo	Republic	1992	160th	$288	Marka	93%	23	Muslim, Eastern Orthodox, Catholic
Botswana Gaborone	Republic	1966	105th	$3,310	Pula	80%	67	Indigenous, Christian
Brazil Brasília	Federal Republic	1889	8th	$4,790	Real	86%	32	Catholic
Brunei Bandar Seri Begawan	Constitutional Monarchy	1984	116th	$14,240	Brunei Dollar	92%	14	Muslim, Buddhist, Christian
Bulgaria Sofia	Republic	1991	82nd	$1,170	Lev	99%	14	Eastern Orthodox, Muslim
Burkina Faso Ouagadougou	Republic	1960	130th	$250	CFA Franc	27%	100	Muslim, Indigenous
Burundi Bujumbura	Republic	1966	157th	$140	Burundi Franc	52%	72	Christian, Indigenous
Cambodia Phnom Penh	Constitutional Monarchy	1953	125th	$300	Riel	70%	76	Buddhist
Cameroon Yaoundé	Republic	1960	86th	$620	CFA Franc	79%	70	Indigenous, Christian, Muslim
Canada Ottawa	Parliamentary Democracy	1867	9th	$19,640	Canadian Dollar	97%	5	Catholic, Protestant
Cape Verde Praia	Republic	1975	169th	$1,090	Escudo	77%	51	Catholic, Protestant
Central African Republic Bangui	Republic	1960	152nd	$320	CFA Franc	51%	93	Indigenous, Protestant, Catholic, Muslim

*Gross National Product

**deaths/1,000 live births

COUNTRY Capital	Type of Government	Date Founded	*GNP Ranking	GNP Per Capita	Currency	Literacy	**Infant Mortality	Primary Religion(s)
Chad N'Djamena	Republic	1960	147th	$230	CFA Franc	48%	96	Muslim, Christian
Chile Santiago	Republic	1823	43rd	$4,820	Chilean Peso	96%	9	Catholic, Protestant
China Beijing	Communist State	1949	7th	$860	Yuan	82%	25	Atheist, Buddhist, Daoist, Confucian
Colombia Bogotá	Republic	1819	39th	$2,180	Colombian Peso	93%	23	Catholic
Comoros Moroni	Republic	1975	181st	$400	Comoran Franc	57%	80	Muslim
Congo, Democratic Republic of the Kinshasa	Dictatorship	1960	103rd	$110	Congolese Franc	66%	97	Catholic, Protestant
Congo, Republic of the Brazzaville	Republic	1960	144th	$670	CFA Franc	84%	95	Christian, Indigenous
Costa Rica San José	Republic	1838	85th	$2,680	Colón	96%	11	Catholic
Côte d'Ivoire Yamoussoukro, Abidjan	Republic	1960	81st	$710	CFA Franc	51%	98	Muslim, Indigenous, Christian
Croatia Zagreb	Republic	1991	69th	$4,060	Kuna	99%	7	Catholic
Cuba Havana	Communist State	1959	72nd	$1,650	Cuban Peso	97%	7	Catholic
Cyprus Nicosia	Republic	1960	92nd	$9,400	Cyprus Pound	98%	8	Eastern Orthodox, Muslim
Czech Republic Prague	Republic	1993	48th	$5,240	Koruna	100%	5	Atheist, Catholic
Denmark Copenhagen	Constitutional Monarchy	1849	25th	$38,890	Krone	100%	5	Protestant
Djibouti Djibouti	Republic	1977	167th	$750	Djibouti Franc	68%	107	Muslim
Dominica Roseau	Republic	1978	179th	$3,040	E. Car. Dollar	94%	15	Catholic, Protestant
Dominican Republic Santo Domingo	Republic	1865	76th	$1,750	Dom. Rep. Peso	85%	34	Catholic
East Timor Dili	Republic	2002	—	—	U.S. Dollar	48%	50	Catholic
Ecuador Quito	Republic	1830	71st	$1,570	Sucre	93%	32	Catholic
Egypt Cairo	Republic	1953	42nd	$1,200	Egyptian Pound	58%	35	Muslim
El Salvador San Salvador	Republic	1841	78th	$1,810	Colón	80%	27	Catholic

*Gross National Product

**deaths/1,000 live births

COUNTRY Capital	Type of Government	Date Founded	*GNP Ranking	GNP Per Capita	Currency	Literacy	**Infant Mortality	Primary Religion(s)
Equatorial Guinea Malabo	Republic	1968	168th	$1,060	CFA Franc	86%	89	Catholic
Eritrea Asmara	Republic	1993	158th	$230	Nakfa	59%	76	Muslim, Christian
Estonia Tallinn	Republic	1991	107th	$3,360	Kroon	100%	12	Protestant
Ethiopia Addis Ababa	Federal Republic	1995	99th	$110	Birr	43%	103	Muslim, Eastern Orthodox, Indigenous
Fiji Islands Suva	Republic	1987	139th	$2,460	Fiji Dollar	94%	13	Christian, Hindu
Finland Helsinki	Republic	1917	31st	$24,790	Euro	100%	4	Protestant
France Paris	Republic	1958	4th	$26,300	Euro	99%	4	Catholic
Gabon Libreville	Republic	1960	110th	$4,120	CFA Franc	63%	55	Christian
Gambia Banjul	Republic	1970	170th	$340	Dalasi	40%	75	Muslim
Georgia T'bilisi	Republic	1991	111th	$860	Lari	99%	51	Eastern Orthodox, Muslim
Germany Berlin	Federal Republic	1949	3rd	$28,280	Euro	99%	4	Protestant, Catholic
Ghana Accra	Republic	1960	95th	$390	Cedi	75%	53	Christian, Indigenous, Muslim
Greece Athens	Republic	1975	32nd	$11,640	Euro	98%	6	Eastern Orthodox
Grenada St. George's	Parliamentary Democracy	1974	174th	$3,140	E. Car. Dollar	98%	17	Catholic, Protestant
Guatemala Guatemala City	Republic	1838	74th	$1,580	Quetzal	71%	38	Catholic, Protestant
Guinea Conakry	Republic	1958	119th	$550	Guinean Franc	36%	93	Muslim
Guinea-Bissau Bissau	Republic	1974	176th	$230	Guinea Peso	42%	110	Indigenous, Muslim
Guyana Georgetown	Republic	1970	162nd	$800	Guy. Dollar	99%	38	Christian, Hindu
Haiti Port-au-Prince	Republic	1804	128th	$380	Gourde	53%	76	Catholic, Protestant
Honduras Tegucigalpa	Republic	1838	113th	$740	Lempira	76%	30	Catholic
Hungary Budapest	Republic	1989	50th	$4,510	Forint	99%	9	Catholic, Protestant

*Gross National Product

**deaths/1,000 live births

COUNTRY Capital	Type of Government	Date Founded	*GNP Ranking	GNP Per Capita	Currency	Literacy	**Infant Mortality	Primary Religion(s)
Iceland Reykjavík	Republic	1944	94th	$26,580	Icelandic Króna	100%	4	Protestant
India New Delhi	Federal Republic	1950	15th	$370	Indian Rupee	60%	60	Hindu, Muslim
Indonesia Jakarta	Republic	1949	23rd	$1,110	Rupiah	89%	38	Muslim
Iran Tehran	Islamic Republic	1979	34th	$1,780	Iranian Rial	79%	44	Muslim
Iraq Baghdad	Transitional Government	1958	65th	$950	Iraqi Dinar	40%	55	Muslim
Ireland Dublin	Republic	1949	44th	$17,790	Euro	98%	5	Catholic
Israel Jerusalem[1]	Republic	1948	37th	$16,180	Shekel	95%	7	Jewish, Muslim
Italy Rome	Republic	1946	6th	$20,170	Euro	99%	6	Catholic
Jamaica Kingston	Parliamentary Democracy	1962	117th	$1,550	Jamaican Dollar	88%	13	Protestant
Japan Tokyo	Constitutional Monarchy	1947	2nd	$38,160	Yen	99%	3	Shinto, Buddhist
Jordan Amman	Constitutional Monarchy	1946	96th	$1,520	Jordanian Dinar	91%	19	Muslim
Kazakhstan Astana	Republic	1991	62nd	$1,350	Tenge	98%	59	Muslim, Eastern Orthodox
Kenya Nairobi	Republic	1964	83rd	$340	Kenyan Shilling	85%	63	Protestant, Catholic, Indigenous
Kiribati Tarawa	Republic	1979	188th	$910	Australian Dollar	98%	51	Catholic, Protestant
Korea, North Pyongyang	Communist State	1948	64th	$1,390	Won	99%	26	Atheist, Buddhist, Confucian
Korea, South Seoul	Republic	1948	11th	$10,550	Won	98%	7	Christian, Buddhist
Kuwait Kuwait	Constitutional Monarchy	1961	58th	$17,390	Kuwaiti Dinar	84%	11	Muslim
Kyrgyzstan Bishkek	Republic	1991	134th	$480	Som	97%	75	Muslim, Eastern Orthodox
Laos Vientiane	Communist State	1975	142nd	$400	Kip	53%	89	Buddhist
Latvia Rīga	Republic	1991	100th	$2,430	Lat	100%	15	Protestant, Catholic, Eastern Orthodox
Lebanon Beirut	Republic	1944	77th	$3,350	Lebanese Pound	87%	26	Muslim, Christian

[1] Most countries maintain embassies in Tel Aviv.

*Gross National Product

**deaths/1,000 live births

COUNTRY Capital	GOVERNMENT Type of Government	Date Founded	ECONOMICS *GNP Ranking	GNP Per Capita	Currency	SOCIAL & CULTURAL Literacy	**Infant Mortality	Primary Religion(s)
Lesotho Maseru	Constitutional Monarchy	1966	150th	$680	Loti	85%	86	Christian, Indigenous
Liberia Monrovia	Republic	1847	154th	$330	Liberian Dollar	58%	132	Indigenous, Christian, Muslim
Libya Tripoli	Military Dictatorship	1969	57th	$5,220	Libyan Dinar	83%	27	Muslim
Liechtenstein Vaduz	Constitutional Monarchy	1719	151st	$40,000	Swiss Franc	100%	5	Catholic
Lithuania Vilnius	Republic	1991	88th	$2,260	Litas	100%	14	Catholic
Luxembourg Luxembourg	Constitutional Monarchy	1868	70th	$45,360	Euro	100%	5	Catholic
Macedonia, Former Yugoslav Republic of Skopje	Republic	1991	135th	$1,100	Macedonia Denar	94%	12	Eastern Orthodox, Muslim
Madagascar Antananarivo	Republic	1960	120th	$250	Ariary	69%	80	Indigenous, Christian
Malawi Lilongwe	Republic	1966	136th	$210	Kwacha	63%	105	Protestant, Catholic, Muslim
Malaysia Kuala Lumpur	Constitutional Monarchy	1963	36th	$4,530	Ringgit	89%	19	Muslim, Buddhist, Daoist, Confucian
Maldives Male	Republic	1965	173rd	$1,180	Rufiyaa	97%	60	Muslim
Mali Bamako	Republic	1960	129th	$260	CFA Franc	46%	119	Muslim
Malta Valletta	Republic	1974	122nd	$9,330	Maltese Lira	93%	6	Catholic
Marshall Islands Majuro	Republic	1986	185th	$1,610	U.S. Dollar	94%	32	Protestant
Mauritania Nouakchott	Islamic Republic	1960	153rd	$440	Ouguiya	42%	74	Muslim
Mauritius Port Louis	Republic	1992	112th	$3,870	Mauritian Rupee	86%	16	Hindu, Catholic, Muslim
Mexico Mexico City	Federal Republic	1823	16th	$3,700	Mexican Peso	93%	24	Catholic
Micronesia, Federated States of Palikir	Republic	1986	180th	$1,920	U.S. Dollar	89%	32	Catholic, Protestant
Moldova Chişinău	Republic	1991	140th	$460	Leu	99%	42	Eastern Orthodox
Monaco Monaco	Constitutional Monarchy	1911	106th	$11,000	Euro	99%	6	Catholic

*Gross National Product

**deaths/1,000 live births

COUNTRY Capital	GOVERNMENT: Type of Government	Date Founded	ECONOMICS: *GNP Ranking	GNP Per Capita	Currency	SOCIAL & CULTURAL: Literacy	**Infant Mortality	Primary Religion(s)
Mongolia Ulaanbaatar	Republic	1992	156th	$390	Tugrik	99%	57	Buddhism
Morocco Rabat	Constitutional Monarchy	1956	54th	$1,260	Dirham	52%	45	Muslim
Mozambique Maputo	Republic	1975	132nd	$140	Metical	48%	199	Indigenous, Christian, Muslim
Myanmar Yangon	Military Dictatorship	1948	41st	$1,500	Kyat	83%	70	Buddhist
Namibia Windhoek	Republic	1990	123rd	$2,110	Namibian Dollar	84%	68	Christian, Indigenous
Nauru Yaren	Republic	1968	187th	$7,270	Australian Dollar	95%	10	Protestant, Catholic
Nepal Kathmandu	Constitutional Monarchy	1990	108th	$220	Nepalese Rupee	45%	71	Hindu
Netherlands Amsterdam	Constitutional Monarchy	1815	12th	$25,830	Euro	99%	4	Catholic, Protestant
New Zealand Wellington	Parliamentary Democracy	1907	47th	$15,820	N. Zealand Dollar	99%	6	Protestant, Catholic
Nicaragua Managua	Republic	1838	143rd	$410	Gold Cordoba	68%	31	Catholic
Niger Niamey	Republic	1960	141st	$200	CFA Franc	18%	124	Muslim
Nigeria Abuja	Federal Republic	1963	55th	$280	Naira	68%	71	Muslim, Christian, Indigenous
Norway Oslo	Constitutional Monarchy	1905	27th	$36,100	Norwegian Krone	100%	4	Protestant
Oman Muscat	Traditional Monarchy	1970	79th	$4,820	Omani Rial	76%	21	Muslim
Pakistan Islamabad	Federal Republic	1956	45th	$500	Pakistani Rupee	46%	77	Muslim
Palau Koror	Republic	1994	186th	$5,000	U.S. Dollar	92%	16	Christian, Indigenous
Panama Panama City	Republic	1903	92nd	$2,670	Balboa	93%	21	Catholic, Protestant
Papua New Guinea Port Moresby	Parliamentary Democracy	1975	115th	$930	Kina	66%	55	Indigenous, Catholic, Protestant
Paraguay Asunción	Republic	1811	80th	$200	Guaraní	94%	28	Catholic
Peru Lima	Republic	1824	46th	$2,610	Nuevo Sol	91%	37	Catholic
Philippines Manila	Republic	1946	38th	$1,200	Philippine Peso	96%	25	Catholic

*Gross National Product

**deaths/1,000 live births

COUNTRY Capital	Type of Government	Date Founded	*GNP Ranking	GNP Per Capita	Currency	Literacy	**Infant Mortality	Primary Religion(s)
Poland Warsaw	Republic	1990	29th	$3,590	Zloty	100%	9	Catholic
Portugal Lisbon	Republic	1910	33rd	$11,010	Euro	93%	6	Catholic
Qatar Doha	Traditional Monarchy	1971	93rd	$11,600	Qatari Riyal	83%	20	Muslim
Romania Bucharest	Republic	1991	56th	$1,410	Leu	99%	18	Eastern Orthodox
Russia Moscow	Federal Republic	1991	13th	$2,680	Ruble	99%	20	Eastern Orthodox
Rwanda Kigali	Republic	1962	146th	$210	Rwandan Franc	70%	103	Catholic, Protestant
St. Kitts and Nevis Basseterre	Parliamentary Democracy	1983	177th	$6,260	E. Car. Dollar	97%	15	Protestant, Catholic
St. Lucia Castries	Parliamentary Democracy	1979	163rd	$3,510	E. Car. Dollar	67%	14	Catholic, Protestant
St. Vincent and the Grenadines Kingstown	Parliamentary Democracy	1979	175th	$2,420	E. Car. Dollar	96%	15	Protestant, Catholic
Samoa Apia	Constitutional Monarchy	1962	182nd	$1,140	Tala	100%	30	Christian
San Marino San Marino	Republic	1600	183rd	$7,830	Euro	96%	6	Catholic
Sao Tome and Principe São Tomé	Republic	1975	189th	$290	Dobra	79%	46	Catholic, Protestant
Saudi Arabia Riyadh	Traditional Monarchy	1932	187th	$7,150	Saudi Riyal	79%	48	Muslim
Senegal Dakar	Republic	1960	109th	$540	CFA Franc	40%	58	Muslim
Serbia and Montenegro Belgrade	Republic	2002	84th	$900	Dinar, Euro	93%	17	Eastern Orthodox, Muslim
Seychelles Victoria	Republic	1976	165th	$6,910	S. Rupee	58%	16	Catholic
Sierra Leone Freetown	Republic	1971	161st	$160	Leone	31%	147	Muslim, Indigenous, Christian
Singapore Singapore	Republic	1965	35th	$32,810	Singapore Dollar	93%	4	Buddhism, Muslim
Slovakia Bratislava	Republic	1993	66th	$3,680	Koruna	100%	9	Catholic, Protestant
Slovenia Ljubljana	Republic	1991	67th	$9,840	Tolar	100%	4	Catholic

*Gross National Product

**deaths/1,000 live births

COUNTRY Capital	GOVERNMENT: Type of Government	GOVERNMENT: Date Founded	ECONOMICS: *GNP Ranking	ECONOMICS: GNP Per Capita	ECONOMICS: Currency	SOCIAL & CULTURAL: Literacy	SOCIAL & CULTURAL: **Infant Mortality	SOCIAL & CULTURAL: Primary Religion(s)
Solomon Islands Honiara	Parliamentary Democracy	1978	171st	$870	Solomon Is. Dollar	54%	23	Protestant, Catholic
Somalia Mogadishu	Transitional Government	1960	159th	$100	Somali Shilling	38%	120	Muslim
South Africa Bloemfontein, Cape Town, Pretoria	Republic	1961	30th	$3,210	Rand	86%	61	Christian, Indigenous
Spain Madrid	Constitutional Monarchy	1978	10th	$14,490	Euro	98%	5	Catholic
Sri Lanka Colombo	Republic	1972	75th	$800	Sri Lankan Rupee	92%	15	Buddhist, Hindu
Sudan Khartoum	Republic	1956	90th	$290	Sudanese Dinar	61%	66	Muslim, Indigenous
Suriname Paramaribo	Republic	1975	164th	$1,320	Guilder	93%	25	Hindu, Protestant, Catholic, Muslim
Swaziland Mbabane	Monarchy	1968	149th	$1,520	Lilangeni	82%	67	Christian, Indigenous
Sweden Stockholm	Constitutional Monarchy	1809	21st	$26,210	Swedish Krona	99%	3	Protestant
Switzerland Bern	Federal Republic	1848	18th	$26,210	Swiss Franc	99%	4	Catholic, Protestant
Syria Damascus	Republic	1946	73rd	$1,120	Syrian Pound	77%	32	Muslim
Taiwan Taipei	Republic	1949	20th	$10,320	Taiwanese Dollar	86%	7	Buddhist, Confucian, Daoist
Tajikistan Dushanbe	Republic	1991	138th	$330	Somoni	99%	113	Muslim
Tanzania Dar es Salaam	Republic	1964	97th	$210	Tanzanian Shilling	78%	104	Muslim, Indigenous, Christian
Thailand Bangkok	Constitutional Monarchy	1932	26th	$2,740	Baht	96%	22	Buddhism
Togo Lomé	Republic	1960	148th	$340	CFA Franc	61%	69	Indigenous, Christian, Muslim
Tonga Nuku'alofa	Constitutional Monarchy	1970	184th	$1,810	Pa'anga	99%	13	Christian
Trinidad and Tobago Port-of-Spain	Republic	1976	102nd	$4,250	T&T Dollar	99%	25	Catholic, Hindu, Protestant
Tunisia Tunis	Republic	1956	68th	$2,110	Tunisian Dinar	74%	27	Muslim
Turkey Ankara	Republic	1923	24th	$3,130	Turkish Lira	87%	44	Muslim
Turkmenistan Ashgabat	Republic	1991	127th	$640	Manat	98%	73	Muslim

*Gross National Product

**deaths/1,000 live births

COUNTRY Capital	GOVERNMENT: Type of Government	GOVERNMENT: Date Founded	ECONOMICS: *GNP Ranking	ECONOMICS: GNP Per Capita	ECONOMICS: Currency	SOCIAL & CULTURAL: Literacy	SOCIAL & CULTURAL: **Infant Mortality	SOCIAL & CULTURAL: Primary Religion(s)
Tuvalu Funafuti	Parliamentary Democracy	1978	190th	$330	Australian Dollar	55%	21	Protestant
Uganda Kampala	Republic	1963	98th	$330	Ugandan Shilling	70%	88	Catholic, Protestant, Indigenous, Muslim
Ukraine Kiev	Republic	1991	49th	$1,335	Hryvnia	100%	21	Eastern Orthodox
United Arab Emirates Abu Dhabi	Federal Monarchy	1971	53rd	$17,400	U.A.E. Dirhem	78%	16	Muslim
United Kingdom London	Constitutional Monarchy	1707	5th	$20,870	Pound Sterling	99%	5	Protestant, Catholic
United States Washington, D.C.	Federal Republic	1776	1st	$29,080	U.S. Dollar	97%	7	Protestant, Catholic
Uruguay Montevideo	Republic	1828	63rd	$6,130	Uruguay Peso	98%	14	Catholic
Uzbekistan Tashkent	Republic	1991	59th	$1,020	Sum	99%	72	Muslim
Vanuatu Port-Vila	Republic	1980	178th	$1,340	Vatu	53%	58	Protestant, Catholic
Vatican City —	Sovereign State under the Pope	1929	—	—	Euro	100%	—	Catholic
Venezuela Caracas	Federal Republic	1821	40th	$3,480	Bolivar	93%	24	Catholic
Vietnam Hanoi	Communist State	1954	60th	$310	Dong	94%	31	Buddhist
Yemen Sanaa	Republic	1990	114th	$270	Rial	50%	65	Muslim
Zambia Lusaka	Republic	1964	121st	$370	Zambian Kwacha	81%	99	Christian, Muslim, Hindu
Zimbabwe Harare	Republic	1980	89th	$720	Zimbabwe Dollar	91%	66	Christian, Indigenous

*Gross National Product

**deaths/1,000 live births

TEACH

Have students write down everything they associate with the word "test." Ask them to list helpful hints for taking tests. Lead a class discussion on successful test-taking strategies. For example, suggest that when taking tests students look for clues in the question that support their answers, eliminate answers that do not make sense, and read the titles or keys of any graphics presented (graphs, charts, time lines, maps).

Standardized Test Skills Handbook

Standardized tests are one way educators measure what you have learned. This handbook is designed to help you practice for standardized test questions. On the pages that follow, you will find a review of the major critical thinking skills that you will need to master to be successful when taking tests.

Contents

Interpreting a Map 787
Interpreting a Political Map 788
Interpreting Charts 789
Making Comparisons 790
Interpreting Primary Sources 791
Interpreting a Political Cartoon 792
Interpreting a Circle Graph 793
Drawing Inferences and Conclusions 794
Comparing Data 795
Categorizing and Analyzing Information 796
Sequencing Events 797

Additional Glencoe TEST PRACTICE RESOURCES:

The following materials are available for further test practice:

- Glencoe Skillbuilder Interactive Workbook, Level 1
- ExamView® Pro Testmaker CD-ROM
- Reading Essentials and Study Guide
- Quizzes, Tests, and Performance Assessment
- 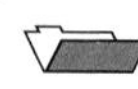 Critical Thinking Skills Activities
-  Standardized Test Skills Practice Workbook
-  Daily Focus Skills Transparencies

Interpreting a Map

Before 1492, people living in Europe in the Eastern Hemisphere had no idea that the continents of North America and South America in the Western Hemisphere existed. That was the year Christopher Columbus first reached the Americas. His voyage of exploration paved the way for other European voyages to the Western Hemisphere. The voyages of the early explorers brought together two worlds. Previously these parts of the globe had no contact with each other. Trade between the hemispheres changed life for people on both sides of the Atlantic Ocean. The trade between the peoples of the Eastern Hemisphere and the Western Hemisphere is referred to as the Columbian Exchange.

NATIONAL GEOGRAPHIC **The Columbian Exchange**

Skills Practice

Although globes are the best, most accurate way to show places on the round earth, people can more easily use maps to represent places. A map is made by taking data from a round globe and placing it on a flat surface. To read a map, first read the title to determine the subject of the map. Then read the map key or the labels on the map to find out what the colors and symbols on the map mean. Use the compass rose to identify the four cardinal directions of north, south, east, and west. Study the map of the Columbian Exchange and answer the questions that follow on a separate sheet of paper.

1. What is the subject of the map?
2. What do the arrows represent?
3. What continents are shown on the map?
4. What foods did Europeans acquire from the Americas?
5. What did the Americas acquire from Europe?
6. What people were brought from Africa to the Americas?
7. In what direction is Europe from the Americas?

Standardized Test Practice

DIRECTIONS: Use the map and your knowledge of social studies to answer the following question on a separate sheet of paper.

1. Which of the following statements about the Columbian Exchange is true?
   - **A** Food products were traded only between Africa and the Americas.
   - **B** Europeans acquired cattle from the Americas.
   - **C** Europeans introduced corn, tomatoes, and beans to Native Americans.
   - **D** Enslaved Africans were brought to the Americas.

TEACH

Write the following on the overhead or board: "In fourteen hundred ninety-two, Columbus sailed the ocean blue." Ask students to analyze the verse. **Ask: What is the significance of 1492? What century is represented by that date? Who was Columbus? To which ocean does the verse refer?**

Review the steps of reading a map with students. (1. Read all the map labels; 2. Identify each symbol and color shown in the map key and locate these on the map; 3. Use this information to look for similarities and differences in the regions shown on the map.)

Skills Practice Answers:

1. the Columbian Exchange
2. trade routes between continents or hemispheres
3. North America, South America, Europe, Africa
4. corn, beans, chocolate
5. cattle, horses, wheat, diseases
6. enslaved people
7. east

Standardized Test Practice Answer:

1. D

Test-Taking Strategy: Have students study the map carefully before answering the question. They should then eliminate answers they know are incorrect or do not make sense.

TEACH

Ask students: **Why did people come to live in the British colonies in North America?** Have students discuss the many reasons why someone might want to go on a dangerous voyage to a new land. *(Students should be able to explain that the various colonies were founded and populated for religious freedom, for profit, for trade, for political freedom, and to escape debt.)*

Remind students to use the various parts of the map to help them interpret it. These map parts include the map key, labels, and compass rose.

Skills Practice Answers:

1. Massachusetts, Rhode Island, New Hampshire, Connecticut
2. New Jersey, Pennsylvania, New York, Delaware
3. New York
4. Georgia
5. Atlantic Ocean
6. in the Southern Colonies; in South Carolina

Interpreting a Political Map

By 1750, or the middle of the eighteenth century, there were 13 British colonies in North America. A colony is a group of people living in one place who are governed by rulers in another place. The British colonists in America were ruled by the monarchy and Parliament of Great Britain. That meant that rulers living 3,000 miles away made laws for the American colonists.

Skills Practice

Political maps illustrate divisions between territories such as nations, states, colonies, or other political units. These divisions are called boundaries. Lines represent the boundaries between political areas. To interpret a political map, read the map title to determine what geographic area and time period it covers. Identify the colonies or other political units on the map. Look at the map key for additional information. Study the map on this page and answer the questions that follow on a separate sheet of paper.

1. List the New England Colonies.
2. Which were the Middle Colonies?
3. Which Middle Colony bordered Pennsylvania to the north?
4. Which was the southernmost early British colony?
5. Name the body of water that formed the eastern border of the colonies.
6. Where was Charles Town located?

NATIONAL GEOGRAPHIC **The Thirteen Colonies, 1750**

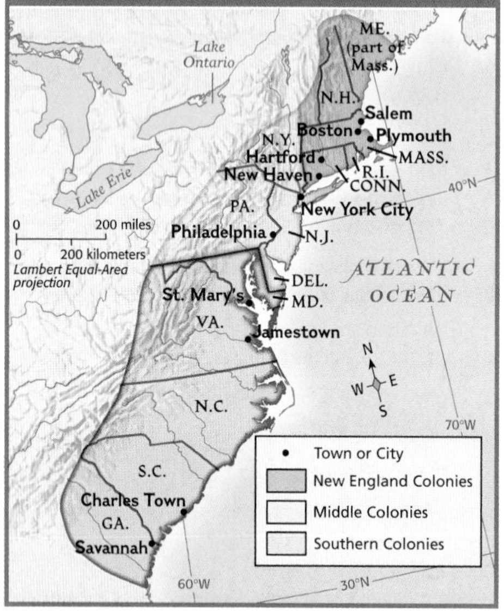

Standardized Test Practice

DIRECTIONS: Use the map and your knowledge of social studies to answer the following questions on a separate sheet of paper.

1. The New England Colony that covered the largest land area was
   - **A** Virginia.
   - **B** Pennsylvania.
   - **C** Massachusetts.
   - **D** New Hampshire.
2. The northernmost Middle Colony is the present-day state of
   - **F** Maryland.
   - **G** New York.
   - **H** Massachusetts.
   - **J** Pennsylvania.
3. The settlement of Plymouth was located
   - **A** near Jamestown.
   - **B** in Massachusetts.
   - **C** in the Southern Colonies.
   - **D** in Virginia.

Standardized Test Practice Answers:

1. C
Test-Taking Strategy: Be sure students identify the New England Colonies before they choose their answer.
2. G
Test-Taking Strategy: Tell students: First locate the Middle Colonies. Next determine which Middle Colony is farthest north.
3. B
Test-Taking Strategy: Have students answer the question before reviewing the choices to see which choice matches their answer.

Interpreting Charts

Government is a necessary part of every nation. It gives citizens stability and provides services that many of us take for granted. However, governments can sometimes have too much power.

The United States was founded on the principle of limited government. Limited governments require all people to follow the laws. Even the rulers must obey rules set for the society. A democracy is a form of limited government. Not all forms of government have limits. In unlimited governments, power belongs to the ruler. No laws exist to limit what the ruler may do. A dictatorship is an example of an unlimited government.

Skills Practice

Charts are visual graphics that categorize information. When reading a chart, be sure to look at all the headings and labels. Study the charts on this page and answer the questions that follow on a separate sheet of paper.

1. What do the charts compare?
2. Which political systems are forms of limited government?
3. Which form of government often uses military rule?
4. In which political system does the king or queen have complete power?

Limited Governments

Representative Democracy	Constitutional Monarchy
People elect leaders to rule	King or queen's power is limited
Individual rights important	Individual rights important
More than one political party	More than one political party
People give consent to be governed	People elect governing body

Unlimited Governments

Dictatorship	Absolute Monarchy
One person or small group rules	King or queen inherits power
Few personal freedoms	Usually some freedoms
Rule by force, often military	Officials are appointed by king or queen
Ruler does not have to obey rules	Monarch has complete authority

Standardized Test Practice

DIRECTIONS: Use the charts and your knowledge of social studies to answer the following questions on a separate sheet of paper.

1. Information found in the charts shows that the most restrictive form of government is a
   - **A** dictatorship.
   - **B** representative democracy.
   - **C** absolute monarchy.
   - **D** constitutional monarchy.
2. Under which type of government do citizens have the most power?
   - **F** unlimited government
   - **G** limited government
   - **H** absolute monarchy
   - **J** dictatorship
3. An example of an unlimited government is
   - **A** the United States in the 1960s.
   - **B** Libya in the 1970s.
   - **C** the United Kingdom in the 1980s.
   - **D** Mexico in the 1990s.

TEACH

Ask how many students play a sport. What kinds of sports? Then tell them that information like this could be explained in text form, but placing the information or statistics in a table or chart would present the information in a more concise and easily interpreted format. Have students practice analyzing a chart by reading the information and answering the questions that follow.

Skills Practice Answers:

1. types of government or limited versus unlimited governments
2. representative democracy, constitutional monarchy
3. dictatorship
4. absolute monarchy

Standardized Test Practice Answers:

1. A
Test-Taking Strategy: Make sure students have a clear understanding of the meaning of key words in the question. The most restrictive government is the one with the fewest freedoms.

2. G
Test-Taking Strategy: Tell students to be sure to read all the headings on the chart.

3. B
Test-Taking Strategy: Students can narrow the answer choices by eliminating choices they know are incorrect.

TEACH

Making comparisons is an important skill in all academic areas. Help students to realize that making comparisons is also a life skill that we use every day by having volunteers give examples of a situation in which they have had to make a comparison recently.

You may wish to create, as a class, a comparison chart of two professional sports teams, two entertainers, and so on.

Skills Practice Answers:

1. The chart compares the two houses of the United States Congress—the House of Representatives and the Senate. It compares the qualifications, number of representatives, and the terms of office for senators and representatives.
2. To become a member of the U.S. Congress (in either house), you must live in the state you represent.

Making Comparisons

The roots of representative democracy in the United States can be traced back to colonial times. In 1607 English settlers founded the colony of Jamestown in present-day Virginia. As the colony developed, problems arose. Later, colonists formed the House of Burgesses to deal with these problems. Citizens of Virginia were chosen as representatives to the House of Burgesses. This became the first legislature, or lawmaking body, in America.

Today citizens of the United States elect representatives to Congress. The major function of Congress is to make laws for the nation. There are two houses, or chambers, of the U.S. Congress. Legislative bodies with two houses are said to be bicameral. The bicameral Congress of the United States includes the Senate and the House of Representatives. Article I of the U.S. Constitution describes how each house will be organized and how its members will be chosen.

The U.S. Congress

House of Representatives	Senate
Qualifications: • Must be 25 years old • Must be U.S. citizen for 7+ years • Must live in the state they represent	**Qualifications:** • Must be 30 years old • Must be U.S. citizen for 9+ years • Must live in the state they represent
Number of Representatives: • 435 total representatives; number of representatives per state is based on state population	**Number of Representatives:** • 100 total senators; two senators elected from each state regardless of state population
Terms of Office: • Two-year terms	**Terms of Office:** • Six-year terms

Skills Practice

When you make a comparison, you identify and examine two or more groups, situations, events, or documents. Then you identify any similarities and differences between the items. Study the information presented on the chart on this page and answer the questions that follow on a separate sheet of paper.

1. What two things does the chart compare?
2. How are the qualifications for each house of the U.S. Congress similar?

Standardized Test Practice

DIRECTIONS: Use the chart and your knowledge of social studies to answer the following questions on a separate sheet of paper.

1. Which of the following statements best reflects information shown in the chart?
   - **A** The Senate has more members than the House of Representatives.
   - **B** Representatives to the House are elected to two-year terms.
   - **C** House members must be residents of their states for at least 9 years.
   - **D** A state's population determines its number of senators.
2. One inference that can be made from information shown on the chart is that
   - **F** Texas elects more senators than Rhode Island.
   - **G** Texas elects more House members than Rhode Island.
   - **H** Texas elects fewer senators than Rhode Island.
   - **J** Texas elects fewer House members than Rhode Island.

Standardized Test Practice Answers:

1. B
Test-Taking Strategy: Tell students: Do not rely on your memory alone to answer the question. Check each answer choice with information presented in the chart.

2. G
Test-Taking Strategy: Ask: What do you know about the populations of Texas and Rhode Island? Which house uses population to determine the number of members?

Interpreting Primary Sources

When Thomas Jefferson wrote the Declaration of Independence, he used the term "unalienable rights." Jefferson was referring to the natural rights that belong to humans. He and the other Founders of our nation believed that government could not take away the rights of the people.

Skills Practice

Primary sources are records of events made by the people who witnessed them. A historical document such as the Declaration of Independence is an example of a primary source. Read the passage below and answer the questions that follow on a separate sheet of paper.

> "We hold these truths to be self-evident, that all men are created equal, that they are endowed by their Creator with certain unalienable Rights, that among these are Life, Liberty, and the pursuit of Happiness . . ."
>
> —Declaration of Independence, July 4, 1776

1. What does the document say about the equality of men?
2. List the three natural, or unalienable, rights to which the document refers.

After gaining independence, American leaders wrote the U.S. Constitution in 1787. The Bill of Rights includes the first 10 amendments, or additions, to the Constitution. The First Amendment protects five basic rights of all American citizens. Study the chart on this page and answer the questions that follow.

1. Which right allows Americans to express themselves without fear of punishment by the government?
2. Which right allows people to worship as they please?
3. Which right allows citizens to publish a pamphlet that is critical of the president?
4. What is the Bill of Rights?

Rights Protected by the First Amendment

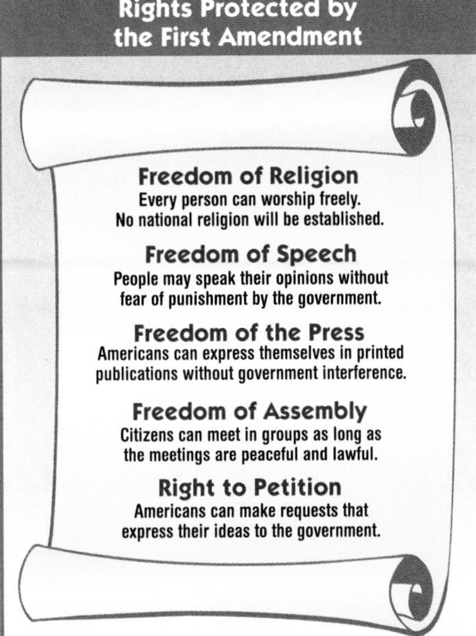

Freedom of Religion
Every person can worship freely.
No national religion will be established.
Freedom of Speech
People may speak their opinions without fear of punishment by the government.
Freedom of the Press
Americans can express themselves in printed publications without government interference.
Freedom of Assembly
Citizens can meet in groups as long as the meetings are peaceful and lawful.
Right to Petition
Americans can make requests that express their ideas to the government.

Standardized Test Practice

DIRECTIONS: Use the chart and your knowledge of social studies to answer the following question on a separate sheet of paper.

1. Which First Amendment right protects citizens who are staging a protest outside a government building?

A freedom of speech
B freedom of the press
C freedom of assembly
D freedom of religion

Standardized Test Skills Handbook

Standardized Test Skills Handbook

TEACH

Have students explain the phrase "Founders of our nation." **Ask: What does the phrase mean? Who were the Founders of the United States? What did they do?** Have students speculate as to why the term *Founders* is capitalized.

Tell students that Thomas Jefferson was one of the most famous of the Founders of our nation because he wrote the Declaration of Independence. Ask students to recall the country from which Americans were declaring independence. Have students locate Great Britain on a map before they read these pages.

Skills Practice Answers:

1. All men are created equal.
2. life, liberty, and the pursuit of happiness

1. freedom of speech
2. freedom of religion
3. freedom of the press
4. The Bill of Rights includes the first 10 amendments to the United States Constitution. These amendments protect basic liberties and rights.

Standardized Test Practice Answer:

1. C

Test-Taking Strategy: Have students check each answer choice against the information presented in the chart. Words in the question may not exactly match information in the chart. Encourage students to look for synonyms, or words of similar meanings, to support their answers.

Standardized Test
Skills Handbook

TEACH

Point out that the main purpose of political cartoons is to comment on a situation and, sometimes, to suggest a course of action. Help students understand that political cartoonists often use caricatures and symbols. (A caricature is an unrealistic drawing of a real person. A symbol is a drawing that represents a concept.)

Skills Practice Answers:

1. a man sitting at a desk writing (about what freedoms to grant to Americans)
2. freedom, liberty, rights, but not too much/many
3. a Founder of our nation (the writer of the U.S. Constitution or Bill of Rights)
4. writing the Bill of Rights
5. They suggest that the nation's Founders had to create a balance between freedoms and rights and the limits to them.
6. Americans' rights are restricted so that one person cannot interfere in the rights of another person. These limits are necessary to keep order in a society of so many people.

Standardized Test Skills Handbook

Interpreting a Political Cartoon

Just as the government of the United States is limited in its powers, freedoms extended to Americans also have limits. The First Amendment was not intended to allow Americans to do whatever they please without regard to others. Limits on freedoms are necessary to keep order in a society of so many people. The government can establish laws to limit certain rights to protect the health, safety, security, or moral standards of a community. Rights can be restricted to prevent one person's rights from interfering with the rights of another. For example, the freedom of speech does not include allowing a person to make false statements that hurt another's reputation.

Skills Practice

The artists who create political cartoons often use humor to express their opinions on political issues. Sometimes these cartoonists are trying to inform and influence the public about a certain topic. To interpret a political cartoon, look for symbols, labels, and captions that provide clues about the message of the cartoonist. Analyze these elements and draw some conclusions. Study the political cartoon on this page and answer the questions that follow on a separate sheet of paper.

1. What is the subject of the cartoon?
2. What words provide clues as to the meaning of the cartoon?
3. Whom does the person in the cartoon represent?
4. What is the person doing?
5. What do the subject's thoughts suggest about the task faced by those involved in planning the new nation's government?
6. What limits are placed on First Amendment rights? Why are these rights limited?

Standardized Test Practice

DIRECTIONS: Use the political cartoon and your knowledge of social studies to answer the following questions on a separate sheet of paper.

1. The most appropriate title for the cartoon is
   - **A** Limits on Government.
   - **B** Parliament at Work.
   - **C** Limiting Rights.
   - **D** Unlimited Government.
2. The sources of our rights as citizens of the United States come from which of the following?
   - **F** the Declaration of Independence and the U.S. Constitution
   - **G** the will of the president
   - **H** unwritten customs and traditions
   - **J** the United Nations charter

Standardized Test Practice Answers:

1. C
Test-Taking Strategy: Encourage students to look for clues. Words found in the cartoon show that the man is trying to grant limited rights.

2. F
Test-Taking Strategy: This question requires students to understand the sources of our rights. Our government is a limited one, based on the Declaration of Independence and the U.S. Constitution.

Interpreting a Circle Graph

"E pluribus unum" is a Latin phrase found on United States coins. It means "Out of many, one." The United States is sometimes called a "nation of immigrants." Unless you are a Native American, your ancestors came to America within the last 500 years.

Groups of people who share a common culture, language, or history are referred to as ethnic groups. American neighborhoods include many different ethnic groups. The circle graph on this page shows the major ethnic groups in the United States.

NATIONAL GEOGRAPHIC **Ethnic Groups in the United States**

African American 12.1%
Asian 3.6%
Native American/Inuit 0.7%
Other 1.9%
Hispanic 12.5%
White 69.2%

Source: U.S. Census Bureau, 2000.

Skills Practice

A circle graph shows percentages of a total quantity. Each part, or slice, of the graph represents a part of the total quantity. To read a circle graph, first read the title. Then study the labels to find out what each part represents. Compare the sizes of the circle slices. Study the circle graph and answer the questions that follow on a separate sheet of paper.

1. What information does this circle graph present?
2. Which ethnic group includes the largest percentage of Americans?
3. Which groups represent less than 1 percent of the people in the United States?
4. What percentage of the United States population is represented by African Americans?
5. The smallest ethnic group has lived in the United States the longest. What is this ethnic group?

Standardized Test Practice

DIRECTIONS: Use the graph and your knowledge of social studies to answer the following questions on a separate sheet of paper.

1. Which group's population is about three times greater than the number of Asians?
   - **A** African American
   - **B** White
   - **C** Native American/Inuit
   - **D** Other
2. How does the Hispanic population compare to the African American population of the United States?
   - **F** It is greater than the African American population.
   - **G** It is the smallest segment of the United States population.
   - **H** It is less than half the size of the African American population.
   - **J** It is slightly less than the African American population.

TEACH

Ask students to name a custom practiced in the United States that originated in another country. Examples include celebrations, types of food, music, dance, or other cultural practices. Lead a discussion focusing on the diverse cultural heritages of Americans. Explain to students that the practice of adopting the cultural traits of another group is called *cultural borrowing*.

Explain to students that a circle graph is like a sliced pie; often it is even called a pie chart. Circle graphs show proportions rather than absolute amounts. They often are used when the information being compared totals 100 percent.

Skills Practice Answers:

1. ethnic groups in the United States
2. White
3. Native American/Inuit
4. 12.1 percent
5. Native American/Inuit

Standardized Test Practice Answers:

1. A
Test-Taking Strategy: Remind students to eliminate answers that do not make sense. Then students should multiply the percentage of Asians by three to find the correct answer.

2. F
Test-Taking Strategy: To answer this question, students must compare two slices of the total circle.

Standardized Test
Skills Handbook

TEACH

To help students become comfortable with making inferences and drawing conclusions, write the following sports page headline on the board: "Another Year of Futility—Hawks Fail to Make the Playoffs Again!" Ask students what information about the team they can draw from the headline. *(Most students will infer that it has been a long time since the Hawks had a successful season.)* Then have students suggest how the writer might feel about the situation. *(Students may suggest that the writer seems upset or frustrated.)* Then point out that students have just been drawing inferences and conclusions.

Skills Practice Answers:

1. immigration to the United States from 1820 to 1860
2. years (from 1820 to 1860)
3. number of immigrants
4. Students' answers will vary. Students may mention push and pull factors that push people out of their homelands to the U.S. and opportunities in the U.S. that pull people to this country.

Standardized Test Skills Handbook

Drawing Inferences and Conclusions

During the mid-nineteenth century, immigration to the United States increased. People from European countries such as Germany and Ireland traveled to America seeking new opportunities. Life, however, was not easy for these immigrants.

Skills Practice

To infer means to evaluate information and arrive at a conclusion. When you make inferences, you "read between the lines." You must use the available facts and your own knowledge of social studies to form a judgment or opinion about the material.

Line graphs are a way of showing numbers visually. They are often used to compare changes over time. Sometimes a graph has more than one line. The lines show different quantities of a related topic. To analyze a line graph read the title and the information on the horizontal and vertical axes. Use this information to draw conclusions. Study the graph on this page and answer the questions that follow on a separate sheet of paper.

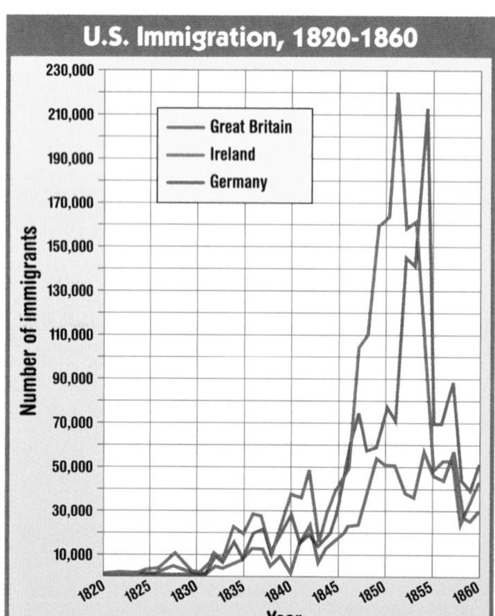

Source: *Historical Statistics of the United States: Colonial Times to 1970.*

1. What is the subject of the line graph?
2. What information is shown on the horizontal axis?
3. What information is shown on the vertical axis?
4. Why do you think these immigrants came to the United States?

Standardized Test Practice

DIRECTIONS: Use the line graph and your knowledge of social studies to answer the following questions on a separate sheet of paper.

1. The country that provided the most immigrants to the United States between the years 1820 and 1860 was
   A Great Britain.
   B Ireland.
   C Germany.
   D France.
2. In about what year did the number of German immigrants to the United States reach a peak?
   F 1845
   G 1852
   H 1855
   J 1860
3. Irish migration to the United States increased in the mid-1800s because of
   A a terrible potato famine in Ireland.
   B the failure of a German revolution in 1848.
   C the nativist movement.
   D the availability of low-paying factory jobs.

Standardized Test Practice Answers:

1. B
Test-Taking Strategy: Remind students to check each answer choice against the graph to eliminate wrong answers.
2. H
Test-Taking Strategy: Students must first find the line that represents Germany and estimate the year of the peak.
3. A
Test-Taking Strategy: Students must make an inference. Ask: What would force people from Ireland to leave their country?

Comparing Data

The world's earliest civilizations developed more than 6,000 years ago. The discovery of farming led to the rise of ancient cities in Mesopotamia and the Nile River valley. These early cities shared one important characteristic—they each arose near waterways. Since water was the easiest way to transport goods, the settlements became centers of trade.

Since then cities have grown all over the world. Every 10 years, the United States Census Bureau collects data to determine the population of the United States. (A census is an official count of people living in an area.) The first census was conducted in 1790. At that time, there were 3.9 million people in the 13 original states. The most recent census occurred in 2000. The results of that census showed that more than 280 million people reside in the 50 states that make up our nation.

POPULATION OF FIVE LARGEST U.S. CITIES, 1790

City	Number of People
New York City	33,131
Philadelphia	28,522
Boston	18,320
Charleston	16,359
Baltimore	13,503

POPULATION OF FIVE LARGEST U.S. CITIES, 2000*

City	Number of People
New York City	8,008,278
Los Angeles	3,694,820
Chicago	2,896,016
Houston	1,953,631
Philadelphia	1,517,550

*Numbers do not include metropolitan areas.

Skills Practice

The charts on this page show populations of the five most populous cities in the United States during different time periods. When comparing information on charts be sure to read the titles and headings to define the data being compared. Study the charts and answer the questions below on a separate sheet of paper.

1. Which U.S. city had the greatest population in 1790?
2. Which U.S. city had the greatest population in 2000?
3. What was the population of Philadelphia in 1790?
4. What was Philadelphia's population in 2000?
5. Which city had the third-largest population in 1790?
6. Which cities are on both lists?

Standardized Test Practice

DIRECTIONS: Use the charts and your knowledge of social studies to answer the following questions on a separate sheet of paper.

1. One inference that can be made from the charts is that the most populous cities in the United States
   - **A** have good weather.
   - **B** were founded early in our nation's history.
   - **C** are port cities.
   - **D** are in the eastern United States.
2. In 1790 the major cities of the United States were all
   - **F** larger than 20,000 people.
   - **G** located in the East.
   - **H** Northern cities.
   - **J** founded for religious reasons.

Standardized Test
Skills Handbook

TEACH

Tell students the following: Determining populations is necessary for many reasons. For example, it is important to know the number of students in schools and school districts. The student population in each school helps officials decide how many teachers to hire. It also determines the amount of money districts receive. Find the total population of students in your school. What percentage of total students makes up each grade level? Create a circle graph that shows this information. *(Students should find the number of students in each grade and convert those numbers to percentages before drawing slices of the circle graph. Check graphs for accuracy.)*

Skills Practice Answers:

1. New York City
2. New York City
3. 28,522
4. 1,517,550
5. Boston
6. New York City, Philadelphia

Standardized Test Practice Answers:

1. C
Test-Taking Strategy: To answer this question students must make an inference, or "read between the lines." Encourage students to read each answer choice, eliminating ones that do not make sense.

2. G
Test-Taking Strategy: To answer this question students must think of the location of each city and then eliminate incorrect answer choices.

TEACH

Have students divide a piece of paper into two columns entitled "Wants" and "Needs." Ask students to list their wants and needs under the appropriate heading. Explain to students that balancing our wants and needs helps us to make decisions about our individual economic situations. Countries of the world use different methods to meet the economic needs of their people.

Tell students that categorizing information helps them deal with large quantities of information in an understandable way.

Skills Practice Answers:

1. command economic system
2. traditional economic system
3. Students should create a circle graph with the following slices: manufacturing and mining, 18 percent; agriculture, 2 percent; service and information industries, 80 percent; 2 percent

Categorizing and Analyzing Information

Economic systems describe the ways in which societies produce and distribute goods and services. Early societies, such as Mesopotamia, used bartering as their system of trade. In the seventeenth and eighteenth centuries, European countries practiced mercantilism in which colonies provided wealth to their parent countries. Great Britain used this idea to gain wealth from its North American colonies. The economy of the United States is based on the principle of free enterprise. Americans have the freedom to own businesses with limited interference from the government.

Because Americans are employed in a variety of industries, our economy is the largest and among the most diverse in the world. The U.S. economy includes the following parts:

- Manufacturing and mining make up 18 percent of the economy.
- Agriculture makes up 2 percent of the economy.
- Service and information industries make up 80 percent of the economy.

Skills Practice

Grouping information into categories is one way of making the information easier to understand. The economic systems of today's world can be classified into four basic groups. Study the chart on this page and answer the questions that follow on a separate sheet of paper.

1. Under which economic system does the government have the most control?
2. Under which system would people be most likely to have the same job as their parents?
3. Use the information about the U.S. economy on this page to create a circle graph. Then answer this question: Industries related to farming represent what percentage of the U.S. economy?

WORLD ECONOMIC SYSTEMS

Traditional	Command	Market	Mixed
Based on customs	Government controls production, prices, and wages	Individuals control production, prices, and wages	Individuals control some aspects of economy
Trades are passed down through generations	Communism; Government owns businesses	Free enterprise; Individuals own businesses	Government regulates selected industries and restricts others

Standardized Test Practice

DIRECTIONS: Use the chart and your knowledge of social studies to answer the following questions on a separate sheet of paper.

1. Which economic system provides individuals with the most economic freedom?
   - **A** traditional
   - **B** command
   - **C** market
   - **D** mixed
2. The United States has this type of economic system.
   - **F** traditional
   - **G** command
   - **H** market
   - **J** mixed

Standardized Test Practice Answers:

1. C
Test-Taking Strategy: Students should look for key words in the question. Encourage students to determine whether any of the key words are used on the chart. Under which category do they appear?

2. J
Test-Taking Strategy: Students should recall that the United States has a mixed economy. Although the economy is based on free enterprise, the government can step in when needed to regulate industry.

Sequencing Events

The free enterprise economic system of the United States has encouraged Americans to invent and produce new technology throughout the history of our nation. Using its rich natural and human resources, Americans are continually advancing the economy through technology. The tremendous economic growth of the United States at certain times in history, such as after the Civil War, resulted from foundations laid early in the nation's history and affects the growth of the United States economy today.

1850

1852 Elisha Otis develops the elevator brake.

1860s The telegraph links the United States and Europe.

1879 Thomas Alva Edison invents the electric lightbulb.

1888 George Eastman invents a small camera.

1893 Charles and J. Frank Duryea make a gasoline-powered car.

1899 John Thurman develops a vacuum cleaner.

1900

Skills Practice

Sequencing information involves placing facts in the order in which they occurred. Listed below are technological advances that occurred at different times in history, transforming the world economy. Find the date of each invention by studying the time line on page 98 of your textbook. On a separate sheet of paper, take notes by writing the date beside each invention. Then sequence the inventions by rewriting them in the order in which they were invented.

• Telephone	• Airplane
• Cellular phone	• Automobile
• Steamboat	• Steam locomotive
• Space shuttle	• Internet
• Radio	• Television

In the late 1800s, innovations in technology and new business combinations helped the United States grow into an industrial power. By the year 1900, the United States's industrial production was the greatest around the world.

Read the time line on this page. Determine the subject of the time line and summarize it in a few words. Then write a title for the time line on a separate sheet of paper.

Standardized Test Practice

DIRECTIONS: Use the events you have sequenced and your knowledge of social studies to answer the following questions on a separate sheet of paper.

1. Which of the following inventions occurred last?
   - **A** steam locomotive
   - **B** telephone
   - **C** airplane
   - **D** steamboat
2. During the late 1700s, 1800s, and early 1900s, new inventions and developments in the area of transportation, such as the steamboat, steam locomotive, and airplane, resulted in
   - **F** increased poverty among urban Americans.
   - **G** an end to westward migration.
   - **H** the creation of new markets for trade.
   - **J** rural growth.
3. In the early 1800s, steamboats dramatically improved the transport of goods and passengers
   - **A** along major roads.
   - **B** along major inland rivers.
   - **C** between the Americas and Africa.
   - **D** in the West.

TEACH

Tell students it is easier to understand the order of events and their relationship to one another if the events are sequenced, or placed in order, on a time line.

Skills Practice Answers:

1. 1787 — Steamboat
2. 1803 — Steam locomotive
3. 1876 — Telephone
4. 1885 — Automobile
5. 1903 — Airplane
6. 1920 — Radio
7. 1926 — Television
8. 1969 — Internet
9. 1981 — Space shuttle
10. 1983 — Cellular phone

The time line lists inventions that occurred from 1852–1899. Possible titles include: The Growth of Industry in the United States; The Growth of Technology in the United States, and Inventions and Developments in the U.S. (1850–1900).

Standardized Test Practice Answers:

1. C
Test-Taking Strategy: Students will have to have correctly sequenced the events to answer this question correctly.
2. H
Test-Taking Strategy: Students should eliminate answers they know are incorrect or that do not make sense.
3. B
Test-Taking Strategy: Students should recall when steamboats were invented and why they were important.

Honoring America

For Americans, the flag has always had a special meaning. It is a symbol of our nation's freedom and democracy. 

Flag Etiquette

Over the years, Americans have developed rules and customs concerning the use and display of the flag. One of the most important things every American should remember is to treat the flag with respect.

- The flag should be raised and lowered by hand and displayed only from sunrise to sunset. On special occasions, the flag may be displayed at night, but it should be illuminated.
- The flag may be displayed on all days, weather permitting, particularly on national and state holidays and on historic and special occasions.
- No flag may be flown above the American flag or to the right of it at the same height.
- The flag should never touch the ground or floor beneath it.
- The flag may be flown at half-staff by order of the president, usually to mourn the death of a public official.
- The flag may be flown upside down only to signal distress.
- When the flag becomes old and tattered, it should be destroyed by burning. According to an approved custom, the Union (stars on blue field) is first cut from the flag; then the two pieces, which no longer form a flag, are burned.

The Star-Spangled Banner

O! say can you see, by the dawn's early light,
What so proudly we hail'd at the twilight's last gleaming,
Whose broad stripes and bright stars through the perilous fight,
O'er the ramparts we watched, were so gallantly streaming?
And the Rockets' red glare, the Bombs bursting in air,
Gave proof through the night that our Flag was still there;
O! say, does that star-spangled banner yet wave
O'er the Land of the free and the home of the brave!

The Pledge of Allegiance

I pledge allegiance to the Flag of the United States of America and to the Republic for which it stands, one Nation under God, indivisible, with liberty and justice for all.

Gazetteer

A gazetteer (GA•zuh•TIHR) is a geographic index or dictionary. It shows latitude and longitude for cities and certain other places. Latitude and longitude are shown in this way: 48°N 2°E, or 48 degrees north latitude and two degrees east longitude. This Gazetteer lists many important geographic features and most of the world's largest independent countries and their capitals. The page numbers tell where each entry can be found on a map in this book. As an aid to pronunciation, most entries are spelled phonetically.

Abidjan [AH•bee•JAHN] Capital of Côte d'Ivoire. 5°N 4°W (p. 539)

Abu Dhabi [AH•boo DAH•bee] Capital of the United Arab Emirates. 24°N 54°E (p. 459)

Abuja [ah•BOO•jah] Capital of Nigeria. 8°N 9°E (p. 539)

Accra [ah•KRUH] Capital of Ghana. 6°N 0° longitude (p. 539)

Addis Ababa [AHD•dihs AH•bah•BAH] Capital of Ethiopia. 9°N 39°E (p. 539)

Adriatic [AY•dree•A•tihk] **Sea** Arm of the Mediterranean Sea between the Balkan Peninsula and Italy. 44°N 14°E (p. 284)

Afghanistan [af•GA•nuh•STAN] Central Asian country west of Pakistan. 33°N 63°E (p. 459)

Albania [al•BAY•nee•uh] Country on the Adriatic Sea, south of Serbia and Montenegro. 42°N 20°E (p. 285)

Algeria [al•JIHR•ee•uh] North African country east of Morocco. 29°N 1°E (p. 459)

Algiers [al•JIHRZ] Capital of Algeria. 37°N 3°E (p. 459)

Alps [ALPS] Mountain ranges extending through central Europe. 46°N 9°E (p. 284)

Amazon [A•muh•ZAHN] **River** Largest river in the world by volume and second-largest in length. 2°S 53°W (p. 180)

Amman [a•MAHN] Capital of Jordan. 32°N 36°E (p. 459)

Amsterdam [AHM•stuhr•DAHM] Capital of the Netherlands. 52°N 5°E (p. 285)

Andes [AN•DEEZ] Mountain system extending north and south along the western side of South America. 13°S 75°W (p. 180)

Andorra [an•DAWR•uh] Small country in southern Europe between France and Spain. 43°N 2°E (p. 285)

Angola [ang•GOH•luh] Southern African country north of Namibia. 14°S 16°E (p. 539)

Ankara [AHNG•kuh•ruh] Capital of Turkey. 40°N 33°E (p. 459)

Antananarivo [AHN•tah•NAH•nah•REE•voh] Capital of Madagascar. 19°S 48°E (p. 539)

Arabian [uh•RAY•bee•uhn] **Peninsula** Large peninsula extending into the Arabian Sea. 28°N 40°E (p. 458)

Argentina [AHR•juhn•TEE•nuh] South American country east of Chile. 36°S 67°W (p. 181)

Armenia [ahr•MEE•nee•uh] European-Asian country between the Black and Caspian Seas. 40°N 45°E (p. 397)

Ashgabat [AHSH•gah•BAHT] Capital of Turkmenistan. 38°N 58°E (p. 397)

Asmara [az•MAHR•uh] Capital of Eritrea. 16°N 39°E (p. 539)

Astana Capital of Kazakhstan. 51°N 72°E (p. 397)

Asunción [ah•SOON•see•OHN] Capital of Paraguay. 25°S 58°W (p. 181)

Athens Capital of Greece. 38°N 24°E (p. 285)

Atlas [AT•luhs] **Mountains** Mountain range on the northern edge of the Sahara. 31°N 5°W (p. 458)

Australia [aw•STRAYL•yuh] Country and continent in Southern Hemisphere. 25°S 135°W (p. 729)

Austria [AWS•tree•uh] Western European country east of Switzerland and south of Germany and the Czech Republic. 47°N 12°E (p. 285)

Azerbaijan [A•zuhr•BY•JAHN] European-Asian country on the Caspian Sea. 40°N 47°E (p. 397)

Baghdad Capital of Iraq. 33°N 44°E (p. 459)

Bahamas [buh•HAH•muhz] Country made up of many islands between Cuba and the United States. 23°N 74°W (p. 180)

Bahrain [bah•RAYN] Country located on the Persian Gulf. 26°N 51°E (p. 459)

Baku [bah•KOO] Capital of Azerbaijan. 40°N 50°E (p. 397)

Balkan [BAWL•kuhn] **Peninsula** Peninsula in southeastern Europe. 42°N 20°E (p. 284)

Baltic [BAWL•tihk] **Sea** Sea in northern Europe that is connected to the North Sea. 55°N 17°E (p. 284)

Bamako [BAH•mah•KOH] Capital of Mali. 13°N 8°W (p. 539)

Bangkok [BANG•KAHK] Capital of Thailand. 14°N 100°E (p. 629)

Bangladesh [BAHNG•gluh•DEHSH] South Asian country bordered by India and Myanmar. 24°N 90°E (p. 629)

GAZETTEER

Bangui [BAHNG•GEE] Capital of the Central African Republic. 4°N 19°E (p. 539)
Banjul [BAHN•JOOL] Capital of Gambia. 13°N 17°W (p. 539)
Barbados [bahr•BAY•duhs] Island country between the Atlantic Ocean and the Caribbean Sea. 14°N 59°W (p. 181)
Beijing [BAY•JIHNG] Capital of China. 40°N 116°E (p. 629)
Beirut [bay•ROOT] Capital of Lebanon. 34°N 36°E (p. 459)
Belarus [BEE•luh•ROOS] Eastern European country west of Russia. 54°N 28°E (p. 285)
Belgium [BEHL•juhm] Western European country south of the Netherlands. 51°N 3°E (p. 285)
Belgrade [BEHL•GRAYD] Capital of Serbia and Montenegro. 45°N 21°E (p. 285)
Belize [buh•LEEZ] Central American country east of Guatemala. 18°N 89°W (p. 181)
Belmopan [BEHL•moh•PAHN] Capital of Belize. 17°N 89°W (p. 181)
Benin [buh•NEEN] West African country west of Nigeria. 8°N 2°E (p. 539)
Berlin [behr•LEEN] Capital of Germany. 53°N 13°E (p. 285)
Bern Capital of Switzerland. 47°N 7°E (p. 285)
Bhutan [boo•TAHN] South Asian country northeast of India. 27°N 91°E (p. 629)
Bishkek [bihsh•KEHK] Capital of Kyrgyzstan. 43°N 75°E (p. 397)
Bissau [bihs•SOW] Capital of Guinea-Bissau. 12°N 16°W (p. 539)
Black Sea Large sea between Europe and Asia. 43°N 32°E (p. 285)
Bloemfontein [BLOOM•FAHN•TAYN] Judicial capital of South Africa. 26°E 29°S (p. 539)
Bogotá [BOH•goh•TAH] Capital of Colombia. 5°N 74°W (p. 181)
Bolivia [buh•LIHV•ee•uh] Country in the central part of South America, north of Argentina. 17°S 64°W (p. 181)
Bosnia and Herzegovina [BAHZ•nee•uh HEHRT•seh•GAW•vee•nuh] Southeastern European country between Croatia and Serbia and Montenegro. 44°N 18°E (p. 285)
Botswana [bawt•SWAH•nah] Southern African country north of the Republic of South Africa. 22°S 23°E (p. 539)
Brasília [brah•ZEEL•yuh] Capital of Brazil. 16°S 48°W (p. 181)
Bratislava [BRAH•tih•SLAH•vuh] Capital of Slovakia. 48°N 17°E (p. 285)
Brazil [bruh•ZIHL] Largest country in South America. 9°S 53°W (p. 181)
Brazzaville [BRAH•zuh•VEEL] Capital of Congo. 4°S 15°E (p. 539)
Brunei [bru•NY] Southeast Asian country on northern coast of the island of Borneo. 5°N 114°E (p. 628)
Brussels [BRUH•suhlz] Capital of Belgium. 51°N 4°E (p. 285)
Bucharest [BOO•kuh•REHST] Capital of Romania. 44°N 26°E (p. 285)
Budapest [BOO•duh•PEHST] Capital of Hungary. 48°N 19°E (p. 285)
Buenos Aires [BWAY•nuhs AR•eez] Capital of Argentina. 34°S 58°W (p. 181)
Bujumbura [BOO•juhm•BUR•uh] Capital of Burundi. 3°S 29°E (p. 539)
Bulgaria [BUHL•GAR•ee•uh] Southeastern European country south of Romania. 42°N 24°E (p. 285)
Burkina Faso [bur•KEE•nuh FAH•soh] West African country south of Mali. 12°N 3°E (p. 539)
Burundi [bu•ROON•dee] East African country at the northern end of Lake Tanganyika. 3°S 30°E (p. 539)

Cairo [KY•ROH] Capital of Egypt. 31°N 32°E (p. 459)
Cambodia [kam•BOH•dee•uh] Southeast Asian country south of Thailand and Laos. 12°N 104°E (p. 629)
Cameroon [KA•muh•ROON] Central African country on the northeast shore of the Gulf of Guinea. 6°N 11°E (p. 539)
Canada [KA•nuh•duh] Northernmost country in North America. 50°N 100°W (p. 119)
Canberra [KAN•BEHR•uh] Capital of Australia. 35°S 149°E (p. 729)
Cape Town Legislative capital of the Republic of South Africa. 34°S 18°E (p. 539)
Cape Verde [VUHRD] Island country off the coast of western Africa in the Atlantic Ocean. 15°N 24°W (p. 539)
Caracas [kah•RAH•kahs] Capital of Venezuela. 11°N 67°W (p. 181)
Caribbean [KAR•uh•BEE•uhn] **Islands** Islands in the Caribbean Sea between North America and South America, also known as West Indies. 19°N 79°W (p. 180)
Caribbean Sea Part of the Atlantic Ocean bordered by the West Indies, South America, and Central America. 15°N 76°W (p. 180)
Caspian [KAS•pee•uhn] **Sea** Salt lake between Europe and Asia that is the world's largest inland body of water. 40°N 52°E (p. 396)
Caucasus [KAW•kuh•suhs] **Mountains** Mountain range between the Black and Caspian Seas. 43°N 42°E (p. 396)
Central African Republic Central African country south of Chad. 8°N 21°E (p. 539)
Chad [CHAD] Country west of Sudan in the African Sahel. 18°N 19°E (p. 539)
Chile [CHEE•lay] South American country west of Argentina. 35°S 72°W (p. 181)
China [CHY•nuh] Country in eastern and central Asia, known officially as the People's Republic of China. 37°N 93°E (p. 629)
Chişinău [KEE•shee•NOW] Capital of Moldova. 47°N 29°E (p. 285)
Colombia [kuh•LUHM•bee•uh] South American country west of Venezuela. 4°N 73°W (p. 181)
Colombo [kuh•LUHM•boh] Capital of Sri Lanka. 7°N 80°E (p. 629)

Comoros [KAH•muh•ROHZ] Small island country in Indian Ocean between the island of Madagascar and the southeast African mainland. 13°S 43°E (p. 539)
Conakry [KAH•nuh•kree] Capital of Guinea. 10°N 14°W (p. 539)
Congo [KAHNG•goh] Central African country east of the Democratic Republic of the Congo. 3°S 14°E (p. 539)
Congo, Democratic Republic of the Central African country north of Zambia and Angola. 1°S 22°E (p. 539)
Copenhagen [KOH•puhn•HAY•guhn] Capital of Denmark. 56°N 12°E (p. 285)
Costa Rica [KAWS•tah REE•kah] Central American country south of Nicaragua. 11°N 85°W (p. 181)
Côte d'Ivoire [KOHT dee•VWAHR] West African country south of Mali. 8°N 7°W (p. 539)
Croatia [kroh•AY•shuh] Southeastern European country on the Adriatic Sea. 46°N 16°E (p. 285)
Cuba [KYOO•buh] Island country in the Caribbean Sea. 22°N 79°W (p. 180)
Cyprus [SY•pruhs] Island country in the eastern Mediterranean Sea, south of Turkey. 35°N 31°E (p. 285)
Czech [CHEHK] **Republic** Eastern European country north of Austria. 50°N 15°E (p. 285)

Dakar [dah•KAHR] Capital of Senegal. 15°N 17°W (p. 539)
Damascus [duh•MAS•kuhs] Capital of Syria. 34°N 36°E (p. 459)
Dar es Salaam (DAHR EHS sah•LAHM] Capital of Tanzania. 7°S 39°E (p. 539)
Denmark [DEHN•MAHRK] Northern European country between the Baltic and North Seas. 56°N 9°E (p. 285)
Dhaka [DA•kuh] Capital of Bangladesh. 24°N 90°E (p. 629)
Djibouti [jih•BOO•tee] East African country on the Gulf of Aden. 12°N 43°E (p. 539)
Doha [DOH•huh] Capital of Qatar. 25°N 51°E (p. 459)
Dominican [duh•MIH•nih•kuhn] **Republic** Country in the Caribbean Sea on the eastern part of the island of Hispaniola. 19°N 71°W (p. 181)
Dublin [DUH•blihn] Capital of Ireland. 53°N 6°W (p. 285)
Dushanbe [doo•SHAM•buh] Capital of Tajikistan. 39°N 69°E (p. 397)

East Timor [TEE•MOHR] Previous province of Indonesia, now under UN administration. 10°S 127°E (p. 629)
Ecuador [EH•kwuh•DAWR] South American country southwest of Colombia. 0° latitude 79°W (p. 181)
Egypt [EE•jihpt] North African country on the Mediterranean Sea. 27°N 27°E (p. 459)
El Salvador [ehl SAL•vuh•DAWR] Central American country southwest of Honduras. 14°N 89°W (p. 181)
Equatorial Guinea [EE•kwuh•TOHR•ee•uhl GIH•nee] Central African country south of Cameroon. 2°N 8°E (p. 539)
Eritrea [EHR•uh•TREE•uh] East African country north of Ethiopia. 17°N 39°E (p. 539)
Estonia [eh•STOH•nee•uh] Eastern European country on the Baltic Sea. 59°N 25°E (p. 285)
Ethiopia [EE•thee•OH•pee•uh] East African country north of Somalia and Kenya. 8°N 38°E (p. 539)
Euphrates [yu•FRAY•TEEZ] **River** River in southwestern Asia that flows through Syria and Iraq and joins the Tigris River. 36°N 40°E (p. 458)

Fiji [FEE•jee] **Islands** Country comprised of an island group in the southwest Pacific Ocean. 19°S 175°E (p. 729)
Finland [FIHN•luhnd] Northern European country east of Sweden. 63°N 26°E (p. 285)
France [FRANS] Western European country south of the United Kingdom. 47°N 1°E (p. 285)
Freetown [FREE•TOWN] Capital of Sierra Leone. 9°N 13°W (p. 539)
French Guiana [gee•A•nuh] French-owned territory in northern South America. 5°N 53°W (p. 181)

Gabon [ga•BOHN] Central African country on the Atlantic Ocean. 0° latitude 12°E (p. 539)
Gaborone [GAH•boh•ROH•NAY] Capital of Botswana. 24°S 26°E (p. 539)
Gambia [GAM•bee•uh] West African country along the Gambia River. 13°N 16°W (p. 539)
Georgetown [JAWRJ•TOWN] Capital of Guyana. 8°N 58°W (p. 181)
Georgia [JAWR•juh] European-Asian country bordering the Black Sea south of Russia. 42°N 43°E (p. 397)
Germany [JUHR•muh•nee] Western European country south of Denmark, officially called the Federal Republic of Germany. 52°N 10°E (p. 285)
Ghana [GAH•nuh] West African country on the Gulf of Guinea. 8°N 2°W (p. 539)
Great Plains The continental slope extending through the United States and Canada. 45°N 104°W (p. 118)
Greece [GREES] Southern European country on the Balkan Peninsula. 39°N 22°E (p. 285)
Greenland [GREEN•luhnd] Island in northwestern Atlantic Ocean and the largest island in the world. 74°N 40°W (p. 119)
Guatemala [GWAH•tay•MAH•lah] Central American country south of Mexico. 16°N 92°W (p. 181)
Guatemala City Capital of Guatemala. 15°N 91°W (p. 181)

Guinea [GIH•nee] West African country on the Atlantic coast. 11°N 12°W (p. 539)
Guinea-Bissau [GIH•nee bih•SOW] West African country on the Atlantic coast. 12°N 20°W (p. 539)
Gulf of Mexico Gulf on part of the southern coast of North America. 25°N 94°W (p. 118)
Guyana [gy•AH•nuh] South American country between Venezuela and Suriname. 8°N 59°W (p. 181)

Haiti [HAY•tee] Country in the Caribbean Sea on the western part of the island of Hispaniola. 19°N 72°W (p. 181)
Hanoi [ha•NOY] Capital of Vietnam. 21°N 106°E (p. 629)
Harare [hah•RAH•RAY] Capital of Zimbabwe. 18°S 31°E (p. 539)
Havana [huh•VA•nuh] Capital of Cuba. 23°N 82°W (p. 181)
Helsinki [HEHL•SIHNG•kee] Capital of Finland. 60°N 24°E (p. 285)
Himalaya [HI•muh•LAY•uh] Mountain ranges in southern Asia, bordering the Indian subcontinent on the north. 30°N 85°E (p. 628)
Honduras [hahn•DUR•uhs] Central American country on the Caribbean Sea. 15°N 88°W (p. 181)
Hong Kong [HAWNG KAWNG] Port and industrial center in southern China. 22°N 115°E (p. 629)
Hungary [HUHNG•guh•ree] Eastern European country south of Slovakia. 47°N 18°E (p. 285)

Iberian [eye•BIHR•ee•uhn] **Peninsula** Peninsula in southwest Europe, occupied by Spain and Portugal. 41°N 1°W (p. 284)
Iceland Island country between the North Atlantic and Arctic Oceans, 65°N 20°W (p. 285)
India [IHN•dee•uh] South Asian country south of China and Nepal. 23°N 78°E (p. 629)
Indonesia [IHN•duh•NEE•zhuh] Southeast Asian island country known as the Republic of Indonesia. 5°S 119°E (p. 629)
Indus [IHN•duhs] **River** River in Asia that begins in Tibet and flows through Pakistan to the Arabian Sea. 27°N 68°E (p. 628)
Iran [ih•RAN] Southwest Asian country that was formerly named Persia. 31°N 54°E (p. 459)
Iraq [ih•RAHK] Southwest Asian country west of Iran. 32°N 43°E (p. 459)
Ireland [EYER•luhnd] Island west of Great Britain occupied by the Republic of Ireland and Northern Ireland. 54°N 8°W (p. 285)
Islamabad [ihs•LAH•muh•BAHD] Capital of Pakistan. 34°N 73°E (p. 629)
Israel [IHZ•ree•uhl] Southwest Asian country south of Lebanon. 33°N 34°E (p. 459)
Italy [IHT•uhl•ee] Southern European country south of Switzerland and east of France. 44°N 11°E (p. 285)

Jakarta [juh•KAHR•tuh] Capital of Indonesia. 6°S 107°E (p. 629)
Jamaica [juh•MAY•kuh] Island country in the Caribbean Sea. 18°N 78°W (p. 181)
Japan [juh•PAN] East Asian country consisting of the four large islands of Hokkaido, Honshu, Shikoku, and Kyushu, plus thousands of small islands. 37°N 134°E (p. 628)
Jerusalem [juh•ROO•suh•luhm] Capital of Israel and a holy city for Christians, Jews, and Muslims. 32°N 35°E (p. 459)
Jordan [JAWRD•uhn] Southwest Asian country south of Syria. 30°N 38°E (p. 459)

Kabul [KAH•buhl] Capital of Afghanistan. 35°N 69°E (p. 459)
Kampala [kahm•PAH•lah] Capital of Uganda. 0° latitude 32°E (p. 539)
Kathmandu [KAT•MAN•DOO] Capital of Nepal. 28°N 85°E (p. 629)
Kazakhstan [kuh•ZAHK•STAHN] Large Asian country south of Russia and bordering the Caspian Sea. 48°N 59°E (p. 397)
Kenya [KEHN•yuh] East African country south of Ethiopia. 1°N 37°E (p. 539)
Khartoum [kahr•TOOM] Capital of Sudan. 16°N 33°E (p. 539)
Kiev [KEE•ihf] Capital of Ukraine. 50°N 31°E (p. 285)
Kigali [kee•GAH•lee] Capital of Rwanda. 2°S 30°E (p. 539)
Kingston [KIHNG•stuhn] Capital of Jamaica. 18°N 77°W (p. 181)
Kinshasa [kihn•SHAH•suh] Capital of the Democratic Republic of the Congo. 4°S 15°E (p. 539)
Kuala Lumpur [KWAH•luh LUM•PUR] Capital of Malaysia. 3°N 102°E (p. 629)
Kuwait [ku•WAYT] Country on the Persian Gulf between Saudi Arabia and Iraq. 29°N 48°E (p. 459)
Kyrgyzstan [KIHR•gih•STAN] Central Asian country on China's western border. 41°N 75°E (p. 397)

Laos [LOWS] Southeast Asian country south of China and west of Vietnam. 20°N 102°E (p. 629)
La Paz [lah PAHS] Administrative capital of Bolivia, and the highest capital in the world. 17°S 68°W (p. 181)
Latvia [LAT•vee•uh] Eastern European country west of Russia on the Baltic Sea. 57°N 25°E (p. 285)

Lebanon [LEH•buh•nuhn] Country south of Syria on the Mediterranean Sea. 34°N 34°E (p. 459)
Lesotho [luh•SOH•TOH] Southern African country within the borders of the Republic of South Africa. 30°S 28°E (p. 539)
Liberia [ly•BIHR•ee•uh] West African country south of Guinea. 7°N 10°W (p. 539)
Libreville [LEE•bruh•VIHL] Capital of Gabon. 1°N 9°E (p. 539)
Libya [LIH•bee•uh] North African country west of Egypt on the Mediterranean Sea. 28°N 15°E (p. 459)
Liechtenstein [LIHKT•uhn•SHTYN] Small country in central Europe between Switzerland and Austria. 47°N 10°E (p. 285)
Lilongwe [lih•LAWNG•GWAY] Capital of Malawi. 14°S 34°E (p. 539)
Lima [LEE•mah] Capital of Peru. 12°S 77°W (p. 181)
Lisbon [LIHZ•buhn] Capital of Portugal. 39°N 9°W (p. 285)
Lithuania [LIH•thuh•WAY•nee•uh] Eastern European country northwest of Belarus on the Baltic Sea. 56°N 24°E (p. 285)
Ljubljana [lee•OO•blee•AH•nuh] Capital of Slovenia. 46°N 14°E (p. 285)
Lomé [loh•MAY] Capital of Togo. 6°N 1°E (p. 539)
London [LUHN•duhn] Capital of the United Kingdom, on the Thames River. 52°N 0° longitude (p. 285)
Luanda [lu•AHN•duh] Capital of Angola. 9°S 13°E (p. 539)
Lusaka [loo•SAH•kah] Capital of Zambia. 15°S 28°E (p. 539)
Luxembourg [LUHK•suhm•BUHRG] Small European country between France, Belgium, and Germany. 50°N 7°E (p. 285)

Macau [muh•KOW] Port in southern China. 22°N 113°E (p. 629)
Macedonia [MA•suh•DOH•nee•uh] Southeastern European country north of Greece. 42°N 22°E (p. 285). Macedonia also refers to a geographic region covering northern Greece, the country Macedonia, and part of Bulgaria.
Madagascar [MA•duh•GAS•kuhr] Island in the Indian Ocean off the southeastern coast of Africa. 18°S 43°E (p. 539)
Madrid [muh•DRIHD] Capital of Spain. 41°N 4°W (p. 285)
Malabo [mah•LAH•boh] Capital of Equatorial Guinea. 4°N 9°E (p. 539)
Malawi [mah•LAH•wee] Southern African country south of Tanzania and east of Zambia. 11°S 34°E (p. 539)
Malaysia [muh•LAY•zhuh] Southeast Asian country with land on the Malay Peninsula and on the island of Borneo. 4°N 101°E (p. 628)
Maldives [MAWL•DEEVZ] Island country southwest of India in the Indian Ocean. 5°N 42°E (p. 629)
Mali [MAH•lee] West African country east of Mauritania. 16°N 0° longitude (p. 539)
Managua [mah•NAH•gwah] Capital of Nicaragua. 12°N 86°W (p. 181)
Manila [muh•NIH•luh] Capital of the Philippines. 15°N 121°E (p. 629)
Maputo [mah•POO•toh] Capital of Mozambique. 26°S 33°E (p. 539)
Maseru [MA•zuh•ROO] Capital of Lesotho. 29°S 27°E (p. 539)
Mauritania [MAWR•uh•TAY•nee•uh] West African country north of Senegal. 20°N 14°W (p. 539)
Mauritius [maw•RIH•shuhs] Island country in the Indian Ocean east of Madagascar. 21°S 58°E (p. 539)
Mbabane [uhm•bah•BAH•nay] Capital of Swaziland. 26°S 31°E (p. 539)
Mediterranean [MEH•duh•tuh•RAY•nee•uhn] **Sea** Large inland sea surrounded by Europe, Asia, and Africa. 36°N 13°E (p. 284)
Mekong [MAY•KAWNG] **River** River in southeastern Asia that begins in Tibet and empties into the South China Sea. 18°N 104°E (p. 628)
Mexico [MEHK•sih•KOH] North American country south of the United States. 24°N 104°W (p. 180)
Mexico City Capital of Mexico. 19°N 99°W (p. 181)
Minsk [MIHNSK] Capital of Belarus. 54°N 28°E (p. 285)
Mississippi [MIH•suh•SIH•pee] **River** Large river system in the central United States that flows southward into the Gulf of Mexico. 32°N 92°W (p. 118)
Mogadishu [MOH•guh•DEE•SHOO] Capital of Somalia. 2°N 45°E (p. 539)
Moldova [mawl•DAW•vuh] Small European country between Ukraine and Romania. 48°N 28°E (p. 285)
Monaco [MAH•nuh•KOH] Small country in southern Europe on the French Mediterranean coast. 44°N 8°E (p. 285)
Mongolia [mahn•GOHL•yuh] Country in Asia between Russia and China. 46°N 100°E (p. 629)
Monrovia [muhn•ROH•vee•uh] Capital of Liberia. 6°N 11°W (p. 539)
Montevideo [MAHN•tuh•vuh•DAY•OH] Capital of Uruguay. 35°S 56°W (p. 181)
Morocco [muh•RAH•KOH] North African country on the Mediterranean Sea and the Atlantic Ocean. 32°N 7°W (p. 459)
Moscow [MAHS•KOW] Capital of Russia. 56°N 38°E (p. 397)
Mount Everest [EHV•ruhst] Highest mountain in the world, in the Himalaya between Nepal and Tibet. 28°N 87°E (p. 628)
Mozambique [MOH•zahm•BEEK] Southern African country south of Tanzania. 20°S 34°E (p. 539)
Muscat [MUHS•KAHT] Capital of Oman. 23°N 59°E (p. 459)
Myanmar [MYAHN•MAHR] Southeast Asian country south of China and India, formerly called Burma. 21°N 95°E (p. 629)

Nairobi [ny•ROH•bee] Capital of Kenya. 1°S 37°E (p. 539)

GAZETTEER

Namibia [nuh•MIH•bee•uh] Southern African country south of Angola on the Atlantic Ocean. 20°S 16°E (p. 539)
Nassau [NA•SAW] Capital of the Bahamas. 25°N 77°W (p. 181)
N'Djamena [uhn•jah•MAY•nah] Capital of Chad. 12°N 15°E (p. 539)
Nepal [NAY•PAHL] Mountain country between India and China. 29°N 83°E (p. 629)
Netherlands [NEH•thuhr•lundz] Western European country north of Belgium. 53°N 4°E (p. 285)
New Delhi [NOO DEH•lee] Capital of India. 29°N 77°E (p. 629)
New Zealand [NOO ZEE•luhnd] Major island country southeast of Australia in the South Pacific. 42°S 175°E (p. 729)
Niamey [nee•AHM•ay] Capital of Niger. 14°N 2°E (p. 539)
Nicaragua [NIH•kuh•RAH•gwuh] Central American country south of Honduras. 13°N 86°W (p. 181)
Nicosia [NIH•kuh•SEE•uh] Capital of Cyprus. 35°N 33°E (p. 285)
Niger [NY•juhr] West African country north of Nigeria. 18°N 9°E (p. 539)
Nigeria [ny•JIHR•ee•uh] West African country along the Gulf of Guinea. 9°N 7°E (p. 539)
Nile [NYL] **River** Longest river in the world, flowing north through eastern Africa. 19°N 33°E (p. 458)
North Korea [kuh•REE•uh] East Asian country in the northernmost part of the Korean Peninsula. 40°N 127°E (p. 629)
Norway [NAWR•WAY] Northern European country on the Scandinavian peninsula. 64°N 11°E (p. 285)
Nouakchott [nu•AHK•SHAHT] Capital of Mauritania. 18°N 16°W (p. 539)

Oman [oh•MAHN] Country on the Arabian Sea and the Gulf of Oman. 20°N 58°E (p. 459)
Oslo [AHZ•loh] Capital of Norway. 60°N 11°E (p. 285)
Ottawa [AH•tuh•wuh] Capital of Canada. 45°N 76°W (p. 119)
Ouagadougou [WAH•gah•DOO•goo] Capital of Burkina Faso. 12°N 2°W (p. 539)

Pakistan [PA•kih•STAN] South Asian country northwest of India on the Arabian Sea. 28°N 68°E (p. 629)
Palau [puh•LOW) Island country in the Pacific Ocean. 7°N 135°E (p. 729)
Panama [PA•nuh•MAH] Central American country on the Isthmus of Panama. 9°N 81°W (p. 180)
Panama City Capital of Panama. 9°N 79°W (p. 181)
Papua New Guinea [PA•pyu•wuh NOO GIH•nee] Island country in the Pacific Ocean north of Australia. 7°S 142°E (p. 729)
Paraguay [PAR•uh•GWY] South American country northeast of Argentina. 24°S 57°W (p. 181)
Paramaribo [PAH•rah•MAH•ree•boh] Capital of Suriname. 6°N 55°W (p. 181)
Paris [PAR•uhs] Capital of France. 49°N 2°E (p. 285)
Persian [PUHR•zhuhn] **Gulf** Arm of the Arabian Sea between Iran and Saudi Arabia. 28°N 51°E (p. 458)
Peru [puh•ROO] South American country south of Ecuador and Colombia. 10°S 75°W (p. 181)
Philippines [FIH•luh•PEENZ] Island country in the Pacific Ocean southeast of China. 14°N 125°E (p. 629)
Phnom Penh [puh•NAWM PEHN] Capital of Cambodia. 12°N 106°E (p. 629)
Poland [POH•luhnd] Eastern European country on the Baltic Sea. 52°N 18°E (p. 285)
Port-au-Prince [POHRT•oh•PRIHNS] Capital of Haiti. 19°N 72°W (p. 181)
Port Moresby [MOHRZ•bee] Capital of Papua New Guinea. 10°S 147°E (p. 729)
Port-of-Spain [SPAYN] Capital of Trinidad and Tobago. 11°N 62°W (p. 181)
Porto-Novo [POHR•toh•NOH•voh] Capital of Benin. 7°N 3°E (p. 539)
Portugal [POHR•chih•guhl] Country west of Spain on the Iberian Peninsula. 39°N 8°W (p. 285)
Prague [PRAHG] Capital of the Czech Republic. 51°N 15°E (p. 285)
Pretoria [prih•TOHR•ee•uh] Executive capital of South Africa. 26°S 28°E (p. 539)
Puerto Rico [PWEHR•toh REE•koh] Island in the Caribbean Sea; U.S. Commonwealth. 19°N 67°W (p. 181)
Pyongyang [pee•AWNG•YAHNG] Capital of North Korea. 39°N 126°E (p. 629)

Qatar [KAH•tuhr] Country on the southwestern shore of the Persian Gulf. 25°N 53°E (p. 459)
Quito [KEE•toh] Capital of Ecuador. 0° latitude 79°W (p. 181)

Rabat [ruh•BAHT] Capital of Morocco. 34°N 7°W (p. 459)
Reykjavík [RAY•kyah•VEEK] Capital of Iceland. 64°N 22°W (p. 285)
Rhine [RYN] **River** River in western Europe that flows into the North Sea. 51°N 7°E (p. 284)
Riga [REE•guh] Capital of Latvia. 57°N 24°E (p. 285)
Rio Grande [REE•oh GRAND] River that forms part of the boundary between the United States and Mexico. 30°N 103°W (p. 119)
Riyadh [ree•YAHD] Capital of Saudi Arabia. 25°N 47°E (p. 459)
Rocky Mountains Mountain system in western North America. 50°N 114°W (p. 118)

Romania [ru•MAY•nee•uh] Eastern European country east of Hungary. 46°N 23°E (p. 285)
Rome [ROHM] Capital of Italy. 42°N 13°E (p. 285)
Russia [RUH•shuh] Largest country in the world, covering parts of Europe and Asia. 60°N 90°E (p. 397)
Rwanda [ruh•WAHN•duh] East African country south of Uganda. 2°S 30°E (p. 539)

Sahara [suh•HAR•uh] Desert region in northern Africa that is the largest hot desert in the world. 24°N 2°W (p. 458)
Saint Lawrence [LAWR•uhns] **River** River that flows from Lake Ontario to the Atlantic Ocean and forms part of the boundary between the United States and Canada. 48°N 70°W (p. 119)
Sanaa [sahn•AH] Capital of Yemen. 15°N 44°E (p. 459)
San José [SAN hoh•ZAY] Capital of Costa Rica. 10°N 84°W (p. 181)
San Marino [SAN muh•REE•noh] Small European country located in the Italian peninsula. 44°N 13°E (p. 285)
San Salvador [san SAL•vuh•DAWR] Capital of El Salvador. 14°N 89°W (p. 181)
Santiago [SAN•tee•AH•goh] Capital of Chile. 33°S 71°W (p. 181)
Santo Domingo [SAN•toh duh•MIHNG•goh] Capital of the Dominican Republic. 19°N 70°W (p. 181)
Sao Tome and Principe [SOW•too•MAY PREEN•see•pee] Small island country in the Gulf of Guinea off the coast of central Africa. 1°N 7°E (p. 539)
Sarajevo [SAR•uh•YAY•voh] Capital of Bosnia and Herzegovina. 43°N 18°E (p. 285)
Saudi Arabia [SOW•dee uh•RAY•bee•uh] Country on the Arabian Peninsula. 23°N 46°E (p. 459)
Senegal [SEH•nih•GAWL] West African country on the Atlantic coast. 15°N 14°W (p. 539)
Seoul [SOHL] Capital of South Korea. 38°N 127°E (p. 629)
Serbia and Montenegro [SUHR•bee•uh MAHN•tuh•NEE•groh] Eastern European country south of Hungary. 44°N 21°E (p. 285)
Seychelles [say•SHEHL] Small island country in the Indian Ocean off eastern Africa. 6°S 56°E (p. 539)
Sierra Leone [see•EHR•uh lee•OHN] West African country south of Guinea. 8°N 12°W (p. 539)
Singapore [SIHNG•uh•POHR] Southeast Asian island country near tip of Malay Peninsula. 2°N 104°E (p. 629)
Skopje [SKAW•PYAY] Capital of the country of Macedonia. 42°N 21°E (p. 285)
Slovakia [sloh•VAH•kee•uh] Eastern European country south of Poland. 49°N 19°E (p. 285)
Slovenia [sloh•VEE•nee•uh] Southeastern European country south of Austria on the Adriatic Sea. 46°N 15°E (p. 285)
Sofia [SOH•fee•uh] Capital of Bulgaria. 43°N 23°E (p. 285)
Solomon [SAH•luh•muhn] **Islands** Island country in the Pacific Ocean northeast of Australia. 7°S 160°E (p. 729)
Somalia [soh•MAH•lee•uh] East African country on the Gulf of Aden and the Indian Ocean. 3°N 45°E (p. 539)
South Africa [A•frih•kuh] Country at the southern tip of Africa, officially the Republic of South Africa. 28°S 25°E (p. 539)
South Korea [kuh•REE•uh] East Asian country on the Korean Peninsula between the Yellow Sea and the Sea of Japan. 36°N 128°E (p. 629)
Spain [SPAYN] Southern European country on the Iberian Peninsula. 40°N 4°W (p. 285)
Sri Lanka [SREE•LAHNG•kuh] Country in the Indian Ocean south of India, formerly called Ceylon. 9°N 83°E (p. 629)
Stockholm [STAHK•HOHLM] Capital of Sweden. 59°N 18°E (p. 285)
Sucre [SOO•kray] Constitutional capital of Bolivia. 19°S 65°W (p. 181)
Sudan [soo•DAN] East African country south of Egypt. 14°N 28°E (p. 539)
Suriname [SUR•uh•NAH•muh] South American country between Guyana and French Guiana. 4°N 56°W (p. 181)
Suva [SOO•vah] Capital of the Fiji Islands. 18°S 177°E (p. 729)
Swaziland [SWAH•zee•LAND] Southern African country west of Mozambique, almost entirely within the Republic of South Africa. 27°S 32°E (p. 539)
Sweden [SWEED•uhn] Northern European country on the eastern side of the Scandinavian peninsula. 60°N 14°E (p. 285)
Switzerland [SWIHT•suhr•luhnd] European country in the Alps south of Germany. 47°N 8°E (p. 285)
Syria [SIHR•ee•uh] Southwest Asian country on the east side of the Mediterranean Sea. 35°N 37°E (p. 459)

Taipei [TY•PAY] Capital of Taiwan. 25°N 122°E (p. 629)
Taiwan [TY•WAHN] Island country off the southeast coast of China; the seat of the Chinese Nationalist government. 24°N 122°E (p. 629)
Tajikistan [tah•JIH•kih•STAN] Central Asian country east of Turkmenistan. 39°N 70°E (p. 397)
Tallinn [TA•luhn] Capital of Estonia. 59°N 25°E (p. 285)
Tanzania [TAN•zuh•NEE•uh] East African country south of Kenya. 7°S 34°E (p. 539)
Tashkent [tash•KEHNT] Capital of Uzbekistan. 41°N 69°E (p. 397)
T'bilisi [tuh•bih•LEE•see] Capital of the Republic of Georgia. 42°N 45°E (p. 397)
Tegucigalpa [tay•GOO•see•GAHL•pah] Capital of Honduras. 14°N 87°W (p. 181)

Tehran [TAY•uh•RAN] Capital of Iran. 36°N 52°E (p. 459)
Thailand [TY•LAND] Southeast Asian country east of Myanmar. 17°N 101°E (p. 629)
Thimphu [thihm•POO] Capital of Bhutan. 28°N 90°E (p. 629)
Tigris [TY•gruhs] **River** River in southeastern Turkey and Iraq that merges with the Euphrates River. 35°N 44°E (p. 458)
Tirana [tih•RAH•nuh] Capital of Albania. 42°N 20°E (p. 285)
Togo [TOH•goh] West African country between Benin and Ghana on the Gulf of Guinea. 8°N 1°E (p. 539)
Tokyo [TOH•kee•OH] Capital of Japan. 36°N 140°E (p. 629)
Trinidad and Tobago [TRIH•nuh•DAD tuh•BAY•goh] Island country near Venezuela between the Atlantic Ocean and the Caribbean Sea. 11°N 61°W (p. 181)
Tripoli [TRIH•puh•lee] Capital of Libya. 33°N 13°E (p. 459)
Tunis [TOO•nuhs] Capital of Tunisia. 37°N 10°E (p. 459)
Tunisia [too•NEE•zhuh] North African country on the Mediterranean Sea between Libya and Algeria. 35°N 10°E (p. 459)
Turkey [TUHR•kee] Country in southeastern Europe and western Asia. 39°N 32°E (p. 459)
Turkmenistan [tuhrk•MEH•nuh•STAN] Central Asian country on the Caspian Sea. 41°N 56°E (p. 397)

Uganda [yoo•GAHN•dah] East African country south of Sudan. 2°N 32°E (p. 539)
Ukraine [yoo•KRAYN] Eastern European country west of Russia on the Black Sea. 49°N 30°E (p. 285)
Ulaanbaatar [OO•LAHN•BAH•TAWR] Capital of Mongolia. 48°N 107°E (p. 629)
United Arab Emirates [EH•muh•ruhts] Country made up of seven states on the eastern side of the Arabian Peninsula. 24°N 54°E (p. 459)
United Kingdom Western European island country made up of England, Scotland, Wales, and Northern Ireland. 57°N 2°W (p. 285)
United States of America Country in North America made up of 50 states, mostly between Canada and Mexico. 38°N 110°W (p. 119)
Uruguay [YUR•uh•GWAY] South American country south of Brazil on the Atlantic Ocean. 33°S 56°W (p. 181)
Uzbekistan [UZ•BEH•kih•STAN] Central Asian country south of Kazakhstan. 42°N 60°E (p. 397)

Vanuatu [VAN•WAH•TOO] Country made up of islands in the Pacific Ocean east of Australia. 17°S 170°W (p. 729)
Vatican [VA•tih•kuhn] **City** Headquarters of the Roman Catholic Church, located in the city of Rome in Italy. 42°N 13°E (p. 285)
Venezuela [VEH•nuh•ZWAY•luh] South American country on the Caribbean Sea between Colombia and Guyana. 8°N 65°W (p. 181)
Vienna [vee•EH•nuh] Capital of Austria. 48°N 16°E (p. 285)
Vientiane [vyehn•TYAHN] Capital of Laos. 18°N 103°E (p. 629)
Vietnam [vee•EHT•NAHM] Southeast Asian country east of Laos and Cambodia. 18°N 107°E (p. 629)
Vilnius [VIL•nee•uhs] Capital of Lithuania. 55°N 25°E (p. 285)

Warsaw [WAWR•SAW] Capital of Poland. 52°N 21°E (p. 285)
Washington, D.C. Capital of the United States, in the District of Columbia. 39°N 77°W (p. 119)
Wellington [WEH•lihng•tuhn] Capital of New Zealand. 41°S 175°E (p. 729)
West Indies [IHN•deez] Caribbean islands between North America and South America. 19°N 79°W (p. 180)
Windhoek [VIHNT•HUK] Capital of Namibia. 22°S 17°E (p. 539)

Yamoussoukro [YAH•moo•SOO•kroh] Second capital of Côte d'Ivoire. 7°N 6°W (p. 539)
Yangon [YAHNG•GOHN] Capital of Myanmar, formerly called Rangoon. 17°N 96°E (p. 629)
Yangtze [YANG•SEE] **River** Principal river of China that begins in Tibet and flows into the East China Sea near Shanghai, also known as the Chang Jiang [CHAHNG jee•AHNG]. 31°N 117°E (p. 628)
Yaoundé [yown•DAY] Capital of Cameroon. 4°N 12°E (p. 539)
Yellow River River in northern and eastern China, also known as the Huang He [HWAHNG HUH]. 35°N 114°E (p. 628)
Yemen [YEH•muhn] Country south of Saudi Arabia on the Arabian Peninsula. 15°N 46°E (p. 459)
Yerevan [YEHR•uh•VAHN] Capital of Armenia. 40°N 44°E (p. 397)

Zagreb [ZAH•GREHB] Capital of Croatia. 46°N 16°E (p. 285)
Zambia [ZAM•bee•uh] Southern African country north of Zimbabwe. 14°S 24°E (p. 539)
Zimbabwe [zihm•BAH•bway] Southern African country northeast of Botswana. 18°S 30°E (p. 539)

absolute location exact position of a place on the earth's surface (p. 5)
acid rain rain containing high amounts of chemical pollutants (pp. 70, 135, 370)
adobe sun-dried clay bricks (p. 202)
airlift system of carrying supplies by aircraft (p. 322)
alluvial plain area that is built up by rich fertile soil left by river floods (p. 517)
altiplano large highland plateau (p. 271)
altitude height above sea level (pp. 193, 243)
apartheid system of laws that separated racial and ethnic groups and limited the rights of blacks in South Africa (p. 606)
aquifer underground rock layer that water flows through (pp. 50, 490)
archipelago group of islands (pp. 219, 690)
artifact object made by early people (p. 27)
atmosphere layer of air surrounding the earth (p. 30)
atoll low-lying, ring-shaped island that surrounds a lagoon (pp. 654, 760)
autobahn superhighway (p. 351)
autonomy self-government (pp. 168, 583)
axis imaginary line that runs through the earth's center between the North and South poles (p. 31); *also* horizontal (bottom) or vertical (side) line of measurement on a graph (p. 11)

bar graph graph in which vertical or horizontal bars represent quantities (p. 11)
basin low area surrounded by higher land (p. 232)
bauxite mineral used to make aluminum (pp. 220, 560)
bazaar marketplace (p. 488)
bedouins nomadic desert peoples of Southwest Asia (p. 505)
bilingual referring to a country that has two official languages (pp. 167, 440)
birthrate number of children born each year for every 1,000 people (p. 88)
blockade to forcibly prevent entry to an area (p. 321)
Boers name for the Dutch who were the first European settlers in South Africa (p. 605)
bog low swampy land (pp. 342, 368)
boomerang Australian weapon that is flat, bent, and made of wood that either strikes a target or curves and sails back to the person who threw it (p. 738)
bush rural areas of Australia (p. 739)

cacao tropical tree whose seeds are used to make chocolate and cocoa (pp. 552, 759)
caliph successor to Muhammad (p. 514)
calligraphy art of beautiful writing (p. 670)
campesino Colombian farmer (p. 257)
canopy umbrella-like covering formed by the tops of trees in a rain forest (pp. 214, 571)
cardinal directions basic directions on the earth: north, south, east, west (p. 8)
cartographer person who makes maps (p. 6)
casbah older section of Algerian cities (p. 492)
cash crop product grown to be sold for export (pp. 256, 438)
cassava plant with roots that can be ground into flour to make bread or porridge (p. 578)
caste social class based on a person's ancestry (p. 640)
caudillo military ruler (p. 243)
channel body of water wider than a strait between two pieces of land (p. 42)
chart graphic way of presenting information clearly (p. 12)
charter written agreement guaranteeing privileges and freedoms (p. 302)
circle graph round or pie-shaped graph showing how a whole is divided (p. 12)
city-state city and its surrounding countryside (p. 467)
civilizations highly developed cultures (pp. 84, 466)
civil war fight among different groups within a country (pp. 492, 554, 710)
clan group of people related to one another (pp. 590, 693)
Classical relating to the ancient Greek and Roman world (p. 294)
climate usual, predictable pattern of weather in an area over a long period of time (p. 52)
climograph combination bar and line graph giving information about temperature and precipitation (p. 13)
coalition government government in which two or more political parties work together to run a country (p. 360)
Cold War period between the late 1940s and late 1980s when the United States and the Soviet Union competed for world influence without actually fighting each other (pp. 319, 414)
collection process in the water cycle during which streams and rivers carry water back to the oceans (p. 49)
colony overseas territory or settlement tied to a parent country (p. 146)
common law unwritten set of laws based on local customs (p. 300)

commonwealth partly self-governing territory (p. 223)
communism economic, social, and political system based on the teachings of Karl Marx, which advocated the elimination of private property (p. 316)
communist state country whose government has strong control over the economy and society as a whole (pp. 221, 369, 413, 663)
compound group of houses surrounded by walls (p. 553)
condensation process in which air rises and cools, which makes the water vapor it holds change back into a liquid (p. 49)
conservation careful use of resources so they are not wasted (p. 71)
constitutional monarchy government in which a king or queen is the official head of state, but elected officials run the government (pp. 342, 493, 694)
consul elected chief official of the Roman Republic (p. 296)
consumer goods household products, clothing, and other goods people buy to use for themselves (pp. 378, 663)
contiguous areas that are joined together inside a common boundary (p. 126)
continent massive land area (p. 35)
continental divide mountainous area from which rivers flow in different directions (p. 352)
continental shelf plateau off each coast of a continent that lies under the ocean and stretches for several miles (p. 40)
cooperative farm owned and operated by the government (p. 222)
copper belt large area of copper mines in northern Zambia (p. 610)
copra dried coconut meat, which is used to make margarine, soap, and other products (p. 759)
coral reef structure at or near the water's surface formed by the skeletons of small sea animals (pp. 129, 577, 736)
cordillera group of mountain ranges that run side by side (pp. 160, 254)
core center of the earth, formed of hot iron mixed with other metals (p. 35)
cottage industry home- or village-based industry in which family members supply their own equipment to make goods (pp. 315, 639)
covenant agreement (p. 473)
crevasse deep crack in the Antarctic ice cap (p. 764)
crop rotation varying what is planted in a field to avoid using up all the minerals in the soil (p. 70)
crust uppermost layer of the earth (p. 35)
cultural diffusion the process of spreading new knowledge and skills to other cultures (p. 84)
culture way of life of a group of people who share similar beliefs and customs (p. 80)
culture region different countries that have cultural traits in common (p. 85)
cuneiform Sumerian writing system using wedge-shaped symbols pressed into clay tablets (p. 467)
current moving streams of water in the world's oceans (p. 56)
cyclone intense storm system with heavy rain and high winds (pp. 617, 646)
czar name for emperor in Russia's past (p. 411)

death rate number of people out of every 1,000 who die in a year (p. 87)
deforestation widespread cutting of forests (pp. 70, 235, 574, 709)
delta area formed from a soil deposit located at the mouth of a river (pp. 42, 469, 646)
democracy government in which leaders rule with consent of the citizens (pp. 83, 294, 429)
desalinization process used to make seawater drinkable (p. 514)
desertification process by which grasslands change to desert (p. 557)
deterrence maintenance of military power for the purpose of discouraging an attack (p. 320)
developed country country in which a great deal of manufacturing is carried out (p. 96)
developing country country that is working toward industrialization (p. 96)
dialect local form of a language that differs from the main language in pronunciation or the meaning of words (p. 81)
dictatorship government under the control of one all-powerful leader (pp. 83, 491)
dike high banks of soil built along rivers to control floods (p. 662)
disciple follower of a specific teacher (p. 475)
divine right of kings belief that royalty ruled by the will of God (p. 306)
dominion self-governing nation that accepts the British monarch as head of state (p. 166)
drought long period of extreme dryness (pp. 55, 556)
dry farming method in which the land is left unplanted every few years so that it can store moisture (p. 358)
dynasty line of rulers from the same family (p. 666)
dzong Buddhist center of prayer and study in Bhutan (p. 651)

earthquake violent and sudden movement of the earth's crust (p. 36)
economic system system that sets rules for how people decide what goods and services to produce and how they are exchanged (p. 93)
ecosystem place where the plants and animals are dependent upon one another and their surroundings for survival (p. 72)
ecotourist person who travels to another country to view its natural wonders (pp. 215, 581)

elevation height above sea level (pp. 9, 40, 440)
elevation profile cutaway diagram showing changes in elevation of land (p. 13)
El Niño combination of temperature, wind, and water effects in the Pacific Ocean that causes heavy rains in some areas and drought in others (p. 55)
embargo order that restricts or prohibits trade with another country (pp. 222, 518)
emigrate to move to another country (p. 91)
emperor absolute ruler of an empire (p. 296)
empire group of lands under one ruler (pp. 267, 468, 680)
enclave small territory entirely surrounded by a larger territory (p. 607)
endangered species plant or animal under the threat of completely dying out (p. 584)
environment natural surroundings (p. 24)
equinox day when day and night are of equal length in both hemispheres (p. 32)
erg huge area of shifting sand dunes in the Sahara (p. 492)
erosion process of wearing away or moving weathered material on the earth's surface (p. 38)
escarpment steep cliff between higher and lower land (p. 233)
estancia ranch (p. 240)
ethnic cleansing forcing people from a different ethnic group to leave their homes (p. 379)
ethnic group people who share a common history, language, religion, and physical characteristics (p. 81)
euro common currency adopted by countries in the European Union (p. 325)
evaporation process in which the sun's heat turns liquid water into water vapor (p. 48)
exclave small part of a country that is separated from the main part (p. 614)
exile inability to live in one's own country because of political beliefs (p. 669)
export to trade goods to other countries (p. 95)

famine lack of food (pp. 88, 701)
fault crack in the earth's crust (pp. 37, 438, 662)
favela slum area (p. 234)
federal republic government divided between national and state powers (pp. 147, 204, 351, 429)
fellahin farmers in Egypt who live in villages and work on small plots of land that they rent from landowners (p. 488)
feudalism political and social system in which a lord gave land to a noble to work, govern, and defend, in return for the noble's loyalty (p. 301)
five pillars of faith basic religious obligations of Islam (p. 477)
fjord steep-sided valley cut into mountains by the action of glaciers (pp. 354, 742)
foothill low hill at the base of a mountain range (p. 267)
fossil preserved remains or impressions of early humans, animals, or plants (p. 27)
fossil fuel coal, oil, or natural gas (p. 135)
free enterprise system economic system in which people start and run businesses with limited government intervention (pp. 131, 415, 578)
free market economy see *free enterprise system* (p. 424)
free port place where goods can be unloaded, stored, and shipped again without needing to pay any import taxes (p. 716)
free trade removing trade barriers so that goods flow freely among countries (pp. 96, 136)
free trade zone area where people can buy goods from other countries without paying extra taxes (p. 223)

gaucho cowhand (p. 240)
genocide mass murder of a people because of their race, religion, ethnicity, politics, or culture (pp. 317, 585)
geographic information systems (GIS) special software that helps geographers gather and use information about a place (pp. 6, 25)
geography the study of the earth in all its variety (p. 22)
geothermal energy electricity produced by natural underground sources of steam (pp. 357, 743)
geyser spring of water heated by molten rock inside the earth so that, from time to time, it shoots hot water into the air (pp. 357, 741)
glacier giant slow-moving sheets of ice (pp. 38, 49, 159)
glasnost Russian policy of "openness" (p. 415)
globalization development of a world culture and an interdependent world economy (p. 100)
Global Positioning System (GPS) group of satellites that travels around the earth which can be used to tell exact locations on the earth (pp. 6, 25)
great circle route ship or airplane route following a great circle; the shortest distance between two points on the earth (p. 6)
greenhouse effect buildup of certain gases in the atmosphere that, like a greenhouse, hold more of the sun's warmth (p. 58)
green revolution great increase in food grains production due to the use of improved seeds, pesticides, and efficient farming techniques (p. 639)
groundwater water that fills tiny cracks and holes in the rock layers below the earth's surface (p. 50)
guild medieval workers' organization (p. 302)

habitat type of environment in which a particular animal species lives (p. 580)

GLOSSARY

GLOSSARY

hacienda large ranch (p. 199)
hajj religious journey to Makkah that Muslims are expected to make at least once during their lifetime if they are able to do so (p. 477)
harmattan dry, dusty wind that blows south from the Sahara (p. 551)
heavy industry manufactured goods such as machinery, mining equipment, and steel (pp. 356, 426)
hemisphere one-half of the globe; the Equator divides the earth into Northern and Southern Hemispheres; the Prime Meridian divides it into Eastern and Western Hemispheres (p. 4)
hieroglyphics form of writing that uses signs and symbols (pp. 198, 471)
high island Pacific island formed by volcanic activity (p. 760)
high-technology industry industry that produces computers and other kinds of electronic equipment (p. 678)
Holocaust systematic murder of more than 6 million European Jews and 6 million others by Adolf Hitler and the Nazis during World War II (pp. 317, 511)
human resources supply of people who can produce goods (p. 314)
human rights basic freedoms and rights that all people should enjoy (p. 669)
humid continental climate weather pattern characterized by long, cold, snowy winters and short, hot summers (p. 64)
humid subtropical climate weather pattern characterized by hot, humid, rainy summers and short, mild winters (p. 65)
hurricane violent tropical storm with high winds and heavy rains (p. 193)
hydroelectric power electricity generated by flowing water (pp. 242, 571, 743)

iceberg chunk of a glacier that has broken away and floats free in the ocean (p. 765)
ice shelf layer of ice above water in Antarctica (p. 765)
immigrant person who moves to a new country to make a permanent home (p. 148)
imperialism system of building foreign empires for military and trade advantages (p. 316)
import to buy goods from another country (p. 95)
indulgences pardons for sins, given or sold by the Catholic Church (p. 305)
industrialize to change an economy to rely more on manufacturing and less on farming (pp. 195, 412)
industrialized country country in which a great deal of manufacturing occurs (p. 604)
intensive cultivation growing crops on every available piece of land (p. 693)
interdependence dependence of countries on one another for goods, raw materials to make goods, and markets in which to sell goods (p. 100)
irrigation farming practice followed in dry areas to collect water and bring it to crops (p. 71)
Islamic republic government run by Muslim religious leaders (p. 519)
island body of land smaller than a continent and surrounded by water (p. 40)
isthmus narrow piece of land that connects two larger pieces of land (pp. 40, 212)

jade shiny, usually green gemstone (p. 197)
jute plant fiber used for making rope, burlap bags, and carpet backing (p. 639)

kibbutz settlement in Israel where the people share property and produce goods (p. 510)
krill tiny, shrimplike animal that lives in waters off Antarctica and is food for many other creatures (p. 766)

lagoon shallow pool of water surrounded by reefs, sandbars, or atolls (p. 654)
land bridge narrow strip of land that joins two larger landmasses (p. 190)
landfill area where trash companies dump the waste they collect (p. 136)
landform individual features of the land (p. 23)
landlocked country with no land bordering a sea or an ocean (pp. 271, 372)
La Niña pattern of unusual weather in the Pacific Ocean that has opposite effects of El Niño (p. 56)
latitude location north or south of the Equator, measured by imaginary lines (parallels) that are numbered in degrees north or south (pp. 5, 192)
leap year year that has an extra day; occurs every fourth year (p. 31)
life expectancy the number of years that an average person is expected to live (p. 428)
light industry making of such goods as clothing, shoes, furniture, and household products (p. 426)
line graph graph in which one or more lines represent changing quantities over time (p. 11)
literacy rate percentage of people who can read and write (p. 215)
llanos grassy plains (p. 242)
local wind pattern of wind caused by landforms in a particular area (p. 56)
longitude location east or west of the Prime Meridian, measured by imaginary lines (meridians) numbered in degrees east or west (p. 5)
low island Pacific island formed of coral and having little vegetation (p. 760)

magma hot, melted rock that sometimes flows to the earth's surface in a volcanic eruption (p. 35)
maize Native American name for corn (p. 198)
majority group group in society that controls most of the wealth and power, though not always the largest group in numbers (p. 430)
mangrove tropical tree with roots that extend both above and beneath the water (p. 550)
manor feudal estate made up of a manor house or castle and land (p. 301)
mantle rock layer about 1,800 miles (2,897 km) thick between the earth's core and the crust (p. 35)
manuka small shrub of New Zealand (p. 741)
map key code that explains the lines, symbols, and colors used on a map (p. 8)
maquiladora factory that assembles parts made in other countries (p. 194)
marine west coast climate weather pattern characterized by rainy and mild winters and cool summers (p. 63)
marsupial mammal that carries its young in a pouch (p. 737)
Mediterranean climate weather pattern characterized by mild, rainy winters and hot, dry summers (p. 64)
megalopolis pattern of heavy urban settlement over a large area (pp. 127, 694)
meridian see *longitude* (p. 5)
messiah in Judaism and Christianity, a savior sent by God (p. 475)
mestizo person with mixed Spanish and Native American background (p. 256)
migrant worker person who travels from place to place when extra help is needed to plant or harvest crops (p. 205)
migrate to move from one place to another (p. 504)
minority group group of people who are different in some characteristic from the group with the most power and wealth in a region (p. 430)
missionary person who spreads religious views (p. 300)
monarchy form of government in which a king or queen inherits the right to rule (p. 83)
monotheism belief in one God (p. 473)
monsoon seasonal wind that blows over a continent for months at a time (p. 639)
moor treeless, windy highland area with damp ground (p. 340)
moshav settlement in Israel where people share property but also own some private property (p. 510)
mosque place of worship for followers of Islam (pp. 380, 488)
multilingual able to speak several languages (p. 348)
multinational company firm that does business in several countries (p. 348)
mural wall painting (p. 198)

national debt money owed by a nation's government (p. 206)
natural resource product of the earth that people use to meet their needs (p. 92)
navigable body of water wide and deep enough to allow the passage of ships (pp. 134, 266, 345)
neutrality refusal to take sides in disagreements and wars between countries (p. 352)
newsprint type of paper used for printing newspapers (p. 163)
nomads people who move from place to place with herds of animals (pp. 373, 439, 680)
nonrenewable resource natural resource such as minerals that cannot be replaced (p. 93)
nuclear energy power made by creating a controlled atomic reaction (p. 428)
nuclear weapon weapon whose destructive power comes from a nuclear reaction (p. 319)

oasis a fertile or green area in a desert (pp. 439, 485)
obsidian hard, black glass created by the cooled molten lava of a volcano (p. 198)
orbit path that a body in the solar system travels around the sun (p. 29)
outback inland regions of Australia (p. 737)
overgraze to allow livestock to strip areas so bare that plants cannot grow back (p. 556)
ozone type of oxygen that forms a layer in the atmosphere and protects all living things on the earth from certain harmful rays of the sun (p. 766)

pagoda many-storied Buddhist temple (p. 670)
pampas vast treeless, grass-covered plains of South America (p. 240)
papyrus Egyptian paper (p. 471)
parallel see *latitude* (pp. 5, 699)
parliamentary democracy government in which voters elect representatives to a lawmaking body which chooses a prime minister to head the government (pp. 166, 216, 341)
peat plants partly decayed in water that can be dried and used for fuel (p. 342)
peninsula piece of land with water on three sides (pp. 40, 191)
perestroika Soviet policy that loosened government controls and permitted its economy to move towards free enterprise (p. 415)
permafrost permanently frozen lower layers of soil in the tundra and subarctic regions (p. 406)
pesticides powerful chemicals that kill crop-destroying insects (pp. 71, 640)
pharaoh ruler of ancient Egypt (p. 470)

GLOSSARY

phosphate mineral salt used in fertilizers (pp. 486, 560, 761)
pictograph graph in which small symbols represent quantities (p. 12)
pidgin language language formed by combining elements of several different languages (p. 760)
plain low-lying stretch of flat or gently rolling land (p. 40)
plantain kind of banana (p. 582)
plantation large farm that grows a single crop for sale (p. 194)
plate huge slab of rock that makes up the earth's crust (pp. 589, 714)
plateau flat land with higher elevation than a plain (p. 40)
plate tectonics theory that the earth's crust is not an unbroken shell but consists of plates, or huge slabs of rock, that move (p. 35)
plaza public square (p. 202)
poaching illegal hunting of protected animals (p. 577)
polder area of land reclaimed from the sea (p. 347)
polis Greek term for "city-state" (p. 294)
polytheism belief in more than one god (p. 467)
pope head of the Roman Catholic Church (pp. 299, 371)
population density average number of people living in a square mile or square kilometer (p. 89)
potash type of mineral salt that is often used in fertilizers (p. 385)
prairie rolling, inland grassy area with very fertile soil (p. 160)
precious gems valuable gemstones, such as rubies, sapphires, and jade (p. 709)
precipitation water that falls back to the earth as rain, snow, sleet, or hail (p. 49)
prime minister official who heads the government in a parliamentary democracy (p. 167)
privatize to transfer the ownership of factories from the government to individual citizens (p. 375)
productivity measurement of the amount of work accomplished in a given time (p. 314)
projection in mapmaking, a way of drawing the round Earth on a flat surface (p. 7)
prophet messenger of God (p. 474)
province regional political division similar to states (p. 158)
pyramid huge stone structure that served as an elaborate tomb or monument (p. 470)

quota number limit on how many items of a particular product can be imported from a particular country (p. 95)

rain forest dense forest that receives high amounts of rain each year (p. 59)
rain shadow dry area on the inland side of coastal mountains (p. 58)
recycling reusing materials instead of throwing them out (p. 136)
refugee person who flees to another country to escape persecution or disaster (pp. 91, 379, 585)
reincarnation rebirth of a soul in a new body (p. 640)
relief differences in height in a landscape; how flat or rugged the surface is (p. 9)
renewable resource natural resource that cannot be used up or can be replaced naturally or grown again (p. 92)
representative democracy government in which the people are represented by elected leaders (p. 146)
republic strong national government headed by elected leaders (pp. 216, 296, 487)
responsibilities duties owed by citizens to their government and other citizens (p. 99)
reunification bringing together the two parts of Germany under one government (p. 351)
revolution one complete orbit around the sun (p. 31); a great and often violent change (p. 306)
rights benefits and protections guaranteed by law (p. 99)
rural area in the countryside (p. 150)

samurai powerful land-owning warriors in Japan (p. 693)
satellite nation nation politically and economically dominated or controlled by another, more powerful country (p. 321)
sauna wooden room heated by water sizzling on hot stones (p. 356)
savanna broad grassland in the Tropics with few trees (pp. 62, 550)
scale bar on a map, a divided line showing the map scale, usually in miles or kilometers (p. 8)
secede to withdraw from a national government (p. 147)
secular nonreligious (p. 492)
selva tropical rain forests in Brazil (p. 232)
serf farm laborer who could be bought and sold along with the land (pp. 301, 412)
service industry business that provides services to people instead of producing goods (pp. 132, 195, 488)
shah title given to kings who ruled Iran (p. 519)
shogun military leader in early Japan (p. 693)
silt small particles of rich soil (p. 484)
sirocco hot, dry winds that blow across Italy from North Africa (p. 360)
sisal plant fiber used to make rope and twine (p. 580)
slash-and-burn farming method of clearing land for planting by cutting and burning forests (p. 616)
smog thick haze of fog and chemicals (p. 206)

socialism economic system in which most businesses are owned and run by the government (p. 709)
sodium nitrate chemical used in fertilizer and explosives (p. 274)
solar system Earth, eight other planets, and thousands of smaller bodies that all revolve around the sun (p. 29)
sorghum tall grass with seeds that are used as grain and to make syrup (p. 610)
spa resort that has hot mineral springs that people bathe in to regain their health (p. 374)
station cattle or sheep ranch in Australia (p. 737)
steppe partly dry grassland often found on the edges of a desert (pp. 67, 383, 406, 438, 680)
strait narrow body of water between two pieces of land (pp. 42, 716)
strike refusal to work, usually by a labor organization, until demands are met (p. 315)
subarctic weather pattern characterized by severely cold, bitter winters and short, cool summers (p. 65)
subcontinent large landmass that is part of another continent but distinct from it (p. 638)
subsistence farm small plot where a farmer grows only enough food to feed his own family (pp. 194, 552)
suburb smaller community that surrounds a city (p. 150)
summer solstice day with the most hours of sunlight and the fewest hours of darkness (p. 32)

taiga huge forests of evergreen trees that grow in subarctic regions (p. 406)
tariff tax added to the value of goods that are imported (p. 95)
terraced field strips of land cut out of a hillside like stair steps so the land can hold water and be used for farming (p. 717)
textiles woven cloth (p. 315)
theocracy form of government in which one individual ruled as both religious leader and king (p. 467)
townships crowded neighborhoods outside cities in South Africa where most nonwhites live (p. 607)
trench valley in the ocean floor (p. 41)
tributary small river that flows into a larger river (p. 645)
Tropics low-latitude region between the Tropic of Cancer and the Tropic of Capricorn (p. 53)
trust territory area temporarily placed under control of another nation (p. 761)
tsetse fly insect whose bite can kill cattle or humans with a deadly disease called sleeping sickness (p. 573)
tsunami huge sea wave caused by an earthquake on the ocean floor (pp. 36, 690)
tundra vast rolling treeless plain in high latitude climates in which only the top few inches of ground thaw in summer (pp. 66, 159, 406)

union labor organization that negotiates for improved worker conditions and pay (p. 315)
urban area in the city (p. 150)
urbanization movement to cities (p. 90)

vaquero cowhand (p. 193)
vassal noble in medieval society who swore loyalty to a lord in return for land (p. 301)

wadi dry riverbed filled by rainwater from rare downpours (p. 513)
water cycle process in which water moves from the oceans to the air to the ground and finally back to the oceans (p. 48)
watershed region drained by a river (p. 584)
water vapor water in the form of gas (p. 48)
weather unpredictable changes in air that take place over a short period of time (p. 52)
weathering natural process that breaks surface rocks into boulders, gravel, sand, and soil (p. 37)
welfare state country that uses tax money to support people who are sick, needy, jobless, or retired (p. 355)
winter solstice day with the fewest hours of sunlight (p. 32)

yurt large circle-shaped tent made of animal skins that can be packed up and moved from place to place (p. 681)

GLOSSARY

SPANISH GLOSSARY

absolute location/ubicación absoluta posición exacta de en lugar en la superficie de la Tierra (pág. 5)
acid rain/lluvia ácida lluvia que contiene grandes cantidades de contaminantes químicos (págs. 70, 135, 370)
adobe/adobe ladrillos secados al Sol (pág. 202)
airlift/puente áereo sistema de transportar suministros por avión (pág. 322)
alluvial plain/llanura aluvial área creada por el suelo fértil que se acumula después de las inundaciones causadas por los ríos (pág. 517)
altiplano/altiplano meseta grande y muy elevada; también se llama altiplanicie (pág. 271)
altitude/altitud altura sobre el nivel del mar (págs. 193, 243)
apartheid/apartheid sistema de leyes que separaba los grupos raciales y étnicos y limitaba los derechos de la población negra (pág. 606)
aquifer/manto acuífero capa de rocas subterránea por la cual corre el agua (págs. 50, 490)
archipelago/archipiélago grupo de islas (págs. 219, 690)
artifact/artefacto objeto construido por pueblos antiguos (pág. 27)
atmosphere/atmósfera capa de aire que rodea la Tierra (pág. 30)
atoll/atolón isla de muy poca elevación que se forma alrededor de una laguna en la forma de un anillo (págs. 654, 760)
autobahn/autobahn autopista muy rápida (pág. 351)
autonomy/autonomía gobernarse por sí mismo (págs. 168, 583)
axis/eje terrestre línea imaginaria que atraviesa el centro de la Tierra entre el Polo Norte y el Polo Sur (pág. 31); también la línea vertical (del lado) u horizontal (de abajo) de una gráfica que se usa para medir (pág. 11)

bar graph/gráfica de barras gráfica en que franjas verticales u horizontales representan cantidades (pág. 11)
basin/cuenca área baja rodeada de tierras más elevadas (pág. 232)
bauxite/bauxita mineral que se usa para hacer aluminio (págs. 220, 560)
bazaar/bazar mercado (pág. 488)
bedouins/beduinos gente nomádica del desierto del sudoeste de Asia (pág. 505)
bilingual/bilingüe se refiere a un país que tiene dos idiomas oficiales (págs. 167, 440)
birthrate/índice de natalidad número de niños que nace cada año por cada mil personas (pág. 88)
blockade/bloquear impedir por la fuerza la entrada a un área (pág. 321)
Boers/bóers los holandeses que fueron los primeros colonos en Sudáfrica (pág. 605)
bog/ciénaga tierra baja y pantanosa (págs. 342, 368)
boomerang/bumerán arma australiana que es plana, curvado y de madera que se lanza para que golpee un objetivo o de la vuelta de la persona que la lanzó (pág. 738)
bush/campo áreas rurales de Australia (pág. 739)

cacao/cacao árbol tropical cuyas semillas se usan para hacer chocolate y cocoa (págs. 552, 759)
caliph/califa sucesor de Mahoma (pág. 514)
calligraphy/caligrafía el arte de escribir con letra muy bella (pág. 670)
campesino/campesino agricultor (pág. 257)
canopy/bóveda techo formado por las copas de los árboles en los bosques húmedos (págs. 214, 571)
cardinal directions/puntos cardinales cuatro direcciones básicas en la Tierra: norte, sur, este, oeste (pág. 8)
cartographer/cartógrafo persona que hace mapas (pág. 6)
casbah/casbah la sección antigua de las ciudades de Argelia; también se llama *alcazaba* (pág. 492)
cash crop/cultivo comercial producto que se cultiva para exportación (págs. 256, 438)
cassava/yuca planta con raíces que se pueden convertir en harina para hacer pan o gachas (pág. 578)
caste/casta clase social basada en la ascendencia de una persona (pág. 640)
caudillo/caudillo gobernante militar (pág. 243)
channel/canal una masa de agua entre dos tierras que tiene más anchura que un estrecho (pág. 42)
chart/cuadro manera gráfica de presentar información con claridad (pág. 12)
charter/cédula acuerdo escrito garantizando privilegios y libertades (pág. 302)
circle graph/gráfica de círculo gráfica redonda que muestra como un todo es dividido (pág. 12)
city-state/ciudad estado ciudad junto con las tierras que la rodean (pág. 467)
civilizations/civilizaciones culturas altamente desarrolladas (págs. 84, 466)
civil war/guerra civil pelea entre distintos grupos dentro de un país (págs. 492, 554, 710)
clan/clan grupo de personas que están emparentadas (págs. 590, 693)

Classical/Clásico relacionado a la antigua Roma y Grecia (pág. 294)
climate/clima el patrón que sigue el estado del tiempo en un área durante muchos años (pág. 52)
climograph/gráfica de clima gráfica que combina barras y líneas para dar información sobre la temperatura y la precipitación (pág. 13)
coalition government/gobierno por coalición gobierno en que dos o más partidos trabajan juntos para dirigir un país (pág. 360)
Cold War/Guerra Fría período entre los fines de los 1940 y los fines de los 1980 en que los Estados Unidos y la Unión Soviética compitieron por tener influencia mundial sin pelear uno contra el otro (págs. 319, 414)
collection/drenaje proceso durante el ciclo hidrológico en que los ríos llevan el agua de regreso a los océanos (pág. 49)
colony/colonia territorio o poblado con lazos a un país extranjero (pág. 146)
common law/derecho común grupo de leyes no escritas basadas en costumbres locales (pág. 300)
commonwealth/estado libre asociado territorio que en parte se gobierna por sí solo (pág. 223)
communism/comunismo sistema económico social y político basado en las enseñanzas de Karl Marx, el cual abogaba por la eliminación de propriedades privadas (pág. 316)
communist state/estado comunista país cuyo gobierno mantiene mucho control sobre la economía y la sociedad en su totalidad (págs. 221, 369, 413, 663)
compound/complejo residencial grupo de viviendas rodeada por una muralla (pág. 553)
condensation/condensación proceso en que el aire sube y se enfría, lo cual hace que el vapor de agua que contiene se convierta de nuevo en líquido (pág. 49)
conservation/conservación uso juicioso de los recursos para no malgastarlos (pág. 71)
constitutional monarchy/monarquía constitucional gobierno en que un rey o reina es el jefe de estado oficial pero los gobernantes son elegidos (págs. 342, 493, 694)
consul/cónsul oficial en jefe electo en la república romana (pág. 296)
consumer goods/bienes de consumo productos para la casa, ropa y otras cosas que la gente compra para su uso personal (págs. 378, 663)
contiguous/contiguas áreas adyacentes dentro de la misma frontera (pág. 126)
continent/continente masa de tierra inmensa (pág. 35)
continental divide/línea divisoria continental área montañosa de la cual los ríos desciendan en diferentes direcciones (pág. 352)
continental shelf/plataforma continental meseta formada por parte de un continente que se extiende por varias millas debajo del mar (pág. 40)
cooperative/cooperativa granja que es propiedad y es operada por el gobierno (pág. 222)
copper belt/cinturón de cobre área extensa de minas de cobre en el norte de Zambia (pág. 610)
copra/copra pulpa seca del coco que se usa para hacer margarina, jabón y otros productos (pág. 759)
coral reef/arrecife coralino estructura formada al nivel del mar o cerca de éste por los esqueletos de pequeños animales marinos (págs. 129, 577, 736)
cordillera/cordillera grupo de cadenas paralelas de montañas (págs. 160, 254)
core/núcleo centro de la Tierra, que está formado de hierro caliente y otros metales (pág. 35)
cottage industry/industria familiar industria basada en una casa o aldea en que los miembros de la familia usan sus propias herramientas para hacer productos (págs. 315, 639)
covenant/alianza pacto entre Dios y los hebreos (pág. 473)
crevasse/grieta rajadura profunda en el casquete de hielo de la Antártida (pág. 764)
crop rotation/rotación de cultivos variar lo que se siembra en un terreno para no agotar todos los minerales que tiene el suelo (pág. 70)
crust/corteza capa de afuera de la Tierra (pág. 35)
cultural diffusion/difusión cultural el proceso de esparcir nuevos conocimientos y habilidades a otras culturas (pág. 84)
culture/cultura modo de vida de un grupo de personas que comparten creencias y costumbres similares (pág. 80)
culture region/región cultural países que tienen los mismos rasgos culturales (pág. 85)
cuneiform/cuneiforme sistema de escritura Sumeria que usa símbolos en forma de cuñas hundidas en tabletas de arcilla (pág. 467)
current/corriente movimiento de las aguas del mar (pág. 56)
cyclone/ciclón tormenta violenta con vientos muy fuertes y mucha lluvia (págs. 617, 646)
czar/zar título de los antiguos emperadores rusos (pág. 411)

death rate/índice de mortalidad número de personas de cada mil que mueren en un año (pág. 87)
deforestation/deforestación la extensa destrucción de los bosques (págs. 70, 235, 574, 709)
delta/delta área formada por el suelo que deposita un río en su desembocadura (págs. 42, 469, 646)
democracy/democracia gobierno en el cual los líderes gobiernan con el consentimiento de los ciudadanos (págs. 83, 294, 429)
desalinization/desalinización proceso de hacer el agua de mar potable (pág. 514)
desertification/desertización proceso por el cual los pastos se convierten en desiertos (pág. 557)

SPANISH GLOSSARY

deterrence/disuasión el mantener el poder militar con el propósito de desalentar un ataque (pág. 320)
developed country/país desarrollado país donde hay mucha manufactura de productos (pág. 96)
developing country/país en vías de desarrollo país que está industrializándose (pág. 96)
dialect/dialecto forma local de un idioma que se diferencia del idioma normal por su pronunciación o por el sentido de algunas palabras (pág. 81)
dictatorship/dictadura gobierno bajo el control de un líder que tiene todo el poder (págs. 83, 491)
dike/dique muros de tierra muy altos construidos a lo largo de los ríos para controlar las inundaciones (pág. 662)
disciple/discípulo partidario de un maestro específico (pág. 475)
divine right of kings/derecho divino de los reyes la creencia de que los reyes governaban por la voluntad de Dios (pág. 306)
dominion/dominio naciones que se gobiernan por sí solas que aceptan al monarca británico como jefe de estado (pág. 166)
drought/sequía largos períodos de sequedad (págs. 55, 556)
dry farming/agricultura en seco método de cultivar en que la tierra se deja sin sembrar cada varios años para que almacene humedad (pág. 358)
dynasty/dinastía serie de gobernantes de la misma familia (pág. 666)
dzong*/ *dzong centro budista en Bután para rezar y estudiar (pág. 651)

earthquake/terremoto movimiento violento e inesperado de la corteza de la Tierra (pág. 36)
economic system/sistema económico sistema que establece reglas que determinan cómo las personas deciden cuáles bienes y servicios van a producir y cómo los van a intercambiar (pág. 93)
ecosystem/ecosistema lugar en el cual las plantas y animales dependen unos de otros y de sus alrededores para sobrevivir (pág. 72)
ecotourist/ecoturista persona que viaja a otro país para ver sus bellezas naturales (págs. 215, 581)
elevation/elevación altura por encima del nivel del mar (págs. 9, 40, 440)
elevation profile/perfil de elevaciones diagrama que muestra los cambios en la elevación de la tierra como si se hubiera hecho un corte vertical del área (pág. 13)
El Niño/El Niño combinación de la temperatura, los vientos y los efectos del agua en el océano Pacífico que causa lluvias fuertes en algunas áreas y sequía en otras (pág. 55)
embargo/embargo orden que limita o prohibe el comercio con otro país (págs. 222, 518)
emigrate/emigrar mudarse a otro país (pág. 91)
emperor/emperador gobernante absoluto de un imperio (pág. 296)
empire/imperio grupo de países bajo un gobernante (págs. 267, 468, 680)
enclave/enclave territorio pequeño totalmente rodeado por un territorio más grande (pág. 607)
endangered species/especie en vías de extinción planta o animal que está en peligro de desaparecer completamente (pág. 584)
environment/medio ambiente alrededores naturales (pág. 24)
equinox/equinoccio día en que el día y la noche tienen la misa duración en los dos hemisferios (pág. 32)
erg/ergio inmensas áreas en el Sahara en que se mueven las dunas de arena (pág. 492)
erosion/erosión proceso de mover los materiales desgastados en la superficie de la Tierra (pág. 38)
escarpment/escarpa acantilado empinado entre una área baja y una alta (pág. 233)
***estancia*/estancia** rancho (pág. 240)
ethnic cleansing/limpieza étnica forzar a personas de un grupo étnico distinto a abandonar el lugar donde viven (pág. 379)
ethnic group/grupo étnico personas que tienen el mismo idioma, historia, religión y los mismos rasgos físicos (pág. 81)
euro/eurodólar moneda común adoptada por los países de la Unión Europea (pág. 325)
evaporation/evaporación proceso mediante el cual el calor del sol convierte el agua líquida en vapor de agua (pág. 48)
exclave/territorio externo parte pequeña de un país que está separada de la parte principal (pág. 614)
exile/exilio tener que vivir fuera de su país nativo por causa de sus creencias políticas (pág. 669)
export/exportar comerciar y mandar bienes a otros países (pág. 95)

famine/hambruna falta de alimentos (págs. 88, 701)
fault/falla fractura en la corteza de la Tierra (págs. 37, 438, 662)
favela/favela barrio pobre y deteriorado (pág. 234)
federal republic/república federal nación en que el poder está dividido entre el gobierno nacional y el de los estados (págs. 147, 204, 351, 429)
fellahin/felás granjeros en Egipto que viven en aldeas y cultivan pequeños terrenos que arriendan de un hacendado (pág. 488)
feudalism/feudalismo sistema político y social en el cual un lord cedía tierra a un noble para que la trabajara, gobernara y defendiera, obligándose éste rendirle fidelidad (pág. 301)
five pillars of faith/cinco pilares de fé obligaciones religiosas básicas del Islam (pág. 477)

fjord/fiordo valle creado por el movimiento de glaciares en las montañas que deja laderas sumamente empinadas (págs. 354, 742)
foothill/estribaciones colinas bajas al pie de una cadena de montañas (pág. 267)
fossil/fósil las huellas o restos preservados de seres humanos, animales o plantas antiguos (pág. 27)
fossil fuel/combustibles fósiles carbón, petróleo o gas natural (pág. 135)
free enterprise system/sistema de libre empresa sistema económico en que la gente empieza y administra negocios con poca intervención del gobierno (págs. 131, 415, 578)
free market economy/economía del libre comercio *véase* free enterprise system (pág. 424)
free port/puerto libre lugar donde las mercancías se pueden descargar, almacenar y embarcar de nuevo sin tener que pagar derechos de importación (pág. 716)
free trade/libre comercio eliminar las barreras al comercio para que se puedan mover productos libremente entre países (págs. 96, 136)
free trade zone/zona de cambio libre área donde la gente puede comprar bienes de otros países sin pagar impuestos adicionales (pág. 233)

gaucho/gaucho vaquero (pág. 240)
genocide/genocidio asesinato en masa de personas a causa de su raza, religión, etnicidad, política o cultura (págs. 317, 585)
geographic information systems (GIS)/sistemas de información geográfica (SIG) programas de computadoras especiales que ayudan a los geógrafos a obtener y usar la información geográfica sobre un lugar (págs. 6, 25)
geography/geografía el estudio de la Tierra y de toda su variedad (pág. 22)
geothermal energy/energía geotérmica electricidad producida por fuentes de vapor subterráneas naturales (págs. 357, 743)
geyser/géiser manantial de agua calentado por rocas fundidas dentro de la Tierra que, de vez en cuando, arroja agua caliente al aire (págs. 357, 741)
glacier/glaciar capa de hielo inmensa que se mueve muy lentamente (págs. 38, 49, 159)
glasnost/glasnost política rusa de "franqueza" (pág. 415)
globalization/globalización desarrollo de una cultura y economía interdependiente mundiales (pág. 100)
Global Positioning System (GPS)/Sistema global de posición (GPS) grupo de satélites que le dan la vuelta a la Tierra y se usan para localizar lugares exactos en la Tierra (págs. 6, 25)
great circle route/línea de rumbo ruta que sigue un círculo máximo; usada por aviones y barcos porque es la distancia más corta entre dos puntos en la Tierra (pág. 6)
greenhouse effect/efecto invernadero la acumulación de ciertos gases en la atmósfera que mantienen más del calor del Sol, como hace un invernadero (pág. 58)
green revolution/revolución verde gran aumento en la producción de granos debido al uso de semillas, pesticidas y técnicas agrícolas perfeccionadas (pág. 639)
groundwater/agua subterránea agua que llena las rajaduras y hoyos en las capas de roca debajo de la superficie de la Tierra (pág. 50)
guild/gremio organización de trabajadores en la época medieval (pág. 302)

habitat/hábitat tipo de ambiente en que vive una especie animal en particular (pág. 580)
hacienda/hacienda un rancho grande (pág. 199)
hajj/*hajj* viaje religioso a La Meca que todo musulmán debe hacer por lo menos una vez en la vida si puede (pág. 477)
harmattan/harmattan viento seco y lleno de polvo que sopla hacia el sur desde el Sahara (pág. 551)
heavy industry/industria pesada manufactura de productos como maquinaria, equipo de minería y acero (págs. 356, 426)
hemisphere/hemisferio una mitad del globo terráqueo; el ecuador divide la Tierra en los hemisferios norte y sur; el primer meridiano la divide en hemisferios este y oeste (pág. 4)
hieroglyphics/jeroglíficos forma de escribir que usa signos y símbolos (págs. 198, 471)
high island/isla oceánica isla del Pacífico formada por actividad volcánica (pág. 760)
high-technology industry/industria de alta tecnología industria que produce computadoras y otras clases de equipo electrónico (pág. 678)
Holocaust/Holocausto matanza sistemática de más de 6 millones de judíos europeos y 6 millones de personas más por Adolfo Hitler y los nazis durante la Segunda Guerra Mundial (págs. 317, 511)
human resources/recursos humanos suministro de personas quienes pueden producir bienes de consumo (pág. 314)
human rights/derechos humanos libertades y derechos básicos que todas las personas deben disfrutar (pág. 669)
humid continental climate/clima húmedo continental patrón del estado del tiempo con inviernos largos, fríos y con mucha nieve y veranos cortos y calurosos (pág. 64)
humid subtropical climate/clima húmedo subtropical patrón del estado del tiempo con veranos calurosos, húmedos y lluviosos e inviernos cortos y templados (pág. 65)
hurricane/huracán tormenta tropical violenta con vientos y lluvias fuertes (pág. 193)

hydroelectric power/energía hidroeléctrica electricidad generada por una corriente de agua (págs. 242, 571, 743)

iceberg/iceberg pedazo de un glaciar que se ha desprendido y flota libremente en los océanos (pág. 765)
ice shelf/plataforma de hielo capa de hielo sobre el mar en la Antártida (pág. 765)
immigrant/inmigrante persona que se muda permanentemente a un país nuevo (pág. 148)
imperialism/imperialismo el sistema de desarrollar imperios extranjeros para ventaja militar y comercial (pág. 316)
import/importar comprar productos de otro país (pág. 95)
indulgences/indulgencias perdón por los pecados concedido o vendido por la Iglesia Católica (pág. 305)
industrialize/industrializar cambiar una economía de manera que dependa más de la manufactura que de la agricultura (págs. 195, 412, 604)
industrialized country/país industrializado país en el cual ocurre mucha manufactura (pág. 604)
intensive cultivation/cultivo intensivo labrar toda la tierra posible (pág. 693)
interdependence/interdependencia países que dependen unos de otros para bienes, materia prima para producir bienes y mercados en los cuales vendan sus productos (pág. 100)
irrigation/irrigación práctica agrícola en áreas secas de colectar agua y llevarla a los cultivos (pág. 71)
Islamic republic/república islámica gobierno dirigido por líderes musulmanes (pág. 519)
island/isla masa de tierra más pequeña que un continente, rodeada de agua (pág. 40)
isthmus/istmo lengua de tierra que conecta a dos masas de tierra más grandes (págs. 40, 212)

jade/jade piedra preciosa reluciente, usualmente de color verde (pág. 197)
jute/yute fibras de una planta que se usan para hacer soga, sacos y el revés de alfombras (pág. 639)

kibbutz/kibutz poblado en Israel donde las personas comparten la propiedad y producen bienes (pág. 510)
krill/krill animales diminutos parecidos a los camarones que viven en las aguas alrededor de la Antártida y sirven de alimento para muchos otros animales (pág. 766)

lagoon/laguna masa de agua poco profunda rodeada por arrecifes, bancos de arena o un atolón (pág. 654)
land bridge/puente de tierra franja de tierra que une a dos masas de tierra mayores (pág. 190)
landfill/vertedero de basura lugar donde las compañías que recogen la basura botan los residuos que colectan (pág. 136)
landform/accidente geográfico característica particular de la tierra (pág. 23)
landlocked/rodeado de tierra país que no tiene tierras bordeadas por un mar u océano (págs. 271, 372)
La Niña/La Niña patrón infrecuente en el estado del tiempo del océano Pacífico que tiene los efectos contrarios a los de El Niño (pág. 56)
latitude/latitud posición al norte o al sur del ecuador, medida por medio de líneas imaginarias (paralelos) que son numeradas con grados norte o sur (págs. 5, 192)
leap year/año bisiesto año que tiene un día adicional; cada cuarto año (pág. 31)
life expectancy/expectativas de vida el número de años que se espera que viva la persona promedio (pág. 428)
light industry/industria ligera fabricación de productos como muebles, ropa, zapatos y artículos para el hogar (pág. 426)
line graph/gráfica lineal gráfica en que una o varias líneas representan cambios de cantidad a través del tiempo (pág. 11)
literacy rate/índice de alfabetización porcentaje de personas que saben leer y escribir (pág. 215)
llanos/llanos planicie cubierta de hierba (pág. 242)
local wind/vientos locales patrones en los vientos causados por los accidentes geográficos de un área en particular (pág. 56)
longitude/longitud posición al este o el oeste del primer meridiano, medida por medio de líneas imaginarias (meridianos) numeradas con grados este u oeste (pág. 5)
low island/isla coralina isla del Pacífico formada por coral que tiene poca vegetación (pág. 760)

magma/magma roca caliente y fundida que a veces fluye hasta la superficie de la Tierra en erupciones volcánicas (pág. 35)
maize/maíz nombre Native Americano del elote (pág. 198)
majority group/grupo mayoritario grupo en una sociedad que controla la mayoría de la riqueza y el poder, el cual no siempre es el grupo más numeroso (pág. 430)

mangrove/mangle árbol tropical con raíces que se extienden por encima y por debajo del agua (pág. 550)

manor/feudo estado feudal compuesto de una casa solariega o castillo y tierra (pág. 301)

mantle/manto capa de rocas de 1,800 millas (2,897 km.) de grueso entre el núcleo y la corteza de la Tierra (pág. 35)

manuka/manuka pequeño arbusto de Nueva Zelanda (pág. 741)

map key/leyenda explicación de las líneas, símbolos y colores usados en un mapa; también se llama clave del mapa (pág. 8)

maquiladora/maquiladora fábrica donde se ensamblan piezas hechas en otros países (pág. 194)

marine west coast climate/clima húmedo marítimo patrón del estado del tiempo con inviernos lluviosos y templados y veranos frescos (pág. 63)

marsupial/marsupial mamífero que lleva a sus crías en una bolsa (pág. 737)

Mediterranean climate/clima húmedo mediterráneo patrón del estado del tiempo con inviernos lluviosos y templados y veranos calurosos y secos (pág. 64)

megalopolis/megalópolis área extensa de mucha urbanización (págs. 127, 694)

meridian/meridiano *véase* longitude (pág. 5)

messiah/Mesías en judaísmo y cristianismo, el salvador enviado por Dios (pág. 475)

mestizo/mestizo persona cuya ascendencia incluye indios americanos y españoles (pág. 256)

migrant worker/trabajador itinerante persona que viaja a distintos lugares donde hacen falta trabajadores para sembrar y cosechar cultivos (pág. 205)

migrate/migrar mudarse de un lugar a otro (pág. 504)

minority group/grupo minoritario grupo de gente quien es diferente en alguna característica del grupo con mayor poder y riqueza en una región (pág. 430)

missionary/misionero persona que difunde ideas religiosas (pág. 300)

monarchy/monarquía tipo de gobierno en que un rey o reina hereda el derecho de gobernar (pág. 83)

monotheism/monoteísmo creencia en un solo Dios (pág. 473)

monsoon/monzón vientos que soplan en un continente por varios meses seguidos en ciertas estaciones del año (pág. 639)

moor/páramo área elevada y sin árboles pero con mucho viento y tierra húmeda (pág. 340)

moshav/*moshav* poblados en Israel en que la gente comparte alguna propiedad pero también tiene propiedad privada (pág. 510)

mosque/mezquita edificio de devoción islámico (págs. 380, 488)

multilingual/multilingüe que puede hablar varios idiomas (pág. 348)

multinational company/multinacional compañía compañía que hace negocios en varios países (pág. 348)

mural/mural pintura hecha sobre una pared (pág. 198)

national debt/deuda pública dinero debido por el gobierno de una nación (pág. 206)

natural resource/recurso natural producto de la Tierra que la gente usa para satisfacer sus necesidades (pág. 92)

navigable/navegable masa de agua ancha y profunda suficiente para que los barcos puedan viajar por ella (págs. 134, 266, 345)

neutrality/neutralidad negarse a ponerse a favor de uno de los adversarios en un desacuerdo o una guerra entre países (pág. 352)

newsprint/papel de periódico tipo de papel en que se imprimen los periódicos (pág. 163)

nomads/nómadas gente que se muda de un lugar a otro con sus manadas o rebaños de animales (págs. 373, 439, 680)

nonrenewable resource/recurso no renovable recurso natural, como minerales, que no puede reemplazarse (pág. 93)

nuclear energy/energía nuclear energía producida por medio de una reacción atómica controlada (pág. 428)

nuclear weapon/arma nuclear arma cuya fuerza destructiva viene de una reacción nuclear (pág. 319)

oasis/oasis área fértil o verde en un desierto (págs. 439, 485)

obsidian/obsidiana piedra vítrea de color negro formada por el enfriamiento de la lava líquida de un volcán (pág. 198)

orbit/órbita trayectoria que los cuerpos en el sistema solar siguen alrededor del Sol (pág. 29)

outback/tierra adentro el interior de Australia (pág. 737)

overgraze/pastar excesivamente cuando el ganado despoja los pastos hasta tal punto que las plantas no pueden crecer de nuevo (pág. 556)

ozone/ozono tipo de oxígeno que forma una capa en la atmósfera que protege a todas las cosas vivas de ciertos rayos del Sol que son peligrosos (pág. 766)

pagoda/pagoda templo budista de muchos pisos (pág. 670)

pampas/pampa llanura de gran extensión en América del Sur sin árboles y cubierta de hierba (pág. 240)
papyrus/papiro papel egipcio (pág. 471)
parallel/paralelos *véase* latitude (págs. 5, 699)
parliamentary democracy/democracia parlamentaria gobierno en que los votantes eligen a representantes a un cuerpo que hace las leyes y que selecciona a un primer ministro para que sea el jefe del gobierno (págs. 166, 216, 341)
peat/turba plantas parcialmente descompuestas en agua que se pueden secar y usar como combustible (pág. 342)
peninsula/península masa de tierra con agua alrededor de tres lados (págs. 40, 191)
perestroika/perestroika política soviética que relajó los controles gubernamentales y permitió que la economía se moviera hacia de libre empresa (pág. 415)
permafrost/permafrost capa de suelo congelada en la tundra y las regiones subárticas; también se llama permagel (pág. 406)
pesticides/pesticidas sustancias químicas poderosas que matan a los insectos que destruyen los cultivos (págs. 71, 640)
pharaoh/faraón soberano del antiguo Egipto (pág. 470)
phosphate/fosfato sal mineral que se usa en los abonos (págs. 486, 560, 761)
pictograph/pictograma gráfica en que pequeños símbolos representan cantidades (pág. 12)
pidgin language/lengua franca lenguaje formado al combinar elementos de varios idiomas distintos (pág. 760)
plain/llanura extensión de tierra plana u ondulante a elevaciones bajas (pág. 40)
plantain/plátano de cocinar tipo de banano (pág. 582)
plantation/plantación granja grande en que se siembra un solo cultivo para venderse (pág. 194)
plate/placa plancha de roca inmensa que forma parte de la corteza de la tierra (págs. 589, 714)
plateau/meseta planicie a elevaciones más altas que las llanuras (pág. 40)
plate tectonics/tectónica de placas teoría que dice que la corteza de la Tierra no es una envoltura enteriza, sino que está formada por placas, o planchas de roca inmensas, que se mueven (pág. 35)
plaza/plaza sitio donde se reúne el público (pág. 202)
poaching/caza furtiva cacería ilegal de animales protegidos (pág. 577)
polder/pólder área de tierra ganada del mar (pág. 347)
polis/polis término griego para "cuidad estado" (pág. 294)
polytheism/politeísmo que cree en más de un dios (pág. 467)
pope/papa líder de la Iglesia Católica Apostólica Romana (págs. 299, 371)
population density/densidad de población promedio de personas que viven en una milla cuadrada o kilómetro cuadrado (pág. 89)
potash/potasa tipo de sal mineral que a menudo se usa en los abonos (pág. 385)
prairie/pradera área de pastos ondulantes en el interior con suelo muy fértil (pág. 160)
precious gems/piedras preciosas valiosas piedras preciosas, como el rubí, el zafiro y el jade (pág. 709)
precipitation/precipitación agua que regresa a la Tierra en la forma de lluvia, nieve, aguanieve o granizo (pág. 49)
prime minister/primer ministro líder del gobierno en una democracia parlamentaria (pág. 167)
privatize/privatizar transferir la propiedad de fábricas de las manos del gobierno a las de individuos (pág. 375)
productivity/productividad la medida de la cantidad de trabajo ejecutado en un tiempo dado (pág. 314)
projection/proyección una de las maneras de dibujar la Tierra redonda en una superficie plana para hacer un mapa (pág. 7)
prophet/profeta mensajero de Dios (pág. 474)
province/provincia división política regional, parecida a un estado (pág. 158)
pyramid/pirámide estructura de piedra gigantesca que sirvió como tumba o monumento elaborado (pág. 470)

quota/cuota límite en la cantidad de un producto que se puede importar de un país en particular (pág. 95)

rain forest/bosque húmedo bosque denso que recibe grandes cantidades de lluvia todos los años (pág. 59)
rain shadow/sombra pluviométrica área seca en el lado interior de montañas costeras (pág. 58)
recycling/reciclaje usar materiales de nuevo en vez de botarlos (pág. 136)
refugee/refugiado persona que huye de un país a otro para evitar la persecución o un desastre (págs. 91, 379, 585)
reincarnation/reencarnación renacimiento del alma en un cuerpo nuevo (pág. 640)
relief/relieve las diferencias en altitud de una zona; lo plana o accidentada que es una superficie (pág. 9)
renewable resource/recurso renovable recurso natural que no se puede gastar, que la naturaleza puede reemplazar o que se puede cultivar de nuevo (pág. 92)

representative democracy/democracia representativa gobierno en que las personas están representadas por dirigentes elegidos (pág. 146)
republic/república gobierno nacional fuerte encabezado por líderes elegidos (págs. 216, 296, 487)
responsibilities/responsabilidades deberes que la genta debe a su gobierno (pág. 99)
reunification/reunificación juntar de nuevo las dos partes de Alemania bajo un mismo gobierno (pág. 351)
revolution/revolución una órbita completa alrededor del Sol (pág. 31); un gran cambio, a menudo violento (pág. 306)
rights/derechos beneficios y protecciones que están garantizados por ley (pág. 99)
rural/rural área en el campo (pág. 150)

samurai/samurai propietarios y guerreros poderosos del Japón (pág. 693)
satellite nation/nación satélite nación dominada o controlada política y económicamente por otro país más poderoso (pág. 321)
sauna/sauna cuarto de madera calentado por agua que hierve sobre piedras calientes (pág. 356)
savanna/sabana pastos extensos en los Trópicos con pocos árboles (págs. 62, 550)
scale bar/barra de medir la escala en un mapa, línea con divisiones que muestra la escala del mapa, generalmente en millas o kilómetros (pág. 8)
secede/secesión separarse de un gobierno nacional (pág. 147)
secular/secular no religioso (pág. 492)
***selva*/selva** bosque húmedo tropical, como el de Brasil (pág. 232)
serf/siervo labrador que podía ser comprado y vendido con la tierra (págs. 301, 412)
service industry/industria de servicio negocio que proporciona servicios a la gente en vez de producir productos (págs. 132, 195, 488)
shah/sha título de los reyes que gobernaban Irán (pág. 519)
shogun/shogun líder militar en Japón antiguo (pág. 693)
silt/cieno pequeñas partículas de suelo fértil (pág. 484)
sirocco/siroco vientos calurosos y secos que soplan a través de Italia desde el norte de África (pág. 360)
sisal/sisal fibra de una planta que se usa para hacer soga y cordel (pág. 580)
slash-and-burn farming/agricultura por tala y quema método de limpiar la tierra para el cultivo en que se cortan y se queman los bosques (pág. 616)
smog/smog neblina espesa compuesta de niebla y sustancias químicas (pág. 206)
socialism/socialismo sistema económico en que la mayoría de negocios son propiedad y están dirigidos por el gobierno (pág. 709)
sodium nitrate/nitrato de sodio sustancia química usada en abonos y explosivos (pág. 274)
solar system/sistema solar la Tierra, ocho planetas adicionales y miles de astros más pequeños que giran alrededor del Sol (pág. 29)
sorghum/sorgo cereal de tallo alto cuyas semillas sirven de alimento y del cual se hace un jarabe para endulzar (pág. 610)
spa/termas balneario con manantiales de agua mineral caliente en que la gente se baña para recobrar su salud (pág. 374)
station/estación rancho donde se crían ganado vacuno u ovejas en Australia (pág. 737)
steppe/estepa pastos parcialmente secos que a menudo se encuentran en los bordes de un desierto (págs. 67, 383, 406, 438, 680)
strait/estrecho masa de agua delgada entre dos masas de tierra (págs. 42, 716)
strike/huelga una negativa a trabajar, usualmente por una organización de trabajo, hasta que las demandas sean solucionadas (pág. 315)
subarctic/subártico patrón del estado del tiempo con inviernos extremadamente fríos y veranos cortos y frescos (pág. 65)
subcontinent/subcontinente masa de tierra grande que forma parte de un continente pero se puede diferenciar de él (pág. 638)
subsistence farm/granja de subsistencia terreno pequeño en el cual un granjero cultiva sólo lo suficiente para alimentar a su propia familia (págs. 194, 552)
suburb/suburbio comunidad pequeña en los alrededores de una ciudad (pág. 150)
summer solstice/solsticio de verano día con más horas de sol y menos horas de oscuridad (pág. 32)

taiga/taiga bosques enormes de árboles de hoja perenne en regiones subárticas (pág. 406)
tariff/arancel impuesto sobre el valor de bienes importados (pág. 95)
terraced field/terrazas franjas, parecidas a escalones, que se cortan en la ladera de una colina para que el suelo aguante el agua y se pueda usar para la agricultura (pág. 717)
textiles/textiles tela tejida (pág. 315)
theocracy/teocracia forma de gobierno en la cual un individuo gobernaba como líder religioso tanto como rey (pág. 467)
townships/municipios barrios abarrotados de gente en las afueras de las ciudades de Sudáfrica donde viven la mayoría de las personas que no son blancas (pág. 607)
trench/fosa marina valle en el fondo del mar (pág. 41)

SPANISH GLOSSARY

tributary/afluente río pequeño que desagua en un río más grande (pág. 645)
Tropics/Trópicos región entre el Trópico de Cáncer y el Trópico de Capricornio (pág. 53)
trust territory/territorio en fideicomiso área que está bajo el control temporario de otra nación (pág. 761)
tsetse fly/mosca tsetsé insecto cuya picada puede matar al ganado o a los seres humanos por medio de la enfermedad del sueño (pág. 573)
tsunami/tsunami ola inmensa causada por un terremoto en el fondo del mar (págs. 36, 690)
tundra/tundra inmensas planicies ondulantes y sin árboles en latitudes altas con climas en que sólo varias pulgadas del suelo de la superficie se deshielan (págs. 66, 159, 406)

union/sindicato organización laboral que negocia para mejorar las condiciones y pago de los trabajadores (pág. 315)
urban/urbano parte de una ciudad (pág. 150)
urbanization/urbanización movimiento hacia las ciudades (pág. 90)

vaquero/vaquero pastor de ganado vacuno (pág. 193)
vassal/vasallo noble en la sociedad medieval quien juraba lealtad a un lord en cambio de tierra (pág. 301)

wadi/uadi lecho de un río seco que llenan los aguaceros poco frecuentes (pág. 513)
water cycle/ciclo hidrológico proceso mediante el cual el agua se mueve de los océanos al aire, del aire a la tierra y de la tierra a los océanos una vez más (pág. 48)
watershed/cuenca fluvial región drenada por un río (pág. 584)
water vapor/vapor de agua agua en forma de gas (pág. 48)
weather/estado del tiempo cambios en la atmósfera que son difíciles de pronosticar y tienen lugar durante un período de tiempo corto (pág. 52)
weathering/desgaste proceso natural que rompe la superficie rocosa en peñas, grava, arena y suelo (pág. 37)
welfare state/estado de bienestar social estado que usa el dinero recaudado por los impuestos para mantener a personas que están enfermas, pobres, sin trabajo o retiradas (pág. 355)
winter solstice/solsticio de invierno día con menos horas de sol (pág. 32)

yurt/*yurt* tienda de campaña grande y circular hecha de pieles de animales que se puede desmantelar y llevar de un lugar a otro (pág. 681)

c=chart	*m=map*
d=diagram	*p=photo*
g=graph	*ptg=painting*

A.D. (anno Domini), 298
Abdullah II, 506
Abidjan, Côte d'Ivoire, 559, 561
Abomey, 559
Aborigines, 726, *ptg737,* 738–739, *p739,* 747
absolute location, 5, *d5*
absolute monarchies, 83
Abuja, Nigeria, *p550,* 553
Acapulco, Mexico, 194
Accra, Ghana, 559, 561
acid rain, 37, 70, 135, 351, 370
Aconcagua, 183, 239, *g652*
addicts, 263
Addis Ababa, Ethiopia, 588
adobe, 202
Adriatic Sea, 381
Afghanistan, 89, 454, 462, *p519,* 520, 523
Africa: ethnic groups of, *m589*; plate tectonics and, 35; population growth in, 76. *See also* Africa, south of the Sahara; Central and East Africa; North Africa and Southwest Asia; Southern Africa; West Africa.
Africa, south of the Sahara, 533–567; climate of, 534; country profiles of, *c542–546*; economy of, 536; extreme points of, 541; gems and minerals of, *m540*; landforms of, 534; people of, 536–537; physical geography of, *m538*; political geography of, *m539*; population comparisons of, *c541*. *See also* Central and East Africa; Southern Africa; West Africa.
African Americans, 152
African National Congress (ANC), 606
Afrikaners, 605–606
Age of Exploration, 305
Age of Revolution, 306–307
Agricultural Revolution, 84
agriculture: in Angola, 614; in Asia, 626; in Australia, 738; in Canada, 116; in Chile, 274; in Colombia, 256; in Comoros, 617; in Ecuador, 268–269; in Egypt, 486; in France, 345; in Indonesia, 715; in Israel, 509, *p510*; in Japan, 693; in Latin America, 178; in Madagascar, 617; in Mexico, 194; in Netherlands, *p347*; of New Zealand, 743; in Sri Lanka, 652; in Taiwan, 679; in United States, 116. *See also* farming.
AIDS: in Africa, 594; in Botswana, 612; in Central and East Africa, 594; in South Africa, 607; in Uganda, 584; in Zimbabwe, 611
airlift, *p322*
air pollution, 37, 69, *p70,* 135, 428, 664, 693
Akkad, 468
Alaska (U.S.), 114, 121, 129
Albania, 288, 380, 381, *p381*
Alberta, Canada, 163
Alexander I, 420
Alexander II, 412–413
Alexander the Great, 295
Alexandria, Egypt, 295, 486
Algeria, 454, 462, 491–492
Algiers, Algeria, 492
Allah, 477. *See also* Islam.
alliances, 316
Allies, 317
alluvial plain, 517
alphabet, 469. *See also* languages.
alpine vegetation, *p68,* 349
Alps, *p281,* 350
Altay Mountains, 660
altiplano: in Bolivia, 271; in Chile, 274
altitude, 193, *d193,* 243. *See also* elevation.
Amazon Basin, 232, 235, 267
Amazon rain forest, 25, *p230–231*
Amazon River, 176, 183, *p230–231,* 232, *p232*
amendments, constitutional, 146
"Americanization," 103
American Revolution, 307
American Samoa, 761
Amharic language, 588
Amman, Jordan, 506
Amnesty International, 676
Amur River, 392
Anatolia, Turkey, 502–503
Andersen, Hans Christian, 357
Andes Mountains, 24, *p177,* 232, *p253, m260,* 266
Andorra, 288, 358
Angel Falls, 183, *p243*
Angkor Wat, *p711*
Angola, 542, 614–615
Ankara, Turkey, 504
Anna Karenina **(Tolstoy),** 435
Annan, Kofi, 99
Antananarivo, Madagascar, 617
Antarctica, 24, *p29,* 66, *p97,* 176, *p722,* 722–733, *p725,* 731, *p764, p 765,* 764–768, *p773*; climate of, 724–726; economy of, 726; endangered environments of, *m730*; extreme points of, 731; landforms of, 724; people of, 726–727; physical geography of, *m728*; political geography of, *m729, m759*; population comparisons of, *c727, c731*
Antarctic Treaty of 1959, 726, 766
anthropologists, 26
Antigua, 184
apartheid, 546, *p546,* 606
Appalachian Mountains, 114, *p115,* 128, 159
apprentices, 302
apricots, *p644*
aqueducts, 297
aquifers, 490, 498
Arab Empire, 514–515
Arabian Desert, 485
Arabian Peninsula, 454
Arabian Sea, 516
Arabs, 456, 491–493, 504
Aral Sea, 439, *p439*
archaeologists, 26, *p505, p667*
archipelago, 219, 690
architecture: in Cambodia, *p711*; earthquakes and, *p37*; Leaning Tower of Pisa (Italy), *p361*; in Micronesia, *p760*; Sydney Opera House (Australia), *p738*
Arctic, *p115,* 159
Arctic Circle, 354
Arctic Ocean, 50, 114, 392, 405
Argentina, 176, 183–184, 239–241
Armenia, 392, 400, 437–438
Arnesen, Liv, *p97*
arrowheads, *p26*
artifacts, *ptg26,* 27
arts, 82, *ptg203,* 282, 303, 395, *p429, p433*
Aryans, 640
Ashanti, 559, 561
Ashgabat, Turkmenistan, 439
Asia, 622–634; climate of, 624–626; country profiles of, *c632–634*; economy of, 626; extreme points in, 631; landforms of, 624; monsoons in, *m630*; people of, 626–627; physical geography of, *m628*; political geography of, *m629*; population comparisons in, *c631*. *See also* Central Asia; China; Eurasian republics; Japan; Mongolia; North Africa and Southwest Asia; North Korea; South Asia; Southeast Asia; South Korea; Taiwan.
Asia Minor, 502
Assembly of First Nations, 170
Asunción, Paraguay, 242
Aswan High Dam, *p484,* 486
asylum, 593, 596

INDEX

Atacama Desert, 176, 183, 273
Atatürk, Kemal, 504
Athens, Greece, *p294,* 294–295, 362
Atlanta, Georgia (U.S.), *p131*
Atlantic Coastal Plain, 127
Atlantic Ocean, 50, 280
Atlas Mountains, *p452–453,* 454, 492, *p492*
atmosphere, 30, 69–70
atoll islands, 654, 760–761, *p763*
atomic bombs, 317, 692
Auckland, New Zealand, 744, *p750*
Aung San Suu Kyi, 710
Australia, *p39, p722–723,* 722–733, *p727,* 731, *p734–736,* 734–740, *p772*; Aborigines of, 747; animals of, 737, 740; climate of, 724–726; country profile of, *c732*; economy of, 726, 737–738; endangered environments of, *m730*; extreme points of, 731; government of, 739; history of, 738–739; landforms of, 724, 736–737; people of, 726–727, 738–739; physical geography of, *m728*; political geography of, *m729*; population comparisons of, *c727, c731*; voting in, *p733*
Australian Capital Territory (Australia), 739
Austria, 288, 353
authority, in European Union, 329
autonomy, 168
Autosub, 51, *p51*
autumnal equinox, 32
axis, of planets, 31, *d31*
Axis Powers, 317
Ayers Rock, *p734–735*
Azerbaijan, 392, 400, 438
Azores, *p34*
Aztec, 178, 199, 201, *p201*

B.C. (before Christ), 298
Babylon, 468
Bach, Johann Sebastian, 352
Baghdad, Iraq, 517, *p517*
Bahamas, 184, 219, 221, 228
Bahrain, 462, 515–516, *p523*
Baja California, 191
Baku, Azerbaijan, 438
Bali, Indonesia, *p625,* 715
Balkan Peninsula, 361, 377
ballet, in Russia, *p434*
Baltic republics, 371
Baltic Sea, 371
Bancroft, Ann, *p97*
Banff National Park, Canada, *p158,* 160
Bangkok, Thailand, 710, *p719*
Bangladesh, *p52,* 632, 646–647
Bantu, 553–554, 573, *p609,* 610, 615
Barbados, 184, 221
Barbuda, 184
Barcelona, Spain, 359
barriers to trade, 95
base map, 28
Basque, 359
bauxite, 220, 560, 715
Bavaria, *p350*
Bay of Bengal, 639, 646
Bay of Fundy, 121
bazaars, 488, *p491*
bears, polar, *p115*
bedouins, 505
Beethoven, Ludwig von, 352
Beijing, China, 666, *p669, p673*
Beirut, Lebanon, 505
Belarus, 288, 385–386
Belgium, 288, 347
Belgrade, Serbia, 380
Belize, 184, 212, 216–217
Benelux countries, 320–321, 347–348
Bengal Famine, 639
Benghazi, Libya, 491
Ben-Gurion, David, 511
Benin, 542, 558, *p559*
Bently Subglacial Trench, 731
Benue River, 553
Berbers, *p482–483,* 491–493, *p492,* 566
Bergen, Norway, *p355*
Berlin, Germany, *p87, p319,* 321–322
Berlin airlift, *p322*
Bern, Switzerland, 352
Bhaktapur, Nepal, *p636–637*
Bhutan, 632, *p651,* 651–652
Bhutto, Benazir, 646
Bible, 468
bilingual country, 167–168, 440
biodiversity, 72
biosphere, 69, 72
birth rate, 88
Bishkek, Kyrgyzstan, 440
bishops of Rome, 299
Black Forest, 351, *p351*
black market, 291
Black Sea, 280, 407, 456, *p502,* 504
blizzards, *p53*
blockade, 321
Blue Nile River, 586
Boers, 605
Boer War, 606
Bogatá, Colombia, 255
Bohemia, 374
bolero, 360
Bolívar, Simón, 243, 256, 272
Bolivia, 183, 184, *p271,* 271–273
Bonaparte, Napoleon, 307, 412, 420, *ptg420,* 434
boomerang, 738
border patrols, in Korea, *p699*
Borneo, 714
Bosnia and Herzegovina, 288, 323, *m369,* 380
Bosporus, 502, *p502*
Botswana, 542, 612
Brahma deity (Hinduism), 640
Brahmaputra River, 624, 646
Brasilia, Brazil, 236, *p238*
Bratislava, Slovakia, 375, *p414*
Brazil, 179, *p179,* 184, *p230–231,* 230–237; Amazon River in, 176; cities of, 236; coffee growing in, 95; culture of, 235–237; economic system of, 233–235; government of, 237; history of, 235–236; landforms of, 232–233; manufacturing in, 178; rain forest in, 187, *p187*
Brazzaville, Congo, 574
British Columbia (Canada), *p156–157,* 161–163
British Isles, 340. *See also* United Kingdom.
Brunei, 632, 717
Brussels, Belgium, 347
Bucharest, Romania, 378
Budapest, Hungary, 373, *p373*
Buddhism, *p622–623,* 626, 641, *p666,* 667, 681, 686, 693, 695, 700, 710, *p710,* 712
Buenos Aires, Argentina, 91, 240, *p247*
Bukhara, Uzbekistan, *p436*
Bulgaria, 288, 378
Burkina Faso, 542, 556, 558
Burundi, 542, 584–585, 595
Bush, George W., 140, *p261,* 263, *p331,* 593
bush (pAustralia), 739
Byzantine Empire, 297, 299, *m301,* 504

Cabinda, 614
cacao, *p553*
Caesar Augustus, 296–297
Cairo, Egypt, 456, 486, 488
Calcutta, India, 642
calendars: in ancient Egypt, 471; Aztec, 201, *p201*
California (U.S.), *p134*
caliph, 514
calligraphy, 670
Calvin, John, 305
Cambodia, 632
camels, *p513, p687*
Cameroon, 542, *p570,* 573–574
campesinos, 257
Canada, 114–123, 156–173; bilingual nature of, 167–168; climate of, 114–116; country profile of, *c122*; economic regions of, 161–163; economy of, 116; ethnic diversity of, 168–169; extreme points of, *c121, m121*; food production of, *m120*; history of, 165–167; landforms of, 114,

INDEX

158–161; native peoples of, 170; North American Free Trade Agreement (NAFTA) and, 136; Nunavut Territory of, 168; people of, 116–117; physical geography of, *m118*; polar bears in, *p115*; political geography of, *m119*; provinces of, *c123*; waterways of, 114
Canadian Shield, 159
Canberra, Australia, 739
Cancún, Mexico, 194
canopy, of forest, 62
Canterbury Plains, 742
Cape Horn, 273
Cape of Good Hope, 305, 604
Cape Town, South Africa, *p532, p602–603, p604*
Cape Verde Islands, 542, 558
capitalism, 94, 424
Captiva Island, Florida (U.S.), *p133*
capybaras, *p242*
cardinal directions, 8, 33
Caribbean islands, 219–223
Caribbean Sea, 191, 213
Carnival: in Brazil, *p236,* 237; in Central America, 217
Carpathian Mountains, 280, 368, 373, 377, 383
carpets, Persian, 507
Carthage, Tunisia (ancient), 491
Casablanca, Morocco, 492–493
casbahs, 492
Cascade Range, 129
cash crops, 256, 438
Caspian Sea, 392, 399, 407, 436, 456, 461
caste system, 640
Castro, Fidel, 222
cataracts, 469
categorizing information, 238, 328
Cathedral of Monterrey, Monterrey, Mexico, *p188–189*
Cather, Willa, 151
Catherine the Great, 411
Catholicism. *See* Roman Catholicism.
Caucasus Mountains, 392, 406, 436–438
caudillos, 243
cause and effect, 416
cave paintings, *ptg26*
Cayenne, French Guiana, 245
Celebes, Indonesia, 714
cell phones, *p676*
Celts, 343
census, 108, *p108*
Central African Republic, 542, 573–574
Central America, 176, 212–217; economic regions and systems, *m213*; economic systems of, 213–215; history of, 215–217; landforms of, 212–213; political geography of, *m213*. *See also* Latin America; *and specific countries of Central America.*
Central and East Africa, 568–601; AIDS in, 594; Burundi, 584–585; Cameroon, 573–574; Central African Republic, 573–574; Congo, 574; Democratic Republic of the Congo, 570–573; Djbouti, 589–590; economic activity of, *m583*; Equatorial Guinea, 575; Eritrea, 588–589; Ethiopia, 588; Gabon, 574; Kenya, 577–579; physical geography of, *m572*; political geography of, *m580*; population density of, *m587*; refugees in, 591–596; Rwanda, 584–585; São Tomé and Principe, 575; sleeping sickness in, 576; Somalia, 590; Sudan, 586–588, 592–593; Tanzania, 579–581; Uganda, 582–584
Central Asia, 436, 438–440. *See also* Russian and Eurasian republics; South Asia.
Central Highlands, 212
Central Lowland, 128
Central Mosque, Kano, Nigeria, *p548–549*
Ceylon (Sri Lanka), 653
Chad, *p532,* 542, 556, 558
Chaldeans, 468
chancellor, of Germany, 351
channel, 42
Chao Phraya River, 710
chaparral, 64
Charlemagne, 300
charters, 302
Chaucer, Geoffrey, 304
Chávez, Hugo, 244
Chavuma, Zambia, *p610*
Chechnya, Russia, 430
Cheetah Conservation Fund, 77
cheetahs, *p76,* 76–77
Chennai, India, 642
Chernobyl Nuclear Power Plant, Ukraine, *p383*
Chiang Kai-shek, 667, 679
Chiapas (Mexico), 205
Chicago, Illinois (U.S.), *p128*
Chihuahuan Desert, *p48*
child labor, *p105, p315*
Children's Environmental Trust Foundation, 251
Chile, 176, 178, 183–184, *p272,* 273–274
Chile Antarctic Territory, 766–767
China, 84, 631, 632, *p658–659,* 658–673; culture of, 669–670; economy of, 663–664; government of, 668–669, 673; history of, 666–667; Korea and, 698; landforms of, 660–662; North Korean refugees in, 672; people of, 669; physical geography of, *m661*; Silk Road and, 686; Three Gorges Dam in, 665; trade and, 105
Chinese gooseberry, *p741*
Chipaya, *p271*
Chişinău, Moldova, 386
chlorofluorocarbons, 772–773
chocolate, *p352, p553*
Christianity, 293, 299–300, 457, 475–476, *p475*; ancient Rome and, 297; in Asia, 626; in China, 686; in Ethiopia, *p586*; in India, 641; in Lebanon, 505; in Melanesia, 760; in South Korea, 700; in Uganda, 583. *See also* Eastern Orthodox Christianity; Roman Catholicism; Russian Orthodox Christianity.
Chunnel, 325
Church of the Resurrection, St. Petersburg, Russia, *p395*
Cinco de Mayo, 203
circle graphs, 12, *g12,* 648, *g648*
Cisneros, Sandra, 151
cities: of Brazil, 236; growth of, 302; of India, *p639*; of Mexico, 202; of Russia, *p431*
city-states, Greek, 295
Ciudad Juárez, Mexico, 194
civic participation, 99
civics, 676
civilizations, early, *m86*. *See also* Egypt; Greece; Mesopotamia.
civil liberties, 673
civil wars, 492, 710
Civil War (U.S.), 147
Clark, Helen, *p749*
Classical Europe, 294
Classical Greece, 282
Cleopatra, 487
climate, 47, 52–59; of Africa, south of the Sahara, 534–536; of Andean countries, *m273*; of Antarctica, 765; of Asia, 624–626; of Australia, Oceania, and Antarctica, 724–726; of Canada, 114–116; of Caribbean islands, 220; dry, 67; of Egypt, 486; of Europe, 280–282; highland, 68; high latitude, 65–66; of Indonesia, 715; of Israel, 508–509; landforms and, 56–58; of Latin America, 176; of Melanesia, 758–759; of Mexico, 192–193; of Micronesia, 760; mid-latitude, 63–65; of Nepal, 650; of Nigeria, 550–551; of North Africa and Southwest Asia, 454–456; ocean currents and, 56; people and, 41; people's impact on, 58–59; of Polynesia, 761; regions of, *m63*; of Russia, 404–405, *m405,* 420–421; of Saudi Arabia, 513; of Southwest Asia, *m509*; of Sri Lanka, 652; stability of, 51; sun and, 53–54; tropical, 62; of Turkey, 503; of United States, 114–116, 130; vegetation zones and, 61–68; weather and, 52–53; of West

INDEX

Africa coastal countries, 558; wind and, 54–56
clothing, *p640*; of ancient soldiers, *p297*; of Inuit, *p166*; in Mexico, *p194*; in West Africa, *p557*
coalition governments, in Italy, 360
coal mining, in Poland, *p370*
coastal plains, 127
Coast Mountains, 160
cocaine, 253, 256, 259–264, *m260*
coca leaves, 256
Code of Hammurabi, 468
Coerr, Eleanor, 692
coffee production: in Brazil, *g234*; in Colombia, *p256*
Cold War, 319–323, 413–414, 428
Colombia, 176, 184, 216, 254–265; economic resources of, 255–256; history and people of, 256–257; illegal drugs and, 259–264; landforms of, 254–255
"Colombian Gold," 253
Colombo, Sri Lanka, 653
colonies, 166
Columbian Exchange, 220, 228, *m229,* 305
Columbus, Christopher, 220, 228, 254, 305
COMECON. *See* Council for Mutual Economic Assistance (COMECON).
command economies, 93, 321, 413
commercial farming, 94
common law, 300
Common Market, 321, 324, 330
commonwealth, 223
communication, 98, *c98*
communism, 221, 283, 291, 316, 320, 324, 331, 367, 369, 378, 386, 394, 401, 424–426, 663, 667, 679, 680, 699; in Cambodia, 711; in Laos, 710; in Vietnam, 712
Comoros, 542, 617–618
comparisons, making, 702
compass rose, 33
computers, 85
concentration camps (World War II), *p318*
conclusions, drawing, 555
condensation, 49
Confucianism, 667, 700
Congo, 542–543, 574
Congo River, 534, 571, 574
coniferous trees, 64, 349
conservation, 71, 499
Constantine the Great (Constantine I), 297, 299, 476, 504
Constantinople, 297, 299, 504
constitution: of Iraq, 523; of Japan, 675; of United Kingdom, 307; of United States, 125, 146, 329
Constitutional Convention (U.S.), 147
constitutional monarchies, 83; of Japan, 694; of Morocco, 493; of Spain, 359; of Sweden, 355; of United Kingdom, 342
consuls, 296
consumer goods, 378
contiguous states, 126
Continental Congress, 147
continental divide, 129, 352
continental drift, 35–36, *m45*
continental rift, 534
continental shelf, 40–41
continents, 22, *m41, g652*
contour maps, 713
convention documents, 593
convents, 300
Cook, James, 738
Cook Strait, 741
Coon Come, Matthew, 170, *p170*
Copán, Honduras, 216
Copenhagen, Denmark, 356–357, *p357*
copper belt, 610
coral reefs, 129, *p758,* 760
cordillera, 160, 254. *See also* mountains.
core, of earth, 34, *d35*
Corpus Christi, *p244*
Cortés, Hernán, 199
Costa Rica, 184, 212–215, *m213, p215,* 216–217
Côte d'Ivoire, 543, 558, 561
cottage industry, 315, 639
Council for Mutual Economic Assistance (COMECON), 321
covenant, 473. *See also* Judaism.
Cree, 170
Crete, 361
Crimean Peninsula, 383
critical thinking, 238, 416, 555, 598, 682, 702
Croatia, 288, 323, *m369,* 379
crop rotation, 70
crops: cash, 438; genetically altered, 332; monoculture, 558. *See also* agriculture; farming.
crucifixion, 475
Crusades, 300
crust, of earth, 34–37, *d35*
Crutzen, Paul, 773
Cuba, 184, 219, 221–222
culture, 78–85, *m84*; of ancient Greece, 295; in architecture, *p37*; of Brazil, 235–237; of Canada, 116–117; of Caribbean islands, 220–222; change in, 84–85; of Chile, 274; of China, 669–670; "clash" of, 103; of Colombia, 257; definition of, 80–83; of Egypt, *p487*; of Japan, 695–696; learning about, 106; of Mexico, 203–204; minority, 430; of Morocco, 493; of Pacific Ocean islands, *p756–757*; of Peru, 267; of Portugal, 359; of Russia, 433–434; of Spain, 359; of Tanzania, 581; of Turkey, 504; of United States, 116–117, *p150,* 150–152; of Zimbabwe, *p611*
cuneiform writing, 467–468
currents, ocean, 56, *m57*
customs, Japanese, *p695*
customs dogs, 262
Cuzco, Peru, 267
cyclones, 617, 646–647
Cyprus, 288, 361
Cyrillic alphabet, 378–379, 386, 432
czars, 411–412
Czechoslovakia, *p414*
Czech Republic, 288, *p366–367, p372,* 374, *p374, p376*

da Gama, Vasco, 305
Dakar, Senegal, 560
Dalai Lama, 669
dalang, 718, *p718*
Dallas, Texas (U.S.), *p152*
Dalol, Denakil Depression, 541
Damascus, Syria, 505
Danube River, 280, 287, 350, 372, *p373,* 377
Daoism, 667
Dardanelles, 502
Dar es Salaam, Tanzania, 581
Darwin, Charles, 270
databases, using, 258
David **(Michelangelo),** *p303*
da Vinci, Leonardo, 282, 304, 308
da Vinci, Leonardo, self-portrait **(da Vinci),** *ptg308*
Day of the Dead, 204
Dayton Peace Accords, 380
Dead Sea, 461, 508
death rate, 87
Death Valley, California (U.S.), 121
debt, foreign, Mexican, 205–206
Deccan Plateau, 639
de Cervantes, Miguel, 304
deciduous trees, 64, 349
Declaration of First Nations (Native Americans), 167
Declaration of Independence (U.S.), 147, 167
deforestation, 70, 235, 616
Delhi, India, 642
Delphi, Greece, *p278*
delta, of rivers, 42, 469, 484, 711
Delta Plan Project, 347
demand, supply and, 93
democracy, 294, 673, 675–676; in Asia, 627; in East Timor, 715; in Indonesia, 715; in Iraq, 523; in modern Russia, 429, 441–446; representative, 146

democratic republic government, 512, 717
Democratic Republic of the Congo, 543, 570–573, *p574*
Deng Xiaoping, 668
Denmark, 288, 356–357
Department of Homeland Security, 140, 149
desalinization, 498
desert climate, *p67,* 130; of Antarctica, 726, 765; of Australia, 724
deserts: in Africa, *p23*; Atacama Desert, 176, 183, 273; Chihuahuan Desert, *p48*; of Egypt, 485–486; Garagum Desert, 439; Gobi, 624, 631, 661, 680; Great Indian Desert, 645; Great Victoria Desert, 731; Kalahari Desert, 536, 612; Namib Desert, 536, 604, 616; Negev Desert, 508; Nubian Desert, 586; Rub' al Khali Desert, 513; Sahara, *p452,* 454, 461, 486, *p490, p556,* 566; Syrian Desert, 504; Taklimakan Desert, 624, 661, 686
desertification, 557
deterrence, 320
development, 96, 105
Dhaka, Bangladesh, *p52,* 647
dialects, 81. *See also* languages.
diamond production, *m571,* 605, 612
Dias, Bartholomeu, 305
Diaspora, 474
dictatorships, 83, 148, 491, 518, 672, 711
directions, 33
displaced persons, 593–594
divine right of kings, 306
Diwali, 642
Djibouti, 541, 543, 589–590
Djibouti, Djibouti, 590
Dnieper River, 383
Dominica, 185
Dominican Republic, 185, 220–223
Don River, 406
Dostoyevsky, Fyodor, 434
drought, 55, 556, 587, 612
drugs, illegal, 253, 256, 259–264, *m260*
Drug Treatment Court, 263
dry climates, 67
dry desert climate, 486, 513
dry farming, 358
dry steppe climate, 130, 437
Dubai, United Arab Emirates, *p452*
Dublin, Ireland, 343
Dushanbe, Tajikistan, 440
Dutch. *See* Netherlands.
dynasties, 666, 698
dzongs, 651
Dzonkha, 651

eagles, *p678*
Eakins, Thomas, 151
Earth: forces shaping, 34–38; layers of, *d35*; as planet, 29–32
earthquakes, 22, 190, 192, 407, 454, 502, *p690, p694,* 714; in Central America, 212; in China, 662; plate tectonics and, 36–37; in Ring of Fire, 624
East Africa. *See* Central and East Africa.
East Berlin, Germany, *p319*
Easter eggs, 382, *p382*
Eastern Desert, 485–486
eastern Europe. *See* Europe, eastern.
Eastern Ghats, 638
Eastern Orthodox Christianity, 299, 378–379, 385, 476
Eastern Roman Empire, 297
East Germany, 321
East Timor, 632, 714, 715
eclipses, *p30,* 344
economic regions and systems, 83, 93–94, *c94, m95*; of Africa, south of the Sahara, 536–537; of Argentina, 240; of Asia, 626; of Australia, 737–738; of Australia, Oceania, and Antarctica, 726; of Bolivia, 272; of Brazil, 233–235; of Canada, 116, *c117, m161,* 161–163; of Caribbean islands, 220; of Central America, 213–215, *m214*; of Central and East Africa, *m583*; of Chile, 274; of China, 663–664; of Colombia, 255–256; command economy as, 413; of Egypt, 486; of Eurasian republics, *m437*; of Europe, 282; of Hungary, 373; of India, 638–640, *p640*; of Indonesia, 715; of Israel, 509–510; of Japan, 692–693; in Kenya, 578–579; of Latin America, 178, *c179*; of Mexico, 193–195; of modern Russia, *p424, m425,* 426–428; of New Zealand, 743; of Nigeria, 551–552, *p553*; of North Africa and Southwest Asia, 456; of Pakistan, 645–646; of Poland, 369; of Portugal, 359; of Russia and Eurasian republics, 394; of Slovakia, 375; of South America, *m240*; in South Asia, *m650*; of Spain, 359; specialization in, 95; of Taiwan, 678–679; of Tanzania, 580–581; of United Kingdom, 341; of United States, 116, *c117,* 131–135, *m132*; of Venezuela, 243
ecosystems, 72
ecotourist, 215, 581
Ecuador, 185, *p253,* 266, 268–269
education, *p646*
Egypt, *p19,* 84, 462, *p464–465, p484,* 484–489; ancient, *m467,* 469–471; climate of, 486; desert areas of, 485–486; economy of, 486; folktales of, 489; modern history of, 487; people of, 487–488; Sinai peninsula and, 485
Eiffel Tower, Paris, France, *p338–339*
Elburz Mountains, 519
elections, *p588,* 733
electrical generation, *p92*
electronic databases, 258
elephants, 536, *p535, p568–569, p598*
Elephant seals, *p765*
elevation, 40, 57, 224, *c224,* 440
***El Gaucho Martín Fierro* (Hernández),** 246
Elizabeth I, 304
ellipses, orbits as, 29
El Niño, 55–56, *d56*
El Salvador, 185, 212, 216
embalming, in ancient Egypt, *p469,* 470
embargo, 222, 518
emeralds, *p254*
emigrants, 91
Emperor penguins, *p725, p764*
emperors, Roman, 296
Empty Quarter, 513
emus, 740, *p740*
endangered spaces, 76
energy resources, 134. *See also* hydroelectric power.
Engels, Friedrich, *ptg416*
England, 304, *p312–313,* 340, *p340*. *See also* Great Britain; United Kingdom.
enterprises, 442
entertainment industry, 135
environment, 24; balance in, 69–72; of China, 664; climate in, 47; endangered in Australia, Oceania, and Antarctica, *m730*; of India, 640; in Indonesia, 715; of Japan, 693; modern European, 326; of modern Russia, 428
environmental refugees, 593
environmental stations, 768, *p768*
Equator, 4, 5, 32, 53, 59–60, 61–62, 176, 192, 243, 266, 534, 573, 715
Equatorial Guinea, 543, 575
equinoxes, 32, *p197*
Eriksson, Lief, 354
Eritrea, 543, 588–589
erosion, 23, 38, 70, 235, 428, 650
escapees, 673
estancias: in Argentina, 240; in Colombia, 256
Estonia, 288, 371
Ethiopia, 541, 543, 588, 592, 595

ethnic cleansing, 379
ethnic groups, 81; of Africa, *m589*; of Australia, 726; of Cambodia, 711; of Canada, *c121,* 168–169; of China, 666; of Ghana, 561; of Indonesia, 715; of Kenya, 579, *p581*; of Latin America, *c183*; of modern Russia, 430; of New Zealand, *p743*; of Nigeria, 552; of Russia, 394–395, *g395*; of Rwanda and Burundi, 585; of South Africa, 605; of Sri Lanka, 653–654; of United States, *c121, p145,* 149–150; of Zimbabwe, 611
ethnocentrism, 746
EU. *See* European Union (EU).
Euphrates River, 454, 456, 466, 505, 517
Eurasia, 404, 680
Eurasia Foundation, 446
Eurasian republics, 436–446; economic activity of, *m437*
euro, 325, *p325,* 329, *p329*
Europe, 278–291, *m328*; Classical, 294–297, *m295*; climate of, 280–282; Cold War and, 319–320, *m320*; country profiles of, *c288–291*; economic systems of, 282; environmental issues and, 326; European union and, 320–321, 324–326, 328–332; extreme points of, 287; influence of, 283; landforms of, 280; languages of, *m286, c385*; Medieval, 299–302; modern era of, 314–318; people of, 282–283; physical geography of, *m284*; political geography of, *m285*; Protestant Reformation in, 304–305; Renaissance in, 303–304; revolutions in, 283; World War I in, 316; World War II in, 317, 318. *See also specific countries of Europe.*
Europe, eastern, 321–323, *p324,* 366–389; Albania, 381; Baltic republics, 371; Belarus, 385–386; Bosnia and Herzegovina, 380; Bulgaria, 378; Croatia, 379; Czech Republic, 374; Hungary, 372–373; Macedonia, 380; Moldova, 386; Poland, 368–371; population density of, *m384*; Romania, 377–378; Serbia and Montenegro, 380; Slovakia, 375; Slovenia, 379; Ukraine, 382–385
Europe, western, 338–365; Andorra, 358; Austria, 353; Belgium, 347; Denmark, 356–357; Finland, 356; France, 345–347; Germany, 350–352; Greece, 361–362; Iceland, 357; Italy, 360–361; Luxembourg, 348; Netherlands, 347–348; Norway, 354–355; Portugal, 358–360; Republic of Ireland, 342–343; Spain, 358–360; Stonehenge, 344; Sweden, 355–356; Switzerland, 352–353; United Kingdom, 340–342
European Atomic Energy Community (EURATOM), 325
European Commission to the United States, 332
European Economic Community, 321
European Russia, 405–406
European Union (EU), 96, 283, 320–321, 324–326, 328–332, 355,356, 359, 362
evaporation, 48
Everglades, Florida (U.S.), *p134*

Fabergé, Carl, *p433,* 434
facts *versus* opinions, 682
fado, 360
Falkland Islands, 241
Fante, 561
Farley, Chris, 260–261, *p260*
farming, 647, 650; in Argentina, 240; in Caribbean islands, 220; commercial, 94; cotton, *p152*; dry, 358; genetically altered crops and, 332; intensive cultivation in, 693; monoculture, 558; in Myanmar, 708; in North Africa and Southwest Asia, 456; slash-and-burn, 616; subsistence, 96, 194, 214, 267, 558, 582, 607, *p607,* 614, 616, 651, 761. *See also* agriculture.
Farsi language, 519
Faulkner, William, 151
faults, in earth's crust, 37, 438
favelas, 234
federal government, 146, 204, 351, 429, 739
Federated States of Micronesia, 732, 760
fellahin, 488–489
Ferdinand and Isabella, of Spain, 304
Fertile Crescent, *m86,* 467, *m467*
fertilizers, 70
feudalism, 301
fiestas, 203, *p204*
figurehead, emperor as, 675
Fiji Islands, 732, *p769*
Filipovic, Zlata, 380
"Final Solution," 318
Finland, 289, 356
fishing, 162
five pillars of faith, 477
fjords, 354, 742
flamenco, 360
Flemish language, 347
flexible structures, *p37*
Florida (U.S.), *p20–21, p133, p134*
food: Canadian production of, *m120*; in Egypt, *p487*; United States production of, *m120. See also* agriculture; farming.
foothills, 267
foreign debt, Mexican, 205–206
foreign trade, 663
Former Yugoslav Republic of Macedonia (F.Y.R.O.M.), 290, 380
Fossey, Dian, 77
fossil fuels, 93, 135
fossils, 27, 764
Fox, Vicente, 204
France, *p279,* 287, 289, *p299,* 300, *p316,* 326, *p338–339, p345,* 345–347; Cambodia and, 711; Caribbean islands and, 221; Comoros and, 618; mountains of, *p23*; New Caledonia and, 758; Seychelles and, 618; vegetation map of, *m349*
Frank, Anne, 348
Franklin, Shirley, *p131*
Freedom House, 672–676
Freedom Tower, 141, *d141*
free enterprise, 94, 116, 131, 161; in China, 663; in Kenya, 578; in Mongolia, 680
free market system, 424; in Russia, 394; in Slovakia, 375
free ports, 716
free trade, 96, 136, 157, 223, 271, 329–330
French Guiana, 185, 239, 245
French language, 165–166, 572
French Polynesia, *p726,* 761–762
French Revolution, 307
freshwater, 41, 49–50
Fuentes, Carlos, 203
Fulani, 552, 558
fur seal, *p722*

Gabon, 543, 574, *p574*
Gaborone, Botswana, 612
Gaelic language, 340
Gagarin, Yuri, 409
Galápagos Islands, *m255,* 268, 270; tortoise of, 270, *p270*
Gambia, 543, 558
Gandhi, Indira, *p641,* 642
Gandhi, Mohandas, 641, *p641,* 676
Ganges Plain, 638
Ganges River, 624, *p638,* 639, 646
Garagum Desert, 439
Gartner, Mike, 446
gauchos, 240, 246, *p246*
Gautama, Siddartha, 651
Gaza Strip, 511–512, *m511*
Gdańsk, Poland, 370
gems, *g571*; in Africa, *m540*
genetically altered crops, 332
Geneva, Switzerland, 352
Genghis Khan, 680

INDEX

genocide, 317
geographic information systems (GIS), 6, 25, 28
geography, 1; defined, 22; five themes of, 2; handbook for, 1–15; human, 3, 24; physical, 2, 22–23, *p23*; six essential elements of, 2–3; terms of, 14–15; tools of, 6, 24–25; uses of, 3, 26
Georgetown, Guyana, 244
Georgia, 392, *c400,* 438
geothermal energy, 357, 743
Germany, 289, 300, 316, *p319,* 326, *p350,* 350–352
geysers, 357, 741
Ghana, 543, 558
Ghana Empire, 557, 566
Giant pandas, *p660*
giant sequoia, *p61*
Gibraltar, 493
giraffes, *p532–533,* 536
GIS. *See* geographic information systems (GIS).
glaciers, 38; of Canada, 159; in Chile, 273
glasnost, 415
Glenn, John, 409
globalization, 99, 101–106, *m102, p103*
Global Positioning System (GPS), 6, 25
global warming, 58–59, 70, 332
Gobi, 624, 631, 661, 680
Golan Heights, 508, *m511*
Goode's Interrupted Equal-Area projection, 7, *m7*
Gorbachev, Mikhail, 323, 415, *p415*
gorillas, 76–77, *p77, p582*
Gothic cathedrals, 282
government, 83, *c83*; of Algeria, 492; of Asia, 627; of Australia, 739; of Bahrain, *p523*; of Brazil, 237; of Canada, 166–167; of China, 668–669, 673; of Czech Republic, 374; of Democratic Republic of the Congo, 573; of Egypt, 487; of Germany, 351; of Greece, 362; of Iraq, *p523*; of Israel, 512; of Italy, 360; of Japan, 693; of the Maldives, 654; of Mesopotamia, 467; of Mexico, 204; of modern Russia, 429; of Morocco, 493; of Nepal, 650; of Nigeria, 554; of Norway, 355; of Pakistan, 646; pollution laws and, 428; of Portugal, 359; of Slovakia, 375; of Spain, 359; of Sweden, 355; of Tanzania, 581; of Uganda, 583–584; of United Kingdom, 341; of United States, *d148*; of Venezuela, 243–244
GPS. *See* Global Positioning System (GPS).
Granada, Nicaragua, *p216*
Gran Chaco, 242
Grand Banks, 162
Grand Canyon, *p40,* 121, 135
Grandfather and His Little Grandson, The **(Tolstoy),** 435
Grand Mosque, Makkah, Saudi Arabia, *p478*
Grand Teton National Park, *p46–47*
graphs, *g11,* 11–12, *g12*; bar, 11, *g11, g13*; circle/pie, 12, *g12,* 648, *g648*; climo-, 13, *g13*; line, 11, *g11, g13*; picto-, 12, *g12*
grasslands, 64
Great Artesian Basin, 737
Great Barrier Reef, *p39,* 724, 736
Great Britain, 287, 314. *See also* England; United Kingdom.
Great Depression, 317
Great Dividing Range, 724, 736
Greater Antilles, 219
Great Indian Desert, 645
Great Lakes, 114, 128, 134, 160
Great Mosque of Djenné, Djenné, Mali, 562
Great Mother Snake, 737
Great Plains, 128, *p128,* 160
Great Pyramid of Khufu, Egypt, 470, 472, *p495*
Great Rift Valley, *p40,* 534, 577, 580, 588, 589, 610
Great Sphinx at Giza, Egypt, 470
Great Victoria Desert, 731
Great Wall of China, *p658–659,* 667
Great War (World War I), 316
Great Zimbabwe, *p609,* 611
Greece, *p278,* 289, *p294,* 361–362, *p362*; classical, 282; empire of, *m295*; Golden Age of, 294–295
Greek Orthodox Christians, 362
Greek theater, *p295*
greenhouse effect, 30, 58–59
Greenland, 51, 66, 356
green revolution, 639
Grenada, 185, 221
groundwater, 50
Guadalajara, Mexico, 194
Guadeloupe, Lesser Antilles, *p210–211,* 221
Guam, 760
Guaraní, 242
Guatemala, *p174,* 185, 212–213, 215–217
Guatemala City, Guatemala, 217
Guayaquil, Ecuador, 269
Guianas, 244–245
guilds, 302, *ptg302*
Guinea, 543, 558
Guinea-Bissau, 543, 558
Gulf Coastal Plain, 127
Gulf of Guinea, 550, 558
Gulf of Mexico, 114, 191
Gulf of Thailand, 711
Gulf of Tonkin, 711
GUM state department store, *p431*
Gutenberg, Johannes, 304
Guyana, 185, 239, 244

habitats, endangered, 76, 640
haciendas, 199
Haifa, Israel, 512
haiku, 695, 697
Haiti, 185, 220–222, 222
Halifax, Nova Scotia (Canada), 162
Hammurabi's Code, 468
Han Chinese, 666
hangul language, 698–699
Hanoi, Vietnam, 712
harambee, 579
Harare, Zimbabwe, 611
Hatsheptsut, 470
Hausa, 552
Hawaii (U.S.), 129
Hawthorne, Nathaniel, 151
heat islands, 58
heavy industry, 356, 426
Helsinki, Finland, 356
hemispheres, 4, *d4*
Henry VII, of England, 304
Hermitage Museum, St. Petersburg, Russia, *p427,* 434
Hernández, José, 246
heroin, 261, *p261*
Herzegovina. *See* Bosnia and Herzegovina.
Hidalgo, Miguel, 200
Hidden Holy Land (Bhutan), 651
hieroglyphics: Egyptian, 470–471; Mayan, 198
highland climate, 68, *p68,* 650
high latitude climates, 65–66
high-technology industry, 678, *p679,* 716, 738
hijackings, 138
Hijrah, 476
Hijuelos, Oscar, 151
Himalaya, 36, 39, 624, 638, 649, 651, 660
Hinduism, 626, *p638,* 640, *p640,* 651, 715, 760
Hindu Kush, 454, 520, 645
Hiroshima, Japan, 692, 694
Hispaniola, 219, 222
historians, 26
history, 82; of Argentina, 240–241; of Australia, 738–739; of Brazil, 235–236; of Canada, 165–167; of Caribbean islands, 220–222; of Central America, 215–217; of Colombia, 256–257; of Democratic Republic of the Congo, 573; of Europe, 292–308, 312–333; of India, 640–641; of Israel, 511–512; of Japan, 693–694; of Kenya, 579; of Libya, 491; of modern Egypt, 487 (*See also* Egypt, ancient); of Mongolia, 680–681; of Morocco, 493; of New Zealand, 743–744; of Nigeria, 553–554; of Sahel countries (West Africa), 556–557; of South Africa, 605–607; of Taiwan, 679;

INDEX

of Tanzania, 581; of Tunisia, 491; of Turkey, 504; of Uganda, 583–584; of United States, 145–149; of Venezuela, 243–244; of Vietnam, 712; of West Africa coastal countries, 559
Hitler, Adolf, *p317,* 317–318, 420
HIV, 584. *See also* AIDS.
Ho Chi Minh City, Vietnam, 712
hockey, *p168*
Hokkaido Island, Japan, 690
Holland. *See* Netherlands.
Holocaust, 317–318, 511
Holy Roman Empire, 300
Homer, Winslow, 151
Honduras, 185, 212, 215, *p215,* 216
Hong Kong, China, *p18,* 664
Honshu Island, Japan, 690
Horn of Africa, 586
Horseshoe Falls, *p171*
host countries, for refugees, 596
Hudson Bay, 159
Hughes, Langston, 151, 152
Hugo, Victor, 347
Huguenots, 305
human geography, 3, 23–24
humanism, 303–304
human resources, 314
human rights, 593, 634
humid continental climate, 64, *p65,* 130, 404
humidity, 48
humid subtropical climate, 65, *p65,* 130, 650
Hungarian Plain, 372
Hungary, *p278,* 289, 331, 372–373
Hurricane Mitch, *p215*
hurricanes, 55, 193, 213, 220
Hussein, Saddam, 518, 522
Hussein I, 506
Hutu, 585
hydroelectric power, 92, 170, 242, 486, 505, 561, 571, 609, 743
hydrosphere, 69, 71
Hyksos, 470

Ibadan, Nigeria, 553
Iberian Peninsula, 358–360
Ibo, Nigeria, 552
ice, 38
ice cap climate, 66, *p66*
Iceland, 289, 357
ice shelves, 51
Idaho (U.S.), 61
Idi Amin, 583
Ilo, Peru, 271
immigrants, 91, 148, 593
imperialism, 316
Inca, 178, 228, *p266,* 267
independence: in Africa, *m615;* in Argentina, *p247;* in Asia, 627; in Australia, 726; of Caribbean islands, 221; in Central America, 216; in Colombia, 256; in Mexico, 200; in Thailand, 710
Independence Day, Mexican, 203, *p204*
India, *p79,* 84, *p622, p625, p627,* 631, 632, 638–643; economy of, 639–640; Guyana and, 244; history of, 640–641; Kashmir, *p93;* landforms of, 638–639; Myanmar and, 709; people of, 641; Taj Mahal in, 643, *p643*
Indian Ocean, 50
Indonesia, *p625,* 631, 632, 714–715, 718
Indonesian puppet theater, 718
indulgences, 304–305, *ptg305*
Indus River, 640, 645
Industrial Revolution, 147, 282, 314, *p314, p315,* 341
industry, 85, 105; in Argentina, 240; in Asia, 626, *p626;* in Australia, 738; in Caribbean islands, 220; in Central America, 215; in Chile, 274; in China, *p663;* of Egypt, 486; entertainment, 132; heavy, 356, 426; in India, 639; in Indonesia, 715; in Japan, 692–693; light, 426; in Malaysia, 716; in Mexico, *p194,* 195; in Myanmar, 709; in New Zealand, 743; in Singapore, 716; in Taiwan, 678, *p679;* textile, 315; in Thailand, 710; in United States, *p116,* 135, *p135*
inferences, making, 328, 380, 555
Information Revolution, 85
initiative, 401
insulation, 51
"intelligent" buildings, *p37*
intensive cultivation, 693
interdependence, 100
interior plains, 128, *p128*
intermediate directions, 33
internally displaced persons (IDPs), 594
International Space Station, 409
Internet, 98, *c98,* 526, 528, *p528,* 682, *p682;* access to, *c107;* conservation and, 77; culture and, 84, 106; global economy and, *p101,* 104, *p104,* 106; World Wide Web on, 106
Internet café, 526
Inuit, 159, *p166,* 168
inventiveness, 443
investments, 663
Iran, 462, 519, 524
Iraq, 84, 462, 517–518, 521–523, *p521–523,* 526
Ireland, Republic of, *p283,* 289, 342–343
"iron curtain," 414
Irrawaddy River, 708
irrigation, 71, 498
Islam, 359, 457, 477, *p478, m518, p527;* in Bangladesh, 647; in China, 686; dating system of, 298; in Egypt, 487; in India, 641, 643; in Indonesia, 715; in Iraq, *p517, m522;* in Israel, 510; in Jordan, 506; in Malaysia, 716; in the Maldives, 654; in Pakistan, 646; in Saudi Arabia, 515; in Tunisia, 491; in Turkey, 503
Islamabad, Pakistan, 646
Islamic republic, 519
islands, 40
Ismail Samani Peak, 440
Israel, 457, 462, *p473,* 474, *p508,* 508–512; Arab conflict with, 525; climate of, 509; economy of, 509–510; history of, 511–512; landforms of, 508–509; neighbors of, *m511;* people of, 510–512
Istanbul, Turkey, 456, *p502,* 504
isthmus, 40, 212
Isthmus of Panama, 215
Itaipu Dam, Paraguay, 242
Italy, 287, *c289,* 296, *p360,* 360–361, *p361*
Ivan the Great (Ivan III), 411, *ptg411*
Ivan the Terrible (Ivan IV), *ptg411*
iwi, 749

jade, 197
Jainism, 641
Jakarta, Indonesia, 715
Jamaica, 185, 219–221, *c224*
Japan, *p622, p626,* 632, *p675,* 675, *p688–689,* 690–697; after World War I, 316; culture of, 695–696; economy of, 692–693; government of, 693; haiku of, 697; history of, 693–694; landforms of, 690–691; people of, 694–695; physical geography of, *m691;* political geography of, *m691;* population density of, *m700*
Jasper National Park, Canada, 160
Java, Indonesia, 714, 718
Jefferson, Thomas, *p147*
Jerusalem, Israel, *p473,* 474, *m474,* 512
Jesus of Nazareth, 297, 475
jet stream, *d56*
Jews, 473–474. *See also* Israel; Judaism.
Jodhpur, India, *p627*
Jordan, 462, *p505,* 506
Jordan River, 509
Joyce, James, 343
Judaism, 300, 370, 457, 473–474. *See also* Israel.
judo, 696
Julius Caesar, 296
Jupiter, 29
Jutland Peninsula, 356

Kaaba, 477, *p478*
Kabale, Uganda, *p547*
Kabuki theater, 696
Kabul, Afghanistan, 520
Kahlo, Frida, 203
Kalahari Desert, 536, 612
Kaliningrad, Russia, 426
Kamchatka Peninsula, 407
Kampala, Uganda, 583, *p584*
kangaroos, 737, 740, *p740*
Kano, Nigeria, *p548–549,* 552, 553
Kanto Plain, 691
Karachi, Pakistan, 646, *p647*
Karakoram Range, 638
karate, 696
Kasai River, 571
Kashmir, *p93,* 644
Kathmandu, Nepal, 650
kauri trees, 742
Kayapo Indians, 235
Kazakh nomads, *p438,* 439
Kazakhstan, 392, 400, 438–439
Kennedy, John F., *p330*
Kenya, *p532,* 541, 544, 577–579, 595; refugees in, 592
Kenyatta, Jomo, 579
Key West, Florida (U.S.), *p20–21*
Khmer, 711, *p711*
Khyber Pass, 454, 520, 645
kibbutz, 510, *p510*
Kiev, Ukraine, 384–385, 410
Kievan Rus, 410
Kikuyu, 579
Kilimanjaro, 534, *p535,* 541, 580, *g652*
Kim Il Sung, 701
Kim Jong Il, 701
kimonos, 695
King Fahd Stadium, *p500–501*
King, Martin Luther, Jr., 148
kings, divine right of, 306
Kingwana language, 572
Kinshasa, Democratic Republic of the Congo, 572, *p573*
Kiribati, 732, 760
kiwi (bird), 742
kiwifruit, *p741*
Knesset, 512
koalas, 737, 740, *p740*
Kobe, Japan, *p690*
Kongfuzi (Confucius), 667
Kongo kingdom, 573
Korea, 698–699, *p703*; division of, 698–699, *p699* (*See also* North Korea; South Korea); landforms of, *m691*
Korean Peninsula, 624, 698–699
Kosciuszko, *g652*
Kosovo, Serbia, *p90,* 380
Kuala Lumpur, Malaysia, 716
Kukulcan, *p197,* 198
kulibini, 442
Kunlun Shan, 660
Kurdish language, 504
Kurokami, Japan, *p694*
Kush, 470
Kush civilization, 587
Kuwait, 456, 462, 515–516, 518, 523
Kyrgyzstan, 392, 400, 439–440
Kyushu Island, Japan, 690

labor: child, *p105, p315*; cost of, 664; globalization and, 102–103
Labrador, Canada, 162
lagoons, 654, 760
Lagos, Nigeria, *p537,* 553, 559
Lake Albert, 570
Lake Assal, 541
Lake Baikal, 392, 399, 407–408, *p417*
Lake Balaton, 372
Lake Edward, 570
Lake Eyre, 731
Lake Kivu, 570
Lake Malawi, 610
Lake Maracaibo, 183, 242
Lake Nasser, *p484*
Lake Nicaragua, *p216*
Lake Superior, 121
Lake Tanganyika, 570
Lake Titicaca, 183, 266
Lake Vänern, 287
Lake Victoria, 541, 580, 582–583
Lake Volta, 561
Lalibela, 586
land bridges, 190–192
landfills, 136
landforms, 23; of Africa, south of the Sahara, 534; of Antarctica, 764–765; of Asia, 624; of Australia, 736–737; of Australia, Oceania, and Antarctica, 724; of Brazil, 232–233; of Canada, 114, 158–161; of Central America, 212–213; of China, 660–662; climate and, 56–58; of Colombia, 254–255; erosion and, 38; of Europe, 280; of India, 638–639; of Israel, 508–509; of Japan, 690–691; of New Zealand, 741–742; of North Africa and Southwest Asia, 454; of Pakistan, 644–645; of Sahel countries (West Africa), 556–557; types of, 39–41; of United States, 114, 126–129; water and, 42; weathering and, 37
Land of the Blue Sky, 680
Landsat images, 24
land use planners, 25
languages, 80–81; Afrikaans, 606; Amharic, 588; Arabic, 504; Bantu, 553–554; Basque, 359; Dzonkha, 651; of Europe, *m286, c385*; Farsi, 519; Flemish, 347; French, 165–166, 572; Gaelic, 340; hangul, 698–699; Kingwana, 572; Kurdish, 504; Lingala, 572; pidgin, 760; Portuguese, 179, 235; Quechua, 268; Setswana, 612; Spanish, *p150,* 179; Swahili, 579, 581; in United States, 150, *p150*; Vietnamese, *p150*; Welsh, 340
La Niña, 55–56
Laos, 632
Laozi, 667
La Paz, Bolivia, 272
Latin America, *p174–175,* 174–187; climates of, 176; country profiles of, *c184–187*; economic systems of, 178, *c179*; ethnic groups in, *c183*; extreme points of, *c183*; modern, 179; mountains of, 176; people of, 178; physical geography of, *m180*; plains of, 176; political geography of, *m181*; population of, *c183*; populations, *c179*; urban population of, *m182. See also specific Latin American countries.*
latitude, 5, *d5,* 53, 60, *m60,* 192
Latvia, 289, 371, *p371*
Laurentian Highlands, 160
Law of Return, 512
Leaning Tower of Pisa, Italy, *p361*
learning, lifetime, 106
Lebanon, 462, 505–506
leeward side, 58
lemurs, ring-tailed, *p617*
Lena River, 392
Lenin, Vladimir, *p402–403,* 413, *ptg416*
Lesotho, 544, 607, *p607*
Lesser Antilles, *p210–211,* 219
leukemia, 692
Liberia, 544, 549, 558
liberties, 138, *d138,* 140. *See also* rights.
library resources, 478
Libreville, Gabon, 574
Libya, 462, 490–491
Libyan Desert, 485–486
lichens, 66
Liechtenstein, 289, 350, 352
lifetime learning, 106
Lighthouse of Commerce, Monterrey, Mexico, *p188–189*
light industry, 426
Lima, Peru, 267
Limpopo River, 610
line graph, 11, *g11, g13*
Lingala language, 572
lions, 536
Lisbon, Portugal, 359
lithosphere, 69–70
Lithuania, 289, 371
Little Mermaid, Copenhagen, Denmark, *p357*
Livingstone, David, 610
llanos, 176, 242, 254
Locke, John, 306
logging, 76, *p76*

Loire River, 326, 345
London, England, *p312–313, p340,* 342, *p342*
longitude, 5, *d5,* 60, *m60,* 613
Los Angeles, California (U.S.), 135
Lost Boys of Sudan, 592–593, *p592–593*
Louvre Museum, Paris, France, *p279*
Lower Egypt, *m467,* 470
Loyalists, in Northern Ireland, 343
Ludwig II, 350
Lusaka, Zambia, 610
Luther, Martin, 305, *ptg305,* 351
Luxembourg, 289, 348
Luxor, Egypt, *p464–465*

macaques, *p622*
Macau, China, 664
Macedonia, Former Yugoslav Republic of (F.Y.R.O.M.), 290, 380
Machu Picchu, *p266,* 267
Madagascar, 42, 541, 544, 617
Madeira Islands, *p71*
Madinah, Saudi Arabia, 476–477
Madison, James, *p147*
Madrid, Spain, 359
Magdalena River, 176
Maghreb, 491
magma, 35. *See also* volcanoes.
Magyars, 372
Mahal, Mumtaz, 643
Maine (U.S.), *p126*
majority group, 81, 430
Makkah, Saudi Arabia, 476–477, *p478,* 514–515, 557, 562, 643
Malabo, Equatorial Guinea, 575
Malacca, Malaysia, 716
malaria, 218
Malawi, 544
Malay, 716
Malay Peninsula, 708, 716
Malaysia, 633, 716, *p716*
Maldives, 633, 654
Male, Maldives, 654
Mali, 544, 556, 557–558
Mali Empire, 557, 566
Malta, *p281,* 290
Malvinas Islands, 241
Mandela, Nelson, 546, 606–607
mangrove swamps, 550
Manitoba, Canada, *p112,* 162–163
manors, 300–301
mantle, of earth, 34–35
manufacturing, *p116. See also* industry.
manuka, 741
Maori, 743, *p743, m746, p746–747,* 746–750, *p748*
maoritanga, 749
Mao Zedong, 667
maps, 6, 7, 8, *p22,* 24–25, *m28;* contour, 10, *m10,* 713; keys to, 8, 33; mental, 144; physical, 9, *m9,* 196; political, 9, *m9;* population, 334; projections, 7, *m7;* thematic, 10, *m10,* 86; vegetation, *m229,* 349, *m349. See also* physical geography; political geography.
Maputo, Mozambique, *p616,* 617
maquiladoras, 194, *p194*
Mardalsfossen, Norway, 287
Mariana Trench, 41
marijuana, 262
marine west coast climate, 63–64, *p65,* 130, 273; in New Zealand, 724
Maritime Provinces, Canada, 159, 162
market economy, 93–94, 369. *See also* free enterprise.
Marrakech, Morocco, 492
Mars, 29
Marshall Islands, 732, 760
Marshall Plan, 319
marsupials, 737, 740, *p740*
martial arts, 696, 700
Martinique, 221
Marx, Karl, 316, *ptg416*
Masai, 577, *p577*
mathematics, in ancient Egypt, 471
Mau Mau, 579
Mauritania, 544, 556, 558
Mauritius, 544, 618
Mawsmai waterfall, 631
Mawsynram, India, 631
Maya, *p175,* 178, 198, 205, 215–216
May Day, 433
McDonald, Andy, 264
McKinley, *g652*
Mecca. *See* Makkah, Saudi Arabia.
medicine, in ancient Egypt, 471
Medieval Europe, 299–302, *m301*
Mediterranean climate, 64, *p65,* 273, 437, 456, 509; in United States, 130
Mediterranean Sea, 280, 360, 407, 454, 467, *p502*
megalopolis, 127, 694
Mekong River, 624, 710
Melanesia, 758–760
Melbourne, Australia, *p727,* 739
mental mapping, 144
Mercator projection, 7, *m7*
Mercury, 29
meridians, 5, *d5,* 60, *m60. See also* longitude.
Mesopotamia, 466–469, *m467*
mestizos, 256, 269, 274
Mexico, *p175, p178,* 186, *p188–189,* 188–209, *p190;* altitude zones of, *c193;* cities and villages of, 202; climates of, 192–193; culture of, 203–204; economic regions of, 193–195; foreign debt of, 205–206; government of, 204; as land bridge, 190–192; manufacturing in, 178; Native American civilizations of, 197–199, 201; North American Free Trade Agreement (NAFTA) and, 136; physical geography of, 196, *m196;* political geography of, *p191;* pollution in, 206; population growth in, 204–205; revolutions in, 200; Spain and, 199
Mexico City, Mexico, 91, 179, 192, *p192,* 194, 199
Mexico Through the Centuries **(Rivera),** *ptg203*
Michelangelo, 282, *p303,* 304
Micronesia, *p760,* 760–761, 301
Middle Ages, 293, 299
mid-latitude climates, 63–65
Midwest United States, 133–134
migrant workers, 205
migration, 476, 504
Milan, Italy, *p360*
military control of government, 627
minerals, 76; in Africa, *m540;* in Antarctica, 766; in Canada, 116; in United States, 116, 132, 134. *See also* economic regions and systems.
minority group, 81, 430. *See also* ethnic groups.
Minsk, Belarus, 386
missionaries, 300
Mississippi River, 114, 121, 128
mixed economies, 94
mobility of population, 150
Mogul Empire, 641
Moldova, 290, 386
Molina, Mario, 773, *p773*
Mombasa, Kenya, 579
Monaco, 290
Mona Lisa **(da Vinci),** *ptg308*
monarchies, 83, 147, 515, 627. *See also* constitutional monarchies.
monasteries, 300
Monet, Claude, 347
Mongol Empire, 680
Mongolia, 631, 633, 678, *p678,* 680–681, *p681*
Mongols, 410–411, *p438,* 439
Monnet, Jean, 330, *p330*
monoculture, 558
Monroe, James, 560–561
Monroe Doctrine, 211
Monrovia, Liberia, 560–561
monsoons, 55, *p625,* 626, *m630,* 639, 646, 654, 701, 708, 715
Mont Blanc, 287
Montenegro, 380. *See also* Serbia and Montenegro.
Monterrey, Mexico, *p188–189,* 194
Montevideo, Uruguay, 241–242
Montreal, Canada, 162
moon, 30
Moorea Lagoon, Tahiti, *p756–757*

INDEX

Morocco, *p452–453,* 454, 462, *p482–483, p492,* 492–493
Morrison, Toni, 151
Moscow, Russia, *p390, p402–403, p422–423,* 426, 430
moshav, 510
***Mosi oa Tunya,* (Victoria Falls),** 534, *p535,* 609
mosques, 522; in Bosnia and Herzegovina, 380
Mother Teresa, 381, 642
mountain gorillas, 76–77, *p77*
mountains, *g652*; of Antarctica, 765; Caribbean islands as, 219–220; climate of, 68; as continental divide, 129, 352; cordillera, 160, 254; highest, *g652*; in France, *p23*; as landforms, 39; of Latin America, 176; rainfall and, 57–58; *See also specific peaks and ranges.*
Mount Cook, 742
Mount Egmont, *p725,* 741
Mount Elbrus, 399, *g652*
Mount Erebus, 765, *p765*
Mount Etna, 22
Mount Everest, *p25,* 39, 624, 631, 649, *g652*
Mount Fuji, *p688–689,* 691
Mount Kenya, 534, 578
Mount McKinley, 121, 129, *p129, g652*
Mount Meru, 711
Mount Nowshak, 461
Mount Oyama Volcano, *p694*
Mount Pinatubo, *p55*
Mount Sinai, 474
mouth, of rivers, 42
movable type, 304
Mozambique, 534, 544, 616–617
Mozambique Channel, 42
Muhammad, 298, 477, 514. *See also* Islam.
Muiden, Netherlands, *p292–293*
Muiderslot Castle, Muiden, Netherlands, *p292–293*
multilingual people, 348
multimedia presentations, 164
multinational companies, 348
Mumbai (Bombay), India, 642
Munich, Germany, 352
murals, Mayan, 198
Murmansk, Russia, 426
Murray-Darling River, 731, 736
Musa, Mansa, 557
Muscat, Oman, 516
Muscovy, 411
Muslims, 300, 477, *p527*; in Albania, 381; in Bangladesh, 647; in Bosnia and Herzegovina, 380; in Bulgaria, 378; in China, 686; in Egypt, 487; in India, 641, 643; in Indonesia, 715; in Iran, 519; in Iraq, *p517, m522*; in Israel, 510; in Jordan, 506; in Lebanon, 505; in Malaysia, 716; in the Maldives, 654; in Pakistan, 646; in Russia, 432; in Saudi Arabia, 515; in Serbia and Montenegro, 380; in Turkey, 503. *See also* Islam.
Myanmar, 633, *p708,* 708–710

Naadam Festival, 681
Naama, Esra, 526
NAFTA. *See* North American Free Trade Agreement (NAFTA).
Nagasaki, Japan, 694
Nairobi, Kenya, 578–579
Namib Desert, 536, 604, *p614,* 616
Namibia, *p614,* 616
Nasser, Gamal Abdel, 487
National Aeronautics and Space Administration (NASA), 768
national debt, of Mexico, 206
National Hockey League Players' Association (NHLPA), 446
Nationalist political party (China), 667
Nationalists, in Northern Ireland, 343
National Socialist German Workers' Party, 317
Native Americans, *p117,* 167; of Amazon Basin, 235; of Bolivia, 273; of Canada, 170; of Caribbean islands, 220; of Central America, 215–216; of Latin America, 178; of Mexico, 197–199, *m198,* 201; of Paraguay, 242; of Peru, 267; of United States, 145–146, 152, *p152*
NATO. *See* North Atlantic Treaty Organization (NATO).
natural resources, 92–93; availability of, 41; in Canada, 116; in United States, 116, 132, 134
Nauru, 732, 760–761
navigable lakes, 266
navigable rivers, 134, 345
Nazis, 291, 317, 413
Ndebele, 611
Nebuchadnezzar, 468
Negev Desert, 508
negotiations, 525
Nehru, Jawaharlal, *p641,* 642
Nepal, 89, 631, 633, *p636–637,* 649–651
Neptune, 29
Netherlands, *p282,* 287, 290, *p292–293, p347,* 347–348; Australia and, 738; Guyana and, 244; Indonesia and, 715; Suriname and, 245
neutrality, of Switzerland, 352
Neva River, 426, *p427*
New Caledonia, 758
Newcomen, Thomas, 315
New Delhi, India, 642
Newfoundland, Canada, 162
New Guinea, *p18,* 631
New York City, New York (U.S.), *p112,* 133, *p145*
New Zealand, 724, *p725,* 732, *p741,* 741–744; economy of, 743; history and people of, 743–744; landforms of, 741–742; Maori of, 746–750
Niagara Falls, *p171*
Nicaragua, 186, 212, 215, 216, *p216*
Nicholas II, 413
Nieuwerkerk aan den Ijssel, Netherlands, 287
Niger, 544, 556, 558
Nigeria, 536, *p537,* 545, *p548–549,* 549, 550–554, 559; climate of, 550–551; economy of, 551–552, *p553*; government of, 554; history of, 553–554; people of, 552–553
Niger River, 550, 553, *p559*
Nile River, 454, *p455,* 461, 469, *p479,* 484, 486, 488, 534, 541, 580
nitrogen, 30
Noah's ark, 468
Nobel Peace Prize, 642, 710
Nobel Prize, 553, 773
Nok, 553
nomads, 84; Aborigines, 738; Berbers, 566; Fulani, 558; of Hungary, 373; of Kazakhstan, 439; of Mongolia, 680; of Syria, 505; Tuareg, 558
nonrenewable resources, 93
Nordic countries, 354–357
North Africa and Southwest Asia, 452–463; climate of, 454–456; country profiles of, *c462–463*; economic regions and systems of, 456; extreme points of, 461; landforms of, 454; oil and gas production of, *m460*; people of, 456–457; physical geography of, *m458, m503*; political geography of, *m459, m503*; today, 483, 484–488, 490–493, 501, 502–527; water crisis in, 498–499, *m498, p498, p499.* *See also* Christianity; Egypt, ancient; Islam; Judaism; Mesopotamia; *specific countries of North Africa.*
North American Free Trade Agreement (NAFTA), 96, 102, 136, 163, 195
North Atlantic Current, 280
North Atlantic Treaty Organization (NATO), 320, 325–326
northeast United States, 133
Northern Hemisphere, 32
Northern Ireland, 341–343, *p343*
Northern Mariana Islands, 760
Northern Territory (Australia), 739

INDEX

North European Plain, 40, 280, 345, 368, 392, *p393,* 405–406
North Island, New Zealand, 741–742, *m742*
North Korea, 633, 698–699, 701; physical geography of, *m691*; political geography of, *m691*; population density of, *m700*; refugees from, 672
Northwest Territories (Canada), 159
Norway, 287, 290, 354–355, *p355*
note taking, 376
Notre Dame Cathedral, Paris, France, *p346*
Novokuznetsk, Siberia (Russia), 446
Nubian Desert, 586
nuclear energy, 93, 428
Nunavut Territory (Canada), 159, 168

oases, 454, 456, *p482–483,* 485
Ob-Irtysh River, 392, 399
obsidian, 198
Oceania, 722–733, 758–762; climate of, 724–726; country profiles of, *c732–733*; economy of, 726; endangered environments of, *m730*; extreme points of, 731; landforms of, 724; people of, 726–727; physical geography of, *m728*; political geography of, *m729, m759*; population comparisons of, *c727, c731*. *See also specific countries.*
oceans, 40–41, *m41,* 50; climate and, 56; currents of, *m57*; earthquakes in, 36; exploring, 51; temperature of, *d56*. *See also* Arctic Ocean; Atlantic Ocean; Indian Ocean; Pacific Ocean; water.
oil and gas production, 456, *p456, m460, g514,* 514–516, 519, *p522,* 551, *p553,* 615, 738; in Argentina, 240; in Brunei, 717; in Indonesia, 715; in Venezuela, 243–244
oil reserves, *g514*
okapi, *p571*
Okavango River, 612
O'Keeffe, Georgia, 151
Olmec, *p80,* 178, 197–198, 215
Omahuru, Ngataua, 746, 750
Oman, 463, 516, *p516,* 523
"one country, two systems" pledge, 664
Ontario (Canada), 162
OPEC. *See* Organization of Petroleum Exporting Countries (OPEC).
Operation Tribute to Freedom, 526
opinions *versus* facts, 682
orbits, of planets, 29
Orczy, Baroness, 306
Organization of Petroleum Exporting Countries (OPEC), 514
origami, 692, *p692*
Orinoco River, 176, 243
Orozco, José Clemente, 203
Ortiz, Simon J., 152
Oslo, Norway, 355
ostriches, *p614*
Ottawa, Ontario (Canada), 162
Ottoman Empire, 297, 504, 506
outback, 724, 737, 739
outlining, 752
oxygen, 30, 231
ozone layer, 70, 766, 768, 772–773, *p773*

Pacific coast, 129, 135
Pacific Ocean, 50, *p756–757, p763*
Pacific Rim, *m702, g702*
Padaung, *p708*
paella, 359
pagodas, 670
Pakehas, 746
Pakistan, *p105,* 454, 633, 640, 641, *p644,* 644–646
Palau, 732, 760
Palestinians, 473, 510–511, 525. *See also* Israel.
Pamir Mountains, 392
pampas, 176, 240, 246
Pamplona, Spain, *p358*
Panama, *p177,* 186, 212, 216
Panama Canal, 215, 218, *d218, p225*
pandas, giant, *p660*
Pangaea, 35, *d45*
Papeete, Tahiti, 762
Papua New Guinea, 732, 758
papyrus, 471
Paraguay, 186, 239, *p239,* 241–242
parallels, 5, *d5,* 60, *m60. See also* latitude.
Paramaribo, Suriname, 245
paramilitary forces, in Colombia, 261
Paricutín, 190, *p190*
Paris, France, *p279, p338–339,* 346–347, *p346*
Parliament, British, 306–307
parliamentary democracy, 166–167; in Australia, 739; in Belize, 216; in Caribbean islands, 221; in Czech Republic, 374; in Nepal, 650; in New Zealand, 744; in Norway, 355; in United Kingdom, 341
parliamentary republic: in Bahrain, 523; in Greece, 362; in Portugal, 359
Parthenon, Athens, Greece, *p294,* 362
Parthian Empire, 686
participation, civic, 99, 291
Partnership for a Drug-Free America, 264
Party of Institutional Revolution (PRI), 204
Pashtuns, 520
Patagonia, Argentina, 239–240
Patriot Act, *See* USA Patriot Act.
Paul, 297
Pax Romana, 296, 297
Paz, Octavio, 203
Pearl Harbor, Hawaii (U.S.), 694
Peloponnesian War, 295
Pemba, 580
penguins, *p725, p764*
peninsulas, 40; Arabian Peninsula, 454; Baja California, 191; Balkan Peninsula, 361, 377; Crimean Peninsula, 383; Europe as, 280; Iberian Peninsula, 358–360; Italian Peninsula, 296, 360; Jutland Peninsula, 356; Kamchatka Peninsula, 407; Korean Peninsula, 698; Malay Peninsula, 708; Sinai Peninsula, 485; Yucatán Peninsula, 191, *m196,* 197, 198
Pentagon (U.S.), 138, 520
Penza, Russia, 446
people: of Africa, south of the Sahara, 536–537; of Algeria, 492; of Argentina, 241; of Asia, 626–627; of Australia, 738–739; of Australia, Oceania, and Antarctica, 726–727; Basque, 359; of Bhutan, 651–652; of Bolivia, 272–273; of Bulgaria, 378; of Canada, 116–117; of China, *p635,* 669; climate and, 58–59; of Colombia, 256–257; of Czech Republic, 374; of Democratic Republic of the Congo, 572–573; of Ecuador, 269; of Egypt, 487–488; of Europe, 282–283; of France, 346–347; of Germany, 351–352; of Greece, 362; of Hungary, 373; of India, 640–641; of Indonesia, 715; of Israel, 510–512; of Italy, 361; of Japan, 694–696; of Jordan, 506; landforms and, 41; of Latin America, 178; of Lebanon, 505–506; of Melanesia, 759–760; of Micronesia, 761; of modern Russia, 431–433; of Mongolia, 680–681; of Morocco, 493; of Nepal, 650–651; of New Zealand, 743–744; of Nigeria, 552–553; of North Africa and Southwest Asia, 456–457; of Pakistan, 646; of Poland, 370–371; of Polynesia, 762; of Republic of Ireland, 343; of Russia and Eurasian republics, 394–395; of Sahel countries (West Africa), 558; of Saudi Arabia, 515; of South Africa,

INDEX

605–607, *p607*; of South Korea, 700; of Sri Lanka, 653–654; of Syria, 505; of Taiwan, 679; of Turkey, 503–504; of Ukraine, 384–385; of United Kingdom, 342; of United States, 116–117; of Venezuela, 244; of Vietnam, 712; of West Africa coastal countries, 560–561
People's Republic of China. *See* China.
perestroika, 415
permafrost, 66, 392
Péron, Juan, 241
Perry, Matthew, 694
persecution, 593
Persian Gulf, 467
Persian rugs, 507
Persian Wars, 295
Peru, *p101, p174,* 183, 186, 266–268, *p275*
Peru Current, 266, 273
Peter, 297
Peter the Great, 410, *ptg410,* 411, 426
Petra, Jordan, *p505*
Petronas Towers, Kuala Lumpur, Malaysia, 716
pharaohs, 469–470
Philip II of Macedonia, 295
Philippines, 633
philosophy, 294–295
Phnom Penh, Cambodia, 711
Phoenicians, 104, 469, 491
Phoenix, Arizona (U.S.), *p263*
phosphate, 486, 560, 761
physical geography, 22–23; of Africa, south of the Sahara, *m538*; of Asia, *m628*; of Australia, Oceania, and Antarctica, *m728*; of Brazil, *m233*; of Canada, *m118*; of Central and East Africa, *m572*; of China, *m661*; of Europe, *m284*; of Japan, *m691*; of Koreas, *m691*; of Latin America, *m180*; of Mexico, 196, *m196*; of North Africa, *m485*; of North Africa and Southwest Asia, *m458*; of Russia and Eurasian republics, *m396*; of South Asia, *m645*; of Southwest Asia, 503; of United States, *m118, m127*; of West Africa, *m552*
pictograph, 12, *g12*
pidgin language, 760
Piedmont, 128
pipelines, water, 498
pirarucu, *p232*
Pisa, Italy, *p361*
plains, of Latin America, 176. *See also* pampas.
plantations: in Central America, 213; in Mexico, 194
Plateau of Mexico, 192
Plateau of Tibet, 40, 624, 660
plateaus, 40, 129
plate tectonics, 35–37, *d36,* 39; in Indonesia, 714
platypus, 740
plazas, in Mexico, 202
Pluto, 29
Poland, 290, *p368,* 368–371, *p370*
polar bears, *p115*
polar ice cap climate, 765
polar science, 768
polders, 347
polis, 294
political geography: of Africa, south of the Sahara, *m539*; of Andean countries, *m255*; of Asia, *m629*; of Australia, Oceania, and Antarctica, *m729*; of Brazil, *m233*; of Canada, *m119*; of Central America, *m213*; of Central and East Africa, *m580*; eastern Europe, *m369*; of Europe, *m285*; of Europe, 1950, *m320*; of Japan, *m691*; of Latin America, *m181*; of Mexico, *p191*; of North Africa and Southwest Asia, *m459*; of North Korea, *m691*; of Oceania and Antarctica, *m759*; of Russia and Eurasian republics, *m397*; of Southeast Asia, 709; of Southern Africa, *m605*; of South Korea, *m691*; of Southwest Asia, 503; of United States, *m119*; of West Africa, *m551*; of western Europe, *m341*
political rights, 673
pollution, 326, 428; air, 37, 69, *p70,* 135, 351, 664, 693; in Mexico, 206; in Russia, 394; water, 71, 498, *p638*
Pol Pot, 711
Polynesia, 761–762
polytheism, 467
Pontic Mountains, 502
popes, 299
Popocatepetl, 192, *p192*
population: of Africa, *c537*; of Africa, south of the Sahara, *c541*; of Asia, *c627*; of Australia, Oceania, and Antarctica, *c727, c731*; of Canada, *c117, c121*; density of, *m89, m149, m205,* 334, *m384,* 487–488, *m560, m653, m700*; of Europe, *c283, c287*; growth of, 76, 87–88, *c88*; of Latin America, *c179, m182, c183*; locations of, 88–90; of Mexico, 204–205; mobility of, 150; movement of, 90–91; of North Africa and Southwest Asia, *c457, c461*; rural, 150, 432, 487–488, *c627, p662*; of Russian and Eurasian republics, *c395, c399*; suburban, 150; trends in, 26; of United States, *c117, c121*; urban, 150, 487–488, *c627*; of Vietnam, 712
population density, 89
porcelain, 670
Port-au-Prince, Haiti, 222
Port Harcourt, Nigeria, 559
Port Louis, Mauritius, 618
ports, free, 716
Portugal, 290, 358–360; Angola and, 615; Brazil and, 236–237; East Timor and, 715; Macau and, 664; population density of, *m334*
Portuguese language, 179, 235
Postel, Sandra, 499
pottery, *p491*
Prague, Czech Republic, *p366–367, p372,* 374, *p376*
Prairie Provinces (Canada), 159, *p162,* 162–163
precipitation, 49. *See also* rainfall.
predictions, making, 598
prefects, 245
prehistory, 27
presentations, multimedia, 164
prevailing winds, *m54*
primary sources, 448, 606
Prime Meridian, 4, 5, 60, 613
prime ministers, 167
printing press, 304
privacy, 139
privatization, 375
productivity, 314
pronunciation, 81. *See also* languages.
Protestantism, 221
Protestant Reformation, 304–305
provinces, 158
public servants, 445
Puerto Rico, 186, 219, 220, 221–223
Puerto Vallarta, Mexico, 194
Punt, 470
Puritans, 305
Putin, Vladimir, 430
Pyongyang, North Korea, *p672,* 701
pyramids: Aztec, 199; Egyptian, 456, 470, 472, *p495*
Pyrenees Mountains, 280, 358–359
pysanky, 382, *p382*

Qaddhafi, Muammar, 491
Qatar, 463, 515, 523
Quebec (Canada), 162, 167
Quebec City, Quebec (Canada), 162, *p165*
Quechua, 268. *See also* Inca.
quipu, 267. *See also* Inca.
Quito, Ecuador, *p253,* 269
quotas, trade, 95
Quran, 477, 519. *See also* Islam.

Rabat, Morocco, 493
racism, 546
radar, 24
radiation, atomic bombs and, 692

INDEX

rainfall: in Amazon Basin, 232; in Botswana, 612; in Egypt, 486; in Israel, 509; in Mexico, 193; mountains and, 57–58. *See also* acid rain.
rain forests, 59, 62, 176; in Africa, 534; Amazon, 25, *p230–231*; in Asia, 626; in Brazil, 187, *p187,* 232–233; in Central America, *p212,* 213–215; in Democratic Republic of the Congo, 571; in Melanesia, 758; in Panama, *p177*; in Rwanda, *p582*; vanishing, 250, *p250*
rain shadow, 58, *d58*
Ramses II, *p484*
recycling, 136, 498
Red Sea, 485
Red Square, Moscow, Russia, *p422–423*
refugees, *p90,* 91, 379, 506; in Africa, *m592*; in Central and East Africa, 591–596; in Ethiopia, 592; host countries for, 596, *p596*; in Taiwan, 679; in Tanzania, *p595*
region, 2, 24
Reims, France, *p299*
reincarnation, 640–641
religion, 80, 82, *c82,* 304–305; in Africa, *c537*; in ancient Egypt, 470; ancient Mexican, *p197*; in Asia, 626; in China, 667; of Europe, *c287*; in India, 640–641; in Japan, 693, *p693,* 695; in Latin America, *p178*; in Mesopotamia, 467; in Russia, 432; tolerance of, 463; in Uganda, 583; in United States, 150. *See also specific religions.*
Rembrandt van Rijn, 348
Renaissance, 282, *p303,* 303–304
renewable resources, 92–93
Renoir, Pierre-Auguste, 347
Repin Institute, Russia, *p429*
report writing, 763
representative democracy, 146
representative government, 83
Republic of South Africa. *See* South Africa.
republic, federal, 146
republic government, 296; of Algeria, 492; of Egypt, 487; of the Maldives, 654
Republic of Ireland, 342–343
resources. *See* natural resources.
reunification, of Germany, 351
revolutions: American, 307; in Europe, 283, 306–307; in Mexico, 200; of planets, 31; Russian, 413
Reykjavik, Iceland, 357
Rhine River, 280, 326, 350
rhinoceroses, 536
Rhodes, Cecil, 611
Rhodesia, 611
Rhodope Mountains, 378
rice production, *g662*
Ridge, Tom, 140, 142
Rīga, Latvia, *p371*
rights, 139, 747; human, 593, 634; political, 673; unalienable, 167; women's, 634
Rimsky-Korsakov, Nikolay, 434
Ring of Fire, 407, 624, 662
ring-tailed lemurs, *p617*
Rio de Janeiro, Brazil, 179, *p179,* 234, *p236*
Rio de la Plata, 176
Rio Grande, 176, 206
Rivera, Diego, 203, *ptg203*
rivers, 42; continental divide and, 352; navigable, 134, 345
Riyadh, Saudi Arabia, *p500–501,* 515
Robinson projection, 7, *m7*
Rocky Mountains, *p112–113,* 114, 129, 160
Roman Catholicism, 299; in Argentina, 241; in Brazil, 236; in Caribbean islands, 221; in Central America, 217; in Chile, 274; in Colombia, 256; in Croatia, 379; in East Timor, 715; in Italy, 361; in Latin America, 176, *p178,* 179; in Philippines, 717; in Poland, 371; in Russia, 432; in Slovakia, 375; in Spain and Portugal, 359; spread of, 476; in Uruguay, 242; in Venezuela, 244. *See also* Christianity.
Romania, 290, *p377,* 377–378
Roman law, 296
Rome, ancient, 282, 296–297; Colosseum of, *p296*; empire of, *m295,* 296
Rome, Italy, 360
Rosetta Stone, *p470*
rotation, of planets, 29, 31
Rotterdam, Netherlands, *p282*
Rousseau, Jean Jacques, 306
Rowland, F. Sherwood, 773
Royal Danish Ballet, *p356*
Rub' al Khali Desert, 454, 513
rubber trees, *p716*
Ruhr Valley, 351
rural population, 150, *c283, p431,* 432, 487–488, *c627, p663*
Russia, 386, *p390–391, p393,* 400, *p402–403,* 402–434, 441–447, *p422–423*; climate of, 392–394, 404–405, 420–421; communism, fall in, 424–426; culture of, 433–434; democracy in, 429, 441–446; early, 410–413; east of Ural Mountains, 406–407; economic regions of, *m425,* 426–428; environmental issues in, 428; ethnic challenges in, 430; European, 405–406; expansion of, *m412*; inland waters of, 407–408; landforms of, 392; modern, 422–451; people of, 431–433; political challenges in, 429–430; Soviet era of, 413–415; in space race, 409; winter temperatures in, *m421*
Russia and Eurasian republics, 390–401; country profiles of, *c400–401*; economy of, 394; extreme points in, 399; people of, 394–395; physical geography of, *m396*; political geography of, *m397*; snow cover in, *m398*
Russian Federation, 442
Russian Orthodox Christianity, 432
Russian Revolution, 412
Rwanda, 545, 584–585

sacred lands (Australia), 747
Sadako and the Thousand Paper Cranes **(Coerr),** 692
safety checks, *d138,* 139, *p139, p140*
saffron, 93, *p93*
Sahara, *p452,* 454, 461, *p479,* 486, *p490,* 493, *p556,* 566
Sahel countries, 556–558
Saint Kitts, 221
Sakhalin, Russia, 399
salt trade of Africa, 566, *p567, m567*
salt water, 50. *See also* desalinization.
Salween River, 708
Samburu, *p581*
Samoa, *p722,* 732, 761
samurai, 693
Sanaa, Yemen, 516
San Andreas Fault, 37
sand, 454
San Francisco, California (U.S.), *p92*
San José, Costa Rica, *p215,* 217
San Juan, Puerto Rico, 223
San Marino, 290, 360
San Martín, José de, 240
San Salvador, Bahamas, 220
Santiago, Chile, *p272,* 273
Santo Domingo, Dominican Republic, 220
San Xavier del Bac, Arizona (U.S.), *p146*
São Francisco River, 176
São Paulo, Brazil, 179, 234
São Tomé and Principe, 545, 575
Sarajevo, Bosnia and Herzegovina, 380
Saskatchewan, Canada, *p162,* 163
satellite nations of Soviet Union, 321, 414
Satpura Range, 638
Saturn, 29
Saudi Arabia, 456, *p457,* 463, *p478, p500–501,* 513–515
saunas, 356
savanna climate, 220
savannas, 550, 570
Scandinavia, 282
Scarlet Pimpernel, The **(Orczy),** 306

INDEX

"scorched earth policy," 420
Scotland, 340
scribes, 468
Scriptures, 475
scuba diving, *p219*
sea anemone, *p758*
seals, *p765*
Sea of Marmara, 502, *p502*
seasons, *d31,* 31–32
secession, 147
secondary sources, 448
secular policies, 492
security, in U.S., 137–143, *d138, p139, p140,* 148–149
Seine River, 326, 345
Seko, Mobutu Sese, 573
selvas, 232
Senate (Rome), 296
Senegal, 545, 558
Seoul, South Korea, *p674, p699,* 700
September 11, 2001, 138, *p138,* 139, 148–149, 520
sequencing information, 238
Sequieros, David Alfero, 203
sequoia, *p61*
Serbia and Montenegro, 290, 323, *m369,* 380
Serengeti Plain, *p568–569,* 579–580
serfs, 301, 412
service industries, 132, 195, 743
Setswana language, 612
Seychelles, 545, 618
Shackleton, Ernest, *p766*
Shah Jahan, 643
shahs, 519
Shakespeare, William, 304, 342
Shanghai, China, 661, *p673*
Shaw, George Bernard, 343
Shepard, Alan, 409
Sherpas, 650
Shi'ite Muslims, 477, 522
Shikoku Island, Japan, 690
Shinto religion, 693, *p693,* 695
shoguns, 693
Shona, 611, *p611*
Siberia (Russia), *p390–391, p400,* 406, *p406, p407,* 413, *p417,* 427, 446
Siberian tigers, *p390–391, p404*
Sicily, 360
Siddartha Gautama, 651
Sierra Leone, 545, 558, 561, 595
Sierra Madre Mountains, 176, 191–192
Sikhism, 641
silk, *p436, p686*
Silk Road, 439, 686, *m687*
Silla kingdom, 698
Sinai Peninsula, 485
Singapore, 633, *p706–707,* 716
Sinhalese, 653–654
sirocco winds, 360
Siva deity (Hinduism), 640, *p640*
Skopje, Macedonia, 380
skydiving, *p20–21*
slash-and-burn farming, 616
slave trade, 147, 559
Slavs, 370, 374, 384, 394, 430
sleeping sickness, 573, 576
Sloan, John, 151
sloth, three-toed, *p177*
Slovakia, 290, *p374,* 375
Slovenia, 291, 323, *m369,* 379
smugglers, drug, 260, 262
snow cover, in Russia, *m398. See also* climate.
soccer, *p268, p329*
social groups, 80–81
socialist government, of Tanzania, 581
social scientists, 80
sodium nitrate, 274
Sofia, Bulgaria, 378
Sögüt, Turkey, 504
Sokkuram shrine (Korea), *p698*
solar eclipses, *p30*
solar energy, 93
solar system, 29–31, *d30*
Solidarity (Poland), 370
Solomon Islands, 732, 758
solstices, 32, 344
Solzhenitsyn, Alexander, 432, 434
Somalia, 470, 545, 590
Songhai Empire, 557, 566
Sotho, 605
souks, 492
source of rivers, 42
sources, primary and secondary, 448
South Africa, *p532,* 536, 545, *p602–603, p604,* 604–607; Namibia and, 616
South America: plate tectonics and, 35. *See also* Latin America; *and specific Latin American countries.*
South Asia, 636–657; Bangladesh, 646–647; Bhutan, 651–652; economic regions and systems of, *m650*; India, 638–643; Maldives, 654; Nepal, 649–651; Pakistan, 644–646; physical geography of, *m645*; population density of, *m653*; Sri Lanka, 652–654
South China Sea, 711
Southeast Asia, 706–721; Brunei, 717; Cambodia, 711; Indonesia, 714–715, 718; Laos, 710; Malaysia, 716; Myanmar, 708–710; political geography of, 709; Singapore, 716–717; Thailand, 710; Vietnam, 711–712
Southern Africa, 602–621; Angola, 614–615; Botswana, 612; Comoros, 617–618; diamond mining in, 608; Madagascar, 617; Malawi, 610; Mauritius, 618; Mozambique, 616–617; Namibia, 616; political geography of, *m605*; Seychelles, 618; South Africa, 604–607; Zambia, 609–610; Zimbabwe, 610–611
Southern Alps, 742
Southern Hemisphere, 32
South Island, New Zealand, 742, *m742*
South Korea, 634, 674, 698–700; physical geography of, *m691*; political geography of, *m691*; population density of, *m700*
south United States, 133
Southwest Asia: climate of, *m509*. *See also* North Africa and Southwest Asia.
Soviet Union, 321, 394, 413–415, 436. *See also* Russia.
Soyinka, Wole, 553
space race, 409
Spaceship Earth, 21
space shuttle, 22
Space Station, International, 409
Spain, 291, *p358,* 358–360; Central America and, 216; Mexico and, 199; Philippines and, 717; population density of, *m334*
Spanish-American War, 223, 717
Spanish language, *p150,* 179
Sparta, Greece, 295
specialization, economic, 95
species, endangered, 76, *m76*
spin, of planets, 29
spreadsheets, 494
Sri Lanka, 634, *p649,* 652–654
St. Basil's Cathedral, Moscow, Russia, *p390*
St. Kitts and Nevis, 186, 221
St. Lawrence River, 160, 166
St. Lawrence Seaway, 114, 134, *d159*
St. Lucia, 186
St. Petersburg, Russia, *p393, p395,* 406, 420, 426–427, *p427,* 434
St. Vincent and the Grenadines, 186
Stalin, Joseph, 384, 413, 420, 444, *p444*
stations, 737
Statue of Liberty, New York (U.S.), *p124–125*
steppe climate, 67, *p67,* 273, 454
steppes, 438, 536, 680; in Russia, 394, 406, *p407*; in Ukraine, 383
Stockholm, Sweden, 356
Stoker, Bram, 378
Stonehenge, United Kingdom, 344, *p344*
storms, 55
Strait of Gibraltar, 492
Strait of Hormuz, 516
Strait of Magellan, 42, 273
Strait of Malacca, 716
straits, 42
Stravinsky, Igor, 434
subarctic climate, 65–66, *p66,* 130

subcontinent, 638
subsistence farming, 96, 759; in Angola, 614; in Bhutan, 651; in Central America, 214; in Lesotho and Swaziland, 607, *p607*; in Mexico, 194; in Micronesia, 761; in Namibia, 616; in Peru, 267; in Uganda, 582; in West Africa, 558
suburban populations, 150
suburbs, 432; of India, *p639*
Sucre, Bolivia, 272
Sudan, 470, 545, 586–588, 592–593
Suez Canal, 485, 487
sultans, 717
Sumatra, Indonesia, 714
Sumer, 456, 467
summer solstice, 32
sumo wrestling, 696
sun, 30–32; Earth's climate and, 53–54
Sunni Muslims, 477, 522
sunscreen ratings, 772, *p772*
Sun Yat-sen, 667
supply and demand, 93; for illegal drugs, 263
Suriname, 186, 239, 245
Suva, Fiji Islands, *p769*
Swahili language, 579, 581
swamps, mangrove, 550
Swaziland, 545, 607
Sweden, 287, 291, *p354,* 355–356
Switzerland, *p281,* 291, *p352,* 352–353
Sydney, Australia, 727, *p738,* 739
Sydney Opera House, Sydney, Australia, *p738*
Syria, *c463,* 504–505
Syrian Desert, 504

Table Mountain, *p602–603,* 604, *p604*
tabulating machines, 108
tae kwon do, 700
Tahiti, 761–762
taiga, 66, 394, 406, *p407*
Taíno, 220
Taipei, Taiwan, 679
Taiwan, *p70,* 634, 667, 675, 678–679
Tajikistan, 392, 401, 440
Tajiks, 520
Taj Mahal, Agra, India, *p622,* 641, 643, *p643*
Taklimakan Desert, 624, 661, 686
Tale of Genji, The, 696
Taliban, *p519,* 520
Tamil Nadu, India, *p625*
Tamils, 653–654
Tan, Amy, 151
Tanganyika, 581
Tanzania, 541, 545, *p568–569,* 579–581; refugees in, 595, *p595*
Taoudenni, 566
tariffs, 95
Tashkent, Uzbekistan, 439
Tasmania, Australia, 736
Tasman Sea, 724
Taurus Mountains, 502
Taxco, Mexico, *p202*
T'bilisi, Georgia, 438
Tchaikovsky, Peter, 395, 412, 434
technology, 97–98, *c98, p116, p135,* 136, 678–679
tectonics. *See* plate tectonics.
Tehran, Iran, 456, 519, *p519, p524*
Tel Aviv-Yafo, Israel, *p508,* 510, 512
telenovelas, 237
temperate climates, 63
temperatures: latitude effects on, 192; ocean, *d56*; winter, *m421*
tenants, 301
Ten Commandments, 474
Tenochtitlán, 199
Teotihuacán, *p199*
Terhazza, 566
terracing, 70, *p71*
terrorism, *p138,* 148–149, 326; defense against, 137–143
Texas (U.S.), *p116, p128, p152,* 200
textiles, 315
Thailand, *p622–623,* 634, *p708*
thematic maps, 10, *m10,* 86, *m86*
theocracy, 470
Theodosius I, 297
Thimphu, Bhutan, 651
thinking, critical, 416, 598, 702
"Third World," 96
Three Gorges Dam, China, 662, 665
three-toed sloth, *p177*
thunderstorms, 55
Tiananmen Square, Beijing, China, 668
Tian Shan, 392, 439, 660
Tibet, 631, 666, *p666,* 669
tierra caliente altitude, 193
Tierra del Fuego (Chile), *p272,* 273
tierra fria altitude, 193
tierra templada altitude, 193
Tigris River, 454, 456, 466, 517
Tijuana, Mexico, 194
Tikal, Guatemala, 216
timberline, 68
time zones, *m447,* 613, *m613*
Timor, 714
Tirana, Albania, 381
Togo, *c546,* 558
Tokyo, Japan, 691
tolerance, religious, 463
Tolstoy, Leo, 434, 435, *ptg435*
Tombouctou, Mali, 557
Tonga, 733, 761
topsoil, 70
Torah, 473
tornadoes, 55
Toronto, Canada, 160, *p160,* 162, *p168*
tourism: in Antarctica, 766; in Argentina, 239; in Australia, 738; in Botswana, 612; in Brazil, 234; in Bulgaria, 378; in Canada, *p158*; in Caribbean islands, *p219,* 220; in Central America, 215; in China, 661; in Egypt, 486; in France, *p316, p345–346,* 345–347; in Georgia, 438; in Greece, 362; in Jordan, *p505*; in Kenya, *p598, g598*; in Laos, 710; in the Maldives, 654; in Melanesia, 759; in Mexico, 194; in Micronesia, 761; in Morocco, 492; in New Zealand, 743; in Norway, 354; in Polynesia, 762; in Portugal, 359; in Puerto Rico, 223; in Russia, 408; in Spain, 359; in Tanzania, 579–580; in United States, *p134,* 135
Toussaint-Louverture, Francois-Dominique, 222
trade: ancient routes of, 104; free, 96, 136, 157, 223, 271, 329–330; restrictions on, 693; slave, 147; water transport and, 468; world, 94–96, 136
traditional economic systems, 93
traits, 80
Transantarctic Mountains, 765
Transdanubia region (Hungary), 372
transportation, 98, *c98*
Transportation Security Administration (TSA), 139
Trans-Siberian Railroad, 413, *p417*
Transylvania, *p378*
Treaty of Waitangi, 748–749
trees: coniferous, 64; deciduous, 64; rubber, *p716*; in vegetation map, 349
trenches, in oceans, 41
Trinidad and Tobago, 186, 220, 221
Tripoli, Libya, 491
tropical climate, 62, 130, 176, 243, 558, 626, 652, 715, 724, 758–761
tropical rain forest climate, 62, *p62,* 534
tropical savanna climate, 62, *p62,* 536, 550
Tropic of Cancer, 32, 53, 192, 255
Tropic of Capricorn, 32, 53, 255
Truman Doctrine, 320
tsetse flies, 573, 576
tsunamis, 36, 690
Tuareg, *p557,* 558
Tucson, Arizona (U.S.), *p146*
tundra, 116, 159, *p400*; in Russia, 392, 406, *p407*; in Scandinavia, 282; in United States, 130

tundra climate, 66, *p66*
Tunis, Tunisia, 491
Tunisia, 463, 491
Turkey, 454, 463, 502–504, 507
Turkish Straits, 502
Turkmenistan, 392, 401, 439
Turpan Depression, 631, 661
Tutankhamen, *p466*
Tutsi, 585
Tuvalu, 733, 761
Twain, Mark, 151
Twelve Tables (Roman law), 296
typhoons, 55, 760

Ubangi River, 574
Uganda, 541, *c546, p547,* 582–584
Ukraine, 291, 382–385, *p383,* 410
Ukrainian Easter eggs, 382, *p382*
Ulaanbaatar, Mongolia, *p680,* 681
unalienable rights, 167
undersea earthquakes, 36
Union of South Africa, 606
Union of Soviet Socialist Republics (USSR), 413. *See also* Russia; Russia and Eurasian republics.
unions, 315
United Arab Emirates, *p452,* 463, 515
United Kingdom, 61, 287, 291, 340–342; Australia and, 726, 739; Botswana and, 612; in Egypt, 487; Guyana and, 244; Hong Kong and, 664; India and, 639, 641; Israel and, 511; Jordan and, 506; Kenya and, 579; Maldives and, 654; Myanmar and, 709; New Zealand and, 744; Parliament of, 306–307; Seychelles and, 618; Singapore and, 717; South Africa and, 605–606; Sri Lanka and, 653; Suriname and, 245; Uganda and, 583; Zambia and, 610. *See also* England; Great Britain.
United Nations, 99, 493, 511, 518, 526, 592, 606–607, 699
United Nations Educational, Scientific, and Cultural Organization (UNESCO), 269
United States (U.S.), 24, 114–155; after World War I, 316; American Revolution in, 307; American Samoa and, 761; Caribbean islands and, 221, 223; climate of, 114–116, 130; culture of, 150–152; economic leadership of, 131–132; economy of, 116, 133–135; ethnic groups of, 149–150; extreme points of, *c121, m121*; flag, *p143*; food production of, *m120*; Grand Teton National Park, Wyoming, *p46–47*; history of, 145–149; landforms of, 114, 126–129; in Mexican history, 200; Micronesia and, 760; North American Free Trade Agreement (NAFTA) and, 136; people of, 116–117; Philippines and, 717; physical geography of, *m118, m127*; political geography of, *m119*; population density of, *m149*; states of, *c122–123*; terrorism and, 137–142; Vietnam and, 712; waterways of, 114
Upper Egypt, *m467,* 470
Upper Volta, 558
Ural Mountains, 394, 404–407, 427
Uranus, 29
urbanization, 90
urban population, 150, *c283, p431,* 487–488, *c627*
urban sprawl, 91
Uruguay, 187, 239, 241–242
U.S. Census Bureau, 108, *p108*
U.S. Coast Guard, 262
U.S. Constitution, 125, 146, 329
U.S. Customs Service, 262, *p262*
U.S. Declaration of Independence, 167
U.S. Department of Defense, 526
U.S. Postal Service, 108
USA Patriot Act, 139
Uzbekistan, 392, 401, 439

Vaidés Peninsula, 183
Vancouver, British Columbia (Canada), *p156–157,* 163
van Gogh, Vincent, 348
vanilla beans, 617
Vanuatu, 733, 758
vaqueros, 193
vassals, 301
Vatican City, 291, 360–361
vegetation, 61–68; in dry climates, 67; in highland climates, 68; in high latitude climates, 65–66, *p66*; in mid-latitude climates, 63–65; regions of, *m64*; spread of, *m229*; in tropical climates, 62
Venezuela, 183, 187, 239, 242–244
Venice, Italy, 360, *p360*
Venus, 29
Verdun, France, *p316*
vernal equinox, 32
Victoria Falls, 534, *p535,* 609
Vienna, Austria, 353, *p353*
Vientiane, Laos, 710
Vietnam, 634, *p634*
Vietnamese language, *p150*
Vikings, 354
Villa, Francisco "Pancho," 200
Villa Las Estrellas, Chile Antarctic Territory, 766–767
Vinson Massif, *g652,* 731, 765
Virgin Islands, 187, 221
Vishnu deity (Hinduism), 640
Vladivostok, Russia, 413, 427
volcanoes, 575, 589, 617, 624, 662, 690–691, *p694,* 715; in Antarctica, 765; in Azores, *p34*; in Caribbean, 219; in Central America, 212; in Chile, 273; in Iceland, 357; in Italy, 360; in Latin America, 176; magma of, 35; in Micronesia, 760; mountains from, 39; Mount Etna, 22; Mt. Pinatubo, *p55*; in New Zealand, 741, 743; in Oceania, 724; Paricutín, *p190*; in Polynesia, 761; Popocatepetl, 192, *p192*; in Russia, 407
Volga River, 392, 406, 408, 427
Volgograd, Russia, *p390,* 406
voting, 733, 744

Waitangi Day, 748
Wales, 340
Walesa, Lech, 370
Walloons, 347
War and Peace **(Tolstoy),** 434, 435
Warsaw, Poland, 370
Warsaw Pact, 321
Washington, D.C. (U.S.), *m33, p53,* 133
Washington (U.S.), 61
Washington, George, *p147*
water: bodies of, 42; in Canada, 114; crisis in North Africa, 498–499, *p498–499*; cycle of, 48–49, *d49*; fresh, 41; management of, 71; in North Africa and Southwest Asia, 454; pollution of, 428; resources of, 49–50; in Russia, 407–408; trade and, 468; in United States, 114; in weathering, 37–38. *See also* oceans.
Water Demand Management Research Network (WDMRN), 499
Watt, James, 315
Wayang kulit, 718
weather, climate and, 52–53
weathering, 37
weaving, 507
Web sites, 528
Weiler, Kaelin, 264
welfare state (Sweden), 355
Wellington, New Zealand, 744
Welsh language, 340
West Africa: coastal countries of, 558–561; Great Mosque of Djenné of, 562; Nigeria, 550–554; physical geography of, *m552*; political geography of, *m551*; population density of,

INDEX

m560; Sahel countries of, 556–558; salt trade of, 566
West Bank, 511–512, *m511*
western Europe. *See* Europe, western.
Western Ghats, 638
Western Sahara (Morocco), 493
western United States, 134–135
West Indies, 219
West Virginia (U.S.), *p115*
White Nile River, 586
Wieliczka, Poland, *p368*
Wilder, Laura Ingalls, 151
Williams, Serena, *p265*
Williams, Venus, *p265*
windmills, *p92*
winds, 38; climate and, 54–56; electricity from, *p92*; landforms and, 56–57; prevailing, *m54*; sirocco, 360
windward side, 57
Winkel Tripel projection, 7, *m7*
winter solstice, 32
Wojtyla, Karol (Pope John Paul II), 371
women's rights, 634
wood-block printing, *p695*
World Health Organization (WHO), 576
world trade, 94–96, 136
World Trade Center, New York (U.S.), 138, 141, 520; memorial on site of, 141, *d141, d143*
World War I, 148, 316, 504
World War II, 148, 317, 370, *p421,* 511, 676, 692, 694, 761
World Wide Web, 106
World Wildlife Federation, 446
writing reports, 763
Wudi (Chinese Emperor), 686
Wyoming (U.S.), *p46–47*

Xhosa, 605
Xi River, 662

Yagua, *p104*
yaks, *p651*
Yalu River, 699, 701
Yamoussoukro, Côte d'Ivoire, 561
Yangon, Myanmar, 709
Yangtze River, 624, 631, 662
Yap Island, Micronesia, *p760*
Yeats, William Butler, 343
yellow fever, 218
Yellow River, 624, 662
Yellowstone National Park, 135
Yeltsin, Boris, 430, *p430*
Yemen, *p456,* 463, 516
Yenisey River, 394
Yerevan, Armenia, 437
Yokohama, Japan, 691
Yoruba, 552; wooden masks of, *p555*
Yucatán Peninsula, 191, *p197,* 198
Yugoslavia, *p90,* 323, 379
yurts, *p438,* 681

Zagreb, Croatia, 379
Zagros Mountains, 454, 519
Zaire (Democratic Republic of the Congo), 573
Zambezi River, 534, 609, 610
Zambia, *c546, p610*
Zanzibar, 580–581
Zapata, Emiliano, 200
Zealand Island, Denmark, 356
Zhang Qian, 686
Zhou Enlai, 667
ziggurat, 467
Zimbabwe, *c546,* 610–611
Zionists, 511
Zlata's Diary **(Filipovic),** 380
Zulu, 605
Zurich, Switzerland, 352
Zvezda space station module, 409

ACKNOWLEDGMENTS

Text

99 From **Millennium Report, April 3, 2000** by Kofi Annan, secretary-general of the United Nations. United Nations Press Release SG/SM/7343 GA/9705, April 3, 2000. Copyright 2001 by United Nations; **152 Survival This Way** by Simon J. Ortiz. Reprinted by permission of the author. **I, Too** in *Collected Poems* by Langston Hughes. Copyright 1994 by the Estate of Langston Hughes. Reprinted by permission of Alfred A. Knopf, a Division of Random House, Inc; **167 A Declaration of First Nations.** Copyright 2001 by Assembly of First Nations National Indian Brotherhood. (http://www.afn.ca/About%AFN/a_declaration_of_first_nations.htm) **235** From **Botoque, Bringer of Fire** in *Folklore, Myths, and Legends, a World Perspective,* edited by Donna Rosenberg. Copyright 1977. NTC Publishing; **246** From **The Gaucho Martín Fierro** adapted from the Spanish and rendered into English verse by Walter Owen. Copyright 1936 by Farrar & Rinehart. Reprinted by permission of Henry Holt and Company, LLC; **306** From **The Scarlet Pimpernel** by Baroness Orzy. Copyright 1961 Doubleday and Company, Inc; **380** From **Zlata's Diary: A Child's Life in Sarajevo** translated with notes by Christina Pribichevich-Zoric. Translation copyright by Fixot et editions Robert Laffont, 1994 Viking, published by the Penguin Group, Penguin Books USA Inc. NY; **432** From **Nobel Lecture, 1972** by Alexander Isayevich Solzhenitsyn in *Bartlett's Familiar Quotations.* Copyright 1992 by Little, Brown and Company Inc, Boston; **435 The Grandfather and His Little Grandson** by Leo Tolstoy in *A Harvest of Russian Children's Literature,* edited by Miriam Morton. Copyright 1967 by Miriam Morton. University of California Press, Berkeley and Los Angeles, CA; **489** From **The Black Prince and Other Egyptian Folk Tales** told by Ahmed and Zane Zagloul. Copyright 1971 by Doubleday & Company, Inc., Garden City, NY; **578** From **Where are those Songs** by Micere G. Mugo. Reprinted by permission of the author; **606** From **Long Walk to Freedom: The Autobiography of Nelson Mandela** by Nelson Mandela. Copyright 1994 by Nelson Rolihlahla Mandela. Little, Brown and Company; **692** From **Sadako and the Thousand Paper Cranes** by Eleanor Coerr. Copyright 1977. The Putnam Publishing Group; **697** From **Haiku, Volume II.** Copyright 1952 by R.H. Blyth. Reprinted by permission of Hokuseido Press; **737** From **Great Mother Snake** an Aboriginal legend. Glencoe would like to acknowledge the artists and agencies who participated in illustrating this program: Ortelius Design, Inc.

Photographs

Cover (top to bottom) AI Interactive, CORBIS, Grant Faint/Getty Images, Getty Images, Pacific Stock, *Pablo Corral Vega/CORBIS, CORBIS, (bkgd) AI Interactive; **1** (t)Dallas & John Heaton/CORBIS, Jamie Herron/CORBIS, Owen Franken/CORBIS; **2, 3, 16–17** Getty Images; **18** (t)CORBIS, (b)Robert Landau/CORBIS; **18–19** S. Purdy Matthews/Getty Images; **20–21** Norman Kent Productions/oi2.com; **22** NASA/National Geographic Image Collection; **23** (t)Richard T. Nowitz/National Geographic Image Collection, (b)Yann Arthus-Bertrand/CORBIS; **25** Galen Rowell/CORBIS; **26** (l)Shelly Grossman/Woodfin Camp, (tr)Christie's Images/CORBIS, (br)Getty Images; **28** file photo; **29** Maria Stenzel/National Geographic Image Collection; **30** Timothy G. Laman/National Geographic Image Collection; **34** Natalie Fobes/National Geographic Image Collection; **37** Michael K. Nichols/National Geographic Image Collection; **39** David Doubilet/National Geographic Image Collection; **40** Michael K. Nichols/National Geographic Image Collection, (inset)Wolfgang Kaehler/CORBIS; **46–47** Digital Vision/Getty Images; **48** George Grall/National Geographic Image Collection; **51** Southampton Oceanography Centre; **52** J. Blair/National Geographic Image Collection; **53** Medford Taylor/National Geographic Image Collection; **55** CORBIS; **61** Phil Schermeister/National Geographic Image Collection; **62** (l)Michael K. Nichols/National Geographic Image Collection, (r)Beverly Joubert/National Geographic Image Collection; **65** (l)James P. Blair/National Geographic Image Collection, (tr)Annie Griffiths Belt/National Geographic Image Collection, (c)Jodi Cobb/National Geographic Image Collection, (br)Raymond K. Gehman/National Geographic Image Collection; **66** (t)Natalie Fobes/National Geographic Image Collection, (c)George F. Mobley/National Geographic Image Collection, (b)Raymond Gehman/CORBIS; **67** (l)James L. Stanfield/National Geographic Image Collection; (r)Phil Schemeister/National Geographic Image Collection; **68** Pat Jerrold Papilio/CORBIS; **69** Bryan & Cherry Alexander; **70** Jodi Cobb/National Geographic Image Collection; **71** Robert Harding/CORBIS; **76** (l)Gerry Ellis/ENP Images, (r)Jose Azel/Aurora/PictureQuest; **77** (t c)Lisa Hoffner/Wildeye Photography, (b)Art Wolfe/Getty Images; **78–79** Anthony Cassidy/Getty Images; **80** Kenneth Garrett/National Geographic Image Collection; **87** Gerd Ludwig/National Geographic Image Collection; **90** AFP/CORBIS; **92** Jim Sugar Photography/CORBIS; **93** Steve McCurry/National Geographic Image Collection; **97** AP/Wide World Photo; **98** (t)Private Collection/The Bridgeman Art Library, (tc bc)Glencoe file, (b)NASA; **99** AFP/CORBIS; **108** Bettmann/CORBIS; **112** (l)Steve McCurry, (r)Michael Lewis; **112–113** David R. Stoecklein; **115** Susie Post, (inset)Norbert Rosing; **116** Richard Nowitz/Phototake/PictureQuest; **117** Eugene Fisher and Barbara Brundege; **124–125** Mitchell Funk/Getty Images; **126** David Hiser/National Geographic Image Collection; **128** (l)Steven L. Raymer/National Geographic Image Collection, (r)Vincent Musl/National Geographic Image Collection; **129** Roy Corral/Getty Images; **131** AP/Wide World Photos; **133** Gregory Scott Doramus/Omnigraphix; **134** (l)Getty Images, (r)Marvin E. Newman/Getty Images; **135** Joel Satore/National Geographic Image Collection; **145** CORBIS; **146** Ira Block/National Geographic Image Collection; **147** The White House Historical Association; **150** Mary Kate Denny/PhotoEdit; **152** CORBIS; **156–157** SuperStock; **158** Raymond K. Gehman/National Geographic Image Collection; **160** Diaphor Agency/Index Stock; **162** David A. Harvey/National Geographic Image Collection; **164** (l)Daniel J. Wiener/National Geographic Image Collection, (r)Aaron Haupt; **165** Marie-Louise Brimberg/National Geographic Image Collection; **166** Michael Evan Sewell/Visual Pursuit; **167** Index Stock Imagery/PictureQuest; **168** Marie-Louise Brimberg/National Geographic Image Collection; **170** Reuters NewMedia/CORBIS; **171** Richard T. Nowitz/National Geographic Image Collection; **174** (l)David Levy/Getty Images, (r)Oliver Benn/Getty Images; **174–175** Kenneth Garrett/National Geographic Society Image Collection; **177** Norbert Wu/Getty Images, (inset)William J. Hebert/Getty Images; **178** Sisse Brimberg; **179** Chad Ehlers/Getty Images; **187** Michael K. Nichols/National Geographic Image Collection; **188–189** Randy Faris/CORBIS; **190** Bettmann/CORBIS; **192** Albert Moldvay/National Geographic Image Collection; **194** Joel Satore/National Geographic Image Collection; **197** Tomasz Tomaszewski/National Geographic Image Collection; **199** Vladimir Pcholkin/Getty Images; **201** James L. Amos/National Geographic Image Collection; **202** David A. Harvey/National Geographic Image Collection; **203** Peter Menzel/Stock Boston; **204** Tomas Tomaszewski/National Geographic Image Collection; **210–211** Sylvain Grandadam/Getty Images; **212** Art Wolfe; **215** (t)Jan Butchofsky-Houser/CORBIS, (b)Vincent Musl/National Geographic Image Collection; **216** Michael S. Yamashita/CORBIS; **219** Jonathan Blair/National Geographic Image Collection; **221** (l)Tony Arruza/CORBIS, (r)Michael K. Nichols/National Geographic Image Collection; **222** Robert A. Tyrrell; **225** George Mobley/National Geographic Image Collection; **228** (l)Getty Images, (r)Giraudon/Art Resource, NY; **229** Loren McIntyre; **230–231** Layne Kennedy/CORBIS; **232** Alex Webb/Magnum; **235** Kennan Ward/CORBIS Stock Market; **236** (l)Jim Zuckerman/CORBIS, (r)Yann Arthus-Bertrand/CORBIS; **238** Jeremy Horner/CORBIS; **239** Louis O. Mazzatenta/National Geographic Image Collection; **242** Robert Caputo/Aurora; **243** Pablo Corral V/CORBIS; **244** Jacques Jangoux/Getty Images; **246** Kit Houghton Photography/CORBIS; **247** Winfield I. Parks, Jr./National Geographic Image Collection; **250** (t bl)Michael & Patricia Fogden, (br)William Albert Allard; **250–251** Stuart Franklin; **251** (t)Marc Van Roosmalen/Conservation International, (b)Michael Doolittle; **252–253** Paul Harris/Getty Images; **256** Richard S. Durrance/National Geographic Image Collection; **266** Frank & Helen Schreider/National Geographic Image Collection; **268** Michael J. Doolittle/The Image Works; **270** Art Wolfe; **271** Maria Stenzel/National Geographic Image Collection; **272** (l)Richard T. Nowitz/National Geographic Image Collection, (r)James L. Stanfield/National Geographic Image Collection; **275** William A. Allard/National Geographic Image Collection; **278** (t)IFA-Bilderteam-Travel/Bruce Coleman Inc., (b)Robert Everts/Getty Images; **278–279** SuperStock; **281** D.C. Lowe/Getty Images, (inset)Chris Haigh/Getty Images; **282** Bert Blokhuis/Getty Images; **283** Ron Sanford/Getty Images; **291** Mary Kate Denny/PhotoEdit; **292–293** Christian Sarramon/CORBIS; **294** Ira Block/National Geographic Image Collection; **295** Vanni Archive/CORBIS; **296** Richard T. Nowitz/National Geographic Image Collection; **297** Museo della Civilta Romana, Rome/Art Resource, NY; **299** Richard List/CORBIS; **302** Archivo Iconografico, SA/CORBIS; **303** David Lees/CORBIS; **304** Sistine Chapel, Vatican, Rome/Fratelli Alinari/SuperStock; **305** The Art Archive; **306** Matt Meadows; **308** (l)Bettmann/CORBIS, (r)Gianni Dagli Orti/CORBIS; **312–313** Philippa Lewis/CORBIS; **314** The Art Archive/Dagli Orti/Musee National d'Art Moderne, Paris; **315** Culver Pictures, Inc.; **316** (l)CORBIS, (r)Craig Aurness/CORBIS; **317** Hulton-Deutsch Collection/CORBIS; **318** V. Yudin/Sovfoto/Eastfoto/PictureQuest; **319** Owen Franken/CORBIS; **322** (l)Culver Pictures/PictureQuest, (r)Bettmann/CORBIS; **324** James Stanfield/National Geographic Image

ACKNOWLEDGMENTS

Collection; **325** AFP/CORBIS; **338–339** Photowood, Inc./CORBIS Stock Market; **340** London Aerial Photo Library/CORBIS; **342** Stephen Beer/Getty Images; **343** Tim Thompson/CORBIS; **344** Adam Woolfitt/CORBIS; **345** James L. Stanfield/National Geographic Image Collection; **346** (t)Brand X/Getty Images, (r)Jonathan P. Blair/National Geographic Image Collection; **347** Michael John Kielty/CORBIS; **350** Ric Ergenbright/CORBIS; **351** Owen Franken/CORBIS; **352** Sisse Brimberg/National Geographic Image Collection; **353** AFP/CORBIS; **354** Tomasz Tomaszewski/National Geographic Image Collection; **355** (l)Buddy May/CORBIS, (r)Richard S. Durrance/National Geographic Image Collection; **356** Sisse Brimberg/National Geographic Image Collection; **357** SuperStock; **358** David Cumming, Eye Ubiquitous/CORBIS; **359** Gerard Degeorge/CORBIS; **360** (t)Getty Images, (b)Vittoriano Rastelli/CORBIS; **361** Louis O. Mazzatenta/National Geographic Image Collection; **362** A. Ramey/PhotoEdit; **366** Brand X/Getty Images; **366–367** Foto World/Getty Images; **368** Tomasz Tomaszewski/National Geographic Image Collection; **370** James L. Stanfield/National Geographic Image Collection; **371** Steven L. Raymer/National Geographic Image Collection; **372** Peter Blakely/CORBIS Saba; **373** Dean Conger/CORBIS; **374** Stephanie Heimann/Sovfoto; **376** James Stanfield/National Geographic Image Collection; **377** Steve Raymer/CORBIS; **378** Peter Wilson/CORBIS; **379** Francoise de Mulder/CORBIS; **380** Aaron Haupt; **381** Catherine Karnow/CORBIS; **382** (l)Kelly-Mooney Photography/CORBIS, (r)Craig Aurness/CORBIS; **383** Gerd Ludwig/National Geographic Image Collection; **390** (l)Bruce Dale, (r)Alain Le Garsmeur/Getty Images; **390–391** Marc Moritsch/National Geographic Society Image Collection; **393** Simeone Huber/Getty Images, (inset)Jay Dickman; **394** B. Klipinitsen, M. Moshkov/Sovfoto/Eastfoto/PictureQuest; **395** Michael Nichols/National Geographic Image Collection; **400** Paul Harris/Getty Images; **401** KS Studios; **402–403** John Lamb/Getty Images; **404** Tom Brakefield/CORBIS; **406** Bryan & Cherry Alexander; **407** (l)Andre Gallant/Getty Images, (c)Wolfgang Kaehler/CORBIS, (r)A. Solomonov/Sovfoto/Easfoto/PictureQuest; **409** NASA; **410** Giraudon/Art Resource, NY; **411** Stock Montage; **414** Marc Garanger/CORBIS; **415** David & Peter Turnley/CORBIS; **416** Farrell Grehan/CORBIS; **417** Wolfgang Kaehler/CORBIS; **420** Giraudon/Art Resource, NY; **421** Sovfoto/Eastfoto/PictureQuest; **422–423** David & Peter Turnley/CORBIS; **424** Gerd Ludwig/National Geographic Image Collection; **427** Steve Kokker/Lonely Planet Images; **429** Sisse Brimberg/National Geographic Image Collection; **430** Shone/Sipa Press; **431** (l)Marc Garanger/CORBIS, (r)David Turnley/CORBIS; **432** Richard Howard/Black Star Publishing/PictureQuest; **433** Kremlin Museums–Moscow–Russia/Bridgeman Art Library; **434** Bob Krist/CORBIS; **435** Roger-Viollet/Musee du Petit Palais, Paris/Bridgeman Art Library, London/New York; **436** Wolfgang Kaehler; **438** Index Stock Imagery/PictureQuest; **439** Gerd Ludwig/National Geographic Image Collection; **448** Gerd Ludwig/National Geographic Image Collection; **449** Michael S. Yamashita/CORBIS; **452** (t)Hugh Sitton/Getty Images, (b)David Coulson; **452–453** X. Richer/Hoaqui, Photo Researchers; **455** James Strachan/Getty Images; **456** Getty Images; **457** Wayne Eastep/Getty Images; **463** AP/Wide World Photo; **464–465** Wolfgang Kaehler; **466** Kenneth Garrett/National Geographic Image Collection; **469** (l)Gianni Dagli Orti/CORBIS, (r)Charles & Josette Lenars/CORBIS; **470** Wolfgang Kaehler; **472** Steve Vidler/SuperStock; **473** Gary Cralle/Getty Images; **475** (t)CMCD/Photodisc, (c)C Squared Studios/Photodisc, (b)Robert Harding/CORBIS; **478** AP/Wide World Photos; **479** Kenneth Garrett/National Geographic Image Collection; **482–483** W.N. Westermann/CORBIS; **484** Stephen Studd/Getty Images; **487** AP/Wide World; **489** Owen Franken/CORBIS; **490** George Steinmetz/National Geographic Image Collection; **491–492** K.M. Westermann/CORBIS; **495** Reza/National Geographic Image Collection; **498** Ed Kashi; **498–499** James L. Stanfield; **499** (l)Ed Kashi, (r)Courtesy of Sandra Postel; **500–501** Wolfgang Kaehler/CORBIS; **502** Patrick Ward/CORBIS; **504** James L. Stanfield/National Geographic Image Collection; **505** Annie Griffiths Belt/National Geographic Image Collection; **507** Arthur Thevenart/CORBIS; **508** I. Talby/Index Stock; **510** Richard T. Nowitz/CORBIS; **513** James L. Stanfield/National Geographic Image Collection; **516** J. Stanfield/National Geographic Image Collection; **517** Charles & Josette Lenars/CORBIS; **519** (l)Alexandra Avakian/National Geographic Image Collection, (r)Jon Spaull/CORBIS; **522** (l)AP/Wide World Photos, (c)Ali Fraidoon/AP, (r)Langeuin Jacques/CORBIS Sygma; **523** (l)Suhaib Salam/Reuters/Newscom, (r)Murad Sezer/AP; **524** Hasan Sarbakhshian/AP; **525** Rina Castelnuovo/AP; **526** Douglas Graham/Roll Call Photos/Newscom; **528** Doug Martin; **532** (l)Hugh Sitton/Getty Images, (r)Jacques Jangoux/Getty Images; **532–533** Manoj Shah/Getty Images; **535** Ian Murphy/Getty Images, (inset)Renee Lynn/Getty Images; **536** Ian Murphy/Getty Images; **537** Will Curtis/Getty Images; **546** David & Peter Turnley/CORBIS; **547** Nicholas Parfitt/Getty Images; **548–549** Paul Almasy/CORBIS; **550** AP/Wide World Photos; **553** (l)AP/Wide World Photos, (r)Robert W. Moore/National Geographic Image Collection; **555** (l)Bowers Museum of Cultural Art/CORBIS, (r)Davis Factor/CORBIS; **556** Steve McCurry/Magnum Photos, Inc.; **557** Carol Beckwith & Angela Fisher/Robert Estall Photo Agency; **559** Robert W. Moore/National Geographic Image Collection; **562** Nik Wheeler/CORBIS; **563** AP/Wide World Photos; **566** Michael A. Hampshire; **567** James L. Stanfield; **568–569** W. Perry Conway/CORBIS; **570** AP/Wide World Photos; **571** Michael K. Nichols/National Geographic Image Collection; **573** Daniel Laine/CORBIS; **574** (l)Ann and Carl Purcell/Words & Pictures/PictureQuest, (r)James A. Sugar/Black Star Publishing/PictureQuest; **576** David Turnley/CORBIS; **577–578** Carol Beckwith & Angela Fisher/Robert Estall Photo Agency; **579** The Purcell Team/CORBIS; **581** Frank Lane Picture Agency/CORBIS; **582** Art Wolfe; **584** Chinch Gryniewicz/Ecoscene/CORBIS; **586** Dave Bartruff/CORBIS; **588** AP/Wide World Photos; **595** AFP Photo/Newscom; **598** Darrell Gulin/CORBIS; **602–603** Pictor; **604** Wolfgang Kaehler; **606** Turnley Collection/CORBIS; **607** Nik Wheeler/CORBIS; **609** Walter Edwards/National Geographic Image Collection; **610** Chris Johns/National Geographic Image Collection; **611** Robert Holmes/CORBIS; **614** Des & Jen Bartlett/National Geographic Image Collection; **616** AP/Wide World Photos; **617** Art Wolfe/Getty Images; **619** National Geographic Society Image Collection; **622** (l)Tim Davis/Getty Images, (r)David Sutherland/Getty Images; **622–623** Waranun Chutchawan-Tipakorn; **625** Hilarie Kavanagh/Getty Images, (inset)Martin Puddy/Getty Images; **626** Paul Chesley/Getty Images; **627** Steve McCurry/National Geographic Image Collection; **634** Steve Raymer/CORBIS; **635** Keren Su/Getty Images; **636–637** Tibor Bognar/CORBIS Stock Market; **638** George F. Mobley/National Geographic Image Collection; **639** Steve McCurry/National Geographic Image Collection; **640** (t)Oriental Museum, Durham University, UK/The Bridgeman Art Library, London/New York, (b)Lindsay Hebberd/CORBIS; **641** (l)SuperStock, (c)Bettmann/CORBIS, (r)Hulton/Archive; **643** Brian Vikander/CORBIS; **644** Jonathan Blair/National Geographic Image Collection; **646** Brian Vikander/CORBIS; **647** Ed Kashi/National Geographic Image Collection; **649** Steve McCurry/National Geographic Image Collection; **651** Paul Chesley/Getty Images; **655** Robert Holmes/CORBIS; **658–659** Christopher Arnesen/Getty Images; **660** Keren Su/CORBIS; **663** (t)Michele Burgess/CORBIS, (b)Kevin R. Morris/CORBIS; **665** Bob Sacha; **666** AFP/CORBIS; **667** The Telegraph Colour Library/FPG; **669** Joseph Sohm/ChromoSohm Inc./CORBIS; **670** (t)Freer Gallery of Art, Washington, DC, (b)Bonhams, London, UK/Bridgeman Art Library; **678** How-Man Wong/CORBIS; **679** Marc Garanger/CORBIS; **680** Nik Wheeler/CORBIS; **681** James L. Stanfield/National Geographic Image Collection; **682** AFP/CORBIS; **686** Cary Wolinsky/Stock Boston; **687** Keren Su/CORBIS; **688–689** Dallas and John Heaton/CORBIS; **690** Reuters NewMedia Inc./CORBIS; **692** Steve Cole/Photodisc; **693** Karen Kasmauski/Matrix; **694** Roger Ressmeyer/CORBIS; **695** (t)Christie's Images/CORBIS, (b)Will & Deni McIntyre/Getty Images; **697** Asian Art & Archaeology, Inc./CORBIS; **698** Carmen Redondo/CORBIS; **699** (l)Nathan Benn/CORBIS, (r)Wolfgang Kaehler/CORBIS; **703** Neil Beer/CORBIS; **706–707** Bob Krist/Getty Images; **708–710** Paul Chesley/National Geographic Image Collection; **711** Kevin R. Morris/CORBIS; **714** Roger Ressmeyer/CORBIS; **716** Earl & Nazima Kowall/CORBIS; **718** David Hanson/Getty Images; **719** AP/Wide World Photos; **722** (l)David Madison/Getty Images, (r)David Hiser/Getty Images; **722–723** Oliver Strewe/Getty Images; **725** Oliver Strewe/Getty Images, (inset)Johnny Johnson/Getty Images; **726** Nicholas DeVore/Getty Images; **727** Glen Allison/Getty Images; **733** Elaine Shay; **734–735** Larry Williams/CORBIS Stock Market; **736** R. Ian Productions P Lloyd/National Geographic Image Collection; **737** Penny Tweedie/CORBIS; **738** (t)Australian Picture Library/CORBIS, (b)Horniman Museum, London, UK/Heini Schneebeli/Bridgeman Art Library; **739** (t)Paul A. Souders/CORBIS, (bl)Earl & Nazima Kowall/CORBIS, (br)Charles Philip Cangialosi/CORBIS; **740** (t)Australian Picture Library/CORBIS, (b)Earl & Nazima Kowall/CORBIS, Charles Philip Cangialosi/CORBIS ; **741** Kevin Fleming/CORBIS; **743** Neil Rabinowitz/CORBIS; **752** Kevin Fleming/CORBIS; **753** Larry Mulvehill/Image Works; **756–757** Dana Edmunds/FPG; **758** Hal Beral/CORBIS; **760** (l)Ben Simmons/CORBIS Stock Market, (r)SuperStock; **763** David Doubllet/National Geographic Image Collection; **764** Wolfgang Kaehler/CORBIS; **765** (l)SuperStock, (r)David Madison/Getty Images; **766** Underwood & Underwood/CORBIS; **768** Galen Rowell/CORBIS; **769** AP/Wide World Photos; **772** Christine Osborne/CORBIS; **772–773** Penny Tweedie/CORBIS; **773** (t)PhotoDisc, (c)Bettmann/CORBIS, (b)George F. Mobley; **774** Getty Images.